CALIFORNIA

HOLT MATH

Holt California Algebra 1

California Resources in the Student Edition and Teacher's Edition

Additional Resources to Support Mastering the California Standards

Focus on California Standards: Benchmark Tests includes pre-tests and post-tests for each of the standards with emphasis on the key standards. The **Standards Doctor** contains complete solutions and error analysis of incorrect answers.

Focus on California Standards: Intervention targets the key standards. It includes scaffolded intervention for skills and problem-solving, alternate teaching strategies, worksheets for skills and problem solving practice, key vocabulary words, and standards review. Also available as a consumable workbook.

California Countdown to Mastery Transparencies provide twenty-four weeks of daily warm-up problems addressing the California Mathematics Content Standards.

California On-Course Mapping: A Teacher's Guide for Planning provides you with a road map for using *Holt California Mathematics* to teach the concepts and skills required by the California Mathematics Content Standards. This booklet provides a **Minimum Course of Study** to ensure that all standards are covered in the course of the year. In addition, it lists available resources for each standard that enable you to adapt the curriculum to provide access to all of your students.

California Premier Online Edition includes the complete *Student Edition*, Homework Help Online, *Lesson Tutorial Videos*, Interactivities with feedback, parent resources, and much more!

California Review for Mastery Workbook includes lesson-by-lesson intervention with instruction, new examples, and practice exercises.

California Standards Virtual File Cabinet CD-ROM enables you to quickly find resources based on your search criteria, including California Mathematics Content Standards, chapter, lesson, and resource type. In addition, you can mark your favorites and even add your own content to the database. In the end, you have a customizable catalog of your favorite resources!

California Standards Practice CD-ROM contains banks of **ExamView®** items organized for teacher convenience in building tests and practice worksheets that reflect the California Mathematics Content Standards.

California Student One Stop CD-ROM solves the backpack problem. The entire *Student Edition*, workbooks, and intervention and enrichment worksheets can be found on one CD-ROM.

California Teacher's One-Stop Planner® CD-ROM is a convenient tool for planning and managing lessons and contains all print-based teaching resources, plus customizable lesson plans.

CALIFORNIA TEACHER'S EDITION

HOLT

Algebra 1

Edward B. Burger
David J. Chard
Earlene J. Hall
Paul A. Kennedy
Steven J. Leinwand
Freddie L. Renfro
Tom W. Roby
Dale G. Seymour
Bert K. Waits

HOLT, RINEHART AND WINSTON
A Harcourt Education Company
Orlando • Austin • New York • San Diego • London

Cover photo: Golden Gate Bridge, San Francisco, California; © George Steinmetz/Corbis

Cover photo: windsurfing, San Simeon, California; © DY Riess MD/Alamy

Cover photo: Joshua tree at sunset, California; © Frank Krahmer/zefa/Corbis

Cover photo: skyscrapers, Los Angeles, California; © Toyohiro Yamada/Getty Images

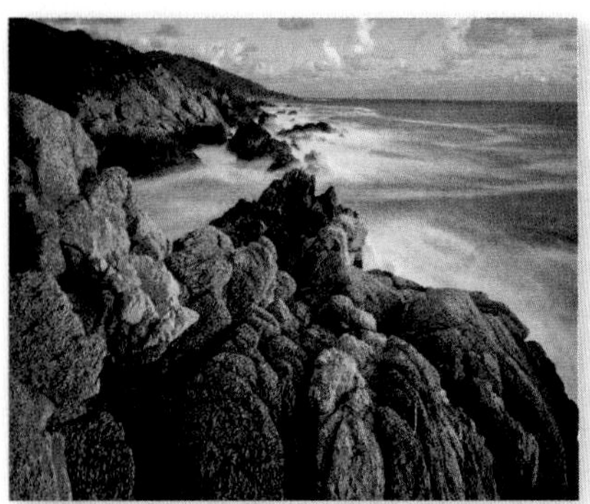

Cover photo: Garapata Beach, Big Sur, California; © David Muench/Corbis

Printed in the United States of America

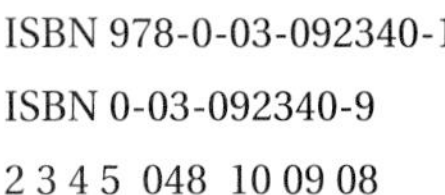

ISBN 978-0-03-092340-1

ISBN 0-03-092340-9

2 3 4 5 048 10 09 08

California Algebra 1 Teacher's Edition

Contents in Brief

Chapter Teacher Material

Student Handbook

California Teacher Advisory Panel

Kay Barrie
Math Department Chair
Rio Vista MS
Fresno, CA

Youshi Berry
Math Teacher
Emerson MS
Pomona, CA

Charlie Bialowas
Math Curriculum Specialist
Anaheim Union HS District
Anaheim, CA

Lorrie Wineberg Buehler
Principal
Baldy View Elementary School
Upland, CA

Mary Chiaverini
Math Teacher
Plaza Vista MS
Irvine, CA

Dennis Deets
Assistant Principal
AB Miller HS
Fontana, CA

Pauline Embree
Math Department Chair
Rancho San Joaquin MS
Irvine, CA

Sandi Enochs
Math Lead Teacher
Desert Hot Springs HS
Desert Hot Springs, CA

Tricia Gough
Math Department Chair
Emerson MS
Pomona, CA

Lee Haines
IB Coordinator/Math Coach
San Bernardino City Schools
San Bernardino, CA

Shannon Kelly
Math Teacher
Centennial HS
Corona, CA

Lisa Kernaghan
Math Teacher/ Administrator
Oak Creek Intermediate School
Oakhurst, CA

Mary Ann Kremenliev
Math Teacher
Foothill MS
Walnut Creek, CA

Carole Kuck
Math Department Chair
Jean Farb MS
San Diego, CA

David V. Mattoon
Math Teacher
Potter Junior HS
Fallbrook, CA

Lynette McClintock
Math/Science Teacher
Thompson MS
Murrieta, CA

Nancy Nazarian-Carroll
Math Teacher
Curtiss MS
Carson, CA

John (Jack) P. Nunes
Math Teacher and Department Leader
Fern Bacon MS
Sacramento, CA

Suzanne O'Rourke
Math Teacher
Antioch MS
Antioch, CA

Jong Sun Park
Math Teacher
Holmes International MS
Northridge, CA

Barbara Parr
Math Teacher
Emerson MS
Bakersfield, CA

Donna Phair
Math Department Chair
William Hopkins Junior HS
Fremont, CA

Donald R. Price
Math Teacher
Alvarado Intermediate School
Irvine, CA

Jennifer Randel
Math/Science Teacher, Grade Level Chair
Thompson MS
Murrieta, CA

Wendy Taub-Hoglund
Teacher Expert Secondary Math
Los Angeles USD
Los Angeles, CA

Matthew Ting
Math Coach
Peary MS
Gardena, CA

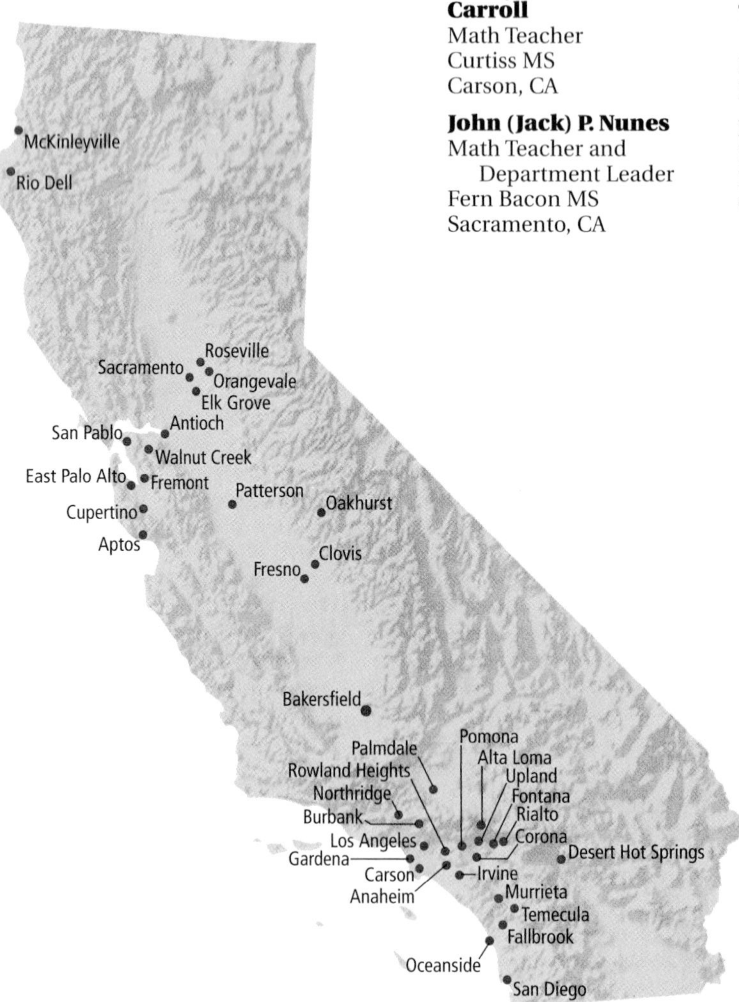

California Reviewers

Youshi Berry
Math Teacher
Emerson MS
Pomona, CA

Charlie Bialowas
Mathematics Curriculum Specialist
Anaheim Union HS District
Anaheim, CA

Lorrie Wineberg Buehler
Principal
Baldy View Elementary School
Upland, CA

Mary Chiaverini
Math Department Head
Plaza Vista MS
Irvine, CA

Michael Davoudian
Math Coach
Luther Burbank MS
Burbank, CA

DeAnn DeBey
Math Teacher
Irvine Unified School District
Irvine, CA

Pauline Embree
Math Department Chair
Rancho San Joaquin MS
Irvine, CA

Tricia Gough
Math Department Chair
Emerson MS
Pomona, CA

Lee Haines
IB Coordinator/Math Coach
San Bernardino City Schools
San Bernardino, CA

Lisa Kernaghan
Math Teacher/Administrator
Oak Creek Intermediate School
Oakhurst, CA

David Mattoon
Math Teacher
Potter Junior HS
Fallbrook, CA

Michael Nagaran
Mathematics Coach
Los Angeles Unified School District
Los Angeles, CA

Nancy Nazarian-Carroll
Math Teacher
Curtiss MS
Carson, CA

John (Jack) P. Nunes
Math Teacher and Department Leader
Fern Bacon MS
Sacramento, CA

Jong Sun Park
Math Teacher
Holmes International MS
Northridge, CA

Raylene Paustain
Teacher on Special Assignment
Clovis Unified School District
Clovis, CA

Donna Phair
Math Department Chair
William Hopkins Junior HS
Fremont, CA

Donald R. Price
Math Teacher
Alvarado Intermediate School
Rowland Heights, CA

Golden T. Quinn
Math Teacher
Audubon MS
Los Angeles, CA

Wendy Taub-Hoglund
Teacher Expert Secondary Math
Los Angeles USD
Los Angeles, CA

California Field Test Participants

Carmencita Ancora
Dana MS
San Diego, CA

Henry Ashe
Vail Ranch MS
Temecula, CA

Susan Battistv
High Tech MS
San Diego, CA

Donna Campbell
Mesa Intermediate School
Palmdale, CA

Todd Cardosa
Encina HS
Sacramento, CA

Lou Catti
Creekside MS
Patterson, CA

Marcie Charlesworth
Excelsior Elementary School
Roseville, CA

Peggy Clarke
Temecula MS
Temecula, CA

Sheryl Cleveland
Golden Valley HS
Bakersfield, CA

Joyanna Deutsch
Forty-Niners Academy
East Palo Alto, CA

Andrea Farrow
Margarita MS
Temecula, CA

Ryan Gallagher
High Tech MS
San Diego, CA

Laura Grant
McKinleyville MS
McKinleyville, CA

Sally Haggerty
Martin Luther King MS
Oceanside, CA

V J Hirsch
Lincoln HS
Los Angeles, CA

Mollie Holmgren
Monument MS
Rio Dell, CA

Rayetta Lawson
Kastner Intermediate School
Fresno, CA

Tami Llewellyn
Ruth Musser MS
Alta Loma, CA

Lisa Madigan
Helms MS
San Pablo, CA

Eric Manabe
Aptos HS
Aptos, CA

David McKinley
Fort Miller MS
Fresno, CA

Viola Okoro
Franklin HS
Elk Grove, CA

William Olmeda
Lincoln HS
Los Angeles, CA

Breeze Patten
Bella Vista MS
Murrieta, CA

Jeff Perkins
Casa Roble HS
Orangevale, CA

Laurie Pines
Homestead HS
Cupertino, CA

Julie Prater
James L. Day MS
Temecula, CA

Wallace Rayford
Frisbie MS
Rialto, CA

Carey Resch
Leroy F. Greene MS
Sacramento, CA

Katherine Ringer
Heritage Intermediate School
Fontana, CA

Wendy Salcedo
Jordan MS
Burbank, CA

Chris Schmidt
Thurgood Marshall MS
San Diego, CA

Mary Ann Sheridan
McKinleyville MS
McKinleyville, CA

Byron Wright
Vail Ranch MS
Temecula, CA

Seunghwan Yom
Abraham Lincoln HS
Los Angeles, CA

California
the golden state

The State Capitol in Sacramento

Big Sur coastline

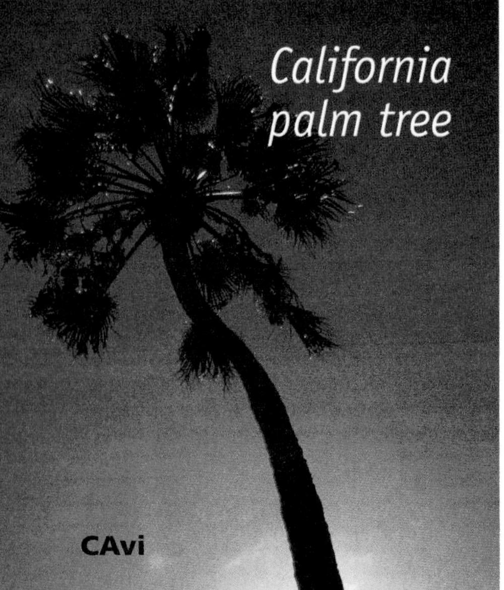
California palm tree

Correlation to the California Mathematics Content Standards for Algebra 1

The following is a correlation of *Holt California Algebra 1* to the California Mathematics Content Standards for Algebra 1. The correlation breaks down standards, when appropriate, to show where specific parts of the standards are addressed.

The symbol 🔑 designates key standards.

The state
bird is the
California Quail

The Poppy is the state flower

California Mathematics Content Standards for Algebra 1

Standard		Taught	Reinforced
1.0 Students identify and use the arithmetic properties of subsets of integers and rational, irrational, and real numbers, including closure properties for the four basic arithmetic operations where applicable.	*arithmetic properties*	42–47	57, 60, 62, 63, 77, 84, 90, 250, 322, 323, 772, EP3, EP24
	closure properties	42–47	57, 61, 62, 322, EP3
1.1 Students use properties of numbers to demonstrate whether assertions are true or false.		48–53	50–53, 57, 61, 62, 322, 361
2.0 Students understand and use such operations as taking the opposite, finding the reciprocal, taking a root, and raising to a fractional power. They understand and use the rules of exponents.	*taking the opposite*	15–19	40, 41, 59, 62, 72–76, 101, 122, 128, 279, 609, EP2, EP4, EP24, EP25
	finding the reciprocal	21–24	40, 41, 59, 62, 74–77, 101, 122, 334, EP2, EP4, EP24, EP25

Standard		Taught	Reinforced
	taking a root	32–37, 422–427	40, 41, 47, 53, 60, 62, 77, 161, 322, 376, 421, 429, 453, 461, 468, 581, 582–587, 596, 597, 611, 614, 616, 700–704, 705–710, 711–715, 716–721, 722–729, 730, 731, 761, 764, 765, 766, 768, 769, EP3, EP19, EP22, EP34
	raising to a fractional power	422–427	429, 466, 468, 539, 772, EP15, EP30
	rules of exponents	26–31, 394–399, 400–405, 406–407, 408–414, 415–421, 422–427	62, 107, 128, 428, 429, 435, 443, 453, 464–466, 468, 469, 472, 473, 493, 503, 539, 551, 573, 620, 641, 648, 695, 746, 753, 772, 773, EP14, EP15, EP30
3.0 Students solve equations and inequalities involving absolute values.	*equations*	114–119	120, 121, 125, 126, 131, 141, 147, 168, 205, 250, 355, 361, 389, 414, 427, 673, EP5, EP25
	inequalities	178–183	185, 189, 190, 251, 262, EP7, EP26

Standard		Taught	Reinforced
🔑4.0 Students simplify expressions before solving linear equations and inequalities in one variable, such as $3(2x - 5) + 4(x - 2) = 12$.	*linear equations*	86–90, 93–98	101, 123, 124, 127, 130, 141, 220, 231, 239, 251, 262, 287, 322, 334, 399, 414, 421, 587, EP4, EP5, EP25
	linear inequalities	157–161, 163–168	169, 185, 188, 190, 191, 194, 220, 231, 250, 251, 268, 296, 334, 405, 472, 604, 641, 658, 721, 737, 744, EP7, EP26
🔑5.0 Students solve multistep problems, including word problems, involving linear equations and linear inequalities in one variable and provide justification for each step.	*linear equations*	85–90, 92–98, 99	100, 101, 107, 114–119, 121, 123–125, 126, 127, 130, 131, 176, 184, 193, 212, 220, 231, 239, 250, 251, 288, 310, 322, 355, 389, 435, 538, 620, 673, 773, EP4, EP5, EP25
	linear inequalities	156–161, 162–168, 169	170–176, 178–183, 184, 185, 188, 189, 190, 191, 193, 195, 220, 231, 239, 250, 251, 296, 303, 389, 538, 604, 620, EP7, EP26

Standard		Taught	Reinforced
6.0 Students graph a linear equation and compute the x- and y-intercepts (e.g., graph $2x + 6y = 4$). They are also able to sketch the region defined by linear inequalities (e.g., they sketch the region defined by $2x + 6y < 4$).	*graph a linear equation*	256–262, 263–268, 290–296, 297	284–287, 288, 289, 301, 303, 310, 312, 313, 314, 316, 318, 323, 329–334, 341, 355, 363, 364–370, 371–376, 378, 379, 380, 383, 384, 388, 389, 443, 453, 461, 511, 597, 648, 704, EP10, EP12, EP28
	compute x- and y-intercepts	263–268, 290–296	275, 277–279, 288, 289, 302, 303, 310, 313, 315, 317, 318, 320, 321, 322, 323, 342, 388, 443, 461, 473, 565, 648, 694, 704, EP10, EP28
	sketch the region defined by linear inequalities	364–370	371–376, 378, 379, 383, 384, 389, 453, 511, 737, EP13, EP29
7.0 Students verify that a point lies on a line, given an equation of the line. Students are able to derive linear equations by using the point-slope formula.	*verify that a point lies on a line*	256–262	287, 289, 300, 314, 318, 322, 323, 342, 539, 559, 620, 683, 694, 710, EP10, EP11, EP18
	derive linear equations by using the point-slope formula	297–303	307, 308, 310, 312, 313, 316, 317, 318, 320, 321, 323, 349, 370, 399, 473, 573, 609, 773, EP11

Standard		Taught	Reinforced
8.0 Students understand the concepts of parallel lines and perpendicular lines and how their slopes are related. Students are able to find the equation of a line perpendicular to a given line that passes through a given point.	*understand parallel lines and how their slopes are related*	304–310	313, 317, 318, 321, 323, 350–353, 382, 472, 483, 493, 538, 587, 621, 658, 678, 715, EP11, EP28
	understand perpendicular lines and how their slopes are related	304–310	313, 317, 318, 323, 388, 389, 527, 539, 678, 694, 715, 772, EP11, EP28
	find the equation of a line perpendicular to a given line through a given point	304–310	313, 317, 318, 323, 388, 389, 473, 772, EP11
9.0 Students solve a system of two linear equations in two variables algebraically and are able to interpret the answer graphically. Students are able to solve a system of two linear inequalities in two variables and to sketch the solution sets.	*solve a system of equations algebraically*	335, 336–342, 343–349, 350–355	363, 381, 382, 384, 385, 387, 388, 389, 356–361, 362, 370, 405, 472, 473, 493, 503, 539, 565, 678, 695, 729, 772, EP13, EP29
	interpret the answer graphically	329–334, 350–355	363, 380, 382, 384, 387, EP12
	solve a system of inequalities and sketch the solution sets	371–376, 377	378, 379, 383, 384, 385, 389, 472, 511, 621, EP13, EP29

Standard		Taught	Reinforced
10.0 Students add, subtract, multiply, and divide monomials and polynomials. Students solve multistep problems, including word problems, by using these techniques.	*add and subtract monomials and polynomials*	436–437, 438–443	446–453, 458, 459, 460, 461, 463, 467, 469, 470, 471, 473, 483, 501, 519, EP15, EP30, EP31
	multiply monomials and polynomials	444–445, 446–453, 455–461	462, 463, 465, 466, 467, 468, 469, 470, 472, 473, 519, 520, 559, 597, 621, 693, 704, 772, 773, EP15, EP30
	divide monomials and polynomials	666, 667–673	685, 689, 690, 691, 695, 704, EP21, EP33
11.0 Students apply basic factoring techniques to second- and simple third-degree polynomials. These techniques include finding a common factor for all terms in a polynomial, recognizing the difference of two squares, and recognizing perfect squares of binomials.	*factoring techniques*	494–495, 496–503, 504, 505–511, 522–527	512, 513, 528, 529, 532, 533, 534, 536, 537, 538, 539, 620, 665, 683, 695, 721, EP16, EP17, EP31
	finding a common factor	486, 487–493	513, 522–527, 529, 531, 533, 534, 535, 537, 538, 539, 620, 695, 721, EP17, EP31
	difference of two squares	514–520	522–527, 529, 533, 534, 535, 539, EP17, EP31
	perfect squares of binomials	514–520	522–527, 528, 529, 533, 534, 538, 539, 683, 695, 744, EP17, EP31

Standard		Taught	Reinforced
12.0 Students simplify fractions with polynomials in the numerator and denominator by factoring both and reducing them to the lowest terms.		642–648	651, 657, 658, 665, 668, 671, 672, 673, 683, 687, 689, 690, 693, 694, 695, 772, EP20, EP21
13.0 Students add, subtract, multiply, and divide rational expressions and functions. Students solve both computationally and conceptually challenging problems by using these techniques.	*rational functions*	626, 627–633, 634–641, 649	650, 651, 686, 687, 690, 691, 693, 695, 773, EP20, EP33
	add and subtract rational expressions	659–665	685, 687, 688, 690, 694, 695, EP20, EP21, EP33
	multiply and divide rational expressions	652–658	685, 687, 688, 690, 694, 695, EP20, EP21, EP33
14.0 Students solve a quadratic equation by factoring or completing the square.	*factoring*	576–581	587, 611, 614, 616, 621, 641, 665, 715, 773, EP19
	completing the square	591–597	602, 604, 611, 615, 616, 633, 744, 773, EP19
15.0 Students apply algebraic techniques to solve rate problems, work problems, and percent mixture problems.	*rate problems*	102–107, 356–361, 659–665, 679–683	65, 121, 126, 153, 382, 483, 501, 510, 512, 550, 551, 689, EP5, EP25, EP29, EP33
	work problems	679–683	640, 650, 685, 689, 690, 695, EP29
	percent mixture problems	356-361, 679-683	382, 388, 685, 689, 773, EP29

Standard		Taught	Reinforced
16.0 Students understand the concepts of a relation and a function, determine whether a given relation defines a function, and give pertinent information about given relations and functions.	*understand relations and functions*	206–212, 213–220	220, 243, 246, 249, 251, 427, 621, EP8, EP27
	determine whether a relation defines a function	206–212, 213–220	212, 223, 243, 244, 246, 247, 249, 250, 251, 319, 349, 427, 520, 527, 633, EP8
	give pertinent information	206–212, 213–220	212, 223, 243, 246, 249, 251, 399, 551
17.0 Students determine the domain of independent variables and the range of dependent variables defined by a graph, a set of ordered pairs, or a symbolic expression.	*graph*	206–212, 213–220	222, 223, 243, 246, 251, 259, 260, 323, 389, 427, 547–551, 564, 621, 703, EP8, EP18
	set of ordered pairs	206–212	212, 220, 223, 243, 246, 247, 287, 427, 520, 527, 550, 648, 729, EP8
	symbolic expression	213–220	244, 249, 259, 260, 323, 511, 565, 629, 631, 632, 633, 637, 639, 640, 641, 650, 651, 695, 701, 702, 703, 710, 715, 729, 731, 768, 773, EP22, EP27, EP28, EP33

Standard		Taught	Reinforced
18.0 Students determine whether a relation defined by a graph, a set of ordered pairs, or a symbolic expression is a function and justify the conclusion.	*graph*	206–212, 213–220	231, 246, 249, 250, 256, 257, 260, 370, 427, EP8, EP10
	set of ordered pairs	206–212	220, 243, 246, 247, 250, 287, 319, 322, 349, 427, 520, 527, 633, EP8, EP27
	symbolic expression	213–220	231, 246, 256, 257, 260, 262, 370, EP27
19.0 Students know the quadratic formula and are familiar with its proof by completing the square.		598–604	608, 611, 615, 616, EP19
20.0 Students use the quadratic formula to find the roots of a second-degree polynomial and to solve quadratic equations.	*find the roots of a second-degree polynomial*	598–604	770, EP19
	solve quadratic equations	598–604	608, 609, 611, 615, 616, 621, 695, 737, 773
21.0 Students graph quadratic functions and know that their roots are the x-intercepts.	*graph quadratic functions*	544–551, 560–565	566, 567, 568–573, 574, 575, 581, 596, 611, 612, 613, 614, 616, 617, 620, 621, 694, 772, 773, EP18
	know that their roots are the x-intercepts	553–559, 568–573, 574–575	566, 567, 613, 616, 621, 773, EP19

Standard		Taught	Reinforced
22.0 Students use the quadratic formula or factoring techniques or both to determine whether the graph of a quadratic function will intersect the x-axis in zero, one, or two points.	*quadratic formula*	598–604, 605–609	615, 616, 620, 621, 694, 772, EP19
	factoring techniques	576–581	596, 600, 694
	both	598–604	605, 617, 772
23.0 Students apply quadratic equations to physical problems, such as the motion of an object under the force of gravity.		568–573, 576–581, 582–587, 591–597	603, 606, 607, 608, 610, 611, 613, 614, 615, 616, 619, 773, EP32
24.0 Students use and know simple aspects of a logical argument.		42–47, 48–53, 99, 108, 169, 280–281, 311, 484–485	30, 31, 57, 60, 61, 62, 65, 67, 107, 119, 147, 153, 176, 183, 233, 267, 268, 270, 271, 278, 296, 305, 306, 308, 309, 310, 311, 317, 322, 355, 398–399, 405, 406–407, 420, 421, 426, 427, 461, 481, 493, 538, 552, 558, 587, 608, 609, 641, 678, 703, 710, 715, 735, 736, 744, EP3, EP28

Standard		Taught	Reinforced
24.1 Students explain the difference between inductive and deductive reasoning and identify and provide examples of each.	*explain the difference*	280–281	311
	identify examples of each	280–281	
	provide examples of each	99, 108, 169, 280–281	30, 31, 108, 233, 267, 270, 271, 278, 310, 355, 398–399, 405, 406–407, 420, 461, 552, 558, 641, 703, 710, 736, 744
24.2 Students identify the hypothesis and conclusion in logical deduction.		38–39	99, 108, 169
24.3 Students use counterexamples to show that an assertion is false and recognize that a single counterexample is sufficient to refute an assertion.	*use counterexamples*	42–47	57, 60, 62, 153, 322, 538
	recognize that a single counterexample is sufficient	42–47	57, 538

Los Angeles skyline

Standard		Taught	Reinforced
25.0 Students use properties of the number system to judge the validity of results, to justify each step of a procedure, and to prove or disprove statements.		42–47, 48–53, 99, 108, 169, 311, 484–485	57, 60, 61, 62, 65, 67, 107, 119, 147, 153, 176, 183, 267, 268, 296, 305, 306, 308, 309, 310, 317, 420, 421, 426, 427, 461, 481, 493, 538, 587, 608, 609, 678, 715, 735, EP3, EP28
25.1 Students use properties of numbers to construct simple, valid arguments (direct and indirect) for, or formulate counterexamples to, claimed assertions.	*construct simple, valid direct arguments*	48–53, 99, 108, 169, 311	57, 60, 61, 62, 65, 67, 107, 119, 147, 176, 183, 267, 268, 296, 305, 306, 308, 309, 310, 317, 420, 421, 426, 427, 461, 493, 538, 587, 608, 609, 678, 715, 735, EP3, EP28
	construct simple, valid indirect arguments	484–485	
	formulate counterexamples	42–47	60, 153, 481

Standard	Taught	Reinforced
25.2 Students judge the validity of an argument according to whether the properties of the real number system and the order of operations have been applied correctly at each step.	99, 169	107, 152, 167, 295, 302, 348, 360, 398, 413, 426, 435, 442, 460, 493, 510, 519, 526, 564, 580, 586, 596, 640, 657, 664, 672, 682, 714, 728, 752, 760
25.3 Given a specific algebraic statement involving linear, quadratic, or absolute value expressions or equations or inequalities, students determine whether the statement is true sometimes, always, or never.	91	96, 118, 147, 182, 571, 586

Golden Gate Bridge

Using Your Book to Master the Standards

Holt California Algebra 1 provides many opportunities for you to master the California Mathematics Content Standards for Algebra 1.

Countdown to Mastery

Countdown to Mastery provides practice with the standards every day.

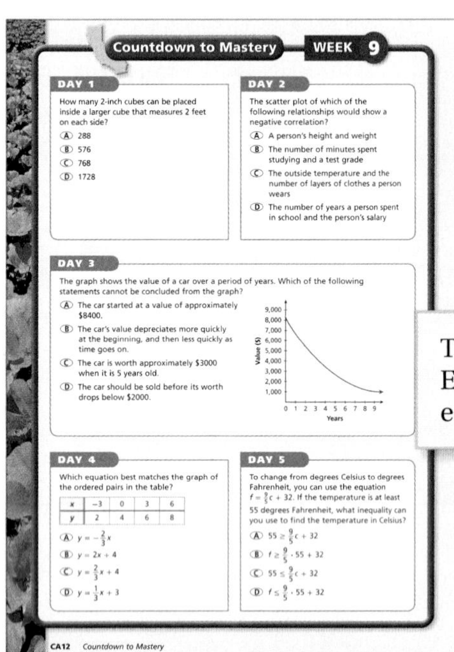

Step 1

✔ Complete one item each day before you start the lesson.

There are 24 pages of standards practice. Each page has five questions, one for each day of the week.

California Standards

The California Standards taught in each lesson are listed at the start of the lesson.

Step 2

✔ Preview the standards before you start the lesson.

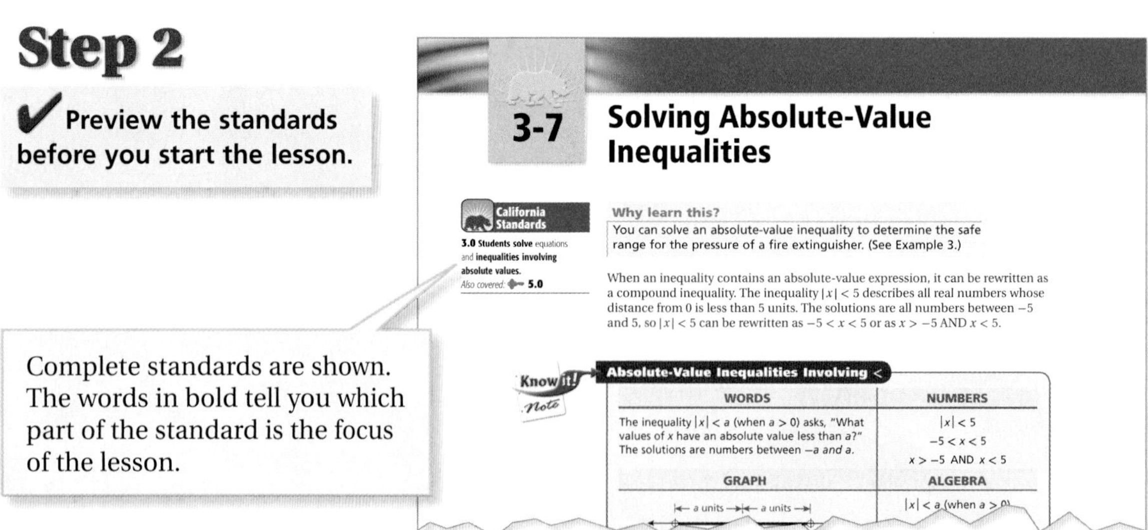

Complete standards are shown. The words in bold tell you which part of the standard is the focus of the lesson.

Use the Spiral Standards Review for constant review of standards taught in previous lessons.

Step 3

✔ **Keep your skills fresh by practicing the standards daily.**

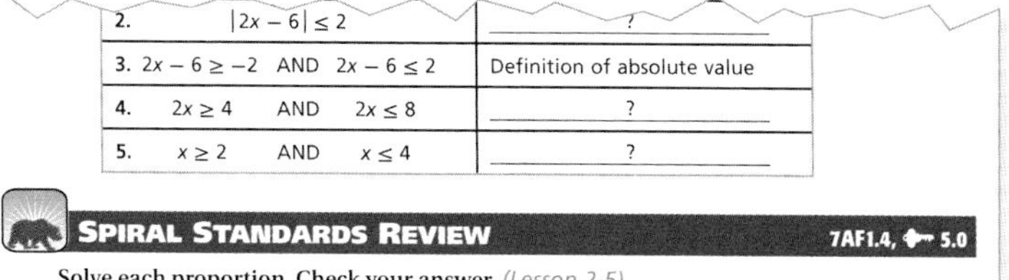

2.	$\lvert 2x - 6\rvert \le 2$	?
3.	$2x - 6 \ge -2$ AND $2x - 6 \le 2$	Definition of absolute value
4.	$2x \ge 4$ AND $2x \le 8$	?
5.	$x \ge 2$ AND $x \le 4$	?

SPIRAL STANDARDS REVIEW 7AF1.4, 🔑 5.0

Solve each proportion. Check your answer. (Lesson 2-5)

61. $\frac{x+1}{4} = \frac{5}{8}$ 62. $\frac{2}{15} = \frac{6}{y-5}$ 63. $\frac{12}{m+2} = \frac{8}{3}$ 64. $\frac{7+g}{10} = \frac{6}{8}$

Describe the solutions of each inequality in words. (Lesson 3-1)

65. $16 > 8m$ 66. $c + 4 < 11$ 67. $-4 \le x + 2$ 68. $0 \ge x + 7$

Solve each compound inequality and graph the solutions. (Lesson 3-6)

69. $-3 < x - 3 < 1$ 70. $-3 \le 2x + 1 \le 9$

71. $x - 2 < -1$ OR $x - 2 > 2$ 72. $x + 4 \le 3$ OR $x + 4 \ge 6$

3-7 Solving Absolute-Value Inequalities 183

If you need help with a problem, go to the lesson referenced at the end of the problem.

Use Mastering the Standards for review of standards taught in the current and previous chapters.

Step 4

✔ **After finishing each chapter, review your knowledge of the standards.**

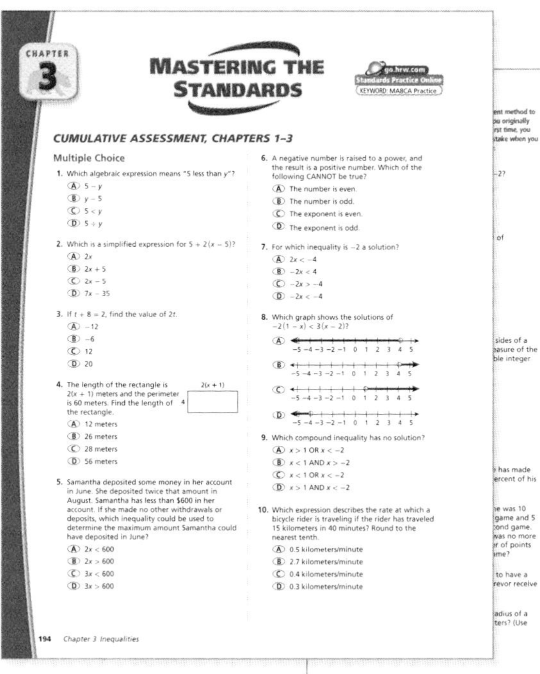

CHAPTER 3

MASTERING THE STANDARDS

CUMULATIVE ASSESSMENT, CHAPTERS 1–3

Multiple Choice

Short Response

Extended Response

194 *Chapter 3 Inequalities*

Cumulative Assessment, Chapters 1–3 195

There are multiple choice, gridded response, short response, and extended response questions to help you check your knowledge of the Algebra 1 standards.

Countdown to Mastery

Each problem in the *Countdown to Mastery* is correlated to the California Mathematics Content Standards. These correlations are shown at the bottom of each page. For the full text of the Algebra 1 standards, see pages CAvi – CAxix.

Countdown to Mastery

WEEK 1

DAY 1

Which expression always represents an odd number?

Ⓐ $n^2 + 1$
Ⓑ $2n + 1$ (circled)
Ⓒ n^2
Ⓓ $n + 1$

DAY 2

Cell phone bills are based on a flat monthly fee and the number of minutes used. In the equation $c = 0.07m + 29.99$, what does the variable m represent?

Ⓐ The number of months billed
Ⓑ The total amount of the bill
Ⓒ The number of minutes used (circled)
Ⓓ The phone number

DAY 3

Look at the table. Which equation best describes the relationship between the number of students and the number of tables in the cafeteria?

Students (n)	Tables (t)
720	18
600	15
960	24

Ⓐ $n = 40t$ (circled)
Ⓑ $n = 35t + 90$
Ⓒ $t = 40n$
Ⓓ $n = 45t - 90$

DAY 4

Which expression represents the verbal phrase "the sum of three times a number and five"?

Ⓐ $3(n + 5)$
Ⓑ $3 + n \cdot 5$
Ⓒ $3n + 5$ (circled)
Ⓓ $3 + (n + 5)$

DAY 5

Sara has $140. What computation will give the number of days she can skate at a skatepark if it costs $30 for a five day pass plus $3 a day for rental of a helmet?

Ⓐ Divide 140 by 5
Ⓑ Divide 140 by 9 (circled)
Ⓒ Divide 140 by 5 and subtract 15
Ⓓ Divide 140 by 30 and subtract 3

Day	California Standards
1	7AF1.1, 7MR1.2
2	7AF1.1
3	7AF1.1, 7MR2.4
4	7AF1.1
5	7NS1.2 (key), 7MR1.1

Countdown to Mastery WEEK 2

DAY 1

Katie has a part-time job for 2 hours after school and 4 hours on Saturdays. If she spends 1 hour each night doing homework, what are Katie's earnings on Thursday? What other information is needed in order to solve this problem?

Ⓐ The number of days Katie works per week

Ⓑ The total amount Katie earns in one week

Ⓒ The average number of hours Katie works per week

Ⓓ The amount of money Katie earns per hour

DAY 2

If $x = 5$, then $2(3x - 4) - 8x + 3 =$

Ⓐ -42

Ⓑ -29

Ⓒ -21

Ⓓ -15

DAY 3

Based on the table, which inequality represents the relationship between x and y?

x	2	3	5	6
y	−3	−8	−10	−9

Ⓐ $x > -y$

Ⓑ $2x < -y$

Ⓒ $x < -y$

Ⓓ $2x > -y$

DAY 4

If you get 18 questions wrong on a test that has 72 questions, what percent of the questions did you get right?

Ⓐ 75%

Ⓑ 72%

Ⓒ 54%

Ⓓ 25%

DAY 5

The Earth's mass is approximately 5,973,600,000,000,000,000,000,000 kilograms. What is this number in scientific notation?

Ⓐ 5.9×10^{-24}

Ⓑ 59×10^{23}

Ⓒ 5.9×10^{24}

Ⓓ 0.59×10^{25}

Day	California Standards
1	7NS1.2 (key), 7MR1.1
2	7AF1.2
3	7AF1.1, 7MR2.4
4	7NS1.3
5	7NS1.1

Countdown to Mastery WEEK 3

DAY 1

Which expression is equivalent to 2^3?

Ⓐ $2 \cdot 3$
Ⓑ $3 + 3$
Ⓒ $2 + 2 + 2$
Ⓓ $2 \cdot 2 \cdot 2$

DAY 2

Which number is not a solution of $-7y + 19 < 75$?

Ⓐ 13
Ⓑ 0
Ⓒ −2
Ⓓ −8

DAY 3

Lydia received a gift card for $25.00 worth of smoothies from the Smoothie Spot. If the cost of each smoothie is $3.25, which table best describes *b*, the balance remaining on the gift card after she buys *n* smoothies?

Ⓐ

n	*b*
1	$21.75
3	$15.25
4	$12.00
7	$2.25

Ⓑ

n	*b*
2	$18.50
4	$12.00
6	$6.50
8	$0

Ⓒ

n	*b*
1	$21.75
2	$18.50
5	$15.25
7	$12.00

Ⓓ

n	*b*
2	$18.50
3	$15.25
5	$7.75
6	$4.50

DAY 4

The band is trying to raise money to take a field trip to the Rock and Roll Hall of Fame. They decide to sell sweatshirts. The equation for the amount of money *a* that they will make for selling *t* sweatshirts is $a = 22t - 350$. In order to make at least $2100, how many sweatshirts do the band members need to sell?

Ⓐ 112
Ⓑ 111
Ⓒ 80
Ⓓ 79

DAY 5

What is the solution to the equation $8x - 10 = 54$?

Ⓐ 5.5
Ⓑ 6.75
Ⓒ 8
Ⓓ 12

Day	California Standards
1	7AF2.1
2	7AF4.1
3	7SDAP1.1
4	7AF4.1
5	7AF4.1

Countdown to Mastery WEEK 4

DAY 1

Which number equals $(5)^{-3}$?

Ⓐ -15

Ⓑ $-\frac{1}{125}$

Ⓒ $\frac{1}{125}$

Ⓓ $\frac{1}{15}$

DAY 2

What is the value of $3x^2 - 5x + 2$ when $x = -4$?

Ⓐ -66

Ⓑ -26

Ⓒ 30

Ⓓ 70

DAY 3

Which graph matches the values from the table?

x	-3	-1	2	4
y	6	2	-4	-8

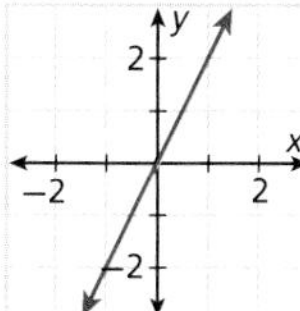

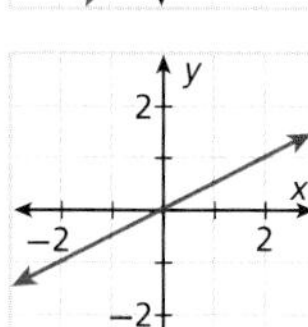

Ⓒ
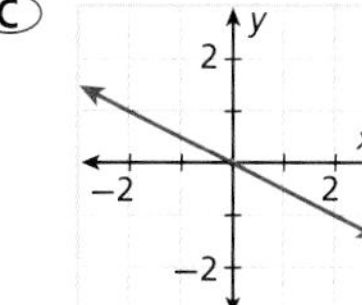

Ⓓ
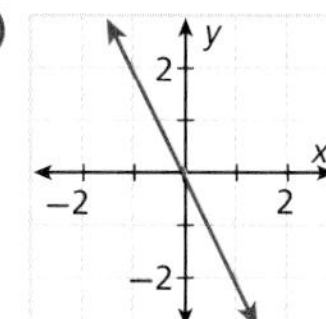

DAY 4

What is $\frac{11}{12} + \frac{4}{15}$?

Ⓐ $\frac{5}{9}$

Ⓑ $\frac{21}{20}$

Ⓒ $\frac{71}{60}$

Ⓓ $\frac{55}{16}$

DAY 5

Which of the following is equivalent to $4(x + 5) - 2(x + 5) = 14$?

Ⓐ $4x + 5 - 2x + 5 = 14$

Ⓑ $4x + 5 - 2x - 5 = 14$

Ⓒ $4x + 20 - 2x + 10 = 14$

Ⓓ $4x + 20 - 2x - 10 = 14$

Day	California Standards
1	7NS2.1
2	7AF1.2
3	7AF1.5
4	7NS2.2
5	1A4.0

Countdown to Mastery WEEK 5

DAY 1

The table shows all of the possible outcomes when flipping a coin twice.

First flip	Second flip
H	H
H	T
T	H
T	T

Which of the following statements must be true?

(A) The probability that two flips will have at least one tail is $\frac{1}{2}$.

(B) The probability that two flips will have the same outcome is $\frac{1}{2}$.

(C) The probability of getting exactly two heads is higher than the probability of getting exactly two tails.

(D) The probability of getting exactly one head and one tail is higher than the probability of getting at least one head.

DAY 2

Which of the following is equivalent to $(4^6)^3$?

(A) 4^2

(B) 4^3

(C) 4^9

(D) 4^{18}

DAY 3

The square root of 200 is between

(A) 11 and 12

(B) 12 and 13

(C) 13 and 14

(D) 14 and 15

DAY 4

A piano regularly sells for $950. It is marked up 45%. How much does the piano sell for now?

(A) $427.50

(B) $522.50

(C) $1377.50

(D) $1472.50

DAY 5

If $|x| = 5$, what is the value of x?

(A) -5 or 0

(B) -5 or 5

(C) 0 or 5

(D) -10 or 10

Day	California Standards
1	6SDAP3.1 🔑
2	7NS2.3 🔑
3	7NS2.4
4	7NS1.7 🔑
5	7NS2.5 🔑

Countdown to Mastery WEEK 6

DAY 1

Which equation represents the data in the table?

x	3	1	−2	6
y	2	4	7	−1

(A) $y = -x + 5$
(B) $y = 2x - 1$
(C) $y = x + 3$
(D) $y = -3x + 11$

DAY 2

A fair number cube is rolled. What is the probability that the number cube will land showing a number that is greater than 3?

(A) 0.17
(B) 0.33
(C) 0.5
(D) 0.67

DAY 3

Ryan's first 5 test scores in Algebra were 80, 87, 84, 92, and 87. What was his mean score?

(A) 85
(B) 86
(C) 87
(D) 92

DAY 4

Jonathan tosses a fair coin 30 times, and it lands showing heads 18 times. Using Jonathan's results, what is the difference between the experimental probability of tossing heads and the theoretical probability of tossing heads?

(A) 0.1
(B) 0.5
(C) 0.6
(D) 1.1

DAY 5

This year the average cost of tuition and fees for a public four-year college is $20,528. In three years the estimated average cost will be $27,914. What is the percent increase of the cost to the nearest percent?

(A) 74%
(B) 36%
(C) 26%
(D) 14%

Day	California Standards
1	7AF1.1, 7MR2.4
2	6SDAP3.3
3	6SDAP1.1
4	6SDAP3.3
5	7NS1.6

COUNTDOWN TO MASTERY

Countdown to Mastery WEEK 7

DAY 1

Daniel's recipe for 24 cookies calls for $2\frac{1}{2}$ cups of flour. How much flour will Daniel need to make 60 cookies?

(A) 1 cup

(B) $6\frac{1}{4}$ cups

(C) $6\frac{1}{2}$ cups

(D) $7\frac{1}{2}$ cups

DAY 2

What is the value of $2x^2 + 3x - 5$ when $x = -2$?

(A) −7

(B) −3

(C) 5

(D) 9

DAY 3

Which graph shows a line where each value of y is three more than half of x?

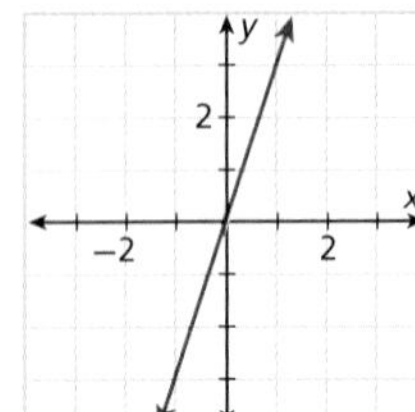

(C)
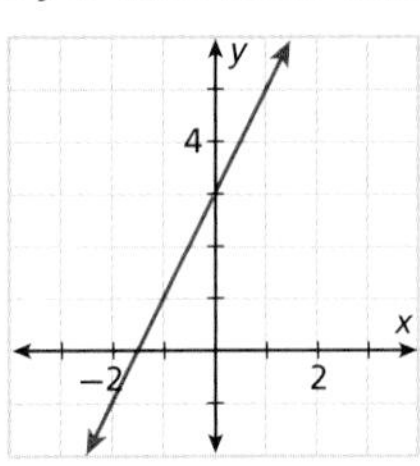

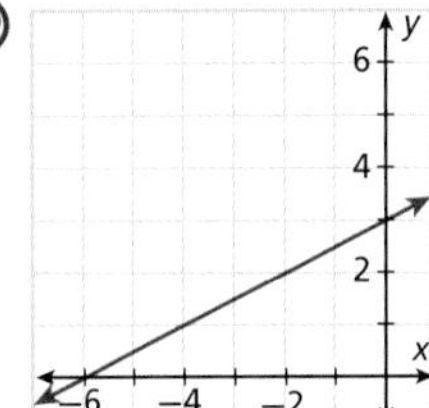

(D)
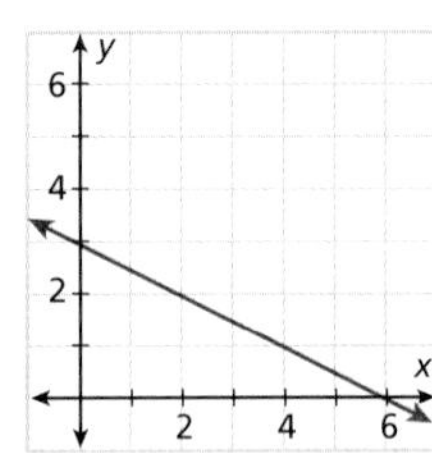

DAY 4

Solve for x.

$$2(x + 4) < 3x - 4$$

(A) $x < 12$

(B) $x > \frac{12}{5}$

(C) $x > 12$

(D) $x < \frac{12}{5}$

DAY 5

Solve for x.

$$3(5x - 8) = 2(2x - 1)$$

(A) $x = \frac{7}{11}$

(B) $x = 2$

(C) $x = 1\frac{1}{2}$

(D) $x = 3$

Day	California Standards
1	7NS1.2
2	7AF1.2
3	7AF1.5
4	1A5.0
5	1A4.0

Countdown to Mastery WEEK 8

DAY 1

A swimming pool charges an annual \$75 membership fee, and it costs \$1.50 each time a member brings a guest. Which equation shows the yearly cost y in terms of the number of guests g?

(A) $y = 75g + 1.5$
(B) $y = -1.5g + 75$
(C) $y = 1.5g + 75$
(D) $y = 1.5g + 75g$

DAY 2

On a certain standardized test, the equation $s = 9q + 218$ is used to determine a student's score. In this equation, s is the score and q is the number of questions answered correctly. If the maximum score on the test is 650, how many questions are on the test?

(A) 96 questions
(B) 72 questions
(C) 48 questions
(D) 24 questions

DAY 3

In the election for class treasurer, 220 ballots were tallied. How many more people voted for Pauley than for Sue?

(A) 10

(B) 22
(C) 29
(D) 37

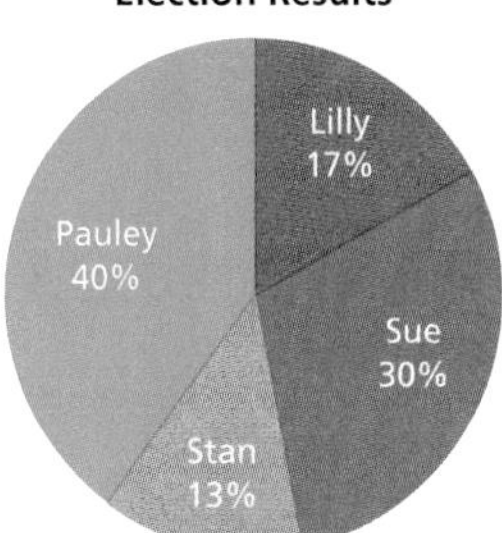

DAY 4

Jaclyn has two hats. The first hat contains 26 slips of paper on which the letters of the alphabet are written, one letter per slip. The second hat contains 10 slips numbered 0 through 9. If Jaclyn draws 1 slip of paper from each hat, what is the probability that she will draw a letter that is a vowel and a number less than 2?

(A) 0.038
(B) 0.046
(C) 0.058
(D) 0.392

DAY 5

The surface area of cube A is 96 square meters. The surface area of cube B is half the surface area of cube A. What is the area of one face of cube B in square meters?

(A) 3.6

(B) 8
(C) 16
(D) 32

Day	California Standards
1	7AF1.1
2	1A5.0
3	7SDAP1.1
4	6SDAP3.5
5	7MG2.3

Countdown to Mastery WEEK 9

DAY 1

How many 2-inch cubes can be placed inside a larger cube that measures 2 feet on each side?

(A) 288

(B) 576

(C) 768

(D) 1728

DAY 2

The scatter plot of which of the following relationships would show a negative correlation?

(A) A person's height and weight

(B) The number of minutes spent studying and a test grade

(C) The outside temperature and the number of layers of clothes a person wears

(D) The number of years a person spent in school and the person's salary

DAY 3

The graph shows the value of a car over a period of years. Which of the following statements cannot be concluded from the graph?

(A) The car started at a value of approximately $8400.

(B) The car's value depreciates more quickly at the beginning, and then less quickly as time goes on.

(C) The car is worth approximately $3000 when it is 5 years old.

(D) The car should be sold before its worth drops below $2000.

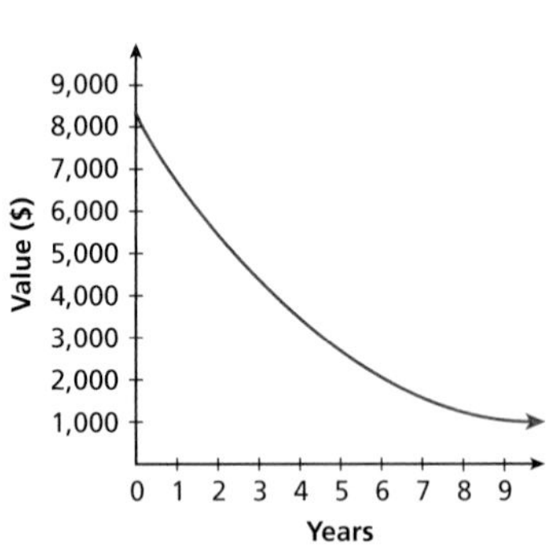

DAY 4

Which equation best matches the graph of the ordered pairs in the table?

x	−3	0	3	6
y	2	4	6	8

(A) $y = -\frac{2}{3}x$

(B) $y = 2x + 4$

(C) $y = \frac{2}{3}x + 4$

(D) $y = \frac{1}{3}x + 3$

DAY 5

To change from degrees Celsius to degrees Fahrenheit, you can use the equation $f = \frac{9}{5}c + 32$. If the temperature is at least 55 degrees Fahrenheit, what inequality can you use to find the temperature in Celsius?

(A) $55 \geq \frac{9}{5}c + 32$

(B) $f \geq \frac{9}{5} \cdot 55 + 32$

(C) $55 \leq \frac{9}{5}c + 32$

(D) $f \leq \frac{9}{5} \cdot 55 + 32$

Day	California Standards
1	7MG2.4
2	7SDAP1.2
3	6SDAP2.5
4	7AF3.3
5	7MG1.1

Countdown to Mastery WEEK 10

COUNTDOWN TO MASTERY

DAY 1

What is the surface area of the figure represented by this net?

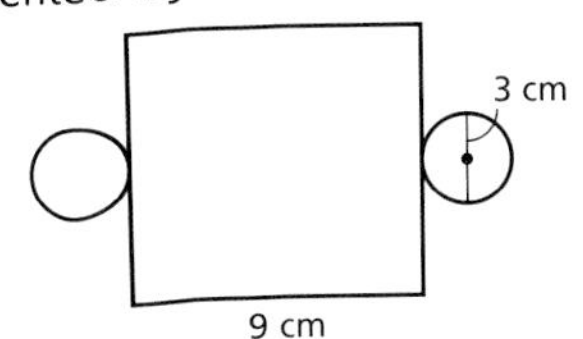

(A) 84.82 square centimeters
(B) 94.25 square centimeters
(C) 98.91 square centimeters
(D) 226.19 square centimeters

DAY 2

What is the area of the shaded region in the figure shown?

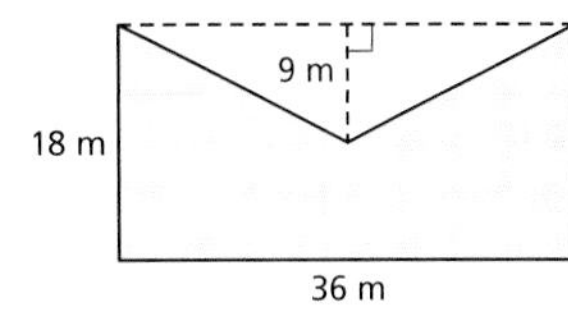

(A) 270 square meters
(B) 486 square meters
(C) 648 square meters
(D) 810 square meters

DAY 3

What is the equation of the graph of the line shown?

(A) $y = 2x$
(B) $y = -2x$
(C) $y = \frac{1}{2}x$
(D) $y = -\frac{1}{2}x$

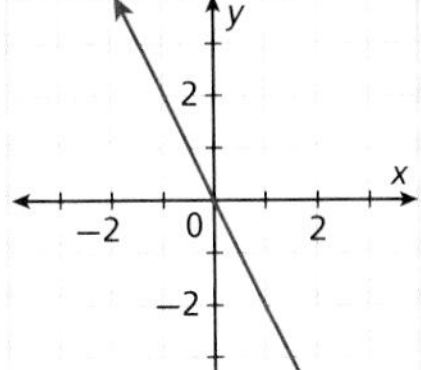

DAY 4

Three thousand rotations in 60 seconds is the same rate as which of the following?

(A) 5 rotations per second
(B) 50 rotations per minute
(C) 500 rotations per second
(D) 3000 rotations per minute

DAY 5

On a certain day, the exchange rate was 60 U.S. dollars for 50 euro. At this rate about how many U.S. dollars were 70 euro worth that day?

(A) \$20
(B) \$43
(C) \$58
(D) \$84

Day	California Standards
1	7MG2.1
2	7MG2.2
3	7AF3.3
4	7MG1.3
5	7MG1.3

COUNTDOWN TO MASTERY

Countdown to Mastery WEEK 13

DAY 1

Which of the following points lies on the line $2x + 3y = 6$?

Ⓐ (0, 2)

Ⓑ (0, 3)

Ⓒ (1, 2)

Ⓓ (3, 1)

DAY 2

A taxi company charges a \$2.50 fee per ride plus an additional \$2.10 per mile traveled. If the taxi fee increases to \$2.75, what characteristic of a graph of this relationship would change?

Ⓐ The slope

Ⓑ The x-intercept

Ⓒ The y-intercept

Ⓓ There would be no changes.

DAY 3

What is the equation of the line shown in the graph?

Ⓐ $y = x - 3$

Ⓑ $y = 2x$

Ⓒ $y = \frac{1}{3}x$

Ⓓ $y = 3x$

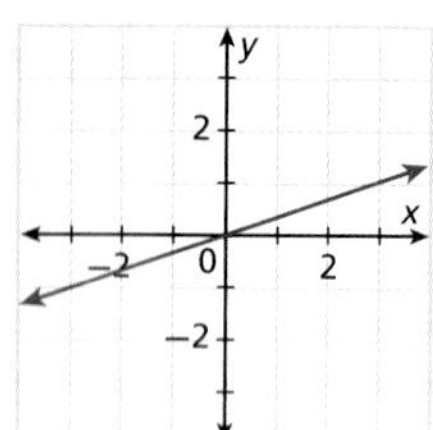

DAY 4

Paul's swimming coach recorded the following data during Paul's swim meet.

Time (s)	Distance (yd)
21.2	25
42.4	50
63.6	75

If Paul continues to swim at the rate shown in the table, how many yards will he swim in 127.2 seconds?

Ⓐ 100

Ⓑ 125

Ⓒ 150

Ⓓ 175

DAY 5

Jessika runs at a speed of 6 miles per hour. She runs for 25 minutes in a straight line at this rate. Approximately what distance does Jessika run?

Ⓐ $1\frac{1}{4}$ miles

Ⓑ 2 miles

Ⓒ $2\frac{1}{2}$ miles

Ⓓ 4 miles

Day	California Standards
1	1A7.0
2	7MG1.3, 7MR1.1
3	1A6.0
4	7AF4.2
5	1A15.0

DAY 1

What is the equation of a line that has a slope of $-\frac{3}{2}$ and passes through the point $(-4, 2)$?

Ⓐ $y = -\frac{3}{2}x - 4$

Ⓑ $y = -\frac{3}{2}x - 20$

Ⓒ $y = -\frac{3}{2}x - 8$

Ⓓ $y = -\frac{3}{2}x + 4$

DAY 2

What is the slope of a line parallel to the line whose equation is $3x - 4y = -8$?

Ⓐ $m = 3$

Ⓑ $m = 2$

Ⓒ $m = \frac{3}{4}$

Ⓓ $m = -3$

DAY 3

Using the line of best fit shown on the scatter plot, which of the following best approximates the amount of monthly rainfall in month 9?

Ⓐ 10 inches

Ⓑ 11 inches

Ⓒ 12 inches

Ⓓ 13 inches

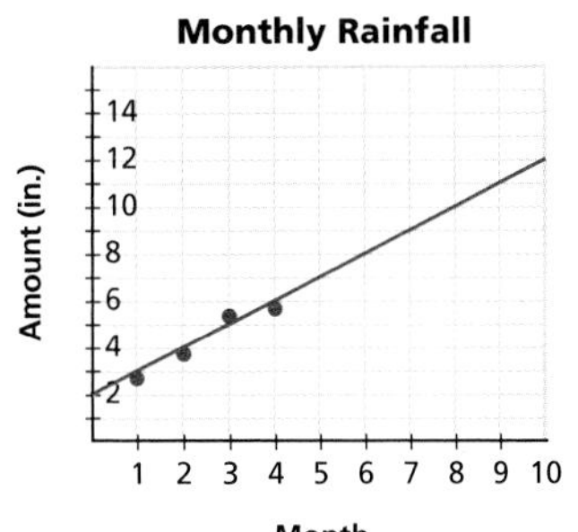

DAY 4

Which relation is a function?

Ⓐ {(11, −2), (12, −1), (13, 0), (21, 8)}

Ⓑ {(1, −2), (2, −1), (3, 0), (1, 4)}

Ⓒ {(1, −2), (1, −1), (1, 0), (1, 1)}

Ⓓ {(11, −2), (10, −1), (10, 9), (11, 9)}

DAY 5

The wholesale cost of a TV at Terry's Video is $1250. The company makes a 40% profit on the sale of this TV. How much did Terry's Video sell the TV for?

Ⓐ $1300

Ⓑ $1650

Ⓒ $1750

Ⓓ $2000

Day	California Standards
1	1A7.0
2	1A8.0
3	7SDAP1.2, 7MR2.3
4	1A16.0
5	7NS1.7

Countdown to Mastery WEEK 15

DAY 1

Pam used the following process to find the y-intercept of the line described by the equation $2x - y = 11$.

Step 1 Subtract $2x$ from both sides. $-y = -2x + 11$
Step 2 Divide each side by -1. $y = 2x - 11$
Step 3 The y-intercept of $y = mx + b$ is b. y-intercept is -11

According to Pam's method, which expression gives the y-intercept of the line described by the equation $ax + by = c$?

Ⓐ $-\frac{a}{b}$ Ⓑ $\frac{b}{a}$ Ⓒ $-\frac{b}{c}$ Ⓓ $\frac{c}{b}$

DAY 2

Which number serves as a counterexample to the statement below?

A prime number plus one is not prime.

Ⓐ 2
Ⓑ 3
Ⓒ 11
Ⓓ 17

DAY 3

The sum of the angle measures of a triangle is 180°. Two angles of a triangle measure 35° and 65°. What can you conclude is the measure of the third angle of the triangle?

Ⓐ 80°
Ⓑ 90°
Ⓒ 100°
Ⓓ It cannot be determined.

DAY 4

What are the x- and y-intercepts of the graph of $y = \frac{2}{5}x - 2$?

Ⓐ x-intercept: -2; y-intercept: 5
Ⓑ x-intercept: $\frac{2}{5}$; y-intercept: -2
Ⓒ x-intercept: 0; y-intercept: -2
Ⓓ x-intercept: 5; y-intercept: -2

DAY 5

A system of equations is set up to determine how many pounds of hazelnut coffee and how many pounds of Colombian coffee were mixed together to make a blend. The total mixture was 20 pounds of coffee. Which of the following is not a possible solution to the system?

Ⓐ (7, 13)
Ⓑ (32, –12)
Ⓒ (11, 9)
Ⓓ (1, 19)

Day	California Standards
1	7AF4.1, 7MR3.3
2	1A24.3
3	1A24.1
4	1A6.0
5	1A15.0

Countdown to Mastery WEEK 16

DAY 1

The equations $|x| = 3$ and $x = |3|$ have the same solution.

Ⓐ This statement is sometimes true.
Ⓑ This statement is always true.
Ⓒ This statement is never true.
Ⓓ This statement is true for positive numbers only.

DAY 2

Which equation represents a line parallel to the one shown?

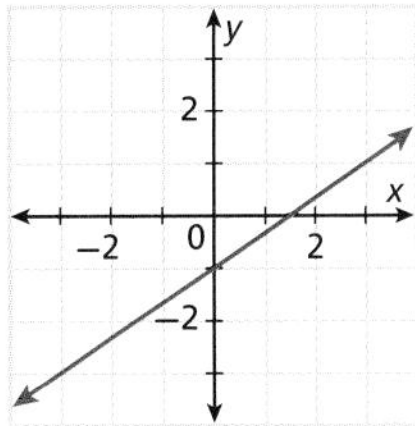

Ⓐ $y = \frac{3}{2}x + 1$
Ⓑ $y = \frac{2}{3}x + 1$
Ⓒ $y = -\frac{3}{2}x - 1$
Ⓓ $y = -\frac{2}{3}x$

DAY 3

When Miles began heating a frozen substance, its temperature was −3°F. Miles recorded the temperature of the substance every 20 minutes. If the temperature continued to rise at about the same rate, which is the best estimate of the temperature after 2 hours of heating?

Ⓐ 6°F
Ⓑ 10°F
Ⓒ 15°F
Ⓓ 18°F

DAY 4

Simplify.

$$(7x^2 + 3x - 1) + (x^2 - 4x + 5)$$

Ⓐ $8x^2 - x + 4$
Ⓑ $8x^2 - x - 6$
Ⓒ $8x^2 + 7x + 4$
Ⓓ $8x^2 + x - 6$

DAY 5

What is the solution to the system of equations graphed below?

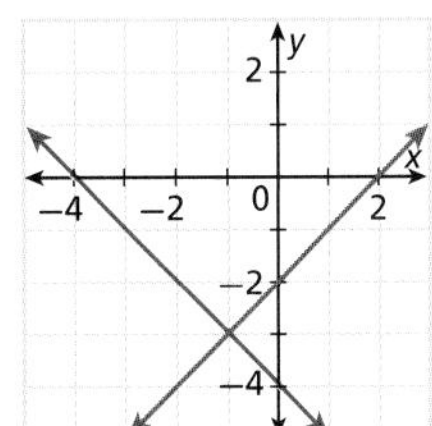

Ⓐ (−1, 3)
Ⓑ (−1, −3)
Ⓒ (−3, −1)
Ⓓ (3, −1)

Day	California Standards
1	1A25.3
2	1A8.0
3	7AF4.2, 7MR2.1
4	1A10.0
5	1A9.0

Countdown to Mastery WEEK 17

DAY 1

A store manager increases the wholesale cost of an item by 35%. Which statement best represents the functional relationship between the wholesale cost of the item and the markup on the item?

Ⓐ The markup is dependent on the wholesale cost.

Ⓑ The wholesale cost is dependent on the markup.

Ⓒ The markup and the wholesale cost are independent of each other.

Ⓓ The relationship cannot be determined.

DAY 2

In one high school 40 of the school's 1100 students work on the school paper. About what percent of the students work on the paper?

Ⓐ 3.6%

Ⓑ 10.3%

Ⓒ 27.5%

Ⓓ 36.4%

DAY 3

The scatter plot shows the percent of households that own a car versus the household income. Based on these data, what is a reasonable estimate for the percent of households that own a car if the household income is $50,000?

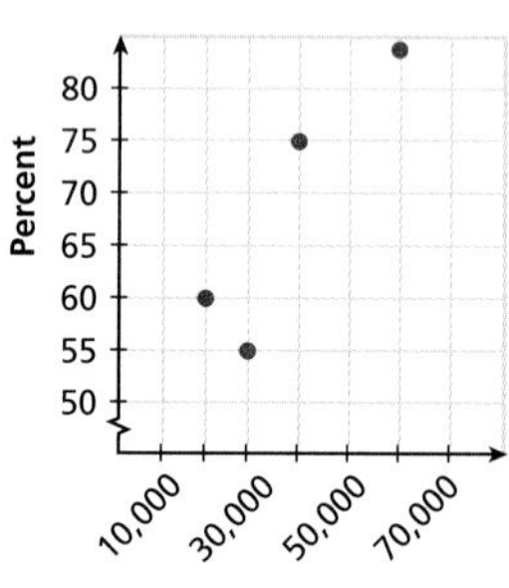

Ⓐ 50%

Ⓑ 65%

Ⓒ 77%

Ⓓ 85%

DAY 4

Greg has two similar rectangular boxes. The dimensions of box 1 are half those of box 2. How many times greater is the volume of box 2 than the volume of box 1?

Ⓐ 3

Ⓑ 8

Ⓒ 9

Ⓓ 27

DAY 5

Which of the following is the prime factored form of the lowest common denominator of $\frac{15}{28} - \frac{5}{12}$?

Ⓐ 3×5

Ⓑ $2 \times 2 \times 3 \times 7$

Ⓒ $3 \times 4 \times 7$

Ⓓ $3 \times 4 \times 4 \times 7$

Day	California Standards
1	7NS1.7
2	7NS1.3
3	7SDAP1.2
4	7MG2.3
5	7NS2.2

Countdown to Mastery WEEK 18

DAY 1

What is the range of the function $f(x) = 2x^2 + 1$ if the domain is $\{-2, 0, 3\}$?

(A) $\{1, 9, 19\}$
(B) $\{0, 8, 18\}$
(C) $\{-9, 1, 19\}$
(D) $\{-2, 0, 3\}$

DAY 2

What is the equation of the line with a slope of $\frac{5}{4}$ and a y-intercept of -2?

(A) $5x + 4y = 2$
(B) $y - 2 = \frac{5}{4}x$
(C) $y = -\frac{5}{4}x + 2$
(D) $5x - 4y = 8$

DAY 3

The graph shows the relationship between a person's height and weight. Which of the following statements would be an invalid conclusion for these data?

(A) The graph shows data for 20 people.
(B) A person who is tall is likely to have a higher weight.
(C) The tallest person in this study weighed the most.
(D) A person who has a lower weight has a fast metabolism.

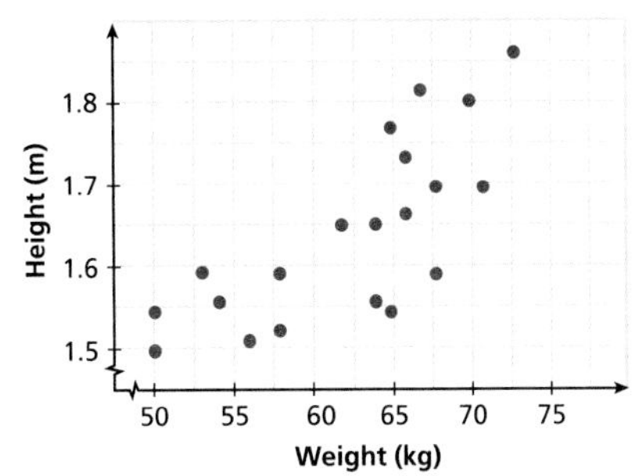

DAY 4

In the figure shown, all the corners form right angles. What is the area of the figure in square centimeters?

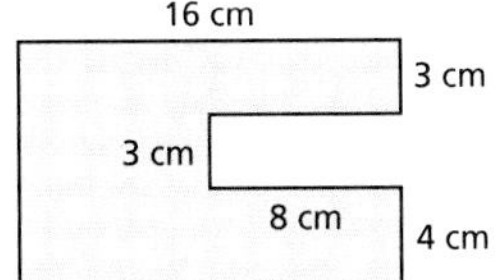

(A) 104 square centimeters
(B) 112 square centimeters
(C) 120 square centimeters
(D) 136 square centimeters

DAY 5

A circle with a 6-inch diameter is cut out of a rectangular piece of cloth. Find the area of the remaining piece of cloth. ($A = \pi r^2$ and $\pi \approx 3.14$)

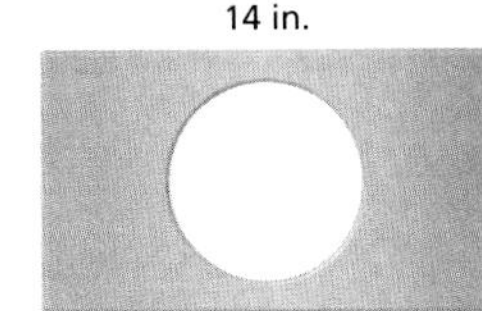

(A) 15.7 square inches
(B) 74.32 square inches
(C) 83.7 square inches
(D) 93.16 square inches

Day	California Standards
1	1A17.0
2	1A7.0
3	7SDAP1.2
4	7MG2.2
5	7MG2.1

Countdown to Mastery WEEK 19

DAY 1

Kristin rode her bicycle 56 miles in 4 hours. What was Kristin's speed in feet per second to the nearest tenth?

Ⓐ 6.8
Ⓑ 20.5
Ⓒ 23.3
Ⓓ 123.0

DAY 2

What is the y-intercept of the line with a slope of $-\frac{1}{3}$ that passes through the point $(-6, 4)$?

Ⓐ 6
Ⓑ 2
Ⓒ −2
Ⓓ −6

DAY 3

The graph of rectangle $JKLM$ is shown. What is the area in square units of rectangle $JKLM$?

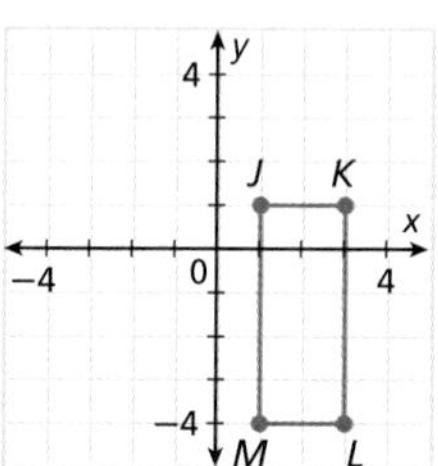

Ⓐ 6
Ⓑ 8
Ⓒ 10
Ⓓ 12

DAY 4

Miguel earns a 15% commission on his sales in addition to a salary of $500 a week. His weekly earnings can be modeled by the equation $p = 0.15s + 500$. What restrictions on the values of p and s best fit this situation?

Ⓐ $p \geq 0$, s can be any value.
Ⓑ $s \geq 0$, p can be any value.
Ⓒ $s \geq 500$, $p \geq 0$
Ⓓ $s \geq 0$, $p \geq 500$

DAY 5

Which is the greatest common factor of the terms in $4x^3 + 2x^2 - 6x$?

Ⓐ x
Ⓑ $x + 2$
Ⓒ $2x$
Ⓓ $2x^3$

Day	California Standards
1	7MG1.1
2	1A6.0
3	7MG3.2
4	7NS1.7
5	1A11.0

Countdown to Mastery WEEK 20

COUNTDOWN TO MASTERY

DAY 1

How many times does the graph of $y = x^2 - 3$ intersect the x-axis?

Ⓐ none
Ⓑ one
Ⓒ two
Ⓓ three

DAY 2

What is the slope of a line parallel to the line shown?

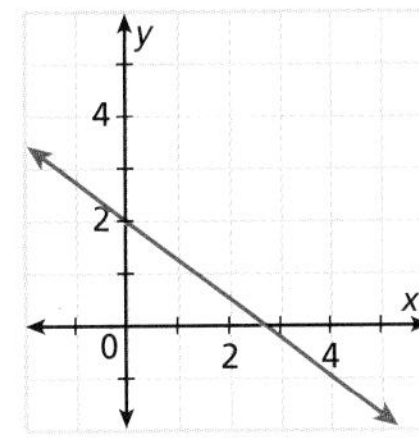

Ⓐ $-\frac{4}{3}$
Ⓑ $-\frac{3}{4}$
Ⓒ $\frac{3}{4}$
Ⓓ $\frac{4}{3}$

DAY 3

The graph shows the proposed balanced in Ashley's bank account. What is the average amount Ashley saves each week?

Ⓐ \$2
Ⓑ \$10
Ⓒ \$15
Ⓓ \$20

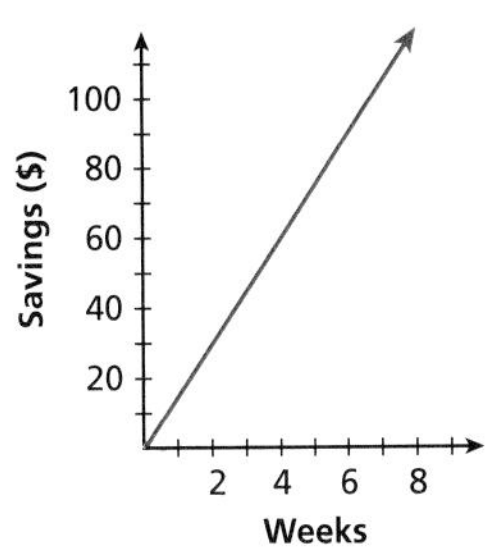

DAY 4

A map has the scale 1 inch:10 miles. On the map the area of a national park is about 12.5 square inches. Approximately how many acres are in the park? (1 square mile = 640 acres)

Ⓐ 800
Ⓑ 8000
Ⓒ 80,000
Ⓓ 800,000

DAY 5

Which is a factor of $4x^2 - 121$?

Ⓐ $2x + 11$
Ⓑ $(2x + 11)^2$
Ⓒ $2(x - 11)$
Ⓓ $4(x - 11)$

Day	California Standards
1	1A22.0
2	1A8.0
3	7AF3.4
4	7MG2.4
5	1A11.0

Countdown to Mastery

Countdown to Mastery — WEEK 21

DAY 1

Simplify the expression.

$$(2a^2b^3c^5)(4ab^2c^4)$$

(A) $6a^3b^5c^9$
(B) $8a^2b^5c^9$
(C) $8a^3b^5c^9$
(D) $8a^2b^6c^{20}$

DAY 2

Simplify the expression.

$$\frac{a^7b^5c^3}{a^2b^3c^2}$$

(A) $a^5b^2c^{-1}$
(B) a^5b^2c
(C) $a^9b^8c^5$
(D) $a^{14}b^{15}c^6$

DAY 3

Peter's solution to find the value of x is shown.

Which property of real numbers did Peter use for Step 1?

(A) Multiplication Property of Equality
(B) Division Property of Equality
(C) Distributive Property of Equality
(D) Zero Product Property of Multiplication

Given: $ax^2 + bx = 0$
Step 1: $x^2 + \frac{b}{a}x = 0$
Step 2: $x\left(x + \frac{b}{a}\right) = 0$
Step 3: $x = 0$ or $x + \frac{b}{a} = 0$
Step 4: $x = 0$ or $x = -\frac{b}{a}$

DAY 4

What are the solutions for the equation $y =(2x - 1)(x + 5)$?

(A) $\frac{1}{2}$ and -5
(B) -1 and 5
(C) 1 and -5
(D) $-\frac{1}{2}$ and 5

DAY 5

What quantity should be added to both sides of this equation to complete the square?

$$x^2 + 14x = 15$$

(A) 7
(B) 28
(C) 49
(D) 196

Day	California Standards
1	7AF2.2
2	7AF2.2
3	1A25.1
4	1A14.0
5	1A14.0

Countdown to Mastery WEEK 22

DAY 1

The graph of the equation $y = x^2 + 6x + 8$ is shown. For what values of x is $y = 0$?

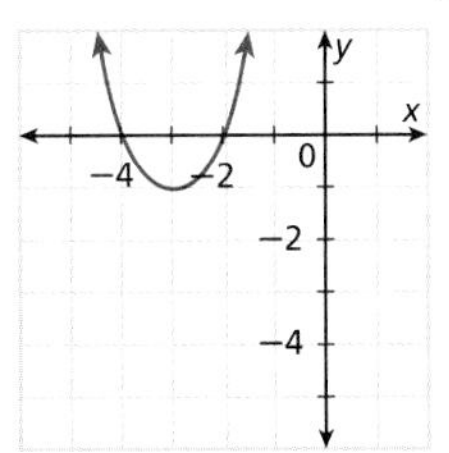

(A) 2 and 4
(B) −2 and −4
(C) −2 and 4
(D) 2 and −4

DAY 2

What is the range of the function shown?

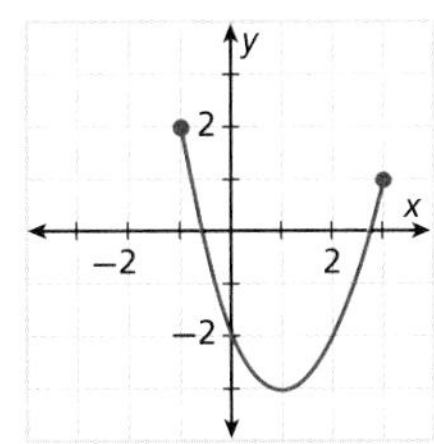

(A) $-2 < y < 3$
(B) $-3 < y \leq 6$
(C) $-3 \leq y \leq 6$
(D) $-2 \leq y \leq 3$

DAY 3

The graph shows the height of a baseball from the time it is thrown until the time it hits the ground. What value is ***not*** shown on the graph?

(A) The amount of time that the ball was in the air
(B) The height at which the ball started
(C) The maximum height that the ball reached
(D) The speed at which the ball was thrown

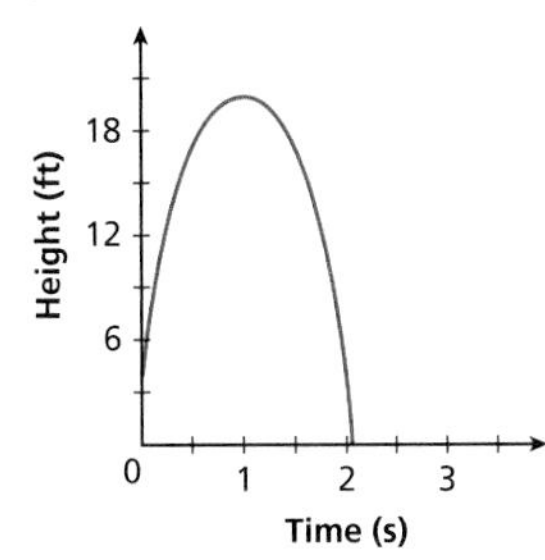

DAY 4

What are the solution(s) of the quadratic equation $x^2 - 10x - 24 = 0$?

(A) $x = -4, 6$
(B) $x = 2, -12$
(C) $x = -2, 12$
(D) $x = 4, -6$

DAY 5

What is the solution to the system of equations?

$$\begin{cases} 3x - 4y = 19 \\ y = 2x - 11 \end{cases}$$

(A) (5, −1)
(B) (−5, −21)
(C) (5, 1)
(D) (−5, −8.5)

Day	California Standards
1	1A21.0
2	1A17.0
3	1A23.0
4	1A14.0
5	1A9.0

Countdown to Mastery — WEEK 23

DAY 1

Which of the following is the graph of $y = -x^2$?

Ⓐ 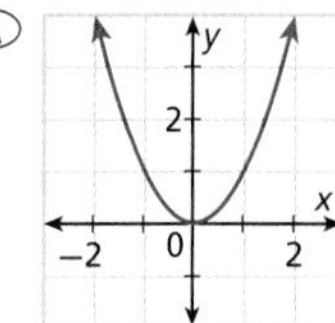

Ⓒ 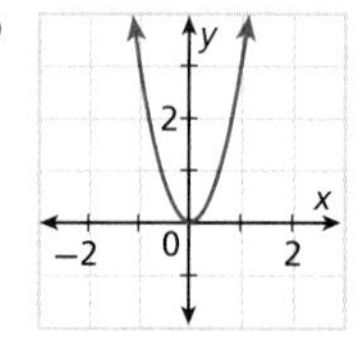

Ⓑ (circled) 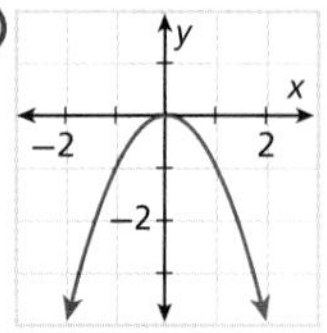

Ⓓ 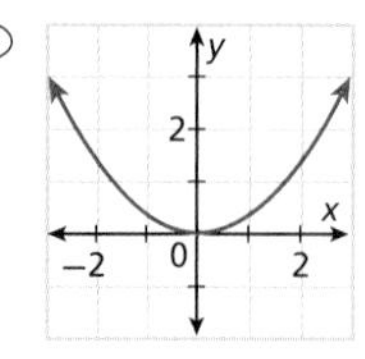

DAY 2

What is the value of x in the triangle shown?

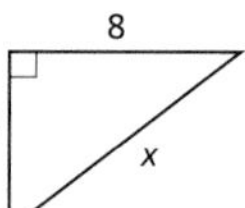

Ⓐ 5

Ⓑ 7

Ⓒ (circled) 10

Ⓓ 14

DAY 3

The graph shows the height of water coming out of a fountain over time. How many seconds pass before the water reaches the ground?

Ⓐ 0

Ⓑ (circled) 2

Ⓒ 4

Ⓓ 18

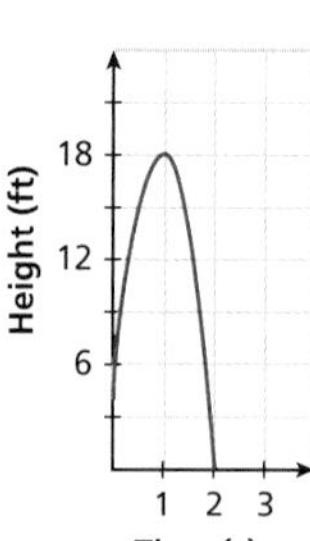

DAY 4

What is one solution to the equation $2x^2 + 7x + 3 = 0$?

Ⓐ $x = 3$

Ⓑ $x = \frac{1}{2}$

Ⓒ (circled) $x = -\frac{1}{2}$

Ⓓ $x = -1$

DAY 5

What is the solution to the system of equations?

$$\begin{cases} 4x + 2y = -8 \\ x - 2y = 13 \end{cases}$$

Ⓐ (25, 6)

Ⓑ (1, 6)

Ⓒ (−1, −6)

Ⓓ (circled) (1, −6)

Day	California Standards
1	7AF3.1
2	7MG3.3 🔑
3	1A23.0 🔑
4	1A20.0 🔑
5	1A9.0 🔑

Countdown to Mastery **WEEK 24**

COUNTDOWN TO MASTERY

DAY 1

What is the surface area of the figure represented by this net?

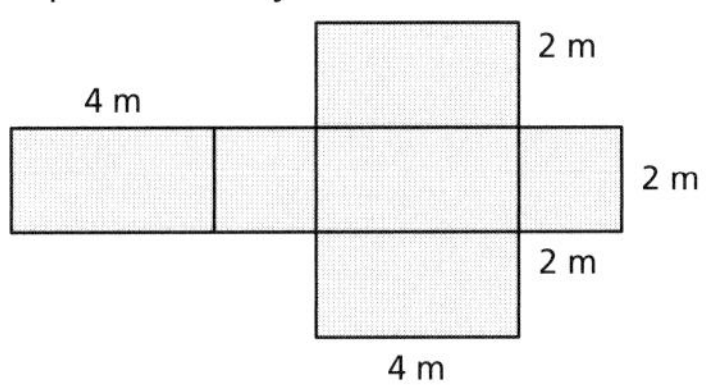

Ⓐ 32 square meters

Ⓑ 36 square meters

Ⓒ 40 square meters

Ⓓ 44 square meters

DAY 2

The graph of the equation $y = \frac{2}{3}x + 2$ is shown. For what value of x is $y = 0$?

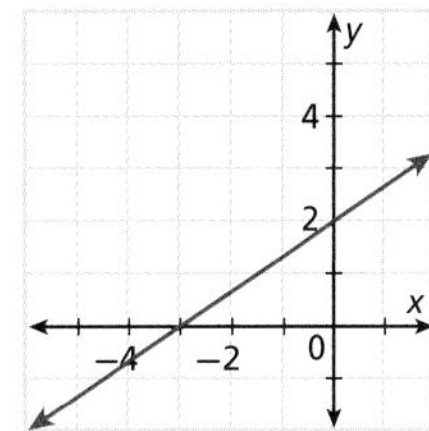

Ⓐ $x = -3$

Ⓑ $x = -2$

Ⓒ $x = 2$

Ⓓ $x = 3$

DAY 3

What values would you use for a, b, and c in the Quadratic Formula to solve $2x^2 = 5x + 140$?

Ⓐ $a = 2;\ b = 5;\ c = 140$

Ⓑ $a = 2;\ b = -5;\ c = -140$

Ⓒ $a = 5;\ b = -2;\ c = 140$

Ⓓ $a = 5;\ b = 2;\ c = 140$

DAY 4

Simplify $\frac{x^2 + 7x}{x^2 - 49}$ to lowest terms.

Ⓐ $-\frac{x}{7}$

Ⓑ $-\frac{1}{7}$

Ⓒ $\frac{x}{x - 7}$

Ⓓ $\frac{x}{x + 7}$

DAY 5

Which fraction equals the product

$$\left(\frac{3t + 4}{5t}\right)\left(\frac{10t}{t + 4}\right)?$$

Ⓐ $\frac{3t + 4}{t + 2}$

Ⓑ $\frac{6t + 8}{t + 4}$

Ⓒ $\frac{6}{1}$

Ⓓ $\frac{8}{1}$

Day	California Standards
1	7MG2.1
2	1A21.0
3	1A19.0
4	1A12.0
5	1A13.0

California Mathematics Content Standards for Algebra 1

The state bird is the California Quail
The Poppy is the state flower

California Mathematics Content Standards for Algebra 1

California
the golden state

The State Capitol in Sacramento

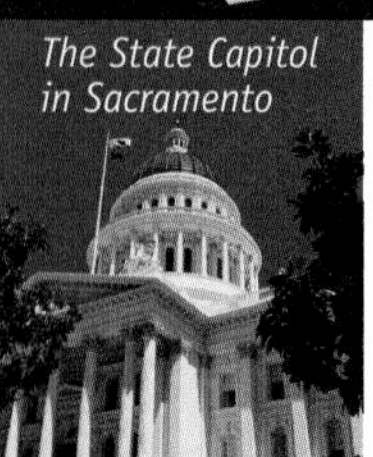

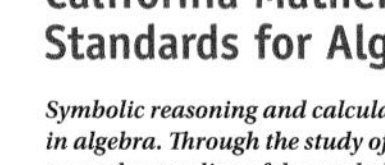

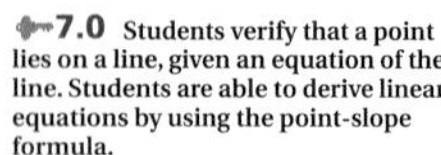

California Mathematics Content Standards for Algebra 1

Symbolic reasoning and calculations with symbols are central in algebra. Through the study of algebra, a student develops an understanding of the symbolic language of mathematics and the sciences. In addition, algebraic skills and concepts are developed and used in a wide variety of problem-solving situations.

1.0 Students identify and use the arithmetic properties of subsets of integers and rational, irrational, and real numbers, including closure properties for the four basic arithmetic operations where applicable:

1.1 Students use properties of numbers to demonstrate whether assertions are true or false.

2.0 Students understand and use such operations as taking the opposite, finding the reciprocal, taking a root, and raising to a fractional power. They understand and use the rules of exponents.

3.0 Students solve equations and inequalities involving absolute values.

4.0 Students simplify expressions before solving linear equations and inequalities in one variable, such as $3(2x - 5) + 4(x - 2) = 12$.

5.0 Students solve multistep problems, including word problems, involving linear equations and linear inequalities in one variable and provide justification for each step.

6.0 Students graph a linear equation and compute the x- and y-intercepts (e.g., graph $2x + 6y = 4$). They are also able to sketch the region defined by linear inequality (e.g., they sketch the region defined by $2x + 6y < 4$).

7.0 Students verify that a point lies on a line, given an equation of the line. Students are able to derive linear equations by using the point-slope formula.

8.0 Students understand the concepts of parallel lines and perpendicular lines and how those slopes are related. Students are able to find the equation of a line perpendicular to a given line that passes through a given point.

9.0 Students solve a system of two linear equations in two variables algebraically and are able to interpret the answer graphically. Students are able to solve a system of two linear inequalities in two variables and to sketch the solution sets.

10.0 Students add, subtract, multiply, and divide monomials and polynomials. Students solve multistep problems, including word problems, by using these techniques.

Continued

Big Sur coastline

California palm tree

California
the golden state

California Mathematics Content Standards for Algebra 1

11.0 Students apply basic factoring techniques to second- and simple third-degree polynomials. These techniques include finding a common factor for all terms in a polynomial, recognizing the difference of two squares, and recognizing perfect squares of binomials.

12.0 Students simplify fractions with polynomials in the numerator and denominator by factoring both and reducing them to the lowest terms.

13.0 Students add, subtract, multiply, and divide rational expressions and functions. Students solve both computationally and conceptually challenging problems by using these techniques.

14.0 Students solve a quadratic equation by factoring or completing the square.

15.0 Students apply algebraic techniques to solve rate problems, work problems, and percent mixture problems.

16.0 Students understand the concepts of a relation and a function, determine whether a given relation defines a function, and give pertinent information about given relations and functions.

17.0 Students determine the domain of independent variables and the range of dependent variables defined by a graph, a set of ordered pairs, or a symbolic expression.

18.0 Students determine whether a relation defined by a graph, a set of ordered pairs, or a symbolic expression is a function and justify the conclusion.

19.0 Students know the quadratic formula and are familiar with its proof by completing the square.

20.0 Students use the quadratic formula to find the roots of a second-degree polynomial and to solve quadratic equations.

21.0 Students graph quadratic functions and know that their roots are the x-intercepts.

22.0 Students use the quadratic formula or factoring techniques or both to determine whether the graph of a quadratic function will intersect the x-axis in zero, one, or two points.

23.0 Students apply quadratic equations to physical problems, such as the motion of an object under the force of gravity.

Continued

Bay Bridge

California the golden state

24.0 Students use and know simple aspects of a logical argument:

24.1 Students explain the difference between inductive and deductive reasoning and identify and provide examples of each.

24.2 Students identify the hypothesis and conclusion in logical deduction.

24.3 Students use counterexamples to show that an assertion is false and recognize that a single counterexample is sufficient to refute an assertion.

San Diego Beach

25.0 Students use properties of the number system to judge the validity of results, to justify each step of a procedure, and to prove or disprove statements:

25.1 Students use properties of numbers to construct simple, valid arguments (direct and indirect) for, or formulate counterexamples to, claimed assertions.

25.2 Students judge the validity of an argument according to whether the properties of the real number system and the order of operations have been applied correctly at each step.

25.3 Given a specific algebraic statement involving linear, quadratic, or absolute value expressions or equations or inequalities, students determine whether the statement is true sometimes, always, or never.

Balboa Park, San Diego

Count on **Holt California Algebra 1** for

Mastering the California Standards

A program created exclusively for California

Holt California Algebra 1 is specifically designed for California students and teachers. The California Mathematics Content Standards are unpacked, taught, and then reinforced throughout our program so that teachers can plan, diagnose, teach, assess, and intervene with the standards in mind.

UNDERSTANDING THE STANDARDS

A special **Unpacking the Standards** section at the start of each chapter helps students understand the new concepts they will learn, defines the Academic Vocabulary, and shows how the standards are applied in the chapter.

CHAPTER 5 **Unpacking the Standards**

The information below "unpacks" the standards. The Academic Vocabulary is highlighted and defined to help you understand the language of the standards. Refer to the lessons listed after each standard for help with the math terms and phrases. The Chapter Concept shows how the standard is applied in this chapter.

California Standard	Academic Vocabulary	Chapter Concept
6.0 Students graph a linear equation and compute the *x*- and *y*-intercepts (e.g., graph $2x + 6y = 4$). They are also able to sketch the region defined by linear inequalities (e.g., they sketch the region defined by $2x + 6y < 4$). (Lessons **5-1, 5-2, 5-3, 5-4, 5-5, 5-6**)	**graph** to represent data with a diagram **compute** to calculate an answer	You graph an equation of a line using various methods: • plotting points that are solutions of an equation and connecting them with a line. • finding the points where a line will intersect the *x*-axis and the *y*-axis, and then connecting those two points with a line.
7.0 Students verify that a point lies on a line, given an	**verify** to check whether or not something is true	You learn that all points on the graph of a line are solutions to ... n. You also write an ... a line given a point and its slope.

Math Background: Teaching the Standards supports the professional development of teachers. This feature addresses the mathematic theory underlying each lesson and also provides greater depth and complexity for each standard by showing how the math will be used in future courses.

Holt's standards-driven content is easy to manage using Holt's **California On-Course Mapping Instruction: A Teacher's Guide for Planning**. Teachers and administrators can see at a glance which lessons and resources address each of the standards.

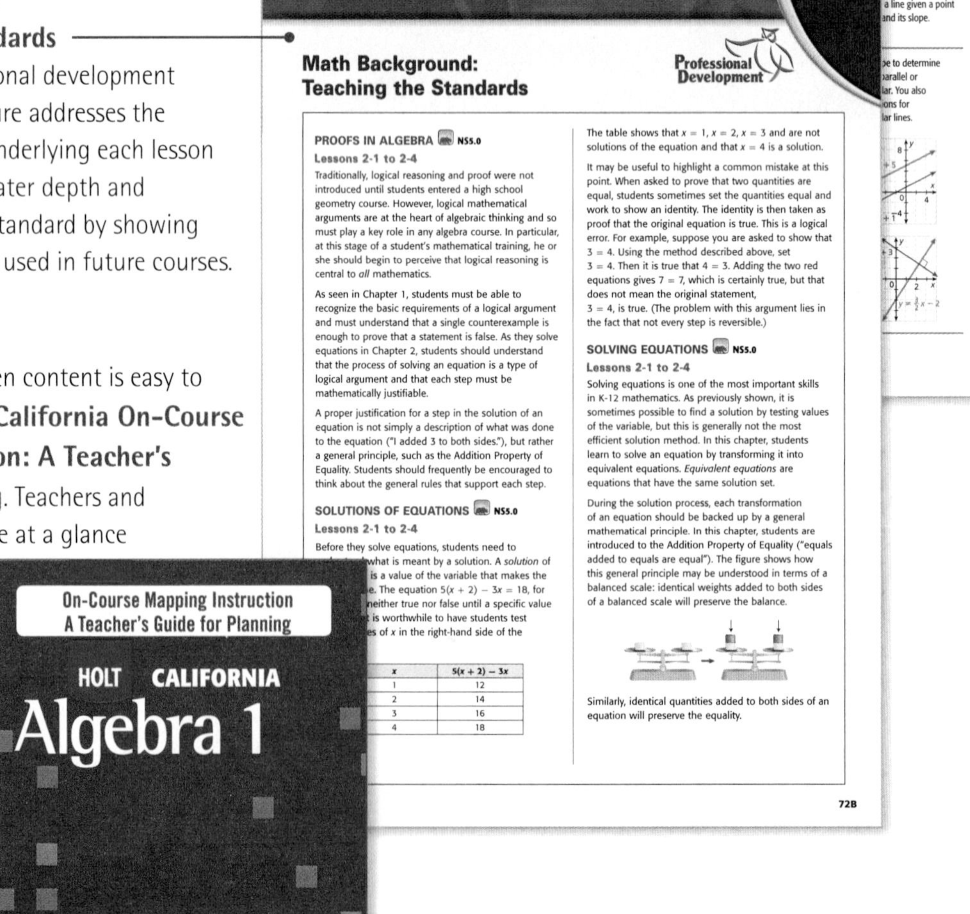

Math Background: Teaching the Standards

Professional Development

PROOFS IN ALGEBRA NS5.0
Lessons 2-1 to 2-4

Traditionally, logical reasoning and proof were not introduced until students entered a high school geometry course. However, logical mathematical arguments are at the heart of algebraic thinking and so must play a key role in any algebra course. In particular, at this stage of a student's mathematical training, he or she should begin to perceive that logical reasoning is central to *all* mathematics.

As seen in Chapter 1, students must be able to recognize the basic requirements of a logical argument and must understand that a single counterexample is enough to prove that a statement is false. As they solve equations in Chapter 2, students should understand that the process of solving an equation is a type of logical argument and that each step must be mathematically justifiable.

A proper justification for a step in the solution of an equation is not simply a description of what was done to the equation ("I added 3 to both sides."), but rather a general principle, such as the Addition Property of Equality. Students should frequently be encouraged to think about the general rules that support each step.

SOLUTIONS OF EQUATIONS NS5.0
Lessons 2-1 to 2-4

Before they solve equations, students need to ... what is meant by a solution. A *solution* of ... is a value of the variable that makes the ... e. The equation $5(x + 2) - 3x = 18$, for ... neither true nor false until a specific value ... t is worthwhile to have students test ... es of x in the right-hand side of the

x	$5(x + 2) - 3x$
1	12
2	14
3	16
4	18

The table shows that $x = 1$, $x = 2$, $x = 3$ and are not solutions of the equation and that $x = 4$ is a solution.

It may be useful to highlight a common mistake at this point. When asked to prove that two quantities are equal, students sometimes set the quantities equal and work to show an identity. The identity is then taken as proof that the original equation is true. This is a logical error. For example, suppose you are asked to show that $3 = 4$. Using the method described above, set $3 = 4$. Then it is true that $4 = 3$. Adding the two red equations gives $7 = 7$, which is certainly true, but that does not mean the original statement, $3 = 4$, is true. (The problem with this argument lies in the fact that not every step is reversible.)

SOLVING EQUATIONS NS5.0
Lessons 2-1 to 2-4

Solving equations is one of the most important skills in K-12 mathematics. As previously shown, it is sometimes possible to find a solution by testing values of the variable, but this is generally not the most efficient solution method. In this chapter, students learn to solve an equation by transforming it into equivalent equations. *Equivalent equations* are equations that have the same solution set.

During the solution process, each transformation of an equation should be backed up by a general mathematical principle. In this chapter, students are introduced to the Addition Property of Equality ("equals added to equals are equal"). The figure shows how this general principle may be understood in terms of a balanced scale: identical weights added to both sides of a balanced scale will preserve the balance.

Similarly, identical quantities added to both sides of an equation will preserve the equality.

72B

Program Highlights

HOLT MATH

PRACTICING THE STANDARDS

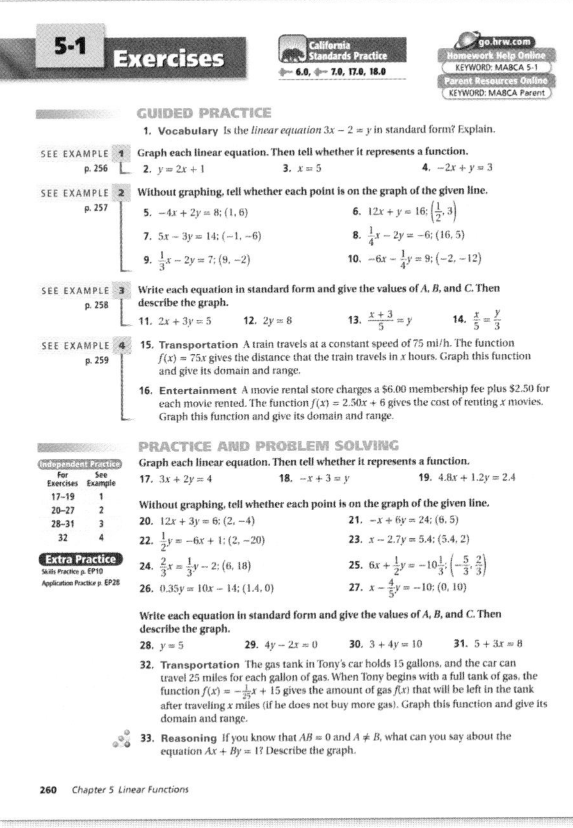

5-1 Exercises

California Standards Practice 6.0, 7.0, 17.0, 18.0

go.hrw.com Homework Help Online KEYWORD: MA8CA 5-1 Parent Resources Online KEYWORD: MA8CA Parent

GUIDED PRACTICE

1. **Vocabulary** Is the *linear equation* $3x - 2 = y$ in standard form? Explain.

SEE EXAMPLE 1 p. 256 Graph each linear equation. Then tell whether it represents a function.

2. $y = 2x + 1$
3. $x = 5$
4. $-2x + y = 3$

SEE EXAMPLE 2 p. 257 Without graphing, tell whether each point is on the graph of the given line.

5. $-4x + 2y = 8$; $(1, 6)$
6. $12x + y = 16$; $\left(\frac{1}{2}, 3\right)$
7. $5x - 3y = 14$; $(-1, -6)$
8. $\frac{1}{4}x - 2y = -6$; $(16, 5)$
9. $\frac{1}{3}x - 2y = 7$; $(9, -2)$
10. $-6x - \frac{1}{4}y = 9$; $(-2, -12)$

SEE EXAMPLE 3 p. 258 Write each equation in standard form and give the values of *A*, *B*, and *C*. Then describe the graph.

11. $2x + 3y = 5$
12. $2y = 8$
13. $\frac{x+3}{5} = y$
14. $\frac{x}{5} = \frac{y}{3}$

SEE EXAMPLE 4 p. 259

15. **Transportation** A train travels at a constant speed of 75 mi/h. The function $f(x) = 75x$ gives the distance that the train travels in *x* hours. Graph this function and give its domain and range.
16. **Entertainment** A movie rental store charges a \$6.00 membership fee plus \$2.50 for each movie rented. The function $f(x) = 2.50x + 6$ gives the cost of renting *x* movies. Graph this function and give its domain and range.

PRACTICE AND PROBLEM SOLVING

Independent Practice	
For Exercises	See Example
17–19	1
20–27	2
28–31	3
32	4

Extra Practice Skills Practice p. EP10 Application Practice p. EP28

Graph each linear equation. Then tell whether it represents a function.

17. $3x + 2y = 4$
18. $-x + 3 = y$
19. $4.8x + 1.2y = 2.4$

Without graphing, tell whether each point is on the graph of the given line.

20. $12x + 3y = 6$; $(2, -4)$
21. $-x + 6y = 24$; $(6, 5)$
22. $\frac{1}{2}y = -6x + 1$; $(2, -20)$
23. $x - 2.7y = 5.4$; $(5.4, 2)$
24. $\frac{2}{3}x = \frac{1}{3}y - 2$; $(6, 18)$
25. $6x + \frac{1}{2}y = -10\frac{1}{3}$; $\left(-\frac{5}{3}, \frac{2}{3}\right)$
26. $0.35y = 10x - 14$; $(1.4, 0)$
27. $x - \frac{4}{5}y = -10$; $(0, 10)$

Write each equation in standard form and give the values of *A*, *B*, and *C*. Then describe the graph.

28. $y = 5$
29. $4y - 2x = 0$
30. $3 + 4y = 10$
31. $5 + 3x = 8$

32. **Transportation** The gas tank in Tony's car holds 15 gallons, and the car can travel 25 miles for each gallon of gas. When Tony begins with a full tank of gas, the function $f(x) = -\frac{1}{25}x + 15$ gives the amount of gas $f(x)$ that will be left in the tank after traveling *x* miles (if he does not buy more gas). Graph this function and give its domain and range.
33. **Reasoning** If you know that $AB = 0$ and $A \neq B$, what can you say about the equation $Ax + By = 1$? Describe the graph.

260 Chapter 5 Linear Functions

Lesson Exercises include correlations to the California standards.

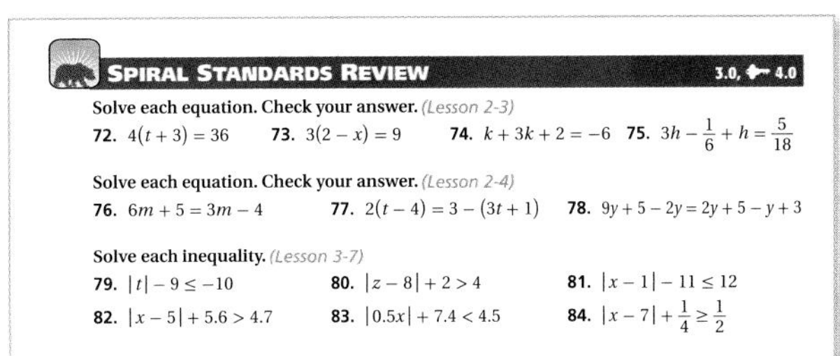

SPIRAL STANDARDS REVIEW 3.0, 4.0

Solve each equation. Check your answer. (Lesson 2-3)

72. $4(t + 3) = 36$
73. $3(2 - x) = 9$
74. $k + 3k + 2 = -6$
75. $3h - \frac{1}{6} + h = \frac{5}{18}$

Solve each equation. Check your answer. (Lesson 2-4)

76. $6m + 5 = 3m - 4$
77. $2(t - 4) = 3 - (3t + 1)$
78. $9y + 5 - 2y = 2y + 5 - y + 3$

Solve each inequality. (Lesson 3-7)

79. $|t| - 9 \leq -10$
80. $|z - 8| + 2 > 4$
81. $|x - 1| - 11 \leq 12$
82. $|x - 5| + 5.6 > 4.7$
83. $|0.5x| + 7.4 < 4.5$
84. $|x - 7| + \frac{1}{4} \geq \frac{1}{2}$

Correlated **Spiral Standards Review** at the end of each lesson keeps previously learned skills sharp.

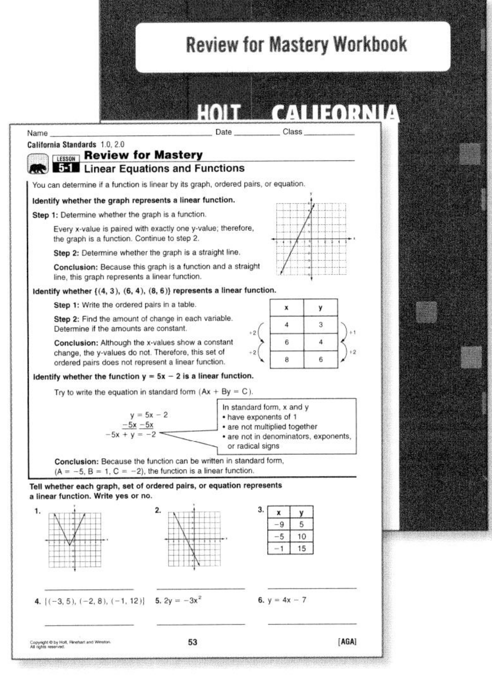

Review for Mastery Workbook

HOLT CALIFORNIA

Name __________ Date __________ Class __________

California Standards 1.0, 2.0

LESSON 5-1 **Review for Mastery**
Linear Equations and Functions

You can determine if a function is linear by its graph, ordered pairs, or equation.

Identify whether the graph represents a linear function.

Step 1: Determine whether the graph is a function.

Every x-value is paired with exactly one y-value; therefore, the graph is a function. Continue to step 2.

Step 2: Determine whether the graph is a straight line.

Conclusion: Because this graph is a function and a straight line, this graph represents a linear function.

Identify whether {(4, 3), (6, 4), (8, 6)} represents a linear function.

Step 1: Write the ordered pairs in a table.

Step 2: Find the amount of change in each variable. Determine if the amounts are constant.

Conclusion: Although the x-values show a constant change, the y-values do not. Therefore, this set of ordered pairs does not represent a linear function.

x	y
4	3
6	4
8	6

Identify whether the function y = 5x − 2 is a linear function.

Try to write the equation in standard form (Ax + By = C).

$y = 5x - 2$
$-5x \quad -5x$
$-5x + y = -2$

In standard form, x and y
• have exponents of 1
• are not multiplied together
• are not in denominators, exponents, or radical signs

Conclusion: Because the function can be written in standard form, (A = −5, B = 1, C = −2), the function is a linear function.

Tell whether each graph, set of ordered pairs, or equation represents a linear function. Write yes or no.

1.
2.
3.

x	y
−9	5
−5	10
−1	15

4. {(−3, 5), (−2, 8), (−1, 12)}
5. $2y = -3x^2$
6. $y = 4x - 7$

53 [AGA]

Review for Mastery Workbook provides reteaching and additional practice for every lesson.

Program Highlights

Standards Practice CD-ROM, powered by ExamView® Version 5 Assessment Suite, provides a bank of practice items searchable by California Mathematics Content Standard, so that you can customize assignments.

California Standards Virtual File Cabinet CD-ROM gives you access to standards-based content in a database that is adaptable, searchable, and expandable.

> *"Students can master the California standards by learning mathematics as a coherent collection of related ideas that fit together naturally."*
>
> — Tom Roby, Holt author

Count on **Holt California Algebra 1** for

Assessment and Strategic Intervention

Holt's at-a-glance system makes it easy to keep students on track.

You need to know how well your students understand the lesson BEFORE they take the test. With *Holt California Algebra 1*, informal and formal assessment options are given at every stage within the chapter. Intervention resources allow you to reteach or review material without merely sending students back to previous lessons in the book.

- **Assess Prior Knowledge** to make sure all students begin the chapter on solid footing.

  Intervene with alternate teaching strategies and basic skills review in ***Are You Ready? Intervention and Enrichment.***

- **Formative Assessment** diagnoses skill development within the chapter.

  Intervene with ***Ready to Go On? Intervention and Enrichment, Lesson Tutorial Videos,*** **Homework Help Online,** and more.

- **Summative Assessment** allows students to demonstrate their mastery of the concepts.

  Intervene with ***Review for Mastery Workbook.***

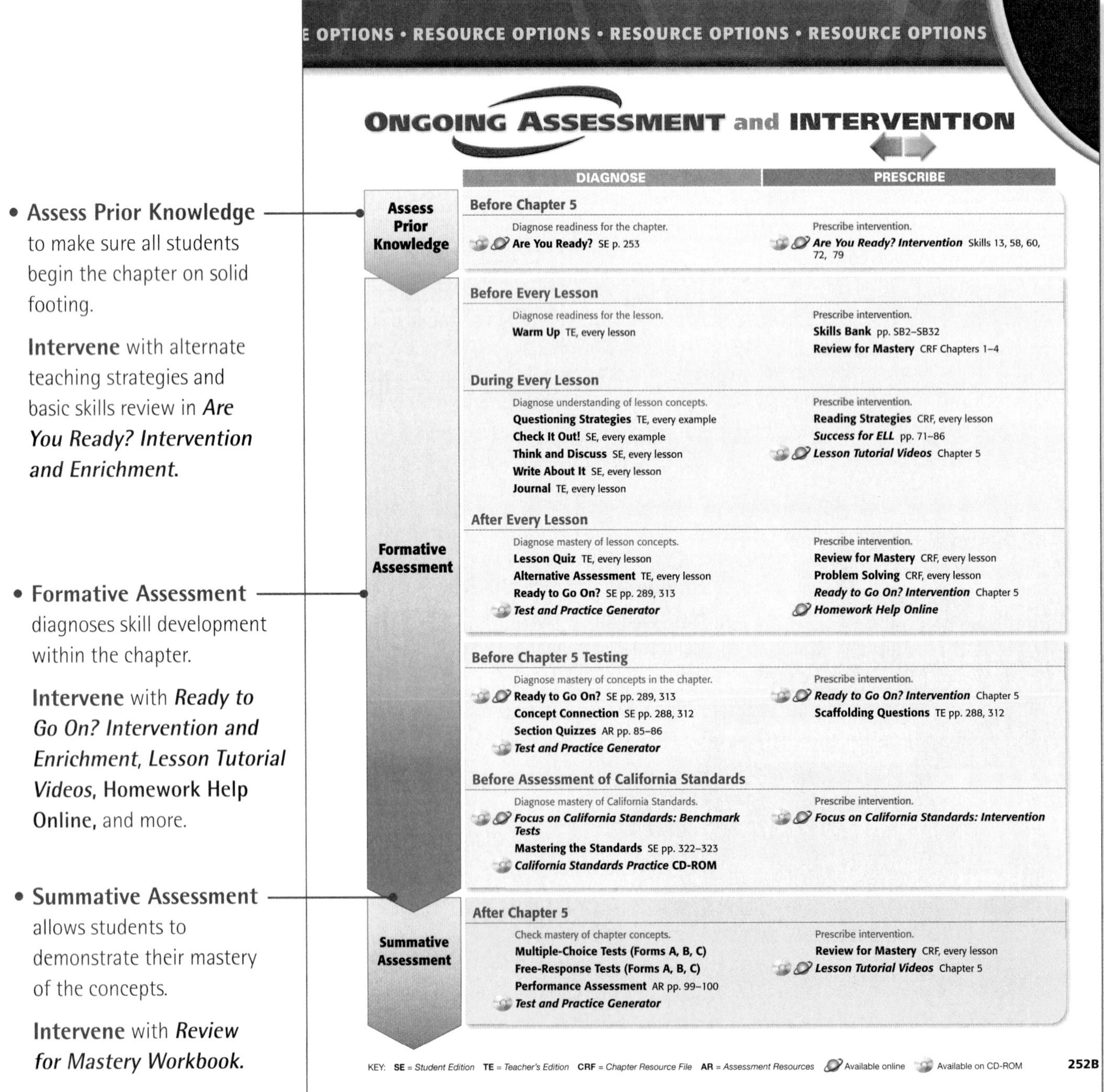

E OPTIONS • RESOURCE OPTIONS • RESOURCE OPTIONS • RESOURCE OPTIONS

ONGOING ASSESSMENT and INTERVENTION

	DIAGNOSE	PRESCRIBE
Assess Prior Knowledge	**Before Chapter 5** Diagnose readiness for the chapter. **Are You Ready?** SE p. 253	Prescribe intervention. ***Are You Ready? Intervention*** Skills 13, 58, 60, 72, 79
Formative Assessment	**Before Every Lesson** Diagnose readiness for the lesson. **Warm Up** TE, every lesson	Prescribe intervention. **Skills Bank** pp. SB2–SB32 **Review for Mastery** CRF Chapters 1–4
	During Every Lesson Diagnose understanding of lesson concepts. **Questioning Strategies** TE, every example **Check It Out!** SE, every example **Think and Discuss** SE, every lesson **Write About It** SE, every lesson **Journal** TE, every lesson	Prescribe intervention. **Reading Strategies** CRF, every lesson ***Success for ELL*** pp. 71–86 ***Lesson Tutorial Videos*** Chapter 5
	After Every Lesson Diagnose mastery of lesson concepts. **Lesson Quiz** TE, every lesson **Alternative Assessment** TE, every lesson **Ready to Go On?** SE pp. 289, 313 ***Test and Practice Generator***	Prescribe intervention. **Review for Mastery** CRF, every lesson **Problem Solving** CRF, every lesson ***Ready to Go On? Intervention*** Chapter 5 ***Homework Help Online***
	Before Chapter 5 Testing Diagnose mastery of concepts in the chapter. **Ready to Go On?** SE pp. 289, 313 **Concept Connection** SE pp. 288, 312 **Section Quizzes** AR pp. 85–86 ***Test and Practice Generator***	Prescribe intervention. ***Ready to Go On? Intervention*** Chapter 5 **Scaffolding Questions** TE pp. 288, 312
	Before Assessment of California Standards Diagnose mastery of California Standards. ***Focus on California Standards: Benchmark Tests*** **Mastering the Standards** SE pp. 322–323 ***California Standards Practice CD-ROM***	Prescribe intervention. ***Focus on California Standards: Intervention***
Summative Assessment	**After Chapter 5** Check mastery of chapter concepts. **Multiple-Choice Tests (Forms A, B, C)** **Free-Response Tests (Forms A, B, C)** **Performance Assessment** AR pp. 99–100 ***Test and Practice Generator***	Prescribe intervention. **Review for Mastery** CRF, every lesson ***Lesson Tutorial Videos*** Chapter 5

KEY: **SE** = *Student Edition* **TE** = *Teacher's Edition* **CRF** = *Chapter Resource File* **AR** = *Assessment Resources* Available online Available on CD-ROM

252B

When students struggle, rereading the same text hoping that it will eventually make sense is a discouraging task. Research shows that they need to try a new approach to the lesson. That's at the core of the assessment and intervention system in *Holt California Algebra 1*

Only from Holt!

Are You Ready? Intervention and Enrichment

- Diagnoses mastery of prerequisite skills
- Strengthens student weaknesses with direct instruction, conceptual models, and scaffolded practice
- Enriches every chapter with critical thinking activities
- Available in print, on CD-ROM, and online

Only from Holt!

Ready to Go On? Intervention and Enrichment

- Diagnoses mastery of newly taught skills
- Addresses deficiencies with alternative instruction and practice
- Checks student progress with post-tests
- Available in print, on CD-ROM, and online

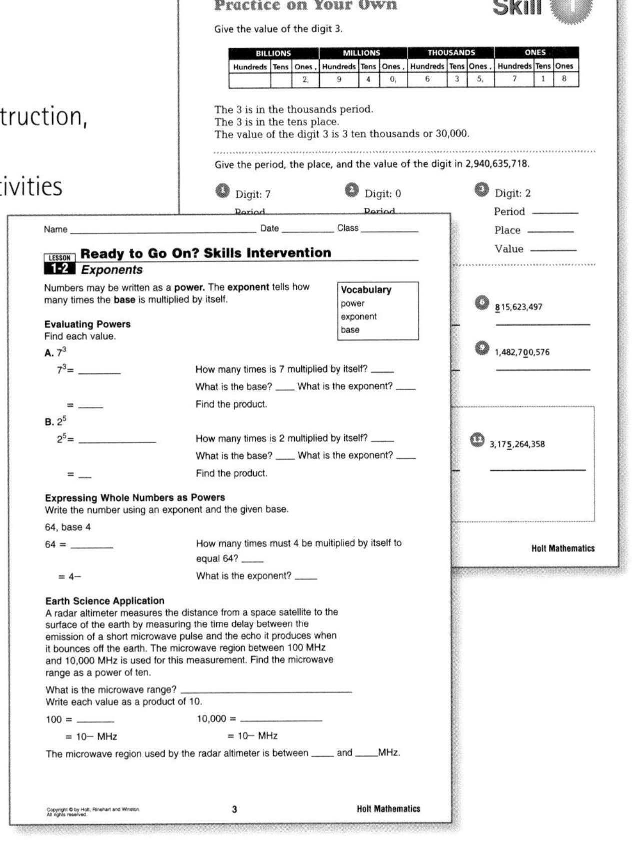

Name ______ Skill ______

Practice on Your Own Skill 1

Give the value of the digit 3.

BILLIONS			MILLIONS			THOUSANDS			ONES		
Hundreds	Tens	Ones ,	Hundreds	Tens	Ones ,	Hundreds	Tens	Ones ,	Hundreds	Tens	Ones
		2,	9	4	0,	6	3	5,	7	1	8

The 3 is in the thousands period.
The 3 is in the tens place.
The value of the digit 3 is 3 ten thousands or 30,000.

Give the period, the place, and the value of the digit in 2,940,635,718.

1. Digit: 7 Period
2. Digit: 0 Period
3. Digit: 2 Period ______ Place ______ Value ______

6. 815,623,497 ______

9. 1,482,700,576 ______

12. 3,175,264,358 ______

Holt Mathematics

Name ______ Date ______ Class ______

LESSON 1-2 **Ready to Go On? Skills Intervention**
Exponents

Numbers may be written as a **power.** The **exponent** tells how many times the **base** is multiplied by itself.

Vocabulary: power, exponent, base

Evaluating Powers
Find each value.

A. 7^3

7^3 = ______ How many times is 7 multiplied by itself? ____
What is the base? ____ What is the exponent? ____
= ____ Find the product.

B. 2^5

2^5 = ______ How many times is 2 multiplied by itself? ____
What is the base? ____ What is the exponent? ____
= __ Find the product.

Expressing Whole Numbers as Powers
Write the number using an exponent and the given base.

64, base 4

64 = ______ How many times must 4 be multiplied by itself to equal 64? ____
= 4– What is the exponent? ____

Earth Science Application
A radar altimeter measures the distance from a space satellite to the surface of the earth by measuring the time delay between the emission of a short microwave pulse and the echo it produces when it bounces off the earth. The microwave region between 100 MHz and 10,000 MHz is used for this measurement. Find the microwave range as a power of ten.

What is the microwave range? ______
Write each value as a product of 10.

100 = ______ 10,000 = ______
= 10– MHz = 10– MHz

The microwave region used by the radar altimeter is between ____ and ____MHz.

Copyright © by Holt, Rinehart and Winston. All rights reserved. 3 Holt Mathematics

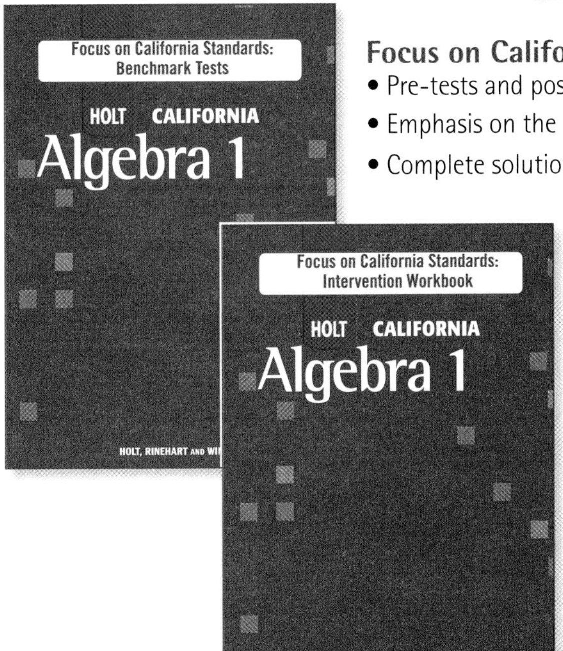

Focus on California Standards: Benchmark Tests

Only from Holt!

- Pre-tests and post-tests for each of the standards
- Emphasis on the key standards
- Complete solutions and error analysis of incorrect answers

Focus on California Standards: Intervention Workbook

Only from Holt!

- Alternative teaching strategies for every standard.
- Scaffolded intervention for skills and problem solving
- Skills and problem-solving practice worksheets
- Key vocabulary worksheets
- Standards review with practice

"*The right support structure can empower every teacher to be highly confident and every student to succeed.*"

— Lee Haines, Holt author

Program Highlights

Count on **Holt California Algebra 1** for

Universal Access

Reach all learners in your classroom every day – no matter what their skill levels.

Not all students "get it" at the same time or in the same way. *Holt California Algebra 1* accommodates the students in your classroom with different skill levels and those who benefit from different approaches.

With leveled practice and tests, content presented in a variety of media, and teaching strategies built in at point-of-use, helping all of your students succeed has never been easier.

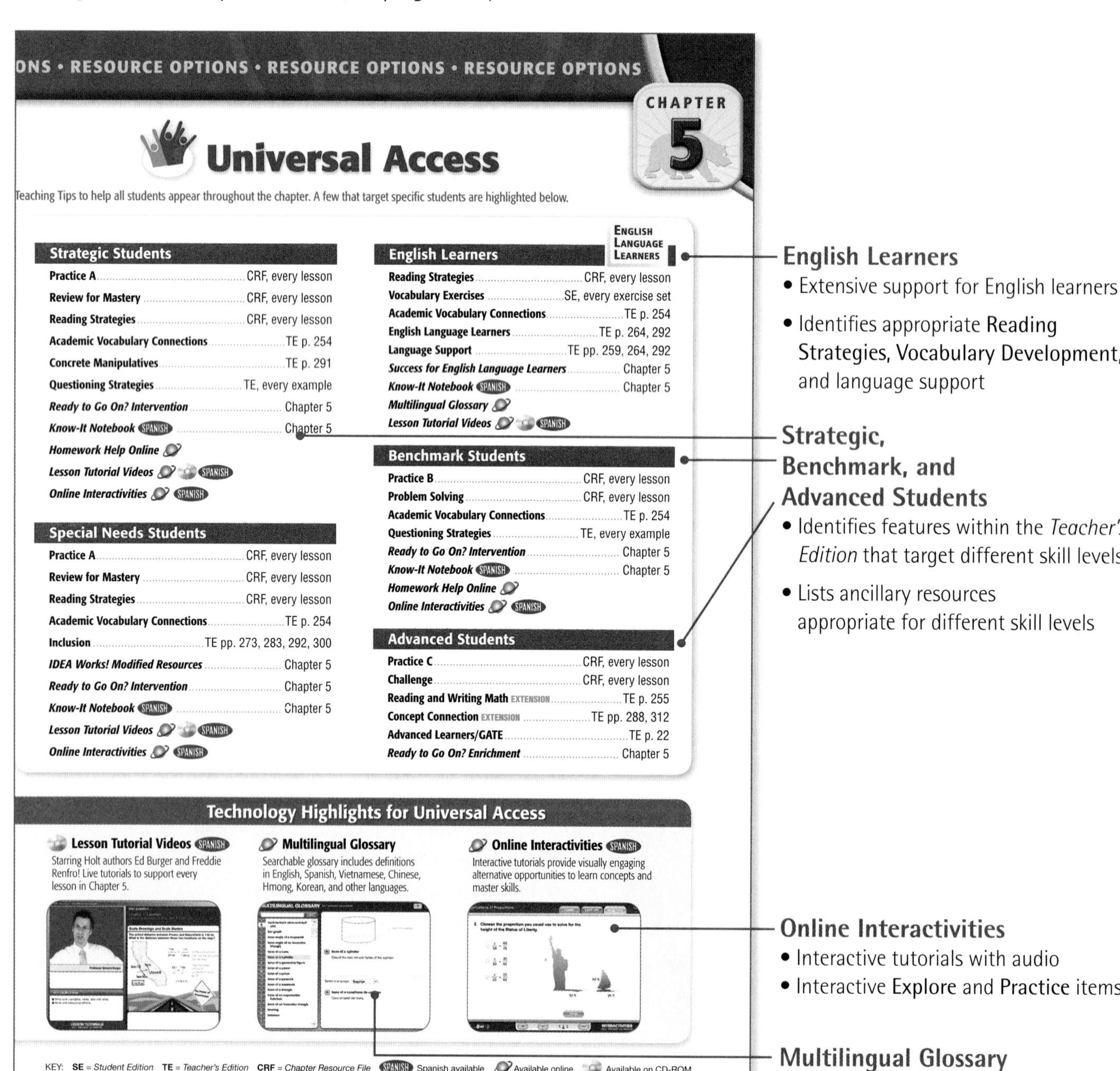

ONS • RESOURCE OPTIONS • RESOURCE OPTIONS • RESOURCE OPTIONS

CHAPTER 5

Universal Access

Teaching Tips to help all students appear throughout the chapter. A few that target specific students are highlighted below.

Strategic Students

Practice A	CRF, every lesson
Review for Mastery	CRF, every lesson
Reading Strategies	CRF, every lesson
Academic Vocabulary Connections	TE p. 254
Concrete Manipulatives	TE p. 291
Questioning Strategies	TE, every example
Ready to Go On? Intervention	Chapter 5
Know-It Notebook SPANISH	Chapter 5
Homework Help Online	
Lesson Tutorial Videos SPANISH	
Online Interactivities SPANISH	

Special Needs Students

Practice A	CRF, every lesson
Review for Mastery	CRF, every lesson
Reading Strategies	CRF, every lesson
Academic Vocabulary Connections	TE p. 254
Inclusion	TE pp. 273, 283, 292, 300
IDEA Works! Modified Resources	Chapter 5
Ready to Go On? Intervention	Chapter 5
Know-It Notebook SPANISH	Chapter 5
Lesson Tutorial Videos SPANISH	
Online Interactivities SPANISH	

English Learners — ENGLISH LANGUAGE LEARNERS

Reading Strategies	CRF, every lesson
Vocabulary Exercises	SE, every exercise set
Academic Vocabulary Connections	TE p. 254
English Language Learners	TE p. 264, 292
Language Support	TE pp. 259, 264, 292
Success for English Language Learners	Chapter 5
Know-It Notebook SPANISH	Chapter 5
Multilingual Glossary	
Lesson Tutorial Videos SPANISH	

Benchmark Students

Practice B	CRF, every lesson
Problem Solving	CRF, every lesson
Academic Vocabulary Connections	TE p. 254
Questioning Strategies	TE, every example
Ready to Go On? Intervention	Chapter 5
Know-It Notebook SPANISH	Chapter 5
Homework Help Online	
Online Interactivities SPANISH	

Advanced Students

Practice C	CRF, every lesson
Challenge	CRF, every lesson
Reading and Writing Math EXTENSION	TE p. 255
Concept Connection EXTENSION	TE pp. 288, 312
Advanced Learners/GATE	TE p. 22
Ready to Go On? Enrichment	Chapter 5

Technology Highlights for Universal Access

Lesson Tutorial Videos SPANISH
Starring Holt authors Ed Burger and Freddie Renfro! Live tutorials to support every lesson in Chapter 5.

Multilingual Glossary
Searchable glossary includes definitions in English, Spanish, Vietnamese, Chinese, Hmong, Korean, and other languages.

Online Interactivities SPANISH
Interactive tutorials provide visually engaging alternative opportunities to learn concepts and master skills.

KEY: **SE** = *Student Edition* **TE** = *Teacher's Edition* **CRF** = *Chapter Resource File* SPANISH Spanish available · Available online · Available on CD-ROM

252D

English Learners
- Extensive support for English learners
- Identifies appropriate **Reading Strategies, Vocabulary Development,** and language support

Strategic, Benchmark, and Advanced Students
- Identifies features within the *Teacher's Edition* that target different skill levels
- Lists ancillary resources appropriate for different skill levels

Online Interactivities
- Interactive tutorials with audio
- Interactive **Explore** and **Practice** items

Multilingual Glossary
- Illustrated glossary in twelve languages
- Audio for English and Spanish terms

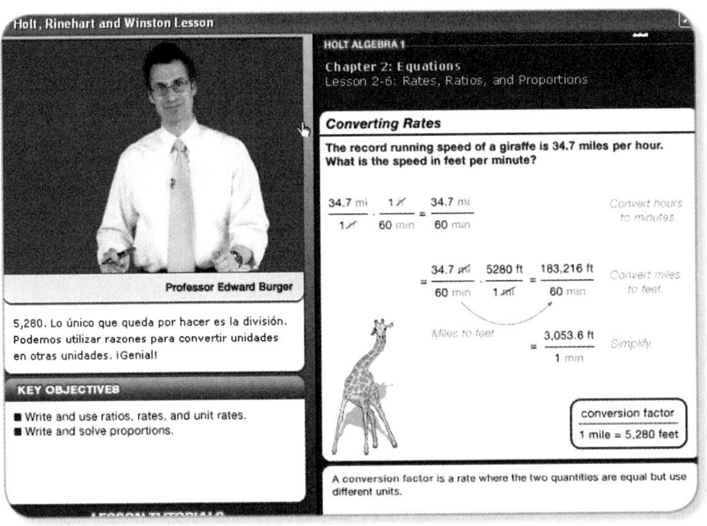

Lesson Tutorial Videos

Only from Holt!

- Illustrate every example!
- Your students' personal take-home tutor
- Closed captioning in English and Spanish
- Available online or on CD-ROM

Math Builders

- Illustrates important standards through a step-by-step layered approach
- Transparent pages in the *Student Edition*

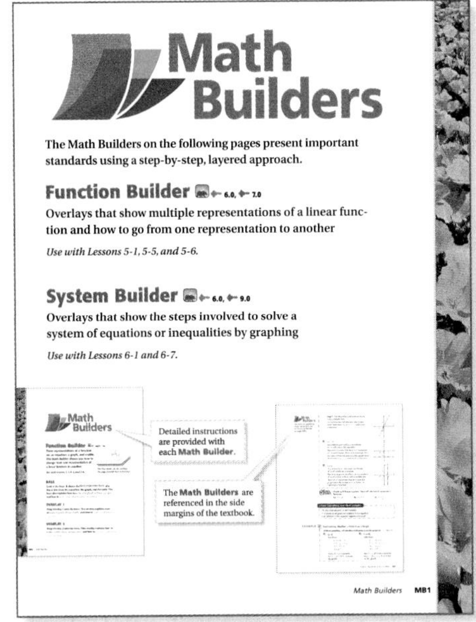

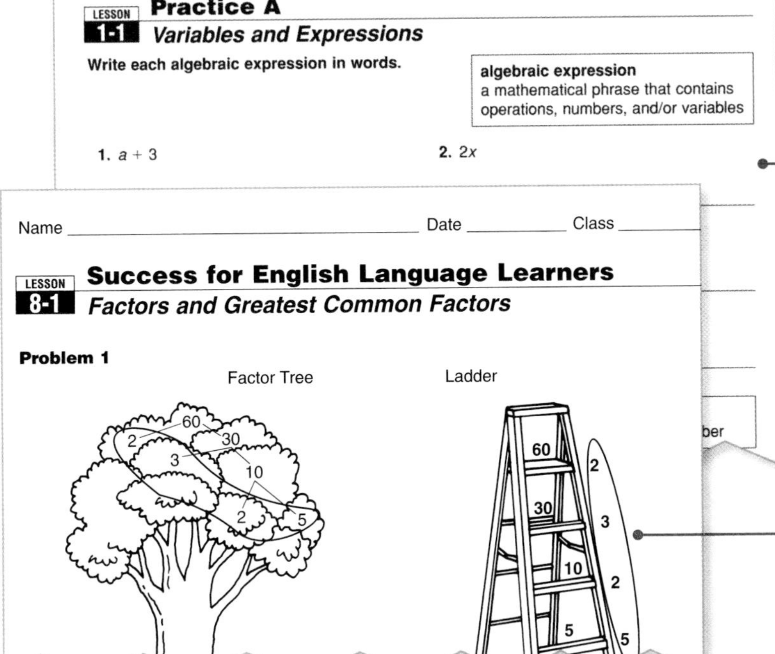

Only from Holt!

IDEA Works!®

Modified Worksheets and Tests

- Adapted format for students with special needs
- Modified practice and problem solving for every lesson
- Modified tests and quizzes for every chapter
- Vocabulary flashcards

Success for English Language Learners

- Same concepts as the student lesson, but fewer words and more visuals
- Alternate teaching strategies for English-language learners

*"Thoughtfully designed and supported instruction **demystifies mathematics for all students** and enhances their understanding of core foundational knowledge and skills."*

– Dr. Edward Burger, Holt author

Program Highlights

Count on Holt California Algebra 1 for

Technology to make your life easier!

The right tools to accomplish your goals

Holt California Algebra 1 empowers you with key management and presentation tools that help you inspire your students and meet their needs while saving you time.

Interactive Answers and Solutions CD-ROM

- Show complete solutions for any exercise at the click of a button!
- Customize answer keys
- Make answer transparencies

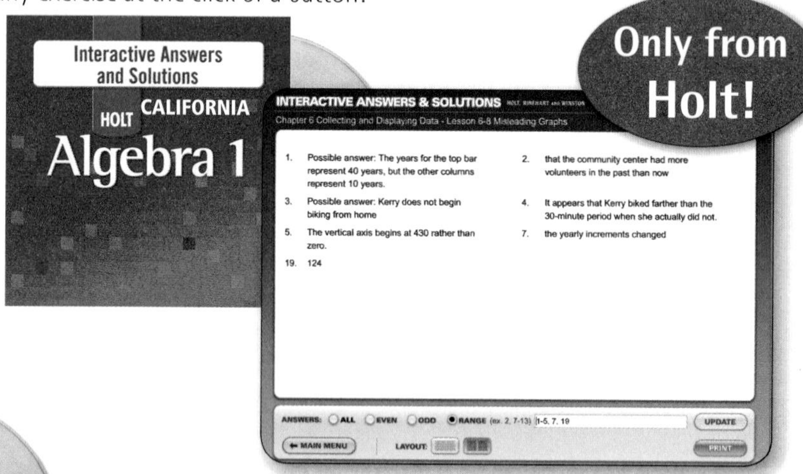

California Teacher's One-Stop Planner® CD-ROM

Everything a math teacher needs to plan and manage lessons is available in one place.

- Complete *Teacher's Edition*
- All print ancillaries and transparencies
- Customizable lesson plans
- Holt Calendar Planner
  - Holt PuzzlePro®
  - MindPoint® Quiz Show
  - ExamView® Version 5 Assessment Suite

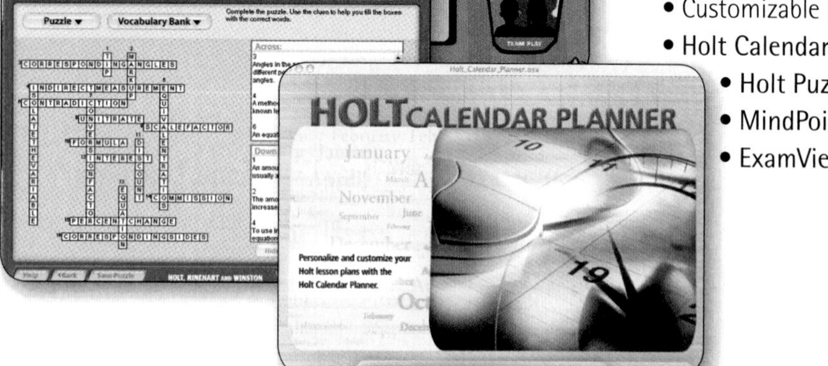

California Student One Stop

- Entire *Student Edition*
- All workbooks
- *Are You Ready? Intervention and Enrichment*
- *Ready to Go On? Intervention and Enrichment*

Program Highlights

California Premier Online Edition

Go home empty-handed and get online.

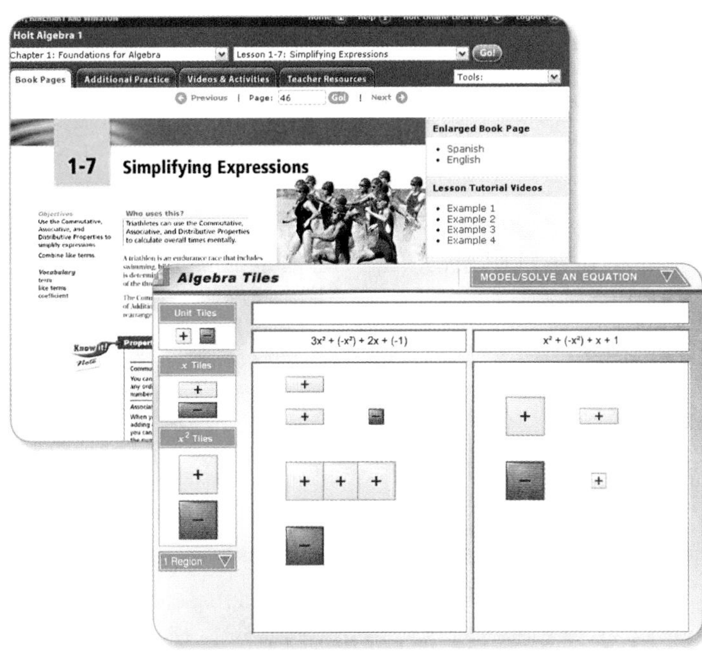

For students:

- Entire *Student Edition*
- *Lesson Tutorial Videos*
- Homework Help Online
- Extra practice broken out by lesson and chapter
- Interactive quizzes and tests
- All workbooks
- Graphing calculator
- Virtual manipulatives
- Parent resources

For teachers:

- Editable lesson plans
- Lesson transparencies
- PowerPoint® presentations for every lesson
- Leveled practice worksheets for every lesson
- Modified worksheets, quizzes, and tests for special needs students
- *Are You Ready?* and *Ready to Go On? Intervention and Enrichment*
- *Success for English Language Learners* teaching strategies and worksheets

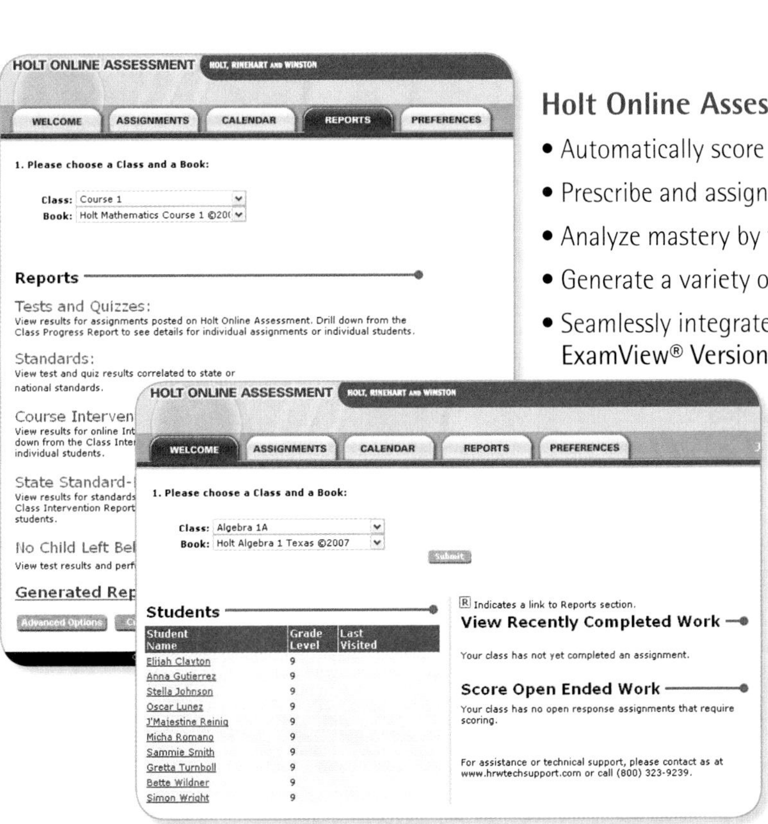

Holt Online Assessment

- Automatically score online assessments
- Prescribe and assign intervention
- Analyze mastery by topic or standard
- Generate a variety of reports
- Seamlessly integrated with ExamView® Version 5 Assessment Suite

California Standards Virtual File Cabinet CD-ROM

- Search for resources by standard, lesson topic, resource type, and other criteria
- Mark your favorites for quick access in the future
- Add your own content to this expandable database

Count on **Action Learning Systems** for

Professional Development strategies that work

Inspire yourself and your students with effective classroom teaching strategies.

Mathematics teachers are responsible for bringing each lesson to life for their students while following the California Mathematics Framework. Holt has partnered with Action Learning Systems to provide professional development that includes engaging opportunities for students to establish and deepen conceptual understanding, to master specific computational and procedural skills, and to develop and apply appropriate problem-solving skills.

Professional Development Strategies from Action Learning Systems:

INSTRUCTIONAL CONVERSATION Builds Conceptual Understanding

Instructional Conversation provides a structure for students to explain their work to a partner using appropriate mathematical vocabulary. Students clarify their understanding of the mathematical process while helping each other explain the steps to the solution.

- Have students read their text to develop an initial understanding of the mathematical concept.
- Generate a class list of students' vocabulary words.
- Choose five to seven words from the class list and have students write the selected words as "Target Vocabulary."
- Organize students into pairs (Student A and Student B).
- Assign a practice problem to the pairs and have them complete the problem using the designated roles:

Student A	Student B
1. Solve the problem. 2. Explain the work using the Target Vocabulary words. The goal is to use each word at least once.	1. Check the work of Student A. Student B cannot do the work for Student A but can assist Student A. 2. While Student A explains the work, Student B gives a point to Student A for each Target Vocabulary word used.

- Once pairs have completed the first problem, ask them to share how many points Student A earned. Students enjoy sharing their success and being challenged to do better next time.
- Post the solution so students can check and correct their work.
- Assign a second problem and direct partners to switch roles.
- Continue the process until the practice problems are completed.

>> **What does *conceptual understanding* mean?**

- Students not only know how to apply skills but also when to apply them and why they are being applied.
- Students are able to apply their knowledge to new problems and to recognize when they have made procedural errors.

QUICK DRAW FOR POINTS Builds Computational and Procedural Skills

Quick Draw for Points clarifies the procedure for solving a multi-step problem. Students are given positive reinforcement as they complete the problems and show all work. The criteria for success are clearly delineated, and as students complete more problems, their level of success increases.

- Introduce the mathematical concept either through modeling a few sample problems or reading the text.
- Generate a class list of how points will be rewarded when the practice problems are completed. For example, if multiplying decimal numbers, a point could be given for each of the following: lining the numbers up vertically starting from the right, counting the number of decimal places in each factor, predicting the number of places to move the decimal in the product, multiplying correctly, and writing the product in words using the correct mathematical vocabulary.
- Give students a set amount of time to complete the first problem. Remind them to show all work to receive the maximum points.
- Assign the first problem. When time is up, have students exchange papers with a partner.
- Identify the key components of the solution and ask students to give their partners points for each part that they included.

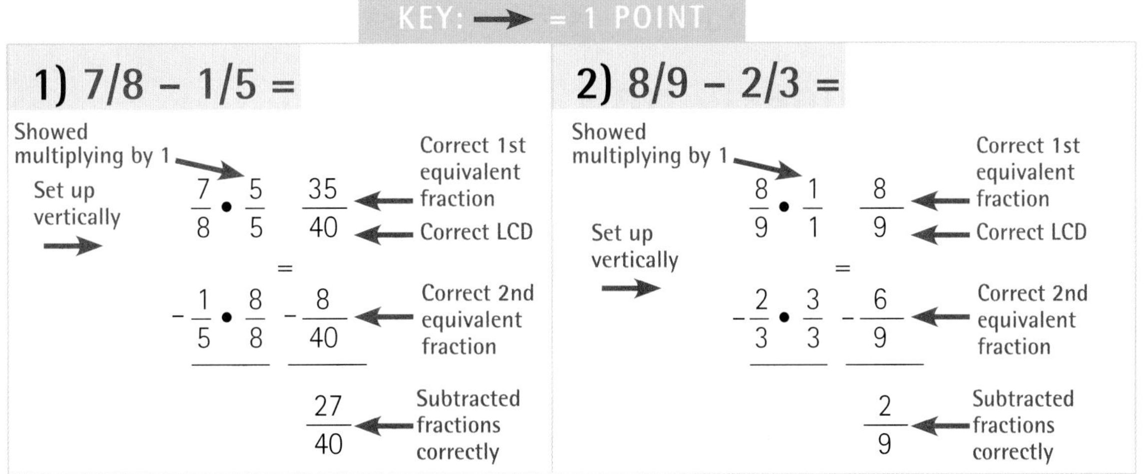

- Give students a prompt to discuss with their partner: for example, "What is one thing that your partner could do next time to get more points?"
- Continue the process for three additional problems. When students have completed four problems, have them summarize the essential steps in solving this type of problem.

> **What should I know about** ***computational and procedural skills*****?**
- Students should learn to use these skills routinely and automatically.
- Students must practice these skills frequently enough to commit them to memory.
- These skills develop over time and increase in depth and complexity through the years.
- Beware—computational skills can be taught in the absence of conceptual understanding.

Action *Learning* Systems, Inc.

Action Learning Systems helps schools and districts focus on—and meet—their ultimate goal of increasing student achievement by offering research-based teaching strategies, training and coaching, and intervention programs. Action Learning Systems and Holt, Rinehart and Winston are working in partnership to provide exceptional professional development services to California schools.

You may download blackline masters of these instructional strategies at **www.actionlearningsystems.com.** Just click on "Resources."

Program Research

Count on **Holt California Algebra 1** to be

Grounded in research, built by experts, proven in classrooms

Holt California Algebra 1 is built on a solid foundation of research, proven to work in the classroom, and built to meet the California Mathematics Content Standards. This research is backed by the expertise of a world-class team of authors who have executed a program that makes students want to learn, helps them *actually* learn, and ensures their success in mastering the California standards.

The Research Underlying the Program

Holt established a pattern of interaction with the educational community throughout all stages of the program's development.

Needs Assessment

- Teacher Interviews
- University Faculty Interviews
- Federal, State, and Local Agencies
- Advisory Panels
- Task Forces
- Academic Conferences
- Surveys with Teachers, Sales, Administrators

Pedagogical Research

- Thorough
- Effective
- Scientifically-Based

Program Development

- Classroom Observation
- Field Testing of Prototypes
- Reviewed by Program and Field Consultants
- Reviewed by Teachers and Administrators

Program Validation

- User Surveys
- Student and Teacher Appraisals
- Field Consultant and Sales Reports

Program Effectiveness

- Post-Implementation Effectiveness Studies
- Valid and Reliable Tests

HOLT MATH

Count on **Holt California Algebra 1** for a

World-class author team

Meet the experts who make Holt California Algebra 1 *a success.*

With a broad range of expertise, award-winning dedication, and a passion for developing strong, effective teaching and learning strategies, our *Holt California Algebra 1* author team is unsurpassed.

Edward B. Burger, Ph.D.
Professor of Mathematics and Chair | Williams College, MA

Student Engagement

"Deep and abstract ideas are challenging to all, but the challenge should be a pleasurable one that students want to conquer. Thus, the mathematics in *Holt California Algebra 1* is developed in a meaningful manner with student readers in mind. While maintaining the integrity of the mathematics, questions such as "What would resonate with real students today?" were asked at every stage of the writing and video production.

Holt California Algebra 1 doesn't just stress the mechanics, it also teaches the ideas behind the mechanics so that students understand not only how the mathematics works but also why. The instruction reflects a balance of computational and procedural basic skills, conceptual understanding, and problem solving. It is designed to stress the deep and profound ideas of mathematics. This emphasis is accomplished through various instructional approaches, including the ***Lesson Tutorial Videos,*** in order to engage all students and capture their imaginations."

SUPPORTING RESEARCH

Ames, R., & Ames, C. (Eds.). (1984). *Research on motivation in education: Vol. 1. Student motivation.* New York: Academic Press.

Brewster, Cori, and Jennifer Fager. (2000). *Increasing Student Engagement and Motivation: From Time-on-Task to Homework.* Portland, Ore.: Northwest Regional Educational Laboratory.

David J. Chard, Ph.D.
Associate Dean, Curriculum and Academic Programs | University of Oregon

Universal Access

"*Holt California Algebra 1* is designed to assist teachers in helping all their students learn conceptual knowledge, skills, and strategies essential to understanding sophisticated mathematics.

Some students often require substantial assistance in developing strategies for problem solving, while others may already have the knowledge necessary to solve problems with little support. In this program, the instructional framework builds the background knowledge essential for ensuring that all students are able to understand and solve increasingly complex problems. Scaffolding in this program takes many forms. For example, the program presents content starting with simple examples and progressing to more difficult content and applications. In addition, the program offers frequent opportunities to review, alternative lessons to help students who did not master content in introductory lessons, and additional examples for extended instruction."

SUPPORTING RESEARCH

Bransford, J. D., Brown, A. L., & Cocking, R. R. (Eds.). (2000). *How people learn: Brain, mind, experience, and school.* Washington, DC: National Research Council.

Gersten, R., Chard, D. J., Baker, S., et al. (2005). *A meta-analysis of research on mathematics instruction for students with learning disabilities.* Signal Hill, CA: Instructional Research Group.

Earlene J. Hall, Ed.D.
Mathematics Supervisor | Detroit Public Schools

Intervention

"Traditionally, mathematics intervention has been offered in an 'extraction type format'. In this series, Holt has provided teachers a tool kit of strategies that address closing the achievement gap through the use of an innovative intervention system. *Holt California Algebra 1* provides intervention at the point of misconception. An ongoing assessment and intervention system in each chapter allows the teacher to diagnose, monitor, and assess students' mastery of the mathematical concepts throughout the chapters.

Within each lesson, at each stage of the developing concept, this program offers teachers scaffolding intervention questions and instructional examples that focus on comprehension of the mathematics content by students impacted by language barriers."

SUPPORTING RESEARCH

All students reaching the top : trategies for closing academic achievement gaps. A report of the National Study Group for the Affirmative Development of Academic Ability. (2004)

Resnick, L. B. , & Klopfer, L.E. (1989). *Toward the Thinking Curriculum: Current Cognitive Research.*

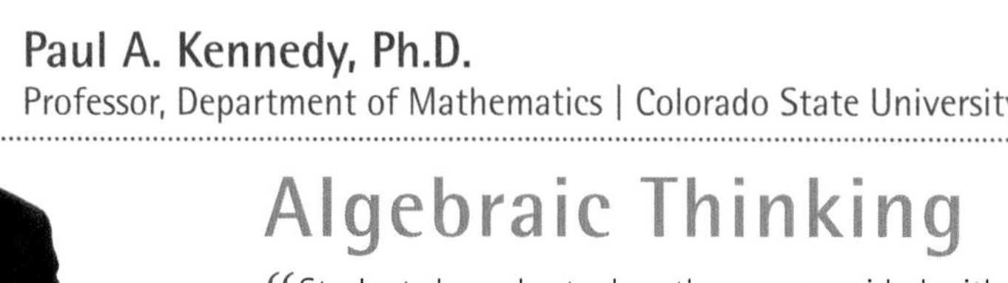

Paul A. Kennedy, Ph.D.
Professor, Department of Mathematics | Colorado State University

Algebraic Thinking

"Students learn best when they are provided with opportunities to link present learning to concrete knowledge. This area in which learning occurs, in between the concrete and the abstract, is what Vygotsky calls the "zone of proximal development." *Holt California Algebra 1* empowers students to make the transition from concrete to abstract with the notion that "abstractions" become new "concretes" so that they can build on what they know to develop true algebraic thinking.

In *Holt California Algebra 1,* content is carefully developed using methods aligned with standard best practices. The idea of "doing and undoing" is developed early and carried throughout the text. In addition, students need to see the relationships between the math they are learning and real-world scenarios."

SUPPORTING RESEARCH

Vygotsky, L.S. (1978). *Mind and society: The development of higher mental processes.* Cambridge, MA: Harvard University Press.

Driscoll, Mark J. (1997). *Fostering algebraic thinking.* Portsmouth, NH.; Heinemann.

Steven J. Leinwand
Principal Research Analyst, American Institutes for Research | Washington, DC

Assessing Student Understanding

“As the mathematics curriculum has broadened to encompass communicating and conceptualizing, problem solving and reasoning, so too must our traditional view of assessment broaden. To reflect today's curriculum and more accurately determine students' progress, assessment should be an integral part of the teaching and learning process. Questioning strategies, such as those found in *Holt California Algebra 1,* can be integral to daily assessment, along with lesson quizzes.

Additionally, assessment should provide opportunities for students to evaluate, reflect upon, and improve their work. The **Are You Ready?** feature allows students to determine if they have the skills to complete the chapter successfully. And more importantly, **Ready to Go On?** provides several opportunities during the course of the chapter for students to see how well they understand the material and to work several times in a chapter to improve their work before the Chapter Test (rather than after).”

SUPPORTING RESEARCH

NCTM Assessment Standards Working Groups (1995). *Assessment standards for school mathematics.* National Council of Teachers of Mathematics. Reston, VA.

National Research Council (1989). *Everybody counts.* Washington, DC: National Academy Press.

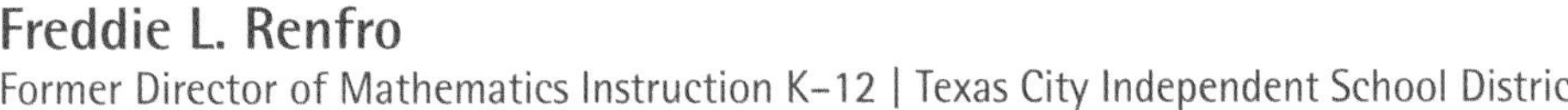

Freddie L. Renfro
Former Director of Mathematics Instruction K–12 | Texas City Independent School District

Universal Access

“Imagine a classroom where diversity in learning is the norm, and the teacher responds to the learners' needs with flexible strategies, open dialogue, and ongoing assessment.

Every child is unique. Finding ways to tailor instruction to meet individual student needs in the classroom can be a manageable task with the right support. In *Holt California Algebra 1,* we promote universal access by including activities that provide a variety of learning approaches: the use of technology, hands-on manipulatives, and student interaction, to name a few.

The *Teacher's Edition* offers suggestions for differentiated assessment as well so that students have the opportunity to demonstrate their understanding in a manner that reflects their skills and abilities.”

SUPPORTING RESEARCH

Tomlinson, C. (1999). *The differentiated classroom: Responding to the needs of all learners.* Alexandria, VA: Association for Supervision and Curriculum Development.

Willis, S. and Mann, Larry. (2000). *Differentiating instruction.* Alexandria, VA: Association for Supervision and Curriculum Development.

Tom Roby, Ph.D.
Associate Professor | University of Connecticut

Mathematical Coherence

"The middle grades mark a key transition for students, from basic arithmetical knowledge to the more abstract topics of algebra and geometry. Students need to understand the fundamental properties of numbers, not just the procedures of arithmetic, in order to become comfortable when numbers are replaced by variables. This transition from the concrete to the abstract can be facilitated by using manipulatives and pictures, as is done systematically in *Holt California Algebra 1*. These manipulatives function like training wheels on a bicycle, helping students to make sense of the procedures, which ultimately helps them develop computational fluency alongside strong conceptual understanding.

The program is carefully designed to address the California Mathematics Content Standards in such a way that topics fit together naturally. Just addressing each topic is not enough, since students can easily find themselves memorizing many specific individual procedures without ever seeing the bigger picture. Ensuring that the mathematics is not only accurate and aligned with a standard, but also coherent within the grade and well articulated from one grade to the next, is key to helping students succeed at this level and in those to come."

SUPPORTING RESEARCH

National Research Council. (2001). *Adding it up: Helping children learn mathematics.* J. Kilpatrick, J. Swafford, and B. Findell (Eds.). Mathematics Learning Study Committee, Center for Education, Division of Behavioral and Social Sciences and Education: Washington, DC: National Academy Press.

Wu, H. H. (2001). *How to prepare students for algebra.* American Educator 25 (2): 10-17.

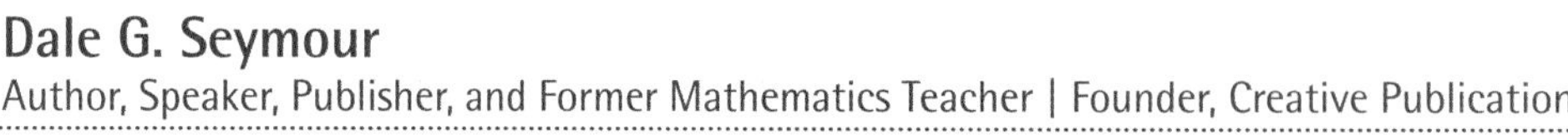

Dale G. Seymour
Author, Speaker, Publisher, and Former Mathematics Teacher | Founder, Creative Publications

Geometry Instructional Design

"Connections in mathematics are key to understanding and appreciating the beauty of mathematics. These connections need to be demonstrated so that students can view mathematics as an integrated whole.

In *Holt California Algebra 1* we use graphical illustrations to help students envision complex mathematical concepts. Many students can comprehend a difficult concept more quickly if they see it as a whole rather than attempt to understand it as an abstraction. Visualizations in the textbook as well as in the series' accompanying posters enable students to make connections among interrelated ideas."

SUPPORTING RESEARCH

Fuys, D., Geddes, D., & Tischler, R. (1988). The van Hiele model of thinking in geometry among adolescents. *Journal for Research in Mathematics Education.*

Gagatsis, A. & Patronis, T. (1990, February). Using geometrical models in a process of reflective thinking in learning and teaching mathematics. *Educational Studies in Mathematics, 21, 1, 29-54.*

Bert K. Waits, Ph.D.
Professor Emeritus of Mathematics | The Ohio State University

Technology to Enhance Learning

"Research has demonstrated that technology, when used appropriately, can improve students' mathematical understanding and problem-solving skills. Similarly, technological tools can help teachers challenge students to use and understand mathematics in real-world scenarios.

Holt California Algebra 1 presents a balanced approach to learning. We stress that students must utilize all available tools, including mental and paper-and-pencil skills and technology, in the mathematics-learning process. This series uses technology not as an end in itself, but rather as a means for understanding and application. Current research supports this use of computer software including spreadsheets, dynamic geometry software, and graphing calculators."

SUPPORTING RESEARCH

Graham, A.T., & J.O.J. Thomas. (2000). Building a versatile understanding of algebraic variables with a graphic calculator. *Educational Studies in Mathematics,* 41 (3), 265-282.

Hallar, Jeannie C., & Karen Norwood. (1999). The effects of a graphing-approach intermediate algebra curriculum on students' understanding of function. *Journal for Research in Mathematics Education,* 30 (2), 220-226.

CONTRIBUTING AUTHORS

Lee Haines, M.A.
Math Academic Coach, San Bernardino City Schools | San Bernardino, CA

Mastering the California Standards

"Moving all students to proficiency on mathematics standards requires accessible content, motivated students, and confident teachers. Holt's *Focus on California Standards: Benchmark Tests* and *Focus on California Standards: Intervention* were designed to provide all three elements.

By deconstructing the standards, emphasizing vocabulary development, and providing sufficient practice, Holt has created a user-friendly intervention program that is custom-made for California, targets the key standards, and motivates students. Since intervention lessons are taught by instructors with a wide range of mathematics backgrounds, teacher support materials were developed to empower every intervention instructor to teach at the level of a highly qualified mathematics teacher."

Robin Scarcella, Ph.D.
Associate Professor and Director of Academic English and ESL Program
University of California, Irvine

Teaching English Learners in the Math Classroom

"Mathematics vocabulary includes content words that are found only in mathematics lessons and are not reinforced in other disciplines or in everyday conversation. Many new words are introduced in a small amount of text, and the grammar can be complex. Fortunately, a variety of motivating and effective means are available to teach reading in the mathematics classroom.

Holt California Algebra 1 incorporates vocabulary development and reading comprehension strategies that enable students to make sense of and remember concepts. Some of these strategies include assessments of prerequisite vocabulary at the start of the chapter, the use of graphic organizers to help students identify and understand critical concepts, and activities that use additional resources like the glossary and index in the *Student Edition.* Additionally, the series encourages students to use the language they are learning through a multitude of opportunities to discuss and write about the mathematics. Language instruction is extended through teaching strategies such as Language Support Tips and ELL Teaching Tips."

California the golden state

CHAPTER 1

Foundations of Algebra

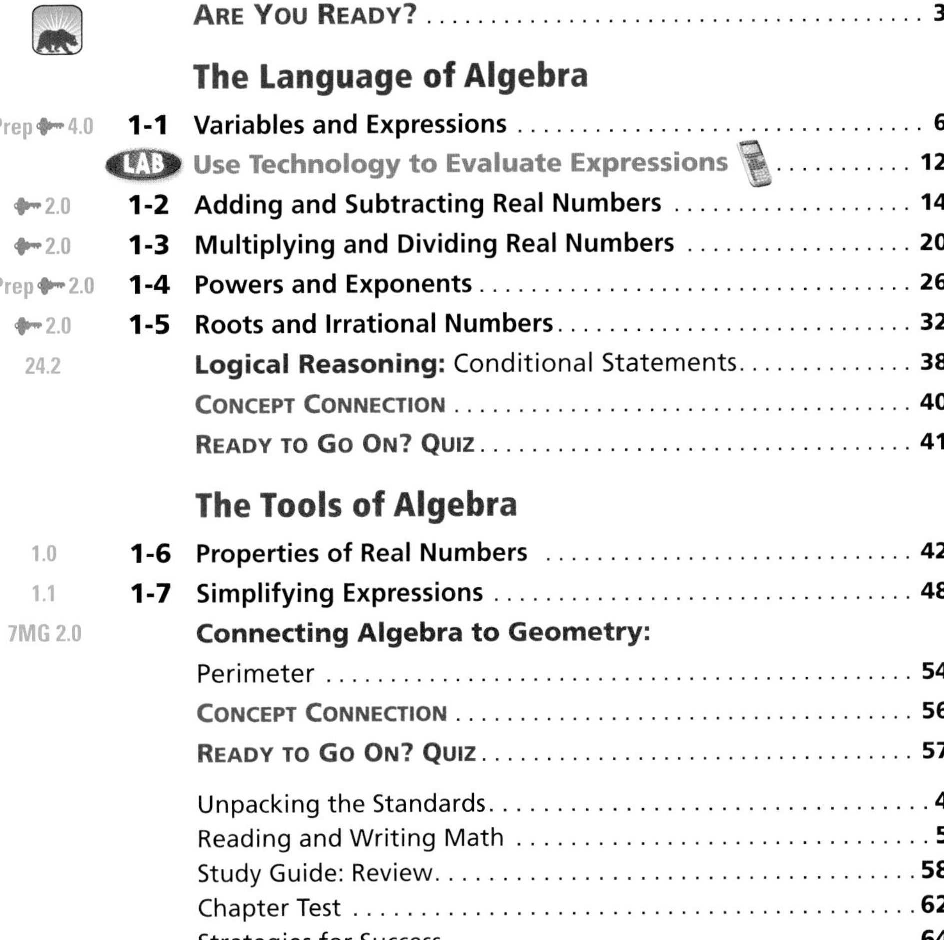

Online Resources
KEYWORD: MA8CA TOC

Tools for Success

Equations

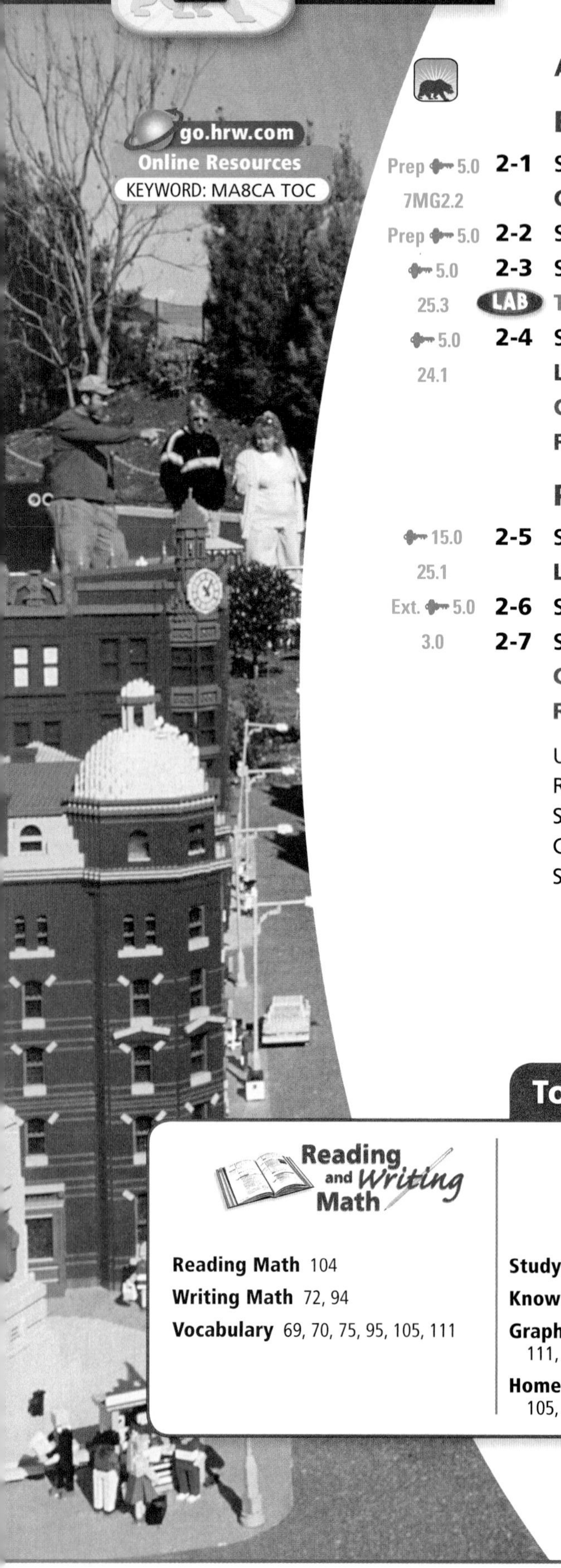

go.hrw.com
Online Resources
KEYWORD: MA8CA TOC

Tools for Success

Inequalities

CHAPTER 3

go.hrw.com
Online Resources
KEYWORD: MA8CA TOC

Tools for Success

MASTERING THE STANDARDS

Functions

Tools for Success

Linear Functions

CHAPTER 5

go.hrw.com
Online Resources
KEYWORD: MA8CA TOC

Tools for Success

MASTERING THE STANDARDS

CHAPTER 6

Systems of Equations and Inequalities

Tools for Success

MASTERING THE STANDARDS

Exponents and Polynomials

CHAPTER 7

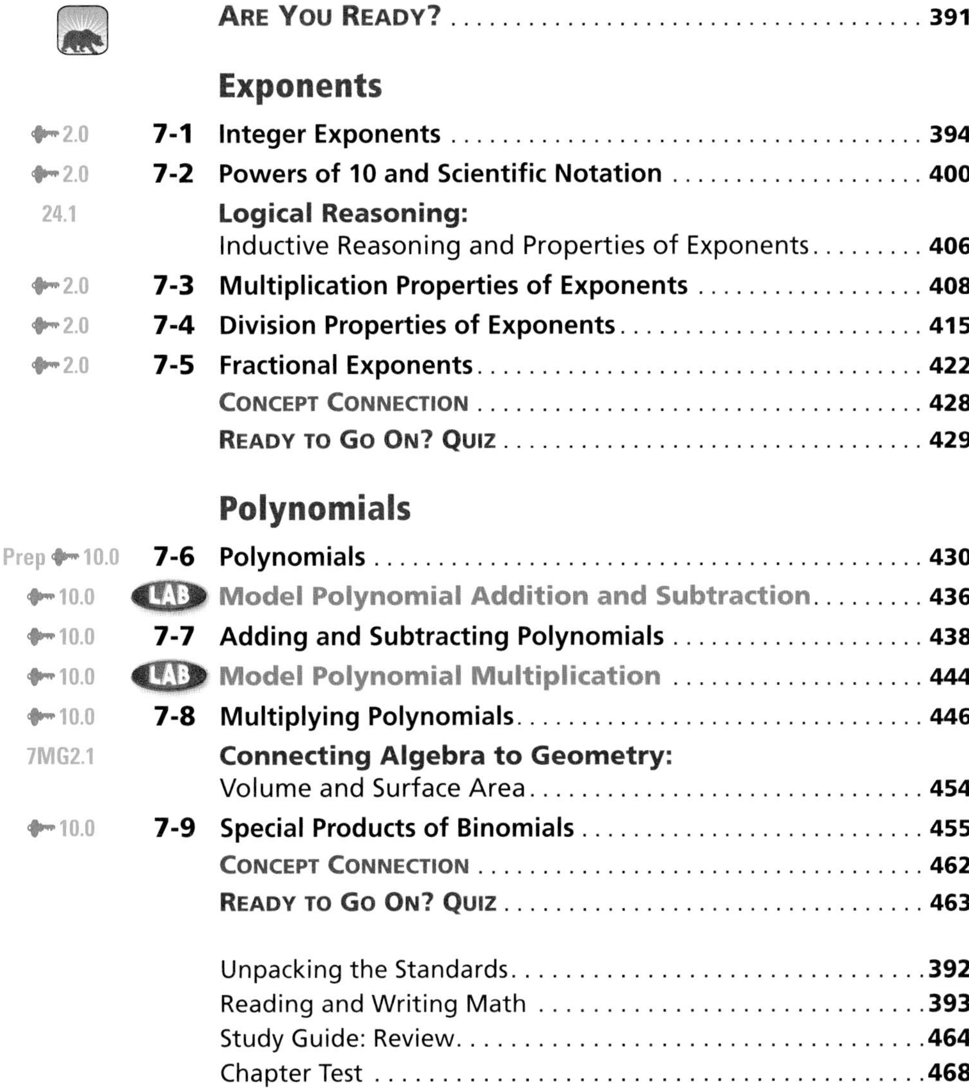

go.hrw.com
Online Resources
KEYWORD: MA8CA TOC

Tools for Success

Reading Math 394, 401, 402

Writing Math 400, 416, 439

Vocabulary 391, 392, 403, 425, 433, 459

Know-It Notes 394, 400, 401, 408, 410, 411, 415, 417, 418, 423

Graphic Organizers 396, 402, 411, 419, 424, 432, 440, 450, 459

Homework Help Online 397, 403, 412, 419, 425, 433, 441, 451, 459

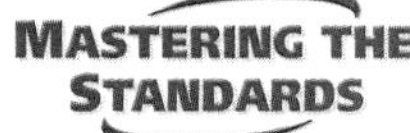

Countdown to Mastery Weeks 14, 15, 16, 17

Spiral Standards Review 399, 405, 414, 421, 427, 435, 443, 453, 461

Ready to Go On? 429, 463

Mastering the Standards 472

Factoring Polynomials

Tools for Success

Quadratic Functions and Equations

CHAPTER 9

go.hrw.com
Online Resources
KEYWORD: MA8CA TOC

Tools for Success

MASTERING THE STANDARDS

CHAPTER 10

Rational Functions and Equations

Tools for Success

Preview of Algebra II

Exponential and Radical Functions

CHAPTER 11

go.hrw.com
Online Resources
KEYWORD: MA8CA TOC

Tools for Success

MASTERING THE STANDARDS

Focus on Problem Solving

The Problem-Solving Plan

To be a good problem solver you need a good problem-solving plan. Using a problem-solving plan along with a problem-solving strategy helps you organize your work and correctly solve the problem. The plan used in this book is outlined below.

UNDERSTAND the Problem

- **What are you asked to find?** Make sure you understand exactly what the problem is asking. Restate the problem in your own words.
- **What information is given in the problem?** List every piece of information the problem gives you.
- **Is all the information relevant?** Sometimes problems have extra information that is not needed to solve the problem. Try to determine what is and is not needed. This helps you stay organized when you are making a plan.
- **Were you given enough information to solve the problem?** Sometimes there simply is not enough information to solve the problem. List what else you need to know to solve the problem.

Make a PLAN

- **What problem-solving strategy or strategies can you use to help you solve the problem?** Think about strategies you have used in the past to solve problems. Would any of them be helpful in solving this problem?
- **Create a step-by-step plan of how you will solve the problem.** Write out your plan in words to help you get a clearer idea of how to solve the problem mathematically.

SOLVE

- **Use your plan to solve the problem.** Translate your plan from words to math. Show each step in your solution and write your answer in a complete sentence.

LOOK BACK

- **Did you completely answer the question that was asked?** Be sure you answered the question that asked and that your answer is complete.
- **Is your answer reasonable?** Your answer should make sense.
- **Could you have used a different strategy to solve the problem?** Solving the problem again with a different strategy is a good way to check your answer.
- **Did you learn anything that could help you solve similar problems in the future?** You may want to take notes about this kind of problem and the strategy you used to solve it.

Using the Problem Solving Plan

During a skating competition, Jules skated around the track 35 times. One lap is 0.9 mile. If Jules finished in 1 hour 30 minutes, what was his average speed?

UNDERSTAND the Problem

You are asked to find Jules's average speed for 35 laps. You know the distance of each lap and the amount of time it took him to finish the competition.

Make a PLAN

Solve a simpler problem by using easier numbers to do the computations.

SOLVE

Find the total distance skated.

$35(0.9)$ — *There were 35 laps that measured 0.9 mile.*

$35(1 - 0.1)$ — *Write 0.9 as 1 − 0.1*

$35(1) - 3.5(0.1)$ — *Use the Distributive Property.*

$35 - 3.5$

31.5

Use the distance formula to find the average speed.

$d = rt$

$31.5 = r \times 1.5$ — *1 hour 30 minutes = 1.5 hours*

$\frac{31.5}{1.5} = r$ — *Solve for r.*

$\frac{315}{15} = r$ — *Multiply the numerator and denominator by 10 to eliminate the decimals.*

$\frac{1}{15}(315) = r$

$\frac{1}{15}(300 + 15) = r$ — *Write 315 as 300 + 15.*

$\frac{1}{15}(300) + \frac{1}{15}(15) = r$ — *Use the Distributive Property.*

$20 + 1 = r$

$21 = r$

Jules skated at an average speed of 21 miles per hour.

LOOK BACK

Each lap is a little less than 1 mile, so 35 laps is less than 35 miles. Round this distance to 30 miles and use $d = rt$ to find the rate when the time is 1.5 hours: 30 mi = $(1.5 \text{ h})r \longrightarrow r = 20$ mi/h. This is close to 21 mi/h.

Using Your Book for Success

Holt California Algebra 1 has many features designed to help you learn and study math. Becoming familiar with these features will prepare you for greater success.

Learn

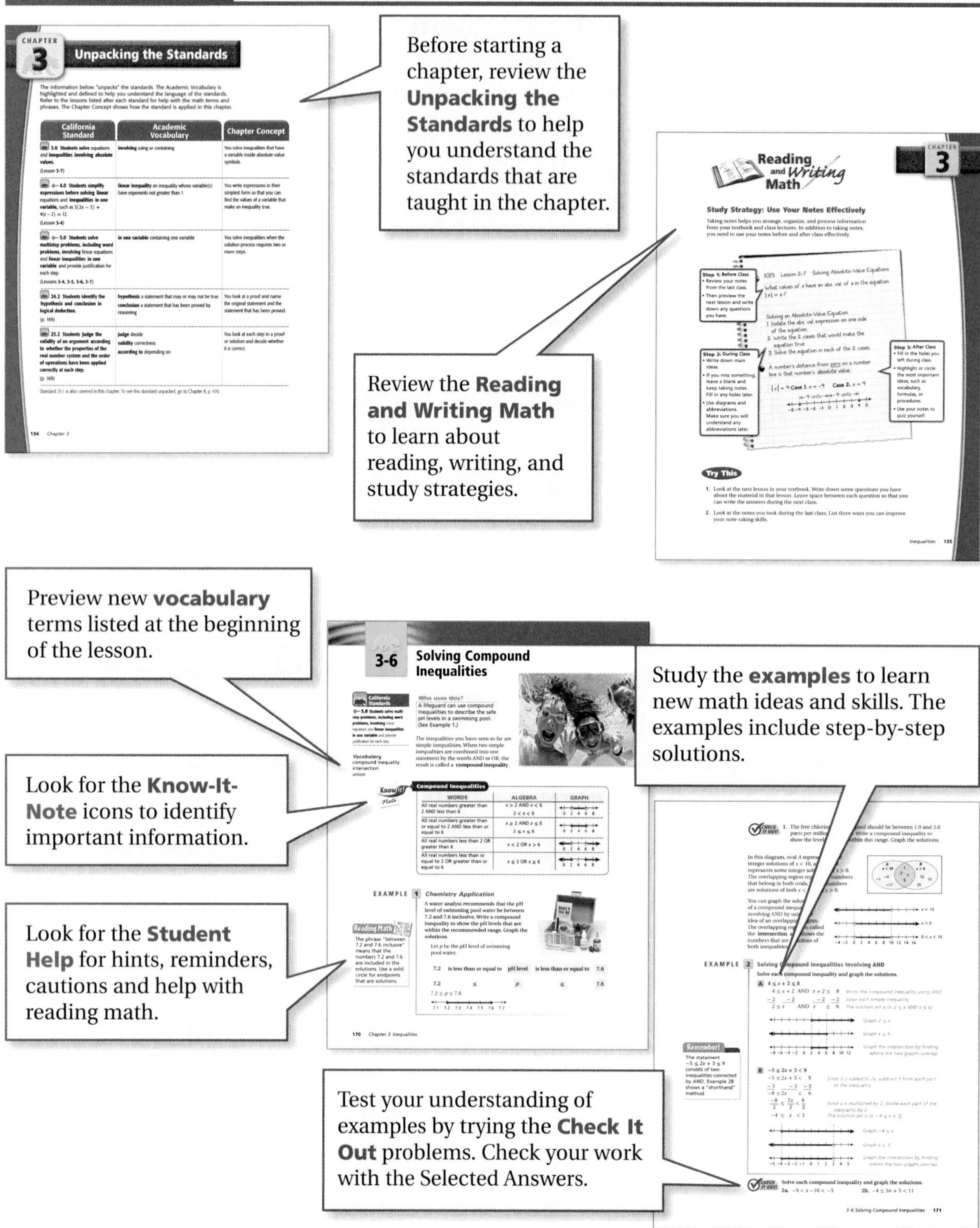

Before starting a chapter, review the **Unpacking the Standards** to help you understand the standards that are taught in the chapter.

Review the **Reading and Writing Math** to learn about reading, writing, and study strategies.

Preview new **vocabulary** terms listed at the beginning of the lesson.

Study the **examples** to learn new math ideas and skills. The examples include step-by-step solutions.

Look for the **Know-It-Note** icons to identify important information.

Look for the **Student Help** for hints, reminders, cautions and help with reading math.

Test your understanding of examples by trying the **Check It Out** problems. Check your work with the Selected Answers.

Practice

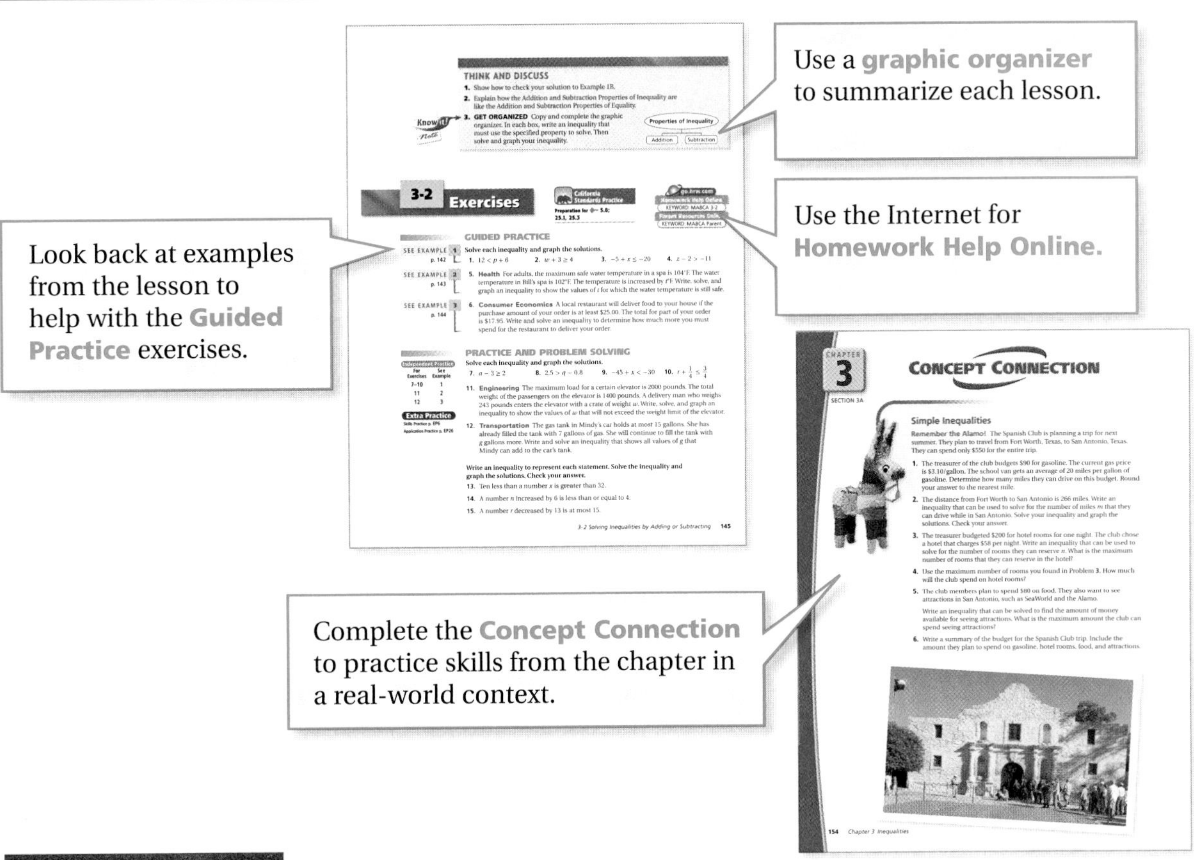

Look back at examples from the lesson to help with the Guided Practice exercises.
Complete the Concept Connection to practice skills from the chapter in a real-world context.

Review

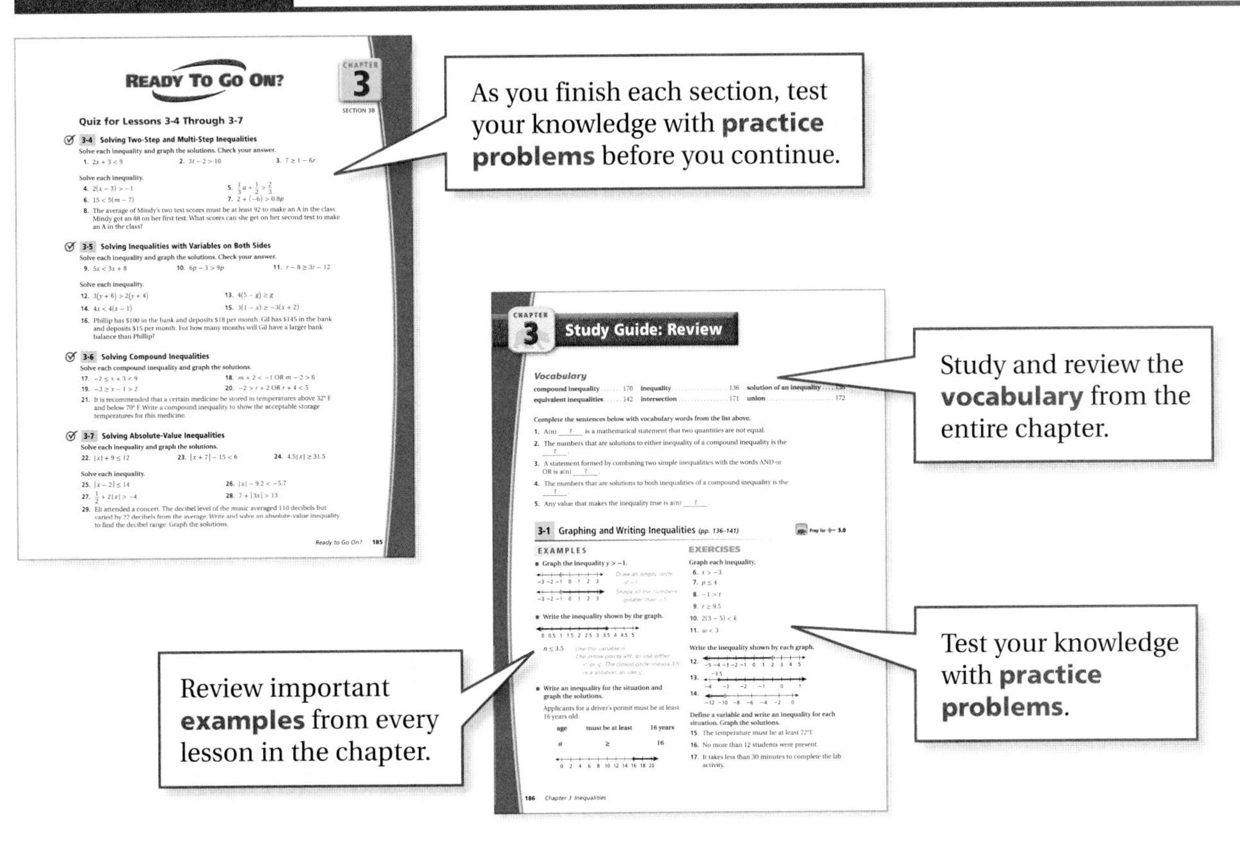

As you finish each section, test your knowledge with practice problems before you continue.
Ready To Go On?
Study Guide: Review
Study and review the vocabulary from the entire chapter.
Test your knowledge with practice problems.
Review important examples from every lesson in the chapter.

Scavenger Hunt

Holt California Algebra 1 is your resource to help you succeed. Use this scavenger hunt to discover some of the many tools Holt provides to help you be an independent learner.

On a separate sheet of paper, write the answers to each question below. Within each answer, one letter will be in a yellow box. After you have answered every question, identify the letters that would be in yellow boxes and rearrange them to reveal the answer to the question at the bottom of the page.

1. What is the last **Vocabulary** term in the Study Guide: Review for Chapter 2?
   UNIT RATE

2. What keyword should you enter for **Homework Help** for Lesson 6-3?
   MA8CA6-3

3. In Lesson 7-3, what is **Example 1** teaching you to find?
   PRODUCTS OF POWERS

4. In Chapter 4, what is the last academic vocabulary word listed in **Unpacking the Standards**?
   JUSTIFY

5. What is the topic of the **Logical Reasoning** on page 311?
   PROVING CONJECTURES

6. To what school subject is **Exercise 35** in Lesson 3-6 linked?
   CHEMISTRY

7. What type of question is featured in Chapter 9 **Strategies for Success**?
   EXTENDED RESPONSE

8. The Chapter 7 **Reading and Writing Math** is about what strategy?
   READ AND UNDERSTAND THE PROBLEM

FACT!

Algebra was used to build what ancient structures?

PYRAMIDS

The Math Builders section in the Student Edition uses transparent pages to allow students to learn important standards through a step-by-step, layered approach. At key points in the text, these pages are referenced in the side margin. The Math Builders are also available on overhead transparencies in *Lesson Transparencies*.

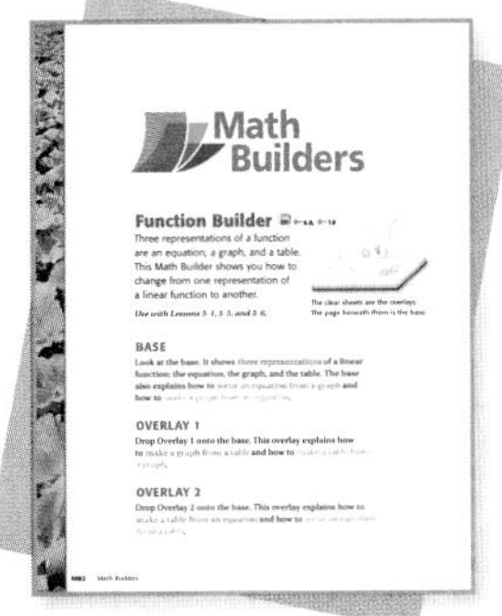

Use with Lessons 5-1, 5-5, and 5-6.

Function Builder

This Math Builder shows how the same functional relationship can often be shown in several different ways.

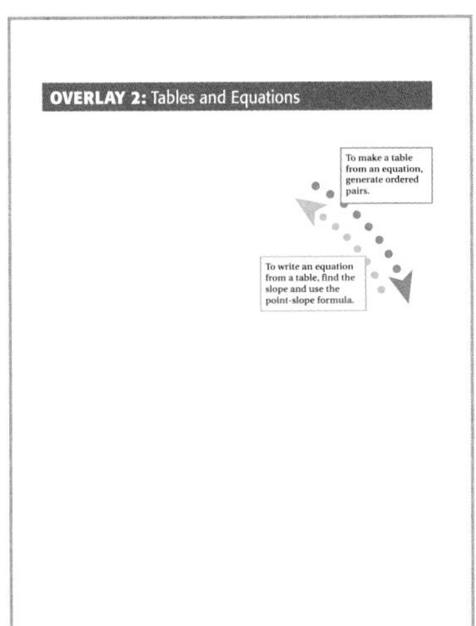

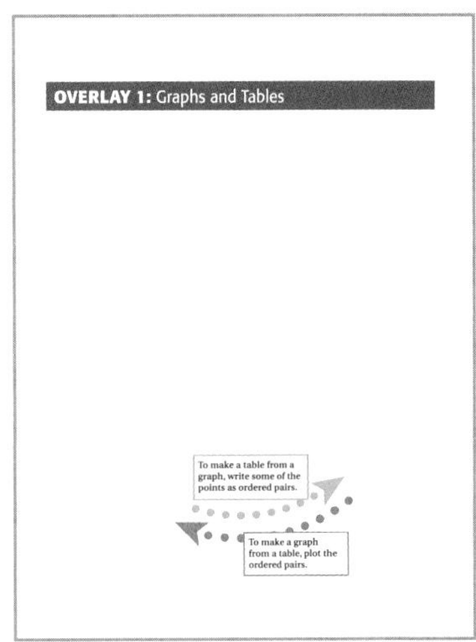

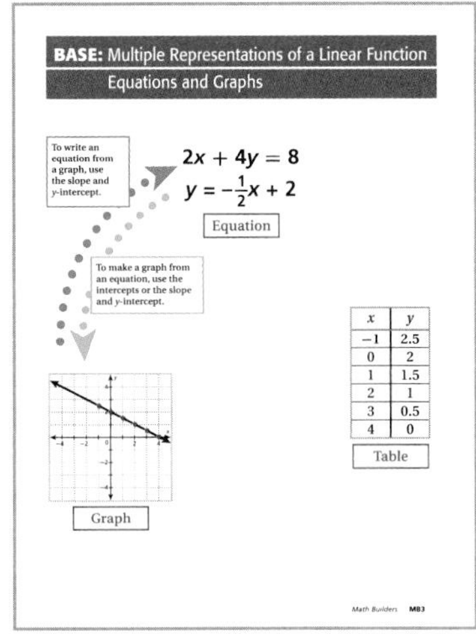

x	y
−1	2.5
0	2
1	1.5
2	1
3	0.5
4	0

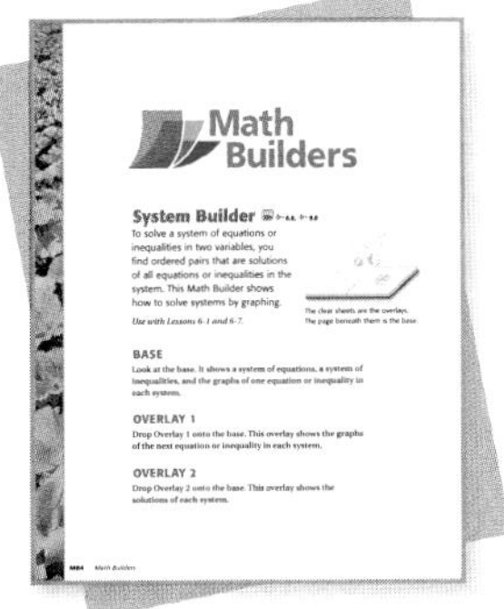

Use with Lessons 6-1 and 6-7.

System Builder

This Math Builder shows you how to find solutions of a system of two linear equations or inequalities in two variables.

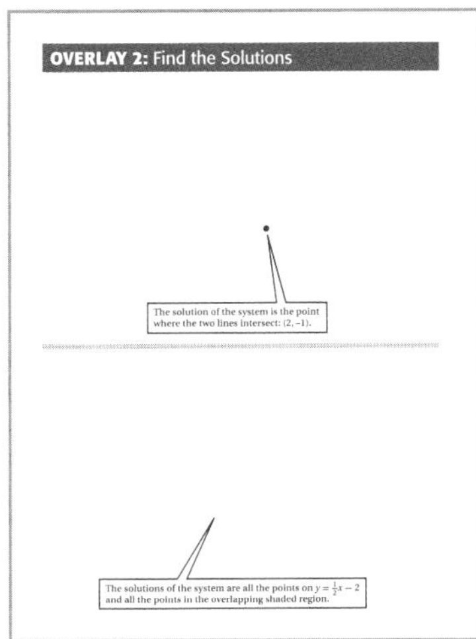

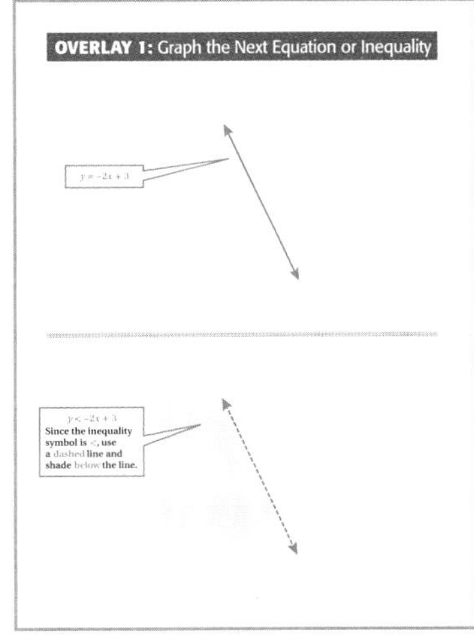

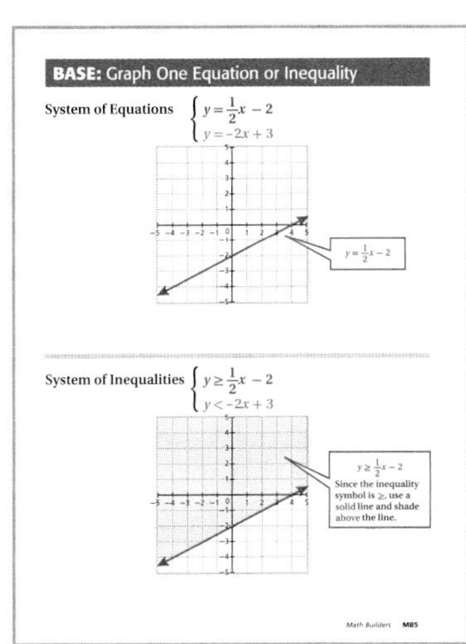

Foundations of Algebra

✔	Grade-level Standard
◄	Review
►	Beyond the Standards
A	Assessment
O	Optional

Pacing Guide

Calendar Planner
Teacher's One-Stop Planner®

Lesson/Lab		California Standards	Time	Advanced Students	Benchmark Students	Strategic Students
1-1	Variables and Expressions	Preparation for 4.0	50 min	O	◄	◄
LAB	Use Technology to Evaluate Expressions		25 min	O	O	O
1-2	Adding and Subtracting Real Numbers	2.0	50 min	✔	✔	✔
1-3	Multiplying and Dividing Real Numbers	2.0	50 min	✔	✔	✔
1-4	Powers and Exponents	Preparation for 2.0	50 min	O	◄	◄
1-5	Roots and Irrational Numbers	2.0	50 min	✔	✔	✔
LR	Conditional Statements	24.2	25 min	✔	✔	✔
Concept Connection		2.0	25 min	A	A	O
Ready to Go On?			25 min	A	A	A
1-6	Properties of Real Numbers	1.0, 24.3, 25.1	50 min	✔	✔	✔
1-7	Simplifying Expressions	1.1, 25.1	50 min	✔	✔	✔
CN	Perimeter	Reinforcement of Grade 7 MG2.0	25 min	O	◄	◄
Concept Connection			25 min	A	A	O
Ready to Go On?			25 min	A	A	A
Study Guide: Review			25 min	✔	✔	✔
Chapter Test		1.0, 1.1, Preparation for 2.0, 2.0, Preparation for 4.0, 24.3, 25.1	50 min	A	A	A

* **Benchmark students** are achieving at or near grade level.

** **Strategic students** may be a year or more below grade level, and may require additional time for intervention.

Countdown to Mastery, Weeks 1, 2

ONGOING ASSESSMENT and INTERVENTION

	DIAGNOSE	PRESCRIBE
Assess Prior Knowledge	**Before Chapter 1**	
	Diagnose readiness for the chapter. ***Are You Ready?*** SE p. 3	Prescribe intervention. ***Are You Ready? Intervention*** Skills 43, 44, 45, 46, 47, 48
Formative Assessment	**Before Every Lesson**	
	Diagnose readiness for the lesson. **Warm Up** TE, every lesson	Prescribe intervention. **Skills Bank** pp. SB1–SB32 **Review for Mastery** CRF Chapter 1
	During Every Lesson	
	Diagnose understanding of lesson concepts. **Questioning Strategies** TE, every example **Check It Out!** SE, every example **Think and Discuss** SE, every lesson **Write About It** SE, every lesson **Journal** TE, every lesson	Prescribe intervention. **Reading Strategies** CRF, every lesson ***Success for ELL*** pp. 1–14 ***Lesson Tutorial Videos*** Chapter 1
	After Every Lesson	
	Diagnose mastery of lesson concepts. **Lesson Quiz** TE, every lesson **Alternative Assessment** TE, every lesson **Ready to Go On?** SE pp. 41, 57 ***Test and Practice Generator***	Prescribe intervention. **Review for Mastery** CRF, every lesson **Problem Solving** CRF, every lesson ***Ready to Go On? Intervention*** Chapter 1 ***Homework Help Online***
	Before Chapter 1 Testing	
	Diagnose mastery of concepts in the chapter. **Ready to Go On?** SE pp. 41, 57 **Concept Connection** SE pp. 40, 56 **Section Quizzes** AR pp. 5–6 ***Test and Practice Generator***	Prescribe intervention. ***Ready to Go On? Intervention*** Chapter 1 **Scaffolding Questions** TE pp. 40, 56
	Before Assessment of California Standards	
	Diagnose mastery of California Standards. ***Focus on California Standards: Benchmark Tests*** **Mastering the Standards** SE pp. 66–67 ***California Standards Practice* CD-ROM**	Prescribe intervention. ***Focus on California Standards: Intervention***
Summative Assessment	**After Chapter 1**	
	Check mastery of chapter concepts. **Multiple-Choice Tests (Forms A, B, C)** **Free-Response Tests (Forms A, B, C)** **Performance Assessment** AR pp. 7–20 ***Test and Practice Generator***	Prescribe intervention. **Review for Mastery** CRF, every lesson ***Lesson Tutorial Videos*** Chapter 1

KEY: **SE** = *Student Edition* **TE** = *Teacher's Edition* **CRF** = *Chapter Resource File* **AR** = *Assessment Resources* Available online Available on CD-ROM

Supporting the Teacher

Chapter 1 Resource File

Family Involvement
pp. 1–4, 45–48

Practice A, B, C
pp. 5–7, 13–15, 21–23, 29–31, 37–39, 49–51, 57–59

Review for Mastery
pp. 8–9, 16–17, 24–25, 29–30, 40–41, 52–53, 60–61

Challenge
pp. 10, 18, 26, 34, 42, 54, 62

Problem Solving
pp. 11, 19, 27, 35, 43, 55, 63

Reading Strategies ELL
pp. 12, 20, 28, 36, 44, 56, 64

Algebra Lab
pp. 65–66, 68–69

Technology Lab
pp. 67

Workbooks

Homework and Practice Workbook SPANISH
Teacher's Edition .... pp. 1–7

Know-It Notebook SPANISH
Teacher's Guide .... Chapter 1

Review for Mastery Workbook SPANISH
Teacher's Guide .... pp. 1–14

Focus on California Standards: Intervention Workbook SPANISH
Teacher's Guide

Teacher Tools

Power Presentations
Complete PowerPoint® presentations for Chapter 1 lessons

Lesson Tutorial Videos SPANISH
Holt authors Ed Burger and Freddie Renfro present tutorials to support the Chapter 1 lessons.

Teacher's One-Stop Planner SPANISH
Easy access to all Chapter 1 resources and assessments, as well as software for lesson planning, test generation, and puzzle creation

IDEA Works!
Key Chapter 1 resources and assessments modified to address special learning needs

Solutions Key .... Chapter 1

Interactive Answers and Solutions

TechKeys

Lab Resources

Project Teacher Support 

Parent Resources

Transparencies

Lesson Transparencies, Volume 1 .... Chapter 1
- Teacher Tools
- Warm-ups
- Teaching Transparencies
- Lesson Quizzes

Alternate Openers: Explorations .... pp. 1–7

Countdown to Mastery .... pp. 1–4

Know-It Notebook .... Chapter 1
- Vocabulary
- Key Concepts
- Graphic Organizers
- Chapter Review
- Big Ideas

Technology Highlights for the Teacher

 **Power Presentations**

Dynamic presentations to engage students. Complete PowerPoint® presentations for every lesson in Chapter 1.

2-1 Solving One-Step Equations

Isolate a variable by using inverse operations which "undo" operations on the variable.

An equation is like a balanced scale. To keep the balance, perform the same operation on both sides.

Inverse Operations	
Operation	**Inverse Operation**
Addition	Subtraction
Subtraction	Addition

 **One-Stop Planner** SPANISH

Easy access to Chapter 1 resources and assessments. Includes lesson planning, test generation, and puzzle creation software.

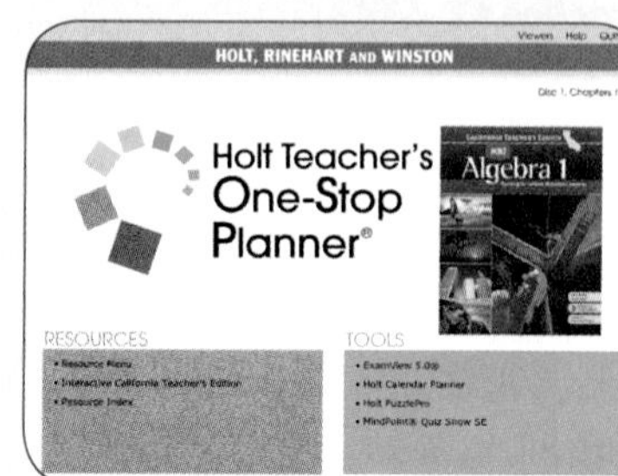

 **Premier Online Edition** SPANISH

Includes Tutorial Videos, Lesson Activities, Lesson Quizzes, Homework Help, Chapter Project and more.

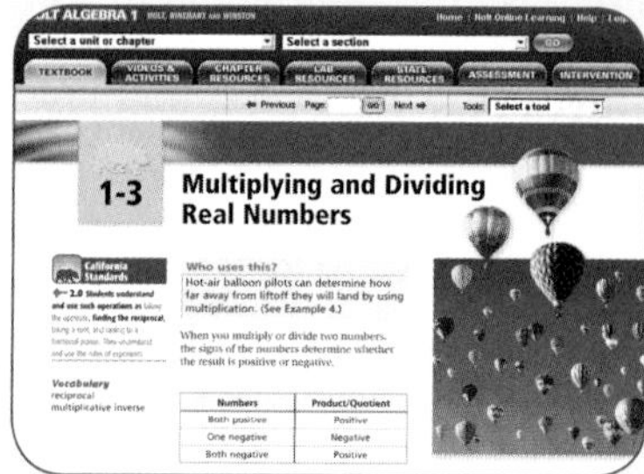

KEY: **SE** = *Student Edition* **TE** = *Teacher's Edition* ELL English Language Learners  Spanish available  Available online  Available on CD-ROM

Universal Access

Teaching Tips to help all students appear throughout the chapter. A few that target specific students are included in the lists below.

Strategic Students

Practice A	CRF, every lesson
Review for Mastery	CRF, every lesson
Reading Strategies	CRF, every lesson
Academic Vocabulary Connections	TE p. 4
Concrete Manipulatives	TE p. 15
Questioning Strategies	TE, every example
Ready to Go On? Intervention	Chapter 1
Know-It Notebook SPANISH	Chapter 1
Homework Help Online	
Lesson Tutorial Videos SPANISH	
Online Interactivities SPANISH 	

Special Needs Students

Practice A	CRF, every lesson
Review for Mastery	CRF, every lesson
Reading Strategies	CRF, every lesson
Academic Vocabulary Connections	TE p. 4
Inclusion	TE pp. 15, 24, 29, 36, 54
IDEA Works! Modified Resources	Chapter 1
Ready to Go On? Intervention	Chapter 1
Know-It Notebook SPANISH	Chapter 1
Lesson Tutorial Videos SPANISH	
Online Interactivities  	

English Learners

ENGLISH LANGUAGE LEARNERS

Reading Strategies	CRF, every lesson
Vocabulary Exercises	SE, every exercise set
Academic Vocabulary Connections	TE p. 4
English Language Learners	TE p. 43
Language Support	TE pp. 34, 43
Success for English Language Learners	Chapter 1
Know-It Notebook SPANISH	Chapter 1
Multilingual Glossary	
Lesson Tutorial Videos 	

Benchmark Students

Practice B	CRF, every lesson
Problem Solving	CRF, every lesson
Academic Vocabulary Connections	TE p. 4
Questioning Strategies	TE, every example
Ready to Go On? Intervention	Chapter 1
Know-It Notebook SPANISH	Chapter 1
Homework Help Online	
Online Interactivities SPANISH	

Advanced Students

Practice C	CRF, every lesson
Challenge	CRF, every lesson
Reading and Writing Math EXTENSION	TE p. 5
Concept Connection EXTENSION	TE pp. 40, 56
Advanced Learners/GATE	TE p. 22
Ready to Go On? Enrichment	Chapter 1

Technology Highlights for Universal Access

Lesson Tutorial Videos SPANISH

Starring Holt authors Ed Burger and Freddie Renfro! Live tutorials to support every lesson in Chapter 1.

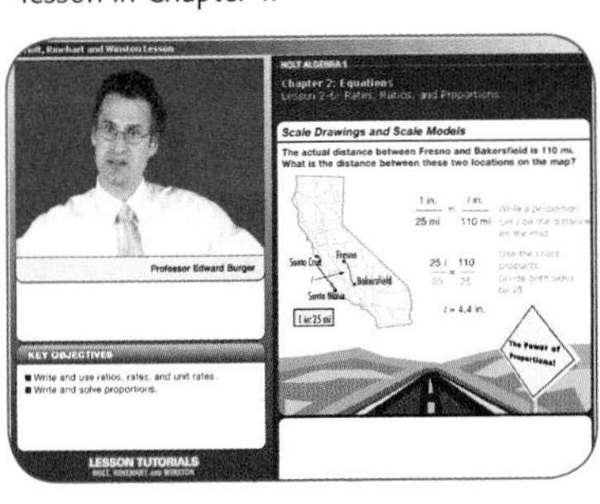

Multilingual Glossary

Searchable glossary includes definitions in English, Spanish, Vietnamese, Chinese, Hmong, Korean, and other languages.

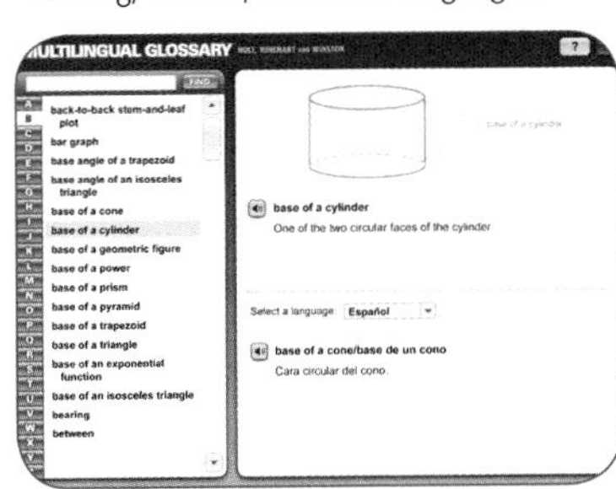

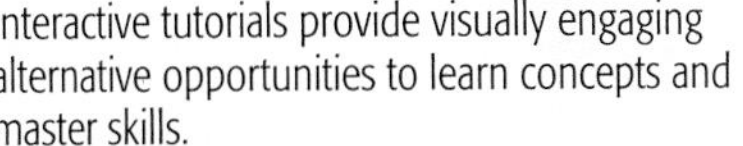

Online Interactivities SPANISH

Interactive tutorials provide visually engaging alternative opportunities to learn concepts and master skills.

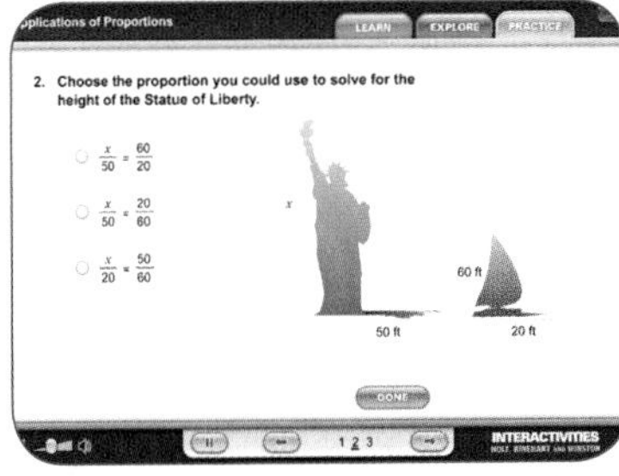

KEY: **SE** = *Student Edition* **TE** = *Teacher's Edition* **CRF** = *Chapter Resource File*  Spanish available  Available online  Available on CD-ROM

Ongoing Assessment

Assessing Prior Knowledge

Determine whether students have the prerequisite concepts and skills for success in Chapter 1.

Are You Ready? SPANISH .... SE p. 3
Warm Up .... TE, every lesson

Chapter and Standards Assessment

Provide review and practice for Chapter 1 and standards mastery.

Concept Connection .... SE pp. 40, 56
Study Guide: Review .... SE pp. 58–61
Strategies for Success .... SE pp. 64–65
Mastering the Standards .... SE pp. 66–67
College Entrance Exam Practice .... SE p. 63
***Countdown to Mastery* Transparencies** .... pp. 1–4
Focus on California Standards: Benchmark Tests
Focus on California Standards: Intervention Workbook
***California Standards Practice* CD-ROM** SPANISH
IDEA Works! Modified Worksheets and Tests

Alternative Assessment

Assess students' understanding of Chapter 1 concepts and combined problem-solving skills.

Alternative Assessment .... TE, every lesson
Performance Assessment .... AR pp. 19–20
Portfolio Assessment .... AR p. xxxiii
Chapter 1 Project

Daily Assessment

Provide formative assessment for each day of Chapter 1.

Questioning Strategies .... TE, every example
Think and Discuss .... SE, every lesson
Check It Out! Exercises .... SE, every example
Write About It .... SE, every lesson
Journal .... TE, every lesson
Lesson Quiz .... TE, every lesson
Alternative Assessment .... TE, every lesson
IDEA Works! Modified Lesson Quizzes .... Chapter 1

Weekly Assessment

Provide formative assessment for each week of Chapter 1.

Concept Connection .... SE pp. 40, 56
Ready to Go On? .... SE pp. 41, 57
Cumulative Assessment .... SE pp. 66–67
Test and Practice Generator SPANISH .... *One-Stop Planner*

Formal Assessment

Provide summative assessment of Chapter 1 mastery.

Section Quizzes .... AR pp. 5–6
Chapter 1 Test SPANISH .... SE p. 62
Chapter Test (Levels A, B, C) .... AR pp. 7–18
• Multiple Choice • Free Response
Cumulative Test .... AR pp. 21–24
Test and Practice Generator SPANISH .... *One-Stop Planner*

Technology Highlights for Ongoing Assessment

Automatically assess readiness and prescribe intervention for Chapter 1 prerequisite skills.

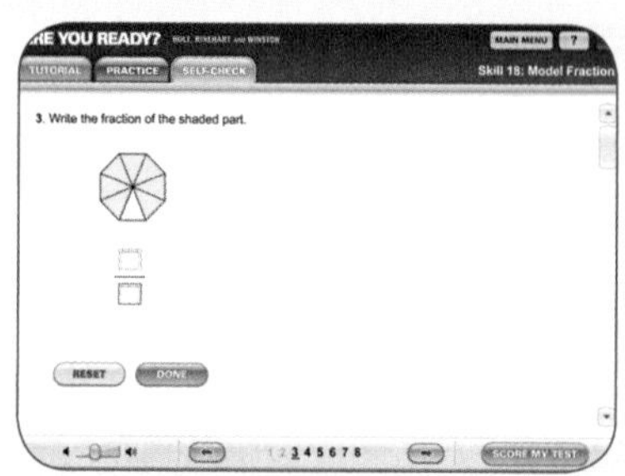

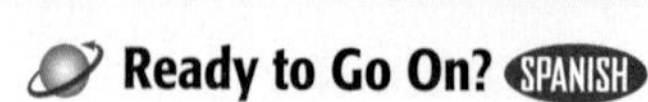

Automatically assess understanding of and prescribe intervention for Sections 1A and 1B.

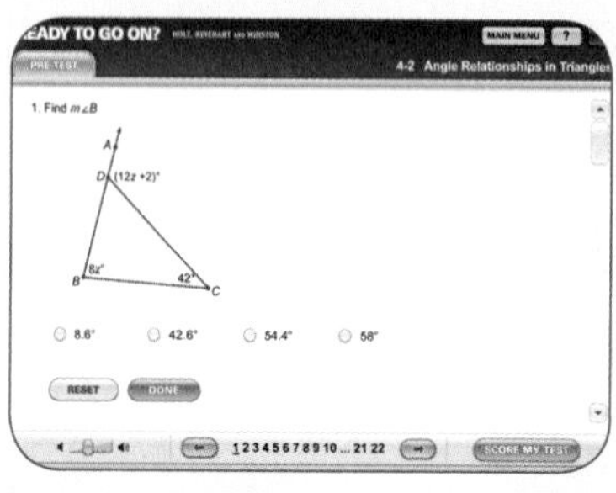

Focus on California Standards: Benchmark Tests and Intervention SPANISH

Automatically assess proficiency with California Algebra I Standards and provide intervention.

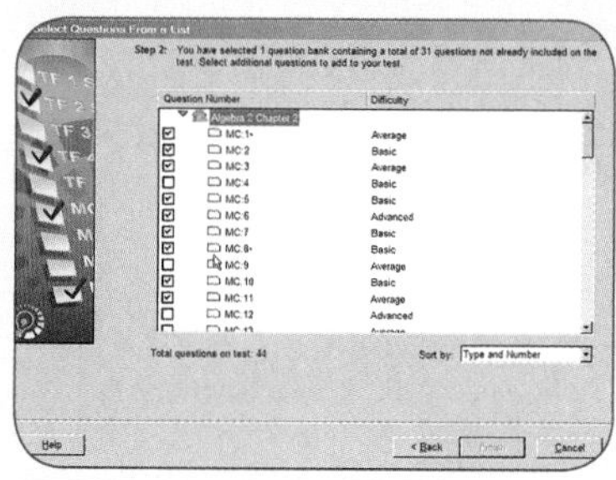

KEY: **SE** = *Student Edition* **TE** = *Teacher's Edition* **AR** = Assessment Resources SPANISH Spanish available 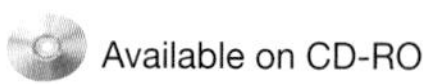 Available online Available on CD-ROM

Formal Assessment

Three levels (A, B, C) of multiple-choice and free-response chapter tests are available in the *Assessment Resources.*

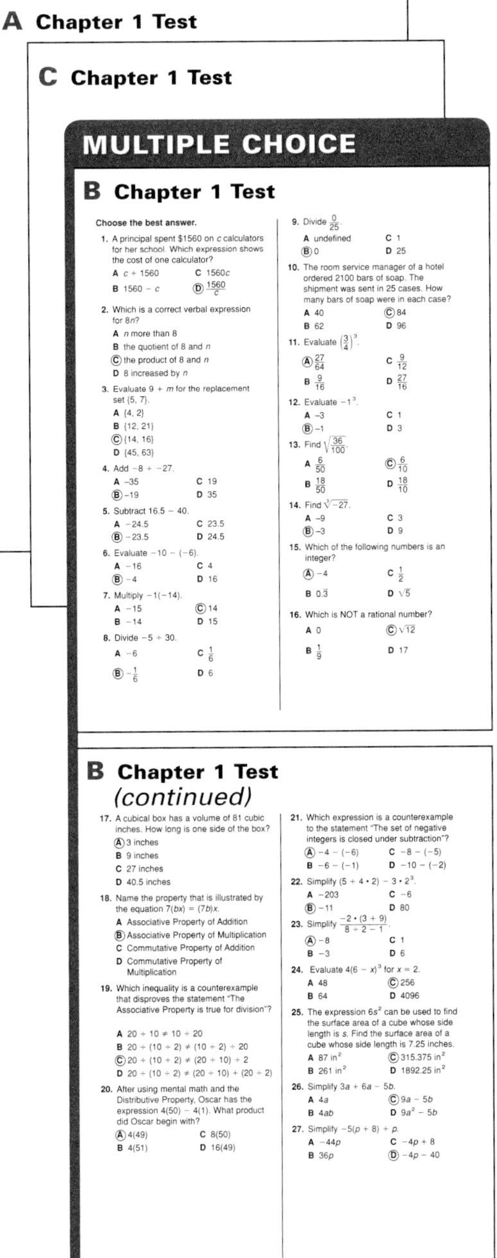

A Chapter 1 Test

C Chapter 1 Test

MULTIPLE CHOICE

B Chapter 1 Test

Choose the best answer.

1. A principal spent $1560 on c calculators for her school. Which expression shows the cost of one calculator?
A c + 1560 C 1560c
B 1560 − c Ⓓ $\frac{1560}{c}$
2. Which is a correct verbal expression for 8n?
A n more than 8
B the quotient of 8 and n
Ⓒ the product of 8 and n
D 8 increased by n
3. Evaluate 9 + m for the replacement set {5, 7}.
A {4, 2}
B {12, 21}
Ⓒ {14, 16}
D {45, 63}
4. Add −8 + −27.
A −35 C 19
Ⓑ −19 D 35
5. Subtract 16.5 − 40.
A −24.5 C 23.5
Ⓑ −23.5 D 24.5
6. Evaluate −10 − (−6).
A −16 C 4
Ⓑ −4 D 16
7. Multiply −1(−14).
A −15 Ⓒ 14
B −14 D 15
8. Divide −5 ÷ 30.
A −6 C $\frac{1}{6}$
Ⓑ $-\frac{1}{6}$ D 6
9. Divide $\frac{0}{25}$.
A undefined C 1
Ⓑ 0 D 25
10. The room service manager of a hotel ordered 2100 bars of soap. The shipment was sent in 25 cases. How many bars of soap were in each case?
A 40 Ⓒ 84
B 62 D 96
11. Evaluate $\left(\frac{3}{4}\right)^3$.
Ⓐ $\frac{27}{64}$ C $\frac{9}{12}$
B $\frac{9}{16}$ D $\frac{27}{16}$
12. Evaluate -1^3.
A −3 C 1
Ⓑ −1 D 3
13. Find $\sqrt{\frac{36}{100}}$.
A $\frac{6}{50}$ Ⓒ $\frac{6}{10}$
B $\frac{18}{50}$ D $\frac{18}{10}$
14. Find $\sqrt[3]{-27}$.
A −9 C 3
Ⓑ −3 D 9
15. Which of the following numbers is an integer?
Ⓐ −4 C $\frac{1}{2}$
B 0.3 D $\sqrt{5}$
16. Which is NOT a rational number?
A 0 Ⓒ $\sqrt{12}$
B $\frac{1}{9}$ D 17

B Chapter 1 Test (continued)

17. A cubical box has a volume of 81 cubic inches. How long is one side of the box?
Ⓐ 3 inches
B 9 inches
C 27 inches
D 40.5 inches
18. Name the property that is illustrated by the equation 7(bx) = (7b)x.
A Associative Property of Addition
Ⓑ Associative Property of Multiplication
C Commutative Property of Addition
D Commutative Property of Multiplication
19. Which inequality is a counterexample that disproves the statement "The Associative Property is true for division"?
A 20 ÷ 10 ≠ 10 ÷ 20
B 20 ÷ (10 ÷ 2) ≠ (10 ÷ 2) ÷ 20
Ⓒ 20 ÷ (10 ÷ 2) ≠ (20 ÷ 10) ÷ 2
D 20 ÷ (10 ÷ 2) ≠ (20 ÷ 10) ÷ (20 ÷ 2)
20. After using mental math and the Distributive Property, Oscar has the expression 4(50) − 4(1). What product did Oscar begin with?
Ⓐ 4(49) C 8(50)
B 4(51) D 16(49)
21. Which expression is a counterexample to the statement "The set of negative integers is closed under subtraction"?
Ⓐ −4 − (−6) C −8 − (−5)
B −6 − (−1) D −10 − (−2)
22. Simplify (5 + 4 • 2) − 3 • 2^3.
A −203 C −6
Ⓑ −11 D 80
23. Simplify $\frac{-2 \cdot (3 + 9)}{8 \div 2 - 1}$.
Ⓐ −8 C 1
B −3 D 6
24. Evaluate $4(6 - x)^3$ for x = 2.
A 48 Ⓒ 256
B 64 D 4096
25. The expression $6s^2$ can be used to find the surface area of a cube whose side length is s. Find the surface area of a cube whose side length is 7.25 inches.
A 87 in² Ⓒ 315.375 in²
B 261 in² D 1892.25 in²
26. Simplify 3a + 6a − 5b.
A 4a Ⓒ 9a − 5b
B 4ab D $9a^2 - 5b$
27. Simplify −5(p + 8) + p.
A −44p C −4p + 8
B 36p Ⓓ −4p − 40

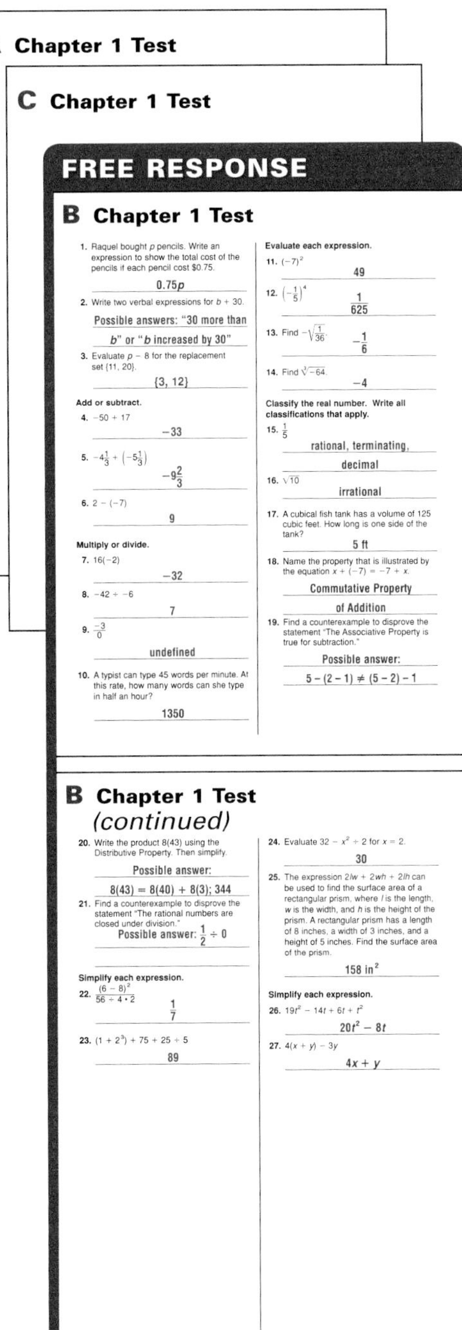

A Chapter 1 Test

C Chapter 1 Test

FREE RESPONSE

B Chapter 1 Test

1. Raquel bought p pencils. Write an expression to show the total cost of the pencils if each pencil cost $0.75. **0.75p**
2. Write two verbal expressions for b + 30. **Possible answers: "30 more than b" or "b increased by 30"**
3. Evaluate p − 8 for the replacement set {11, 20}. **{3, 12}**

Add or subtract.

4. −50 + 17 **−33**
5. $-4\frac{1}{3} + \left(-5\frac{1}{3}\right)$ **$-9\frac{2}{3}$**
6. 2 − (−7) **9**

Multiply or divide.

7. 16(−2) **−32**
8. −42 ÷ −6 **7**
9. $\frac{-3}{0}$ **undefined**
10. A typist can type 45 words per minute. At this rate, how many words can she type in half an hour? **1350**

Evaluate each expression.

11. $(-7)^2$ **49**
12. $\left(-\frac{1}{5}\right)^4$ **$\frac{1}{625}$**
13. Find $-\sqrt{\frac{1}{36}}$. **$-\frac{1}{6}$**
14. Find $\sqrt[3]{-64}$. **−4**

Classify the real number. Write all classifications that apply.

15. $\frac{1}{5}$ **rational, terminating, decimal**
16. $\sqrt{10}$ **irrational**
17. A cubical fish tank has a volume of 125 cubic feet. How long is one side of the tank? **5 ft**
18. Name the property that is illustrated by the equation x + (−7) = −7 + x. **Commutative Property of Addition**
19. Find a counterexample to disprove the statement "The Associative Property is true for subtraction." **Possible answer: 5 − (2 − 1) ≠ (5 − 2) − 1**

B Chapter 1 Test (continued)

20. Write the product 8(43) using the Distributive Property. Then simplify. **Possible answer: 8(43) = 8(40) + 8(3); 344**
21. Find a counterexample to disprove the statement "The rational numbers are closed under division." **Possible answer: $\frac{1}{2} \div 0$**

Simplify each expression.

22. $\frac{(6 - 8)^2}{56 \div 4 \cdot 2}$ **$\frac{1}{7}$**
23. $(1 + 2^3) + 75 \div 25 \div 5$ **89**
24. Evaluate $32 - x^2 \div 2$ for x = 2. **30**
25. The expression 2lw + 2wh + 2lh can be used to find the surface area of a rectangular prism, where l is the length, w is the width, and h is the height of the prism. A rectangular prism has a length of 8 inches, a width of 3 inches, and a height of 5 inches. Find the surface area of the prism. **158 in²**

Simplify each expression.

26. $19t^2 - 14t + 6t + t^2$ **$20t^2 - 8t$**
27. 4(x + y) − 3y **4x + y**

Modified tests and worksheets found in *IDEA Works!*

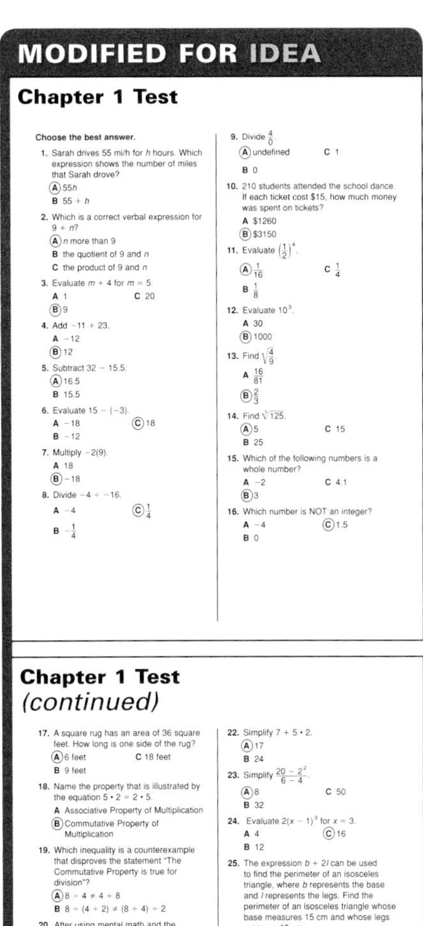

MODIFIED FOR IDEA

Chapter 1 Test

Choose the best answer.

1. Sarah drives 55 mi/h for h hours. Which expression shows the number of miles that Sarah drove?
Ⓐ 55h
B 55 + h
2. Which is a correct verbal expression for 9 + n?
Ⓐ n more than 9
B the quotient of 9 and n
C the product of 9 and n
3. Evaluate m + 4 for m = 5.
A 1 C 20
Ⓑ 9
4. Add −11 + 23.
A −12
Ⓑ 12
5. Subtract 32 − 15.5.
Ⓐ 16.5
B 15.5
6. Evaluate 15 − (−3).
A −18 Ⓒ 18
B −12
7. Multiply −2(9).
A 18
Ⓑ −18
8. Divide −4 ÷ −16.
A −4 Ⓒ $\frac{1}{4}$
B $-\frac{1}{4}$
9. Divide $\frac{4}{0}$.
Ⓐ undefined C 1
B 0
10. 210 students attended the school dance. If each ticket cost $15, how much money was spent on tickets?
A $1260
Ⓑ $3150
11. Evaluate $\left(\frac{1}{2}\right)^4$.
Ⓐ $\frac{1}{16}$ C $\frac{1}{4}$
B $\frac{1}{8}$
12. Evaluate 10^3.
A 30
Ⓑ 1000
13. Find $\sqrt{\frac{4}{9}}$.
A $\frac{16}{81}$
Ⓑ $\frac{2}{3}$
14. Find $\sqrt[3]{125}$.
Ⓐ 5 C 15
B 25
15. Which of the following numbers is a whole number?
A −2 C 4.1
Ⓑ 3
16. Which number is NOT an integer?
A −4 Ⓒ 1.5
B 0

Chapter 1 Test (continued)

17. A square rug has an area of 36 square feet. How long is one side of the rug?
Ⓐ 6 feet C 18 feet
B 9 feet
18. Name the property that is illustrated by the equation 5 • 2 = 2 • 5.
A Associative Property of Multiplication
Ⓑ Commutative Property of Multiplication
19. Which inequality is a counterexample that disproves the statement "The Commutative Property is true for division"?
Ⓐ 8 ÷ 4 ≠ 4 ÷ 8
B 8 ÷ (4 ÷ 2) ≠ (8 ÷ 4) ÷ 2
20. After using mental math and the Distributive Property, Carmella has the expression 7(100) + 7(2). What product did Carmella begin with?
A 7(98) C 7(200)
Ⓑ 7(102)
21. Which expression is a counterexample to the statement "The whole numbers are closed under division"?
Ⓐ 2 ÷ 10
B 10 ÷ 2
22. Simplify 7 + 5 • 2.
Ⓐ 17
B 24
23. Simplify $\frac{20 - 2^2}{6 - 4}$.
Ⓐ 8 C 50
B 32
24. Evaluate $2(x - 1)^2$ for x = 3.
A 4 Ⓒ 16
B 12
25. The expression b + 2l can be used to find the perimeter of an isosceles triangle, where b represents the base and l represents the legs. Find the perimeter of an isosceles triangle whose base measures 15 cm and whose legs measure 10 cm.
Ⓐ 35 cm
B 170 cm
26. Simplify 4x + y + 2x.
Ⓐ 6x + y C 7x
B $6x^2 + y$
27. Simplify 12(n − 1) + 2n.
A 14n − 1
Ⓑ 14n − 12

Create and customize Chapter 1 Tests. Instantly generate multiple test versions, answer keys, and Spanish versions of test items.

SECTION 1A
The Language of Algebra

On page 40, students write and evaluate algebraic expressions to describe the pressure exerted on a diver underwater, as well as the diver's speed of descent and depth.

Exercises designed to prepare students for success on the Concept Connection can be found on pages 10, 18, 24, 30, and 36.

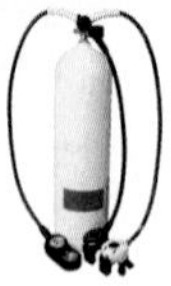

SECTION 1B
The Tools of Algebra

On page 56, students use algebraic properties to determine the cost of supplies needed to decorate a room.

Exercises designed to prepare students for success on the Concept Connection can be found on pages 46 and 52.

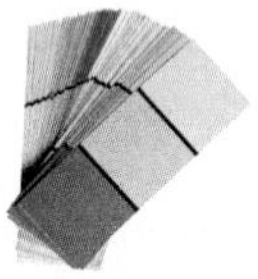

Algebra in *California*

A packet of wildflower seeds usually indicates how many square feet the seeds will cover. If you want to plant the seeds in a square garden, you find the square root of the number of square feet listed on the packet to determine the side length of the garden. Students will learn about square roots in Lesson 1-5 of this chapter.

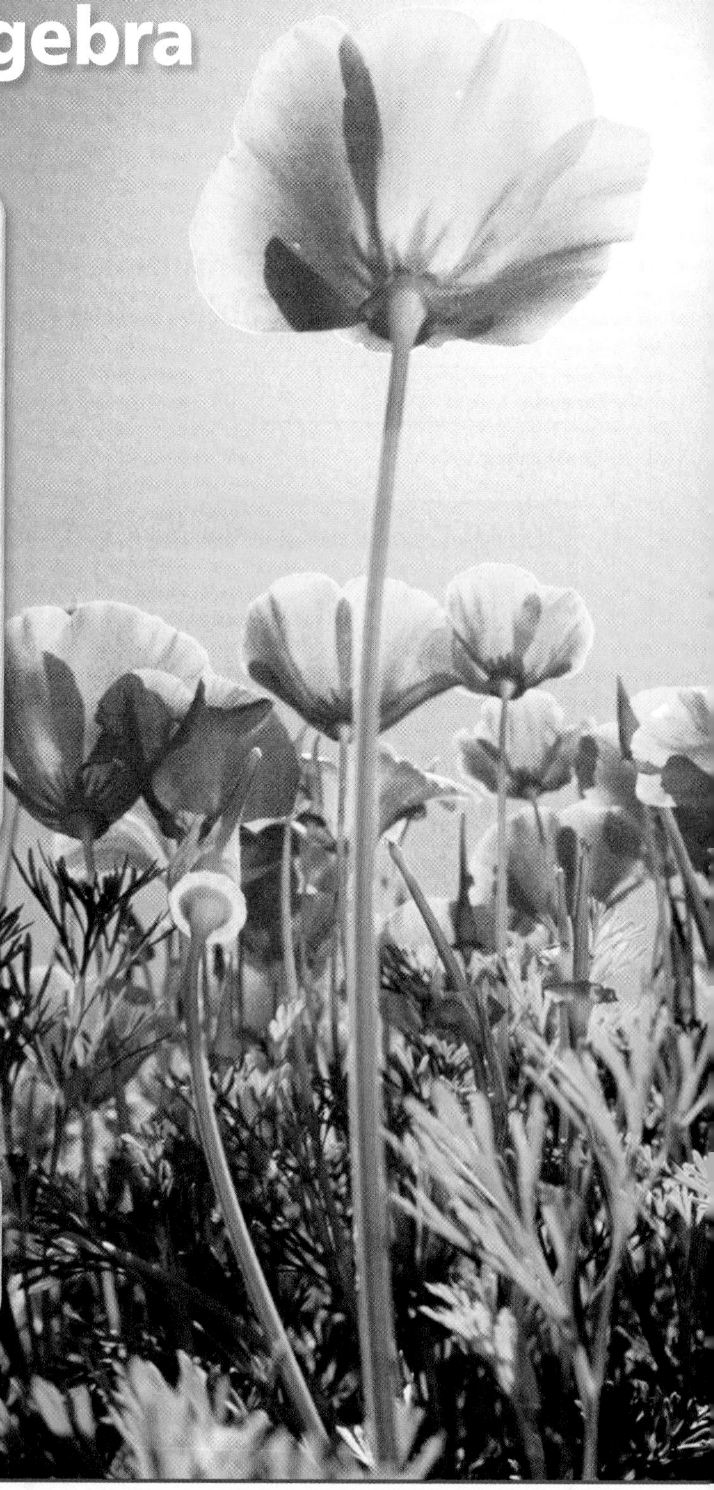

CHAPTER 1

Foundations of Algebra

go.hrw.com
Chapter Project Online
KEYWORD: MA8CA ChProj

You can use square roots to determine the size of a square garden of California poppies. The poppy is the state flower of California.

About the Project

Discovering the "Magic"

The ancient Chinese legend of Lo Shu tells about a 3 x 3 magic square found on a turtle's back. In the Chapter Project, students explore 3 x 3 magic squares and the "magic" behind them.

Project Resources

All project resources for teachers and students are provided online.

ARE YOU READY?

Vocabulary

Match each term on the left with a definition on the right.

1. difference **E**
2. factor **B**
3. perimeter **A**
4. area **D**

A. the distance around a figure
B. a number that is multiplied by another number to form a product
C. a result of division
D. the number of square units a figure covers
E. a result of subtraction

Whole Number Operations

Add, subtract, multiply, or divide.

5. $23 + 6$ **29** 6. $156 \div 12$ **13** 7. 18×96 **1728** 8. $85 - 62$ **23**

Add and Subtract Decimals

Add or subtract.

9. $2.18 + 6.9$ **9.08** 10. $0.32 - 0.18$ **0.14** 11. $29.34 + 0.27$ **29.61** 12. $4 - 1.82$ **2.18**

Multiply Decimals

Multiply.

13. 0.7×0.6 **0.42** 14. 2.5×0.1 **0.25** 15. 1.5×1.5 **2.25** 16. 3.04×0.12 **0.3648**

Divide Decimals

Divide.

17. $6.15 \div 3$ **2.05** 18. $8.64 \div 2$ **4.32** 19. $7.2 \div 0.4$ **18** 20. $92.7 \div 0.3$ **309**

Multiply and Divide Fractions

Multiply or divide. Give your answer in simplest form.

21. $\frac{3}{5} \times \frac{1}{2}$ $\mathbf{\frac{3}{10}}$ 22. $\frac{2}{3} \div \frac{1}{6}$ **4** 23. $\frac{7}{8} \times \frac{4}{7}$ $\mathbf{\frac{1}{2}}$ 24. $4 \div \frac{2}{3}$ **6**

Add and Subtract Fractions

Add or subtract. Give your answer in simplest form.

25. $\frac{2}{5} + \frac{2}{5}$ $\mathbf{\frac{4}{5}}$ 26. $\frac{3}{8} - \frac{1}{8}$ $\mathbf{\frac{1}{4}}$ 27. $\frac{1}{2} + \frac{1}{4}$ $\mathbf{\frac{3}{4}}$ 28. $\frac{2}{3} - \frac{4}{9}$ $\mathbf{\frac{2}{9}}$

ARE YOU READY? CHAPTER 1

Organizer

Objective: Assess students' understanding of prerequisite skills.

Prerequisite Skills

Whole Number Operations
Add and Subtract Decimals
Multiply Decimals
Divide Decimals
Multiply and Divide Fractions
Add and Subtract Fractions

Assessing Prior Knowledge

INTERVENTION

Diagnose and Prescribe

Use this page to determine whether intervention is necessary or whether enrichment is appropriate.

Resources

 ***Are You Ready? Intervention and Enrichment* Worksheets**

 ***Are You Ready?* CD-ROM**

 ***Are You Ready?* Online**

my.hrw.com

ARE YOU READY?
Diagnose and Prescribe

Prerequisite Skill	*Are You Ready? Intervention,* Chapter 1 — Worksheets	CD-ROM	Online
Whole Number Operations	Skill 43	Activity 43	Diagnose and Prescribe Online
Add and Subtract Decimals	Skill 44	Activity 44	
Multiply Decimals	Skill 45	Activity 45	
Divide Decimals	Skill 46	Activity 46	
Multiply and Divide Fractions	Skill 47	Activity 47	
Add and Subtract Fractions	Skill 48	Activity 48	

YES
ENRICH

Are You Ready? Enrichment, Chapter 1

Worksheets
CD-ROM
Online

Organizer

Objective: Help students understand the new concepts they will learn in Chapter 1.

Academic Vocabulary Connections

Becoming familiar with the academic vocabulary on this student page will be helpful to students. Discussing some of the vocabulary terms in the chapter also may be helpful.

1. The word **variable** comes from the word *vary*. What does *vary* mean? Which of the key vocabulary terms above has the opposite meaning? *Vary* means "to change;" constant
2. Another word for *inverse* is *reverse*. The word *additive* relates to the operation of addition. What do you think **additive inverse** is? Something that reverses addition or does the opposite of addition
3. The prefix *ir-* means "not." What relationship do you think **rational numbers** and **irrational numbers** may have? An irrational number is any number that is not rational.

CHAPTER 1

Unpacking the Standards

The information below "unpacks" the standards. The Academic Vocabulary is highlighted and defined to help you understand the language of the standards. Refer to the lessons listed after each standard for help with the math terms and phrases. The Chapter Concept shows how the standard is applied in this chapter.

California Standard	Academic Vocabulary	Chapter Concept
1.0 Students identify and use the arithmetic properties of subsets of integers and rational, irrational, and real numbers, including closure properties for the four basic arithmetic operations where applicable. (Lesson **1-6**)	**identify** know or be able to name **subset** a part of a set or group **property** a feature or characteristic that describes an object or a rule or law that the object satisfies	You learn properties of sets of numbers so that you can identify each set. You also use properties to simplify expressions.
1.1 Students use properties of numbers to demonstrate whether assertions are true or false. (Lesson **1-7**)	**demonstrate** show **assertion** statement that is made without proof	You use properties to decide whether statements about numbers are true or false.
2.0 Students understand and use such operations as taking the opposite, finding the reciprocal, taking a root, and raising to a fractional power. They understand and use the rules of exponents. (Lessons **1-2, 1-3, 1-5**)	**reciprocals** numbers that have a product of 1 ***Example:*** $3 \cdot \frac{1}{3} = \frac{3}{1} \cdot \frac{1}{3} = \frac{3}{3} = 1$ So 3 and $\frac{1}{3}$ are reciprocals.	You perform operations on numbers and find their roots.
24.3 Students use counterexamples to show that an assertion is false and recognize that a single counterexample is sufficient to refute an assertion. (Lesson **1-6**)	**recognize** know or understand **sufficient** enough **refute** show that a statement is not true	You find an example to show that a statement about numbers is false.
25.1 Students use properties of numbers to construct simple, valid arguments (direct and indirect) **for, or formulate counterexamples to, claimed assertions.** (Lessons **1-6, 1-7**)	**construct** make or prepare **valid** true and correct **formulate** make or prepare	You use properties to prove whether a statement about numbers is true or false.

Standard 25.2 is also covered in this chapter. To see this standard unpacked go to Chapter 3, p. 134.

Looking Back

Previously, students

- learned words related to mathematical operations.
- performed operations on whole numbers, decimals and fractions.
- identified numbers on a real number line.

In This Chapter

Students will study

- how to use operations to evaluate and simplify expressions.
- the order of operations.
- properties of the real number system.

Looking Forward

Students can use these skills

- to write and solve equations and inequalities using inverse operations.
- to reason logically about the real numbers.

Reading Strategy: Use Your Book for Success

Understanding how your textbook is organized will help you locate and use helpful information.

Pay attention to the **margin notes.** Know-It Note icons point out key information. Writing Math notes, Helpful Hints, and Caution notes help you understand concepts and avoid common mistakes.

These expressions mean "2 times y":
$2y$ $2(y)$

Helpful Hint

You can write the reciprocal of a number by switch

In the expression -5^2, 5 is the base because the nega

The **Glossary** is found in the back of your textbook. Use it as a resource when you need the definition of an unfamiliar word or property.

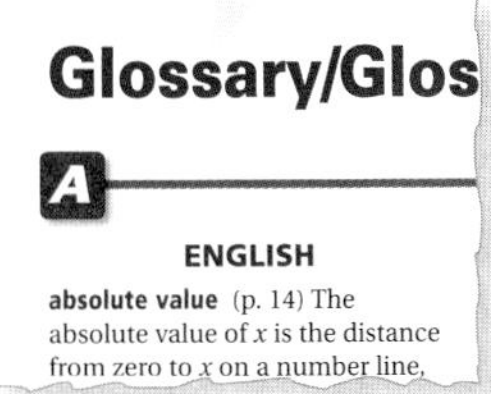

Glossary/Glos
A
ENGLISH
absolute value (p. 14) The absolute value of x is the distance from zero to x on a number line.

The **Index** is located at the end of your textbook. Use it to locate the page where a particular concept is taught.

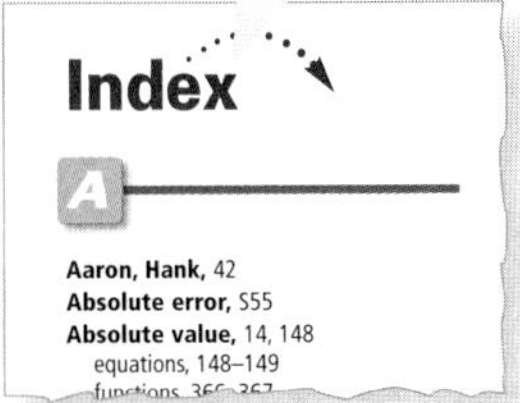

The **Skills Bank** is found in the back of your textbook. These pages review concepts from previous math courses, including geometry skills.

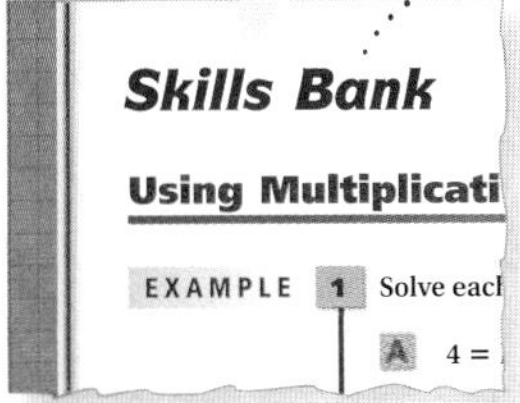

Try This

Use your textbook for the following problems.

1. Use the index to find the page where each word is defined: *algebraic expression, like terms, real numbers.*
2. Use the glossary to find the definition of each word: *additive inverse, constant, perfect square, reciprocal.*
3. Where can you review the concepts of area and perimeter?

Reading and Writing Math CHAPTER 1

Organizer

Objective: Help students apply strategies to understand and retain key concepts.

Online Edition

Resources

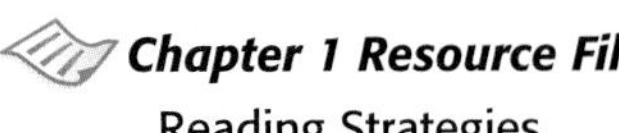

Chapter 1 Resource File
Reading Strategies

Reading Strategy: Use Your Book for Success

Discuss When students know the components of their book, and how to use them, they discover how to become independent learners.

Extend As students ask questions throughout Chapter 1, when appropriate, ask where they might find the answer in their book. Then have them look there.

Ask students what other resources they can use for math help. Answers may include dictionaries and Internet sites.

Answers to *Try This*

1. algebraic expression: 6; like terms: 49; real numbers: 14
2. additive inverse: the opposite of a number; constant: a quantity that does not change; perfect square: a number whose positive square root is a whole number; reciprocal: two numbers are reciprocals if their product is 1.
3. Skills Bank

SECTION

The Language of Algebra

One-Minute Section Planner

Lesson	Lab Resources	Materials
Lesson 1-1 Variables and Expressions • Translate between words and algebra. • Evaluate algebraic expressions. **Preparation for 4.0**		**Optional** highlighters
1-1 Technology Lab Create a Table to Evaluate Expressions • Use a table to evaluate algebraic expressions.		**Required** graphing calculator, spreadsheet program
Lesson 1-2 Adding and Subtracting Real Numbers • Add real numbers. • Subtract real numbers. **2.0**	***Algebra Lab* 1-2** In *Chapter 1 Resource File* ***Technology Lab* 1-2** In *Chapter 1 Resource File*	**Optional** integer chips (MK)
Lesson 1-3 Multiplying and Dividing Real Numbers • Multiply real numbers. • Divide real numbers. **2.0**		**Optional** calculator, index cards
Lesson 1-4 Powers and Exponents • Evaluate expressions containing exponents. **Preparation for 2.0**		
Lesson 1-5 Roots and Irrational Numbers • Evaluate expressions containing roots. • Classify numbers within the real number system. **2.0**	***Algebra Lab* 1-5** In *Chapter 1 Resource File*	**Optional** calculator

MK = *Manipulatives Kit*

Notes

Math Background: Teaching the Standards

Professional Development

THE TRANSITION TO ALGEBRA  1.0

Lesson 1-1

The transition from arithmetic to algebra is a transition from the concrete to the abstract. An essential element of this transition, and one that sometimes causes difficulties for students, is the use of variables.

A *variable*, such as the symbol x, stands for a number. It is important to recognize, however, that variables are used in a variety of settings. For example, the expression $3x$ gives the cost of buying x gallons of gasoline at \$3 per gallon. The expression may be evaluated for any value of x greater than or equal to zero. Variables are used in this way in Lesson 1-1.

Later, students will solve equations such as $3x = 27$. Here, students must understand that the variable stands for a specific number and that solving the equation means finding the replacement value for x that makes the equation true. By way of contrast, the equation $4(x + 5) = 4x + 20$ states a mathematical identity. In this case, there is nothing to "solve"—the statement is true for all real values of x. It is advisable to point out and discuss these different uses of variables as they arise.

OPERATIONS WITH REAL NUMBERS

 1.0, 2.0

Lessons 1-2, 1-3, 1-4

In algebra, students are expected to work with real numbers, and, in particular, to perform arithmetic operations on integers. Students must understand the underlying logic of integer arithmetic and be able to use patterns to develop generalizations about the operations.

For example, students should recognize that for any integer a, the *opposite* of a, $-a$, is the unique integer that satisfies $a + (-a) = 0$. This gives a basis for understanding addition with negative numbers. Using the Commutative and Associative Properties shows that $(2 + 3) + [(-2) + (-3)] = 2 + (-2) + 3 + (-3) = 0 + 0 = 0$. Therefore, $(-2) + (-3) = -(2 + 3)$. In other words, $(-2) + (-3) = -5$.

Students can use patterns to understand integer arithmetic. To see that the product of a positive integer and a negative integer is negative, students can extend the following pattern.

$$\begin{aligned} 3(3) &= 9 \\ 2(3) &= 6 \\ 1(3) &= 3 \\ 0(3) &= 0 \\ -1(3) &= -3 \\ -2(3) &= -6 \end{aligned}$$

-3 -3 -3

Continue the pattern of subtracting 3 at each stage to find the product when multiplying by a negative number.

When presenting division, emphasize that division by 0 is undefined. This is because $\frac{a}{b} = c$ means that $a = bc$ (this is the definition of division). For $\frac{a}{0}$, there is no value of c that makes $a = 0 \cdot c$ when $a \neq 0$.

When $a = 0$, we have $\frac{0}{0}$, which is *indeterminate*. To see why, notice that $a \cdot 0 = 0$ for all values of a. Were it possible to define $\frac{0}{0}$, this would mean that $\frac{0}{0} = a$ for all values of a. That is, $\frac{0}{0} = 1$, $\frac{0}{0} = 2$, $\frac{0}{0} = 3.71$, and so on. There is no unique way to define $\frac{0}{0}$ that is consistent with the definition of division.

RATIONAL AND IRRATIONAL NUMBERS

 1.0

Lesson 1-5

When we express a rational number as a decimal, we usually say it is a repeating decimal or a terminating decimal. However, it can be said that *all* rational numbers are repeating decimals since, for example, $8 = 8.00000\ldots$. We can also write 8 as $7.99999\ldots$ as shown below:

Let $x = 7.99999\ldots$. Then $10x = 79.99999\ldots$ and

$$\begin{aligned} 10x &= 79.99999\ldots \\ -\ x &\quad -\ 7.99999\ldots \\ \hline 9x &= 72 \\ \frac{9x}{9} &= \frac{72}{9} \\ x &= 8 \end{aligned}$$

It is interesting to note that repeating decimals are base dependent. In base 10, the fraction $\frac{1}{3}$ is given by the repeating decimal $0.33333\ldots$, but in base 3 the fraction is given by simply 0.1.

1-1 Organizer

Objectives: Translate between words and algebra.

Evaluate algebraic expressions.

Online Edition
Tutorial Videos

Countdown to Mastery Week 1

Power Presentations with PowerPoint®

Warm Up

Add or subtract.

1. 6 + 104 110 **2.** 12 + 1.9 13.9

3. 23 − 8 15 **4.** $\frac{1}{2} + \frac{1}{5}$ $\frac{7}{10}$

Multiply or divide.

5. 324 ÷ 18 18 **6.** $\frac{1}{4}(24)$ 6

7. 13.5(10) 135 **8.** 18.2 ÷ 2 9.1

Also available on transparency

Math Fact !!

The Rhind papyrus, an ancient Egyptian scroll, was written around 1650 B.C.E. It describes algebraic methods used by the Egyptians.

Answers to *Check It Out!*

Possible answers given.

1a. 4 decreased by n; n less than 4

1b. the quotient of t and 5; t divided by 5

1c. the sum of 9 and q; q added to 9

1d. the product of 3 and h; 3 times h

California Standards

Preparation for 4.0

1-1 Variables and Expressions

California Standards

Preparation for 4.0
Students simplify expressions before solving linear equations and inequalities **in one variable,** such as $3(2x - 5) + 4(x - 2) = 12$.

Vocabulary
variable
constant
numerical expression
algebraic expression
evaluate
replacement set

Why learn this?

Variables and expressions can be used to determine how many plastic drink bottles must be recycled to make enough carpet for a house.

Container City, in East London, UK, is a development of buildings made from recycled sea containers.

A home that is "green built" uses many recycled products, including carpet made from recycled plastic drink bottles. You can determine how many square feet of carpet can be made from a certain number of plastic drink bottles by using *variables, constants,* and *expressions.*

A **variable** is a letter or symbol used to represent a value that can change.

A **constant** is a value that does not change.

A **numerical expression** contains only constants and/or operations.

An **algebraic expression** contains variables, constants, and/or operations.

You will need to translate between algebraic expressions and words to be successful in math. The diagram below shows some of the ways to write mathematical operations with words.

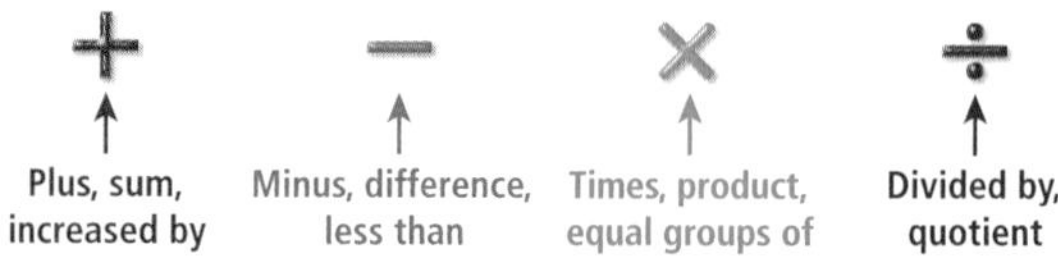

EXAMPLE 1 Translating from Algebra to Words

Give two ways to write each algebraic expression in words.

A $x + 3$
the sum of x and 3
x increased by 3

B $m - 7$
the difference of m and 7
7 less than m

C $2 \cdot y$
2 times y
the product of 2 and y

D $k \div 5$
k divided by 5
the quotient of k and 5

Writing Math

These expressions all mean "2 times y":
$2y$ $2(y)$
$2 \cdot y$ $(2)(y)$
$2 \times y$ $(2)y$

CHECK IT OUT! **Give two ways to write each algebraic expression in words.**

1a. $4 - n$ **1b.** $\frac{t}{5}$ **1c.** $9 + q$ **1d.** $3(h)$

1 Introduce

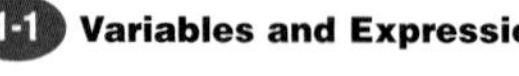

EXPLORATION

1-1 Variables and Expressions

You are going to a concert with some friends to celebrate your birthday. The tickets are $18 each.

1. Complete the table to find the total cost for different numbers of tickets.
2. Explain how to find the total cost for a given number of tickets.

Number of Tickets	Total Cost
1	
2	
3	
4	

3. Suppose n represents the number of tickets. Use a combination of operations, numbers, and the letter n to represent the total cost of n tickets.
4. What is the value of the mathematical statement that you wrote when $n = 6$? What does this represent?

THINK AND DISCUSS

5. Show how to write a mathematical statement for the total cost of the tickets if each ticket costs $23.
6. Describe a situation that can be represented by the mathematical statement $h + 3$.

Motivate

Have students write a shopping list while you call out the items to them. Name the items quickly enough that the students have time to write down abbreviations for them, but not the entire words.

Point out to students that they probably used abbreviations or symbols to represent the words on the shopping list. Today they will learn how algebra can represent words and phrases by using variables, constants, and operation symbols.

Explorations and answers are provided in *Alternate Openers: Explorations Transparencies*.

To translate words into algebraic expressions, read the problem to determine what actions are taking place.

Add	**Subtract**	**Multiply**	**Divide**
↑	↑	↑	↑
Put together, combine	Find how much more or less	Put together equal groups	Separate into equal groups

EXAMPLE 2 **Translating from Words to Algebra**

A **Eve reads 25 pages per hour. Write an expression for the number of pages she reads in h hours.**

h represents the number of hours that Eve reads.

$25 \cdot h$ or $25h$ *Think: h groups of 25 pages.*

B **Sam is 2 years younger than Sue. Sue is y years old. Write an expression for Sam's age.**

y represents Sue's age.

$y - 2$ *Think: "younger than" means "less than."*

C **William runs a mile in 12 minutes. Write an expression for the number of miles that William runs in m minutes.**

m represents the total time William runs.

$\frac{m}{12}$ *Think: How many groups of 12 are in m?*

2. Miriam is 5 cm taller than Jan. Jan is m cm tall. Write an expression for Miriam's height in centimeters. **$m + 5$**

To **evaluate** an expression is to find its value. To evaluate an algebraic expression, substitute numbers for the variables in the expression and then simplify the expression. A **replacement set** is a set of numbers that can be substituted for a variable.

EXAMPLE 3 **Evaluating Algebraic Expressions**

Evaluate each expression for the replacement set {2, 4, 5.7}

A $x + 8$

Substitute each value in the replacement set for x and simplify.

$x + 8$	$x + 8$	$x + 8$
$2 + 8$	$4 + 8$	$5.7 + 8$
10	12	13.7

B $\frac{x}{2}$

Substitute each value in the replacement set for x and simplify.

$\frac{x}{2}$	$\frac{x}{2}$	$\frac{x}{2}$
$\frac{2}{2}$	$\frac{4}{2}$	$\frac{5.7}{2}$
1	2	2.85

Writing Math

One way to indicate a set is to use braces, {}. The items in a set are called elements.

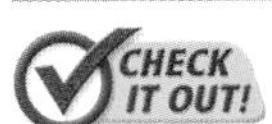

Evaluate each expression for the replacement set {2, 3, 9}.

3a. $\frac{2}{3}n$ **$\frac{4}{3}$; 2; 6** **3b.** $15 - n$ **13; 12; 6** **3c.** $n + 0.15$

3c. 2.15; 3.15; 9.15

Power Presentations with PowerPoint®

Additional Examples

Example 1

Give two ways to write each algebraic expression in words.

Possible answers given.

A. $9 + r$ the sum of 9 and r; 9 increased by r

B. $q - 3$ the difference of q and 3; 3 less than q

C. $7m$ the product of m and 7; m times 7

D. $j \div 6$ the quotient of j and 6; j divided by 6

Example 2

A. John types 62 words per minute. Write an expression for the number of words he types in m minutes. $62m$

B. Roberto is 4 years older than Emily, who is y years old. Write an expression for Roberto's age. $y + 4$

C. Joey earns $5 for each car he washes. Write an expression for the number of cars Joey must wash to earn d dollars. $\frac{d}{5}$

Example 3

Evaluate each expression for the replacement set {6, 7, 2}.

A. $b - 1$ 5; 6; 1

B. $3b$ 18; 21; 6

Also available on transparency

INTERVENTION

Questioning Strategies

EXAMPLE 1

- What words are indicated by each operation symbol?

EXAMPLE 2

- What clues tell you which operation to use?

EXAMPLE 3

- Explain why the value of an algebraic expression is numeric.

2 Teach

Guided Instruction

Before introducing variables and expressions, review elementary problems such as $2 + \square = 7$ and $\frac{10}{\square} = 2$. Tell students that in algebra, the box is replaced by a letter. Be sure students understand that the letter represents a number.

Teaching Tip **Visual** When students translate words into algebraic expressions, encourage them to copy the word phrases and to use a highlighter to call attention to words that indicate what action is taking place.

Universal Access

Through Graphic Organizers

Copy the following table on the board and have students write real-world situations that might be modeled by each expression.

$100 - p$	$\frac{30}{x}$	$b - 1$	$\frac{m}{2}$	$6h$	$14 + s$

Power Presentations with PowerPoint®

Additional Examples

Example 4

Approximately eighty-five 20-ounce plastic bottles must be recycled to produce the fiberfill for a sleeping bag.

A. Write an expression for the number of bottles needed to make *s* sleeping bags. 85*s*

B. Find the number of bottles needed to make 20, 50, and 325 sleeping bags. 1700; 4250; 27,625

Also available on transparency

INTERVENTION

Questioning Strategies

EXAMPLE 4

- How do you think the letter for the variable was chosen?
- Why is multiplication used in the expression?

EXAMPLE 4 Recycling Application

Approximately fourteen 20-ounce plastic drink bottles must be recycled to produce 1 square foot of carpet.

a. Write an expression for the number of bottles needed to make *c* square feet of carpet.

The expression $14c$ models the number of bottles needed to make *c* square feet of carpet.

b. Find the number of bottles needed to make 40, 120, and 224 square feet of carpet.

Evaluate $14c$ for the replacement set {40, 120, 224}.

c	$14c$
40	$14(40) = 560$
120	$14(120) = 1680$
224	$14(224) = 3136$

To make 40 ft^2 of carpet, 560 bottles are needed.
To make 120 ft^2 of carpet, 1680 bottles are needed.
To make 224 ft^2 of carpet, 3136 bottles are needed.

4. To make one sweater, sixty-three 20-ounce plastic drink bottles must be recycled.
   a. Write an expression for the number of bottles needed to make *s* sweaters. **63*s***
   b. Find the number of bottles needed to make 12, 25, and 50 sweaters. **756 bottles; 1575 bottles; 3150 bottles**

THINK AND DISCUSS

1. Write two ways to suggest each of the following, using words or phrases: addition, subtraction, multiplication, division.

2. Explain the difference between a numerical expression and an algebraic expression.

3. GET ORGANIZED Copy and complete the graphic organizer. Next to each operation, write a word phrase in the left box and its corresponding algebraic expression in the right box.

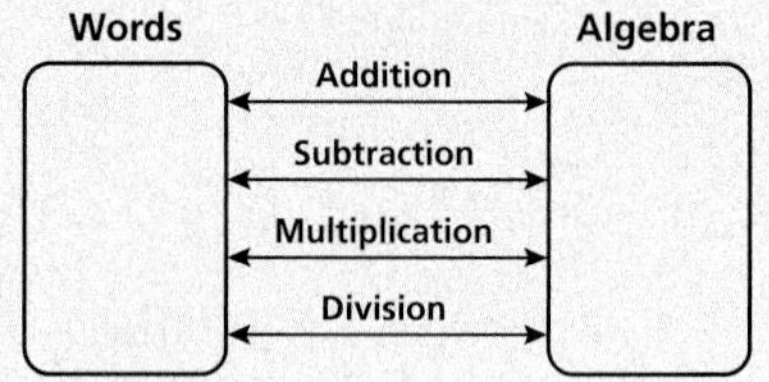

3 Close

Summarize

Have students list key words for each operation. Possible answers: addition–*add, sum*; subtraction–*minus, difference*; multiplication–*times, product*; division–*divided by, quotient* Have students explain the difference between a variable and a constant. A variable is a value that can change. A constant is a value that does not change.

FORMATIVE ASSESSMENT

and INTERVENTION

***Diagnose Before* the Lesson**
1-1 Warm Up, TE p. 6

***Monitor During* the Lesson**
Check It Out! Exercises, SE pp. 6–8
Questioning Strategies, TE pp. 7–8

***Assess After* the Lesson**
1-1 Lesson Quiz, TE p. 11
Alternative Assessment, TE p. 11

Answers to *Think and Discuss*

Possible answers:

1. addition–*increased by, sum of*; subtraction–*decreased by, difference of*; multiplication–*multiplied by, product of*; division–*divided by, quotient of*
2. Both types of expressions may contain numbers and operations. Algebraic expressions may also contain variables.
3. See p. A2.

1-1 Exercises

California Standards Practice
Preparation for 4.0

go.hrw.com
Homework Help Online
KEYWORD: MA8CA 1-1
Parent Resources Online
KEYWORD: MA8CA Parent

GUIDED PRACTICE

1. **Vocabulary** A(n) ___?___ is a value that can change. (*algebraic expression, constant,* or *variable*) **variable**

SEE EXAMPLE 1 p. 6

Give two ways to write each algebraic expression in words.

2. $n - 5$
3. $\frac{f}{3}$
4. $c + 15$
5. $9 - y$
6. $\frac{x}{12}$
7. $t + 12$
8. $8x$
9. $x - 3$

SEE EXAMPLE 2 p. 7

10. George drives at 45 mi/h. Write an expression for the number of miles George travels in h hours. **$45h$**
11. The length of a rectangle is 4 units greater than its width w. Write an expression for the length of the rectangle. **$w + 4$**

SEE EXAMPLE 3 p. 7

Evaluate each expression for the replacement set {3, 4, 9}.

12. $a - 2$ **1; 2; 7**
13. $4a$ **12; 16; 36**
14. $6 \div a$ **2; $\frac{3}{2}$; $\frac{2}{3}$**
15. $2a$ **6; 8; 18**

SEE EXAMPLE 4 p. 8

16. Brianna practices the piano 30 minutes each day.
    a. Write an expression for the number of hours she practices in d days. **$0.5d$**
    b. Find the number of hours Brianna practices in 2, 4, and 10 days. **1; 2; 5**

PRACTICE AND PROBLEM SOLVING

Independent Practice

For Exercises	See Example
17–24	1
25–26	2
27–30	3
31	4

Extra Practice
Skills Practice p. EP2
Application Practice p. EP24

Give two ways to write each algebraic expression in words.

17. $5p$
18. $4 - y$
19. $3 + x$
20. $3y$
21. $-3s$
22. $r \div 5$
23. $14 - t$
24. $x + 0.5$
25. Friday's temperature was 20° warmer than Monday's temperature t. Write an expression for Friday's temperature. **$t + 20$**
26. Ann sleeps 8 hours per night. Write an expression for the number of hours Ann sleeps in n nights. **$8n$**

Evaluate each expression for the replacement set {2, 8, 13}.

27. $r - 1$ **1; 7; 12**
28. $6 + r$ **8; 14; 19**
29. $r \div 2$ **1; 4; $\frac{13}{2}$**
30. $15r$ **30; 120; 195**
31. Jim is paid for overtime when he works more than 40 hours per week.
    a. Write an expression for the number of hours he works overtime when he works h hours. **$h - 40$**
    b. Find the number of hours Jim works overtime when he works 40, 44, 48, and 52 hours. **0; 4; 8; 12**

32. **Write About It** Write a paragraph that explains to another student how to evaluate an expression. **To evaluate an expression is to find its value. To do this, substitute values for the variables and perform all the indicated operations.**

Write an algebraic expression for each verbal expression. Then write a real-world situation that could be modeled by the expression.

33. the product of 2 and x
34. b less than 17
35. 10 more than y

Teacher to Teacher

I like to use the Think and Discuss questions from the previous lesson as a warm-up activity to begin the next class. It helps students refresh their memory of the concepts just learned and practiced. The Think and Discuss questions often begin very useful class discussions and allow students to learn from their peers.

John Bakelaar
Jackson, MS

1-1 Exercises

Assignment Guide

Assign *Guided Practice* exercises as necessary.

If you finished Examples **1–2**
Proficient 17–26, 40–43
Advanced 17–26, 40–43

If you finished Examples **1–4**
Proficient 17–35, 36–40 even, 44, 48–51, 55–64
Advanced 18–26 even, 27–36, 39, 40, 44–64

Homework Quick Check
Quickly check key concepts.
Exercises: 18, 24, 26, 28, 31, 40

Answers

2–9. Possible answers given.

2. 5 less than n; n decreased by 5
3. the quotient of f and 3; f; divided by 3
4. c increased by 15; the sum of c and 15
5. 9 decreased by y; y less than 9
6. one-twelfth x; the quotient of x and 12
7. the sum of t and 12; t increased by 12
8. the product of 8 and x; 8 groups of x
9. x decreased by 3; the difference of x and 3

17–22. Possible answers given.

17. the product of 5 and p; 5 groups of p
18. 4 decreased by y; the difference of 4 and y
19. the sum of 3 and x; 3 increased by x
20. the product of 3 and y; 3 times y
21. negative 3 times s; the product of negative 3 and s
22. the quotient of r and 5; one-fifth r
23–24, 33–35. See p. A12.

California Standards

Standard	Exercises
Prep for 4.0	2–54
6MG2.2	55–57

Exercise 36 involves using algebraic expressions to describe the pressure on a diver's body at different depths. The exercise prepares students for the Concept Connection on page 40.

Teaching Tip **Geometry** In **Exercise 37,** students must write an expression for the area of a rectangle. Remind students that the area of a rectangle is its length times its width.

CONCEPT CONNECTION

36. This problem will prepare you for the Concept Connection on page 40.

The air around you puts pressure on your body equal to 14.7 pounds per square inch (psi). When you are underwater, the water exerts additional pressure on your body. For each foot you are below the surface of the water, the pressure increases by 0.445 psi.

a. What does 14.7 represent in the expression $14.7 + 0.445d$? **air pressure on land**

b. What does d represent in the expression? **depth below the water in feet**

c. What is the total pressure exerted on a person's body when $d = 8$ ft? **18.26 psi**

37. **Geometry** The length of a rectangle is 9 inches. Write an expression for the area of the rectangle if the width is w inches. Find the area of the rectangle if the replacement set for the width is 1, 8, 9, and 11 inches. **$9w$; 9 in^2; 72 in^2; 81 in^2; 99 in^2**

38. **Geometry** The perimeter of any rectangle is the sum of the lengths of its sides. The area of any rectangle is the length ℓ times the width w.

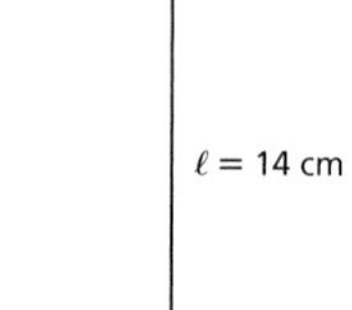

a. Write an expression for the perimeter of a rectangle. **$2\ell + 2w$**

b. Find the perimeter of the rectangle shown. **44 cm**

c. Write an expression for the area of a rectangle. **ℓw**

d. Find the area of the rectangle shown. **112 cm^2**

Complete each table. Evaluate the expression for each value of x.

39.

x	$x + 12$
1	**13**
2	**14**
3	**15**
4	**16**

40.

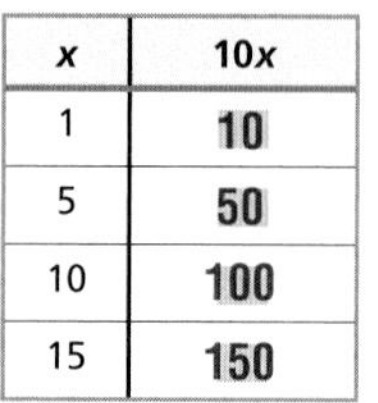

x	$10x$
1	**10**
5	**50**
10	**100**
15	**150**

41.

x	$x \div 2$
12	**6**
20	**10**
26	**13**
30	**15**

LINK

Astronomy

A crater on Canada's Devon Island is geologically similar to the surface of Mars. However, the temperature on Devon Island is about 37°F in summer, and the average summer temperature on Mars is −85°F.

42. **Astronomy** An object's weight on Mars can be found by multiplying 0.38 by the object's weight on Earth.

a. An object weighs p pounds on Earth. Write an expression for its weight on Mars. **$0.38p$**

b. Dana weighs 120 pounds, and her bicycle weighs 44 pounds. How much would Dana and her bicycle together weigh on Mars? **62.32 lb**

43. **Meteorology** Use the bar graph to write an expression for the average annual precipitation in New York, New York.

a. The average annual precipitation in New York is m inches more than the average annual precipitation in Houston, Texas. **$47.84 + m$**

b. The average annual precipitation in New York is s inches less than the average annual precipitation in Miami, Florida. **$58.53 - s$**

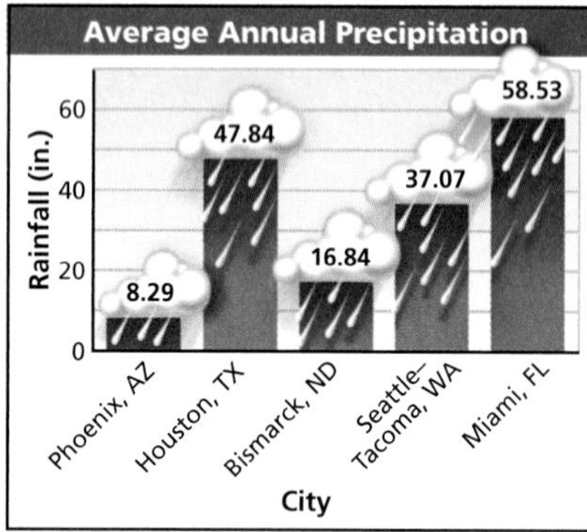

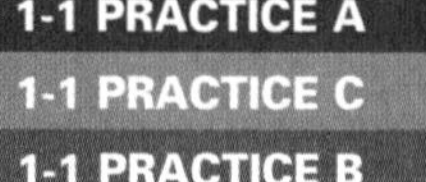

1-1 PRACTICE A
1-1 PRACTICE C
1-1 PRACTICE B

LESSON 1-1 **Practice B**
Variables and Expressions

Give two ways to write each algebraic expression in words.

1. $15 - b$
   the difference of 15 and b
   b less than 15

2. $\frac{x}{16}$
   the quotient of x and 16
   x divided by 16

3. $x + 9$
   the sum of x and 9
   9 more than x

4. $(2)(t)$
   the product of 2 and t
   2 times t

5. $z - 7$
   the difference of z and 7
   7 less than z

6. $4y$
   the product of 4 and y
   4 times y

7. Sophie's math class has 6 fewer boys than girls, and there are g girls. Write an expression for the number of boys. $g - 6$

8. A computer printer can print 10 pages per minute. Write an expression for the number of pages the printer can print in m minutes. $10m$

Evaluate each expression for the replacement set {12, 23, 28.2}.

9. $28.2 + a$ — 40.2, 51.2, 56.4
10. $212.8 - b$ — 200.8, 189.8, 184.6
11. $4.5x$ — 54, 103.5, 126.9
12. $t - 7.8$ — 4.2, 15.2, 20.4
13. $\frac{g}{4}$ — 3, 5.75, 7.05
14. $z - 14.6$ — −2.6, 8.4, 13.6

15. Paula always withdraws 20 dollars more than she needs from the bank.

a. Write an expression for the amount of money Paula withdraws if she needs d dollars. $d + 20$

b. Find the amount of money Paula withdraws if she needs 20, 60, and 75 dollars. 40 dollars; 80 dollars; 95 dollars

1-1 READING STRATEGIES

LESSON 1-1 **Reading Strategies**
Connecting Words and Symbols

To translate between phrases and algebraic expressions, you must connect words with symbols. Look at the examples in the table below.

Operations	Words	Symbols
Addition	"sum of 3 and n" "n more than 3" "3 plus n"	$3 + n$
Subtraction	"difference of 3 and n" "n less than 3" "3 minus n"	$3 - n$
Multiplication	"product of 3 and n" "3 times n" "3 groups of n"	$3n$ $3 \cdot n$ $3 \times n$ $3(n)$
Division	"quotient of 3 and n" "3 divided by n" "3 separated into n groups"	$3 \div n$ $\frac{3}{n}$

Solve each problem.

1. Write "10 times the value of y" in symbols in three different ways.
   Possible answers: $10y$, $10 \cdot y$, and $10(y)$

2. Write "$k \div 6$" in words in two different ways.
   Possible answers: k divided by 6, the quotient of k and 6

3. Write "4 less than b" in symbols. $b - 4$

4. Write "b less than 4" in symbols. $4 - b$

Translate each word phrase into an algebraic expression.

5. Craig types 20 words per minute. Write an expression for the number of words Craig types in m minutes. $20m$

6. Jeana is 58 inches tall. Her sister Janelle is t inches taller. Write an expression for Janelle's height. $58 + t$

1-1 REVIEW FOR MASTERY

LESSON 1-1 **Review for Mastery**
Variables and Expressions

To translate words into algebraic expressions, find words like these that tell you the operation.

+	−	·	÷
add	subtract	multiply	divide
sum	difference	product	quotient
more	less	times	split
increased	decreased	per	ratio

Kenny owns v video games. Stan owns 7 more video games than Kenny. Write an expression for the number of video games Stan owns.

v represents the number of video games Kenny owns.

$v + 7$ *Think: The word "more" indicates addition.*

Order does not matter for addition. The expression $7 + v$ is also correct.

Jenny is 12 years younger than Candy. Write an expression for Jenny's age if Candy is c years old.

c represents Candy's age.

The word "younger" means "less," which indicates subtraction.

$c - 12$ *Think: Candy is older, so subtract 12 from her age.*

Order does matter for subtraction. The expression $12 - c$ is incorrect.

1. Jared can type 35 words per minute. Write an expression for the number of words he can type in m minutes. $35m$

2. Mr. O'Brien's commute to work is 0.5 hour less than Miss Santos's commute. Write an expression for the length of Mr. O'Brien's commute if Miss Santos's commute is h hours. $h - 0.5$

3. Mrs. Knighten bought a box of c crayons and split them evenly between the 25 students in her classroom. Write an expression for the number of crayons each student received. $c \div 25$

4. Enrique collected 152 recyclable bottles, and Latasha collected b recyclable bottles. Write an expression for the number of bottles they collected altogether. $152 + b$

5. Tammy's current rent is r dollars. Next month it will be reduced by \$50. Write an expression for next month's rent in dollars. $r - 50$

44. **Critical Thinking** Compare algebraic expressions and numerical expressions. Give examples of each. **Both algebraic and numerical expressions contain numbers and operations, but algebraic expressions also contain variables.**

Write an algebraic expression for each verbal expression. Then evaluate the algebraic expression for the given values of x.

	Verbal	Algebraic	$x = 12$	$x = 14$
	x reduced by 5	$x - 5$	$12 - 5 = 7$	$14 - 5 = 9$
45.	7 more than x	**$x + 7$**	**19**	**21**
46.	The quotient of x and 2	**$\frac{x}{2}$**	**6**	**7**
47.	The sum of x and 3	**$x + 3$**	**15**	**17**

Multiple Choice **For Exercises 48–50, choose the best answer.**

48. Claire has had her driver's license for 3 years. Bill has had his license for b fewer years than Claire. Which expression can be used to show the number of years Bill has had his driver's license?

Ⓐ $3 + b$ Ⓑ $b + 3$ **Ⓒ $3 - b$** Ⓓ $b < 3$

49. Which expression represents x?

Ⓐ $12 - 5$ Ⓒ $7 - x$

Ⓑ $x + 5$ Ⓓ $12 - 7$

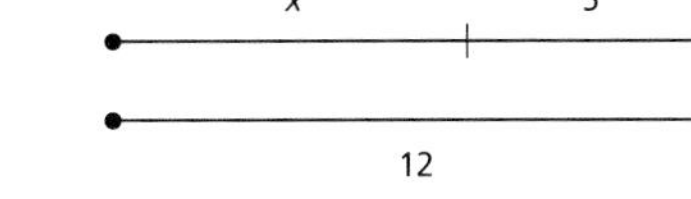

50. Which situation is best modeled by the expression $25 - x$?

Ⓐ George places x more video games on a shelf with 25 games.

Ⓑ Sarah has driven x miles of a 25-mile trip.

Ⓒ Amelia paid 25 dollars of an x dollar lunch that she shared with Ariel.

Ⓓ Jorge has 25 boxes full of x baseball cards each.

CHALLENGE AND EXTEND

Evaluate each expression for the given values of the variables.

51. $2ab$; $a = 6, b = 3$ **36** 52. $2x + y$; $x = 4, y = 5$ **13** 53. $3x \div 6y$; $x = 6, y = 3$ **1**

54. **Multi-Step** An Internet service provider charges $9.95/month for the first 20 hours and $0.50 for each additional hour. Write an expression representing the charges for h hours of use in one month when h is more than 20 hours. What is the charge for 35 hours? **$9.95 + 0.50(h - 20)$; $17.45**

62–64. Possible answers given.

62. Add 8 to the previous term; 36, 44, 52.

63. Multiply the previous term by 3; 729, 2187, 6561.

64. Add 1 to the previous term, then add 2, and then add 3, and so on; 17, 23, 30.

SPIRAL STANDARDS REVIEW

6MG2.2

The sum of the angle measures in a triangle is 180°. Find the measure of the third angle given the other two angle measures. *(Previous course)*

55. 45° and 90° **45°** 56. 120° and 20° **40°** 57. 30° and 60° **90°**

Write an equivalent fraction for each percent. *(Previous course)*

58. 25% **$\frac{1}{4}$** 59. 50% **$\frac{1}{2}$** 60. 75% **$\frac{3}{4}$** 61. 100% **1**

Find a possible pattern and use it to give the next three numbers. *(Previous course)*

62. 4, 12, 20, 28, ... 63. 3, 9, 27, 81, 243, ... 64. 2, 3, 5, 8, 12, ...

Teaching Tip

Multiple Choice For **Exercise 50,** students may recognize choices **B** and **C** as indicating subtraction. Show students that since 25 is written first in the expression, 25 is the full amount being considered. In **C,** $25 is only part of the cost of lunch, but in **B,** 25 miles is the whole trip, so **B** is the answer.

Journal

Have students describe some things in their lives that change, and then relate them to the algebraic definition of "variable."

ALTERNATIVE ASSESSMENT

Instruct students to look through newspapers and magazines to find real-world situations that can be described using words that indicate mathematical operations. Then have them write how they would model each situation with an algebraic expression.

Power Presentations with PowerPoint®

1-1 Lesson Quiz

Give two ways to write each algebraic expression in words.

1, 2. Possible answers given.

1. $j - 3$ the difference of j and 3; 3 less than j

2. $4p$ 4 times p; the product of 4 and p

3. Mark is 5 years older than Juan, who is y years old. Write an expression for Mark's age. $y + 5$

Evaluate each expression for the replacement set {5, 8, 12}.

4. $\frac{d}{2}$ $\frac{5}{2}$; 4; 6 5. $6 + d$ 11; 14; 18

Shemika practices basketball for 2 hours each day.

6. Write an expression for the number of hours she practices in d days. $2d$

7. Find the number of hours she practices in 5, 12, and 20 days. 10 hours; 24 hours; 40 hours

Also available on transparency

1-1 PROBLEM SOLVING

Problem Solving
LESSON 1-1 *1-1 Variables and Expressions*

Write the correct answer.

1. For her book club, Sharon reads for 45 minutes each day. Write an expression for the number of hours she reads in d days. **45d**

2. The minimum wage in 2003 was $5.15. This was w more than the minimum wage in 1996. Write an expression for the minimum wage in 1996. **$5.15 - w$**

3. According to the 2000 census, the number of people per square mile in Florida was about 216 more than the number of people per square mile in Texas. Write an expression for the number of people per square mile in Florida if there were t people per square mile in Texas. **$216 + t$**

4. The cost of a party is $550. The price per person depends on how many people attend the party. Write an expression for the price per person if p people attend the party. Then find the price per person if 25, 50, and 55 people attend the party. **$\frac{550}{p}$** **$22, $11, $10**

Use the table below to answer questions 5–6, which shows the years five states entered the Union. Select the best answer.

State	Year Entered into Union
Florida	1845
Indiana	1816
Pennsylvania	1787
Texas	1845
West Virginia	1863

5. North Carolina entered the Union x years after Pennsylvania. Which expression shows the year North Carolina entered the Union?

A $1845 + x$ **Ⓒ $1787 + x$**

B $1845 - x$ D $1787 - x$

6. The expression $f - 26$ represents the year Alabama entered the Union, where f is the year Florida entered. In which year did Alabama enter the Union?

Ⓕ 1819 H 1837

G 1826 J 1871

7. The number of states that entered the Union in 1889 was half the number of states s that entered in 1788. Which expression shows the number of states that entered the Union in 1889?

A $2s$ C $s + 2$

Ⓑ $s \div 2$ D $2 - s$

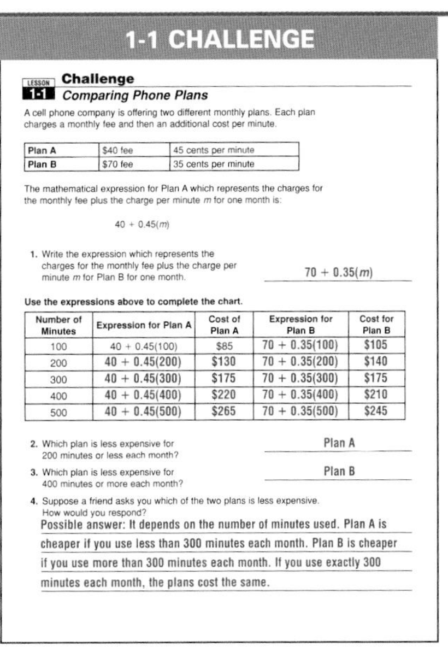

1-1 CHALLENGE

Challenge
LESSON 1-1 *Comparing Phone Plans*

A cell phone company is offering two different monthly plans. Each plan charges a monthly fee and then an additional cost per minute.

Plan A	$40 fee	45 cents per minute
Plan B	$70 fee	35 cents per minute

The mathematical expression for Plan A which represents the charges for the monthly fee plus the charge per minute m for one month is:

$40 + 0.45(m)$

1. Write the expression which represents the charges for the monthly fee plus the charge per minute m for Plan B for one month. **$70 + 0.35(m)$**

Use the expressions above to complete the chart.

Number of Minutes	Expression for Plan A	Cost of Plan A	Expression for Plan B	Cost for Plan B
100	40 + 0.45(100)	$85	**70 + 0.35(100)**	**$105**
200	**40 + 0.45(200)**	**$130**	**70 + 0.35(200)**	**$140**
300	**40 + 0.45(300)**	**$175**	**70 + 0.35(300)**	**$175**
400	**40 + 0.45(400)**	**$220**	**70 + 0.35(400)**	**$210**
500	**40 + 0.45(500)**	**$265**	**70 + 0.35(500)**	**$245**

2. Which plan is less expensive for 200 minutes or less each month? **Plan A**

3. Which plan is less expensive for 400 minutes or more each month? **Plan B**

4. Suppose a friend asks you which of the two plans is less expensive. How would you respond?
Possible answer: It depends on the number of minutes used. Plan A is cheaper if you use less than 300 minutes each month. Plan B is cheaper if you use more than 300 minutes each month. If you use exactly 300 minutes each month, the plans cost the same.

Organizer

Use with Lesson 1-1

Objective: Use a table to evaluate algebraic expressions.

Materials: graphing calculator, spreadsheet program

Online Edition
TechKeys

Countdown to Mastery Week 1

Teach

Discuss

Be sure students are comfortable evaluating expressions using pencil and paper before doing this activity. The concept of a variable is difficult for many beginning algebra students. Use this activity to emphasize that a variable represents a number and that the value of a variable may change.

Technology When using technology to create a table, use an asterisk (*) for multiplication, a forward slash (/) for division, and a caret (^) for exponentiation.

1-1

Use Technology to Evaluate Expressions

You can use a graphing calculator to quickly evaluate expressions for many values of the variable.

Use with Lesson 1-1

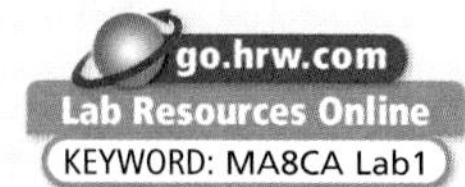

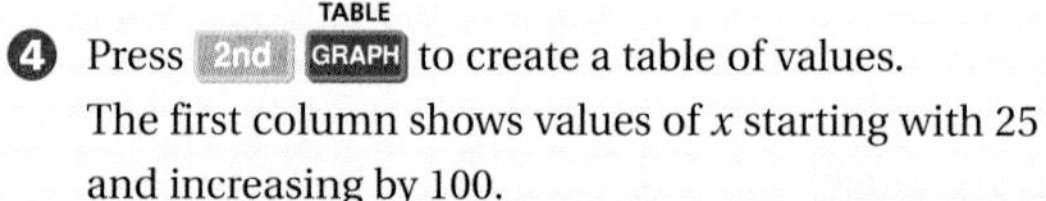

Activity 1

Evaluate $2x + 7$ for $x = 25, 125, 225, 325,$ and 425.

1. Press **Y=** and enter **2X+7** for **Y1**.

2. Determine a pattern for values of x.
   The x-values start with 25 and increase by 100.

3. Press **2nd** **WINDOW** (TBLSET) to view the *Table Setup* window.
   Enter **25** as the starting value in **TblStart=**.
   Enter **100** as the amount by which x changes in **△Tbl=**.

4. Press **2nd** **GRAPH** (TABLE) to create a table of values.
   The first column shows values of x starting with 25 and increasing by 100.
   The second column shows values of the expression $2x + 7$ when x is equal to the value in the first column.
   You can use the arrow keys to view the table when x is greater than 625.
   The answers are 57, 257, 457, 657, and 857.

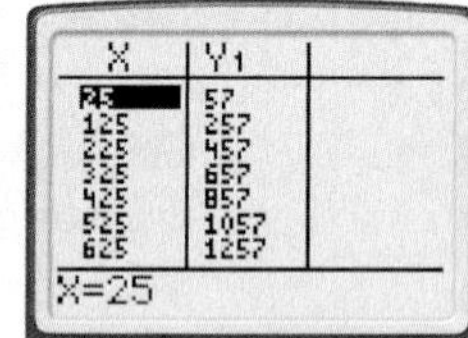

Try This

1. Use the table feature of a graphing calculator to evaluate $5x - 7$ for $x = 4, 6, 8, 10,$ and 12.
   a. What value did you enter in **TblStart=**? **4**
   b. What value did you enter in **△Tbl=**? **2**
2. Use the table feature of a graphing calculator to evaluate $3x + 4$ for $x = -5, -1, 3, 7,$ and 11.
   a. What value did you enter in **TblStart=**? **−5**
   b. What value did you enter in **△Tbl=**? **4**

You can also use a spreadsheet program to evaluate expressions.

Activity 2

Evaluate $2x + 7$ for $x = 3, 5, 7, 9$, and 11.

1. In the first column, enter the values 3, 5, 7, 9, and 11.

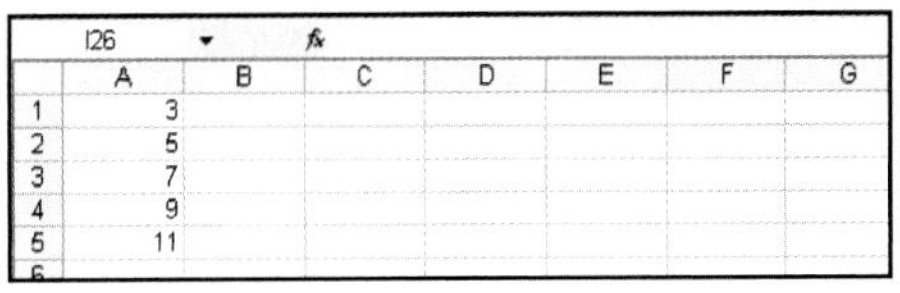

	A	B	C	D	E	F	G
1	3						
2	5						
3	7						
4	9						
5	11						

2. Enter the expression in cell B1.

   To do this, type the following:
   =2*A1+7

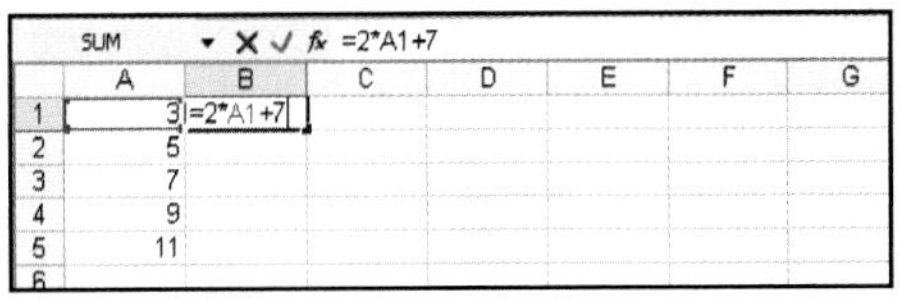

SUM ▾ ✕ ✓ fx =2*A1+7

	A	B	C	D	E	F	G
1	3	=2*A1+7					
2	5						
3	7						
4	9						
5	11						

3. Press Enter.

   The value of $2x + 7$ when $x = 3$ appears in cell B1.

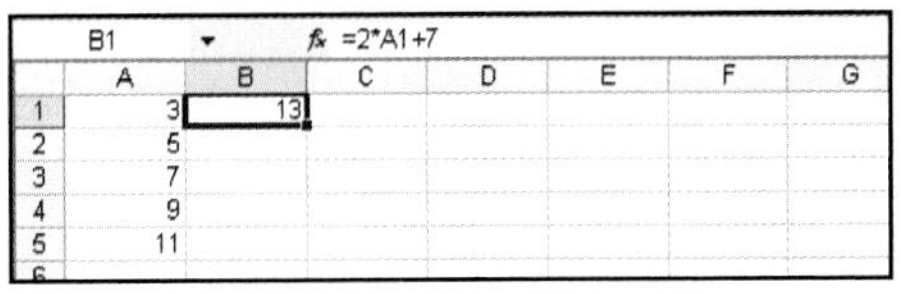

B1 ▾ fx =2*A1+7

	A	B	C	D	E	F	G
1	3	13					
2	5						
3	7						
4	9						
5	11						

4. Copy the formula into cells B2, B3, B4, and B5.

   Use the mouse to click on the lower right corner of cell B1. Hold down the mouse button and drag the cursor through cell B5.

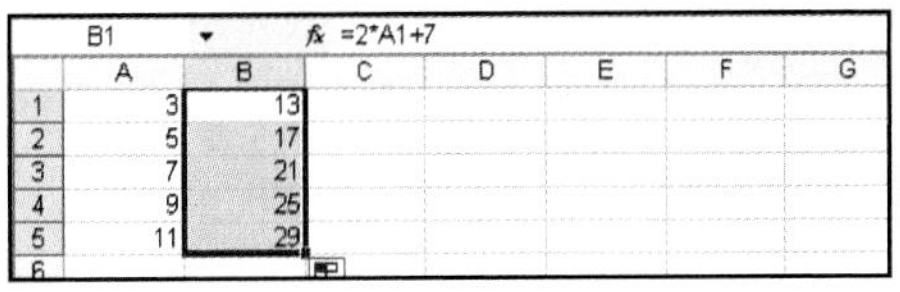

   For each row in column B, the number that is substituted for x is the value in the same row of column A.

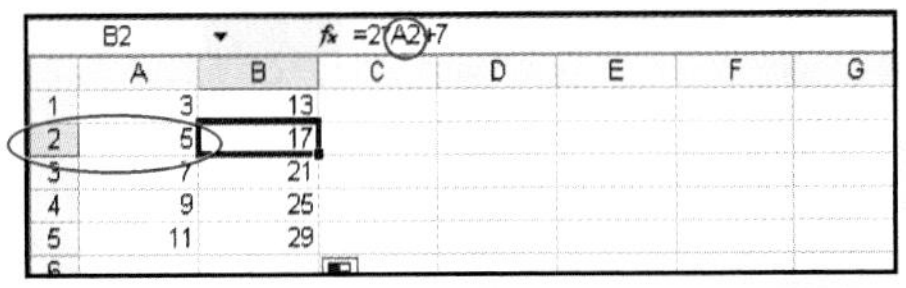

   You can continue the table by entering more values in column A and copying the formula from B1 into more cells in column B.

B1 ▾ fx =2*A1+7

	A	B	C	D	E	F	G
1	3	13					
2	5	17					
3	7	21					
4	9	25					
5	11	29					

B2 ▾ fx =2*A2+7

	A	B	C	D	E	F	G
1	3	13					
2	5	17					
3	7	21					
4	9	25					
5	11	29					

Try This

3. Use a spreadsheet program to evaluate $-2x + 9$ for $x = -5, -2, 1, 4$, and 7.
   a. What values did you enter in column A? **–5; –2; 1; 4; 7**
   b. What did you type in cell B1? **–2*A1+9**
4. Use a spreadsheet program to evaluate $7x - 10$ for $x = 2, 7, 12, 17$, and 22.
   a. What values did you enter in column A? **2; 7; 12; 17; 22**
   b. What did you type in cell B1? **7*A1–10**
5. What is an advantage to using technology to evaluate expressions?

Close

Key Concept

Many different values can be substituted for the variable in an algebraic expression. The table feature of a graphing calculator or a spreadsheet evaluates an expression for many values of the variable(s) at one time.

Assessment

Journal Have students explain how to use a graphing calculator and a spreadsheet program to evaluate expressions.

Answers to Try This

5. Possible answer: using a calculator or a spreadsheet allows you to evaluate an expression for several values of the variable more quickly than evaluating using pencil and paper.

1-1 Technology Lab **13**

1-2 Organizer

Objectives: Add real numbers. Subtract real numbers.

Algebra Lab
In *Chapter 1 Resource File*

Technology Lab
In *Chapter 1 Resource File*

Online Edition
Tutorial Videos

Countdown to Mastery Week 1

Power Presentations with PowerPoint®

Warm Up

Simplify.

1. $|-3|$ 3 **2.** $-|4|$ −4

Write an improper fraction to represent each mixed number.

3. $4\frac{2}{3}$ $\frac{14}{3}$ **4.** $7\frac{6}{7}$ $\frac{55}{7}$

Write a mixed number to represent each improper fraction.

5. $\frac{12}{5}$ $2\frac{2}{5}$ **6.** $\frac{24}{9}$ $2\frac{2}{3}$

Also available on transparency

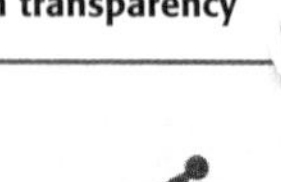

Math Humor

Student 1: How will we ever use negative numbers in the real world?

Student 2: You haven't seen my bank balance!

California Standards

Algebra 1 2.0

1-2 Adding and Subtracting Real Numbers

California Standards

2.0 Students understand and use such operations as taking the opposite, finding the reciprocal, taking a root, and raising to a fractional power. They understand and use the rules of exponents.

Vocabulary
real numbers
absolute value
opposites
additive inverse

Why learn this?
The total length of a penguin's dive can be determined by adding real numbers. (See Example 4.)

The set of all numbers that can be represented on a number line are called **real numbers**. You can use a number line to model addition and subtraction of real numbers.

Addition
To model addition of a positive number, move right. To model addition of a negative number, move left.

Subtraction
To model subtraction of a positive number, move left.
To model subtraction of a negative number, move right.

EXAMPLE 1 Adding and Subtracting Numbers on a Number Line

Add or subtract using a number line.

A $-3 + 6$

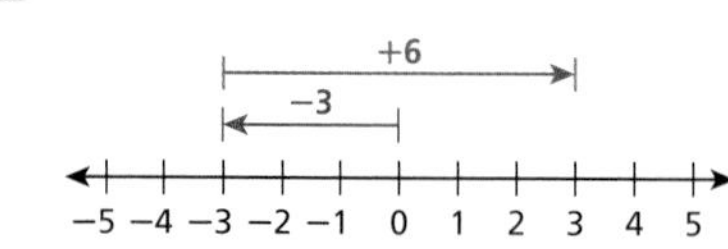

Start at 0. Move left to −3.

To add 6, move right 6 units.

$-3 + 6 = 3$

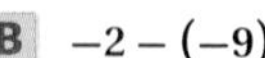

B $-2 - (-9)$

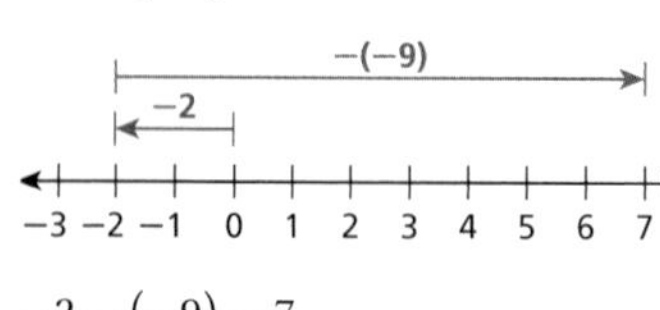

Start at 0. Move left to −2.

To subtract −9, move right 9 units.

$-2 - (-9) = 7$

CHECK IT OUT! Add or subtract using a number line.

1a. $-3 + 7$ **4** **1b.** $-3 - 7$ **−10** **1c.** $-5 - (-6.5)$ **1.5**

The **absolute value** of a number is its distance from zero on a number line. The absolute value of 5 is written as $|5|$.

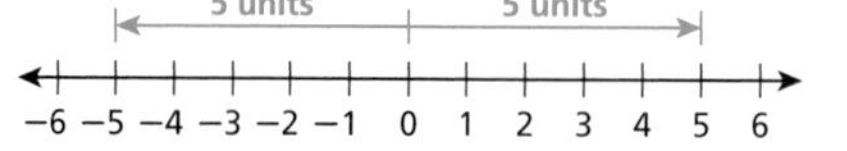

$|5| = 5$

$|-5| = 5$

1 Introduce

EXPLORATION

1-2 Adding and Subtracting Real Numbers

A hot-air balloon flies at an altitude of 700 feet above the ground.

1. A passenger in the balloon sees a kite 500 feet below. Draw a picture of the situation. How far is the kite above the ground?
2. The passenger sees a bird flying 50 feet above the balloon. Draw a picture of the situation. How far is the bird above the ground?
3. The balloon flies over a lake. The passenger spots a marker that is 20 feet below the surface of the lake. Draw a picture of the situation. What is the distance from the balloon to the marker?

700 feet

THINK AND DISCUSS

4. **Explain** how you can use subtraction to find the distance from the balloon to the marker in the lake.
5. **Describe** a situation based on the hot-air balloon that can be modeled by the subtraction problem 700 − 60 = 640.

Motivate

Ask how many students have ever owed money to someone. Pose the following situation: "You borrow \$10 from a friend and spend it. Then you earn \$25 by mowing the lawn. How much money will you have after you pay back your friend?" \$15 Point out that not all of the money you earned for mowing the lawn is really yours. Owing money is like having a negative balance. You must add the \$25 you earned to your −\$10 balance.

Explorations and answers are provided in *Alternate Openers: Explorations Transparencies*.

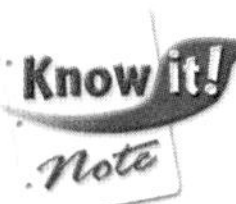

Adding Real Numbers

WORDS	NUMBERS	
Adding Numbers with the Same Sign Add the absolute values and use the sign of the numbers.	$3 + 6$ 9	$-2 + (-9)$ -11
Adding Numbers with Different Signs Subtract the absolute values and use the sign of the number with the greater absolute value.	$-8 + 12$ 4	$3 + (-15)$ -12

EXAMPLE 2 Adding Real Numbers

Add.

A $-3 + (-16)$
$(3 + 16 = 19)$ — *Same signs: add the absolute values.*
-19 — *Both numbers are negative, so the sum is negative.*

B $-13 + 7$
$(13 - 7 = 6)$ — *Different signs: subtract the absolute values.*
-6 — *Use the sign of the number with the greater absolute value.*

C $6.2 + (-4.9)$
$(6.2 - 4.9 = 1.3)$ — *Different signs: subtract the absolute values.*
1.3 — *Use the sign of the number with the greater absolute value.*

Add.

2a. $-5 + (-7)$ **−12** **2b.** $-13.5 + (-22.3)$ **−35.8** **2c.** $52 + (-68)$ **−16**

Two numbers are **opposites** if their sum is 0. A number and its opposite are **additive inverses** and are the same distance from zero. They have the same absolute value.

Inverse Property of Addition

WORDS	NUMBERS	ALGEBRA
The sum of a real number and its opposite is 0.	$6 + (-6) = (-6) + 6 = 0$	For any real number a, $a + (-a) = (-a) + a = 0$

To subtract signed numbers, you can use additive inverses. Subtracting a number is the same as adding the opposite of the number.

Subtracting Real Numbers

WORDS	NUMBERS	ALGEBRA
To subtract a number, add its opposite. Then follow the rules for adding signed numbers.	$3 - 8 = 3 + (-8)$ $= -5$	$a - b = a + (-b)$

2 Teach

Guided Instruction

Show students how to add and subtract on a number line. Use the results from the number line to develop the rules for adding and subtracting real numbers. Emphasize that subtracting is the same as adding the opposite.

Universal Access

Through Concrete Manipulatives

Provide students with integer chips of two different colors. One color represents $+1$, and the other color represents -1. Show students that one chip of each color forms a zero pair. Use these chips to model addition of positive and negative numbers. Integer chips can be found in the Manipulatives Kit (MK).

COMMON ERROR ALERT

Students may incorrectly calculate $-14 - (-12)$, getting -26 as the answer, because there are so many negative signs. Remind students to first write any subtraction as adding the opposite. Then the expression can be written as $-14 + 12$.

Power Presentations with PowerPoint®

Additional Examples

Example 1

Add or subtract using a number line.

A. $-4 + -7$ -11

B. $3 - (-6)$ 9

Example 2

Add.

A. $-\frac{3}{4} + \frac{1}{4}$ $-\frac{1}{2}$

B. $-6 + (-2)$ -8

Also available on transparency

INTERVENTION

Questioning Strategies

EXAMPLE 1

- What would happen if you used a number line to add the numbers in reverse order?
- What would happen if you used a number line to subtract the numbers in reverse order?

EXAMPLE 2

- How could a number line be used to perform addition?

Inclusion When using number lines to add and subtract, some students may find it easier to begin at the first number in the sum or difference, rather than beginning at 0.

Power Presentations with PowerPoint®

Additional Examples

Example 3

Subtract.

A. $-6.7 - 4.1$ -10.8

B. $5 - (-4)$ 9

C. $-2\frac{3}{5} - 2\frac{7}{10}$ -5.3

Example 4

An iceberg extends 75 feet above the sea. The bottom of the iceberg is at an elevation of -247 feet. What is the height of the iceberg? 322 feet

Also available on transparency

INTERVENTION

Questioning Strategies

EXAMPLE 3

- What is the first step in finding the value of an expression that contains subtraction and signed numbers?

EXAMPLE 4

- What does it mean for something to be at a negative elevation?
- What is another way to solve this problem?

Science Link A glacier is a large mass of ice moving across land. An iceberg is a piece of a glacier that has broken off into the sea.

Multiple Representations Another way to describe subtraction is as the distance between two numbers. Students can model this concept on a number line by plotting each number given in the problem and counting from the first number to the second number. The direction of the movement can be used to find the sign of the answer. Because the operation is subtraction, moving left indicates a positive answer and moving right indicates a negative answer.

EXAMPLE 3 Subtracting Real Numbers

Subtract.

A $7 - 10$

$7 - 10 = 7 + (-10)$ *To subtract 10, add −10.*

$(10 - 7 = 3)$ *Different signs: subtract absolute values.*

-3 *Use the sign of the number with the greater absolute value.*

B $-3 - (-12)$

$-3 - (-12) = -3 + 12$ *To subtract −12, add 12.*

$(12 - 3 = 9)$ *Different signs: subtract absolute values.*

9 *Use the sign of the number with the greater absolute value.*

C $-11 - 22$

$-11 - 22 = -11 + (-22)$ *To subtract 22, add −22.*

$(22 + 11 = 33)$ *Same signs: add absolute values.*

-33 *Both numbers are negative, so the sum is negative.*

D $22.5 - (-4)$

$22.5 - (-4) = 22.5 + 4$ *To subtract −4, add 4.*

$(22.5 + 4 = 26.5)$ *Same signs: add absolute values.*

26.5 *Both numbers are positive, so the sum is positive.*

Helpful Hint

On many scientific and graphing calculators, there is one button to express the opposite of a number and a different button to express subtraction.

Subtract.

3a. $13 - 21$ **−8** **3b.** $\frac{1}{2} - \left(-3\frac{1}{2}\right)$ **4** **3c.** $-14 - (-12)$ **−2**

EXAMPLE 4 *Biology Application*

An emperor penguin stands on an iceberg that extends 10 feet above the water. Then the penguin dives to an elevation of −67 feet to catch a fish. What is the total length of the penguin's dive?

Find the difference in the elevations.

elevation of iceberg	minus	elevation of fish
10	−	−67

$10 - (-67)$

$10 - (-67) = 10 + 67$ *To subtract −67, add 67.*

$= 77$ *Same signs: add absolute values.*

The total length of the penguin's dive is 77 feet.

4. What if...? The tallest known iceberg in the North Atlantic rose 550 feet above the ocean's surface. How many feet would it be from the top of the tallest iceberg to the wreckage of the *Titanic*, which is at an elevation of −12,468 feet? **13,018 ft**

3 Close

Summarize

Review the rules for adding and subtracting real numbers on page 15. Have students explain the phrase "add the opposite." Possible answer: To add the opposite means to rewrite a subtraction expression as addition by changing the minus to a plus and writing the additive inverse of the second number.

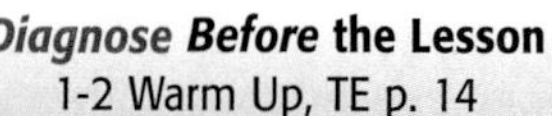

and INTERVENTION

***Diagnose Before* the Lesson**
1-2 Warm Up, TE p. 14

***Monitor During* the Lesson**
Check It Out! Exercises, SE pp. 14–16
Questioning Strategies, TE pp. 15–16

***Assess After* the Lesson**
1-2 Lesson Quiz, TE p. 19
Alternative Assessment, TE p. 19

THINK AND DISCUSS

1. The difference of −7 and −5 is −2. Explain why the difference is greater than −7.
2. **GET ORGANIZED** Copy and complete the graphic organizer. For each pair of points, tell whether the sum and the difference of the first point and the second point are positive or negative.

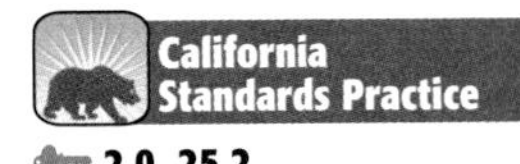

Points	Sum	Difference
A, B		
B, A		
C, B		
D, A		

Answers to *Think and Discuss*

Possible answers:

1. Subtracting a negative number is the same as adding a positive number. This means you move right on the number line, making the sum greater than the first number.
2. See p. A2.

1-2 Exercises

California Standards Practice
2.0, 25.2

GUIDED PRACTICE

1. **Vocabulary** The sum of a number and its ___?___ is always zero. (*opposite* or *absolute value*) **opposite**

SEE EXAMPLE 1 p. 14
Add or subtract using a number line.

2. $-4 + 7$ **3**
3. $-3.5 - 5$ **−8.5**
4. $5.6 - 9.2$ **−3.6**
5. $3 - \left(-6\frac{1}{4}\right)$ $\mathbf{9\frac{1}{4}}$

SEE EXAMPLE 2 p. 15
Add.

6. $91 + (-11)$ **80**
7. $4\frac{3}{4} + \left(-3\frac{3}{4}\right)$ **1**
8. $15.6 + (-17.9)$ **−2.3**

SEE EXAMPLE 3 p. 16
Subtract.

9. $23 - 36$ **−13**
10. $4.3 - 8.4$ **−4.1**
11. $1\frac{1}{5} - 2\frac{4}{5}$ $\mathbf{-1\frac{3}{5}}$

SEE EXAMPLE 4 p. 16
12. **Economics** The Dow Jones Industrial Average (DJIA) reports the average prices of stocks for 30 companies. Use the table to determine the total decrease in the DJIA for the two days. **−616.34**

DJIA 1987	
Friday, Oct. 16	−108.35
Monday, Oct. 19	−507.99

PRACTICE AND PROBLEM SOLVING

Independent Practice

For Exercises	See Example
13–16	1
17–19	2
20–22	3
23	4

Extra Practice
Skills Practice p. EP2
Application Practice p. EP24

Add or subtract using a number line.

13. $-2 + 6$ **4**
14. $6 + (-2)$ **4**
15. $\frac{1}{4} - 12$ $\mathbf{-11\frac{3}{4}}$
16. $-\frac{2}{5} + 6$ $\mathbf{5\frac{3}{5}}$

Add.

17. $-18 + (-12)$ **−30**
18. $-2.3 + 3.5$ **1.2**
19. $-15 + 29$ **14**

Subtract.

20. $12 - 22$ **−10**
21. $-\frac{3}{4} - \left(-\frac{1}{4}\right)$ $\mathbf{-\frac{1}{2}}$
22. $38 - 24.6$ **13.4**
23. **Meteorology** A meteorologist reported that the day's high temperature was 17°F and the low temperature was −6°F. What was the difference between the day's high and low temperatures? **23°F**

1-2 Exercises

Assignment Guide

Assign *Guided Practice* exercises as necessary.

If you finished Examples **1–2**
Proficient 13–19, 24, 26, 53, 54
Advanced 13–19, 53–56

If you finished Examples **1–4**
Proficient 13–23, 28–34 even, 36–56, 60–68
Advanced 13–23, 28–42 even, 43–46, 48–68

Homework Quick Check
Quickly check key concepts.
Exercises: 16, 18, 22, 23, 40, 43

California Standards

Standard	Exercises
2.0	9–11, 20–23, 28, 30, 33, 34, 37, 39, 40, 43, 47–49
25.2	47
7AF4.1	62–64
7MG2.1	60–64

Exercise 48 involves applying the subtraction of real numbers to diving. This exercise prepares students for the Concept Connection on page 40.

Answers

44. Possible answer: $-1-(-5)=4$ (pos) but $-10-(-3)=-7$ (neg.).
45. Possible answer: all neg. numbers are left of 0 on a number line. Adding a neg. number means moving farther to the left, so the final result will always be neg.
46. Possible answer: all neg. numbers are left of 0 on a number line. Subtracting a pos. number means moving farther to the left, so the final result will always be neg.

48a. 1650 ft

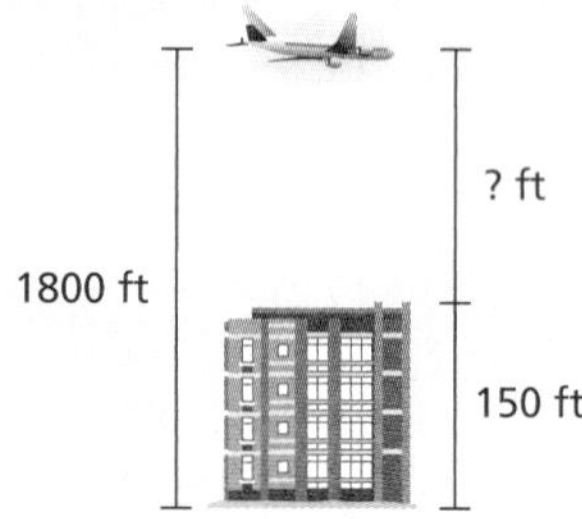

b. 1880 ft

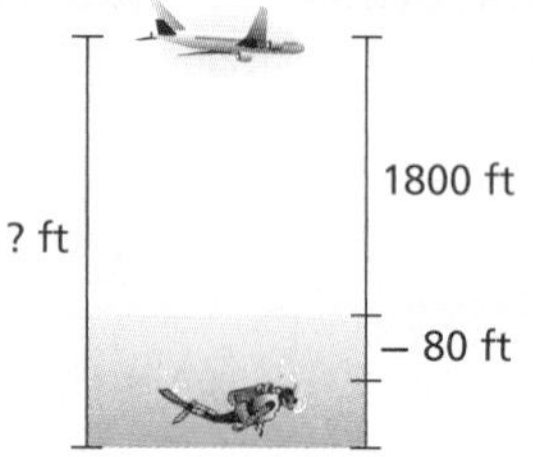

c. 1880 ft; because subtracting a negative number is the same as adding a positive number

Evaluate the expression $n+(-5)$ for each value of n.

24. $n = 312$ **307** **25.** $n = 5.75$ **0.75** **26.** $n = -\frac{7}{12}$ $\mathbf{-5\frac{7}{12}}$ **27.** $n = -7\frac{2}{5}$ $\mathbf{-12\frac{2}{5}}$

Add or subtract.

28. $-8-3$ **−11** **29.** $-9+(-3)$ **−12** **30.** $16-(-16)$ **32** **31.** $100-63$ **37**

32. $5.2-2.5$ **2.7** **33.** $-4.7-(-4.7)$ **0** **34.** $\frac{2}{5}-\frac{7}{8}$ $\mathbf{-\frac{19}{40}}$ **35.** $\frac{2}{5}-\frac{3}{10}$ $\mathbf{\frac{1}{10}}$

36. Business A restaurant manager lost \$415 in business during the month of January. Business picked up in February, and he ended that month with a profit of \$1580.

a. What was the manager's profit after January and February? **\$1165**

b. **What if...?** The restaurant lost \$245 in business during the month of March. What was the manager's profit after January, February, and March? **\$920**

Compare. Write <, >, or =.

37. $-4-(-6)$ **>** $-7-3$ **38.** $|-51|$ **>** $|0|$ **39.** $3-(-3)$ **>** $0-(-3)$

40. $-3-8$ **=** $-22+11$ **41.** $|-10+5|$ **<** $|-15|$ **42.** $9+(-8)$ **=** $-12+13$

43. Travel Death Valley National Park is located in California. Use the table to determine the difference in elevation between the highest and lowest locations. **11,331 ft**

Death Valley National Park	
Location	**Elevation (ft)**
Badwater	−282
Emigrant Pass	5,318
Furnace Creek Airport	−210
Telescope Creek	11,049

Reasoning Tell whether each statement is sometimes, always, or never true. Explain.

44. The difference of two negative numbers is positive. **sometimes**

45. The sum of two negative numbers is negative. **always**

46. The difference of a negative number and a positive number is negative. **always**

47. ///ERROR ANALYSIS/// Which is incorrect? Explain the error.

A; the opposite of −8 should have been added.

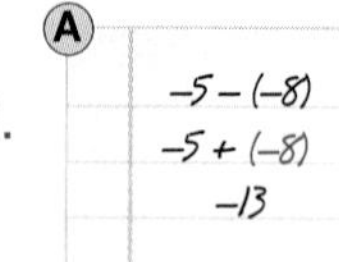

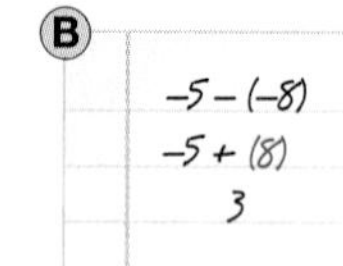

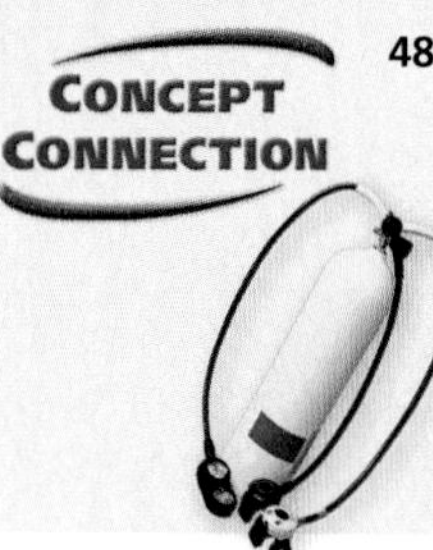

48. This problem will prepare you for the Concept Connection on page 40.

a. A plane flies at a height of 1800 feet directly over a 150-foot-tall building. How far above the building is the plane? Draw a diagram to explain your answer.

b. The same plane then flies directly over a diver who is 80 feet below the surface of the water. How far is the plane above the diver? Draw a diagram to explain your answer.

c. Subtract the diver's altitude of −80 feet from the plane's altitude of 1800 feet. Explain why this distance is greater than 1800 feet.

1-2 PRACTICE A

1-2 PRACTICE C

1-2 PRACTICE B

LESSON 1-2 **Practice B**
Adding and Subtracting Real Numbers

Add or subtract using a number line.

1. $-6+(-8)$ **−14** 2. $2-(-8)$ **10** 3. $10+(-4)$ **6**
4. $-2-(-6)$ **4** 5. $-7+7$ **0** 6. $-0.25-4$ **−4.25**

Add.

7. $-5+23$ **18** 8. $-15+(-9)$ **−24** 9. $24.6+(-45.5)$ **−20.9**
10. $-\frac{3}{8}+5$ $\mathbf{4\frac{5}{8}}$ 11. $16+(-14)$ **2** 12. $-3.3+(-9.1)$ **−12.4**

Subtract.

13. $-35-(-80)$ **45** 14. $12-(-16)$ **28** 15. $8.3-10.7$ **−2.4**
16. $-\frac{2}{3}-5\frac{1}{3}$ **−6** 17. $15-(-22)$ **37** 18. $1-3.5$ **−2.5**

19. The record high temperature for Asheville, North Carolina was 99°F. The record low was −17°F. What is the difference between these two temperatures? **116°F**

20. The balance in Mr. Sanchez's bank account was \$293.74. He accidentally wrote a check for \$300. What is his balance now? **−\$6.26**

Evaluate the expression $18-n$ for each value of n.

21. $n=-13$ **31** 22. $n=8.55$ **9.45** 23. $n=20\frac{1}{5}$ $\mathbf{-2\frac{1}{5}}$

1-2 READING STRATEGIES

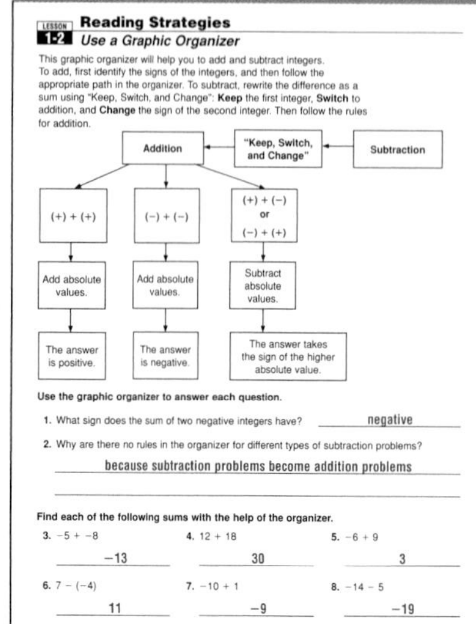

LESSON 1-2 **Reading Strategies**
Use a Graphic Organizer

This graphic organizer will help you to add and subtract integers. To add, first identify the signs of the integers, and then follow the appropriate path in the organizer. To subtract, rewrite the difference as a sum using "Keep, Switch, and Change": **Keep** the first integer, **Switch** to addition, and **Change** the sign of the second integer. Then follow the rules for addition.

Use the graphic organizer to answer each question.

1. What sign does the sum of two negative integers have? **negative**
2. Why are there no rules in the organizer for different types of subtraction problems? **because subtraction problems become addition problems**

Find each of the following sums with the help of the organizer.

3. $-5+-8$ **−13** 4. $12+18$ **30** 5. $-6+9$ **3**
6. $7-(-4)$ **11** 7. $-10+1$ **−9** 8. $-14-5$ **−19**

1-2 REVIEW FOR MASTERY

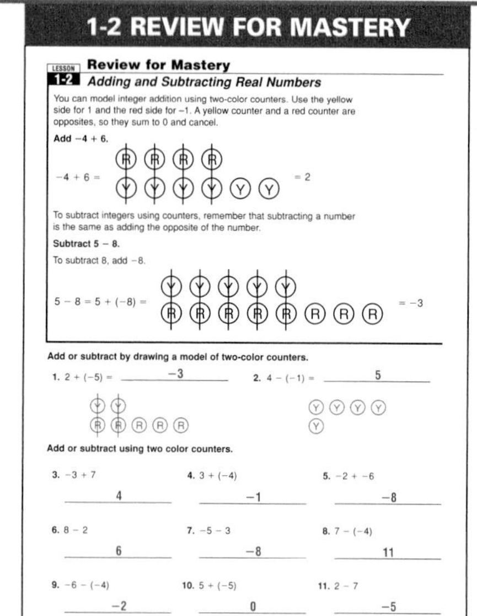

LESSON 1-2 **Review for Mastery**
Adding and Subtracting Real Numbers

You can model integer addition using two-color counters. Use the yellow side for 1 and the red side for −1. A yellow counter and a red counter are opposites, so they sum to 0 and cancel.

Add −4 + 6.

$-4+6=$ [counters] $=2$

To subtract integers using counters, remember that subtracting a number is the same as adding the opposite of the number.

Subtract 5 − 8.

To subtract 8, add −8.

$5-8=5+(-8)=$ [counters] $=-3$

Add or subtract by drawing a model of two-color counters.

1. $2+(-5)=$ **−3** 2. $4-(-1)=$ **5**

Add or subtract using two color counters.

3. $-3+7$ **4** 4. $3+(-4)$ **−1** 5. $-2+-6$ **−8**
6. $8-2$ **6** 7. $-5-3$ **−8** 8. $7-(-4)$ **11**
9. $-6-(-4)$ **−2** 10. $5+(-5)$ **0** 11. $2-7$ **−5**

49. Write About It Explain why addition and subtraction are called inverse operations. Use the following examples in your explanation:

$8 + (-2) = 8 - 2 \qquad 8 - (-2) = 8 + 2$

Multiple Choice For Exercises 50–52, choose the best answer.

50. A rectangle has a length of 23.8 cm and a width of 14.5 cm. What is its perimeter?

Ⓐ 9.3 cm Ⓑ 38.3 cm Ⓒ 62.1 cm **(Ⓓ) 76.6 cm**

51. At midnight, the temperature was −12°F. By noon, the temperature had risen 25°F. During the afternoon, it fell 10°F and fell another 3°F by midnight. What was the temperature at midnight?

(Ⓐ) 0°F Ⓑ 3°F Ⓒ 12°F Ⓓ 24°F

52. The table shows the amounts Mr. Espinosa spent on lunch each day one week. What is the total amount Mr. Espinosa spent for lunch this week?

Day	Monday	Tuesday	Wednesday	Thursday	Friday
Amount ($)	5.40	4.16	7.07	5.40	9.52

Ⓐ $21.83 Ⓑ $22.03 **(Ⓒ) $31.55** Ⓓ $36.95

CHALLENGE AND EXTEND

Simplify each expression.

53. $-1\frac{1}{5} + (-7.8)$ **−9**
54. $-\frac{1}{5} + 2.1$ **1.9**
55. $9.75 + \left(-7\frac{3}{4}\right)$ **2**
56. $-2\frac{3}{10} + 8.5$ **6.2**

For each pattern shown below, describe a possible rule for finding the next term. Then use your rule to write the next 3 terms.

57. 14, 10, 6, 2, … **Subtract 4; −2, −6, −10**

58. $-2, -\frac{8}{5}, -\frac{6}{5}, -\frac{4}{5}, \ldots$ **Add $\frac{2}{5}$; $-\frac{2}{5}$, 0, $\frac{2}{5}$**

59. Geography Sam visited two volcanoes, Cotapaxi and Sangay, and two caves, Sistema Huautla and Sistema Cheve. Cotapaxi, in Ecuador, has an elevation of 19,347 ft. Sangay, also in Ecuador, has an elevation of 17,159 ft. The main entrance of Sistema Huautla, in Mexico, has an elevation of 5051 ft. The main entrance of Sistema Cheve, also in Mexico, has an elevation of 9085 ft. What is the average elevation of these places? **12,660.5 ft**

SPIRAL STANDARDS REVIEW

7AF4.1, 7MG2.1

Give the area of the figure described. *(Previous course)*

60. rectangle; $\ell = 12$ cm, $w = 5$ cm **60 cm²**
61. triangle; $b = 8$ in., $h = 11$ in. **44 in²**

Find the length of the third side of the triangle. *(Previous course)*

62. perimeter = 12 cm **5 cm**
63. perimeter = 30 cm **13 cm**
64. perimeter = 56 cm **25 cm**

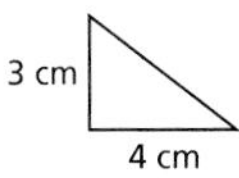

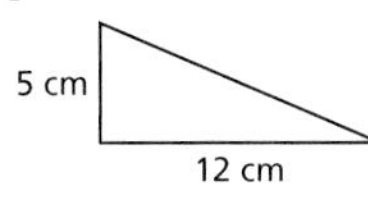

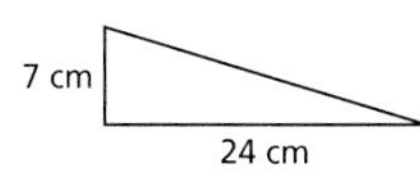

Evaluate each expression for $x = 8$, $y = 4$, and $z = 2$. *(Lesson 1-1)*

65. $x + y$ **12**
66. $\frac{x}{z}$ **4**
67. $x - y$ **4**
68. $\frac{y}{z}$ **2**

Teaching Tip

Multiple Choice For **Exercise 51,** students who chose **C** may have begun at 0° instead of −12°; students who chose **D** may have begun at +12°.

For **Exercise 52,** students should estimate the answer by rounding to the nearest dollar before looking at the answer choices. Choice **C** seems to be the correct one. Students can check this answer by working the problem.

Answer

49. The first example shows that adding the opposite of 2 and subtracting 2 are equal. The second example shows that subtracting the opposite of 2 and adding 2 are equal. After adding two numbers, you can get back to the first number by subtracting the second number.

Journal

Have students explain how they could teach a student who is absent from class to add and subtract real numbers. Have them include at least one example of each operation.

ALTERNATIVE ASSESSMENT

Have students create and solve two real-world problems involving some negative numbers. One problem should involve addition, and the other should involve subtraction.

1-2 Lesson Quiz

Add or subtract using a number line.

1. $-2 + 9$ 7

2. $-5 - (-3)$ −2

Add or subtract.

3. $-23 + 42$ 19

4. $4.5 - (-3.7)$ 8.2

5. $-2\frac{2}{3} + \left(-\frac{5}{6}\right)$ $-3\frac{1}{2}$

6. The temperature at 6:00 A.M. was −23°F. At 3:00 P.M., it was 18°F. Find the difference in the temperatures. 41°F

Also available on transparency

1-2 PROBLEM SOLVING

LESSON 1-2 **Problem Solving**
Adding and Subtracting Real Numbers

Write the correct answer.

1. The Pacific Ocean has an average depth of 12,925 feet, while the Atlantic Ocean has an average depth of 11,730 feet. Find the difference in average depths.
   1195 feet

2. A kite flies 74 feet above the ground. The person flying the kite is 5 feet 6 inches tall. How far above the person is the kite?
   68 feet 6 inches

3. Stock in ABC Company fell 12.67 points on Monday and 31.51 points on Tuesday. Determine the total change in the stock for the two days.
   −44.18 points

4. Muriel scored 30 points lower on her first practice SAT test than she did on her PSAT. She scored 20 points better on her second practice SAT test than she did on her first practice SAT test. How does her second practice SAT test score compare with her PSAT test score?
   10 points lower

Use the table below to answer questions 5–7, which shows some of the world's most extreme elevations. A negative number means the location is *below* sea level. Select the best answer.

Location	Elevation (ft)
Mount Everest	29,028
Aconcagua	22,834
Mount McKinley	20,320
Mariana Trench	−35,840
Puerto Rico Trench	−28,232
Java Trench	−23,376

5. Find the difference in elevation between the Puerto Rico Trench and the Java Trench.
   (A) 4856 ft C 51,608 ft
   B 7608 ft D 59,216 ft

6. Find the difference in elevation between the highest and lowest locations.
   (F) 64,868 ft H 6812 ft
   G 52,404 ft J 5652 ft

7. Denver is called the "Mile High City" because it is approximately 5280 feet above sea level. How much higher in elevation is Denver than the Mariana Trench?
   A 30,560 ft C 35,840 ft
   B 34,308 ft (D) 41,120 ft

1-2 CHALLENGE

LESSON 1-2 **Challenge**
Deposits and Withdrawals

The music club wanted to have a party at the end of the school year. Their advisor stated that if they had over $100 at the end of the school year, they would have a party.

The club's financial transactions for the second half of the school year are shown below. A balance of $500 was carried over from the first half of the school year.

A deposit indicates that a positive amount was added. A withdrawal indicates that a negative amount was added.

Complete the chart to help you answer the questions below.

Transaction Date	Type of Transaction	Amount	Math Expression	Balance
				$500
1/4	Deposit	$50	$500 + $50	$550
1/12	Withdrawal	$100	$550 + (−$100)	$450
1/18	Withdrawal	$15	$450 + (−$25)	$425
1/26	Withdrawal	$200	$425 + (−$200)	$225
2/10	Deposit	$50	$225 + $50	$275
3/8	Deposit	$50	$275 + $50	$325
3/23	Withdrawal	$350	$325 + (−$350)	−$25
4/6	Deposit	$75	−$25 + $75	$50
4/22	Withdrawal	$25	$50 + (−$25)	$25
5/11	Deposit	$100	$25 + $100	$125
5/17	Withdrawal	$200	$125 + (−$200)	−$75
6/7	Deposit	$225	−$75 + $225	$150

1. Did the balance ever go above $600? If so, on what date(s) did this occur?
   no
2. Did the balance ever go below $0? If so, on what date(s) did this occur?
   yes; 3/23 and 5/17
3. What was the ending balance? $150
4. Did the music club get to have a party? yes

1-3 Organizer

Objectives: Multiply real numbers.

Divide real numbers.

Online Edition
Tutorial Videos

Countdown to Mastery Week 1

Power Presentations with PowerPoint®

Warm Up

Multiply or divide.

1. $6(7)$ 42
2. $\frac{1}{2}\left(\frac{3}{4}\right)$ $\frac{3}{8}$
3. $42 \div 7$ 6
4. $\frac{60}{15}$ 4
5. Write $\frac{16}{5}$ as a mixed number. $3\frac{1}{5}$
6. Write $4\frac{3}{8}$ as an improper fraction. $\frac{35}{8}$

Also available on transparency

Astrologer: Hey, what's your sign?
Confused math student: Negative?

California Standards

Algebra 1 2.0

1-3 Multiplying and Dividing Real Numbers

California Standards

2.0 Students understand and use such operations as taking the opposite, **finding the reciprocal,** taking a root, and raising to a fractional power. They understand and use the rules of exponents.

Vocabulary
reciprocal
multiplicative inverse

Who uses this?

Hot-air balloon pilots can determine how far away from liftoff they will land by using multiplication. (See Example 4.)

When you multiply or divide two numbers, the signs of the numbers determine whether the result is positive or negative.

Numbers	Product/Quotient
Both positive	Positive
One negative	Negative
Both negative	Positive

Know it! Note

Multiplying and Dividing Real Numbers

WORDS	NUMBERS	
Multiplying and Dividing Numbers with the Same Sign		
If two numbers have the same sign, their product or quotient is positive.	$4 \cdot 5 = 20$	$-15 \div (-3) = 5$
Multiplying and Dividing Numbers with Different Signs		
If two numbers have different signs, their product or quotient is negative.	$6(-3) = -18$ $(-7)2 = -14$	$-18 \div 2 = -9$ $10 \div (-5) = -2$

EXAMPLE  **Multiplying and Dividing Signed Numbers**

Find the value of each expression.

A $-12 \cdot 5$

-60 *The product of two numbers with different signs is negative.*

B $8\left(-\frac{5}{4}\right)$

$\left(\frac{8}{1}\right)\left(-\frac{5}{4}\right)$ *Multiply.*

$= -\frac{40}{4} = -10$ *The quotient of two numbers with different signs is negative.*

CHECK IT OUT! Find the value of each expression.

1a. $35 \div (-5)$ **−7** **1b.** $-11(-4)$ **44** **1c.** $-6(7)$ **−42**

1 Introduce

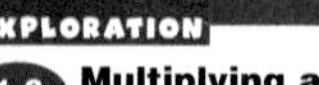

EXPLORATION

1-3 Multiplying and Dividing Real Numbers

You will need a calculator for this Exploration. Use a calculator to find each product or quotient.

1. a. $4 \cdot 5$
   b. $60\left(\frac{7}{3}\right)$
   c. 23.45×3.4
2. a. $-2 \cdot 53$
   b. $-2.5 \div 0.8$
   c. $7.5 \times (-4.1)$
3. a. $-555 \div (-5)$
   b. $-3.2(-7.53)$
   c. $-1500 \times (-0.4)$
4. What patterns do you notice about the signs of the answers?

THINK AND DISCUSS

5. **Explain** when the product or quotient of two real numbers is positive. When is the product or quotient negative?
6. **Discuss** whether the product of five negative numbers is positive or negative. Explain your reasoning.

Motivate

Pose the following situation: You are buying a car by paying $300 per month for 48 months. How much will you pay in all? $14,400 What operation did you use to get your answer? multiplication Suppose you pay a total of $15,000 for a car by making equal monthly payments for 60 months. What is the monthly payment? $250 What operation did you use to get your answer? division

Explorations and answers are provided in *Alternate Openers: Explorations Transparencies.*

Two numbers are **reciprocals** if their product is 1. A number and its reciprocal are called **multiplicative inverses**.

Inverse Property of Multiplication

WORDS	NUMBERS	ALGEBRA
The product of a nonzero real number and its reciprocal is 1.	$4 \cdot \frac{1}{4} = \frac{1}{4} \cdot 4 = 1$ $-3 \cdot \left(-\frac{1}{3}\right) = -\frac{1}{3} \cdot (-3) = 1$	For any real number a ($a \neq 0$), $a \cdot \frac{1}{a} = \frac{1}{a} \cdot a = 1$

To divide by a number, you can multiply by its multiplicative inverse.

EXAMPLE 2 Dividing with Fractions

Divide.

A $-\frac{4}{5} \div \left(-\frac{8}{15}\right)$

$-\frac{4}{5} \div \left(-\frac{8}{15}\right) = -\frac{4}{5}\left(-\frac{15}{8}\right)$ *To divide by $-\frac{8}{15}$, multiply by $-\frac{15}{8}$.*

$= \frac{(-4)(-15)}{5(8)}$ *Multiply the numerators and multiply the denominators.*

$= \frac{60}{40} = \frac{3}{2}$ *$-\frac{4}{5}$ and $-\frac{8}{15}$ have the same sign, so the quotient is positive.*

B $-4 \div 9\frac{1}{4}$

$-4 \div 9\frac{1}{4} = -\frac{4}{1} \div \frac{37}{4}$ *Write 4 as a fraction with a denominator of 1. Write $9\frac{1}{4}$ as an improper fraction.*

$= -\frac{4}{1} \cdot \frac{4}{37}$ *To divide by $\frac{37}{4}$, multiply by $\frac{4}{37}$.*

$= -\frac{4(4)}{1(37)} = -\frac{16}{37}$ *-4 and $9\frac{1}{4}$ have different signs, so the quotient is negative.*

Helpful Hint

You can write the reciprocal of a number by switching the numerator and denominator. A number written without a denominator has a denominator of 1.

CHECK IT OUT! Divide.

2a. $-\frac{3}{4} \div (-9)$ $\frac{1}{12}$ **2b.** $\frac{3}{10} \div \left(-\frac{6}{5}\right)$ $-\frac{1}{4}$ **2c.** $-\frac{5}{6} \div 1\frac{2}{3}$ $-\frac{1}{2}$

The number 0 has special properties for multiplication and division.

Properties of Zero

WORDS	NUMBERS		ALGEBRA	
Multiplication by Zero The product of any number and 0 is 0.	$\frac{1}{3} \cdot 0 = 0$	$0(-17) = 0$	$a \cdot 0 = 0$	$0 \cdot a = 0$
Zero Divided by a Number The quotient of 0 and any nonzero number is 0.	$\frac{0}{6} = 0$	$0 \div \frac{2}{3} = 0$	$\frac{0}{a} = 0$	$(a \neq 0)$
Division by Zero Division by 0 is undefined.	$12 \div 0$ ✗	$\frac{-5}{0}$ ✗	$a \div 0$ ✗	$\frac{a}{0}$ ✗

2 Teach

Guided Instruction

Begin by reminding students that multiplication is repeated addition. So $3(-2) = -2 + (-2) + (-2) = -6$. Review mixed numbers, improper fractions, and reciprocals. Then discuss the rules for multiplying and dividing signed numbers, as well as the properties of zero. Emphasize the difference between $\frac{0}{a}$ and $\frac{a}{0}$ for $a \neq 0$. $\left(\frac{0}{a} = 0, \text{ and } \frac{a}{0} \text{ is undefined.}\right)$ This will be important later when finding the slopes of lines.

Universal Access

Through Cooperative Learning

Pair students and give each student two index cards, one with a plus sign and one with a minus sign. The students take turns placing one of their cards on the table. If the product is positive, student A receives a point, and if the product is negative, student B receives a point. The cards are then picked up, and play continues. Play to a set number of points.

Optional: Play with three cards.

COMMON ERROR ALERT

Some students may think the fraction $-\frac{4}{5}$ can be rewritten as $\frac{-4}{-5}$. Remind them that a negative in both the numerator and the denominator results in a positive fraction because it indicates a negative number divided by a negative number. The fraction $-\frac{4}{5}$ can be rewritten as $\frac{-4}{5}$ or $\frac{4}{-5}$.

Power Presentations with PowerPoint®

Additional Examples

Example 1

Find the value of each expression.

A. $\frac{1}{2}(-10)$ -5

B. $\frac{-48}{-4}$ 12

C. $-3\left(\frac{2}{3}\right)$ -2

Example 2

Divide.

A. $-\frac{1}{2} \div \left(-\frac{5}{6}\right)$ $\frac{3}{5}$

B. $\frac{8}{9} \div \left(-2\frac{2}{3}\right)$ $-\frac{1}{3}$

Also available on transparency

INTERVENTION
Questioning Strategies

EXAMPLE 1

- What is the sign of the product of two negative numbers?

EXAMPLE 2

- Does every number have a reciprocal? Explain.

Communicating Math Ask "How many 3's are in 12?" 4 "What division problem shows this?" $12 \div 3 = 4$ Now ask students to explain how they know that $\frac{1}{2} \div \frac{1}{2} = 1$. There is one $\frac{1}{2}$ in $\frac{1}{2}$. Also, any nonzero number divided by itself is 1.

Power Presentations with PowerPoint®

Additional Examples

Example 3

Multiply or divide if possible.

A. $\frac{0}{15}$ 0

B. $-22 \div 0$ undefined

C. $-8.45(0)$ 0

Example 4

The speed of a hot air balloon is $3\frac{3}{4}$ mi/h. It travels in a straight line for $1\frac{1}{3}$ hours before landing. How many miles away from the liftoff site will the balloon land?

5 miles

Also available on transparency

INTERVENTION

Questioning Strategies

EXAMPLE 3

- Why does $\frac{0}{4} = 0$?
- Why does $\frac{5}{0} \neq 0$?

EXAMPLE 4

- Why does the problem state that the hot air balloon travels in a straight line parallel to the ground?

Advanced Learners/GATE In general, division by 0 is undefined, but the quotient $\frac{0}{0}$ is said to be *indeterminate*. To understand why, have students think of what number times zero would equal zero. There is not one correct answer since it could be any number.

EXAMPLE 3 Multiplying and Dividing with Zero

Multiply or divide if possible.

A $0 \div 16.568$ — *Zero is divided by a nonzero number.*
0 — *The quotient of zero and any nonzero number is 0.*

B $63\frac{7}{8} \div 0$ — *A number is divided by zero.*
undefined — *Division by zero is undefined.*

C $1 \cdot 0$ — *A number is multiplied by zero.*
0 — *The product of any number and 0 is 0.*

Multiply or divide.

3a. $0 \div \left(-8\frac{1}{6}\right)$ **0** **3b.** $2.04 \div 0$ **undefined** **3c.** $(-12{,}350)(0)$ **0**

EXAMPLE 4 *Recreation Application*

A hot-air balloon is taken for a 2.5-hour trip. The wind speed (and the speed of the balloon) is 4.75 mi/h. The balloon travels in a straight line parallel to the ground. How many miles away from the liftoff site will the balloon land?

Find the distance traveled at a rate of 4.75 mi/h for 2.5 hours. To find distance, multiply rate by time.

rate	times	time
4.75	•	2.5

$4.75 \cdot 2.5$

11.875

The hot-air balloon will land 11.875 miles from the liftoff site.

4. What if...? On another hot-air balloon trip, the wind speed is 5.25 mi/h. The trip is planned for 1.5 hours. The balloon travels in a straight line parallel to the ground. How many miles away from the liftoff site will the balloon land? **7.875 mi**

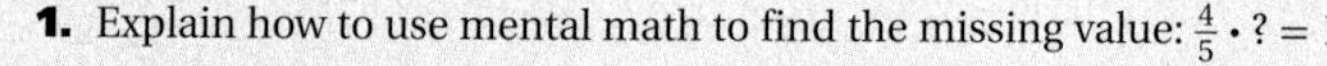

THINK AND DISCUSS

1. Explain how to use mental math to find the missing value: $\frac{4}{5} \cdot ? = 1$.

2. GET ORGANIZED Copy and complete the graphic organizer. In each blank, write "pos" or "neg" to indicate positive or negative.

Multiplying and Dividing Numbers	
Multiplication	**Division**
pos × ___ = pos	pos ÷ ___ = pos
pos × ___ = neg	pos ÷ ___ = neg
neg × ___ = neg	neg ÷ ___ = neg
neg × ___ = pos	neg ÷ ___ = pos

3 Close

Summarize

Review the rules for multiplying and dividing positive and negative numbers on page 20. Remind students that the number of negative factors in an expression determines the sign of the answer.

FORMATIVE ASSESSMENT

and INTERVENTION

***Diagnose Before* the Lesson**
1-3 Warm Up, TE p. 20

***Monitor During* the Lesson**
Check It Out! Exercises, SE pp. 20–22
Questioning Strategies, TE pp. 21–22

***Assess After* the Lesson**
1-3 Lesson Quiz, TE p. 25
Alternative Assessment, TE p. 25

Answers to *Think and Discuss*

1. A number multiplied by its reciprocal is 1. The reciprocal of $\frac{4}{5}$ is $\frac{5}{4}$.
2. See p. A2.

1-3 Exercises

California Standards Practice
2.0

go.hrw.com
Homework Help Online
KEYWORD: MA8CA 1-3
Parent Resources Online
KEYWORD: MA8CA Parent

GUIDED PRACTICE

1. **Vocabulary** How do you find the *reciprocal* of $\frac{1}{2}$? **Switch the numerator and denominator. The reciprocal of $\frac{1}{2}$ is $\frac{2}{1}$, or 2.**

SEE EXAMPLE 1 p. 20

Find the value of each expression.

2. $-72 \div (-9)$ **8**
3. $11(-11)$ **−121**
4. $-7.2 \div 3.6$ **−2**

SEE EXAMPLE 2 p. 21

Divide.

5. $5 \div \frac{5}{7}$ **7**
6. $\frac{4}{5} \div \left(-\frac{7}{5}\right)$ **$-\frac{4}{7}$**
7. $-\frac{2}{3} \div \left(-\frac{1}{3}\right)$ **2**
8. $-\frac{16}{25} \div \left(-\frac{4}{5}\right)$ **$\frac{4}{5}$**

SEE EXAMPLE 3 p. 22

Multiply or divide if possible.

9. $3.8 \div 0$ **undefined**
10. $0(-27)$ **0**
11. $0 \div \frac{2}{3}$ **0**
12. $\frac{7}{8} \div 0$ **undefined**

SEE EXAMPLE 4 p. 22

13. **Entertainment** It is estimated that 7 million people saw off-Broadway shows in 2002. Assume that the average price of a ticket was \$30. How much money was spent on tickets for off-Broadway shows in 2002? **about \$210,000,000**

PRACTICE AND PROBLEM SOLVING

Independent Practice

For Exercises	See Example
14–16	1
17–20	2
21–24	3
25	4

Extra Practice
Skills Practice p. EP2
Application Practice p. EP24

Find the value of each expression.

14. $-30 \div (-6)$ **5**
15. $8(-4)$ **−32**
16. $-25(-12)$ **300**

Divide.

17. $-\frac{3}{20} \div \left(-\frac{1}{6}\right)$ **$\frac{9}{10}$**
18. $\frac{3}{14} \div \frac{15}{28}$ **$\frac{2}{5}$**
19. $-4\frac{1}{2} \div 1\frac{1}{2}$ **−3**
20. $2\frac{3}{4} \div \left(-1\frac{1}{2}\right)$ **$-\frac{11}{6}$**

Multiply or divide if possible.

21. $0 \cdot 15$ **0**
22. $-0.25 \div 0$ **undefined**
23. $0 \div 1$ **0**
24. $\frac{0}{1} \div 3$ **0**

25. **Weather** A cold front changes the temperature by −3°F each day. If the temperature started at 0°F, what will the temperature be after 5 days? **−15°F**

Multiply or divide.

26. $21 \div (-3)$ **−7**
27. $-100 \div 25$ **−4**
28. $-6 \div (-14)$ **$\frac{3}{7}$**
29. $-6.2(10)$ **−62**
30. $\frac{1}{2} \div \frac{1}{2}$ **1**
31. $-3.75(-5)$ **18.75**
32. $-12\frac{1}{2}(-3)$ **$\frac{75}{2}$**
33. $17\left(\frac{1}{17}\right)$ **1**

34. **Critical Thinking** What positive number is the same as its reciprocal? **1**

Evaluate each expression for $a = 4$, $b = -3$, and $c = -\frac{1}{2}$.

35. ab **−12**
36. $a \div c$ **−8**
37. bc **$\frac{3}{2}$**
38. $c \div a$ **$-\frac{1}{8}$**

Let p represent a positive number, n represent a negative number, and z represent zero. Tell whether each expression is positive, negative, zero, or undefined.

39. pn **negative**
40. pnz **zero**
41. $\frac{n}{p}$ **negative**
42. $-pz$ **zero**
43. $-\frac{p}{n}$ **positive**
44. $-(pn)$ **positive**
45. $\frac{pn}{z}$ **undefined**
46. $\frac{z}{n}$ **zero**

1-3 Exercises

Assignment Guide

Assign *Guided Practice* exercises as necessary.

If you finished Examples **1–2**
Proficient 14–20, 35–46, 76–78
Advanced 14–20, 35–38, 43–46, 64–67, 76–81

If you finished Examples **1–4**
Proficient 14–25, 34–67, 71–78, 90–98
Advanced 14–25, 34, 43–56, 63–70, 72–98

Homework Quick Check
Quickly check key concepts.
Exercises: 16, 18, 24, 25, 40, 48

Teaching Tip

Reading Math Help students see that the parentheses in **Exercise 2** are used to enclose a negative number. The parentheses in **Exercise 3** are used to indicate multiplication.

California Standards

Standard	Exercises
2.0	2–8, 17–20, 32, 33, 47–54, 57–62, 64–67
6NS2.3	95–98
6AF1.2	94
7MG2.1	90–93

Inclusion To help students understand **Exercise 63,** write the signs on the board. Students must stand when the sign of the resulting product is positive, and they must sit when the sign of the product is negative. Keep writing additional signs so that students change positions often.

For example:

+	(Students stand)
+ +	stand
+ + −	sit
+ + − +	sit
+ + − + −	stand

If sitting and standing is not possible, thumbs up and thumbs down can be used.

Exercise 72 involves using the formula for rate. This exercise prepares students for the Concept Connection on page 40.

Answers

63c. The product of two negative numbers is positive. The product of a positive number and a negative number is negative.

d. No; it does not matter how many times you multiply by a positive number, the sign does not change.

71. The product of two negative numbers is positive and the product of a negative number and a positive number is negative. You know that the product is positive and one factor is negative, so the second factor must also be negative.

72b.

Time (min)	Depth (ft)
1	15
2	30
5	75

Evaluate the expression $y \div \frac{3}{4}$ for each value of y.

47. $y = \frac{3}{4}$ **1**
48. $y = -\frac{9}{16}$ **$-\frac{3}{4}$**
49. $y = \frac{3}{8}$ **$\frac{1}{2}$**
50. $y = -2\frac{1}{4}$ **−3**

Evaluate the expression $\frac{1}{2} \div m$ for each value of m.

51. $m = -\frac{5}{2}$ **$-\frac{1}{5}$**
52. $m = \frac{7}{8}$ **$\frac{4}{7}$**
53. $m = \frac{4}{9}$ **$\frac{9}{8}$**
54. $m = -5$ **$-\frac{1}{10}$**

LINK

Diving

Florida is home to more than 300 freshwater springs, some of which are explored by cave divers. This chamber of the Diepolder Cave system is about 250 feet deep.

55. **Education** Benjamin must have 120 credit hours of instruction to receive his college degree. Benjamin wants to graduate in 8 semesters without attending summer sessions. How many credit hours must Benjamin take on average each semester to graduate in 8 semesters? **15 h per semester**

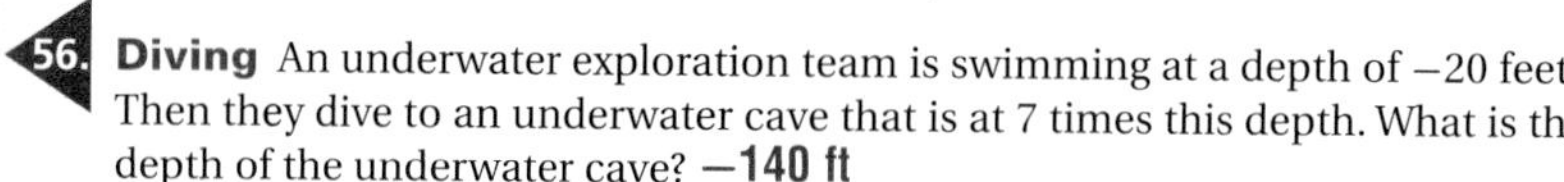

56. **Diving** An underwater exploration team is swimming at a depth of −20 feet. Then they dive to an underwater cave that is at 7 times this depth. What is the depth of the underwater cave? **−140 ft**

Multiply or divide. Then compare using <, >, or =.

57. $10\left(-\frac{1}{2}\right)$ **<** $20 \div 4$
58. $16 \div (-2)$ **<** $-2(-4)$
59. $-2\frac{2}{3} \div 3$ **>** $5(-2.4)$
60. $20 \div 4$ **>** $\frac{3}{4} \div \left(-\frac{1}{2}\right)$
61. $2.1(-3.4)$ **=** $2.1(-3.4)$
62. $0\left(-\frac{3}{5}\right)$ **<** $\frac{1}{2} \div \frac{1}{2}$

63. **Critical Thinking** There is a relationship between the number of negative factors and the sign of the product.
    a. What is the sign of the product of an even number of negative factors? **positive**
    b. What is the sign of the product of an odd number of negative factors? **negative**
    c. Explain why the number of negative factors affects the sign of the product.
    d. Does the number of positive factors affect the sign of the product? Explain.

Write each division expression as a multiplication expression.

64. $12 \div (-3)$ **$12\left(-\frac{1}{3}\right)$**
65. $75 \div 15$ **$75\left(\frac{1}{15}\right)$**
66. $\frac{80}{-8}$ **$80\left(-\frac{1}{8}\right)$**
67. $\frac{-121}{11}$ **$-121\left(\frac{1}{11}\right)$**

Determine whether each statement is sometimes, always, or never true.

68. The quotient of two negative numbers is negative. **never**
69. The quotient of two numbers with the same sign has that sign. **sometimes**
70. The product of two numbers with different signs is positive. **never**
71. **Reasoning** The product of two factors is positive. One of the factors is negative. Show that the second factor must be negative.

CONCEPT CONNECTION

72. This problem will prepare you for the Concept Connection on page 40.
    a. You swam 20 feet in 5 seconds. Use the formula $r = \frac{d}{t}$ to determine how fast you were swimming. **4 ft/s**
    b. A diver descended at a rate of 15 feet per minute. Make a table to show the diver's depth after 1, 2, and 5 minutes.
    c. Show two ways to find how far the diver descended in 5 minutes. Remember that multiplication is repeated addition. **5 • 15 = 75; 15 + 15 + 15 + 15 + 15 = 75**

1-3 PRACTICE A

1-3 PRACTICE C

1-3 PRACTICE B

LESSON 1-3 **Practice B**
Multiplying and Dividing Real Numbers

Find the value of each expression.

1. −24 ÷ −8 **3**
2. 24(−5) **−120**
3. −96 ÷ 3 **−32**
4. −6(20) **−120**
5. −7(−15) **105**
6. 6 ÷ (−1.5) **−4**

Divide.

7. $-\frac{8}{9} \div \frac{2}{3}$ **$-\frac{4}{3} = -1\frac{1}{3}$**
8. $-12 \div \left(-\frac{6}{25}\right)$ **50**
9. $2\frac{1}{4} \div \left(-5\frac{1}{3}\right)$ **$-\frac{27}{64}$**

Multiply or divide.

10. 0 · 4.75 **0**
11. 0 ÷ 10 **0**
12. $-\frac{1}{3} \div 0$ **undefined**
13. When Brianna's first CD sold a million copies, her record label gave her a $5000 bonus. She split the money evenly between herself, her agent, her producer, and her stylist. How much money did each person receive? **$1250**
14. (0.3)(−1.8) **−0.54**
15. $\frac{2}{5}\left(-\frac{5}{2}\right)$ **−1**
16. −15 ÷ (−6) **$\frac{5}{2} = 2\frac{1}{2}$**

Evaluate each expression for $x = 16$, $y = -4$, and $z = -2$.

17. $y \div x$ **$-\frac{1}{4}$**
18. $x \cdot y$ **−64**
19. xz **−32**
20. $z \div y$ **$\frac{1}{2}$**
21. $(y)(z)$ **8**
22. $y \div z$ **2**
23. $x \div z$ **−8**
24. $x \div y$ **−4**
25. $z \div x$ **$-\frac{1}{8}$**

1-3 READING STRATEGIES

LESSON 1-3 **Reading Strategies**
Using Patterns

Studying multiplication patterns can help you understand the rules for assigning signs to products and quotients.

8 • 3 means 3 groups of 8.
So, 8 • 3 = 8 + 8 + 8 = 24.
One rule is **pos × pos = pos**.

Look at the pattern below for the next rule.

8 • 3 = 24
8 • 2 = 16
8 • 1 = 8
8 • 0 = 0
8 • −1 = −8
8 • −2 = −16
8 • −3 = −24
(each step: −1, −8)

The pattern shows that **pos × neg = neg**.

−8 • 3 means 3 groups of −8.
So, −8 • 3 is −8 + −8 + −8, or −24.
Another rule is **neg × pos = neg**.

Look at the pattern below for the next rule.

−8 • 3 = −24
−8 • 2 = −16
−8 • 1 = −8
−8 • 0 = 0
−8 • −1 = 8
−8 • −2 = 16
−8 • −3 = 24
(each step: −1, +8)

The pattern shows that **neg × neg = pos**.

The rules for quotient signs are the same as the rules for product signs.

Solve each problem.

1. Write −5 • 4 as an addition problem, showing 4 groups of −5. **−5 + −5 + −5 + −5**
2. A negative number is multiplied by a positive number. What is the sign of the product? **negative**
3. A negative number is divided by a negative number. What is the sign of the quotient? **positive**

Multiply.

4. 7 • 2 = **14**
5. 3 • −5 = **−15**
6. −1 • 6 = **−6**
7. −4 • −9 = **36**

Use the following to answer problems 8–11.

A. −12 ÷ −3 B. −8 • 2 C. −2 • 2 D. 8 ÷ 2 E. 4 • −2

8. Which expressions result in a negative value? **B, C, E**
9. Which expressions result in a positive value? **A, D**
10. Find the value of each expression. **A: 4, B: −16, C: −4, D: 4, E: −8**
11. Which expression has the least value? **B**

1-3 REVIEW FOR MASTERY

LESSON 1-3 **Review for Mastery**
Multiplying and Dividing Real Numbers

To multiply or divide real numbers, first use the rules below to determine the sign of the result. Then operate with the numbers as if they have no signs.

Multiplication	Division	In General
(+) · (+) = (+)	(+) ÷ (+) = (+)	same sign = (+)
(+) · (−) = (−)	(+) ÷ (−) = (−)	different signs = (−)
(−) · (+) = (−)	(−) ÷ (+) = (−)	different signs = (−)
(−) · (−) = (+)	(−) ÷ (−) = (+)	same sign = (+)

Multiply −5 • 3.

−5 • 3 = −☐ *Different signs mean the product is negative.*
= −[5 • 3] *Multiply the numbers as if they have no signs.*
= −[15] *Multiply.*
= −15

Divide −2 ÷ (−0.5).

−2 ÷ (−0.5) = +☐ *Same signs mean the quotient is positive.*
= +[2 ÷ 0.5] *Divide the numbers as if they have no signs.*
= +[4] *Divide.*
= 4

Determine the sign (+ or −) for each product or quotient.

1. −8 • −4 = **+** 32
2. 156 ÷ (−8) = **−** 19.5
3. −15(4) = **−** 60
4. 6.4 ÷ (−4) = **−** 1.6
5. −0.5(0.4) = **−** 0.2
6. 29.82 ÷ 2.1 = **+** 14.2

Multiply or divide.

7. −3 • 7 **−21**
8. −55 ÷ −11 **5**
9. 6(−4) **−24**
10. −100 ÷ 20 **−5**
11. −6(−8) **48**
12. 5 ÷ (−2) **−2.5**
13. 15.3 ÷ −3 **−5.1**
14. −8.2 • −5 **41**
15. −21 ÷ 10 **−2.1**
16. −2.7(4) **−10.8**
17. 4.5 ÷ 1.5 **3**
18. 3.4 • (−1.5) **−5.1**

Multiple Choice For Exercises 73 and 74, choose the best answer.

73. In which situation below would you multiply 5 • 35 to find the final balance?
   Ⓐ Marc had \$35 in his bank account, and for 5 weeks, he withdrew \$5 a week.
   Ⓑ Marc opened a new bank account, and for the first 5 months, he deposited \$35 a month.
   Ⓒ Marc opened a bank account with \$35. For 5 weeks, he deposited \$5 a week.
   Ⓓ Marc withdrew \$35 a month from his bank account for 5 months.

74. Robyn is buying carpet for her bedroom floor, which is a 15-foot-by-12-foot rectangle. If carpeting costs \$1.25 per square foot, how much will it cost Robyn to carpet her bedroom?
   Ⓐ \$68 Ⓑ \$144 Ⓒ \$180 Ⓓ \$225

75. **Short Response** In music notation, a half note is played $\frac{1}{2}$ the length of a whole note. A quarter note is played $\frac{1}{4}$ the length of a whole note. In a piece of music, the clarinets play 8 half notes. In the same length of time, the flutes play x quarter notes. Determine how many quarter notes the flutes play. Explain your method.

75. Clarinets: 1 half note = $\frac{1}{2}$ whole note; 8 half notes = 4 whole notes; find the number of quarter notes that have the same length as 4 whole notes; $4 \div \frac{1}{4} = 16$; the flutes play 16 quarter notes.

CHALLENGE AND EXTEND

Find the value of each expression.

76. $(-2)(-2)(-2)$ **−8**
77. $\frac{5}{7} \cdot \frac{5}{7}$ **$\frac{25}{49}$**
78. $5\left(-\frac{4}{5}\right)\left(-\frac{3}{4}\right)$ **3**
79. $\left|-\frac{1}{4}\right| \cdot |20|$ **5**
80. $5 \cdot 4 \cdot 3 \cdot 2 \cdot 1$ **120**
81. $\left|-\frac{2}{5}\right| \cdot \left|\frac{5}{2}\right|$ **1**
82. $\frac{1}{2} \cdot \frac{2}{3} \cdot \frac{3}{4} \cdot \frac{4}{5}$ **$\frac{1}{5}$**
83. $\left(-\frac{3}{4}\right)\left(-\frac{3}{4}\right)\left(-\frac{3}{4}\right)$ **$\frac{-27}{64}$**
84. $(2^3)^2$ **64**

For each pattern shown below, describe a possible rule for finding the next term. Then use your rule to write the next 3 terms.

85. −1, 2, −4, 8, ... **Multiply by −2; −16, 32, −64.**
86. $\frac{1}{63}, -\frac{1}{21}, \frac{1}{7}, -\frac{3}{7}, \ldots$ **Multiply by −3; $\frac{9}{7}, \frac{-27}{7}, \frac{81}{7}$.**
87. −5, 10, −15, 20, −25, ...
88. 0.5, 0.25, 0.125, 0.0625, ...
89. A cleaning service charges \$49.00 to clean a one-bedroom apartment. If the work takes longer than 2 hours, the service charges \$18.00 for each additional hour. What would be the total cost for a job that took 4 hours to complete? **\$85**

87. The numbers are alternating positive and negative multiples of 5; 30, −35, 40

88. Multiply by 0.5; 0.03125, 0.015625, 0.0078125

SPIRAL STANDARDS REVIEW

6NS2.3, 6AF1.2, 7MG2.1

Each regular polygon has a side length of 2.1 cm. Find the perimeter. *(Previous course)*

90. 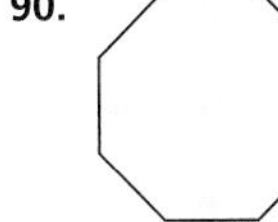 **16.8**
91. 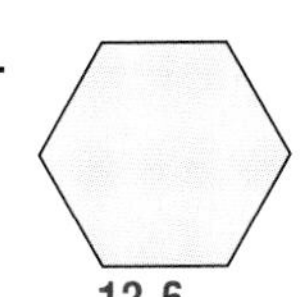 **12.6**
92. 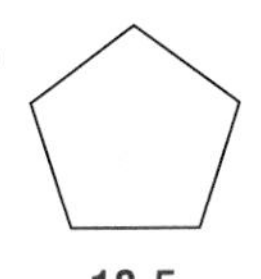 **10.5**
93. 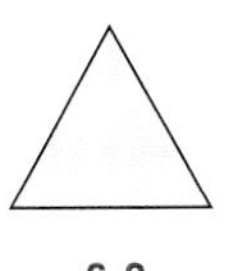 **6.3**

94. A prepaid phone card has a credit of 200 minutes. Write an expression for the number of minutes left on the card after t minutes have been used. *(Lesson 1-1)* **200 − t**

Add or subtract. *(Lesson 1-2)*

95. 12 − 18 **−6**
96. −6 + 14 **8**
97. 3 − (−5) **8**
98. 11 + (−8) **3**

COMMON ERROR ALERT

Students may fail to read the entire question on standardized tests. In **Exercise 74,** some students will find an area of 180 ft², and will immediately mark choice **C.** Remind students to reread the question to determine if additional calculations are required.

Multiple Choice In **Exercise 73,** choices **B** and **D** both seem to require multiplying 5(35). However, choice **D** refers to a withdrawal, which is represented by −35.

Journal

Write a word problem that uses the expression 7(−25). Then solve your word problem.

ALTERNATIVE ASSESSMENT

Have students write the two rules for multiplying and dividing signed numbers and an equation for each rule. One equation must contain a fraction. Next have students write a fraction that equals zero and a fraction that is undefined.

Power Presentations with PowerPoint®

1-3 Lesson Quiz

Find the value of each expression.

1. $\frac{35}{-7}$ −5
2. 2(−6) −12

Multiply or divide if possible.

3. $-3 \div 1\frac{3}{4}$ $-\frac{12}{7}$
4. $-2\frac{1}{3}(0)$ 0
5. $-\frac{3}{4} \div 0$ undefined
6. A cyclist traveled on a straight road for $1\frac{1}{4}$ hours at a speed of 12 mi/h. How many miles did the cyclist travel? 15 miles

Also available on transparency

1-3 PROBLEM SOLVING

LESSON 1-3 Problem Solving
Multiplying and Dividing Real Numbers

Write the correct answer.

1. Jane's grade point average changed by −0.16 points each term. How much did her grade point average change after 4 terms?
   −0.64 points
2. Isari's recipe for strawberry smoothies requires $\frac{1}{2}$ cup of sliced strawberries per smoothie. How many smoothies can she make using 8 cups of strawberries?
   16 smoothies
3. The value of an investor's stock changed by $-1\frac{3}{4}$ points last week. This week, the value changed by 3 times as much. How much did the value of the investor's stock change this week?
   $-5\frac{1}{4}$ points
4. Jogging on pavement burns 13 calories per minute. Jogging on grass burns 1.07 times as many calories per minute. How many calories would you burn by jogging on grass for 5 minutes? (Round your answer to the nearest tenth.)
   69.6 calories

Use the table below for exercises 5–7, which shows the cost of three different types of season tickets during the Dallas Cowboys 2005 season. Select the best answer.

2005 Season Tickets	
Seat Location	**Cost**
Upper Level Sideline	\$730
Upper Level Corner	\$620
Upper Level Far Corner	\$490

5. How much money was spent on Upper Level Sideline season tickets in 2005 if 2500 fans bought Upper Level Sideline season tickets?
   A \$1,315,000 C \$1,757,500
   B \$1,550,000 Ⓓ \$1,825,000
6. Tom and his two brothers gave their father two Upper Level Far Corner season tickets as a gift. If the brothers shared the cost equally, how much did each one pay towards the gift?
   F \$163 Ⓗ \$327
   G \$245 J \$980
7. If sales of Upper Level Corner season tickets totaled \$1,116,000, how many Upper Level Corner season ticket holders were there?
   A 1529 C 2278
   Ⓑ 1800 D 6919
8. Four friends bought a pair of Upper Level Sideline season tickets. If they shared the cost equally, how much did each pay?
   F \$122.50 H \$310
   G \$182.50 Ⓙ \$365

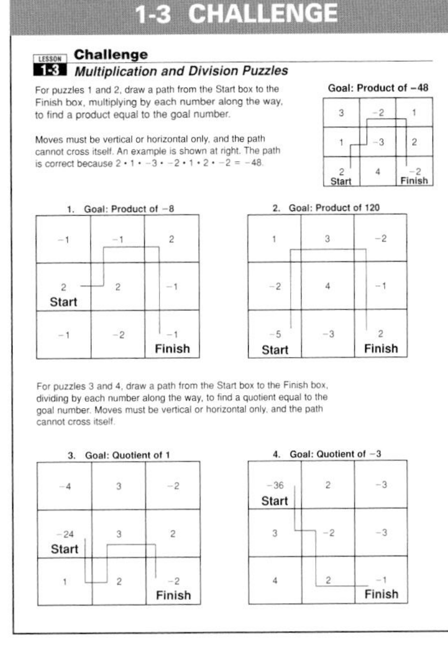

1-3 CHALLENGE

LESSON 1-3 Challenge
Multiplication and Division Puzzles

For puzzles 1 and 2, draw a path from the Start box to the Finish box, multiplying by each number along the way, to find a product equal to the goal number.

Moves must be vertical or horizontal only, and the path cannot cross itself. An example is shown at right. The path is correct because 2 • 1 • −3 • −2 • 1 • 2 • −2 = −48.

Goal: Product of −48

3	−2	1
1	−3	2
2 Start	4	−2 Finish

1. Goal: Product of −8

−1	−1	2
2 Start	2	−1
−1	−2	−1 Finish

2. Goal: Product of 120

1	3	−2
−2	4	−1
−5 Start	−3	2 Finish

For puzzles 3 and 4, draw a path from the Start box to the Finish box, dividing by each number along the way, to find a quotient equal to the goal number. Moves must be vertical or horizontal only, and the path cannot cross itself.

3. Goal: Quotient of 1

−4	3	−2
−24 Start	3	2
1	2	−2 Finish

4. Goal: Quotient of −3

−36 Start	2	−3
3	−2	−3
4	2	−1 Finish

1-4 Organizer

Objective: Evaluate expressions containing exponents.

Online Edition
Tutorial Videos

Countdown to Mastery Week 1

Power Presentations with PowerPoint®

Warm Up

Simplify.

1. 2(2) 4

2. (−2)(−2) 4

3. (−2)(−2)(−2) −8

4. 3(3)(3) 27

5. $\left(-\frac{2}{3}\right)\left(-\frac{2}{3}\right)$ $\frac{4}{9}$

Also available on transparency

Math Fact !!

A *googol* is 1 followed by 100 zeros. It can be expressed as a power of 10, as 10^{100}.

Preparation for 🔑 2.0

1-4 Powers and Exponents

Preparation for 🔑 2.0 Students understand and use such operations as taking the opposite, finding the reciprocal, **taking a root, and raising to a fractional power. They understand and use the rules of exponents.**

Vocabulary
power
base
exponent

Who uses this?
Biologists use exponents to model the growth patterns of living organisms.

When bacteria divide, their number increases exponentially. This means that the number of bacteria is multiplied by the same factor each time the bacteria divide. Instead of writing repeated multiplication to express a product, you can write it as a *power*.

A **power** is an expression written with an *exponent* and a *base* or the value of such an expression. 3^2 is an example of a power.

When a number is raised to the second power, we usually say it is "squared." The area of a *square* is $s \cdot s = s^2$, where s is the side length.

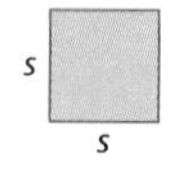

When a number is raised to the third power, we usually say it is "cubed." The volume of a *cube* is $s \cdot s \cdot s = s^3$, where s is the side length.

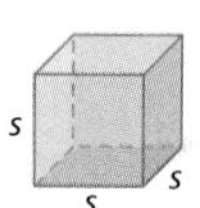

EXAMPLE 1 Writing Powers for Geometric Models

Write the power represented by each geometric model.

A

There are 3 rows of 3 dots. 3 × 3
The factor 3 is used 2 times.

3^2

B

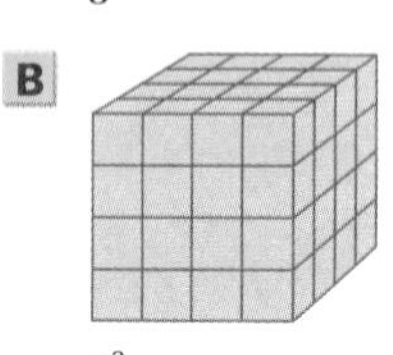

The figure is 4 cubes long, 4 cubes wide, and 4 cubes tall. 4 × 4 × 4
The factor 4 is used 3 times.

4^3

Write the power represented by each geometric model.

1a. 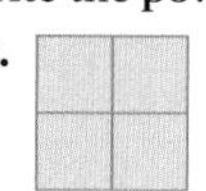 2^2

1b. 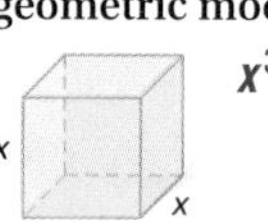 x^3

1 Introduce

1-4 Powers and Exponents

Powers are used to represent repeated multiplication. For example, the expression 8^3 means 8 × 8 × 8.

1. This square has a length and width of 4 inches. The number of one-inch squares needed to fill the region is 4 × 4. Write this using powers.
2. A square has a length and width of 6 inches. How many one-inch squares are needed to fill the region? Write your answer using powers.
3. A cube has a length, width, and height of 4 inches. How many cubes that are 1 inch on each side are needed to fill this cube? Write your answer using powers.
4. Some expressions with powers cannot be modeled using a geometric model. Use multiplication to explain what $(-2)^5$ means. Then evaluate the expression.

THINK AND DISCUSS

5. **Explain** why $(-210)^4$ must be positive.
6. **Describe** what you think is meant by the expression 3^1.

Motivate

Review the idea of repeated addition with students. Ask students to write an example of repeated addition, such as 7 + 7 + 7 + 7 + 7. Show how to write repeated addition as multiplication, 5(7). Now have students write an example of repeated multiplication, such as 4 × 4 × 4 × 4 × 4 × 4. Tell students that they will review how to write repeated multiplication in this lesson.

Explorations and answers are provided in *Alternate Openers: Explorations Transparencies.*

There are no easy geometric models for numbers raised to exponents greater than 3, but you can still write them using repeated multiplication or with a base and exponent.

Reading Exponents			
Words	Multiplication	Power	Value
3 to the first power	3	3^1	3
3 to the second power, or 3 squared	$3 \cdot 3$	3^2	9
3 to the third power, or 3 cubed	$3 \cdot 3 \cdot 3$	3^3	27
3 to the fourth power	$3 \cdot 3 \cdot 3 \cdot 3$	3^4	81
3 to the fifth power	$3 \cdot 3 \cdot 3 \cdot 3 \cdot 3$	3^5	243

EXAMPLE 2 Evaluating Powers

Simplify each expression.

A $(-2)^3$

$(-2)(-2)(-2)$ — *Use −2 as a factor 3 times.*

-8

Caution!

In the expression -5^2, 5 is the base because the negative sign is not in parentheses.
In the expression $(-2)^3$, −2 is the base because of the parentheses.

B -5^2

$-1 \cdot 5 \cdot 5$ — *Think of a negative sign in front of a power as multiplying by −1. Find the product of −1 and two 5's.*

$-1 \cdot 25$

-25

C $\left(\frac{2}{3}\right)^2$

$\frac{2}{3} \cdot \frac{2}{3}$ — *Use $\frac{2}{3}$ as a factor 2 times.*

$\frac{2}{3} \cdot \frac{2}{3} = \frac{4}{9}$

CHECK IT OUT! Simplify each expression.

2a. $(-5)^3$ **−125** **2b.** -6^2 **−36** **2c.** $\left(\frac{3}{4}\right)^3$ $\frac{27}{64}$

EXAMPLE 3 Writing Powers

Write each number as a power of the given base.

A 8; base 2

$2 \cdot 2 \cdot 2$ — *The product of three 2's is 8.*

2^3

B −125; base −5

$(-5)(-5)(-5)$ — *The product of three −5's is −125.*

$(-5)^3$

CHECK IT OUT! Write each number as a power of the given base.

3a. 64; base 8 8^2 **3b.** −27; base −3 $(-3)^3$

2 Teach

Guided Instruction

Before writing expressions as powers, review multiplication of signed numbers, including fractions and decimals. Review the rules for products with an even and odd number of negative factors. Next have students write expressions as powers, such as $4 \times 4 \times 4 = 4^3$. Then have students simplify the expressions.

Universal Access
Through Number Sense

Have students create a table of the common powers listed below. Have them include the value of each power. Suggest to students that they should be able to recall the value of each power.

$2^2, 2^3, 2^4, 2^5, 3^2, 3^3, 4^2, 4^3, 5^2, 5^3, 6^2, 7^2, 8^2, 9^2$

COMMON ERROR ALERT

Students may multiply the exponent by the base, especially when the base is 1. Encourage them to write the power as repeated multiplication.

$$1^5 = 1 \cdot 1 \cdot 1 \cdot 1 \cdot 1 = 1$$
$$2^3 = 2 \cdot 2 \cdot 2 = 8$$

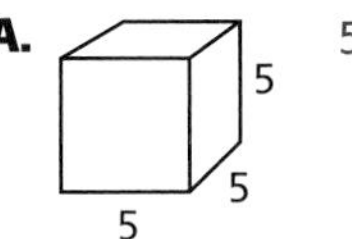

Power Presentations with PowerPoint®

Additional Examples

Example 1

Write the power represented by each geometric model.

A. 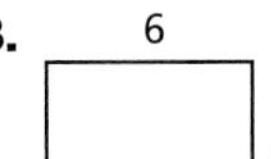 5^3

B. 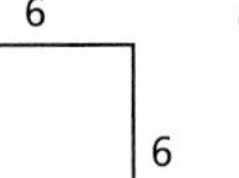 6^2

Example 2

Simplify each expression.

A. $(-6)^3$ -216

B. -10^2 -100

C. $\left(\frac{2}{9}\right)^2$ $\frac{4}{81}$

Example 3

Write each number as a power of the given base.

A. 64; base 8 8^2

B. 81; base −3 $(-3)^4$

Also available on transparency

INTERVENTION
Questioning Strategies

EXAMPLE 1

- What multiplication expression does each model show?

EXAMPLE 2

- When is a negative sign part of the base?

EXAMPLE 3

- How can you determine what exponent to use with the base that is given?

Power Presentations with PowerPoint®

Additional Examples

Example 4

In case of a school closing, the PTA president calls 3 families. Each of these families calls 3 other families, and so on. How many families will have been called in the 4th round of calls?
81

Also available on transparency

INTERVENTION
Questioning Strategies

EXAMPLE 4

- Why do you use the same base to write expressions for the number in each stage of the problem?
- What does the exponent in each expression correspond to?

EXAMPLE 4 *Problem-Solving Application*

A certain bacterium divides into 2 bacteria every hour. There is 1 bacterium on a slide. If each bacterium on the slide divides each hour, how many bacteria will be on the slide after 6 hours?

1 Understand the Problem

The **answer** will be the number of bacteria on the slide after 6 hours.
List the **important information:**

- There is 1 bacterium on a slide that divides into 2 bacteria.
- Each bacterium then divides into 2 more bacteria.

2 Make a Plan

Draw a diagram to show the number of bacteria after each hour.

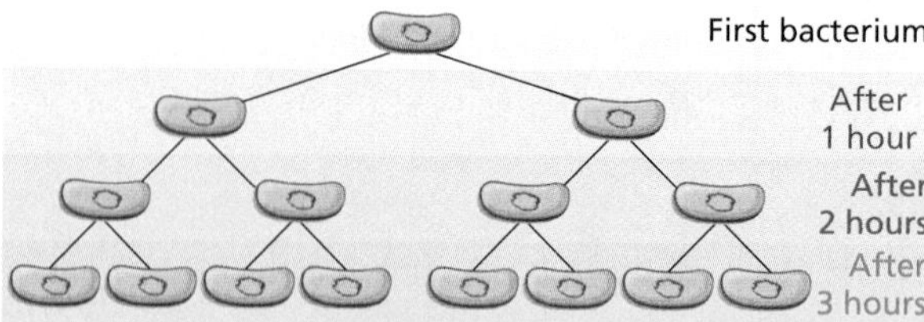

3 Solve

Notice that after each hour, the number of bacteria is a power of 2.

After 1 hour: $1 \cdot 2 = 2$ or 2^1 bacteria on the slide
After 2 hours: $2 \cdot 2 = 4$ or 2^2 bacteria on the slide
After 3 hours: $4 \cdot 2 = 8$ or 2^3 bacteria on the slide

So, after the 6th hour, there will be 2^6 bacteria.

$2^6 = 2 \cdot 2 \cdot 2 \cdot 2 \cdot 2 \cdot 2 = 64$ *Multiply six 2's.*

After 6 hours, there will be 64 bacteria on the slide.

4 Look Back

The numbers become too large for a diagram quickly, but a diagram helps you recognize a pattern. Then you can write the numbers as powers of 2.

CHECK IT OUT! 4. **What if...?** How many bacteria will be on the slide after 8 hours? $2^8 = 256$

THINK AND DISCUSS

1. Express 8^3 in words two ways.
2. **GET ORGANIZED** Copy and complete the graphic organizer. In each box, give an example and tell whether the expression is positive or negative.

	Even Exponent	Odd Exponent
Positive Base		
Negative Base		

3 Close

Summarize

Make sure students recognize the differences between 3^2, 2^3, and $2 \cdot 3$. Explain that 3^2 means to multiply 3 times 3; 2^3 means to multiply 2 times 2 times 2; and $2 \cdot 3$ means to multiply 2 times 3. Review how to determine whether a negative sign is part of the base.

FORMATIVE ASSESSMENT and INTERVENTION

***Diagnose Before* the Lesson**
1-4 Warm Up, TE p. 26

***Monitor During* the Lesson**
Check It Out! Exercises, SE pp. 26–28
Questioning Strategies, TE pp. 27–28

***Assess After* the Lesson**
1-4 Lesson Quiz, TE p. 31
Alternative Assessment, TE p. 31

Answers to *Think and Discuss*

1. eight cubed; eight raised to the third power
2. See p. A2.

California Standards Practice
Preparation for 2.0; 24.1

go.hrw.com
Homework Help Online
KEYWORD: MA8CA 1-4
Parent Resources Online
KEYWORD: MA8CA Parent

GUIDED PRACTICE

1. **Vocabulary** What does the *exponent* in the expression 5^6 tell you? the number of times to use the base as a factor

SEE EXAMPLE 1 p. 26

Write the power represented by each geometric model.

2. 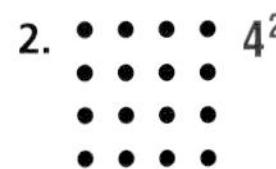 4^2
3. 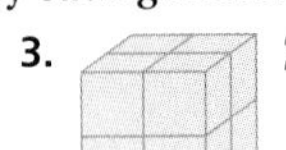 2^3
4. 9, 9 9^2

SEE EXAMPLE 2 p. 27

Simplify each expression.

5. 7^2 49
6. $(-2)^4$ 16
7. $(-2)^5$ −32
8. $-\left(\frac{1}{2}\right)^4$ $-\frac{1}{16}$

SEE EXAMPLE 3 p. 27

Write each number as a power of the given base.

9. 81; base 9 9^2
10. 100,000; base 10 10^5
11. −64; base −4 $(-4)^3$
12. 10; base 10 10^1
13. 81; base 3 3^4
14. 36; base −6 $(-6)^2$

SEE EXAMPLE 4 p. 28

15. **Technology** Jan wants to predict the number of hits she will get on her Web page. Her Web page received 3 hits during the first week it was posted. If the number of hits triples every week, how many hits will the Web page receive during the 5th week? $3^5 = 243$

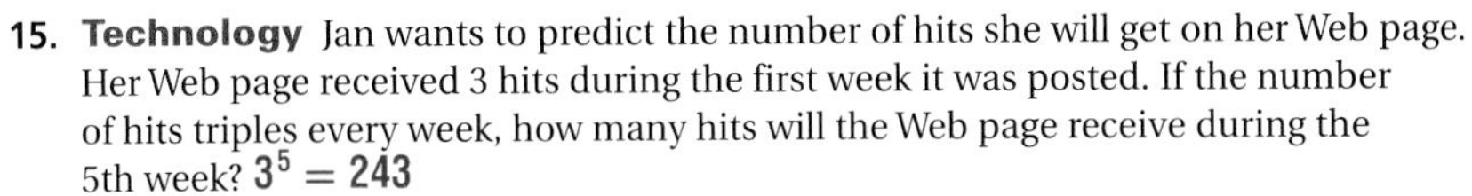

PRACTICE AND PROBLEM SOLVING

Independent Practice

For Exercises	See Example
16–18	1
19–22	2
23–28	3
29	4

Extra Practice
Skills Practice p. EP2
Application Practice p. EP24

Write the power represented by each geometric model.

16. 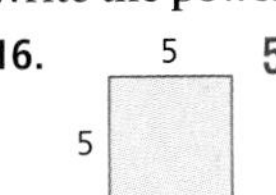 5, 5 5^2
17. 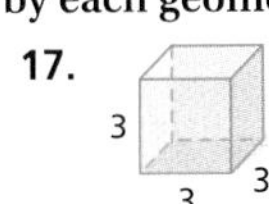 3, 3, 3 3^3
18.  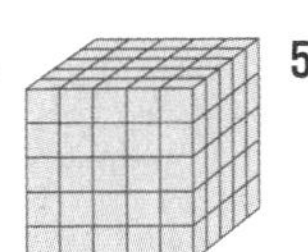 5^3

Simplify each expression.

19. 3^3 27
20. $(-4)^2$ 16
21. -4^2 −16
22. $\left(-\frac{3}{5}\right)^2$ $\frac{9}{25}$

Write each number as a power of the given base.

23. 49; base 7 7^2
24. 1000; base 10 10^3
25. −8; base −2 $(-2)^3$
26. 1,000,000; base 10 10^6
27. 64; base 4 4^3
28. 343; base 7 7^3

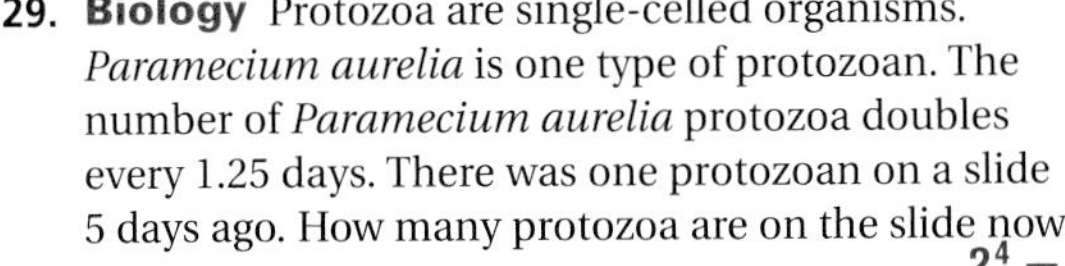

29. **Biology** Protozoa are single-celled organisms. *Paramecium aurelia* is one type of protozoan. The number of *Paramecium aurelia* protozoa doubles every 1.25 days. There was one protozoan on a slide 5 days ago. How many protozoa are on the slide now? $2^4 = 16$

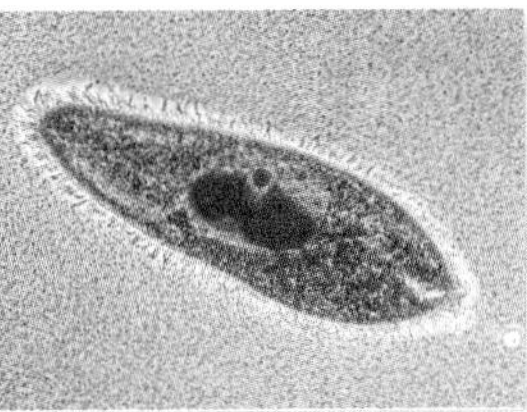

30. **Write About It** A classmate says that any number raised to an even power is positive. Explain whether your classmate is correct.

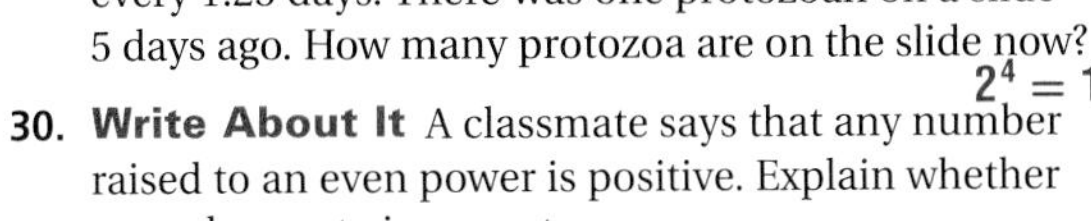

Compare. Write <, >, or =.

31. $3^2 < 3^3$
32. $5^2 < 2^5$
33. $4^2 = 2^4$
34. $1^9 = 1^4$
35. $-2^3 = (-2)^3$
36. $-3^2 < (-3)^2$
37. $10^2 > 2^6$
38. $2^2 = 4^1$

1-4 Exercises

Assignment Guide

Assign *Guided Practice* exercises as necessary.

If you finished Examples **1–2**
Proficient 16–22, 31–42, 44, 60–63
Advanced 16–22, 39–46, 48–53, 60–63

If you finished Examples **1–4**
Proficient 16–30, 39–60, 64–73, 76–86
Advanced 16–30, 39–86

Homework Quick Check
Quickly check key concepts.
Exercises: 16, 20, 24, 29, 39, 44

Teaching Tip

Inclusion In **Exercise 29,** students may have difficulty determining how many times the protozoa double. Suggest to students that they make a diagram like the one in **Example 4** or a chart like the one below:

1 division	1.25 days
2 divisions	2.5 days
⋮	⋮

Answer

30. Any two positive numbers make a positive number when multiplied together. Two negative numbers multiplied together also make a positive number. An even number of negative numbers multiplied together will always make a positive number.

California Standards

Standard	Exercises
Prep for 2.0	1–65, 67–75
24.1	65, 70
6NS2.2	83
6NS2.3	85
6SDAP1.1	76–78
7NS1.2	86

Geometry The figures in **Exercise 47** are squares, so the area can be found using the formula $A = s^2$.

Challenge advanced students to find the area of the yellow region by also using the formula for the area of a triangle, $A = \frac{1}{2}bh$.

Exercise 66 involves converting units to work with the relationships between pressure, force, and area. This exercise prepares students for the Concept Connection on page 40.

Answers

39. $2 \cdot 2 \cdot 2 = 8$

40. $1 \cdot 1 \cdot 1 \cdot 1 \cdot 1 \cdot 1 \cdot 1 = 1$

41. $(-4)(-4)(-4) = -64$

42. $-(4 \cdot 4 \cdot 4) = -64$

43. $(-1)(-1)(-1) = -1$

44. $(-1)(-1)(-1)(-1) = 1$

45. $\left(\frac{1}{3}\right)\left(\frac{1}{3}\right)\left(\frac{1}{3}\right) = \frac{1}{27}$

46. $-(2.2 \cdot 2.2) = -4.84$

64c. If the coin is fair, about half the tosses should result in heads and half should result in tails. So Becky's and Mark's scores increase about equally often. But Becky's score is increasing by a greater factor, so she will probably win.

66a. $\frac{1}{2}$ psi

b. $\frac{4}{9}$ psi

Write each expression as repeated multiplication. Then simplify the expression.

39. 2^3 40. 1^7 41. $(-4)^3$ 42. -4^3

43. $(-1)^3$ 44. $(-1)^4$ 45. $\left(\frac{1}{3}\right)^3$ 46. -2.2^2

47. **Geometry** The diagram shows an ornamental tile design.
   a. What is the area of the whole tile? **36 in^2**
   b. What is the area of the white square? **9 in^2**
   c. What is the total area of the two shaded regions? **27 in^2**

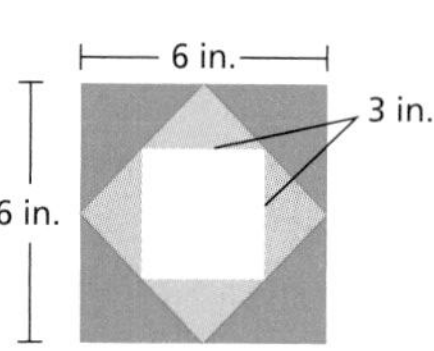

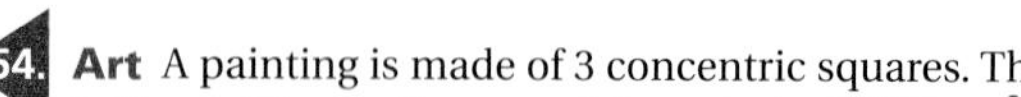

Write each expression using a base and an exponent.

48. $3 \cdot 3 \cdot 3 \cdot 3$ **3^4** 49. $6 \cdot 6$ **6^2** 50. $8 \cdot 8 \cdot 8 \cdot 8 \cdot 8$ **8^5**

51. $(-1)(-1)(-1)(-1)$ **$(-1)^4$** 52. $(-7)(-7)(-7)$ **$(-7)^3$** 53. $\left(\frac{1}{9}\right)\left(\frac{1}{9}\right)\left(\frac{1}{9}\right)$ **$\left(\frac{1}{9}\right)^3$**

LINK Art

German artist Josef Albers began his series *Homage to the Square* in 1949. These paintings of nested squares explored the psychological effects of color combinations.

54. **Art** A painting is made of 3 concentric squares. The side length of the largest square is 24 cm. What is the area of the painting? **576 cm^2**

55. **Estimation** A box is shaped like a cube with edges 22.7 centimeters long. What is the approximate volume of the box? **between 8000 cm^3 and 15,625 cm^3**

Write the exponent that makes each equation true.

56. $2^{■} = 4$ **2** 57. $4^{■} = 16$ **2** 58. $(-2)^{■} = 16$ **4** 59. $5^{■} = 625$ **4**

60. $-2^{■} = -8$ **3** 61. $10^{■} = 100$ **2** 62. $5^{■} = 125$ **3** 63. $3^{■} = 81$ **4**

64. **Entertainment** Mark and Becky play a coin toss game. Both start with one point. Every time the coin comes up heads, Mark doubles his score. Every time the coin comes up tails, Becky triples her score. The results of their game so far are shown in the table.
   a. What is Mark's score? **$2^5 = 32$**
   b. What is Becky's score? **$3^3 = 27$**
   c. **What if...?** If they toss the coin 50 more times, who do you think will win? Why?

Coin Toss Results

Heads	Tails
✓	✓
✓	✓
✓	✓
✓	
✓	

65. **Critical Thinking** The number of zeros in powers of 10 follow a pattern.
   a. Evaluate each of the following: 10^2, 10^3, 10^4. **100, 1000, 10,000**
   b. Use your answers to part *a* to make a prediction about the relationship between the exponent of a power of 10 and the number of zeros in the answer. **The exponent is the same as the number of zeros in the number.**

CONCEPT CONNECTION

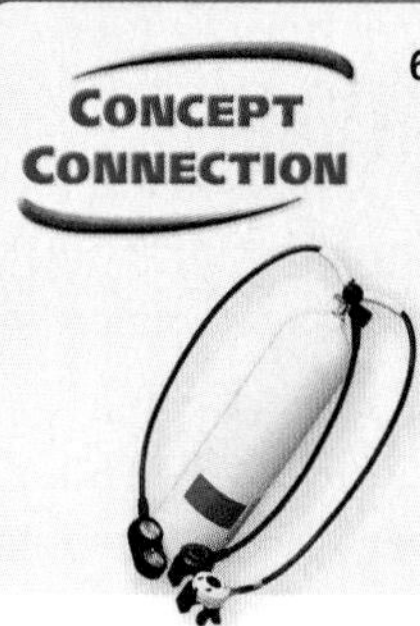

66. This problem will prepare you for the Concept Connection on page 40.
The formula $p = \frac{F}{A}$ shows that pressure p is the amount of force F exerted over an area A in square units.
   a. A bag of flour sits on a block and exerts a force of 50 pounds over an area of 100 in^2. What is the pressure exerted on the block by the bag of flour?
   b. Water pressure exerts 64 pounds on each square foot of a diver's body. What force is exerted on each square *inch* of the diver's body? (*Hint:* Determine how many square inches are in one square foot.)

1-4 PRACTICE A

1-4 PRACTICE C

1-4 PRACTICE B

LESSON 1-4 **Practice B**
Powers and Exponents

Write the power represented by each geometric model.

1. 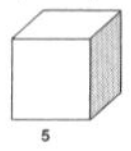 (cube, edge 5) 5^3 2. 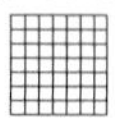 (grid) 7^2 3. 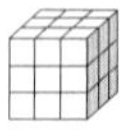 (cube) 3^3

Evaluate each expression.

4. 2^4 **16** 5. $(-3)^3$ **−27** 6. $\left(\frac{2}{5}\right)^2$ **$\frac{4}{25}$**

7. 3^5 **243** 8. $(-10)^4$ **10,000** 9. $\left(\frac{3}{4}\right)^2$ **$\frac{9}{16}$**

Write each number as a power of the given base.

10. 16; base 2 **2^4** 11. 1,000,000; base 10 **10^6** 12. −216; base −6 **$(-6)^3$**

13. 2401; base 7 **7^4** 14. 256; base −4 **$(-4)^4$** 15. $\frac{8}{27}$; base $\frac{2}{3}$ **$\left(\frac{2}{3}\right)^3$**

16. Anna needed to let everyone in the music club know the time of its next meeting. She called two people and asked each of them to call two other people, and so on. If each phone call takes one minute, how many phone calls were made during the fifth minute? **$2^5 = 32$**

1-4 READING STRATEGIES

LESSON 1-4 **Reading Strategies**
Use a Venn Diagram

Examine the Venn diagram below for similarities and differences between the power expression 4^3 and the multiplication expression $4 \cdot 3$.

4^3 / **$4 \cdot 3$**

- 4^3 only:
  - reads "4 to the third power"
  - 4 is a base and 3 is an exponent
  - 4 is a factor 3 times
  - when evaluated, the result is $4 \cdot 4 \cdot 4 = 64$
- Both:
  - both result in a product
  - both involve multiplication
  - both have 4 as a factor
- $4 \cdot 3$ only:
  - reads "4 times 3"
  - 4 is a factor and 3 is a factor
  - 4 is a factor only once
  - when evaluated, the result is $4 \cdot 3 = 12$

Answer the following with the help of the Venn diagram.

1. The expression 3^8 reads "3 to the **eighth** power."
2. Write the expression that represents "5 to the sixth power." **5^6**
3. In the expression 7^4, 7 is the **base** and 4 is the **exponent**.
4. In the expression 6^4, how many times is 6 used as a factor? **4 times**
5. The expression 2^6 **is not** (is/is not) equal in value to the expression $2 \cdot 6$.
6. When evaluated, which expression results in a value of 10, 2^5 or $2 \cdot 5$? **$2 \cdot 5$**
7. When evaluated, which expression results in a value of 1, 1^3 or $1 \cdot 3$? **1^3**

Evaluate each expression.

8. 9^2 **81** 9. 2^4 **16** 10. 1^5 **1**

1-4 REVIEW FOR MASTERY

LESSON 1-4 **Review for Mastery**
Powers and Exponents

A **power** is an expression that represents repeated multiplication of a factor. The factor is the **base**, and the number of times it is used as a factor is the **exponent**. Pay attention to parentheses, which tell you how much of the expression the exponent influences.

Power	Base	Exponent	Expanded Form
5^4	5	4	$5 \cdot 5 \cdot 5 \cdot 5$
-5^4	5	4	$-(5 \cdot 5 \cdot 5 \cdot 5)$
$(-5)^4$	−5	4	$(-5) \cdot (-5) \cdot (-5) \cdot (-5)$

To evaluate a power, perform the repeated multiplication.

Evaluate $\left(-\frac{4}{5}\right)^3$.

There are parentheses, so the exponent influences the negative *and* the fraction.

$\left(-\frac{4}{5}\right)^3 = \left(-\frac{4}{5}\right)\left(-\frac{4}{5}\right)\left(-\frac{4}{5}\right)$

$= \left(+\frac{16}{25}\right)\left(-\frac{4}{5}\right)$ *Multiply two of the factors. A negative times a negative is positive.*

$= -\frac{64}{125}$ *Multiply again. A positive times a negative is negative.*

Write the expanded form of each power.

1. 7^6 **$7 \cdot 7 \cdot 7 \cdot 7 \cdot 7 \cdot 7$** 2. $(-3)^2$ **$(-3) \cdot (-3)$**

3. $\frac{1^7}{2}$ **$\frac{1}{2} \cdot \frac{1}{2} \cdot \frac{1}{2} \cdot \frac{1}{2} \cdot \frac{1}{2} \cdot \frac{1}{2} \cdot \frac{1}{2}$** 4. -6^5 **$-(6 \cdot 6 \cdot 6 \cdot 6 \cdot 6)$**

Evaluate each expression.

5. 3^5 **243** 6. -2^4 **−16** 7. $\left(-\frac{2}{9}\right)^2$ **$\frac{4}{81}$**

8. $(-2)^3$ **−8** 9. 1^8 **1** 10. 0^2 **0**

Multiple Choice For Exercises 67–70, choose the best answer.

67. Which of the following is equal to 9^2?

Ⓐ $9 \cdot 2$ Ⓑ 27 **(Ⓒ) 3^4** Ⓓ -9^2

68. Which power represents the same value as the product $(-16)(-16)(-16)(-16)$?

Ⓐ $(-16)4$ **(Ⓑ) $(-16)^4$** Ⓒ -16^4 Ⓓ $-(16 \cdot 4)$

69. A number raised to the third power is negative. What is true about the number?

Ⓐ The number is positive. Ⓒ The number is even.

(Ⓑ) The number is negative. Ⓓ The number is odd.

70. The table shows the results of raising −1 to consecutive whole numbers. If the pattern in the table continues, what is the value of −1 raised to the 100th power?

$(-1)^n$	$(-1)^1$	$(-1)^2$	$(-1)^3$	$(-1)^4$	$(-1)^5$	$(-1)^6$
Value	−1	1	−1	1	−1	1

Ⓐ -1^{100} Ⓑ −1 **(Ⓒ) 1** Ⓓ 0

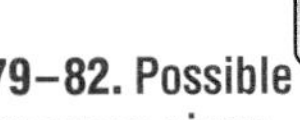

CHALLENGE AND EXTEND

Simplify each expression.

71. $(2^2)(2^2)(2^2)$ **64** 72. $(2^3)(2^3)(2^3)$ **512** 73. $(-4^2)(-4^2)(-4^2)(-4^2)$ **65,536**

74. **Design** The diagram shows the layout of a pool and the surrounding path. The path is 2.5 feet wide.

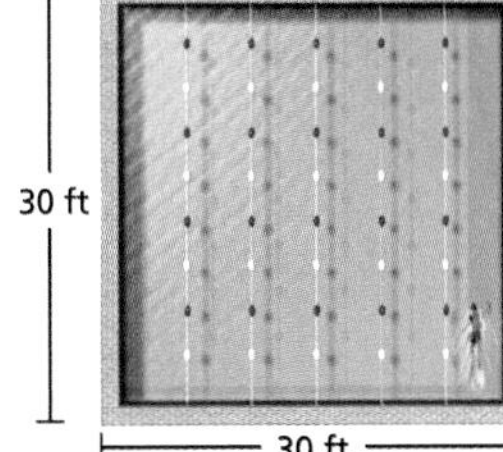

a. What is the total area of the pool and path? **900 ft²**

b. What is the area of the pool? **625 ft²**

c. What is the area of the path? **275 ft²**

d. One bag of pebbles covers 10 square feet. How many bags of pebbles are needed to cover the path? **28 bags**

75. Exponents and powers have special properties.

a. Write both 4^2 and 4^3 as a product of 4's. **$4 \cdot 4$; $4 \cdot 4 \cdot 4$**

b. Write the product of the two expressions from part **a.** Write this product as a power of 4. **$4 \cdot 4 \cdot 4 \cdot 4 \cdot 4 = 4^5$**

c. **Write About It** Add the exponents in the expressions 4^2 and 4^3. Describe any relationship you see between your answer to part **b** and the sum of the exponents. **$2 + 3 = 5$; the sum of the exponents in 4^2 and 4^3 is the exponent in the product 4^5.**

SPIRAL STANDARDS REVIEW

6NS2.2, 6NS2.3, 6SDAP1.1, 7NS1.2

79–82. Possible answers given.

79. 5 minus x; x less than 5

80. 6 times n; the product of 6 and n

81. c divided by d; the quotient of c and d

82. the sum of a and b; b more than a

Find the mean of each data set by dividing the sum of the data by the number of items in the data set. *(Previous course)*

76. 7, 7, 8, 8 **7.5** 77. 1, 3, 5, 7, 9 **5** 78. 10, 9, 9, 12, 12 **10.4**

Give two ways to write each algebraic expression in words. *(Lesson 1-1)*

79. $5 - x$ 80. $6n$ 81. $c \div d$ 82. $a + b$

Multiply or divide if possible. *(Lesson 1-3)*

83. $\frac{4}{5} \div \frac{8}{25}$ **$\frac{5}{2}$** 84. $0 \div \frac{6}{7}$ **0** 85. $-20(-14)$ **280** 86. $\frac{1}{2}\left(-\frac{4}{5}\right)$ **$-\frac{2}{5}$**

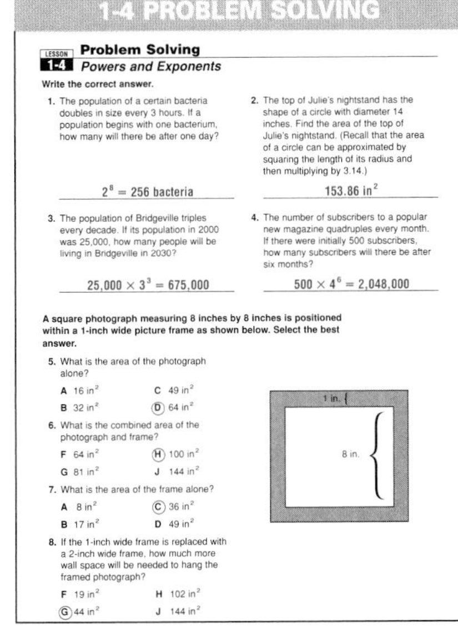

1-4 PROBLEM SOLVING

LESSON 1-4 **Problem Solving**
Powers and Exponents

Write the correct answer.

1. The population of a certain bacteria doubles in size every 3 hours. If a population begins with one bacterium, how many will there be after one day?
$2^8 = 256$ bacteria

2. The top of Julie's nightstand has the shape of a circle with diameter 14 inches. Find the area of the top of Julie's nightstand. (Recall that the area of a circle can be approximated by squaring the length of its radius and then multiplying by 3.14.)
153.86 in²

3. The population of Bridgeville triples every decade. If its population in 2000 was 25,000, how many people will be living in Bridgeville in 2030?
$25{,}000 \times 3^3 = 675{,}000$

4. The number of subscribers to a popular new magazine quadruples every month. If there were initially 500 subscribers, how many subscribers will there be after six months?
$500 \times 4^6 = 2{,}048{,}000$

A square photograph measuring 8 inches by 8 inches is positioned within a 1-inch wide picture frame as shown below. Select the best answer.

5. What is the area of the photograph alone?
A 16 in² C 49 in²
B 32 in² (D) 64 in²

6. What is the combined area of the photograph and frame?
F 64 in² (H) 100 in²
G 81 in² J 144 in²

7. What is the area of the frame alone?
A 8 in² (C) 36 in²
B 17 in² D 49 in²

8. If the 1-inch wide frame is replaced with a 2-inch wide frame, how much more wall space will be needed to hang the framed photograph?
F 19 in² H 102 in²
(G) 44 in² J 144 in²

1 in.
8 in.

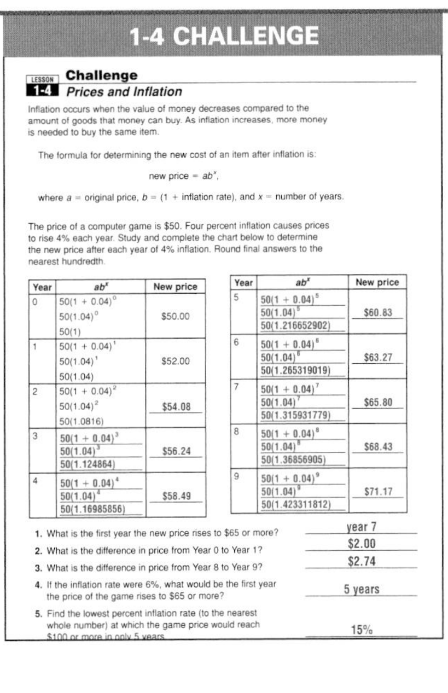

1-4 CHALLENGE

LESSON 1-4 **Challenge**
Prices and Inflation

Inflation occurs when the value of money decreases compared to the amount of goods that money can buy. As inflation increases, more money is needed to buy the same item.

The formula for determining the new cost of an item after inflation is:

new price = ab^x,

where a = original price, b = (1 + inflation rate), and x = number of years.

The price of a computer game is $50. Four percent inflation causes prices to rise 4% each year. Study and complete the chart below to determine the new price after each year of 4% inflation. Round final answers to the nearest hundredth.

Year	ab^x	New price
0	$50(1 + 0.04)^0$ $50(1.04)^0$ $50(1)$	$50.00
1	$50(1 + 0.04)^1$ $50(1.04)^1$ $50(1.04)$	$52.00
2	$50(1 + 0.04)^2$ $50(1.04)^2$ $50(1.0816)$	$54.08
3	$50(1 + 0.04)^3$ $50(1.04)^3$ $50(1.124864)$	$56.24
4	$50(1 + 0.04)^4$ $50(1.04)^4$ $50(1.16985856)$	$58.49

Year	ab^x	New price
5	$50(1 + 0.04)^5$ $50(1.04)^5$ $50(1.216652902)$	$60.83
6	$50(1 + 0.04)^6$ $50(1.04)^6$ $50(1.265319019)$	$63.27
7	$50(1 + 0.04)^7$ $50(1.04)^7$ $50(1.315931779)$	$65.80
8	$50(1 + 0.04)^8$ $50(1.04)^8$ $50(1.36856905)$	$68.43
9	$50(1 + 0.04)^9$ $50(1.04)^9$ $50(1.423311812)$	$71.17

1. What is the first year the new price rises to $65 or more? **year 7**
2. What is the difference in price from Year 0 to Year 1? **$2.00**
3. What is the difference in price from Year 8 to Year 9? **$2.74**
4. If the inflation rate were 6%, what would be the first year the price of the game rises to $65 or more? **5 years**
5. Find the lowest percent inflation rate (to the nearest whole number) at which the game price would reach $100 or more in only 5 years. **15%**

COMMON ERROR ALERT

In **Exercise 64,** students may multiply the number of heads by 2 and the number of tails by 3. Encourage students to write each score in a list as it is doubled or tripled from the previous score.

Teaching Tip **Multiple Choice** In **Exercise 67,** students may not recognize that powers with different bases and exponents may have the same value. Suggest that students first simplify the expressions given in choices **A, C,** and **D.**

Journal

Explain why the value of a power is not always greater than its base. Use examples in your explanation.

ALTERNATIVE ASSESSMENT

Have students write and simplify each of the following: a power containing a positive base with an odd exponent; a power containing a negative base with an odd exponent; a power containing a positive base with an even exponent; and a power containing a negative base with an even exponent.

Power Presentations with PowerPoint®

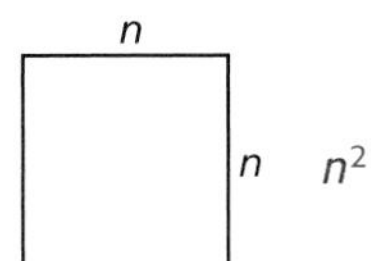

1-4 Lesson Quiz

1. Write the power represented by the geometric model. n n n^2

Simplify each expression.

2. $\left(-\frac{1}{8}\right)^3$ $-\frac{1}{512}$ 3. -6^3 −216

4. 6^3 216 5. $(-2)^6$ 64

Write each number as a power of the given base.

6. 343; base 7 7^3

7. 10,000; base 10 10^4

Also available on transparency

1-5 Organizer

Objectives: Evaluate expressions containing roots.

Classify numbers within the real number system.

Algebra Lab
In *Chapter 1 Resource File*

Online Edition
Tutorial Videos, Interactivity

Countdown to Mastery Week 2

Power Presentations with PowerPoint®

Warm Up

Simplify each expression.

1. 6^2 36 **2.** 11^2 121

3. $(-9)(-9)$ 81 **4.** $\left(\frac{5}{6}\right)\left(\frac{5}{6}\right)$ $\frac{25}{36}$

Write each fraction as a decimal.

5. $\frac{2}{5}$ 0.4 **6.** $\frac{5}{9}$ $0.\overline{5}$

7. $5\frac{3}{8}$ 5.375 **8.** $-1\frac{5}{6}$ $-1.8\overline{3}$

Also available on transparency

Math Humor

Teacher: What kind of roots does a "geom-e-tree" have?
Student: Square roots!

California Standards
Algebra 1 🔑 **2.0**

1-5 Roots and Irrational Numbers

California Standards

🔑 **2.0 Students understand and use such operations as** taking the opposite, finding the reciprocal, **taking a root**, and raising to a fractional power. They understand and use the rules of exponents.

Vocabulary
square root
principal square root
perfect square
cube root
natural numbers
whole numbers
integers
rational numbers
terminating decimal
repeating decimal
irrational numbers

Why learn this?

Square roots can be used to find the side length of a square garden when you know its area. (See Example 3.)

A number that is multiplied by itself to form a product is a **square root** of that product. The radical symbol $\sqrt{\ }$ is used to represent square roots. For nonnegative numbers, the operations of squaring and finding a square root are inverse operations. In other words, for $x \geq 0$, $\sqrt{x} \cdot \sqrt{x} = x$.

Positive real numbers have two square roots. The **principal square root** of a number is the positive square root and is represented by $\sqrt{\ }$. A negative square root is represented by $-\sqrt{\ }$. The symbol $\pm\sqrt{\ }$ is used to represent both square roots.

$$4 \cdot 4 = 4^2 = 16 \longrightarrow \sqrt{16} = 4 \longleftarrow \text{Positive square root of 16}$$

$$(-4)(-4) = (-4)^2 = 16 \rightarrow -\sqrt{16} = -4 \leftarrow \text{Negative square root of 16}$$

A **perfect square** is a number whose positive square root is a whole number. Some examples of perfect squares are shown in the table.

0	1	4	9	16	25	36	49	64	81	100
0^2	1^2	2^2	3^2	4^2	5^2	6^2	7^2	8^2	9^2	10^2

A number that is raised to the third power to form a product is a **cube root** of that product. The symbol $\sqrt[3]{\ }$ indicates a cube root. Since $2^3 = 8$, $\sqrt[3]{8} = 2$. Similarly, the symbol $\sqrt[4]{\ }$ indicates a fourth root: $2^4 = 16$, so $\sqrt[4]{16} = 2$.

EXAMPLE 1 Finding Roots

Find each root.

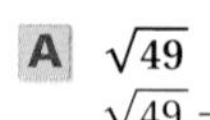

A $\sqrt{49}$

$\sqrt{49} = \sqrt{7^2}$ *Think: What number squared equals 49?*

$= 7$

B $-\sqrt{36}$

$-\sqrt{36} = -\sqrt{6^2}$ *Think: What number squared equals 36?*

$= -6$

C $\sqrt[3]{-125}$

$\sqrt[3]{-125} = \sqrt[3]{(-5^3)}$ *Think: What number cubed equals −125?*

$= -5$ *$(-5)(-5)(-5) = 25(-5) = -125$*

Writing Math

The small number to the left of the root is the *index*. In a square root, the index is understood to be 2. In other words, $\sqrt{\ }$ is the same as $\sqrt[2]{\ }$.

CHECK IT OUT! Find each root.

1a. $\sqrt{4}$ **2** **1b.** $-\sqrt{25}$ **−5** **1c.** $\sqrt[4]{81}$ **3**

1 Introduce

EXPLORATION

1-5 Roots and Irrational Numbers

Explore what happens when you square a set of numbers and then reverse the process.

1. Complete the table by squaring each number. One example has been filled in for you.

Number, n	1	2	3	4	5	6	7	8	9
Square of Number, n^2			9						

2. You can use the symbol $\sqrt{\ }$ to reverse the process. For example, $\sqrt{9} = 3$. Write additional mathematical statements using this symbol and the values in your table.

THINK AND DISCUSS

3. **Show** how you can write a new mathematical statement if you are given that fact that $17^2 = 289$.
4. **Describe** how you can find the value of $\sqrt{121}$.

Motivate

Tell students that you are going to carpet a square room that has an area of 65 square feet. Before you cut the carpet, you need to find the length of the sides. Ask students what must be true about the sides of a square room. Then ask if they think the length of the sides is greater or less than 8 feet.

Explorations and answers are provided in *Alternate Openers: Explorations Transparencies*.

EXAMPLE 2 Finding Roots of Fractions

Find $\sqrt{\frac{1}{4}}$.

$\frac{1}{2} \cdot \frac{1}{2} = \frac{1}{4}$ *Think: What number squared equals $\frac{1}{4}$?*

$\sqrt{\frac{1}{4}} = \frac{1}{2}$

CHECK IT OUT! Find each root.

2a. $\sqrt{\frac{4}{9}}$ **$\frac{2}{3}$** **2b.** $\sqrt[3]{\frac{1}{8}}$ **$\frac{1}{2}$** **2c.** $-\sqrt{\frac{4}{49}}$ **$-\frac{2}{7}$**

Square roots of numbers that are not perfect squares, such as 15, are not whole numbers. A calculator can approximate the value of $\sqrt{15}$ as 3.872983346... Without a calculator, you can use the square roots of perfect squares to help estimate the square roots of other numbers.

EXAMPLE 3 *Gardening Application*

Nancy wants to plant a square garden of wildflowers. She has enough wildflower seeds to cover 19 ft². Estimate to the nearest tenth the side length of a square with an area of 19 ft².

Since the area of the square is 19 ft², then each side of the square is $\sqrt{19}$ ft. 19 is not a perfect square, so find the two consecutive perfect squares that 19 is between: 16 and 25. $\sqrt{19}$ is between $\sqrt{16}$ and $\sqrt{25}$, or 4 and 5. Refine the estimate.

4.3:	$4.3^2 = 18.49$	too low	*$\sqrt{19}$ is greater than 4.3.*
4.4:	$4.4^2 = 19.36$	too high	*$\sqrt{19}$ is less than 4.4.*
4.35:	$4.35^2 = 18.9225$	too low	*$\sqrt{19}$ is greater than 4.35.*

Since 4.35 is too low and 4.4 is too high, $\sqrt{19}$ is between 4.35 and 4.4. Rounded to the nearest tenth, $\sqrt{19} \approx 4.4$.

The side length of the plot is $\sqrt{19} \approx 4.4$ ft.

Writing Math

The symbol ≈ means "is approximately equal to."

CHECK IT OUT! **3. What if...?** Nancy decides to buy more wildflower seeds and now has enough to cover 26 ft². Estimate to the nearest tenth the side length of a square with an area of 26 ft². **about 5.1 ft**

Writing Math

To show that one or more digits repeat continuously, write a bar over those digits.
$1.333333333... = 1.\overline{3}$
$2.14141414... = 2.\overline{14}$

Real numbers can be classified according to their characteristics.

Natural numbers are the counting numbers: 1, 2, 3, ...

Whole numbers are the natural numbers and zero: 0, 1, 2, 3, ...

Integers are the whole numbers and their opposites: −3, −2, −1, 0, 1, 2, 3, ...

Rational numbers are numbers that can be expressed in the form $\frac{a}{b}$, where a and b are both integers and $b \neq 0$. When expressed as a decimal, a rational number is either a *terminating decimal* or a *repeating decimal.*

- A **terminating decimal** has a finite number of digits after the decimal point (for example, 1.25, 2.75, and 4.0).
- A **repeating decimal** has a block of one or more digits after the decimal point that repeat continuously (where all digits are not zeros).

2 Teach

Guided Instruction

Review squaring and cubing numbers before finding square roots and cube roots. When presenting square roots, show why (within the real numbers) there cannot be a negative number under the radical symbol. Ask students to think of a number that when multiplied by itself equals a negative number. Point out how this differs from cube roots, in which there can be a negative number under the radical symbol because a negative number cubed equals a negative number.

Universal Access

Through Graphic Organizers

Prior to class, prepare a list of rational and irrational numbers, including repeating decimals, terminating decimals, and the square roots of non-perfect squares. In class, have students discuss where to place each of the numbers in the following table.

Rational Numbers		Irrational Numbers
Terminating Decimals	Repeating Decimals	

Power Presentations with PowerPoint®

Additional Examples

Example 1

Find each root.

A. $\sqrt{81}$ 9 **B.** $-\sqrt{25}$ −5

C. $\sqrt[3]{-216}$ −6

Example 2

Find each root.

A. $\sqrt{\frac{49}{9}}$ $\frac{7}{3}$ **B.** $\sqrt[3]{\frac{8}{125}}$ $\frac{2}{5}$

C. $-\sqrt{\frac{4}{25}}$ $-\frac{2}{5}$

Example 3

As part of her art project, Shonda will need to make a paper square covered in glitter. Her tube of glitter covers 13 in². Estimate to the nearest tenth the side length of a square with an area of 13 in².

≈3.6 in.

Also available on transparency

INTERVENTION

Questioning Strategies

EXAMPLE 1

- What is the difference between and $-\sqrt{36}$ and $\sqrt{-36}$?
- What are some examples of integers that are not perfect squares?

EXAMPLE 2

- How are the numerators in the answers related to the numerators in the problems? What about the denominators?

EXAMPLE 3

- How can you choose two consecutive whole numbers that the square root of a non-perfect square falls between?

Teaching Tip **Reading Math** Have students read the problem in **Example 3.** Then ask them to identify the information in the problem that will be essential in finding the solution.

Teaching Tip **Technology** Students can verify their answers in **Example 3** by using a calculator to find the roots. Be sure to emphasize that the calculator's answer, even though it has several decimal places, is still only an approximation.

Power Presentations with PowerPoint®

Additional Examples

Example 4

Write all classifications that apply to each number.

A. -32 rational number, integer, terminating decimal

B. $-\sqrt{14}$ irrational number

Also available on transparency

Teaching Tip **Language Support** When teaching the definition of terminating decimal, be sure students know the meaning and pronunciation of *finite*. Some students may be familiar with the concept of infinity. If so, you can point out that *infinite* is the opposite of *finite*.

INTERVENTION

Questioning Strategies

EXAMPLE 4

- How can you recognize repeating decimals and terminating decimals?
- If you know that a number is a natural number, what other classifications automatically apply to that number?
- Which classifications do not include negative numbers?

Irrational numbers are all numbers that are not rational. They cannot be expressed in the form $\frac{a}{b}$ where a and b are both integers and $b \neq 0$. They are neither terminating decimals nor repeating decimals. For example:

0.10100100010000100000... *After the decimal point, this number contains 1 followed by one 0, and then 1 followed by two 0's, and then 1 followed by three 0's, and so on.*

This decimal neither terminates nor repeats, so it is an irrational number.

If a whole number is not a perfect square, then its square root is irrational. For example, 2 is not a perfect square, and $\sqrt{2}$ is irrational.

The real numbers are made up of all rational and irrational numbers.

Know it! Note

Reading Math

Note the symbols for the sets of numbers.
ℝ: real numbers
ℚ: rational numbers
ℤ: integers
𝕎: whole numbers
ℕ: natural numbers

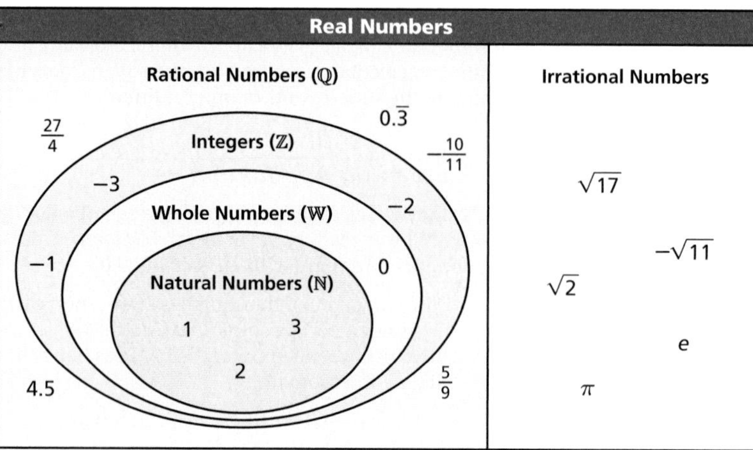

EXAMPLE 4 Classifying Real Numbers

Write all classifications that apply to each real number.

A $\frac{8}{9}$

$\frac{8}{9}$ *is in the form* $\frac{a}{b}$, *where a and b are integers and* $b \neq 0$.

$8 \div 9 = 0.8888\ldots$

$= 0.\overline{8}$ $\frac{8}{9}$ *can be written as a repeating decimal.*

rational, repeating decimal

B 18

$18 = \frac{18}{1}$ *18 can be written in the form* $\frac{a}{b}$.

$18 = 18.0$ *18 can be written as a terminating decimal.*

rational, terminating decimal, integer, whole, natural

C $\sqrt{20}$

irrational   *20 is not a perfect square, so* $\sqrt{20}$ *is irrational.*

CHECK IT OUT! **Write all classifications that apply to each real number.**

4a. $7\frac{4}{9}$ ℚ, rep. dec.

4b. -12 ℚ, term. dec., ℤ

4c. $\sqrt{10}$ irr.

4d. $\sqrt{100}$ ℕ, 𝕎, ℤ, ℚ, term. dec.

3 Close

Summarize

Link the finding of square roots to the different subsets of the real numbers by asking students to think of a number whose square root is

- an integer
- a rational number, but not an integer
- an irrational number

FORMATIVE ASSESSMENT

and INTERVENTION

***Diagnose Before* the Lesson**
1-5 Warm Up, TE p. 32

***Monitor During* the Lesson**
Check It Out! Exercises, SE pp. 32–34
Questioning Strategies, TE pp. 33–34

***Assess After* the Lesson**
1-5 Lesson Quiz, TE p. 37
Alternative Assessment, TE p. 37

THINK AND DISCUSS

1. Write $\frac{2}{3}$ and $\frac{3}{5}$ as decimals. Identify what number classifications the two numbers share and how their classifications are different.
2. **GET ORGANIZED** Copy the graphic organizer and use the flowchart to classify each of the given numbers. Write each number in the box with the most specific classification that applies. 4, $\sqrt{25}$, 0, $\frac{1}{3}$, −15, −2.25, $\frac{1}{4}$, $\sqrt{21}$, 2^4, $(-1)^2$

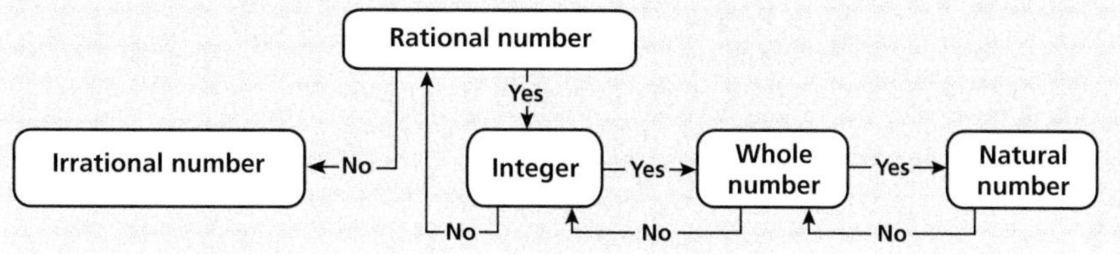

Answers to *Think and Discuss*

1. $\frac{2}{3} = 0.\overline{6}$; $\frac{3}{5} = 0.6$; both numbers are rational. $\frac{2}{3}$ is a repeating decimal; $\frac{3}{5}$ is a terminating decimal.
2. See p. A2.

1-5 Exercises

2.0

Homework Help Online
KEYWORD: MA8CA 1-5
Parent Resources Online
KEYWORD: MA8CA Parent

GUIDED PRACTICE

1. **Vocabulary** Give an example of a *square root* that is not a *rational number*. **Possible answer: $\sqrt{3}$**

SEE EXAMPLE 1 p. 32

Find each root.

2. $\sqrt{64}$ **8**
3. $-\sqrt{225}$ **−15**
4. $\sqrt[3]{-64}$ **−4**
5. $\sqrt[4]{625}$ **5**
6. $\sqrt{81}$ **9**
7. $-\sqrt[3]{27}$ **−3**
8. $-\sqrt[3]{-27}$ **3**
9. $-\sqrt{16}$ **−4**

SEE EXAMPLE 2 p. 33

10. $\sqrt{\frac{1}{16}}$ **$\frac{1}{4}$**
11. $\sqrt[3]{\frac{8}{27}}$ **$\frac{2}{3}$**
12. $-\sqrt{\frac{1}{9}}$ **$-\frac{1}{3}$**
13. $\sqrt{\frac{9}{64}}$ **$\frac{3}{8}$**
14. $\sqrt{\frac{1}{36}}$ **$\frac{1}{6}$**
15. $\sqrt[3]{\frac{1}{64}}$ **$\frac{1}{4}$**
16. $-\sqrt{\frac{4}{81}}$ **$-\frac{2}{9}$**
17. $\sqrt[3]{-\frac{1}{125}}$ **$-\frac{1}{5}$**

SEE EXAMPLE 3 p. 33

18. A contractor is told that a potential client's kitchen floor is in the shape of a square. The area of the floor is 45 ft^2. Estimate to the nearest tenth the side length of the floor. **about 6.7 ft**

SEE EXAMPLE 4 p. 34

Write all classifications that apply to each real number.

19. −27 **$\mathbb{Q}$, term. dec., $\mathbb{Z}$**
20. $\frac{1}{6}$ **$\mathbb{Q}$, rep. dec.**
21. $\sqrt{33}$ **irr.**
22. −6.8 **$\mathbb{Q}$, term. dec.**

PRACTICE AND PROBLEM SOLVING

Find each root.

23. $\sqrt{121}$ **11**
24. $\sqrt[3]{-1000}$ **−10**
25. $-\sqrt{100}$ **−10**
26. $\sqrt[4]{256}$ **4**
27. $\sqrt{\frac{1}{25}}$ **$\frac{1}{5}$**
28. $\sqrt[4]{\frac{1}{16}}$ **$\frac{1}{2}$**
29. $\sqrt[3]{-\frac{1}{8}}$ **$-\frac{1}{2}$**
30. $-\sqrt{\frac{25}{36}}$ **$-\frac{5}{6}$**
31. A new house will have a foundation in the shape of a square. The house will cover 222 square yards. Estimate to the nearest tenth the length of one side of the house. **about 14.9 yd**

1-5 Exercises

Assignment Guide

Assign *Guided Practice* exercises as necessary.

If you finished Examples **1–2**
Proficient 23–30, 36–40, 52
Advanced 23–30, 36–40, 52, 57–64

If you finished Examples **1–4**
Proficient 23–60, 66–75
Advanced 15–41 odd, 42–67

Homework Quick Check
Quickly check key concepts.
Exercises: 25, 29, 31, 33, 35, 36

Reading Math Students may need practice reading roots. If so, ask them to read some of the exercises aloud. For example, **Exercise 2** reads "the square root of 64." **Exercise 4** is "the cube root of −64" and **Exercise 5** is "the fourth root of 625."

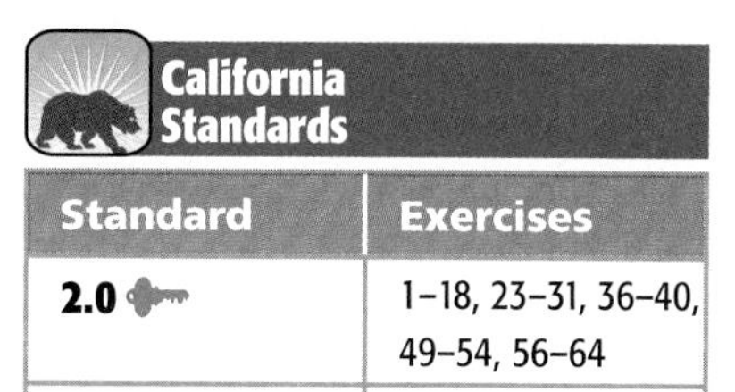

Standard	Exercises
2.0	1–18, 23–31, 36–40, 49–54, 56–64
7NS1.2	66–71

Exercise 50 involves using the Pythagorean Theorem to determine the distance of a diver from a boat. This exercise prepares students for the Concept Connection on page 40.

Inclusion For **Exercises 41–44,** you may want to remind students of the formula relating distance, rate, and time: $d = rt$.

Answers

41. 45; $\mathbb{Q}$, term. dec., $\mathbb{Z}$, $\mathbb{W}$, $\mathbb{N}$
42. $38.\overline{740}$; $\mathbb{Q}$, rep. dec.
43. 34.625; $\mathbb{Q}$, term. dec.
44. $47.\overline{1}$; $\mathbb{Q}$, rep. dec.
49. Possible answer: No; a pos. number has only one cube root because a neg. number cubed results in a neg. number. A pos. number has two fourth roots because a neg. number raised to the fourth power results in a pos. number.

Independent Practice	
For Exercises	See Example
23–26	1
27–30	2
31	3
32–35	4

Extra Practice
Skills Practice p. EP3
Application Practice p. EP24

Write all classifications that apply to each real number.

32. $\frac{5}{12}$ $\mathbb{Q}$, rep. dec. 33. $\sqrt{49}$ 34. -3 35. $\sqrt{18}$ irr.

33. $\mathbb{Q}$, term. dec., $\mathbb{Z}$, $\mathbb{W}$, $\mathbb{N}$

34. $\mathbb{Q}$, term. dec., $\mathbb{Z}$

36. **Geometry** The cube root of the volume of a cube gives the length of one side of the cube.
 a. Find the side length of the cube shown. 7 cm
 b. Find the area of each face of the cube. 49 cm^2

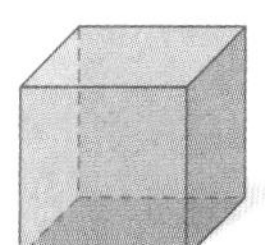

Volume = 343 cm^3

Compare. Write <, >, or =.

37. $8 \;\square\; \sqrt{63}$ > 38. $\sqrt{88} \;\square\; 9$ > 39. $6 \;\square\; \sqrt{40}$ < 40. $\sqrt{\frac{9}{25}} \;\square\; 0.61$ <

Travel During a cross-country road trip, Madeline recorded the distance between several major cities and the time it took her to travel between those cities. Find Madeline's average speed for each leg of the trip and classify that number.

Portland Boise Denver Portland Memphis

Madeline's Cross-Country Road Trip

		Distance (mi)	Time (h)	Speed (mi/h)	Classification
41.	Portland, ME, to Memphis, TN	1485	33		
42.	Memphis, TN, to Denver, CO	1046	27		
43.	Denver, CO, to Boise, ID	831	24		
44.	Boise, ID, to Portland, OR	424	9		

Reasoning Determine whether each statement is sometimes, always, or never true. If it is sometimes true, give one example that makes the statement true and one example that makes it false. If it is always true, explain. If it is never true, rewrite the statement so that it is always true.

45. Mixed numbers are rational numbers. Always; mixed numbers can be written as improper fractions.
46. The decimal form of an irrational number is a repeating decimal.
47. A terminating decimal is a rational number.
48. A negative number is irrational. Sometimes; $-\sqrt{2}$ is irrational, but -6.2 is rational.
49. **Critical Thinking** A positive number has two square roots, one that is positive and one that is negative. Is the same thing true for the cube root of a positive number? What about the fourth root of a positive number? Explain.

46. Never; the dec. form of an irrational number is a nonterminating, nonrepeating decimal.

47. Always; every term. dec. can be written as a fraction whose denom. is a power of 10.

CONCEPT CONNECTION

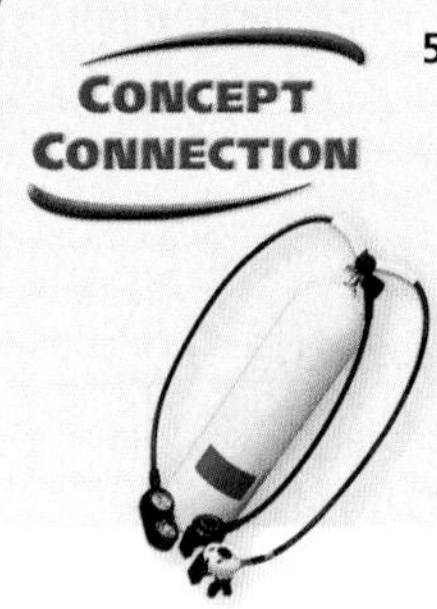

50. This problem will prepare you for the Concept Connection on page 40.
 The equation $a^2 + b^2 = c^2$ relates the lengths of the sides of a right triangle. Sides a and b make the right angle of the triangle.
 a. What is the value of c^2 when $a = 5$ and $b = 12$? Determine the square root of c^2 to find the value of c. 169; 13
 b. A diver is a horizontal distance of 50 feet from a boat and 120 feet beneath the surface of the water. What distance will the diver swim if he swims diagonally to the boat? 130 ft

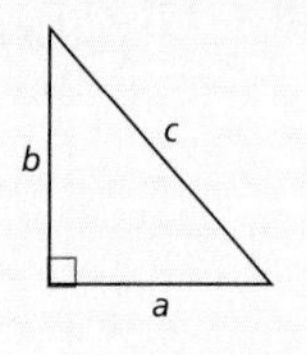

1-5 PRACTICE A
1-5 PRACTICE C
1-5 PRACTICE B

LESSON 1-5 **Practice B**
Roots and Irrational Numbers

Find each square root.

1. $\sqrt{144}$ 12
2. $-\sqrt{36}$ -6
3. $\sqrt{\frac{1}{49}}$ $\frac{1}{7}$
4. $\sqrt{196}$ 14
5. $-\sqrt{64}$ -8
6. $-\sqrt{\frac{4}{25}}$ $-\frac{2}{5}$
7. $\sqrt[3]{27}$ 3
8. $-\sqrt[3]{\frac{8}{125}}$ $-\frac{2}{5}$
9. $\sqrt[4]{\frac{1}{256}}$ 4
10. A contractor needs to cut a piece of glass to fit a square window. The area of the window is 12 ft^2. Find the length of the side of the window to the nearest tenth of a foot. 3.5 feet
11. A piece of cloth must be cut to exactly cover a square table. The area of the table is 27 ft^2. Find the length of the side of the table to the nearest tenth of a foot. 5.2 feet

Write all the classifications that apply to each real number.

12. $\sqrt{2}$ irrational
13. $\frac{2}{3}$ Q, repeating decimal
14. -10 Z, Q, terminating decimal
15. $\sqrt{81}$ N, W, Z, Q, terminating decimal
16. 0 W, Z, Q, terminating decimal
17. 1 N, W, Z, Q, terminating decimal

1-5 READING STRATEGIES

LESSON 1-5 **Reading Strategies**
Understanding Relationships

The flow chart below can help you understand the relationships among different subsets of the real numbers.

Real Numbers: 2.7, −4, 0, 8, $\frac{2}{3}$, $\sqrt{5}$
Rational: 2.7, −4, 0, 8, $\frac{2}{3}$
Irrational: $\sqrt{5}$
Terminating Decimal: 2.7, −4, 0, 8
Repeating Decimal: $\frac{2}{3} = 0.\overline{6}$
Integer: −4, 0, 8
Whole: 0, 8
Natural: 8

Answer true or false for each statement.

1. Real numbers are either rational or irrational. true
2. An irrational number can be a repeating decimal. false
3. Whole numbers include negative numbers. false
4. The number 12 is an integer. true
5. The only integer not included in the natural numbers is 0. false
6. Irrational numbers are not real numbers. false
7. The fraction $\frac{1}{2}$ can be written as a terminating decimal. true
8. All integers are rational numbers. true

1-5 REVIEW FOR MASTERY

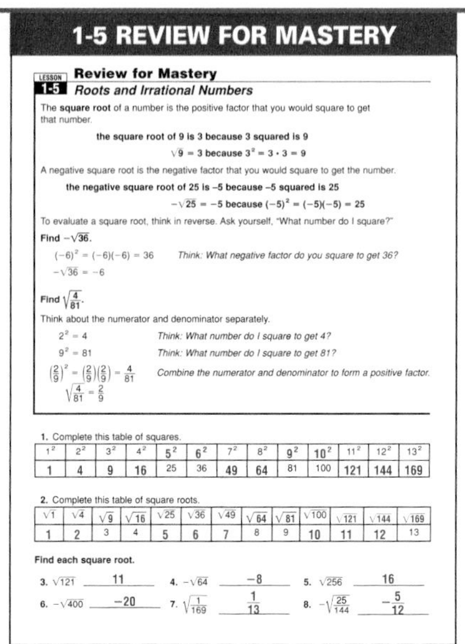

LESSON 1-5 **Review for Mastery**
Roots and Irrational Numbers

The **square root** of a number is the positive factor that you would square to get that number.

the square root of 9 is 3 because 3 squared is 9
$\sqrt{9} = 3$ because $3^2 = 3 \cdot 3 = 9$

A negative square root is the negative factor that you would square to get the number.

the negative square root of 25 is −5 because −5 squared is 25
$-\sqrt{25} = -5$ because $(-5)^2 = (-5)(-5) = 25$

To evaluate a square root, think in reverse. Ask yourself, "What number do I square?"

Find $-\sqrt{36}$.
$(-6)^2 = (-6)(-6) = 36$ *Think: What negative factor do you square to get 36?*
$-\sqrt{36} = -6$

Find $\sqrt{\frac{4}{81}}$.
Think about the numerator and denominator separately.
$2^2 = 4$ *Think: What number do I square to get 4?*
$9^2 = 81$ *Think: What number do I square to get 81?*
$\left(\frac{2}{9}\right)^2 = \left(\frac{2}{9}\right)\left(\frac{2}{9}\right) = \frac{4}{81}$ *Combine the numerator and denominator to form a positive factor.*
$\sqrt{\frac{4}{81}} = \frac{2}{9}$

1. Complete this table of squares.

1^2	2^2	3^2	4^2	5^2	6^2	7^2	8^2	9^2	10^2	11^2	12^2	13^2
1	4	9	16	25	36	49	64	81	100	121	144	169

2. Complete this table of square roots.

$\sqrt{1}$	$\sqrt{4}$	$\sqrt{9}$	$\sqrt{16}$	$\sqrt{25}$	$\sqrt{36}$	$\sqrt{49}$	$\sqrt{64}$	$\sqrt{81}$	$\sqrt{100}$	$\sqrt{121}$	$\sqrt{144}$	$\sqrt{169}$
1	2	3	4	5	6	7	8	9	10	11	12	13

Find each square root.

3. $\sqrt{121}$ 11
4. $-\sqrt{64}$ -8
5. $\sqrt{256}$ 16
6. $-\sqrt{400}$ -20
7. $\sqrt{\frac{1}{169}}$ $\frac{1}{13}$
8. $-\sqrt{\frac{25}{144}}$ $-\frac{5}{12}$

51. **Entertainment** In a board game, players place different-colored stones on a grid. Each player tries to make rows of 5 or more stones in their color while preventing their opponent(s) from doing the same. The square game board has 324 squares on it. How many squares are on each side of the board? **18**

52. **Write About It** Explain why you cannot take the square root of a negative number but you can take the cube root of a negative number.

52. Possible answer: There is no number that when squared results in a neg. number, but when you cube a neg. number, the result is a neg. number.

Multiple Choice For Exercises 53–56, choose the best answer.

53. Which point on the number line is closest to $-\sqrt{11}$?

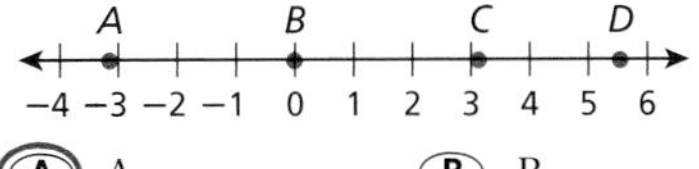

Ⓐ A (circled) Ⓑ B Ⓒ C Ⓓ D

54. What is the area of the figure at right?

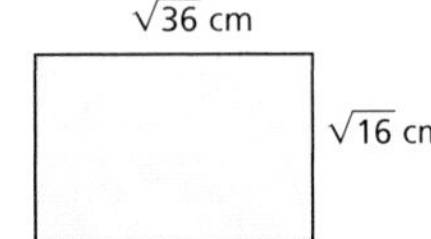

Ⓐ 24 cm^2 (circled) Ⓒ 104 cm^2
Ⓑ 52 cm^2 Ⓓ 576 cm^2

55. Which number is irrational?

Ⓐ $-\sqrt{9}$ Ⓒ 4.0005
Ⓑ $2.\overline{17}$ Ⓓ $\sqrt{40}$ (circled)

56. The square root of 175 is between which two whole numbers?

Ⓐ 11 and 12 Ⓑ 12 and 13 Ⓒ 13 and 14 (circled) Ⓓ 14 and 15

CHALLENGE AND EXTEND

Find each root.

57. $\sqrt{0.81}$ **0.9** 58. $\sqrt{0.25}$ **0.5** 59. $\sqrt[3]{-0.001}$ **−0.1** 60. $\sqrt{2.25}$ **1.5**

Evaluate each expression for $a = 9$ and $b = 7$.

61. $\sqrt{a+b}$ **4** 62. $b\sqrt{a} - a$ **12** 63. $\sqrt[4]{b+a} + ab$ **65** 64. $\sqrt{ab+1}$ **8**

65. **Reasoning** The *Density Property of Real Numbers* states that between any two real numbers, there is another real number.
   a. Does the set of integers have this property? Explain.
   b. Use the Density Property to write a convincing argument that there are infinitely many real numbers between 0 and 1.

65a. No; possible answer: there are no integers between 1 and 2.

65b. Possible answer: Between 0 and 1, there is another real number *r*. Between 0 and *r*, there is another real number *q*. Between 0 and *q*, there is another real number *s*, and so on. Therefore, there must be infinitely many real numbers between 0 and 1.

SPIRAL STANDARDS REVIEW

7NS1.2

Add or subtract. *(Lesson 1-2)*

66. $-14 + (-16)$ **−30** 67. $-\frac{1}{4} - \left(-\frac{3}{4}\right)$ $\frac{1}{2}$ 68. $25 - 17.6$ **7.4**

Multiply or divide. *(Lesson 1-3)*

69. $\frac{1}{8} \div \left(-\frac{2}{3}\right)$ $-\frac{3}{16}$ 70. $(-2.5)(-8)$ **20** 71. $-\frac{21}{6}$ $-\frac{7}{2}$

Simplify each expression. *(Lesson 1-4)*

72. -3^4 **−81** 73. $\left(-\frac{2}{5}\right)^3$ $-\frac{8}{125}$ 74. 14^2 **196** 75. 4^3 **64**

COMMON ERROR ALERT

In **Exercises 57–60,** students may place the decimal point incorrectly. The square root of a decimal number will have half as many digits after the decimal point as the number under the radical.

$\sqrt{1.5129} = 1.23$

4 decimal places 2 decimal places

Students can check their answer by squaring it; they should get the number under the radical symbol.

Multiple Choice If students answered **D** for **Exercise 54,** they may have multiplied 36 by 16. Tell students to simplify the numbers in the diagram before finding the area.

Journal

Have students explain how to estimate the square root of a number that is not a perfect square.

ALTERNATIVE ASSESSMENT

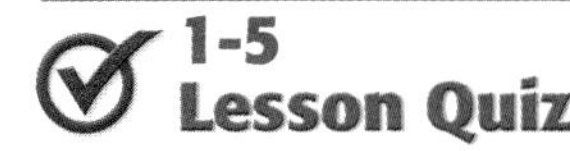

Have students write and solve their own word problems involving the dimensions of a square. Then have them define and give examples of rational numbers and irrational numbers.

Power Presentations with PowerPoint®

1-5 Lesson Quiz

Find each root.

1. $\sqrt{9}$ 3
2. $-\sqrt{\frac{1}{81}}$ $-\frac{1}{9}$
3. $\sqrt[3]{125}$ 5
4. $\sqrt[4]{1}$ 1
5. The area of a square piece of cloth is 68 in^2. Estimate to the nearest tenth the side length of the cloth. ≈ 8.2 in.

Write all classifications that apply to each real number.

6. $-3.\overline{89}$ rational, repeating decimal
7. $\sqrt{500}$ irrational

Also available on transparency

1-5 PROBLEM SOLVING

LESSON 1-5 **Problem Solving**
Roots and Irrational Numbers

1. Jack is building a square pen for his dog. If he wants the area of the pen to be 121 square feet, how long should he make each side of the pen?
   11 ft

2. A cube-shaped box has a volume of 15 ft^3. Estimate the length of one edge to the nearest tenth.
   2.5 ft

3. The Statue of Liberty, which sits on Liberty Island in New York Harbor, is $151\frac{1}{12}$ feet high, from base to torch. Write all classifications that apply to $151\frac{1}{12}$: natural, whole, integer, rational, terminating decimal, repeating decimal, and irrational.
   rational number
   repeating decimal

4. A square note card has an area of 5 in^2. Estimate the length of the side to the nearest tenth. Then write all classifications that apply to the actual side length: natural, whole, integer, rational, terminating decimal, repeating decimal, and irrational.
   2.2
   irrational

Use the table below to answer questions 5–7, which shows the area of four sizes of square-shaped pizzas sold at Town Pizza. Complete the table by finding the length of each side of the four pizzas. Round to the nearest tenth if needed. Select the best answer.

Pizza Size	Area (in^2)	Side length (in.)
Small	100	10
Medium	200	14.1
Large	420.25	20.5
Extra Large	576	24

5. What is the length of each side of an extra large pizza?
   Ⓐ 24 in. (circled) C 26 in.
   B 25 in. D 36 in.

6. Which of the following classifications applies to the length of each side of a large pizza?
   F natural H integer
   G whole Ⓙ rational (circled)

7. Which of the following is NOT a classification for the length of each side of a small pizza?
   A whole C rational
   Ⓑ irrational (circled) D integer

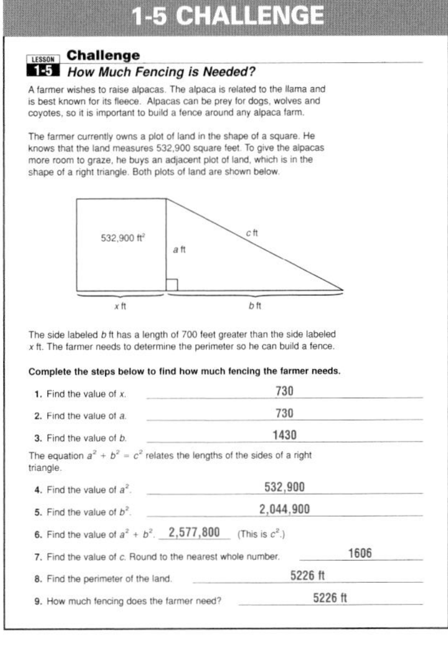

1-5 CHALLENGE

LESSON 1-5 **Challenge**
How Much Fencing is Needed?

A farmer wishes to raise alpacas. The alpaca is related to the llama and is best known for its fleece. Alpacas can be prey for dogs, wolves and coyotes, so it is important to build a fence around any alpaca farm.

The farmer currently owns a plot of land in the shape of a square. He knows that the land measures 532,900 square feet. To give the alpacas more room to graze, he buys an adjacent plot of land, which is in the shape of a right triangle. Both plots of land are shown below.

532,900 ft²
a ft
c ft
x ft
b ft

The side labeled *b* ft has a length of 700 feet greater than the side labeled *x* ft. The farmer needs to determine the perimeter so he can build a fence.

Complete the steps below to find how much fencing the farmer needs.

1. Find the value of *x*. 730
2. Find the value of *a*. 730
3. Find the value of *b*. 1430

The equation $a^2 + b^2 = c^2$ relates the lengths of the sides of a right triangle.

4. Find the value of a^2. 532,900
5. Find the value of b^2. 2,044,900
6. Find the value of $a^2 + b^2$. 2,577,800 (This is c^2.)
7. Find the value of *c*. Round to the nearest whole number. 1606
8. Find the perimeter of the land. 5226 ft
9. How much fencing does the farmer need? 5226 ft

Organizer

Objectives: Identify the hypothesis and conclusion in a conditional statement.
Find the converse of a conditional statement and determine whether it is true.

Online Edition
Student Edition

Countdown to Mastery Week 2

Teach

Discuss

Begin the discussion with non-mathematical "if-then" statements:

- If it rains, then we will not go hiking.
- If it is my birthday, then my parents give me a gift.

Have students practice identifying the hypothesis and conclusion.

Use these non-mathematical examples again when teaching the converse. Have students determine whether the converse of each non-mathematical statement is true.

California Standards

Algebra 1 24.2

Use with Lesson 1-5

Conditional Statements

A **conditional statement** is a statement that can be written in "if-then" form. The **hypothesis** is the part of the statement that follows *if*. The **conclusion** is the part of the statement that follows *then*.

24.2 Students identify the hypothesis and conclusion in logical deduction.

If a and b are real numbers, then $a + b$ is a real number.

Hypothesis: If a and b are real numbers — Conclusion: $a + b$ is a real number

Example 1

Identify the hypothesis and conclusion in each conditional statement.

1. **If a number is even, then the number is divisible by 2.**
   Hypothesis: A number is even. Conclusion: The number is divisible by 2.
2. **If a triangle has an obtuse angle, then the triangle is not a right triangle.**
   Hypothesis: A triangle has an obtuse angle. Conclusion: The triangle is not a right triangle.
3. **If a shape is a rectangle, then the shape has four right angles.**
   Hypothesis: A shape is a rectangle. Conclusion: The shape has four right angles.
4. **If two angles are vertical angles, then the angles are congruent.**
   Hypothesis: Two angles are vertical angles. Conclusion: The angles are congruent.

Try This

Identify the hypothesis and conclusion in each conditional statement.

1. If two lines are perpendicular, then the lines intersect.
2. If an angle is a right angle, then the angle measures 90°.
3. If two numbers are opposites, then the sum of the two numbers is zero.
4. If a number is a whole number, then the number is an integer.

Mathematical properties can often be written as conditional statements.

- Commutative Property of Addition: If a and b are real numbers, then $a + b = b + a$.
- Distributive Property: If a, b, and c are real numbers, then $a(b + c) = ab + ac$.

Try This

Write each mathematical property as a conditional statement.

5. Commutative Property of Multiplication
6. Associative Property of Addition
7. Associative Property of Multiplication

5. If a and b are real numbers, then $ab = ba$.
6. If a, b, and c are real numbers, then $(a + b) + c = a + (b + c)$.
7. If a, b, and c are real numbers, then $a(bc) = (ab)c$.

The **converse of a conditional statement** is formed by exchanging the hypothesis and the conclusion.

Conditional statement:

If a and b are real numbers, then $a + b$ is a real number.

Hypothesis: If a and b are real numbers — Conclusion: then $a + b$ is a real number.

Converse:

If $a + b$ is a real number, then a and b are real numbers.

Hypothesis: If $a + b$ is a real number — Conclusion: then a and b are real numbers.

A conditional statement may be true while its converse is false.

Example 2

Tell whether each conditional statement in Example 1 is true. Then find each statement's converse and tell whether the converse is true.

1. **If a number is even, then the number is divisible by 2.**
   True; all even numbers are divisible by 2.
   Converse: If a number is divisible by 2, then the number is even.
   True; a number that is divisible by 2 is defined to be even.

2. **If a triangle has an obtuse angle, then the triangle is not a right triangle.**
   True; if a triangle has an obtuse angle, then it cannot be a right triangle.
   Converse: If a triangle is not a right triangle, then the triangle has an obtuse angle.
   Not true; a triangle may have three acute angles.

3. **If a shape is a rectangle, then the shape has four right angles.**
   True; all rectangles have four right angles.
   Converse: If a shape has four right angles, then the shape is a rectangle.
   True; a shape with four right angles is defined to be a rectangle.

4. **If two angles are vertical angles, then the angles are congruent.**
   True; vertical angles are always congruent.
   Converse: If two angles are congruent, then the angles are vertical angles.
   Not true; two angles may be congruent without being vertical angles.

Try This

Tell whether each conditional statement is true. Then find each statement's converse and tell whether the converse is true.

8. If two lines are perpendicular, then the lines intersect.

9. If an angle is a right angle, then the angle measures 90°.

10. If two numbers are opposites, then the sum of the two numbers is zero.

11. If a number is a whole number, then the number is an integer.

Answers

8. yes; If two lines intersect, then the lines are perpendicular; no

9. yes; If an angle measures 90°, then the angle is a right angle; yes

10. yes; If the sum of two numbers is zero, then the numbers are opposites; yes

11. yes; If a number is an integer, then the number is a whole number; no

COMMON ERROR ALERT

Students are often confused by statements that are sometimes true. For instance, in **Example 2,** they may think the converse of statement 4 is true because the two angles *could be* vertical angles. Emphasize that in mathematics, a statement must *always* be true to be considered true; a "sometimes-true" statement is considered false.

Geometry In **Example 2,** students may think the converse of statement 3 is false, reasoning that the shape could be a square. Remind them that a square is also considered a rectangle.

Close

Key Concept

A conditional statement may be true, but that does not mean its converse is necessarily true.

Assess

Have students come up with three conditional statements. At least one of them must be a mathematical property. They should identify the hypothesis and conclusion and tell whether each conditional is true. Then they should find the converse of each statement and tell whether it is true.

Extend

Conditional statements are not always in "if-then" form. The words "if" and "then" may not even appear. For example, the statement "All triangles have 3 sides" is conditional and can be rewritten "If a shape is a triangle, then it has 3 sides." Ask students to rewrite the following conditionals in "if-then" form.

- A number is rational if it is an integer. If a number is an integer, then it is rational.
- Thanksgiving is always on Thursday. If today is Thanksgiving, then today is Thursday.

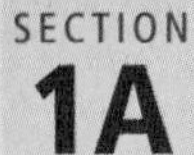

SECTION 1A

CONCEPT CONNECTION

Organizer

Objective: Assess students' ability to apply concepts and skills in Lesson 1-1 through Lesson 1-5 in a real-world format.

PREMIER Online Edition

Problem	Text Reference
1	Lesson 1-1
2	Lesson 1-2
3	Lesson 1-3
4	Lesson 1-4
5	Lesson 1-5

Answers

1.

Depth (ft)	Pressure (psi)
0	14.7
33	29.4
66	44.1
99	58.8
132	73.5

132 ft; continue the table until the pressure reaches 73.5 psi and then find the depth in that row of the table.

4. 6350.37 lb/ft^2; 44.09 psi; the pressure at 66 feet in the table is 44.1 psi, which is approximately the same as 44.09 psi.

California Standards

Algebra 1 2.0

CHAPTER 1 CONCEPT CONNECTION

SECTION 1A

The Language of Algebra

Under Pressure Atmospheric pressure is 14.7 pounds per square inch (psi). Underwater, the water exerts additional pressure. The total pressure on a diver underwater is the atmospheric pressure plus the water pressure.

1. As a diver moves downward in the water, the water pressure increases by 14.7 psi for approximately every 33 ft of water. Make a table to show the total pressure on a diver at 0, 33, 66, and 99 ft below the surface of the water. At what depth would the total pressure equal 73.5 psi? Explain your method.
2. A diver is 40 ft below the surface of the water when a hot-air balloon flies directly over her. The hot-air balloon is 849 ft above the surface of the water. Draw a diagram and write an expression to find the distance between the diver and the balloon when the balloon is directly above her. **$849 - (-40) = 889$ ft**

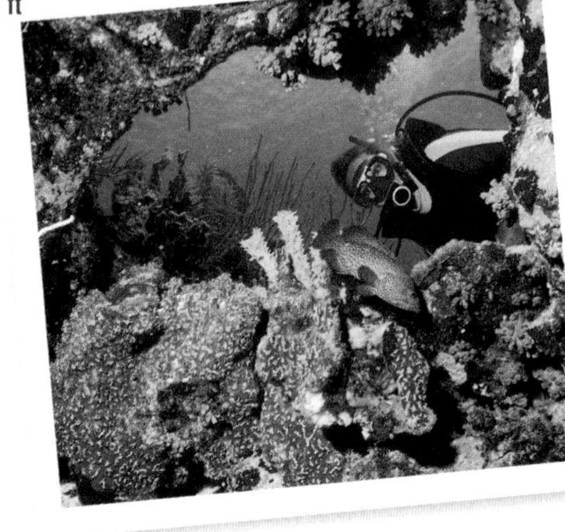

3. The diver swam 62.5 ft in 5 minutes. How fast was she swimming? What total distance will she have traveled after an additional 4 minutes if she maintains this same speed? **12.5 ft/min; 112.5 ft**
4. The total pressure on each square foot of the diver's body is given by the expression $2116.8 + 64.145d$, where d is the depth in feet. At a depth of 66 ft, what is the total pressure on each square foot of her body? What is the total pressure on each square *inch* of her body at this depth? How does your answer compare to your results for problem **1**?
5. The diver realizes that she has drifted horizontally about 30 ft from the boat she left. She is at a depth of 40 ft from the surface. What is the diver's diagonal distance from the boat? **50 ft**

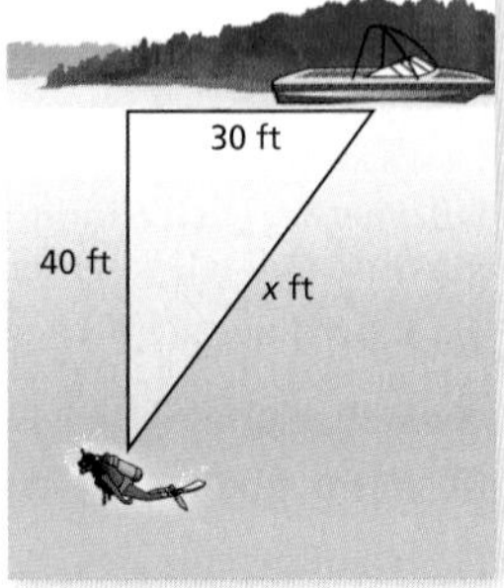

INTERVENTION

Scaffolding Questions

1. How do you decide which values to put in each column of the table? The values for depth are given, and they determine the values for pressure, so depth is in the 1st column, and pressure is in the 2nd column.
2. Can a distance be negative? No.
3. What is speed? a ratio of distance and time How can speed help you find a distance that is traveled? Use the formula $d = rt$.
4. How can you determine the number of square inches in a square foot? divide by 12^2
5. What type of triangle models the distance between the diver and her boat? a right triangle What formula can be used to find this distance? the Pythagorean Theorem

Extension

If the diver swims at a speed of 10 ft/s, how long will it take her to reach the boat? 5 s

CHAPTER 1

SECTION 1A

Quiz for Lessons 1-1 Through 1-5

1-1 Variables and Expressions

Give two ways to write each algebraic expression in words.

1. $4 + n$ 2. $m - 9$ 3. $\frac{g}{2}$ 4. $4z$

5. Bob earns \$15 per hour. Write an expression for the amount of money he earns in h hours. **$15h$**
6. A soccer practice is 90 minutes long. Write an expression for the number of minutes left after m minutes have elapsed. **$90 - m$**

Evaluate each expression for the replacement set {2, 3, 6}.

7. $y \div 2$ **$1; \frac{3}{2}; 3$** 8. $3y$ **6; 9; 18** 9. $3 + y$ **5; 6; 9** 10. $3 - y$ **1; 0; −3**

1-2 Adding and Subtracting Real Numbers

Add or subtract.

11. $81 + (-15)$ **66** 12. $27 - 32$ **−5** 13. $2 - \left(-1\frac{1}{4}\right)$ **$3\frac{1}{4}$** 14. $-7 + (-14)$ **−21**

15. Brandon's bank statement shows a balance of −\$45.00. What will the balance be after Brandon deposits \$70.00? **\$25.00**

1-3 Multiplying and Dividing Real Numbers

Find the value of each expression if possible.

16. $9(-9)$ **−81** 17. $6 \div \frac{3}{5}$ **10** 18. $9.6 \div 0$ **undefined** 19. $-\frac{1}{2}\left(-\frac{1}{2}\right)$ **$\frac{1}{4}$**

20. Simon drove for $2\frac{1}{2}$ hours to get from his house to the beach. Simon averaged 55 miles per hour on the trip. What is the distance from Simon's house to the beach? **137.5 mi**

1-4 Powers and Exponents

Simplify each expression.

21. $(-3)^2$ **9** 22. -3^2 **−9** 23. $\left(-\frac{2}{3}\right)^3$ **$-\frac{8}{27}$** 24. $\left(-\frac{1}{2}\right)^5$ **$-\frac{1}{32}$**

25. The number of bytes in a kilobyte is 2 to the 10th power. Express this number in two ways. **2^{10}; 1024**

1-5 Roots and Irrational Numbers

Find each root.

26. $\sqrt{225}$ **15** 27. $-\sqrt{49}$ **−7** 28. $\sqrt[3]{8}$ **2** 29. $\sqrt{\frac{16}{25}}$ **$\frac{4}{5}$**

30. Mindy is building a patio that is in the shape of a square. The patio will cover 56 square yards. Find the length of a side of the patio to the nearest tenth of a yard. **7.5 yd**

Write all classifications that apply to each real number.

31. $\frac{1}{11}$ 32. $\sqrt{12}$ 33. $\sqrt{900}$ 34. -6

31. $\mathbb{Q}$, repeating decimal
32. irrational number
33. $\mathbb{Q}$, terminating decimal, $\mathbb{Z}$, $\mathbb{W}$, $\mathbb{N}$
34. $\mathbb{Q}$, terminating decimal, $\mathbb{Z}$

READY TO GO ON? SECTION 1A

Organizer

Objective: Assess students' mastery of concepts and skills in Lessons 1-1 through 1-5.

Countdown to Mastery Week 2

Resources

Assessment Resources
Section 1A Quiz

Test & Practice Generator
One-Stop Planner®

INTERVENTION

Resources

***Ready to Go On? Intervention and Enrichment* Worksheets**

***Ready to Go On?* CD-ROM**

***Ready to Go On?* Online**

my.hrw.com

Answers

1–4. See p. A12.

READY TO GO ON? Diagnose and Prescribe

Ready to Go On? Intervention	READY TO GO ON? *Intervention*, Section 1A Worksheets	CD-ROM	Online
Lesson 1-1 Prep for 4.0	1-1 Intervention	Activity 1-1	Diagnose and Prescribe Online
Lesson 1-2 2.0	1-2 Intervention	Activity 1-2	
Lesson 1-3 2.0	1-3 Intervention	Activity 1-3	
Lesson 1-4 Prep for 2.0	1-4 Intervention	Activity 1-4	
Lesson 1-5 2.0	1-5 Intervention	Activity 1-5	

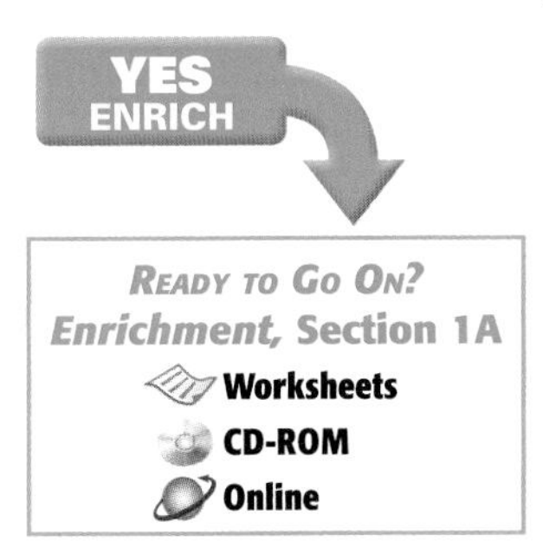

READY TO GO ON? *Enrichment*, Section 1A
Worksheets
CD-ROM
Online

The Tools of Algebra

One-Minute Section Planner

Lesson	Lab Resources	Materials
Lesson 1-6 Properties of Real Numbers • Identify and use properties of real numbers. • Use counterexamples to show that given statements are false. **1.0, 24.0, 24.3, 25.0, 25.1**		
Lesson 1-7 Simplifying Expressions • Use the order of operations and properties of the real number system to simplify expressions. • Combine like terms. **1.1, 25.0, 25.1**		**Optional** graphing calculator

MK = *Manipulatives Kit*

Notes

Math Background: Teaching the Standards

PROPERTIES 1.0, 25.2

Lesson 1-6

Students may have been introduced to properties of addition and multiplication, such as the Commutative, Associative, and Distributive Properties, as early as the elementary grades. At that time, students may have wondered why an "obvious fact" such as $3 \times 4 = 4 \times 3$ requires the complicated name *Commutative Property of Multiplication*.

In algebra, these properties have a key role as part of the underlying logical system that makes it possible to simplify expressions and solve equations. Consider the steps in simplifying the expression $2(x + 3) + x$.

1. $2(x + 3) + x$
2. $= (2x + 6) + x$
3. $= 2x + (6 + x)$
4. $= 2x + (x + 6)$
5. $= (2x + x) + 6$
6. $= 3x + 6$

Although several of these steps would most likely be eliminated in a typical classroom presentation, the details motivate the need for *general* versions of the Commutative, Associative, and Distributive Properties. One can easily verify a specific case of the Distributive Property, such as $4(5 + 1) = 4 \cdot 5 + 4 \cdot 1$, by using simple arithmetic. However, to go from Step 1 to Step 2 in the above process, one must know that $2(x + 3) = 2x + 6$ for any arbitrary value of x. This is precisely what the Distributive Property states: $a(b + c) = ab + ac$ for all real values of a, b, and c. Similarly, Steps 3 and 4 illustrate applications of the Associative and Commutative Properties, respectively.

CLOSURE 1.0

Lesson 1-6

A set is said to be *closed* under an operation if the result of the operation on any two elements in the set is also in the set. For example, the set of whole numbers is closed under addition since the sum of any two whole numbers is also a whole number.

In Algebra 1, closure is important because it offers one way to delineate subsets of the real numbers. For example, the whole numbers are not closed under subtraction (3 and 5 are whole numbers, but $3 - 5 = -2$, which is not a whole number); this suggests a need for the set of integers, which *is* closed under subtraction. In fact, the integers are called the *closure* of the whole numbers with respect to subtraction. Similarly, the rational numbers are the closure of the integers with respect to division.

EXAMPLES AND COUNTEREXAMPLES

24.3, 25.1

Lesson 1-6

As students develop their ability to think abstractly, they must become aware of what does and does not constitute a mathematical proof. In particular, students should understand that specific examples can never be used to prove a general mathematical statement. Based on the fact that $5 + 7 = 12$, $9 + 15 = 24$, and $13 + 49 = 62$, one might conclude that the sum of any two odd numbers is an even number, but the three examples do not form a proof. A more general argument using properties of numbers and operations is required.

Examples *can* be used to prove that a statement is false. In this case, only a single example, called a *counterexample*, is needed. The statement that all odd numbers are prime can be shown to be false with the counterexample of 15, a number that is odd but not prime.

ORDER OF OPERATIONS 25.2

Lesson 1-7

The order of operations is part of the grammatical structure of mathematical language. It provides an agreed-upon sequence of steps for evaluating numerical and algebraic expressions. Note that although the order of operations establishes a unique value for the expression $25 - 18 - 3$ (namely, 4), it may be preferable to write such expressions using parentheses, $(25 - 18) - 3$, to avoid any possible confusion.

1-6 Organizer

Objective: Use the order of operations to simplify expressions.

Online Edition
Tutorial Videos

Countdown to Mastery Week 2

Power Presentations with PowerPoint®

Warm Up

Add.

1. $-6 + (-4)$ -10
2. $17 + (-5)$ 12
3. $(-9) + 7$ -2

Subtract.

4. $12 - (-4)$ 16
5. $-3 - (-5)$ 2
6. $-7 - 15$ -22

Also available on transparency

Math Humor

Question: Why was everyone surprised to find out that the money was counterfeit?

Answer: It contained real numbers.

1-6 Properties of Real Numbers

California Standards

1.0 Students identify and use the arithmetic properties of subsets of integers and rational, irrational, and real numbers, including closure properties for the four basic arithmetic operations where applicable.
24.3 Students use counterexamples to show that an assertion is false and recognize that a single counterexample is sufficient to refute an assertion.
Also covered: **25.1**

Vocabulary
counterexample
closure

Who uses this?
Triathletes can use properties to calculate overall times mentally. (See Exercise 31.)

The Commutative and Associative Properties of Addition and Multiplication allow you to rearrange an expression.

Properties of Addition and Multiplication

WORDS	NUMBERS	ALGEBRA
Commutative Property You can add real numbers in any order. You can multiply real numbers in any order.	$2 + 7 = 7 + 2$ $3 \cdot 9 = 9 \cdot 3$	For real numbers a and b, $a + b = b + a$ $ab = ba$
Associative Property When you are only adding, changing the grouping will not change the sum. When you are only multiplying, changing the grouping will not change the product.	$(6 + 8) + 2 = 6 + (8 + 2)$ $(7 \cdot 4) \cdot 5 = 7 \cdot (4 \cdot 5)$	For real numbers a, b, and c, $(a + b) + c = a + (b + c)$ $(ab)c = a(bc)$

EXAMPLE 1 Identifying Properties

Name the property that is illustrated in each equation.

A $(4 + x) + y = 4 + (x + y)$

$(4 + x) + y = 4 + (x + y)$ *The grouping is different.*

Associative Property of Addition

B $-5 \cdot b = b \cdot (-5)$

$-5 \cdot b = b \cdot (-5)$ *The order is different.*

Commutative Property of Multiplication

C $2 + (6 + m) = 2 + (m + 6)$

$2 + (6 + m) = 2 + (m + 6)$ *The order is different.*

Commutative Property of Addition

Name the property that is illustrated in each equation.

1a. $n + (-7) = -7 + n$ **Comm. Prop. of Add.**

1b. $1.5 + (g + 2.3) = (1.5 + g) + 2.3$ **Assoc. Prop. of Add.**

1c. $(xy)z = (yx)z$ **Comm. Prop. of Mult.**

1 Introduce

EXPLORATION

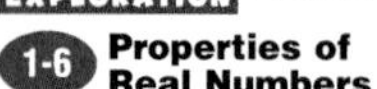

1-6 Properties of Real Numbers

The desks in a classroom are arranged in two sections as shown.

1. Write a product that gives the number of desks in Section A.
2. Write a product that gives the number of desks in Section B.
3. Now add the two products to get an expression for the total number of desks.
4. There is another way to find the total number of desks. First write a sum to find the total number of rows in the classroom. Then multiply this sum by the number of desks in each row.
5. Verify that the expressions you wrote in Steps 3 and 4 give the same total number of desks.
6. The Distributive Property states that $a(b + c) = ab + ac$. Explain how the above problem is an example of this property.

THINK AND DISCUSS

7. **Describe** how you can use the Distributive Property to simplify $7(8 + 4)$ in two different ways.
8. **Discuss** whether the Distributive Property works with subtraction. That is, it is true that $a(b - c) = ab - ac$?

Motivate

Write $18 + 17 + 2 + 3$ on the board. Ask students how they could use mental math to add these numbers. If no one suggests it, show students how changing the order and grouping the numbers differently can make it easier to perform the operations: $(18 + 2) + (17 + 3) = 20 + 20 = 40$. Tell students that this lesson will introduce properties that make it easier to do mental math.

Explorations and answers are provided in *Alternate Openers: Explorations Transparencies.*

California Standards

Algebra 1 1.0, 24.3
Also covered:
24.0 Students use and know simple aspects of a logical argument.
25.0 Students use properties of the number system to judge the validity of results, to justify each step of a procedure, and to prove or **disprove statements.**
25.1 Students use properties of numbers to construct simple, valid arguments (direct and indirect) for, or **formulate counterexamples to, claimed assertions.**

Student to Student

Commutative and Associative Properties

Lorna Anderson
Pearson High School

I used to get the Commutative and Associative Properties mixed up.

To remember the Commutative Property, I think of people commuting back and forth to work. When people commute, they move. I can move numbers around without changing the value of the expression.

For the Associative Property, I think of associating with my friends. They're the group I hang out with. In math, it's about how numbers are grouped.

The Commutative and Associative Properties are true for addition and multiplication. They may not be true for other operations. A **counterexample** is an example that *disproves* a statement, or shows that it is false. One counterexample is enough to disprove a statement.

Caution!

One counterexample is enough to disprove a statement, but one example is not enough to prove a statement.

Counterexamples	
Statement	**Counterexample**
No month has fewer than 30 days.	February has fewer than 30 days, so the statement is false.
Every integer that is divisible by 2 is also divisible by 4.	The integer 18 is divisible by 2 but not by 4, so the statement is false.

EXAMPLE 2 Finding Counterexamples to Statements About Properties

Reasoning

Find a counterexample to disprove the statement "The Associative Property is true for subtraction."

Find three real numbers, a, b, and c, such that $a - (b - c) \neq (a - b) - c$.

Try $a = 10$, $b = 7$, and $c = 2$.

$a - (b - c)$ $\quad$ $(a - b) - c$

$10 - (7 - 2)$ $\quad$ $(10 - 7) - 2$

$10 - 5 = 5$ $\quad$ $3 - 2 = 1$

Since $10 - (7 - 2) \neq (10 - 7) - 2$, this is a counterexample. The statement is false.

CHECK IT OUT! 2. Find a counterexample to disprove the statement "The Commutative Property is true for division."
Possible answer: $6 \div 2 \neq 2 \div 6$

Know it! Note

Distributive Property

NUMBERS	ALGEBRA
$3(4 + 8) = 3(4) + 3(8)$ $3(12) = 12 + 24$ $36 = 36$	For real numbers a, b, and c, $a(b + c) = ab + ac$

The Distributive Property also works with subtraction because subtraction is the same as adding the opposite.

2 Teach

Guided Instruction

After introducing each property, show an example of the property with real numbers before showing an example that involves variables. Emphasize that the properties of this lesson hold for all real numbers and that variables represent real numbers.

Universal Access

Through Cognitive Strategies

Show students how the properties connect to geometric figures. The area of a 3-by-5 rectangle is 3×5 or 5×3 (Comm. Prop. of Mult.). The perimeter of a triangle with sides 6, 7, and 8 is $(6 + 7) + 8$ or $6 + (7 + 8)$ (Assoc. Prop. of Add.). The area of the rectangle below is $3(4 + 5)$ or $3 \bullet 4 + 3 \bullet 5$ (Dist. Prop.).

4 5
3

COMMON ERROR ALERT

When students use the Distributive Property, they may forget to multiply all of the terms in parentheses by the first factor, resulting in errors such as $3(x + 2) = 3x + 2$. Remind students that they must *distribute* the first factor to all of the terms in parentheses.

Power Presentations with PowerPoint®

Additional Examples

Example 1

Name the property that is illustrated in each equation.

A. $7(mn) = (7m)n$ Assoc. Prop. of Mult.

B. $(a + 3) + b = a + (3 + b)$ Assoc. Prop. of Add.

C. $x + (y + z) = x + (z + y)$ Comm. Prop. of Add.

Example 2

Find a counterexample to disprove the statement "The Commutative Property is true for raising to a power."
Poss. ans.: $2^3 = 8$ and $3^2 = 9$, so $2^3 \neq 3^2$

Also available on transparency

INTERVENTION

Questioning Strategies

EXAMPLE 1

- How can you tell when the Commutative Property is being used?
- How is the Associative Property different from the Commulative Property?

EXAMPLE 2

- What would it mean if the Associative Property were true for subtraction?
- What do you need to do in order to find a counterexample that shows that the Associative Property is not true for subtraction?

Teaching Tip

Language Support The word distribute means "to share among many" or "to deliver to members of a group." Point out to students how the everyday meaning of the word is similar to its mathematical meaning.

ENGLISH LANGUAGE LEARNERS

Power Presentations with PowerPoint®

Additional Examples

Example 3

Write each product using the Distributive Property. Then simplify.

A. 5(71) 5(70) + 5(1) = 355

B. 4(38) 4(40) − 4(2) = 152

Example 4

Find a counterexample to show that each statement is false.

A. The prime numbers are closed under addition. 3 and 5 are prime numbers, but 3 + 5 = 8, which is not a prime number.

B. The set of odd numbers is closed under subtraction. 11 and 9 are odd numbers, but 11 − 9 = 2, which is not an odd number.

Also available on transparency

INTERVENTION
Questioning Strategies

EXAMPLE 3

- How can you break one of the factors into a sum with numbers that are easier to work with?

EXAMPLE 4

- What would it mean if the integers were closed under division?
- What is the first thing you should do when you look for a counterexample to the statement "The integers are closed under division"?

EXAMPLE 3 Using the Distributive Property with Mental Math

Helpful Hint

Break the greater factor into a sum or difference that contains a multiple of 10.

Write each product using the Distributive Property. Then simplify.

A 15(103)

$15(103) = 15(100 + 3)$	*Rewrite 103 as 100 + 3.*
$= 15(100) + 15(3)$	*Use the Distributive Property.*
$= 1500 + 45$	*Multiply (mentally).*
$= 1545$	*Add (mentally).*

B 6(19)

$6(19) = 6(20 - 1)$	*Rewrite 19 as 20 − 1.*
$= 6(20) - 6(1)$	*Use the Distributive Property.*
$= 120 - 6$	*Multiply (mentally).*
$= 114$	*Subtract (mentally).*

CHECK IT OUT! Write each product using the Distributive Property. Then simplify.

3a. 9(52) **3b.** 12(98) **3c.** 7(34)

3a. 9(50) + 9(2); 468
3b. 12(100) − 12(2); 1176
3c. 7(30) + 7(4); 238

A set of numbers is said to be closed, or to have **closure**, under an operation if the result of the operation on any two numbers in the set is also in the set.

Know it! Note

Closure Properties of the Real Numbers

WORDS	NUMBERS	ALGEBRA
The real numbers are closed under addition, subtraction, and multiplication.	$6.1 + \sqrt{2}$, $6.1 - \sqrt{2}$, and $6.1 \times \sqrt{2}$ are all real numbers.	For real numbers *a* and *b*, *a* + *b*, *a* − *b*, and *ab* are all real numbers.

EXAMPLE 4 Finding Counterexamples to Statements About Closure

Reasoning

Find a counterexample to show that each statement is false.

A The integers are closed under division.

Find two integers, *a* and *b*, such that the quotient, $\frac{a}{b}$, is not an integer.

Try $a = 1$ and $b = 3$.

$\frac{a}{b} = \frac{1}{3}$

Since $\frac{1}{3}$ is not an integer, this is a counterexample. The statement is false.

B The whole numbers are closed under subtraction.

Find two whole numbers, *a* and *b*, such that the difference, $a - b$, is not a whole number.

Try $a = 4$ and $b = 9$.

$a - b = 4 - 9 = -5$

Since −5 is not a whole number, this is a counterexample. The statement is false.

CHECK IT OUT! Find a counterexample to show that each statement is false.

4a. The set of negative integers is closed under multiplication.

4b. The whole numbers are closed under the operation of taking a square root.

4a. Possible answer: −2 and −1 are neg. integers, but (−2)(−1) = 2, which is not a neg. integer.

4b. Possible answer: 15 is a whole number, but $\sqrt{15}$ is not a whole number.

3 Close

Summarize

Ask students which property is illustrated in each equation.

- $m + (n + p) = (m + n) + p$ Assoc. Prop. of Add.
- $m(n + p) = mn + mp$ Dist. Prop.
- $m + n = n + m$ Comm. Prop. of Add.
- $m(np) = (mn)p$ Assoc. Prop. of Mult.

FORMATIVE ASSESSMENT and INTERVENTION

***Diagnose Before* the Lesson**
1-6 Warm Up, TE p. 40

***Monitor During* the Lesson**
Check It Out! Exercises, SE pp. 42–44
Questioning Strategies, TE pp. 43–44

***Assess After* the Lesson**
1-6 Lesson Quiz, TE p. 47
Alternative Assessment, TE p. 47

THINK AND DISCUSS

1. Tell which property is being described: When adding three numbers, you can add the first number to the sum of the second and third numbers. You can also add the third number to the sum of the first and second numbers. The result is the same.

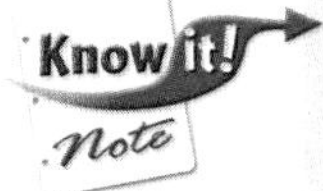

2. **GET ORGANIZED** Copy and complete the graphic organizer below. In each box, give an example to illustrate the given property.

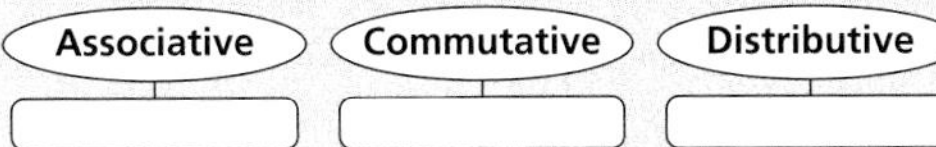

1-6 Exercises

1.0, 24.3, 25.1

GUIDED PRACTICE

1. **Vocabulary** The __?__ Property of Addition states the following: $(a + b) + c = a + (b + c)$. (*Associative, Commutative, or Distributive*) **Associative**

SEE EXAMPLE 1 p. 42

Name the property that is illustrated in each equation.

2. $16 + r = r + 16$
3. $4 + (x + 3y) = (4 + x) + 3y$
4. $(4 + 12) + 9 = (12 + 4) + 9$
5. $m \cdot (-20) = -20m$

SEE EXAMPLE 2 p. 43

6. Find a counterexample to disprove the statement "The Commutative Property is true for subtraction." **Possible answer: $5 - 2 \neq 2 - 5$**

SEE EXAMPLE 3 p. 44

Write each product using the Distributive Property. Then simplify.

7. $14(1002)$
8. $16(19)$
9. $9(38)$
10. $8(57)$
11. $12(112)$
12. $7(109)$

SEE EXAMPLE 4 p. 44

Reasoning Find a counterexample to show that each statement is false.

13. The natural numbers are closed under division.
14. The set of negative integers is closed under the operation of taking the absolute value.

PRACTICE AND PROBLEM SOLVING

Name the property that is illustrated in each equation.

15. $(3 + s) + t = (s + 3) + t$
16. $(5.2 + p) + 2q = 5.2 + (p + 2q)$
17. $(5x)y = 5(xy)$
18. $-2(a + b) = -2(b + a)$
19. $-16a = a(-16)$
20. $-4.1 + 3x = 3x + (-4.1)$
21. Find a counterexample to disprove the statement "The Associative Property is true for division." **Possible answer: $(24 \div 12) \div 2 = 1$, but $24 \div (12 \div 2) = 4$.**

1-6 Exercises

Answers to *Think and Discuss*

1. Associative Property of Addition.
2. See p. A2.

Assignment Guide

Assign *Guided Practice* exercises as necessary.

If you finished Examples **1–2**
Proficient 15–21, 33, 34
Advanced 15–21, 33, 34

If you finished Examples **1–4**
Proficient 15–42, 43–49 odd 51–61
Advanced 15–29, 31–37 odd, 38–61

Homework Quick Check
Quickly check key concepts.
Exercises: 16, 21, 22, 28, 34

Answers

2. Comm. Prop. of Add.
3. Assoc. Prop. of Add.
4. Comm. Prop. of Add.
5. Comm. Prop. of Mult.
7. $14(1000) + 14(2)$; 14,028
8. $16(20) - 16(1)$; 304
9. $9(40) - 9(2)$; 342
10. $8(60) - 8(3)$; 456
11. $12(100) + 12(12)$; 1344
12. $7(100) + 7(9)$; 763
13. Possible answer: 2 and 5 are nat. numbers but $2 \div 5$ is not a nat. number
14. Possible answer: -7 is a neg. int., but $|-7| = 7$, which is not a neg. int.
15. Comm. Prop. of Add.
16. Assoc. Prop. of Add.
17. Assoc. Prop. of Mult.
18. Comm. Prop. of Add.
19. Comm. Prop. of Mult.
20. Comm. Prop. of Add.

Standard	Exercises
1.0	1–46, 48–50
2.0 🔑	58–61
24.3	6, 13, 14, 21, 28, 29, 42
25.1	6, 13, 14, 21, 28, 29, 42

CONCEPT CONNECTION Exercise 37 involves using the Distributive Property to find the total area of three rectangular walls. This exercise prepares students for the Concept Connection on page 56.

Answers

37c. By the Dist. Prop., $8 \cdot 12 + 8 \cdot 14 + 8 \cdot 16 = 8(12 + 14 + 16)$.

43. Yes; the product of any two numbers in the set is in the set.

44. No; $1 + 1 = 2$, which is not in the set.

45. No; $-2(2) = -4$, which is not in the set.

46. Yes; the set consists of multiples of 3. When you multiply two multiples of 3, you get another multiple of 3, so the set is closed under mult.

48. Yes; the operation is based on mult., which is comm.

49. Yes; the operation is based on mult. and add. Since the real numbers are closed under these operations, the real numbers are closed under $\odot$.

50. Possible answer: $1 \odot (2 \odot 3) = 8$ and $(1 \odot 2) \odot 3 = 10$. So $1 \odot (2 \odot 3) \neq (1 \odot 2) \odot 3$.

Independent Practice	
For Exercises	See Example
15–20	1
21	2
22–27	3
28–29	4

Extra Practice
Skills Practice p. EP3
Application Practice p. EP24

Write each product using the Distributive Property. Then simplify.

22. $9(62)$ **$9(60) + 9(2)$; 558** **23.** $8(29)$ **$8(30) - 8(1)$; 232** **24.** $11(25)$ **$11(20) + 11(5)$; 275**

25. $6(53)$ **$6(50) + 6(3)$; 318** **26.** $12(999)$ **$12(1000) - 12(1)$; 11,988** **27.** $3(149)$ **$3(150) - 3(1)$; 447**

Reasoning **Find a counterexample to show that each statement is false.**

28. The set of odd numbers is closed under addition.

28. Possible answer: 5 and 7 are odd, but $5 + 7 = 12$, which is not odd.

29. The terminating decimals are closed under division.

29. Possible answer: 2.5 and 7.5 are term. decimals, but $2.5 \div 7.5 = 0.\overline{3}$, which is not a term. decimal.

30. Estimation Tavon bought 5 spiral notebooks. The notebooks cost $1.97 each.

a. Estimate the total amount that Tavon spent on the notebooks. **about $10**

b. Show how to use the Distributive Property to calculate the exact amount that Tavon spent. **$5(2.00) - 5(0.03) = \$9.85$**

31. Sports In a triathlon, athletes race in swimming, biking, and running events. The athlete with the least total time to complete the events is the winner.

Times from Triathlon

Athlete	Swim (min:s)	Bike (min:s)	Run (min:s)
Amy	18:51	45:17	34:13
Julie	17:13	40:27	23:32
Mardi	19:09	38:58	25:32

a. Use mental math and the properties in this lesson to find the total time for each athlete. (*Hint:* 1 minute = 60 seconds)

31a. Amy: 98:21; Julie: 81:12; Mardi: 83:39

b. Use the total times for the athletes to determine the order in which they finished the triathlon. **Julie, Mardi, Amy**

Name the property that is illustrated in each equation.

32. $(3m + 5p) + 12r = 3m + (5p + 12r)$ **32. Assoc. Prop. of Add.**

33. $3(2r - 7) = 3(2r) - 3(7)$ **Dist. Prop.**

34. $y - 2 = -2 + y$ **Comm. Prop. of Add.**

35. $45x - 35 = 5(9x - 7)$ **Dist. Prop.**

36. Gardening A gardener is planting several rows of cauliflower and several rows of strawberries. There will be 6 plants per row.

a. There are s rows of strawberries and c rows of cauliflower. Write an expression that can be used to find the total number of plants. **$6s + 6c$**

b. Write an equivalent expression using the Distributive Property. **$6(s + c)$**

c. Find the total number of plants when there are 8 rows of strawberries and 9 rows of cauliflower. **102**

Section 1
s rows
?

Section 2
c rows
?

CONCEPT CONNECTION

37. This problem will prepare you for the Concept Connection on page 56.

Jared is painting three rectangular walls in his apartment. The walls have widths of 12 feet, 14 feet, and 16 feet. The ceiling is 8 feet high.

a. Find the total area of the walls by first calculating the area of each wall and then adding the areas together. **336 ft^2**

b. Find the total area of the walls by first adding the widths of the walls and then multiplying this sum by the height. **336 ft^2**

c. Use a property to explain why parts **a** and **b** give the same result.

1-6 PRACTICE A
1-6 PRACTICE C
1-6 PRACTICE B

LESSON 1-6 **Practice B**
Properties of Real Numbers

Name the property that is illustrated in each equation.

1. $h + (y + 4.1) = (h + y) + 4.1$ **Associative Property**
2. $t \cdot 1.5 = 1.5t$ **Commutative Property**
3. $s \cdot p = p \cdot s$ **Commutative Property**
4. $(o + z) + 8 = (z + o) + 8$ **Commutative Property**
5. Find a counterexample to disprove the statement "The Associative Property is true for subtraction." **Possible answer: $30 - (15 - 10) \neq (30 - 15) - 10$**
6. Find a counterexample to disprove the statement "The Commutative Property is true for division." **Possible answer: $10 \div 2 \neq 2 \div 10$**

Write each product using the Distributive Property. Then simplify.

7. $14(12)$ **$14(10) + 14(2)$; 168**
8. $5(47)$ **$5(50) - 5(3)$; 235**
9. $4(106)$ **$4(100) + 4(6)$; 424**

Find a counterexample to show that each statement is false.

10. The repeating decimals are closed under subtraction. **Possible answer: $0.\overline{6} - 0.1\overline{6} = 0.5$**
11. The whole numbers are closed under division. **Possible answer: $10 \div 4 = 2.5$**
12. The negative integers are closed under subtraction. **Possible answer: $-5 - (-6) = 1$**

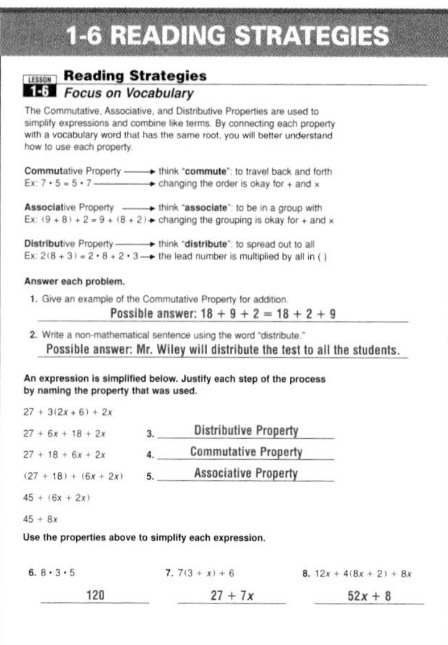

1-6 READING STRATEGIES

LESSON 1-6 **Reading Strategies**
Focus on Vocabulary

The Commutative, Associative, and Distributive Properties are used to simplify expressions and combine like terms. By connecting each property with a vocabulary word that has the same root, you will better understand how to use each property.

Commutative Property → think "**commute**": to travel back and forth
Ex: $7 \cdot 5 = 5 \cdot 7$ → changing the order is okay for + and ×

Associative Property → think "**associate**": to be in a group with
Ex: $(9 + 8) + 2 = 9 + (8 + 2)$ → changing the grouping is okay for + and ×

Distributive Property → think "**distribute**": to spread out to all
Ex: $2(8 + 3) = 2 \cdot 8 + 2 \cdot 3$ → the lead number is multiplied by all in ( )

Answer each problem.

1. Give an example of the Commutative Property for addition. **Possible answer: $18 + 9 + 2 = 18 + 2 + 9$**
2. Write a non-mathematical sentence using the word "distribute." **Possible answer: Mr. Wiley will distribute the test to all the students.**

An expression is simplified below. Justify each step of the process by naming the property that was used.

$27 + 3(2x + 6) + 2x$
$27 + 6x + 18 + 2x$ 3. **Distributive Property**
$27 + 18 + 6x + 2x$ 4. **Commutative Property**
$(27 + 18) + (6x + 2x)$ 5. **Associative Property**
$45 + (6x + 2x)$
$45 + 8x$

Use the properties above to simplify each expression.

6. $8 \cdot 3 \cdot 5$ **120**
7. $7(3 + x) + 6$ **$27 + 7x$**
8. $12x + 4(8x + 2) + 8x$ **$52x + 8$**

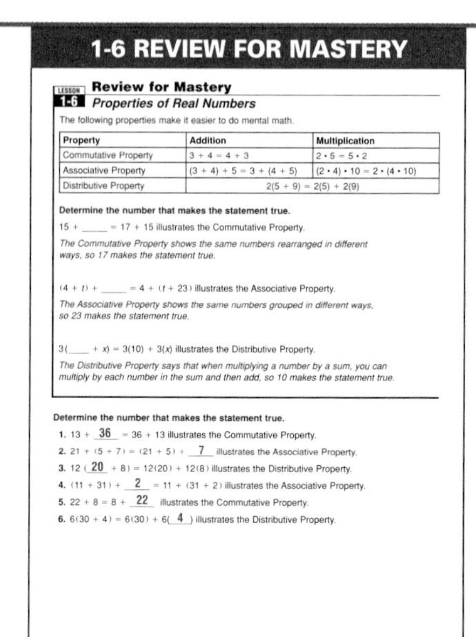

1-6 REVIEW FOR MASTERY

LESSON 1-6 **Review for Mastery**
Properties of Real Numbers

The following properties make it easier to do mental math.

Property	Addition	Multiplication
Commutative Property	$3 + 4 = 4 + 3$	$2 \cdot 5 = 5 \cdot 2$
Associative Property	$(3 + 4) + 5 = 3 + (4 + 5)$	$(2 \cdot 4) \cdot 10 = 2 \cdot (4 \cdot 10)$
Distributive Property	$2(5 + 9) = 2(5) + 2(9)$	

Determine the number that makes the statement true.

$15 +$ ____ $= 17 + 15$ illustrates the Commutative Property.

The Commutative Property shows the same numbers rearranged in different ways, so 17 makes the statement true.

$(4 + t) +$ ____ $= 4 + (t + 23)$ illustrates the Associative Property.

The Associative Property shows the same numbers grouped in different ways, so 23 makes the statement true.

$3($____ $+ x) = 3(10) + 3(x)$ illustrates the Distributive Property.

The Distributive Property says that when multiplying a number by a sum, you can multiply by each number in the sum and then add, so 10 makes the statement true.

Determine the number that makes the statement true.

1. $13 +$ **36** $= 36 + 13$ illustrates the Commutative Property.
2. $21 + (5 + 7) = (21 + 5) +$ **7** illustrates the Associative Property.
3. $12($**20** $+ 8) = 12(20) + 12(8)$ illustrates the Distributive Property.
4. $(11 + 31) +$ **2** $= 11 + (31 + 2)$ illustrates the Associative Property.
5. $22 + 8 = 8 +$ **22** illustrates the Commutative Property.
6. $6(30 + 4) = 6(30) + 6($**4**$)$ illustrates the Distributive Property.

38. Possible answer: If you add two numbers that have no digits to the right of the dec. pt., the sum will also have no digits to the right of the dec. pt. So, the sum of two integers is another integer. Therefore, the integers are closed under addition.

38. **Critical Thinking** Explain why the integers are closed under addition. (*Hint:* When written as a decimal, an integer has no digits to the right of the decimal point. What can you say about the sum of two such numbers?)

39. **Write About It** Describe a real-world situation that can be represented by the Distributive Property. Translate your situation into an algebraic expression. Define each variable you use. **Possible answer: A store sells items for \$0.99. Brian buys n notebooks and p pens. He spends a total of $0.99(n + p)$, or $0.99n + 0.99p$.**

Multiple Choice For Exercises 40–42, choose the best answer.

40. Which equation is an example of the Distributive Property?
   - (A) $(25 + 18) + 33 = 25 + (18 + 33)$
   - (B) $33 + (25 \cdot 18) = (25 \cdot 18) + 33$
   - **(C)** $33 \cdot 25 + 33 \cdot 18 = 33 \cdot (25 + 18)$
   - (D) $3 + 25 \cdot 33 + 18 = 18 + 33 \cdot 25 + 3$

41. Which property is illustrated in the equation $(4 + x) + 15 = 4 + (x + 15)$?
   - **(A)** Associative Property
   - (B) Closure Property
   - (C) Commutative Property
   - (D) Distributive Property

42. Which pair of numbers can be used as a counterexample to disprove the statement "The integers are closed under division"?
   - (A) -2 and 2
   - (B) 3 and 3
   - **(C)** 5 and 7
   - (D) 6.5 and 8.2

CHALLENGE AND EXTEND

Explain whether each set is closed under the given operation.

43. $\{-1, 0, 1\}$; multiplication
44. $\{-1, 0, 1\}$; addition
45. $\{-2, 0, 2\}$; multiplication
46. $\{0, 3, 6, 9, 12, 15...\}$; multiplication

Consider a new operation on the real numbers, $\odot$, that is defined as follows: For real numbers a and b, $a \odot b = ab + 1$. For example, $4 \odot 7 = 4 \cdot 7 + 1 = 28 + 1 = 29$.

47. Find $-3 \odot 2$ and $5 \odot 12$. **-5; 61**
48. Is the Commutative Property true for the operation $\odot$? Explain why or why not.
49. Are the real numbers closed under the operation $\odot$? Explain why or why not.
50. Find a counterexample to show that the Associative Property is not true for the operation $\odot$. (*Hint:* Find three numbers, a, b, and c, for which $a \odot (b \odot c) \neq (a \odot b) \odot c$.

SPIRAL STANDARDS REVIEW

2.0

Evaluate each expression for the replacement set {3, 5, 6}. (Lesson 1-1)

51. $4 - r$ **1, −1, −2**
52. $2 \div r$ **$\frac{2}{3}, \frac{2}{5}, \frac{1}{3}$**
53. $9r$ **27, 45, 54**
54. $r + 8$ **11, 13, 14**

Write the power represented by each geometric model. (Lesson 1-4)

55. **4^2**

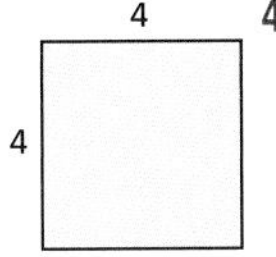

56. **5^2**

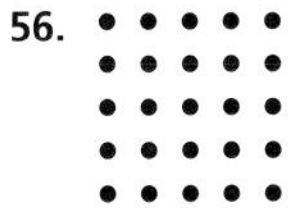

57. **3^3**

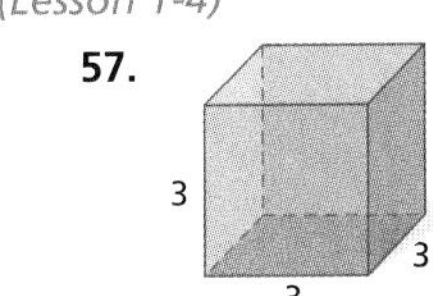

Find each root. (Lesson 1-5)

58. $\sqrt{400}$ **20**
59. $-\sqrt{81}$ **−9**
60. $\sqrt[3]{8}$ **2**
61. $\sqrt[4]{\frac{16}{81}}$ **$\frac{2}{3}$**

1-6 PROBLEM SOLVING

LESSON 1-6 **Problem Solving**
Properties of Real Numbers

Write the correct answer.

1. An English teacher gives students 1 point for reading a magazine article, 5 points for reading a chapter of a book, and 20 points for completing an entire book. If Sue reads 4 magazine articles, 7 chapters, and completes 2 books this term, how many points will she earn?
   79

2. A recipe for banana nut muffins calls for $2\frac{1}{2}$ cups of flour, 1 cup of banana, $\frac{1}{2}$ cup of chopped nuts, $\frac{3}{4}$ cup of sugar, and 1 cup of milk. Find the total number of cups of ingredients.
   $5\frac{3}{4}$ cups

3. A shelf holds 30 DVDs. Belinda has c shelves of comedies, and a shelves of action movies. Write an expression for the total number of DVDs. Rewrite the expression using the Distributive Property.
   $30c + 30a$; $30(c + a)$

4. Lucy is $(k + 5)$ years old. She has a brother who is 3 times as old as she is. Write an expression for Lucy's brother's age. Rewrite the expression using the Distributive Property.
   $3(k + 5)$; $3k + 3 \cdot 5$

Use the table below for questions 5–7, which shows expected flight times to and from New York City and five other cities. The legs of each trip vary in time due to the wind. Select the best answer.

Expected Flight Times

City	Inbound (h)	Outbound (h)
Mexico City	5.5	4.5
Paris	7.25	8.0
San Diego	5.4	4.75
Atlanta	2.3	2
Rome	7.75	8.5

5. Find the sum of the expected outbound flight times.
   - A 23 h
   - B 26 h
   - **(C)** 27.75 h
   - D 28.25 h

6. If Marty plans to travel from New York to Paris and back in February, and then from New York to Rome and back in April, what will be his total flight time for both trips?
   - F 15.25 h
   - G 16.25 h
   - H 31.0 h
   - **(J)** 31.5 h

7. Juan's flight time to San Diego was x hours longer than expected. His flight back was y hours less than expected. Which expression shows Juan's total flight time?
   - A $10.15xy$
   - B $5.4x - 4.75y$
   - **(C)** $10.15 + x - y$
   - D $5.4x(4.75y)$

8. Last month, Heather flew from New York to Atlanta and back twice a week for 3 weeks. What was her total flight time if there were no delays?
   - F 12.9 h
   - G 13.8 h
   - H 19.8 h
   - **(J)** 25.8 h

1-6 CHALLENGE

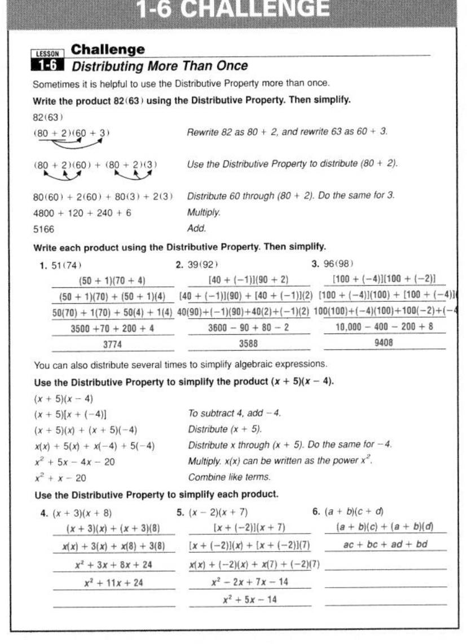

LESSON 1-6 **Challenge**
Distributing More Than Once

Sometimes it is helpful to use the Distributive Property more than once.

Write the product 82(63) using the Distributive Property. Then simplify.

$82(63)$	
$(80 + 2)(60 + 3)$	*Rewrite 82 as 80 + 2, and rewrite 63 as 60 + 3.*
$(80 + 2)(60) + (80 + 2)(3)$	*Use the Distributive Property to distribute (80 + 2).*
$80(60) + 2(60) + 80(3) + 2(3)$	*Distribute 60 through (80 + 2). Do the same for 3.*
$4800 + 120 + 240 + 6$	*Multiply.*
5166	*Add.*

Write each product using the Distributive Property. Then simplify.

1. $51(74)$
   - $(50 + 1)(70 + 4)$
   - $(50 + 1)(70) + (50 + 1)(4)$
   - $50(70) + 1(70) + 50(4) + 1(4)$
   - $3500 + 70 + 200 + 4$
   - 3774

2. $39(92)$
   - $[40 + (-1)](90 + 2)$
   - $[40 + (-1)](90) + [40 + (-1)](2)$
   - $40(90) + (-1)(90) + 40(2) + (-1)(2)$
   - $3600 - 90 + 80 - 2$
   - 3588

3. $96(98)$
   - $[100 + (-4)][100 + (-2)]$
   - $[100 + (-4)](100) + [100 + (-4)]($
   - $100(100) + (-4)(100) + 100(-2) + (-$
   - $10,000 - 400 - 200 + 8$
   - 9408

You can also distribute several times to simplify algebraic expressions.

Use the Distributive Property to simplify the product $(x + 5)(x - 4)$.

$(x + 5)(x - 4)$	
$(x + 5)[x + (-4)]$	*To subtract 4, add −4.*
$(x + 5)(x) + (x + 5)(-4)$	*Distribute (x + 5).*
$x(x) + 5(x) + x(-4) + 5(-4)$	*Distribute x through (x + 5). Do the same for −4.*
$x^2 + 5x - 4x - 20$	*Multiply. x(x) can be written as the power x^2.*
$x^2 + x - 20$	*Combine like terms.*

Use the Distributive Property to simplify each product.

4. $(x + 3)(x + 8)$
   - $(x + 3)(x) + (x + 3)(8)$
   - $x(x) + 3(x) + x(8) + 3(8)$
   - $x^2 + 3x + 8x + 24$
   - $x^2 + 11x + 24$

5. $(x - 2)(x + 7)$
   - $[x + (-2)](x + 7)$
   - $[x + (-2)](x) + [x + (-2)](7)$
   - $x(x) + (-2)(x) + x(7) + (-2)(7)$
   - $x^2 - 2x + 7x - 14$
   - $x^2 + 5x - 14$

6. $(a + b)(c + d)$
   - $(a + b)(c) + (a + b)(d)$
   - $ac + bc + ad + bd$

COMMON ERROR ALERT

Students may not see that the Commutative Property of Addition applies to **Exercise 34**. Show them that the left side of the equation can be rewritten as $y + (-2)$.

Multiple Choice If students answered **D** for **Exercise 42,** they may not understand that in order to find a counterexample to the statement, they need to find two *integers* whose quotient is not an integer.

Journal

Have students write their own mnemonics for remembering the Commutative, Associative, and Distributive Properties.

ALTERNATIVE ASSESSMENT

Ask students to demonstrate how the Commutative, Associative, and Distributive Properties can be used to perform mental math.

Power Presentations with PowerPoint®

1-6 Lesson Quiz

Name the property that is illustrated in each equation.

1. $6(rs) = (6r)s$ Assoc. Prop of Mult.
2. $(3 + n) + p = (n + 3) + p$ Comm. Prop. of Add.
3. $(3 + n) + p = 3 + (n + p)$ Assoc. Prop. of Add.
4. Find a counterexample to disprove the statement "The Commutative Property is true for division." Poss. ans.: $3 \div 6 \neq 6 \div 3$

Write each product using the Distributive Property. Then simplify.

5. $8(21)$ $8(20) + 8(1) = 168$
6. $5(97)$ $5(100) - 5(3) = 485$

Find a counterexample to show that each statement is false.

7. The natural numbers are closed under subtraction. Poss. ans.: 6 and 8 are nat., but $6 - 8 = -2$, which is not nat.
8. The set of even numbers is closed under division. Poss. ans.: 12 and 4 are even, but $12 \div 4 = 3$, which is not even.

Also available on transparency

1-7 Organizer

Objectives: Use the order of operations and properties of the real number system to simplify expressions.

Combine like terms.

Online Edition
Tutorial Videos

Countdown to Mastery Week 2

Power Presentations with PowerPoint®

Warm Up

Evaluate.

1. 4^2 16
2. $|5 - 16|$ 11
3. -2^3 −8
4. $|3 - 7|$ 4

Translate each word phrase into a numerical or algebraic expression.

5. the product of 8 and 6 8×6
6. the difference of 10y and 4 $10y - 4$

Simplify each fraction.

7. $\frac{16}{2}$ 8
8. $\frac{8}{56}$ $\frac{1}{7}$

Also available on transparency

Math Humor

Q: Why was the math teacher upset with Cupid?

A: He kept changing "like terms" to "love terms."

California Standards

Algebra 1 1.1, 25.1
Also covered:
25.0 Students use properties of the number system to judge the validity of results, **to justify each step of a procedure, and to prove** or disprove **statements.**

1-7 Simplifying Expressions

California Standards

1.1 Students use properties of numbers to demonstrate whether assertions are true or false.
25.1 Students use properties of numbers to construct simple, valid arguments (direct and indirect) for, or formulate counterexamples to, claimed assertions.

Vocabulary
order of operations
terms
like terms
coefficient

Who uses this?
Sports statisticians can simplify expressions to calculate data. (See Example 2.)

When an expression contains more than one operation, the **order of operations** tells you which operation to perform first.

Order of Operations	
First:	Perform operations inside grouping symbols.
Second:	Evaluate powers.
Third:	Perform multiplication and division from left to right.
Fourth:	Perform addition and subtraction from left to right.

Grouping symbols include parentheses ( ), brackets [ ], and braces { }. If an expression contains more than one set of grouping symbols, begin with the innermost set. Follow the order of operations within that set of grouping symbols and then work outward.

EXAMPLE 1 Simplifying Numerical Expressions

Simplify each expression.

A $-4^2 + 24 \div 3 \cdot 2$

$-4^2 + 24 \div 3 \cdot 2$ *There are no grouping symbols.*
$-16 + 24 \div 3 \cdot 2$ *Evaluate powers. The exponent applies only to the 4.*
$-16 + 8 \cdot 2$ *Divide.*
$-16 + 16$ *Multiply.*
0 *Add.*

Helpful Hint

Fraction bars, radical symbols, and absolute-value symbols can also be used as grouping symbols. Remember that a fraction bar indicates division.

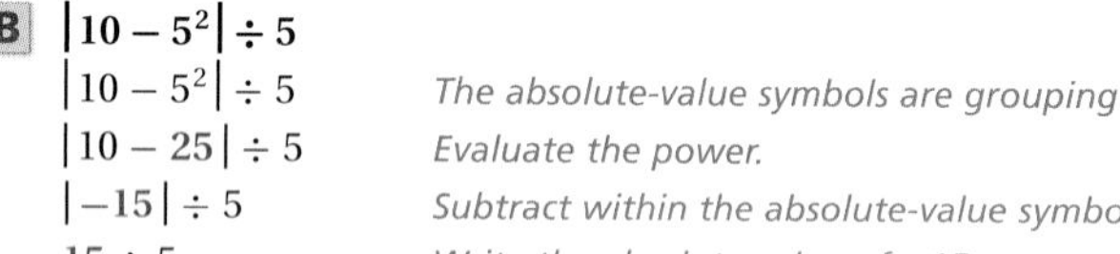

B $|10 - 5^2| \div 5$

$|10 - 5^2| \div 5$ *The absolute-value symbols are grouping symbols.*
$|10 - 25| \div 5$ *Evaluate the power.*
$|-15| \div 5$ *Subtract within the absolute-value symbols.*
$15 \div 5$ *Write the absolute value of −15.*
3 *Divide.*

C $3[2(3 + 4)] - 1$

$3[2(3 + 4)] - 1$ *There are two sets of grouping symbols.*
$3[2(7)] - 1$ *Add within the innermost parentheses.*
$3[14] - 1$ *Multiply within the brackets.*
$42 - 1$ *There are no powers. Multiply.*
41 *Subtract.*

CHECK IT OUT! Simplify each expression.

1a. $8 \div \frac{1}{2} \cdot 3$ **48**
1b. $3\sqrt{50 - 1}$ **21**
1c. $\frac{(5 + 2)(-8)}{(-2)^3 - 3}$ $\mathbf{\frac{56}{11}}$

1 Introduce

EXPLORATION

1-7 Simplifying Expressions

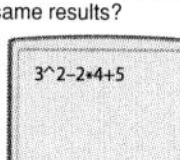

You will need a graphing calculator for this Exploration.

1. Enter -4^2 on your calculator as shown. Then press ENTER. What is the result?
2. Now enter $(-4)^2$ on your calculator. What is the result this time?
3. How are the expressions -4^2 and $(-4)^2$ different?
4. Find the value of the following expression without using a calculator: $3^2 - 2 \cdot 4 + 5$. Compare your answer with those of other students. Did everyone get the same results?
5. Now find the value of $3^2 - 2 \cdot 4 + 5$ by entering the expression on your calculator as shown. How does the calculator's answer compare to your answer and those of your classmates?

THINK AND DISCUSS

6. Explain why everyone must agree on the order in which operations are performed when simplifying an expression.

Motivate

Write $15 - 5 + 3^2$ on the board. Ask students to simplify the expression and share their answers. If any students get different answers, discuss why a standard order of operations is important. If everyone gets the correct answer, change the expression to $(15 - 5 + 3)^2$ or $15 - (5 + 3)^2$ and use this as a basis for discussing how grouping symbols can affect the order of operations.

Explorations and answers are provided in *Alternate Openers: Explorations Transparencies.*

EXAMPLE 2 Sports Application

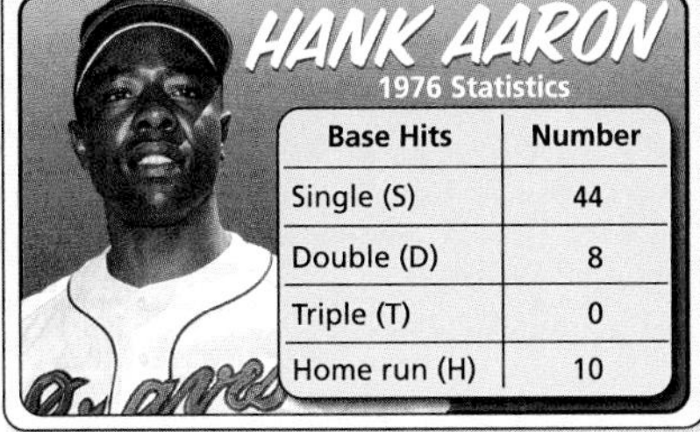

Base Hits	Number
Single (S)	44
Double (D)	8
Triple (T)	0
Home run (H)	10

Hank Aaron's last season in the Major League was in 1976. A player's total number of bases can be found using the expression $S + 2D + 3T + 4H$. Use the table to find Hank Aaron's total bases for 1976.

$S + 2D + 3T + 4H$

$44 + 2(8) + 3(0) + 4(10)$ — *First substitute values for each variable.*

$44 + 16 + 0 + 40$ — *Multiply.*

$60 + 0 + 40$ — *Add from left to right.*

100 — *Add.*

Hank Aaron's total number of bases for 1976 was 100.

2. Another formula for a player's total number of bases is Hits $+ D + 2T + 3H$. Use this expression to find Hank Aaron's total bases for 1959, when he had 223 hits, 46 doublesd, 7 triples, and 39 home runs. **400**

The **terms** of an expression are the parts that are added or subtracted. **Like terms** contain the same variables raised to the same powers. Constants are also like terms.

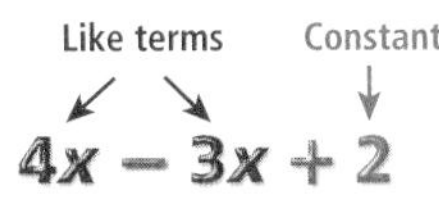

A **coefficient** is a number multiplied by a variable. Like terms may have different coefficients. A variable written without a coefficient has a coefficient of 1.

Like terms can be combined. To combine like terms, use the Distributive Property.

Distributive Property	Example
$ax - bx = (a - b)x$	$7x - 4x = (7 - 4)x$ $= 3x$

Notice that you can combine like terms by adding or subtracting the coefficients. Keep the variables and exponents the same.

EXAMPLE 3 Combining Like Terms

Simplify each expression by combining like terms.

A $12x + 30x$

$12x + 30x$ — *12x and 30x are like terms.*

$42x$ — *Add the coefficients.*

B $6.8y^2 - y^2 + 4y$

$6.8y^2 - y^2 + 4y$ — *$6.8y^2$ and y^2 are like terms.*

$6.8y^2 - 1y^2 + 4y$ — *A variable without a coefficient has a coefficient of 1.*

$5.8y^2 + 4y$ — *Subtract the coefficients of the like terms.*

Caution!

Add or subtract only the coefficients. $6.8y^2 - y^2 \neq 6.8$

Power Presentations with PowerPoint®

Additional Examples

Example 1

Simplify each expression.

A. $15 - 2 \cdot 3 + 1$ 10

B. $12 + 3^2 + 10 \div 2$ 26

C. $\frac{2(-4) + 22}{4^2 - 9}$ 2

Example 2

A shop offers gift-wrapping services at three price levels. The amount of money collected for wrapping gifts on a given day can be found using the expression $2B + 4S + 7D$. On Friday the shop wrapped 10 basic packages B, 6 super packages S, and 5 deluxe packages D. Use the expression to find the amount of money collected for gift-wrapping on Friday. $79

Also available on transparency

Questioning Strategies

EXAMPLE 1

- How do you know which operation to perform first?
- What are two purposes of the fraction bar?

EXAMPLE 2

- Why is it unreasonable to substitute negative values for the variables?
- Why do the given formulas make sense?

2 Teach

Guided Instruction

Before starting the lesson, review the rules for adding, subtracting, multiplying, and dividing real numbers. Suggest that students refer to the chart on page 48 when they are working the Check It Out problems.

Universal Access

Through Auditory Cues

Have students replace variables with the names of everyday objects to determine whether terms can be combined.

$5a + 3c$
Read: 5 apples + 3 chairs
(cannot be combined)

$5a + 3a$
Read: 5 apples + 3 apples = 8 apples
$5a + 3a = 8a$

Power Presentations with PowerPoint®

Additional Examples

Example 3

Simplify each expression by combining like terms.

A. $72p - 25p$ $47p$

B. $\frac{3}{4}x^4 + x^4$ $\frac{7}{4}x^4$

C. $0.5m + 2.5n$ $0.5m + 2.5n$

Example 4

Use properties and operations to show that $14x + 4(2 + x)$ simplifies to $18x + 8$.

$14x + 4(2 + x)$	
$14x + 4(2) + 4(x)$	Distrib. Prop.
$14x + 8 + 4x$	Multiply.
$14x + 4x + 8$	Comm. Prop. of Add.
$(14x + 4x) + 8$	Assoc. Prop. of Add.
$18x + 8$	Combine like terms.

Also available on transparency

INTERVENTION

Questioning Strategies

EXAMPLE 3

- What must be true about the coefficients of two like terms if adding them results in 0?

EXAMPLE 4

- How do you decide which property to use first?

Reasoning The problems in **Example 4** reframe the simplification process into a logical "proof." Convey to students that they should always be able to justify every step in mathematics, even though the justifications are not always written down.

Simplify each expression by combining like terms.

C $4n + 11n^2$

$4n + 11n^2$ *$4n$ and $11n^2$ are not like terms.*

$4n + 11n^2$ *Do not combine the terms.*

Simplify each expression by combining like terms.

3a. $16p + 84p$ **$100p$** **3b.** $-20t - 8.5t$ **$-28.5t$** **3c.** $3m^2 + m^3 - m^2$ **$2m^2 + m^3$**

EXAMPLE 4 Simplifying Algebraic Expressions

Reasoning

Use properties and operations to show that the first expression simplifies to the second expression.

A $2(x + 6) + 3x, 5x + 12$

	Statements	Reasons
1.	$2(x + 6) + 3x$	
2.	$[2x + 2(6)] + 3x$	Distributive Property
3.	$(2x + 12) + 3x$	Multiply.
4.	$3x + (2x + 12)$	Commutative Property of Addition
5.	$(3x + 2x) + 12$	Associative Property of Addition
6.	$5x + 12$	Combine like terms.

B $4x + 2 - 3x + 4, x + 6$

	Statements	Reasons
1.	$4x + 2 - 3x + 4$	
2.	$4x - 3x + 2 + 4$	Commutative Property of Addition
3.	$(4x - 3x) + (2 + 4)$	Associative Property of Addition
4.	$x + 6$	Combine like terms.

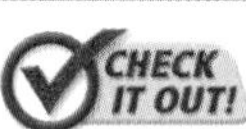

4. Use properties and operations to show that $6(x - 4) + 9$ simplifies to $6x - 15$.

1. Not always; subt. should be performed before add. if it comes before add. from left to right or it is within grouping symbols.

2. 1; possible answers: $3r^8$; $8r$

3. See p. A2.

THINK AND DISCUSS

1. Explain whether you always perform addition before subtraction when simplifying a numerical or algebraic expression.

2. Identify the coefficient for the term r^8. Then give a like term and an unlike term.

3. GET ORGANIZED Copy and complete the graphic organizer. In each box, give an example of an expression that can be simplified using the given method. Then simplify your expressions.

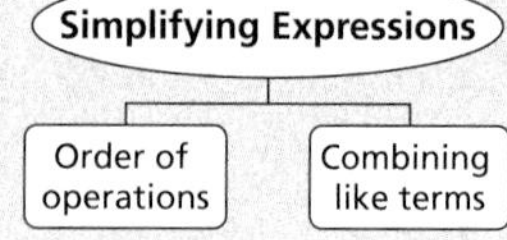

3 Close

Summarize

Review the order of operations. List all the possible grouping symbols, including fraction bars and the symbols for absolute value and roots. Emphasize that knowing and following the order of operations is necessary to the study of algebra and all other advanced math.

FORMATIVE ASSESSMENT

and INTERVENTION

***Diagnose Before* the Lesson**
1-7 Warm Up, TE p. 48

***Monitor During* the Lesson**
Check It Out! Exercises, SE pp. 48–50
Questioning Strategies, TE pp. 49–50

***Assess After* the Lesson**
1-7 Lesson Quiz, TE p. 53
Alternative Assessment, TE p. 53

Answers to Check It Out

4.

Statements	Reasons
1. $6(x - 4) + 9$	
2. $6(x) - 6(4) + 9$	Dist. Prop.
3. $6x - 24 + 9$	Multiply.
4. $6x - 15$	Combine like terms.

1-7 Exercises

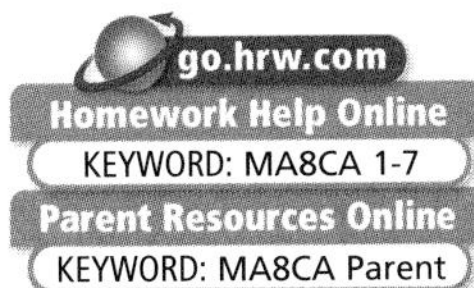

California Standards Practice
1.1, 25.1, 25.2

go.hrw.com
Homework Help Online KEYWORD: MA8CA 1-7
Parent Resources Online KEYWORD: MA8CA Parent

GUIDED PRACTICE

1. **Vocabulary** Explain why the *order of operations* is necessary for simplifying numerical expressions. **Possible answer: Using the order of operations makes sure that everyone gets the same value for an expression.**

SEE EXAMPLE 1 p. 48

Simplify each expression.

2. $5 - [12 \div (-2)]$ **11**
3. $30 - 5 \cdot 3$ **15**
4. $50 - 6 + 8$ **52**
5. $\frac{0 - 24}{6 \div 2}$ **−8**
6. $\frac{2 + 3(6)}{2^2}$ **5**
7. $-44 \div \sqrt{12 \div 3}$ **−22**

SEE EXAMPLE 2 p. 49

8. **Geometry** The surface area of a cylinder can be found using the expression $2\pi r(h + r)$. Find the surface area of the cylinder shown. Use 3.14 for π and give your final answer to the nearest tenth. **188.4 ft²**

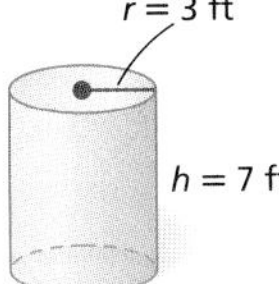

SEE EXAMPLE 3 p. 49

Simplify each expression by combining like terms.

9. $6x + 10x$ **16x**
10. $35x - 15x$ **20x**
11. $-3a + 9a$ **6a**
12. $-8r - r$ **−9r**
13. $17x^2 + x + 3x^2$ **$20x^2 + x$**
14. $3.2x + 4.7x$ **7.9x**

SEE EXAMPLE 4 p. 50

Reasoning Use properties and operations to show that the first expression simplifies to the second expression.

15. $5(x + 3) - 7x$, $15 - 2x$
16. $9(a - 3) - 4$, $9a - 31$
17. $6x - x - 3x^2 + 2x$, $7x - 3x^2$
18. $12x + 8x + t - 7x$, $13x + t$

PRACTICE AND PROBLEM SOLVING

Independent Practice

For Exercises	See Example
19–27	1
28	2
29–36	3
37–40	4

Extra Practice
Skills Practice p. EP3
Application Practice p. EP24

Simplify each expression.

19. $3 + 4(-5)$ **−17**
20. $20 - 4 + 5 - 2$ **19**
21. $41 + 12 \div 2$ **47**
22. $3[(-9) + (-2)(-6)]$ **9**
23. $10^2 \div (10 - 20)$ **−10**
24. $(6 + 2 \cdot 3) \div (9 - 7)^2$ **3**
25. $-4|2.5 - 6|$ **−14**
26. $\frac{8 - 8}{2 - 1}$ **0**
27. $\sqrt{3^2 - 5} \div 8$ **$\frac{1}{4}$**
28. **Geometry** The perimeter of a rectangle can be found using the expression $2(\ell + w)$. Find the perimeter of the rectangle shown. **24 in.**

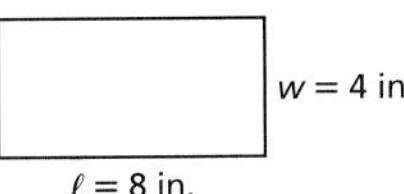

Simplify each expression by combining like terms.

29. $3x + 9x$ **12x**
30. $14x^2 - 5x^2$ **$9x^2$**
31. $-7x + 8x$ **x**
32. $3x^2 - 4$ **$3x^2 - 4$**
33. $5x^2 - 2x + 3x^2$ **$8x^2 - 2x$**
34. $3x + 2 - 2x - 1$ **x + 1**
35. $7y - 3 + 6y - 7$ **13y − 10**
36. $4a - 2a + 2$ **2a + 2**

Reasoning Use properties and operations to show that the first expression simplifies to the second expression.

37. $4(y + 6) + 9$, $4y + 33$
38. $-7(x + 2) + 4x$, $-3x - 14$
39. $5x - 3x + 3x^2 + 9x$, $11x + 3x^2$
40. $8x + 2x - 3y - 9x$, $x - 3y$

18.

Statements	Reasons
1. $12x + 8x + t - 7x$	
2. $12x + 8x - 7x + t$	Comm. Prop. of Add.
3. $13x + t$	Combine like terms.

37. $4(y + 6) + 9$; $4y + 24 + 9$ (Dist. Prop.); $4y + 33$ (Combine like terms.)

38. $-7(x + 2) + 4x$; $-7x - 14 + 4x$ (Dist. Prop.); $-7x + 4x - 14$ (Comm. Prop. of Add.); $-3x - 14$ (Combine like terms.)

39. $5x - 3x + 3x^2 + 9x$; $5x - 3x + 9x + 3x^2$ (Comm. Prop. of Add.); $11x + 3x^2$ (Combine like terms.)

40. $8x + 2x - 3y - 9x$; $8x + 2x - 9x - 3y$ (Comm. Prop. of Add.); $x - 3y$ (Combine like terms.)

1-7 Exercises

Assignment Guide

Assign *Guided Practice* exercises as necessary.

If you finished Examples **1–2**
Proficient 19–28, 41–47, 51
Advanced 19–28, 41–47, 51

If you finished Examples **1–4**
Proficient 19–62, 70–81
Advanced 19–40, 42–50 even, 52–81

Homework Quick Check
Quickly check key concepts.
Exercises: 22, 26, 28, 34, 38, 40

Answers

15.

Statements	Reasons
1. $5(x + 3) - 7x$	
2. $5x + 5(3) - 7x$	Dist. Prop.
3. $5x + 15 - 7x$	Multiply.
4. $15 + 5x - 7x$	Comm. Prop. of Add.
5. $15 - 2x$	Combine like terms.

16.

Statements	Reasons
1. $9(a - 3) - 4$	
2. $9(a) - 9(3) - 4$	Dist. Prop.
3. $9a - 27 - 4$	Multiply.
4. $9a - 31$	Combine like terms.

17.

Statements	Reasons
1. $6x - x - 3x^2 + 2x$	
2. $6x - x + 2x - 3x^2$	Comm. Prop. of Add.
3. $7x - 3x^2$	Combine like terms.

California Standards

Standard	Exercises
1.1	15–18, 37–40, 69
2.0	78–81
25.1	15–18, 37–40, 69
25.2	54
7NS1.2	70–77

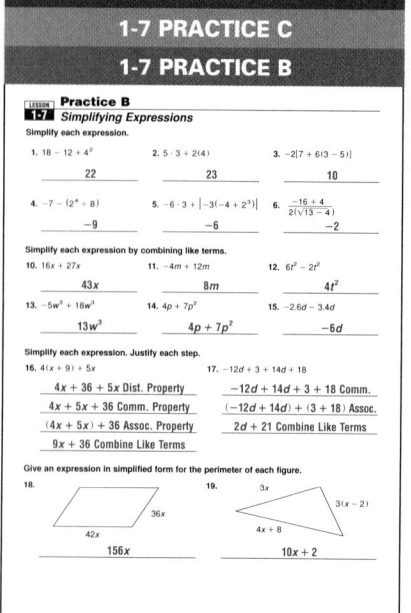

CONCEPT CONNECTION **Exercise 55** requires students to simplify an expression that involves π. This exercise prepares students for using formulas that involve π in the Concept Connection on page 56.

Answers

53. Possible answer: To make a sandwich, you need to get out the ingredients, put the ingredients on either slice of bread, and then put the two sides together. You would not want to put the second slice of bread on top before putting the ingredients in the middle.

California LINK

Sports

As a gymnast at UCLA, Mohini Bhardwaj set records for most perfect 10s in a season, most career perfect 10s, and most 10s in a meet. She later participated in the 2004 Olympic Games.

41. Simplify each expression.

a. $50 + 10 \div 2$ **55** b. $50 \cdot 10 - 2$ **498** c. $50 \cdot 10 \div 2$ **250**

d. $50 \div 10 \cdot 2$ **10** e. $50 - 10 \cdot 2$ **30** f. $50 + 10 \cdot 2$ **70**

Evaluate each expression for the given value of the variable.

42. $5 + 2x - 9$ for $x = 4$ **4** **43.** $30 \div 2 - d$ for $d = 14$ **1** **44.** $51 - 91 + g$ for $g = 20$ **−20**

45. $2(3 + n)$ for $n = 4$ **14** **46.** $4(b - 4)^2$ for $b = 5$ **4** **47.** $12 + [20(5 - k)]$ for $k = 1$ **92**

Geometry **Give an expression in simplified form for the perimeter of each figure.**

48. **6w**

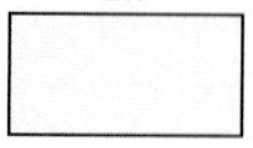

49. **6p + 9**

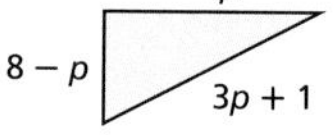

50. **8s + 12**

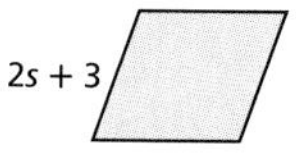

51. Sports At the 2004 Summer Olympics, U.S. gymnast Paul Hamm received the scores shown in the table during the individual all-around competition.

2004 Summer Olympics Individual Scores for Paul Hamm						
Event	Floor	Pommel horse	Rings	Vault	Parallel bars	Horizontal bar
Score	9.725	9.700	9.587	9.137	9.837	9.837

a. Write a numerical expression to show the average of Hamm's scores. (*Hint:* The average of a set of values is the sum of the values divided by the number of values in the set.) $\frac{57.823}{6}$

b. Simplify the expression to find Hamm's average score. **9.637**

52. Critical Thinking Are parentheses required when translating the word phrase "the sum of 8 and the product of 3 and 2" into a numerical phrase? Explain.

53. Write About It Many everyday processes must be done in a certain order to be completed successfully. Describe a process that requires several steps and tell why the steps must be followed in a certain order.

54. ///ERROR ANALYSIS/// Which simplification is incorrect? Explain the error.

52. No; the order of operations tells you to do mult. before add.

54. A; the Dist. Prop. was applied incorrectly (6 was not distributed to −2).

(A)
$24 + 6(x - 2)$
$24 + 6x - 2$
$22 + 6x$

(B)
$24 + 6(x - 2)$
$24 + 6x - 12$
$6x + 12$

CONCEPT CONNECTION

55. This problem will help prepare you for the Concept Connection on page 56.

a. The diagram shows a pattern of shapes that can be folded to make a cylinder. How is the length ℓ of the rectangle related to the circumference of (distance around) each circle? **equal**

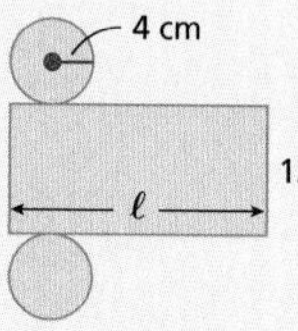

b. An expression for the area of each circle is πr^2. Write an expression for the area of the rectangle. **96π**

c. Use these expressions to write an expression for the total area of the figures. Leave the symbol π in your expression. $2(16\pi) + 96\pi = 128\pi$

1-7 PRACTICE A

1-7 PRACTICE C

1-7 PRACTICE B

LESSON 1-7 **Practice B**
Simplifying Expressions

Simplify each expression.

1. $18 - 12 + 4^2$ **22**
2. $5 \cdot 3 + 2(4)$ **23**
3. $-2[7 + 6(3 - 5)]$ **10**
4. $-7 - (2^4 + 8)$ **−9**
5. $-6 \cdot 3 + |-3(-4 + 2^3)|$ **−6**
6. $\frac{-16 + 4}{2(\sqrt{13} - 4)}$ **−2**

Simplify each expression by combining like terms.

10. $16x + 27x$ **43x**
11. $-4m + 12m$ **8m**
12. $6t^2 - 2t^2$ **$4t^2$**
13. $-5w^3 + 18w^3$ **$13w^3$**
14. $4p + 7p^2$ **$4p + 7p^2$**
15. $-2.6d - 3.4d$ **−6d**

Simplify each expression. Justify each step.

16. $4(x + 9) + 5x$
4x + 36 + 5x Dist. Property
4x + 5x + 36 Comm. Property
(4x + 5x) + 36 Assoc. Property
9x + 36 Combine Like Terms

17. $-12d + 3 + 14d + 18$
−12d + 14d + 3 + 18 Comm.
(−12d + 14d) + (3 + 18) Assoc.
2d + 21 Combine Like Terms

Give an expression in simplified form for the perimeter of each figure.

18.

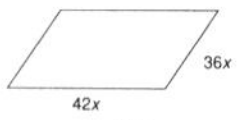

156x

19.

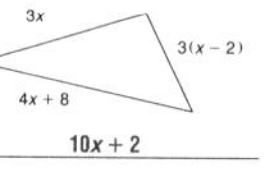

10x + 2

1-7 READING STRATEGIES

LESSON 1-7 **Reading Strategies**
Use a Mnemonic

You can remember the correct order of operations by using the mnemonic **P**lease **E**xcuse **M**y **D**ear **A**unt **S**ally. The first letter of each word in the phrase represents an operation, as shown below.

1. **P**arentheses — **P**lease
2. **E**xponents — **E**xcuse
3. **M**ultiplication — **M**y
   Division — **D**ear
4. **A**ddition — **A**unt
   Subtraction — **S**ally

Notice the order used in the example below.
$6^2 \div (7 - 4) + 8 \cdot 2$
$6^2 \div 3 + 8 \cdot 2$ *Parentheses*
$36 \div 3 + 8 \cdot 2$ *Exponents*
$12 + 16$ *Multiplication and Division left to right*
28 *Addition and Subtraction left to right*

Make up your own mnemonic for remembering the order of operations. It can be funny, serious, creative, or personal. Just make sure it's something that YOU will remember.

P ____________

E ____________

M ____________

D ____________

A ____________

S ____________

Use your mnemonic to simplify the following expressions.

1. $15 - 4 + 2^3$ **19**
2. $6 - (12 + 9) \div 3$ **−1**
3. $-5(3 + 7^2 - 44)$ **−40**
4. $2[8 - (4 + 1)]$ **6**
5. $4^2[4(3^3 - 1 \cdot 2)]$ **1600**
6. $\frac{-5 - 13}{-3^2}$ **2**

1-7 REVIEW FOR MASTERY

LESSON 1-7 **Review for Mastery**
Simplifying Expressions

Expressions can contain more than one operation, and then can also include grouping symbols, like parentheses ( ), brackets [ ], and braces { }. Operations must be performed in a certain order.
I. Perform operations inside grouping symbols, with the innermost group being done first.
II. Evaluate powers (exponents).
III. Perform multiplication and division in order from left to right.
IV. Perform addition and subtraction in order from left to right.

Simplify the expression $6^2 - 3(5 - 1) + 2$.

$6^2 - 3(5 - 1) + 2$
$6^2 - 3 \cdot \mathbf{4} + 2$ *Evaluate 5 − 1.*
$\mathbf{36} - 3 \cdot 4 + 2$ *Evaluate 6^2.*
$36 - \mathbf{12} + 2$ *Evaluate 3 · 4.*
$\mathbf{24} + 2$ *Add and subtract from left to right.*
26

Simplify each expression.

1. $6 \div 2 \cdot 4 - 3$ **9**
2. $18 \div 3^2 - 5 + 2$ **−1**
3. $3 + 5 \cdot 3 - 8 \div 2$ **14**
4. $3 + 3 \div 3 + 3$ **7**
5. $7^2 + 4^2 \cdot 3$ **97**
6. $6 + 10 \div 2 \cdot 5 - 1$ **30**

Simplify each expression.

7. $2^2 + 6(8 - 5) \div 2$ **13**
8. $\frac{(3 + 2)(4 + 3) + 5^2}{6 - 2^2}$ **30**
9. $4(3 - |2 - 6| + 5)$ **16**

Multiple Choice For Exercises 56–58, choose the best answer.

56. Ariel has 19 more CDs than her sister Tiffany has. Victor has 3 times as many CDs as Ariel has. Tiffany has x CDs. Which expression can be used to show how many CDs the three have in total?

Ⓐ $19 + 3x$ Ⓑ $51 + 3x$ Ⓒ $76 + 3x$ **Ⓓ** $76 + 5x$

57. Which expression can be used to represent the perimeter of the rectangle?

Ⓐ $16k$ Ⓒ $3k + 13$
Ⓑ $32k$ **Ⓓ** $6k + 26$

$3 + k$
$2(k + 5)$

58. The perimeter of the Norman window shown is approximated by the expression $2(3 + 8) + 3.14(3)$. Which is the closest approximation of the perimeter of the window?

Ⓐ 23.4 ft **Ⓒ** 31.4 ft
Ⓑ 28.4 ft Ⓓ 51.4 ft

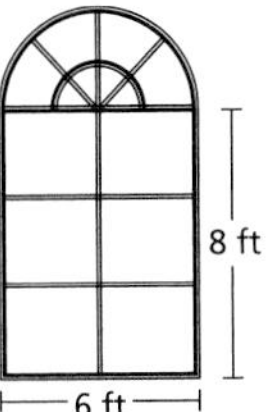

59. **Gridded Response** Evaluate $\sqrt{\frac{54 - (-2)(5)}{20 - 4^2}}$. **4**

CHALLENGE AND EXTEND

Simplify each expression.

60. $\frac{3 + 9 \cdot 2}{2 - 3^2}$ **−3**

61. $[(-6 \cdot 4) \div |-6 \cdot 4|]^2$ **1**

62. $\sqrt{\frac{8 + 10^2}{13 + (-10)}}$ **6**

63. $4[3(x + 9) + 2]$ **12x + 116**

64. $-[3(x - 2) + 5(x - 2)]$ **−8x + 16**

65. $(2b + 5) - (8b + 6) + 3(b - 2)$ **−3b − 7**

66. $\frac{1}{2}[(10 - g) + (-6 + 3g)]$ **2 + g**

67. Possible answer: $2 \cdot 4 + 5 - 8$

67. Use the numbers 2, 4, 5, and 8 to write an expression that has a value of 5. You may use any operations, and you must use each of the numbers at least once.

68. Possible answer: $2(9 - 6) - 5$

68. Use the numbers 2, 5, 6, and 9 to write an expression that has a value of 1. You may use any operations, and you must use each of the numbers at least once.

69. **Reasoning** Fill in the missing reasons to show that $\frac{a + b}{c} = \frac{a}{c} + \frac{b}{c}$.

	Statements	Reasons
1.	$\frac{a + b}{c} = \frac{1}{c}(a + b)$	Definition of division
2.	$= \frac{1}{c}(a) + \frac{1}{c}(b)$	a. **Dist. Prop.**
3.	$= \frac{a}{c} + \frac{b}{c}$	b. **Multiply.**

SPIRAL STANDARDS REVIEW

7NS1.2, 2.0

Add or subtract. (Lesson 1-2)

70. $51 - (-49)$ **100** 71. $-5 + \left(-1\frac{1}{3}\right)$ **$-6\frac{1}{3}$** 72. $-3 + (-8)$ **−11** 73. $2.9 - 5.3$ **−2.4**

Evaluate each expression. (Lesson 1-4)

74. 2^6 **64** 75. 18^2 **324** 76. $-\left(\frac{1}{2}\right)^3$ **$-\frac{1}{8}$** 77. $\left(-\frac{1}{2}\right)^2$ **$\frac{1}{4}$**

Find each root. (Lesson 1-5)

78. $\sqrt[3]{64}$ **4** 79. $\sqrt{324}$ **18** 80. $\sqrt{\frac{36}{49}}$ **$\frac{6}{7}$** 81. $-\sqrt{121}$ **−11**

COMMON ERROR ALERT

Students may always perform multiplication before division, or addition before subtraction. Tell students to write division as multiplication by the reciprocal and subtraction as addition of the opposite. Then perform all multiplication from left to right or all addition from left to right.

Multiple Choice In **Exercise 56,** students may try to use a different variable for the number of CDs each person has. Tell students to start by writing an expression for the number of CDs Tiffany has. Then have students write expressions for the number of CDs Ariel and Victor have, using the same variable. Then students can find the total number of CDs.

Journal

Have students describe what might happen if there were no order of operations. Require them to include formulas used in science or geometry.

ALTERNATIVE ASSESSMENT

Have students write a problem that includes at least three of the following: parentheses, exponents, multiplication, division, addition, subtraction, and combining like terms. Have them explain their step-by-step solution.

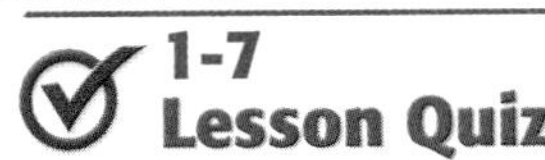

1-7 Lesson Quiz

Simplify each expression.

1. $165 + 27 + 3 + 5$ 200
2. $\frac{1}{3}(2)(12)$ 8
3. The volume of a storage box can be found using the expression $\ell w(w + 2)$. Find the volume of the box if $\ell = 3$ feet and $w = 2$ feet. 24 ft^3

Simplify each expression by combining like terms.

4. $\frac{2}{5}x^3 + \frac{1}{5}x^3$ $\frac{3}{5}x^3$
5. $14c^2 - 9c$ $14c^2 - 9c$
6. Use properties and operations to show that $24a + b^2 + 3a + 2b^2$ simplifies to $27a + 3b^2$. Check students' work.

Also available on transparency

1-7 PROBLEM SOLVING

LESSON 1-7 Problem Solving
Simplifying Expressions

Write the correct answer.

1. A can of soup is in the shape of a cylinder with radius 3.8 cm and height 11 cm. What is the surface area of the can to the nearest tenth? Use 3.14 for π. (Hint: The expression $2\pi r^2 + 2\pi rh$ represents the surface area of a cylinder, where r is the radius and h is the height.)

$r = 3.8$ cm, $h = 11$ cm, Soup

353.2 cm^2

2. One Boston household used the following amounts of electricity to run its heating system during the winter.

Month	Kilowatt-Hours Used
December	1500
January	1463
February	2260

Write an expression that can be used to find the average number of kilowatt hours used. Then simplify the expression. **Possible answer: $(1500 + 1463 + 2260) \div 3$; 1741**

3. In a polygon with n sides, the sum of the measures of the interior angles is $180(n - 2)°$. What is the sum of the measures of the interior angles of a hexagon?

720°

4. In a regular polygon with n sides, the measure of each interior angle is $\frac{180(n-2)°}{n}$. What is the measure of an interior angle of an octagon?

135°

Select the best answer.

5. Anthony had 10 packages of markers. Each package contained 8 markers. He gave his 3 best friends 2 packages each. Which expression shows how many markers he kept for himself?

A $10 \cdot 8 - 10 \cdot 3 \cdot 2$ C $10 \cdot 8 - 3 \cdot 2$
Ⓑ $8(10 - 3 \cdot 2)$ D $8(10 + 3 \cdot 2)$

6. The area of the wall hanging below can be approximated by simplifying $14^2 + \frac{1}{2} \cdot 14 \cdot 8 + \frac{1}{2}(3.14)(7^2)$.

8 in.
14 in.

Which is closest to the area of the wall hanging?

F 160.93 sq in. **Ⓗ** 328.93 sq in.
G 273.98 sq in. J 372.78 sq in.

7. Each month, Mrs. Li pays her phone company \$28 for phone service, and \$0.07 per minute for long distance calls. Which expression represents her bill for a month in which long distance calls totaled 4 hours?

A $4[28 + 60(0.07)]$ C $28 + 0.07 + 4$
Ⓑ $28 + 4(60)(0.07)$ D $28 + 0.07(4)$

1-7 CHALLENGE

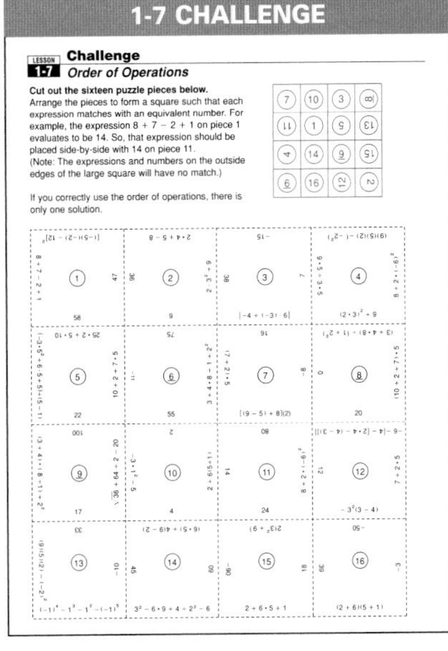
LESSON 1-7 Challenge
Order of Operations

Cut out the sixteen puzzle pieces below.
Arrange the pieces to form a square such that each expression matches with an equivalent number. For example, the expression 8 + 7 − 2 + 1 on piece 1 evaluates to be 14. So, that expression should be placed side-by-side with 14 on piece 11.
(Note: The expressions and numbers on the outside edges of the large square will have no match.)

If you correctly use the order of operations, there is only one solution.

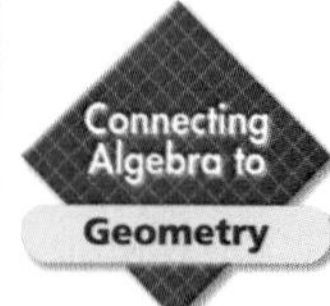

Organizer

See Skills Bank page SB15

Objective: Apply algebra skills of simplifying expressions to finding perimeters of polygons.

Teach

Remember

Students review and apply the concept of perimeter as the sum of the side lengths of a polygon.

INTERVENTION  For additional review and practice on finding the perimeter of polygons, see Skills Bank page SB15.

Inclusion To make sure every side of the polygon is added, have students write a blank that can be filled in with an expression for the length of each side. For example, a triangle has three sides, so students should first write three blanks:

________ + ________ + ________

Close

Assess

Have students draw a rectangle and label the length and width with algebraic expressions. Have them write and simplify an expression for the perimeter. Then have them double the length of each side and write and simplify an expression for the perimeter of the new figure.

California Standards

Reinforcement of 7MG2.0

Perimeter

The distance around a geometric figure is called the *perimeter*. You can use what you have learned about combining like terms to simplify expressions for perimeter.

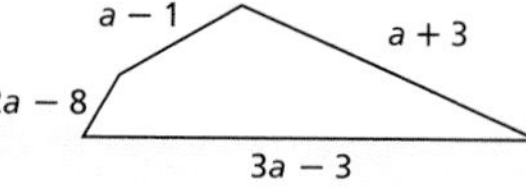

Reinforcement of 7MG2.0 **Students compute the perimeter,** area, and volume **of common geometric objects** and use the results to find measures of less common objects. **They know how perimeter,** area, and volume **are affected by changes of scale.**

A closed figure with straight sides is called a *polygon*. To find the perimeter of a polygon, add the lengths of the sides.

Example 1

A **Write an expression for the perimeter of the quadrilateral.**

$a - 1$, $a + 3$, $2a - 8$, $3a - 3$

Add the lengths of the four sides.

$P = (a + 3) + (2a - 8) + (3a - 3) + (a - 1)$

Combine like terms to simplify.

$P = (a + 2a + 3a + a) + (3 - 8 - 3 - 1)$

$= 7a - 9$ *This is a general expression for the perimeter.*

B **Find the perimeter of this quadrilateral for $a = 5$.**

Substitute 5 for a.

$P = 7(5) - 9$ *Multiply; then subtract.*

$= 35 - 9$

$= 26$ *This is the perimeter when $a = 5$.*

Try This

Write and simplify an expression for the perimeter of each figure.

1. **$6x + 3$**

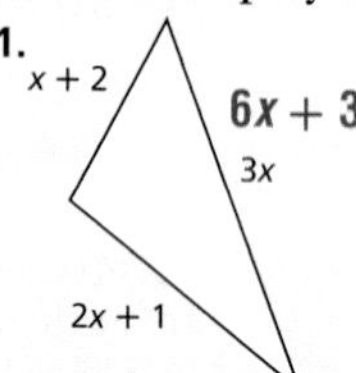

2. **$5b + 3$**

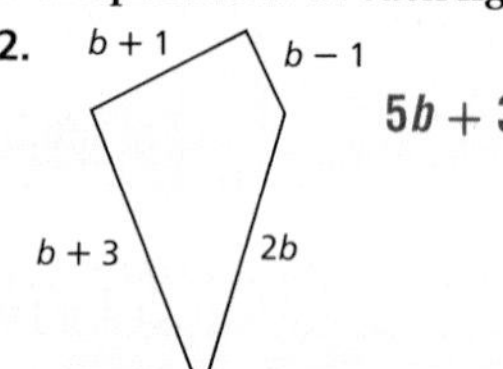

3. **$6m$**

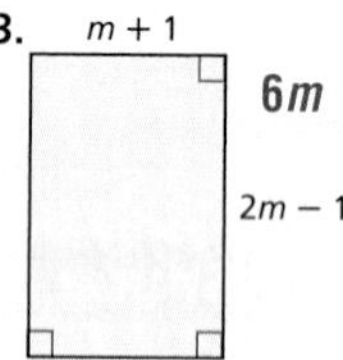

Find the perimeter of each figure for the given value of the variable.

4. $k = 3$ **10**

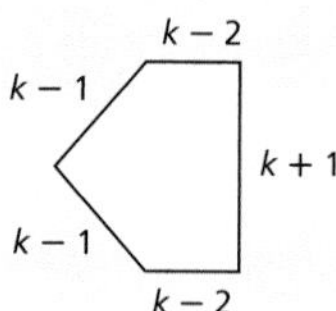

5. $n = 10$ **68**

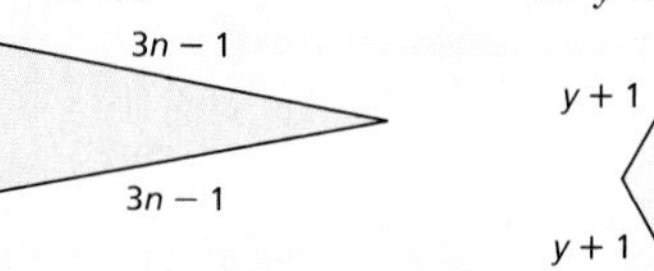

6. $y = 4$ **34**

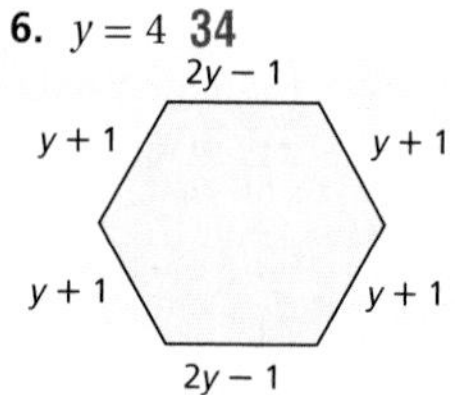

Combining like terms is one way to explore what happens to the perimeter when you double the sides of a triangle or other polygon.

Example 2

What happens to the perimeter of this triangle when you double the length of each side?

Write an expression for the perimeter of the smaller triangle. Combine like terms to simplify the expression.

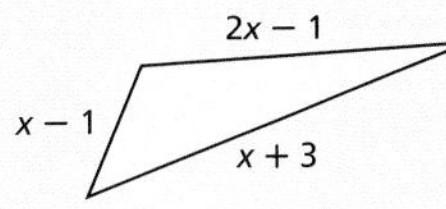

$(x - 1) + (2x - 1) + (x + 3)$

$(x + 2x + x) + (-1 - 1 + 3)$

$4x + 1$ *Perimeter of small triangle*

Double the length of each side of the triangle.

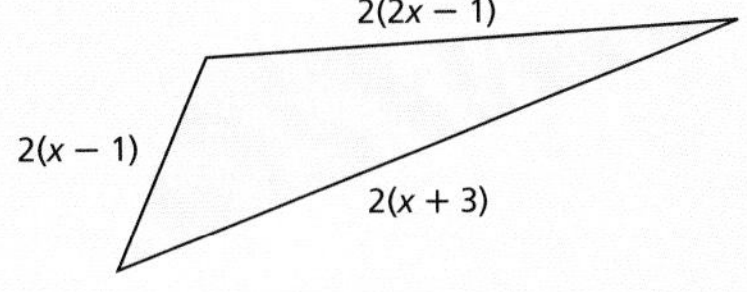

$2(x - 1) = 2x - 2$

$2(2x - 1) = 4x - 2$

$2(x + 3) = 2x + 6$

Find the perimeter of the larger triangle. Combine like terms to simplify.

$(2x - 2) + (4x - 2) + (2x + 6)$ *Add the lengths of the sides.*

$(2x + 4x + 2x) + (-2 - 2 + 6)$ *Use the Associative Property and combine like terms.*

$8x + 2$ *Perimeter of large triangle*

Use the Distributive Property to show that the new perimeter is twice the original perimeter.

$8x + 2 = 2(4x + 1)$

Try This

Each set of expressions represents the side lengths of a triangle. Use the Distributive Property to show that doubling the side lengths doubles the perimeter.

7.	**8.**	**9.**	**10.**
$2p + 1$	$c - 1$	$w + 5$	$h - 2$
$3p + 2$	$2c + 1$	$w + 5$	$3h$
$5p$	$3c - 1$	$3w - 1$	$2h + 3$

Solve each problem.

11. Use the triangles in Example 2. Find the side lengths and perimeters for $x = 5$.

12. The sides of a quadrilateral are $2x - 1$, $x + 3$, $3x + 1$, and $x - 1$. Double the length of each side. Then find an expression for the perimeter of the new figure.
$4x - 2$, $2x + 6$, $6x + 2$, $2x - 2$; $14x + 4$

13. What happens to the perimeter of this trapezoid when you triple the length of each side? Use the variables *a*, *b*, *b*, and *c* for the lengths of the sides. Explain your answer using the Distributive Property.
It triples; $a + b + b + c = a + 2b + c$; $3a + 3b + 3b + 3c = 3a + 6b + 3c$; $3a + 6b + 3c = 3(a + 2b + c)$

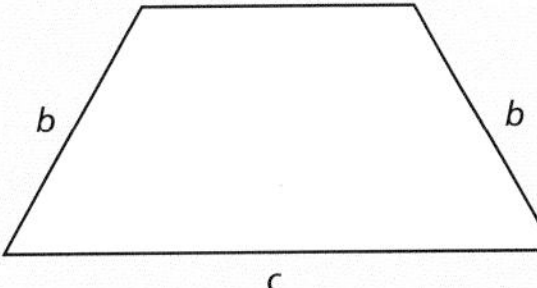

Visual It may benefit some students to draw a diagram when one is not provided, as in Try This problems 7–10.

Answers

7. Perimeter: $10p + 3$; Double perimeter: $20p + 6$; Distrib. Prop: $20p + 6 = 2(10p + 3)$

8. Perimeter: $6c - 1$; Double perimeter: $12c - 2$; Distrib. Prop: $12c - 2 = 2(6c - 1)$

9. Perimeter: $5w + 9$; Double perimeter: $10w + 18$; Distrib. Prop: $10w + 18 = 2(5w + 9)$

10. Perimeter: $6h + 1$; Double perimeter: $12h + 2$; Distrib. Prop: $12h + 2 = 2(6h + 1)$

11. small triangle: 9, 4, 8; 21; large triangle: 18, 8, 16; 42

SECTION 1B

Organizer

Objective: Assess students' ability to apply concepts and skills in Lessons 1-6 and 1-7 in a real-world format.

PREMIER Online Edition

Problem	Text Reference
1	Skills Bank, p. SB16
2	Lesson 1-3
3	Lesson 1-7
4	Skills Bank, p. SB21
5	Lesson 1-7

Answers

1. 108 ft^2, 108 ft^2, 126 ft^2, 126 ft^2; 636 ft^2

5. Lori can buy 25 stickers, or 5 packages.

Packages	Cost($)
1	6
2	12
3	18
4	24
5	30

Stickers	Cost($)
5	6.00
10	12.00
15	18.00
20	24.00
25	30.00

CHAPTER 1

SECTION 1B

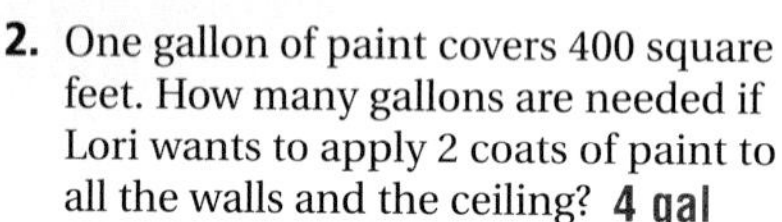

The Tools of Algebra

Design Time Lori's family and Marie's family are redecorating a room in each other's home. They have three days for the decorating project, which will be filmed for a local TV show.

1. Lori decides to paint Marie's room a shade of blue. She measures the height and width of each wall in the rectangular room. She finds that two walls have a width of 12 feet and the other two have a width of 14 feet. The ceiling is 9 feet high. Find the area of each wall. Find the total area of all four walls plus the ceiling.
2. One gallon of paint covers 400 square feet. How many gallons are needed if Lori wants to apply 2 coats of paint to all the walls and the ceiling? **4 gal**
3. Lori decided to build a bedside table in the shape of a cylinder and cover it with yellow fabric on the top and the side. The fabric costs $2.50 per square yard. The table has a radius of 1 foot and a height of 2 feet. What is the cost to cover the table? Use 3.14 for π. **$4.35**

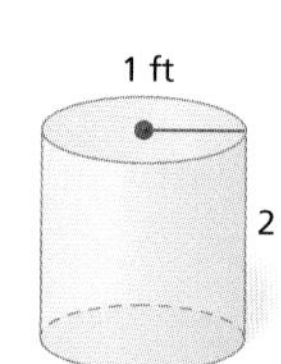
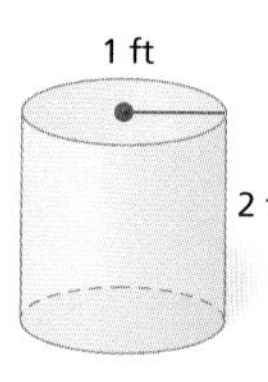

4. Lori will fill a vase with multicolored beads and place it on the bedside table. The vase is in the approximate shape of a cone. The height of the vase is 10 inches, and the radius of the vase at the top is 3 inches. Find the volume of the vase. Use 3.14 for π. (*Hint:* The formula for the volume of a cone is $V = \frac{1}{3}\pi r^2 h$, where r is the radius of the cone and h is the height of the cone.) **about 94.2 in^3**

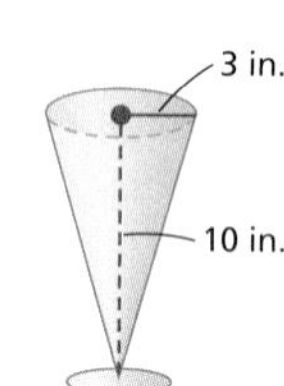

5. Lori wants to create a border around the room using stickers. She can purchase a package of 5 stickers for $6.00. Make a table to show the cost of 1, 2, 3, 4, and 5 packages of stickers. Make another table to show the cost based on the number of stickers (not the number of packages). How many stickers can Lori purchase if she has $32 left in her budget?

56 *Chapter 1 Foundations of Algebra*

INTERVENTION

Scaffolding Questions

1. How can you find the area of one wall? width times height How can you find the area of the ceiling? width of one wall times width of adjacent wall
2. Why is the number of gallons rounded up to the next whole number? Paint is sold in full gallons.
3. How can you find the area of the top of the table? πr^2 How can you find the area of the side? $2\pi rh$ How do you convert ft^2 into yd^2? divide by 3^2
4. How do you find the volume of a cone? $\frac{1}{3}\pi r^2 h$
5. What are the input values in the second table? multiples of 5

Extension

Paint is sometimes sold in quarts. How many gallons and quarts of paint would Lori need to buy in order to have the least amount of paint left over? 3 gallons and 1 quart

CHAPTER 1

SECTION 1B

Quiz for Lessons 1-6 and 1-7

1-6 Properties of Real Numbers

Name the property that is illustrated in each equation. **1. Assoc. Prop. of Add.**

1. $11 + (3 + 4) = (11 + 3) + 4$
2. $12 \cdot 26 = 26 \cdot 12$ **Comm. Prop. of Mult.**
3. $6 + 8 + 2 = 6 + 2 + 8$ **Comm. Prop. of Add.**
4. $ar + 25 = 25 + ar$ **Comm. Prop. of Add.**
5. $a(bc) + 2 = 2 + a(bc)$ **Comm. Prop. of Add.**
6. $5 + (pq)t = 5 + p(qt)$ **Assoc. Prop. of Mult.**

7. Find a counterexample to disprove the statement "The Associative Property is true for subtraction." **Possible answer: $(8 - 2) - 2 \neq 8 - (2 - 2)$**

Write each product using the Distributive Property. Then simplify.

8. $4(29)$ **$4(20) + 4(9)$; 116**
9. $3(204)$ **$3(200) + 3(4)$; 612**
10. $5(37)$ **$5(30) + 5(7)$; 185**
11. $6(28)$ **$6(20) + 6(8)$; 168**
12. $7(85)$ **$7(80) + 7(5)$; 595**
13. $8(32)$ **$8(30) + 8(2)$; 256**

Find a counterexample to show that each statement is false.

14. The set of negative numbers is closed under division. **Possible answer: $-5 \div (-1) = 5$**
15. The real numbers are closed under the operation of taking a square root. **Possible answer: $\sqrt{-9}$ is undefined.**
16. The set of negative numbers is closed under subtraction. **Possible answer: $-1 - (-4) = 3$**

1-7 Simplifying Expressions

Simplify each expression.

17. $75 + 32 + 25$ **132**
18. $5 \cdot 18 \cdot 20$ **1800**
19. $\frac{1}{4} \cdot 19 \cdot 8$ **38**
20. $2(3 + 5)^2$ **128**
21. $6 \div 2 + 2^2$ **7**
22. $2(3)(2 + 1)$ **18**
23. $4k + 15k$ **$19k$**
24. $x^2 + 22x^2$ **$23x^2$**
25. $-2g + 5g$ **$3g$**
26. $5j + 12j$ **$17j$**
27. $16c - 4c$ **$12c$**
28. $17p^3 + 15p^3$ **$32p^3$**
29. $2(5y + 2x) + 3(2y)$ **$16y + 4x$**
30. $3x + 6y + 2x$ **$5x + 6y$**
31. $12x^4 - 3x^2 + 5x^2$ **$12x^4 + 2x^2$**

Use properties and operations to show that the first expression simplifies to the second expression.

32. $3(x + 2) - 3x, 6$
33. $x - 6x^2 + 3x + 4x^2, 4x - 2x^2$
34. $-2(3x + 2y + 4x - 5y), -14x + 6y$

READY TO GO ON? SECTION 1B

Organizer

Objective: Assess students' mastery of concepts and skills in Lessons 1-6 and 1-7.

Resources

Assessment Resources
Section 1B Quiz

INTERVENTION

Resources

Ready to Go On? Intervention and Enrichment Worksheets

Ready to Go On? CD-ROM

Ready to Go On? Online

my.hrw.com

Answers

32–34. See p. A12.

READY TO GO ON?

Diagnose and Prescribe

Ready to Go On? Intervention	*Ready to Go On? Intervention*, Section 1B		
	Worksheets	CD-ROM	Online
Lesson 1-6 — 1.0, 24.3, 25.1	1-6 Intervention	Activity 1-6	Diagnose and Prescribe Online
Lesson 1-7 — 1.1, 25.1	1-7 Intervention	Activity 1-7	

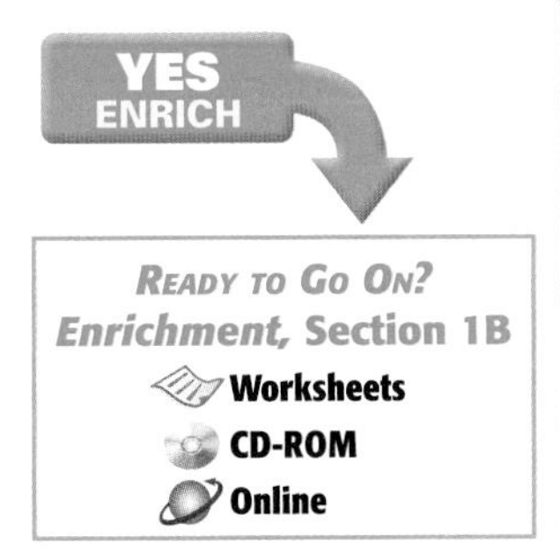

Ready to Go On? Enrichment, Section 1B
Worksheets
CD-ROM
Online

Study Guide: Review

Organizer

Objective: Help students organize and review key concepts and skills presented in Chapter 1.

Online Edition
Multilingual Glossary

Resources

PuzzlePro
One-Stop Planner®

Multilingual Glossary Online
go.hrw.com
KEYWORD: MA8CA Glossary

Lesson *Tutorial Videos* CD-ROM

Test & Practice Generator
One-Stop Planner®

Answers

1. constant
2. whole numbers
3. coefficient
4. term
5. $1.99g$
6. $t + 3$
7. $-5; 0; 5$
8. $-5; 0; 5$
9. $-4; 1; 6$
10. $150 \div m$; 30; 25; 15

Study Guide: Review

Vocabulary

Complete the sentences below with vocabulary words from the list above.

1. A(n) ___?___ is a value that does not change.
2. The ___?___ include the natural numbers and zero.
3. A(n) ___?___ is the numerical factor of a term that contains a variable.
4. A ___?___ is a part of an expression to be added or subtracted.

1-1 Variables and Expressions *(pp. 6–11)*

Prep for 4.0

EXAMPLES

- **Barbara has saved d dollars for a \$65 sweater. Write an expression for the amount of money she still needs to buy the sweater.**

  $65 - d$ — *Think: d dollars less than the price of the sweater.*

- **Evaluate $b - 7$ for the replacement set $\{-1, 3, 15\}$.**

  $b - 7 = -1 - 7$
  $= -8$ — *Substitute the values for the variables.*
  $b - 7 = 3 - 7$
  $= -4$
  $b - 7 = 15 - 7$
  $= 8$

EXERCISES

5. Grapes cost \$1.99 per pound. Write an expression for the cost of g pounds of grapes.
6. Today's temperature is 3 degrees warmer than yesterday's temperature t. Write an expression for today's temperature.

Evaluate each expression for the replacement set $\{-5, 0, 5\}$.

7. $p(1)$
8. $p \div 1$
9. $p + 1$
10. Each member of the art club will make the same number of posters to advertise their club. They will make 150 posters total. Write an expression for how many posters each member will make if there are m members. Find how many posters each member will make if there are 5, 6, and 10 members.

1-2 Adding and Subtracting Real Numbers *(pp. 14–19)*

 2.0

EXAMPLES

Add or subtract.

- $-4 + (-9)$

$-4 + (-9)$ *The signs are the same.*

$4 + 9 = 13$ *Add the absolute values and use the sign of the numbers.*

-13

- $-8 - (-3)$

$-8 - (-3)$

$-8 + 3$ *To subtract −3, add 3.*

-5

EXERCISES

Add or subtract.

11. $-2 + (-12)$ **12.** $-6 + 1.4$ **13.** $9\frac{1}{4} + \left(-4\frac{3}{4}\right)$

14. $\frac{1}{2} - \frac{3}{2}$ **15.** $-8 - 16$ **16.** $6.7 - (-7.6)$

17. $3\frac{1}{3} - \left(-1\frac{2}{3}\right)$

18. A trail starts at an elevation of 2278 feet. It descends 47 feet to a campsite. What is the elevation of the campsite?

1-3 Multiplying and Dividing Real Numbers *(pp. 20–25)*

 2.0

EXAMPLES

Multiply or divide.

- $-12(9)$

$-12(9) = -108$ *The signs are different. The product is negative.*

- $-\frac{5}{6} \div \left(-\frac{3}{4}\right)$

$-\frac{5}{6} \div \left(-\frac{3}{4}\right) = -\frac{5}{6}\left(-\frac{4}{3}\right)$ *To divide by $-\frac{3}{4}$, multiply by $-\frac{4}{3}$.*

$= \frac{(-5)(-4)}{6(3)}$ *Multiply numerators and denominators.*

$= \frac{20}{18} = \frac{10}{9}$ *Simplify.*

EXERCISES

Multiply or divide if possible.

19. $-5(-18)$ **20.** $0 \cdot 10$ **21.** $-4(3.8)$

22. $-56 \div 7$ **23.** $0 \div 0.75$ **24.** $9 \div 0$

Divide.

25. $4 \div \frac{4}{9}$ **26.** $-\frac{1}{2} \div \frac{3}{4}$ **27.** $\frac{6}{7} \div \frac{2}{5}$

28. An exercise program recommends that a person walk at least 10,000 steps every day. At this rate, how many steps would the person walk in 1 year?

1-4 Powers and Exponents *(pp. 26–31)*

 Prep for 2.0

EXAMPLES

- Simplify -3^4.

$-3^4 = -1 \cdot 3 \cdot 3 \cdot 3 \cdot 3$ *Find the product of −1 and four 3's.*

$= -81$

EXERCISES

Write each expression as repeated multiplication. Then simplify the expression.

29. 4^3 **30.** $(-3)^3$ **31.** $(-3)^4$

32. -5^2 **33.** $\left(\frac{2}{3}\right)^3$ **34.** $\left(-\frac{4}{5}\right)^2$

Answers

11. -14
12. -4.6
13. $4\frac{1}{2}$
14. -1
15. -24
16. 14.3
17. 5
18. 2231 ft
19. 90
20. 0
21. -15.2
22. -8
23. 0
24. undefined
25. 9
26. $-\frac{2}{3}$
27. $\frac{15}{7}$
28. 3,650,000 steps
29. $4 \cdot 4 \cdot 4 = 64$
30. $(-3)(-3)(-3) = -27$
31. $(-3)(-3)(-3)(-3) = 81$
32. $-1 \cdot 5 \cdot 5 = -25$
33. $\left(\frac{2}{3}\right)\left(\frac{2}{3}\right)\left(\frac{2}{3}\right) = \frac{8}{27}$
34. $\left(-\frac{4}{5}\right)\left(-\frac{4}{5}\right) = \frac{16}{25}$

Answers

35. 2^4
36. $(-10)^3$
37. $(-8)^2$
38. 12^1
39. 729 in^3
40. 6
41. 14
42. −13
43. −12
44. $\frac{5}{6}$
45. $\frac{1}{3}$
46. 4
47. $\frac{9}{11}$
48. 3
49. rat. number, term. dec., int., whole number, nat. number
50. rat. number, term. dec., int., whole number
51. rat. number, term. dec., int.
52. rat. number, term. dec.
53. irrational number
54. rat. number, repeating dec.
55. rat. number, term. dec., int., whole number, nat. number
56. rat. number, term. dec.
57. rat. number, term. dec.
58. 3.6 ft
59. 4.1 ft
60. Assoc. Prop. of Add.
61. Assoc. Prop. of Mult.
62. Comm. Prop. of Add.
63. Comm. Prop. of Mult.
64. Possible answer: $6 \div 3 \div 2 \neq 3 \div 6 \div 2$

■ **Write −216 as a power of −6.**

$-216 = (-6)(-6)(-6)$ *The product of three −6's is −216.*

$= (-6)^3$

Write each number as a power of the given base.

35. 16; base 2

36. −1000; base −10

37. 64; base −8

38. 12; base 12

39. The interior of a safe is shaped like a cube with edges 9 inches long. What is the volume of the interior of the safe?

1-5 Roots and Irrational Numbers *(pp. 32–37)*

2.0

EXAMPLES

Find each root.

■ $-\sqrt{64}$

$-\sqrt{64} = -\sqrt{8^2}$

$= -8$

■ $\sqrt{\frac{16}{81}}$

$\sqrt{\frac{16}{81}} = \sqrt{\left(\frac{4}{9}\right)^2}$

$= \frac{4}{9}$

■ **Classify −7. Write all classifications that apply.**

$-7 = \frac{-7}{1} = -7.0$

rational

terminating decimal

integer

EXERCISES

Find each root.

40. $\sqrt{36}$ **41.** $\sqrt{196}$ **42.** $-\sqrt{169}$

43. $-\sqrt{144}$ **44.** $\sqrt{\frac{25}{36}}$ **45.** $\sqrt[3]{\frac{1}{27}}$

46. $\sqrt[3]{64}$ **47.** $\sqrt{\frac{81}{121}}$ **48.** $\sqrt[4]{81}$

Write all classifications that apply to each real number.

49. 21 **50.** 0 **51.** −13

52. 0.8 **53.** $\sqrt{3}$ **54.** $\frac{5}{6}$

55. $\sqrt{9}$ **56.** 1.61 **57.** −4.5

58. A tabletop is shaped like a square with an area of 13 square feet. Find the length of one side of the table to the nearest tenth of a foot.

59. Bobbie's new square rug covers an area of 17 square feet. Estimate the side length of the rug to the nearest tenth.

1-6 Properties of Real Numbers *(pp. 42–47)*

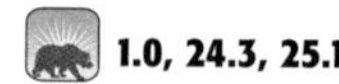

1.0, 24.3, 25.1

EXAMPLES

Name the property that is illustrated in each equation.

■ $(x + 12x) + 4x = x + (12x + 4x)$

The grouping is different.

Associative Property of Addition

■ $x \cdot 7 = 7 \cdot x$

The order is different.

Commutative Property of Multiplication

EXERCISES

Name the property that is illustrated in each equation.

60. $(5 + 2) + 3 = 5 + (2 + 3)$

61. $w(xy) = (wx)y$

62. $(5x + 8) + 6 = (8 + 5x) + 6$

63. $7(3x + 1) = (3x + 1)7$

64. Find a counterexample to disprove the statement "The Commutative Property is true for division."

Write each product using the Distributive Property. Then simplify.

■ $5(25)$

$5(25) = 5(20 + 5)$ *Rewrite 25 as 20 + 5.*

$= 5(20) + 5(5)$ *Use the Distributive Property.*

$= 100 + 25$ *Mulitply.*

$= 125$ *Add.*

Write each product using the Distributive Property. Then simplify.

65. $3(27)$ **66.** $6(12)$

67. $8(17)$ **68.** $7(22)$

69. Find a counterexample to disprove the statement "The irrational numbers are closed under multiplication."

1-7 Simplifying Expressions *(pp. 48–53)*

 **1.1, 25.1**

EXAMPLES

Simplify each expression.

■ $-6f^2 - 8f + 3f^2$

$-6f^2 + 3f^2 - 8f$ *Commutative Property*

$-3f^2 - 8f$ *Combine like terms.*

■ $3x - 4y$

$3x - 4y$ *There are no like terms. It cannot be simplified.*

■ $5x^2 - 3(x - 2) - x$

$5x^2 - 3x - 3(-2) - x$ *Distributive Property*

$5x^2 - 3x + 6 - x$ *Multiply.*

$5x^2 - 3x - x + 6$ *Commutative Property*

$5x^2 - 4x + 6$ *Combine like terms.*

■ **Use properties and operations to show that $4(x + 2) + 5$ simplifies to $4x + 13$.**

Statements	Reasons
1. $4(x + 2) + 5$	
2. $[4x + 4(2)] + 5$	Distributive Property
3. $(4x + 8) + 5$	Multiply.
4. $4x + (8 + 5)$	Associative Property of Addition
5. $4x + 13$	Combine like terms.

EXERCISES

Simplify each expression.

70. $18 + 26 - 8 + 4$ **71.** $60 \cdot 27 \cdot \frac{1}{6}$

72. $2^2 + 12 \cdot 3 - 9$ **73.** $3 \cdot 5 - 14 + \sqrt{4}$

74. $\frac{1}{2} + 5 \cdot 4 + 15$ **75.** $\left[\frac{(6 \cdot 7)}{4 - 1}\right] 2 + 12$

76. The cost in dollars of magazine subscriptions at a particular company can be found by using the expression $\frac{1}{2}(m - 1) + 4$, where m equals the number of subscriptions. Use the expression to find the price of 5 subscriptions.

Simplify each expression.

77. $20x - 16x$ **78.** $2y^2 + 5y^2$

79. $6(x + 4) - 2x$ **80.** $-2(x^2 - 1) + 4x^2$

81. $-2y + 3y^2 - 3y + y$ **82.** $7y + 3y - a - 2y$

83. Rita bought a sandwich, 2 bottles of water, and an apple for lunch. The sandwich cost \$4.99, the bottles of water cost \$1.48 each, and the apple cost \$0.89. How much did Rita spend on lunch?

Use properties and operations to show that the first expression simplifies to the second expression.

84. $2(x + 5) - 3$, $2x + 7$

85. $(5 + y - 3) + 4y$, $5y + 2$

Answers

65. $3(20) + 3(7) = 81$

66. $6(10) + 6(2) = 72$

67. $8(10) + 8(7) = 136$

68. $7(20) + 7(2) = 154$

69. Possible answer: $\sqrt{2} \cdot \sqrt{2} = 2$

70. 40

71. 270

72. 31

73. 3

74. 35.5

75. 40

76. \$6

77. $4x$

78. $7y^2$

79. $4x + 24$

80. $2x^2 + 2$

81. $-4y + 3y^2$

82. $8y - a$

83. \$8.84

84.

Statements	Reasons
1. $2(x + 5) - 3$	
2. $2x + 2(5) - 3$	Distributive Property
3. $2x + 10 - 3$	Multiply.
4. $2x + 7$	Combine like terms

85.

Statements	Reasons
1. $(5 + y - 3) + 4y$	
2. $(5 - 3 + y) + 4y$	Comm. Prop. of Add.
3. $(2 + y) + 4y$	Combine like terms.
4. $2 + (y + 4y)$	Assoc. Prop. of Add.
5. $2 + 5y$	Combine like terms.
6. $5y + 2$	Comm. Prop. of Add.

Organizer

Objective: Assess students' mastery of concepts and skills in Chapter 1.

Online Edition

Resources

Assessment Resources

Chapter 1 Tests

- Free Response (Levels A, B, C)
- Multiple Choice (Levels A, B, C)
- Performance Assessment

***IDEA Works!* CD-ROM**

Modified Chapter 1 Test

CHAPTER TEST

Evaluate each expression for the replacement set {2, 3, 6}.

1. $6 - a$ **4; 3; 0**
2. $a(3)$ **6; 9; 18**
3. $6 \div a$ **3; 2; 1**
4. $\frac{a}{6}$ $\mathbf{\frac{1}{3}; \frac{1}{2}; 1}$
5. $a - 3$ **−1; 0; 3**
6. Write two verbal expressions for $n - 5$. **Possible answer: 5 less than *n*; the difference of *n* and 5**
7. Nate runs 8 miles each week. Write an expression for the number of miles he runs in n weeks. Find the number of miles Nate runs in 5 weeks. **8*n*; 40 mi**

Add or subtract.

8. $-5 + 8$ **3**
9. $-3 - 4$ **−7**
10. $4 + (-7)$ **−3**
11. $7 - (-2)$ **9**

The table shows the lowest temperatures recorded in four states.

12. What is the difference between the lowest temperatures in Hawaii and Alaska? **92°F**
13. What is the difference between the lowest temperatures in Texas and Nebraska? **24°F**

Lowest Temperatures in Four States	
Location	**Temperature (°F)**
Prospect Creek, Alaska	−80
Camp Clarke, Nebraska	−47
Mauna Kea, Hawaii	12
Seminole, Texas	−23

Multiply or divide if possible.

14. $(-3)(-6)$ **18**
15. $-\frac{1}{2} \div \frac{1}{4}$ **−2**
16. $12 \div (-3)$ **−4**
17. $0 \div (-4)$ **0**

Simplify each expression.

18. 5^4 **625**
19. $\left(-\frac{4}{5}\right)^3$ $\mathbf{-\frac{64}{125}}$
20. $\sqrt{25}$ **5**
21. $-\sqrt{36}$ **−6**

Write all classifications that apply to each real number.

22. 30 **rat., term. dec., int., whole, nat.**
23. $\sqrt{6}$ **irr.**
24. −12 **rat., term. dec., int.**
25. $\frac{1}{2}$ **rat., term. dec.**

Name the property that is illustrated in each equation.

26. $7 \cdot 13 = 13 \cdot 7$ **Comm. Prop. of Mult.**
27. $(1 + 32) + 6 = 1 + (32 + 6)$ **Assoc. Prop. of Add.**
28. $(qs)r = (sq)r$ **Comm. Prop. of Mult.**
29. $4 + (24 + 3) = 4 + (3 + 24)$ **Comm. Prop. of Add.**

Simplify each expression.

30. $5\frac{1}{4} + 7 + 2\frac{3}{4}$ **15**
31. $-2(x + 5) + 4x$ $\mathbf{2x - 10}$
32. $3x + 2x^2 - x$ $\mathbf{2x + 2x^2}$
33. $\frac{1}{2}y + \frac{3}{4}y$ $\mathbf{\frac{5}{4}y}$
34. $t^2 + 5t + 3t + 2t^2$ $\mathbf{3t^2 + 8t}$
35. $5k - 4k + 6$ $\mathbf{k + 6}$
36. Find a counterexample to disprove the statement "The rational numbers are closed under the operation of taking the square root." **Possible answer: $\sqrt{7}$ is not rational.**

Use properties and operations to show that the first expression simplifies to the second expression.

37. $5(x + 4) - 10$, $5x + 10$
38. $(x - 2 + 6x) + x$, $8x - 2$

Answers

37.

Statements	Reasons
1. $5(x + 4) - 10$	
2. $5x + 5(4) - 10$	Distrib. Prop.
3. $5x + 20 - 10$	Multiply.
4. $5x + (20 - 10)$	Assoc. Prop. of Add.
5. $5x + 10$	Combine like terms.

38.

Statements	Reasons
1. $(x - 2 + 6x) + x$	
2. $(x + 6x - 2) + x$	Comm. Prop. of Add.
3. $7x - 2 + x$	Combine like terms.
4. $7x + x - 2$	Comm. Prop. of Add.
5. $8x - 2$	Combine like terms.

California Standards

Standard	Exercises
1.0	26–29, 36
1.1	37, 38
Prep for 2.0	1–5, 8, 10, 14
2.0	9, 11–13, 15–21, 23, 36
Prep for 4.0	6, 7, 30–35
24.3	36
25.1	37, 38

COLLEGE ENTRANCE EXAM PRACTICE

FOCUS ON SAT

The SAT is a 3-hour test that is often used to predict academic success at the college level. SAT scores are used to compare the math and verbal reasoning skills of students from all over the world.

In each section of SAT questions, the easier questions are at the beginning of the section and harder questions come later. Answer as many of the easy questions as you can first, and then move on to the more challenging questions.

You may want to time yourself as you take this practice test. It should take you about 8 minutes to complete.

1. The number 0 is NOT an example of which of the following?

(A) Real numbers
(B) Rational numbers
(C) Whole numbers
(D) Integers
(E) Natural numbers

2. A clothing store opens with 75 pairs of jeans on a sale table. By noon, 10 pairs have been sold. As of 2:00, another 8 pairs have been sold. A clerk then restocks with 12 pairs. Receipts show that 18 pairs of jeans were sold after 2:00. How many pairs of jeans are left at the end of the day?

(A) 51
(B) 27
(C) 123
(D) 36
(E) 23

3. If Jack is three times as old as his sister Judy, which of the following expressions represents Jack's age if Judy is j years old?

(A) $3j > j$
(B) $3j$
(C) $j + 3$
(D) $3 - j$
(E) $\frac{1}{3}j$

4. Which of the following is equal to -3^4?

(A) -64
(B) 12
(C) -12
(D) 81
(E) -81

5. What is the result after applying the following sequence of operations to a number n in the given order?

1. Subtract 2.
2. Divide by 3.
3. Add 7.
4. Multiply by -1.

(A) $\frac{n-2}{3} + 7(-1)$
(B) $\frac{(-n-2)+7}{3}$
(C) $-\left(-\frac{2}{3} + 7\right)n$
(D) $-\left(\frac{n-2}{3} + 7\right)$
(E) $n - \frac{2}{3} + 7(-1)$

6. Which property is illustrated by the equation $8(7) + 8(6) = 8(7 + 6)$?

(A) Distributive Property
(B) Associative Property of Multiplication
(C) Commutative Property of Addition
(D) Commutative Property of Multiplication
(E) Associative Property of Addition

COLLEGE ENTRANCE EXAM PRACTICE

Objective: Provide practice for college entrance exams such as the SAT.

Online Edition

Resources

College Entrance Exam Practice

Questions on the SAT represent the following content areas:

Number and Operation, 30–32%

Algebra and Functions, 28–32%

Geometry and Measurement, 27–30%

Data Analysis, Statistics, and Probability, 10–12%

Items on this page focus on:
- Number and Operation

Text References:

Item	1	2	3	4	5	6
Lesson	1-5	1-2	1-1	1-4	1-7	1-6

Teaching Tip

Multiple Choice

1. Students may choose **C** because they do not remember the difference between whole numbers and natural numbers. Remind students that whole numbers are all of the natural numbers and 0.

2. Students who chose **B** may have subtracted the 12 pairs restocked instead of adding them. Students who chose **D** may have found the total number of pairs of jeans sold for the day.

3. Students may choose **A** if they did not read the question carefully; the inequality in **A** is true, but the question asked for an expression for Jack's age. Students who choose answer **E** may think that Judy is three times as old as Jack.

4. Students may choose **D** because they used -3 as the base of the power. Remind students that the exponent applies only to the number right before it, and that -3^4 can be thought of as $(-1)(3^4)$.

5. Students may choose **E** if they did not perform each step on the entire expression obtained from the previous step. Remind students of the need to use grouping symbols when translating words into algebraic expressions.

6. Students may choose **B** because they do not understand the Distributive Property. Ask students about the meaning of the word *distribute* and discuss how it can be applied to an algebraic expression.

Organizer

Objective: Provide opportunities to learn and practice common test-taking strategies.

 **Online Edition**

Teaching Tip **Multiple Choice** This Strategy for Success focuses on using logic and estimation to eliminate answer choices. While this strategy may not always yield a single answer, it may save students time by eliminating some of the choices. In addition, it helps students analyze items before they begin to work.

Multiple Choice: Eliminate Answer Choices

You can answer some problems without doing many calculations. Use logic to eliminate answer choices and save time.

EXAMPLE 1

Which number is the square of 123,765?

Ⓐ 15,317,775,225 Ⓒ 15,317,775,230

Ⓑ 15,317,775,233 Ⓓ 15,317,775,227

Your calculator will not help you on this question. Due to rounding, any of the answer choices are possible.

But you can use this fact to eliminate three of the answer choices:

The square of any number ending in 5 is also a number ending in 5.

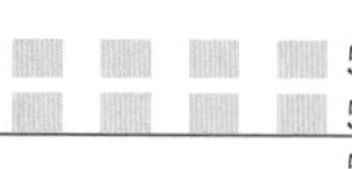

The only answer choice that ends in 5 is A, 15,317,775,225.

EXAMPLE 2

What is a possible area of the wooden triangle shown?

Ⓐ 11 square feet Ⓒ 14 square feet

Ⓑ 20 square feet Ⓓ 24 square feet

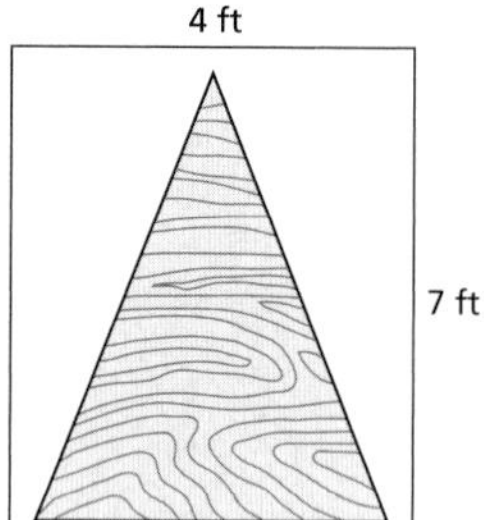

The triangle is inside a rectangle with an area of $7 \times 4 = 28$ square feet.

If the triangle had the same base and height as the rectangle, its area would be half the area of the rectangle, 14 square feet.

However, the triangle fits inside the rectangle, so its area must be less than 14 square feet.

The only answer choice that is less than 14 square feet is A, 11 square feet.

Try to eliminate unreasonable answer choices. Some choices may be too great or too small, have incorrect units, or not be divisible by a necessary number.

Read each test item and answer the questions that follow.

Item A

The top speed of a three-toed sloth is 0.12 miles per hour. About how many feet can a sloth travel in an hour?

Ⓐ 0.12 feet
Ⓑ 600 feet
Ⓒ 2.27 feet
Ⓓ 7500 inches

1. Are there any answer choices you can eliminate immediately? If so, which choices and why?
2. Describe how you can use estimation to find the correct answer.

Item B

A city park is shaped like a triangle. The Liberty Street side of the park is 120 feet long, and the First Avenue side is 50 feet long.

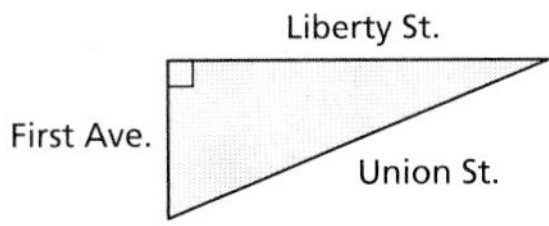

What is the approximate length of the side of the park that faces Union Street?

Ⓐ 25 feet
Ⓑ 110 inches
Ⓒ 65 feet
Ⓓ 130 feet

3. Can any of the answer choices be eliminated immediately? If so, which choices and why?
4. Are there any properties you can use to solve this problem? If so, what are they?
5. Describe how to find the correct answer without doing any calculations.

Item C

Approximately how long will the average 18-year-old have slept in his lifetime?

Ⓐ 6 weeks
Ⓑ 6 months
Ⓒ 6 years
Ⓓ 6 decades

6. Which answer choice can be eliminated immediately? Why?
7. Explain how to use mental math to solve this problem.

Item D

Sheila's paychecks for February and March were equal. If she worked every day during both months, for which month was her daily pay lower?

Ⓐ February
Ⓑ March
Ⓒ Her daily pay did not change.
Ⓓ Cannot be determined

8. What do you need to know to solve this problem?
9. Describe how you can find the correct answer.

Item E

Greg tripled the number of baseball cards he had last week. Which of these could be the number of cards Greg has now?

Ⓐ 100
Ⓑ 200
Ⓒ 150
Ⓓ 250

10. The number of cards that Greg has now must be divisible by what number? How can you tell if a number is divisible by this number?
11. Describe how to find the answer to this problem.

Answers

Possible answers:

1. **D;** the units are incorrect
2. 0.12 mi is about $\frac{1}{10}$ mile, and 1 mile is about 5000 ft, so the answer should be close to $\frac{1}{10}(5000)$, or 500 ft. **B** is the only choice close to 500 ft.
3. **B;** the units are incorrect
4. Pythagorean Theorem, Triangle Inequality Theorem
5. Union Street is the hypotenuse of a right triangle, which means it is the longest side. So Union Street must be longer than 120 ft and 50 ft. **D** is the only choice greater than both of these distances.
6. **D;** 6 decades = 60 years, which is longer than 18 years.
7. People sleep 6–8 hours each day, or 6 to 8 out of each 24. This is about $\frac{1}{4}$ to $\frac{1}{3}$ of each day An 18-year-old will spend about $\frac{1}{4}$ to $\frac{1}{3}$ of 18 years asleep, which is about 4.5 to 6 years. **C** is the correct response.
8. the number of days in February and in March
9. February always has fewer days than March. If Sheila made the same amount of money each month, her daily pay must have been lower in March. **B** is the correct response.
10. 3; the sum of the digits will be divisible by 3.
11. Add the digits of each response and check if the sum is divisible by 3. **C** is the only choice divisible by 3.

Answers to Test Items

A. B
B. D
C. C
D. B
E. C

California Standards

Algebra 1 15.0, 25.1

MASTERING THE STANDARDS

Organizer

Objective: Provide review and practice for Chapter 1.

Online Edition

Resources

Assessment Resources

Chapter 1 Cumulative Test

Focus on California Standards Benchmark Tests and Intervention

California Standards Practice CD-ROM

go.hrw.com
KEYWORD: MA8CA Practice

MASTERING THE STANDARDS

CUMULATIVE ASSESSMENT, CHAPTER 1

Multiple Choice

1. Eric is collecting gifts for a charity event. He needs 150 gifts. So far he has collected x gifts. Which expression represents how many gifts Eric still needs to collect?

(A) $150 + x$ (C) $x - 150$
(B) $150 - x$ (D) $150 \div x$

2. An online store sells birdhouses for $34.95 each. For each order, there is a one-time shipping and handling fee of $7.50. Which expression can be used to represent the cost of ordering x birdhouses?

(A) $x + 34.95 + 7.50$
(B) $(34.95 + 7.50)x$
(C) $7.50x + 34.95$
(D) $34.95x + 7.50$

3. The number of CDs in Olivia's collection can be found using the expression $6S + 8E + 10T + 15F$. Use the table to find the total number of CDs in Olivia's collection.

Stacks of CDs	Number
Stack of 6 (S)	4
Stack of 8 (E)	2
Stack of 10 (T)	3
Stack of 15 (F)	1

(A) 10 **(C)** 85
(B) 39 (D) 49

4. The equation $C = \frac{5}{9}(F - 32)$ relates the Celsius temperature C to the Fahrenheit temperature F. What is the Celsius temperature if the Fahrenheit temperature is -13 degrees?

(A) -45°C **(C)** -25°C
(B) -39.2°C (D) -10.6°C

5. Which equation is NOT true?

(A) $55 + 27 + 45 = 100 + 27$
(B) $5 \cdot 7 \cdot \frac{2}{5} = 2 \cdot 7$
(C) $14(126) = 14(100) + 14(26)$
(D) $31(152) = 30(150) + 1(2)$

6. The radius of a ball is 4 inches. What is the volume of the ball in cubic inches?

(A) 16π in^3
(B) $\frac{64\pi}{3}$ in^3
(C) $\frac{256\pi}{3}$ in^3
(D) $\frac{4096\pi}{3}$ in^3

7. Which of the following real numbers can be written as a terminating decimal?

(A) π
(B) $\frac{3}{2}$
(C) $\frac{4}{9}$
(D) $\frac{1}{3}$

8. At one time, a U.S. dollar had the same value as 11.32 Mexican pesos. To the nearest hundredth, how many Mexican pesos were equal to 16 U.S. dollars at that time?

(A) 1.41 pesos
(B) 4.68 pesos
(C) 27.32 pesos
(D) 181.12 pesos

California Standards

Standard	Items
6AF1.3	5
7AF1.1	1, 2, 3, 8, 9, 11, 12, 15a, 16
7AF1.2	4, 6
7AF1.3 🔑	14a, 15c
7AF1.4	7
7MG2.1	10, 13
25.2	14b, 15b
25.1	14c

Teaching Tip

Multiple Choice For **Item 8,** students may confuse the operations of multiplication and division. Students who chose **A** may have divided 16 by 11.32. Encourage students to write down the information in their own words:

$$\$1 = 11.32 \text{ pesos}$$
$$\$16 = ? \text{ pesos}$$

Students should see that the answer will be greater than 11.32.

Read each question carefully. Be sure you understand what the question is asking before looking at the answer choices or beginning your calculations.

9. Tickets to a festival cost \$5.00 each, and lunch costs \$8.50 per person. Renting a bus to transport everyone to and from the festival costs \$47.00. Which expression gives the cost of x people going to the festival?

(A) $5.00 + 8.50 + 47.00$

(B) $5.00x + 8.50 + 47.00$

(C) $5.00 + 8.50x + 47.00$

(D) $5.00x + 8.50x + 47.00$

10. Tariq cut a rectangular piece of paper in half to make two triangles, as shown.

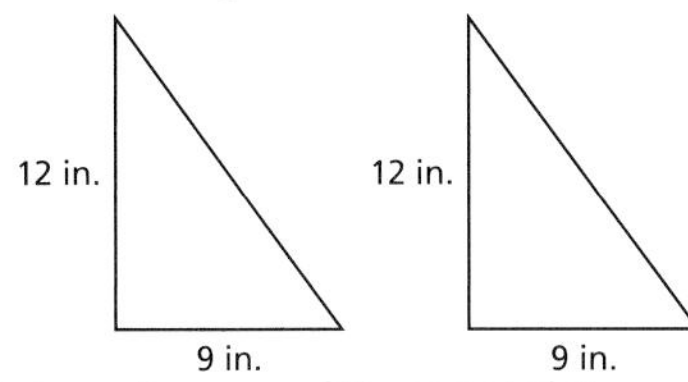

What was the area of the rectangle?

(A) 42 in.

(B) 54 in^2

(C) 72 in.

(D) 108 in^2

Gridded Response

11. A scientist prepares 4 beakers of an acid solution. Each beaker contains 70.9 milliliters of the solution. How many milliliters of acid solution did the scientist prepare in all? **283.6**

12. At an accident scene, an insurance inspector finds a skid mark 60 feet long. The inspector can determine how fast the car was going in miles per hour when the driver applied the breaks by using the expression $\sqrt{21d}$, where d is the length of the skid mark in feet. To the nearest tenth, what was the speed of the car that left the skid mark? **35.5**

13. What is the area in square meters of the robot sumo-wrestling ring shown below? Use 3.14 for π. Round to the nearest tenth. **1.8**

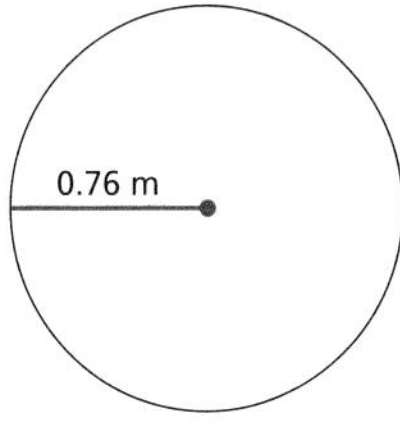

Short Response

14. Use the table to answer the questions below.

Statements	Reasons
1. $3(2 + z - 4) + 7z$	
2. $3(2 - 4 + z) + 7z$	?
3. $3(-2 + z) + 7z$	Combine like terms.
4. $(3(-2) + 3(z)) + 7z$	Distributive Property
5. $(-6 + 3z) + 7z$	Multiply.
6. $-6 + (3z + 10z)$	Associative Property of Addition
7. $-6 + 10z$	Combine like terms.
8. $10z - 6$	Commutative Property of Addition

a. What property was used to get from step 1 to step 2? **Comm. Prop. of Add.**

b. Can $10z - 6$ be simplified any further? **no**

c. Would the expression be the same if step 4 was used before step 3? Explain.
yes; $3(-2) = 3(2) - 3(4)$

15. As part of a challenge problem, a math teacher writes the following expression on the board:

$$-(-x).$$

a. If x is 12, what is the value of the expression? **12**

b. If x is a negative number, is the value of the expression positive or negative? Explain how you found your answer.

c. Simplify the expression. ***x***

Extended Response

16. Fatima enrolled in a traveler rewards program. She begins with 10,000 bonus points. For every trip she takes, she collects 3000 bonus points.

a. Write an expression for the number of bonus points Fatima has after x trips. **$10{,}000 + 3000x$**

b. Make a table showing the number of bonus points Fatima has after 0, 1, 2, 3, 4, and 5 trips.

c. When Fatima has collected 20,000 bonus points, she earns a free vacation. How many trips does Fatima need to take to earn a free vacation? **4 trips**

Short-Response Rubric

Items 14–15

2 Points = The student's answer is an accurate and complete execution of the task or tasks.

1 Point = The student's answer contains attributes of an appropriate response but is flawed.

0 Points = The student's answer contains no attributes of an appropriate response.

Extended-Response Rubric

Item 16

4 Points = The student correctly writes an expression in part **a** and a complete table in part **b,** and answers part **c,** showing all work.

3 Points = The student correctly writes an expression in part **a** and a complete table in part **b** but does not answer part **c.**

2 Points = The student answers all parts correctly but does not show any work or explanation, or the student correctly answers parts **a** and **b** but does not correctly answer part **c.**

1 Point = The student does not give a correct expression in part **a** but performs the correct operations in the other parts of the problem, or the student attempts to answer all parts of the problem, but does not correctly answer any part.

0 Points = The student does not answer correctly and does not attempt all parts of the problem.

Answers

15b. negative; possible answer: The innermost negative sign makes the negative number positive. The negative sign on the outside then makes the number negative again.

16b.

Trips	Bonus Points
0.	10,000
1	13,000
2	16,000
3	19,000
4	22,000
5	25,000

Equations

✔	Grade-level Standard
◄	Review
►	Beyond the Standards
A	Assessment
O	Optional

Pacing Guide

Calendar Planner
Teacher's **One-Stop** Planner®

Lesson/Lab		California Standards	Time	Advanced Students	Benchmark Students	Strategic Students
2-1	Solving One-Step Equations	**Preparation for 5.0, 2.0**	50 min	O	◄	◄
CN	Area of Composite Figures	**Reinforcement of Grade 7 MG2.2**	25 min	O	◄	◄
2-2	Solving Two-Step Equations	**Preparation for 5.0**	50 min	O	◄	◄
2-3	Solving Multi-Step Equations	**4.0, 5.0**	50 min	✔	✔	✔
LAB	True Equations	**25.3**	25 min	✔	✔	✔
2-4	Solving Equations with Variables on Both Sides	**4.0, 5.0**	50 min	✔	✔	✔
LR	Deductive Reasoning	**5.0, 24.1, 24.2, 25.1, 25.2**	50 min	✔	✔	✔
Concept Connection		**5.0**	25 min	A	A	O
Ready to Go On?			25 min	A	A	A
2-5	Solving Proportions	**15.0**	75 min	O	◄	◄
LR	Proving Conditional Statements	**Extension of 5.0, 24.1, 24.2, 25.1**	25 min	✔	✔	✔
2-6	Solving Literal Equations for a Variable	**Extension of 5.0**	50 min	►	O	O
2-7	Solving Absolute-Value Equations	**3.0, 5.0**	50 min	✔	✔	✔
Concept Connection		**3.0**	25 min	A	A	O
Ready to Go On?			25 min	A	A	A
Study Guide: Review			50 min	✔	✔	✔
Chapter Test		**3.0, 5.0, 15.0**	50 min	A	A	A

* **Benchmark students** are achieving at or near grade level.
** **Strategic students** may be a year or more below grade level, and may require additional time for intervention.

Countdown to Mastery, Weeks 3, 4, 5

ONGOING ASSESSMENT and INTERVENTION

	DIAGNOSE	PRESCRIBE
Assess Prior Knowledge	**Before Chapter 2**	
	Diagnose readiness for the chapter.	Prescribe intervention.
	 **Are You Ready?** SE p. 69	 ***Are You Ready? Intervention*** Skills 48, 51, 55, 58, 60
Formative Assessment	**Before Every Lesson**	
	Diagnose readiness for the lesson.	Prescribe intervention.
	Warm Up TE, every lesson	**Skills Bank** pp. SB1–SB32 **Review for Mastery** CRF Chapters 1–2
	During Every Lesson	
	Diagnose understanding of lesson concepts.	Prescribe intervention.
	Questioning Strategies TE, every example **Check It Out!** SE, every example **Think and Discuss** SE, every lesson **Write About It** SE, every lesson **Journal** TE, every lesson	**Reading Strategies** CRF, every lesson ***Success for ELL*** pp. 15–28 ***Lesson Tutorial Videos*** Chapter 2
	After Every Lesson	
	Diagnose mastery of lesson concepts.	Prescribe intervention.
	Lesson Quiz TE, every lesson **Alternative Assessment** TE, every lesson **Ready to Go On?** SE pp. 101, 121 ***Test and Practice Generator***	**Review for Mastery** CRF, every lesson **Problem Solving** CRF, every lesson ***Ready to Go On? Intervention*** Chapter 2 ***Homework Help Online***
	Before Chapter 2 Testing	
	Diagnose mastery of concepts in the chapter.	Prescribe intervention.
	Ready to Go On? SE pp. 101, 121 **Concept Connection** SE pp. 100, 120 **Section Quizzes** AR pp. 25–26 ***Test and Practice Generator***	 ***Ready to Go On? Intervention*** Chapter 2 **Scaffolding Questions** TE pp. 100, 120
	Before Assessment of California Standards	
	Diagnose mastery of California Standards.	Prescribe intervention.
	 ***Focus on California Standards: Benchmark Tests*** **Mastering the Standards** SE pp. 130–131 ***California Standards Practice* CD-ROM**	 ***Focus on California Standards: Intervention***
Summative Assessment	**After Chapter 2**	
	Check mastery of chapter concepts.	Prescribe intervention.
	Multiple-Choice Tests (Forms A, B, C) **Free-Response Tests (Forms A, B, C)** **Performance Assessment** AR pp. 27–40 ***Test and Practice Generator***	**Review for Mastery** CRF, every lesson ***Lesson Tutorial Videos*** Chapter 2

KEY: **SE** = *Student Edition* **TE** = *Teacher's Edition* **CRF** = *Chapter Resource File* **AR** = *Assessment Resources* Available online Available on CD-ROM

Supporting the Teacher

Chapter 2 Resource File

Family Involvement
pp. 1–4, 37–40

Practice A, B, C
pp. 5–7, 13–15, 21–23, 29–31, 41–43, 49–51, 57–59

Review for Mastery
pp. 8–9, 16–17, 24–25, 32–33, 44–45, 52–53, 60–61

Challenge
pp. 10, 18, 26, 34, 46, 54, 62

Problem Solving
pp. 11, 19, 27, 35, 47, 55, 63

Reading Strategies ELL
pp. 12, 20, 28, 36, 48, 56, 64

Workbooks

Homework and Practice Workbook 
Teacher's Edition .... pp. 8–14

Know-It Notebook SPANISH
Teacher's Guide .... Chapter 2

Review for Mastery Workbook SPANISH
Teacher's Guide .... pp. 15–28

Focus on California Standards: Intervention Workbook SPANISH
Teacher's Guide

Teacher Tools

Power Presentations
Complete PowerPoint® presentations for Chapter 2 lessons

Lesson Tutorial Videos SPANISH
Holt authors Ed Burger and Freddie Renfro present tutorials to support the Chapter 2 lessons.

Teacher's One-Stop Planner SPANISH
Easy access to all Chapter 2 resources and assessments, as well as software for lesson planning, test generation, and puzzle creation

IDEA Works!
Key Chapter 2 resources and assessments modified to address special learning needs

Solutions Key .... Chapter 2

Interactive Answers and Solutions

TechKeys

Lab Resources

Project Teacher Support 

Parent Resources

Transparencies

Lesson Transparencies, Volume 1 .... Chapter 2
- Teacher Tools
- Warm-ups
- Teaching Transparencies
- Lesson Quizzes

Alternate Openers: Explorations .... pp. 8–14

Countdown to Mastery .... pp. 5–8

Know-It Notebook .... Chapter 2
- Vocabulary
- Key Concepts
- Graphic Organizers
- Chapter Review
- Big Ideas

Technology Highlights for the Teacher

Power Presentations

Dynamic presentations to engage students. Complete PowerPoint® presentations for every lesson in Chapter 2.

2-1 Solving One-Step Equations

Isolate a variable by using inverse operations which "undo" operations on the variable.

An equation is like a balanced scale. To keep the balance, perform the same operation on both sides.

Inverse Operations	
Operation	**Inverse Operation**
Addition	Subtraction
Subtraction	Addition

One-Stop Planner SPANISH

Easy access to Chapter 2 resources and assessments. Includes lesson planning, test generation, and puzzle creation software.

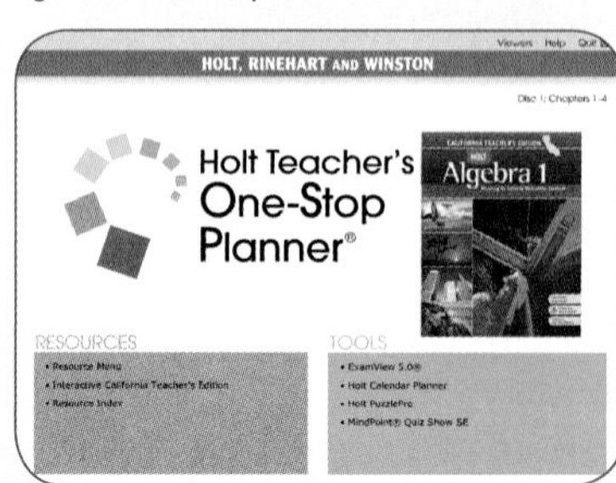

Premier Online Edition SPANISH

Includes Tutorial Videos, Lesson Activities, Lesson Quizzes, Homework Help, Chapter Project and more.

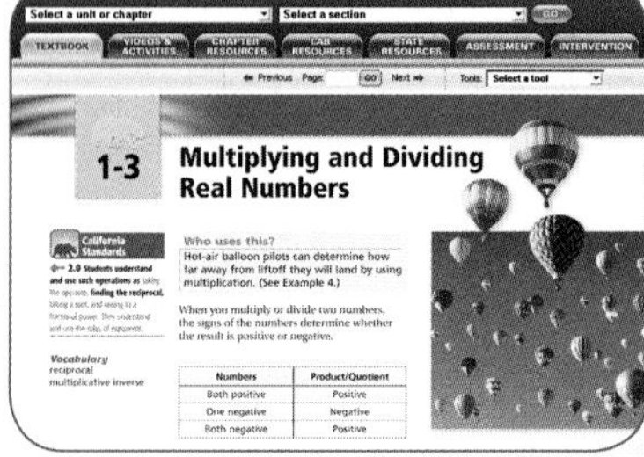

KEY: **SE** = *Student Edition* **TE** = *Teacher's Edition*   English Language Learners  Spanish available  Available online  Available on CD-ROM

Universal Access

Teaching Tips to help all students appear throughout the chapter. A few that target specific students are included in the lists below.

Strategic Students

Practice A .... CRF, every lesson
Review for Mastery .... CRF, every lesson
Reading Strategies .... CRF, every lesson
Academic Vocabulary Connections .... TE p. 70
Concrete Manipulatives .... TE pp. 73, 80, 115
Questioning Strategies .... TE, every example
Ready to Go On? Intervention .... Chapter 2
Know-It Notebook SPANISH .... Chapter 2
Homework Help Online
Lesson Tutorial Videos SPANISH
Online Interactivities SPANISH

Special Needs Students

Practice A .... CRF, every lesson
Review for Mastery .... CRF, every lesson
Reading Strategies .... CRF, every lesson
Academic Vocabulary Connections .... TE p. 70
Inclusion .... TE pp. 74, 80
IDEA Works! Modified Resources .... Chapter 2
Ready to Go On? Intervention .... Chapter 2
Know-It Notebook SPANISH .... Chapter 2
Lesson Tutorial Videos SPANISH
Online Interactivities SPANISH

English Learners

ENGLISH LANGUAGE LEARNERS

Reading Strategies .... CRF, every lesson
Vocabulary Exercises .... SE, every exercise set
Academic Vocabulary Connections .... TE p. 70
English Language Learners .... TE pp. 89, 106
Language Support .... TE pp. 89, 106, 112
Success for English Language Learners .... Chapter 2
Know-It Notebook SPANISH .... Chapter 2
Multilingual Glossary
Lesson Tutorial Videos SPANISH

Benchmark Students

Practice B .... CRF, every lesson
Problem Solving .... CRF, every lesson
Academic Vocabulary Connections .... TE p. 70
Questioning Strategies .... TE, every example
Ready to Go On? Intervention .... Chapter 2
Know-It Notebook SPANISH .... Chapter 2
Homework Help Online
Online Interactivities SPANISH

Advanced Students

Practice C .... CRF, every lesson
Challenge .... CRF, every lesson
Reading and Writing Math EXTENSION .... TE p. 71
Concept Connection EXTENSION .... TE pp. 100, 120
Advanced Learners/GATE .... TE p. 86
Ready to Go On? Enrichment .... Chapter 2

Technology Highlights for Universal Access

Lesson Tutorial Videos SPANISH

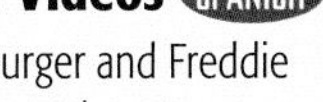

Starring Holt authors Ed Burger and Freddie Renfro! Live tutorials to support every lesson in Chapter 2.

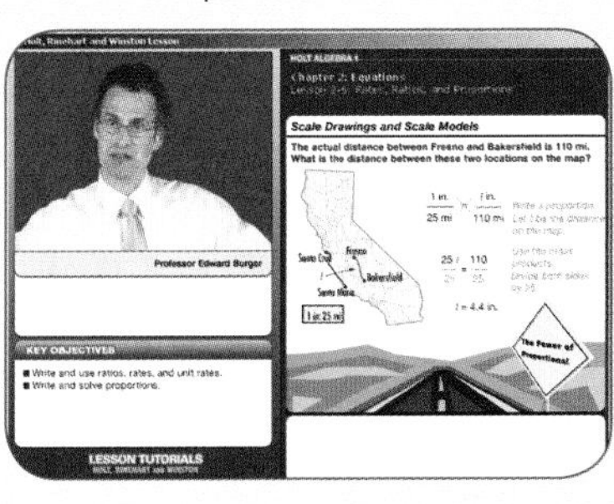

Multilingual Glossary

Searchable glossary includes definitions in English, Spanish, Vietnamese, Chinese, Hmong, Korean, and other languages.

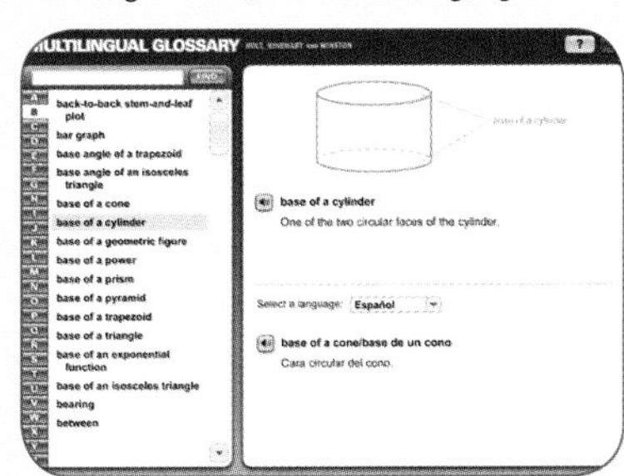

Online Interactivities SPANISH

Interactive tutorials provide visually engaging alternative opportunities to learn concepts and master skills.

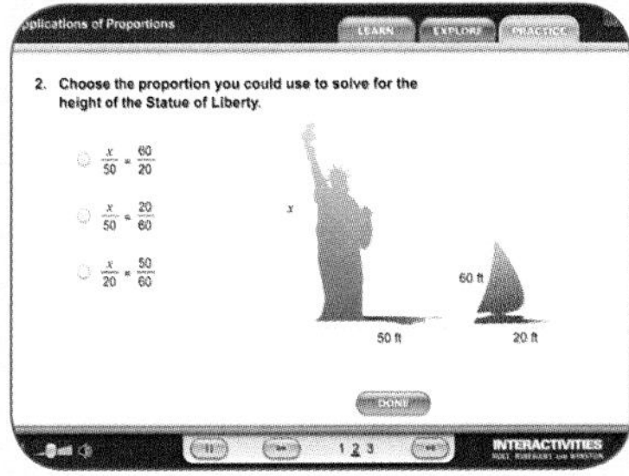

KEY: **SE** = *Student Edition* **TE** = *Teacher's Edition* **CRF** = *Chapter Resource File* SPANISH Spanish available  Available online  Available on CD-ROM

Ongoing Assessment

Assessing Prior Knowledge

Determine whether students have the prerequisite concepts and skills for success in Chapter 2.

Are You Ready? SPANISH .... SE p. 69
Warm Up .... TE, every lesson

Chapter and Standards Assessment

Provide review and practice for Chapter 2 and standards mastery.

Concept Connection .... SE pp. 100, 120
Study Guide: Review .... SE pp. 122–125
Strategies for Success .... SE pp. 128–129
Mastering the Standards .... SE pp. 130–131
College Entrance Exam Practice .... SE p. 127
***Countdown to Mastery* Transparencies** .... pp. 5–8
Focus on California Standards: Benchmark Tests
Focus on California Standards: Intervention Workbook
***California Standards Practice* CD-ROM** SPANISH
IDEA Works! Modified Worksheets and Tests

Alternative Assessment

Assess students' understanding of Chapter 2 concepts and combined problem-solving skills.

Alternative Assessment .... TE, every lesson
Performance Assessment .... AR pp. 39–40
Portfolio Assessment .... AR p. xxxiii
Chapter 2 Project

Daily Assessment

Provide formative assessment for each day of Chapter 2.

Questioning Strategies .... TE, every example
Think and Discuss .... SE, every lesson
Check It Out! Exercises .... SE, every example
Write About It .... SE, every lesson
Journal .... TE, every lesson
Lesson Quiz .... TE, every lesson
Alternative Assessment .... TE, every lesson
IDEA Works! Modified Lesson Quizzes .... Chapter 2

Weekly Assessment

Provide formative assessment for each week of Chapter 2.

Concept Connection .... SE pp. 100, 120
Ready to Go On? .... SE pp. 101, 121
Cumulative Assessment .... SE pp. 130–131
Test and Practice Generator SPANISH .. *One-Stop Planner*

Formal Assessment

Provide summative assessment of Chapter 2 mastery.

Section Quizzes .... AR pp. 25–26
Chapter 2 Test SPANISH .... SE p. 126
Chapter Test (Levels A, B, C) .... AR pp. 27–38
• Multiple Choice • Free Response
Cumulative Test .... AR pp. 41–44
Test and Practice Generator SPANISH .. *One-Stop Planner*

Technology Highlights for Ongoing Assessment

Are You Ready? SPANISH

Automatically assess readiness and prescribe intervention for Chapter 2 prerequisite skills.

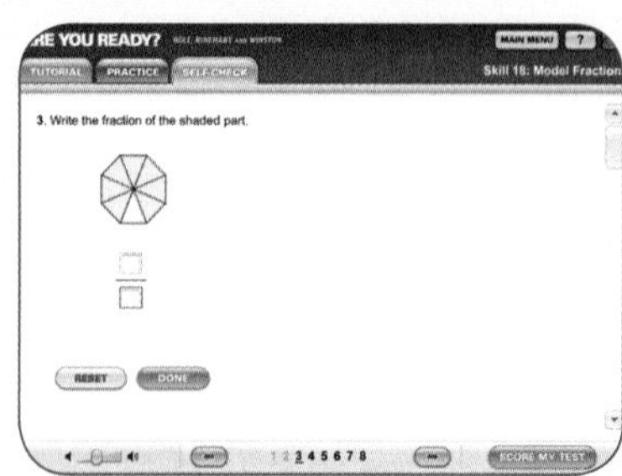

Ready to Go On? SPANISH

Automatically assess understanding of and prescribe intervention for Sections 2A and 2B.

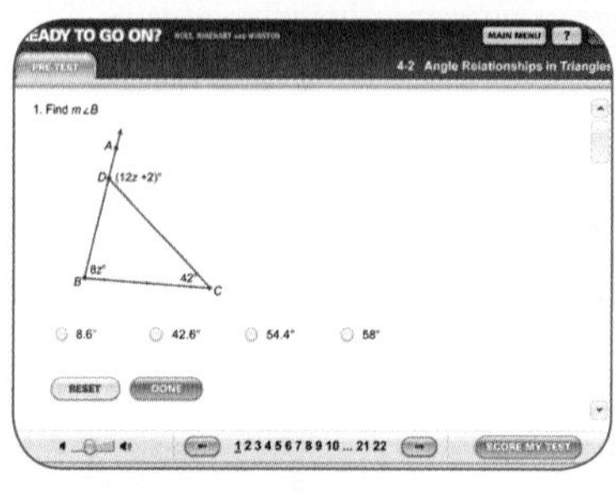

Focus on California Standards: Benchmark Tests and Intervention SPANISH

Automatically assess proficiency with California Algebra I Standards and provide intervention.

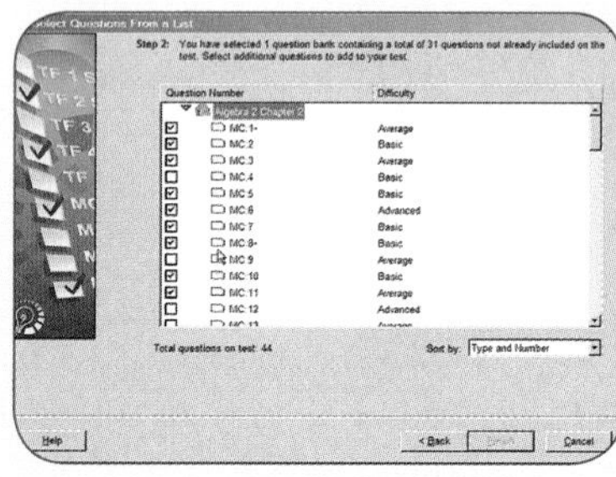

KEY: **SE** = *Student Edition* **TE** = *Teacher's Edition* **AR** = Assessment Resources SPANISH Spanish available Available online  Available on CD-ROM

Three levels (A, B, C) of multiple-choice and free-response chapter tests are available in the *Assessment Resources*.

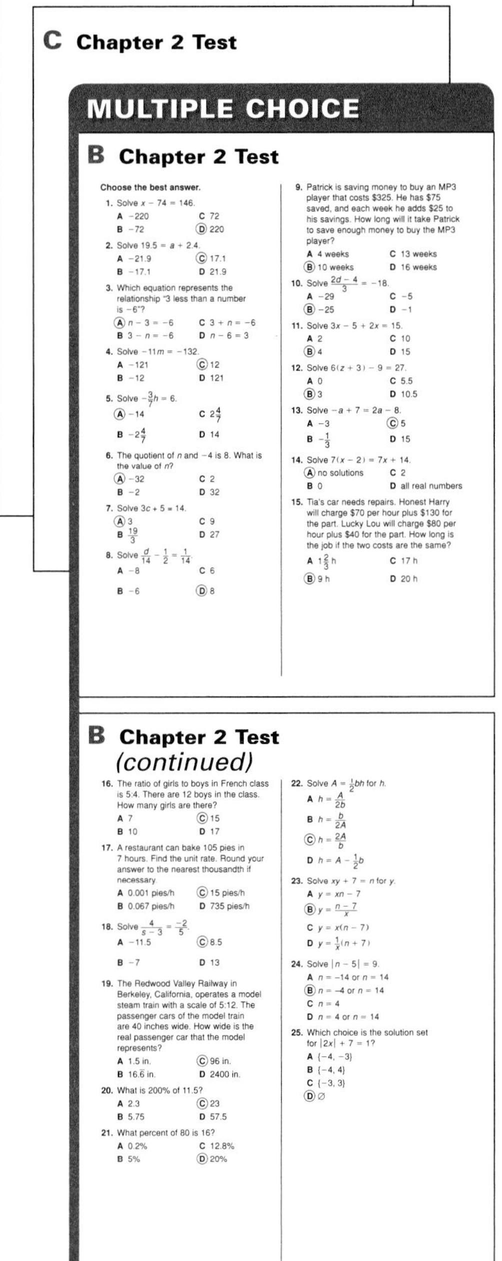

A Chapter 2 Test

C Chapter 2 Test

MULTIPLE CHOICE

B Chapter 2 Test

Choose the best answer.

1. Solve $x - 74 = 146$.
   A −220 C 72
   B −72 (D) 220
2. Solve $19.5 = a + 2.4$.
   A −21.9 (C) 17.1
   B −17.1 D 21.9
3. Which equation represents the relationship "3 less than a number is −6"?
   (A) $n - 3 = -6$ C $3 + n = -6$
   B $3 - n = -6$ D $n - 6 = 3$
4. Solve $-11m = -132$.
   A −121 (C) 12
   B −12 D 121
5. Solve $-\frac{3}{7}h = 6$.
   (A) −14 C $2\frac{4}{7}$
   B $-2\frac{4}{7}$ D 14
6. The quotient of n and −4 is 8. What is the value of n?
   (A) −32 C 2
   B −2 D 32
7. Solve $3c + 5 = 14$.
   (A) 3 C 9
   B $\frac{19}{3}$ D 27
8. Solve $\frac{d}{14} - \frac{1}{2} = \frac{1}{14}$.
   A −8 C 6
   B −6 (D) 8
9. Patrick is saving money to buy an MP3 player that costs $325. He has $75 saved, and each week he adds $25 to his savings. How long will it take Patrick to save enough money to buy the MP3 player?
   A 4 weeks C 13 weeks
   (B) 10 weeks D 16 weeks
10. Solve $\frac{2d - 4}{3} = -18$.
   A −29 C −5
   (B) −25 D −1
11. Solve $3x - 5 + 2x = 15$.
   A 2 C 10
   (B) 4 D 15
12. Solve $6(z + 3) - 9 = 27$.
   A 0 C 5.5
   (B) 3 D 10.5
13. Solve $-a + 7 = 2a - 8$.
   A −3 (C) 5
   B $-\frac{1}{3}$ D 15
14. Solve $7(x - 2) = 7x + 14$.
   (A) no solutions C 2
   B 0 D all real numbers
15. Tia's car needs repairs. Honest Harry will charge $70 per hour plus $130 for the part. Lucky Lou will charge $80 per hour plus $40 for the part. How long is the job if the two costs are the same?
   A $1\frac{2}{3}$ h C 17 h
   (B) 9 h D 20 h

B Chapter 2 Test (continued)

16. The ratio of girls to boys in French class is 5:4. There are 12 boys in the class. How many girls are there?
   A 7 (C) 15
   B 10 D 17
17. A restaurant can bake 105 pies in 7 hours. Find the unit rate. Round your answer to the nearest thousandth if necessary.
   A 0.001 pies/h (C) 15 pies/h
   B 0.067 pies/h D 735 pies/h
18. Solve $\frac{4}{s - 3} = \frac{-2}{5}$.
   A −11.5 (C) 8.5
   B −7 D 13
19. The Redwood Valley Railway in Berkeley, California, operates a model steam train with a scale of 5:12. The passenger cars of the model train are 40 inches wide. How wide is the real passenger car that the model represents?
   A 1.5 in. (C) 96 in.
   B 16.6 in. D 2400 in.
20. What is 200% of 11.5?
   A 2.3 (C) 23
   B 5.75 D 57.5
21. What percent of 80 is 16?
   A 0.2% C 12.8%
   B 5% (D) 20%
22. Solve $A = \frac{1}{2}bh$ for h.
   A $h = \frac{A}{2b}$
   B $h = \frac{b}{2A}$
   (C) $h = \frac{2A}{b}$
   D $h = A - \frac{1}{2}b$
23. Solve $xy + 7 = n$ for y.
   A $y = xn - 7$
   (B) $y = \frac{n - 7}{x}$
   C $y = x(n - 7)$
   D $y = \frac{1}{x}(n + 7)$
24. Solve $|n - 5| = 9$.
   A $n = -14$ or $n = 14$
   (B) $n = -4$ or $n = 14$
   C $n = 4$
   D $n = 4$ or $n = 14$
25. Which choice is the solution set for $|2x| + 7 = 1$?
   A {−4, −3}
   B {−4, 4}
   C {−3, 3}
   (D) ∅

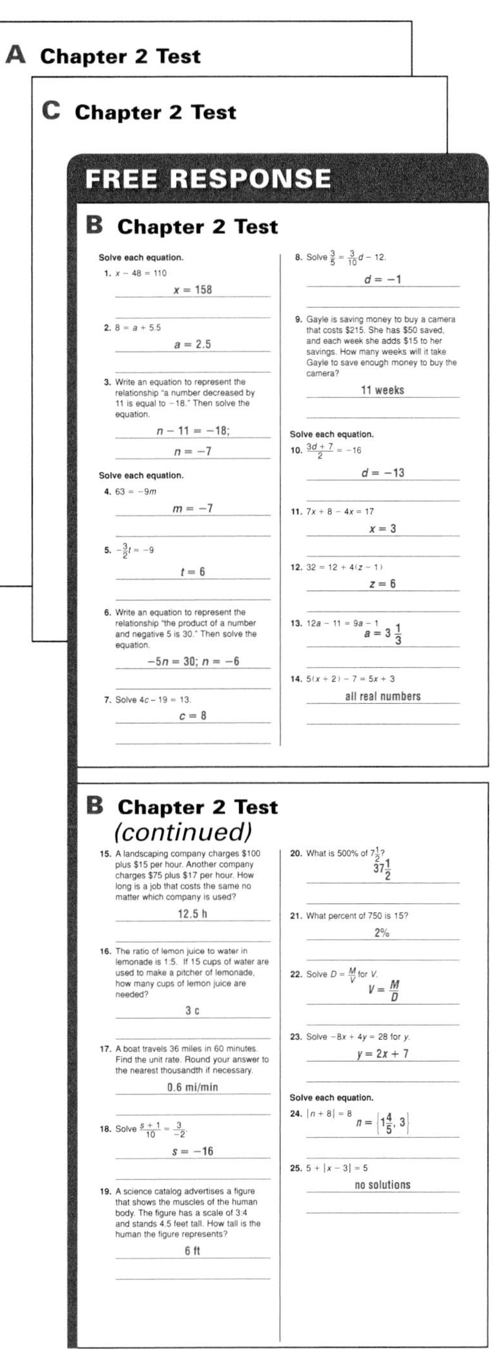

A Chapter 2 Test

C Chapter 2 Test

FREE RESPONSE

B Chapter 2 Test

Solve each equation.

1. $x - 48 = 110$
   $x = 158$
2. $8 = a + 5.5$
   $a = 2.5$
3. Write an equation to represent the relationship "a number decreased by 11 is equal to −18." Then solve the equation.
   $n - 11 = -18$; $n = -7$

Solve each equation.

4. $63 = -9m$
   $m = -7$
5. $-\frac{3}{2}t = -9$
   $t = 6$
6. Write an equation to represent the relationship "the product of a number and negative 5 is 30." Then solve the equation.
   $-5n = 30$; $n = -6$
7. Solve $4c - 19 = 13$.
   $c = 8$
8. Solve $\frac{3}{5} = \frac{3}{10}d - 12$.
   $d = -1$
9. Gayle is saving money to buy a camera that costs $215. She has $50 saved, and each week she adds $15 to her savings. How many weeks will it take Gayle to save enough money to buy the camera?
   11 weeks

Solve each equation.

10. $\frac{3d + 7}{2} = -16$
   $d = -13$
11. $7x + 8 - 4x = 17$
   $x = 3$
12. $32 = 12 + 4(z - 1)$
   $z = 6$
13. $12a - 11 = 9a - 1$
   $a = 3\frac{1}{3}$
14. $5(x + 2) - 7 = 5x + 3$
   all real numbers

B Chapter 2 Test (continued)

15. A landscaping company charges $100 plus $15 per hour. Another company charges $75 plus $17 per hour. How long is a job that costs the same no matter which company is used?
   12.5 h
16. The ratio of lemon juice to water in lemonade is 1:5. If 15 cups of water are used to make a pitcher of lemonade, how many cups of lemon juice are needed?
   3 c
17. A boat travels 36 miles in 60 minutes. Find the unit rate. Round your answer to the nearest thousandth if necessary.
   0.6 mi/min
18. Solve $\frac{s + 1}{10} = \frac{3}{-2}$.
   $s = -16$
19. A science catalog advertises a figure that shows the muscles of the human body. The figure has a scale of 3:4 and stands 4.5 feet tall. How tall is the human the figure represents?
   6 ft
20. What is 500% of $7\frac{1}{2}$?
   $37\frac{1}{2}$
21. What percent of 750 is 15?
   2%
22. Solve $D = \frac{M}{V}$ for V.
   $V = \frac{M}{D}$
23. Solve $-8x + 4y = 28$ for y.
   $y = 2x + 7$

Solve each equation.

24. $|n + 8| = 8$
   $n = \{1\frac{4}{5}, 3\}$
25. $5 + |x - 3| = 5$
   no solutions

Modified tests and worksheets found in *IDEA Works!*

MODIFIED FOR IDEA

Chapter 2 Test

Choose the best answer.

1. Solve $x - 7 = 25$.
   A 18
   (B) 32
2. Solve $54 = a + 22$.
   (A) 32
   B 76
3. Which equation represents the relationship "3 more than a number is 7"?
   A $n + 7 = 3$
   (B) $n + 3 = 7$
   C $3n = 7$
4. Solve $-8m = 48$.
   A −6
   (B) 6
   C 40
5. Solve $\frac{h}{7} = 6$.
   A −42 (C) 42
   B −13
6. The product of 9 and n is −27. What is the value of n?
   A −243
   (B) −3
7. Solve $2c - 5 = 7$.
   A 1
   (B) 6
8. Solve $\frac{d}{3} - 9 = -12$.
   (A) −9 C 6
   B −3
9. Karla bought a student discount card for the cafeteria. The card cost $6 and allows her to buy each meal for $3. After one week, Karla spent $15. How many meals did she buy?
   A 2 meals
   (B) 3 meals
10. Solve $-3 + 5x - 12 = 15$.
   A 0
   (B) 6
11. Solve $2(z + 1) = 16$.
   A 4 C 9
   (B) 7
12. Solve $a + 6 = 3a - 8$.
   A −1
   B 2
   (C) 7
13. Solve $6(x - 1) = 6x - 1$.
   (A) no solutions
   B all real numbers

Chapter 2 Test (continued)

14. Yoga Fun charges a $63 starting fee plus $12 per class. Yoga For All charges no starting fee and $15 per class. For how many classes will the cost be the same at both places?
   A 3
   B 5
   (C) 21
15. The ratio of boys to girls in Art class is 1:2. There are 12 girls in the class. How many boys are there?
   (A) 6 B 24
16. Nina can braid 144 inches of rope in 3 hours. Find her unit rate. Round your answer to the nearest thousandth, if necessary.
   A 0.002 in./h
   B 0.021 in./h
   (C) 48 in./h
17. Solve $\frac{4}{3} = -\frac{2}{9}$.
   A −4.5 (B) −18
18. What is 30% of 15?
   A 0.5 (C) 4.5
   B 2
19. What percent of 50 is 10?
   (A) 20%
   B 500%
20. Solve $V = IR$ for R.
   (A) $R = \frac{V}{I}$
   B $R = \frac{I}{V}$
21. Solve $y + w = x$ for y.
   A $y = w - x$
   (B) $y = x - w$
22. Solve $|3n| = 21$.
   A $n = 7$
   (B) $n = -7$ or $n = 7$

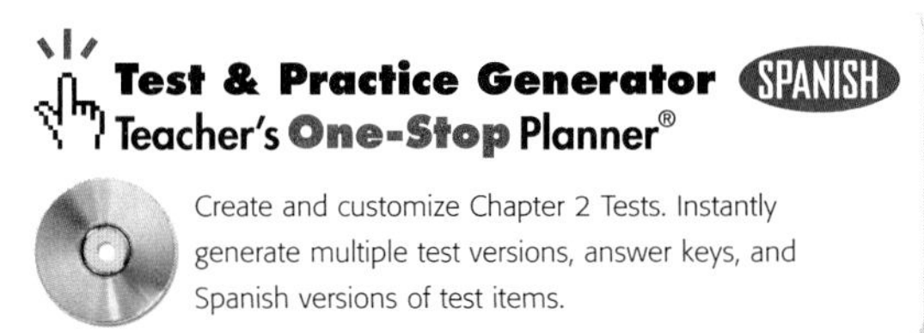

Create and customize Chapter 2 Tests. Instantly generate multiple test versions, answer keys, and Spanish versions of test items.

CHAPTER 2

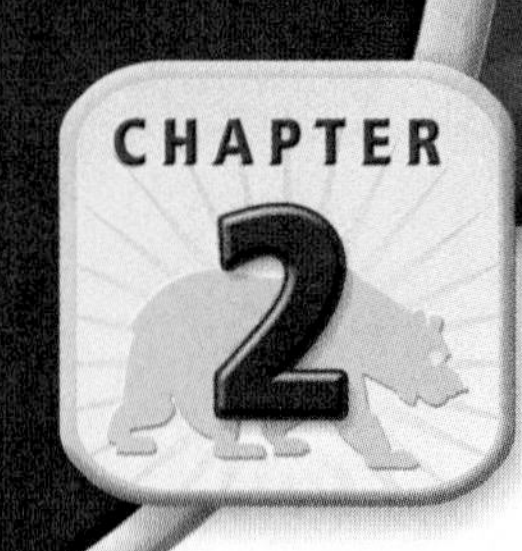

SECTION **2A**

Equations

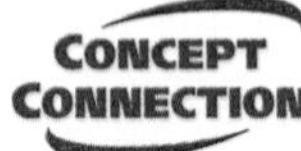

CONCEPT CONNECTION On page 100, students write, solve, and graph equations to model real-world firefighting situations.

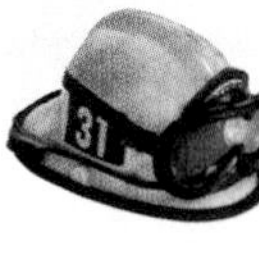

Exercises designed to prepare students for success on the Concept Connection can be found on pages 76, 83, 89, and 96.

SECTION **2B**

Proportions and Formulas

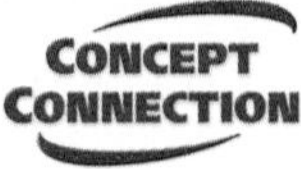

CONCEPT CONNECTION On page 120, students apply proportions and formulas to describe frequencies and wavelengths of musical notes.

Exercises designed to prepare students for success on the Concept Connection can be found on pages 106, 112, and 118.

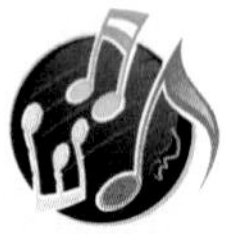

Algebra in *California*

Miniland USA at LEGOLAND in Carlsbad consists of reproductions of American landmarks built to a scale of 1 : 20. Students will investigate scale models in Lesson 2-5 of this chapter.

CHAPTER 2

Equations

go.hrw.com
Chapter Project Online
KEYWORD: MA8CA ChProj

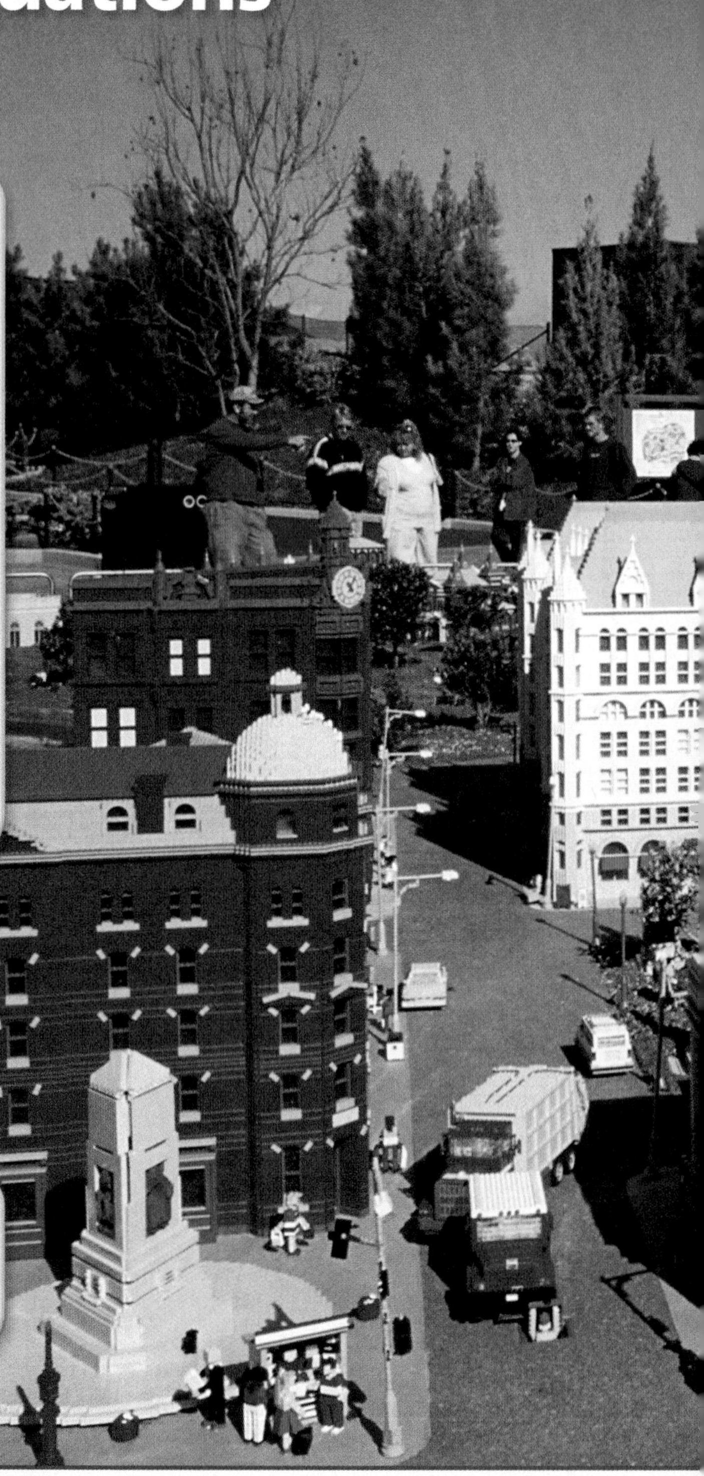

A common use of equations and proportional relationships is the construction of scale models.

LEGOLAND
Carlsbad, CA

About the Project

All in Proportion

In the Chapter Project, students make careful measurements and use scale and proportion to design their own miniature quilts.

Project Resources

All project resources for teachers and students are provided online.

Materials:

- All in Proportion worksheet
- colored paper, ruler, scissors, glue

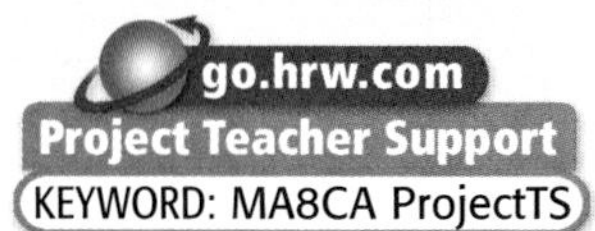

go.hrw.com
Project Teacher Support
KEYWORD: MA8CA ProjectTS

ARE YOU READY?

Vocabulary

Match each term on the left with a definition on the right.

1. constant **E**
2. expression **A**
3. order of operations **C**
4. variable **D**

A. a mathematical phrase that contains operations, numbers, and/or variables

B. a mathematical statement that two expressions are equivalent

C. a process for evaluating expressions

D. a symbol used to represent a quantity that can change

E. a value that does not change

Order of Operations

Simplify each expression.

5. $(7 - 3) \div 2$ **2**
6. $4 \cdot 6 \div 3$ **8**
7. $12 - 3 + 1$ **10**
8. $2 \cdot 10 \div 5$ **4**
9. $125 \div 5^2$ **5**
10. $7 \cdot 6 + 5 \cdot 4$ **62**

Add and Subtract Integers

Add.

11. $-15 + 19$ **4**
12. $-6 - (-18)$ **12**
13. $6 + (-8)$ **−2**
14. $-12 + (-3)$ **−15**

Add and Subtract Fractions

Perform each indicated operation. Give your answer in the simplest form.

15. $\frac{1}{4} + \frac{2}{3}$ $\mathbf{\frac{11}{12}}$
16. $1\frac{1}{2} - \frac{3}{4}$ $\mathbf{\frac{3}{4}}$
17. $\frac{3}{8} + \frac{2}{3}$ $\mathbf{\frac{25}{24}}$
18. $\frac{3}{2} - \frac{2}{3}$ $\mathbf{\frac{5}{6}}$

Evaluate Expressions

Evaluate each expression for the given value of the variable.

19. $2x + 3$ for $x = 7$ **17**
20. $3n - 5$ for $n = 7$ **16**
21. $13 - 4a$ for $a = 2$ **5**
22. $3y + 5$ for $y = 5$ **20**

Connect Words and Algebra

23. Janie bought 4 apples and 6 bananas. Each apple cost $0.75, and each banana cost $0.60. Write an expression representing the total cost. **4(0.75) + 6(0.60)**
24. A rectangle has a width of 13 inches and a length of ℓ inches. Write an expression representing the area of the rectangle. $\mathbf{13\ell}$
25. Write a phrase that could be modeled by the expression $n + 2n$. **Possible answer: a number plus 2 times itself**

ARE YOU READY? CHAPTER 2

Organizer

Objective: Assess students' understanding of prerequisite skills.

Assessing Prior Knowledge

INTERVENTION

Diagnose and Prescribe

Use this page to determine whether intervention is necessary or whether enrichment is appropriate.

Resources

Are You Ready? Intervention and Enrichment **Worksheets**

 ***Are You Ready?*** **CD-ROM**

 ***Are You Ready?*** **Online**

ARE YOU READY?
Diagnose and Prescribe

NO INTERVENE

Prerequisite Skill	Are You Ready? Intervention, Chapter 2 – Worksheets	CD-ROM	Online
Order of Operations	Skill 55	Activity 55	Diagnose and Prescribe Online
Add and Subtract Integers	Skill 51	Activity 51	
Add and Subtract Fractions	Skill 48	Activity 48	
Evaluate Expressions	Skill 60	Activity 60	
Connect Words and Algebra	Skill 58	Activity 58	

YES ENRICH

Are You Ready? Enrichment, Chapter 2
- Worksheets
- CD-ROM
- Online

Organizer

Objective: Help students understand the new concepts they will learn in Chapter 2.

Online Edition
Multilingual Glossary

Academic Vocabulary Connections

Becoming familiar with the academic vocabulary on this student page will be helpful to students. Discussing some of the vocabulary terms in the chapter also may be helpful.

1. The word **equation** begins with the root *equa-*. List some other words that begin with *equa-*. What do all these words have in common? Possible answer: *Equal*, *equality*, and *equalize*; they all have something to do with being the same.
2. The word *literal* means "of letters." How might a **literal equation** be different from an equation like $3 + 5 = 8$? It may contain letters (variables).
3. One definition of **identity** is "exact sameness." An equation consists of two expressions. If an equation is an *identity*, what do you think is true about the expressions? They are the same.

CHAPTER 2

Unpacking the Standards

The information below "unpacks" the standards. The Academic Vocabulary is highlighted and defined to help you understand the language of the standards. Refer to the lessons listed after each standard for help with the math terms and phrases. The Chapter Concept shows how the standard is applied in this chapter.

California Standard	Academic Vocabulary	Chapter Concept
3.0 Students solve equations and inequalities **involving absolute values**. (Lesson 2-7)	**absolute value** a number's distance from 0 on a number line ***Example:*** number line −2 0 2 Both 2 and −2 are 2 units from 0. So $\lvert 2\rvert = 2$ and $\lvert -2\rvert = 2$.	You solve equations that have a variable inside absolute-value symbols.
4.0 Students simplify expressions before solving linear equations and inequalities **in one variable, such as $3(2x - 5) + (4x - 2) = 12$.** (Lessons 2-3, 2-4)	**simplify** (simplification) make things easier **linear equation** an equation whose variable(s) have exponents not greater than 1 **in one variable** containing one variable	You write expressions in their simplest form so that you can find the value of a variable that makes an equation true.
5.0 Students solve multistep problems, including word problems, involving linear equations and linear inequalities **in one variable** and provide **justification** for each step. (Lessons 2-3, 2-4, 2-7)	**multistep** more than one step **involving** needing the use of **justification** a correct reason	You solve equations when the solution process requires two or more steps.
15.0 Students apply algebraic techniques to solve rate problems, work problems, and percent mixture problems. (Lesson 2-5)	**algebraic** having to do with algebra **technique** a way of doing something	You use what you learn in algebra to solve real-world problems about rates.
25.3 Given a specific algebraic statement involving linear, quadratic, or absolute value expressions or **equations** or inequalities, **students determine whether the statement is true sometimes, always, or never.** (Lab 2-4)	**specific** single, exactly one **determine** tell or find out	You decide whether an equation is true for all values of the variable, for some values of the variable, or for no values of the variable.

Standards 2.0, 24.1, 24.2, 25.1, and 25.2 are also covered in this chapter. To see these standards unpacked go to Chapter 5, p. 254; Chapter 3, p. 134; and Chapter 1, p. 4.

Looking Back

Previously, students

- used variables to represent quantities.
- wrote expressions to represent situations.
- practiced using operations in algebra.

In This Chapter

Students will study

- how to use variables to write equations.
- how to write equations to represent situations.
- how to use operations to solve equations.

Looking Forward

Students can use these skills

- to write equations in two or more variables.
- to represent situations using equations with more than one variable.
- to find solutions to equations in two or more variables.

English-Language Arts Reading 8.1.3

Study Strategy: Use Your Own Words

Explaining a concept using your own words will help you better understand it. For example, learning to solve equations might seem difficult if the textbook doesn't use the same words that you would use.

As you work through each lesson:

- Identify the important ideas from the explanation in the book.
- Use your own words to explain the important ideas you identified.

What Arturo Reads	What Arturo Writes
To evaluate an expression is to find its value.	Evaluate an expression–find the value.
To evaluate an algebraic expression, substitute numbers for the variables in the expression and then simplify the expression.	Substitute a number for each variable (letter), and find the answer.
A replacement set is a set of numbers that can be substituted for a variable.	Replacement set–numbers that can be substituted for a letter.

Rewrite each paragraph in your own words.

1. Two numbers are opposites if their sum is 0. A number and its opposite are on opposite sides of zero on a number line, but are the same distance from zero.
2. The Commutative and Associative Properties of Addition and Multiplication allow you to rearrange an expression to simplify it.
3. The terms of an expression are the parts to be added or subtracted. Like terms are terms that contain the same variables raised to the same powers. Constants are also like terms.

Reading and Writing Math

CHAPTER 2

Organizer

Objective: Apply study strategies to understand and retain key concepts.

Online Edition

Resources

Chapter 2 Resource File
Reading Strategies

Study Strategy: Use Your Own Words

ENGLISH LANGUAGE LEARNERS

Discuss Students benefit from listening to each other explain their methods for solving equations.

Encourage students to find many ways to say the same thing.

Extend As students work through Chapter 2, have them discuss how they would rephrase word problems in the exercises. Ask them to first divide the problem into parts, and then identify the information given and what the problem asks.

Have students relate the new math concepts in the exercises to what they already know.

Answers to *Try This*

Possible answers:

1. Opposites–numbers that add to 0 and are the same distance from 0 on a number line, but on opposite sides.
2. Use Commutative, Associative Properties of Addition, Multiplication to simplify expressions.
3. Terms–things that are added or subtracted in an expression. Like terms–same variables raised to same powers, also constants.

Reading 8.1.3 Use word meanings within the appropriate context and show ability to verify those meanings by definition, **restatement,** example, comparison, or contrast.

Equations

One-Minute Section Planner

Lesson	Lab Resources	Materials
Lesson 2-1 Solving One-Step Equations • Solve one-step equations in one variable. **Preparation for 5.0**		**Optional** balance scale with weights, pencil holder
Lesson 2-2 Solving Two-Step Equations • Solve two-step equations in one variable. **Preparation for 5.0**		**Optional** algebra tiles (MK)
Lesson 2-3 Solving Multi-Step Equations • Solve equations in one variable that contain more than one operation. **4.0, 5.0**		
2-4 Technology Lab True Equations • Use a computer spreadsheet to help determine whether an equation is sometimes, always, or never true. **25.3**		**Required** computer spreadsheet
Lesson 2-4 Solving Equations with Variables on Both Sides • Solve equations in one variable that contain variable terms on both sides. **4.0, 5.0**		**Optional** colored pencils (MK), index cards, graphing calculator

MK = *Manipulatives Kit*

Notes

Math Background: Teaching the Standards

PROOFS IN ALGEBRA 5.0

Lessons 2-1 to 2-4

Traditionally, logical reasoning and proof were not introduced until students entered a high school geometry course. However, logical mathematical arguments are at the heart of algebraic thinking and so must play a key role in any algebra course. In particular, at this stage of a student's mathematical training, he or she should begin to perceive that logical reasoning is central to *all* mathematics.

As seen in Chapter 1, students must be able to recognize the basic requirements of a logical argument and must understand that a single counterexample is enough to prove that a statement is false. As they solve equations in Chapter 2, students should understand that the process of solving an equation is a type of logical argument and that each step must be mathematically justifiable.

A proper justification for a step in the solution of an equation is not simply a description of what was done to the equation ("I added 3 to both sides."), but rather a general principle, such as the Addition Property of Equality. Students should frequently be encouraged to think about the general rules that support each step.

SOLUTIONS OF EQUATIONS 5.0

Lessons 2-1 to 2-4

Before they solve equations, students need to understand what is meant by a solution. A *solution* of an equation is a value of the variable that makes the equation true. The equation $5(x + 2) - 3x = 18$, for example, is neither true nor false until a specific value replaces x. It is worthwhile to have students test various values of x in the left-hand side of the equation.

x	$5(x + 2) - 3x$
1	12
2	14
3	16
4	18

The table shows that $x = 1$, $x = 2$, and $x = 3$ are not solutions of the equation and that $x = 4$ is a solution.

It may be useful to highlight a common mistake at this point. When asked to prove that two quantities are equal, students sometimes set the quantities equal and work to show an identity. The identity is then taken as proof that the original equation is true. This is a logical error. For example, suppose you are asked to show that $3 = 4$. Using the method described above, set $3 = 4$. Then it is true that $4 = 3$. Adding the two red equations gives $7 = 7$, which is certainly true, but that does not mean the original statement, $3 = 4$, is true. (The problem with this argument lies in the fact that not every step is reversible.)

SOLVING EQUATIONS 5.0

Lessons 2-1 to 2-4

Solving equations is one of the most important skills in K-12 mathematics. As previously shown, it is sometimes possible to find a solution by testing values of the variable, but this is generally not the most efficient solution method. In this chapter, students learn to solve an equation by transforming it into equivalent equations. *Equivalent equations* are equations that have the same solution set.

During the solution process, each transformation of an equation should be backed up by a general mathematical principle. In this chapter, students are introduced to the Addition Property of Equality ("equals added to equals are equal"). The figure shows how this general principle may be understood in terms of a balanced scale: identical weights added to both sides of a balanced scale will preserve the balance.

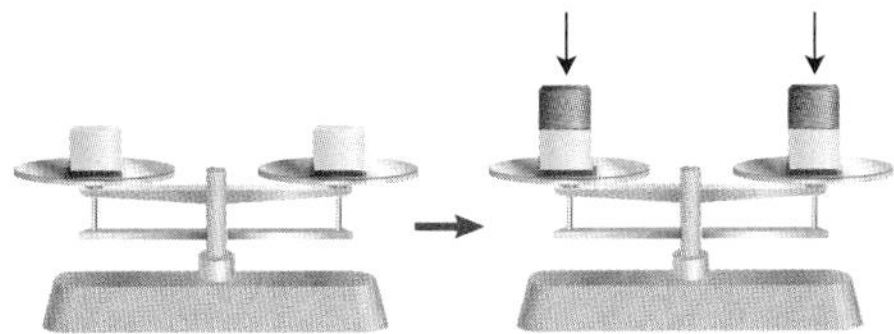

In the same way, identical quantities added to both sides of an equation will preserve the equality. A similar analogy can be made for the Subtraction Property of Equality.

2-1 Organizer

Objective: Solve one-step equations in one variable.

Online Edition
Tutorial Videos, Interactivity

Countdown to Mastery Week 3

Power Presentations with PowerPoint®

Warm Up

Evaluate.

1. $-\frac{2}{3} + 4\frac{1}{3}$ $3\frac{2}{3}$
2. $-0.51 + (-0.29)$ -0.8
3. $0.96 \div 6$ 0.16
4. $(-9)(-9)$ 81
5. $\left(\frac{5}{6}\right)\left(\frac{6}{5}\right)$ 1

Evaluate each expression for $a = 3$ and $b = -2$.

6. $a + 5$ 8 7. $12b$ -24

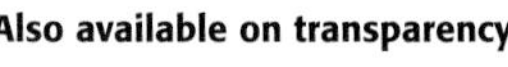

Also available on transparency

Math Humor

Parent: Why do you have that sheet of paper in a bowl of water?

Student: It's my homework. I'm trying to *dissolve* an equation.

2-1 Solving One-Step Equations

California Standards

Preparation for 5.0 Students solve multistep problems, including word problems, involving linear equations and linear inequalities **in one variable** and provide justification for each step.
Also covered: **2.0**

Vocabulary
equation
solution of an equation
solution set

Why learn this?
You can use an equation to calculate your maximum heart rate. (See Example 4.)

An **equation** is a mathematical statement that two expressions are equal.

A **solution of an equation** is a value of the variable that makes the equation true. A **solution set** is the set of all solutions. Finding the solutions of an equation is also called *solving the equation.*

To find solutions, perform inverse operations until you have *isolated the variable.* A variable is isolated when it appears by itself on one side of an equation, and not at all on the other side.

Inverse Operations
Add x. ⟷ Subtract x.
Multiply by x. ⟷ Divide by x.

An equation is like a balanced scale. To keep the balance, you must perform the same inverse operation on both sides.

Know it! Note

Addition and Subtraction Properties of Equality

WORDS	NUMBERS	ALGEBRA
Addition Property of Equality You can add the same number to both sides of an equation, and the statement will still be true.	$3 = 3$ $3 + 2 = 3 + 2$	$a = b$ $a + c = b + c$
Subtraction Property of Equality You can subtract the same number from both sides of an equation, and the statement will still be true.	$7 = 7$ $7 - 5 = 7 - 5$	$a = b$ $a - c = b - c$

EXAMPLE 1 Solving Equations by Using Addition or Subtraction

Solve each equation.

A $x - 10 = 4$

$$x - 10 = 4$$
$$\underline{+10 \quad +10}$$
Since 10 is subtracted from x, add 10 to both sides to undo the subtraction.

$$x = 14$$
The solution set is {14}.

Check $x - 10 = 4$
$14 - 10 \mid 4$
$4 \mid 4$ ✓
To check your solution, substitute 14 for x in the original equation.

Writing Math

Solution sets are written in set notation using braces, { }. Solutions may be given in set notation, or they may be given in the form $x = 14$.

1 Introduce

EXPLORATION

2-1 Solving One-Step Equations

Each of the following problems shows a scale that is balanced.

1. How many ■ are equal to one ▲ ?
2. How many ● are equal to one ◣ ?
3. How many ● are equal to one ★ ?

THINK AND DISCUSS

4. Describe how you solved each problem.

Motivate

Place a balance scale with equal weights on each side where all students can see it. Ask them what will happen if you add or subtract an equal amount of weight on both sides. Demonstrate each. Tell the students that equations are like balance scales; both sides must always be kept equal, which means that you must perform the same operation on both sides.

Explorations and answers are provided in *Alternate Openers: Explorations Transparencies*.

California Standards

Preparation for 5.0
Also covered:
2.0 Students understand and use such operations as taking the opposite, finding the reciprocal, taking a root, and raising to a fractional power. They understand and use the rules of exponents.

Solve each equation.

B $0.7 = r + 0.4$

$0.7 = r + 0.4$
$\underline{-0.4} \quad \underline{-0.4}$ *Since 0.4 is added to r, subtract 0.4 from both sides to undo the addition.*

$0.3 = r$ *The solution set is {0.3}.*

Solve each equation. Check your answer.

1a. $n - 3.2 = 5.6$ **8.8** **1b.** $-6 = k - 6$ **0** **1c.** $6 + t = 14$ **8**

Multiplication and Division Properties of Equality

WORDS	NUMBERS	ALGEBRA
Multiplication Property of Equality You can multiply both sides of an equation by the same number, and the statement will still be true.	$6 = 6$ $6(3) = 6(3)$	$a = b$ $ac = bc$
Division Property of Equality You can divide both sides of an equation by the same nonzero number, and the statement will still be true.	$8 = 8$ $\frac{8}{4} = \frac{8}{4}$	$a = b$ $(c \neq 0), \frac{a}{c} = \frac{b}{c}$

EXAMPLE 2 Solving Equations by Using Multiplication or Division

Solve each equation.

A $13 = -2w$

$\frac{13}{-2} = \frac{-2w}{-2}$ *Since w is multiplied by −2, divide both sides by −2 to undo the multiplication.*

$w = -\frac{13}{2}$, or -6.5 *The solution set is {−6.5}.*

B $-4 = \frac{k}{-5}$

$(-5)(-4) = (-5)\left(\frac{k}{-5}\right)$ *Since k is divided by −5, multiply both sides by −5 to undo the division.*

$20 = k$ *The solution set is {20}.*

Check $-4 = \frac{k}{-5}$ *To check your solution, substitute 20 for k in the original equation.*

$-4 \mid \frac{20}{-5}$

$-4 \mid -4$ ✓

Solve each equation. Check your answer.

2a. $\frac{p}{5} = 10$ **50** **2b.** $0.5y = -10$ **−20** **2c.** $\frac{c}{8} = 7$ **56**

When solving equations, you will sometimes find it easier to add an opposite to both sides instead of subtracting, or to multiply by a reciprocal instead of dividing. This is often true when an equation contains negative numbers or fractions.

COMMON ERROR ALERT

When solving problems using division, some students may automatically divide the larger number by the smaller number every time. For example, a student may try to solve $6x = 3$ by dividing both sides by 3. Remind students that they must isolate the variable, and that the variable in this equation is being multiplied by 6, not by 3.

Power Presentations with PowerPoint®

Additional Examples

Example 1

Solve each equation.

A. $y - 8 = 24$ 32

B. $4.2 = t + 1.8$ 2.4

Example 2

Solve each equation.

A. $-8 = \frac{j}{3}$ −24

B. $-4.8 = -6v$ 0.8

Also available on transparency

INTERVENTION
Questioning Strategies

EXAMPLE 1

- How do you know which operation to use to isolate the variable?
- How do you know which number to add or subtract from both sides?

EXAMPLE 2

- How do you know which operation to use to isolate the variable?
- How do you know which number to multiply or divide both sides by?

2 Teach

Guided Instruction

Before solving equations, review how to determine whether a given value is a solution of an equation. Emphasize that when solving equations, you want to find the value of the variable that makes the equation true. So the answer will be in the form *variable = number*. This is why you want to isolate the variable. Discuss how to find a solution by using the inverse operation to undo the operation in the equation. Finally, demonstrate how to check the answer by substituting it into the original equation.

Universal Access
Through Concrete Manipulatives

Have one student hold a closed container of pencils in one hand and 5 pencils in the other hand. Have another student hold 12 pencils. Tell the class that both students have the same number of pencils. Ask the class how they can figure out the number of pencils in the container without opening it. Give or take pencils away from each student as suggestions are made. When the class has arrived at an answer, check by counting the number of pencils in the container.

Power Presentations with PowerPoint®

Additional Examples

Example 3

Solve each equation.

A. $\frac{5}{6}w = -20$ -24

B. $-\frac{5}{11} + p = -\frac{2}{11}$ $\frac{3}{11}$

Example 4

Ciro deposits $\frac{1}{4}$ of the money he earns from mowing lawns into a college education fund. This year Ciro added $285 to his college education fund. Write and solve an equation to find how much money Ciro earned mowing lawns this year. $\frac{1}{4}m = 285$: $1140

Also available on transparency

INTERVENTION

Questioning Strategies

EXAMPLE 3

- How are these problems like the problems in Examples 1 and 2? How are they different?

EXAMPLE 4

- What is the unknown quantity in the situation?
- What operation is needed to solve the equation?

Inclusion Students often have difficulty assigning a variable to represent a quantity in a real-world problem. Reinforce that a variable represents what is unknown. Students can copy a problem and circle the unknown quantity. This is the quantity that should be represented by the variable.

EXAMPLE **3** **Solving Equations by Using Opposites or Reciprocals**

Solve each equation.

A $-8 + b = 2$

$$-8 + b = 2$$
$$\underline{+8 \quad\quad +8}$$
$$b = 10$$

Since −8 is added to b, add 8 to both sides. The solution set is {10}.

B $\frac{5}{9}v = 35$

$$\left(\frac{9}{5}\right)\frac{5}{9}v = \left(\frac{9}{5}\right)35$$

The reciprocal of $\frac{5}{9}$ is $\frac{9}{5}$. Since v is multiplied by $\frac{5}{9}$, multiply both sides by $\frac{9}{5}$.

$$v = 63$$

The solution set is {63}.

Solve each equation. Check your answer.

3a. $-2.3 + m = 7$ **9.3**   **3b.** $-\frac{3}{4} + z = \frac{5}{4}$ **2**   **3c.** $\frac{1}{6}w = 102$ **612**

EXAMPLE **4** **Fitness Application**

A person's maximum heart rate is the highest rate, in beats per minute, that the person's heart should reach. A person's age added to his or her maximum heart rate is 220. Write and solve an equation to find the maximum heart rate of a 15-year-old.

Age	added to	maximum heart rate	is	220.
a	$+$	r	$=$	220

$$a + r = 220$$

Write an equation to represent the relationship.

$$15 + r = 220$$
$$\underline{-15 \quad\quad -15}$$
$$r = 205$$

Substitute 15 for a. Since 15 is added to r, subtract 15 from both sides to undo the addition.

The maximum heart rate for a 15-year-old is 205 beats per minute.

4. The distance in miles from the airport that a plane should begin descending divided by 3 equals the plane's height above the ground in thousands of feet. A plane is 10,000 feet above the ground. Write and solve an equation to find the distance from the airport at which this plane should begin descending. $\frac{m}{3} = 10$; **30 mi**

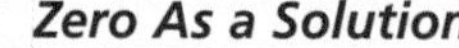

Student to Student

Zero As a Solution

Ama Walker
Carson High School

I used to get confused when I got a solution of 0. But my teacher reminded me that 0 is a number just like any other number, so it can be a solution of an equation. Just check your answer and see if it works.

$$x + 6 = 6$$
$$\underline{-6 \quad -6}$$
$$x = 0$$

Check

$x + 6 = 6$	
$0 + 6$	6
6	6 ✓

3 Close

Summarize

Ask students what they would do to each side to solve each of the following equations.

$-3 + x = 14$ Add 3.

$-14 = h + 6$ Subtract 6.

$-4y = 20$ Divide by -4.

$\frac{x}{33} = -9$ Multiply by 33.

FORMATIVE ASSESSMENT

and INTERVENTION

***Diagnose Before* the Lesson**
2-1 Warm Up, TE p. 72

***Monitor During* the Lesson**
Check It Out! Exercises, SE pp. 72–74
Questioning Strategies, TE pp. 73–74

***Assess After* the Lesson**
2-1 Lesson Quiz, TE p. 77
Alternative Assessment, TE p. 77

THINK AND DISCUSS

1. Describe how the Addition and Subtraction Properties of Equality are like a balanced scale.
2. By what number would you multiply both sides of the equation $\frac{b}{4} = 10$ to isolate the variable?

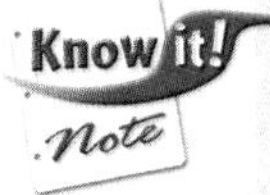

3. **GET ORGANIZED** Copy and complete the graphic organizer. In each box, write an example of an equation that can be solved by using the given property and solve it.

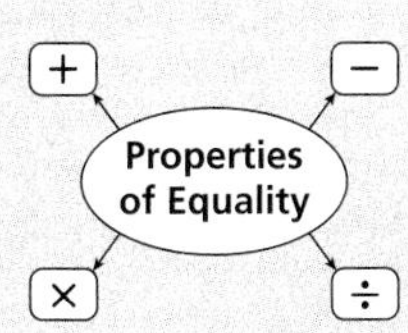

Answers to *Think and Discuss*

1. Possible answer: If a scale is balanced, then you can add or remove the same weight on both sides without affecting the balance. Similarly, in an equation, the Addition and Subtraction Properties of Equality say that you can add or subtract the same value on both sides without affecting the equality.
2. 4
3. See p. A2.

2-1 Exercises

Preparation for 5.0; 2.0, 25.2

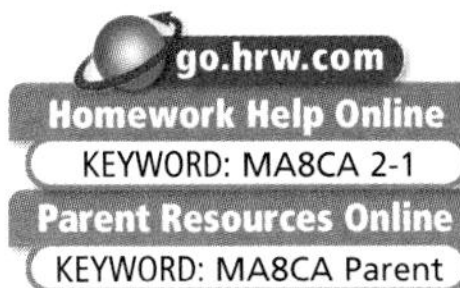

GUIDED PRACTICE

1. **Vocabulary** Will the *solution of an equation* such as $x - 3 = 9$ be a variable or a number? Explain. **Possible answer: The solution of an equation is a number. It is a value for the variable that works in the equation.**

Solve each equation. Check your answer.

SEE EXAMPLE 1 p. 72

2. $s - 5 = 3$ **8**
3. $17 = w - 4$ **21**
4. $k - 8 = -7$ **1**
5. $t + 5 = -25$ **−30**
6. $b + \frac{2}{3} = 2$ $\mathbf{\frac{4}{3}}$
7. $4.2 = m + 3.6$ **0.6**

SEE EXAMPLE 2 p. 73

8. $\frac{k}{4} = 8$ **32**
9. $\frac{g}{1.9} = 10$ **19**
10. $-2 = \frac{w}{-7}$ **14**
11. $4x = 28$ **7**
12. $4m = 10$ $\mathbf{\frac{5}{2}}$
13. $-9j = -45$ **5**

SEE EXAMPLE 3 p. 74

14. $-10 + d = 7$ **17**
15. $20 = -12 + v$ **32**
16. $-4.6 + q = 5$ **9.6**
17. $\frac{1}{2}d = 7$ **14**
18. $-\frac{2}{3} + c = \frac{2}{3}$ $\mathbf{\frac{4}{3}}$
19. $\frac{2}{3}s = -6$ **−9**

SEE EXAMPLE 4 p. 74

20. **Geology** In 1668, the Hope diamond was reduced from its original weight by about 45 carats, resulting in a diamond weighing about 67 carats. Write and solve an equation to find how many carats the original diamond weighed. **$w - 45 = 67$; 112 carats**

PRACTICE AND PROBLEM SOLVING

Independent Practice	
For Exercises	See Example
21–28	1
29–36	2
37–44	3
45	4

Extra Practice
Skills Practice p. EP4
Application Practice p. EP25

Solve each equation. Check your answer.

21. $1 = k - 8$ **9**
22. $m + 20 = 3$ **−17**
23. $x - 7 = 10$ **17**
24. $v + 2300 = -800$ **−3100**
25. $b + \frac{1}{2} = \frac{1}{2}$ **0**
26. $q - 0.5 = 1.5$ **2**
27. $4\frac{2}{3} = r - \frac{1}{3}$ **5**
28. $2 = d + \frac{1}{4}$ $\mathbf{\frac{7}{4}}$
29. $\frac{x}{2} = 12$ **24**
30. $11 = -2z$ $\mathbf{-\frac{11}{2}}$
31. $5t = -15$ **−3**
32. $1.6 = \frac{d}{3}$ **4.8**
33. $-\frac{j}{6} = 6$ **−36**
34. $-12 = -12u$ **1**
35. $-8.4 = -4n$ **2.1**
36. $\frac{h}{8.1} = -4$ **−32.4**

2-1 Exercises

Assignment Guide

Assign *Guided Practice* exercises as necessary.

If you finished Examples **1–2**
Proficient 21–36, 56–58
Advanced 21–36, 56–59, 61–63

If you finished Examples **1–4**
Proficient 21–49, 51–61, 70–78
Advanced 22–44 even, 45–78

Homework Quick Check
Quickly check key concepts.
Exercises: 22, 26, 30, 36, 38, 42, 45

California Standards

Standard	Exercises
7NS1.2	70–72
1.0	76–78
2.0	2–69
Prep for 5.0	2–69, 73–75
25.2	50

Exercise 55 involves using rates to predict how quickly a fire will spread and how much land it will cover. This exercise prepares students for the Concept Connection on page 100.

Answer

53. Possible answer: If you add 5 years to Sue's age, you get her cousin's age. Her cousin is 25. How old is Sue? x represents Sue's age. $x = 20$; this means Sue is 20 years old.

Solve each equation. Check your answer.

37. $-12 + f = 3$ **15**
38. $-9 = -4 + g$ **−5**
39. $\frac{4}{7}t = -2 - \frac{7}{2}$
40. $-\frac{4}{5}g = -12$ **15**
41. $26 = -4 + y$ **30**
42. $\frac{5}{2}k = 5$ **2**
43. $-9 = \frac{3}{4}d$ **−12**
44. $-5.2 + a = -8$ **−2.8**
45. **Nutrition** An orange contains about 80 milligrams of vitamin C, which is 10 times as much as an apple contains. Write and solve an equation to find the amount of vitamin C in an apple. **$10x = 80$; 8 mg**

Write an equation to represent each relationship. Then solve the equation.

46. Ten less than a number is equal to 12. **$x - 10 = 12$; $x = 22$**
47. Five times a number is 45. **$5x = 45$; $x = 9$**
48. The quotient of a number and 3 is −8. **48. $\frac{x}{3} = -8$; $x = -24$**
49. Eight more than a number is 16. **$x + 8 = 16$; $x = 8$**
50. **ERROR ANALYSIS** Below are two possible solutions to $x + 12.5 = 21.6$. Which is incorrect? Explain the error. **Solution B is incorrect. The Addition Property of Equality was used.**

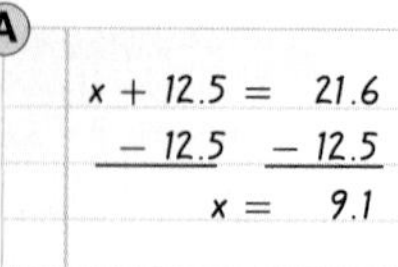

A
x + 12.5 = 21.6
− 12.5 − 12.5
x = 9.1

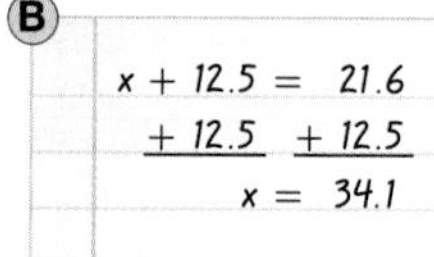

B
x + 12.5 = 21.6
+ 12.5 + 12.5
x = 34.1

California LINK — Oceanography

© 2001 MBARI

The ocean near Monterey reaches depths of more than 10,000 ft. Below 330 ft, there is little, if any, light. Many deep sea animals, such as jelly fish, make their own light (bioluminescence) to help them survive.

51. **Oceanography** The Atlantic Ocean's greatest depth (in feet) is 17,366 feet greater than its average depth. Use the information in the graph to write and solve an equation to find the average depth of the Atlantic Ocean. **$30{,}246 = a + 17{,}366$; 12,880 ft**

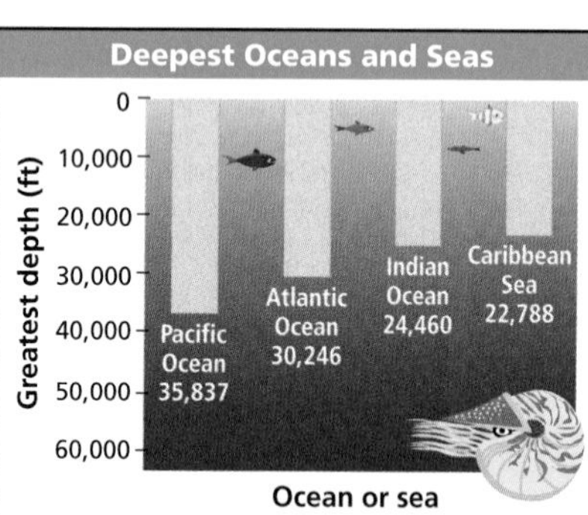

Deepest Oceans and Seas
Greatest depth (ft)
0
10,000
20,000
30,000
40,000
50,000
60,000
Pacific Ocean 35,837
Atlantic Ocean 30,246
Indian Ocean 24,460
Caribbean Sea 22,788
Ocean or sea

52. **Consumer Economics** Dion's long-distance phone bill was \$13.80. His long-distance calls cost \$0.05 per minute. Write and solve an equation to find the number of minutes he was charged for. **$0.05x = 13.80$; $x = 276$**

53. **Write About It** Describe a real-world situation that can be modeled by $x + 5 = 25$. Solve the equation and tell what the solution means in the context of your problem.
54. **Critical Thinking** Without solving, tell whether the solution of $-2 + z = 10$ is greater than 10 or less than 10. Explain. **Possible answer: greater than 10 because you will add a positive number to both sides**

55. This problem will help prepare you for the Concept Connection on page 100.
Rates are often used to describe how quickly something is moving or changing.
    a. A wildfire spreads at a rate of 1000 acres per day. How many acres will the fire cover in 2 days? **2000 acres**
    b. How many acres will the fire cover in 5 days? **5000 acres**
    c. Another wildfire spread for 7 days and covered a total of 780 square miles. How can you estimate the number of square miles the fire covered per day? **Divide 780 by 7.**

2-1 PRACTICE A
2-1 PRACTICE C
2-1 PRACTICE B

LESSON 2-1 Practice B
Solving One-Step Equations

Solve each equation. Check your answers.

1. $g - 7 = 15$ — $g = 22$
2. $t + 4 = 6$ — $t = 2$
3. $13 = m - 7$ — $m = 20$
4. $x + 3.4 = 9.1$ — $x = 5.7$
5. $n - \frac{3}{8} = \frac{1}{8}$ — $n = \frac{1}{2}$
6. $p - \frac{1}{3} = \frac{2}{3}$ — $p = 1$
7. $-49 = 7y$ — $y = -7$
8. $-15 = -\frac{3n}{5}$ — $n = 25$
9. $9m = 6$ — $m = \frac{2}{3}$
10. $\frac{v}{-3} = -6$ — $v = 18$
11. $2.8 = 4b$ — $b = 0.7$
12. $\frac{3r}{4} = \frac{1}{8}$ — $r = \frac{1}{6}$
13. Marietta was given a raise of \$0.75 an hour, which brought her hourly wage to \$12.25. Write and solve an equation to determine Marietta's hourly wage before her raise. Show that your answer is reasonable.
$x + 0.75 = 12.25$; \$11.50; Marietta received a raise, so her previous wage should be less than \$12.25.
14. Brad grew $4\frac{1}{4}$ inches this year and is now $56\frac{7}{8}$ inches tall. Write and solve an equation to find Brad's height at the start of the year. Show that your answer is reasonable.
$x + 4\frac{1}{4} = 56\frac{7}{8}$; $52\frac{5}{8}$ in.; Brad's height increased, so his previous height should be less than $56\frac{7}{8}$ inches.
15. Lola spends one-third of her allowance on movies. She spends \$8 per week at the movies. Write and solve an equation to determine Lola's weekly allowance.
$\frac{1}{3}x = 8$; \$24
16. The perimeter of a regular pentagon is 41.5 cm. Write and solve an equation to determine the length of each side of the pentagon.
$5x = 41.5$; 8.3 cm

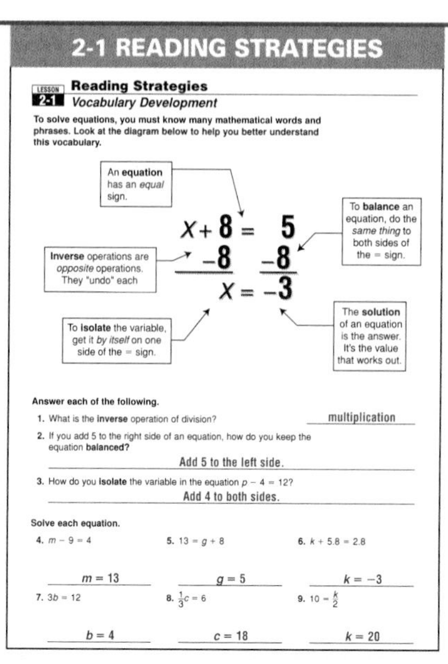

2-1 READING STRATEGIES

LESSON 2-1 Reading Strategies
Vocabulary Development

To solve equations, you must know many mathematical words and phrases. Look at the diagram below to help you better understand this vocabulary.

$$\begin{array}{r} x + 8 = 5 \\ -8 \quad -8 \\ \hline x = -3 \end{array}$$

An **equation** has an *equal* sign.
Inverse operations are *opposite* operations. They "undo" each
To **balance** an equation, do the *same thing* to both sides of the = sign.
To **isolate** the variable, get it *by itself* on one side of the = sign.
The **solution** of an equation is the answer. It's the value that works out.

Answer each of the following.

1. What is the **inverse** operation of division? **multiplication**
2. If you add 5 to the right side of an equation, how do you keep the equation **balanced?** **Add 5 to the left side.**
3. How do you **isolate** the variable in the equation $p - 4 = 12$? **Add 4 to both sides.**

Solve each equation.

4. $m - 9 = 4$ — $m = 13$
5. $13 = g + 8$ — $g = 5$
6. $k + 5.8 = 2.8$ — $k = -3$
7. $3b = 12$ — $b = 4$
8. $\frac{1}{3}c = 6$ — $c = 18$
9. $10 = \frac{k}{2}$ — $k = 20$

2-1 REVIEW FOR MASTERY

LESSON 2-1 Review for Mastery
Solving One-Step Equations

Any addition equation can be solved by adding the opposite. If the equation involves subtraction, it helps to first rewrite the subtraction as addition.

Solve $x + 4 = 10$. (Find the opposite of this number.)

$x + 4 = 10$ *The opposite of 4 is −4.*
$-4 \quad -4$ *Add −4 to each side.*
$x = 6$

Check: $x + 4 = 10$; $6 + 4 \stackrel{?}{=} 10$; $10 \stackrel{?}{=} 10$ ✓

Solve $-5 = x - 8$. (Find the opposite of this number.)

$-5 = x + -8$ *Rewrite subtraction as addition.*
The opposite of −8 is 8.
$+8 \quad +8$ *Add 8 to each side.*
$3 = x$

Check: $-5 = x - 8$; $-5 \stackrel{?}{=} 3 - 8$; $-5 \stackrel{?}{=} -5$ ✓

Rewrite each equation with addition. Then state the number that should be added to each side.

1. $x - 7 = 12$ — $x + -7 = 12$; 7
2. $x - 8 = -5$ — $x + -8 = -5$; 3
3. $-4 = x - 2$ — $-4 = x + -2$; 2

Solve each equation. Check your answers.

4. $x + 4 = 12$ — 8
5. $21 = x + 2$ — 19
6. $x + 3 = 8$ — 5
7. $x + 10 = -6$ — −16
8. $-8 = x - 2$ — −6
9. $x + 5 = -2$ — −7

Geometry The angles in each pair are complementary. Write and solve an equation to find each value of x. (*Hint:* The measures of complementary angles add to 90°.)

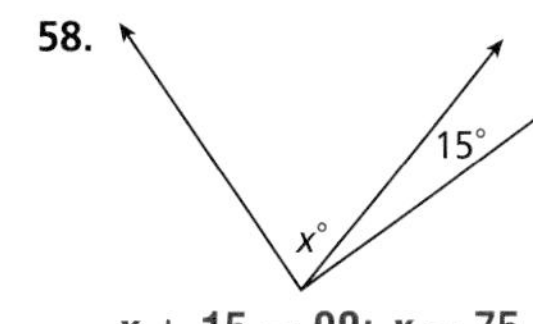

56. $63 + x = 90$; $x = 27$

57. $42 + x = 90$; $x = 48$

58. $x + 15 = 90$; $x = 75$

Multiple Choice For Exercises 59 and 60, choose the best answer.

59. Which situation is best represented by $x - 32 = 8$?
   - Ⓐ Logan withdrew $32 from her bank account. After her withdrawal, her balance was $8. How much was originally in her account?
   - Ⓑ Daniel has 32 baseball cards. Joseph has 8 fewer baseball cards than Daniel has. How many baseball cards does Joseph have?
   - Ⓒ Room A contains 32 desks. Room B has 8 fewer desks. How many desks are in Room B?
   - Ⓓ Janelle bought a bag of 32 craft sticks for a project. She used 8 craft sticks. How many craft sticks does she have left?

60. For which equation is $m = 10$ a solution?
   - Ⓐ $5 = 2m$
   - Ⓒ $\frac{m}{2} = 5$
   - Ⓑ $5m = 2$
   - Ⓓ $\frac{m}{10} = 2$

61. **Short Response** Luisa bought 6 cans of cat food that each cost the same amount. She spent a total of $4.80.
   - a. Write an equation that can be used to determine the cost of one can of cat food. $6x = 4.80$
   - b. Solve your equation to find the cost of one can of cat food. **$0.80**

CHALLENGE AND EXTEND

Solve each equation. Check your answer.

62. $3\frac{1}{5} + b = \frac{4}{5}$ $-\frac{12}{5}$

63. $x - \frac{7}{4} = \frac{2}{3}$ $\frac{29}{12}$

64. $\left(1\frac{1}{3}\right)x = 2\frac{2}{3}$ 2

65. $\left(3\frac{1}{5}\right)b = \frac{4}{5}$ $\frac{1}{4}$

66. If $p - 4 = 2$, find the value of $5p - 20$. **10**

67. If $2p = 4$, find the value of $6p + 10$. **22**

68. If $3x = 15$, find the value of $12 - 4x$. **−8**

69. If $2 + n = -11$, find the value of $6n$. **−78**

SPIRAL STANDARDS REVIEW

7NS1.2, 1.0, 2.0

Multiply or divide. *(Lesson 1-3)*

70. $-63 \div (-7)$ **9**

71. $\frac{3}{7} \div \left(-\frac{4}{7}\right)$ $-\frac{3}{4}$

72. $(-12)(-6)$ **72**

Give the side length of a square with the given area. *(Lesson 1-5)*

73. 225 m^2 **15 m**

74. 36 ft^2 **6 ft**

75. 100 cm^2 **10 cm**

Write each product using the Distributive Property. Then simplify. *(Lesson 1-6)*

76. 11(104) **11(100) + 11(4); 1144**

77. 12(43) **12(40) + 12(3); 516**

78. 3(46) **3(40) + 3(6); 138**

Teaching Tip

Geometry In **Exercises 56–58,** students are asked to write equations for complementary angles. Two angles are complementary if their sum is 90°. Remind students that complementary angles need not be adjacent. The angles below are complementary.

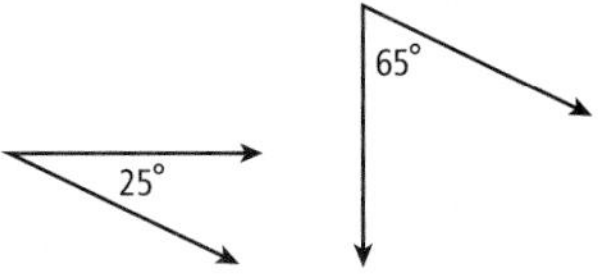

Teaching Tip

Multiple Choice In **Exercise 59,** 32 is being subtracted from x, so students should look for a situation that shows a decrease of 32. Choice **A** has a withdrawal of $32.

Journal

Have students explain the properties of equality and how they are used to solve equations.

ALTERNATIVE ASSESSMENT

Have students write and solve four equations. Each equation should be solved by using a different property of equality.

Power Presentations with PowerPoint®

2-1 Lesson Quiz

Solve each equation.

1. $r - 4 = -8$ −4
2. $\frac{5}{12} = s - \frac{11}{12}$ $\frac{16}{12}$, or $\frac{4}{3}$
3. $\frac{x}{100} = 0.028$ 2.8
4. $8y = 4$ $\frac{1}{2}$
5. $\frac{2}{5}m = 16$ 40
6. This year a high school had 578 sophomores enrolled. This is 89 less than the number enrolled last year. Write and solve an equation to find the number of sophomores enrolled last year. $s - 89 = 578$; $s = 667$

Also available on transparency

2-1 PROBLEM SOLVING

LESSON 2-1 Problem Solving
Solving One-Step Equations

Write the correct answer.

1. Michelle deposited $120 into her bank account. She now has $3345 in her account. Write and solve an equation to find how much money m was in her account before she made the deposit.
   $m + 120 = 3345$; $3225
2. Max lost 23 pounds while on a diet. He now weighs 184 pounds. Write and solve an equation to find his initial weight w.
   $w - 23 = 184$; 207 lbs
3. Maria earned $10.50 per hour working at an ice cream shop. She earned $147 each week before taxes. Write and solve an equation to find the number of hours h she worked each week.
   $10.50h = 147$; 14 hours
4. Ben is saving $\frac{1}{5}$ of his weekly pay to buy a car. Write and solve an equation to find what weekly pay w results in savings of $61.50.
   $\frac{1}{5}w = 61.50$; $307.50

Use the table below to answer questions 5–7. Select the best answer.
The table shows the maximum speed in miles per hour for various animals.

Animal	mi/h
Falcon	200
Zebra	40
Cat (domestic)	30
Black Mamba Snake	20
Snail	0.03

5. The speed of a snail is how many times that of a cat?
   - Ⓐ $\frac{1}{1000}$
   - C 100
   - B $\frac{1}{100}$
   - D 1000
6. A cheetah's maximum speed of 70 mi/h is x times faster than a black mamba snake's maximum speed. Which equation shows this relationship?
   - F $20 + x = 70$
   - H $70 = \frac{20}{x}$
   - G $20 = 70x$
   - Ⓙ $70 = 20x$
7. Use your equation in problem 6 to find how many times faster a cheetah is than a black mamba snake if they are both traveling at their maximum speed.
   - A 0.3 times
   - C 10 times
   - Ⓑ 3.5 times
   - D 50 times

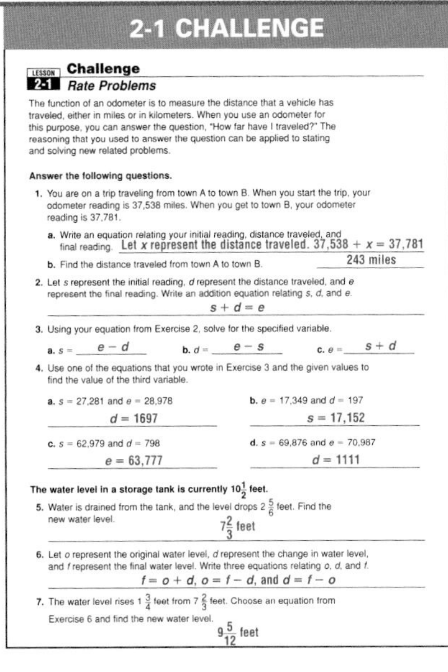

2-1 CHALLENGE

LESSON 2-1 Challenge
Rate Problems

The function of an odometer is to measure the distance that a vehicle has traveled, either in miles or in kilometers. When you use an odometer for this purpose, you can answer the question, "How far have I traveled?" The reasoning that you used to answer the question can be applied to stating and solving new related problems.

Answer the following questions.

1. You are on a trip traveling from town A to town B. When you start the trip, your odometer reading is 37,538 miles. When you get to town B, your odometer reading is 37,781.
   - a. Write an equation relating your initial reading, distance traveled, and final reading. Let x represent the distance traveled. $37{,}538 + x = 37{,}781$
   - b. Find the distance traveled from town A to town B. 243 miles
2. Let s represent the initial reading, d represent the distance traveled, and e represent the final reading. Write an addition equation relating s, d, and e.
   $s + d = e$
3. Using your equation from Exercise 2, solve for the specified variable.
   - a. $s = e - d$
   - b. $d = e - s$
   - c. $e = s + d$
4. Use one of the equations that you wrote in Exercise 3 and the given values to find the value of the third variable.
   - a. $s = 27{,}281$ and $e = 28{,}978$ — $d = 1697$
   - b. $e = 17{,}349$ and $d = 197$ — $s = 17{,}152$
   - c. $s = 62{,}979$ and $d = 798$ — $e = 63{,}777$
   - d. $s = 69{,}876$ and $e = 70{,}987$ — $d = 1111$

The water level in a storage tank is currently $10\frac{1}{2}$ feet.

5. Water is drained from the tank, and the level drops $2\frac{5}{6}$ feet. Find the new water level.
   $7\frac{2}{3}$ feet
6. Let o represent the original water level, d represent the change in water level, and f represent the final water level. Write three equations relating o, d, and f.
   $f = o + d$, $o = f - d$, and $d = f - o$
7. The water level rises $1\frac{3}{4}$ feet from $7\frac{2}{3}$ feet. Choose an equation from Exercise 6 and find the new water level.
   $9\frac{5}{12}$ feet

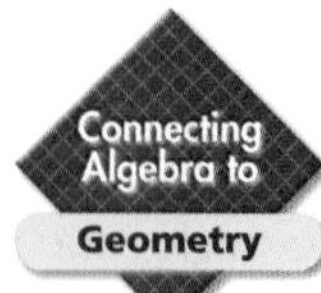

Organizer

See Skills Bank page SB16

Objective: Apply algebra skills to finding areas of geometric figures.

Online Edition

Countdown to Mastery Week 3

Teach

Remember

Students review and apply area formulas for geometric figures.

INTERVENTION For additional review and practice on finding the area of geometric figures, see Skills Bank page SB16.

Visual Have students decide how to divide the composite figure and then draw and label each part separately.

Close

Assess

Have students divide the figure in **Exercise 1** differently than the first time they found the area. Have them show algebraically that the area is still the same.

California Standards

Reinforcement of 7MG2.2

Area of Composite Figures

Review the area formulas for squares, rectangles, and triangles in the table below.

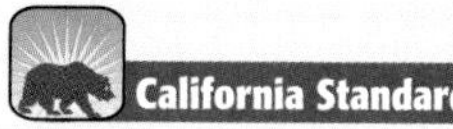

Reinforcement of 7MG2.2 Estimate and **compute the area of more complex or irregular two-** and three-**dimensional figures by breaking the figure down into more basic geometric objects.**

Squares	Rectangles	Triangles
s	ℓ, w	h, b
$A = s^2$	$A = \ell w$	$A = \frac{1}{2}bh$

A *composite figure* is a figure that is composed of basic shapes. You can divide composite figures into combinations of squares, rectangles, and triangles to find their areas.

Example

Find the area of the figure shown.

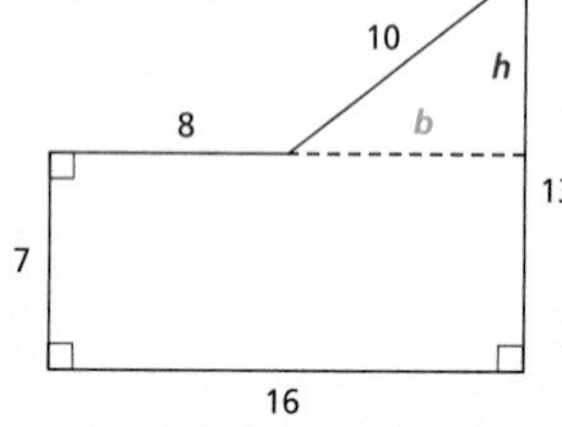

Divide the figure into a rectangle and a right triangle. Notice that you do not know the base or the height of the triangle. Use b and h to represent these lengths.

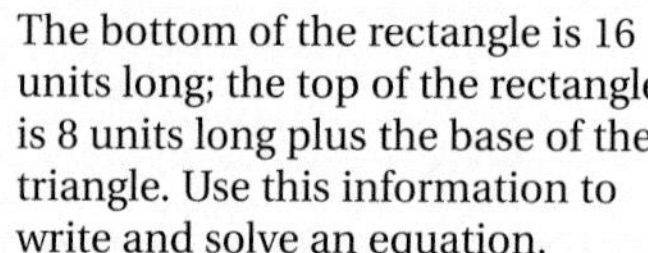

The bottom of the rectangle is 16 units long; the top of the rectangle is 8 units long plus the base of the triangle. Use this information to write and solve an equation.

$$\begin{aligned} b + 8 &= 16 \\ -8 &\;\; -8 \\ \hline b &= 8 \end{aligned}$$

The right side of the figure is 13 units long: 7 units from the rectangle plus the height of the triangle. Use this information to write and solve an equation.

$$\begin{aligned} h + 7 &= 13 \\ -7 &\;\; -7 \\ \hline h &= 6 \end{aligned}$$

The area of the figure is the sum of the areas of the rectangle and the triangle.

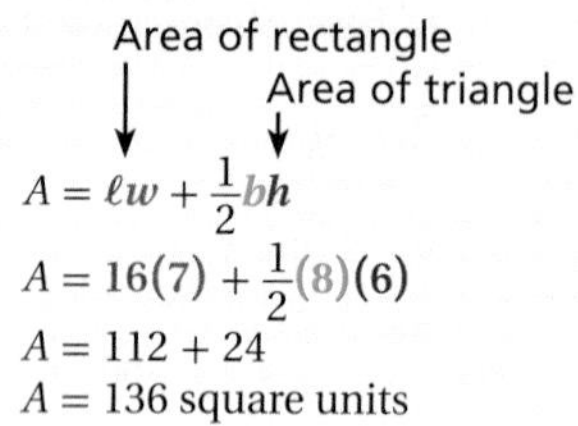

$A = \ell w + \frac{1}{2}bh$

$A = 16(7) + \frac{1}{2}(8)(6)$

$A = 112 + 24$

$A = 136$ square units

Try This

Find the area of each composite figure.

1. 314 units^2

18, 17, 10, 25

2. 672 units^2

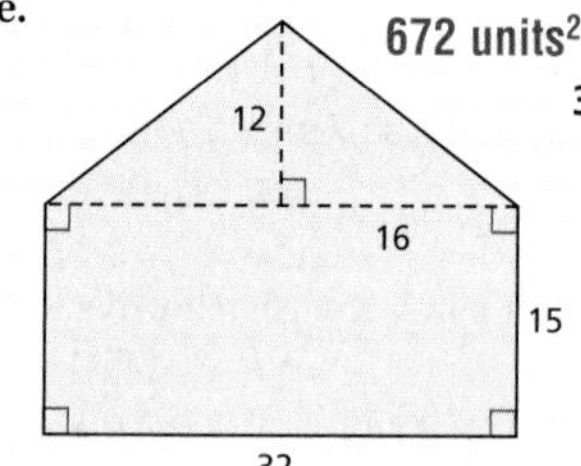

3. 330 units^2

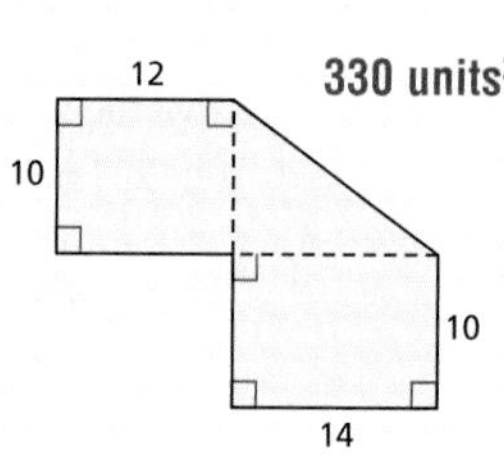

2-2 Solving Two-Step Equations

Preparation for 🔑 5.0 Students solve multistep problems, including word problems, involving linear equations and linear inequalities **in one variable** and provide justification for each step.

Vocabulary
equivalent equations

Why learn this?
Equations containing two operations can model the cost of a music club membership. (See Example 3.)

Many equations contain more than one operation, such as $2x + 5 = 11$.

This equation contains multiplication and addition. Equations that contain two operations require two steps to solve. Identify the operations in the equation and the order in which they are applied to the variable. Then use inverse operations to undo them in reverse order one at a time.

$$2x + 5 = 11$$

Operations in the Equation		To Solve
❶ First x is **multiplied** by 2.		❶ **Subtract** 5 from both sides of the equation.
❷ Then 5 is **added**.		❷ Then **divide** both sides by 2.

$$2x + 5 = 11$$
$$\underline{\quad -5 \quad -5}$$ Subtract 5 from both sides of the equation.
$$2x = 6$$
$$\frac{2x}{2} = \frac{6}{2}$$ Divide both sides of the equation by 2.
$$x = 3$$ The solution set is {3}.

Each time you perform an inverse operation, you create an equation that is *equivalent* to the original equation. **Equivalent equations** have the same solutions, or the same solution set. In the example above, $2x + 5 = 11$, $2x = 6$, and $x = 3$ are all equivalent equations.

EXAMPLE 1 Solving Two-Step Equations

Solve $10 = 6 - 2x$.

$$10 = 6 - 2x$$ *First x is multiplied by −2. Then 6 is added.*
$$\underline{-6 \quad -6}$$ *Subtract 6 from both sides.*
$$4 = -2x$$ *4 = −2x is equivalent to 10 = 6 − 2x.*
$$\frac{4}{-2} = \frac{-2x}{-2}$$ *Since x is multiplied by −2, divide both sides by −2 to undo the multiplication.*
$$-2 = x$$ *The solution set is {−2}.*

Helpful Hint

Check your answer.

$10 = 6 - 2x$	
10	$6 - 2(-2)$
10	$6 - (-4)$
10	$6 + 4$
10	10 ✓

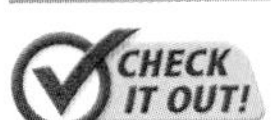

Solve each equation. Check your answer.

1a. $-4 + 7x = 3$ 1 **1b.** $1.5 = 1.2y - 5.7$ 6 **1c.** $\frac{n}{7} + 2 = 2$ 0

2-2 Organizer

Objective: Solve two-step equations in one variable.

Online Edition
Tutorial Videos

Countdown to Mastery Week 3

Power Presentations with PowerPoint®

Warm Up

Solve each equation.

1. $3 + x = 11$ 8

2. $x - 7 = 19$ 26

3. $6x = 15$ $\frac{5}{2}$

4. $\frac{x}{3} = 4$ 12

Find a common denominator.

5. $\frac{1}{2}, \frac{1}{3}$ Possible answer: 6

6. $\frac{1}{5}, \frac{1}{2}, \frac{1}{4}$ Possible answer: 20

Also available on transparency

Teacher: Why don't you have your homework?

Student: I divided by zero, and the paper vanished into thin air!

1 Introduce

EXPLORATION

2-2 Solving Two-Step Equations

Juan wants to rent a bike while on vacation. The sign posted on the rental stand says "$10 fee plus $3 per hour."

1. Juan writes the expression $10 + 3h$ to find the cost of renting a bike for h hours. Complete the table.

Hours h	Cost $10 + 3h$
1	
2	
3	
4	
5	

2. Find the hours that correspond to the costs in the table.

Hours h	Cost $10 + 3h$
	28
	34
	40
	43
	46

THINK AND DISCUSS

3. **Explain** how you evaluated $10 + 3h$ for a given value of h.

4. **Describe** how you completed the table in Problem 2. What process did you use?

Motivate

Have each student secretly choose a number. Ask the students to double their number and add 10. Then ask one student for his or her answer. Ask the rest of the class how they could figure out this student's original number. Subtract 10 and divide by 2. Ask how many steps were used to find the answer and why. Two, because there were two operations.

Explorations and answers are provided in *Alternate Openers: Explorations Transparencies*.

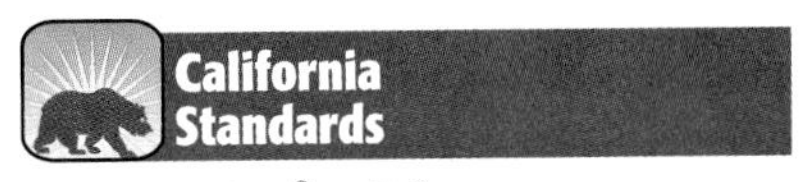

Preparation for 🔑 5.0

Power Presentations with PowerPoint®

Additional Examples

Example 1

Solve each equation.

A. $18 = 4a + 10$ 2

B. $5t - 2 = -32$ -6

Example 2

Solve each equation.

A. $\frac{y}{8} - \frac{3}{4} = \frac{5}{4}$ 16

B. $\frac{2}{3}r + \frac{3}{4} = \frac{7}{12}$ $-\frac{1}{4}$

Also available on transparency

INTERVENTION

Questioning Strategies

EXAMPLE 1

- What steps need to be taken to isolate the variable? Why?

EXAMPLE 2

- What happens to the fractions in an equation when both sides are multiplied by the LCD?

Inclusion To help students remember which operation to undo first, begin by reviewing the order of operations. Then explain that when undoing operations, they should use a backward order of operations. For instance, in the equation $3x + 5 = 20$, they should undo addition first, because addition comes before multiplication in a backward order of operations.

EXAMPLE 2 Solving Two-Step Equations That Contain Fractions

Solve each equation.

A $\frac{q}{15} - \frac{1}{5} = \frac{3}{5}$

Method 1 Use fraction operations.

$$\frac{q}{15} - \frac{1}{5} = \frac{3}{5}$$

$$\underline{\quad + \frac{1}{5} \quad + \frac{1}{5}}$$ *Since $\frac{1}{5}$ is subtracted from $\frac{q}{15}$, add $\frac{1}{5}$ to both sides to undo the subtraction.*

$$\frac{q}{15} = \frac{4}{5}$$

$$15\left(\frac{q}{15}\right) = 15\left(\frac{4}{5}\right)$$ *Since q is divided by 15, multiply both sides by 15 to undo the division.*

$$q = \frac{15 \cdot 4}{5}$$ *Simplify.*

$$q = \frac{60}{5}$$

$$q = 12$$ *The solution set is {12}.*

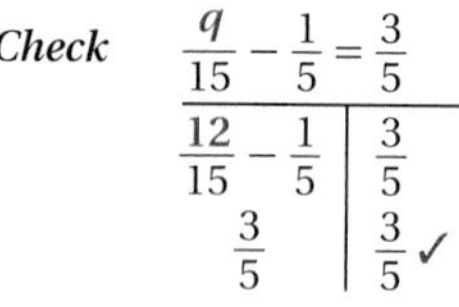

You can multiply both sides of the equation by any common denominator of the fractions. Using the LCD is the most efficient.
To review fraction operations, including LCD, see Skills Bank pages SB8–SB9.

Method 2 Multiply by the least common denominator (LCD) to clear the fractions.

$$\frac{q}{15} - \frac{1}{5} = \frac{3}{5}$$

$$15\left(\frac{q}{15} - \frac{1}{5}\right) = 15\left(\frac{3}{5}\right)$$ *Multiply both sides by 15, the LCD of the fractions.*

$$15\left(\frac{q}{15}\right) - 15\left(\frac{1}{5}\right) = 15\left(\frac{3}{5}\right)$$ *Distribute 15 on the left side.*

$$q - 3 = 9$$

$$\underline{\quad +3 \quad +3}$$ *Simplify. Since 3 is subtracted from q, add 3 to both sides to undo the subtraction.*

$$q = 12$$ *The solution set is {12}.*

Check

$$\frac{q}{15} - \frac{1}{5} = \frac{3}{5}$$ *To check your solution, substitute 12 for q in the original equation.*

$$\frac{12}{15} - \frac{1}{5} \;\Big|\; \frac{3}{5}$$

$$\frac{3}{5} \;\Big|\; \frac{3}{5} \checkmark$$

B $\frac{j}{4} + 2 = 9$

$$\frac{j}{4} + 2 = 9$$

$$\underline{\quad -2 \quad -2}$$ *Since 2 is added to $\frac{j}{4}$, subtract 2 from both sides to undo the addition.*

$$\frac{j}{4} = 7$$

$$4\left(\frac{j}{4}\right) = 4(7)$$ *Since j is divided by 4, multiply both sides by 4 to undo the division.*

$$j = 28$$ *The solution set is {28}.*

Solve each equation. Check your answer.

2a. $\frac{2x}{5} - \frac{1}{2} = 5$ $\frac{55}{4}$ **2b.** $\frac{3}{4}u + \frac{1}{2} = \frac{7}{8}$ $\frac{1}{2}$ **2c.** $\frac{1}{5}n - \frac{1}{3} = \frac{8}{3}$ 15

2 Teach

Guided Instruction

Review with students what they have learned about solving one-step equations. The goal of solving a two-step equation is the same as the goal of solving a one-step equation: to isolate the variable.

Continue to use the concept of a balance scale throughout this lesson—whatever operation is performed on one side of the equation must also be performed on the other side in order to "keep the balance."

Universal Access

Through Concrete Manipulatives

Algebra tiles can model two-step equations. To solve $3x - 2 = 4$:

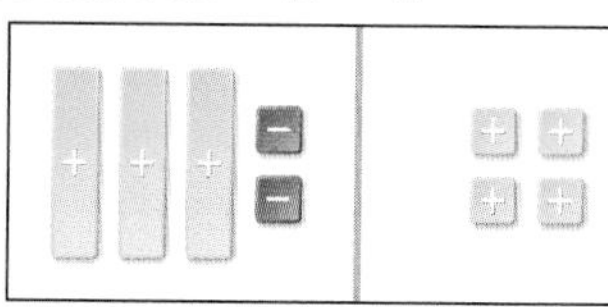

Add 2 positive tiles to each side. On the left, remove the 2 negative tiles and the 2 positive tiles. Divide the 6 unit tiles on the right into 3 equal groups to show division by 3. The solution is $x = 2$.

EXAMPLE 3 Problem-Solving Application

Alex belongs to the Student Music Club and bought a discount card for $19.95. After one year, Alex has spent $63.40. Write and solve an equation to find how many CDs Alex bought during the year.

Student Music Club
Discount Card
CDs $3.95 each

 **Understand the Problem**

The **answer** will be the number of CDs that Alex bought during the year.

List the important information:

- Alex paid $19.95 for a student discount card.
- Alex paid $3.95 for each CD he purchased.
- After one year, Alex has spent $63.40.

 **Make a Plan**

Let *c* represent the number of CDs that Alex purchased. That means Alex has spent $3.95*c*. However, Alex must also add the amount he spent on the card. Write an equation to represent this situation.

total cost	=	cost of CDs	+	cost of discount card
63.40	=	3.95*c*	+	19.95

 **Solve**

$$63.40 = 3.95c + 19.95$$
$$\underline{-19.95 \qquad\qquad -19.95}$$
$$43.45 = 3.95c$$

Since 19.95 is added to 3.95c, subtract 19.95 from both sides to undo the addition.

$$\frac{43.45}{3.95} = \frac{3.95c}{3.95}$$
$$11 = c$$

Since c is multiplied by 3.95, divide both sides by 3.95 to undo the multiplication.

Alex bought 11 CDs during the year.

 **Look Back**

Check that the answer is reasonable. The cost per CD is about $4, so if Alex bought 11 CDs, this amount is about 11(4) = $44.

Add the cost of the discount card, which is about $20: 44 + 20 = 64. So the total cost was about $64, which is close to the amount given in the problem, $63.40.

CHECK IT OUT!

3a. Sara paid $15.95 to become a member at a gym. She then paid a monthly membership fee. Her total cost for 12 months was $735.95. How much was the monthly fee? **$60**

3b. Lynda has 12 records in her collection. She adds the same number of new records to her collection each month. After 7 months Lynda has 26 records. How many records does Lynda add each month? **2**

COMMON ERROR ALERT

When clearing fractions in an equation, students may forget to multiply every term by the LCD, especially when one of the terms is not a fraction. For instance, in **Example 2,** they may write $15 \cdot \frac{q}{15} - \frac{1}{5} = 15 \cdot \frac{3}{5}$ and then fail to multiply 15 by $-\frac{1}{5}$ on the left side. Remind them to use parentheses to show multiplication by the LCD and to distribute the LCD to each term.

Power Presentations with PowerPoint®

Additional Example

Example 3

Jan joined the dining club at the local café for a fee of $29.95. Being a member entitles her to save $2.50 every time she buys lunch. Jan calculates that she has saved a total of $12.55 so far by joining the club. Write and solve an equation to find how many times Jan has eaten lunch at the café. $12.55 = 2.50c - 29.95$; $c = 17$

Also available on transparency

INTERVENTION
Questioning Strategies

EXAMPLE 3

- How do you decide what the variable will represent?
- What operations are needed to solve the equation?

3 Close

Summarize

Ask students what they would do as a first step in solving each of the following equations:

- $7x - 3 = 29$ Add 3 to both sides.
- $-\frac{1}{3}x + \frac{3}{4} = \frac{7}{12}$ Multiply both sides by 12, or subtract $\frac{3}{4}$ from both sides.

FORMATIVE ASSESSMENT and INTERVENTION

***Diagnose Before* the Lesson**
2-2 Warm Up, TE p. 79

***Monitor During* the Lesson**
Check It Out! Exercises, SE pp. 79–81
Questioning Strategies, TE pp. 80–81

***Assess After* the Lesson**
2-2 Lesson Quiz, TE p. 84
Alternative Assessment, TE p. 84

Answers to *Think and Discuss*

1. Possible answer: To solve $2x + 1 = 7$, first subtract 1 from both sides, and then divide both sides by 2. To solve $2x - 1 = 7$, first add 1 to both sides and then divide by 2.
2. See p. A2.

2-2 Exercises

Assignment Guide

Assign *Guided Practice* exercises as necessary.

If you finished Examples **1–3**
Proficient 14–37, 46–54, 62–81
Advanced 14–26 even, 27–31 odd, 33–81

Homework Quick Check
Quickly check key concepts.
Exercises: 14, 18, 22, 24, 26

California Standards

Standard	Exercises
1.0	66–73
Prep for 5.0	1–48, 50–61
6AF1.1	74–81
7NS1.4	62
7NS1.5	63–65

THINK AND DISCUSS

1. Explain the steps you would follow to solve $2x + 1 = 7$. How is this procedure different from the one you would follow to solve $2x - 1 = 7$?

2. **GET ORGANIZED** Copy and complete the graphic organizer. In each box, write and solve a two-step equation. Use addition, subtraction, multiplication, and division.

Solving Two-Step Equations	

2-2 Exercises

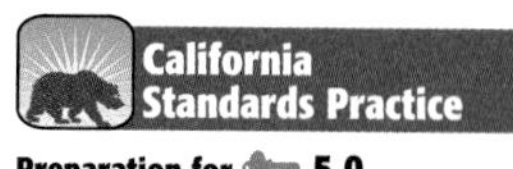

Preparation for 5.0

GUIDED PRACTICE

SEE EXAMPLE 1 p. 79

Solve each equation. Check your answer.

1. $4a + 3 = 11$ **2**
2. $8 = 3r - 1$ **3**
3. $\frac{x}{6} + 4 = 15$ **66**
4. $x + 0.3 = 3.3$ **3**
5. $15y + 31 = 61$ **2**
6. $9 - c = -13$ **22**

SEE EXAMPLE 2 p. 80

7. $\frac{1}{3}y + \frac{1}{4} = \frac{5}{12}$ $\mathbf{\frac{1}{2}}$
8. $\frac{2}{7}j - \frac{1}{7} = \frac{3}{14}$ $\mathbf{\frac{5}{4}}$
9. $\frac{x}{8} - \frac{1}{2} = 6$ **52**
10. $\frac{1}{2} + 12x = \frac{9}{2}$ $\mathbf{\frac{1}{3}}$
11. $\frac{5}{6}x - \frac{1}{3} = \frac{5}{2}$ $\mathbf{\frac{17}{5}}$
12. $3 - \frac{1}{2}r = 12$ **−18**

SEE EXAMPLE 3 p. 81

13. **Transportation** Paul bought a student discount card for the bus. The card cost \$7 and allows him to buy daily bus passes for \$1.50. After one month, Paul spent \$29.50. How many daily bus passes did Paul buy? **15 passes**

PRACTICE AND PROBLEM SOLVING

Independent Practice	
For Exercises	See Example
14–19	1
20–25	2
26	3

Extra Practice
Skills Practice p. EP4
Application Practice p. EP25

Solve each equation. Check your answer.

14. $5 = 2g + 1$ **2**
15. $6h - 7 = 17$ **4**
16. $15 = \frac{a}{3} - 2$ **51**
17. $3x + 3 = 18$ **5**
18. $0.6g + 11 = 5$ **−10**
19. $32 = 5 - 3t$ **−9**
20. $2d + \frac{1}{5} = \frac{3}{5}$ **0.2**
21. $1 = 2x + \frac{1}{2}$ $\mathbf{\frac{1}{4}}$
22. $\frac{z}{2} + 1 = \frac{3}{2}$ **1**
23. $\frac{2}{3} = \frac{4j}{6}$ **1**
24. $\frac{3}{4} = \frac{3}{8}x - \frac{3}{2}$ **6**
25. $\frac{1}{5} - \frac{x}{5} = -\frac{2}{5}$ **3**
26. **Consumer Economics** Jennifer is saving money to buy a bike. The bike costs \$245. She has \$125 saved, and each week she adds \$15 to her savings. How many weeks will it take her to save enough money to buy the bike? **8 weeks**

82 Chapter 2 Equations

2-2 READING STRATEGIES

LESSON 2-2 Reading Strategies
Recognize Errors

There are several common errors that students make when they solve two-step equations. Study the following problems so that you can recognize and avoid these errors.

$6x + 3 = 15$ $\frac{+3}{6x} = \frac{+3}{18}$ $\frac{6x}{6} = \frac{18}{6}$ $x = 3$ **Error:** Remember to use *inverse operations* to isolate the variable. The inverse of addition is subtraction.	$10y + 2 = 7$ $\frac{-2}{10y} = \frac{-2}{5}$ $\frac{10y}{5} = \frac{5}{5}$ $2 = y$ **Error:** You do not always divide a larger number by a smaller one. Divide both sides by the value that multiplies y to undo the multiplication.	$\frac{5x}{2} - \frac{1}{4} = 1$ $4(\frac{5x}{2} - \frac{1}{4}) = 1$ $4 \cdot \frac{5x}{2} - 4 \cdot \frac{1}{4} = 1$ $10x - 1 = 1$ $+1 \quad +1$ $10x = 2$ $\frac{10x}{10} = \frac{2}{10}$ $x = \frac{1}{5}$ **Error:** When you clear fractions, be sure to multiply *both sides* by the LCD.

Answer each question.

1. What is the correct solution for each equation shown above?
$x = 2$ $\quad y = \frac{1}{2}$ $\quad x = \frac{1}{2}$
2. Would you add 10 or subtract 10 on each side of the equation when you solve $14 = 3x - 10$? Explain.
Add; addition is the inverse operation of subtraction.

Tell whether the solution of each equation is correct or incorrect. If incorrect, describe the error.

3. $31 = 7 + 4y$; $y = 6$
correct
4. $3w - 6 = 27$; $w = 7$
Incorrect; 6 was subtracted from both sides of the equation.
5. $12x + 5 = 9$; $x = 3$
Incorrect; after writing $12x = 4$, both sides were divided by 4 instead of 12.

2-2 REVIEW FOR MASTERY

LESSON 2-2 Review for Mastery
Solving Two-Step Equations

When solving two-step equations, first identify the operations and the order in which they are applied to the variable. Then use inverse operations.

	Operations	Solve using Inverse Operations
$4x - 3 = 15$	• x is multiplied by 4. • Then 3 is subtracted.	• Add 3 to both sides. • Then divide both sides by 4.
$\frac{x}{3} + 2 = 9$	• x is divided by 3. • Then 2 is added.	• Add −2 to both sides. • Then multiply both sides by 3.

The order of the inverse operations is the order of operations in reverse.

Solve $5x - 7 = 13$.

		Check:
$5x - 7 = 13$	*x is multiplied by 5. Then 7 is subtracted.*	$5x - 7 = 13$
$+7 \quad +7$	*Add 7 to both sides.*	$5(4) - 7 \stackrel{?}{=} 13$
$5x = 20$		$20 - 7 \stackrel{?}{=} 13$
$\frac{5x}{5} = \frac{20}{5}$	*Divide both sides by 5.*	$13 \stackrel{?}{=} 13$ ✓
$x = 4$		

Solve each equation. Check your answers.

1. $3x - 8 = 4$
4
2. $\frac{b}{2} - 4 = 26$
60
3. $3y + 4 = 9$
$\frac{5}{3}$
4. $14 = 3x - 1$
5

Write an equation to represent each relationship. Then solve.

27. Seven less than twice a number equals 19. $2x - 7 = 19$; $x = 13$

28. Eight decreased by 3 times a number equals 2. $8 - 3x = 2$; $x = 2$

29. 30 increased by 5 times a number equals 80. $30 + 5x = 80$; $x = 10$

30. 30 less than 4 times a number is equal to 14. $4x - 30 = 14$; $x = 11$

31. The sum of 64 and 3 times a number is -2. $64 + 3x = -2$; $x = -22$

32. 6 added to twice a number is equal to -8. $6 + 2x = -8$; $x = -7$

LINK History

Martin Luther King Jr. entered college at age 15. During his life he earned 3 degrees and was awarded 20 honorary degrees.

Source: lib.lsu.edu

33. **History** In 1963, Dr. Martin Luther King Jr. began his famous "I have a dream" speech with the words "Five score years ago, a great American, in whose symbolic shadow we stand, signed the Emancipation Proclamation." The Proclamation was signed by President Abraham Lincoln in 1863.
    a. Using the dates given, write and solve an equation that can be used to find the number of years in a score. $1963 - 5s = 1863$; $s = 20$
    b. How many score would represent 60? **3**

Solve each equation. Check your answer.

34. $3t + 44 = 50$	35. $3x - 6 = 18$	36. $15 = \frac{c}{3} - 2$	37. $2x + 6.5 = 15.5$
38. $3.9w - 17.9 = -2.3$	39. $20 = x - 3x$	40. $5x + 9 = 39$	41. $15 + 5.5m = 70$
42. $7j + 3 = 24$	43. $\frac{3}{4} + \frac{x}{2} = 3$	44. $50 = 3t - 4$	45. $14.5 = 5.5n - 2$

34. 2
35. 8
36. 51
37. 4.5
38. 4
39. -10
40. 6
41. 10
42. 3
43. 4.5
44. 18
45. 3

Biology Use the graph for Exercises 46 and 47.

46. The maximum height of an ostrich is 20 inches more than 4 times the maximum height of a kiwi. Write and solve an equation to find the maximum height of a kiwi. $4k + 20 = 108$; 22 in.

47. Five times the maximum height of a kakapo minus 70 equals the maximum height of an emu. Write and solve an equation to find the maximum height of a kakapo. $5k - 70 = 60$; 26 in.

48. **Transportation** A taxi company charges \$1.10 plus \$0.95 per mile. Karen's total fare was \$12.50. How many miles did Karen travel? **12**

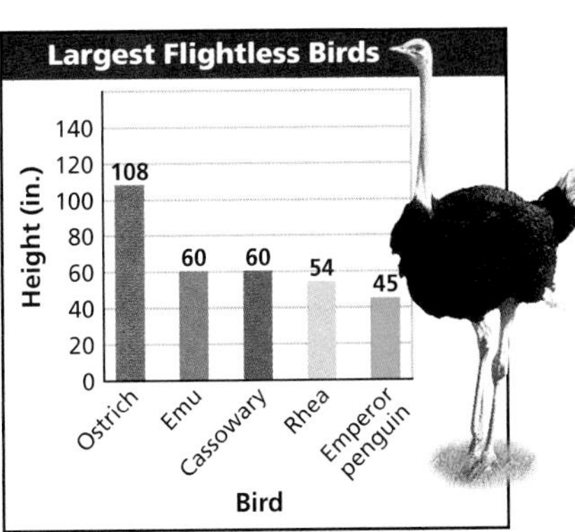

Source: The Top Ten of Everything

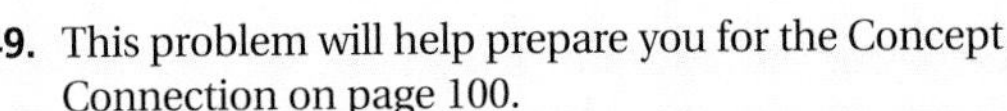

CONCEPT CONNECTION

49. This problem will help prepare you for the Concept Connection on page 100.
    a. The cost of fighting a particular forest fire is \$225 per acre. Complete the table.
    b. Write an equation for the relationship between the cost c of fighting the fire and the number of acres n. $c = 225n$

Cost of Fighting Fire

Acres	Cost (\$)
100	22,500
200	**45,000**
500	**112,500**
1000	**225,000**
1500	**337,500**
n	**$225n$**

CONCEPT CONNECTION **Exercise 49** involves using a known rate to find data values. This exercise prepares students for the Concept Connection on page 100.

2-2 PROBLEM SOLVING

LESSON 2-2 Problem Solving
Solving Two-Step Equations

Write the correct answer.

1. Stephen belongs to a movie club in which he pays an annual fee of \$39.95 and then rents DVDs for \$0.99 each. In one year, Stephen spent \$55.79. Write and solve an equation to find how many DVDs d he rented.
   $39.95 + 0.99d = 55.79$
   16 DVDs

2. In 2003, the population of Zimbabwe was about 12.6 million, which was 1 million more than 4 times the population in 1950. Write and solve an equation to find the population p of Zimbabwe in 1950.
   $12.6 = 4p + 1$
   2.9 million

3. Maggie's brother is three years younger than twice her age. The sum of their ages is 24. How old is Maggie?
   9 years old

4. Kate is saving to take an SAT prep course that costs \$350. So far, she has saved \$180, and she adds \$17 to her savings each week. How many more weeks must she save to be able to afford the course?
   10 weeks

Use the graph below to answer questions 5–7. Select the best answer. The graph shows the population density (number of people per square mile) of various states given in the 2000 census.

5. One seventeenth of Rhode Island's population density minus 17 equals the population density of Colorado. What is Rhode Island's population density?
   A 425 C 714
   B 697 (D) 1003

6. One more than sixteen times the population density of New Mexico equals the population density of Texas. To the nearest whole number, what is New Mexico's population density?
   (F) 5 H 13
   G 8 J 63

7. Three times the population density of Missouri minus 26 equals the population density of California. What is Missouri's population density?
   A 64 C 98
   (B) 81 D 729

Population Density

California	Colorado	Massachusetts	New Jersey	Texas
217	42	810	1135	80

2-2 CHALLENGE

LESSON 2-2 Challenge
Using Two-Step Equations to Solve Geometry Problems

Many concepts of algebra can be applied to a wide range of geometry problems.

Suppose that you want to design a box. The base of the box will be a square that is 10 inches on each side, and the box will be h inches tall. The surface area of the box (that is, the area of cardboard needed to make the box, assuming no overlap) is given by $4 \cdot 10 \cdot h + 2 \cdot 10 \cdot 10$, or $40h + 200$. For a surface area of 360 square inches, you would solve $40h + 200 = 360$ in order to find the height of the box.

h in.
10 in.
10 in.

The base of a rectangular box is to be a square that is 10 inches on each side. For each given surface area, find the corresponding height of the box.

1. 360 square inches 4 inches
2. 520 square inches 8 inches
3. 240 square inches 1 inch
4. 560 square inches 9 inches
5. 800 square inches 15 inches
6. 480 square inches 7 inches

Now suppose that you want to design a cylindrical box whose base is a circle with a radius of 5 inches. The surface area of the cylindrical box is given by $50\pi + 10\pi h$.

The base of a cylindrical box will be a circle with a radius of 5 inches. For each given surface area, find the corresponding height of the box.

7. 80π square inches 3 inches
8. 120π square inches 7 inches
9. 110π square inches 6 inches
10. 160π square inches 11 inches
11. 200π square inches 15 inches
12. 90π square inches 4 inches

Another geometric application of two-step equations relates to the interior angles of a polygon. If the polygon has n sides, the sum of the measures of its angles is $180n - 360$ degrees.

120° 110°
60° 70°

For example, in a triangle, $n = 3$, so the measures of the angles add up to 180°. For a trapezoid, $n = 4$, so the measures of the angles add up to 360°.

In the following exercises, the sum of the measures of the interior angles of a polygon is given. Find the number of sides of the polygon.

13. 540° 5 sides
14. 1800° 12 sides
15. 900° 7 sides
16. 2880° 18 sides

2-2 PRACTICE A
2-2 PRACTICE C
2-2 PRACTICE B

LESSON 2-2 Practice B
Solving Two-Step Equations

Solve each equation. Check your answers.

1. $-4x + 7 = 11$ $x = -1$
2. $17 = 5y - 3$ $y = 4$
3. $-4 = 2p + 10$ $p = -7$
4. $3m + 4 = 1$ $m = -1$
5. $12.5 = 2g - 3.5$ $g = 8$
6. $-13 = -h - 7$ $h = 6$
7. $-6 = \frac{y}{5} + 4$ $y = -50$
8. $\frac{7}{9} = 2n + \frac{1}{9}$ $n = \frac{1}{3}$
9. $-\frac{4}{5}t + \frac{2}{5} = \frac{2}{3}$ $t = -\frac{1}{3}$
10. $-2x - 10 = 8$ $x = -9$
11. $-2b + 8 = -16$ $b = 12$
12. $18 = 4q - 2$ $q = 5$
13. If $3x - 8 = -2$, find the value of $x - 6$. -4
14. If $-3y + 5 = -4$, find the value of $5y$. 15

Answer each of the following.

15. For her cellular service, Vera pays \$32 a month, plus \$0.75 for each minute over the allowed minutes in her plan. Write an expression that shows how much Vera's bill will be for one month. $32 + 0.75x$
16. Vera received a bill for \$47 last month. For how many minutes did she use her phone beyond the allowed minutes? 20 minutes

Multiple Choice In **Exercise 53,** students who chose **C** most likely subtracted 3 from each side of the original equation instead of adding 3. Remind them to identify the operations in the equation and then use *inverse* operations when solving.

Journal

Have students explain what equivalent equations are. They should give an example and include the term *solution set* in their explanation.

ALTERNATIVE ASSESSMENT

Have students explain how to solve a two-step equation to a friend who missed the lesson. Students should write and solve a word problem as part of their explanation.

Power Presentations with PowerPoint®

2-2 Lesson Quiz

Solve each equation.

1. $4y + 8 = 2$ $\quad -\frac{3}{2}$
2. $3 + 2x = 11$ $\quad 4$
3. $\frac{3}{4}a + 14 = 8$ $\quad -8$
4. $\frac{1}{4} = \frac{m}{2} - \frac{1}{8}$ $\quad \frac{3}{4}$
5. Nancy bought 5 rolls of color film and 6 rolls of black-and-white film. The 5 rolls of color film cost \$15, and Nancy's total was \$39. Write and solve an equation to find the cost of one roll of black-and-white film. $6b + 15 = 39$; \$4

Also available on transparency

50. Possible answer: Subtract 2 from both sides or add m to both sides.

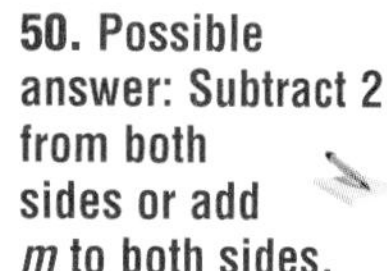

51. Possible answer: Undo any addition or subtraction on this term by using inverse operations. Then undo any multiplication or division on this term by using inverse operations.

50. Critical Thinking The equation $2 - m = 17$ has more than one solution method. Give at least two different "first steps" to solve this equation.

51. Write About It Write a series of steps that you can use to solve any two-step equation.

Multiple Choice For Exercises 52 and 53, choose the best answer.

52. The equation $c = 48 + 0.06m$ represents the cost c of renting a car and driving m miles. Which statement best describes this cost?

Ⓐ The cost is a flat rate of \$0.06 per mile.
Ⓑ The cost is \$0.48 for the first mile and \$0.06 for each additional mile.
Ⓒ The cost is a \$48 fee plus \$0.06 per mile.
Ⓓ The cost is a \$6 fee plus \$0.48 per mile.

53. Which equation is equivalent to $4m - 3 = 21$?

Ⓐ $4m + 3 = 24$ Ⓒ $4m = 18$
Ⓑ $4m - 3 = 18$ **Ⓓ** $4m = 24$

54. Gridded Response A telemarketer earns \$150 a week plus \$2 for each call that results in a sale. Her pay last week was \$204. How many of her calls last week resulted in sales? **27**

CHALLENGE AND EXTEND

Solve each equation. Check your answer.

55. $\frac{11}{2} + 3x = \frac{-5^2}{2}$ **−6** **56.** $\frac{15}{2^2}x - 15 = \frac{33}{2^2}$ $\mathbf{\frac{31}{5}}$

57. $-5.2x + 1.69 = -8.71$ **2** **58.** $\frac{1}{2}x - 12.75 = 21.25$ **68**

59. $169 = 37x - 4^2$ **5** **60.** $8.49 = 4.6x - 5.31$ **3**

61. Business The formula $p = nc - e$ gives the profit p when a number of items n are each sold at a cost c and expenses e are subtracted.

a. If $p = 2500$, $n = 2000$, and $e = 800$, what is the value of c? **1.65**
b. If $p = 2500$, $n = 1000$, and $e = 800$, what is the value of c? **3.3**
c. **What if...?** If n is divided in half while p and e remain the same, what is the effect on c? **c doubles.**

SPIRAL STANDARDS REVIEW — 6AF1.1, 7NS1.4, 7NS1.5, 1.0

Write all classifications that apply to each real number. (Lesson 1-5)

62. $\sqrt{3}$ **irrational** **63.** -58 **64.** $2\frac{1}{3}$ **65.** 0.17

Write each product using the Distributive Property. Then simplify. (Lesson 1-6)

66. 8(61) **67.** 9(28) **68.** 11(28) **69.** 13(21)
70. 3(45) **71.** 7(19) **72.** 9(72) **73.** 8(33)

Solve each equation. (Lesson 2-1)

74. $17 = k + 4$ **13** **75.** $x - 18 = 3$ **21** **76.** $a + 6 = -12$ **−18** **77.** $-7 = q - 7$ **0**
78. $12b = 60$ **5** **79.** $7 = \frac{z}{4}$ **28** **80.** $3a = 24$ **8** **81.** $\frac{t}{6} = -7$ **−42**

63. integer, rational, terminating decimal
64. repeating decimal, rational
65. terminating decimal, rational
66. 8(60) + 8(1); 488
67. 9(20) + 9(8); 252
68. 11(20) + 11(8); 308
69. 13(20) + 13(1); 273
70. 3(40) + 3(5); 135
71. 7(10) + 7(9); 133
72. 9(70) + 9(2); 648
73. 8(30) + 8(3); 264

2-3 Solving Multi-Step Equations

California Standards

4.0 Students simplify expressions before solving linear equations and inequalities in one variable, such as $3(2x - 5) + 4(x - 2) = 12$.

5.0 Students solve multi-step problems, including word problems, involving linear equations and linear inequalities **in one variable** and provide justification for each step.

Why learn this?

Martial arts instructors can model enrollment costs with multi-step equations.

A martial arts school is offering a special where students can enroll for half price, after a $12.50 application fee.

Ten students enrolled and paid a total of $325. To find the regular price of enrollment, you can solve an equation.

$$10\left(\frac{p}{2} + 12.50\right) = 325$$

(Number of students → 10; Regular price of enrollment → p; Application fee → 12.50; Total cost → 325)

Notice that this equation contains multiplication, division, and addition. An equation that contains multiple operations will require multiple steps to solve. You will create an equivalent equation at each step.

EXAMPLE 1 Solving Multi-Step Equations

Solve $\frac{4x + 1}{5} = 5$. Check your answer.

$5\left(\frac{4x + 1}{5}\right) = 5(5)$ — *Since 4x + 1 is divided by 5, multiply both sides by 5 to undo the division.*

$4x + 1 = 25$

$\underline{-1 \quad -1}$ — *Since 1 is added to 4x, subtract 1 from both sides to undo the addition.*

$4x = 24$

$\frac{4x}{4} = \frac{24}{4}$ — *Since x is multiplied by 4, divide both sides by 4 to undo the multiplication.*

$x = 6$ — *The solution set is {6}.*

Check $\frac{4x + 1}{5} = 5$ — *To check your solution, substitute 6 for x in the original equation.*

$\frac{4(6) + 1}{5}$	5
$\frac{24 + 1}{5}$	5
$\frac{25}{5}$	5
5	5 ✓

CHECK IT OUT! Solve each equation. Check your answer.

1a. $\frac{5m + 13}{2} = 1$ $-\frac{11}{5}$ **1b.** $\frac{4 - 2z}{4} = -2$ **6**

2-3 Organizer

Objective: Solve equations in one variable that contain more than one operation.

Online Edition Tutorial Videos

Countdown to Mastery Week 3

Power Presentations with PowerPoint®

Warm Up

Evaluate each expression.

1. $12\left(\frac{3 + (-7)}{12}\right)$ -4

2. $26 - 4(7 - 5)$ 18

Simplify each expression.

3. $10c + c$ $11c$

4. $8.2b + 3.8b - 12b$ 0

5. $5m + 2(2m - 7)$ $9m - 14$

6. $6x - (2x + 5)$ $4x - 5$

Also available on transparency

Q: How do equations get into shape?

A: They do multi-step aerobics.

1 Introduce

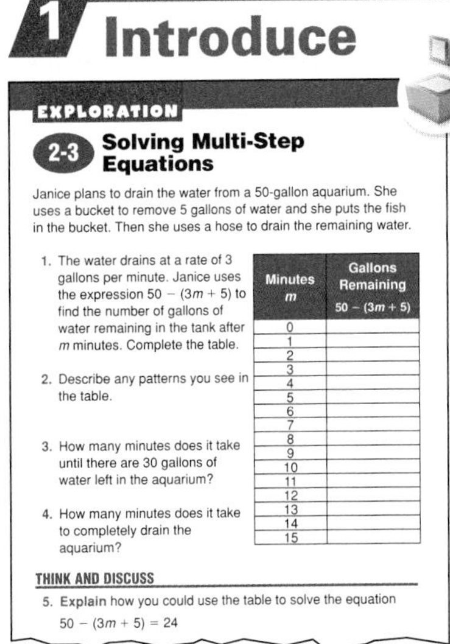

EXPLORATION

2-3 Solving Multi-Step Equations

Janice plans to drain the water from a 50-gallon aquarium. She uses a bucket to remove 5 gallons of water and she puts the fish in the bucket. Then she uses a hose to drain the remaining water.

1. The water drains at a rate of 3 gallons per minute. Janice uses the expression $50 - (3m + 5)$ to find the number of gallons of water remaining in the tank after m minutes. Complete the table.

Minutes m	Gallons Remaining $50 - (3m + 5)$
0	
1	
2	
3	
4	
5	
6	
7	
8	
9	
10	
11	
12	
13	
14	
15	

2. Describe any patterns you see in the table.

3. How many minutes does it take until there are 30 gallons of water left in the aquarium?

4. How many minutes does it take to completely drain the aquarium?

THINK AND DISCUSS

5. Explain how you could use the table to solve the equation $50 - (3m + 5) = 24$

Motivate

Tell students that in the morning, you: get in your car, start it, drive to school, turn off the car, and get out. To undo this chain of events, you: get in the car, start it, drive home, turn off the car, and get out. Stress that your "undoing" must go exactly in reverse order; otherwise you might get out of the car while it is still running.

Solving equations with several operations is similar. The variable is isolated by reversing the order of operations that were used on it.

Explorations and answers are provided in *Alternate Openers: Explorations Transparencies.*

California Standards

Algebra 1 4.0, 5.0

Power Presentations with PowerPoint®

Additional Examples

Example 1

Solve each equation.

A. $\frac{2x+1}{3} = 7$ 10

B. $7 = \frac{3x-4}{2}$ 6

Example 2

Solve each equation.

A. $8x - 21 - 5x = -15$ 2

B. $4 = 2x + 5 - 6x$ $\frac{1}{4}$

Example 3

Solve each equation.

A. $5(p-2) = -15$ −1

B. $10y - (4y + 8) = -20$ −2

Also available on transparency

INTERVENTION

Questioning Strategies

EXAMPLE 1

- What are the operations in the equation?
- What operations will you use to solve the equation?

EXAMPLES 2–3

- How do you know what signs go with each term in the equation?

You may have to combine like terms or use the Distributive Property before you begin solving.

EXAMPLE 2 Simplifying Before Solving Equations

Solve $6x + 3 - 8x = 13$.

$6x + 3 - 8x = 13$	
$6x - 8x + 3 = 13$	*Use the Commutative Property of Addition.*
$-2x + 3 = 13$	*Combine like terms.*
$-3 \quad -3$	*Since 3 is added to −2x, subtract 3 from both sides to undo the addition.*
$-2x = 10$	
$\frac{-2x}{-2} = \frac{10}{-2}$	*Since x is multiplied by −2, divide both sides by −2 to undo the multiplication.*
$x = -5$	*The solution set is {−5}.*

CHECK IT OUT! Solve each equation. Check your answer.

2a. $2a + 3 - 8a = 8$ $-\frac{5}{6}$ **2b.** $-8 - 2d + 2 = 4$ −5 **2c.** $4x - 8 + 2x = 40$ 8

Helpful Hint

You can think of a negative sign as a coefficient of −1.
$-(x + 2) = -1(x + 2)$
$-x = -1x$

EXAMPLE 3 Simplifying Using the Distributive Property

Solve each equation.

A $9 = 6 - (x + 2)$

$9 = 6 + (-1)(x + 2)$	*Write subtraction as addition of the opposite.*
$9 = 6 + (-1)(x) + (-1)(2)$	*Distribute −1.*
$9 = 6 - x - 2$	*Simplify.*
$9 = 6 - 2 - x$	*Commutative Property of Addition*
$9 = 4 - x$	*Combine like terms.*
$-4 \quad -4$	*Since 4 is added to −x, subtract 4 from both sides.*
$5 = -x$	
$\frac{5}{-1} = \frac{-x}{-1}$	*Since x is multiplied by −1, divide both sides by −1.*
$-5 = x$	

B $4(x + 1) + 2(x - 7) = 50$

$4(x + 1) + 2(x - 7) = 50$	
$4(x) + 4(1) + 2(x) + 2(-7) = 50$	*Distribute 4 and 2.*
$4x + 4 + 2x - 14 = 50$	*Simplify.*
$4x + 2x + 4 - 14 = 50$	*Commutative Property of Addition*
$6x - 10 = 50$	*Combine like terms.*
$+10 \quad +10$	*Since 10 is subtracted from 6x, add 10 to both sides.*
$6x = 60$	
$\frac{6x}{6} = \frac{60}{6}$	*Since x is multiplied by 6, divide both sides by 6.*
$x = 10$	

2 Teach

Guided Instruction

Remind students that the goal in solving equations is to isolate the variable. Emphasize using the Distributive Property as needed before combining like terms and make special note of distributing a negative number. Encourage students to work carefully and do all their work on paper. Trying to solve multi-step equations mentally often results in careless errors.

Universal Access

Advanced Learners/GATE

Have students create their own multi-step equation by writing a simple equation and performing operations, one at a time, on both sides. For example:

$x = 3$	
$x + 2 = 5$	Add 2.
$4(x + 2) = 20$	Multiply by 4.

Then have students solve their own multi-step equation. They should get back to the equation they started with.

Solve each equation. Check your answer.

3a. $3(a+1)-4=5$ **2** **3b.** $-4(2-y)=8$ **4** **3c.** $d+3(d-4)=20$ **8**

EXAMPLE 4 ***Fitness Application***

A martial arts school is offering a special where a new student can enroll for half price, after paying a $12.50 application fee. Ten students enrolled, and the instructor collected a total of $325. Write and solve an equation to find the regular price of enrollment.

Let p represent the regular price of enrollment.

10 students each paid	(half the regular price	plus	$12.50)	for a total of	$325
10	$\left(\frac{p}{2}\right.$	+	$\left.12.50\right)$	=	325

$10\left(\frac{p}{2}+12.50\right) = 325$

$10\left(\frac{p}{2}\right)+10(12.50) = 325$ *Distribute 10.*

$5p+125 = 325$ *Simplify.*

$5p+125 = 325$

$\underline{\quad -125 \quad -125}$ *Since 125 is added to 5p, subtract 125 from both sides to undo the addition.*

$5p = 200$

$\frac{5p}{5} = \frac{200}{5}$ *Since p is multiplied by 5, divide both sides by 5 to undo the multiplication.*

$p = 40$

The regular price of enrollment is $40.

4a. At a local gym, there is a joining fee of $59.95 and a monthly membership fee. Sara and Martin both joined this gym. Their combined cost for 12 months was $1319.90. How much is the monthly fee? **$50**

4b. Lily and 4 of her friends want to enroll in a yoga class. After enrollment, the studio requires a $7 processing fee. The 5 girls pay a total of $125.75. How much does the class cost? **$18.15**

THINK AND DISCUSS

1. What would be your first step in solving the equation $3(z+12)=16$?
2. When an equation contains several operations, how do you know which operation to undo first?

3. **GET ORGANIZED** Copy and complete the graphic organizer. In each box, write and solve a multi-step equation. Use addition, subtraction, multiplication, and division at least one time each.

Solving Multi-Step Equations	

Power Presentations with PowerPoint®

Additional Example

Example 4

Lin sold 4 more shirts than Greg. Fran sold 3 times as many shirts as Lin. In total, the three sold 51 shirts. How many shirts did Greg sell? 7

Also available on transparency

INTERVENTION

Questioning Strategies

EXAMPLE 4

- What quantity are you trying to find?
- How can you use the information in the problem to write an equation?

3 Close

Summarize

Ask students what they would do as a first step in solving each of the following equations:

- $5y-2(y-6)=43$ Distribute -2.
- $25=-m-9+3m$ Combine like terms.
- $\frac{5-3t}{8}=4$ Multiply by 8.

FORMATIVE ASSESSMENT

and INTERVENTION

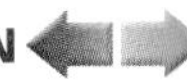

***Diagnose Before* the Lesson**
2-3 Warm Up, TE p. 85

***Monitor During* the Lesson**
Check It Out! Exercises, SE pp. 85–87
Questioning Strategies, TE pp. 86–87

***Assess After* the Lesson**
2-3 Lesson Quiz, TE p. 90
Alternative Assessment, TE p. 90

Answers to *Think and Discuss*

1. Distribute 3.
2. First undo addition/subtraction, and then undo multiplication/division.
3. See p. A2.

2-3 Exercises

Assignment Guide

Assign *Guided Practice* exercises as necessary.

If you finished Examples **1–2**
Proficient 20–28, 47, 50–55, 61–63, 66, 70
Advanced 20–28, 40, 41, 47, 50–52, 61–63, 70, 72

If you finished Examples **1–4**
Proficient 20–39, 46–57, 61–63, 65–71, 79–89
Advanced 20–36 even, 37–52, 53–59 odd, 61–89

Homework Quick Check
Quickly check key concepts.
Exercises: 20, 24, 30, 32, 36

California Standards

Standard	Exercises
1.0	79, 80
4.0 🔑	7–19, 23–65, 71–77
5.0 🔑	1–64, 71–77
25.2	65
7AF1.3 🔑	81–86
7AF4.1 🔑	87–89

2-3 Exercises

California Standards Practice
🔑 4.0, 🔑 5.0, 25.2

go.hrw.com
Homework Help Online
KEYWORD: MA8CA 2-3
Parent Resources Online
KEYWORD: MA8CA Parent

GUIDED PRACTICE

SEE EXAMPLE 1 p. 85

Solve each equation. Check your answer.

1. $\frac{d+3}{4} = 2$ **5**
2. $\frac{3x-2}{8} = 2$ **6**
3. $\frac{6a-1}{7} = 1$ $\mathbf{\frac{4}{3}}$
4. $\frac{n+3}{4} = 12$ **45**
5. $\frac{2h-5}{2} = 0.5$ **3**
6. $\frac{10k+9}{4} = 5$ $\mathbf{\frac{11}{10}}$

SEE EXAMPLE 2 p. 86

7. $9 - 2c + c = -13$ **22**
8. $15y + 21 + 10 = 61$ **2**
9. $8 = 3r - 5 + 4$ **3**
10. $42 = 4d - 6d + 6$ **−18**
11. $2x + 0.3 - x = 3.3$ **3**
12. $2a + 3 + 2a = 11$ **2**

SEE EXAMPLE 3 p. 86

13. $3(x - 4) = 36$ **16**
14. $t(4 - 1) + 9 = 27$ **6**
15. $5(1 - 2w) + 8w = 15$ **−5**
16. $17 = 4(a - 2) + 2a$ $\mathbf{\frac{25}{6}}$
17. $\frac{1}{2}(m - 6) = 12$ **30**
18. $2\left(\frac{x}{4} - 1\right) = 8$ **20**

SEE EXAMPLE 4 p. 87

19. Kathryn organized her books onto 4 shelves. The top shelf holds 5 books, the second shelf holds 7, and the 2 bottom shelves hold the same number of books. Kathryn has a total of 24 books. How many books does each bottom shelf hold? **6**

PRACTICE AND PROBLEM SOLVING

Independent Practice

For Exercises	See Example
20–22	1
23–28	2
29–34	3
35–36	4

Extra Practice
Skills Practice p. EP4
Application Practice p. EP25

Solve each equation. Check your answer.

20. $\frac{x-1}{2} = 5$ **11**
21. $6 = \frac{2w+3}{5}$ $\mathbf{\frac{27}{2}}$
22. $\frac{-3+y}{4} = 25$ **103**
23. $5x - 2x + 3 = 24$ **7**
24. $11 = 2g + 6 - 5$ **5**
25. $2 + 0.5g + 9 = 61$ **100**
26. $4h - 7 + 2h = 7$ $\mathbf{\frac{7}{3}}$
27. $34 = -5 - 6t + 3t$ **−13**
28. $1.5v - 0.9v + 2.1 = 4.5$ **4**
29. $3(d + 5) = 23$ $\mathbf{\frac{8}{3}}$
30. $8(x + 2) = 32$ **2**
31. $-12 = 5(k - 2)$ $\mathbf{-\frac{2}{5}}$
32. $15 = 3(k - 6)$ **11**
33. $5 = \frac{1}{2}(x - 6)$ **16**
34. $6(y - 4) = 0$ **4**

35. Consumer Economics Amanda and Casey's total restaurant bill, including tip, was $34. Amanda's portion of the bill was twice as much as Casey's, and they each left a tip of $2. How much did each person pay? **Amanda: $20; Casey: $10**

36. Marissa is buying a shirt for each of her brothers and each of her 2 sisters. Each shirt costs $7.50, and she spends a total of $30. How many brothers does Marissa have? **2**

Solve each equation. Check your answer.

37. $5(w + 10) = 45$ **−1**
38. $9(p - 2) = 54$ **8**
39. $\frac{1}{2} = \frac{1}{4}(y - 8)$ **10**
40. $2x + \frac{3}{4} + \frac{6}{4} = 16.75$ **7.25**
41. $2.3w - 3.2 + 4.1 = -6$ **−3**
42. $19 = -4(h + 5) + h$ **−13**
43. $3(2x - 4) + \frac{x}{2} = 1$ **2**
44. $2.5(4 - 2m) = 50$ **−8**
45. $-4(d + 1) + 2(d - 2) = \frac{10}{3}$ $\mathbf{-\frac{17}{3}}$

Write an equation to represent each relationship. Then solve.

46. Three increased by a number, all multiplied by 6, equals 36. $\mathbf{6(3 + x) = 36;\ x = 3}$

47. Sixteen plus seven decreased by 4 times some number equals 3. $\mathbf{16 + 7 - 4x = 3;\ x = 5}$

48. Three times the sum of a number and 4, minus the number, is equal to 18. $\mathbf{3(x + 4) - x = 18,\ x = 3}$

49. One-half of a number added to twice the difference of the number and 5 equals 0. $\mathbf{\frac{1}{2}x + 2(x - 5) = 0;\ x = 4}$

2-3 READING STRATEGIES

LESSON 2-3 **Reading Strategies**
Follow a Procedure

Use the example below to understand the procedure for solving multi-step equations. Not all problems will require all the steps.

Solve $-2(x - 5) + 4x = 17$.

$-2(x - 5) + 4x = 17$
$-2x + 10 + 4x = 17$ → 1. Use the Distributive Property.

$-2x + 10 + 4x = 17$
$2x + 10 = 17$ → 2. Identify and combine like terms.

$2x + 10 = 17$
$-10 \quad -10$ → 3. "Undo" addition (and subtraction).

$\frac{2x}{2} = \frac{7}{2}$ → 4. "Undo" division (and multiplication).
$x = 3.5$

Answer each question.

1. If an equation does not need the Distributive Property, what should you look for next?
like terms

2. In the equation $5(x - 3) = 25$, what should you do after using the Distributive Property?
add 15 to both sides

3. Describe how you would solve $\frac{1}{5}(x + 3) = 28$.
Divide both sides by $\frac{1}{5}$, then subtract 3 from both sides.

Solve each equation using the procedure shown. Show all your steps.

4. $3(n - 1) = 12$ **$n = 5$**
5. $3(d - 4) = 9$ **$d = 7$**
6. $-4(j + 2) - 3j = 6$ **$j = -2$**

2-3 REVIEW FOR MASTERY

LESSON 2-3 **Review for Mastery**
Solving Multi-Step Equations

Solving a multi-step equation is similar to solving a two-step equation. You use inverse operations to write an equivalent equation at each step.

	Operations	Solve Using Inverse Operations
$\frac{3x-1}{2} = 7$	• x is multiplied by 3. • Then 1 is subtracted. • Then the result is divided by 2.	• Multiply both sides by 2. • Add 1 to both sides. • Divide both sides by 3.

Solve $\frac{3x-1}{2} = 7$. Check your answer.

		Check:
$2\left(\frac{3x-1}{2}\right) = 2(7)$	*Multiply both sides by 2.*	$\frac{3x-1}{2} = 7$
$3x - 1 = 14$		$\frac{3(5)-1}{2} \stackrel{?}{=} 7$
$+1 = +1$	*Add 1 to both sides.*	$\frac{15-1}{2} \stackrel{?}{=} 7$
$3x = 15$		$\frac{14}{2} \stackrel{?}{=} 7$
$\frac{3x}{3} = \frac{15}{3}$ $x = 5$	*Divide both sides by 3.*	$7 \stackrel{?}{=} 7$ ✓

Solve each equation. Check your answers.

1. $\frac{5y+3}{4} = 7$ **5**
2. $\frac{3+2m}{3} = 9$ **12**
3. $\frac{6x-4}{5} = 4$ **4**
4. $\frac{2r-3}{5} = 3$ **9**

Geometry Write and solve an equation to find the value of x for each triangle. (*Hint:* The sum of the angle measures in any triangle is 180°.)

50. $2x + 100 = 180;\ x = 40$

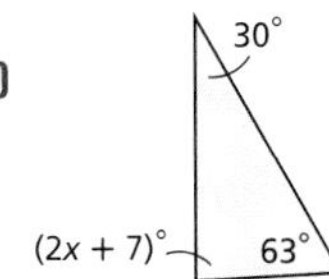

51. 115°, x°, x°

$2x + 115 = 180;\ x = 32.5$

52.

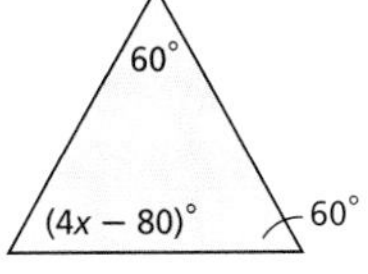

$4x + 40 = 180;\ x = 35$

Solve each equation.

53. $x + 3 - 2x + 5 = 10$ **−2**

54. $9x - 5 - 6x - 1.3 = 0$ **2.1**

55. $-5 = 7g + 5 - 6g$ **−10**

56. $3(x - 2) - 5(2x + 1) = 3$ **−2**

57. $5(2y - 7) + 8(y + 6) = 31$ **1**

58. $4x - 3(6 + x) - 1 = 2$ **21**

59. $17 - (4 - 6z) + 4 = 42$ $\frac{25}{6}$

60. $42r - 2(13 - 5r) + 7 = 85$ **2**

61. The sum of two consecutive whole numbers is 5. What are the two numbers? (*Hint:* Let n represent the first number. Then $n + 1$ is the next consecutive whole number.) **2, 3**

62. Stan's, Mark's, and Wayne's ages are consecutive whole numbers. Stan is the youngest, and Wayne is the oldest. The sum of their ages is 111. Find their ages. **Stan: 36; Mark: 37; Wayne: 38**

63. The sum of two consecutive even whole numbers is 206. What are the two numbers? (*Hint:* Let n represent the first number. What expression can you use to represent the second number?) **102 and 104**

64. **Multi-Step** Alexis and Martin helped the school set chairs in rows for an assembly. They put the same number of chairs in each row. Using the 92 chairs available, Alexis made 4 rows with 2 chairs left over while Martin made 5 rows with no chairs left over.

a. Let c represent the number of chairs in each row. Write an equation that can be used to find c. $4c + 2 + 5c = 92$

b. Solve your equation from part **a.** $c = 10$

c. Alexis and Martin are asked to remove 2 chairs from each row. Then how many of the 92 chairs were not used for the assembly? **20**

65. **///ERROR ANALYSIS///** Below are two possible solutions to $3x + 5 - 4x = 19$. Which is incorrect? Explain the error.

65. A; possible answer: when using the Commutative Property of Addition, each sign should stay with its term.

A

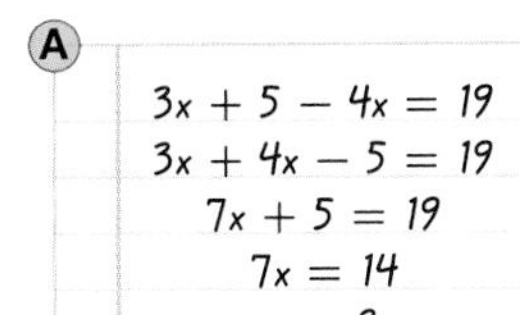

B

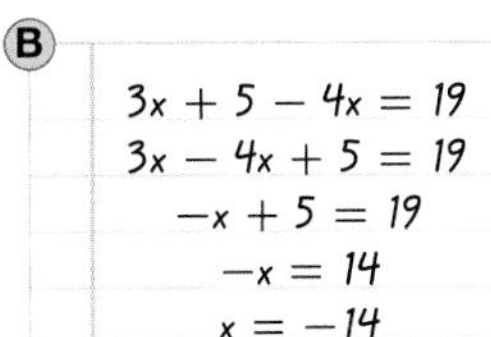

CONCEPT CONNECTION

66. This problem will help prepare you for the Concept Connection on page 100.

a. Suppose firefighters can extinguish a wildfire at a rate of 60 acres per day. Use this information to complete the table.

b. Use the last row in the table to write an equation for acres A extinguished in terms of the number of days d. $A = 60d$

Days	Acres
1	60
2	**120**
3	180
4	**240**
5	**300**
d	**60d**

CONCEPT CONNECTION **Exercise 66** involves using a known value to find data values. This exercise prepares students for the Concept Connection on page 100.

Language Support In **Exercises 61–63,** the word *consecutive* may be unfamiliar to students. Explain that the term refers to two or more items adjacent to each other in a sequence. For example, Monday and Tuesday are consecutive days; the numbers 2, 4, and 6 are consecutive even numbers. Ask students to think of examples and nonexamples of consecutive items.

ENGLISH LANGUAGE LEARNERS

2-3 PROBLEM SOLVING

LESSON 2-3 **Problem Solving**
Solving Multi-Step Equations

Write the correct answer.

1. A theater has a discount pass that costs \$9. With the pass, admission is \$6.50 per movie. Mike, Tyrell, and Juanita all bought a pass and went to see movies together. They spent a total of \$183. Write and solve an equation to find out how many movies they saw.
$3(9 + 6.5m) = 183;\ 8$

2. Jeremy bought postcards on a trip. He sent 5 cards to his aunt. He sent half of the remaining cards to friends. Then he sent one of the remaining cards to his sister. He was left with 4 cards. Write and solve an equation to find out how many postcards Jeremy bought.
$\frac{p - 5}{2} - 1 = 4;\ 15$

3. Maggie's brother is three years younger than twice her age. The sum of their ages is 24. How old is Maggie?
9

4. At Café Primo, a bowl of granola is 2.5 times more expensive than a pot of tea. Karla bought granola and tea, and put \$1.50 in the tip jar. She spent a total of \$6.75. What is the price of a pot of tea?
\$1.50

The table shows prices of school supplies. Use the table for questions 5–7. Select the best answer.

5. The number of notebooks that Mei bought is 2 more than the number of pens she bought. She spent a total of \$12. How many pens did she buy?
A 1   (B) 2   C 4   D 6

6. Kyle bought twice as many notebooks as highlighters. He also bought a stapler for \$6.50. He spent a total of \$26. How many highlighters did he buy?
F 2   (G) 3   H 6   J 8

7. Jorge gets \$2 off the price of each pack of paper at the store. He buys 3 packs of paper and one notebook, and spends a total of \$7.50. What is the regular price of a pack of paper?
A \$2.75   B \$3.25   C \$3.50   (D) \$3.75

Item	Price
Notebook	\$2.25
Pen	\$1.50
Highlighter	\$2.00

2-3 CHALLENGE

LESSON 2-3 **Challenge**
Using Multi-Step Equations to Solve Money Problems

You can use multi-step equations to solve different types of money problems. Consider the following example.

Maria is selling tickets to her school's talent show. Adult tickets cost \$5 and children's tickets cost \$3. Maria sells a total of 50 tickets. She takes in a total of \$214. How many adult tickets and children's tickets does she sell?

To solve this problem, let x be the number of adult tickets that Maria sells. Then $50 - x$ is the number of children's tickets that she sells. The following equation shows that the money Maria takes in by selling adult tickets plus the money she takes in by selling children's tickets is equal to her total revenue from ticket sales.

5 × (number of adult tickets) + 3 × (number of children's tickets) = total revenue

Substituting the expressions for the number of adult tickets and children's tickets gives $5x + 3(50 - x) = 214$

1. Solve the above equation to find the number of adult tickets Maria sells. 32
2. How many children's tickets does Maria sell? 18

Admission to a water park costs \$14 for adults and \$8 for children. During one 15-minute period, a total of 40 people enter the park. The cashier collects a total of \$416 during this time.

3. Write an equation that you can use to find the number of adults that enter the park during this time.
$14x + 8(40 - x) = 416$
4. How many adults and how many children enter the park? 16 adults; 24 children

Tyrone has a jar that contains nickels and dimes. He counts the coins in the jar and finds that there are 102 coins altogether. The total value of the coins is \$8.10.

5. Write an equation that you can use to find the number of nickels in the jar.
$0.05x + 0.1(102 - x) = 8.1$
6. Find the number of nickels and dimes in the jar. 42 nickles; 60 dimes

2-3 PRACTICE A

2-3 PRACTICE C

2-3 PRACTICE B

LESSON 2-3 **Practice B**
Solving Multi-Step Equations

Solve each equation. Check your answers.

1. $\frac{7x + 3}{2} = 12$ $x = 3$
2. $\frac{3c - 4}{2} = 10$ $c = 8$
3. $\frac{4m - 6}{5} = -2$ $m = -1$
4. $\frac{2 - 5y}{2} = 6$ $y = -2$
5. $5x - 6 - 7x = 2$ $x = -4$
6. $-4x + 12 - 3x = 5$ $x = 1$
7. $-d - 5 + 2d = 16$ $d = 21$
8. $-(x - 10) = 7$ $x = 3$
9. $-2(b + 5) = -6$ $b = -2$
10. $8 = 4(q - 2) + 4$ $q = 3$
11. $4(d + 6) + 1 = -11$ $d = -9$
12. $1 - (r + 2) = 9$ $r = -10$
13. If $3x - 2 + 5x = 2$, find the value of $3x$. $\frac{3}{2}$
14. If $1 - 3(y + 2) = -32$, find the value of $\frac{y}{3}$. 3

Answer each of the following.

15. The two angles shown form a right angle. Write and solve an equation to find x. [(3x − 5)°, (2x)°] $3x - 5 + 2x = 90;\ 19$
16. At a restaurant, three friends all ordered the daily special. Each person had a coupon for \$2 off the price of the special. They left a \$6 tip and spent a total of \$38.85. What is the regular price of the daily special? \$12.95

Multiple Choice If students are having trouble with **Exercise 70,** suggest they solve the equation themselves without looking at the given solution. Have them write out each step and then check where their solution differs from the one shown, if at all.

Journal

Have students describe how multi-step equations are different from one-step equations and two-step equations. Then have them describe similarities.

ALTERNATIVE ASSESSMENT

Have students create a multi-step equation. Ask students to describe the solution steps and explain why each step is performed. Check that students understand reversing the order of operations applied to the variable.

Power Presentations with PowerPoint®

2-3 Lesson Quiz

Solve each equation.

1. $2y + 29 - 8y = 5$ 4
2. $3(x - 9) = 30$ 19
3. $x - (12 - x) = 38$ 25
4. $\frac{z}{6} - \frac{5}{8} = \frac{7}{8}$ 9
5. If $3b - (6 - b) = -22$, find the value of $7b$. -28
6. Josie bought 4 cases of sports drinks for an upcoming meet. After talking to her coach, she bought 3 more cases and spent an additional $6.95. Her receipts totaled $74.15. Write and solve an equation to find how much each case of sports drinks cost. $4c + 3c + 6.95 = 74.15$; $9.60

Also available on transparency

67. **Critical Thinking** The equation $3(2x - 5) + 4(x - 2) = 12$ requires several properties of multiplication and addition to solve. Name the properties. **Dist. Prop., Comm. Prop. of Add., Comm. Prop. of Mult., Assoc. Prop. of Add.**

68. **Write About It** Write a series of steps that you can use to solve any multi-step equation.

68. Possible answer: Simplify both sides if necessary. Find the term containing the variable. Undo any addition or subtraction on this term by using inverse operations. Then undo any multiplication or division on this term by using inverse operations.

Multiple Choice For Exercises 69 and 70, choose the best answer.

69. Josh and Howard collect comic books. Josh has 12 more than Howard has, and together they want to triple their collection for a total of 66 comic books. Which equation can be used to find the number of comic books Howard owns?

Ⓐ $3(2h - 12) = 66$ Ⓒ $3h + 12 = 66$

Ⓑ $2h + 6 = 66$ **Ⓓ** $3(2h + 12) = 66$

70. What is the first incorrect step in the solution shown?

$$\frac{4g - 3}{7} = 3$$
Step 1: $4g - 3 = 21$
Step 2: $4g = 18$
Step 3: $g = 4.5$

Ⓐ Step 1 Ⓒ Step 3

Ⓑ Step 2 Ⓓ All steps are correct.

71. **Gridded Response** A band earns $50 a show plus a bonus for every show they play. Last month they played 5 times for a total of $300. How much is the bonus? **$10**

CHALLENGE AND EXTEND

Solve each equation. Check your answer.

72. $\frac{9}{2}x + 18 + 3x = \frac{11}{2}$ $-\frac{5}{3}$
73. $12\left(\frac{1}{4}x - 1\right) = 12$ **8**
74. $(x + 6) - (2x + 7) - 3x = -9$ **2**
75. $(4x + 2) - (12x + 8) + 2(5x - 3) = 6 + 11$ $\frac{29}{2}$
76. $2(5 - y) - 5(y + 3) = -26$ **3**
77. $t(3 + 2) - 6(t - 5) - 22 = 6$ **2**
78. Given the equation $\frac{3x + 2(x + 6)}{2(5 + 4)} = 14$, answer the following questions.
   a. Find two equivalent equations.

   b. **Reasoning** Without solving the equation, predict what would happen to the solution if the numerator changed to $3x + 3(x + 6)$.

78a. possible answer: $\frac{5x + 12}{18} = 14$, $5x + 12 = 252$

b. The solution would decrease.

SPIRAL STANDARDS REVIEW

7AF1.3, 7AF4.1, 1.0

Name the property that is illustrated in each equation. (Lesson 1-6)

79. $-19 + n = n - 19$ **Comm. Prop. of Add.**
80. $6(k + b) = (k + b)6$ **Comm. Prop. of Mult.**

Simplify each expression by combining like terms. (Lesson 1-7)

81. $5m + 3m$ $8m$
82. $22c^2 - 14c$ $22c^2 - 14c$
83. $102v + 16v$ $118v$
84. $51b - b$ $50b$
85. $12c + x$ $12c + x$
86. $\frac{1}{2}p + \frac{1}{2}$ $\frac{1}{2}p + \frac{1}{2}$

Solve each equation. Check your answer. (Lesson 2-2)

87. $10w + 4 = 34$ **3**
88. $11 = 3d - 4$ **5**
89. $38 = -6d + 2$ **−6**

2-4

True Equations

Use with Lesson 2-4

An equation such as $2x + 2 = 6$ is neither true nor false until a value is substituted for x. In Lessons 2-1 through 2-3, you have been solving equations like this one to find the value or values of x that make the equation true. These equations are considered "sometimes true"— they are true when x equals a solution and false when x equals any other value.

Equations may also be "always true" or "never true".

25.3 Given a specific algebraic statement involving linear, quadratic, or absolute value expressions or **equations** or inequalities, **students determine whether the statement is true sometimes, always, or never.**

Activity

Determine whether each equation is sometimes, always, or never true.

$3 + x = x + 3$ $\quad$ $2x = x + 3$ $\quad$ $3x + 2 = x + 2x$

Use a spreadsheet to test several values of x in each equation.

1. Set up a column for x and a column for each equation. Under x, enter several values.

	A	B	C	D
1	x	3 + x = x + 3	2x = x + 3	3x+2=x+2x
2	-4	=3+A2=A2+3	=2*A2=A2+3	=3*A2+2=A2+2*A2
3	-3			

2. Enter the formulas as shown into row 2. These formulas will return TRUE if the equation is true for the value of x and FALSE if it is not.

3. Use the mouse to click on the lower right corner of cell B2. Hold down the mouse button and drag the cursor down to the last row in which you have entered an x-value. The equation $3 + x = x + 3$ appears to always be true. In fact, you know it is always true because it is an example of the Commutative Property of Addition.

	A	B	C	D
1	x	3 + x = x + 3	2x = x + 3	3x+2=x+2x
2	-4	TRUE	FALSE	FALSE
3	-3	TRUE	FALSE	FALSE
4	-2	TRUE	FALSE	FALSE
5	-1	TRUE	FALSE	FALSE
6	0	TRUE	FALSE	FALSE
7	1	TRUE	FALSE	FALSE
8	2	TRUE	FALSE	FALSE
9	3	TRUE	TRUE	FALSE
10	4	TRUE	FALSE	FALSE
11	5	TRUE	FALSE	FALSE

4. Repeat Step 3 for columns C and D.
The equation $2x = x + 3$ is true only when $x = 3$. In other words, it is sometimes true. The equation $3x + 2 = x + 2x$ appears to never be true. If you simplify the right side of this equation, you get $3x + 2 = 3x$. You can see that this equation is never true because $3x + 2$ will always be greater than $3x$ for any value of x.

To test more values of x, enter more values of x into column A and copy the formulas as described above.

Try This

Determine whether each equation is sometimes, always, or never true.

1. $4a + 2 = 3a$ **sometimes**
2. $-3z = 4z - 7z$ **always**
3. $5c + 8 = 5c + 8$ **always**
4. $6x = 2x - 8x$ **sometimes**
5. $4x + 10 = 7x$ **sometimes**
6. $6 + 2a = a + 5 + a$ **never**
7. $-4 + 3c + 6 = 2c + 2 + c$ **always**
8. $6g + 8 = -9 + 6g$ **never**
9. $3y + 4 = -2 + 5y$ **sometimes**

Organizer

Use with Lesson 2-4

Objective: Use a computer speadsheet to help determine whether an equation is sometimes, always, or never true.

Materials: computer spreadsheet

Teach

Discuss

Describe how to enter each equation and each value of x into columns in the spreadsheet. Explain that the spreadsheet will be used to help decide whether an equation is sometimes, always, or never true when values for x are substituted into the equation.

Discuss any observations and conclusions students have made after they have competed the lab activity.

Close

Key Concept

Students should understand that the spreadsheet is sufficient proof only in the case that the equation is sometimes true. Because it is impossible for the spreadsheet to test all values of x, the fact that every cell shows TRUE or FALSE does not prove the equation is always true or never true; it merely suggests it. To show that an equation is always true or never true requires more reasoning beyond examining the spreadsheet.

Assessment

Journal Have students write the equation $4(x + 2) = 4(2 + x)$ and determine whether the equation is sometimes, always, or never true for different values of x. Then ask them to explain what property justifies their answer.

Algebra 1 25.3

2-4 Organizer

Objective: Solve equations in one variable that contain variable terms on both sides.

Online Edition
Tutorial Videos

Countdown to Mastery Week 3

Power Presentations with PowerPoint®

Warm Up

Simplify.

1. $4x - 10x$ $-6x$
2. $-7(x - 3)$ $-7x + 21$
3. $\frac{1}{3}(6x + 9)$ $2x + 3$
4. $15 - (x - 2)$ $17 - x$

Solve.

5. $3x + 2 = 8$ 2
6. $\frac{1}{3}x - \frac{1}{3} = 9$ 28

Also available on transparency

Q: Why did the variable add its opposite?

A: To get to the other side.

California Standards

Algebra 1 🔑 **4.0,** 🔑 **5.0**

2-4 Solving Equations with Variables on Both Sides

California Standards

🔑 **4.0 Students simplify expressions before solving linear equations** and inequalities **in one variable,** such as $3(2x - 5) + 4(x - 2) = 12$.

🔑 **5.0 Students solve multistep problems, including word problems, involving linear equations** and linear inequalities **in one variable** and provide justification for each step.

Vocabulary
identity

Why learn this?
You can compare prices and find the best value.

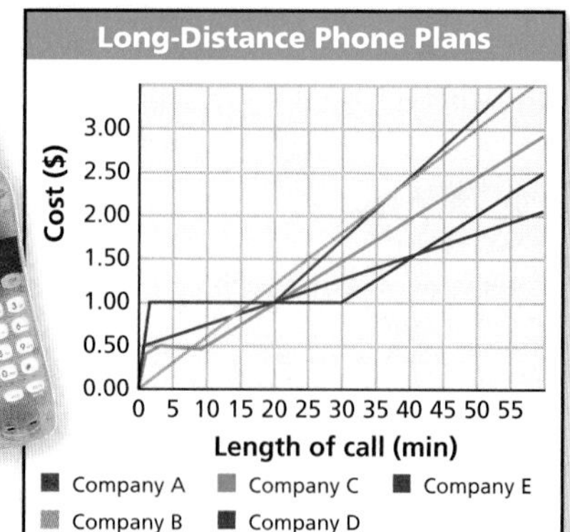

Many phone companies offer low rates for long-distance calls without requiring customers to sign up for their services. To compare rates, solve an equation with variables on both sides.

To solve an equation like this, use inverse operations to "collect" variable terms on one side of the equation.

Helpful Hint

Equations are often easier to solve when the variable has a positive coefficient. Keep this in mind when deciding on which side to "collect" variable terms.

EXAMPLE 1 Solving Equations with Variables on Both Sides

Solve each equation.

A $7k = 4k + 15$

$$7k = 4k + 15$$
$$\underline{-4k \quad -4k}$$
To collect the variable terms on one side, subtract 4k from both sides.
$$3k = 15$$
$$\frac{3k}{3} = \frac{15}{3}$$
Since k is multiplied by 3, divide both sides by 3 to undo the multiplication.
$$k = 5$$

B $5x - 2 = 3x + 4$

$$5x - 2 = 3x + 4$$
$$\underline{-3x \quad -3x}$$
To collect the variable terms on one side, subtract 3x from both sides.
$$2x - 2 = 4$$
$$\underline{+2 \quad +2}$$
Since 2 is subtracted from 2x, add 2 to both sides to undo the subtraction.
$$2x = 6$$
$$\frac{2x}{2} = \frac{6}{2}$$
Since x is multiplied by 2, divide both sides by 2 to undo the multiplication.
$$x = 3$$

Check $5x - 2 = 3x + 4$ *To check your solution, substitute 3 for x in the original equation.*

$5(3) - 2$	$3(3) + 4$
$15 - 2$	$9 + 4$
13	13 ✓

Solve each equation. Check your answer.

1a. $4b + 2 = 3b$ **−2**

1b. $0.5 + 0.3y = 0.7y - 0.3$ **2**

To solve more complicated equations, you may need to first simplify by using the Distributive Property or combining like terms.

1 Introduce

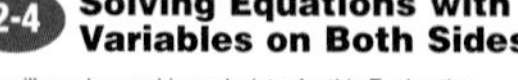

2-4 Solving Equations with Variables on Both Sides

You will need a graphing calculator for this Exploration.

A receptionist is buying plants to decorate the lobby of an office building. The receptionist wants to have the plants delivered. Flower City charges $50 plus $6 per plant. Plants for Less charges $8 per plant.

1. Write an expression that gives the cost of buying plants from Flower City.
2. Write an expression that gives the cost of buying plants from Plants for Less.
3. On your graphing calculator, press [Y=]. Then enter the expressions from Problems 1 and 2 in Y_1 and Y_2.
4. Use your calculator's table feature to find out what number of plants costs the same from both companies.

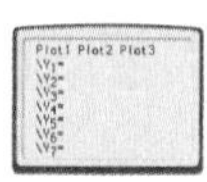

THINK AND DISCUSS

5. **Explain** which company the receptionist should use if 20 plants are needed for the lobby.
6. **Describe** another method you could use to find the number of plants that costs the same from both companies.

Motivate

Draw a balance scale on the board. On one side, draw a 6-ounce weight and an unknown weight. On the other side, draw a 4-ounce weight and two unknown weights. Ask students what the unknown weight must be in order to balance the scale. 2 oz

Remind students that adding or removing an equal amount on both sides of a balanced scale will maintain the balance. This is true even when the weight being added or removed is unknown.

Explorations and answers are provided in *Alternate Openers: Explorations Transparencies*.

EXAMPLE 2 Simplifying Each Side Before Solving Equations

Solve each equation.

A $2(y+6) = 3y$

$$\begin{aligned} 2(y+6) &= 3y \\ 2(y) + 2(6) &= 3y \\ 2y + 12 &= 3y \\ -2y \quad & \quad -2y \\ 12 &= y \end{aligned}$$

Distribute 2 to the expression in parentheses.

To collect the variable terms on one side, subtract 2y from both sides.

Check $2(y+6) = 3y$

$2(12+6)$	$3(12)$
$2(18)$	36
36	36 ✓

To check your solution, substitute 12 for y in the original equation.

B $2k - 5 = 3(1 - 2k)$

$$\begin{aligned} 2k - 5 &= 3(1-2k) \\ 2k - 5 &= 3(1) - 3(2k) \\ 2k - 5 &= 3 - 6k \\ +6k \quad & \quad +6k \\ 8k - 5 &= 3 \\ +5 \quad & \quad +5 \\ 8k &= 8 \\ \frac{8k}{8} &= \frac{8}{8} \\ k &= 1 \end{aligned}$$

Distribute 3 to the expression in parentheses.

To collect the variable terms on one side, add 6k to both sides.

Since 5 is subtracted from 8k, add 5 to both sides.

Since k is multiplied by 8, divide both sides by 8.

C $3 - 5b + 2b = -2 - 2(1 - b)$

$$\begin{aligned} 3 - 5b + 2b &= -2 - 2(1-b) \\ 3 - 5b + 2b &= -2 - 2(1) - 2(-b) \\ 3 - 5b + 2b &= -2 - 2 + 2b \\ 3 - 3b &= -4 + 2b \\ +3b \quad & \quad +3b \\ 3 &= -4 + 5b \\ +4 \quad & \quad +4 \\ 7 &= 5b \\ \frac{7}{5} &= \frac{5b}{5} \\ 1.4 &= b \end{aligned}$$

Distribute −2 to the expression in parentheses.

Combine like terms.

Add 3b to both sides.

Since −4 is added to 5b, add 4 to both sides.

Since b is multiplied by 5, divide both sides by 5.

Solve each equation. Check your answer.

2a. $\frac{1}{2}(b+6) = \frac{3}{2}b - 1$ **4**

2b. $3x + 15 - 9 = 2(x+2)$ **−2**

An **identity** is an equation that is always true, no matter what value is substituted for the variable. The solution set of an identity is all real numbers. Some equations are always false. Their solution sets are empty. In other words, their solution sets contain no elements.

COMMON ERROR ALERT

Students may try to combine the like terms that they see in an equation. For example, $5x - 2 = 3x + 4$ becomes $8x - 2 = 4$. Remind students that they must instead "undo" the addition of $3x$ on the right side.

Power Presentations with PowerPoint®

Additional Examples

Example 1

Solve $7n - 2 = 5n + 6$. 4

Example 2

Solve $4 - 6a + 4a = -1 - 5(7 - 2a)$. $\frac{10}{3}$

Also available on transparency

INTERVENTION

Questioning Strategies

EXAMPLE 1

- How do you decide which variable term to add or subtract from one side of the equation?

EXAMPLE 2

- How are the equations in the second example different from those in the first example?
- How do you know when one side of an equation is not simplified?
- How do you simplify each side of an equation?
- Why is it important to simplify each side of an equation before you add or subtract terms on each side?

Visual To remind students to include negative values in their multiplication when distributing, as in **Example 2C,** circle the negative number that is to be distributed, perhaps with a colored pencil (MK).

2 Teach

Guided Instruction

Before solving equations with variables on both sides, review the steps used to solve equations with a variable on one side. Then review how to combine like terms and how to simplify using the Distributive Property. Show students that adding or subtracting the variable terms on each side, before adding and subtracting constant terms, results in a one-step equation like those from earlier lessons.

Universal Access

Through Cooperative Learning

Give each student a card with an expression such as $2x + 4$ or $3x - 7$ written on it. Have students pair up and solve the equation that is formed by setting their expressions equal to each other. Students should pair up with as many students as time allows. For advanced learners, expressions should require simplifying.

Power Presentations with PowerPoint®

Additional Examples

Example 3

Solve each equation.

A. $10 - 5x + 1 = 7x + 11 - 12x$
all real numbers

B. $12x - 3 + x = 5x - 4 + 8x$
no solution

Example 4

Jon and Sara are planting tulip bulbs. Jon has planted 60 bulbs and is planting at a rate of 44 bulbs per hour. Sara has planted 96 bulbs and is planting at a rate of 32 bulbs per hour. In how many hours will Jon and Sara have planted the same number of bulbs? How many bulbs will that be? 3 h; 192 bulbs

Also available on transparency

Number Sense Encourage students to add and subtract variable terms so that the result is a positive coefficient. Often this means to subtract the variable term with the lesser coefficient on both sides.

INTERVENTION 
Questioning Strategies

EXAMPLE 3

- Which is the solution of an equation if the last line is a true statement? a false statement?

EXAMPLE 4

- Which phrase in the question indicates what the variable will represent?

EXAMPLE 3 Infinitely Many Solutions or No Solutions

Solve each equation.

A $x + 4 - 6x = 6 - 5x - 2$

$x + 4 - 6x = 6 - 5x - 2$ *Identify like terms.*

$4 - 5x = 4 - 5x$ *Combine like terms on the left and the right.*

The statement $4 - 5x = 4 - 5x$ is true for all values of x. The equation $x + 4 - 6x = 6 - 5x - 2$ is an identity. All values of x will make the equation true. In other words, all real numbers are solutions.

B $-8x + 6 + 9x = -17 + x$

$-8x + 6 + 9x = -17 + x$ *Identify like terms.*

$x + 6 = -17 + x$ *Combine like terms.*

$\underline{-x} \quad \underline{-x}$ *Subtract x from both sides.*

$6 = -17$ ✗ *False statement; the solution set is ∅.*

The equation $-8x + 6 + 9x = -17 + x$ is always false. There is no value of x that will make the equation true. There are no solutions.

Writing Math

The empty set can be written as ∅ or {}.

CHECK IT OUT! Solve each equation.

3a. $4y + 7 - y = 10 + 3y$ ∅

3b. $2c + 7 + c = -14 + 3c + 21$ **all real numbers**

EXAMPLE 4 Consumer Application

The long-distance rates of two phone companies are shown in the table. How long is a call that costs the same amount no matter which company is used? What is the cost of that call?

Phone Company	Charges
Company A	36¢ plus 3¢ per minute
Company B	6¢ per minute

Let m represent minutes, and write expressions for each company's cost.

When is	36¢	plus	3¢ per minute	times number of minutes	the same as	6¢ per minute	times number of minutes	?
	36	+	3	(m)	=	6	(m)	

$36 + 3m = 6m$

$\underline{\quad -3m \quad -3m}$ *To collect the variable terms on one side, subtract 3m from both sides.*

$36 = 3m$

$\frac{36}{3} = \frac{3m}{3}$ *Since m is multiplied by 3, divide both sides by 3 to undo the multiplication.*

$12 = m$

The charges will be the same for a 12-minute call using either phone service. To find the cost of this call, evaluate either expression for $m = 12$:

$$36 + 3m = 36 + 3(12) = 36 + 36 = 72 \qquad 6m = 6(12) = 72$$

The cost of a 12-minute call through either company is 72¢.

CHECK IT OUT! **4.** Four times Greg's age, decreased by 3 is equal to 3 times Greg's age, increased by 7. How old is Greg? **10 years old**

3 Close

Summarize

Draw the triangle below on the board:

$(7x - 6)°$ $(2x + 4 + 4x)°$

Tell students that the triangle is isosceles and that the labeled angles have the same measure. Have them write and solve an equation for x, explaining each step. Then have them find the measure of each angle.

$x = 10$; each angle measures 64°.

FORMATIVE ASSESSMENT and INTERVENTION 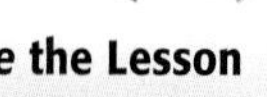

***Diagnose Before* the Lesson**
2-4 Warm Up, TE p. 92

***Monitor During* the Lesson**
Check It Out! Exercises, SE pp. 92–94
Questioning Strategies, TE pp. 93–94

***Assess After* the Lesson**
2-4 Lesson Quiz, TE p. 98
Alternative Assessment, TE p. 98

THINK AND DISCUSS

1. Tell which of the following is an identity. Explain your answer.
   a. $4(a + 3) - 6 = 3(a + 3) - 6$ **b.** $8.3x - 9 + 0.7x = 2 + 9x - 11$

2. **GET ORGANIZED** Copy and complete the graphic organizer. In each box, write an example of an equation that has the indicated number of solutions.

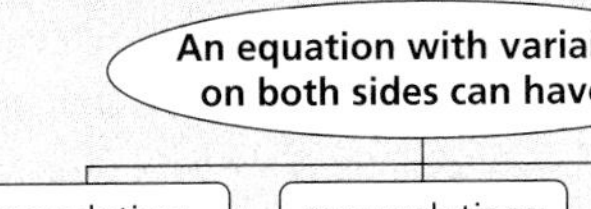

2-4 Exercises

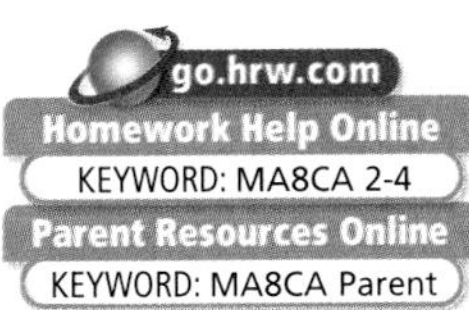

GUIDED PRACTICE

1. **Vocabulary** How can you recognize an *identity*?

SEE EXAMPLE 1 p. 92

Solve each equation. Check your answer.

2. $2c - 5 = c + 4$ **9**
3. $8r + 4 = 10 + 2r$ **1**
4. $2x - 1 = x + 11$ **12**
5. $28 - 0.3y = 0.7y - 12$ **40**

SEE EXAMPLE 2 p. 93

6. $-2(x + 3) = 4x - 3$ $-\frac{1}{2}$
7. $3c - 4c + 1 = 5c + 2 + 3$ $-\frac{2}{3}$
8. $1 + \frac{3}{5}(q - 4) = \frac{2}{5}(q + 1)$ **9**
9. $5 - (t + 3) = -1 + 2(t - 3)$ **3**

SEE EXAMPLE 3 p. 94

10. $7x - 4 = -2x + 1 + 9x - 5$
11. $8x + 6 - 9x = 2 - x - 15$ $\varnothing$
12. $6y = 8 - 9 + 6y$ $\varnothing$
13. $6 - 2x - 1 = 4x + 8 - 6x - 3$ **all real numbers**

SEE EXAMPLE 4 p. 94

14. **Consumer Economics** A house-painting company charges \$376 plus \$12 per hour. Another painting company charges \$280 plus \$15 per hour.
    a. How long is a job for which both companies will charge the same amount? **32 h**
    b. What will that cost be? **\$760**

PRACTICE AND PROBLEM SOLVING

Solve each equation. Check your answer.

15. $7a - 17 = 4a + 1$ **6**
16. $2b - 5 = 8b + 1$ **−1**
17. $4x - 2 = 3x + 4$ **6**
18. $2x - 5 = 4x - 1$ **−2**
19. $8x - 2 = 3x + 12.25$ **2.85**
20. $5x + 2 = 3x$ **−1**
21. $3c - 5 = 2c + 5$ **10**
22. $-17 - 2x = 6 - x$ **−23**
23. $3(t - 1) = 9 + t$ **6**
24. $5 - x - 2 = 3 + 4x + 5$ **−1**
25. $2(x + 4) = 3(x - 2)$ **14**
26. $3m - 10 = 2(4m - 5)$ **0**
27. $5 - (n - 4) = 3(n + 2)$ $\frac{3}{4}$
28. $6(x + 7) - 20 = 6x$ $\varnothing$
29. $8(x + 1) = 4x - 8$ **−4**
30. $x - 4 - 3x = -2x - 3 - 1$
31. $-2(x + 2) = -2x + 1$ $\varnothing$
32. $2(x + 4) - 5 = 2x + 3$

30. all real numbers

32. all real numbers

Answers to *Think and Discuss*

1. Equation b, $8.3x - 9 + 0.7x = 2 + 9x - 11$, is an identity. The equation simplifies to $9x - 9 = 9x - 9$, which is true for all values of x.
2. See p. A3.

2-4 Exercises

Assignment Guide

Assign *Guided Practice* exercises as necessary.

If you finished Examples **1–2**
Proficient 15–30, 38–52 even, 54, 60, 63
Advanced 15–30, 42–52 even, 54, 64, 65, 68, 69

If you finished Examples **1–4**
Proficient 15–37, 38–52 even, 53–63, 66–69, 73–85
Advanced 15–34, 36, 42–52 even, 54–85

Homework Quick Check
Quickly check key concepts.
Exercises: 20, 26, 32, 34, 36, 54

Answers

1. Possible answer: After simplifying, the expressions on either side of the equal sign are the same.
10. all real numbers

California Standards

Standard	Exercises
4.0	6–13, 22–32, 34–36, 48–51, 62, 63, 65, 66, 69
5.0	2–71
25.3	34–36
6NS2.1	75
6AF1.2	72, 73
7NS1.2	74–81
7AF4.1	82–85

Teaching Tip

Geometry For **Exercise 53,** remind students that perimeter is the distance around a figure. Students may benefit from writing $P_1 = P_2$, and then substituting P_1 and P_2 with expressions for each perimeter.

CONCEPT CONNECTION **Exercise 54** involves writing an equation to represent a real-world relationship. This exercise prepares students for the Concept Connection on page 100.

Independent Practice	
For Exercises	See Example
15–22	1
23–29	2
30–32	3
33	4

Extra Practice
Skills Practice p. EP5
Application Practice p. EP25

33. **Multi-Step** Justin and Tyson are beginning an exercise program to train for football season. Justin weighs 150 lb and hopes to gain 2 lb per week. Tyson weighs 195 lb and hopes to lose 1 lb per week.
   a. If the plan works, in how many weeks will the boys weigh the same amount? **15**
   b. What will that weight be? **180 lb**

Reasoning Tell whether each equation is sometimes, always, or never true.

34. $5(x + 3) - 2 = 5x + 13$ **always**
35. $2n + 1 = 2(n + 1) - 1$ **always**
36. $3(k - 1) - 3(2k + 2) = 24$ **sometimes (when $k = -11$)**

Solve each equation. Check your answer.

37. $2x - 2 = 4x + 6$ **−4**
38. $3x + 5 = 2x + 2$ **−3**
39. $4x + 3 = 5x - 4$ **7**
40. $-\frac{2}{5}p + 2 = \frac{1}{5}p + 11$ **−15**
41. $5x + 24 = 2x + 15$ **−3**
42. $5x - 10 = 14 - 3x$ **3**
43. $12 - 6x = 10 - 5x$ **2**
44. $5x - 7 = -6x - 29$ **−2**
45. $1.8x + 2.8 = 2.5x + 2.1$ **1**
46. $2.6x + 18 = 2.4x + 22$ **20**
47. $1 - 3x = 2x + 8$ **$-\frac{7}{5}$**
48. $\frac{1}{2}(8 - 6h) = h$ **1**
49. $\frac{1}{3}(x + 1) = \frac{2}{9}x + \frac{7}{9}$ **4**
50. $9x - 8 + 4x = 7x + 16$ **4**
51. $3(2x - 1) + 5 = 6(x + 1)$ **∅**

52. **Travel** Rapid Rental Car company charges a \$40 rental fee, \$15 for gas, and \$0.25 per mile driven. For the same car, Capital Cars charges \$45 for rental and gas and \$0.35 per mile.
   a. Find the number of miles for which the companies' charges will be the same. Then find that charge. **100 mi; \$80**
   b. The Barre family estimates that they will drive about 95 miles during their vacation to Hershey, Pennsylvania. Which company should they rent their car from? Explain. **Capital Cars; the cost would be less.**
   c. **What if...?** The Barres have extended their vacation and now estimate that they will drive about 120 miles. Should they still rent from the same company as in part **b**? Why or why not? **No; now Rapid Rental would be cheaper.**
   d. Give a general rule for deciding which company to rent from. **Less than 100 mi—use Capital; more than 100 mi—use Rapid.**

53. **Geometry** The triangles shown have the same perimeter. What is the value of x? **9**

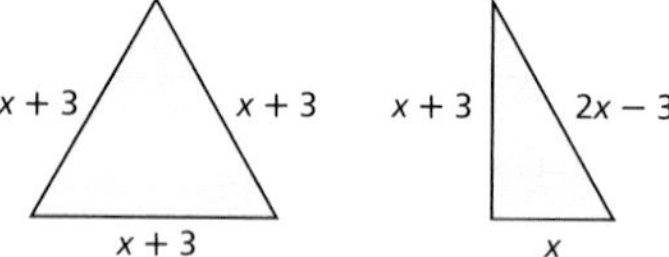

54c. $80d$

d. $420 + 60d = 80d$; $d = 21$ days; the number of days it will take the firefighters to put out the fire

CONCEPT CONNECTION

54. This problem will prepare you for the Concept Connection on page 100.
   a. A fire currently covers 420 acres and continues to spread at a rate of 60 acres per day. How many total acres will be covered in the next 2 days? **540 acres**
   b. Write an expression for the total area covered by the fire in d days. **$420 + 60d$**
   c. The firefighters estimate that they can put out the fire at a rate of 80 acres per day. Write an expression for the total area that the firefighters can put out in d days.
   d. Set the expressions in parts **b** and **c** equal. Solve for d. What does d represent?

2-4 PRACTICE A

2-4 PRACTICE C

2-4 PRACTICE B

LESSON 2-4 **Practice B**
Solving Equations with Variables on Both Sides

Solve each equation. Check your answers.

1. $3d + 8 = 2d - 17$ **$d = -25$**
2. $2n - 7 = 5n - 10$ **$n = 1$**
3. $p - 15 = 13 - 6p$ **$p = 4$**
4. $-t + 5 = t - 19$ **$t = 12$**
5. $15x - 10 = -9x + 2$ **$x = \frac{1}{2}$**
6. $1.8r + 9 = -5.7r - 6$ **$r = -2$**
7. $2y + 3 = 3(y + 7)$ **$y = -18$**
8. $4n + 6 - 2n = 2(n + 3)$ **all real numbers**
9. $6m - 8 = 2 + 9m - 1$ **$m = -3$**
10. $-v + 5 + 6v = 1 + 5v + 3$ **no solution**
11. $2(3b - 4) = 8b - 11$ **$b = \frac{3}{2}$**
12. $5(r - 1) = 2(r - 4) - 6$ **$r = -3$**

Answer each of the following.

13. Janine has job offers at two companies. One company offers a starting salary of \$28,000 with a raise of \$3000 each year. The other company offers a starting salary of \$36,000 with a raise of \$2000 each year.
   a. After how many years would Janine's salary be the same with both companies? **8 years**
   b. What would that salary be? **\$52,000**
14. Xian and his cousin both collect stamps. Xian has 56 stamps, and his cousin has 80 stamps. Both have recently joined different stamp-collecting clubs. Xian's club will send him 12 new stamps per month, and his cousin's club will send him 8 new stamps per month.
   a. After how many months will Xian and his cousin have the same number of stamps? **6 months**
   b. How many stamps will that be? **128 stamps**

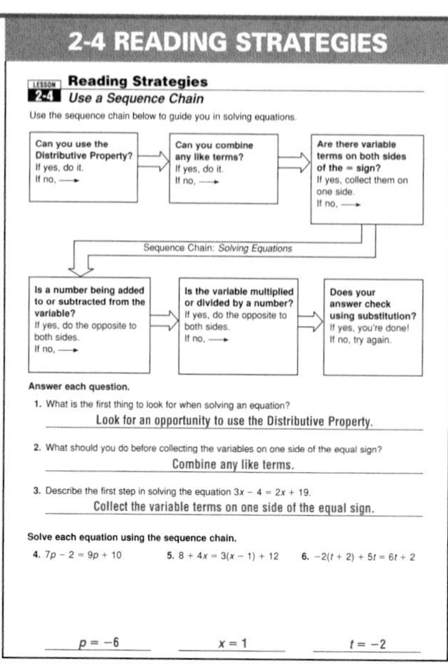

2-4 READING STRATEGIES

LESSON 2-4 **Reading Strategies**
Use a Sequence Chain

Use the sequence chain below to guide you in solving equations.

Can you use the Distributive Property? If yes, do it. If no, →

Can you combine any like terms? If yes, do it. If no, →

Are there variable terms on both sides of the = sign? If yes, collect them on one side. If no, →

Sequence Chain: *Solving Equations*

Is a number being added to or subtracted from the variable? If yes, do the opposite to both sides. If no, →

Is the variable multiplied or divided by a number? If yes, do the opposite to both sides. If no, →

Does your answer check using substitution? If yes, you're done! If no, try again.

Answer each question.

1. What is the first thing to look for when solving an equation? **Look for an opportunity to use the Distributive Property.**
2. What should you do before collecting the variables on one side of the equal sign? **Combine any like terms.**
3. Describe the first step in solving the equation $3x - 4 = 2x + 19$. **Collect the variable terms on one side of the equal sign.**

Solve each equation using the sequence chain.

4. $7p - 2 = 9p + 10$ **$p = -6$**
5. $8 + 4x = 3(x - 1) + 12$ **$x = 1$**
6. $-2(t + 2) + 5t = 6t + 2$ **$t = -2$**

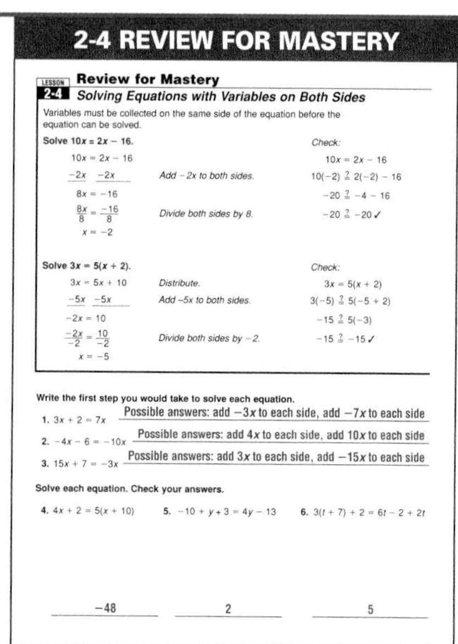

2-4 REVIEW FOR MASTERY

LESSON 2-4 **Review for Mastery**
Solving Equations with Variables on Both Sides

Variables must be collected on the same side of the equation before the equation can be solved.

Solve $10x = 2x - 16$.

		Check:
$10x = 2x - 16$		$10x = 2x - 16$
$-2x \quad -2x$	*Add −2x to both sides.*	$10(-2) \stackrel{?}{=} 2(-2) - 16$
$8x = -16$		$-20 \stackrel{?}{=} -4 - 16$
$\frac{8x}{8} = \frac{-16}{8}$	*Divide both sides by 8.*	$-20 \stackrel{?}{=} -20$ ✓
$x = -2$		

Solve $3x = 5(x + 2)$.

		Check:
$3x = 5x + 10$	*Distribute.*	$3x = 5(x + 2)$
$-5x \quad -5x$	*Add −5x to both sides.*	$3(-5) \stackrel{?}{=} 5(-5 + 2)$
$-2x = 10$		$-15 \stackrel{?}{=} 5(-3)$
$\frac{-2x}{-2} = \frac{10}{-2}$	*Divide both sides by −2.*	$-15 \stackrel{?}{=} -15$ ✓
$x = -5$		

Write the first step you would take to solve each equation.

1. $3x + 2 = 7x$ **Possible answers: add $-3x$ to each side, add $-7x$ to each side**
2. $-4x - 6 = -10x$ **Possible answers: add $4x$ to each side, add $10x$ to each side**
3. $15x + 7 = -3x$ **Possible answers: add $3x$ to each side, add $-15x$ to each side**

Solve each equation. Check your answers.

4. $4x + 2 = 5(x + 10)$ **−48**
5. $-10 + y + 3 = 4y - 13$ **2**
6. $3(t + 7) + 2 = 6t - 2 + 2t$ **5**

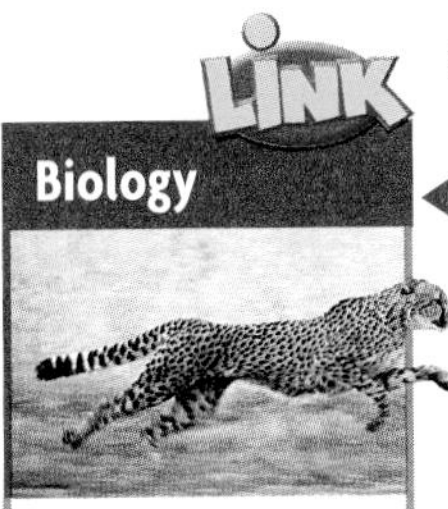

A cheetah's body is well designed for fast running. Its tail acts like a boat's rudder to help it make sharp turns. Its spine acts like a spring to propel it forward.

Source: www.cheetahspot.com

56d. $\frac{1}{18}$ **h, or about** $3\frac{1}{3}$ **min**

56e. No; covering 300 yd takes the cheetah about 0.003 h, or about 11 s.

57. Possible answer: Simplify both sides if necessary. Collect the variable terms on one side by using inverse operations. Then isolate the variable using inverse operations.

55. **Critical Thinking** Write an equation with variables on both sides that has no solution. **Possible answer:** $2x + 6 = x + 5 + x$

56. **Biology** The graph shows the maximum recorded speeds of the four fastest mammals.

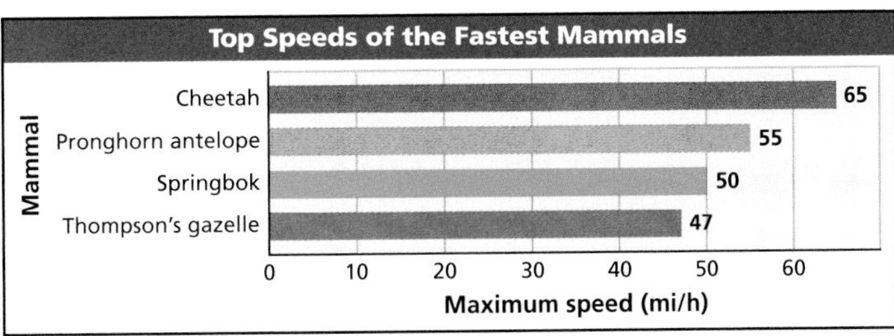

Source: The Top 10 of Everything

a. Write an expression for the distance in miles that a Thompson's gazelle can run at top speed in x hours. **$47x$**

b. Write an expression for the distance in miles that a cheetah can run at top speed in x hours. **$65x$**

c. A cheetah and a Thompson's gazelle are running at their top speeds. The cheetah is one mile behind the gazelle. Write an expression for the distance the cheetah must run to catch up with the gazelle. **$47x + 1$**

d. Write and solve an equation that represents how long the cheetah will have to run at top speed to catch up with the gazelle. **$47x + 1 = 65x$**

e. A cheetah can maintain its top speed for only 300 yards. Will the cheetah be able to catch the gazelle? Explain. (*Hint:* 1 mile = 1760 yards)

57. **Write About It** Write a series of steps that you can use to solve any equation with variables on both sides.

Multiple Choice **For Exercises 58–61, choose the best answer.**

58. Lindsey's monthly magazine subscription costs \$1.25 per issue. Kenzie's monthly subscription costs \$1.50 per issue, but she received her first 2 issues free. Which equation can be used to find the number of months after which the girls will have paid the same amount?

   (A) $1.25m = 1.50m - 2$
   (B) $1.25m = 1.50m - 2m$
   (C) $1.25m = 1.50(m - 2)$
   (D) $1.25m = 3m - 1.50$

59. What is the numerical solution of the equation *7 times a number equals 3 less than 5 times that number*?

   (A) -1.5
   (B) 0.25
   (C) $\frac{2}{3}$
   (D) 4

60. Three packs of markers cost \$9.00 less than 5 packs of markers. Which equation best represents this situation?

   (A) $5x + 9 = 3x$
   (B) $3x + 9 = 5x$
   (C) $3x - 9 = 5x$
   (D) $9 - 3x = 5x$

61. Nicole has \$120. If she saves \$20 per week, in how many days will she have \$500?

   (A) 19
   (B) 25
   (C) 133
   (D) 175

62. **Gridded Response** Solve $-2(x - 1) + 5x = 2(2x - 1)$. **4**

COMMON ERROR ALERT

In **Exercise 51,** students may write 0 instead of *no solution*, thinking that they are writing "zero solutions." Remind students that no solution means that there is no number, including zero, that will make the statement true.

Multiple Choice In **Exercise 58,** only Kenzie's cost (the right side) needs to be analyzed. Have students simplify the right side of **C** so that every choice is in simplified form. Tell students that the cost of two issues at \$1.50 each is \$3.00. This amount is subtracted from the total cost of m issues at \$1.50 per issue.

If students chose **C** in **Exercise 60,** they are probably subtracting \$9 from the lesser cost. Tell students to replace the word *cost* with *is the same as*, to see where the equal sign should go. The correct choice, **B,** is the result of then adding 9 to both sides.

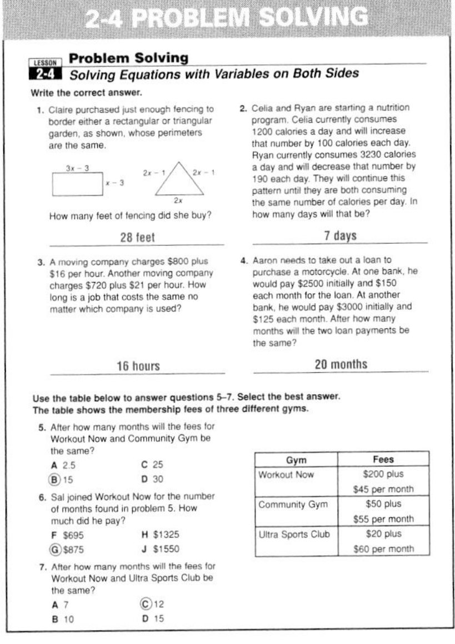

2-4 PROBLEM SOLVING

LESSON 2-4 **Problem Solving**
Solving Equations with Variables on Both Sides

Write the correct answer.

1. Claire purchased just enough fencing to border either a rectangular or triangular garden, as shown, whose perimeters are the same.

   How many feet of fencing did she buy?
   28 feet

2. Celia and Ryan are starting a nutrition program. Celia currently consumes 1200 calories a day and will increase that number by 100 calories each day. Ryan currently consumes 3230 calories a day and will decrease that number by 190 each day. They will continue this pattern until they are both consuming the same number of calories per day. In how many days will that be?
   7 days

3. A moving company charges \$800 plus \$16 per hour. Another moving company charges \$720 plus \$21 per hour. How long is a job that costs the same no matter which company is used?
   16 hours

4. Aaron needs to take out a loan to purchase a motorcycle. At one bank, he would pay \$2500 initially and \$150 each month for the loan. At another bank, he would pay \$3000 initially and \$125 each month. After how many months will the two loan payments be the same?
   20 months

Use the table below to answer questions 5–7. Select the best answer. The table shows the membership fees of three different gyms.

Gym	Fees
Workout Now	\$200 plus \$45 per month
Community Gym	\$50 plus \$55 per month
Ultra Sports Club	\$20 plus \$60 per month

5. After how many months will the fees for Workout Now and Community Gym be the same?
   A 2.5 **(B)** 15 C 25 D 30

6. Sal joined Workout Now for the number of months found in problem 5. How much did he pay?
   F \$695 **(G)** \$875 H \$1325 J \$1550

7. After how many months will the fees for Workout Now and Ultra Sports Club be the same?
   A 7 B 10 **(C)** 12 D 15

2-4 CHALLENGE

LESSON 2-4 **Challenge**
Finding a Formula to Solve Linear Equations

A linear equation in one variable can take on many different appearances. Each of the equations below is an equation in one variable.

$2x - 5 = 12$ $\quad$ $2(x + 1) = 5$ $\quad$ $3x - 4 = -2x + 1$

Although these equations look different, you can transform each of them into the standard form for a linear equation in one variable.

In Exercises 1–4, each equation has the form $ax + b = 0$. Solve each equation.

1. $3x + 7 = 0$ $\quad$ **$x = -\frac{7}{3}$**
2. $-2x - 8 = 0$ $\quad$ **$x = -4$**
3. $\frac{2}{3}x - 5 = 0$ $\quad$ **$x = 7\frac{1}{2}$**
4. $-4.1x - 8.2 = 0$ $\quad$ **$x = -2$**

You can always transform a given linear equation in one variable into the form $ax + b = 0$.

In Exercises 5–8, write each equation in the form $ax + b = 0$. Do not solve the resulting equation.

5. $3(x + 5) = x + 21$
   $2x + (-6) = 0$ or $-2x + 6 = 0$
6. $-2(-4 - 6x) = -10 + 3x$
   $9x + 18 = 0$ or $-9x + (-18) = 0$
7. $-7(-3 - x) = -2(3 - x)$
   $5x + 27 = 0$ or $-5x + (-27) = 0$
8. $8 - 2(x - 5) = x - 3$
   $3x + (-21) = 0$ or $-3x + 21 = 0$

9. a. Solve $ax + b = 0$ for x. **$x = -\frac{b}{a}$**

   b. Explain how to write your answer to part **a** as a formula that you can use to solve a linear equation in x. **After writing the equation in the form $ax + b = 0$, substitute the values of a and b into the formula found in part a.**

Solve the specified equation by using your formula from Exercise 9.

10. Exercise 5 **$x = 3$**
11. Exercise 6 **$x = -2$**
12. Exercise 7 **$x = -5\frac{2}{5}$**
13. Exercise 8 **$x = 7$**

14. a. Let $ax + b = 0$, where $a = 0$ and $b = 0$. How many solutions does the equation have? **infinitely many solutions**

    b. Let $ax + b = 0$, where $a = 0$ and $b \neq 0$. How many solutions does the equation have? **no solution**

CHALLENGE AND EXTEND

Solve each equation.

63. $4x + 2[4 - 2(x + 2)] = 2x - 4$ **2**

64. $\frac{x+5}{2} + \frac{x-1}{2} = \frac{x-1}{3}$ $-\frac{7}{2}$

65. $\frac{2}{3}w - \frac{1}{4} = \frac{2}{3}\left(w - \frac{1}{4}\right)$ **∅**

66. $-5 - 7 - 3f = -f - 2(f + 6)$ **all real numbers**

67. $\frac{2}{3}x + \frac{1}{2} = \frac{3}{5}x - \frac{5}{6}$ **−20**

68. $x - \frac{1}{4} = \frac{x}{3} + 7\frac{3}{4}$ **12**

69. Find three consecutive integers such that twice the greatest integer is 2 less than 3 times the least integer. **6, 7, 8**

70. Find three consecutive integers such that twice the least integer is 12 more than the greatest integer. **14, 15, 16**

71. Rob had twice as much money as Sam. Then Sam gave Rob 1 quarter, 2 nickels, and 3 pennies. Rob then gave Sam 8 dimes. If they now have the same amount of money, how much money did Rob originally have? Check your answer. **$1.68**

SPIRAL STANDARDS REVIEW

6NS2.1, 6AF1.2, 7NS1.2, 7AF4.1

Write an expression for the perimeter of each figure. *(Lesson 1-1)*

72. square with side x cm **$4x$ cm**

73. equilateral triangle with side y cm **$3y$ cm**

Multiply or divide. *(Lesson 1-3)*

74. $6.1 \div 0$ **undefined**

75. $3(-21)$ **−63**

76. $0 \div \frac{7}{8}$ **0**

77. $\frac{2}{5} \div \frac{1}{10}$ **4**

78. $5 \div (-5)$ **−1**

79. $\frac{-16}{-8}$ **2**

80. $-1000 \div (-0.001)$ **1,000,000**

81. $500(-0.25)$ **−125**

Solve each equation. *(Lesson 2-2)*

82. $4x - 44 = 8$ **13**

83. $2x - 6 = 24$ **15**

84. $-1 = \frac{x}{4} - 3$ **8**

85. $2x + 6 = 12$ **3**

Career Path

go.hrw.com
Career Resources Online
KEYWORD: MA8CA Career

Beth Simmons
Biology major

Q: **What math classes did you take in high school?**
A: Algebra 1 and 2, Geometry, and Precalculus

Q: **What math classes have you taken in college?**
A: Two calculus classes and a calculus-based physics class

Q: **How do you use math?**
A: I use math a lot in physics. Sometimes I would think a calculus topic was totally useless, and then we would use it in physics class! In biology, I use math to understand populations.

Q: **What career options are you considering?**
A: When I graduate, I could teach, or I could go to graduate school and do more research. I have a lot of options.

Journal

Have students explain the difference between solving an equation that is an identity and solving an equation that has no solution.

ALTERNATIVE ASSESSMENT

Have students write and solve

- an equation with variables on both sides,
- an equation with variables on both sides that needs to be simplified on both sides before solving,
- an equation with infinitely many solutions, and
- an equation with no solutions.

Power Presentations with PowerPoint®

2-4 Lesson Quiz

Solve each equation.

1. $7x + 2 = 5x + 8$ 3

2. $4(2x - 5) = 5x + 4$ 8

3. $6 - 7(a + 1) = -3(2 - a)$ $\frac{1}{2}$

4. $4(3x + 1) - 7x = 6 + 5x - 2$ all real numbers

5. $\frac{2}{3}(3x + 9) = 8x$ 1

6. A painting company charges $250 base plus $16 per hour. Another painting company charges $210 base plus $18 per hour. How long is a job for which the two companies costs are the same? 20 h

Also available on transparency

Deductive Reasoning and Equations

Use with Lessons 2-1 through 2-4

Deductive reasoning is the process of using logic along with known facts, definitions, and properties to reach a conclusion. In mathematics, deductive reasoning can be used to prove whether given statements are true.

You may not realize it, but you use deductive reasoning every time you solve an equation. In fact, solving an equation can be thought of as a proof.

24.1 Students explain the difference between inductive and deductive reasoning and identify and **provide examples of each.**
Also covered: **5.0, 24.2, 25.1, 25.2**

Example

Solve $3(x + 5) + 2(x + 3) = 26$. Give a reason for each step in your solution process. Identify the conditional statement that is proved and its hypothesis and conclusion.

One way to write down deductive reasoning is to use two columns—one for each step or statement and one for the facts, definitions, and/or properties that support each step.

Statements	Reasons
1. $3(x + 5) + 2(x + 3) = 26$	Given
2. $3x + 15 + 2x + 6 = 26$	Distributive Property
3. $(3x + 2x) + (15 + 6) = 26$	Commutative and Associative Properties of Addition
4. $5x + 21 = 26$	Combine like terms.
5. $5x = 5$	Subtraction Property of Equality (Subtract 21 from both sides.)
6. $x = 1$	Division Property of Equality (Divide both sides by 5.)

The above proves the conditional statement "If $3(x + 5) + 2(x + 3) = 26$, then $x = 1$."

Hypothesis: $3(x + 5) + 2(x + 3) = 26$ Conclusion: $x = 1$

Try This

Solve each equation. Give a reason for each step in your solution process. Identify the conditional statement that is proved and its hypothesis and conclusion.

1. $x - 2 = 4$
2. $x + 6 = 16$
3. $-5x = 25$
4. $\frac{x}{4} = 13$
5. $-2x + 5 = 9$
6. $6x - 5 = 2x - 21$
7. $6(x - 5) = 10$
8. $6x + 1 + x = 10 - 12$
9. What is the error in the solution below? Write a correct solution.

Statements	Reasons
1. $5x + 1 = 7$	Given
2. $5x = 8$	Addition Property of Equality (Add 1 to both sides.)
3. $x = \frac{8}{5}$	Division Property of Equality (Divide both sides by 5.)

Organizer

Objective: Examine the underlying deductive reasoning used when solving an equation.

Online Edition
Student Edition

Countdown to Mastery Week 4

Teach

Discuss

This page illustrates that algebraic procedures are really mathematical proofs in disguise.

Review conditional statements with students. (See pp. 38–39.) Be sure they understand that some conditional statements are true and others are false. For example, the statement "If today is Tuesday, then tomorrow is Sunday" is false. In math, reasoning is used to show whether a conditional statement is true or false.

Answers

1–9. See pp. A12–A13.

Close

Key Concept

Reasoning is always used when doing math. If asked, you should be able to justify any step in a procedure with a property, definition, operation, theorem, etc.

Assess

Choose one or more equations from Section 2A and have students solve them as shown on this page. Then have students trade papers and evaluate each other's work. (25.2)

Extend

When both "if *x*, then *y*" and "if *y*, then *x*" are true (in other words, when both a conditional and its converse are true), we say "*x* if and only if *y*." Such a statement is called a *biconditional* statement. Ask students whether the conditional statements in this activity are biconditionals. yes Challenge them to come up with their own biconditionals, either mathematical or non-mathematical.

Algebra 1 24.1
Also covered:
5.0 Students solve multistep problems, including word problems, **involving linear equations** and linear inequalities **in one variable and provide justification for each step.**
24.2 Students identify the hypothesis and conclusion in logical deduction.
25.0 Students use properties of the number system to judge the validity of results, to justify each step of a procedure, and to prove or disprove **statements.**
25.1 Students use properties of numbers to construct simple, valid arguments (direct and indirect) for, or formulate counterexamples to, claimed assertions.
25.2 Students judge the validity of an argument according to whether the properties of the real number system and the order of operations **have been applied correctly at each step.**

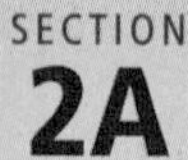

SECTION 2A

CONCEPT CONNECTION

Organizer

Objective: Assess students' ability to apply concepts and skills in Lesson 2-1 through Lesson 2-4 in a real-world format.

Problem	Text Reference
1	Skills Bank p. SB25
2	Lesson 2-1
3	Lesson 2-2
4	Lesson 2-1

CHAPTER 2

SECTION 2A

CONCEPT CONNECTION

Equations and Formulas

All Fired Up A large forest fire in the western United States has been burning for 14 days, spreading to cover approximately 3850 acres. Firefighters have been doing their best to contain the fire, but hot temperatures and high winds have prompted them to request additional help.

1. Find the average number of acres the fire covered each day for the first 14 days. **275 acres**
2. When the fire began, officials estimated that, with no additional firefighting help, the fire would spread to cover 9075 acres before being contained. Write and solve an equation to find the total number of days it would take for the fire to cover 9075 acres. **$275d = 9075$; 33 days**
3. Additional help arrives on day 15, and when the firefighters contain the fire, it has spread to cover a total of only 5775 acres. How many days did it take to contain the fire after the help arrived? **7 days**
4. The total cost of fighting the fire was approximately $1,440,000. Write and solve an equation to find the approximate cost per day of fighting the fire. **$21c = 1{,}440{,}000$; $68,571.43**

INTERVENTION

Scaffolding Questions

1. How do you find an average? Divide the total by the number of days.
2. How many acres have already been burned by the fire? 3850 What is the rate of spread of the fire that you found in **Problem 1**? 275 acres per day
3. How many acres were covered during the first 14 days? 3850 How many acres were covered during the additional *d* days that the help was there? 275*d* How many total acres were covered? 5775
4. What information do you need to find the cost per day? total cost and total number of days How can you find the total number of days? Add 14 to the answer to Problem 3.

Extension

How many acres of land were saved by bringing in additional firefighters? How much time was saved by bringing in additional firefighters? 3300 acres; 12 days

California Standards

5.0 Students solve multistep problems, including word problems, involving linear equations and linear inequalities **in one variable** and provide justification for each step.

CHAPTER 2

SECTION 2A

Quiz for Lessons 2-1 Through 2-4

2-1 Solving One-Step Equations

Solve each equation.

1. $x - 32 = -18$ **14**
2. $1.1 = m - 0.9$ **2**
3. $j + 4 = -17$ **−21**
4. $\frac{9}{8} = g + \frac{1}{2}$ $\frac{5}{8}$
5. $\frac{h}{3} = -12$ **−36**
6. $-2.8 = \frac{w}{-3}$ **8.4**
7. $42 = 3c$ **14**
8. $-0.1b = 3.7$ **−37**
9. When she first purchased it, Soledad's computer had 400 GB of hard drive space. After six months, there were only 313 GB available. Write and solve an equation to find the amount of hard drive space that Soledad used in the first six months. $313 + s = 400$; **87 GB**

2-2 Solving Two-Step Equations

Solve each equation.

10. $2k + 15 = 29$ **7**
11. $-6a - 12 = 24$ **−6**
12. $7 + 3b = -11$ **−6**
13. $1.6 = 0.4n - 2$ **9**
14. $2r + 20 = 200$ **90**
15. $21 = 3g - 6$ **9**
16. $\frac{3}{5}k + 5 = 7$ $\frac{10}{3}$
17. $2.5x + 4.5 = -8$ **−5**
18. Christine's video store membership cost \$5.00, and it costs \$3.50 to rent a DVD. Christine spent \$29.50 her first month. How many DVDs did she rent? **7**
19. A fund-raiser raised \$2400, which was $\frac{3}{5}$ of the goal. Write and solve an equation to find the amount of the goal. $\frac{3}{5}g = 2400$; **\$4000**

2-3 Solving Multi-Step Equations

Solve each equation.

20. $4(x - 7) = 2$ **7.5**
21. $\frac{2}{3} - \frac{y}{4} = \frac{5}{12}$ **1**
22. $5n + 6 - 3n = -12$ **−9**
23. $\frac{3}{4}(8 + 2y) = 3$ **−2**
24. A taxicab company charges \$2.10 plus \$0.80 per mile. Carmen paid a fare of \$11.70. Write and solve an equation to find the number of miles she traveled. $2.10 + 0.80m = 11.70$; **12 mi**
25. If $2(x + 3) = 24$, find the value of $x - 6$. **3**

2-4 Solving Equations with Variables on Both Sides

Solve each equation.

26. $4x - 3 = 2x + 5$ **4**
27. $3(2x - 5) = 2(3x - 2)$ $\varnothing$
28. $2(2t - 3) = 6(t + 2)$ **−9**
29. $7(x + 5) = -7(x + 5)$ **−5**
30. On the first day of the year, Diego had \$700 in his savings account and started spending \$35 a week. His brother Juan had \$450 and started saving \$15 a week. After how many weeks will the brothers have the same amount? What will that amount be? **5 weeks; \$525**

READY TO GO ON?

SECTION 2A

Organizer

Objective: Assess students' mastery of concepts and skills in Lessons 2-1 through 2-4.

PREMIER Online Edition

Countdown to Mastery Week 4

Resources

Assessment Resources
Section 2A Quiz

INTERVENTION

Resources

Ready to Go On? Intervention and Enrichment **Worksheets**

Ready to Go On? **CD-ROM**

Ready to Go On? **Online**

my.hrw.com

READY TO GO ON?
Diagnose and Prescribe

Ready to Go On? Intervention	*Ready to Go On? Intervention,* Section 2A: Worksheets	CD-ROM	Online
Lesson 2-1 Prep for 5.0	2-1 Intervention	Activity 2-1	Diagnose and Prescribe Online
Lesson 2-2 Prep for 5.0	2-2 Intervention	Activity 2-2	
Lesson 2-3 4.0, 5.0	2-3 Intervention	Activity 2-3	
Lesson 2-4 4.0, 5.0	2-4 Intervention	Activity 2-4	

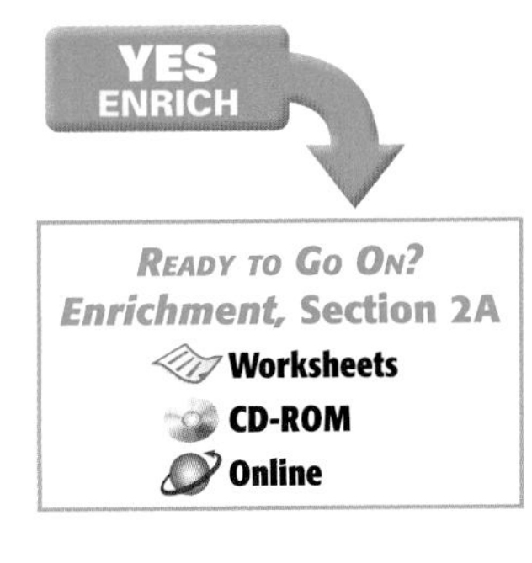

YES
ENRICH
READY TO GO ON?
Enrichment, Section 2A
Worksheets
CD-ROM
Online

Proportions and Formulas

One-Minute Section Planner

Lesson	Lab Resources	Materials
Lesson 2-5 Solving Proportions • Write and use ratios, rates, and unit rates. • Write and solve proportions. **15.0**		
Lesson 2-6 Solving Literal Equations for a Variable • Solve a formula for a given variable. • Solve an equation in two or more variables for one of the variables. **Extension of 5.0**		
Lesson 2-7 Solving Absolute-Value Equations • Solve equations in one variable that contain absolute-value expressions. **3.0, 5.0**		

MK = *Manipulatives Kit*

Notes

Math Background: Teaching the Standards

EQUATIONS AND SOLUTIONS  5.0

Lesson 2-5

A *proportion* is an equation that states that two ratios are equal. The method for solving a proportion, such as $\frac{x}{3} = \frac{5}{8}$, is the same as the method for solving any equation; it requires that the equation be transformed into simpler equivalent equations via a series of mathematically justifiable steps. For example, a possible first step in solving $\frac{x}{3} = \frac{5}{8}$ is to multiply both sides by $3 \cdot 8$, or 24. This step is justified by the Multiplication Property of Equality. The resulting equation, $8x = 15$, can be solved by dividing both sides by 8 (Division Property of Equality).

Performing the above multiplication step on a general proportion leads to the Cross Product Property: If $\frac{a}{b} = \frac{c}{d}$, where $b \neq 0$ and $d \neq 0$, then $ad = bc$. To see why this is true, multiply both sides of the proportion by *bd*.

$\frac{a}{b} = \frac{c}{d}$	
$(bd)\frac{a}{b} = (bd)\frac{c}{d}$	*Multiplication Prop. of Eq.*
$\frac{bda}{b} = \frac{bdc}{d}$	*Multiply.*
$da = bc$	*Simplify.*
$ad = bc$	*Commutative Prop. of Mult.*

(Students will see this argument on p. 108.)

Students often use the Cross Product Property without understanding its underlying mathematics; it is simply a "trick." Understanding the mathematical reasons *why* they may use this property is important for students. More generally, students should realize that there are no tricks in mathematics; every step or operation can be justified with a property, definition, etc.

ABSOLUTE-VALUE EQUATIONS 3.0

Lesson 2-7

The absolute value of a number is the number's distance from 0 on a number line. More generally, $|x - a|$ represents the distance between x and a. Thus, the equation $|x - 1| = 3$ asks, "Which values of x are 3 units away from 1?"

As the figure shows, there are two values of x that are 3 units away from 1, -2 and 4. So, this absolute-value equation has two solutions.

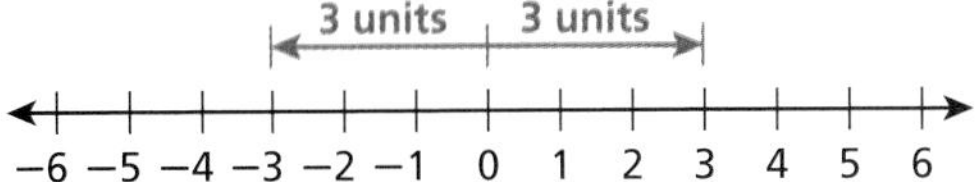

SET THEORY

Lesson 2-7

Beginning in Lesson 2-4 and continuing in Lesson 2-7, students encounter equations that have two solutions, infinitely many solutions, or no solutions. It is convenient to express these various solution possibilities by using set notation.

A *set* is a collection of objects, or *elements*. The *empty set* (or *null set*), denoted as $\varnothing$ or { }, is the set that has no elements. (The empty set should not be confused with the set containing the single element 0.) Thus, when an equation has no solutions, we say that its solution set is the empty set, or that its solution set is empty.

The *universal set* is the set containing all elements under consideration. In Algebra 1, the universal set may generally be assumed to be the real numbers.

Sets that contain a finite number of elements are often described by listing the elements within braces: {2, 4, 6}. For sets that have many or infinitely many elements, *set-builder notation*, $\{x : P(x)\}$, may be used to describe the set of all numbers x for which the rule $P(x)$ is true. For example, $\{x : x > 0\}$ is the set of all numbers x for which $x > 0$; in other words, the set of positive real numbers.

If every element of set A is an element of set B, then set A is a *subset* of set B, denoted $A \subset B$. Subset terminology is useful in describing relationships among sets of numbers. For example, the whole numbers are a subset of the integers, and the integers are a subset of the rational numbers.

2-5 Organizer

Objectives: Write and use ratios, rates, and unit rates.

Write and solve proportions.

Online Edition
Tutorial Videos

Countdown to Mastery Week 4

Power Presentations with PowerPoint®

Warm Up

Solve each equation.

1. $\frac{x}{4} = 12$ 48 **2.** $5m = 18$ 3.6

Multiply.

3. $8\left(\frac{7}{8}\right)$ 7 **4.** $12\left(\frac{5}{6}\right)$ 10

Change each percent to a decimal.

5. 73% 0.73 **6.** 112% 1.12

7. 0.6% 0.006 **8.** 1% 0.01

Change each fraction to a decimal.

9. $\frac{1}{2}$ 0.5 **10.** $\frac{1}{3}$ $0.\overline{3}$

Also available on transparency

California Standards

Algebra 1 🔑 15.0

2-5 Solving Proportions

California Standards

🔑 **15.0 Students apply algebraic techniques to solve rate problems,** work problems, and percent mixture problems.

Vocabulary

ratio	proportion
rate	unit rate
cross products	percent
scale	scale
scale drawing	scale model

Why learn this?

Proportions are used to draw accurate maps. (See Example 5.)

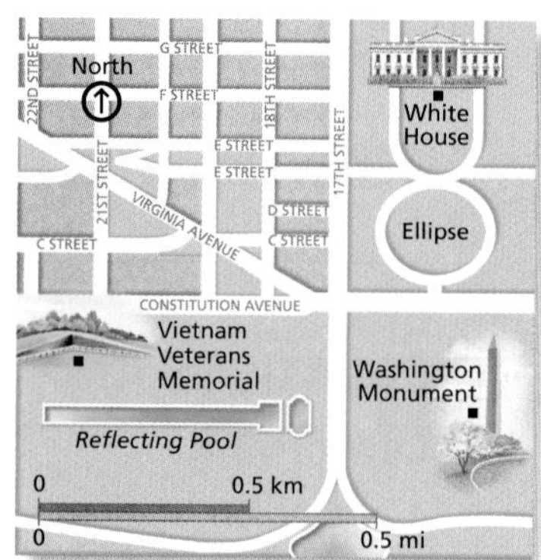

A **ratio** is a comparison of two quantities. The ratio of a to b can be written $a{:}b$ or $\frac{a}{b}$, where $b \neq 0$.

A statement that two ratios are equal, such as $\frac{1}{12} = \frac{2}{24}$, is called a **proportion**.

EXAMPLE 1 Using Ratios

The ratio of faculty members to students at a college is 1:15. There are 675 students. How many faculty members are there?

$\frac{\text{faculty} \rightarrow 1}{\text{students} \rightarrow 15}$ *Write a ratio comparing faculty to students.*

$\frac{1}{15} = \frac{x}{675}$ *Write a proportion. Let x be the number of faculty members.*

$675\left(\frac{x}{675}\right) = 675\left(\frac{1}{15}\right)$ *Since x is divided by 675, multiply both sides by 675.*

$x = 45$ There are 45 faculty members.

1. The ratio of red marbles to green marbles is 6:5. There are 18 red marbles. How many green marbles are there? **15**

A common application of proportions is *rates.* A **rate** is a ratio of two quantities with different units, such as $\frac{34 \text{ mi}}{2 \text{ gal}}$. Rates are usually written as *unit rates.* A **unit rate** is a rate with a second quantity of 1 unit, such as $\frac{17 \text{ mi}}{1 \text{ gal}}$ or 17 mi/gal. You can convert any rate to a unit rate.

EXAMPLE 2 Finding Unit Rates

Takeru Kobayashi of Japan ate 53.5 hot dogs in 12 minutes to win a contest. Find the unit rate. Round your answer to the nearest hundredth.

$\frac{53.5}{12} = \frac{x}{1}$ *Write a proportion to find an equivalent ratio with a second quantity of 1.*

$4.46 \approx x$ *Divide on the left side to find x.*

The unit rate is approximately 4.46 hot dogs per minute.

Find each unit rate. Round to the nearest hundredth if necessary.

2a. Cory earns \$52.50 in 7 hours. **\$7.50/h**

2b. A machine seals 138 envelopes in 23 minutes. **6 envelopes/min**

1 Introduce

EXPLORATION

2-5 Solving Proportions

You can use fractions to compare quantities. For example, the number of triangles compared to the number of stars is $\frac{3}{4}$.

1. Write a fraction to compare the number of squares to the number of triangles.
2. Write a fraction to compare the number of stars to the number of hearts.
3. What do you notice about the fractions you wrote in Problems 1 and 2?
4. Put the numbers 2, 3, 4, and 6 in the squares to complete the following equation. $\frac{\square}{\square} = \frac{\square}{\square}$
5. Can you use the numbers 2, 3, 4, and 6 to complete the equation in a different way? If so, how?

THINK AND DISCUSS

6. **Show** how you can complete the equation in Problem 4 using the numbers 4, 6, 8, and 12.
7. **Discuss** whether it is possible to complete the equation using the numbers 2, 3, 6, and 8.

Motivate

Show students the following table.

Cell Phone Plan	Number of Minutes	Cost
A	800	\$50
B	600	\$40

See whether students can find the cost per minute for each plan. A: 6.25 cents; B: 6.67 cents
Explain that these are *unit* rates, because they are the cost for one unit (one minute). Unit rates allow you to compare items of different sizes.

Explorations and answers are provided in *Alternate Openers: Explorations Transparencies.*

In the proportion $\frac{a}{b} = \frac{c}{d}$, the products $a \cdot d$ and $b \cdot c$ are called **cross products**. You can solve a proportion for a missing value by using the Cross Products Property.

Cross Products Property

WORDS	NUMBERS	ALGEBRA
In a proportion, cross products are equal.	$\frac{2}{3} \times \frac{4}{6}$ $2 \cdot 6 = 3 \cdot 4$	If $\frac{a}{b} \times \frac{c}{d}$ and $b \neq 0$ and $d \neq 0$, then $ad = bc$.

EXAMPLE 3 Solving Proportions

Solve each proportion.

A $\frac{5}{9} = \frac{3}{w}$

$\frac{5}{9} \times \frac{3}{w}$

$5(w) = 9(3)$ *Use cross products.*

$5w = 27$

$\frac{5w}{5} = \frac{27}{5}$ *Divide both sides by 5.*

$w = \frac{27}{5}$

B $\frac{8}{x+10} = \frac{1}{12}$

$\frac{8}{x+10} \times \frac{1}{12}$

$8(12) = 1(x+10)$ *Use cross products.*

$96 = x + 10$

$-10 \quad -10$ *Subtract 10 from both sides.*

$86 = x$

Solve each proportion. Check your answer.

3a. $\frac{-5}{2} = \frac{y}{8}$ **−20**

3b. $\frac{g+3}{5} = \frac{7}{4}$ **5.75**

Another common application of proportions is *percents.* A **percent** is a ratio that compares a number to 100. For example, $25\% = \frac{25}{100}$.

You can use the proportion $\frac{\text{part}}{\text{whole}} = \frac{\text{percent}}{100}$ to find unknown values.

EXAMPLE 4 Percent Problems

A **Find 50% of 20.**

Method 1 Use a proportion.

$\frac{\text{part}}{\text{whole}} = \frac{\text{percent}}{100}$ *Use the percent proportion.*

$\frac{x}{20} = \frac{50}{100}$ *Let x represent the part.*

$100x = 1000$ *Find the cross products. Since x is multiplied by 100, divide both sides by 100 to undo the multiplication.*

$\frac{100x}{100} = \frac{1000}{100}$

$x = 10$

50% of 20 is 10.

2 Teach

Guided Instruction

Before teaching this lesson, review solving one-step equations with multiplication and division. When solving proportions, remind students to use the Distributive Property when a numerator or denominator has more than one term.

Be sure students can convert between fractions, decimals, and percents before solving percent problems. Have them practice stating whether a problem is about finding the part, the whole, or the percent before solving.

Universal Access

Through Number Sense

Encourage students to quickly find 50% and 25% of any number by dividing in half, then in half again. For example:

	50%	25%
80	40	20
48	24	12

Students can check the reasonableness of an answer. If asked to find 35% of 48, the student knows the answer is between 12 and 24.

COMMON ERROR ALERT

Students may be confused as to when to change a percent to a decimal. When using the proportion method shown in **Example 4A,** the percent is not changed to decimal form because the percent number is divided by 100 as part of the proportion.

Power Presentations with PowerPoint®

Additional Examples

Example 1

The ratio of the number of bones in the human ears to the number of bones in the skull is 3:11. There are 22 bones in the skull. How many bones are in the ears? 6

Example 2

Ralf Laue of Germany flipped a pancake 416 times in 120 seconds to set the world record. Find the unit rate. Round your answer to the nearest hundredth. about 3.47 flips/s

Example 3

Solve each proportion.

A. $\frac{3}{9} = \frac{5}{m}$ 15

B. $\frac{6}{y-3} = \frac{2}{7}$ 24

Also available on transparency

INTERVENTION

Questioning Strategies

EXAMPLE 1

- How do you know whether the number of students should be written as the first or second quantity in the ratio?
- What does the ratio 1:15 mean?

EXAMPLE 2

- In the ratio $\frac{53.5}{12}$, what does 53.5 represent? What does 12 represent?
- When you solve this proportion, what are you solving for?

EXAMPLE 3

- How could you solve these equations by multiplying both sides by the same number?

Power Presentations with PowerPoint®

Additional Examples

Example 4

A. Find 30% of 80. 24

B. 230 is what percent of 200? 115%

C. 20 is 0.4% of what number? 5000

Example 5

A contractor has a blueprint for a house drawn to the scale 1 in.:3 ft.

A. A wall on the blueprint is 6.5 inches long. How long is the actual wall? 19.5 ft

B. One wall of the house will be 12 feet long when it is built. How long is the wall on the blueprint? 4 in.

Also available on transparency

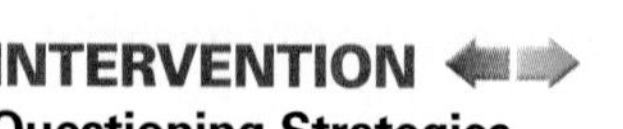

Questioning Strategies

EXAMPLE 4

- Identify any similarities you see between using an equation and using a proportion.
- How can you determine the reasonableness of your answer?

EXAMPLE 5

- If the scale is represented by a ratio less than 1, what do we know about the actual object?
- If the scale is represented by a ratio greater than 1, what do we know about the actual object?

B **440 is what percent of 400?**

Method 2 Use an equation.

$440 = x \cdot 400$	*Write an equation. Let x represent the percent.*
$440 = 400x$	
$\frac{440}{400} = \frac{400x}{400}$	*Since x is multiplied by 400, divide both sides by 400 to undo the multiplication.*
$1.1 = x$	*The answer is a decimal.*
$110\% = x$	*Write the decimal as a percent. This answer is reasonable; 440 is more than 100% of 400.*
440 is 110% of 400.	

4a. Find 20% of 60. **12**

4b. 48 is 15% of what number? **320**

Proportions are used to create *scale drawings* and *scale models.* A **scale** is a ratio between two sets of measurements, such as 1 in:5 mi. A **scale drawing** or **scale model** uses a scale to represent an object as smaller or larger than the actual object. A map is an example of a scale drawing.

EXAMPLE 5 Scale Drawings and Scale Models

On the map, the distance from Chicago to Evanston measures 0.625 in. What is the actual distance?

$\frac{\text{map}}{\text{actual}} \to \frac{1 \text{ in.}}{18 \text{ mi}}$	*Write the scale as a fraction.*
$\frac{1}{18} = \frac{0.625}{x}$	*Let x be the actual distance.*
$x \cdot 1 = 18(0.625)$	*Use cross products to solve.*
$x = 11.25$	

The actual distance is 11.25 mi.

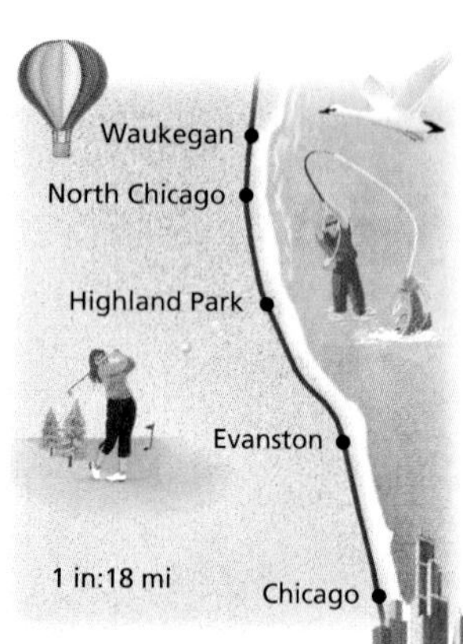

A scale written without units, such as 32:1, means that 32 units of any measure correspond to 1 unit of that same measure.

5a. The actual distance between North Chicago and Waukegan is 4 mi. What is this distance on the map above? **about 0.2 in.**

5b. A scale model of a human heart is 16 ft long. The scale is 32 : 1. How many inches long is the actual heart that the model represents? **6 in.**

THINK AND DISCUSS

1. Explain two ways to solve the proportion $\frac{t}{4} = \frac{3}{5}$.

2. GET ORGANIZED Copy and complete the graphic organizer. In each box, write an example of each use of ratios.

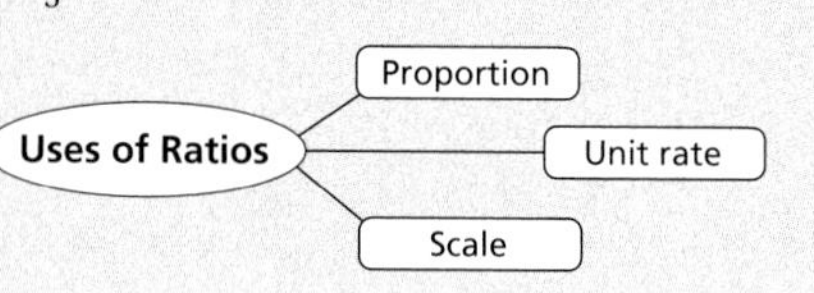

3 Close

Summarize

Review with students how to solve proportions and how to use proportions to solve application problems. Caution students to be careful when writing proportions to represent applications. The variable that is the first quantity of one ratio must also be the first quantity of the other. The variable that is the second quantity of one ratio must also be the second quantity of the other.

FORMATIVE ASSESSMENT and INTERVENTION

***Diagnose Before* the Lesson**
2-5 Warm Up, TE p. 102

***Monitor During* the Lesson**
Check It Out! Exercises, SE pp. 102–104
Questioning Strategies, TE pp. 103–104

***Assess After* the Lesson**
2-5 Lesson Quiz, TE p. 107
Alternative Assessment, TE p. 107

Answers to *Think and Discuss*

1. Possible answer: Use cross products and then use inverse operations to isolate *t*.
2. See p. A3.

2-5 Exercises

California Standards Practice
5.0, 15.0, 25.1, 25.2

Homework Help Online
KEYWORD: MA8CA 2-5
Parent Resources Online
KEYWORD: MA8CA Parent

GUIDED PRACTICE

Vocabulary Apply the vocabulary from this lesson to answer each question.

1. What does it mean when two ratios form a *proportion*? **The ratios are equal.**
2. In your own words, write a definition of *percent*. **Possible answer: Percent is a ratio to a total of 100.**

SEE EXAMPLE 1 p. 102

3. The ratio of the sale price of a jacket to the original price is 3:4. The original price is \$64. What is the sale price? **\$48**
4. **Chemistry** The ratio of hydrogen atoms to oxygen atoms in water is 2:1. If an amount of water contains 341 trillion atoms of oxygen, how many hydrogen atoms are there? **682 trillion**

SEE EXAMPLE 2 p. 102

Find each unit rate.

5. A computer's fan rotates 2000 times in 40 seconds. **50 rotations/s**
6. Twelve cows produce 224,988 pounds of milk. **18,749 lb/cow**

SEE EXAMPLE 3 p. 103

Solve each proportion. Check your answer.

7. $\frac{3}{z} = \frac{1}{8}$ **24**
8. $\frac{x}{3} = \frac{1}{5}$ **$\frac{3}{5}$**
9. $\frac{b}{4} = \frac{3}{2}$ **6**
10. $\frac{f+3}{12} = \frac{7}{2}$ **39**
11. $\frac{-1}{5} = \frac{3}{2d}$ **−7.5**
12. $\frac{3}{14} = \frac{s-2}{21}$ **6.5**

SEE EXAMPLE 4 p. 103

13. Find 75% of 40. **30**
14. Find $12\frac{1}{2}$% of 168. **21**
15. Find 115% of 57. **65.55**
16. Find 70% of 8. **5.6**
17. What percent of 40 is 25? **62.5%**
18. What percent of 225 is 180? **80%**

SEE EXAMPLE 5 p. 104

19. **Archaeology** Stonehenge II in Hunt, Texas, is a scale model of the ancient construction in Wiltshire, England. The scale of the model to the original is 3:5. The Altar Stone of the original construction is 4.9 meters tall. Write and solve a proportion to find the height of the Texas model of the Altar Stone. **$\frac{3}{5} = \frac{h}{4.9}$; 2.94 m**

PRACTICE AND PROBLEM SOLVING

Independent Practice

For Exercises	See Example
20–21	1
22–23	2
24–27	3
28–33	4
34	5

Extra Practice
Skills Practice p. EP5
Application Practice p. EP25

20. **Gardening** The ratio of the height of a bonsai ficus tree to the height of a full-size ficus tree is 1:9. The bonsai ficus is 6 inches tall. What is the height of a full-size ficus? **54 in.**
21. **Manufacturing** At one factory, the ratio of defective light bulbs produced to total light bulbs produced is about 3:500. How many light bulbs are expected to be defective when 12,000 are produced? **72**

Find each unit rate.

22. Four gallons of gasoline weigh 25 pounds. **6.25 lb/gal**
23. Fifteen ounces of gold cost \$6,058.50. **\$403.90/oz**

Solve each proportion. Check your answer.

24. $\frac{v}{6} = \frac{1}{2}$ **3**
25. $\frac{2}{5} = \frac{4}{y}$ **10**
26. $\frac{2}{h} = \frac{-5}{6}$ **−2.4**
27. $\frac{3}{10} = \frac{b+7}{20}$ **−1**

2-5 Exercises

Assignment Guide

Assign *Guided Practice* exercises as necessary.

If you finished Examples **1–3**
Proficient 20–27, 35–38, 44, 46
Advanced 20–27, 35–38, 43, 44, 46–48, 51

If you finished Examples **1–5**
Proficient 20–46, 52–63
Advanced 20–34 even, 35–63

Homework Quick Check
Quickly check key concepts.
Exercises: 20, 22, 24, 28, 32, 34

California Standards

Standard	Exercises
2.0	54–57
5.0	61–63
15.0	5, 6, 22, 23, 44, 46
25.1	53
25.2	45
7AF2.1	58–60

CONCEPT CONNECTION **Exercise 44** involves using proportions to find frequencies. This exercise prepares students for the Concept Connection on page 120.

Language Support Students may not understand the word *interval* in **Exercise 44.** Explain that an interval is "a space".

ENGLISH LANGUAGE LEARNERS

Answers

53.
$$\frac{3}{x} = \frac{5}{x-1}$$
$$(x)\frac{3}{x} = (x)\frac{5}{x-1}$$
$$3 = \frac{5x}{x-1}$$
$$3(x-1) = \frac{5x}{x-1}(x-1)$$
$$3(x-1) = 5x$$

42. Possible answers: $\frac{1}{2} = \frac{3}{6}$; $\frac{1}{4} = \frac{5}{20}$; $\frac{3}{7} = \frac{6}{14}$; they are proportions because their cross products are equal; possible answers: $\frac{1}{2} \neq \frac{5}{6}$; $\frac{1}{2} \neq \frac{6}{7}$; $\frac{3}{4} \neq \frac{2}{3}$; they are not proportions because their cross products are not equal.

Find each value. Round to the nearest tenth if necessary.

28. 60% of 80 **48** **29.** 35% of 90 **31.5** **30.** $\frac{1}{2}$% of 500 **2.5** **31.** 210% of 30 **63**

32. What percent of 52 is 13? **25%** **33.** What percent of 9 is 27? **300%**

34. Science The image shows a dust mite as seen under a microscope. The actual length of this dust mite is 0.3 millimeter. Use a ruler to measure the length of the dust mite in the image in millimeters. What is the scale of the drawing? **1:100**

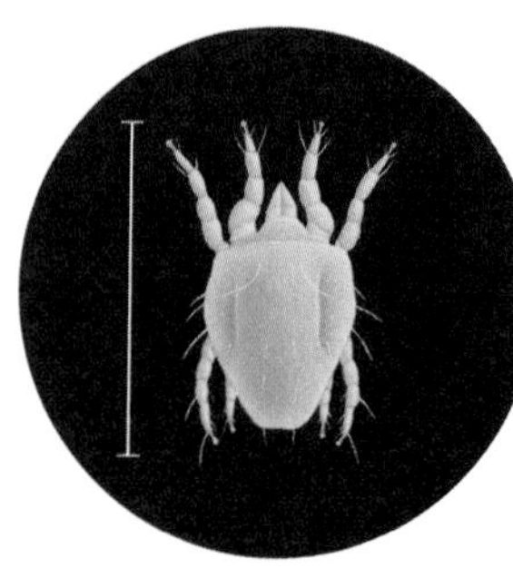

Solve each proportion.

35. $\frac{x-1}{3} = \frac{x+1}{5}$ **4** **36.** $\frac{m}{3} = \frac{m+4}{7}$ **3**

37. $\frac{1}{x-3} = \frac{3}{x-5}$ **2** **38.** $\frac{a}{2} = \frac{a-4}{30}$ $-\frac{2}{7}$

39. $\frac{3}{2y} = \frac{16}{y+2}$ $\frac{6}{29}$ **40.** $\frac{n+3}{5} = \frac{n-1}{2}$ $\frac{11}{3}$

41. Multi-Step According to the 2000 U.S. Census, 138,053,563 Americans are male and 143,368,343 Americans are female. About what percent of the population is male? female? Round your answers to the nearest percent. **49%; 51%**

42. Write About It Give three examples of proportions. How do you know they are proportions? Then give three nonexamples of proportions. How do you know they are not proportions?

43. Entertainment The numbers of various types of movies rented over a period of time are indicated in the graph.

a. What percent of the movies rented were comedies? **40%**

b. What type of movie made up 25% of the rentals? **action**

c. What percent of the movies rented were in the "other" category? **3%**

d. **What if...?** If 25 of the comedy rentals had instead been action rentals, what percent of the movies rented would have been comedies? Round your answer to the nearest tenth. **36.9%**

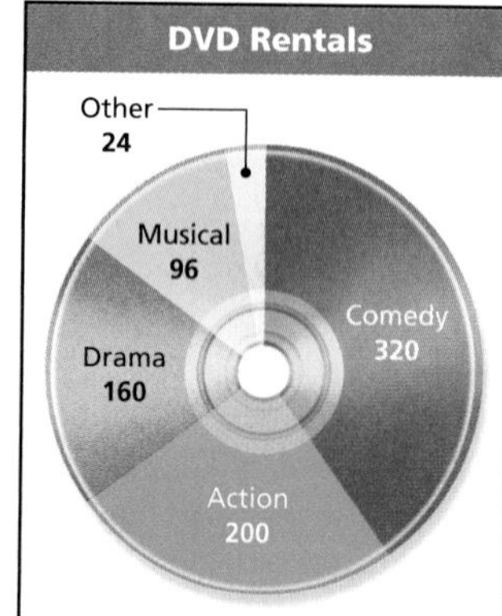

CONCEPT CONNECTION

44. This problem will help prepare you for the Concept Connection on page 120.

Two notes are separated by an interval of a fourth if the ratio of the notes' frequencies is 4:3. The note D_4 has a frequency of 297 hertz (Hz).

a. Write and solve a proportion that you can use to find the frequency of a note that has higher pitch (that is, a greater frequency) than the note D_4 and is separated from the note D_4 by an interval of a fourth. $\frac{4}{3} = \frac{x}{297}$; **396 Hz**

b. Find the frequency of a note with a higher pitch that is separated by an interval of a fourth from the note you found in part **a.** **528 Hz**

2-5 PRACTICE A

2-5 PRACTICE C

2-5 PRACTICE B

LESSON 2-5 **Practice B**
Solving Proportions

1. The ratio of freshman to sophomores in a drama club is 5:6. There are 18 sophomores in the drama club. How many freshmen are there? **15**

Find each unit rate.

2. Four pounds of apples cost $1.96. **$0.49/lb**

3. Sal washed 5 cars in 50 minutes. **0.1 cars/min**

Solve each proportion.

4. $\frac{y}{4} = \frac{10}{8}$ $y = 5$ 5. $\frac{2}{x} = \frac{30}{-6}$ $x = -0.4$ 6. $\frac{3}{12} = \frac{-24}{m}$ $m = -96$

7. $\frac{3t}{10} = \frac{1}{2}$ $t = \frac{5}{3}$ 8. $\frac{32}{4} = \frac{b+4}{3}$ $b = 20$ 9. $\frac{7}{x} = \frac{1}{0.5}$ $x = 3.5$

Find each value. Round to the nearest tenth if necessary.

10. 80% of 120 **96** 11. 115% of 6 **6.9**

12. What percent of 128 is 32? **25%** 13. 3 is what percent of 36? **8.3%**

14. Sam is building a model of an antique car. The scale of his model to the actual car is 1:10. His model is $18\frac{1}{2}$ inches long. How long is the actual car? **185 in.**

15. The scale on a map of Virginia shows that 1 centimeter represents 30 miles. The actual distance from Richmond, VA to Washington, DC is 110 miles. On the map, how many centimeters are between the two cities? Round your answer to the nearest tenth. **3.7 cm**

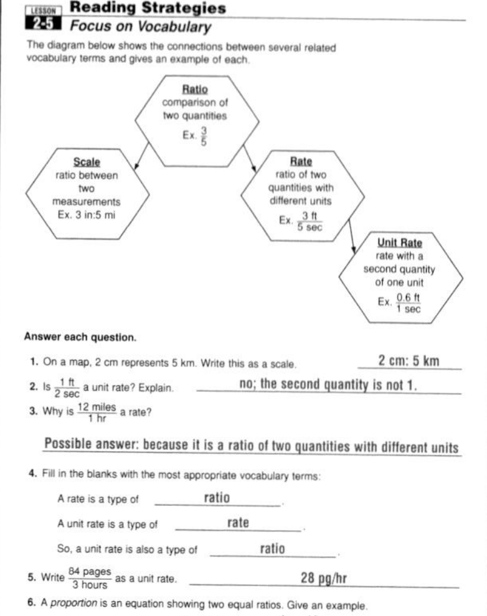

2-5 READING STRATEGIES

LESSON 2-5 **Reading Strategies**
Focus on Vocabulary

The diagram below shows the connections between several related vocabulary terms and gives an example of each.

Answer each question.

1. On a map, 2 cm represents 5 km. Write this as a scale. **2 cm: 5 km**

2. Is $\frac{1 \text{ ft}}{2 \text{ sec}}$ a unit rate? Explain. **no; the second quantity is not 1.**

3. Why is $\frac{12 \text{ miles}}{1 \text{ hr}}$ a rate?

Possible answer: because it is a ratio of two quantities with different units

4. Fill in the blanks with the most appropriate vocabulary terms:

A rate is a type of **ratio**.

A unit rate is a type of **rate**.

So, a unit rate is also a type of **ratio**.

5. Write $\frac{84 \text{ pages}}{3 \text{ hours}}$ as a unit rate. **28 pg/hr**

6. A *proportion* is an equation showing two equal ratios. Give an example.

Possible answer: $\frac{1}{2} = \frac{12}{24}$

2-5 REVIEW FOR MASTERY

LESSON 2-5 **Review for Mastery**
Solving Proportions

Use cross products to solve proportions.

Solve $\frac{x}{10} = \frac{4}{25}$.

$\frac{x}{10} \times \frac{4}{25}$

$25x = 40$ *Multiply x by 25. Write the product on the left. Multiply 10 by 4. Write the product on the right.*

$\frac{25x}{25} = \frac{40}{25}$ *Divide both sides by 25.*

$x = 1.6$

Sometimes it is necessary to use the Distributive Property.

Solve $\frac{4}{x+2} = \frac{2}{5}$.

$\frac{4}{x+2} \times \frac{2}{5}$ *Multiply 4 by 5 and x + 2 by 2.*

$20 = 2(x + 2)$

$20 = 2x + 4$ *Distribute 2.*

$-4 \quad -4$ *Subtract 4 from both sides.*

$\frac{16}{2} = \frac{2x}{2}$ *Divide both sides by 2.*

$8 = x$

Solve each proportion.

1. $\frac{x}{20} = \frac{1}{8}$ $x = 2.5$ 2. $\frac{5}{12} = \frac{1.25}{k}$ $k = 3$

3. $\frac{3}{4} = \frac{a+5}{21}$ $a = 10.75$ 4. $\frac{3}{y-3} = \frac{1}{9}$ $y = 30$

45. Possible answer: The denominator in the first ratio is the number of varsity members, but in the second ratio it is the total number of people on the team.

45. **///ERROR ANALYSIS///** Below is a bonus question that appeared on an algebra test and a student's response.

> The ratio of junior varsity members to varsity members on the track team is 3:5. There are 24 members on the team. Write a proportion to find the number of junior varsity members.
>
> $\frac{3}{5} = \frac{x}{24}$

The student did not receive the bonus points. Why is this proportion incorrect?

Multiple Choice For Exercises 46 and 47, choose the best answer.

46. One day the U.S. dollar was worth approximately 100 Japanese yen. An exchange of 2500 yen was made that day. What was the value of the exchange in dollars?

(A) \$25 (B) \$2,400 (C) \$2,500 (D) \$270,000

47. Which proportion can be used to find 14% of 60?

(A) $\frac{x}{100} = \frac{60}{14}$ (B) $\frac{14}{100} = \frac{60}{x}$ (C) $\frac{x}{100} = \frac{14}{60}$ (D) $\frac{14}{100} = \frac{x}{60}$

48. **Gridded Response** Raul surveyed 35 students about their preferred lunch. Fourteen preferred chicken. Half of those students preferred chicken with barbecue sauce. What percent should Raul report as preferring chicken with barbecue sauce? **20**

CHALLENGE AND EXTEND

49. **Geometry** Complementary angles are two angles whose measures add to 90°. The ratio of the measures of two complementary angles is 4:5. What are the measures of the angles? **40°; 50°**

50. **Population** The population density of Jackson, Mississippi, is 672.2 people per square kilometer. What is the population density in people per square meter? Show that your answer is reasonable. (*Hint:* There are 1000 meters in 1 kilometer. How many square meters are in 1 square kilometer?) **0.0006722 people/m²**

Find each value. Round to the nearest tenth if necessary.

51. What percent of 16 is 2.75? **17.2%**

52. 22 is 73.5% of what number? **29.9**

53. **Reasoning** Without using cross products, show that $\frac{3}{x} = \frac{5}{x-1}$ is equivalent to $3(x-1) = 5x$.

SPIRAL STANDARDS REVIEW

7AF2.1, 2.0, 4.0

Evaluate each expression. (Lesson 1-4)

54. 8^2 **64**

55. $(-3)^3$ **−27**

56. $(-3)^2$ **9**

57. $-\left(\frac{1}{2}\right)^5$ $-\frac{1}{32}$

Write the power represented by each geometric model. (Lesson 1-4)

58. 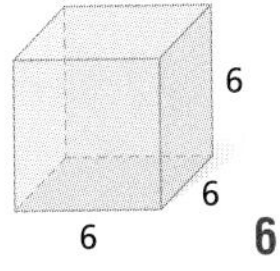

6^3

59. 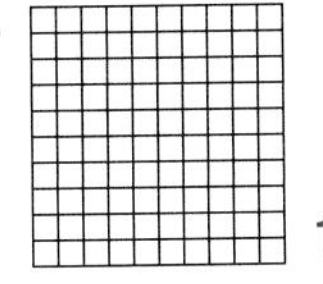
10^2

60. 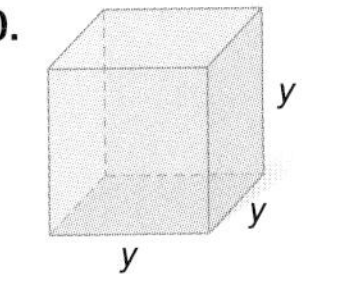

y^3

Solve each equation. Check your answer. (Lesson 2-4)

61. $2x - 12 = 5x + 3$ **−5**

62. $3a - 4 = 6 - 7a$ **1**

63. $3x - 4 = 2x + 4$ **8**

Teaching Tip **Multiple Choice** Encourage students to eliminate answers that are clearly incorrect. When converting from yen to dollars in **Exercise 46,** the amount should decrease based on the exchange rate given. Therefore, **C** and **D** can be excluded immediately.

Teaching Tip **Geometry** In **Exercise 49,** point out that if the ratios of the angle measures are 4:5, then one measure is 4 times a number and the other is 5 times the same number. This leads to the equation $4x + 5x = 90$, which students can solve.

Journal

Have students write about how to find and use unit rates to get the best deal. They should include proportions in their explanation.

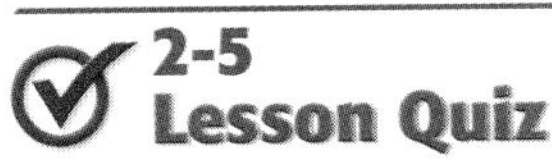

ALTERNATIVE ASSESSMENT

Have students use a map to determine the actual distances between 3 towns. Then have them plan a trip to visit all 3 towns and return to their starting point. They should also explain how much more gas a vehicle that gets 12 mi/gal will need for this trip than a vehicle that gets 25 mi/gal.

Power Presentations with PowerPoint®

2-5 Lesson Quiz

1. In a school, the ratio of boys to girls is 4:3. There are 216 boys. How many girls are there? 162

Find each unit rate. Round to the nearest hundredth if necessary.

2. Nuts cost \$10.75 for 3 pounds. \$3.58/lb

3. Sue washes 25 cars in 5 hours. 5 cars/h

Solve each proportion.

4. $\frac{8}{12} = \frac{g}{9}$ 6 5. $\frac{3}{z-4} = \frac{2}{8}$ 16

6. Find 20% of 80. 16

7. What percent of 160 is 20? 12.5%

8. 35% of what number is 40? 114.3

9. A scale model of a car is 9 in. long. The scale is 1:18. How many inches long is the actual car the model represents? 162 in.

Also available on transparency

2-5 PROBLEM SOLVING

LESSON 2-5 **Problem Solving**
Solving Proportions

Write the correct answer.

1. A bakery bakes 4 dozen loaves of bread every 18 hours. Find the unit rate to the nearest hundredth. **2.67 loaves/hour**

2. At one time, the ratio of in-state to out-of-state tuition at Texas A & M University in College Station, Texas was about 3:11. About how much was the out-of-state tuition if the in-state tuition at that time was about \$2400? **\$8800**

3. The total recommended daily allowance of fat is 65 g. One serving of pumpkin pie contains 12 total grams of fat. What percentage of the recommended daily allowance is this? Round to the nearest tenth. **18.5%**

4. The total recommended daily allowance of saturated fat is 20 g. A certain nutrition bar contains 15% of the recommended daily allowance of saturated fat. How many grams of saturated fat are in the bar? **3 g**

Use the table below to answer questions 5–7. Select the best answer. The table shows the ratio of female to male students at various institutions in 2002.

Institution	female:male
Massachusetts Institute of Technology	41:59
Tulane University	53:47
US Naval Academy	1:19
Georgia Institute of Technology	29:71
University of Massachusetts at Amherst	51:49
Baylor University	29:21

5. If there are 209 women at the US Naval Academy, how many men are there?
A 11 (C) 3971
B 190 D 4180

6. If there are 7282 male students at the Georgia Institute of Technology, how many females are there?
F 2427 H 8282
(G) 2974 J 17,828

7. If there are 4959 male students at Baylor University, which proportion can be used to find the number of female students?
A $\frac{21}{4959} = \frac{x}{21}$ C $\frac{21}{29} = \frac{x}{4959}$
B $\frac{21}{4959} = \frac{x}{29}$ (D) $\frac{29}{21} = \frac{x}{4959}$

8. For which institution is the ratio of female to male students the greatest?
(F) Baylor University
G Tulane University
H University of Massachusetts at Amherst
J US Naval Academy

2-5 CHALLENGE

LESSON 2-5 **Challenge**
Using Cross Products to Derive New Proportions

In Lessson 2-6, you learned that in a true proportion, the cross products are equal.

If $\frac{a}{b} = \frac{c}{d}$, then $ad = bc$.

The proof to the statement above is shown at right.

$\frac{a}{b} = \frac{c}{d}$
$bd\left(\frac{a}{b}\right) = bd\left(\frac{c}{d}\right)$ Multiplication Property of Equality
$da = bc$ Inverse Property of Multiplication
$ad = bc$ Commutative Property of Multiplication

Using $\frac{a}{b} = \frac{c}{d}$, you can write and prove that other proportions involving a, b, c, and d are true.

In each proportion, assume that the denominator is not equal to 0.

1. Let $\frac{a}{b} = \frac{c}{d}$, where $a = 5$, $b = 7$, $c = 15$, and $d = 21$. Verify that the product of the means is equal to the product of the extremes. **bc: 7 • 15 = 105; ad: 5 • 21 = 105**

2. a. Let $\frac{a}{b} = \frac{c}{d}$. What can be done to each side of $\frac{a}{b} = \frac{c}{d}$ in order to get $\frac{d}{c} = \frac{b}{a}$? **Multiply each side by $\frac{bd}{ac}$**

b. Justify each step in the reasoning below in order to show that $\frac{d}{c} = \frac{b}{a}$.

$\frac{a}{b} = \frac{c}{d}$
$ad = bc$ **Cross-Product Property**
$\left(\frac{1}{ac}\right)ad = \left(\frac{1}{ac}\right)bd$ **Multiplication Property of Equality**
$\frac{d}{c} = \frac{b}{a}$ **Identity Property of Multiplication**

3. Let $\frac{a}{b} = \frac{c}{d}$. Show that $\frac{d}{b} = \frac{c}{a}$. Write your reasons to the right of your steps.

$\frac{a}{b} = \frac{c}{d}$
$ad = bc$ **Cross-Product Property**
$\left(\frac{1}{ab}\right)ad = \left(\frac{1}{ab}\right)bc$ **Multiplication Property of Equality**
$\frac{d}{b} = \frac{c}{a}$ **Identity Property of Multiplication**

Organizer

Objective: Use deductive reasoning to prove conditional statements.

Online Edition
Student Edition

Countdown to Mastery Week 4

Teach

Discuss

Students have seen how to prove a conditional statement false by finding a counterexample. In this Logical Reasoning, they will learn how to prove a conditional statement true.

The strategy is to assume the hypothesis is true and reason to the conclusion. This proves that *if* the hypothesis is true, *then* the conclusion is true.

Review deductive reasoning. Emphasize that students must have a definition, property, or operation to support each step.

At the last step of their proofs, students may want to write "Conclusion" or "Given" as the reason. Stress that they must be able to justify going from the previous step to the conclusion.

Answers

2. See p. A13.

Use with Lesson 2-5

Proving Conditional Statements

In Lesson 2-5, you used the Cross Products Property:

If $\frac{a}{b} = \frac{c}{d}$ $(b \neq 0 \text{ and } d \neq 0)$, then $ad = bc$.

Notice that the Cross Products Property is a conditional statement. You can use deductive reasoning to prove that it is true.

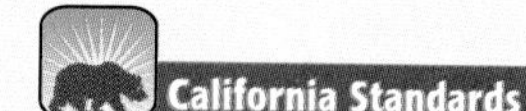

25.1 Students use properties of numbers to construct simple, valid arguments (direct and indirect) **for,** or formulate counterexamples to, **claimed assertions.**

Also covered: **Ext. of 5.0, 24.1, 24.2**

Example

Prove the Cross Products Property: If $\frac{a}{b} = \frac{c}{d}$ $(b \neq 0 \text{ and } d \neq 0)$, then $ad = bc$.

Statements	Reasons
1. $\frac{a}{b} = \frac{c}{d}$ $(b \neq 0 \text{ and } d \neq 0)$	Given
2. $\left(\frac{a}{b}\right)bd = \left(\frac{c}{d}\right)bd$	Multiplication Property of Equality (Multiply both sides by *bd*.)
3. $\frac{abd}{b} = \frac{cbd}{d}$	Multiply.
4. $ad = cb$	Simplify.
5. $ad = bc$	Commutative Property of Multiplication

Try This

1. Below is an incomplete proof of the following statement: If a and b are even, then $a + b$ is even. Fill in the blanks to complete the proof.

Statements	Reasons
1. *a* and *b* are **even**.	Given
2. *a* and *b* are each divisible by **2**. In other words, they can each be written as the product of **2** and some other number: $a = 2m$ and $b = 2n$.	Definition of **even number**
3. $a + b = 2m + 2n$	Substitute **2m** for *a* and **2n** for *b*.
4. $a + b = 2(\quad)$ **m + n**	**Dist. Prop**
5. Because $a + b$ is divisible by 2, **a + b** is even.	Definition of **even number**

2. Prove the following statement: If a and b are even, then ab is even.

Close

Key Concept

When proving a conditional statement, assume the hypothesis is true and use deductive reasoning to reach the conclusion.

Assess

Have students define *conditional statement, hypothesis*, and *conclusion*. Then have them define *deductive reasoning*. Finally, have them explain how to use deductive reasoning to show that a conditional statement is true. They may use any of the examples on this page in their explanation.

Extend

For a conditional statement "if *x*, then *y*," the *contrapositive* is "if not *y*, then not *x*." The contrapositive is equivalent to the conditional. For this reason, mathematicians may sometimes prove a conditional by proving its contrapositive. Ask students to write the contrapositive of each statement below.

- If it is raining, then the grass is wet. If the grass is not wet, then it is not raining.
- If an angle measures 90°, then it is a right angle. If an angle is not a right angle, then it does not measure 90°.

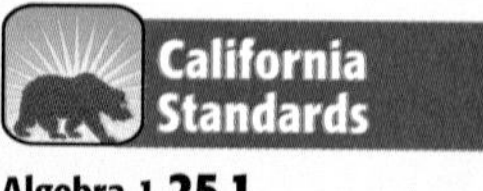

Algebra 1 25.1
Also covered:
Ext of 5.0 Students solve multistep problems, including word problems, **involving linear equations** and inequalities in one variable **and provide justification for each step.**
24.1 Students explain the difference between inductive and deductive reasoning and indentify and **provide examples** of each.
24.2 Students identify the hypothesis and conclusion in logical deduction.

2-6 Solving Literal Equations for a Variable

California Standards

Extension of 5.0 Students solve multistep problems, including word problems, involving linear equations and linear inequalities in one variable and provide justification for each step.

Vocabulary
formula
literal equation

Who uses this?
Athletes can "rearrange" the distance formula to calculate their average speed.

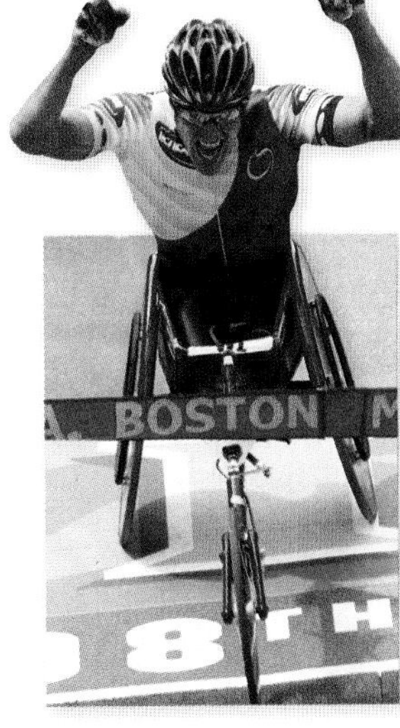

Many wheelchair athletes compete in marathons, which cover about 26.2 miles. Using the time t it took to complete the race, the distance d, and the *formula* $d = rt$, racers can find their average speed r.

A **formula** is an equation that states a rule for a relationship among quantities.

In the formula $d = rt$, d is isolated. You can "rearrange" a formula to isolate any variable by using inverse operations. This is called *solving for a variable.*

Know it! Note

Solving for a Variable	
Step 1	Locate the variable you are asked to solve for in the equation.
Step 2	Identify the operations on this variable and the order in which they are applied.
Step 3	Use inverse operations to undo operations and isolate the variable.

EXAMPLE 1 ***Sports Application***

In 2004, Ernst Van Dyk won the wheelchair race of the Boston Marathon with a time of about 1.3 hours. The race was about 26.2 miles. What was his average speed? Use the formula $d = rt$ and round your answer to the nearest tenth.

The question asks for speed, so first solve the formula $d = rt$ for r.

$d = rt$ — *Locate r in the equation.*

$\frac{d}{t} = \frac{rt}{t}$ — *Since r is multiplied by t, divide both sides by t to undo the multiplication.*

$\frac{d}{t} = r$, or $r = \frac{d}{t}$

Now use this formula and the information given in the problem.

$r = \frac{d}{t} \approx \frac{26.2}{1.3}$

≈ 20.2

Van Dyk's average speed was about 20.2 miles per hour.

Helpful Hint

A nonzero number divided by itself equals 1. For $t \neq 0$, $\frac{t}{t} = 1$.

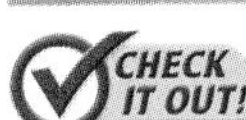

1. Solve the formula $d = rt$ for t. Find the time in hours that it would take Van Dyk to travel 26.2 miles if his average speed was 18 miles per hour. Round to the nearest hundredth. **about 1.46 h**

2-6 Organizer

Objectives: Solve a formula for a given variable.

Solve an equation in two or more variables for one of the variables.

Online Edition
Tutorial Videos

Countdown to Mastery Week 4

Power Presentations with PowerPoint®

Warm Up

Solve each equation.

1. $5 + x = -2$ -7

2. $8m = 43$ $\frac{43}{8}$

3. $\frac{c + 5}{4} = 6$ 19

4. $0.3s + 0.6 = 1.5$ 3

5. $10k - 6 = 9k + 2$ 8

Also available on transparency

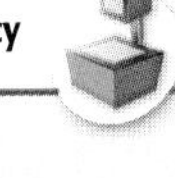

Math Humor

Q: If you give 15 cents to one friend and 10 cents to another friend, what time is it?

A: A quarter to two.

1 Introduce

EXPLORATION

2-6 Solving Literal Equations for a Variable

Mei is planning a rectangular plot for her vegetable garden. She wants the plot to have an area of 24 ft^2.

ℓ ; $\ell w = 24\ ft^2$; w

1. Mei considers various lengths for the plot. Complete the table to show the corresponding width for each length.
2. Explain how you found each width.
3. Write an equation that gives the width w of the plot for any length ℓ.

Length ℓ (ft)	Width w (ft)	Area A (ft^2)
1		24
2		24
3		24
4		24
6		24
8		24

THINK AND DISCUSS

4. **Explain** how you can use your equation to find the width of the plot when the length is 15 feet.
5. **Describe** how the equation you wrote in Problem 3 is related to the original area equation $\ell w = 24$.

Motivate

Show students these two equivalent equations that relate the area of a rectangle to its length and width: $A = \ell w$ and $\ell = \frac{A}{w}$. Explain that the first equation is more convenient if you know the length and the width and want to find the area. The second equation is more convenient if you know the area and the width and want to find the length.

Explorations and answers are provided in *Alternate Openers: Explorations Transparencies.*

California Standards

Extension of 5.0

Power Presentations with PowerPoint®

Additional Examples

Example 1

The formula $C = \pi d$ gives the circumference of a circle C in terms of its diameter d. The circumference of a bowl is 18 inches. What is the bowl's diameter? Leave the symbol π in your answer. $\frac{18}{\pi}$ in.

Example 2

A. The formula for the area of a triangle is $A = \frac{1}{2}bh$, where b is the length of the base and h is the height. Solve for h.

$h = \frac{2A}{b}$

B. Solve the formula for a person's typing speed for e.

$e = \frac{ms - w}{-10}$

Example 3

A. Solve $x + y = 15$ for x.

$x = 15 - y$

B. Solve $pq = x$ for q. $q = \frac{x}{p}$

Also available on transparency

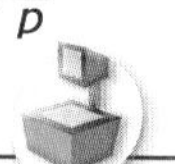

INTERVENTION

Questioning Strategies

EXAMPLES **1–3**

- How is solving for a variable similar to solving an equation? How is it different?

EXAMPLE 2 Solving Formulas for a Variable

A The formula for a Fahrenheit temperature in terms of degrees Celsius is $F = \frac{9}{5}C + 32$. Solve for C.

$F = \frac{9}{5}C + 32$ — *Locate C in the equation.*

$\underline{-32 \quad\quad -32}$ — *Since 32 is added to $\frac{9}{5}C$, subtract 32 from both sides to undo the addition.*

$F - 32 = \frac{9}{5}C$

$\left(\frac{5}{9}\right)(F - 32) = \left(\frac{5}{9}\right)\frac{9}{5}C$ — *Since C is multiplied by $\frac{9}{5}$, divide both sides by $\frac{9}{5}$ (multiply by $\frac{5}{9}$) to undo the multiplication.*

$\frac{5}{9}(F - 32) = C$

Remember!

Dividing by a fraction is the same as multiplying by the reciprocal.

B The formula for a person's typing speed is $s = \frac{w - 10e}{m}$, where s is speed in words per minute, w is number of words typed, e is number of errors, and m is number of minutes typing. Solve for w.

$s = \frac{w - 10e}{m}$ — *Locate w in the equation.*

$m(s) = m\left(\frac{w - 10e}{m}\right)$ — *Since w − 10e is divided by m, multiply both sides by m to undo the division.*

$ms = w - 10e$

$\underline{+10e \quad\quad +10e}$ — *Since 10e is subtracted from w, add 10e to both sides to undo the subtraction.*

$ms + 10e = w$

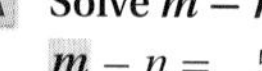

CHECK IT OUT! **2.** The formula for an object's final velocity f is $f = i - gt$, where i is the object's initial velocity, g is acceleration due to gravity, and t is time. Solve for i. $i = f + gt$

A formula is a type of *literal equation.* A **literal equation** is an equation with two or more variables. To solve for one of the variables, use inverse operations.

EXAMPLE 3 Solving Literal Equations for a Variable

A Solve $m - n = 5$ for m.

$m - n = 5$ — *Locate m in the equation.*

$\underline{+n \quad +n}$ — *Since n is subtracted from m, add n to both sides to undo the subtraction.*

$m = 5 + n$

B Solve $\frac{m}{k} = x$ for k.

$\frac{m}{k} = x$ — *Locate k in the equation.*

$k\left(\frac{m}{k}\right) = kx$ — *Since k appears in the denominator, multiply both sides by k.*

$m = kx$

$\frac{m}{x} = \frac{kx}{x}$ — *Since k is multiplied by x, divide both sides by x to undo the multiplication.*

$\frac{m}{x} = k$

CHECK IT OUT! **3a.** Solve $5 - b = 2t$ for t. **3b.** Solve $D = \frac{m}{V}$ for V. $V = \frac{m}{D}$

3a. $t = \frac{5 - b}{2}$

2 Teach

Guided Instruction

Solve $x + 7 = 9$ and $\frac{x}{7} = 9$. Then replace the 7 with y and solve for x again. Show that the procedures are the same, but the answers are in a different form.

Teaching Tip **Visual** Have students circle the variable for which they are solving. On the board, circle this variable as well, or write the variable in a different color.

3 Close

Summarize

Ask students to identify the first step in solving each of the following literal equations for x.

$abx = c$ Divide both sides by ab.

$ax + b = c$ Subtract b from both sides.

$\frac{x - a}{b} = c$ Multiply both sides by b.

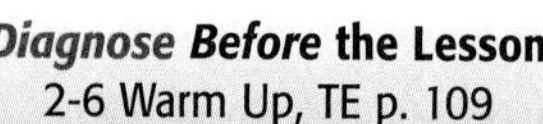

FORMATIVE ASSESSMENT and INTERVENTION

***Diagnose Before* the Lesson**
2-6 Warm Up, TE p. 109

***Monitor During* the Lesson**
Check It Out! Exercises, SE pp. 109–110
Questioning Strategies, TE pp. 110

***Assess After* the Lesson**
2-6 Lesson Quiz, TE p. 113
Alternative Assessment, TE p. 113

THINK AND DISCUSS

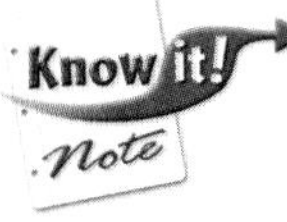

1. Describe a situation in which a formula could be used more easily if it were "rearranged." Include the formula in your description.
2. Explain how to solve $P = 2\ell + 2w$ for w.
3. **GET ORGANIZED** Copy and complete the graphic organizer. Write a formula that is used in each subject. Then solve the formula for each of its variables.

Common Formulas	
Subject	**Formula**
Geometry	
Physical science	
Earth science	

Answers to *Think and Discuss*

1. Possible answer: The formula $d = rt$ is more useful in the form $\frac{d}{r} = t$ when you need to determine the time it takes to travel a certain distance at a certain speed.
2. Isolate w on the right side of the equation by subtracting 2ℓ from both sides and then dividing both sides by 2.
3. See p. A3.

2-6 Exercises

California Standards Practice
Extension of 5.0

go.hrw.com
Homework Help Online
KEYWORD: MA8CA 2-6
Parent Resources Online
KEYWORD: MA8CA Parent

GUIDED PRACTICE

SEE EXAMPLE 1 p. 109

1. **Vocabulary** Explain why a *formula* is a type of *literal equation.*
2. **Construction** The formula $a = 46c$ gives the floor area a in square meters that can be wired using c circuits.
   a. Solve $a = 46c$ for c. $c = \frac{a}{46}$
   b. If a room is 322 square meters, how many circuits are required to wire this room? **7 circuits**

SEE EXAMPLE 2 p. 110

3. The formula for the volume of a rectangular prism with length ℓ, width w, and height h is $V = \ell wh$. Solve this formula for w.

SEE EXAMPLE 3 p. 110

4. Solve $st + 3t = 6$ for s. $s = \frac{6 - 3t}{t}$
5. Solve $m - 4n = 8$ for m. $m = 4n + 8$
6. Solve $\frac{f + 4}{g} = 6$ for f. $f = 6g - 4$
7. Solve $b + c = \frac{10}{a}$ for a. $a = \frac{10}{b + c}$

PRACTICE AND PROBLEM SOLVING

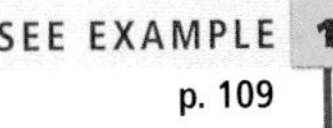

Independent Practice	
For Exercises	See Example
8	1
9	2
10–13	3

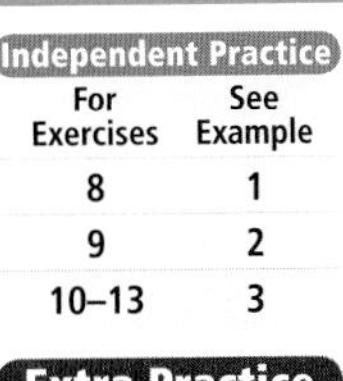

Extra Practice
Skills Practice p. EP5
Application Practice p. EP25

8. **Geometry** The formula $C = 2\pi r$ relates the circumference C of a circle to its radius r. (Recall that π is the constant ratio of circumference to diameter.)
   a. Solve $C = 2\pi r$ for r. $r = \frac{C}{2\pi}$
   b. If a circle's circumference is 15 inches, what is its radius? Leave the symbol π in your answer. $\frac{7.5}{\pi}$ **in.**

C is the distance around the circle.
r is the distance from the center of the circle to any point on the circle.

9. **Finance** The formula $A = P + I$ shows that the total amount of money A received from an investment equals the principal P (the original amount of money invested) plus the interest I. Solve this formula for I. $I = A - P$

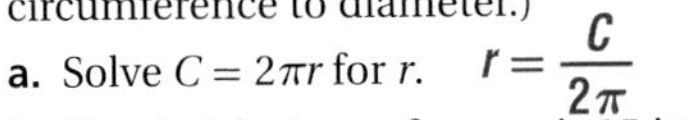

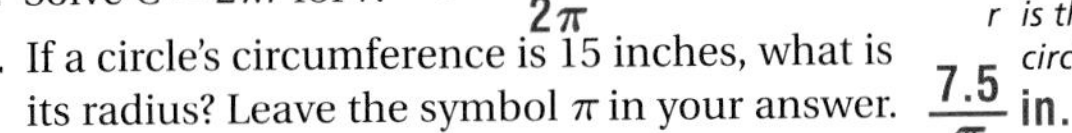

10. Solve $-2 = 4r + s$ for s. $s = -2 - 4r$
11. Solve $xy - 5 = k$ for x. $x = \frac{k + 5}{y}$
12. Solve $\frac{m}{n} = p - 6$ for n. $\frac{m}{p - 6} = n$
13. Solve $\frac{x - 2}{y} = z$ for y. $\frac{x - 2}{z} = y$

Assignment Guide

Assign *Guided Practice* exercises as necessary.

If you finished Examples **1–3**
Proficient 8–13, 20–41, 46–54
Advanced 8–13, 20–28 even, 29–54

Homework Quick Check
Quickly check key concepts.
Exercises: 8, 9, 10, 12, 24, 28, 30

Answers

1. A literal equation contains more than one variable. A formula shows how to determine the value of one variable when you know the value(s) of one or more other variables. So a formula always contains more than one variable, making it a literal equation.
3. $w = \frac{V}{\ell h}$

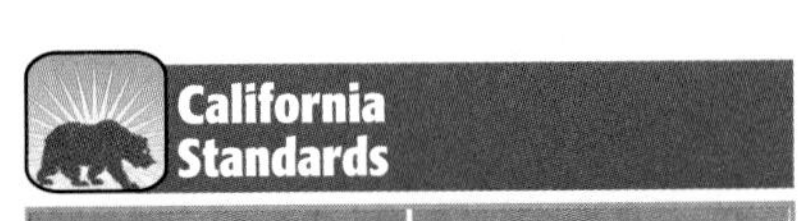

California Standards

Standard	Exercises
Ext. of 5.0	4, 6, 7, 11–19, 22–28, 31, 35, 36–45
6NS2.1	46, 47
6AF1.1	51–54
7AF1.2	48–50

Teaching Tip

Language Support **Exercise 30** is about baseball and may use terms unfamiliar to some students. Have students familiar with baseball discuss the meanings of *run, earned run, inning*, etc.

Exercise 34 involves rewriting a formula in a more useful form to find the frequency of a note. This exercise prepares students for the Concept Connection on page 120.

Answers

14. $n = \frac{S + 360}{180}$
15. $x = 5(a + g)$
16. $b = \frac{2A}{h}$
17. $x = \frac{y - b}{m}$
18. $n = \frac{a - 1}{3}$
19. $T = \frac{PV}{nR}$
20. $T = R - M$
21. $T = M + R$
22. $R = \frac{PV}{nT}$
23. $b = \frac{c - 2a}{2}$
24. $c = \frac{-4p}{9}$
25. $r = 7 - ax$
26. $y = \frac{2 - 3x}{7}$
27. $x = \frac{5 - 4y}{3}$
28. $b = \frac{y - 3x}{3}$
32. Possible answer: Use inverse operations to isolate the indicated variable on one side of the equation. Be sure the variable is the only expression on one side of the equation and doesn't appear on the other side.

Solve for the indicated variable.

14. $S = 180n - 360$ for n **15.** $\frac{x}{5} - g = a$ for x **16.** $A = \frac{1}{2}bh$ for b

17. $y = mx + b$ for x **18.** $a = 3n + 1$ for n **19.** $PV = nRT$ for T

20. $T + M = R$ for T **21.** $M = T - R$ for T **22.** $PV = nRT$ for R

23. $2a + 2b = c$ for b **24.** $5p + 9c = p$ for c **25.** $ax + r = 7$ for r

26. $3x + 7y = 2$ for y **27.** $4y + 3x = 5$ for x **28.** $y = 3x + 3b$ for b

29a. Possible answer: $t \approx \frac{d}{500}$
b. Possible answer: about 2.6 h
c. Possible answer: $d \approx 500t$
d. Possible answer: about 4000 mi

29. Estimation The table shows the flying time and distance traveled for five flights on a certain airplane.

a. Use the data in the table to write a rule that *estimates* the relationship between flying time t and distance traveled d.

b. Use your rule from part **a** to estimate the time that it takes the airplane to fly 1300 miles.

c. Solve your rule for d.

d. Use your rule from part **c** to estimate the distance the airplane can fly in 8 hours.

Flying Times		
Flight	Time (h)	Distance (mi)
A	2	1018
B	3	1485
C	4	2103
D	5	2516
E	6	2886

30. Sports To find a baseball pitcher's earned run average (ERA), you can use the formula $Ei = 9r$, where E represents ERA, i represents number of innings pitched, and r represents number of earned runs allowed. Solve the equation for E. What is a pitcher's ERA if he allows 5 earned runs in 18 innings pitched? **$E = \frac{9r}{i}$; 2.5**

31. $a = \frac{t - g}{-0.0035}$

31. Meteorology For altitudes up to 36,000 feet, the relationship between temperature and altitude can be described by the formula $t = -0.0035a + g$, where t is the temperature in degrees Fahrenheit, a is the altitude in feet, and g is the ground temperature in degrees Fahrenheit. Solve this formula for a.

32. Write About It In your own words, explain how to solve a literal equation for one of the variables.

33. Possible answer: The variable a appears in 2 terms. Use the Distributive Property to write $a - ab$ as $a(1 - b)$, and then divide both sides by $1 - b$.

33. Critical Thinking How is solving $a - ab = c$ for a different from the problems in this lesson? How might you solve this equation for a?

CONCEPT CONNECTION

34. This problem will help prepare you for the Concept Connection on page 120.

The formula $s = fw$ relates the speed of sound s in meters per second, the frequency of a note f in Hertz (Hz), and the wavelength of the note's sound wave w in meters.

a. Solve the formula for f. **$f = \frac{s}{w}$**

b. The speed of sound is approximately 340 m/s. The note A_4 has a wavelength of approximately 0.773 m. Find the frequency of the note A_4 to the nearest whole number. **440 Hz**

c. As the wavelength of a note increases, what happens to the frequency? Explain.

c. The frequency decreases. As the wavelength increases, the speed of sound is divided by greater and greater numbers, so the quotient decreases.

2-6 PRACTICE A

2-6 PRACTICE C

2-6 PRACTICE B

LESSON 2-6 **Practice B**
Solving Literal Equations for a Variable

Answer each of the following.

1. The formula $C = 2\pi r$ relates the radius r of a circle to its circumference C. Solve the formula for r. $r = \frac{C}{2\pi}$

2. The formula $y = mx + b$ is called the slope-intercept form of a line. Solve this formula for m. $m = \frac{y - b}{x}$

Solve each equation for the variable indicated.

3. $4c = d$ for c $c = \frac{d}{4}$
4. $n - 6m = 8$ for n $n = 8 + 6m$
5. $2p + 5r = q$ for p $p = \frac{q - 5r}{2}$
6. $-10 = xy + z$ for x $x = \frac{-10 - z}{y}$
7. $\frac{a}{b} = c$ for b $b = \frac{a}{c}$
8. $\frac{h - 4}{j} = k$ for j $j = \frac{h - 4}{k}$

Answer each of the following.

9. The formula $c = 5p + 215$ relates c, the total cost in dollars of hosting a birthday party at a skating rink, to p, the number of people attending.
   a. Solve the formula $c = 5p + 215$ for p. $p = \frac{c - 215}{5}$
   b. If Allie's parents are willing to spend $300 for a party, how many people can attend? 17
10. The formula for the area of a triangle is $A = \frac{1}{2}bh$, where b represents the length of the base and h represents the height.
   a. Solve the formula $A = \frac{1}{2}bh$ for b. $b = \frac{2A}{h}$
   b. If a triangle has an area of 192 mm^2, and the height measures 12 mm, what is the measure of the base? 32 mm

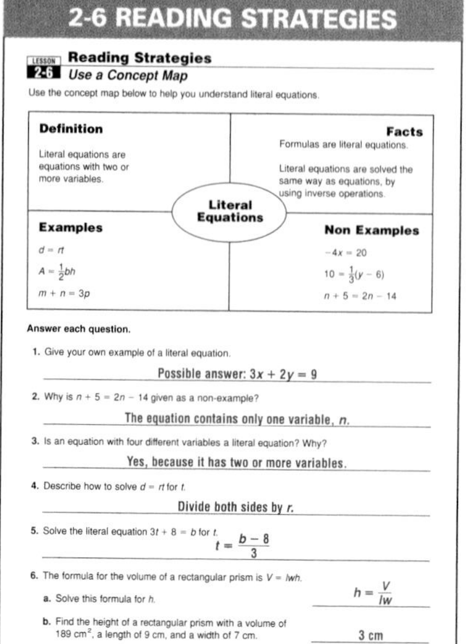

2-6 READING STRATEGIES

LESSON 2-6 **Reading Strategies**
Use a Concept Map

Use the concept map below to help you understand literal equations.

Literal Equations

Definition: Literal equations are equations with two or more variables.

Facts: Formulas are literal equations. Literal equations are solved the same way as equations, by using inverse operations.

Examples: $d = rt$; $A = \frac{1}{2}bh$; $m + n = 3p$

Non Examples: $-4x = 20$; $10 = \frac{1}{3}(y - 6)$; $n + 5 = 2n - 14$

Answer each question.

1. Give your own example of a literal equation. Possible answer: $3x + 2y = 9$
2. Why is $n + 5 = 2n - 14$ given as a non-example? The equation contains only one variable, n.
3. Is an equation with four different variables a literal equation? Why? Yes, because it has two or more variables.
4. Describe how to solve $d = rt$ for t. Divide both sides by r.
5. Solve the literal equation $3t + 8 = b$ for t. $t = \frac{b - 8}{3}$
6. The formula for the volume of a rectangular prism is $V = lwh$.
   a. Solve this formula for h. $h = \frac{V}{lw}$
   b. Find the height of a rectangular prism with a volume of 189 cm^2, a length of 9 cm, and a width of 7 cm. 3 cm

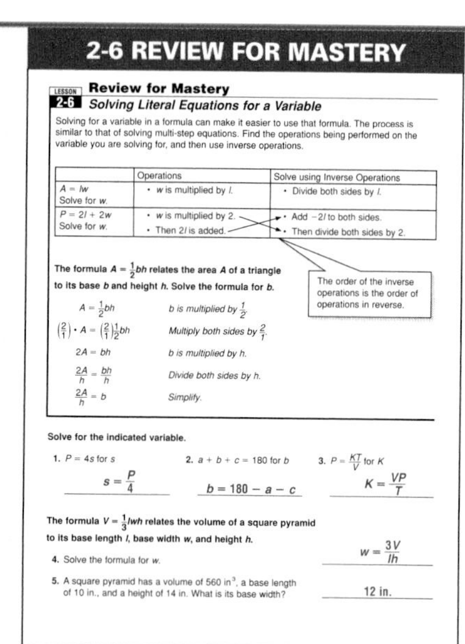

2-6 REVIEW FOR MASTERY

LESSON 2-6 **Review for Mastery**
Solving Literal Equations for a Variable

Solving for a variable in a formula can make it easier to use that formula. The process is similar to that of solving multi-step equations. Find the operations being performed on the variable you are solving for, and then use inverse operations.

	Operations	Solve using Inverse Operations
$A = lw$ Solve for w.	• w is multiplied by l.	• Divide both sides by l.
$P = 2l + 2w$ Solve for w.	• w is multiplied by 2. • Then $2l$ is added.	• Add $-2l$ to both sides. • Then divide both sides by 2.

The order of the inverse operations is the order of operations in reverse.

The formula $A = \frac{1}{2}bh$ relates the area A of a triangle to its base b and height h. Solve the formula for b.

$A = \frac{1}{2}bh$ — *b is multiplied by $\frac{1}{2}$.*
$\left(\frac{2}{1}\right) \cdot A = \left(\frac{2}{1}\right)\frac{1}{2}bh$ — *Multiply both sides by $\frac{2}{1}$.*
$2A = bh$ — *b is multiplied by h.*
$\frac{2A}{h} = \frac{bh}{h}$ — *Divide both sides by h.*
$\frac{2A}{h} = b$ — *Simplify.*

Solve for the indicated variable.

1. $P = 4s$ for s $s = \frac{P}{4}$
2. $a + b + c = 180$ for b $b = 180 - a - c$
3. $P = \frac{KT}{V}$ for K $K = \frac{VP}{T}$

The formula $V = \frac{1}{3}lwh$ relates the volume of a square pyramid to its base length l, base width w, and height h.

4. Solve the formula for w. $w = \frac{3V}{lh}$
5. A square pyramid has a volume of 560 in^3, a base length of 10 in., and a height of 14 in. What is its base width? 12 in.

Multiple Choice For Exercises 35–37, choose the best answer.

35. Which equation is the result of solving $9 + 3x = 2y$ for x?

(A) $\frac{9 + 3y}{2} = x$ (B) $\frac{2}{3}y - 9 = x$ **(C)** $x = \frac{2}{3}y - 3$ (D) $x = 2y - 3$

36. Which of the following is a correct method for solving $2a - 5b = 10$ for b?

(A) Add $5b$ to both sides, then divide both sides by 2.
(B) Subtract $5b$ from both sides, then divide both sides by 2.
(C) Divide both sides by 5, then add $2a$ to both sides.
(D) Subtract $2a$ from both sides, then divide both sides by -5.

37. Anna wants to make a cardboard box with a length of 7 inches, a width of 5 inches, and a volume of 210 cubic inches. In the formula for the volume of a rectangular prism, which variable does Anna need to solve for in order to build the box?

(A) V (B) ℓ (C) w **(D)** h

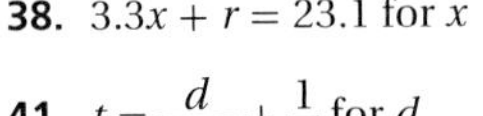

CHALLENGE AND EXTEND

Solve for the indicated variable.

38. $3.3x + r = 23.1$ for x
39. $\frac{2}{5}a - \frac{3}{4}b = c$ for a
40. $\frac{3}{5}x + 1.4y = \frac{2}{5}$ for y
41. $t = \frac{d}{500} + \frac{1}{2}$ for d
42. $s = \frac{1}{2}gt^2$ for g
43. $v^2 = u^2 + 2as$ for s
44. Solve $y = mx + 6$ for m. What can you say about y if $m = 0$?
45. **Entertainment** The formula $S = \frac{h \cdot w \cdot f \cdot t}{35{,}000}$ gives the approximate size in kilobytes (Kb) of a compressed video. The variables h and w represent the height and width of the frame measured in pixels, f is the number of frames per second (fps) the video plays, and t is the time the video plays in seconds. Estimate the time the movie trailer shown will play if it plays at 15 fps and has a size of 2370 Kb. **120 s**

38. $x = \frac{23.1 - r}{3.3}$
39. $a = \frac{5}{2}\left(c + \frac{3}{4}b\right)$
40. $y = \frac{\frac{2}{5} - \frac{3}{5}x}{1.4}$
41. $d = 500\left(t - \frac{1}{2}\right)$
42. $g = \frac{2s}{t^2}$
43. $s = \frac{v^2 - u^2}{2a}$
44. $m = \frac{y - 6}{x}$; if $m = 0$, $y = 6$

SPIRAL STANDARDS REVIEW

6NS2.1, 6AF1.1, 7AF1.2

46. Jill spent $\frac{1}{4}$ of the money she made baby-sitting. She made \$40 baby-sitting. How much did she spend? *(Previous course)* **\$10**

47. In one class, $\frac{3}{5}$ of the students are boys. There are 30 students in the class. How many are girls? *(Previous course)* **12**

Evaluate each expression for the given value of x. *(Lesson 1-7)*

48. $3 + 2 \cdot x + 4$ for $x = 3$ **13**
49. $24 \div 4 - x$ for $x = 12$ **−6**
50. $43 - 62 + x$ for $x = 15$ **−4**

Solve each equation. *(Lesson 2-1)*

51. $18 = -2 + w$ **20**
52. $2 = -3 + c$ **5**
53. $-8 + k = 4$ **12**
54. $-15 + a = -27$ **−12**

COMMON ERROR ALERT

Students may subtract when they should divide. In **Exercise 30,** for example, they may write $r = 9e - i$. Ask students which operation is being performed on r and what will "undo" it.

Teaching Tip

Multiple Choice In **Exercise 35,** students who chose **B** or **D** most likely did not divide every term by 3.

Students who chose **A** in **Exercise 36** probably solved the equation for a. Encourage students to read the question carefully.

Journal

Have students discuss the differences in solving the following literal equations for x: $\frac{x}{7} - y = t$ and $\frac{x - y}{7} = t$.

ALTERNATIVE ASSESSMENT

Have students explain how to solve for each of the three variables in the following literal equation: $q + r = \frac{p}{5}$.

Power Presentations with PowerPoint®

2-6 Lesson Quiz

Solve for the indicated variable.

1. $V = \frac{1}{3}Ah$ for h $h = \frac{3V}{A}$
2. $P = R - C$ for C $C = R - P$
3. $2x + 7y = 14$ for y
$y = \frac{14 - 2x}{7}$
4. $\frac{m}{x} = k - 6$ for m
$m = x(k - 6)$
5. $R = \frac{C - S}{t}$ for C $C = Rt + S$

Euler's formula, $V - E + F = 2$, relates the number of vertices V, the number of edges E, and the number of faces F of a polyhedron.

6. Solve Euler's formula for F.
$F = 2 - V + E$
7. How many faces does a polyhedron with 8 vertices and 12 edges have? 6

Also available on transparency

2-6 PROBLEM SOLVING

LESSON 2-6 **Problem Solving**
Solving Literal Equations for a Variable

Use the table below, which shows some track and field gold medal winners, to answer questions 1–4. Round all answers to the nearest tenth.

2000 Summer Olympics		
Gold Medal Winner	Race	Time (s)
M. Greene, USA	100 m	9.87
K. Kenteris, Greece	200 m	20.09
M. Johnson, USA	400 m	43.84
A. Garcia, Cuba	110 m hurdles	13.00

1. Solve the formula $d = rt$ for r. $r = \frac{d}{t}$
2. Find Johnson's average speed in meters per second. 9.1 m/s
3. Find Garcia's average speed in meters per second. 8.5 m/s
4. The world record of 19.32 seconds in the 200-meter race was set by Michael Johnson in 1996. Find the difference between Johnson's average speed and Kenteris' average speed. 0.4 m/s

Select the best answer.

5. The cost to mail a letter in the United States is \$0.34 for the first ounce and \$0.23 for each additional ounce. Solve $C = 0.34 + 0.23(z - 1)$ for z.
A $z = \frac{C - 0.34}{0.23}$
(B) $z = \frac{C - 0.34}{0.23} + 1$
C $z = \frac{C + 0.11}{0.23}$
D $z = C - 0.56$

6. The formula $V = \frac{Bh}{3}$ shows how to find the volume of a pyramid. Solve for B.
(F) $B = \frac{3V}{h}$ H $B = 3Vh$
G $B = 3V - h$ J $B = 3V + h$

7. Degrees Celsius and degrees Fahrenheit are related by the equation $C = \frac{5}{9}(F - 32)$. Solve for F.
A $F = 9C + 27$ C $F = \frac{5}{9}C + 32$
B $F = \frac{9}{5}C$ **(D)** $F = \frac{9}{5}C + 32$

8. The cost of operating an electrical device is given by the formula $C = \frac{Wtc}{1000}$ where W is the power in watts, t is the time in hours, and c is the cost in cents per kilowatt-hour. Solve for W.
F $W = 1000C - tc$
G $W = \frac{Ctc}{1000}$
H $W = 1000C + tc$
(J) $W = \frac{1000C}{tc}$

2-6 CHALLENGE

LESSON 2-6 **Challenge**
A Formula of Interest

When you put your money in a savings account, the bank may pay you *simple interest*. Let P represent the dollar amount of your deposit (the principal), let r represent the interest rate, and let t represent the number of years. The amount of interest you earn, I, is given by the *simple interest formula*: $I = Prt$.

Note that banks typically use percents to describe their interest rates. Percent means "per hundred," so an interest rate of 5% means that you should use $r = \frac{5}{100}$, or 0.05.

Use the simple interest formula to solve the following problems:

1. If $P = 2500$, $r = 0.03$, and $t = 5$, what is I? $I = 375$
2. If $r = 0.025$, $t = 3$, and $I = 150$, what is P? $P = 2000$
3. If $P = 500$, $r = 0.06$, and $I = 150$, what is t? $t = 5$ years
4. If $P = 3000$, $t = 4$, and $I = 384$, what is r? $r = 0.032$ or 3.2%
5. Kevin is making a deposit of \$1800 at his local bank. The bank pays 6.5% simple interest ($r = 0.065$). If Kevin leaves his deposit at the bank for 3 years, how much interest will he earn? \$351
6. Cecelia made a deposit of \$600 at a bank paying 4% simple interest ($r = 0.04$). How long should she leave her deposit at the bank in order to earn \$72 in interest? 3 years
7. Darryl opened an account at a bank which paid 5.5% simple interest ($r = 0.055$). After 6 years, he had earned \$726 in interest. What was the amount of his original deposit? \$2200
8. Sophia deposited \$150 at a savings and loan association paying simple interest. If she earned \$27 in interest after 6 years, what was the interest rate? 0.03 or 3%
9. Nathan made a deposit of \$650 at a bank paying 3.8% simple interest ($r = 0.038$). If he leaves his deposit at the bank for 10 years, how much interest will he earn? \$247
10. Susie made a deposit of \$980 at a credit union paying 7% simple interest ($r = 0.07$). How long should she leave her deposit at the credit union in order to earn \$343 in interest? 5 years
11. Guillermo deposited \$1350 at a bank paying simple interest. If he earned \$109.35 in 3 years, what was the interest rate? 0.027 or 2.7%

2-7 Organizer

Objective: Solve equations in one variable that contain absolute-value expressions.

Online Edition
Tutorial Videos

Countdown to Mastery Week 5

Power Presentations with PowerPoint®

Warm Up

Solve.

1. $x - 10 = 4$ 14

2. $s + 5 = -2$ -7

3. $32 = -8y$ -4

4. $\frac{m+4}{2} = 7$ 10

5. $-14 = x - 5$ -9

6. $2t + 5 = 45$ 20

Also available on transparency

Math Humor

Question: How is the equation $|x| = 8$ similar to a chemist's laboratory?

Answer: Both have multiple solutions.

California Standards

Algebra 1 3.0, 5.0

2-7 Solving Absolute-Value Equations

California Standards

3.0 Students solve equations and inequalities **involving absolute values.**

5.0 Students solve multistep problems, including word problems, involving linear equations and linear inequalities **in one variable** and provide justification for each step.

Why learn this?

Engineers can solve absolute-value equations to calculate the length of the deck of a bridge. (See Example 3.)

Recall that the absolute value of a number is that number's distance from zero on a number line. For example, $|-5| = 5$ and $|5| = 5$.

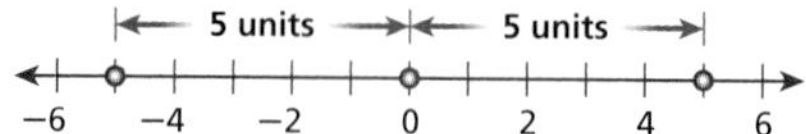

For any nonzero absolute value, there are exactly two numbers with that absolute value. For example, both 5 and -5 have an absolute value of 5.

To write this statement using algebra, you would write $|x| = 5$. This equation asks, "What values of x have an absolute value of 5?" The solutions are 5 and -5. Notice that this equation has two solutions.

Know it! Note

Absolute-Value Equations

WORDS	NUMBERS
The equation $\lvert x\rvert = a$ asks, "What values of x have an absolute value of a?" The solutions are a and the opposite of a.	$\lvert x\rvert = 5$ $x = 5$ or $x = -5$
GRAPH	**ALGEBRA**
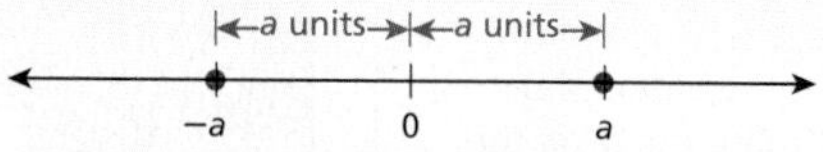 (number line: $-a$, 0, a; a units each side of 0)	$\lvert x\rvert = a$ $x = a$ or $x = -a$ $(a \geq 0)$

To solve absolute-value equations, perform inverse operations to isolate the absolute-value expression on one side of the equation. Then you must consider two cases.

EXAMPLE 1 Solving Absolute-Value Equations

Solve each equation.

A $|x| = 4$

$|x| = 4$ *Think: What numbers are 4 units from 0?*

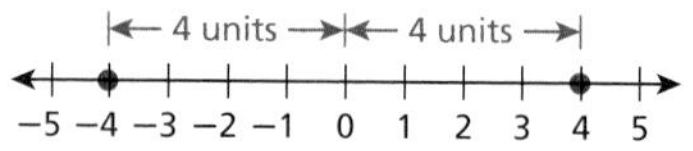

(number line from -5 to 5: 4 units on each side of 0, points at -4 and 4)

Case 1	**Case 2**
$x = -4$	$x = 4$

Rewrite the equation as two cases.

The solutions are -4 and 4. You can write the solution set as $\{-4, 4\}$.

Helpful Hint

Be sure to check both solutions when you solve an absolute-value equation.

$\lvert x\rvert = 4$		$\lvert x\rvert = 4$	
$\lvert -4\rvert$	4	$\lvert 4\rvert$	4
4	4 ✓	4	4 ✓

1 Introduce

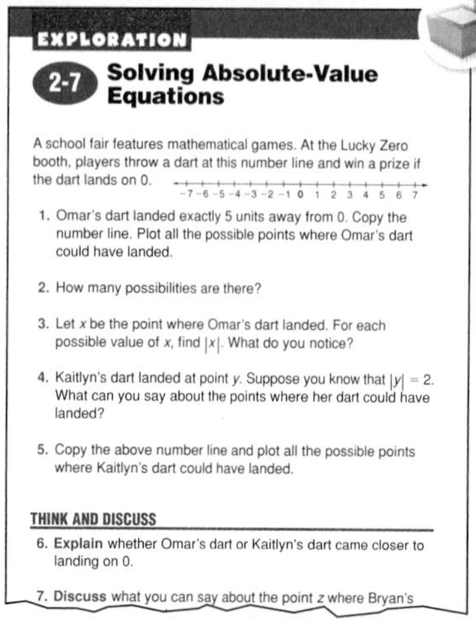

EXPLORATION

Solving Absolute-Value Equations

A school fair features mathematical games. At the Lucky Zero booth, players throw a dart at this number line and win a prize if the dart lands on 0.

1. Omar's dart landed exactly 5 units away from 0. Copy the number line. Plot all the possible points where Omar's dart could have landed.
2. How many possibilities are there?
3. Let x be the point where Omar's dart landed. For each possible value of x, find $|x|$. What do you notice?
4. Kaitlyn's dart landed at point y. Suppose you know that $|y| = 2$. What can you say about the points where her dart could have landed?
5. Copy the above number line and plot all the possible points where Kaitlyn's dart could have landed.

THINK AND DISCUSS

6. **Explain** whether Omar's dart or Kaitlyn's dart came closer to landing on 0.
7. **Discuss** what you can say about the point z where Bryan's

Motivate

Present the following situation to the class. In a game show, two contestants guess the price of a DVD player. The contestants each make different guesses, and both differ from the actual price by \$15. The actual price of the DVD player is \$169. What guesses do the contestants make? 154, 184

Tell students they will learn how to use absolute-value equations to solve problems like this.

Explorations and answers are provided in *Alternate Openers: Explorations Transparencies.*

Solve each equation.

B $4|x+2|=24$

$$\frac{4|x+2|}{4}=\frac{24}{4}$$ *Since $|x+2|$ is multiplied by 4, divide both sides by 4 to undo the multiplication.*

$$|x+2|=6$$ *Think: What numbers are 6 units from 0?*

Case 1	Case 2
$x+2=-6$	$x+2=6$
$-2 \quad -2$	$-2 \quad -2$
$x=-8$	$x=4$

Rewrite the equation as two cases. Since 2 is added to x, subtract 2 from both sides of the equation.

The solution set is $\{-8, 4\}$.

Solve each equation. Check your answer.

1a. $|x|-3=4$ **−7, 7** **1b.** $8=|x-2.5|$ **−5.5, 10.5**

The table summarizes the steps for solving absolute-value equations.

Solving an Absolute-Value Equation
1. Use inverse operations to isolate the absolute-value expression.
2. Rewrite the resulting equation as two cases that do not involve absolute values.
3. Solve the equation in each of the two cases.

Not all absolute-value equations have two solutions. If the absolute-value expression equals 0, there is one solution. If an equation states that an absolute value is negative, there are no solutions.

EXAMPLE 2 Special Cases of Absolute-Value Equations

Solve each equation.

A $|x+3|+4=4$

$|x+3|+4=4$ *Since 4 is added to $|x+3|$, subtract 4 from both sides to undo the addition.*

$-4 \quad -4$

$|x+3|=0$

$x+3=0$ *There is only one case. Since 3 is added to x, subtract 3 from both sides to undo the addition.*

$-3 \quad -3$

$x=-3$

The solution set is $\{-3\}$.

B $5=|x+2|+8$

$5=|x+2|+8$ *Since 8 is added to $|x+2|$, subtract 8 from both sides to undo the addition.*

$-8 \quad -8$

$-3=|x+2|$ ✗ *Absolute value cannot be negative.*

This equation has no solution. The solution set is the empty set, ∅.

Absolute value must be nonnegative because it represents a distance.

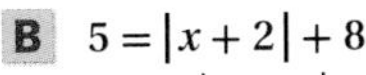

Solve each equation.

2a. $2-|2x-5|=7$ **∅** **2b.** $-6+|x-4|=-6$ **4**

2 Teach

Guided Instruction

Review with students the concept of absolute value. Remind them that the absolute value of a number represents its distance from 0. Because distance can be in the positive or negative direction, there can be as many as two possible solutions for an absolute-value equation. Because distance is always nonnegative, there is no solution when an absolute-value expression is equal to a negative number.

Universal Access

Through Concrete Manipulatives

To help students focus on first isolating the absolute-value expression, have them place a small object or piece of paper over the absolute-value expression in an equation. Then have them "isolate" the object or piece of paper by using inverse operations. Lastly, have students remove the small object or piece of paper and rewrite the equation with two cases.

COMMON ERROR ALERT

In **Example 1B,** students may try to distribute 4 over the absolute value bars. Remind students that their first step should be to isolate the absolute-value expression by dividing both sides by the number in front of the absolute-value bars.

Power Presentations with PowerPoint®

Additional Examples

Example 1

Solve each equation.

A. $|x|=12$ −12, 12

B. $3|x+7|=24$ −15, 1

Example 2

Solve each equation.

A. $-8=|x+2|-8$ −2

B. $3+|x+4|=0$ ∅

Also available on transparency

INTERVENTION

Questioning Strategies

EXAMPLE 1

- What does *absolute value* mean?
- How is the absolute-value sign similar to parentheses? How is it different?
- Why must you consider two cases when solving absolute-value equations?

EXAMPLE 2

- How can you tell when an absolute-value equation has one solution?
- How can you tell when an absolute-value equation has no solution?

Auditory When reading absolute-value expressions aloud, students often confuse expressions of the type $|x+4|$ and $|x|+4$. Be sure they read the first equation as "the absolute value of the quantity x plus four" and the second equation as "the absolute value of x plus four."

Power Presentations with PowerPoint®

Additional Examples

Example 3

A support beam for a building must be 3.5 meters long. It is acceptable for the beam to differ from the ideal length by 3 millimeters. Write and solve an absolute-value equation to find the minimum and maximum acceptable lengths for the beam.

$|x - 3.5| = 0.003$; 3.497 m; 3.503 m

Also available on transparency

INTERVENTION

Questioning Strategies

EXAMPLE 3

- What is the relationship between millimeters and meters?
- What must be true about the minimum and maximum lengths when you plot these values on a number line?

Answers to *Think and Discuss*

1. Divide both sides by $\frac{1}{5}$ (or multiply both sides by 5). Then write two cases: $x - 3 = -10$ and $x - 3 = 10$. Solve these equations to get $x = -7$ or $x = 13$.
2. See p. A3.

EXAMPLE 3 ***Engineering Application***

Sydney Harbour Bridge in Australia is 1149 meters long. Because of changes in temperature, the bridge can expand or contract by as much as 420 millimeters. Write and solve an absolute-value equation to find the minimum and maximum lengths of the bridge.

First convert millimeters to meters.

420 mm = 0.4 2 0 m *Move the decimal point three places to the left.*

The length of the bridge can vary by 0.42 m, so find two numbers that are 0.42 units away from 1149 on a number line.

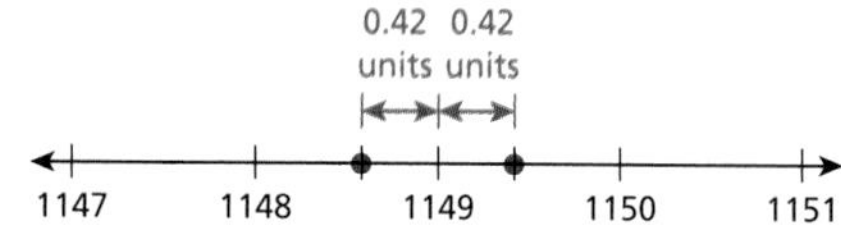

You can find these numbers by using the absolute-value equation $|x - 1149| = 0.42$. Solve the equation by rewriting it as two cases.

Case 1	**Case 2**	
$x - 1149 = -0.42$	$x - 1149 = 0.42$	*Since 1149 is subtracted from x, add 1149 to both sides of each equation.*
$+1149 \quad +1149$	$+1149 \quad +1149$	
$x = 1148.58$	$x = 1149.42$	

The minimum length of the bridge is 1148.58 m, and the maximum length is 1149.42 m.

3. $|x - 134| = 0.18$; **min. height: 133.82 m; max. height: 134.18 m**

CHECK IT OUT! 3. Sydney Harbour Bridge is 134 meters tall. The height of the bridge can rise or fall by 180 millimeters because of changes in temperature. Write and solve an absolute-value equation to find the minimum and maximum heights of the bridge.

THINK AND DISCUSS

1. **Explain** the steps you would use to solve the equation $\frac{1}{5}|x - 3| = 2$.

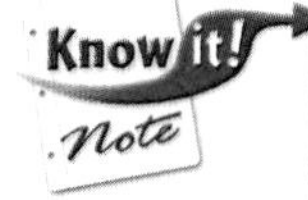

2. **GET ORGANIZED** Copy and complete the graphic organizer. In each box, write an example of an absolute-value equation that has the indicated number of solutions, and then solve.

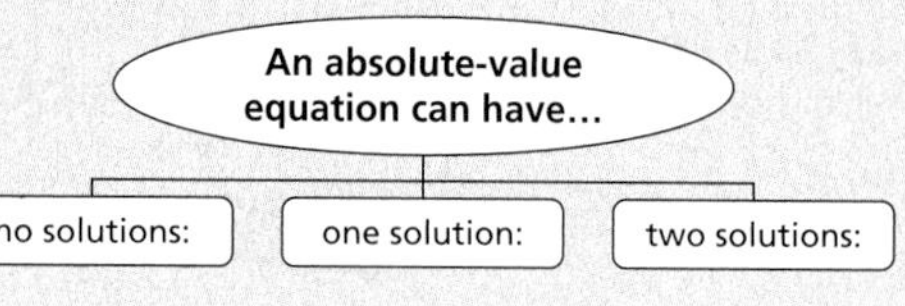

3 Close

Summarize

Ask students to summarize the steps in solving an absolute-value equation.

1. Isolate the absolute-value expression.
2. Rewrite the equation as two cases.
3. Solve for the variable in both cases.
4. Check.

Then ask, "When will there be two solutions? one solution? no solution?" When the expression equals a positive number, equals zero, and equals a negative number, respectively.

FORMATIVE ASSESSMENT

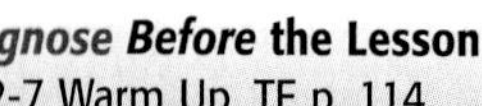

and INTERVENTION

***Diagnose Before* the Lesson**
2-7 Warm Up, TE p. 114

***Monitor During* the Lesson**
Check It Out! Exercises, SE pp. 115–116
Questioning Strategies, TE pp. 115–116

***Assess After* the Lesson**
2-7 Lesson Quiz, TE p. 119
Alternative Assessment, TE p. 119

2-7 Exercises

California Standards Practice
3.0, 5.0, 25.1, 25.3

go.hrw.com
Homework Help Online
KEYWORD: MA8CA 2-7
Parent Resources Online
KEYWORD: MA8CA Parent

GUIDED PRACTICE

SEE EXAMPLE 1 p. 114

Solve each equation.

1. $|x| = 6$ **−6, 6**
2. $9 = |x + 5|$ **−14, 4**
3. $|3x| + 2 = 8$ **−2, 2**
4. $2|x| = 18$ **−9, 9**
5. $\left|x + \frac{1}{2}\right| = 1$ **$-\frac{3}{2}, \frac{1}{2}$**
6. $|x - 3| - 6 = 2$ **−5, 11**

SEE EXAMPLE 2 p. 115

7. $-8 = |x|$ **∅**
8. $|x| = 0$ **0**
9. $|x + 4| = -7$ **∅**
10. $7 = |3x + 9| + 7$ **−3**
11. $|2.8 - x| + 1.5 = 1.5$ **2.8**
12. $5|x + 7| + 14 = 8$ **∅**

SEE EXAMPLE 3 p. 116

13. **Communication** Barry's walkie-talkie has a range of 2 mi. Barry is traveling on a straight highway and is at mile marker 207. Write and solve an absolute-value equation to find the minimum and maximum mile marker from 207 that Barry's walkie-talkie will reach. **$|x - 207| = 2$; mile markers 205 and 209**

PRACTICE AND PROBLEM SOLVING

Independent Practice

For Exercises	See Example
14–22	1
23–28	2
29	3

Extra Practice
Skills Practice p. EP5
Application Practice p. EP25

Solve each equation.

14. $|x| = \frac{1}{5}$ **$-\frac{1}{5}, \frac{1}{5}$**
15. $|2x - 4| = 22$ **−9, 13**
16. $18 = 3|x - 1|$ **−5, 7**
17. $-2|x| = -4$ **−2, 2**
18. $3|x| - 12 = 18$ **−10, 10**
19. $|x - 42.04| = 23.24$ **18.8, 65.28**
20. $\left|\frac{2}{3}x - \frac{2}{3}\right| = \frac{2}{3}$ **0, 2**
21. $|3x + 1| = 13$ **$-\frac{14}{3}$, 4**
22. $|-2x + 3| = 5.8$ **−1.4, 4.4**
23. $|4x| + 9 = 9$ **0**
24. $8 = 7 - |x|$ **∅**
25. $|x| + 6 = 12 - 6$ **0**
26. $|x - 3| + 14 = 5$ **∅**
27. $0 = \left|\frac{2}{3} - x\right|$ **$\frac{2}{3}$**
28. $3 + |x - 1| = 3$ **1**

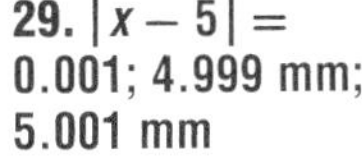
29. $|x - 5| = 0.001$; 4.999 mm; 5.001 mm

29. **Space Shuttle** The diameter of a valve for the space shuttle must be within 0.001 mm of 5 mm. Write and solve an absolute-value equation to find the boundary values for the acceptable diameters of the valve.

5 mm

30. The two numbers that are 5 units from 3 on the number line are represented by the equation $|n - 3| = 5$. What are these two numbers? Graph the solutions. **8, −2**

31. $|x - 7| = 2$; 5, 9

31. Write and solve an absolute-value equation that represents two numbers x that are 2 units from 7 on a number line. Graph the solutions.

32. $|x - 6.5| = 0.04$; 6.54 mm; 6.46 mm

32. **Manufacturing** A quality control inspector at a bolt factory examines random bolts that come off the assembly line. Any bolt whose diameter differs by more than 0.04 mm from 6.5 mm is sent back. Write and solve an absolute-value equation to find the maximum and minimum diameters of an acceptable bolt.

33. $|x - 1500| = 75$; 1575 bricks; 1425 bricks

33. **Construction** A brick company guarantees to fill a contractor's order to within 5% accuracy. A contractor orders 1500 bricks. Write and solve an absolute-value equation to find the maximum and minimum number of bricks guaranteed.

34. **Multi-Step** A machine prints posters and then trims them to the correct size. The equation $|\ell - 65.1| = 0.2$ gives the maximum and minimum acceptable lengths for the posters in inches. Does a poster with a length of 64.8 inches fall within the acceptable range? Why or why not? **No; the acceptable range is from 64.9 to 65.3.**

2-7 Exercises

Assignment Guide

Assign *Guided Practice* Exercises as necessary.

If you finished Examples **1–3**
Proficient 14–29, 32–50, 53–56
Advanced 14–28 even, 29, 32–66

Homework Quick Check
Quickly check key concepts.
Exercises: 16, 24, 28, 29, 32

Answers

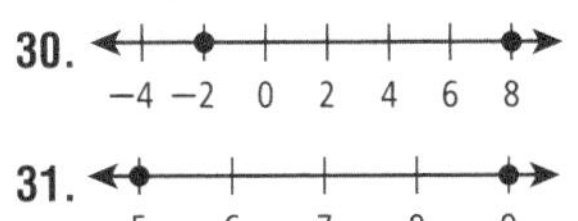

California Standards

Standard	Exercises
3.0	1–37, 41–43, 50, 52
5.0	1–34, 42, 43, 50, 52
25.1	51
25.3	39–41
6AF1.1	53–56
6NS1.3	57–60

Exercise 44 involves using absolute-value equations to describe frequencies. This exercise prepares students for the Concept Connection on page 120.

Answers

39. When the abs.-value expression is equal to a pos. number, there are 2 solutions. If the abs.-value expression is equal to 0, there is 1 solution, and if the abs.-value expression is equal to a neg. number, there are no solutions.
40. When x is nonneg., the expressions are equal, but when x is neg., the expressions are not equal.
41. Abs. value represents a distance, so it can never be neg.

Write an absolute-value equation whose solutions are graphed on the number line.

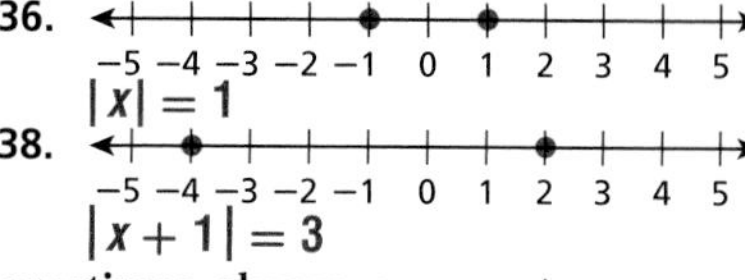

35. −5 −4 −3 −2 −1 0 1 2 3 4 5 — $|x| = 3$
36. −5 −4 −3 −2 −1 0 1 2 3 4 5 — $|x| = 1$
37. −5 −4 −3 −2 −1 0 1 2 3 4 5 — $|x - 2| = 3$
38. −5 −4 −3 −2 −1 0 1 2 3 4 5 — $|x + 1| = 3$

Reasoning Tell whether each statement is sometimes, always, or never true. Explain.

39. An absolute-value equation has two solutions. **sometimes**
40. The value of $|x + 4|$ is equal to the value of $|x| + 4$. **sometimes**
41. The absolute value of a number is nonnegative. **always**
42. **Temperature** A thermostat is set so that the temperature in a laboratory freezer stays within 2.5°F of 2°F. Write and solve an absolute-value equation to find the maximum and minimum temperatures in the freezer. **$|x - 2| = 2.5$; −0.5°F; 4.5°F**
43. **Recreation** To ensure safety, boaters must be aware of wind conditions while they are on the water. A particular anemometer gives a measurement of wind speed within a certain amount of the true wind speed, as shown in the table.

Measured Wind Speed (mi/h)	True Wind Speed (mi/h)
20	15–25
22	17–27
24	19–29
26	21–31
28	23–33
30	25–35

a. Use the table to write an absolute-value equation for the minimum and maximum possible true wind speeds t for the measured wind speed shown on the anemometer.
b. Solve your equation from part **a.** Check that the solution is correct by comparing it to the values given in the table when the measured wind speed is 24 mi/h.
c. Will your equation work for all of the values in the table? Explain.
d. Explain what your equation says about the instrument's measurements.

43a. $|t - 24| = 5$
b. 19; 29
c. yes, if you change the left side so that the measured wind speed is being subtracted from t
d. The measurements are correct to within 5 mi/h.

Concept Connection

44. This problem will help prepare you for the Concept Connection on page 120.
A violin can produce a range of notes. The center of the violin's frequency range is 1666 Hz.
a. Write an absolute-value expression that gives the distance on the number line of a violin note's frequency f from the value 1666. **$|f - 1666|$**
b. The lowest and highest notes that a violin can produce have frequencies that differ by 1470 Hz from the frequency at the center of the range. Write an absolute-value equation for the frequencies of these notes. **$|f - 1666| = 1470$**
c. Find the least and greatest frequencies that a violin can produce.
196 Hz; 3136 Hz

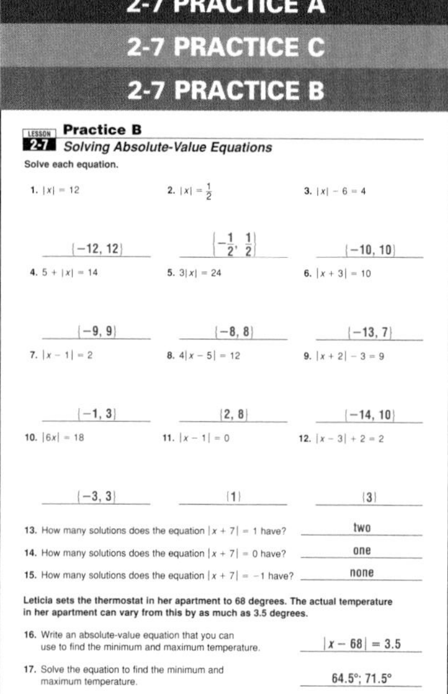

2-7 PRACTICE A
2-7 PRACTICE C
2-7 PRACTICE B

LESSON 2-7 **Practice B**
Solving Absolute-Value Equations

Solve each equation.

1. $|x| = 12$ — $\{-12, 12\}$
2. $|x| = \frac{1}{2}$ — $\{-\frac{1}{2}, \frac{1}{2}\}$
3. $|x| - 6 = 4$ — $\{-10, 10\}$
4. $5 + |x| = 14$ — $\{-9, 9\}$
5. $3|x| = 24$ — $\{-8, 8\}$
6. $|x + 3| = 10$ — $\{-13, 7\}$
7. $|x - 1| = 2$ — $\{-1, 3\}$
8. $4|x - 5| = 12$ — $\{2, 8\}$
9. $|x + 2| - 3 = 9$ — $\{-14, 10\}$
10. $|6x| = 18$ — $\{-3, 3\}$
11. $|x - 1| = 0$ — $\{1\}$
12. $|x - 3| + 2 = 2$ — $\{3\}$
13. How many solutions does the equation $|x + 7| = 1$ have? two
14. How many solutions does the equation $|x + 7| = 0$ have? one
15. How many solutions does the equation $|x + 7| = -1$ have? none

Leticia sets the thermostat in her apartment to 68 degrees. The actual temperature in her apartment can vary from this by as much as 3.5 degrees.

16. Write an absolute-value equation that you can use to find the minimum and maximum temperature. $|x - 68| = 3.5$
17. Solve the equation to find the minimum and maximum temperature. 64.5°; 71.5°

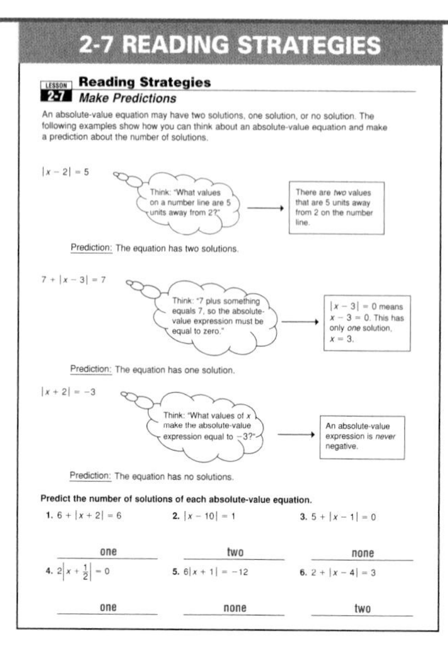

2-7 READING STRATEGIES

LESSON 2-7 **Reading Strategies**
Make Predictions

An absolute-value equation may have two solutions, one solution, or no solution. The following examples show how you can think about an absolute-value equation and make a prediction about the number of solutions.

$|x - 2| = 5$
Think: "What values on a number line are 5 units away from 2?" → There are *two* values that are 5 units away from 2 on the number line.
Prediction: The equation has two solutions.

$7 + |x - 3| = 7$
Think: "7 plus something equals 7, so the absolute-value expression must be equal to zero." → $|x - 3| = 0$ means $x - 3 = 0$. This has only *one* solution, $x = 3$.
Prediction: The equation has one solution.

$|x + 2| = -3$
Think: "What values of x make the absolute-value expression equal to −3?" → An absolute-value expression is *never* negative.
Prediction: The equation has no solutions.

Predict the number of solutions of each absolute-value equation.

1. $6 + |x + 2| = 6$ — one
2. $|x - 10| = 1$ — two
3. $5 + |x - 1| = 0$ — none
4. $2\left|x + \frac{1}{2}\right| = 0$ — one
5. $6|x + 1| = -12$ — none
6. $2 + |x - 4| = 3$ — two

2-7 REVIEW FOR MASTERY

LESSON 2-7 **Review for Mastery**
Solving Absolute-Value Equations

There are three steps in solving an absolute-value equation. First use inverse operations to isolate the absolute-value expression. Then rewrite the equation as two cases that do not involve absolute values. Finally, solve these new equations.

Solve $|x - 3| + 4 = 8$.

Step 1: Isolate the absolute-value expression.
$|x - 3| + 4 = 8$
$-4 \quad -4$ *Subtract 4 from both sides.*
$|x - 3| = 4$

Step 2: Rewrite the equation as two cases.
$|x - 3| = 4$
Case 1 / **Case 2**

Step 3: Solve.
Case 1: $x - 3 = -4$; $+3 \quad +3$; $x = -1$
Case 2: $x - 3 = 4$; $+3 \quad +3$; $x = 7$
Add 3 to both sides.

Write the solution set as $\{-1, 7\}$.

Solve each equation.

1. $|x - 2| - 3 = 5$ — $\{-6, 10\}$
2. $|x + 7| + 2 = 10$ — $\{-15, 1\}$
3. $4|x - 5| = 20$ — $\{0, 10\}$
4. $|2x| + 1 = 7$ — $\{-3, 3\}$

45. Possible answer: no; when an absolute-value expression equals 0, there is only one equation to solve. When an absolute-value expression equals a negative number, there is no equation to solve.

46. No; no matter what value of a is chosen, there will always be two solutions: $a + 1$ and $a - 1$.

45. Write About It Do you agree with the following statement: "To solve an absolute-value equation, you need to solve two equations." Why or why not?

46. Critical Thinking Is there a value of a for which the equation $|x - a| = 1$ has exactly one solution? Explain.

Multiple Choice For Exercises 47–49, choose the best answer.

47. Which situation could be modeled by the equation $|x - 65| = 3$?

Ⓐ Two numbers on the number line are 65 units away from 3.

Ⓑ The length of a carpet is 3 inches less than 65 inches.

(C) The maximum and minimum weights of wrestlers on the team are within 3 kg of 65 kg.

Ⓓ The members of an exercise club for seniors are all between 63 and 67 years old.

48. For which of the following is $n = -3$ a solution?

Ⓐ $|n - 1| = 2$ Ⓑ $|n + 2| = -1$ Ⓒ $|n - 2| = 1$ **(D)** $|n + 1| = 2$

49. The minimum and maximum sound levels at a rock concert are 90 decibels and 95 decibels. Which equation models this situation?

Ⓐ $|x - 90| = 5$ **(B)** $|x - 92.5| = 2.5$ Ⓒ $|x - 92.5| = 5$ Ⓓ $|x - 95| = 2.5$

CHALLENGE AND EXTEND

50. 18 in.; the solutions to the equation are 18 and −46, but since x represents a length, the negative solution is not reasonable.

50. The perimeter of a rectangle is 100 inches. The length of the rectangle is $|2x - 4|$ inches, and the width is x inches. What are the possible values of x? Explain.

51. Reasoning Fill in the missing reasons to justify each step in solving the equation $3|2x + 1| = 21$.

Statements	Reasons
1. $3\|2x + 1\| = 21$	1. Given
2. $\|2x + 1\| = 7$	2. **Div. Prop. of Eq.**
3. $2x + 1 = -7$ or $2x + 1 = 7$	3. Definition of absolute value
4. $2x = -8$ or $2x = 6$	4. **Subtr. Prop. of Eq.**
5. $x = -4$ or $x = 3$	5. **Div. Prop. of Eq.**

52. Solve $|x| = |x + 1|$. (*Hint:* Consider two cases: $x \geq 0$ and $x < 0$.) $-\frac{1}{2}$

SPIRAL STANDARDS REVIEW

6AF1.1, 6NS1.3

Solve each equation. Check your answer. (Lesson 2-1)

53. $5 = p - 4.5$ **9.5** **54.** $-2 = y + 6\frac{1}{2}$ $-8\frac{1}{2}$ **55.** $-12 + q = 3$ **15** **56.** $y - 4.3 = -5.7$ **−1.4**

Solve each proportion. Check your answer. (Lesson 2-5)

57. $\frac{m}{8} = \frac{3}{4}$ **6** **58.** $\frac{16}{y} = \frac{12}{18}$ **24** **59.** $\frac{4}{5} = \frac{12}{x + 6}$ **9** **60.** $\frac{-2}{3} = \frac{5}{2x}$ **−3.75**

Solve for the indicated variable. (Lesson 2-6)

61. $m + 5n = 7$ for m $m = 7 - 5n$ **62.** $S = T + R$ for T $T = S - R$ **63.** $2y + 3x = 1$ for y $y = \frac{1 - 3x}{2}$

64. $\frac{3 + w}{z} = x$ for w $w = xz - 3$ **65.** $c + d = \frac{5}{e}$ for e $e = \frac{5}{c + d}$ **66.** $6M - N = S$ for N $N = 6M - S$

COMMON ERROR ALERT

When writing an absolute-value equation of the form $|x - k| = a$, students sometimes confuse the values that should be used for k and a. In **Exercise 42,** students may write $|x - 2.5| = 2$. Explain that the value that represents the variation (in this case, 2.5) should appear alone on one side of the equation, so the correct equation is $|x - 2| = 2.5$.

Multiple Choice In **Exercise 48,** choice **B** can be immediately eliminated because an absolute value is never negative. Therefore, the equation in **B** has no solution.

Journal

Have students write a step-by-step guide to solving absolute-value equations. Ask students to solve a sample equation to illustrate the steps.

ALTERNATIVE ASSESSMENT

Have students write and solve absolute-value equations that have two solutions, one solution, and no solution.

Power Presentations with PowerPoint®

2-7 Lesson Quiz

Solve each equation.

1. $15 = |x|$ −15, 15
2. $2|x - 7| = 14$ 0, 14
3. $|x + 1| - 9 = -9$ −1
4. $|5 + x| - 3 = -2$ −6, −4
5. $7 + |x - 8| = 6$ ∅
6. Inline skates typically have wheels with a diameter of 74 mm. The wheels are manufactured so that the diameters vary from this value by at most 0.1 mm. Write and solve an absolute-value equation to find the minimum and maximum diameters of the wheels. $|x - 74| = 0.1$; 73.9 mm; 74.1 mm

Also available on transparency

2-7 PROBLEM SOLVING

LESSON 2-7 **Problem Solving**
Solving Absolute-Value Equations

Write the correct answer.

1. A machine manufactures wheels with a diameter of 70 cm. It is acceptable for the diameter of a wheel to be within 0.02 cm of this value. Write and solve an absolute-value equation to find the minimum and maximum acceptable diameters.
$|x - 70| = 0.02$; 69.98 cm; 70.02 cm

2. A pedestrian bridge is 53 meters long. Due to changes in temperature, the bridge may expand or contract by as much as 21 millimeters. Write and solve an absolute-value equation to find the minimum and maximum lengths of the bridge.
$|x - 53| = 0.021$; 52.979 m; 53.021 m

3. Two numbers on a number line are represented by the absolute-value equation $|n - 5| = 6$. What are the two numbers?
−1 and 11

4. A jewelry maker cuts pieces of wire to shape into earrings. The equation $|x - 12.2| = 0.3$ gives the minimum and maximum acceptable lengths of the wires in centimeters. What is the minimum acceptable length of a wire?
11.9 cm

The table shows the recommended daily intake of several minerals for adult women. Use the table for questions 5–7. Select the best answer.

5. Which absolute-value equation gives the minimum and maximum recommended intakes for zinc?
A $|x - 8| = 32$ C $|x - 16| = 24$
(B) $|x - 24| = 16$ D $|x - 40| = 32$

6. For which mineral are the minimum and maximum recommended intakes given by the absolute-value equation $|x - 31.5| = 13.5$?
F Fluoride H Zinc
(G) Iron J None of these

7. Jason writes an equation for the minimum and maximum intakes of fluoride. He writes it in the form $|x - b| = c$. What is the value of b?
A 3 **(C)** 6.5
B 3.5 D 7

Mineral	Daily Minimum (mg)	Daily Maximum (mg)
Fluoride	3	10
Iron	18	45
Zinc	8	40

Source: http://www.supplementquality.com/news/multi_mineral_chart.html

2-7 CHALLENGE

LESSON 2-7 **Challenge**
Writing an Absolute-Value Equation Given the Solutions

It is sometimes useful to write an equation that has a given solution set. For example, consider the solution set {−3, 7}. To write an absolute-value equation with this solution set, first plot the points on a number line.

Find the value that is midway between −3 and 7. One way to do this is to find the mean:

$\frac{-3 + 7}{2} = \frac{4}{2} = 2.$

Now find the distance of −3 and 7 from this midpoint. The distance is 5 units.

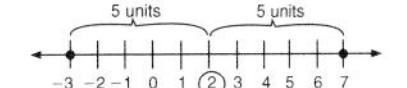

The required absolute-value equation is $|x - m| = d$, where m is the midpoint and d is the distance of each solution from the midpoint. Therefore, the absolute-value equation with the solution set {−3, 7} is $|x - 2| = 5$.

1. Show how to check that −3 and 7 are solutions of $|x - 2| = 5$.
$|(-3) - 2| = |-5| = 5$; $|7 - 2| = |5| = 5$

2. Are there other absolute-value equations with the same solution set? If so, give an example of such an equation. (*Hint:* Consider performing the same operation on each side of the equation $|x - 2| = 5$.)
yes; possible answer: $|x - 2| + 1 = 6$

Write an absolute-value equation with the given solution set. Possible answers given.

3. {1, 9} $|x - 5| = 4$
4. {−4, 8} $|x - 2| = 6$
5. {−5, 11} $|x - 3| = 8$
6. {−9, −1} $|x + 5| = 4$
7. $\{-\frac{1}{3}, \frac{1}{3}\}$ $|x| = \frac{1}{3}$
8. {5, 6} $|x - 5.5| = 0.5$
9. {−4.5, 9.5} $|x - 2.5| = 7$
10. $\{-\frac{1}{2}, \frac{5}{2}\}$ $|x - 1| = \frac{3}{2}$

Organizer

Objective: Assess students' ability to apply concepts and skills in Lesson 2-5 through Lesson 2-7 in a real-world format.

PREMIER Online Edition

Problem	Text Reference
1	Lesson 2-5
2	Lesson 2-6
3	Lesson 2-7

CHAPTER 2

SECTION 2B

Proportions and Formulas

Make a Note of It Sounds are produced by vibrating objects, such as guitar strings. The number of vibrations per second is called the frequency, and the frequency determines the note that you hear. The table shows the approximate frequency for the notes in a scale, where 1 Hertz (Hz) = 1 vibration/second.

Musical Notes	
Note	**Frequency (Hz)**
C	264
D	297
E	330
F	352
G	396
A	440
B	495
C	528

1. Notes that sound pleasing when played at the same time have a special relationship. For example, two notes whose frequencies have a ratio of 5:4 are said to be separated by an interval of a third. Which note is separated by an interval of a third from the note F? **A**

2. The speed of sound is approximately 340 m/s. The following formula relates the speed of sound s, the frequency f, and the wavelength w.

$$s = fw$$

Solve the formula for w to find the wavelength for the note G. $w = \frac{s}{f}$; **approx. 0.86 m/s**

3. A piano can produce a wide range of notes. The center of the piano's frequency range is of 2106.75 Hz, while the frequencies at the extreme ends of the range differ from this value by 2079.25 Hz. Write and solve an absolute-value equation to find the minimum and maximum frequencies for notes on a piano. $|x - 2106.75| = 2079.25$; **27.5 Hz; 4186 Hz**

INTERVENTION

Scaffolding Questions

1. How can you set up a proportion to solve this problem? What should you do to solve the proportion? $\frac{5}{4} = \frac{x}{352}$; set cross products equal to each other.
2. How should you solve the formula for w? Divide both sides by f to isolate the variable w. What frequency should you use for the note G? 396 Hz
3. What absolute-value expression represents the distance of a value on the number line from 2106.75? $|x - 2106.75|$

Extension

The scale shown in the table can be extended indefinitely by repeating the pattern of ratios between the frequencies of consecutive notes. Find the frequencies of the next three notes in the scale. 594 Hz; 660 Hz; 704 Hz

California Standards

Algebra 1 3.0

READY TO GO ON?

CHAPTER 2

SECTION 2B

Quiz for Lessons 2-5 Through 2-7

2-5 Solving Proportions

1. Last week, the ratio of laptops to desktops sold at a computer store was 2:3. Eighteen desktop models were sold. How many laptop models were sold? **12**
2. Anita read 150 pages in 5 hours. What is her reading rate in pages per minute? $\frac{1}{2}$ **page/min**

Find the unit rate.

3. Twenty-six crackers contain 156 Calories. **6 Calories/cracker**
4. A store developed 1024 photographs in 8 hours. **128 photographs/h**

Solve each proportion.

5. $\frac{-18}{n} = \frac{9}{2}$ **−4**
6. $\frac{d}{5} = \frac{2}{4}$ **2.5**
7. $\frac{4}{12} = \frac{r+2}{16}$ $\mathbf{\frac{10}{3}}$
8. $\frac{-3}{7} = \frac{6}{x+6}$ **−20**

Find each value. Round to the nearest tenth if necessary.

9. Find 40% of 25. **10**
10. Find 130% of 9. **11.7**
11. 35 is what percent of 70? **50%**
12. What percent of 400 is 640? **160%**
13. 16 is 80% of what number? **20**
14. 200% of what number is 28? **14**
15. A volunteer at the zoo is responsible for feeding the animals in 15 exhibits in the reptile house. This represents 20% of the total exhibits in the reptile house. How many exhibits are in the reptile house? **75**

2-6 Solving Literal Equations for a Variable

16. Solve $5j + s = t - 2$ for t. $t = 5j + s + 2$
17. Solve $h + p = 3(k - 8)$ for k. $k = \frac{h+p}{3} + 8$
18. Solve $2x + 3y = 12$ for x. $x = 6 - \frac{3}{2}y$
19. Solve $\frac{x}{r} = v$ for x. $x = vr$
20. The formula for the area of a triangle is $A = \frac{1}{2}bh$. Solve the formula for h. If the area of a triangle is 48 cm^2, and its base measures 12 cm, what is the height of a triangle? $h = \frac{2A}{b}$; **8 cm**

2-7 Solving Absolute-Value Equations

Solve each equation.

21. $|r| = 7$ **7, −7**
22. $|h + 4| = 11$ **7, −15**
23. $|2x + 4| = 0$ **−2**
24. $16 = 7|p + 3| + 30$ **∅**
25. Collette is a contestant on a game show. She can win a car if she can guess the price of the car within \$725. The price of the car is \$16,785. Write and solve an absolute-value equation to find the values for the maximum and minimum price that Collette can guess to win the car. $|p - 16{,}785| = 725$; **min = \$16,060; max = \$17,510**

READY TO GO ON? SECTION 2B

Organizer

Objective: Assess students' mastery of concepts and skills in Lessons 2-5 through 2-7.

Countdown to Mastery Week 5

Resources

Assessment Resources
Section 2B Quiz

Test & Practice Generator
One-Stop Planner®

INTERVENTION

Resources

Ready to Go On? Intervention and Enrichment **Worksheets**

Ready to Go On? **CD-ROM**

Ready to Go On? **Online**

my.hrw.com

READY TO GO ON? Diagnose and Prescribe

NO INTERVENE

Ready to Go On? Intervention	Ready to Go On? Intervention, Section 2B: Worksheets	CD-ROM	Online
Lesson 2-5 **15.0**	2-5 Intervention	Activity 2-5	Diagnose and Prescribe Online
Lesson 2-6 **Ext. of 5.0**	2-6 Intervention	Activity 2-6	
Lesson 2-7 **3.0, 5.0**	2-7 Intervention	Activity 2-7	

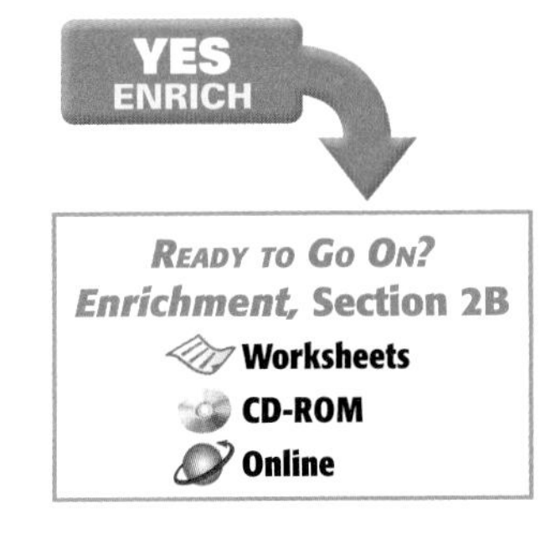

YES ENRICH

Ready to Go On? Enrichment, Section 2B
Worksheets
CD-ROM
Online

Study Guide: Review

Organizer

Objective: Help students organize and review key concepts and skills in Chapter 2.

Online Edition
Multilingual Glossary

Resources

PuzzlePro
One-Stop Planner®

***Multilingual Glossary* Online**

go.hrw.com
KEYWORD: MA8CA Glossary

***Lesson Tutorial Videos* CD-ROM**

Test & Practice Generator
One-Stop Planner®

Answers

1. literal equation
2. ratio
3. $b = 36$
4. $x = -2$
5. $a = -21$
6. $y = 18$
7. $z = \frac{9}{8}$
8. $w = \frac{7}{3}$
9. $t = 5.1$
10. $x = 25.5$
11. $x = 7$
12. $s = -7$
13. $f = 120$
14. $m = 15$
15. $j = 7$
16. $n = 36$
17. $k = 0.875$
18. $c = 12.5$
19. $27 + s = 108$; 81
20. $213

Study Guide: Review

Vocabulary

cross products 103	literal equation 110	scale drawing 104
deductive reasoning 99	percent 103	scale model 104
equation 72	proportion 102	solution of an equation 72
equivalent equations 79	rate 102	solution set 72
formula 109	ratio 102	unit rate 102
identity 93	scale 104	

Complete the sentences below with vocabulary words from the list above.

1. A formula is a type of a(n) ___?___.

2. A(n) ___?___ is used to compare two quantities.

2-1 Solving One-Step Equations *(pp. 72–77)*

2.0, Prep for 5.0

EXAMPLES

Solve each equation. Check your answer.

■ $x - 12 = -8$

$$\begin{aligned} x - 12 &= -8 \\ \underline{+12} \quad & \underline{+12} \\ x &= 4 \end{aligned}$$

Add 12 to both sides.

Check $x - 12 = -8$

$4 - 12$	-8
-8	-8 ✓

■ $-8x = 148$

$$\frac{-8x}{-8} = \frac{148}{-8}$$

Divide both sides by −8.

$$x = -18.5$$

Check $-8x = 148$

$-8(-18.5)$	148
148	148 ✓

EXERCISES

Solve each equation. Check your answer.

3. $b - 16 = 20$

4. $4 + x = 2$

5. $9 + a = -12$

6. $-7 + y = 11$

7. $z - \frac{1}{4} = \frac{7}{8}$

8. $w + \frac{2}{3} = 3$

9. $7.2 + t = 12.3$

10. $22.5 = x - 3$

11. $35 = 5x$

12. $-6s = 42$

13. $\frac{f}{15} = 8$

14. $3m = 45$

15. $4j = 28$

16. $\frac{n}{3} = 12$

17. $4k = 3.5$

18. $\frac{c}{5} = 2.5$

19. Robin needs 108 signatures for her petition. So far, she has 27. Write and solve an equation to determine how many more signatures she needs.

20. Mrs. Wilson gave some money to each of her 6 children. Each child received $35.50. How much money did Mrs. Wilson give to her 6 children in total?

2-2 Solving Two-Step Equations *(pp. 79–84)*

Prep for 5.0

EXAMPLES

Solve each equation.

- $\frac{z}{2.4} + 2 = 14$

$$\frac{z}{2.4} + 2 = 14$$
$$-2 \quad -2 \qquad \text{Subtract 2 from both sides.}$$
$$\frac{z}{2.4} = 12$$
$$(2.4)\frac{z}{2.4} = (2.4)12 \qquad \text{Multiply both sides by 2.4.}$$
$$z = 28.8$$

- $5x - 6 = 79$

$$5x - 6 = 79$$
$$+6 \quad +6 \qquad \text{Add 6 to both sides.}$$
$$5x = 85$$
$$\frac{5x}{5} = \frac{85}{5} \qquad \text{Divide both sides by 5.}$$
$$x = 17$$

EXERCISES

Solve each equation. Check your answer.

21. $4t - 13 = 57$

22. $5 - 2y = 15$

23. $3z + 1 = 19$

24. $18 = 30 - 3h$

25. $\frac{k}{5} - 6 = 2$

26. $\frac{1}{6}f + \frac{3}{4} = \frac{1}{2}$

27. $6h - 7 = 25$

28. $17 = 29 - 4k$

29. $\frac{1}{4} + \frac{3}{4}t = 10$

30. $18 - 4a = 34$

31. $0.2x + 0.5 = 0.9$

32. $-0.6x + 1 = 0.4$

33. Thomas had the same score for 3 different quizzes. On one quiz he received 5 extra bonus points. His total score for the 3 quizzes was 281 points. What was his score on each quiz?

2-3 Solving Multi-Step Equations *(pp. 85–90)*

4.0, 5.0

EXAMPLE

Solve each equation.

- $\frac{3x}{5} - \frac{x}{4} + \frac{1}{2} = \frac{6}{5}$

$$20\left(\frac{3x}{5} - \frac{x}{4} + \frac{1}{2}\right) = 20\left(\frac{6}{5}\right) \qquad \text{Multiply by the LCD.}$$
$$12x - 5x + 10 = 24 \qquad \text{Combine like terms.}$$
$$7x + 10 = 24$$
$$-10 \quad -10 \qquad \text{Subtract 10 from both sides.}$$
$$7x = 14$$
$$\frac{7x}{7} = \frac{14}{7} \qquad \text{Divide both sides by 7.}$$
$$x = 2$$

- $3(b + 1) = -9$

$$3(b) + 3(1) = -9 \qquad \text{Distribute 3.}$$
$$3b + 3 = -9$$
$$-3 \quad -3 \qquad \text{Subtract 3 from both sides.}$$
$$3b = -12$$
$$\frac{3b}{3} = \frac{-12}{3} \qquad \text{Divide both sides by 3.}$$
$$b = -4$$

EXERCISES

Solve each equation. Check your answer.

34. $a - 12 + 2a = 27$

35. $5y + 3 - 7y = 15$

36. $4 + 3a - 6 = 43$

37. $3(x + 2) = 24$

38. $h(5 - 2) + 8 = 17$

39. $8(z + 10) + z = 98$

40. $-6 = 2.5(w - 2)$

41. $0.3x - 1.1 - x = 0.3$

42. If $8n + 22 = 70$, find the value of $3n$.

43. If $0 = 6n - 36$, find the value of $n - 5$.

44. The sum of the measures of two angles is 180°. One angle measures $3a$, and the other angle measures $2a - 25$ Find a. Then find the measure of each angle.

45. A drama club sold 120 child tickets and 80 adult tickets to a play. A child ticket cost $3 less than an adult ticket. The club collected a total of $640 from ticket sales. What is the cost of an adult ticket? a child ticket?

Answers

21. $t = 17.5$
22. $y = -5$
23. $z = 6$
24. $h = 4$
25. $k = 40$
26. $f = -\frac{3}{2}$
27. $h = \frac{16}{3}$
28. $k = 3$
29. $t = 13$
30. $a = -4$
31. $x = 2$
32. $x = 1$
33. 92
34. $a = 13$
35. $y = -6$
36. $a = 15$
37. $x = 6$
38. $h = 3$
39. $z = 2$
40. $w = -0.4$
41. $x = -2$
42. 18
43. 1
44. $a = 41$; 123°; 57°
45. $5; $2

Answers

46. $x = -2$
47. $r = -2$
48. $a = 1$
49. $x = -\frac{2}{3}$
50. $\varnothing$
51. all real numbers
52. $x = 3.5$
53. $c = \frac{18}{7}$
54. $x = 7$
55. $x = 6$
56. $n = -2$
57. $x = 3$
58. 9
59. 16:1, $\frac{16}{1}$, 16 to 1
60. $n = 1.6$
61. $x = 54$
62. 1.37 ft

2-4 Solving Equations with Variables on Both Sides *(pp. 92–98)*

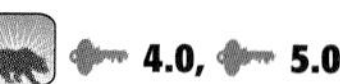

EXAMPLE

Solve each equation.

- $3y - 5 = 2y + 5$

$$\begin{aligned} 3y - 5 &= 2y + 5 \\ -2y \quad &\quad -2y && \text{Subtract } 2y \text{ from both sides.} \\ y - 5 &= 5 \\ +5 \quad &\quad +5 && \text{Add 5 to both sides.} \\ y &= 10 \end{aligned}$$

- $x + 7 = 12 + 3x - 7x$

$$\begin{aligned} x + 7 &= 12 - 4x && \text{Combine like terms.} \\ +4x \quad &\quad +4x && \text{Add } 4x \text{ to both sides.} \\ 5x + 7 &= 12 \\ -7 \quad &\quad -7 && \text{Subtract 7 from both sides.} \\ 5x &= 5 \\ \frac{5x}{5} &= \frac{5}{5} && \text{Divide both sides by 5.} \\ x &= 1 \end{aligned}$$

EXERCISES

Solve each equation. Check your answer.

46. $4x + 2 = 3x$

47. $-3r - 8 = -5r - 12$

48. $-a - 3 + 7 = 3a$

49. $-(x - 4) = 2x + 6$

50. $\frac{2}{3}n = 4n - \frac{10}{3}n - \frac{1}{2}$

51. $0.2(7 + 2t) = 0.4t + 1.4$

52. $0.5x - 1.7 = 0.3x - 1$

53. $-2c + 8 = 5c - 10$

54. $7x - 28 = 3x$

55. $9x - 3 = 6x + 15$

56. $\frac{3}{4}n + 1 = \frac{5}{4}n + 2$

57. $\frac{1}{3}x + \frac{2}{3} = \frac{5}{3}x$

58. One photo shop charges \$0.36 per print. Another photo shop charges \$2.52 plus \$0.08 per print. Juan finds that the cost of developing his photos is the same at either shop. How many photos does Juan have to develop?

2-5 Solving Proportions *(pp. 102–107)*

EXAMPLES

- Solve $\frac{3w - 7}{21} = \frac{3}{7}$.

$$\begin{aligned} \frac{3w - 7}{21} &\times \frac{3}{7} \\ 7(3w - 7) &= 21(3) && \text{Use cross products.} \\ 21w - 49 &= 63 \\ +49 \quad &\quad +49 && \text{Add 49 to both sides.} \\ 21w &= 112 \\ \frac{21w}{21} &= \frac{112}{21} && \text{Divide both sides by 21.} \\ w &= \frac{16}{3} \end{aligned}$$

EXERCISES

59. In the ninth grade there are 320 students and 20 teachers. What is the student-to-teacher ratio?

Solve each proportion. Check your answer.

60. $\frac{n}{8} = \frac{2}{10}$

61. $\frac{2}{9} = \frac{12}{x}$

62. Amelia Earhart made her 1932 solo flight across the Atlantic Ocean in a Lockheed Vega. One model of the plane is $\frac{1}{30}$ the size of the real airplane. The wingspan of the Lockheed was 41 feet. What is the wingspan of the model? Round your answer to the nearest hundredth.

■ **Earth has a surface area of approximately 197 million square miles. About 58 million square miles is land. Find the percent of Earth's surface area that is water.**

197 million − 58 million = 139 million

$$\frac{\text{part}}{\text{whole}} = \frac{\text{percent}}{100}$$

$$\frac{139 \text{ million}}{197 \text{ million}} = \frac{n}{100}$$

$197n = 13{,}900$ *Use cross products.*

$n = 70.56$

About 71% of Earth's surface area is water.

63. Find 2.3% of 230.

64. Find 115% of 2700.

65. What percent of 18 is 12? Round your answer to the nearest tenth of a percent.

66. What percent of 14 is 56?

67. 90% of what number is 120? Round your answer to the nearest tenth.

68. 90 is 37.5% of what number?

69. A student answered 32 questions correctly and 8 incorrectly. What percent of the questions were answered correctly?

2-6 Solving Literal Equations for a Variable *(pp. 109–113)*

 Ext. of 5.0

EXAMPLE

■ **Solve $A = P + Prt$ for r.**

$$\begin{aligned} A &= P + Prt \\ -P \quad & -P \\ A - P &= Prt \end{aligned}$$ *Subtract P from both sides.*

$$\frac{A-P}{Pt} = \frac{Prt}{Pt}$$ *Divide both sides by Pt.*

$$\frac{A-P}{Pt} = r$$

EXERCISES

Solve for the indicated variable.

70. $C = \frac{360}{n}$ for n

71. $S = \frac{n}{2}(a + \ell)$ for a

72. $0.25x + y = 225$ for x

73. The formula $a = \frac{d}{g}$ gives the average gas mileage a of a vehicle that uses g gallons of gas to travel d miles. Use the formula to find how many gallons of gas a vehicle with an average gas mileage of 20.2 miles per gallon will use to travel 75 miles. Round your answer to the nearest tenth.

2-7 Solving Absolute-Value Equations *(pp. 114–119)*

 3.0, 5.0

EXAMPLE

■ **Solve $3|y + 4| = 30$.**

$$\frac{3|y+4|}{3} = \frac{30}{3}$$ *Divide both sides by 3.*

$$|y + 4| = 10$$

Case 1	Case 2
$y + 4 = 10$	$y + 4 = -10$
$-4 \quad -4$	$-4 \quad -4$
$y = 6$	$y = -14$

EXERCISES

Solve each equation. Check your answer.

74. $|x + 6| = 21$

75. $7|y - 5| = 14$

76. $3|y| + 4 = 31$

77. $12 = |x - 5.4|$

78. $|g + 6| + 12 = 14$

79. $|x| = \frac{5}{7}$

80. Jason is driving his car at 55 mi/h. He needs to keep his car within 5 mi/h of his current speed. Write and solve an absolute-value equation to find Jason's maximum and minimum speeds.

Answers

63. 5.29

64. 3105

65. 66.7%

66. 400%

67. 133.3

68. 240

69. 80%

70. $n = \frac{360}{C}$

71. $a = \frac{2S}{n} - \ell$

72. $x = \frac{225 - y}{0.25}$

73. 3.7 gal

74. $x = 15, -27$

75. $y = 7, 3$

76. $y = 9, -9$

77. $x = 17.4, -6.6$

78. $g = -4, -8$

79. $x = \frac{5}{7}, -\frac{5}{7}$

80. $|x - 5| = 55$; min. speed: 50 mi/h; max speed: 60 mi/h

Organizer

Objective: Assess students' mastery of concepts and skills in Chapter 2.

Online Edition

Resources

Assessment Resources

Chapter 2 Tests
- Free Response (Levels A, B, C)
- Multiple Choice (Levels A, B, C)
- Performance Assessment

***IDEA Works!* CD-ROM**

Modified Chapter 2 Test

California Standards

Standard	Exercises
3.0	41–46
5.0	7–12, 25–30
15.0	23, 24, 34
6AF1.1	1–6

Solve each equation.

1. $y - 7 = 2$ **9**
2. $x + 12 = 19$ **7**
3. $-5 + z = 8$ **13**
4. $9x = 72$ **8**
5. $\frac{m}{-8} = -2.5$ **20**
6. $\frac{7}{8}a = 42$ **48**
7. $15 = 3 - 4x$ **−3**
8. $\frac{2a}{3} + \frac{1}{5} = \frac{7}{6}$ **1.45**
9. $8 - (b - 2) = 11$ **−1**
10. $-2x + 4 = 5 - 3x$ **1**
11. $3(q - 2) + 2 = 5q - 7 - 2q$ **∅**
12. $5z = -3(z + 7)$ **−2.625**
13. $m - 2.7 = -1.5m + 1$ **1.48**
14. $x - 3.6 = 10.2 - 3.2$ **10.6**
15. $c + 13.5 = 20$ **6.5**

Solve for the indicated variable.

16. $r - 2s = 14$ for s $s = \frac{r - 14}{2}$
17. $V = \frac{1}{3}bh$ for b $b = \frac{3V}{h}$
18. $P = 2(\ell + w)$ for ℓ $\ell = \frac{P}{2} - w$
19. $2x + a = 4$ for x $x = \frac{4 - a}{2}$
20. $4x + 6y = 12$ for x $x = 3 - \frac{3}{2}y$
21. $\frac{x}{r} = n$ for r $r = \frac{x}{n}$

22. The ratio of red marbles to blue marbles in a bag is 4 : 7. There are 16 red marbles. How many blue marbles are there? **28**

Find each unit rate. Round to the nearest hundredth if necessary.

23. A store sells 3 videotapes for $4.99. **$1.66/videotape**
24. Twenty-five students use 120 sheets of paper. **4.8 sheets/student**

Solve each proportion.

25. $\frac{5}{4} = \frac{x}{12}$ **15**
26. $\frac{8}{2z} = \frac{15}{60}$ **16**
27. $\frac{x + 10}{10} = \frac{18}{12}$ **5**
28. $\frac{x}{8} = \frac{1}{4}$ **2**
29. $\frac{5}{12} = \frac{-4}{f}$ **−9.6**
30. $\frac{3}{10} = \frac{x + 1}{15}$ **3.5**
31. $\frac{c - 4}{5} = \frac{-c}{2}$ $\frac{8}{7}$
32. $\frac{3n}{2} = \frac{2}{3}$ $\frac{4}{9}$
33. $\frac{w}{6} = \frac{5}{2}$ **15**

34. The scale on a map is 1 inch : 500 miles. If two cities are 875 miles apart, how far apart are they on the map? **1.75 in.**

35. Order the following from least to greatest: 0.625, $\frac{1}{8}$, $\frac{1}{2}$, 1, 20%, 30%. $\frac{1}{8}$, **20%, 30%,** $\frac{1}{2}$, **0.625, 1**

36. What is 23% of 46? **10.58**

37. 37.5 is 60% of what number? **62.5**

38. What percent of 175 is 35? **20%**

39. What is 29% of 32? **9.28**

40. 84.41 is 23% of what number? **367**

Solve each equation.

41. $|x - 14| = 21$ **35, −7**
42. $13 = |y + 2| - 3$ **14, −18**
43. $4|z| = 20$ **5, −5**
44. $3|x| + 5 = 8$ **1, −1**
45. $3|g + 1| + 5 = 7$ $-\frac{5}{3}, -\frac{1}{3}$
46. $|2v| = 6$ **3, −3**

COLLEGE ENTRANCE EXAM PRACTICE

FOCUS ON ACT

The ACT Mathematics Test is one of four tests in the ACT. You have 60 minutes to answer 60 multiple-choice questions. The questions cover material typically taught through the end of eleventh grade. You will need to know some basic formulas.

You may want to time yourself as you take this practice test. It should take you about 6 minutes to complete.

HOT TIP! There is no penalty for incorrect answers on the ACT. If you are unsure of the correct answer, eliminate as many answer choices as possible. Then make your best guess. Be sure you have marked an answer for every question before time runs out.

1. At a certain high school, the ratio of left-handed to right-handed basketball players is 1:4. If there are a total of 20 players on the team, how many players are right-handed?

   (A) 1
   (B) 4
   (C) 5
   (D) 12
   (E) 16

2. If $y - 3 = \frac{2}{5}(x + 1)$, then $x = ?$

   (F) $\frac{5(y-3)-2}{2}$
   (G) $y - \frac{22}{5}$
   (H) $\frac{2(y-3)}{5} - 1$
   (J) $\frac{2(y+1)+15}{5}$
   (K) $\frac{5}{2}y - 4$

3. What is $\frac{1}{5}$% of 20?

   (A) 0.004
   (B) 0.04
   (C) 0.4
   (D) 4
   (E) 100

4. If $x - 3 = 4 - 2(x + 5)$, then $x = ?$

   (F) −3
   (G) −1
   (H) 1
   (J) $\frac{3}{2}$
   (K) $\frac{11}{3}$

5. If $\triangle ABC \sim \triangle DEF$, what is the length of $\overline{AC}$?

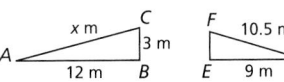

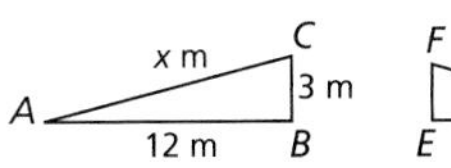

   (A) 2.6 meters
   (B) 3.5 meters
   (C) 7 meters
   (D) 14 meters
   (E) 15 meters

6. A movie theater makes 30% of its revenue from concession sales. If concession sales were \$174,000, what was the total revenue?

   (F) \$52,200
   (G) \$121,800
   (H) \$248,570
   (J) \$580,000
   (K) \$746,000

COLLEGE ENTRANCE EXAM PRACTICE

CHAPTER 2

Organizer

Objective: Provide practice for college entrance exams such as the ACT.

PREMIER **Online Edition**

Resources

College Entrance Exam Practice

Questions on the ACT represent the following content areas:

Pre-Algebra, 23%
Elementary Algebra, 17%
Intermediate Algebra, 15%
Coordinate Geometry, 15%
Plane Geometry, 23%
Trigonometry, 7%

Items on this page focus on:

- Pre-Algebra
- Elementary Algebra
- Plane Geometry

Text References:

Item	1	2	3	4	5	6
Lesson	2-5	2-6	2-5	2-4	2-5	2-5

Teaching Tip

Multiple Choice

1. Students who chose **B** most likely found the number of *left*-handed players. Remind students to read each question carefully.
2. Students who chose **H** probably multiplied the left side of the equation by $\frac{2}{5}$ and eliminated $\frac{2}{5}$ from the right side. Remind students that the inverse operation for multiplication is division, so they should *divide* both sides of the equation by $\frac{2}{5}$.
3. Students who chose **D** probably found $\frac{1}{5}$ of 20 instead of $\frac{1}{5}$% of 20. Remind students that percent means "part of 100," so they should divide $\frac{1}{5}$ by 100 before multiplying by 20.
4. Students who chose **F** may have subtracted 3 from both sides instead of adding 3. Remind students that they should always check their answers to avoid errors caused by simple mistakes.
5. Students who chose **B** probably used the ratio $\frac{3}{9}$ instead of $\frac{12}{9}$. Remind students to look over the problem carefully and be aware of which sides are corresponding.
6. Students who chose **F** most likely found 30% of the concession sales. Remind students how to set up an equation to find the whole when the percent and the part are known.

Organizer

Objective: Provide opportunities to learn and practice common test-taking strategies.

Online Edition

Teaching Tip **Gridded Response** This Strategy for Success focuses on how to correctly fill in a grid when answering a gridded-response item. Students often solve the test item correctly, but fill in the answer grid incorrectly. This stategy involves students reviewing the rules for how to fill in a grid, and then looking at filled-in grids and identifying why the response was marked as incorrect.

Gridded-response test items appear on many standardized tests, such as the PSAT and the SAT.

CHAPTER 2

Gridded Response: Fill in Answer Grids Correctly

When responding to a test item that requires you to place your answer in a grid, you must fill out the grid on your answer sheet correctly, or the item will be marked as incorrect.

EXAMPLE 1

Gridded Response: Simplify the expression $12^2 - 3(10 + 4)$.

$$12^2 - 3(10 + 4)$$
$$12^2 - 3(14)$$
$$144 - 3(14)$$
$$144 - 42$$
$$102$$

The expression simplifies to 102.

- Write your answer in the answer boxes at the top of the grid.
- Put only one digit in each box. Do not leave a blank box in the middle of an answer.
- Shade the bubble for each digit in the same column as the digit in the answer box.

EXAMPLE 2

Gridded Response: Evaluate the expression $ba \div c$ for $a = -7$, $b = 2$, and $c = -6$.

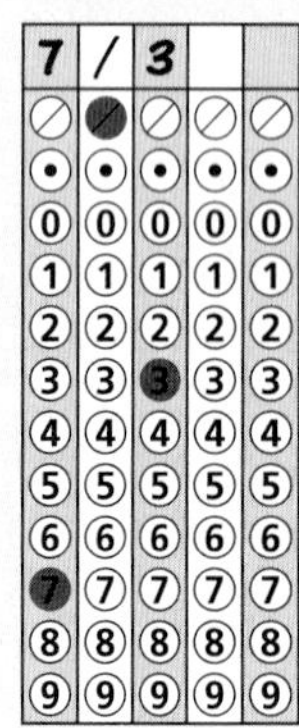

$$ba \div c$$
$$(2)(-7) \div (-6)$$
$$-14 \div (-6)$$
$$\frac{7}{3} = 2\frac{1}{3} = 2.\overline{3}$$

The expression simplifies to $\frac{7}{3}$, $2\frac{1}{3}$, or $2.\overline{3}$.

- Mixed numbers and repeating decimals cannot be gridded, so you must grid the answer as $\frac{7}{3}$.
- Write your answer in the answer boxes at the top of the grid.
- Put only one digit or symbol in each box. On some grids, the fraction bar and the decimal point have a designated box. Do not leave a blank box in the middle of an answer.
- Shade the bubble for each digit or symbol in the same column as the digit in the answer box.

Grid formats may vary from test to test. The grid in this book is used often, but it is not used on every test that has gridded response questions. Always examine the grid when taking a standardized test to be sure you know how to fill it in correctly.

Read each sample and then answer the questions that follow.

Sample A
A student correctly evaluated an expression and got $\frac{8}{15}$ as a result. Then the student filled in the grid as shown.

1. What error did the student make when filling out the grid?
2. Explain how to fill in the answer correctly.

Sample B
The square root of 6.25 is 2.5. This answer is displayed in the grid.

3. What error did the student make when filling in the grid?
4. Explain how to fill in the answer correctly.

Sample C
A student correctly simplified the expression $2\frac{1}{8} + 3\frac{5}{8} + \frac{7}{8}$. Then the student filled in the grid as shown.

5. What answer does the grid show?
6. Explain why you cannot fill in a mixed number.
7. Write the answer in two forms that could be entered in the grid correctly.

Sample D
A student added −10 and 25 and got an answer of 15. Then the student filled in the grid as shown.

8. What error does the grid show?
9. Another student got an answer of −15. Explain why the student knew this answer was wrong.

Answers

Possible answers:

1. There should not be a space between the fraction bar and the next number.
2. Do not leave spaces in the middle of the answer.
3. The decimal point must be shaded.
4. Shade 2, the decimal point, and 5.
5. 65 eighths
6. Because the whole number and numerator of a mixed number would be written next to each other, they would look together like the numerator of an improper fraction.
7. 6.625 or $\frac{53}{8}$
8. Negative numbers cannot be entered into the grid.
9. The student knew that there was no bubble to fill in for a negative sign. You should be able to fill in a correct answer, so the student knew that the negative answer was not correct.

Answers to Test Items

A. See answers to Problems 1 and 2.
B. See answers to Problems 3 and 4.
C. See answer to Problem 7.
D. See answer to Problem 9.

California Standards
2.0, 6NS2.1, 6NS2.3

MASTERING THE STANDARDS

Organizer

Objective: Provide review and practice for Chapters 1–2.

Resources

Assessment Resources

Chapter 2 Cumulative Test

Focus on California Standards Benchmark Tests and Intervention

California Standards Practice CD-ROM

go.hrw.com
KEYWORD: MA8CA Practice

California Standards

Standard	Items
6NS1.4	2
6NS2.0	1
6AF1.1	10, 12, 17
6AF2.2	15
6AF2.3	3, 4, 14
7NS2.5	6
7MG1.2	5, 7
3.0	4, 18
4.0	9, 11
5.0	8, 13, 16, 19

CUMULATIVE ASSESSMENT, CHAPTERS 1–2

Multiple Choice

1. What operation does ◊ represent if $x \lozenge 2.2 = 4.5$ when $x = 9.9$?

Ⓐ Addition
Ⓑ Subtraction
Ⓒ Multiplication
Ⓓ Division

2. A couple earns $4819.25 a month. They pay 9.5% of their monthly income as the monthly payment on their car. To the nearest dollar, how much does the couple pay for their monthly car payment?

Ⓐ $458 Ⓒ $4578
Ⓑ $507 Ⓓ $4810

3. Naomi runs 8 miles each day. If she slows her pace by half, she runs this distance in 2 hours and 40 minutes. What is her normal pace?

Ⓐ 6 miles per hour
Ⓑ 8 miles per hour
Ⓒ 4.75 miles per hour
Ⓓ 6.75 miles per hour

4. A clock loses 5 minutes every day. How much time will it lose in 2 hours?

Ⓐ 0.417 second Ⓒ 240 seconds
Ⓑ 25 seconds Ⓓ 600 seconds

5. A statue is 8 feet tall. The display case for a model of the statue is 18 inches tall. Which scale allows for the tallest model of the statue that will fit in the display case?

Ⓐ 1 inch:2 inches Ⓒ 1 inch:5 inches
Ⓑ 1 inch:7 inches Ⓓ 1 inch:10 inches

6. What is the value of $-|6^2|$?

Ⓐ −36 Ⓒ −8
Ⓑ −12 Ⓓ −3

7. Mr. Phillips wants to install hardwood flooring in his den. The flooring costs $25.86 per square yard. The blueprint below shows his house. What other information do you need in order to find the total cost of the flooring?

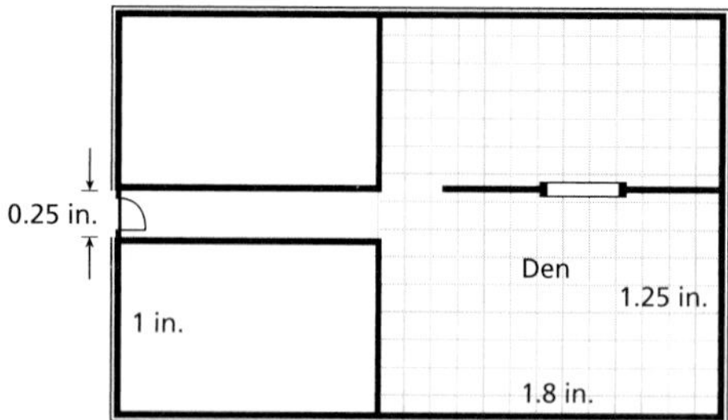

Ⓐ The lengths and widths of the adjoining rooms in the blueprint
Ⓑ The total area of the blueprint
Ⓒ The scale of inches in the blueprint to yards in the house
Ⓓ The width of the den

8. What value of n makes the equation below have no solution?

$$2x + 2 = nx - 3$$

Ⓐ −2
Ⓑ 0
Ⓒ 2
Ⓓ 3

9. Which of the equations below represents the second step of the solution process?

Step 1: $3(5x - 2) + 27 = -24$
Step 2: ☐
Step 3: $15x + 21 = -24$
Step 4: $15x = -45$
Step 5: $x = -3$

Ⓐ $3(5x + 27) - 2 = -24$
Ⓑ $3(5x + 25) = -24$
Ⓒ $15x - 2 + 27 = -24$
Ⓓ $15x - 6 + 27 = -24$

Teaching Tip **Multiple Choice** For **Item 4,** students may have trouble finding the answer in the correct units. For instance, if students chose **A,** they may have mistaken minutes for seconds. If they chose **D,** they may have found how much time the clock loses in 2 days, not 2 hours. Encourage students to use proportions to compare and convert units.

If you are stuck on a problem, skip it and come back later. Another problem might remind you of something that will help. If you feel yourself become tense, take a few deep breaths to relax.

10. Cass drove 3 miles to school, and then she drove m miles to a friend's house. The total mileage for these two trips was 8 miles. Which equation CANNOT be used to determine the number of miles Cass drove?

Ⓐ $3 + m = 8$
Ⓑ $3 - m = 8$ (circled)
Ⓒ $8 - 3 = m$
Ⓓ $8 - m = 3$

11. If $\frac{20}{x} = \frac{4}{x-5}$, which of the following is a true statement?

Ⓐ $x(x - 5) = 80$
Ⓑ $20x = 4(x - 5)$
Ⓒ $20(x - 5) = 4x$ (circled)
Ⓓ $24 = 2x - 5$

Gridded Response

12. Four times a number is two less than six times the same number minus ten. What is the number? **6**

13. On August 1st, Melissa invested $6000 in a retirement account. A portion of her account record is shown below. Her balance can be found using the equation $B = 192m + 6000$, where B is the balance and m is the number of months after August. Find the missing balance, in dollars, in the table.

Date	Balance ($)
8/1	6000
9/1	6192
10/1	6384
1/1	**6960**

14. At 2:45 P.M. you are 112 miles from Dallas. You want to be in Dallas at 4:30 P.M. What is the average number of miles per hour you must travel to be on time? **64**

15. A cyclist travels 45 miles in 4 hours. How many feet does she travel in one second? **16.5**

16. A bike rental shop charges a one-time charge of $8 plus an hourly fee to rent a bike. Dan paid $24.50 to rent a bike for $5\frac{1}{2}$ hours. Find the bike shop's hourly fee in dollars. **3**

Short Response

17. Alex buys 5 calendars to give as gifts. Each calendar has the same price. When the cashier rings up Alex's calendars, the total cost before tax is $58.75.

a. Write and solve an equation to find the cost of each calendar. **$5c = 58.75$; $11.75**

b. The total cost of Alex's calendars after tax is $63.45. Find the percent sales tax. Show your work and explain in words how you found your answer. **8%**

c. Alex's friend Keisha buys some calendars for the same price. She uses her 15% discount card. The total cost before tax is $39.95. How many calendars did Keisha buy? Show your work and explain in words how you found your answer. **4**

18. A student's solution for the absolute-value equation $6|x + 4| = 36$ was {2}. Explain why this answer is incorrect.

Extended Response

19. Korena is putting a decorative border around her rectangular flower garden. The total perimeter of the garden is 200 feet.

a. Draw three different rectangles that could represent Korena's flower garden. Label the dimensions of your rectangles.

b. Use the table to show the lengths and widths of five different rectangles that could represent Korena's flower garden. Do not use any of your rectangles from part a. **Possible answers:**

Possible Dimensions of Korena's Garden		
Length (ℓ)	Width (w)	Perimeter (P)
30	**70**	**200**
25	**75**	**200**
50	**50**	**200**
15	**85**	**200**
10	**90**	**200**

c. The length of Korena's garden is 4 times its width. Explain how to use the perimeter formula $P = 2\ell + 2w$ to find the dimensions of Korena's garden.

d. Find the dimensions of Korena's garden. **20 ft by 80 ft**

19c. Substitute $4w$ for ℓ in $P = 2\ell + 2w$, and solve for w. Substitute this value for w in $P = 2\ell + 2w$ and solve for ℓ.

Short-Response Rubric

Items 17–18

2 Points = The student's answer is an accurate and complete execution of the task or tasks.

1 Point = The student's answer contains attributes of an appropriate response but is flawed.

0 Points = The student's answer contains no attributes of an appropriate response.

Extended-Response Rubric

Item 19

4 Points = The student correctly draws three different rectangles in part **a,** lists five more different rectangles in part **b,** answers and explains part **c,** and answers part **d,** showing all work.

3 Points = The student correctly draws some rectangles in part **a** and lists some rectangles in part **b** but does not identify eight different possibilities, or the student correctly answers parts **a, b,** and **c** but does not correctly answer part **d.**

2 Points = The student answers all parts correctly but does not show any work or explanation, or the student correctly answers parts **a** and **b** but does not correctly answer parts **c** and **d.**

1 Point = The student finds four or fewer rectangles to fit the situation but does not correctly answer other parts of the problem, or the student attempts to answer all parts of the problem but does not correctly answer any part.

0 Points = The student does not answer correctly and does not attempt all parts of the problem.

Answers

18. Possible answer: The student was correct in finding one-half of the solution set. Since it is an absolute-value equation, the answer −10 needs to be included.

19a. Possible answer:

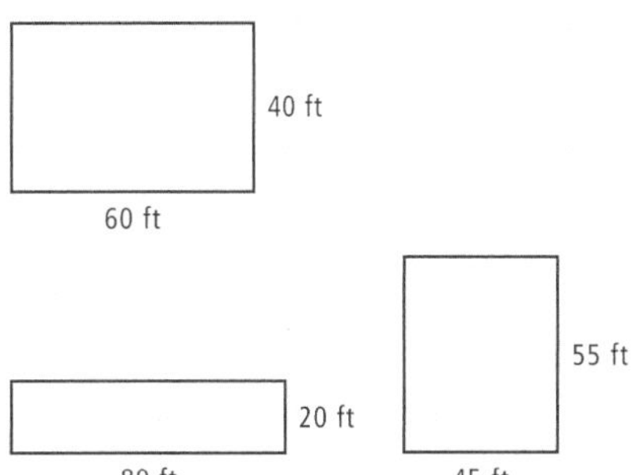

Inequalities

✔	Grade-level Standard
◄	Review
►	Beyond the Standards
A	Assessment
O	Optional

Pacing Guide

Calendar Planner
Teacher's One-Stop Planner®

Lesson/Lab	California Standards	Time	Advanced Students	Benchmark Students*	Strategic Students**
3-1 Graphing and Writing Inequalities	Preparation for 5.0	50 min	O	◄	◄
3-2 Solving Inequalities by Adding or Subtracting	Preparation for 5.0	50 min	O	◄	◄
3-3 Solving Inequalities by Multiplying or Dividing	Preparation for 5.0	50 min	O	◄	◄
Concept Connection	Preparation for 5.0	25 min	A	A	O
Ready to Go On?		25 min	A	A	A
3-4 Solving Two-Step and Multi-Step Inequalities	4.0, 5.0	100 min	✔	✔	✔
3-5 Solving Inequalities with Variables on Both Sides	4.0, 5.0	50 min	✔	✔	✔
LR Deductive Reasoning and Inequalities	5.0, 24.2, 25.1, 25.2	25 min	✔	✔	✔
3-6 Solving Compound Inequalities	5.0	50 min	✔	✔	✔
CN Triangle Inequality	Reinforcement of Grade 7 NS1.1	25 min	O	◄	◄
3-7 Solving Absolute-Value Inequalities	3.0, 5.0	50 min	✔	✔	✔
Concept Connection	5.0	25 min	A	A	O
Ready to Go On?		25 min	A	A	A
Study Guide: Review		50 min	✔	✔	✔
Chapter Test	3.0, 4.0, 5.0	50 min	A	A	A

* **Benchmark students** are achieving at or near grade level.

** **Strategic students** may be a year or more below grade level, and may require additional time for intervention.

Countdown to Mastery, Weeks 5, 6, 7

ONGOING ASSESSMENT and INTERVENTION

	DIAGNOSE	PRESCRIBE
Assess Prior Knowledge	**Before Chapter 3**	
	Diagnose readiness for the chapter.	Prescribe intervention.
	Are You Ready? SE p. 133	***Are You Ready? Intervention*** Skills 16, 56, 57, 60, 68
Formative Assessment	**Before Every Lesson**	
	Diagnose readiness for the lesson.	Prescribe intervention.
	Warm Up TE, every lesson	**Skills Bank** pp. SB1–SB32 **Review for Mastery** CRF Chapters 1–3
	During Every Lesson	
	Diagnose understanding of lesson concepts.	Prescribe intervention.
	Questioning Strategies TE, every example **Check It Out!** SE, every example **Think and Discuss** SE, every lesson **Write About It** SE, every lesson **Journal** TE, every lesson	**Reading Strategies** CRF, every lesson ***Success for ELL*** pp. 29–42 ***Lesson Tutorial Videos*** Chapter 3
	After Every Lesson	
	Diagnose mastery of lesson concepts.	Prescribe intervention.
	Lesson Quiz TE, every lesson **Alternative Assessment** TE, every lesson **Ready to Go On?** SE pp. 155, 185 ***Test and Practice Generator***	**Review for Mastery** CRF, every lesson **Problem Solving** CRF, every lesson ***Ready to Go On? Intervention*** Chapter 3 ***Homework Help Online***
	Before Chapter 3 Testing	
	Diagnose mastery of concepts in the chapter.	Prescribe intervention.
	Ready to Go On? SE pp. 155, 185 **Concept Connection** SE pp. 154, 184 **Section Quizzes** AR pp. 45–46 ***Test and Practice Generator***	***Ready to Go On? Intervention*** Chapter 3 **Scaffolding Questions** TE pp. 154, 184
	Before Assessment of California Standards	
	Diagnose mastery of California Standards.	Prescribe intervention.
	Focus on California Standards: Benchmark Tests **Mastering the Standards** SE pp. 194–195 ***California Standards Practice* CD-ROM**	***Focus on California Standards: Intervention***
Summative Assessment	**After Chapter 3**	
	Check mastery of chapter concepts.	Prescribe intervention.
	Multiple-Choice Tests (Forms A, B, C) **Free-Response Tests (Forms A, B, C)** **Performance Assessment** AR pp. 47–60 ***Test and Practice Generator***	**Review for Mastery** CRF, every lesson ***Lesson Tutorial Videos*** Chapter 3

KEY: **SE** = *Student Edition* **TE** = *Teacher's Edition* **CRF** = *Chapter Resource File* **AR** = *Assessment Resources* Available online Available on CD-ROM

Supporting the Teacher

Chapter 3 Resource File

Family Involvement
pp. 1–4, 29–32

Practice A, B, C
pp. 5–7, 13–15, 21–23, 33–35, 41–43, 49–51, 57–59

Review for Mastery
pp. 8–9, 16–17, 24–25, 36–37, 44–45, 52–53, 60–61

Challenge
pp. 10, 18, 26, 38, 46, 54, 62

Problem Solving
pp. 11, 19, 27, 39, 47, 55, 63

Reading Strategies ELL
pp. 12, 20, 28, 40, 48, 56, 64

Algebra Lab
pp. 65, 66–67

Workbooks

Homework and Practice Workbook SPANISH
Teacher's Edition .... pp. 15–21

Know-It Notebook SPANISH
Teacher's Guide .... Chapter 3

Review for Mastery Workbook SPANISH
Teacher's Guide .... pp. 29–42

Focus on California Standards: Intervention Workbook SPANISH
Teacher's Guide

Teacher Tools

Power Presentations
Complete PowerPoint® presentations for Chapter 3 lessons

Lesson Tutorial Videos SPANISH
Holt authors Ed Burger and Freddie Renfro present tutorials to support the Chapter 3 lessons.

Teacher's One-Stop Planner SPANISH
Easy access to all Chapter 3 resources and assessments, as well as software for lesson planning, test generation, and puzzle creation

IDEA Works!
Key Chapter 3 resources and assessments modified to address special learning needs

Solutions Key .... Chapter 3

Interactive Answers and Solutions

TechKeys

Lab Resources

Project Teacher Support

Parent Resources

Transparencies

Lesson Transparencies, Volume 1 .... Chapter 3
- Teacher Tools
- Warm-ups
- Teaching Transparencies
- Lesson Quizzes

Alternate Openers: Explorations .... pp. 15–21

Countdown to Mastery .... pp. 9–13

Know-It Notebook .... Chapter 3
- Vocabulary
- Key Concepts
- Graphic Organizers
- Chapter Review
- Big Ideas

Technology Highlights for the Teacher

Power Presentations

Dynamic presentations to engage students. Complete PowerPoint® presentations for every lesson in Chapter 3.

2-1 Solving One-Step Equations

Isolate a variable by using inverse operations which "undo" operations on the variable.

An equation is like a balanced scale. To keep the balance, perform the same operation on both sides.

Inverse Operations	
Operation	**Inverse Operation**
Addition	Subtraction
Subtraction	Addition

One-Stop Planner SPANISH

Easy access to Chapter 3 resources and assessments. Includes lesson planning, test generation, and puzzle creation software.

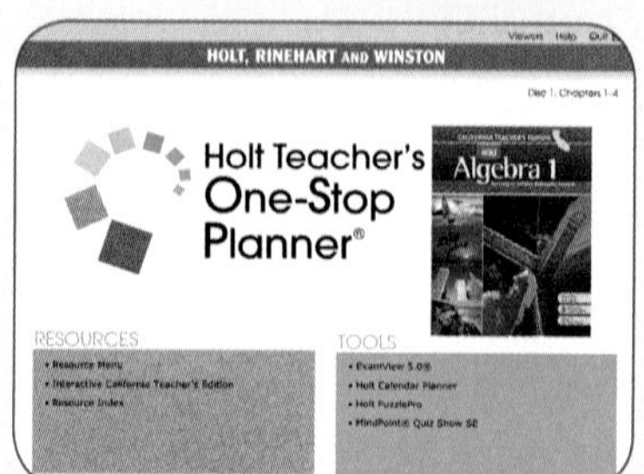

Premier Online Edition SPANISH

Includes Tutorial Videos, Lesson Activities, Lesson Quizzes, Homework Help, Chapter Project and more.

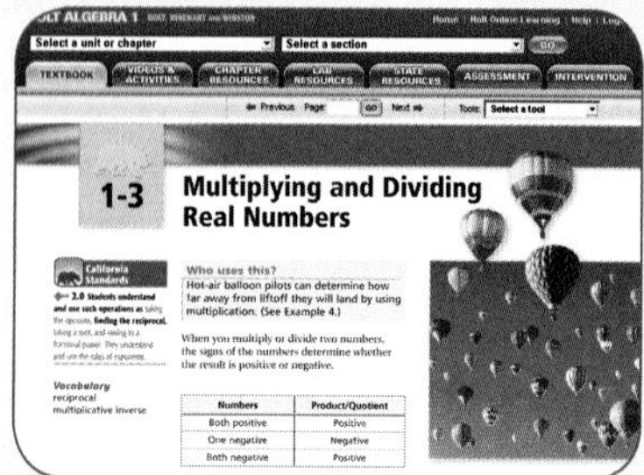

KEY: **SE** = *Student Edition* **TE** = *Teacher's Edition*  English Language Learners  Spanish available  Available online  Available on CD-ROM

Universal Access

Teaching Tips to help all students appear throughout the chapter. A few that target specific students are included in the lists below.

Strategic Students

Practice A	CRF, every lesson
Review for Mastery	CRF, every lesson
Reading Strategies	CRF, every lesson
Academic Vocabulary Connections	TE p. 134
Modeling	TE pp. 149, 171
Questioning Strategies	TE, every example
Ready to Go On? Intervention	Chapter 3
Know-It Notebook SPANISH	Chapter 3
Homework Help Online	
Lesson Tutorial Videos SPANISH	
Online Interactivities SPANISH	

Special Needs Students

Practice A	CRF, every lesson
Review for Mastery	CRF, every lesson
Reading Strategies	CRF, every lesson
Academic Vocabulary Connections	TE p. 134
Inclusion	TE pp. 139, 152, 160, 171
IDEA Works! Modified Resources	Chapter 3
Ready to Go On? Intervention	Chapter 3
Know-It Notebook SPANISH	Chapter 3
Lesson Tutorial Videos SPANISH	
Online Interactivities SPANISH	

English Learners

ENGLISH LANGUAGE LEARNERS

Reading Strategies	CRF, every lesson
Vocabulary Exercises	SE, every exercise set
Academic Vocabulary Connections	TE p. 134
English Language Learners	TE pp. 145, 172
Language Support	TE pp. 145, 172
Success for English Language Learners	Chapter 3
Know-It Notebook SPANISH	Chapter 3
Multilingual Glossary	
Lesson Tutorial Videos SPANISH	

Benchmark Students

Practice B	CRF, every lesson
Problem Solving	CRF, every lesson
Academic Vocabulary Connections	TE p. 134
Questioning Strategies	TE, every example
Ready to Go On? Intervention	Chapter 3
Know-It Notebook SPANISH	Chapter 3
Homework Help Online	
Online Interactivities SPANISH	

Advanced Students

Practice C	CRF, every lesson
Challenge	CRF, every lesson
Reading and Writing Math EXTENSION	TE p. 135
Concept Connection EXTENSION	TE pp. 154, 184
Ready to Go On? Enrichment	Chapter 3

Technology Highlights for Universal Access

Lesson Tutorial Videos SPANISH

Starring Holt authors Ed Burger and Freddie Renfro! Live tutorials to support every lesson in Chapter 3.

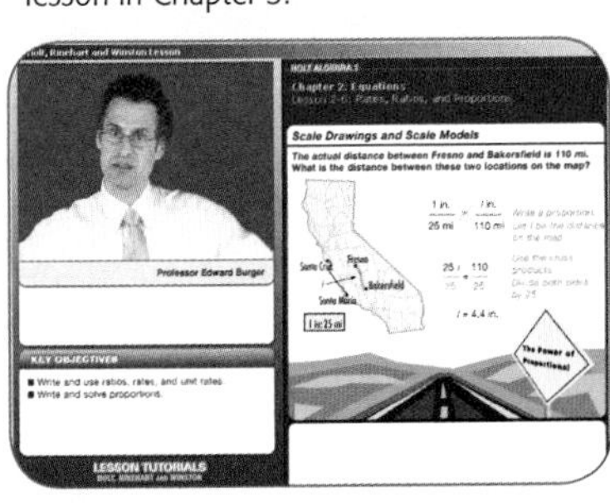

Multilingual Glossary

Searchable glossary includes definitions in English, Spanish, Vietnamese, Chinese, Hmong, Korean, and other languages.

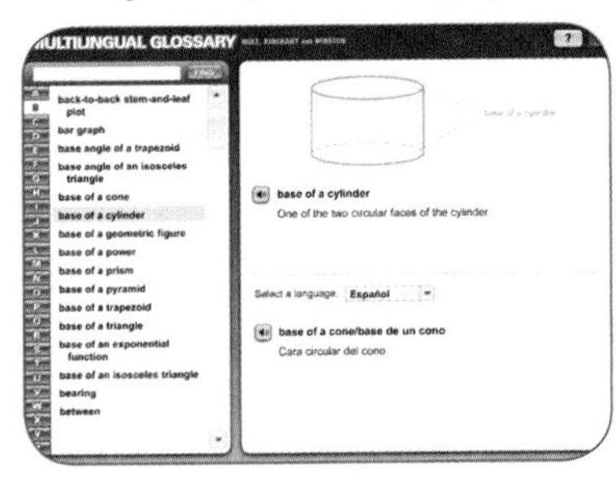

Online Interactivities SPANISH

Interactive tutorials provide visually engaging alternative opportunities to learn concepts and master skills.

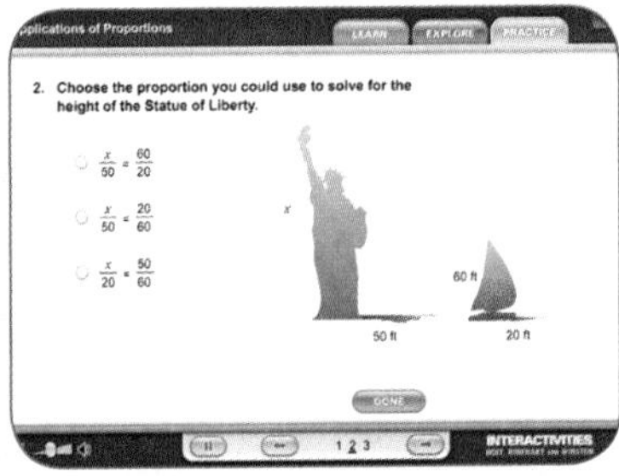

KEY: **SE** = *Student Edition* **TE** = *Teacher's Edition* **CRF** = *Chapter Resource File* SPANISH Spanish available  Available online Available on CD-ROM

Ongoing Assessment

Assessing Prior Knowledge

Determine whether students have the prerequisite concepts and skills for success in Chapter 3.

Are You Ready? SPANISH .... SE p. 133
Warm Up .... TE, every lesson

Chapter and Standards Assessment

Provide review and practice for Chapter 3 and standards mastery.

Concept Connection .... SE pp. 154, 184
Study Guide: Review .... SE pp. 186–189
Strategies for Success .... SE pp. 192–193
Mastering the Standards .... SE pp. 194–195
College Entrance Exam Practice .... SE p. 191
***Countdown to Mastery* Transparencies** .... pp. 9–13
Focus on California Standards: Benchmark Tests
Focus on California Standards: Intervention Workbook
***California Standards Practice* CD-ROM** SPANISH
IDEA Works! Modified Worksheets and Tests

Alternative Assessment

Assess students' understanding of Chapter 3 concepts and combined problem-solving skills.

Alternative Assessment .... TE, every lesson
Performance Assessment .... AR pp. 59–60
Portfolio Assessment .... AR p. xxxiii
Chapter 3 Project

Daily Assessment

Provide formative assessment for each day of Chapter 3.

Questioning Strategies .... TE, every example
Think and Discuss .... SE, every lesson
Check It Out! Exercises .... SE, every example
Write About It .... SE, every lesson
Journal .... TE, every lesson
Lesson Quiz .... TE, every lesson
Alternative Assessment .... TE, every lesson
IDEA Works! Modified Lesson Quizzes .... Chapter 3

Weekly Assessment

Provide formative assessment for each week of Chapter 3.

Concept Connection .... SE pp. 154, 184
Ready to Go On? .... SE pp. 155, 185
Cumulative Assessment .... SE pp. 194–195
Test and Practice Generator SPANISH .... *One-Stop Planner*

Formal Assessment

Provide summative assessment of Chapter 3 mastery.

Section Quizzes .... AR pp. 45–46
Chapter 3 Test SPANISH .... SE p. 190
Chapter Test (Levels A, B, C) .... AR pp. 47–58
• Multiple Choice • Free Response
Cumulative Test .... AR pp. 61–64
Test and Practice Generator SPANISH .... *One-Stop Planner*

Technology Highlights for Ongoing Assessment

Are You Ready? SPANISH

Automatically assess readiness and prescribe intervention for Chapter 3 prerequisite skills.

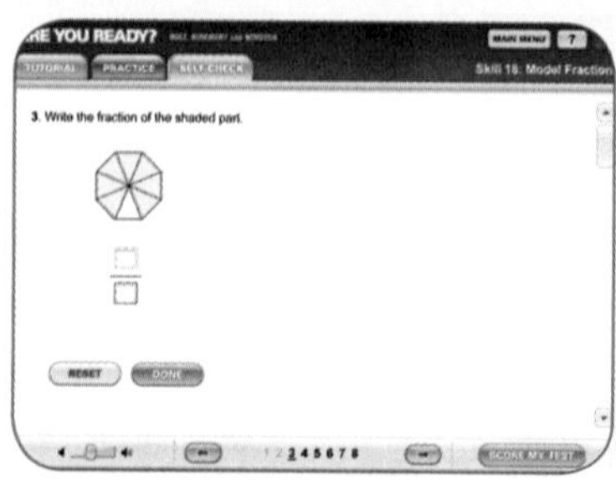

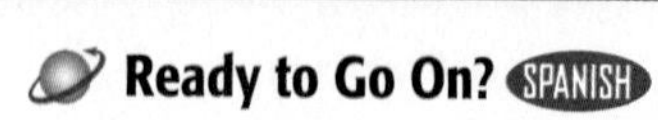

Ready to Go On? SPANISH

Automatically assess understanding of and prescribe intervention for Sections 3A and 3B.

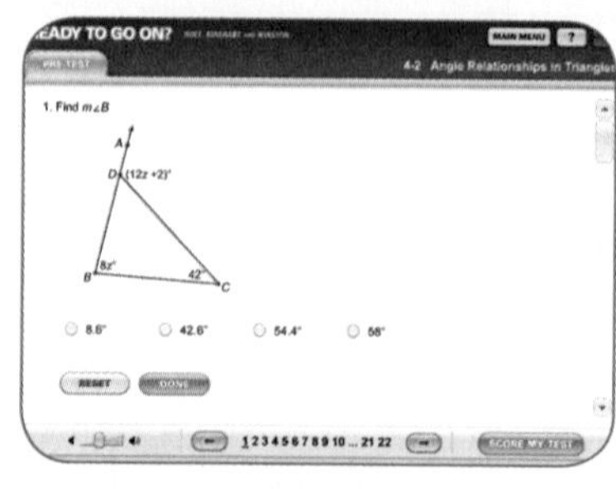

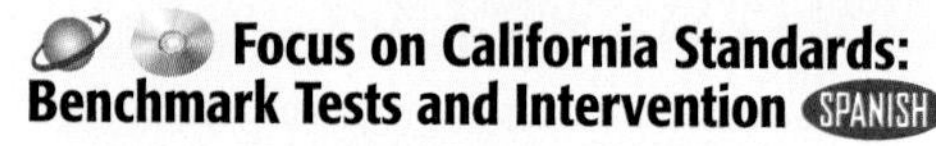

Focus on California Standards: Benchmark Tests and Intervention SPANISH

Automatically assess proficiency with California Algebra I Standards and provide intervention.

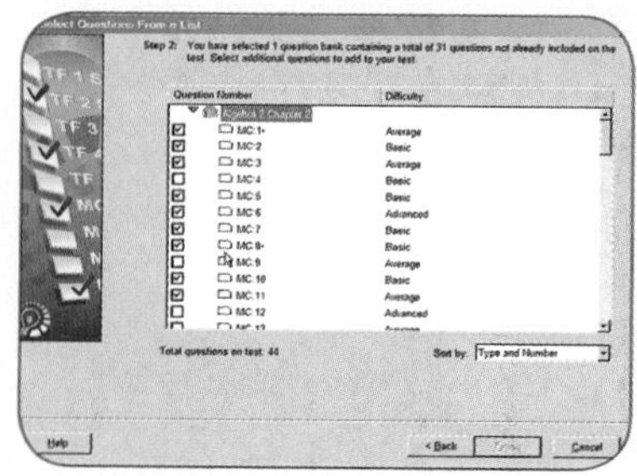

KEY: **SE** = *Student Edition* **TE** = *Teacher's Edition* **AR** = Assessment Resources  Spanish available  Available online 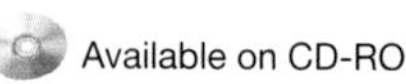 Available on CD-ROM

Three levels (A, B, C) of multiple-choice and free-response chapter tests are available in the *Assessment Resources.*

Modified tests and worksheets found in *IDEA Works!*

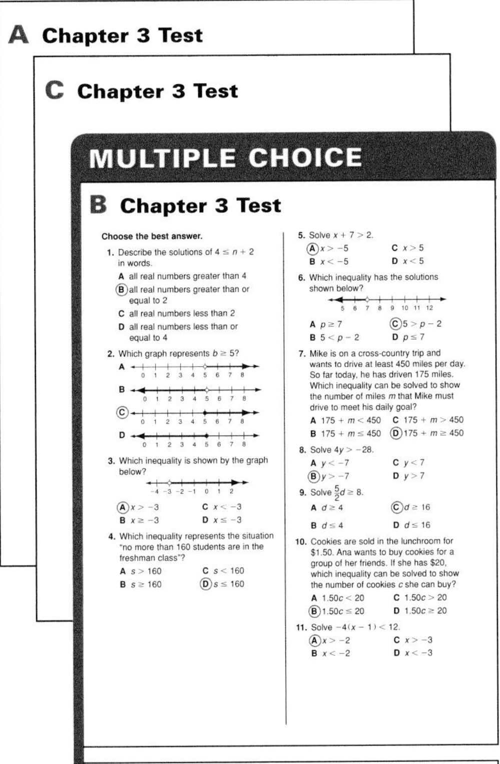

A Chapter 3 Test

C Chapter 3 Test

MULTIPLE CHOICE

B Chapter 3 Test

Choose the best answer.

1. Describe the solutions of $4 \le n + 2$ in words.
   A all real numbers greater than 4
   Ⓑ all real numbers greater than or equal to 2
   C all real numbers less than 2
   D all real numbers less than or equal to 4
2. Which graph represents $b \ge 5$?
3. Which inequality is shown by the graph below?
   Ⓐ $x > -3$ C $x < -3$
   B $x \ge -3$ D $x \le -3$
4. Which inequality represents the situation "no more than 160 students are in the freshman class"?
   A $s > 160$ C $s < 160$
   B $s \ge 160$ Ⓓ $s \le 160$
5. Solve $x + 7 > 2$.
   Ⓐ $x > -5$ C $x > 5$
   B $x < -5$ D $x < 5$
6. Which inequality has the solutions shown below?
   A $p \ge 7$ Ⓒ $5 > p - 2$
   B $5 < p - 2$ D $p \le 7$
7. Mike is on a cross-country trip and wants to drive at least 450 miles per day. So far today, he has driven 175 miles. Which inequality can be solved to show the number of miles m that Mike must drive to meet his daily goal?
   A $175 + m < 450$ C $175 + m > 450$
   B $175 + m \le 450$ Ⓓ $175 + m \ge 450$
8. Solve $4y > -28$.
   A $y < -7$ C $y < 7$
   Ⓑ $y > -7$ D $y > 7$
9. Solve $\frac{5}{2}d \ge 8$.
   A $d \ge 4$ Ⓒ $d \ge 16$
   B $d \le 4$ D $d \le 16$
10. Cookies are sold in the lunchroom for \$1.50. Ana wants to buy cookies for a group of her friends. If she has \$20, which inequality can be solved to show the number of cookies c she can buy?
    A $1.50c < 20$ C $1.50c > 20$
    Ⓑ $1.50c \le 20$ D $1.50c \ge 20$
11. Solve $-4(x - 1) < 12$.
    Ⓐ $x > -2$ C $x > -3$
    B $x < -2$ D $x < -3$

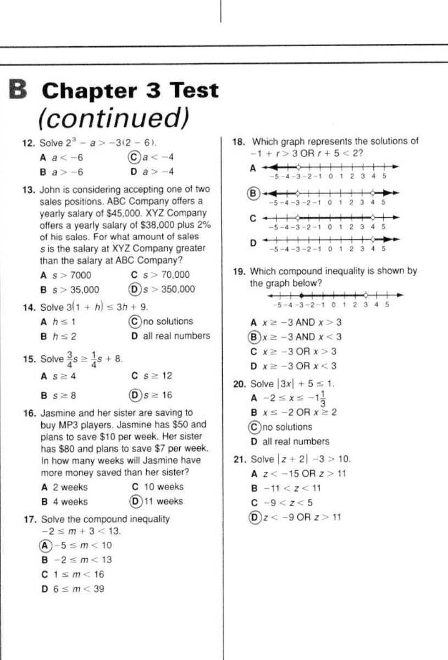

B Chapter 3 Test (continued)

12. Solve $2^3 - a > -3(2 - 6)$.
    A $a < -6$ Ⓒ $a < -4$
    B $a > -6$ D $a > -4$
13. John is considering accepting one of two sales positions. ABC Company offers a yearly salary of \$45,000. XYZ Company offers a yearly salary of \$38,000 plus 2% of his sales. For what amount of sales s is the salary at XYZ Company greater than the salary at ABC Company?
    A $s > 7000$ C $s > 70{,}000$
    B $s > 35{,}000$ Ⓓ $s > 350{,}000$
14. Solve $3(1 + h) \le 3h + 9$.
    A $h \le 1$ Ⓒ no solutions
    B $h \le 2$ D all real numbers
15. Solve $\frac{3}{4}s \ge \frac{1}{4}s + 8$.
    A $s \ge 4$ C $s \ge 12$
    B $s \ge 8$ Ⓓ $s \ge 16$
16. Jasmine and her sister are saving to buy MP3 players. Jasmine has \$50 and plans to save \$10 per week. Her sister has \$80 and plans to save \$7 per week. In how many weeks will Jasmine have more money saved than her sister?
    A 2 weeks C 10 weeks
    B 4 weeks Ⓓ 11 weeks
17. Solve the compound inequality $-2 \le m + 3 < 13$.
    Ⓐ $-5 \le m < 10$
    B $-2 \le m < 13$
    C $1 \le m < 16$
    D $6 \le m < 39$
18. Which graph represents the solutions of $-1 + r > 3$ OR $r + 5 < 2$?
19. Which compound inequality is shown by the graph below?
    A $x \ge -3$ AND $x > 3$
    Ⓑ $x \ge -3$ AND $x < 3$
    C $x \ge -3$ OR $x > 3$
    D $x \ge -3$ OR $x < 3$
20. Solve $|3x| + 5 \le 1$.
    A $-2 \le x \le -1\frac{1}{3}$
    B $x \le -2$ OR $x \ge 2$
    Ⓒ no solutions
    D all real numbers
21. Solve $|z + 2| - 3 > 10$.
    A $z < -15$ OR $z > 11$
    B $-11 < z < 11$
    C $-9 < z < 5$
    Ⓓ $z < -9$ OR $z > 11$

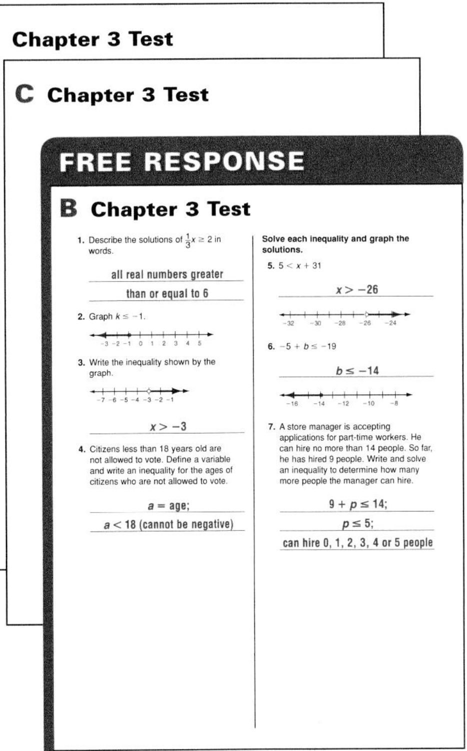

A Chapter 3 Test

C Chapter 3 Test

FREE RESPONSE

B Chapter 3 Test

1. Describe the solutions of $\frac{1}{3}x \ge 2$ in words.
   all real numbers greater than or equal to 6
2. Graph $k \le -1$.
3. Write the inequality shown by the graph.
   $x > -3$
4. Citizens less than 18 years old are not allowed to vote. Define a variable and write an inequality for the ages of citizens who are not allowed to vote.
   a = age; $a < 18$ (cannot be negative)

Solve each inequality and graph the solutions.

5. $5 < x + 31$
   $x > -26$
6. $-5 + b \le -19$
   $b \le -14$
7. A store manager is accepting applications for part-time workers. He can hire no more than 14 people. So far, he has hired 9 people. Write and solve an inequality to determine how many more people the manager can hire.
   $9 + p \le 14$; $p \le 5$; can hire 0, 1, 2, 3, 4 or 5 people

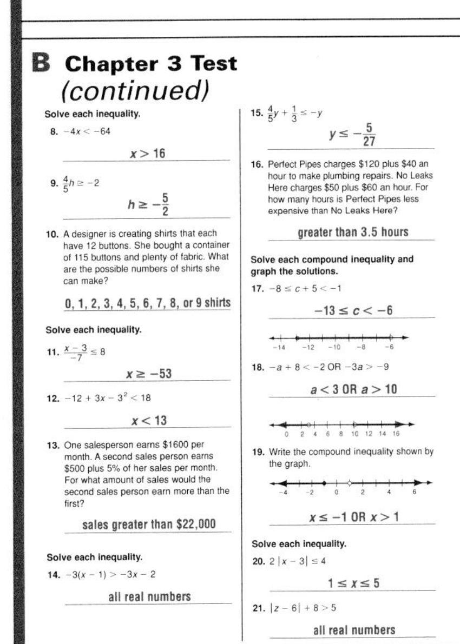

B Chapter 3 Test (continued)

Solve each inequality.

8. $-4x < -64$
   $x > 16$
9. $\frac{4}{5}h \ge -2$
   $h \ge -\frac{5}{2}$
10. A designer is creating shirts that each have 12 buttons. She bought a container of 115 buttons and plenty of fabric. What are the possible numbers of shirts she can make?
    0, 1, 2, 3, 4, 5, 6, 7, 8, or 9 shirts

Solve each inequality.

11. $\frac{x-3}{-7} \le 8$
    $x \ge -53$
12. $-12 + 3x - 3^2 < 18$
    $x < 13$
13. One salesperson earns \$1600 per month. A second sales person earns \$500 plus 5% of her sales per month. For what amount of sales would the second sales person earn more than the first?
    sales greater than \$22,000

Solve each inequality.

14. $-3(x - 1) > -3x - 2$
    all real numbers
15. $\frac{4}{5}y + \frac{1}{3} \le -y$
    $y \le -\frac{5}{27}$
16. Perfect Pipes charges \$120 plus \$40 an hour to make plumbing repairs. No Leaks Here charges \$50 plus \$60 an hour. For how many hours is Perfect Pipes less expensive than No Leaks Here?
    greater than 3.5 hours

Solve each compound inequality and graph the solutions.

17. $-8 \le c + 5 < -1$
    $-13 \le c < -6$
18. $-a + 8 < -2$ OR $-3a > -9$
    $a < 3$ OR $a > 10$
19. Write the compound inequality shown by the graph.
    $x \le -1$ OR $x > 1$

Solve each inequality.

20. $2|x - 3| \le 4$
    $1 \le x \le 5$
21. $|z - 6| + 8 > 5$
    all real numbers

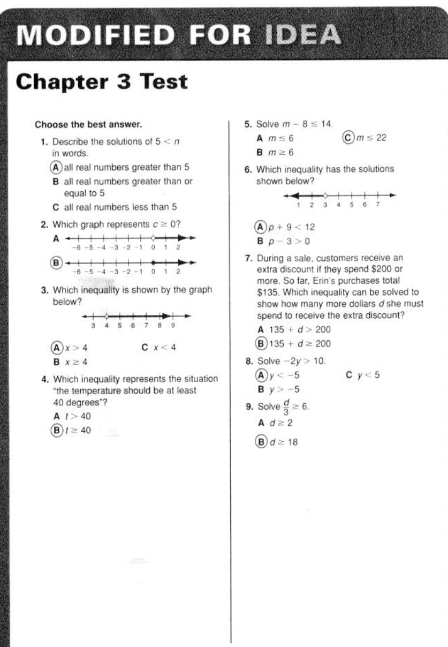

MODIFIED FOR IDEA

Chapter 3 Test

Choose the best answer.

1. Describe the solutions of $5 < n$ in words.
   Ⓐ all real numbers greater than 5
   B all real numbers greater than or equal to 5
   C all real numbers less than 5
2. Which graph represents $c \ge 0$?
3. Which inequality is shown by the graph below?
   Ⓐ $x > 4$ C $x < 4$
   B $x \ge 4$
4. Which inequality represents the situation "the temperature should be at least 40 degrees"?
   A $t > 40$
   Ⓑ $t \ge 40$
5. Solve $m - 8 \le 14$.
   A $m \le 6$ Ⓒ $m \le 22$
   B $m \ge 6$
6. Which inequality has the solutions shown below?
   Ⓐ $p + 9 < 12$
   B $p - 3 > 0$
7. During a sale, customers receive an extra discount if they spend \$200 or more. So far, Erin's purchases total \$135. Which inequality can be solved to show how many more dollars d she must spend to receive the extra discount?
   A $135 + d > 200$
   Ⓑ $135 + d \ge 200$
8. Solve $-2y > 10$.
   Ⓐ $y < -5$ C $y < 5$
   B $y > -5$
9. Solve $\frac{d}{3} \ge 6$.
   A $d \ge 2$
   Ⓑ $d \ge 18$

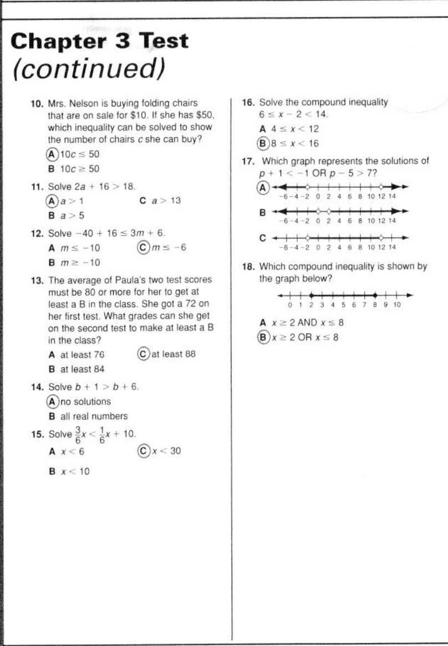

Chapter 3 Test (continued)

10. Mrs. Nelson is buying folding chairs that are on sale for \$10. If she has \$50, which inequality can be solved to show the number of chairs c she can buy?
    Ⓐ $10c \le 50$
    B $10c \ge 50$
11. Solve $2a + 16 > 18$.
    Ⓐ $a > 1$ C $a > 13$
    B $a > 5$
12. Solve $-40 + 16 \le 3m + 6$.
    A $m \le -10$ Ⓒ $m \le -6$
    B $m \ge -10$
13. The average of Paula's two test scores must be 80 or more for her to get at least a B in the class. She got a 72 on her first test. What grades can she get on the second test to make at least a B in the class?
    A at least 76 Ⓒ at least 88
    B at least 84
14. Solve $b + 1 > b + 6$.
    Ⓐ no solutions
    B all real numbers
15. Solve $\frac{3}{6}x < \frac{1}{6}x + 10$.
    A $x < 6$ Ⓒ $x < 30$
    B $x < 10$
16. Solve the compound inequality $6 \le x - 2 < 14$.
    A $4 \le x < 12$
    Ⓑ $8 \le x < 16$
17. Which graph represents the solutions of $p + 1 < -1$ OR $p - 5 > 7$?
18. Which compound inequality is shown by the graph below?
    A $x \ge 2$ AND $x \le 8$
    Ⓑ $x \ge 2$ OR $x \le 8$

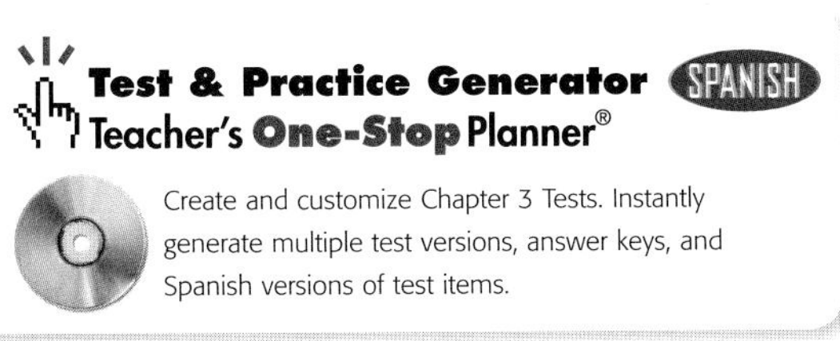

Test & Practice Generator SPANISH
Teacher's One-Stop Planner®

Create and customize Chapter 3 Tests. Instantly generate multiple test versions, answer keys, and Spanish versions of test items.

SECTION 3A
Simple Inequalities

On page 154, students write, solve, and graph inequalities to model the cost of travel, lodging, and entertainment while on a vacation.

Exercises designed to prepare students for success on the Concept Connection can be found on pages 140, 146, and 152.

SECTION 3B
Multi-Step and Compound Inequalities

On page 184, students write, solve, and graph inequalities to determine the costs associated with recording a CD at a studio.

Exercises designed to prepare students for success on the Concept Connection can be found on pages 160, 166, 175 and 182.

Algebra in *California*

County fairs often feature a variety of competitions. You can use inequalities to determine minimum scores needed to win a competition, as shown in Lesson 3-4 of this chapter.

CHAPTER 3

Inequalities

go.hrw.com
Chapter Project Online
KEYWORD: MA8CA ChProj

You can use inequalities to determine what is needed to win a competition at a county fair.

Los Angeles County Fair
Pomona, CA

About the Project

For a Good Cause

A car wash is a great way to raise money for an organization. In the chapter project students plan a car wash and decide how much to charge. Then students decide how many custom T-shirts to buy in order to promote the event. Students must write and solve inequalities to help them make these decisions.

Project Resources

All project resources for teachers and students are provided online.

Materials:

- none

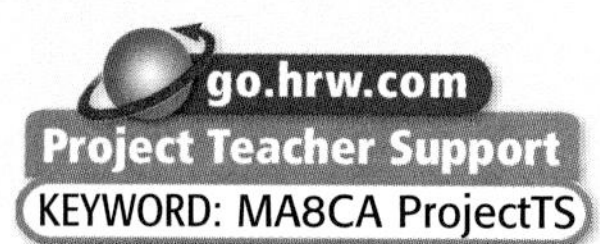

ARE YOU READY?

Vocabulary

Match each term on the left with a definition on the right.

1. equation B
2. evaluate E
3. inverse operations F
4. like terms D
5. solution of an equation C

A. mathematical phrase that contains operations, numbers, and/or variables
B. mathematical statement that two expressions are equivalent
C. value of a variable that makes a statement true
D. terms that contain the same variable raised to the same power
E. to find the value of an expression
F. operations that "undo" each other

Evaluate Expressions

Evaluate each expression for $a = 2$ and $b = 6$.

6. $b - a$ 4
7. ab 12
8. $b \div a$ 3
9. $a + b$ 8

Compare and Order Real Numbers

Compare. Write <, >, or =.

10. 10 < 21
11. 5.27 > 5.23
12. 20% = 0.2
13. $\frac{1}{3} < \frac{2}{5}$

Combine Like Terms

Simplify each expression by combining like terms.

14. $6x + x$ $7x$
15. $-8a + 3a$ $-5a$
16. $9x^2 - 15x^2$ $-6x^2$
17. $2.1x + 4.3x$ $6.4x$

Distributive Property

Simplify each expression.

18. $2(x + 3)$ $2x + 6$
19. $(3 - d)5$ $15 - 5d$
20. $4(r - 1)$ $4r - 4$
21. $3(4 + m)$ $12 + 3m$

Solve One-Step Equations

Solve.

22. $s - 3 = 8$ 11
23. $-7x = 21$ -3
24. $y + 11 = 2$ -9
25. $\frac{h}{2} = 6$ 12
26. $t + 2 = -2$ -4
27. $6x = 42$ 7
28. $r - 8 = -13$ -5
29. $\frac{y}{3} = -12$ -36

Organizer

Objective: Assess students' understanding of prerequisite skills.

Prerequisite Skills

- Evaluate Expressions
- Compare and Order Real Numbers
- Combine Like Terms
- Distributive Property
- Solve One-Step Equations

Assessing Prior Knowledge

INTERVENTION

Diagnose and Prescribe

Use this page to determine whether intervention is necessary or whether enrichment is appropriate.

Resources

 ***Are You Ready? Intervention and Enrichment* Worksheets**

 ***Are You Ready?* CD-ROM**

 ***Are You Ready?* Online**

my.hrw.com

ARE YOU READY? Diagnose and Prescribe

NO INTERVENE

Prerequisite Skill	*Are You Ready? Intervention,* Chapter 3: Worksheets	CD-ROM	Online
Evaluate Expressions	Skill 60	Activity 60	Diagnose and Prescribe Online
Compare and Order Real Numbers	Skill 16	Activity 16	
Combine Like Terms	Skill 57	Activity 57	
Distributive Property	Skill 56	Activity 56	
Solve One-Step Equations	Skill 68	Activity 68	

YES ENRICH

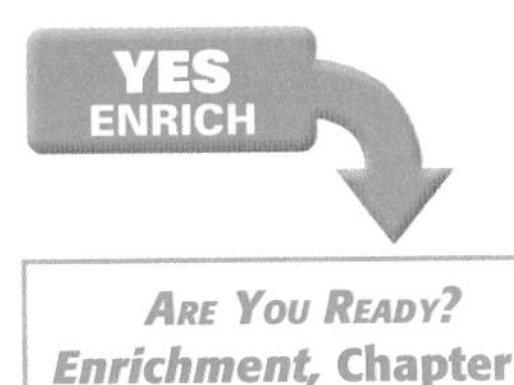

Are You Ready? Enrichment, Chapter 3
- Worksheets
- CD-ROM
- Online

Unpacking the Standards

Organizer

Objective: Help students understand the new concepts they will learn in Chapter 3.

Academic Vocabulary Connections

Becoming familiar with the academic vocabulary on this student page will be helpful to students. Discussing some of the vocabulary terms in the chapter also may be helpful.

1. The prefix *in-* means "not." An *equality* states that two things are equal. Use these meanings to write your own definition for the word **inequality**. An inequality states that two things are not equal.
2. The word *compound* means "consisting of two or more parts." What do you think a **compound inequality** might be? An inequality made of two or more simple inequalities
3. The **intersection** of two roads is the place where the two roads overlap. What do you think the *intersection* of two graphs would be? the place where the two graphs overlap
4. The word **union** begins with the root *uni-*. List some other words that begin with *uni-*. What do all of these words have in common? *Unite, unify, unit, unicycle, uniform, universal;* each word refers to a common whole, or single action, purpose, or thing.

CHAPTER 3

Unpacking the Standards

The information below "unpacks" the standards. The Academic Vocabulary is highlighted and defined to help you understand the language of the standards. Refer to the lessons listed after each standard for help with the math terms and phrases. The Chapter Concept shows how the standard is applied in this chapter.

California Standard	Academic Vocabulary	Chapter Concept
3.0 Students solve equations and **inequalities involving absolute values.** (Lesson **3-7**)	**involving** using or containing	You solve inequalities that have a variable inside absolute-value symbols.
4.0 Students simplify expressions before solving linear equations and **inequalities in one variable,** such as $3(2x - 5) + 4(x - 2) = 12$. (Lesson **3-4**)	**linear inequality** an inequality whose variable(s) have exponents not greater than 1	You write expressions in their simplest form so that you can find the values of a variable that make an inequality true.
5.0 Students solve multistep problems, including word problems, involving linear equations and **linear inequalities in one variable** and provide justification for each step. (Lessons **3-4, 3-5, 3-6, 3-7**)	**in one variable** containing one variable	You solve inequalities when the solution process requires two or more steps.
24.2 Students identify the hypothesis and conclusion in logical deduction. (p. 169)	**hypothesis** a statement that may or may not be true **conclusion** a statement that has been proved by reasoning	You look at a proof and name the original statement and the statement that has been proved.
25.2 Students judge the validity of an argument according to whether the properties of the real number system and the order of operations have been applied correctly at each step. (p. 169)	**judge** decide **validity** correctness **according to** depending on	You look at each step in a proof or solution and decide whether it is correct.

Standard 25.1 is also covered in this chapter. To see this standard unpacked, go to Chapter 8, p. 476.

134 Chapter 3

Looking Back

Previously, students:

- learned the properties of equality.
- solved equations by using inverse operations.
- solved multi-step equations and equations with variables on both sides.

In This Chapter

Students will study:

- the properties of inequality.
- solving inequalities by using inverse operations.
- solving multi-step inequalities and inequalities with variables on both sides.

Looking Forward

Students can use these skills:

- to solve inequalities in two variables.
- to solve systems of inequalities in two variables
- to solve nonlinear inequalities.

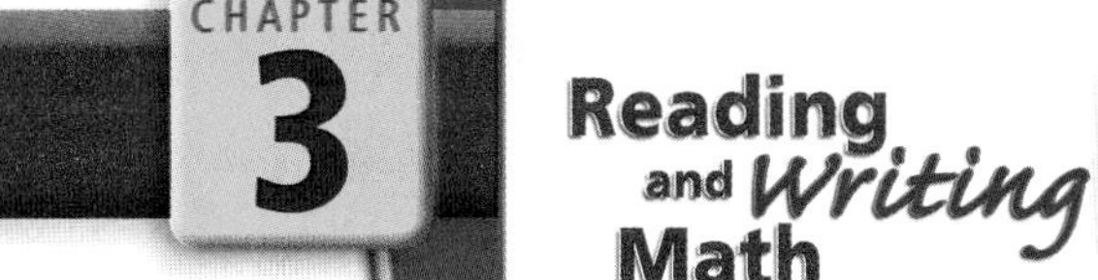

Study Strategy: Use Your Notes Effectively

Taking notes helps you arrange, organize, and process information from your textbook and class lectures. In addition to taking notes, you need to use your notes before and after class effectively.

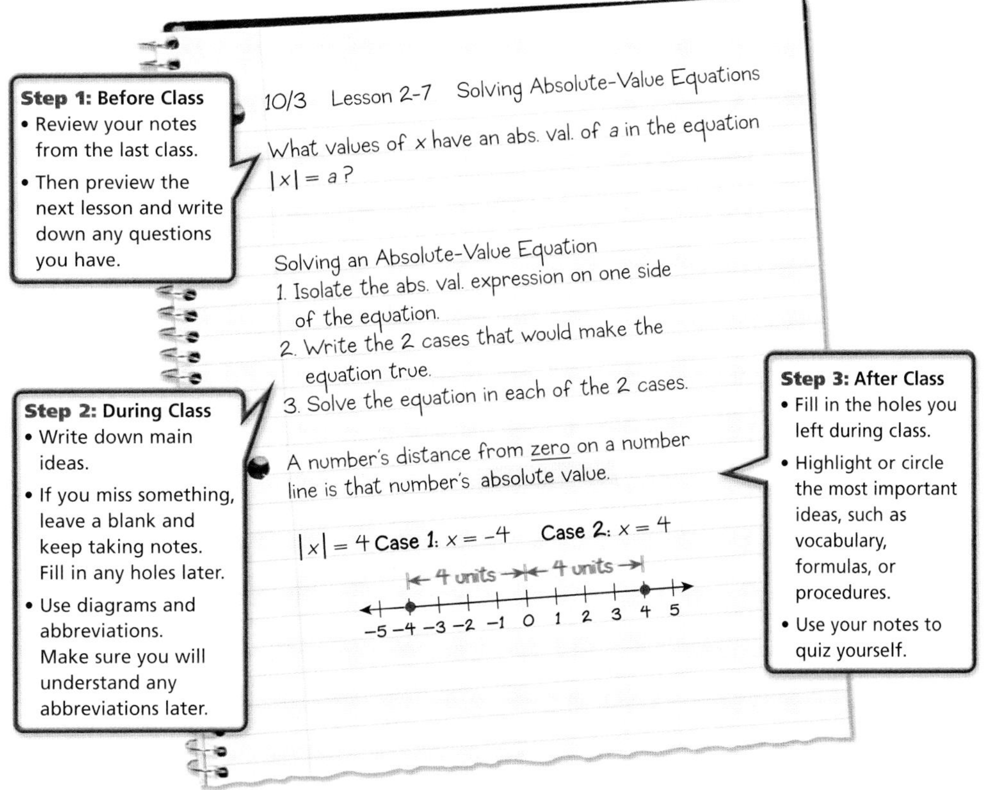

Step 1: Before Class
• Review your notes from the last class.
• Then preview the next lesson and write down any questions you have.
10/3 Lesson 2-7 Solving Absolute-Value Equations
What values of x have an abs. val. of a in the equation |x| = a?
Solving an Absolute-Value Equation
1. Isolate the abs. val. expression on one side of the equation.
2. Write the 2 cases that would make the equation true.
3. Solve the equation in each of the 2 cases.
A number's distance from zero on a number line is that number's absolute value.
|x| = 4 Case 1: x = -4 Case 2: x = 4
4 units 4 units
-5 -4 -3 -2 -1 0 1 2 3 4 5
Step 2: During Class
• Write down main ideas.
• If you miss something, leave a blank and keep taking notes. Fill in any holes later.
• Use diagrams and abbreviations. Make sure you will understand any abbreviations later.
Step 3: After Class
• Fill in the holes you left during class.
• Highlight or circle the most important ideas, such as vocabulary, formulas, or procedures.
• Use your notes to quiz yourself.

Try This

1. Look at the next lesson in your textbook. Write down some questions you have about the material in that lesson. Leave space between each question so that you can write the answers during the next class.
2. Look at the notes you took during the last class. List three ways you can improve your note-taking skills.

Reading and Writing Math

CHAPTER 3

Organizer

Objective: Help students apply strategies to understand and retain key concepts.

Resources

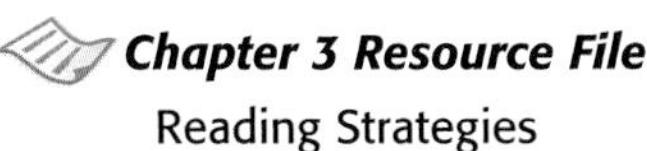

Reading Strategies

Study Strategy: Use Your Notes Effectively

Discuss Writing information down helps you retain more than just reading about or listening to it.

Notes are most helpful when they are well organized. Students may wish to divide their notebooks into sections for class notes, definitions, formulas, homework, scrap work, review, etc.

Extend Abbreviations can be used when taking notes to save space and time. Some students use *b/c* for *because* or *s/t* for *sometimes*. Ask students to share other abbreviations they use.

Answers to *Try This*

1–2. Check students' work.

Simple Inequalities

One-Minute Section Planner

Lesson	Lab Resources	Materials
Lesson 3-1 Graphing and Writing Inequalities • Identify solutions of inequalities in one variable. • Write and graph inequalities in one variable. **Preparation for 5.0**		
Lesson 3-2 Solving Inequalities by Adding or Subtracting • Solve one-step inequalities by using addition. • Solve one-step inequalities by using subtraction. **Preparation for 5.0**	***Algebra Lab 3-2*** In *Chapter 3 Resource File*	**Optional** index cards
Lesson 3-3 Solving Inequalities by Multiplying or Dividing • Solve one-step inequalities by using multiplication. • Solve one-step inequalities by using division. **Preparation for 5.0**		

MK = *Manipulatives Kit*

Notes

Math Background: Teaching the Standards

INEQUALITIES 5.0

Lessons 3-1 to 3-3

One of the basic building blocks of mathematics is the Law of Trichotomy. This axiom says that given any two real numbers, a and b, exactly one of the following is true:

$$a = b\ ,\ a < b\ ,\ \text{or}\ a > b.$$

In the first case, a and b are related by an equality. In the second and third cases, a and b are related by an *inequality.*

To understand inequalities, it is necessary to understand their connection to the real number line. For example, the inequality $-2 < 3$, which states that -2 is less than 3, means that -2 is to the left of 3 on the number line.

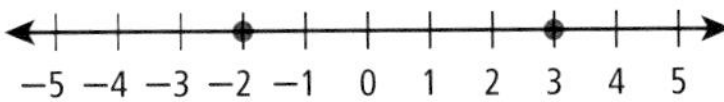

A *solution* of an inequality is any value of the variable that makes the inequality true. Thus, the solution set of $x < 3$ contains every value on the number line to the left of 3, since any of these values, when substituted in the inequality, result in a true statement. This solution set, consisting of infinitely many elements, can be shown as a ray on the number line. (The open circle at 3 indicates that $x = 3$ is not a solution.)

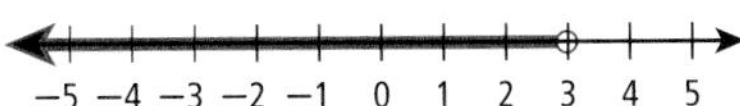

SOLVING INEQUALITIES 5.0

Lessons 3-1 to 3-3

Solving an inequality in one variable is similar to solving an equation in one variable. The goal is to isolate the variable on one side of the inequality by writing a series of equivalent inequalities–that is, a series of inequalities with the same solution set.

The Addition and Subtraction Properties of Inequality are analogous to their counterparts for equations: the same quantity may be added to or subtracted from both sides of an inequality. For multiplication and division there is an important caveat.

Consider the inequality $a > b$. By the Subtraction Property of Inequality, $a - a > b - a$ or, equivalently, $0 > b - a$. Applying the Subtraction Property of Inequality again shows that $0 - b > b - a - b$ or $-b > -a$, which is the same as $-a < -b$. In other words, when both sides of the inequality are multiplied by -1, the direction of the inequality is reversed. More generally, the direction of the inequality is reversed when both sides of an inequality are multiplied or divided by any negative number.

TRANSFORMATIONS

Lessons 3-1 to 3-3

We can use transformations to examine solutions of inequalities. For example, compare the graph of $x < 3$ with the graph of $x - 2 < 3$.

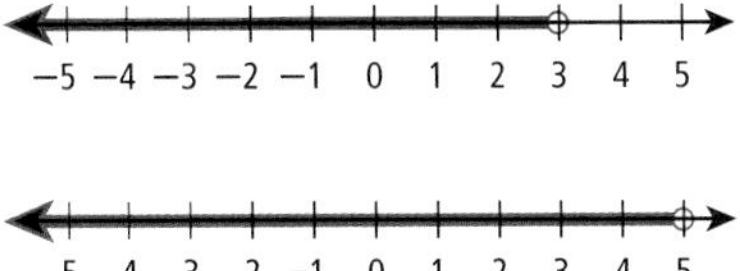

Notice that the graphs are identical except that the graph of $x - 2 < 3$ has been shifted 2 units to the right. In general, the graph of $x - a < k$ is the same as that of $x < k$, but shifted a units to the right (if $a > 0$) or $|a|$ units to the left (if $a < 0$).

The coefficient of x represents the stretching or shrinking of the graph. For example, the graph of $6x < 3$ is shown below.

As compared to the graph of $x < 3$, the ray is contracted toward the origin by a factor of 6.

Finally, the graph of $-x < 3$ is shown below.

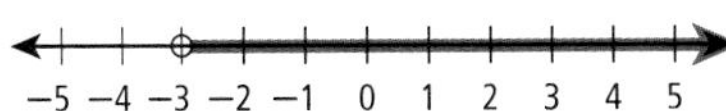

Comparing this to the graph of $x < 3$ shows that the negative sign in front of x reflects the ray about the origin.

3-1 Organizer

Objectives: Identify solutions of inequalities in one variable.

Write and graph inequalities in one variable.

Online Edition
Tutorial Videos, Interactivity

Countdown to Mastery Week 5

Power Presentations with PowerPoint®

Warm Up

Compare. Write <, >, or =.

1. -3 < 2 2. 6.5 > 6.3
3. $\frac{1}{2}$ > $-\frac{3}{4}$ 4. 0.25 = $\frac{1}{4}$

Tell whether the inequality $x < 5$ is true or false for the following values of x.

5. $x = -10$ T 6. $x = 5$ F
7. $x = 4.99$ T 8. $x = -\frac{1}{5}$ T

Also available on transparency

Q: Why did the Moore family name their son Lester?

A: So he could be called either "Moore" or "Les."

California Standards

Preparation for 🔑 5.0

3-1 Graphing and Writing Inequalities

Preparation for 🔑 5.0 Students solve multistep problems, including word problems, involving linear equations and **linear inequalities in one variable** and provide justification for each step.

Vocabulary
inequality
solution of an inequality

Who uses this?
Members of a crew team can use inequalities to be sure they fall within a range of weights. (See Example 4.)

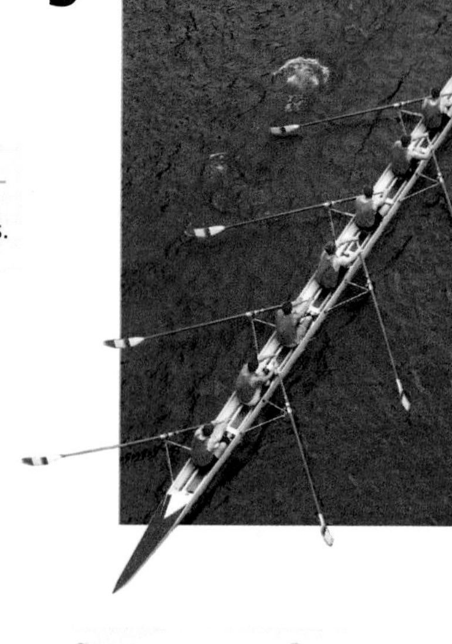

The athletes on a lightweight crew team must weigh 165 pounds or less. The acceptable weights for these athletes can be described using an *inequality*.

An **inequality** is a statement that two quantities are not equal. The quantities are compared by using one of the following signs:

$<$	$>$	$\leq$	$\geq$	$\neq$
$A < B$	$A > B$	$A \leq B$	$A \geq B$	$A \neq B$
A is less than *B*.	*A* is greater than *B*.	*A* is less than or equal to *B*.	*A* is greater than or equal to *B*.	*A* is not equal to *B*.

A **solution of an inequality** is any value that makes the inequality true. The set of all solutions of an inequality is its solution set.

EXAMPLE 1 Identifying Solutions of Inequalities

Describe the solutions of $3 + x < 9$ in words.

Test values of x that are positive, negative, and 0.

x	-2.75	0	5.99	6	6.01	6.1
$3 + x$	0.25	3	8.99	9	9.01	9.1
$3 + x \overset{?}{<} 9$	$0.25 \overset{?}{<} 9$	$3 \overset{?}{<} 9$	$8.99 \overset{?}{<} 9$	$9 \overset{?}{<} 9$	$9.01 \overset{?}{<} 9$	$9.1 \overset{?}{<} 9$
Solution?	Yes	Yes	Yes	No	No	No

When the value of x is a number less than 6, the value of $3 + x$ is less than 9.
When the value of x is 6, the value of $3 + x$ is equal to 9.
When the value of x is a number greater than 6, the value of $3 + x$ is greater than 9.

The solutions of $3 + x < 9$ are numbers less than 6.

1. Describe the solutions of $2p > 8$ in words. **all real numbers greater than 4**

1 Introduce

3-1 Graphing and Writing Inequalities

You can use a number line to help you see relationships among numbers.

1. Plot the following numbers on the number line: −5, 6, −3.5, 0, 1.5, −2, −7.
   −10 −8 −6 −4 −2 0 2 4 6 8 10
2. Which of the numbers that you plotted are greater than or equal to −5?
3. Name and plot three additional numbers that are greater than or equal to −5.
   −10 −8 −6 −4 −2 0 2 4 6 8 10
4. Draw a ray connecting all the numbers that are greater than or equal to −5.
   −10 −8 −6 −4 −2 0 2 4 6 8 10

THINK AND DISCUSS

5. **Describe** how the ray would be different if you plot and connect numbers that are less than or equal to −5.
6. **Explain** how you could draw a ray to show all numbers that are greater than or equal to $4\frac{1}{2}$.

Motivate

Make some statements like "There are fewer than 30 students in this class" and "The temperature will be at least 70 degrees tomorrow." Ask students what the phrases "fewer than" and "at least" mean. Ask students for other phrases that indicate a comparison.

Explorations and answers are provided in *Alternate Openers: Explorations Transparencies.*

An inequality like $3 + x < 9$ has too many solutions to list. One way to show all the solutions is to use a graph on a number line.

The solutions are shaded and an arrow shows that the solutions continue past those shown on the graph. To show that an endpoint is a solution, draw a solid circle at the number. To show that an endpoint is not a solution, draw an empty circle.

Know it! Note

Graphing Inequalities

WORDS	ALGEBRA	GRAPH
All real numbers less than 5	$x < 5$	−4 −3 −2 −1 0 1 2 3 4 5 6
All real numbers greater than −1	$x > -1$	−4 −3 −2 −1 0 1 2 3 4 5 6
All real numbers less than or equal to $\frac{1}{2}$	$x \le \frac{1}{2}$	−2 $-1\frac{1}{2}$ −1 $-\frac{1}{2}$ 0 $\frac{1}{2}$ 1
All real numbers greater than or equal to 0	$x \ge 0$	−4 −3 −2 −1 0 1 2 3 4 5 6

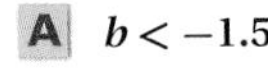

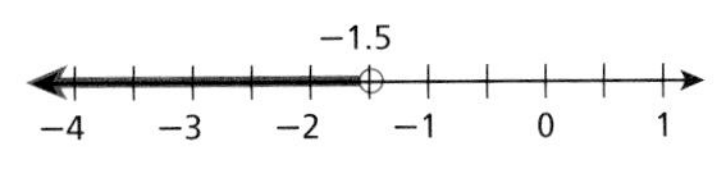

EXAMPLE 2 Graphing Inequalities

Graph each inequality.

A $b < -1.5$

−1.5

−4 −3 −2 −1 0 1

Draw an empty circle at −1.5.

Shade all the numbers less than −1.5 and draw an arrow pointing to the left.

B $r \ge 2$

−4 −3 −2 −1 0 1 2 3 4 5 6

Draw a solid circle at 2.

Shade all the numbers greater than 2 and draw an arrow pointing to the right.

CHECK IT OUT! Graph each inequality.

2a. $c > 2.5$ **2b.** $2^2 - 4 \ge w$ **2c.** $m \le -3$

2a. 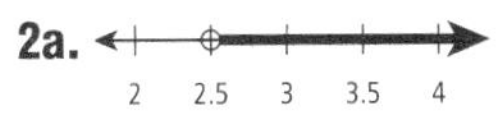
2 2.5 3 3.5 4

2b. 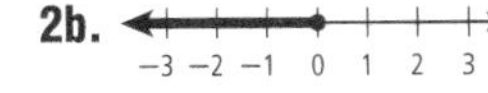
−3 −2 −1 0 1 2 3

2c. 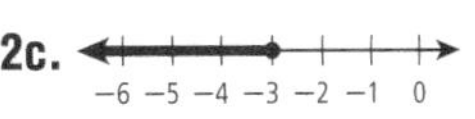
−6 −5 −4 −3 −2 −1 0

Student to Student: Graphing Inequalities

Victor Solomos
Palmer High School

To know which direction to shade a graph, I write inequalities with the variable on the left side of the inequality symbol. I know that the symbol has to point to the same number after I rewrite the inequality.

For example, I write $4 < y$ as $y > 4$.

Now the inequality symbol points in the direction that I should draw the shaded arrow on my graph.

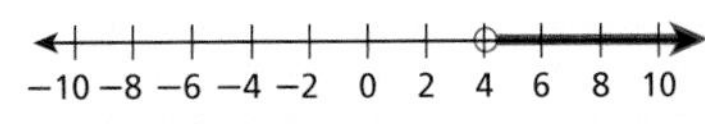
−10 −8 −6 −4 −2 0 2 4 6 8 10

2 Teach

Guided Instruction

Review the inequality symbols before identifying solutions of inequalities. Focus on building an understanding of inequalities, rather than solving inequalities. Procedures for solving will be addressed in subsequent lessons.

Discuss with students the similarities and differences between equations and inequalities. For example, have students describe the similarities and differences between $x = 3$ and $x < 3$, $x \le 3$, $x > 3$, and $x \ge 3$.

Universal Access

Through Cognitive Strategies

Use the DISC method to graph inequalities:

***D**raw*—Draw a number line and a circle at the endpoint.

***I**nclude?*—Look at the inequality sign to determine whether the circle should be solid or empty.

***S**hade*—Shade in the correct direction.

***C**heck*—Substitute a value on the solution side into the expression to check that the inequality is true.

COMMON ERROR ALERT

When students find that $x = 6$ does not make the inequality in **Example 1** true, some students believe the solution should be numbers less than 5. Remind them of the numbers between 5 and 6.

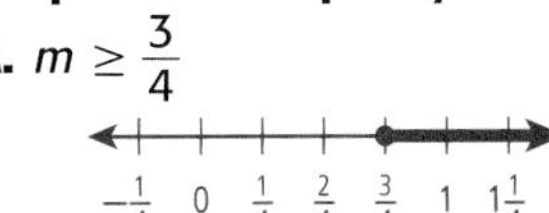

Power Presentations with PowerPoint®

Additional Examples

Example 1

Describe the solutions of $x - 6 \ge 4$ in words. all real numbers greater than or equal to 10

Example 2

Graph each inequality.

A. $m \ge \frac{3}{4}$

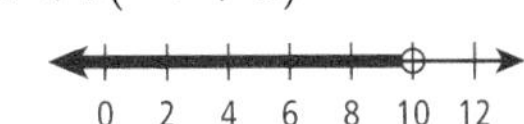
$-\frac{1}{4}$ 0 $\frac{1}{4}$ $\frac{2}{4}$ $\frac{3}{4}$ 1 $1\frac{1}{4}$

B. $t < 5(-1 + 3)$

0 2 4 6 8 10 12

Also available on transparency

INTERVENTION

Questioning Strategies

EXAMPLE 1

- Why is it important to test values for the variable that are positive, negative, and zero?

EXAMPLE 2

- How do you decide which way to shade the graph?

Teaching Tip **Communicating Math** Some people refer to a solid circle as "closed" and an empty circle as "open."

Teaching Tip **Geometry** A set of points that extend indefinitely in one direction is a *ray*. Many of the graphs in these exercises are rays.

Teaching Tip **Reading Math** Before **Example 4,** have students use the phrases "no more than," "no less than," "at most," and "at least" in everyday sentences. **ENGLISH LANGUAGE LEARNERS**

Power Presentations with PowerPoint®

Additional Examples

Example 3

Write the inequality shown by each graph.

A. 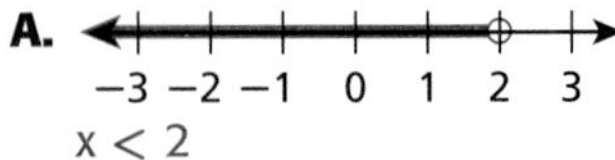

$x < 2$

B. 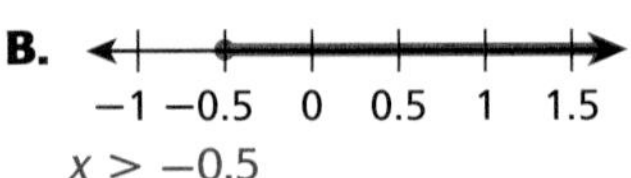

$x \geq -0.5$

Example 4

Ray's dad told him not to turn on the air conditioner unless the temperature is at least 85°F. Define a variable and write an inequality for the temperatures at which Ray can turn on the air conditioner. Graph the solutions.

$t \geq 85$

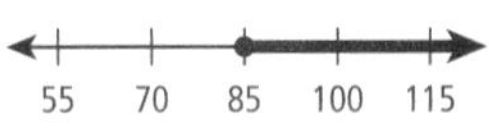

Also available on transparency

INTERVENTION

Questioning Strategies

EXAMPLE 3

- What does an empty or solid circle tell you? What does the direction of the arrow tell you?

EXAMPLE 4

- Do you think all the values that were shaded are reasonable answers in this situation?

Critical Thinking Discuss with students what types of problems might have answers that can only be whole numbers, positive numbers, etc.

EXAMPLE 3 Writing an Inequality from a Graph

Write the inequality shown by each graph.

A 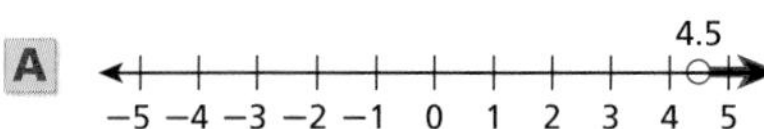

Use any variable. The arrow points to the right, so use either > or ≥.
The empty circle at 4.5 means that 4.5 is not a solution, so use >.

$h > 4.5$

B 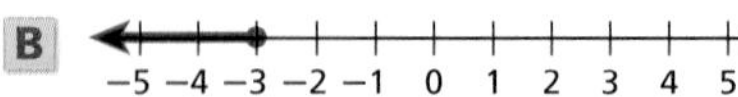

Use any variable. The arrow points to the left, so use either < or ≤.
The solid circle at −3 means that −3 is a solution, so use ≤.

$m \leq -3$

3. Write the inequality shown by the graph.

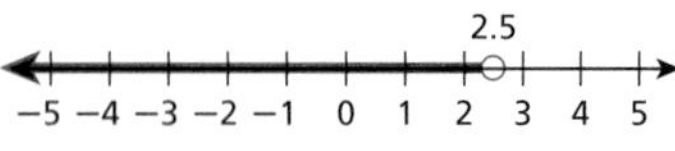

$x < 2.5$

EXAMPLE 4 *Sports Application*

The members of a lightweight crew team can weigh no more than 165 pounds each. Define a variable and write an inequality for the acceptable weights of the team members. Graph the solutions.

Reading Math

"No more than" or "at most" means "less than or equal to." (≤)

"At least" means "greater than or equal to." (≥)

Let w represent the weights that are allowed.

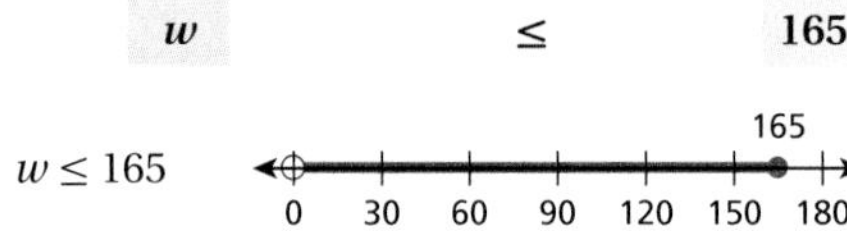

Athletes may weigh	no more than	165 pounds.
w	$\leq$	165

$w \leq 165$

Stop the graph at 0 because a person's weight must be a positive number.

4. A store's employees earn at least $8.25 per hour. Define a variable and write an inequality for the amount the employees may earn per hour. Graph the solutions.

4. d = amount employee can earn per hour; $d \geq 8.25$

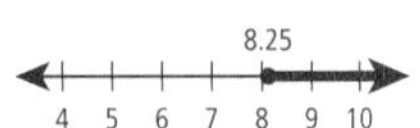

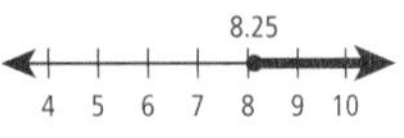

THINK AND DISCUSS

1. Compare the solutions of $x > 2$ and $x \geq 2$.

2. GET ORGANIZED Copy and complete the graphic organizer. Draw a graph in the first row and write the correct inequality in the second row.

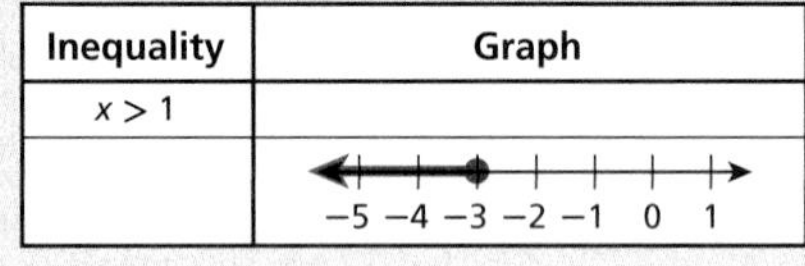

Inequality	Graph
$x > 1$	
	−5 −4 −3 −2 −1 0 1

3 Close

Summarize

Make sure students can describe the solutions of inequalities in words. Stress the need to test positive and negative values as well as zero. Remind students that there are many numbers between each integer.

When graphing inequalities that represent real-world situations, students should consider which values are reasonable in the context.

FORMATIVE ASSESSMENT and INTERVENTION 

***Diagnose Before* the Lesson**
3-1 Warm Up, TE p. 136

***Monitor During* the Lesson**
Check It Out! Exercises, SE pp. 136–138
Questioning Strategies, TE pp. 137–138

***Assess After* the Lesson**
3-1 Lesson Quiz, TE p. 141
Alternative Assessment, TE p. 141

Answers to *Think and Discuss*

1. Both graphs include the real numbers greater than 2. The graph of $x \geq 2$ also includes 2.
2. See p. A3.

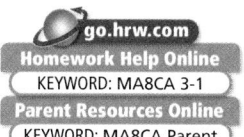

3-1 Exercises

California Standards Practice
Preparation for 5.0

go.hrw.com
Homework Help Online
KEYWORD: MA8CA 3-1
Parent Resources Online
KEYWORD: MA8CA Parent

GUIDED PRACTICE

1. **Vocabulary** How is a *solution of an inequality* like a solution of an equation?
A solution of an inequality makes the inequality true when substituted for the variable.

SEE EXAMPLE 1 p. 136

Describe the solutions of each inequality in words.

2. $g - 5 \geq 6$ 3. $-2 < h + 1$ 4. $20 > 5t$ 5. $5 - x \leq 2$

SEE EXAMPLE 2 p. 137

Graph each inequality.

6. $x < -5$ 7. $c \geq 3\frac{1}{2}$ 8. $(4 - 2)^3 > m$ 9. $p \geq \sqrt{17 + 8}$

SEE EXAMPLE 3 p. 138

Write the inequality shown by each graph.

10. 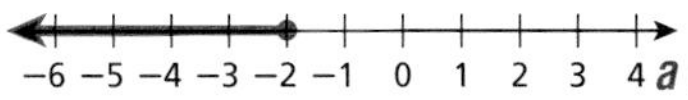

$a \leq -2$

11. 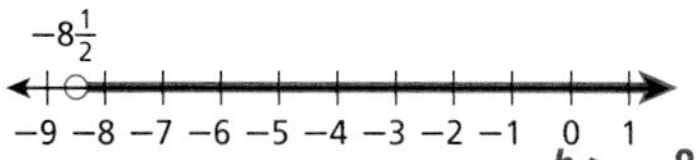

$b > -8\frac{1}{2}$

12. 

$c < 5.5$

13. 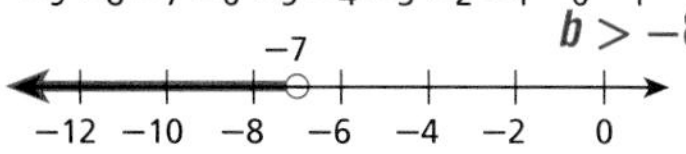

$d < -7$

14. 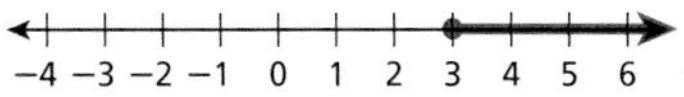

$e \geq 3$

15. 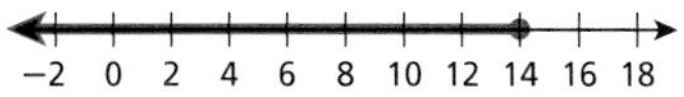

$f \leq 14$

SEE EXAMPLE 4 p. 138

Define a variable and write an inequality for each situation. Graph the solutions.

16. There must be at least 20 club members present in order to hold a meeting. **m = members present; $m \geq 20$**
17. A trainer advises an athlete to keep his heart rate under 140 beats per minute. **r = heart rate; $r < 140$**

PRACTICE AND PROBLEM SOLVING

Independent Practice

For Exercises	See Example
18–21	1
22–25	2
26–31	3
32–33	4

Extra Practice
Skills Practice p. EP6
Application Practice p. EP26

Describe the solutions of each inequality in words.

18. $-2t > -8$ 19. $0 > w - 2$ 20. $3k > 9$ 21. $\frac{1}{2}b \leq 6$

Graph each inequality.

22. $7 < x$ 23. $t \leq -\frac{1}{2}$ 24. $d > 4(5 - 8)$ 25. $t \leq 3^2 - 2^2$

Write the inequality shown by each graph.

26. 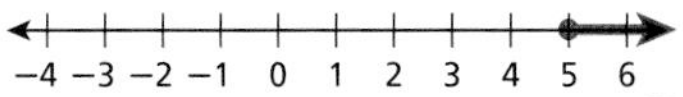

$u \geq 5$

27. 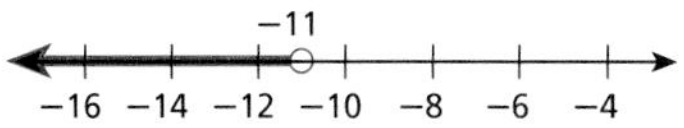

$v < -11$

28. 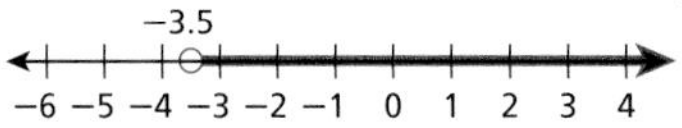

$w > -3.5$

29. 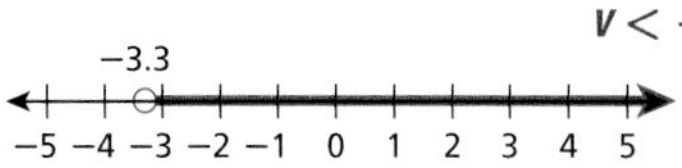

$x > -3.3$

30. 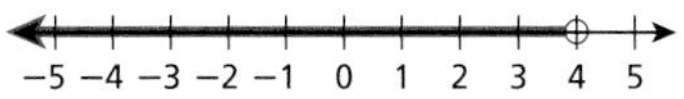

$y < 4$

31. 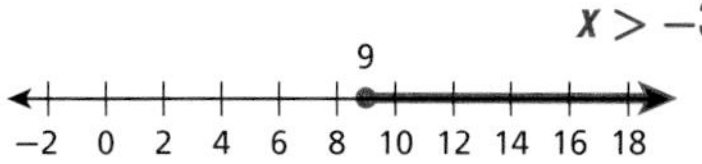

$z \geq 9$

Define a variable and write an inequality for each situation. Graph the solutions.

32. The maximum speed allowed on Main Street is 25 miles per hour. **s = speed; $s \leq 25$**
33. Applicants must have at least 5 years of experience. **y = years of experience; $y \geq 5$**

3-1 Exercises

Assignment Guide

Assign *Guided Practice* exercises as necessary.

If you finished Examples **1–2**
Proficient 18–25, 34–41, 62–64, 67
Advanced 18–25, 34–41, 62–66

If you finished Examples **1–4**
Proficient 18–33, 34–48 even, 54–68, 70–80
Advanced 18–33, 38–45, 54–56, 58–80

Homework Quick Check
Quickly check key concepts.
Exercises: 18, 22, 28, 32, 40, 42

Teaching Tip

Inclusion For exercises like **Exercises 32–33,** have students ask themselves a question to decide whether the boundary number is allowed. For example, for **Exercise 32,** ask "Is 25 miles per hour allowed?" Yes, so the graph should have a solid circle.

Answers

2. all real numbers greater than or equal to 11
3. all real numbers greater than −3
4. all real numbers less than 4
5. all real numbers greater than or equal to 3
6. 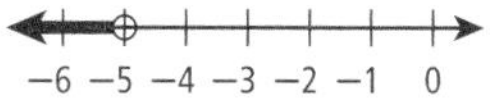

7. 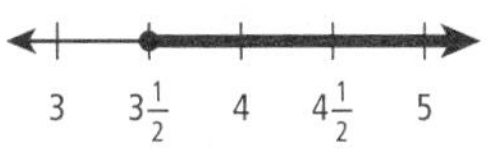

8. 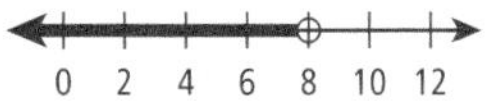

9. 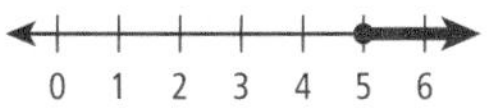

16. 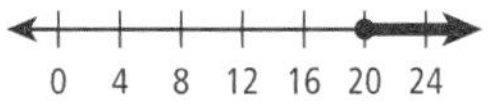

17. 

18. all real numbers less than 4
19. all real numbers less than 2
20. all real numbers greater than 3
21. all real numbers less than or equal to 12

22. 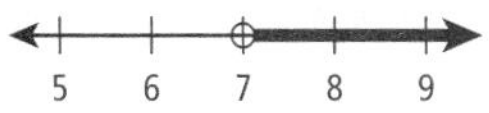

23. 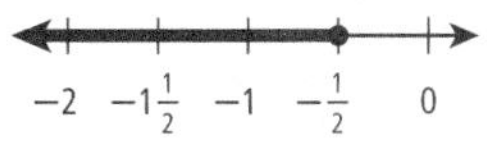

24. 

25. 

32. 

33. 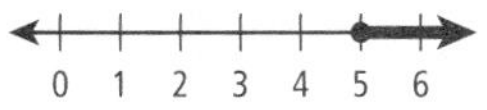

California Standards

Standard	Exercises
3.0	80
4.0	78, 79
Prep for 5.0	2–9, 16–25, 32, 33, 38–49, 55, 58–60, 62–68
6NS2.3	70–73
7AF1.3	74–76

Exercise 55 involves using inequalities to describe how much money can be spent shopping while on a trip. This exercise prepares students for the Concept Connection on page 154.

Answers

34. x is greater than 7.
35. h is less than −5.
36. d is less than or equal to 23.
37. r is greater than or equal to −2.

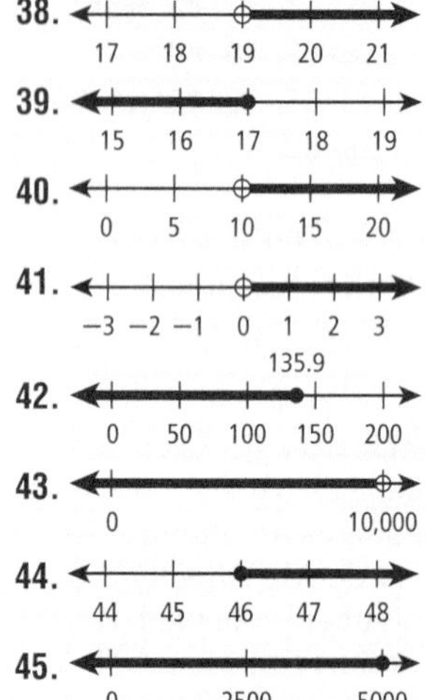

46. Possible answer: x represents the distance in miles between the two locations.
47. Possible answer: x represents the age in years of a child at a child-care center when x is positive.
48. Possible answer: x represents the hour on an analog clock when x is a natural number.
49. Possible answer: x represents the number of millions of albums sold by a popular band.

Write each inequality in words.

34. $x > 7$ **35.** $h < -5$ **36.** $d \leq 23$ **37.** $r \geq -2$

Write each inequality with the variable on the left. Graph the solutions.

38. $19 < g$ $g > 19$ **39.** $17 \geq p$ $p \leq 17$ **40.** $10 < e$ $e > 10$ **41.** $0 < f$ $f > 0$

Define a variable and write an inequality for each situation. Graph the solutions.

42. The highest temperature ever recorded on Earth was 135.9°F at Al Aziziyah, Libya, on September 13, 1922. **42.** t = temperature; $t \leq 135.9$

43. Businesses with profits less than \$10,000 per year will be shut down. p = profits; $p < 10{,}000$

44. You must be at least 46 inches tall to ride the Indiana Jones Adventure ride at Disney's California Adventure Park. h = height; $h \geq 46$

45. Due to a medical condition, a hiker can hike only in areas with an elevation no more than 5000 feet above sea level. e = elevation; $e \leq 5000$

Write a real-world situation that could be described by each inequality.

46. $x \geq 0$ **47.** $x < 10$ **48.** $x \leq 12$ **49.** $x > 8.5$

Match each inequality with its graph.

50. $x \geq 5$ **A** — **A.** −2 −1 0 1 2 3 4 5 6 7 8

51. $x < 5$ **D** — **B.** −2 −1 0 1 2 3 4 5 6 7 8

52. $x > 5$ **B** — **C.** −2 −1 0 1 2 3 4 5 6 7 8

53. $x \leq 5$ **C** — **D.** −2 −1 0 1 2 3 4 5 6 7 8

54. ///ERROR ANALYSIS/// Two students graphed the inequality $4 > b$. Which graph is incorrect? Explain the error. **A is incorrect; it should be drawn with an empty circle.**

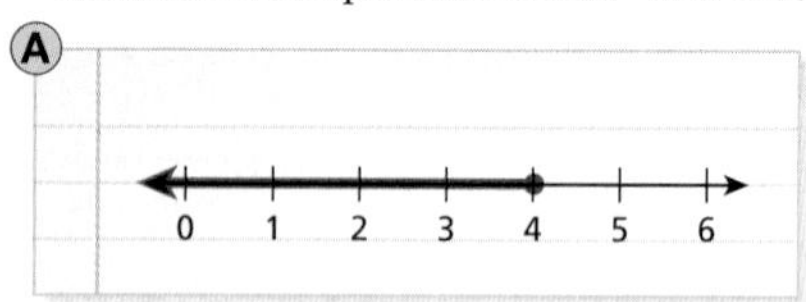

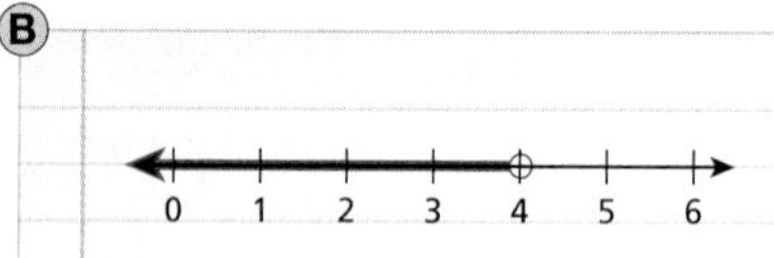

55a. $125 - s \geq 90$; $s \leq 35$ **55b.** 0 5 15 25 35 **55c.** $s + 15 \leq 35$; $s \leq 20$ where s is nonnegative

55. This problem will prepare you for the Concept Connection on page 154.

a. Mirna earned \$125 baby-sitting during the spring break. She needs to save \$90 for the German Club trip. She wants to spend the remainder of the money shopping. Write an inequality to show how much she can spend.

b. Graph the inequality you wrote in part **a**.

c. Mirna spends \$15 on a bracelet. Write an inequality to show how much money she has left to spend.

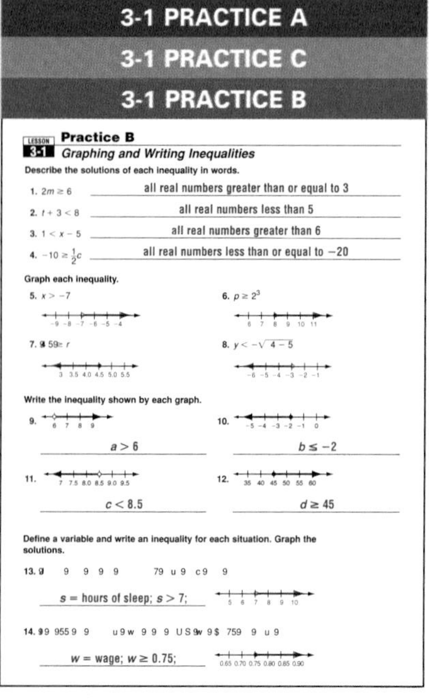

3-1 PRACTICE A

3-1 PRACTICE C

3-1 PRACTICE B

LESSON 3-1 **Practice B**
Graphing and Writing Inequalities

Describe the solutions of each inequality in words.

1. $2m \geq 6$ all real numbers greater than or equal to 3
2. $t + 3 < 8$ all real numbers less than 5
3. $1 < x - 5$ all real numbers greater than 6
4. $-10 \geq \frac{1}{2}c$ all real numbers less than or equal to −20

Graph each inequality.

5. $x > -7$ (−9 −8 −7 −6 −5 −4)
6. $p \geq 2^3$ (6 7 8 9 10 11)
7. 9 59= r (3 3.5 4.0 4.5 5.0 5.5)
8. $y < -\sqrt{4-5}$ (−6 −5 −4 −3 −2 −1)

Write the inequality shown by each graph.

9. (6 7 8 9) $a > 6$
10. (−5 −4 −3 −2 −1 0) $b \leq -2$
11. (7 7.5 8.0 8.5 9.0 9.5) $c < 8.5$
12. (35 40 45 50 55 60) $d \geq 45$

Define a variable and write an inequality for each situation. Graph the solutions.

13. 9 9 9 9 9 79 u 9 c9 9
s = hours of sleep; $s > 7$; (5 6 7 8 9 10)

14. 99 9559 9 u9w 9 9 9 US9w 9$ 759 9 u 9
w = wage; $w \geq 0.75$; (0.65 0.70 0.75 0.80 0.85 0.90)

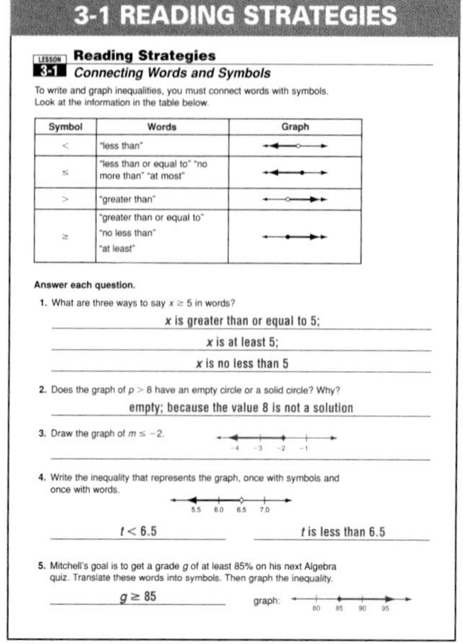

3-1 READING STRATEGIES

LESSON 3-1 **Reading Strategies**
Connecting Words and Symbols

To write and graph inequalities, you must connect words with symbols. Look at the information in the table below.

Symbol	Words	Graph
<	"less than"	
≤	"less than or equal to" "no more than" "at most"	
>	"greater than"	
≥	"greater than or equal to" "no less than" "at least"	

Answer each question.

1. What are three ways to say $x \geq 5$ in words?
x is greater than or equal to 5;
x is at least 5;
x is no less than 5

2. Does the graph of $p > 8$ have an empty circle or a solid circle? Why?
empty; because the value 8 is not a solution

3. Draw the graph of $m \leq -2$. (−4 −3 −2 −1)

4. Write the inequality that represents the graph, once with symbols and once with words. (5.5 6.0 6.5 7.0)
$t < 6.5$ — t is less than 6.5

5. Mitchell's goal is to get a grade g of at least 85% on his next Algebra quiz. Translate these words into symbols. Then graph the inequality.
$g \geq 85$ graph: (80 85 90 95)

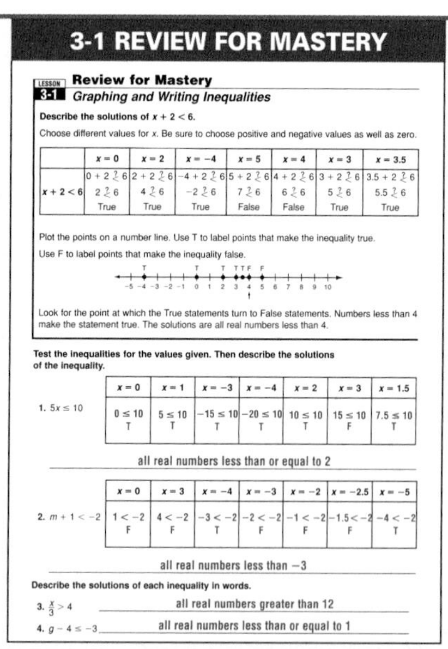

3-1 REVIEW FOR MASTERY

LESSON 3-1 **Review for Mastery**
Graphing and Writing Inequalities

Describe the solutions of $x + 2 < 6$.

Choose different values for x. Be sure to choose positive and negative values as well as zero.

	$x = 0$	$x = 2$	$x = -4$	$x = 5$	$x = 4$	$x = 3$	$x = 3.5$
$x + 2 < 6$	$0 + 2 \overset{?}{<} 6$ $2 \overset{?}{<} 6$ True	$2 + 2 \overset{?}{<} 6$ $4 \overset{?}{<} 6$ True	$-4 + 2 \overset{?}{<} 6$ $-2 \overset{?}{<} 6$ True	$5 + 2 \overset{?}{<} 6$ $7 \overset{?}{<} 6$ False	$4 + 2 \overset{?}{<} 6$ $6 \overset{?}{<} 6$ False	$3 + 2 \overset{?}{<} 6$ $5 \overset{?}{<} 6$ True	$3.5 + 2 \overset{?}{<} 6$ $5.5 \overset{?}{<} 6$ True

Plot the points on a number line. Use T to label points that make the inequality true.

Use F to label points that make the inequality false.

(T T T T T F F; −5 −4 −3 −2 −1 0 1 2 3 4 5 6 7 8 9 10)

Look for the point at which the True statements turn to False statements. Numbers less than 4 make the statement true. The solutions are all real numbers less than 4.

Test the inequalities for the values given. Then describe the solutions of the inequality.

1. $5x \leq 10$

$x = 0$	$x = 1$	$x = -3$	$x = -4$	$x = 2$	$x = 3$	$x = 1.5$
$0 \leq 10$ T	$5 \leq 10$ T	$-15 \leq 10$ T	$-20 \leq 10$ T	$10 \leq 10$ T	$15 \leq 10$ F	$7.5 \leq 10$ T

all real numbers less than or equal to 2

2. $m + 1 < -2$

$x = 0$	$x = 3$	$x = -4$	$x = -3$	$x = -2$	$x = -2.5$	$x = -5$
$1 < -2$ F	$4 < -2$ F	$-3 < -2$ T	$-2 < -2$ F	$-1 < -2$ F	$-1.5 < -2$ F	$-4 < -2$ T

all real numbers less than −3

Describe the solutions of each inequality in words.

3. $\frac{x}{3} > 4$ all real numbers greater than 12
4. $g - 4 \leq -3$ all real numbers less than or equal to 1

56. **Critical Thinking** Graph all positive integer solutions of the inequality $x < 5$.

57. **Write About It** Explain how to write an inequality that is modeled by a graph. What characteristics do you look for in the graph?

58. **Write About It** You were told in the lesson that the phrase "no more than" means "less than or equal to" and the phrase "at least" means "greater than or equal to."
   a. What does the phrase "at most" mean? **less than or equal to**
   b. What does the phrase "no less than" mean? **greater than or equal to**

Multiple Choice For Exercises 59–61, choose the best answer.

59. Which is NOT a solution of the inequality $5 - 2x \geq -3$?
   (A) 0 (B) 2 (C) 4 **(D) 5**

60. Which is NOT a solution of the inequality $3 - x < 2$?
   (A) 1 (B) 2 (C) 3 (D) 4

61. Which graph represents the solutions of $-2 \leq 1 - t$?

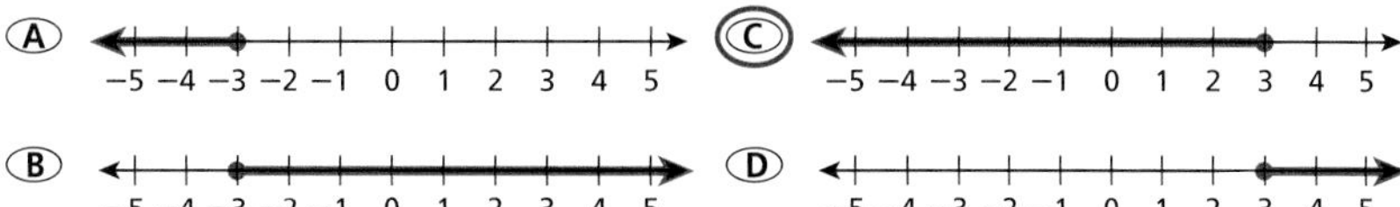

CHALLENGE AND EXTEND

Reasoning Describe the values for x and y that make each inequality true.

62. $x + y \leq |x + y|$ **all real numbers**
63. $x^2 < xy$ **any numbers such that $|x| < |y|$**
64. $x - y \geq y - x$ **any numbers such that y is less than or equal to x**

Complete each statement. Write < or >.

65. If $a > b$, then b **<** a.
66. If $x > y$ and $y > z$, then x **>** z.
67. Name a value of x that makes the statement $0.35 < x < 1.27$ true. **any number between 0.35 and 1.27**
68. Is $\frac{5}{6}$ a solution of $x < 1$? How many solutions of $x < 1$ are between 0 and 1?

68. yes; infinitely many

69. **Write About It** Explain how to graph all the solutions of $x \neq 5$.
   Draw an empty circle at 5. Then draw arrows going left and right from 5.

SPIRAL STANDARDS REVIEW

6NS2.3, 7AF1.3, 3.0, 4.0

Add or subtract. *(Lesson 1-2)*

70. $-7 + 5$ **−2**
71. $6 - (-4)$ **10**
72. $8 - 13$ **−5**
73. $12 + (-5)$ **7**

Simplify each expression. *(Lesson 1-7)*

74. $x + 3x$ **4x**
75. $x + (x + 1) + (x + 2)$ **3x + 3**
76. $5 + (x + 3) + 5 + 2(x + 3)$ **3x + 19**

Solve each equation. Check your answer. *(Lesson 2-3)*

77. $2b - 6 = b + 3$ **9**
78. $-3(2 - x) = 5x + 2$ **−4**
79. $2(y + 1) = 2y + 1$ **∅**

80. Carrie is reading a book and wants to find the first page of a specific chapter. She is now on page 217. She knows that the chapter she is looking for starts within 40 pages of where she is now. Write and solve an absolute-value equation to find maximum and minimum page numbers where Carrie should look. *(Lesson 2-7)*
   min = 177, max. = 257

Multiple Choice Choices **B** and **C** in **Exercise 61** include zero as a solution. Substitute 0 for t to determine whether the inequality is true or false.

Answers

56.

57. Look for a solid or empty circle. A solid circle tells you to use ≤ or ≥, and an empty circle tells you to use < or >. Then look at the direction of the arrow. An arrow pointing left tells you to use < or ≤, and an arrow pointing right tells you to use > or ≥.

Journal

The phrase "x is not less than 7" means that x is greater than or equal to 7. The mathematical expression is $x \geq 7$. Explain the meaning of the following expressions and write a mathematical expression for each:

1) x is not greater than 7.
2) x is not less than or equal to 7.
3) x is not greater than or equal to 7.

ALTERNATIVE ASSESSMENT

Write four inequalities using each of the following inequality symbols: <, ≤, >, ≥. Then graph each inequality.

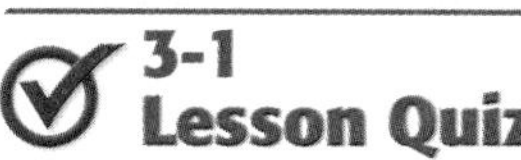

Power Presentations with PowerPoint®

3-1 Lesson Quiz

1. Describe the solutions of $7 < x + 4$ in words. all real numbers greater than 3
2. Graph $h \geq -4.75$

Write the inequality shown by each graph.

3. $x \geq 3$
4. $x < -5.5$
5. A cell phone plan offers free minutes for no more than 250 minutes per month. Define a variable and write an inequality for the possible number of free minutes. Graph the solutions. m = number of minutes; $m \leq 250$

Also available on transparency

3-1 PROBLEM SOLVING

LESSON 3-1 Problem Solving
Graphing and Writing Inequalities

Write the correct answer.

1. A citizen must be at least 35 years old in order to run for the Presidency of the United States. Define a variable and write an inequality for this situation.
   a = age of person; $a \geq 35$
2. A certain elevator can hold no more than 2500 pounds. Define a variable and write an inequality for this situation.
   w = weight; $w \leq 2500$
3. Approximately 30% of the land on Earth is forested, but this percent is decreasing due to construction. Write and graph an inequality for this situation.
   f = percent forested; $f \leq 30$
4. Khalil weighed 125 pounds before he started to gain weight to play football. Write and graph an inequality for this situation.
   w = weight; $w \geq 125$

The Sanchez family is visiting an amusement park. When they enter the park, they receive a brochure which lists several requirements and restrictions. Select the best answer.

5. You must be at least 50 inches tall to ride The Wild Tornado roller coaster. Which of the following inequalities fits this situation?
   A $h \leq 50$ **(C) $h \geq 50$**
   B $h < 50$ D $h > 50$
6. Children less than 12 years old must be accompanied by an adult inside The Haunted House. Which of the following inequalities shows the ages of children who require an adult inside the house?
   F $y \leq 12$ H $y \geq 12$
   (G) $y < 12$ J $y > 12$
7. Totland is an area of the amusement park set aside for children who are 6 years old or younger. Which of the following inequalities represents the ages of children who are allowed in Totland?
   (A) $a \leq 6$ C $a \geq 6$
   B $a < 6$ D $a > 6$
8. The Bumpy Cars will not be turned on if there are 5 or more empty cars. Which of the following inequalities shows the possible numbers of empty cars if the ride is going to start?
   F $c \leq 5$ H $c \geq 5$
   (G) $c < 5$ J $c > 5$

3-1 CHALLENGE

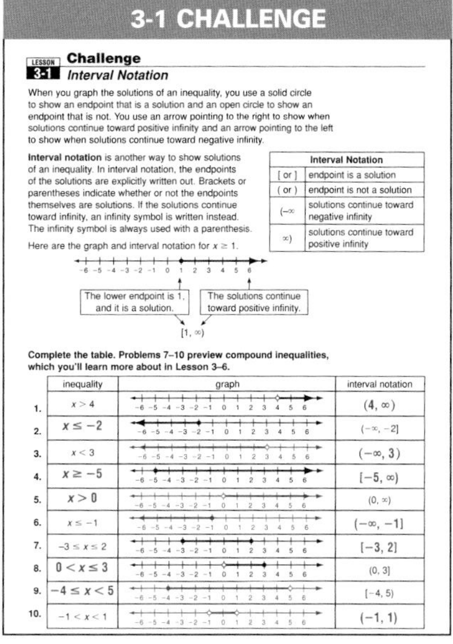

LESSON 3-1 Challenge
Interval Notation

When you graph the solutions of an inequality, you use a solid circle to show an endpoint that is a solution and an open circle to show an endpoint that is not. You use an arrow pointing to the right to show when solutions continue toward positive infinity and an arrow pointing to the left to show when solutions continue toward negative infinity.

Interval notation is another way to show solutions of an inequality. In interval notation, the endpoints of the solutions are explicitly written out. Brackets or parentheses indicate whether or not the endpoints themselves are solutions. If the solutions continue toward infinity, an infinity symbol is written instead. The infinity symbol is always used with a parenthesis.

Interval Notation	
[or]	endpoint is a solution
(or)	endpoint is not a solution
(−∞	solutions continue toward negative infinity
∞)	solutions continue toward positive infinity

Here are the graph and interval notation for $x \geq 1$.

The lower endpoint is 1, and it is a solution.
The solutions continue toward positive infinity.
[1, ∞)

Complete the table. Problems 7–10 preview compound inequalities, which you'll learn more about in Lesson 3-6.

	inequality	graph	interval notation
1.	$x > 4$		(4, ∞)
2.	$x \leq -2$		(−∞, −2]
3.	$x < 3$		(−∞, 3)
4.	$x \geq -5$		[−5, ∞)
5.	$x > 0$		(0, ∞)
6.	$x \leq -1$		(−∞, −1]
7.	$-3 \leq x \leq 2$		[−3, 2]
8.	$0 < x \leq 3$		(0, 3]
9.	$-4 \leq x < 5$		[−4, 5)
10.	$-1 < x < 1$		(−1, 1)

3-2 Organizer

Objectives: Solve one-step inequalities by using addition.

Solve one-step inequalities by using subtraction.

Algebra Lab
In *Chapter 3 Resource File*

Online Edition
Tutorial Videos

Countdown to Mastery Week 5

Power Presentations with PowerPoint®

Warm Up

Write an inequality for each situation.

1. The temperature must be at least -10°F. $x \geq -10$
2. The temperature must be no more than 90°F. $x \leq 90$

Solve each equation.

3. $x - 4 = 10$ 14
4. $15 = x + 1.1$ 13.9

Also available on transparency

Math Humor

Q: Why did the parents think their little variable was sick?

A: The nurse said he had to be isolated.

California Standards

Preparation for 5.0

3-2 Solving Inequalities by Adding or Subtracting

California Standards

Preparation for 5.0 Students solve multistep problems, including word problems, involving linear equations and **linear inequalities in one variable** and provide justification for each step.

Vocabulary
equivalent inequality

Who uses this?

You can use inequalities to determine how many more photos you can take. (See Example 2.)

Solving one-step inequalities is much like solving one-step equations. To solve an inequality, you need to isolate the variable using the properties of inequality and inverse operations. At each step, you will create an inequality that is equivalent to the original inequality. **Equivalent inequalities** have the same solution set.

Know it! Note

Properties of Inequality

Addition and Subtraction

WORDS	NUMBERS	ALGEBRA
Addition You can add the same number to both sides of an inequality, and the statement will still be true.	$3 < 8$ $3 + 2 < 8 + 2$ $5 < 10$	$a < b$ $a + c < b + c$
Subtraction You can subtract the same number from both sides of an inequality, and the statement will still be true.	$9 < 12$ $9 - 5 < 12 - 5$ $4 < 7$	$a < b$ $a - c < b - c$

These properties are also true for inequalities that use the symbols $>$, $\geq$, and $\leq$.

In Lesson 3-1, you saw that one way to show the solution set of an inequality is by using a graph. Another way is to use *set-builder notation*.

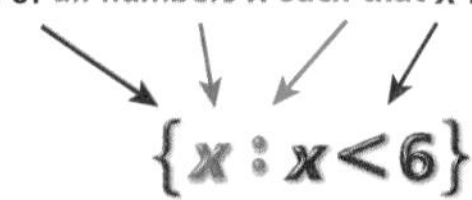

Read the above as "**the set of** all numbers x such that x **is less than 6.**"

EXAMPLE  **Using Addition and Subtraction to Solve Inequalities**

Solve each inequality and graph the solutions.

A $x + 9 < 15$

$x + 9 < 15$ *Since 9 is added to x, subtract 9 from both sides to undo the addition.*

$\underline{-9 \quad -9}$

$x \quad < 6$ *The solution set is $\{x : x < 6\}$.*

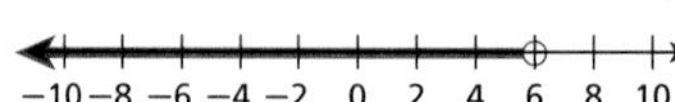

1 Introduce

EXPLORATION

3-2 Solving Inequalities by Adding or Subtracting

Use number lines to graph inequalities and to find patterns.

1. Graph the solutions of $x \leq 5$ on the number line.

−10 −8 −6 −4 −2 0 2 4 6 8 10

2. Test each value in the table to determine if it is a solution of the inequality $x + 2 \leq 7$. Record your results.

x	−7	−5.5	−3	−1.5	0	2	5	6.5	8
Solution of $x + 2 \leq 7$? (Yes/No)									

3. Plot the values that are solutions of $x + 2 \leq 7$ on the number line. Then connect the points to form a ray.

−10 −8 −6 −4 −2 0 2 4 6 8 10

4. What do you notice about the solutions you graphed in Step 1 and in Step 3?
5. How is the inequality $x + 2 \leq 7$ related to the inequality $x \leq 5$?

THINK AND DISCUSS

6. Explain how the solutions of $x \geq 3$ are related to the solutions of $x + 7 \geq 10$.

Motivate

Pose the following situation: Maria's mother told her that she should practice piano for at least 45 minutes. She has already practiced for 20 minutes. Ask students how they would determine the number of minutes that Maria still needs to practice. Tell students that they could use a one-step inequality to solve the problem.

Explorations and answers are provided in *Alternate Openers: Explorations Transparencies.*

Solve each inequality and graph the solutions.

B $d - 3 > -6$

$d - 3 > -6$ *Since 3 is subtracted from d, add 3 to both sides to undo the subtraction.*

$\underline{+3 \quad +3}$

$d \quad > -3$

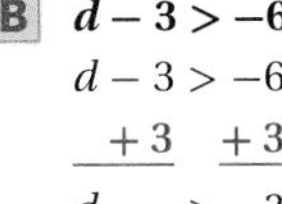

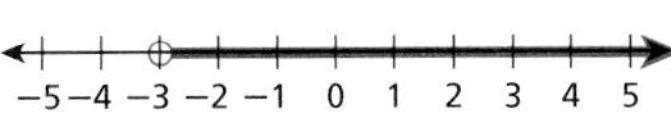

C $0.7 \geq n - 0.4$

$0.7 \geq n - 0.4$ *Since 0.4 is subtracted from n, add 0.4 to both sides to undo the subtraction.*

$\underline{+0.4 \quad +0.4}$

$1.1 \geq n$

$n \leq 1.1$

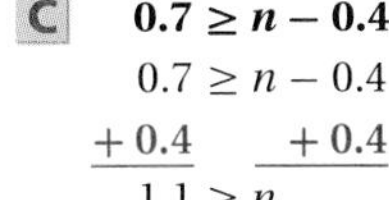

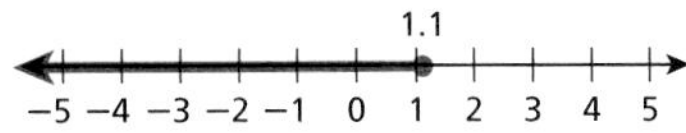

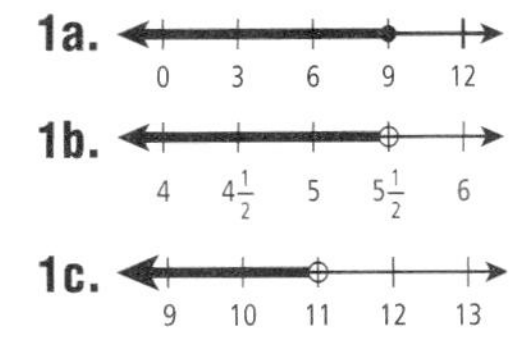

1a. (graph: 0, 3, 6, 9, 12)

1b. (graph: 4, $4\frac{1}{2}$, 5, $5\frac{1}{2}$, 6)

1c. (graph: 9, 10, 11, 12, 13)

CHECK IT OUT! Solve each inequality and graph the solutions.

1a. $s + 1 \leq 10$ $s \leq 9$ **1b.** $2\frac{1}{2} > -3 + t$ $t < 5\frac{1}{2}$ **1c.** $q - 3.5 < 7.5$ $q < 11$

Since there can be an infinite number of solutions to an inequality, it is not possible to check all the solutions. You can check the endpoint and the direction of the inequality symbol.

Caution!

In Step 1, the endpoint should be a solution of the related equation, but it may or may not be a solution of the inequality.

The solutions of $x + 9 < 15$ are given by $x < 6$.

Step 1 Check the endpoint.

Substitute 6 for x in the related equation $x + 9 = 15$. The endpoint should be a solution of the equation.

$x + 9 = 15$	
$6 + 9$	15
15	15 ✓

Step 2 Check the inequality symbol.

Substitute a number less than 6 for x in the original inequality. The number you choose should be a solution of the inequality.

$x + 9 < 15$		
$4 + 9$	<	15
13	<	15 ✓

EXAMPLE **2** ***Problem Solving Application***

The memory in Tenea's camera phone holds up to 20 pictures. Tenea has already taken 16 pictures. Write, solve, and graph an inequality to show how many more pictures Tenea could take.

1 Understand the Problem

The **answer** will be an inequality and a graph.

List the important information:

- Tenea can take up to, or *at most*, 20 pictures.
- Tenea has taken 16 pictures already.

2 Make a Plan

Write an inequality. Let p represent the remaining number of pictures Tenea can take.

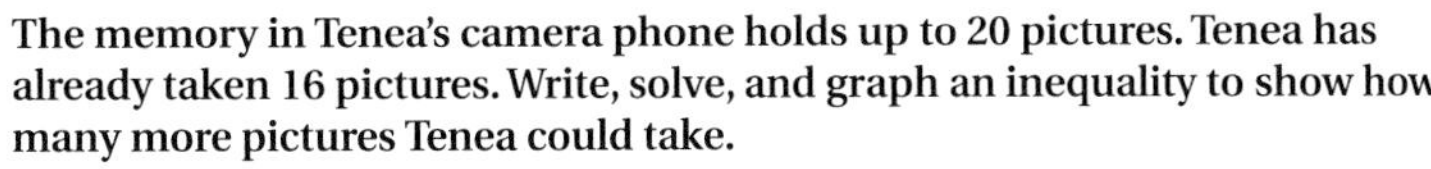

Number taken	plus	number remaining	is at most	20 pictures.
16	+	p	≤	20

2 Teach

Guided Instruction

Discuss which operations are used to undo addition and subtraction when solving equations. Tell students to solve an inequality as they would an equation. Encourage students to always check the endpoint and the inequality symbol.

Visual Some students may find it easier to rewrite the original inequality with the variable on the left, so that when the inequality is solved, the inequality symbol points in the direction of the shading.

Universal Access

Through Cooperative Learning

Have students work in pairs. Each pair should make two sets of index cards: one set with one-step inequalities and another with the corresponding solutions and graphs. Have each pair trade cards with another pair. The students can then work together to match each inequality to its graph.

COMMON ERROR ALERT

Students may assume that the symbol in the original inequality statement indicates the direction of the arrow in the graph. Remind students that this is only true when the variable is on the left side.

Power Presentations with PowerPoint®

Additional Examples

Example 1

Solve each inequality and graph the solutions.

A. $x + 12 < 20$ $x < 8$

(graph: 0, 2, 4, 6, 8)

B. $d - 5 > -7$ $d > -2$

(graph: −3, −2, −1, 0, 1, 2, 3)

C. $0.9 \geq n - 0.3$ $n \leq 1.2$

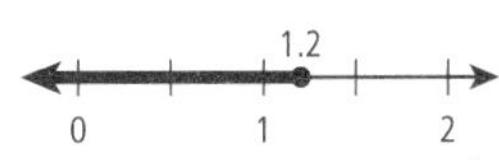

Example 2

Sami has a gift card. She has already used \$14 of the total value, which was \$30. Write, solve, and graph an inequality to show how much more she can spend. $14 + g \leq 30$; $g \leq 16$

Also available on transparency

INTERVENTION

Questioning Strategies

EXAMPLE **1**

- How is solving inequalities similar to solving equations?
- How is the solution of an inequality different from the solution of an equation?

EXAMPLE **2**

- What will the solution represent?
- What two things need to be checked when checking the solutions to an inequality?

Power Presentations with PowerPoint®

Additional Examples

Example 3

Mrs. Lawrence wants to buy an antique bracelet at an auction. She is willing to bid no more than \$550. So far, the highest bid is \$475. Write and solve an inequality to determine the amount Mrs. Lawrence can add to the bid. Check your answer.

$475 + x \leq 550$; $x \leq 75$

Also available on transparency

INTERVENTION

Questioning Strategies

EXAMPLE 3

- What words in the problem tell you which inequality symbol to use?

3 Solve

$$\begin{aligned} 16 + p &\leq 20 \\ -16 \quad & \quad -16 \\ p &\leq 4 \end{aligned}$$

Since 16 is added to p, subtract 16 from both sides to undo the addition.

It is not reasonable for Tenea to take a negative or fractional number of pictures, so graph the nonnegative integers less than or equal to 4.

Tenea could take 0, 1, 2, 3, or 4 more pictures.

4 Look Back

Check Check the endpoint, 4.

$$16 + p = 20$$

$16 + 4$	20
20	20 ✓

Check a number less than 4.

$$16 + p \leq 20$$

$16 + 2$	$\leq$	20
18	$\leq$	20 ✓

Adding 0, 1, 2, 3, or 4 more pictures will not exceed 20.

CHECK IT OUT! **2.** The Recommended Daily Allowance (RDA) of iron for a female in Sarah's age group (14–18 years) is 15 mg per day. Sarah has consumed 11 mg of iron today. Write and solve an inequality to show how many more milligrams of iron Sarah can consume without exceeding the RDA.

$11 + m \leq 15$; $m \leq 4$; Sarah can consume 4 mg or less without exceeding the RDA.

EXAMPLE 3 *Sports Application*

Josh can bench press 220 pounds. He wants to bench press at least 250 pounds. Write and solve an inequality to determine how many more pounds Josh must lift to reach his goal. Check your answer.

Let *p* represent the number of additional pounds Josh must lift.

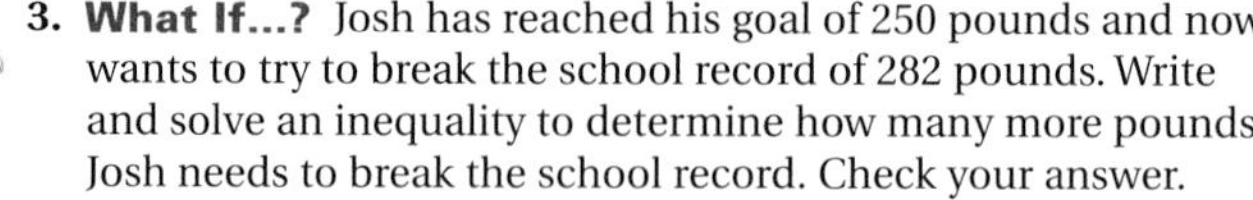

220 pounds	plus	additional pounds	is at least	250 pounds.
220	+	*p*	≥	250

$$\begin{aligned} 220 + p &\geq 250 \\ -220 \quad & \quad -220 \\ p &\geq 30 \end{aligned}$$

Since 220 is added to p, subtract 220 from both sides to undo the addition.

Check Check the endpoint, 30.

$$220 + p = 250$$

$220 + 30$	250
250	250 ✓

Check a number greater than 30.

$$220 + p \geq 250$$

$220 + 40$	$\geq$	250
260	$\geq$	250 ✓

Josh must lift at least 30 additional pounds to reach his goal.

3. $250 + p > 282$; $p > 32$; Josh needs to bench press more than 32 additional pounds to break the school record.

CHECK IT OUT! **3. What If...?** Josh has reached his goal of 250 pounds and now wants to try to break the school record of 282 pounds. Write and solve an inequality to determine how many more pounds Josh needs to break the school record. Check your answer.

3 Close

Summarize

Remind students to solve one-step inequalities by using inverse operations. For the following solutions, ask students what two points they would check. Possible answers:

$12 < c$ 12, 15

$d \geq -3$ −3, 0

$-7 > b$ −10, −7

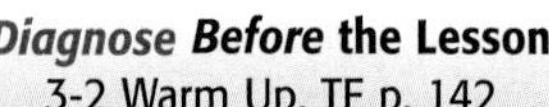

FORMATIVE ASSESSMENT and INTERVENTION

***Diagnose Before* the Lesson**
3-2 Warm Up, TE p. 142

***Monitor During* the Lesson**
Check It Out! Exercises, SE pp. 143–144
Questioning Strategies, TE pp. 143–144

***Assess After* the Lesson**
3-2 Lesson Quiz, TE p. 147
Alternative Assessment, TE p. 147

THINK AND DISCUSS

1. Show how to check your solution to Example 1B.
2. Explain how the Addition and Subtraction Properties of Inequality are like the Addition and Subtraction Properties of Equality.
3. **GET ORGANIZED** Copy and complete the graphic organizer. In each box, write an inequality that must use the specified property to solve. Then solve and graph your inequality.

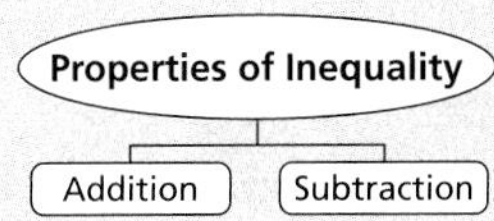

Answers to *Think and Discuss*

1.

$d - 3 = -6$		$d - 3 > -6$		
$(-3) - 3$	-6	$(0) - 3$	$>$	-6
-6	-6 ✓	-3	$>$	-6 ✓

2. You can add or subtract the same number on both sides of an equation or an inequality, and the statement will still be true.
3. See p. A3.

3-2 Exercises

Preparation for 5.0; 25.1, 25.3

GUIDED PRACTICE

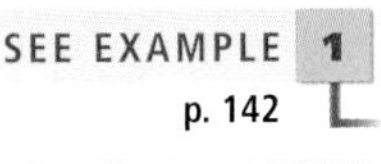

SEE EXAMPLE 1 p. 142

Solve each inequality and graph the solutions.

1. $12 < p + 6$ **$p > 6$**
2. $w + 3 \geq 4$ **$w \geq 1$**
3. $-5 + x \leq -20$ **$x \leq -15$**
4. $z - 2 > -11$ **$z > -9$**

SEE EXAMPLE 2 p. 143

5. **Health** For adults, the maximum safe water temperature in a spa is 104°F. The water temperature in Bill's spa is 102°F. The temperature is increased by t°F. Write, solve, and graph an inequality to show the values of t for which the water temperature is still safe. **$102 + t \leq 104$; $t \leq 2$ where t is nonnegative**

SEE EXAMPLE 3 p. 144

6. **Consumer Economics** A local restaurant will deliver food to your house if the purchase amount of your order is at least \$25.00. The total for part of your order is \$17.95. Write and solve an inequality to determine how much more you must spend for the restaurant to deliver your order. **$17.95 + d \geq 25.00$; $d \geq 7.05$**

PRACTICE AND PROBLEM SOLVING

Independent Practice

For Exercises	See Example
7–10	1
11	2
12	3

Extra Practice
Skills Practice p. EP6
Application Practice p. EP26

Solve each inequality and graph the solutions.

7. $a - 3 \geq 2$ **$a \geq 5$**
8. $2.5 > q - 0.8$ **$q < 3.3$**
9. $-45 + x < -30$ **$x < 15$**
10. $r + \frac{1}{4} \leq \frac{3}{4}$ **$r \leq \frac{1}{2}$**
11. **Engineering** The maximum load for a certain elevator is 2000 pounds. The total weight of the passengers on the elevator is 1400 pounds. A delivery man who weighs 243 pounds enters the elevator with a crate of weight w. Write, solve, and graph an inequality to show the values of w that will not exceed the weight limit of the elevator. **$1643 + w \leq 2000$; $w \leq 357$ where w is nonnegative**
12. **Transportation** The gas tank in Mindy's car holds at most 15 gallons. She has already filled the tank with 7 gallons of gas. She will continue to fill the tank with g gallons more. Write and solve an inequality that shows all values of g that Mindy can add to the car's tank. **$7 + g \leq 15$; $g \leq 8$ where g is nonnegative**

Write an inequality to represent each statement. Solve the inequality and graph the solutions. Check your answer.

13. Ten less than a number x is greater than 32. **$x - 10 > 32$; $x > 42$**
14. A number n increased by 6 is less than or equal to 4. **$n + 6 \leq 4$; $n \leq -2$**
15. A number r decreased by 13 is at most 15. **$r - 13 \leq 15$; $r \leq 28$**

3-2 Exercises

Assignment Guide

Assign *Guided Practice* exercises as necessary.

If you finished Examples **1–3**
Proficient 7–25, 30–42, 47–60
Advanced 8–12 even, 13–25, 30–60

Homework Quick Check
Quickly check key concepts.
Exercises: 8, 10, 12, 14, 31

Language Support
Exercise 11 requires that students understand the phrases "maximum load," "not exceed," and "weight limit." Have students discuss which phrase indicates the inequality symbol for this problem.

ENGLISH LANGUAGE LEARNERS

Answers

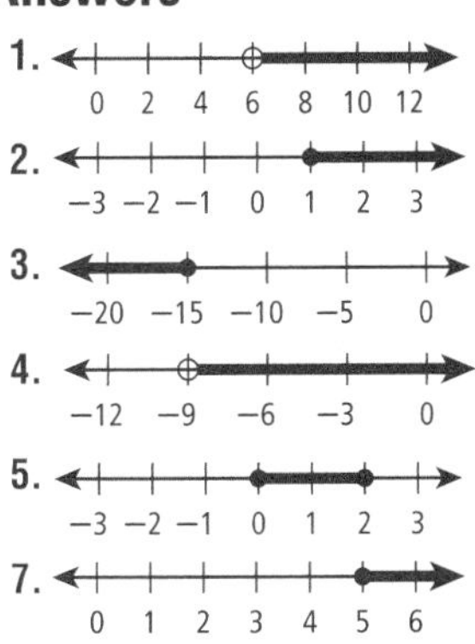

9. 0 5 10 15 20
10. −1 $-\frac{1}{2}$ 0 $\frac{1}{2}$ 1
11. 0 357
13. 40 41 42 43 44
14. −3 −2 −1 0 1 2 3
15. 26 27 28 29 30

California Standards

Standard	Exercises
3.0	53–58
Prep for 5.0	1–29, 31, 35, 37–42
25.1	46
25.3	43–45
6AF1.2	59, 60

Teaching Tip **Math Background** In **Exercise 27,** students may need to be reminded that subtraction is addition of the opposite.

CONCEPT CONNECTION **Exercise 35** involves using inequalities to describe the number of miles that can be driven on a trip. This exercise prepares students for the Concept Connection on page 154.

Answers

16. $x \le -2$
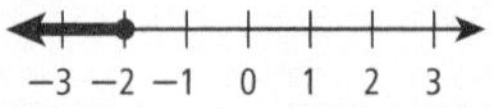

17. $q > 51$
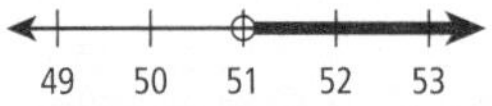

18. $x < 6\frac{2}{5}$
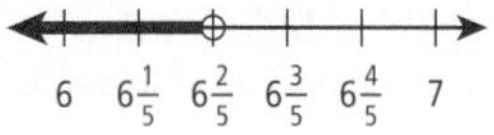

19. $p \le 0.8$
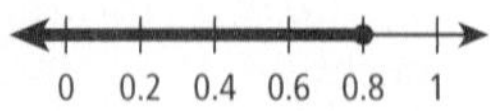

20. $x \ge 0$

21. $c > -202$
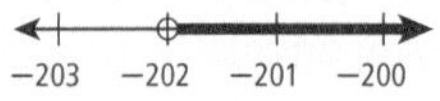

22. $y > 1$
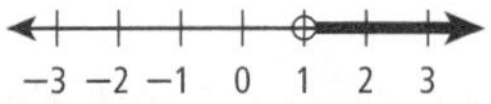

23. $x \ge 0$

25.

30. It is a reasonable answer. If you round each number to the nearest multiple of 10 and then solve the inequality $12 + x < 22$, the solution is $x < 10$.

31. $936 + 4254 + p \le 45{,}611$; $5190 + p \le 45{,}611$; $p \le 40{,}421$ where p is nonnegative

33. When you isolate the variable in each inequality, you get $x \ge 2$ and $x \ge 2$.

34–35. See p. A13.

Solve each inequality and graph the solutions. Check your answer.

16. $x + 4 \le 2$
17. $-12 + q > 39$
18. $x + \frac{3}{5} < 7$
19. $4.8 \ge p + 4$
20. $-12 \le x - 12$
21. $4 < 206 + c$
22. $y - \frac{1}{3} > \frac{2}{3}$
23. $x + 1.4 \ge 1.4$

24. Use the inequality $s + 12 \ge 20$ to fill in the missing numbers.
    a. $s \ge$ **8** b. $s +$ **22** ≥ 30 c. $s - 8 \ge$ **0**

LINK Health

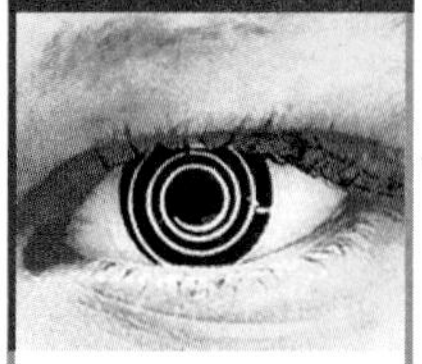

Special-effects contact lenses are sometimes part of costumes for movies. All contact lenses should be worn under an eye doctor's supervision.

25. **Health** A particular type of contact lens can be worn up to 30 days in a row. Alex has been wearing these contact lenses for 21 days. Write, solve, and graph an inequality to show how many more days Alex could wear his contact lenses.
$21 + d \le 30$; $d \le 9$ where d is nonnegative

Solve each inequality and match the solution to the correct graph.

26. $1 \le x - 2$ **$x \ge 3$; C**

A. 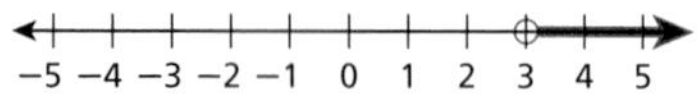

27. $8 > x - (-5)$ **$x < 3$; B**

B. 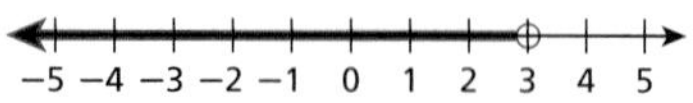

28. $x + 6 > 9$ **$x > 3$; A**

C. 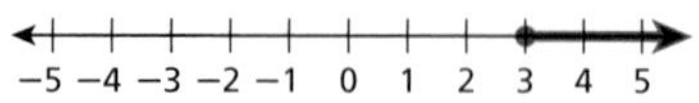

29. $-4 \ge x - 7$ **$x \le 3$; D**

D. 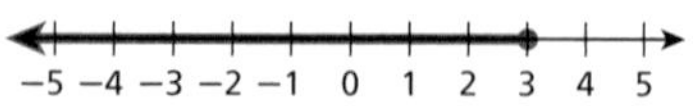

30. **Estimation** Is $x < 10$ a reasonable estimate for the solutions to the inequality $11.879 + x < 21.709$? Explain your answer.

31. **Sports** At the Seattle Mariners baseball team's home games, there are 45,611 seats in the four areas listed in the table. Suppose all the suite level and club level seats during a game are filled. Write and solve an inequality to determine how many people p could be sitting in the other types of seats.

Mariners Home Game Seating

Type of Seat	Number of Seats
Main bowl	24,399
Upper bowl	16,022
Club level	4,254
Suite level	936

32. If a scale is unbalanced and the same amount is added to or subtracted from both sides, the scale should maintain the same amount of imbalance.

32. **Critical Thinking** Recall that in Chapter 2 a balance scale was used to model solving equations. Describe how a balance scale could model solving inequalities.

33. **Critical Thinking** Explain why $x + 4 \ge 6$ and $x - 4 \ge -2$ have the same solutions.

34. **Write About It** How do the solutions of $x + 2 \ge 3$ differ from the solutions of $x + 2 > 3$? How do the graphs of the solutions differ?

CONCEPT CONNECTION

35. This problem will prepare you for the Concept Connection on page 154.
    a. Daryl finds that the distance from Columbus, Ohio, to Washington, D.C, is 411 miles. What is the round-trip distance?
    b. Daryl can afford to drive a total of 1000 miles. Write an inequality to show the number of miles m he can drive while in Washington, D.C.
    c. Solve the inequality and graph the solutions on a number line.

3-2 PRACTICE A

3-2 PRACTICE C

3-2 PRACTICE B

LESSON 3-2 **Practice B**
Solving Inequalities by Adding or Subtracting

Solve each inequality and graph the solutions.

1. $b + 8 > 15$ **$b > 7$**
2. $t - 5 \ge -2$ **$t \ge 3$**
3. $-4 + x \ge 1$ **$x \ge 5$**
4. $g + 8 < 2$ **$g < -6$**
5. $-9 \ge m - 9$ **$m \le 0$**
6. $15 > d + 19$ **$d < -4$**

Answer each question.

7. Jessica makes overtime pay when she works more than 40 hours in a week. So far this week she has worked 29 hours. She will continue to work h hours this week. Write, solve, and graph an inequality to show the values of h that will allow Jessica to earn overtime pay. **$29 + h > 40$; $h > 11$**
8. Henry's MP3 player has 512MB of memory. He has already downloaded 287MB and will continue to download m more megabytes. Write and solve an inequality that shows how many more megabytes he can download. **$287 + m \le 512$; $m \le 225$**
9. Eleanor needs to read at least 97 pages of a book for homework. She has read 34 pages already. Write and solve an inequality that shows how many more pages p she must read. **$34 + p \ge 97$; $p \ge 63$**

3-2 READING STRATEGIES

LESSON 3-2 **Reading Strategies**
Follow a Procedure

There are two parts to checking solutions to inequalities: checking the endpoint and checking the direction of the inequality symbol.

Check that $x > -3$ represents the solutions to $x - 4 > -7$.

Step 1: $x - 4 = -7$; $-3 - 4 = -7$; $-7 = -7$ ✓ — Write the related equation. Substitute −3 for x in the related equation. If the statement is true, the value is an endpoint.

Step 2: $x - 4 > -7$; $10 - 4 > -7$; $6 > -7$ ✓ — Write the original inequality. Substitute a value greater than −3 in the original inequality. If the statement is true, the symbol is correct.

Both steps check, so $x > -3$ correctly represents the solutions.

Answer each question.

1. Which Step confirms that the endpoint is correct? **Step 1**
2. What is being checked in Step 2? **the direction of the inequality symbol**
3. Describe Step 1 when checking that $8 \le m$ represents the solutions to $14 \le m + 6$. **Substitute 8 for m in $14 = m + 6$.**
4. Give a value that could be used in Step 2 when checking that $8 \le m$ represents the solutions to $14 \le m + 6$. **Possible answer: 9**

For each problem, check that the given solutions represent the inequality by using the two-step procedure shown above.

	Step 1	Step 2	correct?
5. $t + 5 < -9$; $t > -14$	$t + 5 = -9$; $-14 + 5 = -9$; $-9 = -9$	$t + 5 < -9$; $-13 + 5 < -9$; $-8 < -9$	no
6. $b - 6 \ge 2$; $b \ge 8$	$b - 6 = 2$; $8 - 6 = 2$; $2 = 2$	$b - 6 \ge 2$; $9 - 6 \ge 2$; $3 \ge 2$	yes

3-2 REVIEW FOR MASTERY

LESSON 3-2 **Review for Mastery**
Solving Inequalities by Adding or Subtracting

The method for solving one-step inequalities by adding is just like the method for solving one-step equations by adding.

Solve $x - 2 = 1$ and graph the solution.
$x - 2 = 1$; $+2$ $+2$ Add 2 to each side. $x = 3$

Solve $x - 2 \ge 1$ and graph the solutions.
$x - 2 \ge 1$; $+2$ $+2$ Add 2 to each side. $x \ge 3$

Solve $-4 = a - 3$ and graph the solution.
$-4 = a - 3$; $+3$ $+3$ Add 3 to each side. $-1 = a$

Solve $-4 > a - 3$ and graph the solutions.
$-4 > a - 3$; $+3$ $+3$ Add 3 to each side. $-1 > a$; $a < -1$

Solve each inequality and graph the solutions.

1. $b - 4 < 3$ **$b < 7$**
2. $x - 5 < -2$ **$x < 3$**
3. $-10 > -6 + x$ **$x < -4$**
4. $1 \le f - 3$ **$f \ge 4$**

Multiple Choice For Exercises 36–39, choose the best answer.

36. Which is a reasonable solution of $4.7367 + p < 20.1784$?

Ⓐ 15 　 B 16 　 C 24 　 D 25

37. Which statement can be modeled by $x + 3 \leq 12$?

Ⓐ Sam has 3 bottles of water. Together, Sam and Dave have at most 12 bottles of water.

B Jennie sold 3 cookbooks. To earn a prize, Jennie must sell at least 12 cookbooks.

C Peter has 3 baseball hats. Peter and his brothers have fewer than 12 baseball hats.

D Kathy swam 3 laps in the pool this week. She must swim more than 12 laps.

38. Which represents the solutions of $p + 3 < 1$?

Ⓐ 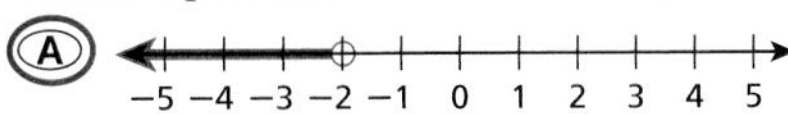

B $\{p : p \leq -27\}$

C −5 −4 −3 −2 −1 0 1 2 3 4 5

D $\{p : p > 2\}$

39. Which inequality is NOT equivalent to $n + 12 \leq 26$?

A $n \leq 14$ 　 B $n + 6 \leq 20$ 　 C $10 \geq n - 4$ 　 Ⓓ $n - 12 \leq 14$

CHALLENGE AND EXTEND

Solve each inequality and graph the solutions. Check your answer.

40. $6\frac{9}{10} \geq 4\frac{4}{5} + x$ $x \leq 2\frac{1}{10}$ **41.** $r - 1\frac{2}{5} \leq 3\frac{7}{10}$ $r \leq 5\frac{1}{10}$ **42.** $6\frac{2}{3} + m > 7\frac{1}{6}$ $m > \frac{1}{2}$

Reasoning Determine whether each statement is *sometimes, always,* or *never* true. Explain.

43. $a + b > a - b$ Sometimes; when b is positive, the inequality is true.

44. If $a > c$, then $a + b > c + b$. Always; adding the same number to both sides keeps the statement true.

45. If $a > b$ and $c > d$, then $a + c > b + d$.

45. Always; a and c are the two greater numbers, so their sum will be greater than that of the two lesser numbers.

46. **Reasoning** If $x + b > c$ and $x > 0$ are equivalent, show that $b = c$.

SPIRAL STANDARDS REVIEW 6AF1.2, 3.0

Solve each equation for the indicated variable. *(Lesson 2-6)*

47. $2x + 3y = 9$ for y **48.** $P = 4s$ for s $s = \frac{P}{4}$ **49.** $2a + ab = c$ for a $a = \frac{c}{2 + b}$

47. $y = 3 - \frac{2}{3}x$

50. $p + e = f$ for e $e = f - p$ **51.** $2s - k = 11$ for k $k = 2s - 11$ **52.** $5m + n = 0$ for m $m = -\frac{n}{5}$

Solve each equation. Check your answer. *(Lesson 2-7)*

53. $|x| + 2 = 6$ 4, −4 **54.** $|z - 12| = 24$ 36, −12 **55.** $4|d| = 20$ 5, −5

56. $|-3r + 1| = 14$ 5, $-\frac{13}{3}$ **57.** $|6b + 2| - 4 = 22$ 4, $-\frac{14}{3}$ **58.** $0 = |3 - 2c|$ $\frac{3}{2}$

Write the inequality shown by each graph. *(Lesson 3-1)*

59. −4 −3 −2 −1 0 1 2 3 4 5 6 **60.** −4 −3 −2 −1 0 1 2 3 4 5 6

59. $x \geq -1$

60. $x < 4$

Teaching Tip **Multiple Choice** If students have difficulty selecting the correct statement in **Exercise 37,** remind them that the inequality indicates 12 is the greatest value the expression can equal.

Answers

40. (number line: 2, $2\frac{1}{10}$, $2\frac{2}{10}$, $2\frac{3}{10}$, $2\frac{4}{10}$)

41. (number line: 5, $5\frac{1}{10}$, $5\frac{2}{10}$, $5\frac{3}{10}$, $5\frac{4}{10}$)

42. (number line: −1, $-\frac{1}{2}$, 0, $\frac{1}{2}$, 1)

46. See p. A13.

Journal

Explain why the solutions to the inequality $x + 3 \geq 12$ are not only those numbers greater than or equal to 12.

Have students write a real-world situation that can be modeled by a one-step inequality. Ask students to write, solve, and graph the inequality and explain the meaning of the solution in the context of the situation.

Power Presentations with PowerPoint®

3-2 Lesson Quiz

Solve each inequality and graph the solutions.

1. $13 < x + 7$ $x > 6$

0 2 4 6 8

2. $-6 + h \geq 15$ $h \geq 21$

15 18 21 24 27

3. $6.7 + y \leq -2.1$ $y \leq -8.8$

−8.8

−10 −8 −6 −4 −2 0

4. A certain restaurant has room for 120 customers. On one night, there are 72 customers dining. Write and solve an inequality to show how many more people can eat at the restaurant.

$x + 72 \leq 120$; $x \leq 48$ where x is a natural number

Also available on transparency

3-2 PROBLEM SOLVING

LESSON 3-2 **Problem Solving**
Solving Inequalities by Adding or Subtracting

Write the correct answer.

1. Sumiko is allowed to watch no more than 10 hours of television each week. She has watched 4 hours of television already. Write and solve an inequality to show how many more hours of television Sumiko can watch.
$4 + h \leq 10$; $h \leq 6$

2. A satellite will be released into an orbit of more than 400 miles above the Earth. The rocket carrying it is currently 255 miles above Earth. Write and solve an inequality to show how much higher the rocket must climb before it releases the satellite.
$m + 255 > 400$; $m > 145$

3. Wayne's homework is to solve at least 20 questions from his textbook. So far, he has completed 9 of them. Write, solve, and graph an inequality to show how many more problems Wayne must complete.
$q + 9 \geq 20$; $q \geq 11$
9 10 11 12 13 14 15 16

4. Felix wants to get at least one hour of exercise each day. Today, he has run for 40 minutes. Write, solve, and graph an inequality that shows how much longer Felix needs to exercise to reach his goal.
$40 + e \geq 60$; $e \geq 20$
0 10 20 30 40 50 60 70

The high school has been raising money for charity and the class that raises the most will be awarded a party at the end of the year. The table below shows how much money each class has raised so far. Use this information to answer questions 5–7.

Class	Amount Raised ($)
Seniors	870
Juniors	650
Sophomores	675
First-Years	590

5. The school has a goal of raising at least $3000. Which inequality shows how much more money m they need to raise to reach their goal?
Ⓐ $m \geq 215$ 　 C $m \leq 215$
B $m < 215$ 　 D $m > 2785$

6. The juniors would like to raise more money than the seniors. The seniors have completed their fundraising for the year. Which expression shows how much more money j the juniors must raise to overtake the seniors?
F $j \leq 220$ 　 H $j \geq 220$
G $j < 220$ 　 Ⓙ $j > 220$

7. A local business has agreed to donate no more than half as much as the senior class raises. Which inequality shows how much money b the business will contribute?
A $\frac{1}{2}(870) \leq b$ 　 Ⓒ $\frac{1}{2}(870) \geq b$
B $870 \leq \frac{1}{2}b$ 　 D $870 \geq \frac{1}{2}b$

3-2 CHALLENGE

LESSON 3-2 **Challenge**
Solving One-Step Inequalities by Adding and Subtracting

Susan has 200 feet of fencing and wants to use it to enclose a rectangular garden. She knows that the formula for the perimeter of a rectangle is $P = 2(L + W)$. Susan also knows that the area A of a rectangle is found by using $A = LW$.

W L

Answer the following questions in order to help Susan plan how to use the fencing.

1. Susan can either use some or all of the fencing. Write an inequality that describes how much fencing she could use. $0 < P \leq 200$

2. Would a length of 70 feet and a width of 40 feet satisfy the inequality in Exercise 1? Explain.
No; because $2(70 + 40) = 220$ feet is greater than 200 feet

3. a. If Susan decides to use all of the fencing and chooses a length of 20 feet, find the width. 80 feet
b. What would the length be if she chooses a width of 20 feet? 80 feet
c. Given these dimensions, find the area of the garden. 1600 square feet

4. a. If Susan decides to use all of the fencing and chooses a length of 40 feet, find the width. 60 feet
b. What would the length be if she chooses a width of 40 feet? 60 feet
c. Given these dimensions, find the area of the garden. 2400 square feet

5. What conclusion can you draw from Exercises 3 and 4?
If the dimensions are reversed, the area remains the same.

6. a. If Susan would like the length and the width to be as close to one another as possible and to be whole numbers, what might the dimensions be? 50 feet by 50 feet
b. Given her intention in part **a**, what shape is she trying to achieve? a square
c. Given your answer to part **a**, find the area of the garden. 2500 square feet

7. Susan's friend, Jack, has 160 feet of fencing. He wants to use all his fencing to make a garden with the greatest possible area. Without using inequalities, what dimensions should he choose? 40 feet by 40 feet

3-3 Organizer

Objectives: Solve one-step inequalities by using multiplication.

Solve one-step inequalities by using division.

Online Edition
Tutorial Videos

Countdown to Mastery Week 5

Power Presentations with PowerPoint®

Warm Up

Solve each equation.

1. $-5a = 30$ $\quad -6$
2. $-\frac{2}{5}x = 4$ $\quad -10$
3. $\frac{y}{-5} = \frac{-3}{8}$ $\quad 1\frac{7}{8}$
4. $-\frac{3}{4}x = \frac{6}{11}$ $\quad -\frac{8}{11}$

Graph each inequality.

5. $x \geq -10$

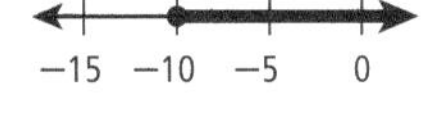

6. $x < -3$

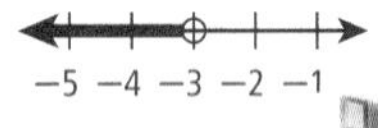

Also available on transparency

Q: What did the teacher do to prepare for class?

A: She made a "less-than" plan. (Lesson plan)

California Standards

Preparation for 5.0

3-3 Solving Inequalities by Multiplying or Dividing

Preparation for 5.0 Students solve multistep problems, including word problems, involving linear equations and **linear inequalities in one variable** and provide justification for each step.

Who uses this?

You can solve an inequality to determine how much you can buy with a certain amount of money. (See Example 3.)

Jonny Hawkins/CartoonResource.com

"This is all I have, so I'll take 3 pencils, 3 notebooks, a binder, and 0.9 calculators."

Remember, solving inequalities is similar to solving equations. To solve an inequality that contains multiplication or division, undo the operation by dividing or multiplying both sides of the inequality by the same number.

The rules below show the properties of inequality for multiplying or dividing by a positive number. The rules for multiplying or dividing by a negative number appear later in this lesson.

Properties of Inequality

Multiplication and Division by Positive Numbers

WORDS	NUMBERS	ALGEBRA
Multiplication You can multiply both sides of an inequality by the same *positive* number, and the statement will still be true.	$7 < 12$ $7(3) < 12(3)$ $21 < 36$	If $a < b$ and $c > 0$, then $ac < bc$.
Division You can divide both sides of an inequality by the same *positive* number, and the statement will still be true.	$15 < 35$ $\frac{15}{5} < \frac{35}{5}$ $3 < 7$	If $a < b$ and $c > 0$, then $\frac{a}{c} < \frac{b}{c}$.

These properties are also true for inequalities that use the symbols >, ≥, and ≤.

EXAMPLE 1 Multiplying or Dividing by a Positive Number

Solve each inequality and graph the solutions.

A $3x > -27$

$3x > -27$ *Since x is multiplied by 3, divide both sides by 3 to undo the multiplication.*

$\frac{3x}{3} > \frac{-27}{3}$

$x > -9$ *The solution set is {x:x > −9}.*

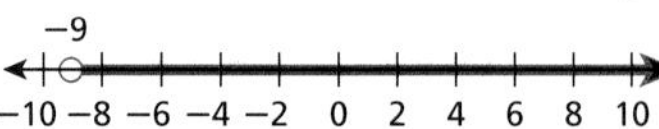

1 Introduce

EXPLORATION

3-3 Solving Inequalities by Multiplying or Dividing

Investigate what happens when both sides of an inequality are multiplied by a negative number.

1. Complete each inequality with < or >.
   2 ☐ 3 −2 ☐ 4 7 ☐ −1 −6 ☐ −9
2. Complete each inequality with < or >.
   −2 ☐ −3 2 ☐ −4 −7 ☐ 1 6 ☐ 9
3. Describe any patterns that you notice.
4. Complete each inequality with < or >.
   −10 ☐ −15 10 ☐ −20 −35 ☐ 5 30 ☐ 45
5. How do the inequalities in Step 4 compare to those in Step 1?

THINK AND DISCUSS

6. **Explain** how an inequality changes when you multiply the two numbers in the inequality by −1.
7. **Describe** a general rule that you can use when multiplying both sides of an inequality by a negative number.

Motivate

Pose the following situation: "Bradley has $50 of birthday money to spend at a resale store. He wants to buy some used video games that cost $11 each." Ask students how they could determine the number of video games Bradley can buy. Tell students that they could use a one-step inequality. Tell students that there are special rules when multiplying or dividing both sides of an inequality by a negative number.

Explorations and answers are provided in *Alternate Openers: Explorations Transparencies*.

1a. 0 2 4 6 8 10 12

1b. −18 −16 −14 −12 −10

1c. 34 35 36 37 38

Solve each inequality and graph the solutions.

B $\frac{2}{3}r < 6$

$\frac{2}{3}r < 6$ *Since r is multiplied by $\frac{2}{3}$, multiply both sides by the reciprocal of $\frac{2}{3}$.*

$\frac{3}{2}\left(\frac{2}{3}r\right) < \frac{3}{2}(6)$

$r < 9$ *The solution set is {r : r < 9}.*

9

−8 −6 −4 −2 0 2 4 6 8 10 12

CHECK IT OUT! **Solve each inequality and graph the solutions. Check your answer.**

1a. $4k > 24$ $k > 6$ **1b.** $-50 \geq 5q$ $q \leq -10$ **1c.** $\frac{3}{4}g > 27$ $g > 36$

What happens when you multiply or divide both sides of an inequality by a negative number?

Look at the number line below.

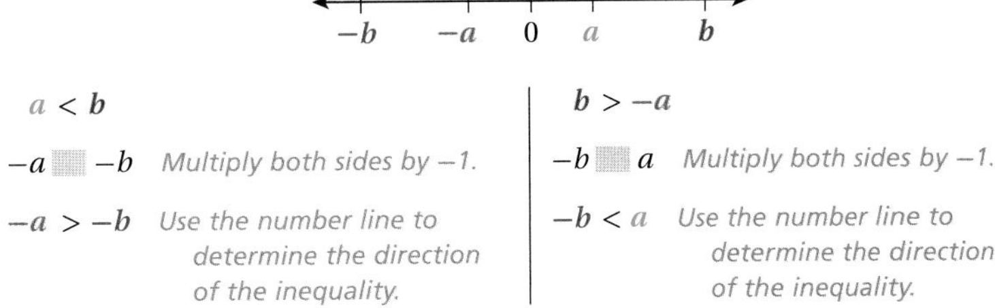

$-b$ $-a$ 0 a b

$a < b$	$b > -a$
$-a$ ▒ $-b$ *Multiply both sides by −1.*	$-b$ ▒ a *Multiply both sides by −1.*
$-a > -b$ *Use the number line to determine the direction of the inequality.*	$-b < a$ *Use the number line to determine the direction of the inequality.*

Notice that when you multiply (or divide) both sides of an inequality by a negative number, you must reverse the inequality symbol.

Properties of Inequality

Multiplication and Division by Negative Numbers

WORDS	NUMBERS	ALGEBRA
Multiplication If you multiply both sides of an inequality by the same *negative* number, you must reverse the inequality symbol for the statement to still be true.	$8 > 4$ $8(-2) < 4(-2)$ $-16 < -8$ $-16 < -8$	If $a > b$ and $c < 0$, then $ac < bc$.
Division If you divide both sides of an inequality by the same *negative* number, you must reverse the inequality symbol for the statement to still be true.	$12 > 4$ $\frac{12}{-4} < \frac{4}{-4}$ $-3 < -1$ $-3 < -1$	If $a > b$ and $c < 0$, then $\frac{a}{c} < \frac{b}{c}$.

These properties are also true for inequalities that use the symbols <, ≥, and ≤.

COMMON ERROR ALERT

Students may change the inequality symbol when any number in the expression is negative. Remind them that the inequality symbol is changed only when multiplying or dividing both sides by a negative number.

Power Presentations with PowerPoint®

Additional Examples

Example 1

Solve each inequality and graph the solutions.

A. $7x > -42$ $x > -6$

−8 −6 −4 −2 0

B. $2.4 \leq \frac{m}{3}$ $m \geq 7.2$

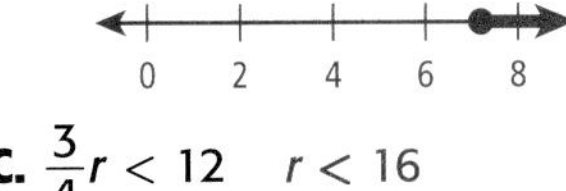

C. $\frac{3}{4}r < 12$ $r < 16$

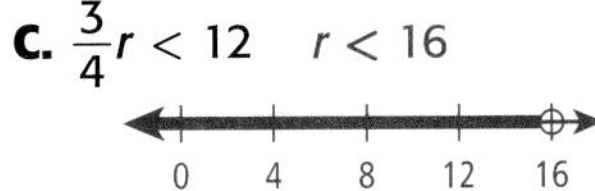

Also available on transparency

INTERVENTION

Questioning Strategies

EXAMPLE 1

- How do you know whether to multiply or divide?

2 Teach

Guided Instruction

Review solving one-step equations using multiplication and division. Multiply both sides of a true inequality, like 2 < 6, by both a positive and negative number, to show that the expression is still true after it is multiplied by the positive number, but false after it is multiplied by the negative number. The false expression becomes true when the inequality sign is changed. Remind students how to check their solutions.

Universal Access

Through Modeling

Draw a number line with 1 and 3 plotted.

Ask if it is correct to write $1 < 3$. yes

Multiply both numbers by −1 and plot the products.

Ask if it is correct to write $-1 < -3$. no Why? −1 is further to the right. Ask if it is correct to write $-1 > -3$. yes What changed? the direction of the sign Show the division of two numbers by a negative.

Power Presentations with PowerPoint®

Additional Examples

Example 2

Solve each inequality and graph the solutions.

A. $-12x > 84$ $x < -7$

B. $-8 \le \frac{x}{-3}$ $x \le 24$

Example 3

Jill has a $20 gift card to an art supply store where 4 oz tubes of paint are $4.30 each after tax. What are the possible numbers of tubes that Jill can buy?

0, 1, 2, 3, or 4 tubes

Also available on transparency

INTERVENTION

Questioning Strategies

EXAMPLE 2

- What must be done to both sides of an inequality to make the inequality symbol change?

EXAMPLE 3

- Why are the solutions of the inequality graphed as individual points?

Caution!

Do not change the direction of the inequality symbol just because you see a negative sign. For example, you do not change the symbol when solving $4x < -24$.

EXAMPLE 2 Multiplying or Dividing by a Negative Number

Solve each inequality and graph the solutions.

A $-8x > 72$

$\frac{-8x}{-8} < \frac{72}{-8}$ *Since x is multiplied by −8, divide both sides by −8. Change > to <.*

$x < -9$

B $-3 \le \frac{x}{-5}$

$-5(-3) \ge -5\left(\frac{x}{-5}\right)$ *Since x is divided by −5, multiply both sides by −5. Change ≤ to ≥.*

$15 \ge x$

$x \le 15$

CHECK IT OUT! Solve each inequality and graph the solutions. Check your answer.

2a. $10 \ge -x$ **$x \ge -10$**

2b. $4.25 > -0.25h$ **$h > -17$**

EXAMPLE 3 *Consumer Application*

Ryan has a $16 gift card for a health store where a smoothie costs $2.50 with tax. What are the possible numbers of smoothies that Ryan can buy?

Let *s* represent the number of smoothies Ryan can buy.

$2.50	times	number of smoothies	is at most	$16.00.
2.50	•	*s*	≤	16.00

$2.50s \le 16.00$

$\frac{2.50s}{2.50} \le \frac{16.00}{2.50}$ *Since s is multiplied by 2.50, divide both sides by 2.50. The symbol does not change.*

$s \le 6.4$ *Ryan can buy only a whole number of smoothies.*

Ryan can buy 0, 1, 2, 3, 4, 5, or 6 smoothies.

CHECK IT OUT! **3.** A pitcher holds 128 ounces of juice. What are the possible numbers of 10-ounce servings that one pitcher can fill?
$10g \le 128$; $g \le 12.8$; 0, 1, 2, 3, 4, 5, 6, 7, 8, 9, 10, 11, or 12 servings

THINK AND DISCUSS

1. Compare the Multiplication and Division Properties of Inequality and the Multiplication and Division Properties of Equality.

2. GET ORGANIZED Copy and complete the graphic organizer. In each cell, write and solve an inequality.

Solving Inequalities by Using Multiplication and Division		
	By a Positive Number	By a Negative Number
Divide		
Multiply		

3 Close

Summarize

Remind students that solving one-step inequalities is like solving one-step equations, except they must remember to change the sign of the inequality when multiplying or dividing by a negative number. Write the following on the board, and ask if the inequality sign would change when solving.

$2x > -10$	no
$-3b \le 12$	yes
$5 > -10n$	yes
$-16 < 4t$	no

FORMATIVE ASSESSMENT and INTERVENTION

***Diagnose Before* the Lesson**
3-3 Warm Up, TE p. 148

***Monitor During* the Lesson**
Check It Out! Exercises, SE pp. 149–150
Questioning Strategies, TE pp. 149–150

***Assess After* the Lesson**
3-3 Lesson Quiz, TE p. 153
Alternative Assessment, TE p. 153

Answers to *Think and Discuss*

1. They are alike because you can multiply or divide by a positive number on both sides and the inequality or equation will still be true. They are different because you have to reverse the inequality symbol if you multiply or divide by a negative number.
2. See p. A3.

3-3 Exercises

California Standards Practice

Preparation for 🔑 5.0; 24.3, 25.1, 25.2

Homework Help Online
KEYWORD: MA8CA 3-3

Parent Resources Online
KEYWORD: MA8CA Parent

GUIDED PRACTICE

SEE EXAMPLE 1 p. 148

Solve each inequality and graph the solutions. Check your answer.

1. $3b > 27$
2. $-40 \geq 8b$
3. $\frac{d}{3} > 6$
4. $24d \leq 6$
5. $1.1m \leq 1.21$
6. $\frac{2}{3}k > 6$
7. $9s > -18$
8. $\frac{4}{5} \geq \frac{r}{2}$

SEE EXAMPLE 2 p. 150

9. $-2x < -10$
10. $\frac{b}{-2} \geq 8$
11. $-3.5n < 1.4$
12. $4 > -8g$
13. $\frac{d}{-6} < \frac{1}{2}$
14. $-10h \geq -6$
15. $12 > \frac{t}{-6}$
16. $-\frac{1}{2}m \geq -7$

SEE EXAMPLE 3 p. 150

17. **Travel** Tom saved \$550 to go on a school trip. The cost for a hotel room, including tax, is \$80 per night. Write an inequality to show the number of nights Tom can stay at the hotel. **$80n \leq 550$; $n \leq 6.875$; 0, 1, 2, 3, 4, 5, or 6 nights**

PRACTICE AND PROBLEM SOLVING

Independent Practice

For Exercises	See Example
18–29	1
30–41	2
42	3

Extra Practice

Skills Practice p. EP6
Application Practice p. EP26

Solve each inequality and graph the solutions. Check your answer.

18. $10 < 2t$
19. $\frac{1}{3}j \leq 4$
20. $-80 < 8c$
21. $21 > 3d$
22. $\frac{w}{4} \geq -2$
23. $\frac{h}{4} \leq \frac{2}{7}$
24. $6y < 4.2$
25. $12c \leq -144$
26. $\frac{4}{5}x \geq \frac{2}{5}$
27. $6b \geq \frac{3}{5}$
28. $-25 > 10p$
29. $\frac{b}{8} \leq -2$
30. $-9a > 81$
31. $\frac{1}{2} < \frac{r}{-3}$
32. $-6p > 0.6$
33. $\frac{y}{-4} > -\frac{1}{2}$
34. $-\frac{1}{6}f < 5$
35. $-2.25t < -9$
36. $24 \leq -10w$
37. $-11z > 121$
38. $\frac{3}{5} < \frac{f}{-5}$
39. $-k \geq 7$
40. $-2.2b < -7.7$
41. $16 \geq -\frac{4}{3}p$
42. **Camping** The rope Roz brought with her camping gear is 54 inches long. Roz needs to cut shorter pieces of rope that are each 18 inches long. What are the possible number of pieces Roz can cut? **$18r \leq 54$; $r \leq 3$; 0, 1, 2, or 3**

Solve each inequality and graph the solutions. Check your answer.

43. $-8x < 24$
44. $3t \leq 24$
45. $\frac{1}{4}x < 5$
46. $\frac{4}{5}p \geq -24$
47. $54 \leq -9p$
48. $3t > -\frac{1}{2}$
49. $-\frac{3}{4}b > -\frac{3}{2}$
50. $216 > 3.6r$

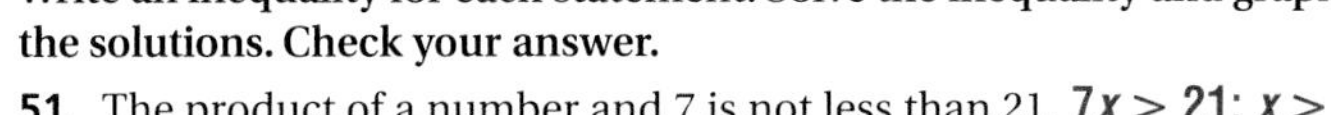

Write an inequality for each statement. Solve the inequality and graph the solutions. Check your answer.

51. The product of a number and 7 is not less than 21. **$7x \geq 21$; $x \geq 3$**
52. The quotient of h and -6 is at least 5. **$\frac{h}{-6} \geq 5$; $h \leq -30$**
53. The product of $-\frac{4}{5}$ and b is at most -16. **$-\frac{4}{5}b \leq -16$; $b \geq 20$**
54. Ten is no more than the quotient of t and 4. **$10 \leq \frac{t}{4}$; $t \geq 40$**

55. **Write About It** Explain how you know whether to reverse the inequality symbol when solving an inequality.
56. **Geometry** The area of a rectangle is at most 21 square inches. The width of the rectangle is 3.5 inches. What are the possible measurements for the length of the rectangle? **$\ell \leq 6$ in. where ℓ is positive**

55. You reverse the symbol only when you multiply or divide both sides of the inequality by the same negative number.

3-3 Exercises

Assignment Guide

Assign *Guided Practice* exercises as necessary.

If you finished Examples **1–3**
Proficient 18–56, 61–70, 72, 78–87
Advanced 18–42, 44–50 even, 51–56, 61, 63, 66–87

Homework Quick Check
Quickly check key concepts.
Exercises: 20, 34, 42, 50, 54, 61

Answers

1. $b > 9$
2. $b \leq -5$
3. $d > 18$
4. $d \leq \frac{1}{4}$
5. $m \leq 1.1$
6. $k > 9$
7. $s > -2$
8. $r \leq \frac{8}{5}$
9. $x > 5$
10. $b \leq -16$
11. $n > -0.4$
12. $g > -\frac{1}{2}$
13. $d > -3$
14. $h \leq 0.6$
15. $t > -72$

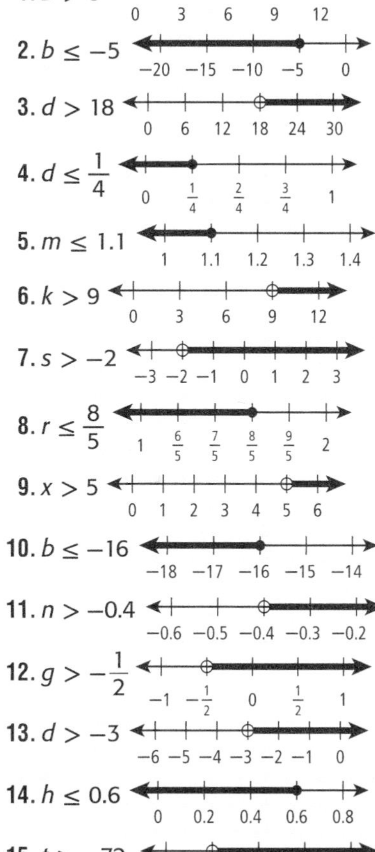

16. $m \leq 14$
18. $t > 5$
19. $j \leq 12$
20. $c > -10$
21. $d < 7$
22. $w \geq -8$
23. $h \leq \frac{8}{7}$
24. $y < 0.7$

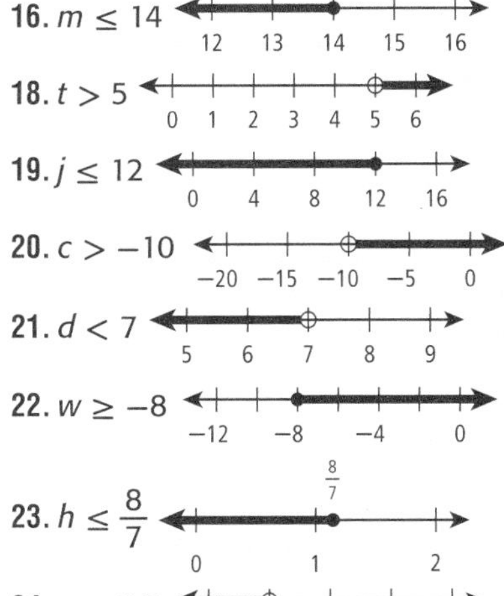

25. $c \leq -12$
26. $x \geq \frac{1}{2}$
27. $b \geq \frac{1}{10}$
28. $p < -2.5$
29. $b \leq -16$
30. $a < -9$

31–41, 43–50. See p. A13.

51–54. For graphs see p. A13.

California Standards

Standard	Exercises
Prep for 5.0 🔑	1–62, 64–74, 84–87
15.0 🔑	81–83
24.3	77
25.1	76, 77
25.2	64
6AF1.1 🔑	84–87
7AF2.1	78–80

Teaching Tip **Inclusion** Some students may get confused in **Exercise 59** because the inequality changes direction twice: once when dividing both sides by a negative number, and again when rewriting the expression with the variable on the left. Encourage students to write down every step, and not to attempt to do two steps at once.

CONCEPT CONNECTION **Exercise 66** involves writing and solving an inequality in which the reasonable answers are only whole numbers. This exercise prepares students for the Concept Connection on page 154.

Answer

66b. 

Solve each inequality and match the solution to the correct graph.

57. $-0.5t \geq 1.5$
$t \leq -3$; C

58. $\frac{1}{9}t \leq -3$
$t \leq -27$; D

59. $-13.5 \leq -4.5t$
$t \leq 3$; A

60. $\frac{t}{-6} \leq -\frac{1}{2}$ $t \geq 3$; B

A. −5 −4 −3 −2 −1 0 1 2 3 4 5

B. −5 −4 −3 −2 −1 0 1 2 3 4 5

C. −5 −4 −3 −2 −1 0 1 2 3 4 5

D. −45 −36 −27 −18 −9 0 9

Animals

Sun Lin is the third panda to be born at the San Diego Zoo. Pandas at the zoo eat bamboo, vegetables, and special biscuits. Su Lin is sometimes given honey and fruit as a treat.

Source: San Diego Zoo.

61. **Animals** A wildlife shelter is home to native species of birds, mammals, and reptiles. If mixed seed is sold in 20 lb bags, what is the least number of bags of mixed seed needed for one year at this shelter? **26 bags**

Food Consumed at a Wildlife Shelter per Week	
Type of Food	Amount of Food (lb)
Grapes	4
Mixed seed	10
Peanuts	5
Raw meat	10
Grains	5

62. **Education** In order to earn an A in a college math class, a student must score no less than 90% of all possible points. One semester, students who earned an A had at least 567 points. Write an inequality to show the range of points possible. **$567 \leq p \leq 630$**

63. **Critical Thinking** Explain why you cannot solve an inequality by multiplying both sides by zero. **Multiplying both sides of an inequality by zero makes both sides equal zero, so there is no longer an inequality to solve.**

64. **///ERROR ANALYSIS///** Two students have different answers for a homework problem. Which answer is incorrect? Explain the error.

A is incorrect. Both sides are divided by a positive number, so the inequality symbol should not be reversed.

Ⓐ 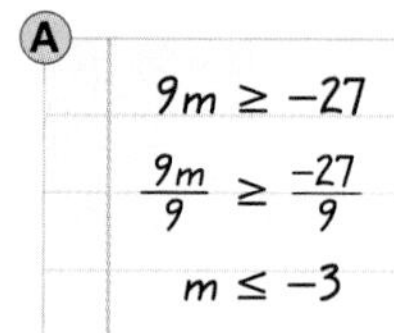

Ⓑ 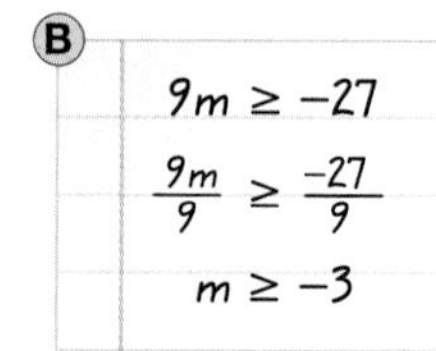

65. Jan has a budget of $800 for catering. The catering company charges $12.50 per guest. Write and solve an inequality to show the numbers of guests Jan can invite. **$12.5g \leq 800$; $g \leq 64$ where g is nonnegative**

CONCEPT CONNECTION

66. This problem will prepare you for the Concept Connection on page 154.
    a. The Swimming Club can spend a total of $250 for hotel rooms for its spring trip. One hotel costs $75 per night. Write an inequality to find the number of rooms the club can reserve at this hotel. Let n be the number of rooms. **$75n \leq 250$**
    b. Solve the inequality you wrote in part **a.** Graph the solutions on a number line. Make sure your answer is reasonable. **$n \leq 3.33$; n must be a natural number**
    c. Another hotel offers a rate of $65 per night. Does this allow the club to reserve more rooms? Explain your reasoning. **$65n \leq 250$; $n \leq 3.85$; no, they still can reserve only 3 or fewer rooms.**

3-3 PRACTICE A

3-3 PRACTICE C

3-3 PRACTICE B

LESSON 3-3 **Practice B**
Solving Inequalities by Multiplying or Dividing

Solve each inequality and graph the solutions.

1. $4a > 32$ — $a > 8$
2. $-7y < 21$ — $y > -3$
3. $1.5n \leq -18$ — $n \leq -12$
4. $-\frac{3}{8}c \geq 9$ — $c \leq -24$
5. $\frac{y}{5} > 4$ — $y > 20$
6. $2s \leq -3$ — $s \leq -1.5$
7. $-\frac{1}{3}b < -6$ — $b > 18$
8. $\frac{z}{-8} \geq -0.25$ — $z \leq 2$

Write and solve an inequality for each problem.

9. Phil has a strip of wood trim that is 16 feet long. He needs 5-foot pieces to trim some windows. What are the possible numbers of pieces he can cut?
$5p \leq 16$; $p \leq 3.2$; 0, 1, 2, or 3 pieces
10. A teacher buys a 128-ounce bottle of juice and serves it in 5-ounce cups. What are the possible numbers of cups she can fill?
$5s \leq 128$; $s \leq 25.6$; 0 to 25 cups
11. At an online bookstore, Kendra bought 4 copies of the same book for the members of her book club. She got free shipping because her total was at least $50. What was the minimum price of each book?
$4b \geq 50$; $b \geq 12.50$; $12.50 each

3-3 READING STRATEGIES

LESSON 3-3 **Reading Strategies**
Recognize Errors

The rules for solving inequalities are the same as for solving equations, with one exception. Analyze the problems below to avoid common errors.

$-4n > 28$; $\frac{-4n}{-4} > \frac{28}{-4}$; $n < -7$ **Correct:** When dividing by a negative number, you must reverse the inequality symbol.	$\frac{x}{-8} \leq 2$; $(-8)\frac{x}{-8} \leq 2(-8)$; $x \geq -16$ **Correct:** When multiplying by a negative number, you must reverse the inequality symbol.
$\frac{t}{-5} \geq 4$; $(-5)\frac{t}{-5} \geq 4(-5)$; $t < -20$ **Error:** Don't drop the "or equal to" part of the inequality symbol.	$3p < -4.5$; $\frac{3p}{3} < \frac{-4.5}{3}$; $p > -1.5$ **Error:** Do not reverse the inequality symbol just because there is a negative in the problem.

Answer each question.

1. Would you reverse the inequality symbol when solving $2x > -20$? Explain.
No; because you are dividing by a positive number.
2. What are the *correct* answers for the two errors shown above?
$t \leq -20$; $p < -1.5$

Tell whether the solution for each of the inequalities shown below is correct or incorrect. If incorrect, describe the error.

3. $-2a \geq -6$; $a \leq 3$ — Correct
4. $\frac{m}{-2} \leq 9$; $m > -18$ — Incorrect; ≤ was reversed to >, instead of ≥.
5. $15 > -15t$; $t < -1$ — Incorrect; The sign was not reversed.

3-3 REVIEW FOR MASTERY

LESSON 3-3 **Review for Mastery**
Solving Inequalities by Multiplying or Dividing

The inequality sign must be reversed when multiplying by a negative number.

Multiplying by a positive number:

$2 < 5$ *True*
$3 \cdot 2 \overset{?}{<} 3 \cdot 5$ *Multiply both sides by a positive number.*
$6 \overset{?}{<} 15$ ✓ *Statement is true.*

Multiplying by a negative number:

$2 < 5$ *True*
$(-3) \cdot 2 \overset{?}{<} (-3) \cdot 5$ *Multiply both sides by a negative number.*
$-6 \overset{?}{<} -15$ ✗ *Statement is false.*
$-6 > -15$ ✓ *Reverse inequality sign so statement is true.*

Solve $\frac{x}{3} > -2$ and graph the solution.

$\frac{x}{3} > -2$
$3 \cdot \frac{x}{3} > 3 \cdot (-2)$ *Multiply both sides by 3.*
$x > -6$

Solve $\frac{x}{-4} \geq 1$ and graph the solutions.

$\frac{x}{-4} \geq 1$
$(-4) \cdot \frac{x}{-4} \geq (-4) \cdot 1$ *Multiply both sides by −4.*
$x \leq -4$ Reverse inequality sign.

Solve each inequality and graph the solutions.

1. $\frac{x}{3} \geq -2$ — $x \geq -6$
2. $-\frac{3}{4}g < -3$ — $g > 4$

Solve each inequality.

3. $-1 < \frac{v}{-5}$ — $v < 5$
4. $\frac{5}{6}m > 10$ — $m > 12$

Multiple Choice For Exercises 67–69, choose the best answer.

67. Which inequality does NOT have the same solutions as $-\frac{2}{3}y > 4$?

Ⓐ $12 < -2y$ Ⓒ $-\frac{3}{4}y > \frac{9}{2}$

(B) $\frac{y}{2} < -12$ Ⓓ $-3y > 18$

68. The solutions of which inequality are NOT represented by the graph?

−5 −4 −3 −2 −1 0 1 2 3 4 5

Ⓐ $\frac{x}{2} \geq -2$ Ⓒ $3x \geq -12$

(B) $-5x \geq 20$ Ⓓ $-7x \leq 28$

69. Which inequality can be used to find the number of 39-cent stamps you can purchase for $4.00?

Ⓐ $0.39s \geq 4.00$ Ⓒ $\frac{s}{0.39} \leq 4.00$

(B) $0.39s \leq 4.00$ Ⓓ $\frac{4.00}{0.39} \leq s$

70. **Short Response** Write three different inequalities that are equivalent to $x > 4$. Show your work and explain each step.

Possible answer: $2x > 8$, $\frac{1}{4}x > 1$, $3x > 12$

CHALLENGE AND EXTEND

71. $g \leq -\frac{14}{5}$
72. $x < 12.375$
73. $m > \frac{4}{15}$
74. $f \geq 4$

Solve each inequality. Check your answer.

71. $2\frac{1}{3} \leq -\frac{5}{6}g$ 72. $\frac{2x}{3} < 8.25$ 73. $2\frac{5}{8}m > \frac{7}{10}$ 74. $3\frac{3}{5}f \geq 14\frac{2}{5}$

75. **Estimation** What is the greatest possible integer solution of the inequality $3.806x < 19.902$? $x = 5$

76. **Reasoning** The Transitive Property of Equality states that if $a = b$ and $b = c$, then $a = c$. Is there a Transitive Property of Inequality using the symbol $<$? If so, explain. If not, give a counterexample.

77. **Reasoning** The Symmetric Property of Equality states that if $a = b$, then $b = a$. Is there a Symmetric Property of Inequality? If so, explain. If not, give a counterexample. no; $0 < 1$ but $1 \not< 0$

SPIRAL STANDARDS REVIEW

6AF1.1, 7AF2.1, 15.0

Write the power represented by each geometric model. (Lesson 1-4)

78. 3^2

79. 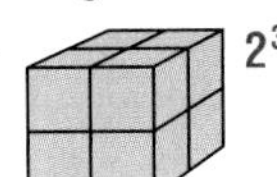 2^3

80. 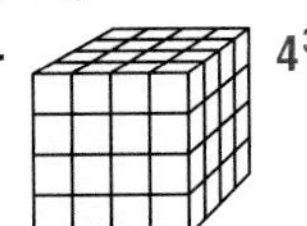 4^3

Find the unit rate. (Lesson 2-5)

81. Twelve gallons of gas cost $22.68. $1.89/gal

82. A tree grows four feet in six years. $\frac{2}{3}$ ft/yr

83. A student types 105 words in 3 minutes. 35 words/min

Solve each inequality and graph the solutions. Check your answer. (Lesson 3-2)

84. $x + 5 \geq 3$ $x \geq -2$ 85. $t - \frac{1}{4} < \frac{3}{4}$ $t < 1$ 86. $4 > x - 1$ $x < 5$ 87. $6 > b - 8$ $b < 14$

84. −3 −2 −1 0 1 2 3
85. −3 −2 −1 0 1 2 3
86. 0 1 2 3 4 5 6
87. 12 13 14 15 16

Teaching Tip **Multiple Choice** In **Exercise 69,** students who chose **A** or **D** may understand that the cost is multiplied by the number of stamps, but not that the cost must be less than or equal to $4. Students who chose **C** may not understand the relationship between the cost of the stamps and the number of stamps that can be purchased.

Answer

76. Yes; if $a < b$, then b is to the right of a on the number line. If $b < c$, then c is to the right of b on the number line. Therefore, c is to the right of a, and $a < c$. Similar arguments hold for $\leq$, $>$, and $\geq$.

Journal

Have students explain why someone might change the direction of the inequality symbol twice when solving a one-step inequality with multiplication or division.

ALTERNATIVE ASSESSMENT

Have students work in groups to explain solving one-step inequalities. The report should include using each property of inequality, at least one real-world problem, and an explanation of why and when the inequality symbol is changed.

Power Presentations with PowerPoint®

3-3 Lesson Quiz

Solve each inequality and graph the solutions.

1. $8x < -24$ $x < -3$

−6 −5 −4 −3 −2 −1 0

2. $-5x \geq 30$ $x \leq -6$

−8 −6 −4 −2 0

3. $\frac{x}{5} > 4$ $x > 20$

0 10 20 30 40

4. $\frac{x}{-8} \leq \frac{-3}{4}$ $x \geq 6$

0 2 4 6 8

5. A soccer coach plans to order more shirts for her team. Each shirt costs $9.85. She has $77 left in her uniform budget. What are the possible numbers of shirts she can buy? 0, 1, 2, 3, 4, 5, 6, or 7 shirts

Also available on transparency

3-3 PROBLEM SOLVING

LESSON 3-3 **Problem Solving**
Solving Inequalities by Multiplying or Dividing

Write and solve an inequality for each situation.

1. Karin has $3 to spend in the arcade. The game she likes costs 50¢ per play. What are the possible numbers of times that she can play?

$0.50g \leq 3$; $g \leq 6$;
0, 1, 2, 3, 4, 5, or 6

2. Tyrone has $21 and wants to buy juice drinks for his soccer team. There are 15 players on his team. How much can each drink cost so that Tyrone can buy one drink for each person?

$15d \leq 21$; $d \leq 1.40$;
up to $1.40

3. A swimming pool is 7 feet deep and is being filled at the rate of 2.5 feet per hour. How long can the pool be left unattended without the water overflowing?

$2.5h \leq 7$; $h \leq 2.8$;
up to 2.8 hours

4. Megan is making quilts that require 11 feet of cloth each. She has 50 feet of cloth. What are the possible numbers of quilts that she can make?

$11q \leq 50$; $q \leq 4.54$;
0, 1, 2, 3, or 4

Alyssa, Reggie, and Cassie are meeting some friends at the movies and have stopped at the refreshment stand. The table below shows some of the items for sale and their prices. Use this information to answer questions 5–7.

Menu Item	Price ($)
Popcorn	3.50
Drink	3.00
Hot Dog	2.50
Nachos	2.50
Fruit Snack	2.00

5. Alyssa has $7 and would like to buy fruit snacks for as many of her friends as possible. Which inequality below can be solved to find the number of fruit snacks f she can buy?

(A) $2f \leq 7$ C $7f \leq 2$
B $2f < 7$ D $7f < 2$

6. Reggie brought $13 and is going to buy popcorn for the group. Which answer below shows the possible numbers of popcorns p Reggie can buy for his friends?

F 0, 1, or 2 H 0, 1, 2, 3, or 4
(G) 0, 1, 2, or 3 J 0, 1, 2, 3, 4, or 5

7. The movie theater donates 12% of its sales to charity. From Cassie's purchases, the theater will donate at least $2.15. Which inequality below shows the amount of money m that Cassie spent at the refreshment stand?

(A) $m \geq 17.92$ C $m \geq 25.80$
B $m \leq 17.92$ D $m \leq 25.80$

3-3 CHALLENGE

LESSON 3-3 **Challenge**
A Mathematical Lens

You will need a centimeter ruler for this activity.

1. Consider the inequality $-1 < 3$. Write the inequality you get when you multiply both sides by -2. $2 > -6$

2. On the top number line, plot a point at −1. On the bottom number line, plot the value you get when you multiply by −2. Use your ruler to connect the two points with a straight segment.

3. Similarly, on the top, plot a point at 3. On the bottom, plot the value you get when you multiply by −2. Connect the two points with a segment.

4. Explain how the graph illustrates that you *reverse* an inequality when you multiply both sides by a negative number.

The segments cross each other showing that the value that was lesser (−1) now corresponds to the value that is greater (2), and vice versa.

5. The two segments should intersect along the dashed segment connecting the zeroes. Measure the two pieces of the dashed segment. How is the ratio of the two lengths related to the factor −2?

The ratio of these lengths is the absolute value of −2: $\frac{\text{bottom}}{\text{top}} = \frac{2.4 \text{ cm}}{1.2 \text{ cm}} = 2$.

6. Try it again. Multiply both sides of the inequality $9 < 15$ by $-\frac{1}{3}$. Plot points and connect them. Do you see the same patterns? yes; the segments cross each other and the ratio of the lengths of the pieces of the dashed segment is still the absolute value of the factor: $\frac{\text{bottom}}{\text{top}} = \frac{0.9 \text{ cm}}{2.7 \text{ cm}} = \frac{1}{3}$.

7. Where along the dashed line would the segments intersect if you multiplied both sides of any inequality by −1?

The segments would intersect at the midpoint of the dashed line.

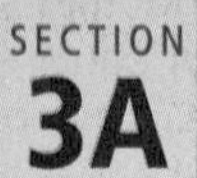

3A CONCEPT CONNECTION

Organizer

Objective: Assess students' ability to apply concepts and skills in Lessons 3-1 through 3-3 in a real-world format.

Premier Online Edition

Problem	Text Reference
1	Lesson 3-1
2	Lesson 3-2
3	Lesson 3-3
4	Lesson 1-3
5	Lessons 1-2 and 1-3

Answers

1. 581 mi
2. $532 + m \leq 581$; $m \leq 49$ where m is nonnegative

3. $58n \leq 200$; $n \leq 3.45$; they can reserve a maximum of 3 rooms.

CHAPTER 3 CONCEPT CONNECTION

SECTION 3A

Simple Inequalities

Remember the Alamo! The Spanish Club is planning a trip for next summer. They plan to travel from Fort Worth, Texas, to San Antonio, Texas. They can spend only $550 for the entire trip.

1. The treasurer of the club budgets $90 for gasoline. The current gas price is $3.10/gallon. The school van gets an average of 20 miles per gallon of gasoline. Determine how many miles they can drive on this budget. Round your answer to the nearest mile.
2. The distance from Fort Worth to San Antonio is 266 miles. Write an inequality that can be used to solve for the number of miles m that they can drive while in San Antonio. Solve your inequality and graph the solutions. Check your answer.
3. The treasurer budgeted $200 for hotel rooms for one night. The club chose a hotel that charges $58 per night. Write an inequality that can be used to solve for the number of rooms they can reserve n. What is the maximum number of rooms that they can reserve in the hotel?
4. Use the maximum number of rooms you found in Problem **3.** How much will the club spend on hotel rooms? **$58(3) = \$174$**
5. The club members plan to spend $80 on food. They also want to see attractions in San Antonio, such as SeaWorld and the Alamo.

   Write an inequality that can be solved to find the amount of money available for seeing attractions. What is the maximum amount the club can spend seeing attractions? **$344 + a \leq 550$; $206**
6. Write a summary of the budget for the Spanish Club trip. Include the amount they plan to spend on gasoline, hotel rooms, food, and attractions.

6.

Gasoline	$90
Hotel rooms	$174
Food	$80
Attractions	+ $206
	$550

INTERVENTION

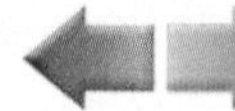

Scaffolding Questions

1. What equation relates the number of gallons, price per gallon, and total price? total price = (price per gallon)(gallons)
2. How can you find the total distance for the round trip? Double the distance between the cities.
3. Should you round your answer up or down? Round down, because they don't have enough money for 4 nights.
4. What operation should you use to find the cost of the hotel rooms? multiplication

5–6. What values do you need to find the amount left for seeing attractions? total budgeted amount, cost of gas, cost of hotel rooms, and cost of food

Extension

Explain any adjustments you would make to the budget. Possible answer: Transfer money from the hotel room budget to food or attractions. Students may want to make other changes.

California Standards

Preparation for 5.0

CHAPTER 3

SECTION 3A

Quiz for Lessons 3-1 Through 3-3

3-1 Graphing and Writing Inequalities

Describe the solutions of each inequality in words.

1. $-2 < r$ 2. $t - 1 \leq 7$ 3. $2s \geq 6$ 4. $4 > 5 - x$

Graph each inequality.

5. $x > -2$ 6. $m \leq 1\frac{1}{2}$ 7. $g < \sqrt{8+1}$ 8. $h \geq 2^3$

Write the inequality shown by each graph.

9. 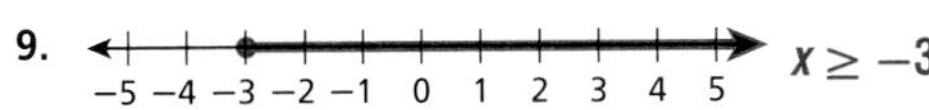 $x \geq -3$

10. $y < 5$

11. $z \leq -1.5$

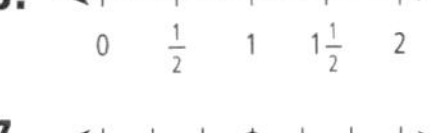

Write an inequality for each situation and graph the solutions.

12. You must purchase at least 5 tickets to receive a discount. $t \geq 5$ where t is a natural number
13. Children under 13 are not admitted to certain movies without an adult. $a < 13$ where a is positive
14. A cell phone plan allows up to 250 free minutes per month. $m \leq 250$ where m is nonnegative

3-2 Solving Inequalities by Adding and Subtracting

Solve each inequality and graph the solutions. Check your answer.

15. $k + 5 \leq 7$ 16. $4 > p - 3$ 17. $r - 8 \geq -12$ 18. $-3 + p < -6$

19. Allie must sell at least 50 gift baskets for the band fund-raiser. She already sold 36 baskets. Write and solve an inequality to determine how many more baskets Allie must sell for the fund-raiser. $36 + b \geq 50$; $b \geq 14$; Allie must sell at least 14 more baskets.
20. Dante has at most \$12 to spend on entertainment each week. So far this week, he spent \$7.50. Write and solve an inequality to determine how much money Dante can spend on entertainment the rest of the week. $7.50 + m \leq 12$; $m \leq 4.50$; Dante can spend \$4.50 at most.

3-3 Solving Inequalities by Multiplying and Dividing

Solve each inequality and graph the solutions. Check your answer.

21. $-4x < 8$ $x > -2$ 22. $\frac{d}{3} \geq -3$ $d \geq -9$ 23. $\frac{3}{4}t \leq 12$ $t \leq 16$ 24. $8 > -16c$ $c > -\frac{1}{2}$

25. A spool of ribbon is 80 inches long. Riley needs to cut strips of ribbon that are 14 inches long. What are the possible numbers of strips that Riley can cut? $14r \leq 80$; $r \leq 5.7$; Riley can cut 0, 1, 2, 3, 4, or 5 strips of ribbon.

READY TO GO ON? SECTION 3A

Organizer

Objective: Assess students' mastery of concepts and skills in Lessons 3-1 through 3-3.

Countdown to Mastery Week 6

Resources

Assessment Resources

Section 3A Quiz

INTERVENTION

Resources

***Ready to Go On? Intervention and Enrichment* Worksheets**

***Ready to Go On?* CD-ROM**

***Ready to Go On?* Online**

Answers

1–4, 15–18. See p. A13.
21–24. For graphs, see p. A13.

READY TO GO ON? Diagnose and Prescribe

Ready to Go On? Intervention	*Ready to Go On? Intervention,* Section 3A		
	Worksheets	CD-ROM	Online
Lesson 3-1 Prep for 5.0	3-1 Intervention	Activity 3-1	Diagnose and Prescribe Online
Lesson 3-2 Prep for 5.0	3-2 Intervention	Activity 3-2	
Lesson 3-3 Prep for 5.0	3-3 Intervention	Activity 3-3	

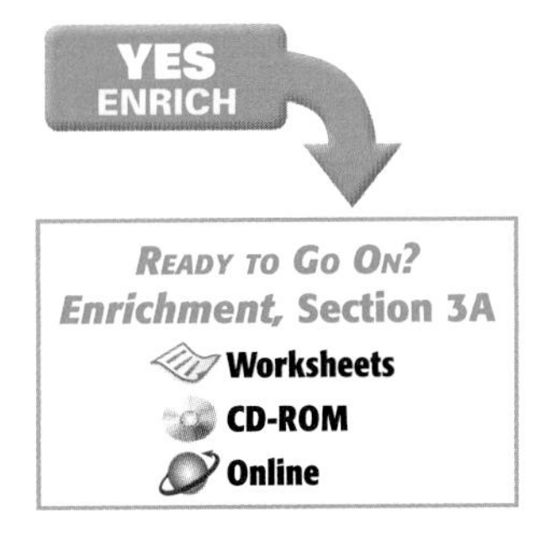

Multi-Step and Compound Inequalities

One-Minute Section Planner

Lesson	Lab Resources	Materials
Lesson 3-4 Solving Two-Step and Multi-Step Inequalities • Solve inequalities that contain more than one operation. **4.0, 5.0**		
Lesson 3-5 Solving Inequalities with Variables on Both Sides • Solve inequalities that contain variable terms on both sides. **4.0, 5.0**	***Algebra Lab 3-5*** In *Chapter 3 Resource File*	**Optional** graphing calculator
Lesson 3-6 Solving Compound Inequalities • Solve compound inequalities in one variable. • Graph solution sets of compound inequalities in one variable. **5.0**		**Optional** blank transparency, yellow and blue transparency markers, graphing calculator
Lesson 3-7 Solving Absolute-Value Inequalities • Solve inequalities in one variable involving absolute-value expressions. **3.0, 5.0**		

MK = *Manipulatives Kit*

Notes

Math Background: Teaching the Standards

COMPOUND INEQUALITIES   5.0

Lesson 3-6

A *compound inequality* is a pair of inequalities linked by the word AND or by the word OR. To understand compound inequalities, it is important to understand the logic behind the words AND and OR and to recognize the uses of these words in basic set theory.

Consider the compound inequality $x \geq -2$ AND $x < 4$. If a value of x is a solution of the compound inequality, the word AND means that both inequalities must be true. The first two number lines below show solutions of the two inequalities; the third number line shows the points that both graphs have in common.

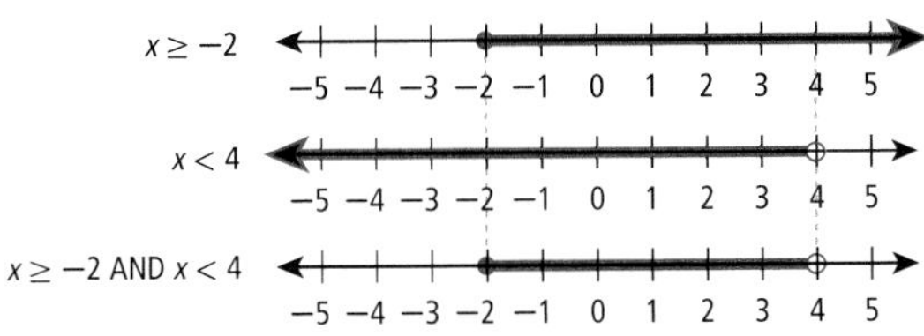

Thus, the solution set of the compound inequality $x \geq -2$ AND $x < 4$ is the *intersection* of the solution sets of $x \geq -2$ and $x < 4$. Graphically, this intersection is a line segment without one of its endpoints. Note that compound inequalities involving AND can often be written in a shorthand form: $-2 \leq x < 4$.

Now consider the compound inequality $x < -2$ OR $x \geq 4$. If a value of x is a solution of this compound inequality, the word OR means that x must be a solution of at least one of the two inequalities. Here the solution set is the *union* of the solution sets of $x < -2$ and $x \geq 4$. This is shown in the third number line below.

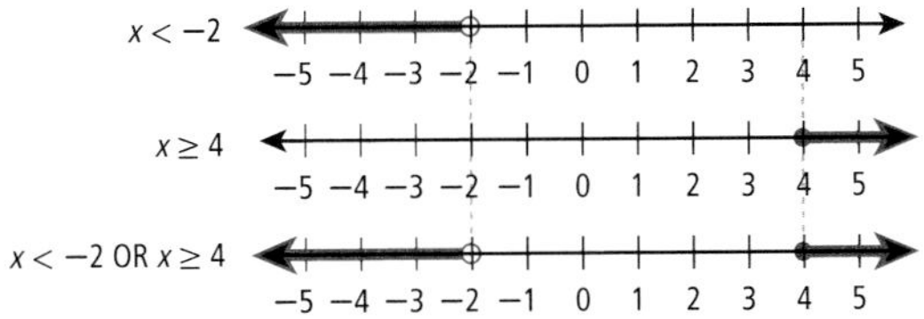

When working with compound inequalities that involve OR, students may be tempted to combine the two inequalities in a single statement, such as $-2 > x \geq 4$. This is a logical error. (For instance, the statement asserts that $-2 > 4$, which is false.) Many compound inequalities involving AND can be written in this shorthand form, but inequalities involving OR cannot.

ABSOLUTE-VALUE INEQUALITIES   3.0

Lesson 3-7

Compound inequalities may be written using absolute-value expressions. Since the absolute value of x gives the distance of x from 0 on a number line, an inequality such as $|x| < 3$ represents all points less than 3 units from 0; that is, $x > -3$ AND $x < 3$, or $-3 < x < 3$. Similarly, $|x| > 3$ is the set of all points more than 3 units from 0, which is the compound inequality $x < -3$ OR $x > 3$.

One of the key ideas of Lesson 3-7 is that absolute-value inequalities may be used to express a range of values. The absolute value of $x - a$ gives the distance between x and a on a number line. Therefore, the absolute-value inequality $|x - a| < k$ states that the distance between x and a is less than k. In other words, the inequality represents the set of all values of x that are less than k units from a.

This idea is useful in a variety of real-world applications. For example, suppose that a machine is set to cut pieces of fabric that are 2 meters long. For quality-assurance purposes, the pieces of fabric may differ from this length by at most 3 millimeters or 0.003 meters. The range of acceptable lengths is expressed by the inequality $|x - 2| \leq 0.003$. That is, the distance on a number line from x to 2 is at most 0.003. Equivalently, the relationship can be expressed with the compound inequality $-0.003 \leq x - 2 \leq 0.003$. By the Addition Property of Inequality, it is permissible to add 2 to each part of the inequality, which gives the range of acceptable lengths as $1.997 \leq x \leq 2.003$.

3-4 Organizer

Objective: Solve inequalities that contain more than one operation.

Online Edition
Tutorial Videos

Countdown to Mastery Week 6

Power Presentations with PowerPoint®

Warm Up

Solve each equation.

1. $2x - 5 = -17$ -6
2. $\frac{2x-4}{3} = 8$ 14

Solve each inequality and graph the solutions.

3. $5 < t + 9$ $t > -4$

(number line: −6 −5 −4 −3 −2 −1 0)

4. $\frac{a}{-2} \geq 4$ $a \leq -8$

(number line: −16 −12 −8 −4 0)

Also available on transparency

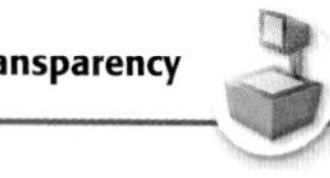

Math Humor

Q: What did the doctor say to the multi-step inequality?

A: I can solve your problem with a few operations.

California Standards

Algebra 1 4.0, 5.0

3-4 Solving Two-Step and Multi-Step Inequalities

California Standards

4.0 Students simplify expressions before solving linear equations and **inequalities in one variable,** such as $3(2x - 5) + 4(x - 2) = 12$.

5.0 Students solve multi-step problems, including word problems, involving linear equations and **linear inequalities in one variable** and provide justification for each step.

Why learn this?

Contestants at a county fair can solve an inequality to find how many pounds a prize-winning pumpkin must weigh. (See Example 3.)

At the county fair, contestants can enter contests that judge animals, recipes, crops, art projects, and more. Sometimes an average score or average weight is used to determine the winner of the blue ribbon. A contestant can use a multi-step inequality to determine what score or weight is needed in order to win.

Inequalities that contain more than one operation require more than one step to solve. Use inverse operations to undo the operations in the inequality one at a time.

EXAMPLE 1 Solving Multi-Step Inequalities

Solve each inequality and graph the solutions.

A $160 + 4f \leq 500$

$$\begin{aligned} 160 + 4f &\leq 500 \\ -160 \quad & \quad -160 \\ 4f &\leq 340 \\ \frac{4f}{4} &\leq \frac{340}{4} \\ f &\leq 85 \end{aligned}$$

Since 160 is added to 4f, subtract 160 from both sides to undo the addition.

Since f is multiplied by 4, divide both sides by 4 to undo the multiplication.

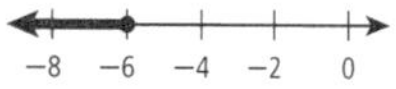

The solution set is $\{f : f \leq 85\}$.

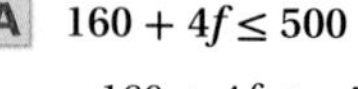

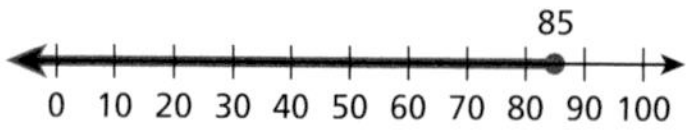

B $7 - 2t \leq 21$

$$\begin{aligned} 7 - 2t &\leq 21 \\ -7 \quad & \quad -7 \\ -2t &\leq 14 \\ \frac{-2t}{-2} &\geq \frac{14}{-2} \\ t &\geq -7 \end{aligned}$$

Since 7 is added to −2t, subtract 7 from both sides to undo the addition.

Since t is multiplied by −2, divide both sides by −2 to undo the multiplication.

Change ≤ to ≥.

The solution set is $\{t : t \geq -7\}$.

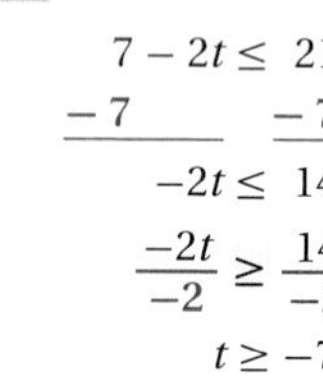

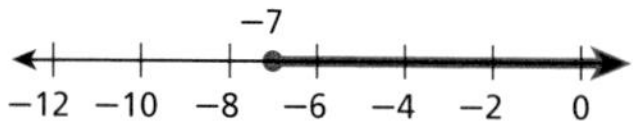

Remember!

Subtracting a number is the same as adding its opposite.
$7 - 2t = 7 + (-2t)$

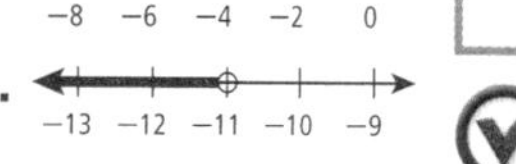

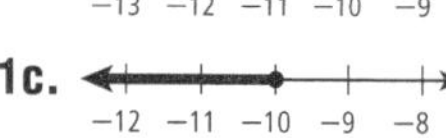

1c. (number line: −12 −11 −10 −9 −8)

Solve each inequality and graph the solutions. Check your answer.

1a. $-12 \geq 3x + 6$ $x \leq -6$ **1b.** $\frac{x+5}{-2} > 3$ $x < -11$ **1c.** $\frac{1-2n}{3} \geq 7$ $n \leq -10$

1 Introduce

EXPLORATION

3-4 Solving Two-Step and Multi-Step Inequalities

Explore the similarities and differences between solving equations and inequalities.

1. Consider the following steps in solving the equation $\frac{5x-1}{2} = 7$. Fill in the rectangles to explain what was done at each step.

$\frac{5x-1}{2} = 7$
$5x - 1 = 14$
$5x = 15$
$x = 3$

2. Use the same steps to solve the inequality $\frac{5x-1}{2} > 7$.
3. How is the solution of the inequality $\frac{5x-1}{2} > 7$ different from the solution of the equation $\frac{5x-1}{2} = 7$?
4. What would you need to do differently if the inequality was $\frac{5x-1}{-2} > 7$?

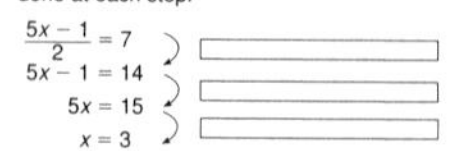

THINK AND DISCUSS

5. **Explain** how solving an inequality is similar to solving an equation.
6. **Explain** how solving an inequality is different from solving an equation.

Motivate

An online movie-rental company has two movie-rental plans. Plan A costs \$10 per month plus \$3.00 for each movie rental. Plan B costs \$20 per month for unlimited movie rentals. Discuss with students how to determine the number of movie rentals in one month for which plan A is less than plan B.

Tell students that they could use a two-step inequality, which they will learn to solve in this lesson.

Explorations and answers are provided in *Alternate Openers: Explorations Transparencies.*

To solve more complicated inequalities, you may first need to simplify the expressions on one or both sides.

EXAMPLE 2 Simplifying Before Solving Inequalities

Solve each inequality and graph the solutions.

A $-4 + (-8) < -5c - 2$

$-12 < -5c - 2$	*Combine like terms. Since 2 is subtracted from $-5c$, add 2 to both sides to undo the subtraction.*
$\underline{+2 \qquad +2}$	
$-10 < -5c$	*Since c is multiplied by -5, divide both sides by -5 to undo the multiplication.*
$\frac{-10}{-5} > \frac{-5c}{-5}$	*Change < to >.*
$2 > c$ (or $c < 2$)	*The solution set is $\{c : c < 2\}$.*

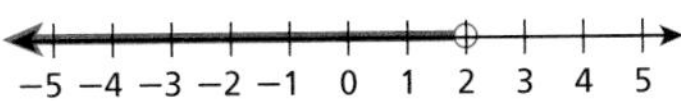

B $-3(3 - x) < 4^2$

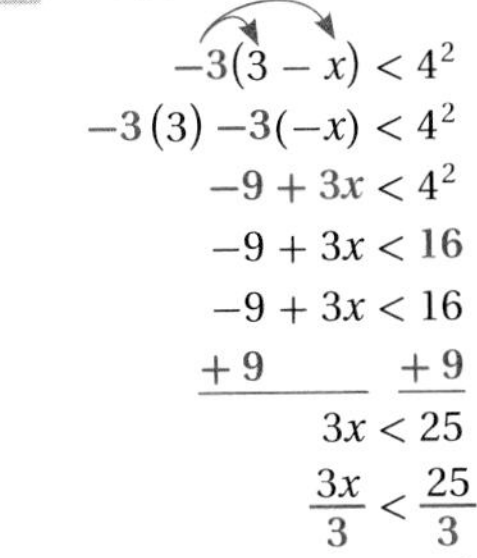

$-3(3 - x) < 4^2$	
$-3(3) - 3(-x) < 4^2$	
$-9 + 3x < 4^2$	*Distribute -3 on the left side.*
$-9 + 3x < 16$	*Simplify the right side.*
$-9 + 3x < 16$	*Since -9 is added to $3x$, add 9 to both sides to undo the addition.*
$\underline{+9 \qquad +9}$	
$3x < 25$	*Since x is multiplied by 3, divide both sides by 3 to undo the multiplication.*
$\frac{3x}{3} < \frac{25}{3}$	
$x < 8\frac{1}{3}$	*The solution set is $\{x : x < 8\frac{1}{3}\}$.*

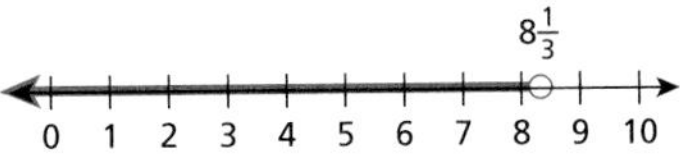

C $\frac{4}{5}x + \frac{1}{2} > \frac{3}{5}$

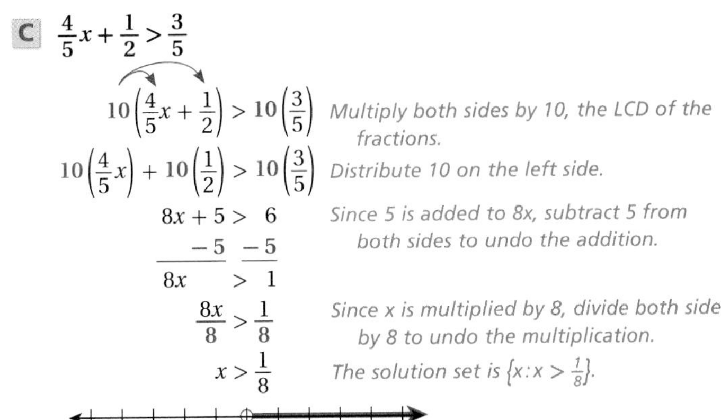

$10\left(\frac{4}{5}x + \frac{1}{2}\right) > 10\left(\frac{3}{5}\right)$	*Multiply both sides by 10, the LCD of the fractions.*
$10\left(\frac{4}{5}x\right) + 10\left(\frac{1}{2}\right) > 10\left(\frac{3}{5}\right)$	*Distribute 10 on the left side.*
$8x + 5 > 6$	*Since 5 is added to 8x, subtract 5 from both sides to undo the addition.*
$\underline{-5 \quad -5}$	
$8x > 1$	
$\frac{8x}{8} > \frac{1}{8}$	*Since x is multiplied by 8, divide both sides by 8 to undo the multiplication.*
$x > \frac{1}{8}$	*The solution set is $\{x : x > \frac{1}{8}\}$.*

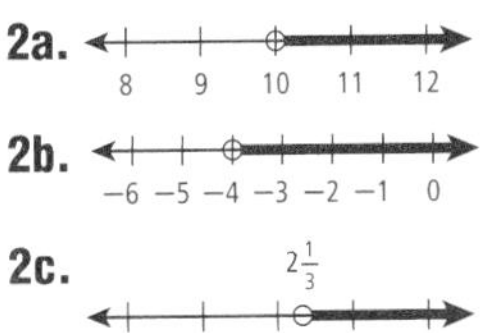

Solve each inequality and graph the solutions. Check your answer.

2a. $2m + 5 > 5^2$ $\quad m > 10$

2b. $3 + 2(x + 4) > 3$ $\quad x > -4$

2c. $\frac{5}{8} < \frac{3}{8}x - \frac{1}{4}$ $\quad x > 2\frac{1}{3}$

COMMON ERROR ALERT

When the variable is on the right side of the inequality, some students may have difficulty rewriting it with the variable on the left. For example, a student might rewrite $2 > c$ as $c > 2$. Suggest that they choose a number for c that makes the inequality true. If $2 > 1$, then $1 < 2$, so if $2 > c$, then $c < 2$.

Power Presentations with PowerPoint®

Additional Examples

Example 1

Solve each inequality and graph the solutions.

A. $45 + 2b > 61$ $\quad b > 8$

0 4 8 12 16

B. $8 - 3y \geq 29$ $\quad y \leq -7$

−8 −7 −6 −5 −4

Example 2

Solve each inequality and graph the solutions.

A. $2 - (-10) > -4t$ $\quad t > -3$

−6 −5 −4 −3 −2 −1 0

B. $-4(2 - x) \leq 8$ $\quad x \leq 4$

−2 0 2 4 6

C. $\frac{2}{3}f + \frac{1}{2} > \frac{1}{3}$ $\quad f > -\frac{1}{4}$

$-\frac{1}{2}$ $-\frac{1}{4}$ 0 $\frac{1}{4}$ $\frac{1}{2}$

Also available on transparency

INTERVENTION

Questioning Strategies

EXAMPLE 1

- What operations would you use to solve this inequality? Why?

EXAMPLE 2

- What is the difference between simplifying and solving?

2 Teach

Guided Instruction

Review the properties of inequality and remind students that the inequality symbol must be reversed when multiplying or dividing both sides of an inequality by a negative number. Also remind students to check their solution by substituting the endpoint and another point into the original inequality.

Universal Access

Through Visual Cues

Give students several multi-step inequalities. Ask students to identify the operations performed on the variable (in order). Ask students to identify the steps to solve the inequality (in order). They can make a chart, as shown below.

Inequality	Operations on Variable	Operations to Solve
$5 > \frac{3p + 2}{4}$	1. Multiply by 3.	3. Divide by 3.
	2. Add 2.	2. Subtract 2.
	3. Divide by 4.	1. Multiply by 4.

Power Presentations with PowerPoint®

Additional Examples

Example 3

To rent a certain vehicle, Rent-A-Ride charges \$55.00 per day with unlimited miles. The cost of renting a similar vehicle at We Got Wheels is \$38.00 per day plus \$0.20 per mile. For what number of miles is the cost at Rent-A-Ride less than the cost at We Got Wheels? more than 85 miles

Also available on transparency

INTERVENTION

Questioning Strategies

EXAMPLE 3

- How do you know which inequality symbol to use?

EXAMPLE 3 *Gardening Application*

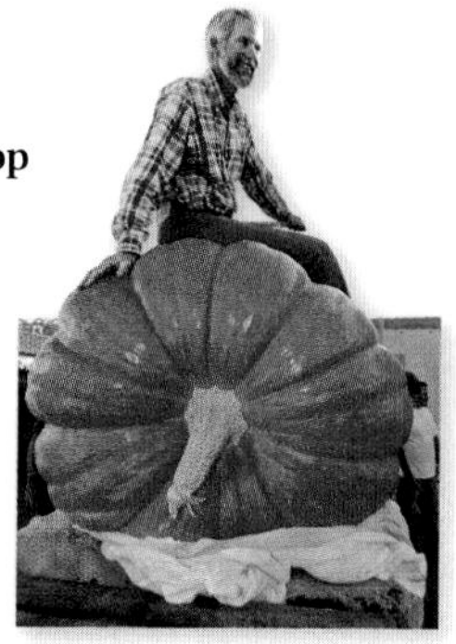

To win the blue ribbon for the Heaviest Pumpkin Crop at the county fair, the average weight of John's two pumpkins must be greater than 819 lb. One of his pumpkins weighs 887 lb. What is the least number of pounds the second pumpkin could weigh in order for John to win the blue ribbon?

Let p represent the weight of the second pumpkin. The average weight of the pumpkins is the sum of each weight divided by 2.

(887	plus	p)	divided by	2	must be greater than	819.
(887	+	p)	÷	2	>	819

$$\frac{887+p}{2} > 819$$

Since 887 + p is divided by 2, multiply both sides by 2 to undo the division.

$$2\left(\frac{887+p}{2}\right) > 2(819)$$

$$887 + p > 1638$$

Since 887 is added to p, subtract 887 from both sides to undo the addition.

$$\underline{-887 \qquad -887}$$

$$p > 751$$

The second pumpkin must weigh more than 751 pounds.

Check Check the endpoint, 751.

$$\frac{887+p}{2} = 819$$

$\frac{887+751}{2}$	819
$\frac{1638}{2}$	819
819	819 ✓

Check a number greater than 751.

$$\frac{887+p}{2} > 819$$

$\frac{887+755}{2}$	>	819
$\frac{1642}{2}$	>	819
821	>	819 ✓

CHECK IT OUT!

3. The average of Jim's two test scores must be at least 90 to make an A in the class. Jim got a 95 on his first test. What grades can Jim get on his second test to make an A in the class?
Jim's score must be at least 85.

THINK AND DISCUSS

1. The inequality $v \geq 25$ states that 25 is the ___?___. (*value of v, minimum value of v,* or *maximum value of v*)

2. Describe two sets of steps for solving the inequality $\frac{x+5}{3} > 7$.

Know it! Note

3. GET ORGANIZED Copy and complete the graphic organizer.

Solving Multi-Step Equations and Inequalities

How are they alike? | How are they different?

3 Close

Summarize

Have students solve and graph the following inequalities.

$8 - 3x < 20$ $x > -4$

$5 - 13 \geq 16t$ $t \leq -\frac{1}{2}$

$-2(1 - y) < 4^2$ $y < 9$

$\frac{1}{5}p - \frac{1}{3} > \frac{2}{3}$ $p > 5$

FORMATIVE ASSESSMENT and INTERVENTION

***Diagnose Before* the Lesson**
3-4 Warm Up, TE p. 156

***Monitor During* the Lesson**
Check It Out! Exercises, SE pp. 156–158
Questioning Strategies, TE pp. 157–158

***Assess After* the Lesson**
3-4 Lesson Quiz, TE p. 161
Alternative Assessment, TE p. 161

Answers to *Think and Discuss*

1. minimum value of v
2. 1. Multiply both sides by 3, and then subtract 5 from both sides.
   2. Divide the left side to get $\frac{x}{3} + \frac{5}{3}$, subtract $\frac{5}{3}$ from both sides, and then multiply both sides by 3.
3. See p. A3.

3-4 Exercises

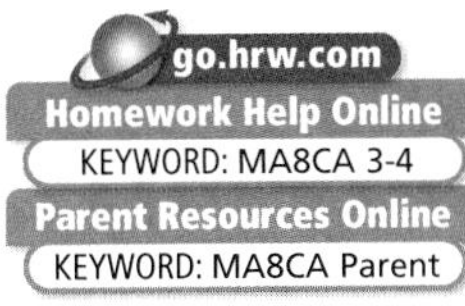

go.hrw.com
Homework Help Online
KEYWORD: MA8CA 3-4
Parent Resources Online
KEYWORD: MA8CA Parent

GUIDED PRACTICE

SEE EXAMPLE 1 p. 156

Solve each inequality and graph the solutions. Check your answer.

1. $2m + 1 > 13$ 2. $2d + 21 \leq 11$ 3. $6 \leq -2x + 2$ 4. $4c - 7 > 5$

5. $\frac{4 + x}{3} > -4$ 6. $1 < 0.2x - 0.7$ 7. $\frac{3 - 2x}{3} \leq 7$ 8. $2x + 5 \geq 2$

SEE EXAMPLE 2 p. 157

9. $4(x + 2) > 6$ 10. $\frac{1}{4}x + \frac{2}{3} < \frac{3}{4}$ 11. $4 - x + 6^2 \geq 21$

12. $4 - x > 3(4 - 2)$ 13. $0.2(x - 10) > -1.8$ 14. $3(j + 41) \leq 35$

SEE EXAMPLE 3 p. 158

15. **Business** A sales representative is given a choice of two paycheck plans. One choice includes a monthly base pay of $300 plus 10% of his sales. The second choice is a monthly salary of $1200. For what amount of sales would the representative make more money with the first plan?
$300 + 0.1x > 1200$; sales of more than $9000

PRACTICE AND PROBLEM SOLVING

Independent Practice

For Exercises	See Example
16–27	1
28–36	2
37	3

Extra Practice
Skills Practice p. EP7
Application Practice p. EP26

Solve each inequality and graph the solutions. Check your answer.

16. $4r - 9 > 7$ 17. $3 \leq 5 - 2x$ 18. $\frac{w + 3}{2} > 6$ 19. $11w + 99 < 77$

20. $9 \geq \frac{1}{2}v + 3$ 21. $-4x - 8 > 16$ 22. $8 - \frac{2}{3}z \leq 2$ 23. $f + 2\frac{1}{2} < -2$

24. $\frac{3n - 8}{5} \geq 2$ 25. $-5 > -5 - 3w$ 26. $10 > \frac{5 - 3p}{2}$ 27. $2v + 1 > 2\frac{1}{3}$

28. $4(x + 3) > -24$ 29. $4 > x - 3(x + 2)$ 30. $-18 \geq 33 - 3h$

31. $-2 > 7x - 2(x - 4)$ 32. $9 - (9)^2 > 10x - x$ 33. $2a - (-3)^2 \geq 13$

34. $6 - \frac{x}{3} + 1 > \frac{2}{3}$ 35. $12(x - 3) + 2x > 6$ 36. $15 \geq 19 + 2(q - 18)$

37. **Communications** One cell phone company offers a plan that costs $29.99 and includes unlimited night and weekend minutes. Another company offers a plan that costs $19.99 and charges $0.35 per minute during nights and weekends. For what numbers of night and weekend minutes does the second company's plan cost more than the first company's plan?
$29.99 < 19.99 + 0.35x$; starting at 29 min

Solve each inequality and graph the solutions. Check your answer.

38. $-12 > -4x - 8$ 39. $5x + 4 \leq 14$ 40. $\frac{2}{3}x - 5 > 7$

41. $x - 3x > 2 - 10$ 42. $5 - x - 2 > 3$ 43. $3 < 2x - 5(x + 3)$

44. $\frac{1}{6} - \frac{2}{3}m \geq \frac{1}{4}$ 45. $4 - (r - 2) > 3 - 5$ 46. $0.3 - 0.5n + 1 \geq 0.4$

47. $6^2 > 4(x + 2)$ 48. $-4 - 2n + 4n > 7 - 2^2$ 49. $\frac{1}{4}(p - 10) \geq 6 - 4$

50. Use the inequality $-4t - 8 \leq 12$ to fill in the missing numbers.
a. $t \geq$ **−5** b. $t + 4 \geq$ **−1** c. $t -$ **−5** ≥ 0
d. $t + 10 \geq$ **5** e. $3t \geq$ **−15** f. $\frac{t}{\mathbf{1}} \geq -5$

Answers

10. $x < \frac{1}{3}$
11. $x \leq 19$
12. $x < -2$
13. $x > 1$
14. $j \leq -29\frac{1}{3}$
16. $r > 4$
17. $x \leq 1$
18. $w > 9$
19. $w < -2$
20. $v \leq 12$
21. $x < -6$
22. $z \geq 9$
23. $f < -4.5$
24. $n \geq 6$

25–36, 38–49. See pp. A13–A14.

3-4 Exercises

Assignment Guide

Assign *Guided Practice* exercises as necessary.

If you finished Examples **1–2**
Proficient 16–36, 38–49, 50–54, 68–70
Advanced 16–36, 38–48 even, 50–54, 68–76

If you finished Examples **1–3**
Proficient 16–37, 38–48 even, 50–70, 77–86
Advanced 16–26 even, 28–37, 38–48 even, 50–86

Homework Quick Check
Quickly check key concepts.
Exercises: 18, 32, 37, 46, 53, 60

Math Background There is more than one way to solve problems with fractions. **Exercise 44** could be solved by subtracting $\frac{1}{6}$ and then multiplying by $-\frac{3}{2}$, by subtracting $\frac{1}{6}$ and then dividing by $-\frac{2}{3}$, or by multiplying by the LCD and then solving.

Answers

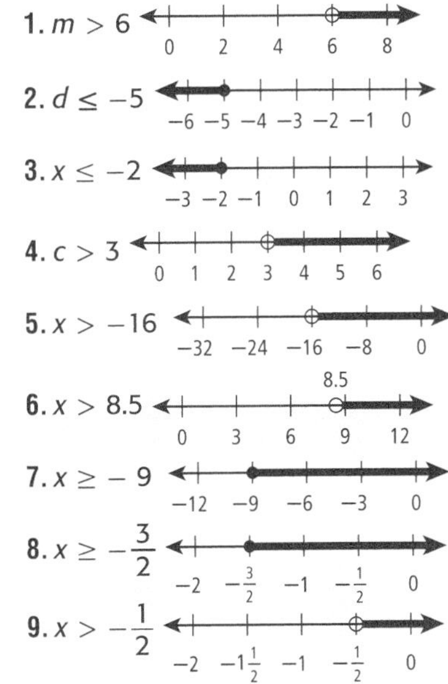

Standard	Exercises
2.0	77–82
4.0	9, 11–14, 28, 29, 31–36, 41–43, 45, 47–49, 53, 56–60, 68–70
5.0	1–62, 64–70, 83
6AF1.1	84–86

Teaching Tip **Reading Math** In **Exercise 53,** students may incorrectly interpret the inequality as $4n + 12 \leq 16$. Remind students that the product of a sum requires parentheses.

Teaching Tip **Inclusion** In **Exercise 60,** students must write an inequality using the formula for the area of a triangle where the height is a sum, $\frac{1}{2}(5)(2x + 3) < 55$. Students may distribute 5 and $\frac{1}{2}$ before using inverse operations, or they may multiply both sides by $\frac{2}{5}$ before using inverse operations.

CONCEPT CONNECTION **Exercise 61** involves using an inequality to find the number of CDs a band can purchase. This exercise prepares students for the Concept Connection on page 184.

Answers

51. $\frac{1}{2}x + 9 < 33;\ x < 48$

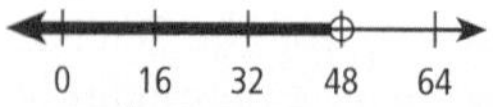

52. $6 \leq 4 - 2x;\ x \leq -1$

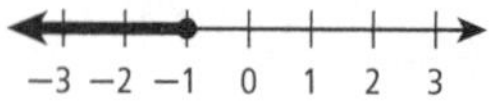

53. $4(x + 12) \leq 16;\ x \leq -8$

54. $\frac{1}{2}x + \frac{2}{3}x < 14;\ x < 12$

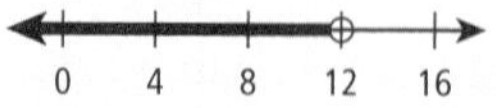

59. $225 + 400 < 275 + 15m;$ $23\frac{1}{3} < m$; 24 months or more

60a. $\frac{1}{2}(5)(2x + 3) < 55$

Write an inequality for each statement. Solve the inequality and graph the solutions.

51. One-half of a number, increased by 9, is less than 33.
52. Six is less than or equal to the sum of 4 and $-2x$.
53. The product of 4 and the sum of a number and 12 is at most 16.
54. The sum of half a number and two-thirds of the number is less than 14.

Solve each inequality and match the solution to the correct graph.

55. $4x - 9 \geq 7$ — $x \geq 4$; B
56. $-0.6 \geq 0.3(x - 2)$ — $x \leq 0$; D
57. $-2x - 6 \geq -4 + 2$ — $x \leq -2$; A
58. $\frac{1}{2} - \frac{1}{3}x \leq \left(\frac{2}{3} + \frac{1}{3}\right)^2$ — $x \geq -\frac{3}{2}$; C

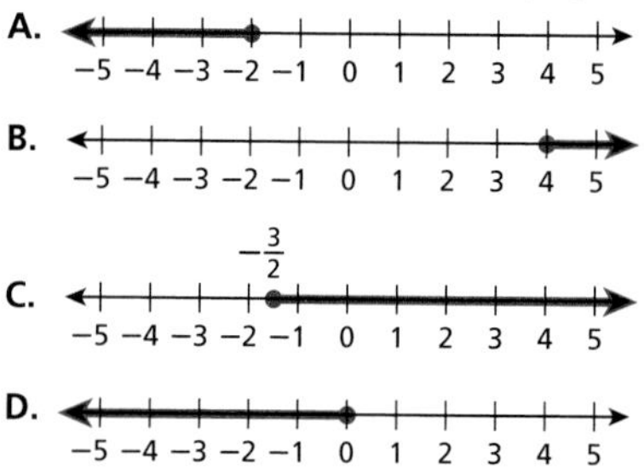

A. number line −5 to 5, closed point at −2, shaded left
B. number line −5 to 5, closed point at 4, shaded right
C. number line −5 to 5, closed point at $-\frac{3}{2}$, shaded right
D. number line −5 to 5, closed point at 0, shaded left

59. **Entertainment** A digital video recorder (DVR) records television shows on an internal hard drive. To use a DVR, you need a subscription with a DVR service company. Two companies advertise their charges for a DVR machine and subscription service.

EASY ELECTRONICS
$225 for DVR machine
$400 for lifetime subscription

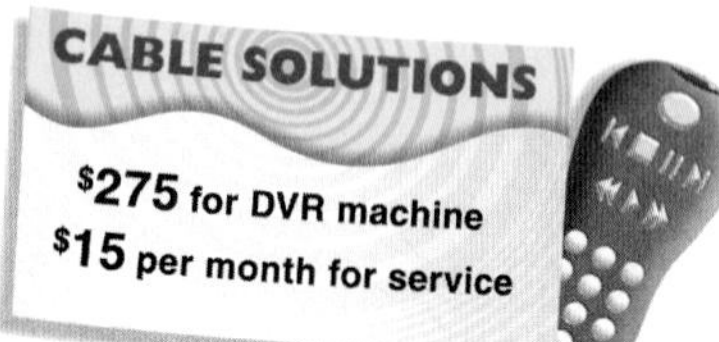

For what numbers of months will a consumer pay less for the machine and subscription at Easy Electronics than at Cable Solutions?

60. **Geometry** The area of the triangle shown is less than 55 square inches.
    a. Write an inequality that can be used to find x.
    b. Solve the inequality you wrote in part **a.** $x < 9.5$
    c. What is the maximum height of the triangle? less than 22 in.

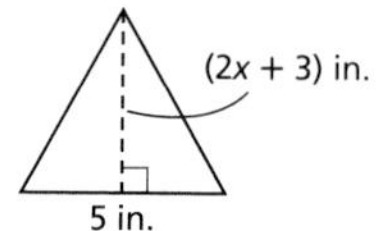

CONCEPT CONNECTION

61. This problem will prepare you for the Concept Connection on page 184.
    a. A band wants to create a CD of their last concert. They received a donation of $500 to cover the cost. The CDs cost $350 plus $3 per CD. Complete the table to find a relationship between the number of CDs and the total cost.

Number	Process	Cost
1	350 + 3	353
2	350 + 3(2)	356
3	350 + 3(3)	359
10	350 + 3(10)	380
n	350 + 3(n)	350 + 3n

    b. Write an equation for the cost C of the CDs based on the number of CDs n. $c = 350 + 3n$
    c. Write an inequality that can be used to determine how many CDs can be made with the $500 donation. Solve the inequality and determine how many CDs the band can have made from the $500 donation. Check your answer. $350 + 3n \leq 500$; $n \leq 50$; 50 CDs or fewer

3-4 PRACTICE A
3-4 PRACTICE C
3-4 PRACTICE B

LESSON 3-4 **Practice B**
Solving Two-Step and Multi-Step Inequalities

Solve each inequality and graph the solutions.

1. $-3a + 10 < -11$ — $a > 7$
2. $4x - 12 \geq 20$ — $x \geq 8$
3. $\frac{2k - 3}{-5} > 7$ — $k < -16$
4. $-\frac{1}{5}z + \frac{2}{3} \leq 2$ — $z \geq -6\frac{2}{3}$
5. $6(n - 8) \geq -18$ — $n \geq 5$
6. $10 - 2(3x + 4) < 11$ — $x > -1\frac{1}{2}$
7. $7 + 2c - 4^2 \leq -9$ — $c \leq 0$
8. $15p + 3(p - 1) > 3(2^3)$ — $p > 1\frac{1}{2}$

Write and solve an inequality for each problem.

9. A full-year membership to a gym costs $325 upfront with no monthly charge. A monthly membership costs $100 upfront and $30 per month. For what numbers of months is it less expensive to have a monthly membership?
   $30m + 100 < 325$; $m < 7.5$; 1, 2, 3, 4, 5, 6, or 7 months
10. The sum of the lengths of any two sides of a triangle must be greater than the length of the third side. What are the possible values of x for this triangle? (triangle sides: (3x) cm, (x + 5) cm, 40 cm)
   $x + 5 + 3x > 40$; $x > 8.75$

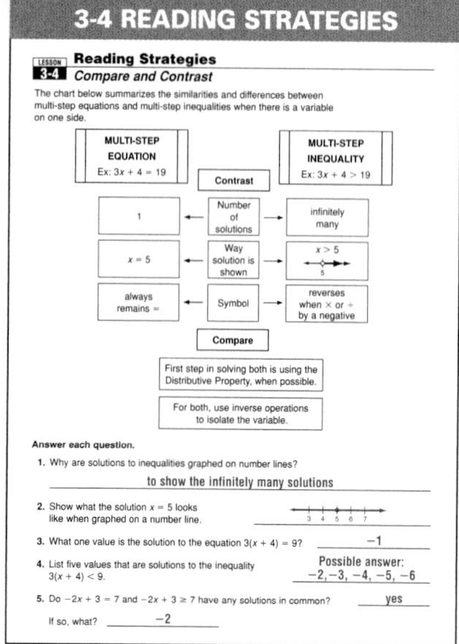
3-4 READING STRATEGIES

LESSON 3-4 **Reading Strategies**
Compare and Contrast

The chart below summarizes the similarities and differences between multi-step equations and multi-step inequalities when there is a variable on one side.

MULTI-STEP EQUATION Ex: 3x + 4 = 19	Contrast	MULTI-STEP INEQUALITY Ex: 3x + 4 > 19
1	Number of solutions	infinitely many
x = 5	Way solution is shown	x > 5
always remains =	Symbol	reverses when × or ÷ by a negative

Compare

First step in solving both is using the Distributive Property, when possible.

For both, use inverse operations to isolate the variable.

Answer each question.

1. Why are solutions to inequalities graphed on number lines? to show the infinitely many solutions
2. Show what the solution $x = 5$ looks like when graphed on a number line.
3. What one value is the solution to the equation $3(x + 4) = 9$? −1
4. List five values that are solutions to the inequality $3(x + 4) < 9$. Possible answer: −2, −3, −4, −5, −6
5. Do $-2x + 3 = 7$ and $-2x + 3 \geq 7$ have any solutions in common? yes
   If so, what? −2

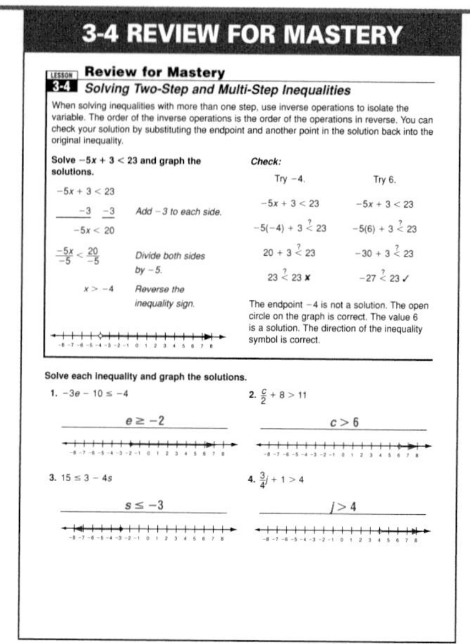
3-4 REVIEW FOR MASTERY

LESSON 3-4 **Review for Mastery**
Solving Two-Step and Multi-Step Inequalities

When solving inequalities with more than one step, use inverse operations to isolate the variable. The order of the inverse operations is the order of the operations in reverse. You can check your solution by substituting the endpoint and another point in the solution back into the original inequality.

Solve $-5x + 3 < 23$ and graph the solutions.

$-5x + 3 < 23$
$-3 \quad -3$ — *Add −3 to each side.*
$-5x < 20$
$\frac{-5x}{-5} < \frac{20}{-5}$ — *Divide both sides by −5.*
$x > -4$ — *Reverse the inequality sign.*

Check:

Try −4.	Try 6.
$-5x + 3 < 23$	$-5x + 3 < 23$
$-5(-4) + 3 \overset{?}{<} 23$	$-5(6) + 3 \overset{?}{<} 23$
$20 + 3 \overset{?}{<} 23$	$-30 + 3 \overset{?}{<} 23$
$23 \overset{?}{<} 23$ ✗	$-27 \overset{?}{<} 23$ ✓

The endpoint −4 is not a solution. The open circle on the graph is correct. The value 6 is a solution. The direction of the inequality symbol is correct.

Solve each inequality and graph the solutions.

1. $-3e - 10 \leq -4$ — $e \geq -2$
2. $\frac{c}{2} + 8 > 11$ — $c > 6$
3. $15 \leq 3 - 4s$ — $s \leq -3$
4. $\frac{3}{4}j + 1 > 4$ — $j > 4$

62. **Critical Thinking** What is the least whole number that is a solution of $4r - 4.9 > 14.95$? **$r = 5$**

63. **Write About It** Describe two sets of steps to solve $2(x + 3) > 10$.

63. 1. Divide both sides by 2, and then subtract 3 from both sides. 2. Distribute 2 on the left side, subtract 6 from both sides, then divide both sides by 2.

Multiple Choice For Exercises 64–66, choose the best answer.

64. What are the solutions of $3y > 2x + 4$ when $y = 6$?

(A) $7 > x$ (circled) (B) $x > 7$ (C) $x > 11$ (D) $11 > x$

65. Cecilia has $30 to spend at a carnival. Admission costs $5.00, lunch will cost $6.00, and each ride ticket costs $1.25. Which inequality represents the number of ride tickets x that Cecilia can buy?

(A) $30 - (5 - 6) + 1.25x \le 30$
(B) $5 + 6 + 1.25x \le 30$ (circled)
(C) $30 - (5 + 6) \le 1.25x$
(D) $30 + 1.25x \le 5 + 6$

66. Which statement is modeled by $2p + 5 < 11$?

(A) The sum of 5 and 2 times p is at least 11.
(B) Five added to the product of 2 and p is less than 11. (circled)
(C) Two times p plus 5 is at most 11.
(D) The product of 2 and p added to 5 is 11.

67. **Gridded Response** A basketball team scored 8 points more in its second game than in its first. In its third game, the team scored 42 points. The total number of points scored in the three games was more than 150. What is the least number of points the team might have scored in its *second* game? **59**

CHALLENGE AND EXTEND

Solve each inequality and graph the solutions. Check your answer.

68. $3(x + 2) - 6x + 6 \le 0$ **$x \ge 4$**

69. $-18 > -(2x + 9) - 4 + x$ **$x > 5$**

70. $\frac{2 + x}{2} - (x - 1) > 1$ **$x < 2$**

Write an inequality for each statement. Graph the solutions.

71. x is a positive number. **$x > 0$**

72. x is a negative number. **$x < 0$**

73. x is a nonnegative number. **$x \ge 0$**

74. x is not a positive number. **$x \le 0$**

75. x times negative 3 is positive. **$-3x > 0$**

76. The opposite of x is greater than 2. **$-x > 2$**

SPIRAL STANDARDS REVIEW

Find each square root. *(Lesson 1-5)*

77. $\sqrt{49}$ **7**

78. $-\sqrt{144}$ **−12**

79. $\sqrt{\frac{4}{9}}$ **$\frac{2}{3}$**

80. $\sqrt{196}$ **14**

81. $-\sqrt{1}$ **−1**

82. $\sqrt{10{,}000}$ **100**

83. Video rental store A charges a membership fee of $25 and $2 for each movie rental. Video rental store B charges a membership fee of $10 and $2.50 for each movie. Find the number of movie rentals for which both stores' charges are the same. *(Lesson 2-4)* **30 movies**

Solve each inequality and graph the solutions. Check your answer. *(Lesson 3-3)*

84. $2x < -8$ **$x < -4$**

85. $\frac{a}{-2} \le -3$ **$a \ge 6$**

86. $\frac{1}{4} < \frac{t}{12}$ **$t > 3$**

Teaching Tip **Multiple Choice** For **Exercise 66,** the verbal translation for the left side of the inequality is correct for all four choices. Choice **D** can be eliminated because is means "equal." "At least" and "at most" are both or-equal-to symbols.

Answers

68–76, 84–86. For graphs, see p. A14.

Journal

Write about the differences and similarities in solving a multi-step inequality and a multi-step equation. Include a comparison of the solutions and the methods of checking the solutions.

ALTERNATIVE ASSESSMENT

Instruct students to write a real-world problem that can be modeled by an inequality that requires at least two steps to solve. Ask students to solve the inequality explaining each step. Students should explain the meaning of the solution in the context of the problem.

Power Presentations with PowerPoint®

3-4 Lesson Quiz

Solve each inequality and graph the solutions.

1. $13 - 2x \ge 21$ $x \le -4$

−6 −5 −4 −3 −2 −1 0

2. $-11 + 2 < 3p$ $p > -3$

−6 −5 −4 −3 −2 −1 0

3. $2^3 < -2(3 - t)$ $t > 7$

4 5 6 7 8

4. $\frac{1}{3}n + \frac{1}{2} < \frac{2}{3}$ $n < \frac{1}{2}$

−1 $-\frac{1}{2}$ 0 $\frac{1}{2}$ 1

5. A video store has two movie-rental plans. Plan A includes a $25 membership fee plus $1.25 for each movie rental. Plan B costs $40 for unlimited movie rentals. For what number of movie rentals is plan B less than plan A?
more than 12 movies

Also available on transparency

3-4 PROBLEM SOLVING

LESSON 3-4 **Problem Solving**
Solving Two-Step and Multi-Step Inequalities

Write and solve an inequality for each situation.

1. Jillene is playing in a basketball tournament and scored 24 points in her first game. If she averages over 20 points for both games, she will receive a trophy. How many points can Jillene score in the second game and receive a trophy?
$\frac{p + 24}{2} > 20$; $p > 16$

2. Marcus has accepted a job selling cell phones. He will be paid $1500 plus 15% of his sales each month. He needs to earn at least $2430 to pay his bills. For what amount of sales will Marcus be able to pay his bills?
$1500 + 0.15s \ge 2430$; $s \ge 6200$

3. A 15-foot-tall cedar tree is growing at a rate of 2 feet per year beneath power lines that are 58 feet above the ground. The power company will have to prune or remove the tree before it reaches the lines. How many years can the power company wait before taking action?
$15 + 2y < 58$; $y < 21.5$

4. Binh brought $23 with her to the county fair. She purchased a $5 T-shirt and now wants to buy some locally grown plants for $2.50 each. What are the numbers of plants that she can purchase with her remaining money?
$5 + 2.5p \le 23$; $p \le 7.2$; 0, 1, 2, 3, 4, 5, 6, or 7 plants

Benedict, Ricardo, and Charlie are considering opportunities for summer work. The table below shows the jobs open to them and the pay for each. Use this information to answer questions 5–7.

Job	Pay
Mowing Lawns	$15 per lawn
Baby-Sitting	$5.50 per hour
Tutoring	$9 per session

5. Benedict has saved $91 from last year and would like to baby-sit to earn enough to buy a mountain bike. A good quality bike costs at least $300. What numbers of hours h can Benedict baby-sit to reach his goal?
A $h \ge 14$
B $h \ge 23$
(C) $h \ge 38$ (circled)
D $h \ge 71$

6. Ricardo has agreed to tutor for the school. He owes his older brother $59 and would like to end the summer with at least $400 in savings. How many sessions s can Ricardo tutor to meet his goal?
F $s \ge 31$
G $s \ge 38$
(H) $s \ge 51$ (circled)
J $s \ge 83$

7. Charlie has agreed to mow his neighbor's lawn each week and will also baby-sit some hours. If he makes $100 or more each week, his parents will charge him rent. How many hours h should Charlie agree to baby-sit each week to avoid paying rent?
(A) $h \le 15$ (circled)
B $h \ge 15$
C $h \le 21$
D $h \ge 21$

3-4 CHALLENGE

LESSON 3-4 **Challenge**
Solving Multi-Step Inequalities

As you have already seen, when you solve a linear equation, you find a definite value. If the variable is equal to 3, then the number line is divided into three parts: the number 3, those numbers greater than 3, and those numbers less than 3. When you deal with multiple inequalities, you divide the number line into even more parts.

In Exercises 1–3, use the number line below.

−4 −3 −2 −1 0 1 2 3 4 5 6 7 8 9 10 x

1. Draw a graph showing the solutions to $x \ge 3$ and $x < 7$.
2. What integers satisfy both of these inequalities? **3, 4, 5, 6**
3. What inequalities describe your response in Exercise 2? **$x \ge 3$ and $x \le 6$ where x is an integer.**

On a certain freeway, the minimum allowable speed is 40 miles per hour, and the maximum allowable speed is 55 miles per hour.

Use the information above to answer Exercises 4–6.

4. Write an inequality for each driving situation.
   a. A motorist is driving too fast. **$x > 55$**
   b. A motorist is driving too slow. **$x > 0$ and $x < 40$**
5. Is it technically correct to say that the speed limit is exactly 55 miles per hour?
   No, since there is a lower limit as well as an upper limit
6. Write multiple inequalities for each situation.
   a. The driver's speed is within the speed limits. **$x \ge 40$ and ≤ 55**
   b. The driver's speed is outside of the speed limits. **$x > 0$ and $x < 40$ or $x > 55$**

People use multiple inequalities when they deal with real-estate situations.

7. John and Marsha would like to buy a house priced at $185,000, plus or minus $5,000.
   a. What are the maximum and minimum house price that they are willing to pay? **maximum: $190,000 minimum: $180,000**
   b. Write a pair of inequalities describing their price range. **$x \ge \$180{,}000$ and $x \le \$190{,}000$**
8. Use inequalities to describe the following sentence: "We sell houses priced at $80,000, plus or minus $5000, to houses priced at $250,000, plus or minus $5000." **$x \ge \$75{,}000$ and $x \le \$245{,}000$**

3-5 Organizer

Objective: Solve inequalities that contain variable terms on both sides.

Algebra Lab
In *Chapter 3 Resource File*

Online Edition
Tutorial Videos

Countdown to Mastery Week 6

Power Presentations with PowerPoint®

Warm Up

Solve each equation.

1. $2x = 7x + 15$ $\quad x = -3$
2. $3y - 21 = 4 - 2y$ $\quad y = 5$
3. $2(3z + 1) = -2(z + 3)$
   $z = -1$
4. $3(p - 1) = 3p + 2$
   no solution
5. Solve and graph $5(2 - b) > 5^2$. $\quad b < -3$

−6 −5 −4 −3 −2 −1 0

Also available on transparency

Math Humor

Q: What did Miss Manners say to the inequality symbol?

A: It's not polite to point.

California Standards

Algebra 1 4.0, 5.0

3-5 Solving Inequalities with Variables on Both Sides

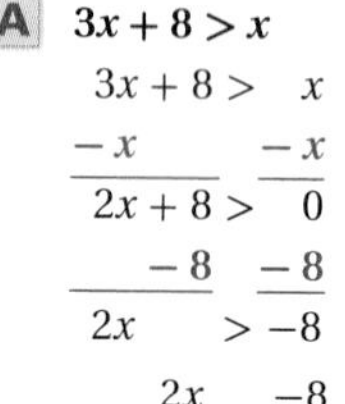

California Standards

4.0 Students simplify expressions before solving linear equations and **inequalities in one variable,** such as $3(2x - 5) + 4(x - 2) = 12$.

5.0 Students solve multistep problems, including word problems, involving linear equations and **linear inequalities in one variable** and provide justification for each step.

Who uses this?

Business owners can use inequalities to find the most cost-efficient services. (See Example 2.)

Some inequalities have variable terms on both sides of the inequality symbol. You can solve these inequalities like you solved equations with variables on both sides.

Use the properties of inequality to "collect" all the variable terms on one side and all the constant terms on the other side.

EXAMPLE 1 Solving Inequalities with Variables on Both Sides

Solve each inequality and graph the solutions.

A $3x + 8 > x$

$3x + 8 > x$ — *To collect the variable terms on one side, subtract x from both sides.*

$-x \quad -x$

$2x + 8 > 0$ — *Since 8 is added to 2x, subtract 8 from both sides to undo the addition.*

$-8 \quad -8$

$2x > -8$

$\frac{2x}{2} > \frac{-8}{2}$ — *Since x is multiplied by 2, divide both sides by 2 to undo the multiplication.*

$x > -4$ — *The solution set is {x:x > −4}.*

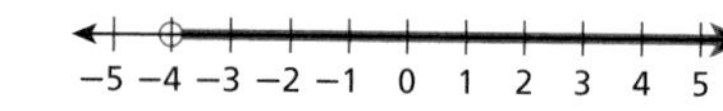

Helpful Hint

Your first step can also be to subtract 3x from both sides to get $8 > -2x$. When you divide by a negative number, remember to reverse the inequality symbol.

B $6x - 1 \leq 3.5x + 4$

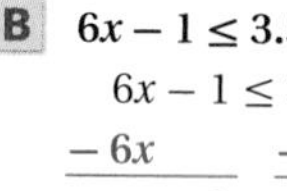

$6x - 1 \leq 3.5x + 4$ — *Subtract 6x from both sides.*

$-6x \quad -6x$

$-1 \leq -2.5x + 4$ — *Since 4 is added to −2.5x, subtract 4 from both sides to undo the addition.*

$-4 \quad -4$

$-5 \leq -2.5x$

$\frac{-5}{-2.5} \geq \frac{-2.5x}{-2.5}$ — *Since x is multiplied by −2.5, divide both sides by−2.5 to undo the multiplication. Reverse the inequality symbol.*

$2 \geq x$

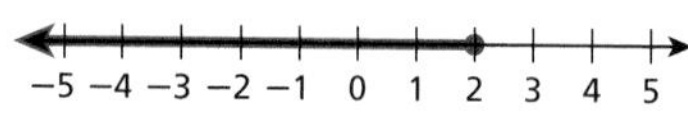

The solution set is {x:x ≤ 2}.

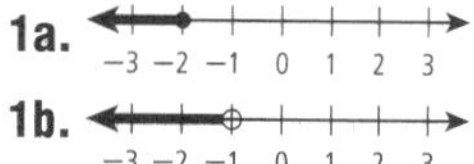

Solve each inequality and graph the solutions. Check your answer.

1a. $4x \geq 7x + 6$ $\quad x \leq -2$ $\qquad$ **1b.** $5t + 1 < -2t - 6$ $\quad t < -1$

1 Introduce

EXPLORATION

3-5 Solving Inequalities with Variables on Both Sides

You will need a graphing calculator for this Exploration. Using a graphing calculator, follow the steps below to explore the inequality $5x < 2x + 9$.

1. Press Y=. Enter **5X** for **Y1** and **2X + 9** for **Y2**.
2. Press 2nd GRAPH. Use the arrow keys to scroll up and down the table. For which values of x is **Y1** less than **Y2**?
3. Substitute several of the x-values from step 2 in the inequality $5x < 2x + 9$. Are they solutions of the inequality?
4. What are the solutions of $5x < 2x + 9$? Graph the solutions on a number line.

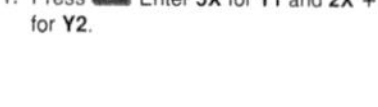

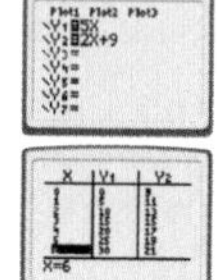

THINK AND DISCUSS

5. **Discuss** whether the table shows *all* solutions of $5x < 2x + 9$.
6. **Explain** how you could use a calculator to find solutions of

Motivate

Present two ski-ticket plans to students. Plan A costs $45 per day and includes equipment and the lift ticket; plan B costs $350 for the season and includes equipment but not the $20 lift ticket. Discuss with students how to determine the number of days for which plan A costs less than plan B. $45x < 350 + 20x$ Tell students that they could use an inequality with variables on both sides, which they will learn to solve in this lesson.

Explorations and answers are provided in *Alternate Openers: Explorations Transparencies.*

EXAMPLE 2 ***Business Application***

The *Daily Info* charges a fee of \$650 plus \$80 per week to run an ad. The *People's Paper* charges \$145 per week. For how many weeks will the total cost at *Daily Info* be less expensive than the cost at *People's Paper*?

People's Paper
STUDENT HOUSING COSTS RISING AGAIN!
Daily Info
CITY RAISES FUNDS FOR NEW HIGHWAY PROJECTS
SUMMER CLASSES WILL START EARLIER THIS YEAR

Let w be the number of weeks the ad runs in the paper.

Daily Info fee	plus	\$80 per week	times	number of weeks	is less expensive than	*People's Paper* charge per week	times	number of weeks.
\$650	+	\$80	•	w	<	\$145	•	w

$650 + 80w < 145w$

$\underline{-80w \quad -80w}$ *Subtract 80w from both sides.*

$650 < 65w$ *Since w is multiplied by 65, divide both sides by 65 to undo the multiplication.*

$\frac{650}{65} < \frac{65w}{65}$

$10 < w$

The total cost at *Daily Info* is less than the cost at *People's Paper* if the ad runs for more than 10 weeks.

CHECK IT OUT!

2. A-Plus Advertising charges a fee of \$24 plus \$0.10 per flyer to print and deliver flyers. Print and More charges \$0.25 per flyer. For how many flyers is the cost at A-Plus Advertising less than the cost at Print and More? **more than 160 flyers**

You may need to simplify one or both sides of an inequality before solving it. Look for like terms to combine and places to use Distributive Property.

EXAMPLE 3 **Simplifying Each Side Before Solving**

Solve each inequality and graph the solutions.

A $3x > 6(1 - x)$

$3x > 6(1 - x)$ *Distribute 6 on the right side of the inequality.*

$3x > 6(1) - 6(x)$

$3x > 6 - 6x$

$\underline{+6x \quad +6x}$ *Add 6x to both sides so that the coefficient of x is positive.*

$9x > 6$

$\frac{9x}{9} > \frac{6}{9}$ *Since x is multiplied by 9, divide both sides by 9 to undo the multiplication.*

$x > \frac{2}{3}$ *The solution set is $\{x : x > \frac{2}{3}\}$.*

$-\frac{1}{3}$ 0 $\frac{1}{3}$ $\frac{2}{3}$ 1 $1\frac{1}{3}$ $1\frac{2}{3}$ 2 $2\frac{1}{3}$ $2\frac{2}{3}$ 3

Power Presentations with PowerPoint®

Additional Examples

Example 1

Solve each inequality and graph the solutions.

A. $y \le 4y + 18$ $y \ge -6$

−8 −6 −4 −2 0

B. $4m - 3 < 2m + 6$ $m < \frac{9}{2}$

$\frac{8}{2}$ $\frac{9}{2}$ $\frac{10}{2}$ $\frac{11}{2}$ $\frac{12}{2}$

Example 2

The Home Cleaning Company charges \$312 to power-wash the siding of a house plus \$12 for each window. Power Clean charges \$36 per window, and the price includes power-washing the siding. How many windows must a house have to make the total cost from The Home Cleaning Company less expensive than Power Clean?

more than 13 windows

Example 3

Solve each inequality and graph the solutions.

A. $2(k - 3) > 6 + 3k - 3$

$k < -9$

−12 −9 −6 −3 0

B. $0.9y \ge 0.4y - 0.5$ $y \ge -1$

−3 −2 −1 0 1 2 3

Also available on transparency

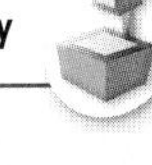

INTERVENTION

Questioning Strategies

EXAMPLE 1

- How do you decide on which side of the inequality to gather the variable terms?

EXAMPLE 2

- How do you know which inequality symbol to use?

EXAMPLE 3

- How can you tell when an expression is simplified?

2 Teach

Guided Instruction

Before solving inequalities with variables on both sides, review the steps used to solve equations with variables on both sides. Be sure students understand what identities and contradictions are.

Teaching Tip

Visual Cues To help students focus on simplifying first, tell them to cover up the right side of the inequality and simplify the left side. Then cover the left side and simplify the right side.

Universal Access

Through Communication

Give students one inequality at a time. For each, ask the following questions.

- On which side of the inequality would you gather the variables? Why?
- Would the inequality symbol need to be reversed?

Example: $3x + 1 < 4x$

Possible answers: right, to keep the variable positive, no; left, to keep the variable on the left side of the inequality, yes

Power Presentations with PowerPoint®

Additional Examples

Example 4

Solve each inequality.

A. $2x - 7 \le 5 + 2x$
$-7 \le 5$
all real numbers

B. $2(3y - 2) - 4 \ge 3(2y + 7)$
$-8 \ge 21$
no solutions

Also available on transparency

INTERVENTION

Questioning Strategies

EXAMPLE 4

- How can you tell whether the solution of an inequality is *all real numbers* or *no solutions*?

Helpful Hint

In Example 3B, you can also multiply each term in the inequality by the same power of 10 to clear the decimals.
$10(1.6x) \le 10(-0.2x) + 10(0.9)$
$16x \le -2x + 9$

Solve each inequality and graph the solutions.

B $1.6x \le -0.2x + 0.9$

$1.6x \le -0.2x + 0.9$

$\underline{+0.2x \quad +0.2x}$ *Since −0.2x is added to 0.9, subtract −0.2x from both sides. Subtracting −0.2x is the same as adding 0.2x.*

$1.8x \le 0.9$

$\frac{1.8x}{1.8} \le \frac{0.9}{1.8}$ *Since x is multiplied by 1.8, divide both sides by 1.8 to undo the multiplication.*

$x \le \frac{1}{2}$

−2 −1½ −1 −½ 0 ½ 1

CHECK IT OUT! **Solve each inequality and graph the solutions. Check your answer.**

3a. $5(2 - r) \ge 3(r - 2)$ $r \le 2$

−3 −2 −1 0 1 2 3

3b. $0.5x - 0.3 + 1.9x < 0.3x + 6$ $x < 3$

0 1 2 3 4 5 6

Some inequalities are true no matter what value is substituted for the variable. For these inequalities, the solution set is all real numbers.

Some inequalities are false no matter what value is substituted for the variable. These inequalities have no solutions. Their solution set is the empty set, ∅.

If both sides of an inequality are fully simplified and the same variable term appears on both sides, then the inequality has all real numbers as solutions or it has no solutions. Look at the other terms in the inequality to decide which is the case.

EXAMPLE 4 All Real Numbers as Solutions or No Solutions

Solve each inequality.

A $x + 5 \ge x + 3$

$x + 5 \ge x + 3$

The same variable term (x) appears on both sides. Look at the other terms.

For any number x, adding 5 will always result in a greater number than adding 3.

All values of x make the inequality true.
All real numbers are solutions.

B $2(x + 3) < 5 + 2x$

$2x + 6 < 5 + 2x$ *Distribute 2 on the left side.*

The same variable term ($2x$) appears on both sides. Look at the other terms.

For any number $2x$, adding 6 will never result in a lesser number than adding 5.

No values of x make the inequality true.
There are no solutions. The solution set is ∅.

CHECK IT OUT! **Solve each inequality.**

4a. $4(y - 1) \ge 4y + 2$ ∅

4b. $x - 2 < x + 1$ all real numbers

3 Close

Summarize

Have students solve the following and explain each step.

$a + 8 > 3a$ $a < 4$

$2(x - 3) > x - 5^2$ $x > -19$

$4(1 - t) < -2(2t + 3)$ ∅

FORMATIVE ASSESSMENT and INTERVENTION

***Diagnose Before* the Lesson**
3-5 Warm Up, TE p. 162

***Monitor During* the Lesson**
Check It Out! Exercises, SE pp. 162–164
Questioning Strategies, TE pp. 163–164

***Assess After* the Lesson**
3-5 Lesson Quiz, TE p. 168
Alternative Assessment, TE p. 168

THINK AND DISCUSS

1. Explain how you would collect the variable terms to solve the inequality $5c - 4 > 8c + 2$.
2. **GET ORGANIZED** Copy and complete the graphic organizer. In each box, give an example of an inequality of the indicated type.

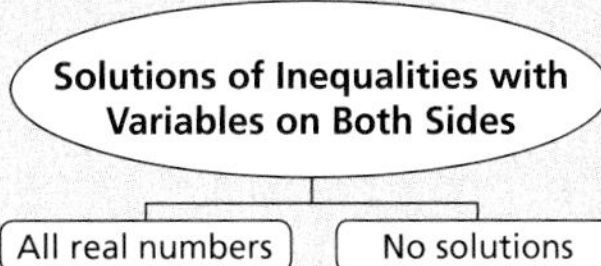

Answers to *Think and Discuss*

Possible answers:

1. Subtract 5c from both sides of the inequality so that all variable terms are on the right side. Then subtract 2 from both sides so that all constant terms are on the left side.
2. See p. A3.

3-5 Exercises

4.0, 5.0, 25.2

GUIDED PRACTICE

SEE EXAMPLE 1 p. 162

Solve each inequality and graph the solutions. Check your answer.

1. $2x > 4x - 6$ $x < 3$
2. $7y + 1 \leq y - 5$ $y \leq -1$
3. $27x + 33 > 58x - 29$ $x < 2$
4. $-3r < 10 - r$ $r > -5$
5. $5c - 4 > 8c + 2$ $c < -2$
6. $4.5x - 3.8 \geq 1.5x - 2.3$ $x \geq \frac{1}{2}$

SEE EXAMPLE 2 p. 163

7. **School** The school band will sell pizzas to raise money for new uniforms. The supplier charges $100 plus $4 per pizza. If the band members sell the pizzas for $7 each, how many pizzas will they have to sell to make a profit?
   $100 + 4p < 7p$; $p > 33.33$; they'll have to sell at least 34 pizzas.

SEE EXAMPLE 3 p. 163

Solve each inequality and graph the solutions. Check your answer.

8. $5(4 + x) \leq 3(2 + x)$ $x \leq -7$
9. $-4(3 - p) > 5(p + 1)$ $p < -17$
10. $2(6 - x) < 4x$ $x > 2$
11. $4x > 3(7 - x)$ $x > 3$
12. $\frac{1}{2}f + \frac{3}{4} \geq \frac{1}{4}f$ $f \geq -3$
13. $-36.72 + 5.65t < 0.25t$ $t < 6.8$

SEE EXAMPLE 4 p. 164

Solve each inequality.

14. $2(x - 2) \leq -2(1 - x)$ all real numbers
15. $4(y + 1) < 4y + 2$ $\emptyset$
16. $4v + 1 < 4v - 7$ $\emptyset$
17. $b - 4 \geq b - 6$ all real numbers
18. $3(x - 5) > 3x$ $\emptyset$
19. $2k + 7 \geq 2(k + 14)$ $\emptyset$

PRACTICE AND PROBLEM SOLVING

Solve each inequality and graph the solutions. Check your answer.

20. $3x \leq 5x + 8$ $x \geq -4$
21. $9y + 3 > 4y - 7$ $y > -2$
22. $1.5x - 1.2 < 3.1x - 2.8$ $x > 1$
23. $7 + 4b \geq 3b$ $b \geq -7$
24. $7 - 5t < 4t - 2$ $t > 1$
25. $2.8m - 5.2 > 0.8m + 4.8$ $m > 5$
26. **Geometry** Write and solve an inequality to find the values of x for which the area of the rectangle is greater than the area of the triangle.
   $12(x + 2) > \frac{1}{2}(10)(x + 16)$; $x > 8$

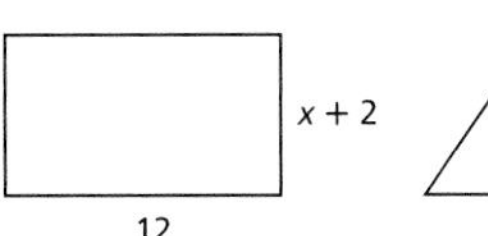

3-5 Exercises

Assignment Guide

Assign *Guided Practice* exercises as necessary.

If you finished Examples **1–2**
Proficient 20–26, 42, 44, 49, 52–56, 66
Advanced 20–26, 42, 44, 49, 52–56, 66

If you finished Examples **1–4**
Proficient 20–38, 40–48 even, 49–51, 56–66, 73–76
Advanced 24, 26, 27–38, 40–48 even, 49–51, 56–59, 61–76

Homework Quick Check
Quickly check key concepts.
Exercises: 24, 26, 28, 38, 46, 49

Answers

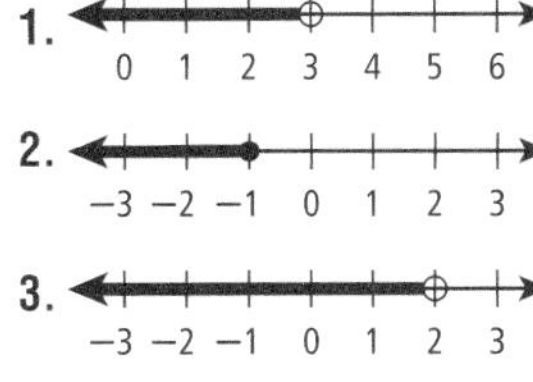

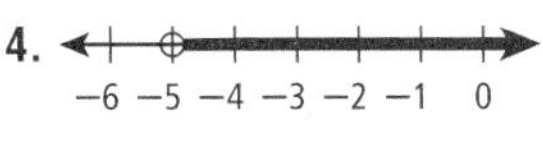

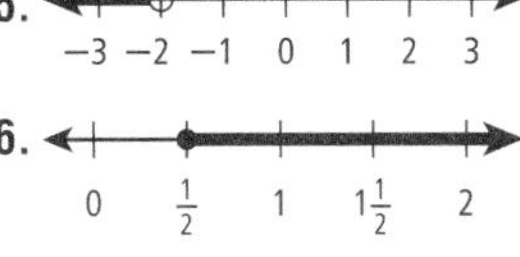

8. −9 −8 −7 −6 −5

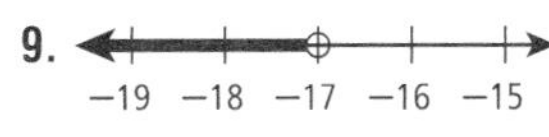

10. −3 −2 −1 0 1 2 3

11. 0 1 2 3 4 5 6

12. −6 −5 −4 −3 −2 −1 0

13. 6 6.2 6.4 6.6 6.8

20. −6 −5 −4 −3 −2 −1 0

21. −3 −2 −1 0 1 2 3

22. −3 −2 −1 0 1 2 3

23. −9 −8 −7 −6 −5

24. −3 −2 −1 0 1 2 3

25. 0 1 2 3 4 5 6

California Standards

Standard	Exercises
3.0	74
4.0	8–11, 14, 15, 18, 19, 26–29, 33, 35–38, 40, 41, 43, 45–48, 63, 67, 69
5.0	1–56, 60, 63, 65–73
25.2	60
7AF1.1	75, 76

CONCEPT CONNECTION Exercise 51 requires writing and solving multi-step inequalities in order to solve problems relating cost and profit. This exercise prepares students for the Concept Connection on page 184.

Answers

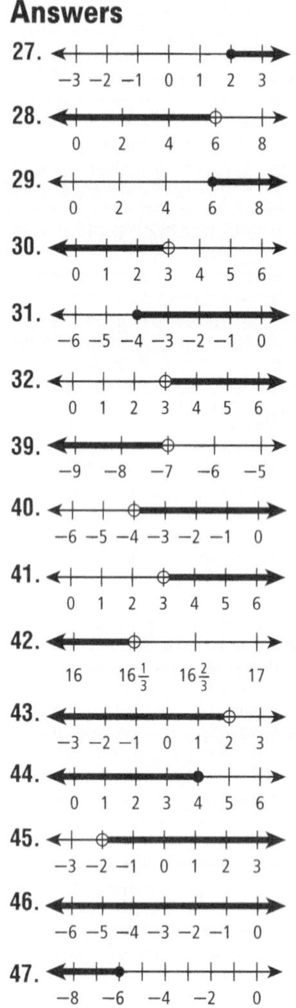

Independent Practice	
For Exercises	See Example
20–25	1
26	2
27–32	3
33–38	4

Extra Practice
Skills Practice p. EP7
Application Practice p. EP26

Solve each inequality and graph the solutions. Check your answer.

27. $4(2 - x) \le 5(x - 2)$ **$x \ge 2$**
28. $-3(n + 4) < 6(1 - n)$ **$n < 6$**
29. $9(w + 2) \le 12w$ **$w \ge 6$**
30. $4.5 + 1.3t > 3.8t - 3$ **$t < 3$**
31. $\frac{1}{2}r + \frac{2}{3} \ge \frac{1}{3}r$ **$r \ge -4$**
32. $2(4 - n) < 3n - 7$ **$n > 3$**

Solve each inequality.

33. $3(2 - x) < -3(x - 1)$ **∅**
34. $7 - y > 5 - y$ **all real numbers**
35. $3(10 + z) \le 3z + 36$ **all real numbers**
36. $-5(k - 1) \ge 5(2 - k)$ **∅**
37. $4(x - 1) \le 4x$ **all real numbers**
38. $3(v - 9) \ge 15 + 3v$ **∅**

Solve each inequality and graph the solutions. Check your answer.

39. $3t - 12 > 5t + 2$ **$t < -7$**
40. $-5(y + 3) - 6 < y + 3$ **$y > -4$**
41. $3x + 9 - 5x < x$ **$x > 3$**
42. $18 + 9p > 12p - 31$ **$p < 16\frac{1}{3}$**
43. $2(x - 5) < -3x$ **$x < 2$**
44. $-\frac{2}{5}x \le \frac{4}{5} - \frac{3}{5}x$ **$x \le 4$**
45. $-2(x - 7) - 4 - x < 8x + 32$ **$x > -2$**
46. $-3(2r - 4) \ge 2(5 - 3r)$ **all real numbers**
47. $-7x - 10 + 5x \ge 3(x + 4) + 8$ **$x \le -6$**
48. $-\frac{1}{3}(n + 8) + \frac{1}{3}n \le 1 - n$ **$n \le \frac{11}{3}$**

LINK

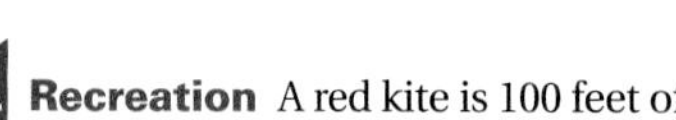

Recreation

The American Kitefliers Association has over 4000 members in 35 countries. Kitefliers participate in festivals, competitions, and kite-making workshops.

49. **Recreation** A red kite is 100 feet off the ground and is rising at 8 feet per second. A blue kite is 180 feet off the ground and is rising at 5 feet per second. How long will it take for the red kite to be higher than the blue kite? Round your answer to the nearest second. **$s > 26.67$; 27 s**

50. **Education** The table shows the enrollment in Howard High School and Phillips High School for three school years.

School Enrollment

	Year 1	Year 2	Year 3
Howard High School	1192	1188	1184
Phillips High School	921	941	961

a. How much did the enrollment change each year at Howard? **decreased by 4**
b. Use the enrollment in year 1 and your answer from part **a** to write an expression for the enrollment at Howard in any year x. **$1192 - 4x$**
c. How much did the enrollment change each year at Phillips? **increased by 20**
d. Use the enrollment in year 1 and your answer from part **c** to write an expression for the enrollment at Phillips in any year x. **$921 + 20x$**
e. Assume that the pattern in the table continues. Use your expressions from parts **b** and **d** to write an inequality that can be solved to find the year in which the enrollment at Phillips High School will be greater than the enrollment at Howard High School. Solve your inequality. **$1192 - 4x < 921 + 20x$; $x \ge 12$ where x is a whole number**

CONCEPT CONNECTION

51. This problem will prepare you for the Concept Connection on page 184.
a. The school orchestra is creating a CD of their last concert. To create the CDs, there is a fee of \$400 and a charge of \$4.50 per CD. Write an expression for the cost of creating the CDs based on the number of CDs n. **$400 + 4.50n$**
b. The orchestra plans to sell the CDs for \$12. Write an expression for the amount the orchestra earns from the sale of n CDs. **$12n$**
c. In order for the orchestra to make a profit, the amount they make selling the CDs must be greater than the cost of creating the CDs. Write an inequality that can be solved to find the number of CDs the orchestra must sell in order to make a profit. Solve your inequality. Check your answer. **$400 + 4.50n < 12n$; $n > 53\frac{1}{3}$; 54 CDs or more**

3-5 PRACTICE A
3-5 PRACTICE C
3-5 PRACTICE B

LESSON 3-5 **Practice B**
Solving Inequalities with Variables on Both Sides

Solve each inequality and graph the solutions.

1. $2x + 30 \ge 7x$ **$x \le 6$**
2. $2k + 6 < 5k - 3$ **$k > 3$**
3. $3b - 2 \le 2b + 1$ **$b \le 3$**
4. $2(3n + 7) > 5n$ **$n > -14$**
5. $5s - 9 < 2(s - 6)$ **$s < -1$**
6. $-3(3x + 5) \ge -5(2x - 2)$ **$x \ge 25$**
7. $1.4z + 2.2 > 2.6z - 0.2$ **$z < 2$**
8. $\frac{7}{8}p - \frac{1}{4} \le \frac{1}{2}p$ **$p \le \frac{2}{3}$**

Solve each inequality.

9. $v + 1 > v - 6$ **all real numbers**
10. $3(x + 4) \le 3x$ **∅**
11. $-2(8 - 3x) \ge 6x + 2$ **∅**

Write and solve an inequality for each problem.

12. Ian wants to promote his band on the Internet. Site A offers website hosting for \$4.95 per month with a \$49.95 startup fee. Site B offers website hosting for \$9.95 per month with no startup fee. For how many months would Ian need to keep the website for Site B to be less expensive than Site A? **$9.95m < 4.95m + 49.95$; $m < 9.99$; for 0 to 9 months**
13. For what values of x is the area of the rectangle greater than the perimeter? **$7(x + 2) > 7 + (x + 2) + 7 + (x + 2)$; $x > 0.8$**

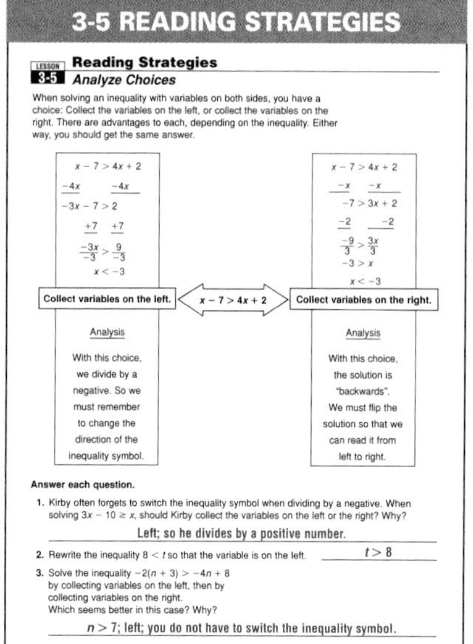

3-5 READING STRATEGIES

LESSON 3-5 **Reading Strategies**
Analyze Choices

When solving an inequality with variables on both sides, you have a choice: Collect the variables on the left, or collect the variables on the right. There are advantages to each, depending on the inequality. Either way, you should get the same answer.

$x - 7 > 4x + 2$

Collect variables on the left.
$x - 7 > 4x + 2$
$-4x \quad -4x$
$-3x - 7 > 2$
$+7 \quad +7$
$\frac{-3x}{-3} > \frac{9}{-3}$
$x < -3$

Analysis: With this choice, we divide by a negative. So we must remember to change the direction of the inequality symbol.

Collect variables on the right.
$x - 7 > 4x + 2$
$-x \quad -x$
$-7 > 3x + 2$
$-2 \quad -2$
$\frac{-9}{3} > \frac{3x}{3}$
$-3 > x$
$x < -3$

Analysis: With this choice, the solution is "backwards". We must flip the solution so that we can read it from left to right.

Answer each question.

1. Kirby often forgets to switch the inequality symbol when dividing by a negative. When solving $3x - 10 \ge x$, should Kirby collect the variables on the left or the right? Why? **Left; so he divides by a positive number.**
2. Rewrite the inequality $8 < t$ so that the variable is on the left. **$t > 8$**
3. Solve the inequality $-2(n + 3) > -4n + 8$ by collecting variables on the left, then by collecting variables on the right. Which seems better in this case? Why? **$n > 7$; left; you do not have to switch the inequality symbol.**

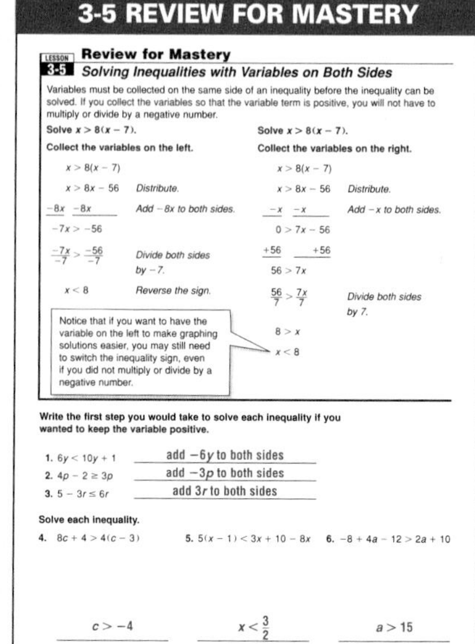

3-5 REVIEW FOR MASTERY

LESSON 3-5 **Review for Mastery**
Solving Inequalities with Variables on Both Sides

Variables must be collected on the same side of an inequality before the inequality can be solved. If you collect the variables so that the variable term is positive, you will not have to multiply or divide by a negative number.

Solve $x > 8(x - 7)$.
Collect the variables on the left.

$x > 8(x - 7)$
$x > 8x - 56$ — *Distribute.*
$-8x \quad -8x$ — *Add −8x to both sides.*
$-7x > -56$
$\frac{-7x}{-7} > \frac{-56}{-7}$ — *Divide both sides by −7.*
$x < 8$ — *Reverse the sign.*

Solve $x > 8(x - 7)$.
Collect the variables on the right.

$x > 8(x - 7)$
$x > 8x - 56$ — *Distribute.*
$-x \quad -x$ — *Add −x to both sides.*
$0 > 7x - 56$
$+56 \quad +56$
$56 > 7x$
$\frac{56}{7} > \frac{7x}{7}$ — *Divide both sides by 7.*
$8 > x$
$x < 8$

Notice that if you want to have the variable on the left to make graphing solutions easier, you may still need to switch the inequality sign, even if you did not multiply or divide by a negative number.

Write the first step you would take to solve each inequality if you wanted to keep the variable positive.

1. $6y < 10y + 1$ **add $-6y$ to both sides**
2. $4p - 2 \ge 3p$ **add $-3p$ to both sides**
3. $5 - 3r \le 6r$ **add $3r$ to both sides**

Solve each inequality.

4. $8c + 4 > 4(c - 3)$ **$c > -4$**
5. $5(x - 1) < 3x + 10 - 8x$ **$x < \frac{3}{2}$**
6. $-8 + 4a - 12 > 2a + 10$ **$a > 15$**

Write an inequality to represent each relationship. Solve your inequality.

$52.\ 2x + 4 > \frac{2}{3}x;\ x > -3$

52. Four more than twice a number is greater than two-thirds of the number.

53. Ten less than five times a number is less than six times the number decreased by eight. $5x - 10 < 6x - 8;\ x > -2$

54. The sum of a number and twenty is less than four times the number decreased by one. $x + 20 < 4x - 1;\ x > 7$

$55.\ \frac{3}{4}x \geq x - 5;\ x \leq 20$

55. Three-fourths of a number is greater than or equal to five less than the number.

56. Entertainment Use the table to determine how many movies you would have to rent for Video View to be less expensive than Movie Place. **20 videos or more**

	Membership Fee ($)	Cost per Rental ($)
Movie Place	None	2.99
Video View	19.99	1.99

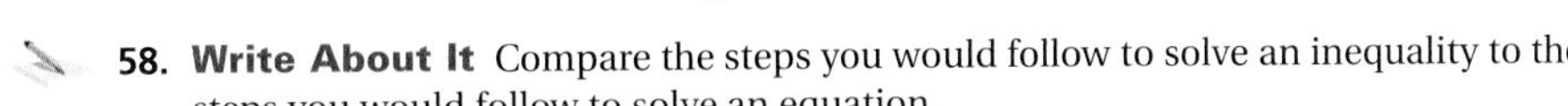

57. Geometry In an acute triangle, all angles measure less than 90°. Also, the sum of the measures of any two angles is greater than the measure of the third angle. Can the measures of an acute triangle be x, $x - 1$, and $2x$? Explain.

58. Write About It Compare the steps you would follow to solve an inequality to the steps you would follow to solve an equation.

59. Critical Thinking How can you tell just by looking at the inequality $x > x + 1$ that it has no solutions? **x can never be greater than itself plus 1.**

60. ///ERROR ANALYSIS/// Two students solved the inequality $5x < 3 - 4x$. Which is incorrect? Explain the error.

B is incorrect; the student should have added $4x$ to both sides to undo the subtraction.

Ⓐ
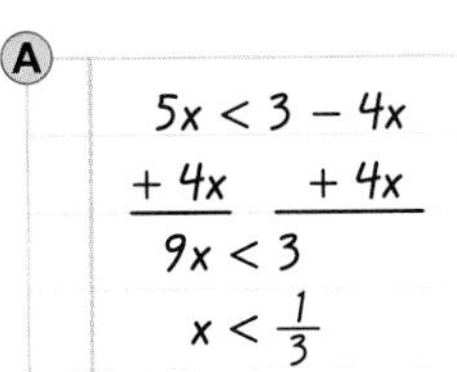

Ⓑ
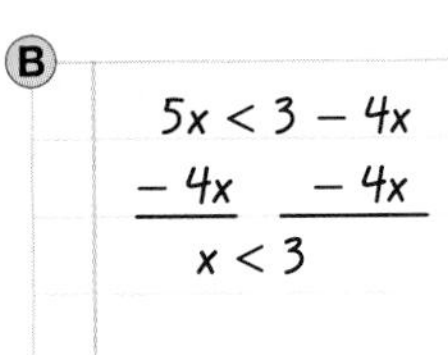

Multiple Choice For Exercises 61–64, choose the best answer.

61. If $a - b > a + b$, which statement is true?

Ⓐ The value of a is positive.
Ⓑ The value of b is positive.
Ⓒ The value of a is negative.
Ⓓ The value of b is negative.

62. If $-a < b$, which statement is always true?

Ⓐ $a < b$ Ⓑ $a > b$ Ⓒ $a < -b$ **Ⓓ $a > -b$**

63. Which is a solution of the inequality $7(2 - x) > 4(x - 2)$?

Ⓐ -2 Ⓑ 2 Ⓒ 4 Ⓓ 7

64. Which is the graph of $-3x < -6$?

Ⓐ
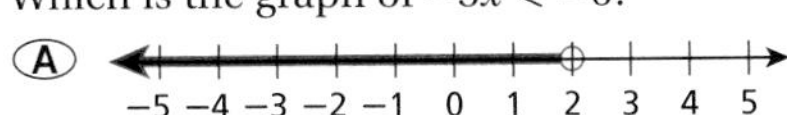

Ⓒ
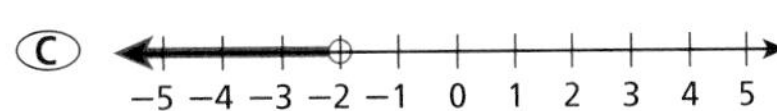

Ⓑ
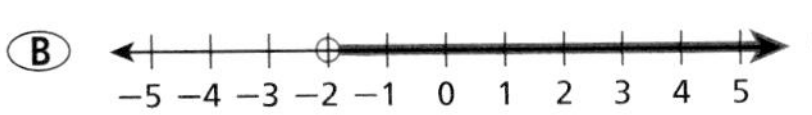

Ⓓ
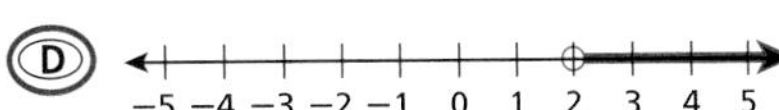

Teaching Tip

Geometry For **Exercise 57,** the largest angle is already greater than either of the other two, so students only need to check if the sum of the two smaller angles (x and $x - 1$) is greater than the largest angle ($2x$). The problem could also be solved by writing and solving an equation. Set the sum of the angles equal to 180, solve for x, and then substitute x back into each expression. One angle is greater than 90, so it is not acute.

Multiple Choice In **Exercise 61,** tell students to solve for either variable. Both will result in the inequality $b < 0$. In **Exercise 63,** students who chose **C** or **D** may not have changed the inequality sign when dividing both sides by a negative number. Students who chose **B** chose the boundary point, which is not included.

Answers

57. No; the sum of the angles with measures x and $x - 1$ would need to be greater than $2x$. $x + (x - 1) > 2x$: $2x - 1 > 2x$ has no solutions.

58. The steps are identical except when you multiply or divide both sides of an inequality by a negative number.

3-5 PROBLEM SOLVING

LESSON 3-5 Problem Solving
Solving Inequalities With Variables on Both Sides

Write and solve an inequality for each situation.

1. Rosa has decided to sell pet rocks at an art fair for $5 each. She has paid $50 to rent a table at the fair and it costs her $2 to package each rock with a set of instructions. For what numbers of sales will Rosa make a profit?
$5r > 50 + 2r;$ $r > 17$

2. Jamie has a job paying $25,000 and expects to receive a $1000 raise each year. Wei has a job paying $19,000 a year and expects a $1500 raise each year. For what span of time is Jamie making more money than Wei?
$25{,}000 + 1000y > 19{,}000 + 1500y;\ y < 12$

3. Sophia types 75 words per minute and is just starting to write a term paper. Patton already has 510 words written and types at a speed of 60 words per minute. For what numbers of minutes will Sophia have more words typed than Patton?
$75m > 510 + 60m;$ $m > 34$

4. Keith is racing his little sister Pattie and has given her a 15 foot head start. She runs 5 ft/sec and he is chasing at 8 ft/sec. For how long can Pattie stay ahead of Keith?
$15 + 5s > 8s;$ $s < 5$

The table below shows the population of four cities in 2004 and the amount of population change from 2003. Use this table to answer questions 5–6.

City	Population (2004)	Population Change (from 2003)
Lakewood, CO	141,301	−830
Vallejo, CA	118,349	−1155
Carrollton, TX	117,823	+1170
Manchester, NH	109,310	+261

5. If the trends in this table continue, after how many years y will the population of Manchester, NH, be more than the population of Vallejo, CA? Round your answer to the nearest tenth of a year.
A $y > 0.2$ Ⓑ $y > 6.4$ C $y > 34.6$ D $y > 78.6$

6. If the trends in this table continue, for how long x will the population of Carrollton, TX be less than the population of Lakewood, CO? Round your answer to the nearest tenth of a year.
Ⓕ $x < 11.7$ G $x < 14.6$ H $x < 20.1$ J $x < 28.3$

3-5 CHALLENGE

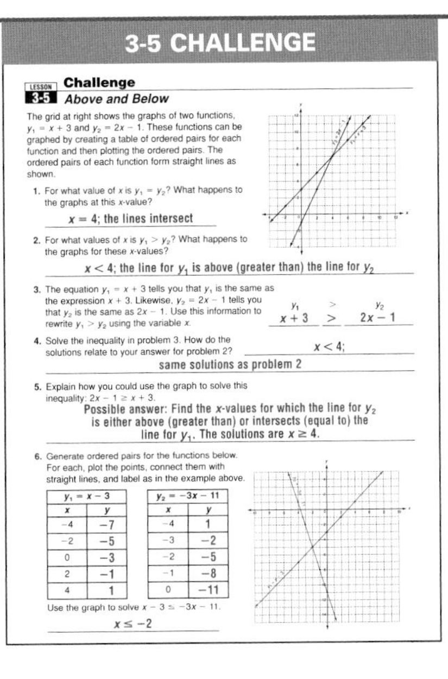

LESSON 3-5 Challenge
Above and Below

The grid at right shows the graphs of two functions, $y_1 = x + 3$ and $y_2 = 2x - 1$. These functions can be graphed by creating a table of ordered pairs for each function and then plotting the ordered pairs. The ordered pairs of each function form straight lines as shown.

1. For what value of x is $y_1 = y_2$? What happens to the graphs at this x-value?
$x = 4$; the lines intersect

2. For what values of x is $y_1 > y_2$? What happens to the graphs for these x-values?
$x < 4$; the line for y_1 is above (greater than) the line for y_2

3. The equation $y_1 = x + 3$ tells you that y_1 is the same as the expression $x + 3$. Likewise, $y_2 = 2x - 1$ tells you that y_2 is the same as $2x - 1$. Use this information to rewrite $y_1 > y_2$ using the variable x.
$x + 3 > 2x - 1$

4. Solve the inequality in problem 3. How do the solutions relate to your answer for problem 2?
$x < 4$; same solutions as problem 2

5. Explain how you could use the graph to solve this inequality: $2x - 1 \geq x + 3$.
Possible answer: Find the x-values for which the line for y_2 is either above (greater than) or intersects (equal to) the line for y_1. The solutions are $x \geq 4$.

6. Generate ordered pairs for the functions below. For each, plot the points, connect them with straight lines, and label as in the example above.

$y_1 = x - 3$	
x	y
−4	−7
−2	−5
0	−3
2	−1
4	1

$y_2 = -3x - 11$	
x	y
−4	1
−3	−2
−2	−5
−1	−8
0	−11

Use the graph to solve $x - 3 \leq -3x - 11$.
$x \leq -2$

65. Short Response Write a real-world situation that could be modeled by the inequality $7x + 4 > 4x + 13$. Explain how the inequality relates to your situation.

Possible answer: parking lot A starts with 4 cars and 7 more cars park each hour. Parking lot B starts with 13 cars and 4 more cars park each hour. The inequality helps you find that parking lot A has more cars than parking lot B after 3 hours.

CHALLENGE AND EXTEND

Solve each inequality. Check your answer.

66. $2\frac{1}{2} + 2x \geq 5\frac{1}{2} + 2\frac{1}{2}x$ $x \leq -6$

67. $1.6x - 20.7 > 6.3x - (-2.2x)$ $x < -3$

68. $1.3x - 7.5x < 8.5x - 29.4$ $x > 2$

69. $-4w + \frac{-8 - 37}{9} \leq \frac{75 - 3}{9} + 3w$ $w \geq -1\frac{6}{7}$

70. Replace the square and circle with numbers so that all real numbers are solutions of the inequality. $\square - 2x < \bigcirc - 2x$ Check students' work: the number in the square should be less than the number in the circle.

71. Replace the square and circle with numbers so that the inequality has no solutions. $\square - 2x < \bigcirc - 2x$ Check students' work: the number in the square should be greater than the number in the circle.

72. Critical Thinking Explain whether there are any numbers that can replace the square and circle so that all real numbers are solutions of the inequality. $\square + 2x < \bigcirc + x$

72. Check students' work: if the same number is added to both sides and x is negative, all real numbers are solutions of the inequality.

SPIRAL STANDARDS REVIEW

7AF1.1, 3.0, 5.0

73. The ratio of the width of a rectangle to the length is 2:5. The length is 65 inches. Find the width. *(Lesson 2-5)* $\frac{2}{5} = \frac{w}{65}$; $w = 26$ in.

74. Roman recorded the temperature for the last 7 days. The average temperature was 82 degrees and rose or fell by 8 degrees. Write and solve an absolute-value equation to find the minimum and maximum temperatures over the last 7 days. *(Lesson 2-7)* $|t - 82| = 8$; min. temp: 74°, max temp: 90°

Define a variable and write an inequality for each situation. Graph the solutions. *(Lesson 3-1)*

75. Participants must be at least 14 years old. y = years; $y \geq 14$

76. The maximum speed on a certain highway is 60 miles per hour. s = speed; $s \leq 60$ where s is nonnegative

Career Path

go.hrw.com
Career Resources Online
KEYWORD: MA8CA Career

Katie Flannigan
Culinary Arts program

Q: What math classes did you take in high school?
A: Algebra 1, Geometry, and Algebra 2

Q: What math classes have you taken since high school?
A: I have taken a basic accounting class and a business math class.

Q: How do you use math?
A: I use math to estimate how much food I need to buy. I also use math when adjusting recipe amounts to feed large groups of people.

Q: What are your future plans?
A: I plan to start my own catering business. The math classes I took will help me manage the financial aspects of my business.

Answers

75. 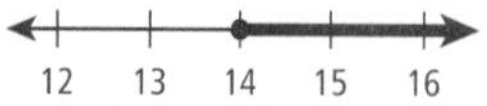

76. 

Journal

Given $n \geq 4n + 9$, have students explain how they decide on which side of the inequality to gather the variable terms and why. Then have students solve the inequality, explaining each step.

ALTERNATIVE ASSESSMENT

Have students write, solve, and graph an inequality that has variables on both sides and that needs to be simplified before applying inverse operations.

Power Presentations with PowerPoint®

3-5 Lesson Quiz

Solve each inequality and graph the solutions.

1. $t < 5t + 24$ $t > -6$

2. $5x - 9 \leq 4.1x - 81$
$x \leq -80$

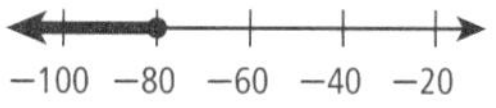

3. $4b + 4(1 - b) > b - 9$
$b < 13$

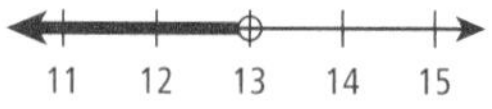

4. Rick bought a photo printer and supplies for \$186.90, which will allow him to print photos for \$0.29 each. A photo store charges \$0.55 to print each photo. How many photos must Rick print before his total cost is less than getting prints made at the photo store? Rick must print more than 718 photos.

Solve each inequality.

5. $2y - 2 \geq 2(y + 7)$ $\varnothing$

6. $2(-6r - 5) < -3(4r + 2)$
all real numbers

Also available on transparency

Deductive Reasoning and Inequalities

Use with Lessons 3-1 through 3-5

Just as you do solving equations, you use deductive reasoning every time you solve an inequality.

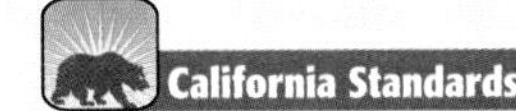

California Standards

5.0 Students solve multi-step problems, including word problems, **involving** linear equations and **linear inequalities in one variable and provide justification for each step.**
Also covered: **4.0, 24.2, 25.1, 25.2**

Example

Solve $2(x - 3) - 5x \geq -18$. Give a reason for each step in your solution process. Identify the conditional statement that is proved and its hypothesis and conclusion.

Statements	Reasons
1. $2(x - 3) - 5x \geq -18$	Given
2. $2x - 6 - 5x \geq -18$	Distributive Property
3. $(2x - 5x) - 6 \geq -18$	Commutative and Associative Properties of Addition
4. $-3x - 6 \geq -18$	Combine like terms.
5. $-3x \geq -12$	Addition Property of Inequality (Add 6 to both sides.)
6. $x \leq 4$	Division Property of Inequality (Divide both sides by −3. Reverse the inequality symbol.)

The above proves the conditional statement "If $2(x - 3) - 5x \geq -18$, then $x \leq 4$."

Hypothesis: $2(x - 3) - 5x \geq -18$ Conclusion: $x \leq 4$

Try This

Solve each inequality. Give a reason for each step in your solution process. Identify the conditional statement that is proved and its hypothesis and conclusion.

1. $x + 5 < 9$
2. $x - 9 \leq -12$
3. $8x > 64$
4. $\frac{x}{12} \leq -7$
5. $2x + 15 < 29$
6. $5(3 + x) < 20$
7. $16 - x \geq 3x + 8 - 5x$
8. $-4(x + 3) > 6(3 - x)$
9. What is the error in the solution below? Write a correct solution.

Statements	Reasons
1. $3x + 9 - 4x \geq 15$	Given
2. $x + 9 \geq 15$	Combine like terms.
3. $x \geq 6$	Subtraction Property of Inequality (Subtract 9 from both sides.)

Close

Key Concept

Reasoning is always used when doing math. If asked, you should be able to justify any step in a procedure with a property, definition, operation, etc.

Assess

Divide students into groups of three or four. Give each group an inequality from the previous lessons. One student writes the first step of the solution and its reason and passes it to the second student, who writes the second step, and so on. The group should discuss the completed solution.

Extend

Challenge students to justify statements that combine equations and inequalities:

- If $2x + 7 = 13$, then $x < 5$.
- If $2x - 3x = 4x + 10$, then $x \geq -2$.

Have students come up with their own conditional statements to justify.

Organizer

Objective: Examine the underlying deductive reasoning used when solving an inequality.

Online Edition
Student Edition

Countdown to Mastery Week 6

Teach

Discuss

Reinforce to students that there is a reason for everything we do in mathematics, even though we often do not write the reasons down when solving problems.

Watch for students who combine more than one step in their solutions. It is not incorrect to do this, but all of the reasons must be listed. For example, if a student goes from $5(x + 3) + 2x$ to $7x + 15$, the reasons should be: Distributive Property, Associative and Commutative Properties, and combine like terms.

Answers

1.

Statements	Reasons
1. $x + 5 < 9$	Given
2. $x < 4$	Subtr. Prop. of Ineq. (subtract 5 from both sides.)

If $x + 5 < 9$, then $x < 4$. Hypothesis: $x + 5 < 9$; Conclusion: $x < 4$

2–9. See pp. A14–A15.

California Standards

5.0
Also covered:
4.0 Students simplify expressions before solving linear equations and **inequalities in one variable,** such as $3(2x - 5) + 4(x - 2) = 12$.
24.2 Students identify the hypothesis and conclusion in logical deduction.
25.0 Students use properties of the number system to judge the validity of results, to justify each step of a procedure, and to prove or disprove **statements.**
25.1 Students use properties of numbers to construct simple, valid arguments (direct and indirect) for, or formulate counterexamples to, claimed assertions.
25.2 Students judge the validity of an argument according to whether the properties of the real number system and the order of operations have been applied correctly at each step.

3-6 Organizer

Objectives: Solve compound inequalities in one variable.

Graph solution sets of compound inequalities in one variable.

Online Edition
Tutorial Videos, Interactivity

Countdown to Mastery Week 7

Power Presentations with PowerPoint®

Warm Up

Solve each inequality.

1. $x + 3 \leq 10$ $x \leq 7$

2. $23 < -2x + 3$ $-10 > x$

Solve each inequality and graph the solutions.

3. $4x + 1 \leq 25$ $x \leq 6$

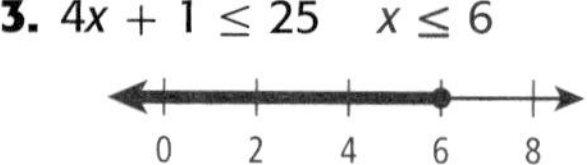

4. $0 \geq 3x + 3$ $-1 \geq x$

−3 −2 −1 0 1 2 3

Also available on transparency

Math Humor

Q: How does a math teacher get a compound fracture?

A: She breaks her hAND.

3-6 Solving Compound Inequalities

California Standards

5.0 Students solve multi-step problems, including word problems, involving linear equations and **linear inequalities in one variable** and provide justification for each step.

Vocabulary
compound inequality
intersection
union

Who uses this?
A lifeguard can use compound inequalities to describe the safe pH levels in a swimming pool. (See Example 1.)

The inequalities you have seen so far are simple inequalities. When two simple inequalities are combined into one statement by the words AND or OR, the result is called a **compound inequality**.

Know it! Note

Compound Inequalities

WORDS	ALGEBRA	GRAPH
All real numbers greater than 2 AND less than 6	$x > 2$ AND $x < 6$ $2 < x < 6$	0 2 4 6 8
All real numbers greater than or equal to 2 AND less than or equal to 6	$x \geq 2$ AND $x \leq 6$ $2 \leq x \leq 6$	0 2 4 6 8
All real numbers less than 2 OR greater than 6	$x < 2$ OR $x > 6$	0 2 4 6 8
All real numbers less than or equal to 2 OR greater than or equal to 6	$x \leq 2$ OR $x \geq 6$	0 2 4 6 8

EXAMPLE 1 ***Chemistry Application***

A water analyst recommends that the pH level of swimming pool water be between 7.2 and 7.6 inclusive. Write a compound inequality to show the pH levels that are within the recommended range. Graph the solutions.

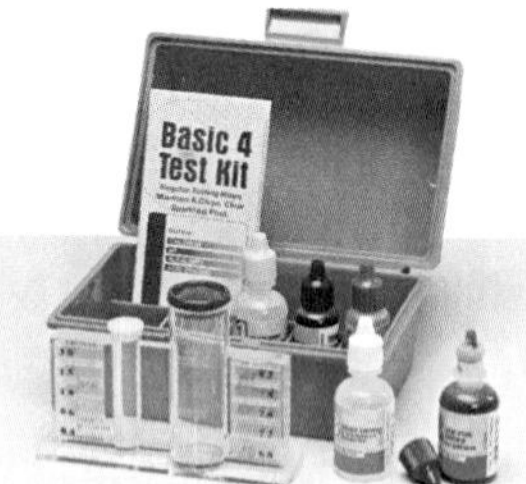

Reading Math

The phrase "between 7.2 and 7.6 *inclusive*" means that the numbers 7.2 and 7.6 are included in the solutions. Use a solid circle for endpoints that are solutions.

Let p be the pH level of swimming pool water.

7.2	is less than or equal to	pH level	is less than or equal to	7.6
7.2	$\leq$	p	$\leq$	7.6

$7.2 \leq p \leq 7.6$

7.1 7.2 7.3 7.4 7.5 7.6 7.7

1 Introduce

EXPLORATION

3-6 Solving Compound Inequalities

You will need a graphing calculator for this Exploration. Using a graphing calculator, follow the steps below to find the values of x when $2x + 1$ is between −3 and 7.

1. Press [Y=]. Enter **2X + 1** for **Y1**, **−3** for **Y2**, and **7** for **Y3**.
2. Press [GRAPH] to graph the functions.
3. Press [TRACE] and use the arrow keys to move the cursor. Find the x-values where the graph of $y = 2x + 1$ crosses the horizontal lines.
4. For which values of x is $2x + 1$ between −3 and 7?
5. Press [2nd] [GRAPH] to examine these functions in a table. For which values of x is $2x + 1$ between −3 and 7? Graph these values on a number line.

−10 −8 −6 −4 −2 0 2 4 6 8 10

THINK AND DISCUSS

6. **Explain** how the solution to this problem is different from the solutions to problems you studied earlier in the chapter.
7. **Explain** how the graph of this solution looks different from the graphs you studied earlier in the chapter.

Motivate

Read the sentences and follow-up questions below.

Max will take his brother or sister to the concert.

How many people will Max take? 1 How do you know? the word *or*

Max will take his brother and sister to the concert.

How many people will Max take? 2 How do you know? the word *and*

The words *or* and *and* can be used to represent the solutions of a compound inequality.

Explorations and answers are provided in *Alternate Openers: Explorations Transparencies.*

California Standards

Algebra 1 5.0

1. The free chlorine level in a pool should be between 1.0 and 3.0 parts per million inclusive. Write a compound inequality to show the levels that are within this range. Graph the solutions.
$1.0 \le c \le 3.0$

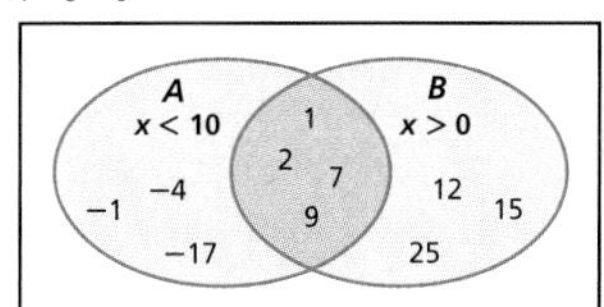

In this diagram, oval A represents some integer solutions of $x < 10$, and oval B represents some integer solutions of $x > 0$. The overlapping region represents numbers that belong in both ovals. Those numbers are solutions of *both* $x < 10$ *and* $x > 0$.

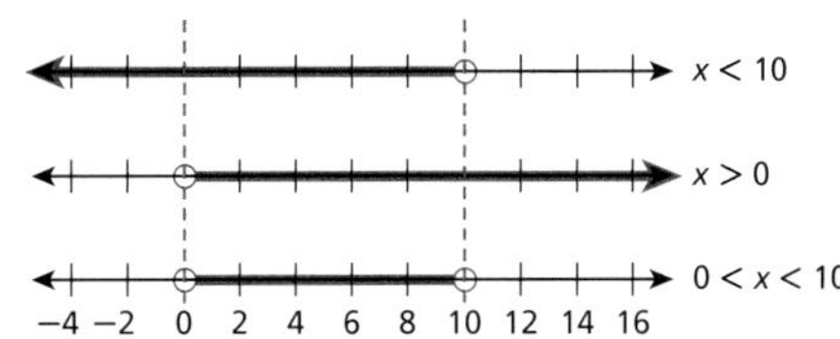

You can graph the solutions of a compound inequality involving AND by using the idea of an overlapping region. The overlapping region is called the **intersection** and shows the numbers that are solutions of both inequalities.

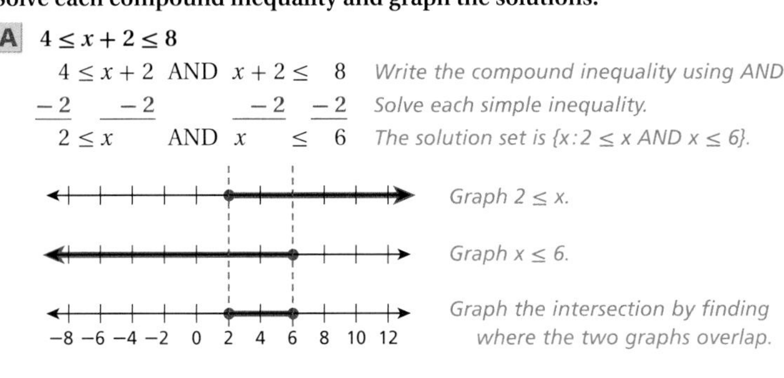

EXAMPLE 2 Solving Compound Inequalities Involving AND

Solve each compound inequality and graph the solutions.

A $4 \le x + 2 \le 8$

$4 \le x + 2$ AND $x + 2 \le 8$	*Write the compound inequality using AND.*
$\underline{-2}\quad \underline{-2}\qquad \underline{-2}\quad \underline{-2}$	*Solve each simple inequality.*
$2 \le x$ AND $x \le 6$	*The solution set is {x: 2 ≤ x AND x ≤ 6}.*

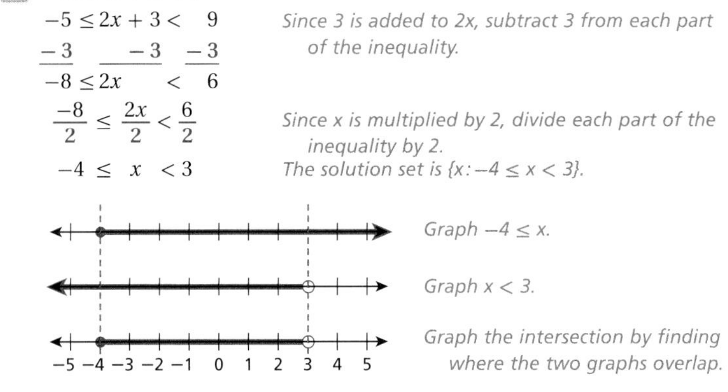

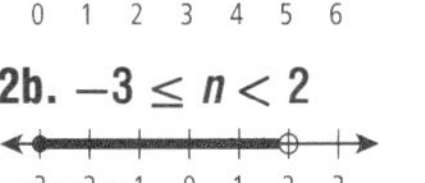

The statement $-5 \le 2x + 3 \le 9$ consists of two inequalities connected by AND. Example 2B shows a "shorthand" method.

B $-5 \le 2x + 3 < 9$

$-5 \le 2x + 3 < 9$	*Since 3 is added to 2x, subtract 3 from each part of the inequality.*
$\underline{-3}\qquad \underline{-3}\quad \underline{-3}$	
$-8 \le 2x < 6$	
$\frac{-8}{2} \le \frac{2x}{2} < \frac{6}{2}$	*Since x is multiplied by 2, divide each part of the inequality by 2.*
$-4 \le x < 3$	*The solution set is {x: −4 ≤ x < 3}.*

Graph $-4 \le x$.

Graph $x < 3$.

Graph the intersection by finding where the two graphs overlap.

−5 −4 −3 −2 −1 0 1 2 3 4 5

2a. $1 < x < 5$

0 1 2 3 4 5 6

2b. $-3 \le n < 2$

−3 −2 −1 0 1 2 3

Solve each compound inequality and graph the solutions.

2a. $-9 < x - 10 < -5$ **2b.** $-4 \le 3n + 5 < 11$

2 Teach

Guided Instruction

Review solving multi-step inequalities. Solve compound inequalities with AND, and then OR, and then discuss the differences between the two. Help students make the connection between AND and intersection (∩), and between OR and union (∪).

Universal Access

Through Modeling

Assign each student a number. (Assign 1–20 to twenty students.) Then have students stand when you read statements that describe their number. For instance:

- greater than 15 OR less than 2;
- less than 12 AND greater than or equal to 8;
- greater than or equal to 3 AND less than or equal to 3;
- greater than 2 OR less than 3

COMMON ERROR ALERT

Students may be confused when using the shorthand method for AND in **Example 2B.** When reading the expression $a < x < b$, students can say, "x is greater than a AND x is less than b." Students can also say, "a is less than x AND x is less than b." This shortcut expression exists only for the AND statement.

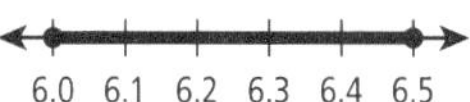

Power Presentations with PowerPoint®

Additional Examples

Example 1

The pH level of a popular shampoo is between 6.0 and 6.5 inclusive. Write a compound inequality to show the pH levels of this shampoo. Graph the solutions. $6.0 \le p \le 6.5$

6.0 6.1 6.2 6.3 6.4 6.5

Example 2

Solve each compound inequality and graph the solutions.

A. $-5 < x + 1 < 2$ $-6 < x < 1$

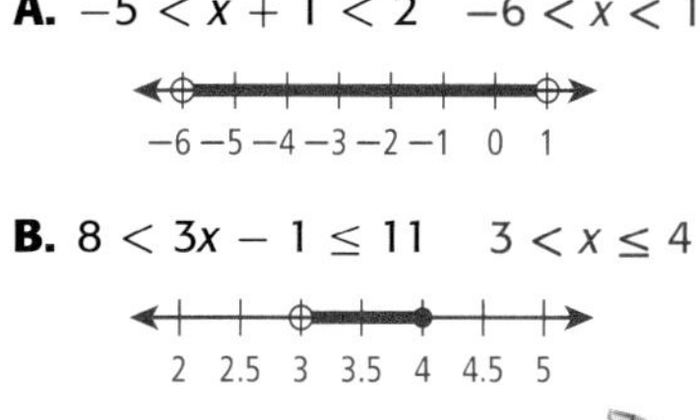

Also available on transparency

INTERVENTION

Questioning Strategies

EXAMPLE 1

- How would the solution change if the range of given values were not inclusive?

EXAMPLE 2

- How do you write a compound inequality as two simple inequalities?

Inclusion Show students that they can check their answers to compound inequalities in the same way they did for simple inequalities, but now they will have to check both parts of their answer.

Power Presentations with PowerPoint®

Additional Examples

Example 3

Solve each compound inequality and graph the solutions.

A. $8 + t \geq 7$ OR $8 + t < 2$

$t \geq -1$ OR $t < -6$

−6 −5 −4 −3 −2 −1 0

B. $4x \leq 20$ OR $3x > 21$

$x \leq 5$ OR $x > 7$

2 3 4 5 6 7 8

Example 4

Write the compound inequality shown by each graph.

A. −10 −8 −6 −4 −2 0 2

$x \leq -8$ OR $x > 0$

B. 5

−4 −2 0 2 4 6 8

$m > -2$ AND $m < 5$

Also available on transparency

INTERVENTION

Questioning Strategies

EXAMPLE 3

- Describe a characteristic of the solutions graph of a compound inequality involving OR.

EXAMPLE 4

- How do you know whether a graph represents a compound inequality that involves AND or OR?

Teaching Tip **Language Support** Discuss the everyday meanings of *intersection* and *union*. The intersection of two streets is where they cross each other. A labor union is an organization of workers who join together.

ENGLISH LANGUAGE LEARNERS

In this diagram, circle A represents some integer solutions of $x < 0$, and circle B represents some integer solutions of $x > 10$. The combined shaded regions represent numbers that are solutions of *either* $x < 0$ *or* $x > 10$.

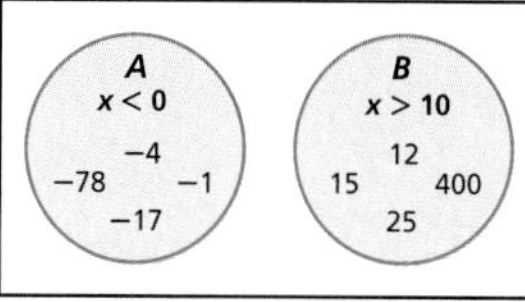

You can graph the solutions of a compound inequality involving OR by using the idea of combining regions. The combined regions are called the **union** and show the numbers that are solutions of either inequality.

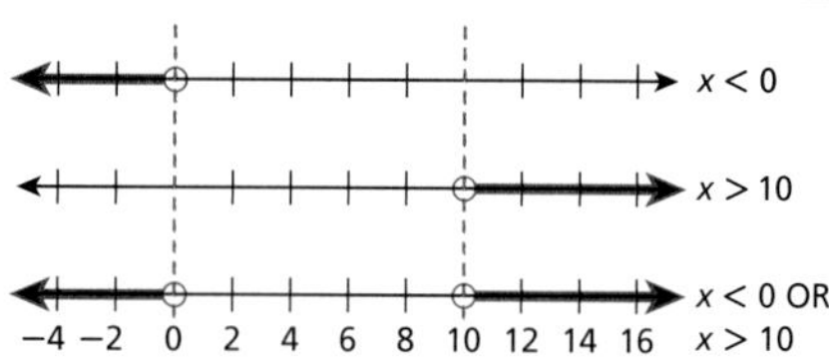

EXAMPLE 3 **Solving Compound Inequalities Involving OR**

Solve each compound inequality and graph the solutions.

A $-4 + a > 1$ OR $-4 + a < -3$

$$\begin{aligned} -4 + a &> 1 \text{ OR } -4 + a < -3 \\ \underline{+4} \quad \underline{+4} &\quad \underline{+4} \quad \underline{+4} \\ a &> 5 \text{ OR } \quad a < 1 \end{aligned}$$

Solve each simple inequality.
The solution set is {a:a > 5 OR a < 1}.

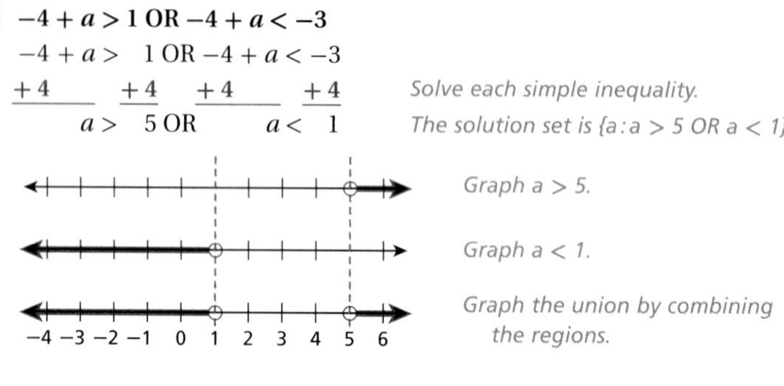

B $2x \leq 6$ OR $3x > 12$

$2x \leq 6$ OR $3x > 12$

$\frac{2x}{2} \leq \frac{6}{2}$ $\frac{3x}{3} > \frac{12}{3}$

$x \leq 3$ OR $x > 4$

Solve each simple inequality.
The solution set is {x:x ≤ 3 OR x > 4}.

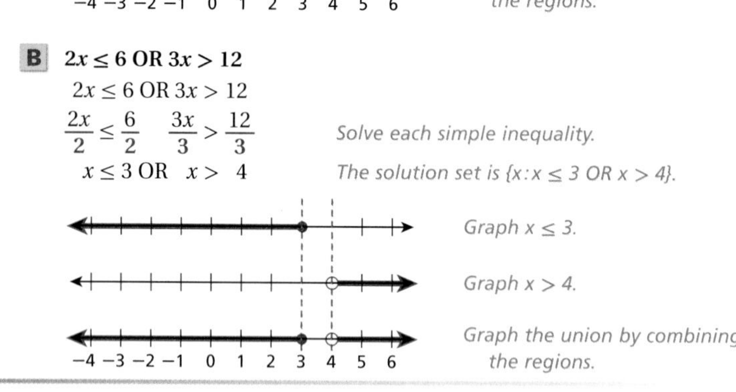

Helpful Hint

AND inequalities can sometimes be combined into one expression.
$1 < x < 5$
OR inequalities cannot be combined as one expression.
$x < 1$ OR $x > 5$

CHECK IT OUT! Solve each compound inequality and graph the solutions.

3a. $2 + r < 12$ OR $r + 5 > 19$ **$r < 10$ OR $r > 14$**

3b. $7x \geq 21$ OR $2x < -2$ **$x \geq 3$ OR $x < -1$**

3a. 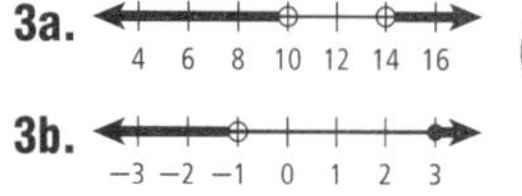

3b. 

Every solution of a compound inequality involving AND must be a solution of both parts of the compound inequality. If no numbers are solutions of *both* simple inequalities, then the compound inequality has no solutions.

The solutions of a compound inequality involving OR are not always two separate sets of numbers. Some numbers may be solutions of both parts of the compound inequality.

EXAMPLE 4 Writing a Compound Inequality from a Graph

Write the compound inequality shown by each graph.

A

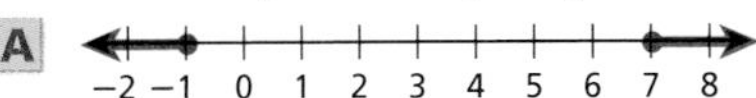

The shaded portion of the graph is not between two values, so the compound inequality involves OR.

On the left, the graph shows an arrow pointing left, so use either $<$ or $\leq$. The solid circle at -1 means -1 is a solution, so use $\leq$.

$x \leq -1$

On the right, the graph shows an arrow pointing right, so use either $>$ or $\geq$. The solid circle at 7 means 7 is a solution, so use $\geq$.

$x \geq 7$

The compound inequality is $x \leq -1$ OR $x \geq 7$.

B

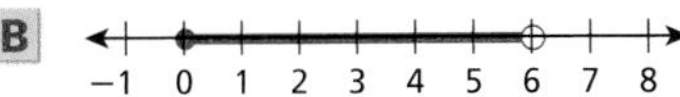

The shaded portion of the graph is between the values 0 and 6, so the compound inequality involves AND.

The shaded values are to the right of 0, so use $>$ or $\geq$. The solid circle at 0 means 0 is a solution, so use $\geq$.

$x \geq 0$

The shaded values are to the left of 6, so use $<$ or $\leq$. The empty circle at 6 means 6 is not a solution, so use $<$.

$x < 6$

The compound inequality is $x \geq 0$ AND $x < 6$ or $0 \leq x \leq 6$.

Write the compound inequality shown by each graph.

4a. 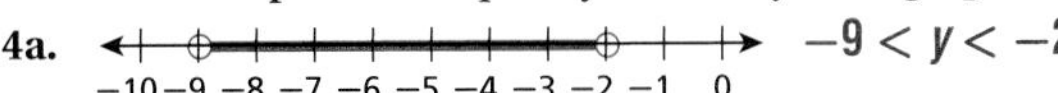 $-9 < y < -2$

4b. $x \leq -3$ OR $x \geq 2$

THINK AND DISCUSS

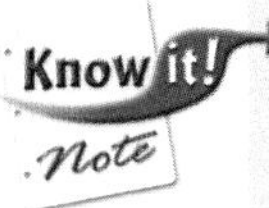

1. Describe how to write the compound inequality $y > 4$ AND $y \leq 12$ without using the joining word AND.

2. GET ORGANIZED Copy and complete the graphic organizers. Write three solutions in each of the three sections of the diagram. Then write each of your nine solutions in the appropriate column or columns of the table.

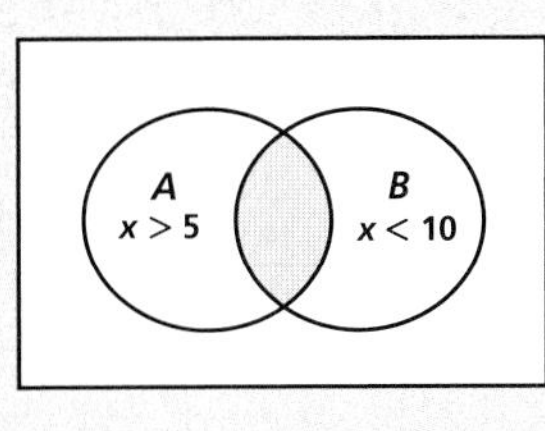

$x > 5$ AND $x < 10$	$x > 5$ OR $x < 10$

Teaching Tip **Visual** Use color to help students compare AND and OR statements. On a transparency, graph the solutions of $x < 3$ with a yellow marker and the solutions of $x < 7$ with a blue marker. Show that the solution set for $x < 3$ AND $x < 7$ is the green area described by $x < 3$. Then discuss the solution set for $x < 3$ OR $x < 7$. The solution is anywhere the graph is shaded, as described by $x < 7$.

Teaching Tip **Multiple Representations** Sometimes a parenthesis is used for an empty circle and a square bracket is used for a solid circle. The values described by $a < x \leq b$ can also be written as $(a, b]$, a notation used more often in higher-level math. The symbols may also be used on a graph.

3 Close

Summarize

Remind students that solving compound inequalities requires solving two separate inequalities.

Emphasize that an AND statement represents an intersection, and the solutions will be those values that make both inequalities true.

An OR statement represents a union, and the solutions combine two sets of numbers, which may or may not overlap. The solutions make either inequality true.

FORMATIVE ASSESSMENT and INTERVENTION

***Diagnose Before* the Lesson**
3-6 Warm Up, TE p. 170

***Monitor During* the Lesson**
Check It Out! Exercises, SE pp. 171–173
Questioning Strategies, TE pp. 171–172

***Assess After* the Lesson**
3-6 Lesson Quiz, TE p. 176
Alternative Assessment, TE p. 176

Answers to *Think and Discuss*

1. $y > 4$ can be written as $4 < y$. Write $y \leq 12$ on the right side of that inequality and drop one of the y's: $4 < y \leq 12$.
2. See p. A3.

3-6 Exercises

Assignment Guide

Assign *Guided Practice* exercises as necessary.

If you finished Examples **1–2**
Proficient 15–19, 30–35, 45
Advanced 15–19, 30–35, 42, 43, 45, 51

If you finished Examples **1–4**
Proficient 15–29, 30–40 even, 42–54, 57–66
Advanced 15–29, 34, 36–40 even, 42–66

Homework Quick Check
Quickly check key concepts.
Exercises: 15, 18, 20, 26, 34, 42

Answers

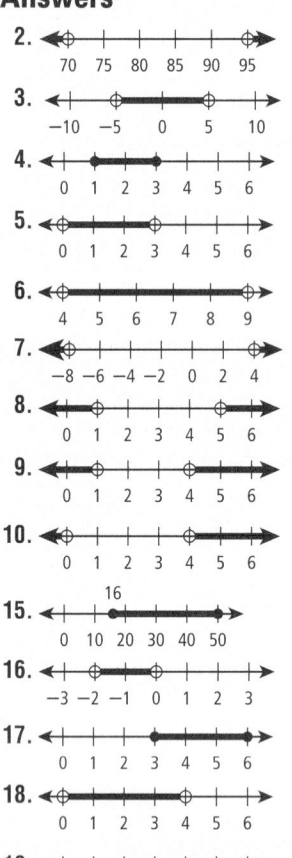

2. 70 75 80 85 90 95
3. −10 −5 0 5 10
4. 0 1 2 3 4 5 6
5. 0 1 2 3 4 5 6
6. 4 5 6 7 8 9
7. −8 −6 −4 −2 0 2 4
8. 0 1 2 3 4 5 6
9. 0 1 2 3 4 5 6
10. 0 1 2 3 4 5 6
15. 16; 0 10 20 30 40 50
16. −3 −2 −1 0 1 2 3
17. 0 1 2 3 4 5 6
18. 0 1 2 3 4 5 6
19. 0 1 2 3 4 5 6

20–23. For graphs, see p. A15.

California Standards

Standard	Exercises
5.0 🔑	3–10, 16–23, 29, 36–44, 47, 48, 50–56, 60–62, 64–66
25.1	57–59

3-6 Exercises

California Standards Practice
🔑 5.0

go.hrw.com
Homework Help Online
KEYWORD: MA8CA 3-6
Parent Resources Online
KEYWORD: MA8CA Parent

GUIDED PRACTICE

1. **Vocabulary** The graph of a(n) __?__ shows all values that are solutions to both simple inequalities that make a compound inequality. (*union* or *intersection*) **intersection**

SEE EXAMPLE 1 p. 170

2. **Biology** An iguana needs to live in a warm environment. The temperature in a pet iguana's cage should be between 70° F and 95°F inclusive. Write a compound inequality to show the temperatures that are within the recommended range. Graph the solutions. $70 \le t \le 95$

SEE EXAMPLE 2 p. 171

Solve each compound inequality and graph the solutions.

3. $-3 < x + 2 < 7$ $\;-5 < x < 5$
4. $5 \le 4x + 1 \le 13$ $\;1 \le x \le 3$
5. $2 < x + 2 < 5$ $\;0 < x < 3$
6. $11 < 2x + 3 < 21$ $\;4 < x < 9$

SEE EXAMPLE 3 p. 172

7. $x + 2 < -6$ OR $x + 2 > 6$ $\;x < -8$ OR $x > 4$
8. $r - 1 < 0$ OR $r - 1 > 4$ $\;r < 1$ OR $r > 5$
9. $n + 2 < 3$ OR $n + 3 > 7$ $\;n < 1$ OR $n > 4$
10. $x - 1 < -1$ OR $x - 5 > -1$ $\;x < 0$ OR $x > 4$

SEE EXAMPLE 4 p. 173

Write the compound inequality shown by each graph.

11. −6 −5 −4 −3 −2 −1 0 1 2 3 4 $\;-5 \le a \le -3$
12. −5 −4 −3 −2 −1 0 1 2 3 4 5 $\;b \le -3$ OR $b > 3$
13. 0 1 2 3 4 5 6 7 8 9 10 $\;c < 1$ OR $c \ge 9$
14. −10 −8 −6 −4 −2 0 2 4 6 8 10 $\;4 \le d < 8$

PRACTICE AND PROBLEM SOLVING

For Exercises	See Example
15	1
16–19	2
20–23	3
24–27	4

Extra Practice
Skills Practice p. EP7
Application Practice p. EP26

15. **Meteorology** Earth's atmosphere is made of several layers. A layer called the stratosphere extends from about 16 km above Earth's surface to about 50 km above Earth's surface. Write a compound inequality to show the altitudes that are within the range of the stratosphere. Graph the solutions. $16 \le k \le 50$

Solve each compound inequality and graph the solutions.

16. $-1 < x + 1 < 1$ $\;-2 < x < 0$
17. $1 \le 2n - 5 \le 7$ $\;3 \le n \le 6$
18. $-2 < x - 2 < 2$ $\;0 < x < 4$
19. $5 < 3x - 1 < 17$ $\;2 < x < 6$
20. $x - 4 < -7$ OR $x + 3 > 4$ $\;x < -3$ OR $x > 1$
21. $2x + 1 < 1$ OR $x + 5 > 8$ $\;x < 0$ OR $x > 3$
22. $x + 1 < 2$ OR $x + 5 > 8$ $\;x < 1$ OR $x > 3$
23. $x + 3 < 0$ OR $x - 2 > 0$ $\;x < -3$ OR $x > 2$

Write the compound inequality shown by each graph.

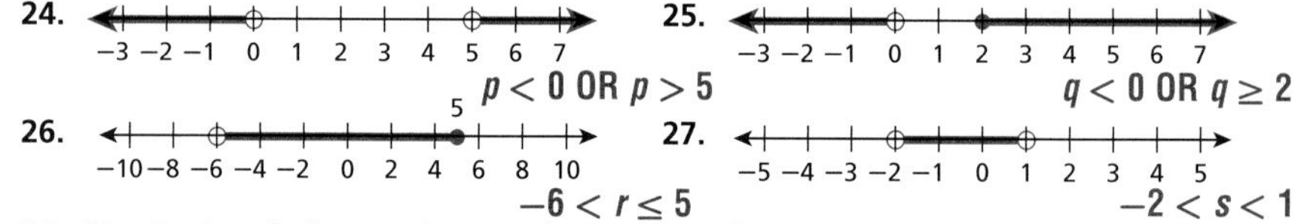

24. $p < 0$ OR $p > 5$
25. $q < 0$ OR $q \ge 2$
26. 5; $-6 < r \le 5$
27. $-2 < s < 1$

28. **Music** A typical acoustic guitar has a range of three octaves. When the guitar is tuned to "concert pitch," the range of frequencies for those three octaves is between 82.4 Hz and 659.2 Hz inclusive. Write a compound inequality to show the frequencies that are within the range of a typical acoustic guitar. Graph the solutions.

28. $82.4 \le f \le 659.2$
82.4 659.2

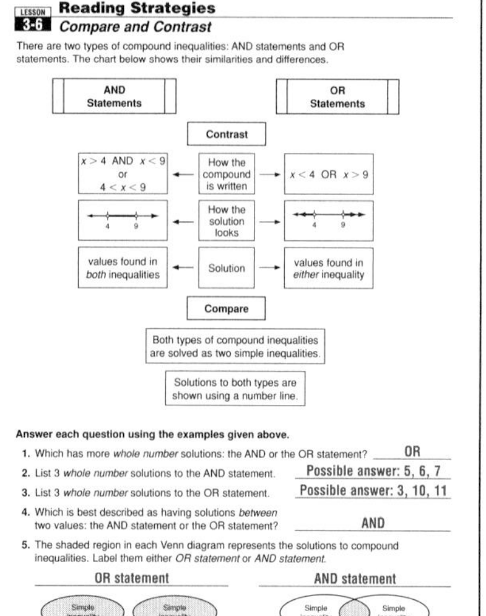

3-6 READING STRATEGIES

LESSON 3-6 **Reading Strategies**
Compare and Contrast

There are two types of compound inequalities: AND statements and OR statements. The chart below shows their similarities and differences.

AND Statements	Contrast	OR Statements
$x > 4$ AND $x < 9$ or $4 < x < 9$	How the compound is written	$x < 4$ OR $x > 9$
4 9	How the solution looks	4 9
values found in *both* inequalities	Solution	values found in *either* inequality

Compare

Both types of compound inequalities are solved as two simple inequalities.

Solutions to both types are shown using a number line.

Answer each question using the examples given above.

1. Which has more *whole number* solutions: the AND or the OR statement? **OR**
2. List 3 *whole number* solutions to the AND statement. **Possible answer: 5, 6, 7**
3. List 3 *whole number* solutions to the OR statement. **Possible answer: 3, 10, 11**
4. Which is best described as having solutions *between* two values: the AND statement or the OR statement? **AND**
5. The shaded region in each Venn diagram represents the solutions to compound inequalities. Label them either *OR statement* or *AND statement*.

OR statement — Simple inequality, Simple inequality
AND statement — Simple inequality, Simple inequality

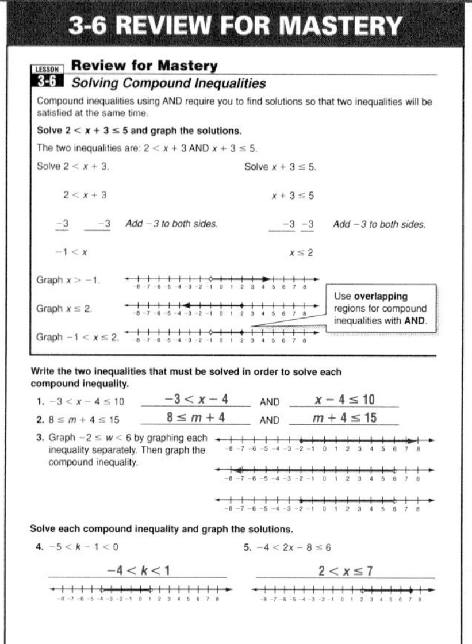

3-6 REVIEW FOR MASTERY

LESSON 3-6 **Review for Mastery**
Solving Compound Inequalities

Compound inequalities using AND require you to find solutions so that two inequalities will be satisfied at the same time.

Solve $2 < x + 3 \le 5$ and graph the solutions.

The two inequalities are: $2 < x + 3$ AND $x + 3 \le 5$.

Solve $2 < x + 3$.
$2 < x + 3$
$-3 \quad -3$ *Add −3 to both sides.*
$-1 < x$

Solve $x + 3 \le 5$.
$x + 3 \le 5$
$-3 \quad -3$ *Add −3 to both sides.*
$x \le 2$

Graph $x > -1$. −8 −7 −6 −5 −4 −3 −2 −1 0 1 2 3 4 5 6 7 8
Graph $x \le 2$. −8 −7 −6 −5 −4 −3 −2 −1 0 1 2 3 4 5 6 7 8
Graph $-1 < x \le 2$. −8 −7 −6 −5 −4 −3 −2 −1 0 1 2 3 4 5 6 7 8

Use **overlapping** regions for compound inequalities with **AND**.

Write the two inequalities that must be solved in order to solve each compound inequality.

1. $-3 < x - 4 \le 10$ $\;-3 < x - 4$ AND $x - 4 \le 10$
2. $8 \le m + 4 \le 15$ $\;8 \le m + 4$ AND $m + 4 \le 15$
3. Graph $-2 \le w < 6$ by graphing each inequality separately. Then graph the compound inequality.

Solve each compound inequality and graph the solutions.

4. $-5 < k - 1 < 0$ $\;-4 < k < 1$
5. $-4 < 2x - 8 \le 6$ $\;2 < x \le 7$

29. This problem will prepare you for the Concept Connection on page 184.

Jenna's band is going to record a CD at a recording studio. They will pay \$225 to use the studio for one day and \$80 per hour for sound technicians. Jenna has \$200 and hopes to raise an additional \$350 by taking pre-orders for the CDs.

a. Explain how the inequality $200 \le 225 + 80n \le 550$ can be used to find the number of hours Jenna and her band can afford to use the studio and sound technicians.

b. Solve the inequality. Are there any numbers in the solution set that are not reasonable in this situation? **$-0.3125 \le n \le 4.0625$; n cannot be negative**

c. How much more money does Jenna need to raise if she wants to use the studio and sound technicians for 6 hours? **They need an additional \$155 to use the studio for 6 h.**

Write and graph a compound inequality for the numbers described.

30. all real numbers between −6 and 6 **$-6 < x < 6$**

31. all real numbers less than or equal to 2 and greater than or equal to 1 **$1 \le x \le 2$**

32. all real numbers greater than 0 and less than 15 **$0 < x < 15$**

33. all real numbers between −10 and 10 inclusive **$-10 \le x \le 10$**

34. **Transportation** The cruise-control function on Georgina's car should keep the speed of the car within 3 mi/h of the set speed. Write a compound inequality to show the acceptable speeds s if the set speed is 55 mi/h. Graph the solutions. **$52 \le x \le 58$**

35. **Chemistry** Water is not a liquid if its temperature is above 100°C or below 0°C. Write a compound inequality for the temperatures t when water is not a liquid. **$t < 0$ OR $t > 100$**

LINK

Chemistry

The element gallium is in a solid state at room temperature but becomes a liquid at about 30°C. Gallium stays in a liquid state until it reaches a temperature of about 2204°C.

Solve each compound inequality and graph the solutions.

36. $5 \le 4b - 3 \le 9$ **$2 \le b \le 3$**

37. $-3 < x - 1 < 4$ **$-2 < x < 5$**

38. $r + 2 < -2$ OR $r - 2 > 2$ **$r < -4$ OR $r > 4$**

39. $2a - 5 < -5$ OR $3a - 2 > 1$ **$a < 0$ OR $a > 1$**

40. $x - 4 \ge 5$ AND $x - 4 \le 5$ **$x \ge 9$ AND $x \le 9$**

41. $n - 4 < -2$ OR $n + 1 > 6$ **$n < 2$ OR $n > 5$**

42. **Sports** The ball used in a soccer game may not weigh more than 16 ounces or less than 14 ounces at the start of the match. After $1\frac{1}{2}$ ounces of air was added to a ball, the ball was approved for use in a game. Write and solve a compound inequality to show how much the ball might have weighed before the air was added. **$12.5 \le w \le 14.5$**

43. **Meteorology** Tornado damage is rated using the Fujita scale shown in the table. A tornado has a wind speed of 200 miles per hour. Write and solve a compound inequality to show how many miles per hour the wind speed would need to increase for the tornado to be rated "devastating" but not "incredible." **$7 \le m \le 60$**

Fujita Tornado Scale

Category	Type	Wind Speed (mi/h)
F0	Weak	40 to 72
F1	Moderate	73 to 112
F2	Significant	113 to 157
F3	Severe	158 to 206
F4	Devastating	207 to 260
F5	Incredible	261 to 318

44. Possible answer: Margaret is expecting between 25 and 35 guests; $25 \le g \le 35$ where g is a natural number.

44. Give a real world situation that can be described by a compound inequality. Write the inequality that describes your situation.

45. **Write About It** How are the graphs of the compound inequality $x < 3$ AND $x < 7$ and the compound inequality $x < 3$ OR $x < 7$ different? How are the graphs alike? Explain.

CONCEPT CONNECTION **Exercise 29** involves using inequalities to find the number of hours a band can afford to rent a recording studio. This exercise prepares students for the Concept Connection on page 184.

Answers

29a. $225 + 80n$ gives the cost of the studio and technicians. They will spend between \$200 and \$550.

30.

−6 −4 −2 0 2 4 6

31. −3 −2 −1 0 1 2 3

32. 0 5 10 15 20

33. −20 −10 0 10 20

34. 52 54 56 58

36. 0 1 2 3 4 5 6

37. −2 0 2 4 6 (5)

38. −8 −4 0 4 8

39. −3 −2 −1 0 1 2 3

40. 7 8 9 10 11

41. 0 1 2 3 4 5 6

45. Both graphs include numbers less than 3. The graph of $x < 3$ AND $x < 7$ does not include numbers greater than or equal to 3. The graph of $x < 3$ OR $x < 7$ also includes all numbers less than 7.

3-6 PROBLEM SOLVING

LESSON 3-6 **Problem Solving**
Solving Compound Inequalities

Write and solve an inequality for each situation.

1. The Mexican Tetra is a tropical fish that requires a water temperature between 68 and 77 degrees Fahrenheit, inclusive. An aquarium is heated 8 degrees so that a Tetra can live in it. What temperatures could the water have been before the heating?
$68 \le t + 8 \le 77$;
$60 \le t \le 69$

2. Nerissa's car can travel between 380 and 410 miles on a full tank of gas. She filled her gas tank and drove 45 miles. How many more miles can she drive without running out of gas?
$380 \le m + 45 \le 410$;
$335 \le m \le 365$

3. A local company is hiring trainees with less than 1 year of experience and managers with 5 or more years of experience. Graph the solutions.
$y < 1$ OR $y \ge 5$

4. Marty's allowance is doubled and is now between \$10 and \$15, inclusive. What amounts could his allowance have been before the increase? Graph the solutions.
$10 \le 2a \le 15$;
$5 \le a \le 7.5$

The elliptical orbits of celestial objects bring them closer to and farther from the Sun at different times. The closest (perihelion) and furthest (aphelion) points are given for three objects below. Use this data to answer questions 5–7.

Celestial Object	Perihelion (in 10^6 km)	Aphelion (in 10^6 km)
Uranus	2741.3	3003.6
Neptune	4444.5	4545.7
Pluto	4435.0	7304.3

5. Which inequality represents the distances d from the sun to Neptune?
A $d \le 4444.5$
B $d \le 4545.7$
Ⓒ $4444.5 \le d \le 4545.7$
D $d = 4444.5$ OR $d \ge 4545.7$

6. A NASA probe is traveling between Uranus and Neptune. It is currently between their orbits. Which inequality shows the possible distance p from the probe to the Sun?
F $1542.1 < p < 1703.2$
Ⓖ $2741.3 < p < 4545.7$
H $3003.6 < p < 4444.5$
J $7185.8 < p < 7549.3$

7. At what distances o do the orbits of Neptune and Pluto overlap?
A $4435.0 \le o \le 4444.5$
Ⓑ $4435.0 \le o \le 4545.7$
C $4444.5 \le o \le 7304.3$
D $4545.7 \le o \le 7304.3$

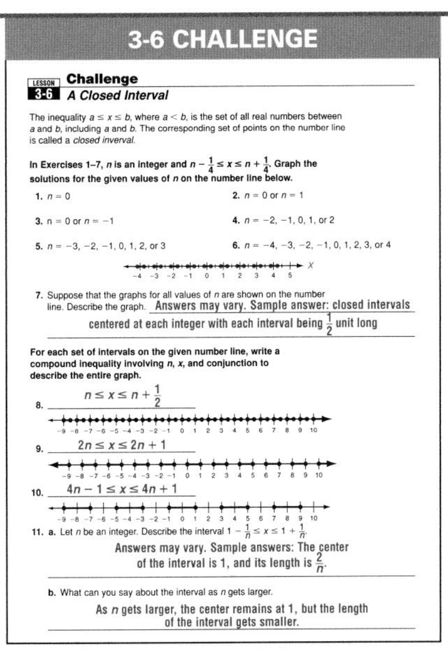
3-6 CHALLENGE

LESSON 3-6 **Challenge**
A Closed Interval

The inequality $a \le x \le b$, where $a < b$, is the set of all real numbers between a and b, including a and b. The corresponding set of points on the number line is called a *closed inverval.*

In Exercises 1–7, n is an integer and $n - \frac{1}{4} \le x \le n + \frac{1}{4}$. Graph the solutions for the given values of n on the number line below.

1. $n = 0$
2. $n = 0$ or $n = 1$
3. $n = 0$ or $n = -1$
4. $n = -2, -1, 0, 1,$ or 2
5. $n = -3, -2, -1, 0, 1, 2,$ or 3
6. $n = -4, -3, -2, -1, 0, 1, 2, 3,$ or 4

7. Suppose that the graphs for all values of n are shown on the number line. Describe the graph. Answers may vary. Sample answer: closed intervals centered at each integer with each interval being $\frac{1}{2}$ unit long

For each set of intervals on the given number line, write a compound inequality involving n, x, and conjunction to describe the entire graph.

8. $n \le x \le n + \frac{1}{2}$
9. $2n \le x \le 2n + 1$
10. $4n - 1 \le x \le 4n + 1$

11. a. Let n be an integer. Describe the interval $1 - \frac{1}{n} \le x \le 1 + \frac{1}{n}$.
Answers may vary. Sample answers: The center of the interval is 1, and its length is $\frac{2}{n}$.

b. What can you say about the interval as n gets larger.
As n gets larger, the center remains at 1, but the length of the interval gets smaller.

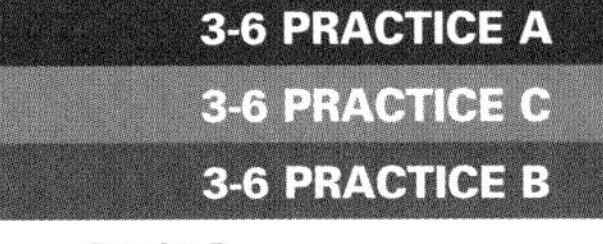
3-6 PRACTICE A
3-6 PRACTICE C
3-6 PRACTICE B

LESSON 3-6 **Practice B**
Solving Compound Inequalities

Write the compound inequality shown by each graph.

1. $-2 < x < 4$
2. $x < -3$ OR $x \ge 3$
3. $x \le -15$ OR $x \ge -8$
4. $0 \le x < 20$

Solve each compound inequality and graph the solutions.

5. $-15 < x - 8 < -4$ $-7 < x < 4$
6. $12 \le 4n < 28$ $3 \le n < 7$
7. $-2 \le 3b + 7 \le 13$ $-3 \le b \le 2$
8. $x - 3 < -3$ OR $x - 3 \ge 3$ $x < 0$ OR $x \ge 6$
9. $5k \le -20$ OR $2k \ge 8$ $k \le -4$ OR $k \ge 4$
10. $2s + 3 \le 7$ OR $3s + 5 > 26$ $s \le 2$ OR $s > 7$

Write a compound inequality for each problem. Graph the solutions.

11. The human ear can distinguish sounds between 20 Hz and 20,000 Hz, inclusive. $20 \le h \le 20{,}000$

12. For a man to box as a welterweight, he must weigh more than 140 lbs, but at most 147 lbs. $140 < w \le 147$

Teaching Tip

Multiple Choice In **Exercise 48,** students who chose **A** solved only the second inequality.

In **Exercise 49,** students can start by looking at the open circle at 2 and determining that the correct symbol is $<$. This narrows the choices down to **B** or **D.** The closed circle at 5 makes the answer **B.**

Journal

Explain the difference between graphing an inequality involving AND, and graphing an inequality involving OR.

Alternative Assessment

Have students write and graph a compound inequality with AND, and one with OR, such that solving each individual inequality involves two steps.

Power Presentations with PowerPoint®

3-6 Lesson Quiz

1. The target heart rate during exercise for a 15-year-old is between 154 and 174 beats per minute inclusive. Write a compound inequality to show the heart rates that are within the target range. Graph the solutions. $154 \le h \le 174$

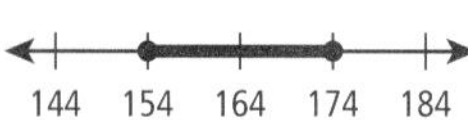

Solve each compound inequality and graph the solutions.

2. $2 \le 2w + 4 \le 12$
   $-1 \le w \le 4$

   −2 −1 0 1 2 3 4

3. $3 + r > -2$ OR $3 + r < -7$
   $r > -5$ OR $r < -10$

   −10 −9 −8 −7 −6 −5 −4

Write the compound inequality shown by each graph.

4. −7

   −10 −8 −6 −4 −2 0 2

   $x < -7$ OR $x \ge 0$

5. −2 −1 0 1 2 3 4

   $-2 \le a < 4$

Also available on transparency

46. **Critical Thinking** If there is no solution to a compound inequality, does the compound inequality involve OR or AND? Explain.

46. An inequality with OR always has solutions because the two simple inequalities do not have to be true at the same time. A compound inequality with no solutions must involve AND.

Multiple Choice For Exercises 47–50, choose the best answer.

47. Which of the following describes the solutions of $-x + 1 > 2$ OR $x - 1 > 2$?
    (A) all real numbers greater than 1 or less than 3
    (B) all real numbers greater than 3 or less than 1
    (C) all real numbers greater than −1 or less than 3
    (D) all real numbers greater than 3 or less than −1

48. Which of the following describes the solutions of $x - 3 < 2$ AND $x + 3 > 2$?
    (A) $\{x : x > -1\}$
    (C) 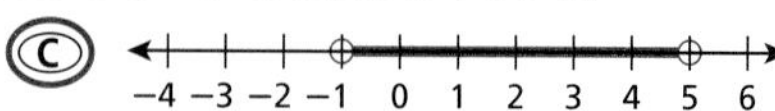
    (B) 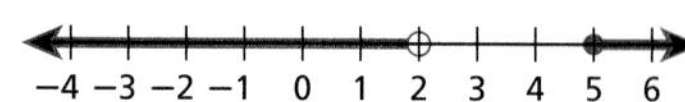
    (D) $\{x : x < -1$ OR $x > 5\}$

49. Which compound inequality is shown by the graph?

    −4 −3 −2 −1 0 1 2 3 4 5 6

    (A) $x \le 2$ OR $x > 5$
    (C) $x \le 2$ OR $x \ge 5$
    (B) $x < 2$ OR $x \ge 5$
    (D) $x < 2$ OR $x > 5$

50. Which of the following is a solution of $x + 1 \ge 3$ AND $x + 1 \le 3$?
    (A) 0 (B) 1 **(C)** 2 (D) 3

CHALLENGE AND EXTEND

Solve and graph each compound inequality.

51. $2c - 10 < 5 - 3c < 7c$ **$0.5 < c < 3$**
52. $5p - 10 < p + 6 < 3p$ **$3 < p < 4$**
53. $2s \le 18 - s$ OR $5s \ge s + 36$
54. $9 - x \ge 5x$ OR $20 - 3x \le 17$

53. $s \le 6$ OR $s \ge 9$

54. $x \le 1\frac{1}{2}$ OR $x \ge 1$

55. Write a compound inequality that represents all values of x that are NOT solutions to $x < -1$ OR $x > 3$. **$-1 \le x \le 3$**
56. For the compound inequality $x + 2 \ge a$ AND $x - 7 \le b$, find values of a and b for which the only solution is $x = 1$. **$a = 3$; $b = -6$**

SPIRAL STANDARDS REVIEW

5.0, 25.1

Use properties and operations to show that the first expression simplifies to the second expression. *(Lesson 1-7)*

57. $4(x - 3) + 7, 4x - 5$
58. $5x - 4y - x + 3y, 4x - y$
59. $6a - 3(a - 1), 3a + 3$

Solve each equation. Check your answer. *(Lesson 2-4)*

60. $7x + 3 = 4x$ **−1**
61. $19 - 5t = t + 1$ **3**
62. $k - \frac{1}{2} = 6k + \frac{3}{4}$ **$-\frac{1}{4}$**
63. Solve the formula $\frac{d}{r} = t$ for d. Find the distance in miles that a car would travel in 4 hours if its average speed was 31.71 mi/h. Round to the nearest tenth. *(Lesson 2-6)* **$d = rt$; 126.8 mi**

Solve each inequality and graph the solutions. Check your answer. *(Lesson 3-4)*

64. $3m - 5 < 1$ **$m < 2$**
65. $2(x + 4) > 6$ **$x > -1$**
66. $11 \le 7 - 2x$ **$x \le -2$**

Answers

51.–53. 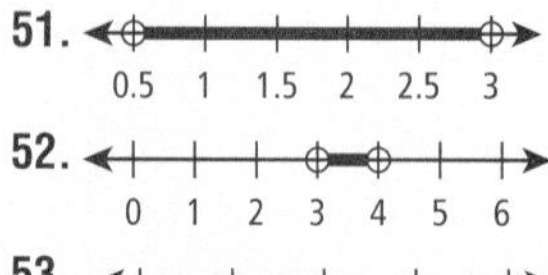

54. 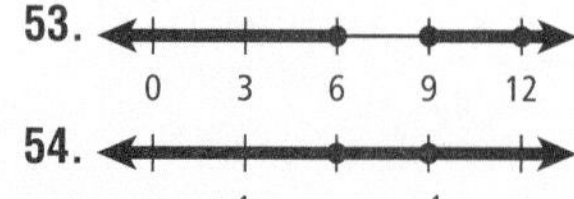

57. $4(x - 3) + 7$
    $4x - 12 + 7$ Distribute 4.
    $4x - 5$ Combine like terms.

58. $5x - 4y - x + 3y$
    $5x - x - 4y + 3y$ Comm. Prop. of Add.
    $4x - y$ Combine like terms.

59. $6a - 3(a - 1)$
    $6a - 3a + 3$ Distribute 3.
    $3a + 3$ Combine like terms.

64. 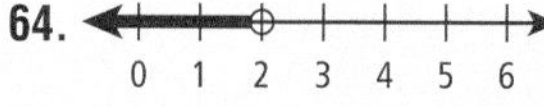

65. −3 −2 −1 0 1 2 3

66. −6 −5 −4 −3 −2 −1 0

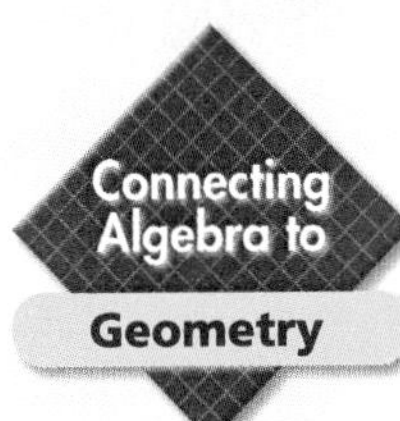

Triangle Inequality

For any triangle, the sum of the lengths of any two sides is greater than the length of the third side.

California Standards

Reinforcement of 7NS1.1 Read, write, and compare rational numbers in scientific notation (positive and negative powers of 10), **compare rational numbers in general.**

The sides of this triangle are labeled *a*, *b*, and *c*. You can use the Triangle Inequality to write three statements about the triangle.

$a + b > c$ $\quad$ $a + c > b$ $\quad$ $b + c > a$

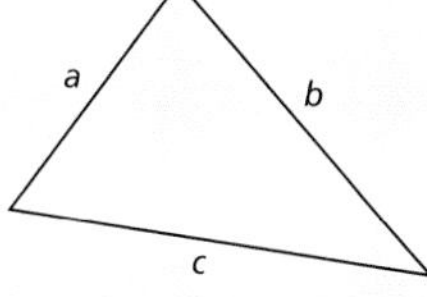

Unless all three of the inequalities are true, the lengths *a*, *b*, and *c* cannot form a triangle.

Example 1

Can three side lengths of 25 cm, 15 cm, and 5 cm form a triangle?

a. $25 + 15 > 5$
$40 > 5$ *True*

b. $25 + 5 > 15$
$30 > 15$ *True*

c. $15 + 5 > 25$
$20 > 25$ *False*

One of the inequalities is false, so the three lengths will not make a triangle. The situation is shown in the figure to the right.

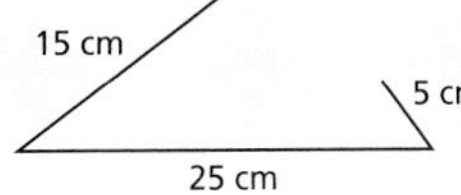

Example 2

Two sides of a triangle measure 8 ft and 10 ft. What is the range of lengths of the third side?

Start by writing three statements about the triangle. Use x for the unknown side length.

a. $8 + 10 > x$
$18 > x$
The third side must be shorter than 18 ft.

b. $8 + x > 10$
$8 + x - 8 > 10 - 8$
$x > 2$
The third side must be longer than 2 ft.

c. $x + 10 > 8$
$x + 10 - 10 > 8 - 10$
$x > -2$
This provides no new useful information.

From part **a,** the third side must be shorter than 18 ft. And from part **b,** it must be longer than 2 ft. An inequality showing this is $2 < x < 18$.

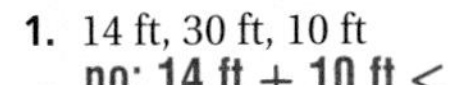

Try This

Decide whether the three lengths given can form a triangle. If not, explain.

1. 14 ft, 30 ft, 10 ft
no; 14 ft + 10 ft < 30 ft

2. 11 cm, 8 cm, 17 cm
yes

3. $6\frac{1}{2}$ yd, 3 yd, $2\frac{3}{4}$ yd
no; 3 yd + $2\frac{3}{4} < 6\frac{1}{2}$ yd

Write a compound inequality for the range of lengths of the third side of each triangle.

4. 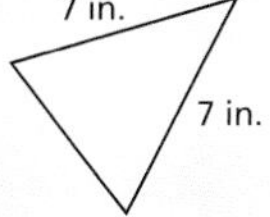

5. 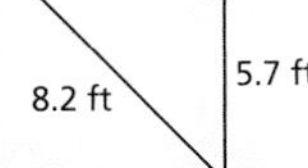

6. 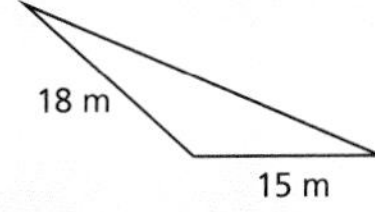

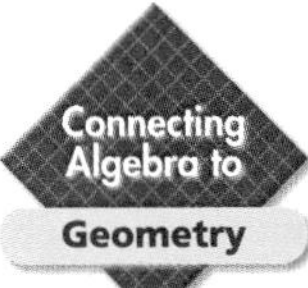

Organizer

See Skills Bank page SB15

Objective: Apply the algebra skills of solving inequalities to finding possible side lengths of triangles.

Online Edition

Teach

Remember

Students review and apply the geometric properties of triangles.

INTERVENTION For additional review and practice on finding the perimeter of geometric figures, see Skills Bank page SB15.

Teaching Tip

Concrete Manipulatives Students may better understand the Triangle Inequality if they attempt to make triangles from various lengths of straw or spaghetti.

Close

Assess

Have students give three possible side lengths for the third side of the triangles in **Problems 4–6.**

Answers

4. 0 in. $< x <$ 14 in.
5. 2.5 ft $< x <$ 13.9 ft
6. 3 m $< x <$ 33 m

California Standards

Reinforcement of 7NS1.1

3-7 Organizer

Objective: Solve inequalities in one variable involving absolute-value expressions.

Online Edition
Tutorial Videos

Countdown to Mastery Week 7

Power Presentations with PowerPoint®

Warm Up

Solve each inequality and graph the solutions.

1. $x + 7 < 4$ $x < -3$

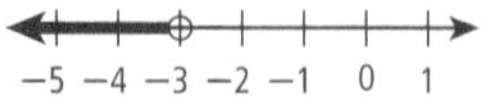

−5 −4 −3 −2 −1 0 1

2. $14x \geq 28$ $x \geq 2$

−1 0 1 2 3 4 5 6

3. $5 + 2x > 1$ $x > -2$

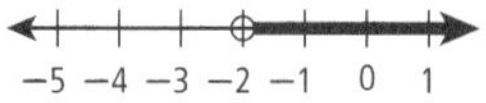

−5 −4 −3 −2 −1 0 1

Also available on transparency

Math Humor

Q: What does an absolute-value expression work on when it goes to the gym?

A: Its "abs"!

3-7 Solving Absolute-Value Inequalities

California Standards

3.0 Students solve equations and **inequalities involving absolute values.**

Also covered: **5.0**

Why learn this?

You can solve an absolute-value inequality to determine the safe range for the pressure of a fire extinguisher. (See Example 3.)

When an inequality contains an absolute-value expression, it can be rewritten as a compound inequality. The inequality $|x| < 5$ describes all real numbers whose distance from 0 is less than 5 units. The solutions are all numbers between −5 and 5, so $|x| < 5$ can be rewritten as $-5 < x < 5$ or as $x > -5$ AND $x < 5$.

Know it! Note

Absolute-Value Inequalities Involving <

WORDS	NUMBERS
The inequality $\vert x\vert < a$ (when $a > 0$) asks, "What values of x have an absolute value less than a?" The solutions are numbers between $-a$ *and* a.	$\vert x\vert < 5$ $-5 < x < 5$ $x > -5$ AND $x < 5$
GRAPH	**ALGEBRA**
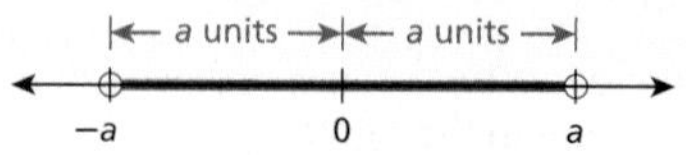 ← a units →← a units → $-a$ 0 a	$\vert x\vert < a$ (when $a > 0$) $-a < x < a$ $x > -a$ AND $x < a$

The same properties are true for inequalities that use the symbol ≤.

EXAMPLE 1 **Solving Absolute-Value Inequalities Involving <**

Solve each inequality and graph the solutions.

A $|x| + 3 < 12$

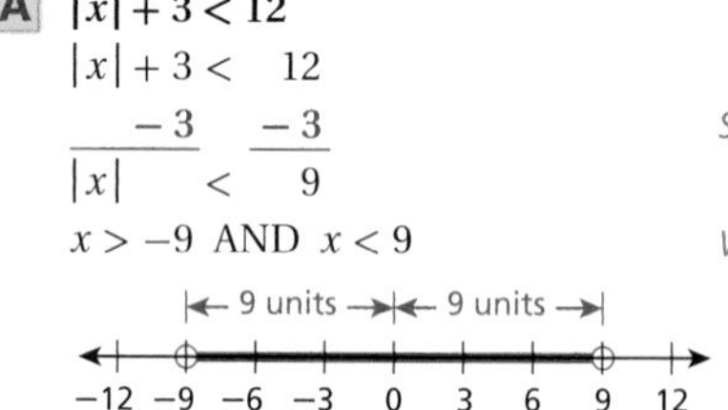

$|x| + 3 < 12$
$\underline{-3} \quad \underline{-3}$
$|x| < 9$ *Since 3 is added to |x|, subtract 3 from both sides to undo the addition.*
$x > -9$ AND $x < 9$ *Write as a compound inequality. The solution set is {x: −9 < x < 9}.*

← 9 units →← 9 units →
−12 −9 −6 −3 0 3 6 9 12

B $|x + 4| \leq 2$

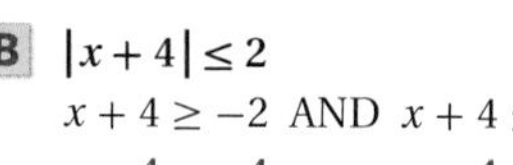

$x + 4 \geq -2$ AND $x + 4 \leq 2$ *Write as a compound inequality.*
$\underline{-4} \quad \underline{-4} \qquad \underline{-4} \quad \underline{-4}$ *Solve each inequality.*
$x \geq -6$ AND $x \leq -2$ *Write as a compound inequality. The solution set is {x: −6 ≤ x ≤ −2}.*

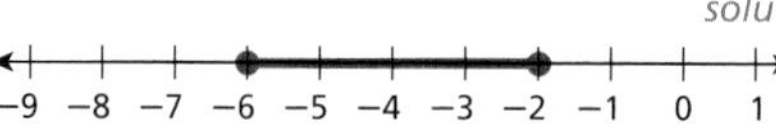

−9 −8 −7 −6 −5 −4 −3 −2 −1 0 1

Helpful Hint

Just as you do when solving absolute-value equations, you first isolate the absolute-value expression when solving absolute-value inequalities.

1 Introduce

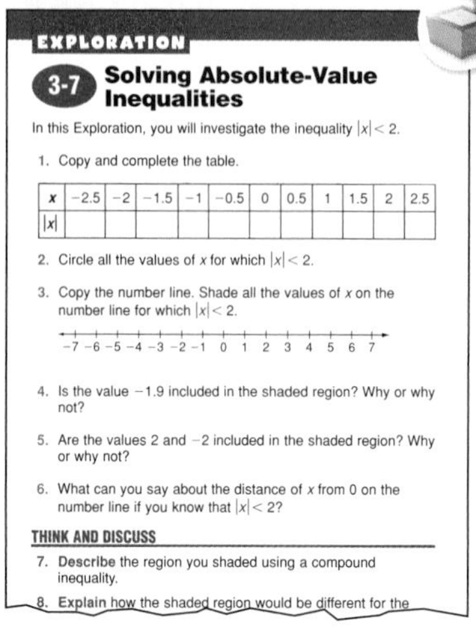

EXPLORATION

3-7 Solving Absolute-Value Inequalities

In this Exploration, you will investigate the inequality $|x| < 2$.

1. Copy and complete the table.

x	−2.5	−2	−1.5	−1	−0.5	0	0.5	1	1.5	2	2.5
$\vert x\vert$											

2. Circle all the values of x for which $|x| < 2$.
3. Copy the number line. Shade all the values of x on the number line for which $|x| < 2$.

−7 −6 −5 −4 −3 −2 −1 0 1 2 3 4 5 6 7

4. Is the value −1.9 included in the shaded region? Why or why not?
5. Are the values 2 and −2 included in the shaded region? Why or why not?
6. What can you say about the distance of x from 0 on the number line if you know that $|x| < 2$?

THINK AND DISCUSS

7. **Describe** the region you shaded using a compound inequality.
8. **Explain** how the shaded region would be different for the

Motivate

Present the following situation to the class: To get a B on an exam, a student's score must be no more than 5 points away from 85. Ask students what scores result in a B. Plot these values on a number line. Then explain that an absolute-value inequality can be used to describe the set of scores.

Explorations and answers are provided in *Alternate Openers: Explorations Transparencies.*

California Standards

Algebra 1 3.0

Also covered:

5.0 Students solve multi-step problems, including word problems, involving linear equations and **linear inequalities in one variable** and provide justification for each step.

Solve each inequality and graph the solutions.

1a. $2|x| \le 6$ $-3 \le x \le 3$

–5 –4 –3 –2 –1 0 1 2 3 4 5

1b. $|x+3| - 4.5 \le 7.5$ $-15 \le x \le 9$

–20 –15 –10 –5 0 5 10 15

The inequality $|x| > 5$ describes all real numbers whose distance from 0 is greater than 5 units. The solutions are all numbers less than –5 or greater than 5. The inequality $|x| > 5$ can be rewritten as the compound inequality $x < -5$ OR $x > 5$.

Absolute-Value Inequalities Involving >

WORDS	NUMBERS
The inequality $|x| > a$ (when $a > 0$) asks, "What values of x have an absolute value greater than a?" The solutions are numbers less than $-a$ or greater than a.	$|x| > 5$ $x < -5$ OR $x > 5$
GRAPH	**ALGEBRA**
a units, a units; $-a$, 0, a	$|x| > a$ (when $a > 0$) $x < -a$ OR $x > a$

The same properties are true for inequalities that use the symbol ≥.

EXAMPLE **2** **Solving Absolute-Value Inequalities Involving >**

Solve each inequality and graph the solutions.

A $|x| - 20 > -13$

$|x| - 20 > -13$

$+20 \quad +20$ *Since 20 is subtracted from $|x|$, add 20 to both sides to undo the subtraction.*

$|x| > 7$

$x < -7$ OR $x > 7$ *Write as a compound inequality. The solution set is {x: x < –7 OR x > 7}.*

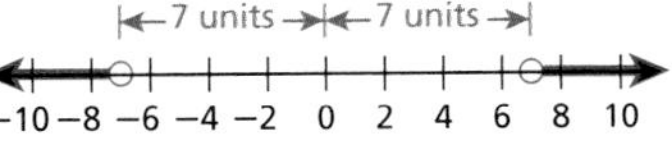

B $|x-8| + 5 \ge 11$

$|x-8| + 5 \ge 11$

$-5 \quad -5$ *Since 5 is added to $|x-8|$, subtract 5 from both sides to undo the addition.*

$|x-8| \ge 6$

$x - 8 \le -6$ OR $x - 8 \ge 6$ *Write as a compound inequality. Solve each inequality.*

$+8 \quad +8 \qquad +8 \quad +8$

$x \le 2$ OR $x \ge 14$ *Write as a compound inequality. The solution set is {x: x ≤ 2 OR x ≥ 14}.*

–2 0 2 4 6 8 10 12 14 16 18

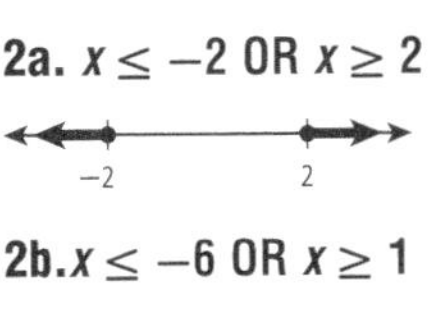

Solve each inequality and graph the solutions.

2a. $|x| + 10 \ge 12$

2b. $\left|x + 2\frac{1}{2}\right| + \frac{1}{2} \ge 4$

2 Teach

Guided Instruction

Remind students that the absolute value of a number is its distance from 0 on a number line. Then briefly review how to solve compound inequalities.

Use number lines and simple absolute-value inequalities like $|x| < 5$ and $|x| > 5$ to show why less-than symbols indicate an AND statement and greater-than symbols indicate an OR statement.

Universal Access

Through Auditory Cues

Stress the word *than* when saying "less than" and stress the suffix *-er* when saying "greater." Then the appropriate compound word almost rhymes with the inequality in the following phrase: "Less than is AND, greater is OR."

COMMON ERROR ALERT

In **Example 1B**, students may try to subtract 4 from both sides of the inequality as a first step. Remind students that they must first remove the absolute-value symbol by writing two cases.

Power Presentations with PowerPoint®

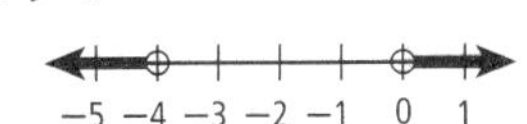

Additional Examples

Example 1

Solve each inequality and graph the solutions.

A. $|x| - 3 < -1$ $-2 < x < 2$

–3 –2 –1 0 1 2 3

B. $|x - 1| \le 2$ $-1 \le x \le 3$

–3 –2 –1 0 1 2 3

Example 2

Solve each inequality and graph the solutions.

A. $|x| + 14 \ge 19$ $x \le -5$ or $x \ge 5$

–10 –5 0 5 10

B. $3 + |x + 2| > 5$ $x < -4$ or $x > 0$

–5 –4 –3 –2 –1 0 1

Also available on transparency

INTERVENTION

Questioning Strategies

EXAMPLE **1**

- Why does an absolute-value inequality with a less-than symbol indicate an AND statement?

EXAMPLE **2**

- Why does an absolute-value inequality with a greater-than symbol indicate an OR statement?

Visual Have students read an absolute-value inequality as "the distance from zero" to help them visualize what the graph will look like. For example, $|x| < 3$ can be read as "the distance from zero is less than 3."

Power Presentations with PowerPoint®

Additional Examples

Example 3

A pediatrician recommends that a baby's bath water be 95°F, but it is acceptable for the temperature to vary from this amount by as much as 3°F. Write and solve an absolute-value inequality to find the range of acceptable temperatures. Graph the solutions.

$|t - 95| \leq 3$; $92 \leq t \leq 98$

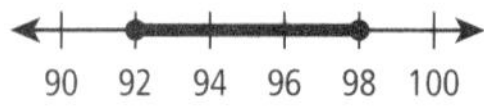

Example 4

Solve each inequality.

A. $|x + 4| - 5 > -8$ all real numbers

B. $|x - 2| + 9 < 7$ ∅

Also available on transparency

INTERVENTION

Questioning Strategies

EXAMPLE 3

- How can you use an inequality to represent the phrase "at most"?

EXAMPLE 4

- How can you tell when an absolute-value inequality will have all real numbers as its solution?
- How can you tell when an absolute-value inequality will have no solution?

EXAMPLE 3 *Safety Application*

Some fire extinguishers contain pressurized water. The water pressure should be 162.5 psi (pounds per square inch), but it is acceptable for the pressure to differ from this value by at most 12.5 psi. Write and solve an absolute-value inequality to find the range of acceptable pressures. Graph the solutions.

Let p represent the actual water pressure of a fire extinguisher.

The difference between p and the ideal pressure is at most 12.5 psi.

$$p - 162.5 \quad \leq \quad 12.5$$

$$|p - 162.5| \leq 12.5$$

$$p - 162.5 \geq -12.5 \text{ AND } p - 162.5 \leq 12.5$$ *Solve the two inequalities.*

$$\underline{+162.5 \quad +162.5} \qquad \underline{+162.5 \quad +162.5}$$

$$p \geq 150 \text{ AND } p \leq 175$$

140 145 150 155 160 165 170 175 180 185 190

The range of acceptable pressures is $150 \leq p \leq 175$.

3. A dry-chemical fire extinguisher should be pressurized to 125 psi, but it is acceptable for the pressure to differ from this value by at most 75 psi. Write and solve an absolute-value inequality to find the range of acceptable pressures. Graph the solution.

3. $|p - 125| \leq 75$; $50 \leq p \leq 200$

25 50 75 100 125 150 175 200 225

When solving an absolute-value inequality, you may get a statement that is true for all values of the variable. In this case, all real numbers are solutions of the original inequality. If you get a false statement when solving an absolute-value inequality, the original inequality has no solutions. Its solution set is ∅.

EXAMPLE 4 Special Cases of Absolute-Value Inequalities

Solve each inequality.

A $|x - 6| + 7 > 2$

$$|x - 6| + 7 > 2$$

$$\underline{\quad -7 \quad -7}$$ *Subtract 7 from both sides.*

$$|x - 6| > -5$$ *Absolute-value expressions are always nonnegative. Therefore, the statement is true for all values of x.*

The solution set is all real numbers.

Remember!

An absolute value represents a distance, and distance cannot be less than 0.

B $|x + 12| - 5 \leq -6$

$$|x + 12| - 5 \leq -6$$

$$\underline{\quad +5 \quad +5}$$ *Add 5 to both sides.*

$$|x + 12| \leq -1$$ *Absolute-value expressions are always nonnegative. Therefore, the statement is false for all values of x.*

The inequality has no solutions. The solution set is ∅.

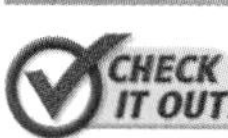

Solve each inequality.

4a. $|x| - 9 \geq -11$ **all real numbers**

4b. $4|x - 3.5| \leq -8$ ∅

3 Close

Summarize

Solve each absolute-value inequality.

1. $4 + |x| < 16$ $-12 < x < 12$
2. $|x - 3| + 5 \leq -8$ ∅
3. $|x + 1| - 4 \geq 3$ $x \leq -8$ or $x \geq 6$
4. $2|x + 6| > -10$ all real numbers

FORMATIVE ASSESSMENT

and INTERVENTION

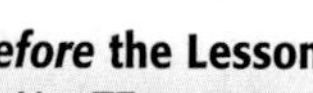

***Diagnose Before* the Lesson**
3-7 Warm Up, TE p. 178

***Monitor During* the Lesson**
Check It Out! Exercises, SE pp. 178–180
Questioning Strategies, TE pp. 178–180

***Assess After* the Lesson**
3-7 Lesson Quiz, TE p. 183
Alternative Assessment, TE p. 183

THINK AND DISCUSS

1. Describe how the solutions of $7|x| \le 21$ are different from the solutions of $7|x| < 21$.
2. **GET ORGANIZED** Copy and complete the graphic organizer. In each box, write an example of the indicated type of absolute-value inequality and then solve.

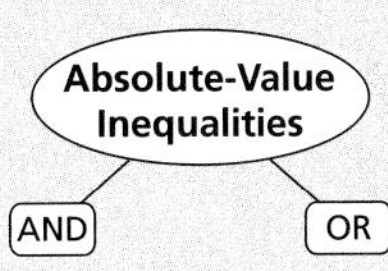

Answers to *Think and Discuss*

Possible answers:

1. The solutions of $7|x| \le 21$ are all values of x between -3 and 3, inclusive. The solutions of $7|x| < 21$ are all values of x between -3 and 3, not including these values.
2. See p. A3.

3-7 Exercises

California Standards Practice 3.0, 5.0, 25.1, 25.3

go.hrw.com Homework Help Online KEYWORD: MA8CA 3-7
Parent Resources Online KEYWORD: MA8CA Parent

GUIDED PRACTICE

Solve each inequality and graph the solutions.

SEE EXAMPLE 1 p. 178

1. $|x| - 5 \le -2$
2. $|x+1| - 7.8 < 6.2$
3. $|3x| + 2 < 8$
4. $4|x| \le 20$
5. $|x-5| + 1 < 2$
6. $\left|x + \frac{1}{2}\right| - \frac{1}{2} \le 3\frac{1}{2}$

SEE EXAMPLE 2 p. 179

7. $|x| - 6 > 16$
8. $|x| + 2.9 > 8.6$
9. $2|x| \ge 8$
10. $|x+2| > 7$
11. $|x-3| + 2 \ge 4$
12. $|x+5| - 4\frac{1}{2} \ge 7\frac{1}{2}$

SEE EXAMPLE 3 p. 180

13. **Nutrition** A nutritionist recommends that an adult male consume 55 grams of fat per day. It is acceptable for the fat intake to differ from this amount by at most 25 grams. Write and solve an absolute-value inequality to find the range of fat intake that is acceptable. Graph the solutions.

SEE EXAMPLE 4 p. 180

Solve each inequality.

14. $|x| + 8 \le 2$ ∅
15. $|x+3| < -5$ ∅
16. $|x+4| \ge -8$ all real numbers
17. $|x-5| + \frac{1}{3} > -1$ all real numbers
18. $|3x| + 7 > 2$ all real numbers
19. $|x-7| + 3.5 \le 2$ ∅

PRACTICE AND PROBLEM SOLVING

Independent Practice	
For Exercises	See Example
20–25	1
26–31	2
32	3
33–38	4

Extra Practice
Skills Practice p. EP7
Application Practice p. EP26

Solve each inequality and graph the solutions.

20. $|x| + 6 \le 10$
21. $|x-3| < 1$
22. $|x-2| - 8 \le -3$
23. $|5x| < 15$
24. $|x-2.4| + 4 \le 6.4$
25. $4 + |x+3| < 7$
26. $|x-1| > 2$
27. $6|x| \ge 60$
28. $|x-4| + 3 > 8$
29. $2|x+2| \ge 16$
30. $3 + |x-4| > 4$
31. $\left|x - \frac{1}{2}\right| + 9 > 10\frac{1}{2}$
32. The thermostat for a sauna is set to 175°F, but the actual temperature of the sauna may vary by as much as 12°F. Write and solve an absolute-value inequality to find the range of possible temperatures. Graph the solutions.

Solve each inequality.

33. $12 + |x| \le 10$ ∅
34. $\left|x + \frac{3}{5}\right| - 2 > -4$ all real numbers
35. $|x+1| + 5 \ge 4$ all real numbers
36. $|4x| - 3 < -6$ ∅
37. $3|x-4| \le -9$ ∅
38. $|2x| + 9 \ge 9$ all real numbers

3-7 Exercises

Assignment Guide

Assign *Guided Practice* exercises as necessary.

If you finished Examples **1–2**
Proficient 20–31, 39, 40, 45–48
Advanced 20–31, 39, 40, 45–48, 58, 59

If you finished Examples **1–4**
Proficient 20–44, 46–52 even, 53–58, 61–72
Advanced 20–44 even, 45–72

Homework Quick Check
Quickly check key concepts.
Exercises: 22, 28, 32, 34, 50

Answers

1. $-3 \le x \le 3$

2. $-15 < x < 13$

3. $-2 < x < 2$

4. $-5 \le x \le 5$

Answers

5. $4 < x < 6$

6. $-4\frac{1}{2} \le x \le 3\frac{1}{2}$

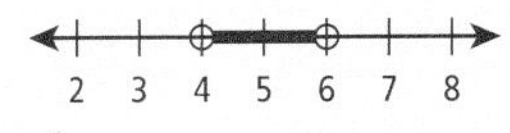

7. $x < -22$ OR $x > 22$

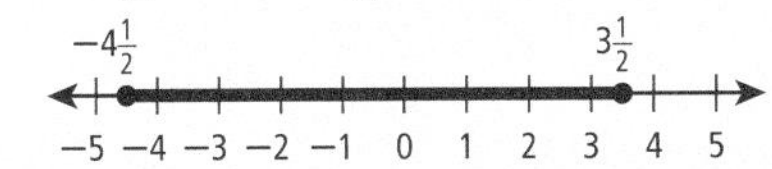

8. $x < -5.7$ OR $x > 5.7$

9. $x \le -4$ OR $x \ge 4$

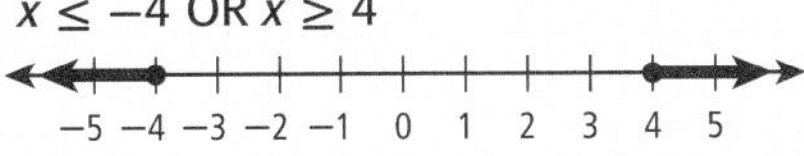

10. $x < -9$ OR $x > 5$

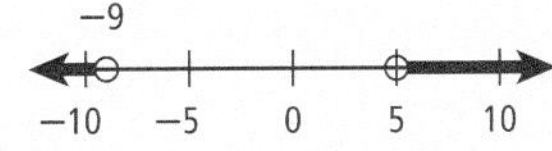

11. $x \le 1$ OR $x \ge 5$

12. $x \le -17$ OR $x \ge 7$

13. $|x - 55| \le 25$; $30 \le x \le 80$

20–32. See p. A15.

California Standards

Standard	Exercises
3.0	1–38, 42–44, 49–52, 55–57, 60
5.0	1–38, 42–44, 49–52, 55–57, 60, 61–64, 69–72
25.1	60
25.3	39–41
7AF1.4	65–68

Exercise 52 involves using absolute-value inequalities to determine the range of possible prices for a CD. This exercise prepares students for the Concept Connection on page 184.

Answers

39. Absolute-value expressions are always nonneg.
40. Absolute-value expressions are always nonneg.
41. Possible answer: $|x + 1| > -5$ has all real numbers as solutions, but $|x - 7| < 0$ has no solutions.
42. $|x| \leq 15$; $-15 \leq x \leq 15$

    −15 15

43. $|x - 2| \leq 3$; $-1 \leq x \leq 5$

    −1 5

44. $|x - 8| \geq 2$; $x \leq 6$ or $x \geq 10$

    6 10

45. $|a| \leq 2$
46. $|b| > 3$
47. $|c| \geq 6\frac{1}{2}$
48. $|d| < 7$
49. a. 10,010 Hz
    b. $|x - 10{,}010| \leq 9990$
50. European eel: $|x - 23| \leq 11$; Rainbow trout: $|x - 15| \leq 11$; Sea bass: $|x - 21| \leq 9$

Reasoning Tell whether each statement is sometimes, always, or never true. Explain.

39. The value of $|x + 1|$ is greater than -5. **always**
40. The value of $|x - 7|$ is less than 0. **never**
41. An absolute-value inequality has all real numbers as solutions. **sometimes**

Write and solve an absolute-value inequality for each expression. Graph the solutions on a number line.

42. All numbers whose absolute value is less than or equal to 15
43. All numbers less than or equal to 3 units from 2 on the number line
44. All numbers at least 2 units from 8 on the number line

Write an absolute-value inequality for each graph.

45. −5 −4 −3 −2 −1 0 1 2 3 4 5
46. −5 −4 −3 −2 −1 0 1 2 3 4 5
47. $-6\frac{1}{2}$ $6\frac{1}{2}$ −10 −8 −6 −4 −2 0 2 4 6 8 10
48. −7 7 −10 −8 −6 −4 −2 0 2 4 6 8 10

49. **Multi-Step** The frequency of a sound wave determines its pitch. The human ear can detect a wide range of frequencies, from 20 Hz (very low notes) to 20,000 Hz (very high notes).
    a. What frequency is at the middle of the range?
    b. Write an inequality for the range of frequencies the human ear can detect.

50. **Biology** The diagram shows the temperature range at which several fish species can survive. For each species, write an absolute-value inequality that gives the range of temperatures at which it can survive.

51. **Entertainment** On a game show, a contestant must guess a secret two-digit number. The secret number is 23. Write an inequality that shows that the contestant's guess is more than 12 numbers away from the secret number. $|n - 23| > 12$

Temperature Range of Fish

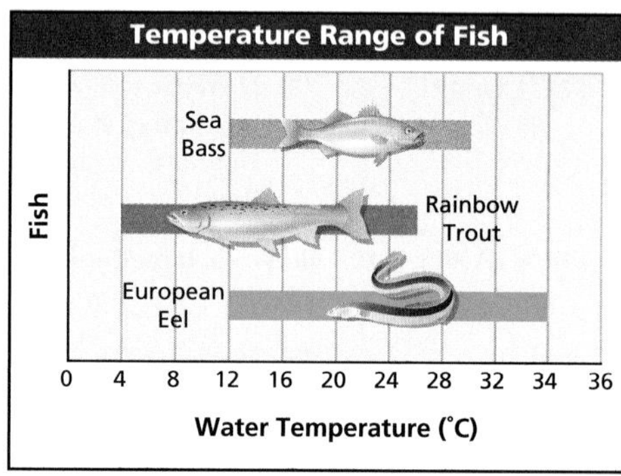

52. This problem will help prepare you for the Concept Connection on page 184.
    The manager of a band recommends that the band sell its CDs for \$8.75. The band decides to sell the CDs for p dollars.
    a. Write an absolute-value expression that tells how far the band's price is from the recommended price. $|p - 8.75|$
    b. The band wants the price of its CD to be no more than \$1.25 from the recommended price. Write an absolute-value inequality that gives the range of possible prices for the CD. $|p - 8.75| \leq 1.25$
    c. Solve inequality. Write the solution as a compound inequality. $\$7.50 \leq p \leq \$10.00$

3-7 PRACTICE A

3-7 PRACTICE C

3-7 PRACTICE B

LESSON 3-7 **Practice B**
Solving Absolute-Value Inequalities

Solve each inequality and graph the solutions.

1. $|x| - 2 \leq 3$ — $x \geq -5$ AND $x \leq 5$
2. $|x + 1| + 5 < 7$ — $x > -3$ AND $x < 1$
3. $3|x - 6| \leq 9$ — $x \geq 3$ AND $x \leq 9$
4. $|x + 3| - 1.5 < 2.5$ — $x > -7$ AND $x < 1$
5. $|x| + 17 > 20$ — $x < -3$ OR $x > 3$
6. $|x - 6| - 7 > -3$ — $x < 2$ OR $x > 10$
7. $\frac{1}{2}|x + 5| \geq 2$ — $x \leq -9$ OR $x \geq -1$
8. $2|x - 2| \geq 3$ — $x \leq 0.5$ OR $x \geq 3.5$
9. The organizers of a drama club wanted to sell 350 tickets to their show. The actual sales were no more than 35 tickets from this goal. Write and solve an absolute-value inequality to find the range of the number of tickets that may have been sold.
   $|x - 350| \leq 35$; $315 \leq x \leq 385$
10. The temperature at noon in Los Angeles on a summer day was 88°. During the day, the temperature varied from this by as much as 7.5°. Write and solve an absolute-value inequality to find the range of possible temperatures for that day.
    $|x - 88| \leq 7.5$; $80.5 \leq x \leq 95.5$

3-7 READING STRATEGIES

LESSON 3-7 **Reading Strategies**
Use a Model

You can use a number line to help you solve absolute-value inequalities that have the form $|x - b| \leq c$ or $|x - b| < c$. The following steps show how to use this method to solve $|x - 1| \leq 3$.

Step 1: Plot the value of b on the number line. In $|x - 1| \leq 3$, $b = 1$.

Step 2: Plot the two points that are c units away from b. In this case, $c = 3$. (3 units, 3 units)

Step 3: Shade the points in between. The solution is $-2 \leq x \leq 4$.

Answer each question.

1. When you use a number line to solve the inequality $|x - 5| < 4$, which point should you plot first? **5**
2. Which points should you plot next? **1 and 9**
3. Graph the solutions of $|x - 5| < 4$ on the number line.
4. When you use a number line to solve the inequality $|x + 1| \leq 2$, which point should you plot first? (*Hint:* The inequality can be written as $|x - (-1)| \leq 2$) **−1**
5. Which points should you plot next? **−3 and 1**
6. Graph the solutions of $|x + 1| \leq 2$ on the number line.
7. Use this method to graph the solutions of $|x + 2| < 1$.

3-7 REVIEW FOR MASTERY

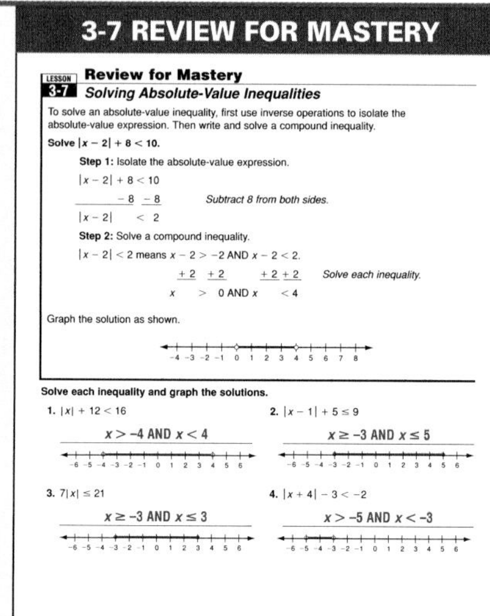

LESSON 3-7 **Review for Mastery**
Solving Absolute-Value Inequalities

To solve an absolute-value inequality, first use inverse operations to isolate the absolute-value expression. Then write and solve a compound inequality.

Solve $|x - 2| + 8 < 10$.

Step 1: Isolate the absolute-value expression.

$|x - 2| + 8 < 10$
$\quad -8 \quad -8$ *Subtract 8 from both sides.*
$|x - 2| < 2$

Step 2: Solve a compound inequality.

$|x - 2| < 2$ means $x - 2 > -2$ AND $x - 2 < 2$.
$+2 \quad +2 \qquad +2 \quad +2$ *Solve each inequality.*
$x > 0$ AND $x < 4$

Graph the solution as shown.

Solve each inequality and graph the solutions.

1. $|x| + 12 < 16$ — $x > -4$ AND $x < 4$
2. $|x - 1| + 5 \leq 9$ — $x \geq -3$ AND $x \leq 5$
3. $7|x| \leq 21$ — $x \geq -3$ AND $x \leq 3$
4. $|x + 4| - 3 < -2$ — $x > -5$ AND $x < -3$

53. **Critical Thinking** For which values of k does the inequality $|x| + 1 < k$ have no solutions? Explain.

54. **Write About It** Describe how to use an absolute-value inequality to find all the values on a number line that are within 5 units of -6.

Multiple Choice **For Exercises 55–57, choose the best answer.**

55. What is the solution set of the inequality $3 + |x + 4| < 6$?
   - (A) $\{x: -13 < x < 5\}$
   - (B) $\{x: -7 < x < -1\}$
   - (C) $\{x: -6 < x < -2\}$
   - (D) $\{x: 1 < x < 7\}$

56. A thermometer gives temperature readings that may be inaccurate by at most 2°F. The actual temperature is 75°F. Which absolute-value inequality describes the range of temperatures that may be shown on the thermometer?
   - (A) $|x - 75| \le 2$
   - (B) $|x + 75| \le 2$
   - (C) $|x - 75| \ge 2$
   - (D) $|x + 75| \ge 2$

57. The inequality $|w - 156| \le 3$ describes the weights of members of a wrestling team. Which statement is NOT true?
   - (A) All of the team members weigh no more than 159 pounds.
   - (B) A team member may weigh 152 pounds.
   - (C) Every member of the team is at most 3 pounds away from 156 pounds.
   - (D) There are no team members who weigh 160 pounds.

CHALLENGE AND EXTEND

Write an absolute-value inequality for each graph.

58. 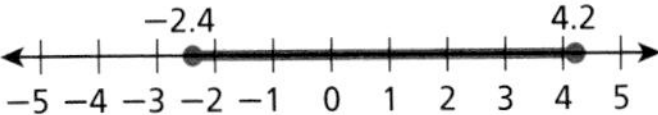

59. 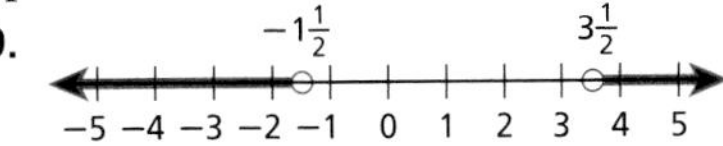

58. Possible answer: $|x - 0.9| \le 3.3$

59. Possible answer: $|x - 1| > 2\frac{1}{2}$

60. **Reasoning** Fill in the missing reasons to justify each step in solving $|2x - 6| + 5 \le 7$.

Statements	Reasons
1. $|2x - 6| + 5 \le 7$	Given
2. $|2x - 6| \le 2$	Subtr. Prop. of Ineq.
3. $2x - 6 \ge -2$ AND $2x - 6 \le 2$	Definition of absolute value
4. $2x \ge 4$ AND $2x \le 8$	Add. Prop. of Ineq.
5. $x \ge 2$ AND $x \le 4$	Div. Prop. of Ineq.

SPIRAL STANDARDS REVIEW

7AF1.4, 5.0

Solve each proportion. Check your answer. *(Lesson 2-5)*

61. $\frac{x+1}{4} = \frac{5}{8}$ $1\frac{1}{2}$
62. $\frac{2}{15} = \frac{6}{y-5}$ 50
63. $\frac{12}{m+2} = \frac{8}{3}$ $2\frac{1}{2}$
64. $\frac{7+g}{10} = \frac{6}{8}$ $\frac{1}{2}$

Describe the solutions of each inequality in words. *(Lesson 3-1)*

65. $16 > 8m$
66. $c + 4 < 11$
67. $-4 \le x + 2$
68. $0 \ge x + 7$

Solve each compound inequality and graph the solutions. *(Lesson 3-6)*

69. $-3 < x - 3 < 1$
70. $-3 \le 2x + 1 \le 9$
71. $x - 2 < -1$ OR $x - 2 > 2$
72. $x + 4 \le 3$ OR $x + 4 \ge 6$

3-7 PROBLEM SOLVING

LESSON 3-7 **Problem Solving**
Solving Absolute-Value Inequalities

Write the correct answer.

1. A carpenter cuts boards that are 2 meters long. It is acceptable for the length to differ from this value by at most 0.05 meters. Write and solve an absolute-value inequality to find the range of acceptable lengths.
   $|x - 2| \le 0.05$;
   $1.95 \le x \le 2.05$

2. During a workout, Vince tries to keep his heart rate at 134 beats per minute. His actual heart rate varies from this value by as much as 8 beats per minute. Write and solve an absolute-value inequality to find Vince's range of heart rates.
   $|x - 134| \le 8$;
   $126 \le x \le 142$

3. Mai thinks of a secret number. She says that her secret number is more than 11 units away from 50. Write an absolute-value inequality that gives the possible values of Mai's number.
   $|x - 50| > 11$

4. Boxes of cereal are supposed to weigh 15.3 ounces each. A quality-control manager finds that the boxes are no more than 0.4 ounces away from this weight. Write an absolute-value inequality that gives the range of possible weights of the boxes.
   $|x - 15.3| \le 0.4$

The table gives the typical lifespan for several mammals. Use the table for questions 5–7. Select the best answer.

5. Which absolute-value inequality gives the number of years a goat may live?
   - A $|x - 6| \le 24$
   - (B) $|x - 15| \le 9$
   - C $|x - 24| \le 6$
   - D $|x - 30| \le 9$

6. Which mammal has a lifespan that can be represented by the absolute-value inequality $|x - 12.5| \le 2.5$?
   - F Antelope
   - (G) Koala
   - H Otter
   - J Wolf

7. The inequality $|x - 17| \le c$ gives the number of years a panda may live. What is the value of c?
   - (A) 3
   - B 6
   - C 14
   - D 20

Mammal	Lifespan (years)	Mammal	Lifespan (years)
Antelope	10 to 25	Otter	15 to 20
Goat	6 to 24	Panda	14 to 20
Koala	10 to 15	Wolf	13 to 15

Source: http://www.sandiegozoo.org/animalbytes/a-mammal.html

3-7 CHALLENGE

LESSON 3-7 **Challenge**
Solving More Complex Absolute-Value Inequalities

When you solve a multi-step inequality, you may need to simplify expressions, combine like terms, or use the Distributive Property. This also applies when you solve inequalities that involve absolute values.

For example, to solve $3(|x| + 4) < 18$, you can first use the Distributive Property on the left side of the equation to write $3|x| + 12 < 18$.

1. Show how to finish solving the above inequality. Graph the solutions.
   $3|x| < 6$; $|x| < 2$; $x > -2$ AND $x < 2$

In some cases, you may need to combine like terms. For example, to solve $6|x| - 5 + 3|x| \ge 22$, first combine the absolute-value terms to write $9|x| - 5 \ge 22$.

2. Show how to finish solving the above inequality. Graph the solutions.
   $9|x| \ge 27$; $|x| \ge 3$; $x \le -3$ OR $x \ge 3$

Solve each inequality and graph the solutions.

3. $5|x| + 1 - 3|x| \le 3$
   $x \ge -1$ AND $x \le 1$

4. $2(5 + |x|) < 13$
   $x > -\frac{3}{2}$ AND $x < \frac{3}{2}$

5. $7|x + 1| - 5|x + 1| > 4$
   $x < -3$ OR $x > 1$

8. $3(|x - 2| + 1) \ge -1$
   all real numbers

COMMON ERROR ALERT

When writing an absolute-value inequality of the form $|x - k| \le a$, students sometimes confuse the values that should be used for k and a. In **Exercise 43**, students may write $|x - 3| \le 2$. Explain that the value that is at the center of the range (in this case, 2) should appear inside the absolute-value expression, so the correct inequality is $|x - 2| \le 3$.

Multiple Choice If students answered **C** or **D** for **Exercise 56**, remind them that the range of values is represented by AND, which corresponds to a less-than symbol. Therefore, choices **C** and **D** can be eliminated at once.

Answers

53, 54, 65–72. See p. A15.

Journal

Have students compare the steps they would use to solve $|x + 1| - 5 < 4$ with the steps they would use to solve $|x + 1| - 5 > 4$.

ALTERNATIVE ASSESSMENT

Have students write and solve an absolute-value inequality that involves AND and an absolute-value inequality that involves OR.

Power Presentations with PowerPoint®

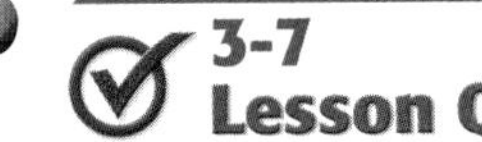

3-7 Lesson Quiz

Solve each inequality and graph the solutions.

1. $3|x| > 15$ $x < -5$ or $x > 5$
   (−10 −5 0 5 10)

2. $|x + 3| + 1 < 3$ $-5 < x < -1$
   (−6 −5 −4 −3 −2 −1 0)

3. A number, n, is no more than 7 units away from 5. Write and solve an absolute-value inequality to show the range of possible values for n.
   $|n - 5| \le 7$; $-2 \le n \le 12$

Solve each inequality

4. $|3x| + 1 < 1$ ∅
5. $|x + 2| - 3 \ge -6$ all real numbers

Also available on transparency

Organizer

Objective: Assess students' ability to apply concepts and skills in Lessons 3-4 through 3-7 in a real-world format.

Online Edition

Problem	Text Reference
1	Lesson 3-4
2	Lesson 3-4
3	Lesson 3-4
4	Lesson 3-5
5	Lesson 3-5
6	Lesson 3-6

Algebra 1 5.0

SECTION 3B

Multi-Step and Compound Inequalities

Guitar Picks Cullen and his band are interested in recording a CD of their music. The recording studio charges $450 to record the music and then charges $5 for each CD. The band is required to spend at least $1000 for the total of the recording and CD charges.

1. Write an equation for the cost C of the CDs based on the number of CDs n. $C = 450 + 5n$
2. Write an inequality that can be used to determine the minimum number of CDs that must be burned at this studio to meet the $1000 total. $450 + 5n \geq 1000$
3. Solve your inequality from Problem 2. Check your answer. $n \geq 110$ where n is a natural number
4. The band orders the minimum number of CDs found in Problem 3. They want to sell the CDs and make at least as much money as they spent for the recording studio and making the CDs. Write an inequality that can be solved to determine the minimum amount the band should charge for their CDs. $110x \geq 1000$
5. Solve your inequality from Problem 4. Check your answer. $x \geq 9.09$
6. If the band has 30 more CDs made than the minimum number found in Problem 4 and charges the minimum price found in Problem 5, will they make a profit? If so, how much profit will the band make?

6. yes;
$450 + 5(110 + 30) = 1150$;
$140(9.09) = 1272.60$;
$1272.60 - 1150.00 =$
$122.60 profit

INTERVENTION

Scaffolding Questions

1. What is the cost if Cullen's band purchases only 1 CD? $455 What is the cost if the band purchases 10 CDs? $500

2–3. What inequality symbol is indicated by the phrase "at least"? greater than or equal to Should the graph be shaded or have individual points? Explain. individual points, because they must buy whole numbers of CDs

4–5. What expression can be used to represent the amount made from selling the CDs? $110x$ Should the endpoint on your graph have an empty or a solid circle? solid

6. How is the profit from the sale of CDs determined? sales minus cost

Extension

Write and solve an inequality to find the number of CDs they would need to purchase and sell for $9 each in order to make at least $200 profit. $200 \leq 9x - (450 + 5x)$; $x \geq 162.5$; at least 163 CDs

CHAPTER 3

SECTION 3B

Quiz for Lessons 3-4 Through 3-7

3-4 Solving Two-Step and Multi-Step Inequalities

Solve each inequality and graph the solutions. Check your answer.

1. $2x + 3 < 9$ **$x < 3$**
2. $3t - 2 > 10$ **$t > 4$**
3. $7 \geq 1 - 6r$ **$r \geq -1$**

Solve each inequality.

4. $2(x - 3) > -1$ **$x > 2.5$**
5. $\frac{1}{3}a + \frac{1}{2} > \frac{2}{3}$ **$a > \frac{1}{2}$**
6. $15 < 5(m - 7)$ **$m > 10$**
7. $2 + (-6) > 0.8p$ **$p < -5$**
8. The average of Mindy's two test scores must be at least 92 to make an A in the class. Mindy got an 88 on her first test. What scores can she get on her second test to make an A in the class? **Mindy must make a score of 96 or higher.**

3-5 Solving Inequalities with Variables on Both Sides

Solve each inequality and graph the solutions. Check your answer.

9. $5x < 3x + 8$ **$x < 4$**
10. $6p - 3 > 9p$ **$p < -1$**
11. $r - 8 \geq 3r - 12$ **$r \leq 2$**

Solve each inequality.

12. $3(y + 6) > 2(y + 4)$ **$y > -10$**
13. $4(5 - g) \geq g$ **$g \leq 4$**
14. $4x < 4(x - 1)$ **$\emptyset$**
15. $3(1 - x) \geq -3(x + 2)$ **all real numbers**
16. Phillip has \$100 in the bank and deposits \$18 per month. Gil has \$145 in the bank and deposits \$15 per month. For how many months will Gil have a larger bank balance than Phillip? **15 mo**

3-6 Solving Compound Inequalities

Solve each compound inequality and graph the solutions.

17. $-2 \leq x + 3 < 9$ **$-5 \leq x < 6$**
18. $m + 2 < -1$ OR $m - 2 > 6$ **$m < -3$ OR $m > 8$**
19. $-3 \geq x - 1 > 2$ **$\emptyset$**
20. $-2 > r + 2$ OR $r + 4 < 5$ **$r < 1$**
21. It is recommended that a certain medicine be stored in temperatures above 32° F and below 70° F. Write a compound inequality to show the acceptable storage temperatures for this medicine. **$32 < t < 70$**

3-7 Solving Absolute-Value Inequalities

Solve each inequality and graph the solutions.

22. $|x| + 9 \leq 12$ **$-3 \leq x \leq 3$**
23. $|x + 7| - 15 < 6$ **$-28 < x < 14$**
24. $4.5|x| \geq 31.5$ **$x \leq -7$ OR $x \geq 7$**

Solve each inequality.

25. $|x - 2| \leq 14$ **$-12 \leq x \leq 16$**
26. $|x| - 9.2 < -5.7$ **$-3.5 < x < 3.5$**
27. $\frac{1}{2} + 2|x| > -4$ **all real numbers**
28. $7 + |3x| > 13$ **$x < -2$ OR $x > 2$**
29. Eli attended a concert. The decibel level of the music averaged 110 decibels but varied by 22 decibels from the average. Write and solve an absolute-value inequality to find the decibel range. Graph the solutions. **$|d - 110| \leq 22$; $88 \leq d \leq 132$**

READY TO GO ON? SECTION 3B

Organizer

Objective: Assess students' mastery of concepts and skills in Lessons 3-4 through 3-7.

Countdown to Mastery Week 7

Resources

Assessment Resources
Section 3B Quiz

Test & Practice Generator
One-Stop Planner®

INTERVENTION

Resources

Ready to Go On? Intervention and Enrichment **Worksheets**

Ready to Go On? **CD-ROM**

Ready to Go On? **Online**

my.hrw.com

Answers

1–3, 9–11, 17–20, 22–24, 29. For graphs, see p. A15.

READY TO GO ON?
Diagnose and Prescribe

Ready to Go On? Intervention	*Ready to Go On? Intervention,* Section 3B: Worksheets	CD-ROM	Online
Lesson 3-4 4.0	3-4 Intervention	Activity 3-4	Diagnose and Prescribe Online
Lesson 3-5 4.0	3-5 Intervention	Activity 3-5	
Lesson 3-6 5.0	3-6 Intervention	Activity 3-6	
Lesson 3-7 3.0	3-7 Intervention	Activity 3-7	

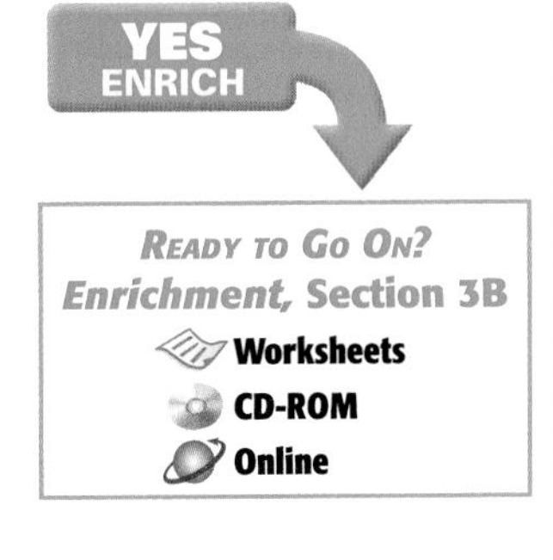

***Ready to Go On? Enrichment,* Section 3B**
Worksheets
CD-ROM
Online

CHAPTER 3 **Study Guide: Review**

Organizer

Objective: Help students organize and review key concepts and skills presented in Chapter 3.

Online Edition
Multilingual Glossary

Resources

PuzzlePro
One-Stop Planner®

Multilingual Glossary Online
go.hrw.com
KEYWORD: MA8CA Glossary

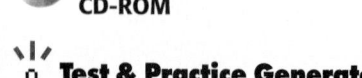

Lesson Tutorial Videos
CD-ROM

Test & Practice Generator
One-Stop Planner®

Answers

1. inequality
2. union
3. compound inequality
4. intersection
5. solution of an inequality

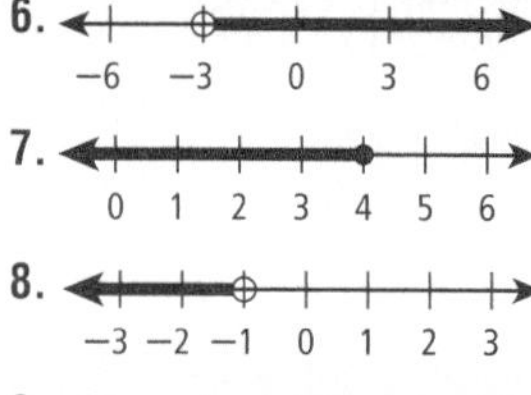

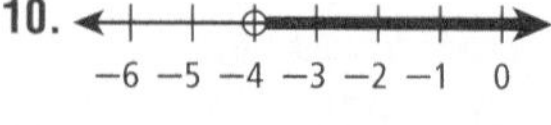

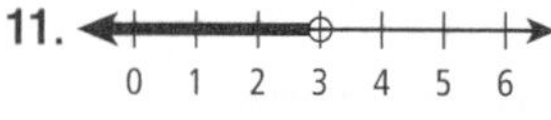

12. $a < 2$
13. $k \geq -3.5$
14. $q < -10$
15. t = temperature; $t \geq 72$

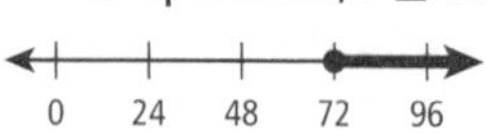

16. s = students; $s \leq 12$ where s is a natural number

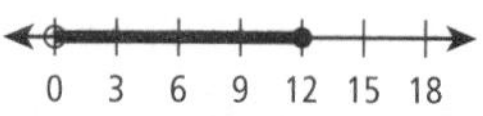

17. m = minutes; $m < 30$ where m is nonnegative

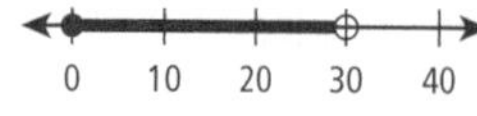

CHAPTER 3

Study Guide: Review

Vocabulary

compound inequality 170	**inequality** 136	**solution of an inequality** 136
equivalent inequalities 142	**intersection** 171	**union** 172

Complete the sentences below with vocabulary words from the list above.

1. A(n) ___?___ is a mathematical statement that two quantities are not equal.
2. The numbers that are solutions to either inequality of a compound inequality is the ___?___.
3. A statement formed by combining two simple inequalities with the words AND or OR is a(n) ___?___.
4. The numbers that are solutions to both inequalities of a compound inequality is the ___?___.
5. Any value that makes the inequality true is a(n) ___?___.

3-1 Graphing and Writing Inequalities *(pp. 136–141)*

Prep for 5.0

EXAMPLES

■ **Graph the inequality $y > -1$.**

−3 −2 −1 0 1 2 3 — *Draw an empty circle at −1.*

−3 −2 −1 0 1 2 3 — *Shade all the numbers greater than −1.*

■ **Write the inequality shown by the graph.**

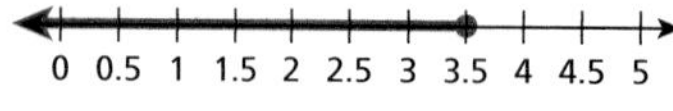

$n \leq 3.5$ — *Use the variable n.* *The arrow points left, so use either < or ≤. The closed circle means 3.5 is a solution, so use ≤.*

■ **Write an inequality for the situation and graph the solutions.**

Applicants for a driver's permit must be at least 16 years old.

age	must be at least	16 years
a	$\geq$	16

0 2 4 6 8 10 12 14 16 18 20

EXERCISES

Graph each inequality.

6. $x > -3$
7. $p \leq 4$
8. $-1 > t$
9. $r \geq 9.5$
10. $2(3 - 5) < k$
11. $w < 3$

Write the inequality shown by each graph.

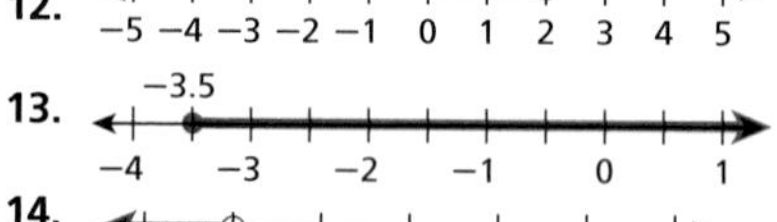

Define a variable and write an inequality for each situation. Graph the solutions.

15. The temperature must be at least 72°F.
16. No more than 12 students were present.
17. It takes less than 30 minutes to complete the lab activity.

3-2 Solving Inequalities by Adding or Subtracting *(pp. 142–147)*

Prep for 5.0

EXAMPLES

Solve each inequality and graph the solutions.

■ $x + 6 > 2$

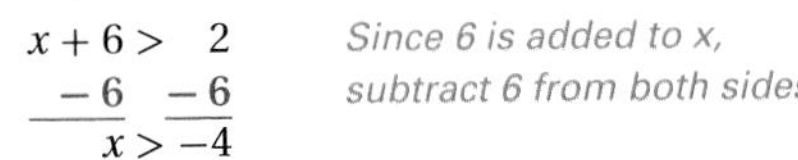

$x + 6 > 2$ — *Since 6 is added to x, subtract 6 from both sides.*

$\underline{-6 \quad -6}$

$x > -4$

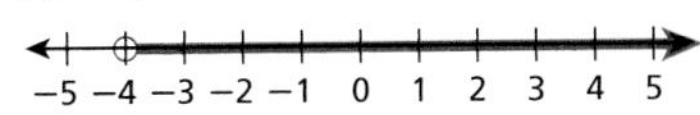

■ $n - 1.3 < 3.2$

$n - 1.3 < 3.2$ — *Since 1.3 is subtracted from x, add 1.3 to both sides.*

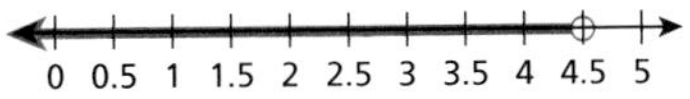

$\underline{+1.3 \quad +1.3}$

$n < 4.5$

EXERCISES

Solve each inequality and graph the solutions. Check your answer.

18. $t + 3 < 10$

19. $k - 7 \le -5$

20. $-1 < m + 4$

21. $x + 2.3 \ge 6.8$

22. $w - 3 < 6.5$

23. $4 > a - 1$

24. $h - \frac{1}{4} < \frac{3}{4}$

25. $5 > 7 + v$

26. Tammy wants to run at least 10 miles per week. So far this week, she ran 4.5 miles. Write and solve an inequality to determine how many more miles Tammy must run this week to reach her goal.

27. Rob has a gift card for $50. So far, he has selected a shirt that costs $32. Write and solve an inequality to determine the amount Rob could spend without exceeding the gift card limit.

3-3 Solving Inequalities by Multiplying or Dividing *(pp. 148–153)*

Prep for 5.0

EXAMPLES

■ **Solve $\frac{p}{-3} \le 6$ and graph the solutions.**

$\frac{p}{-3} \le 6$ — *Since p is divided by −3, multiply both sides by −3.*

$-3 \cdot \frac{p}{-3} \ge -3 \cdot 6$

$p \ge -18$ — *Change ≤ to ≥.*

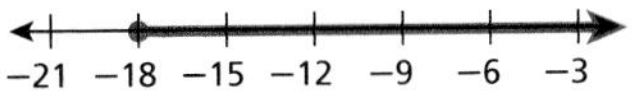

■ **What possible numbers of pizzas that cost $5.50 each can be purchased with $30?**

Let n represent the number of pizzas that can be purchased.

$5.50	times	number of pizzas	is at most	$30.
5.50	•	n	≤	30

$5.50n \le 30$

$\frac{5.50n}{5.50} \le \frac{30}{5.50}$ — *Since n is multiplied by 5.50, divide both sides by 5.50.*

$n \le 5\frac{5}{11}$

Only a whole number of pizzas can be purchased, so 0, 1, 2, 3, 4, or 5 pizzas can be purchased.

EXERCISES

Solve each inequality and graph the solutions. Check your answer.

28. $3a \le 15$

29. $-18 < 6t$

30. $\frac{p}{4} > 2$

31. $\frac{2}{5}x \le -10$

32. $-3n < -18$

33. $\frac{g}{-2} > 6$

34. $-2k < 14$

35. $-3 > \frac{1}{3}r$

36. $27 < -9h$

37. $-0.4g > -1$

38. What are the possible numbers of notebooks costing $1.39 that can be purchased with $10?

39. The senior class is selling lanyards as a fundraiser. The profit for each lanyard is $0.75. Write and solve an inequality to determine the number of lanyards the class must sell to make a profit of at least $250.

Answers

18. $t < 7$

19. $k \le 2$

20. $m > -5$

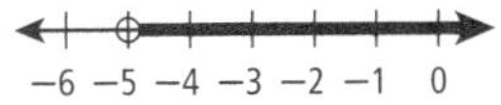

21. $x \ge 4.5$

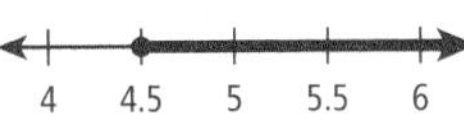

22. $w < 9.5$

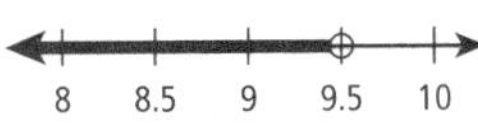

23. $a < 5$

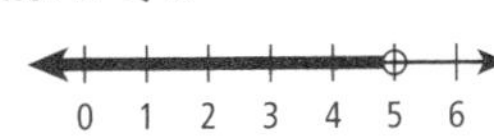

24. $h < 1$

25. $v < -2$

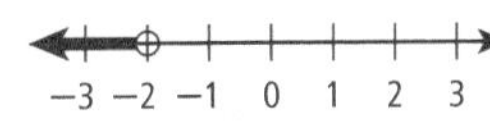

26. $4.5 + m \ge 10$; $m \ge 5.5$; Tammy must run 5.5 mi or more.

27. $32 + d \le 50$; $d \le 18$; Rob can spend $18 or less.

28. $a \le 5$

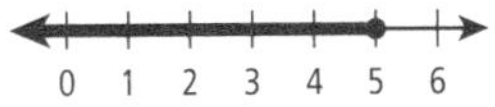

29. $t > -3$

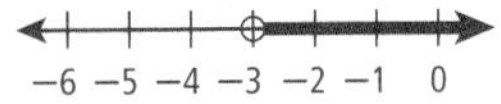

30. $p > 8$

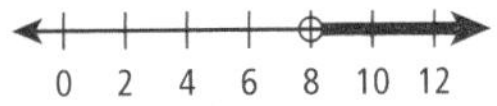

31. $x \le -25$

32. $n > 6$

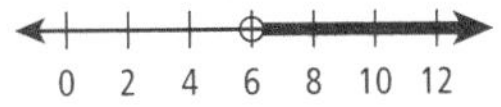

33. $g < -12$

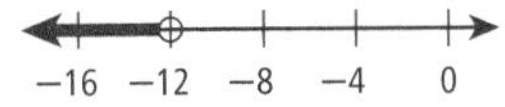

34. $k > -7$

35. $r < -9$

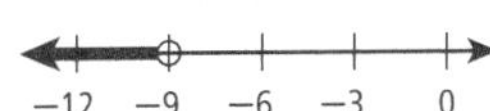

36. $h < -3$

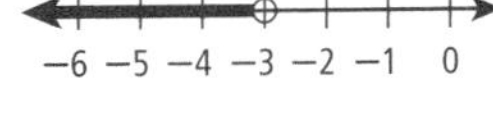

37. $g < 2.5$

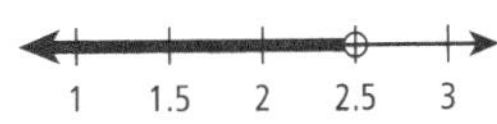

38. 0, 1, 2, 3, 4, 5, 6, 7

39. $0.75n \ge 250$; $n \ge 333\frac{1}{3}$; they must sell at least 334 lanyards.

Study Guide: Review 187

Answers

40. $x < 5$

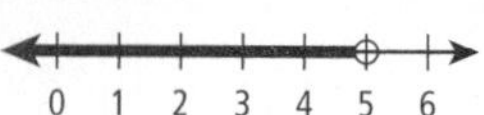

41. $t \geq 6$

42. $m > -11$

43. $x < -1$

44. $h > -3$

45. $x > 1\frac{1}{2}$

46. $b \leq 10$

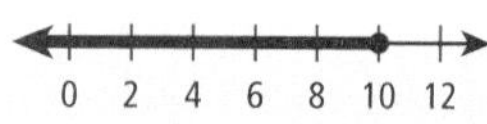

47. $y > 3\frac{1}{2}$

48. $n > -15$

49. 0, 1, 2, 3, 4, 5, 6, 7, 8, 9, 10, 11, 12, or 13

50. $m < -1$

51. $y \geq -2$

52. $c < -3$

53. $q \leq -4$

54. $x > 2$

55. $t < 3$

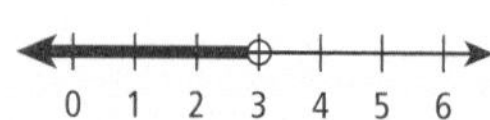

56. $\varnothing$

57. all real numbers

3-4 Solving Two-Step and Multi-Step Inequalities *(pp. 156–161)*

EXAMPLES

Solve each inequality and graph the solution.

■ $18 + 3t > -12$

$$18 + 3t > -12$$
$$\underline{-18 \qquad -18}$$
$$3t > -30$$

Since 18 is added to 3t, subtract 18 from both sides.

$$\frac{3t}{3} > \frac{-30}{3}$$
$$t > -10$$

Since t is multiplied by 3, divide both sides by 3.

■ $3^2 - 5 \leq 2(1 + x)$

$$3^2 - 5 \leq 2(1 + x)$$
$$9 - 5 \leq 2(1 + x)$$

Simplify the left side using order of operations.

$$4 \leq 2(1 + x)$$
$$4 \leq 2(1) + 2(x)$$

Distribute 2 on the right side.

$$4 \leq 2 + 2x$$
$$\underline{-2 \quad -2}$$
$$2 \leq 2x$$

Since 2 is added to 2x, subtract 2 from both sides

$$\frac{2}{2} \leq \frac{2x}{2}$$
$$1 \leq x$$

Since x is multiplied by 2, divide both sides by 2.

EXERCISES

Solve each inequality and graph the solutions. Check your answer.

40. $3x + 4 < 19$
41. $7 \leq 2t - 5$
42. $\frac{m + 3}{2} > -4$
43. $2(x + 5) < 8$
44. $-4(2 - 5) > (-3)^2 - h$
45. $\frac{1}{5}x + \frac{1}{2} > \frac{4}{5}$
46. $0.5(b - 2) \leq 4$
47. $\frac{1}{3}y - \frac{1}{2} > \frac{2}{3}$
48. $6 - 0.2n < 9$
49. Carl's Cable Company charges \$55 for monthly service plus \$4 for each pay-per-view movie. Teleview Cable Company charges \$110 per month with no fee for movies. For what number of movies is the cost of Carl's Cable Company less than the cost of Teleview?

3-5 Solving Inequalities with Variables on Both Sides *(pp. 162–168)*

EXAMPLES

■ **Solve $b + 16 < 3b$ and graph the solutions.**

$$b + 16 > 3b$$
$$\underline{-b \qquad -b}$$
$$16 > 2b$$

Subtract b from both sides so that the coefficient of b is positive.

$$\frac{16}{2} > \frac{2b}{2}$$
$$8 > b$$

Since b is multiplied by 2, divide both sides by 2.

Solve each inequality.

■ $3(1 - k) > 4 - 3k$

$$3(1) - 3(k) > 4 - 3k$$

Distribute the 3.

$$3 - 3k > 4 - 3k$$
$$\underline{+3k \qquad +3k}$$
$$3 > 4$$

Add 3k to both sides. False statement

There are no solutions.

EXERCISES

Solve the inequality and graph the solutions.

50. $5 + 2m < -3m$
51. $y \leq 6 + 4y$
52. $4c - 7 > 9c + 8$
53. $-3(2 - q) \geq 6(q + 1)$
54. $2(5 - x) < 3x$
55. $3.5t - 1.8 < 1.6t + 3.9$

Solve each inequality.

56. $d - 2 < d - 4$
57. $2(1 - x) > -2(1 + x)$
58. $4(1 - p) < 4(2 + p)$
59. $3w + 1 > 3(w - 1)$
60. $5(4 - k) < 5k$
61. $3(c + 1) > 3c + 5$
62. Hanna has a savings account with a balance of \$210 and deposits \$16 per month. Faith has a savings account with a balance of \$175 and deposits \$20 per month. Write and solve an inequality to determine the number of months Hanna's account balance will be greater than Faith's account balance.

58. $p > -\frac{1}{2}$

59. all real numbers

60. $k > 2$

61. $\varnothing$

62. $210 + 16m > 175 + 20m$; $8.75 > m$

3-6 Solving Compound Inequalities *(pp. 170–176)*

EXAMPLES

Solve each compound inequality and graph the solutions.

■ $-3 < c + 5 \leq 11$
$\quad\;\; -5 \quad -5 \quad -5$
$\quad -8 < c \leq 6$

Since 5 is added to c, subtract 5 from each part of the inequality.

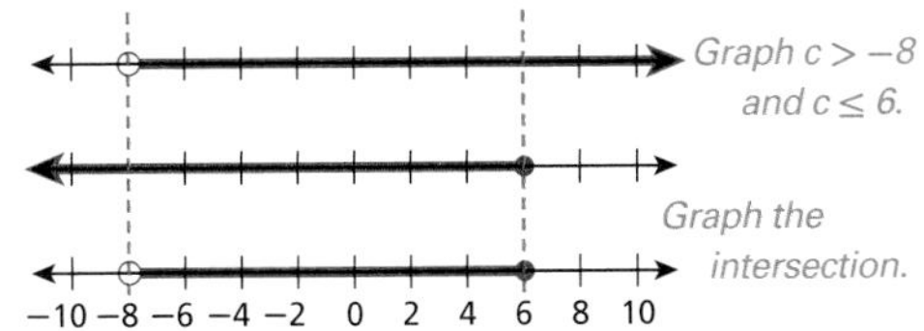

■ $-2 + t \geq 2$ OR $t + 3 < 1$
$\quad +2 \quad +2 \qquad -3 \quad -3$
$\quad t \geq 4$ OR $t < -2$

Solve the simple inequalities.

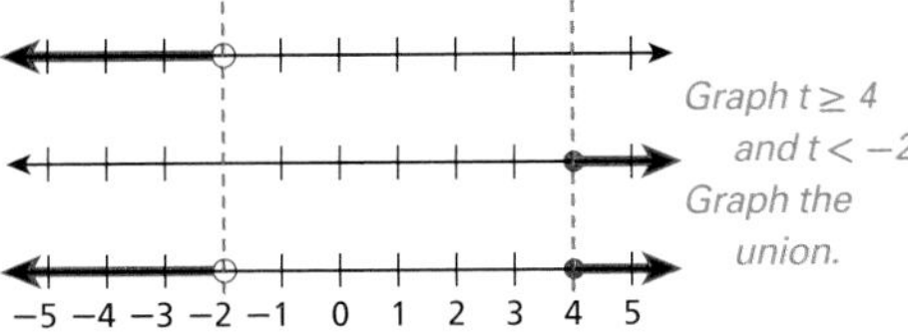

EXERCISES

Solve each compound inequality and graph the solutions.

63. $-4 < t + 6 < 10$ **64.** $-8 < k - 2 \leq 5$

65. $-3 + r > 4$ OR $r + 1 < -1$

66. $2 > n + 3 > 5$

67. $12 \geq p + 7 > 5$

68. $3 < s + 9$ OR $1 > s - 4$

69. One day, the high temperature was 84°F and the low temperature was 68°F. Write a compound inequality to represent the day's temperatures.

70. The table shows formulas for the recommended heart rates during exercise for a person who is a years old. Write and solve a compound inequality to determine the heart rate range for a 16-year-old person.

Recommended Heart Rate Range	
Lower Limit	$0.5 \times (220 - a)$
Upper Limit	$0.9 \times (220 - a)$

3-7 Solving Absolute-Value Inequalities *(pp. 178–183)*

EXAMPLES

Solve each inequality and graph the solutions.

■ $|x| + 4 < 9$
$|x| + 4 < 9$
$\quad\; -4 \quad -4$
$|x| < 5$

Subtract 4 from both sides.

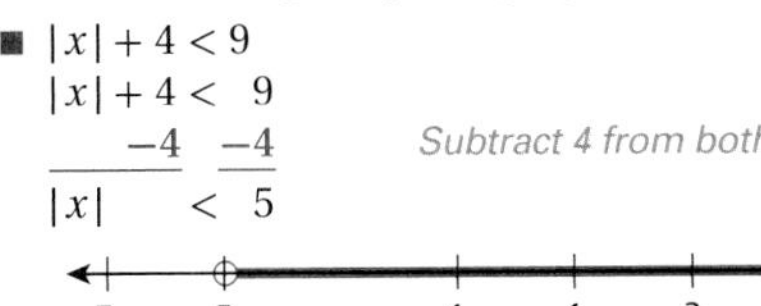

$x > -5$ AND $x < 5$ *Write as a compound inequality.*

■ $|x - 3| + 7 \geq 13$
$\quad -7 \quad -7$
$|x - 3| \geq 6$ *Add 9 to both sides.*

$x - 3 \leq -6$ OR $x - 3 \geq 6$ *Solve the two inequalities.*
$\quad +3 \quad +3 \qquad +3 \quad +3$
$x \leq -3$ OR $x \geq 9$

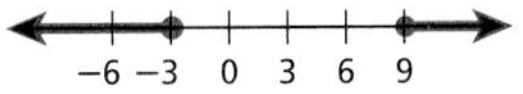

EXERCISES

Solve the inequality and graph the solutions.

71. $|x| - 7 \leq 15$ **72.** $|x + 4| > 8$

73. $6|x| \leq 24$ **74.** $|x + 9| + 11 < 20$

75. $3|x| \geq 9$ **76.** $4|2x| < 24$

Solve the inequality.

77. $|x| - 5.4 > 8.5$ **78.** $|5.2 + x| < 7.3$

79. $|x - 7| + 10 \geq 12$ **80.** $14|x| - 15 \geq 41$

81. $\left|x - \frac{1}{2}\right| + 4 \leq \frac{5}{2}$ **82.** $|x + 5.5| - 6.4 \leq 4.9$

83. The water depth for a pool is set to 6 ft, but the actual depth of the pool may vary by as much as 4 in. Write and solve an absolute-value inequality to find the range of possible water depths in inches. Graph the solutions.

Answers

63. $-10 < t < 4$

64. $-6 < k \leq 7$

65. $r > 7$ OR $r < -2$

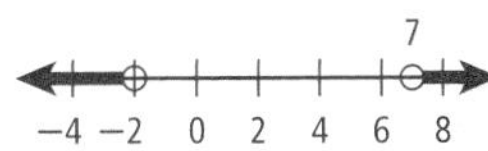

66. ∅

67. $-2 < p \leq 5$

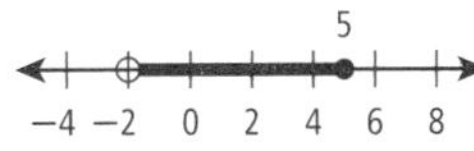

68. all real numbers

69. $68 \leq t \leq 84$

70. $102 \leq n \leq 183.6$

71. $-22 \leq x \leq 22$

72. $x < -12$ OR $x > 4$

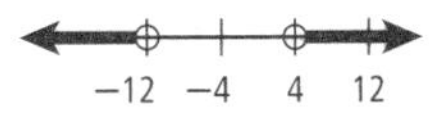

73. $-4 \leq x \leq 4$

74. $-18 < x < 0$

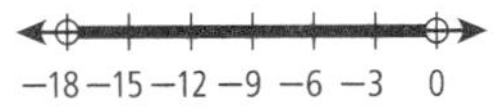

75. $x \leq -3$ OR $x \geq 3$

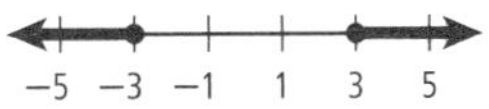

76. $-3 < x < 3$

77. $x < -13.9$ OR $x > 13.9$

78. $-12.5 < x < 2.1$

79. $x \leq 5$ OR $x \geq 9$

80. $x \leq -4$ OR $x \geq 4$

81. ∅

82. $-16.8 \leq x \leq 5.8$

83. $|d - 72| \leq 4$; $68 \leq d \leq 76$

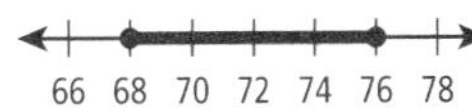

Organizer

Objective: Assess students' mastery of concepts and skills in Chapter 3.

Online Edition

Resources

Assessment Resources

Chapter 3 Tests

- Free Response (Levels A, B, C)
- Multiple Choice (Levels A, B, C)
- Performance Assessment

***IDEA Works!* CD-ROM**

Modified Chapter 3 Test

Answers

1. all real numbers greater than or equal to −6
2. all real numbers greater than 4
3. all real numbers less than or equal to −2
4. all real numbers less than or equal to 8
5. (number line: −6 −5 −4 −3 −2 −1 0)
6. (number line: 2 2.5 3 3.5 4)
7. (number line: −6 −5 −4 −3 −2 −1 0)
8. (number line: −16 −12 −8 −4 0)

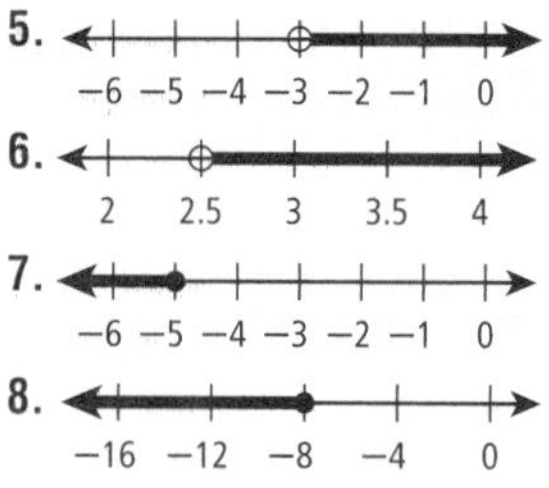

California Standards

Algebra 1 **3.0, 4.0, 5.0**

Describe the solutions of each inequality in words.

1. $-6 \le m$ **2.** $3t > 12$ **3.** $-x \ge 2$ **4.** $2 + b \le 10$

Graph each inequality.

5. $b > -3$ **6.** $2.5 < c$ **7.** $y \le -\sqrt{25}$ **8.** $3 - (4 + 7) \ge h$

Write the inequality shown by each graph.

9. 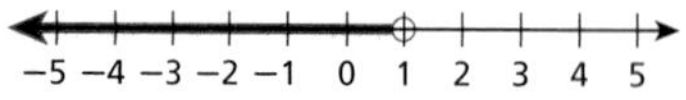 (number line −5 to 5) $d < 1$ **10.** (number line −5 to 0, point at −4.5) $p \ge -4.5$

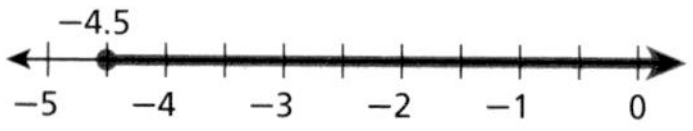

Write an inequality for the situation and graph the solutions.

11. Madison must run a mile in no more than 9 minutes to qualify for the race.
$m \le 9$ where m is nonnegative

Solve each inequality and graph the solutions.

12. $d - 5 > -7$ $d > -2$ **13.** $f + 4 < -3$ $f < -7$ **14.** $4.5 \ge s + 3.2$ $s \le 1.3$ **15.** $g + (-2) \le 9$ $g \le 11$

16. Students need at least 75 hours of volunteer service to meet their graduation requirement. Samir has already completed 48 hours. Write and solve an inequality to determine how many more hours he needs to complete.
$48 + h \ge 75$; $h \ge 27$; Samir needs at least 27 more hours.

Solve each inequality and graph the solutions.

17. $-2c \le 2$ $c \ge -1$ **18.** $3 > \frac{k}{2}$ $k < 6$ **19.** $\frac{4}{5}x \le -8$ $x \le -10$ **20.** $\frac{b}{3} > -7$ $b > -21$

21. Marco needs to buy premium gasoline for his car. He has $20 in his wallet. Write and solve an inequality to determine how many gallons of gas Marco can buy.
$2.25g \le 20$; $g \le 8.89$; Marco can buy 8.89 gallons or less.

Gasoline Prices ($)		
Regular	Plus	Premium
2.05	2.12	2.25

Solve each inequality and graph the solutions.

22. $3x - 8 < 4$ $x < 4$ **23.** $-2(c - 3) > 4$ $c < 1$ **24.** $5 \le \frac{3}{4}n - 2^4$ $n \ge 28$ **25.** $3 - 2a \le -15 + (-9)$ $a \ge 13\frac{1}{2}$

Solve each inequality.

26. $2k - 6 > 3k + 2$ $k < -8$ **27.** $2(5 - f) \le f + 12$ $f \ge -\frac{2}{3}$ **28.** $\frac{3}{2}d \le -\frac{1}{2}d + 6$ $d \le 3$

Solve each compound inequality and graph the solutions.

29. $-1 \le x - 3 < 3$ $2 \le x < 6$ **30.** $t + 7 < 3$ OR $t - 1 > 4$ $t < -4$ OR $t > 5$ **31.** $4 \le d - 2 < 5$ $6 \le d < 7$

32. The driving school instructor has asked Lina to stay within 2 miles of the posted speed limits. The current road has a speed limit of 45 mi/h. Write a compound inequality to show Lina's acceptable speeds s. $43 \le s \le 47$

Solve each inequality.

33. $|x - 3| + 7 < 17$ $-7 < x < 13$ **34.** $6|x| + 4 \ge 16$ $x \le -2$ OR $x \ge 2$ **35.** $|x + 12| \le 23$ $-35 \le x \le 11$

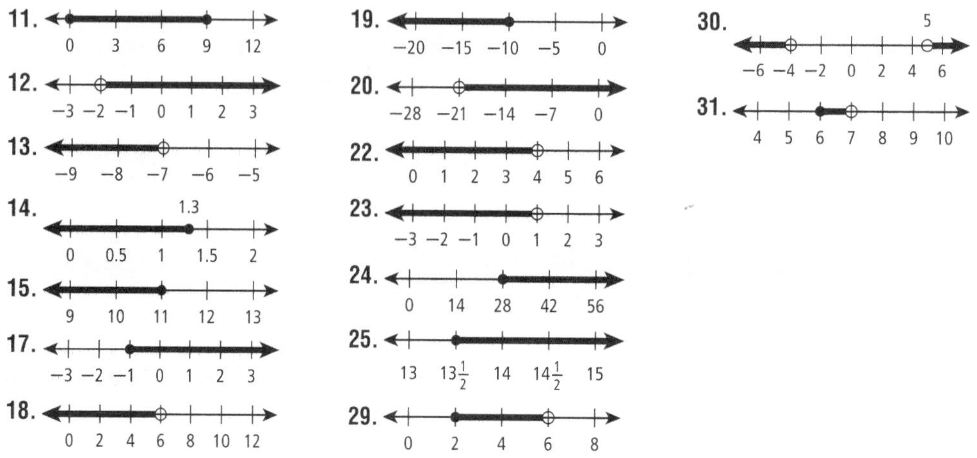

11. (number line: 0 3 6 9 12)
12. (number line: −3 −2 −1 0 1 2 3)
13. (number line: −9 −8 −7 −6 −5)
14. (number line: 0 0.5 1 1.5 2; 1.3)
15. (number line: 9 10 11 12 13)
17. (number line: −3 −2 −1 0 1 2 3)
18. (number line: 0 2 4 6 8 10 12)
19. (number line: −20 −15 −10 −5 0)
20. (number line: −28 −21 −14 −7 0)
22. (number line: 0 1 2 3 4 5 6)
23. (number line: −3 −2 −1 0 1 2 3)
24. (number line: 0 14 28 42 56)
25. (number line: 13 $13\frac{1}{2}$ 14 $14\frac{1}{2}$ 15)
29. (number line: 0 2 4 6 8)
30. (number line: −6 −4 −2 0 2 4 6; 5)
31. (number line: 4 5 6 7 8 9 10)

FOCUS ON SAT STUDENT-PRODUCED RESPONSES

Ten questions on the SAT require you to enter your answer in a special grid like the one shown. You do not have to write your answer in the boxes at the top of the grid, but doing this may help you avoid errors when filling in the grid. The circles must be filled in correctly for you to receive credit.

You cannot enter a zero in the first column of the grid. This is to encourage you to give a more accurate answer when you need to round. For example, $\frac{1}{16}$ written as a decimal is 0.0625. This should be entered in the grid as .063 instead of 0.06.

You may want to time yourself as you take this practice test. It should take you about 9 minutes to complete.

1. Mailing a standard-sized letter in 2005 by first-class mail cost \$0.37 for a letter weighing 1 ounce or less and \$0.23 for each additional ounce. How much did it cost, in dollars, to send a standard-sized letter that weighed 3 ounces?
   0.83

2. If $p = q - 2$ and $\frac{q}{3} = 9$, what is the value of p?
   25

3. Give the maximum value of x if $12 - 3(x + 1) \geq \frac{1}{2}(3 - 5)$.
   $\frac{10}{3}$

4. Give the minimum value of x if $2x + y \leq 7x - 9$ and $y = -3$.
   $\frac{6}{5}$

5. For what integer value of x is $2x - 9 < 5$ and $x - 1 > 4$? **6**

6. What is the minimum value of z that satisfies the inequality $z - 7.3 \geq 4.1$?
   11.4

7. To be eligible for financial aid, Alisa must work at least 15 hours per week in a work-study program. She wants to spend at least 5 more hours studying than working each week. What is the minimum number of hours per day (Monday through Friday) that she must study to meet this goal and be eligible for financial aid?
   4

8. For all real numbers a and b, define the operation # as follows:
   $$a \# b = 2a - b$$
   Given $a = 3$ and $a \# b = 1$, what is the value of b?
   5

COLLEGE ENTRANCE EXAM PRACTICE

Organizer

Objective: Provide practice for college entrance exams such as the SAT.

 **Online Edition**

Resources

Questions on the SAT represent the following math content areas:

Number and Operations, 30–32%

Algebra and Functions, 28–32%

Geometry and Measurement, 27–30%

Data Analysis, Statistics, and Probability, 10–12%

Items on this page focus on:
- Number and Operations
- Algebra and Functions

Text References:

Item	1	2	3	4	5	6	7
Lesson	3-6	3-3	3-4	3-5	3-2	3-3	3-4

Student-Produced Responses

1. Students who answered 1.06 may have found the cost of 3 additional ounces instead of 2 additional ounces.
2. Students who answered 1 may have divided by 3 when solving for q in the second equation, instead of multiplying.
3. Students who gave an answer greater than $\frac{10}{3}$ may have forgotten to reverse the inequality symbol when multiplying by a negative number.
4. Students who have an answer less than -24 may have substituted -3 for x instead of y. Urge students to read each test item carefully.
5. Students who gave an answer other than 6 that is between 5 and 7 may have solved correctly, but did not remember to give an integer answer.
6. Students who gave an answer of 3.2 or less may have subtracted instead of adding.
7. Students may have difficulty working with two inequalities. Suggest that students first write the inequality and then test several values to determine whether their answer is reasonable.
8. Students may have difficulty approaching the problem. Suggest that students write the given equation and then substitute 1 for the expression on the left side and 3 for a on the right side.

Organizer

Objective: Provide opportunities to learn and practice common test-taking strategies.

Online Edition

Teaching Tip

Short Response This Strategy for Success focuses on writing full-credit answers to short-response test items. Students benefit from knowing how their answers will be scored. By seeing examples of answers that do not earn full credit, students are reminded that they must pay attention to all parts of the question to receive full credit for an answer.

Short Response: Understand Short Response Scores

To answer a short-response question completely, you must show how you solved the problem and explain your answer. Short response questions are scored using a 2-point scoring rubric. A sample scoring rubric is provided below.

EXAMPLE 1

Short Response An online company offers free shipping if the cost of the order is at least $35. Your order currently totals $26.50. Write an inequality to show how much more you need to spend to qualify for free shipping. Solve the inequality and explain what your answer means.

2-point response:

Let c be the amount I must add to my order.
c plus the amount I already ordered must be at least $35.

$c \quad + \quad 26.50 \quad \geq \quad 35$

$c + 26.50 \geq 35$

$c + 26.50 - 26.50 \geq 35 - 26.50$

$c \geq 8.50$

Check:
$8.50 + 26.50 \geq 35$ ✓

To get free shipping on the order, I must spend at least $8.50 more since $8.50 + $26.50 is at least $35.

The student wrote and solved an inequality correctly. The student defined the variable used in the inequality, answered the question in a complete sentence, and showed an explanation for the work done.

1-point response:

$c + 26.50 > 35$

$c > 8.50$

$8.50

The student did not define the variable. The student gave a correct answer, but the inequality symbol shown in the student's work is incorrect. No explanation was given.

0-point response:

$9.25

The student gave an answer that satisfies the problem, but the student did not show any work or give explanation.

Scoring Rubric:

2 points: The student writes and correctly solves an inequality, showing all work. Student defines the variable, answers the question in a complete sentence, and provides an explanation.

1 point: The student writes and correctly solves an inequality but does not show all work, does not define the variable, or does not provide an explanation.

1 point: The student writes and solves an inequality but gives an incorrect answer. The student shows all work and provides an explanation for the answer.

0 points: The student gives no response or provides a solution without showing any work or explanation.

Read short-response test items carefully. If you are allowed to write in the test booklet, underline or circle the parts of the question that tell you what your answer must include. Be sure to explain how you get your answer in complete sentences.

Read each sample and answer the questions that follow by using the scoring rubric below.

Scoring Rubric:

2 points: The student demonstrates a thorough understanding of the concept, correctly answers the question, shows all work, and provides a complete explanation.

1 point: The student correctly answers the question but does not show all work or does not provide an explanation.

1 point: The student makes minor errors resulting in an incorrect solution but shows and explains understanding of the concept.

0 points: The student gives no response or provides a solution without showing any work or explanation.

Sample A

Short Response Write a real-world situation that can be modeled by the inequality $25s - 75 \geq 250$. Solve for s and explain how the value of s relates to your situation.

Student's Answer

A painter rents a booth at the county fair for $75. The artist sells his paintings for $25 each. If he makes at least $250 in profit, he can buy a new easel.

The artist has to sell at least 13 paintings.

1. What score should the student's answer receive? Explain your reasoning.
2. What additional information, if any, should the student's answer include in order to receive full credit?

Sample B

Short Response How do the solutions of $3s - 10 < 15 - 2s$ and $-34 + 9s \leq 4s - 9$ differ? How are the solutions alike? Include a graph in your explanation.

Student's Answer

Solve both inequalities.

$$\begin{array}{ll} 3s - 10 < 15 - 2s & -34 + 9s \leq 4s - 9 \\ \underline{+2s \qquad\quad +2s} & \underline{\quad -4s \quad -4s} \\ 5s - 10 < 15 & -34 + 5s \leq -9 \\ \underline{+10 \quad +10} & \underline{+34 \qquad\quad +34} \\ 5s < 25 & 5s \leq 25 \\ \frac{5s}{5} < \frac{25}{5} & \frac{5s}{5} \leq \frac{25}{5} \\ s < 5 & s \leq 5 \end{array}$$

Blue graph: $s<5$ Red graph: $s\leq5$

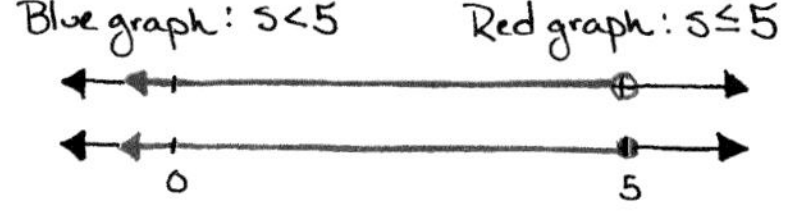

3. What score should the student's answer receive? Explain your reasoning.
4. What additional information, if any, should the student's answer include in order to receive full credit?

Sample C

Short Response Explain the difference between the solution of the equation $x - 6 = 2x + 9$ and the solutions of the inequality $x - 6 < 2x + 9$.

Student's Answer

The equation has a solution of x = –15, and the inequality has a solution of x > –15. The equation is true only when x equals –15. The inequality is true for all values greater than –15.

5. What score should the student's answer receive? Explain your reasoning.
6. What additional information, if any, should the student's answer include in order to receive full credit?

Answers

1. 1; the student did not show how he or she got the answer 13.
2. The student should explain how he or she got the answer by showing each step he or she followed to solve the inequality.
3. 1; the student did not explain how the graphs and solutions differ or how they are alike.
4. The student should explain that the solutions of the two inequalities are the same except that one includes 5 and the other does not.
5. 1; the student did not show the steps he or she followed to solve the equation or the inequality.
6. The student should show each step he or she followed to solve the equation and the inequality.

Answers to Test Items

A. See answer to Problem 2.
B. See answer to Problem 4.
C. See answer to Problem 6.

Algebra 1 5.0

MASTERING THE STANDARDS

Organizer

Objective: Provide review and practice for Chapters 1–3.

Online Edition

Resources

Assessment Resources

Chapter 3 Cumulative Test

Focus on California Standards Benchmark Tests and Intervention

California Standards Practice CD-ROM

go.hrw.com
KEYWORD: MA8CA Practice

California Standards

Standard	Items
6NS1.4	14
6AF1.1	3
7NS1.1	13
7AF1.1	1, 5, 18
7AF1.3	2
7AF4.0	7
7MG1.3	10
7MG2.1	4, 17
2.0	6
4.0	8
5.0	8, 9, 12, 15, 16, 19–21

CUMULATIVE ASSESSMENT, CHAPTERS 1–3

Multiple Choice

1. Which algebraic expression means "5 less than y"?

Ⓐ $5 - y$
Ⓑ $y - 5$
Ⓒ $5 < y$
Ⓓ $5 \div y$

2. Which is a simplified expression for $5 + 2(x - 5)$?

Ⓐ $2x$
Ⓑ $2x + 5$
Ⓒ $2x - 5$
Ⓓ $7x - 35$

3. If $t + 8 = 2$, find the value of $2t$.

Ⓐ -12
Ⓑ -6
Ⓒ 12
Ⓓ 20

4. The length of the rectangle is $2(x + 1)$ meters and the perimeter is 60 meters. Find the length of the rectangle.

$2(x + 1)$ 4

Ⓐ 12 meters
Ⓑ 26 meters
Ⓒ 28 meters
Ⓓ 56 meters

5. Samantha deposited some money in her account in June. She deposited twice that amount in August. Samantha has less than $600 in her account. If she made no other withdrawals or deposits, which inequality could be used to determine the maximum amount Samantha could have deposited in June?

Ⓐ $2x < 600$
Ⓑ $2x > 600$
Ⓒ $3x < 600$
Ⓓ $3x > 600$

6. A negative number is raised to a power, and the result is a positive number. Which of the following CANNOT be true?

Ⓐ The number is even.
Ⓑ The number is odd.
Ⓒ The exponent is even.
Ⓓ The exponent is odd.

7. For which inequality is -2 a solution?

Ⓐ $2x < -4$
Ⓑ $-2x < 4$
Ⓒ $-2x > -4$
Ⓓ $-2x < -4$

8. Which graph shows the solutions of $-2(1 - x) < 3(x - 2)$?

Ⓐ 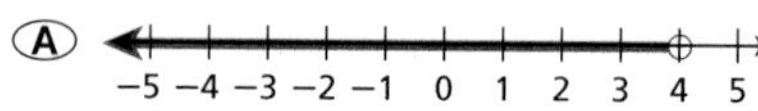

Ⓑ 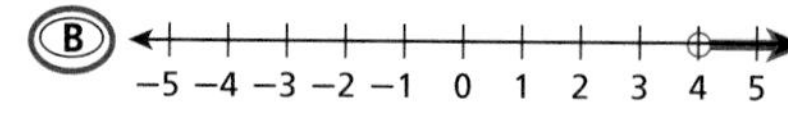

Ⓒ 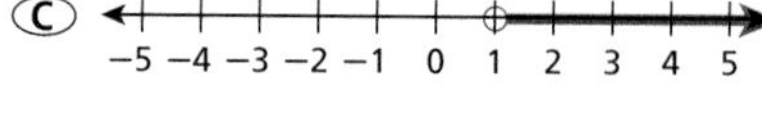

Ⓓ −5 −4 −3 −2 −1 0 1 2 3 4 5

9. Which compound inequality has no solution?

Ⓐ $x > 1$ OR $x < -2$
Ⓑ $x < 1$ AND $x > -2$
Ⓒ $x < 1$ OR $x < -2$
Ⓓ $x > 1$ AND $x < -2$

10. Which expression describes the rate at which a bicycle rider is traveling if the rider has traveled 15 kilometers in 40 minutes? Round to the nearest tenth.

Ⓐ 0.5 kilometers/minute
Ⓑ 2.7 kilometers/minute
Ⓒ 0.4 kilometers/minute
Ⓓ 0.3 kilometers/minute

Teaching Tip

Multiple Choice In **Item 3,** if students chose **B,** they chose the value of t instead of $2t$. If they chose **C,** they may have forgotten the negative sign when they multiplied. If they chose **D,** they most likely added 8 to both sides instead of subtracting 8 from both sides when solving.

Some students may have difficulty answering **Item 9.** Encourage students to graph the simple inequalities in each answer choice and then determine the solutions of the compound inequality.

To check your answer, use a different method to solve the problem from the one you originally used. If you made a mistake the first time, you are unlikely to make the same mistake when you solve the problem a different way.

11. Which inequality is equivalent to $p < -2$?

Ⓐ $p + 1 < -2$

Ⓑ $p + 4 < 2$

Ⓒ $2p + 1 < -4$

Ⓓ $3p < -12$

12. What is the greatest integer solution of $5 - 3m > 11$?

Ⓐ 0

Ⓑ −1

Ⓒ −2

Ⓓ −3

Gridded Response

13. The sum of the measures of any two sides of a triangle must be greater than the measure of the third side. What is the greatest possible integer value for x? **26**

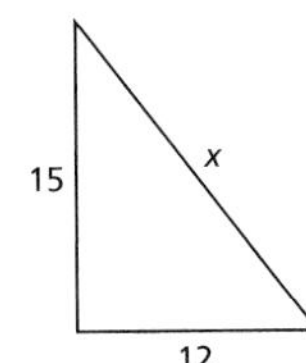

14. Brian plays basketball. In the past, he has made 4 out of every 5 free throws. What percent of his free throws has Brian made? **80**

15. Amy's bowling score in her third game was 10 points less than her score in the first game and 5 points more than her score in the second game. The total points for all three games was no more than 275. What is the highest number of points Amy could have scored in her first game? **100**

16. Trevor needs a 93 on his second quiz to have a quiz average of 90. What score did Trevor receive on his first quiz? **87**

17. What is the length in meters of the radius of a circle that has area of 314 square meters? (Use 3.14 for π.) **10**

Short Response

18. Write 2 different inequalities that are equivalent to $n > 3$ such that

a. the first inequality uses the symbol > and requires addition or subtraction to solve.

b. the second inequality uses the symbol < and requires multiplication or division to solve.

19. Alison has twice as many videogames as Kyle. Maurice has 5 more videogames than Alison. The total number of videogames is less than 40.

a. Write an inequality to represent this situation.

b. Solve the inequality to determine the greatest number of videogames Maurice could have.

20. Donna's Deli delivers lunches for \$7 per person plus a \$35 delivery fee. Larry's Lunches delivers lunches for \$11 per person.

a. Write an expression to represent the cost of x lunches from Donna's Deli. Write an expression to represents the cost of ordering x lunches from Larry's Lunches.

b. Write an inequality to determine the number of lunches for which the cost of Larry's Lunches is less than the cost of Donna's Deli.

c. Solve the inequality and explain what the answer means. Which restaurant charges less for an order of 10 lunches?

Extended Response

21. Aleya has two employment opportunities. Company A offered her a yearly salary of \$31,000. Company B offered her a similar position with a yearly salary of \$27,000 plus 2.5% of her total sales for the year.

a. Let x represent Aleya's total sales for the year at company B. Write an expression to represent the total income after one year at company B.

b. Use your expression from part **a** to write an inequality that could be solved to determine the amount of sales for which the yearly income at company A would be greater than that at company B.

c. Solve the inequality from part **b** and explain the meaning of the solution in relation to Aleya's decision to work for company A or company B.

d. How much more than the salary at company A would Aleya make after one year at company B if her total sales for the year was \$200,000?

Short-Response Rubric

Items 18–20

2 Points = The student's answer is an accurate and complete execution of the task or tasks.

1 Point = The student's answer contains attributes of an appropriate response but is flawed.

0 Points = The student's answer contains no attributes of an appropriate response.

Extended-Response Rubric

Item 21

4 Points = The student correctly writes an expression in part **a** and an inequality in part **b.** The solution in part **c** is correct, and the student correctly explains what the answer means in the context of the problem. The student gives a correct answer to part **d.**

3 Points = The student correctly writes an expression in part **a** and an inequality in part **b.** The solution in part **c** is correct, but the student does not explain the meaning of the answer in the context of the problem. The student gives a correct answer to part **d.**

2 Points = The student answers all parts correctly but does not show any work or explanation; or the student correctly answers parts **a** and **b** but does not correctly answer parts **c** and **d.**

1 Point = The student correctly writes an expression in part **a** but does not correctly answer the other parts of the problem; or the student attempts to answer all parts of the problem but does not correctly answer any part.

0 Points = The student does not answer correctly and does not attempt all parts of the problem.

Answers

18a. Possible answer: $n + 5 > 8$

b. Possible answer: $-2n < -6$

19a. $k + 2k + (2k + 5) < 40$

b. Maurice can have up to 17 videos.

20a. $35 + 7x$; $11x$

b. $35 + 7x > 11x$

c. $x < 8.75$; Larry's costs less when 8 lunches or fewer are ordered. Donna's costs less for 10 lunches.

21a. $27{,}000 + 0.025x$

b. $31{,}000 > 27{,}000 + 0.025x$

c. $x < 160{,}000$; Aleya should work for company A if her sales will be less than \$160,000.

d. $27{,}000 + 0.025(200{,}000)$; $2700 + 5000$; $32{,}000$; $32{,}000 - 31{,}000 =$ \$1000

Functions

✔	Grade-level Standard
◀	Review
▶	Beyond the Standards
A	Assessment
O	Optional

Pacing Guide

Calendar Planner
Teacher's One-Stop Planner®

Lesson/Lab	California Standards	Time	Advanced Students	Benchmark Students*	Strategic Students**
4-1 Graphing Relationships	**Review of Grade 7 AF1.5**	50 min	O	◀	◀
4-2 Relations and Functions	**16.0, 17.0, 18.0**	50 min	✔	✔	✔
4-3 Writing and Graphing Functions	**16.0, 17.0, 18.0**	75 min	✔	✔	✔
LAB Connect Equations, Tables, and Graphs	**16.0**	25 min	✔	✔	✔
Concept Connection	**17.0**	25 min	A	A	O
Ready to Go On?		25 min	A	A	A
4-4 Scatter Plots and Trend Lines	**Review of Grade 7 SDAP1.2**	50 min	O	◀	◀
CN Median-Fit Line	**Reinforcement of Grade 6 SDAP1.1, Reinforcement of Grade 7 SDAP1.2**	25 min	▶	O	O
LR Inductive Reasoning	**24.1**	25 min	✔	✔	✔
4-5 Arithmetic Sequences	**Preparation for Algebra II 22.0**	50 min	▶	O	O
Concept Connection	**Review of Grade 7 SDAP1.2**	25 min	A	A	O
Ready to Go On?		25 min	A	A	A
Study Guide: Review		50 min	✔	✔	✔
Chapter Test	**16.0, 17.0, 18.0**	50 min	A	A	A

* **Benchmark students** are achieving at or near grade level.

** **Strategic students** may be a year or more below grade level, and may require additional time for intervention.

Countdown to Mastery, Weeks 7, 8, 9

ONGOING ASSESSMENT and INTERVENTION

	DIAGNOSE	PRESCRIBE
Assess Prior Knowledge	**Before Chapter 4**	
	Diagnose readiness for the chapter.	Prescribe intervention.
	Are You Ready? SE p. 197	***Are You Ready? Intervention*** Skills 60, 69, 72, 79
Formative Assessment	**Before Every Lesson**	
	Diagnose readiness for the lesson.	Prescribe intervention.
	Warm Up TE, every lesson	**Skills Bank** pp. SB1–SB32
		Review for Mastery CRF Chapters 1–4
	During Every Lesson	
	Diagnose understanding of lesson concepts.	Prescribe intervention.
	Questioning Strategies TE, every example	**Reading Strategies** CRF, every lesson
	Check It Out! SE, every example	***Success for ELL*** pp. 43–52
	Think and Discuss SE, every lesson	***Lesson Tutorial Videos*** Chapter 4
	Write About It SE, every lesson	
	Journal TE, every lesson	
	After Every Lesson	
	Diagnose mastery of lesson concepts.	Prescribe intervention.
	Lesson Quiz TE, every lesson	**Review for Mastery** CRF, every lesson
	Alternative Assessment TE, every lesson	**Problem Solving** CRF, every lesson
	Ready to Go On? SE pp. 223, 241	***Ready to Go On? Intervention*** Chapter 4
	Test and Practice Generator	***Homework Help Online***
	Before Chapter 4 Testing	
	Diagnose mastery of concepts in the chapter.	Prescribe intervention.
	Ready to Go On? SE pp. 223, 241	***Ready to Go On? Intervention*** Chapter 4
	Concept Connection SE pp. 222, 240	**Scaffolding Questions** TE pp. 222, 240
	Section Quizzes AR pp. 65–66	
	Test and Practice Generator	
	Before Assessment of California Standards	
	Diagnose mastery of California Standards.	Prescribe intervention.
	Focus on California Standards: Benchmark Tests	***Focus on California Standards: Intervention***
	Mastering the Standards SE pp. 250–251	
	***California Standards Practice* CD-ROM**	
Summative Assessment	**After Chapter 4**	
	Check mastery of chapter concepts.	Prescribe intervention.
	Multiple-Choice Tests (Forms A, B, C)	**Review for Mastery** CRF, every lesson
	Free-Response Tests (Forms A, B, C)	***Lesson Tutorial Videos*** Chapter 4
	Performance Assessment AR pp. 67–80	
	Test and Practice Generator	

KEY: **SE** = *Student Edition* **TE** = *Teacher's Edition* **CRF** = *Chapter Resource File* **AR** = *Assessment Resources* Available online  Available on CD-ROM

Supporting the Teacher

Chapter 4 Resource File

Family Involvement
pp. 1–4, 29–32

Practice A, B, C
pp. 5–7, 13–15, 21–23, 33–35, 41–43

Review for Mastery
pp. 8–9, 16–17, 24–25, 36–37, 44–45

Challenge
pp. 10, 18, 26, 38, 46

Problem Solving
pp. 11, 19, 27, 39, 47

Reading Strategies ELL
pp. 12, 20, 28, 40, 48

Algebra Lab
pp. 51–52, 53–54, 55–56, 57–58

Technology Lab
pp. 49–50

Workbooks

Homework and Practice Workbook SPANISH
Teacher's Edition  pp. 22–26

Know-It Notebook SPANISH
Teacher's Guide .... Chapter 4

Review for Mastery Workbook SPANISH
Teacher's Guide .... pp. 43–52

Focus on California Standards: Intervention Workbook SPANISH
Teacher's Guide

Teacher Tools

Power Presentations
Complete PowerPoint® presentations for Chapter 4 lessons

Lesson Tutorial Videos SPANISH
Holt authors Ed Burger and Freddie Renfro present tutorials to support the Chapter 4 lessons.

Teacher's One-Stop Planner SPANISH
Easy access to all Chapter 4 resources and assessments, as well as software for lesson planning, test generation, and puzzle creation

IDEA Works!
Key Chapter 4 resources and assessments modified to address special learning needs

Solutions Key .... Chapter 4

Interactive Answers and Solutions

TechKeys

Lab Resources

Project Teacher Support

Parent Resources 

Transparencies

Lesson Transparencies, Volume 1 .... Chapter 4
- Teacher Tools
- Warm-ups
- Teaching Transparencies
- Lesson Quizzes

Alternate Openers: Explorations .... pp. 22–26

Countdown to Mastery .... pp. 14–17

Know-It Notebook .... Chapter 4
- Vocabulary
- Key Concepts
- Graphic Organizers
- Chapter Review
- Big Ideas

Technology Highlights for the Teacher

 Power Presentations

Dynamic presentations to engage students. Complete PowerPoint® presentations for every lesson in Chapter 4.

2-1 Solving One-Step Equations

Isolate a variable by using inverse operations which "undo" operations on the variable.

An equation is like a balanced scale. To keep the balance, perform the same operation on both sides.

Inverse Operations	
Operation	Inverse Operation
Addition	Subtraction
Subtraction	Addition

 One-Stop Planner SPANISH

Easy access to Chapter 4 resources and assessments. Includes lesson planning, test generation, and puzzle creation software.

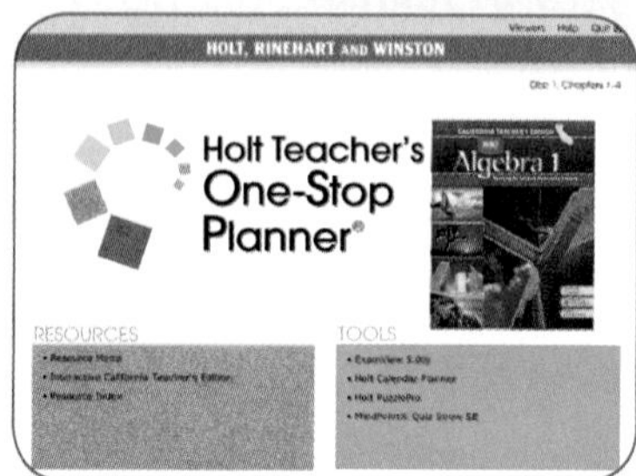

 Premier Online Edition SPANISH

Includes Tutorial Videos, Lesson Activities, Lesson Quizzes, Homework Help, Chapter Project and more.

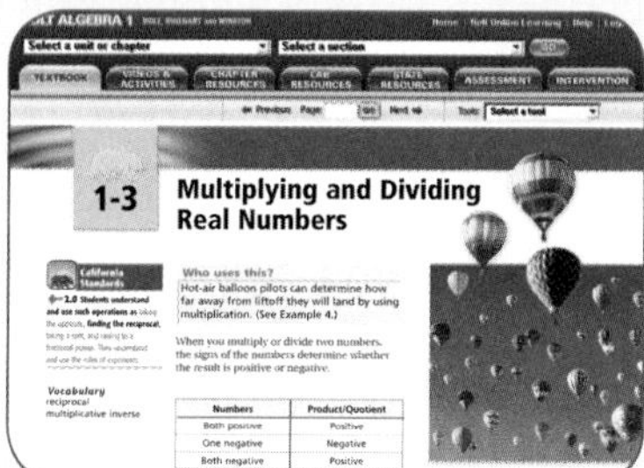

KEY: **SE** = *Student Edition* **TE** = *Teacher's Edition*  English Language Learners  Spanish available  Available online  Available on CD-ROM

Universal Access

Teaching Tips to help all students appear throughout the chapter. A few that target specific students are included in the lists below.

Strategic Students

- **Practice A** ..... CRF, every lesson
- **Review for Mastery** ..... CRF, every lesson
- **Reading Strategies** ..... CRF, every lesson
- **Academic Vocabulary Connections** ..... TE p. 198
- **Modeling** ..... TE p. 203
- **Questioning Strategies** ..... TE, every example
- ***Ready to Go On? Intervention*** ..... Chapter 4
- ***Know-It Notebook*** SPANISH ..... Chapter 4
- ***Homework Help Online***
- ***Lesson Tutorial Videos*** SPANISH
- ***Online Interactivities*** SPANISH

Special Needs Students

- **Practice A** ..... CRF, every lesson
- **Review for Mastery** ..... CRF, every lesson
- **Reading Strategies** ..... CRF, every lesson
- **Academic Vocabulary Connections** ..... TE p. 198
- **Inclusion** ..... TE pp. 202, 215, 217
- ***IDEA Works! Modified Resources*** ..... Chapter 4
- ***Ready to Go On? Intervention*** ..... Chapter 4
- ***Know-It Notebook*** SPANISH ..... Chapter 4
- ***Lesson Tutorial Videos*** SPANISH
- ***Online Interactivities*** SPANISH

English Learners

ENGLISH LANGUAGE LEARNERS

- **Reading Strategies** ..... CRF, every lesson
- **Vocabulary Exercises** ..... SE, every exercise set
- **Academic Vocabulary Connections** ..... TE p. 198
- **English Language Learners** ..... TE p. 236
- **Language Support** ..... TE pp. 227, 236
- ***Success for English Language Learners*** ..... Chapter 4
- ***Know-It Notebook*** SPANISH ..... Chapter 4
- ***Multilingual Glossary***
- ***Lesson Tutorial Videos*** SPANISH

Benchmark Students

- **Practice B** ..... CRF, every lesson
- **Problem Solving** ..... CRF, every lesson
- **Academic Vocabulary Connections** ..... TE p. 198
- **Questioning Strategies** ..... TE, every example
- ***Ready to Go On? Intervention*** ..... Chapter 4
- ***Know-It Notebook*** SPANISH ..... Chapter 4
- ***Homework Help Online***
- ***Online Interactivities*** SPANISH

Advanced Students

- **Practice C** ..... CRF, every lesson
- **Challenge** ..... CRF, every lesson
- **Reading and Writing Math** EXTENSION ..... TE p. 199
- **Concept Connection** EXTENSION ..... TE pp. 222, 240
- ***Ready to Go On? Enrichment*** ..... Chapter 4

Technology Highlights for Universal Access

Lesson Tutorial Videos 

Starring Holt authors Ed Burger and Freddie Renfro! Live tutorials to support every lesson in Chapter 4.

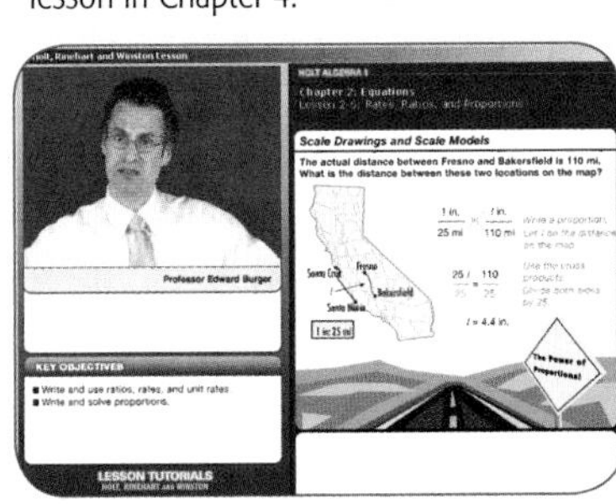

Multilingual Glossary

Searchable glossary includes definitions in English, Spanish, Vietnamese, Chinese, Hmong, Korean, and other languages.

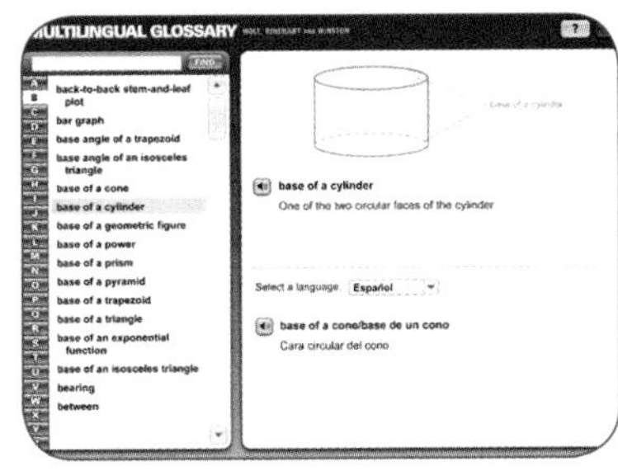

Online Interactivities 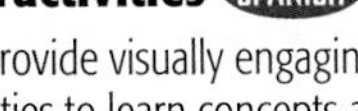

Interactive tutorials provide visually engaging alternative opportunities to learn concepts and master skills.

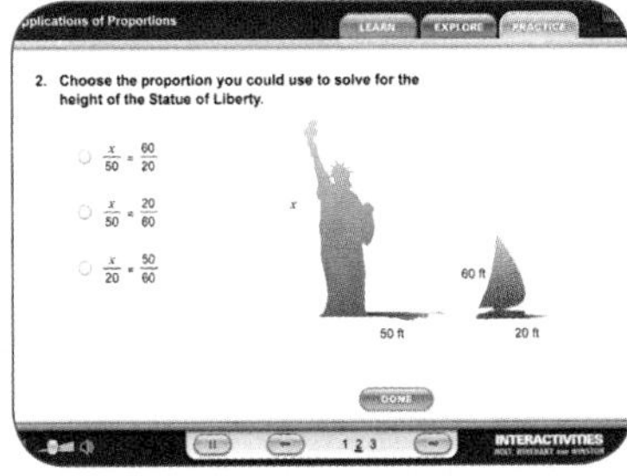

KEY: **SE** = *Student Edition* **TE** = *Teacher's Edition* **CRF** = *Chapter Resource File* SPANISH Spanish available  Available online 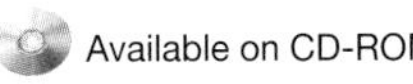 Available on CD-ROM

Ongoing Assessment

Assessing Prior Knowledge

Determine whether students have the prerequisite concepts and skills for success in Chapter 4.

Are You Ready? SPANISH .... SE p. 197
Warm Up .... TE, every lesson

Chapter and Standards Assessment

Provide review and practice for Chapter 4 and standards mastery.

Concept Connection .... SE pp. 222, 240
Study Guide: Review .... SE pp. 242–245
Strategies for Success .... SE pp. 248–249
Mastering the Standards .... SE pp. 250–251
College Entrance Exam Practice .... SE p. 247
***Countdown to Mastery* Transparencies** .... pp. 14–17
Focus on California Standards: Benchmark Tests
Focus on California Standards: Intervention Workbook
***California Standards Practice* CD-ROM** SPANISH
IDEA Works! Modified Worksheets and Tests

Alternative Assessment

Assess students' understanding of Chapter 4 concepts and combined problem-solving skills.

Alternative Assessment .... TE, every lesson
Performance Assessment .... AR pp. 79–80
Portfolio Assessment .... AR p. xxxiii
Chapter 4 Project

Daily Assessment

Provide formative assessment for each day of Chapter 4.

Questioning Strategies .... TE, every example
Think and Discuss .... SE, every lesson
Check It Out! Exercises .... SE, every example
Write About It .... SE, every lesson
Journal .... TE, every lesson
Lesson Quiz .... TE, every lesson
Alternative Assessment .... TE, every lesson
IDEA Works! Modified Lesson Quizzes .... Chapter 4

Weekly Assessment

Provide formative assessment for each week of Chapter 4.

Concept Connection .... SE pp. 222, 240
Ready to Go On? .... SE pp. 223, 241
Cumulative Assessment .... SE pp. 250–251
Test and Practice Generator SPANISH .... *One-Stop Planner*

Formal Assessment

Provide summative assessment of Chapter 4 mastery.

Section Quizzes .... AR pp. 65–66
Chapter 4 Test SPANISH .... SE p. 246
Chapter Test (Levels A, B, C) .... AR pp. 67–78
• Multiple Choice • Free Response
Cumulative Test .... AR pp. 81–84
Test and Practice Generator SPANISH .... *One-Stop Planner*

Technology Highlights for Ongoing Assessment

Automatically assess readiness and prescribe intervention for Chapter 4 prerequisite skills.

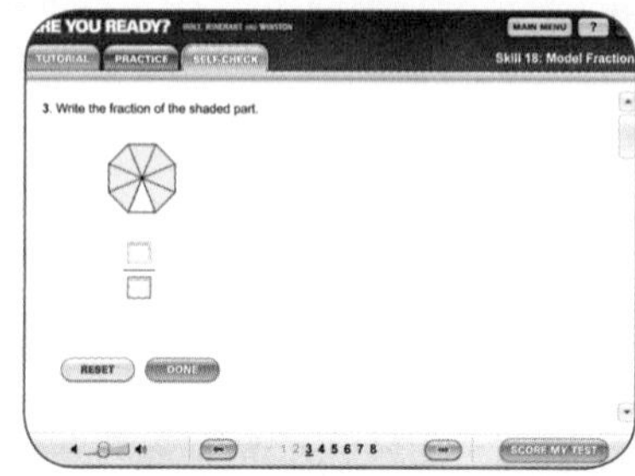

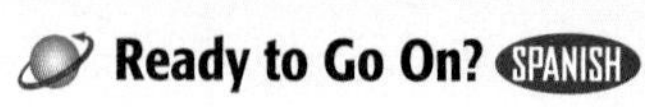

Automatically assess understanding of and prescribe intervention for Sections 4A and 4B.

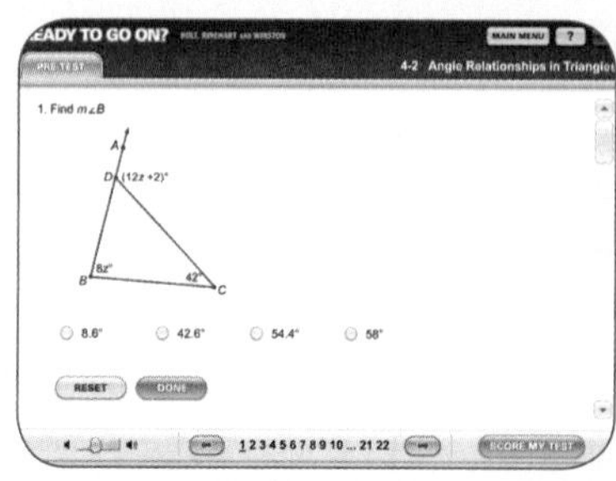

Focus on California Standards: Benchmark Tests and Intervention SPANISH

Automatically assess proficiency with California Algebra I Standards and provide intervention.

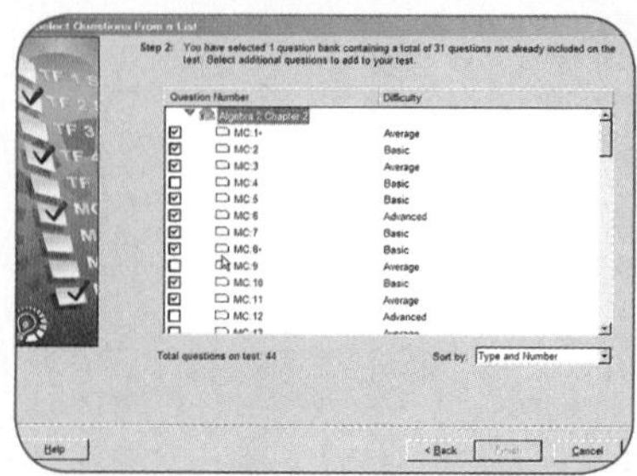

KEY: **SE** = *Student Edition* **TE** = *Teacher's Edition* **AR** = Assessment Resources  Spanish available Available online  Available on CD-ROM

Formal Assessment

Three levels (A, B, C) of multiple-choice and free-response chapter tests are available in the *Assessment Resources.*

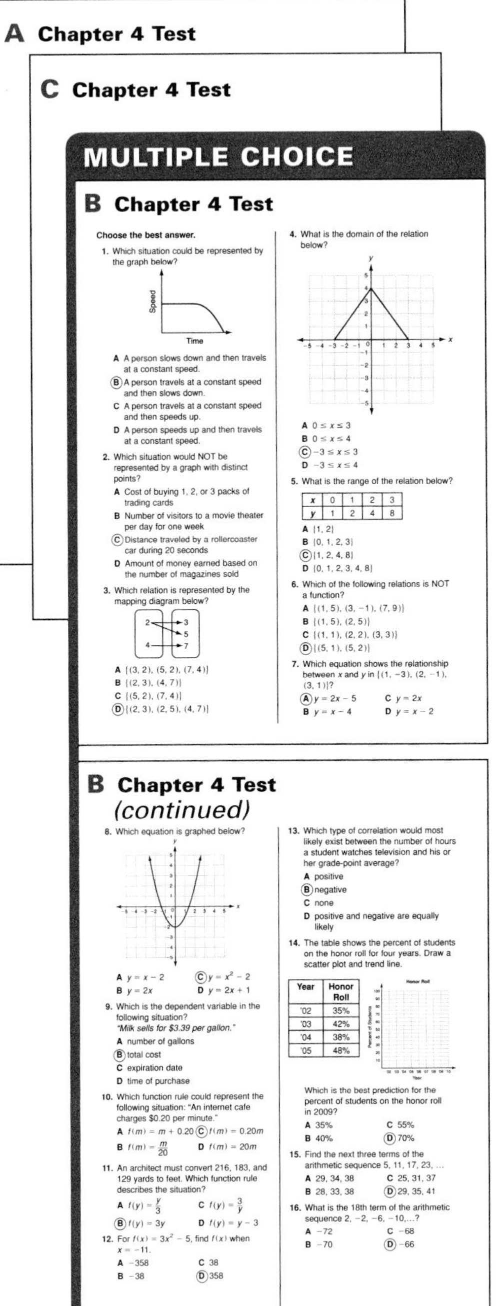

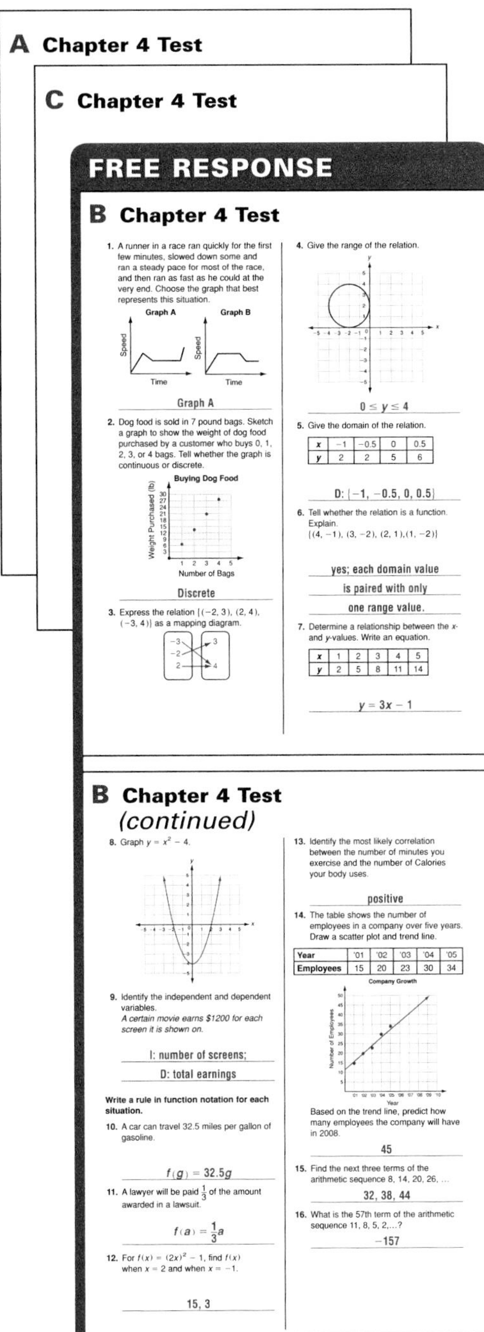

Modified tests and worksheets found in *IDEA Works!*

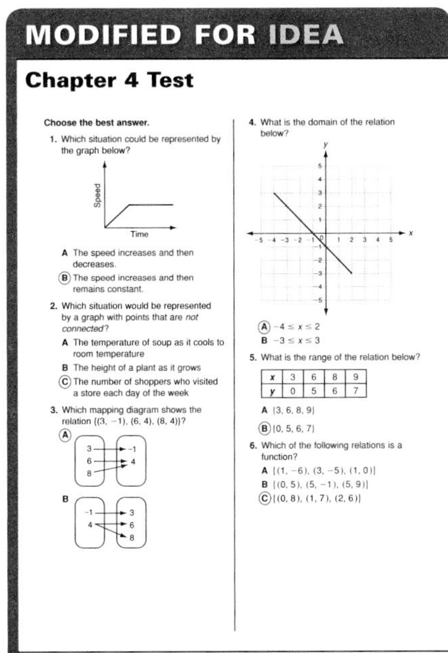

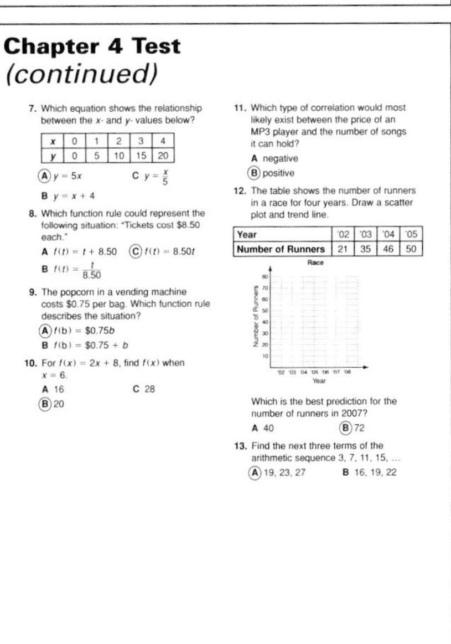

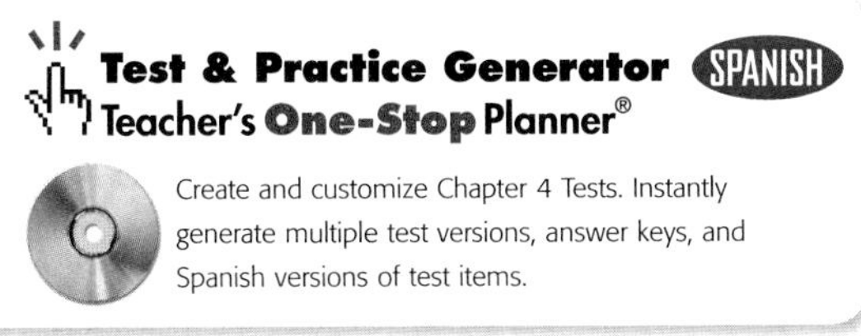

Create and customize Chapter 4 Tests. Instantly generate multiple test versions, answer keys, and Spanish versions of test items.

CHAPTER 4

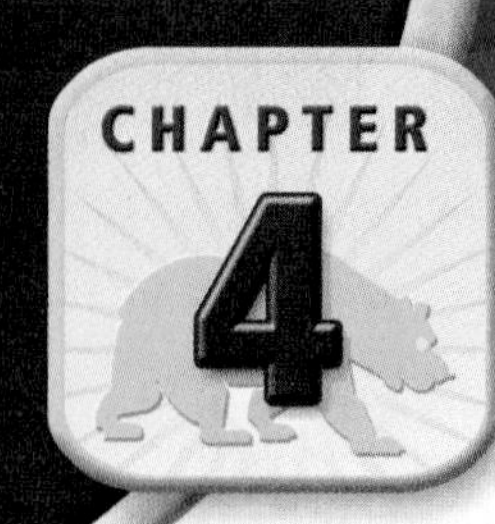

SECTION 4A
Function Concepts

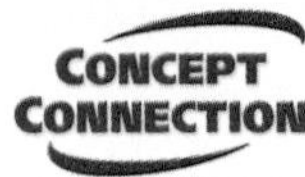

CONCEPT CONNECTION On page 222, students use a graph to write and solve an equation that models real-world pool-draining situations.

Exercises designed to prepare students for success on the Concept Connection can be found on pages 204, 211, and 219.

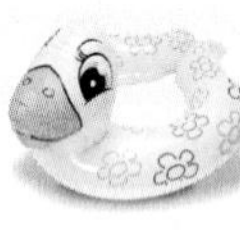

SECTION 4B
Applying Functions

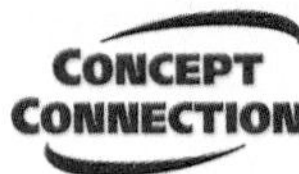

CONCEPT CONNECTION On page 240, students create a scatter plot and trend line to model a real-world travel situation.

Exercises designed to prepare students for success on the Concept Connection can be found on pages 230 and 238.

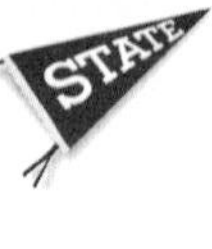

Algebra in *California*

The sea otter is a large otter that is found in the Pacific Ocean, including off the coast of California. To track wildlife populations, scientists may use scatter plots and trend lines. Students will study these topics in Lesson 4-4 of this chapter.

CHAPTER 4

Functions

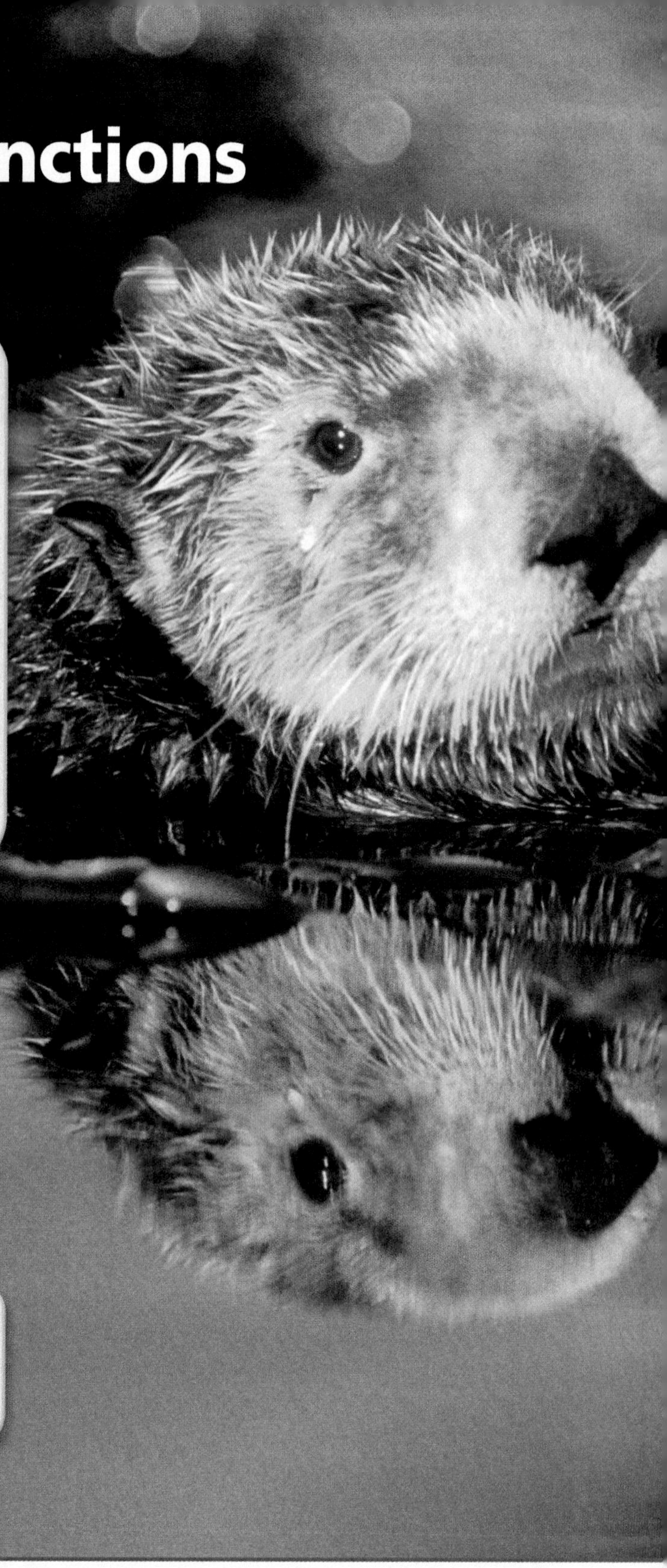

go.hrw.com
Chapter Project Online
KEYWORD: MA8CA ChProj

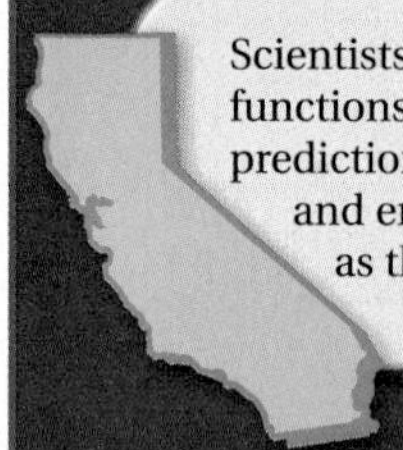

Scientists can use data along with functions to model and make predictions about populations and endangered species, such as this sea otter.

About the Project

Is That Your Foot?

In the first activity of the Chapter Project, students determine their walking rate and then graph a function to predict how far they can walk in 8 hours. In the second activity, students determine whether there is a correlation between foot length and height by creating and interpreting a scatter plot and its trend line.

Project Resources

All project resources for teachers and students are provided online.

Materials:

- Activity 1: stopwatch, tape measure (ft) (MK)
- Activity 2: tape measure (cm)

go.hrw.com
Project Teacher Support
KEYWORD: MA8CA ProjectTS

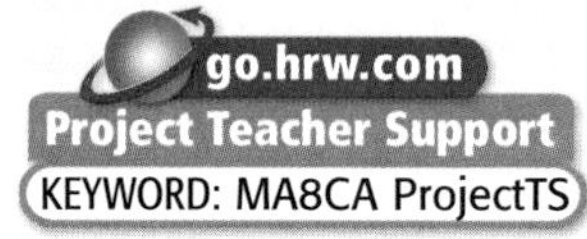

ARE YOU READY?

Vocabulary

Match each term on the left with a definition on the right.

1. absolute value D
2. algebraic expression C
3. input F
4. output B
5. x-axis E

A. a letter used to represent a value that can change
B. the value generated for y
C. a group of numbers, symbols, and variables with one or more operations
D. the distance of a number from zero on the number line
E. the horizontal number line in the coordinate plane
F. a value substituted for x

Ordered Pairs

Graph each point on the same coordinate plane.

6. $(-2, 4)$ 7. $(0, -5)$ 8. $(1, -3)$ 9. $(4, 2)$
10. $(3, -2)$ 11. $(-1, -2)$ 12. $(-1, 3)$ 13. $(-4, 0)$

Evaluate Expressions

Evaluate each expression for $x = -2$.

14. $-2x - 1$ 3
15. $x + 1$ −1
16. $-x^2$ −4
17. $\frac{1}{2}x + 2$ 1
18. $(x + 1)^2$ 1
19. $(x - 1)^2$ 9

Solve Multi-Step Equations

Solve each equation. Check your answer.

20. $17x - 15 = 12$ $\frac{27}{17}$
21. $-7 + 2t = 7$ 7
22. $-6 = \frac{p}{3} + 9$ −45
23. $5n - 10 = 35$ 9
24. $3r - 14 = 7$ 7
25. $9 = \frac{x}{2} + 1$ 16
26. $-2.4 + 1.6g = 5.6$ 5
27. $34 - 2x = 12$ 11
28. $2(x + 5) = -8$ −9

Solve for a Variable

Solve each equation for the indicated variable.

29. $A = \ell w$ for w $w = \frac{A}{\ell}$
30. $V = \ell wh$ for w $w = \frac{V}{\ell h}$
31. $A = bh$ for h $h = \frac{A}{b}$
32. $C = 2\pi r$ for r $r = \frac{C}{2\pi}$
33. $I = Prt$ for P $P = \frac{I}{rt}$
34. $V = \frac{1}{3}\ell wh$ for h $h = 3\frac{V}{\ell w}$

ARE YOU READY? CHAPTER 4

Organizer

Objective: Assess students' understanding of prerequisite skills.

Prerequisite Skills

Ordered Pairs
Evaluate Expressions
Solve Muti-Step Equations
Solve for a Variable

Assessing Prior Knowledge

INTERVENTION

Diagnose and Prescribe

Use this page to determine whether intervention is necessary or whether enrichment is appropriate.

Resources

Are You Ready? Intervention and Enrichment **Worksheets**

Are You Ready? **CD-ROM**

Are You Ready? **Online**

my.hrw.com

Answers

6–13. See p. A15.

ARE YOU READY?
Diagnose and Prescribe

NO INTERVENE

Prerequisite Skill	*Are You Ready? Intervention,* Chapter 4		
	Worksheets	CD-ROM	Online
Ordered Pairs	Skill 79	Activity 79	Diagnose and Prescribe Online
Evaluate Expressions	Skill 60	Activity 60	
Solve Multi-Step Equations	Skill 69	Activity 69	
Solve for a Variable	Skill 72	Activity 72	

YES ENRICH

Are You Ready? Enrichment, Chapter 4
Worksheets
CD-ROM
Online

Unpacking the Standards

Organizer

Objective: Help students understand the new concepts they will learn in Chapter 4.

 *Multilingual Glossary* Online

go.hrw.com

KEYWORD: MA8CA Glossary

Academic Vocabulary Connections

Becoming familiar with the academic vocabulary on this student page will be helpful to students. Discussing some of the vocabulary terms in the chapter also may be helpful.

1. What does the word *dependent* mean? What do you think is true about the value of a **dependent variable**? Possible answer: relying on someone or something else; the value of a dependent variable relies on the value of something else.
2. The word *correlation* means "relationship." What might it mean if two sets of data have **no correlation**? They have no relationship.

CHAPTER 4

Unpacking the Standards

The information below "unpacks" the standards. The Academic Vocabulary is highlighted and defined to help you understand the language of the standards. Refer to the lessons listed after each standard for help with the math terms and phrases. The Chapter Concept shows how the standard is applied in this chapter.

California Standard	Academic Vocabulary	Chapter Concept
16.0 Students understand the concepts of a relation and a function, determine whether a given relation defines a function, and give pertinent information about given relations and functions. (Lessons **4-2, 4-3**)	**concept(s)** the most basic meaning **pertinent** related to	You learn to determine if a relation is also a function given a graph, a table, and a mapping diagram. You find the domain and range of relations.
17.0 Students determine the domain of independent variables and the range of dependent variables defined by a graph, a set of ordered pairs, **or a symbolic expression.** (Lessons **4-2, 4-3**)	**determine** find out **symbolic** using a symbol or symbols to represent something else	You identify the domain of independent variables and the range of dependent variables defined by a graph, a table, and a mapping diagram.
18.0 Students determine whether a relation defined by a graph, a set of ordered pairs, **or a symbolic expression is a function and justify the conclusion.** (Lessons **4-2, 4-3**)	**defined by** to show something clearly **justify** to give a reason or explanation	You identify functions defined by a graph, a table, and a mapping diagram. You also graph equations and use the vertical-line test to determine whether the equation represents a function.

198 *Chapter 4*

Looking Back

Previously, students

- graphed ordered pairs in the coordinate plane.
- studied equations containing one variable and their solutions.
- represented and interpreted data using bar graphs and circle graphs.

In This Chapter

Students will study

- sets of ordered pairs as relations and functions.
- equations containing two variables and their solutions.
- representing and interpreting data using scatter plots and trend lines.

Looking Forward

Students can use these skills

- to study linear, quadratic, and other specific functions.
- to solve linear equations, inequalities, and systems in two variables.
- to interpret data using linear regression.

Reading Strategy: Read and Interpret Math Symbols

It is essential that as you read through each lesson of the textbook, you can interpret mathematical symbols.

Common Math Symbols

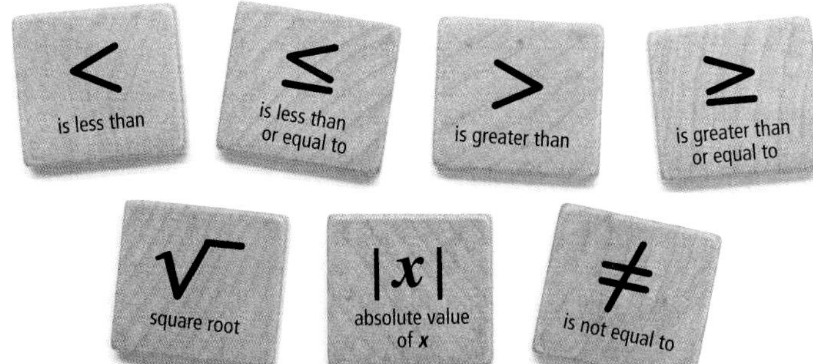

You must be able to translate symbols into words . . .

Using Symbols	Using Words
$3\left(\frac{x}{12}\right) - 1 = 21$	Three times the quotient of x and 12, minus 1 equals 21.
$25x + 6 \geq 17$	Twenty-five times x plus 6 is greater than or equal to 17.
$\lvert x \rvert > 14$	The absolute value of x is greater than 14.
$\sqrt{60 + x} \leq 40$	The square root of the sum of 60 and x is less than or equal to 40.

. . . and words into symbols.

Using Words	Using Symbols
The height of the shed is at least 9 feet.	$h \geq 9$ ft
The distance is at most one tenth of a mile.	$d \leq 0.1$ mi
The silo contains more than 600 cubic feet of corn.	$c > 600$ ft^3

Try This

Translate the symbols into words.

1. $x \leq \sqrt{10}$
2. $\lvert x \rvert + 2 > 45$
3. $-5 \leq x < 8$
4. $-6 - \frac{1}{5}x = -32$

Translate the words into symbols.

5. There are less than 15 seconds remaining.
6. The tax is 8.25 percent of the cost.
7. Ann counted over 100 pennies.
8. Joe can spend at least \$22 but no more than \$30.

Organizer

Objective: Help students apply strategies to understand and retain key concepts.

Resources

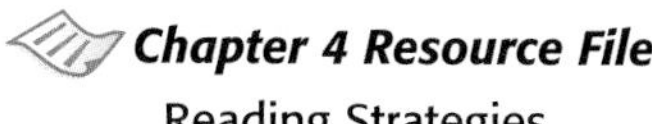

Reading Strategies

ENGLISH LANGUAGE LEARNERS

Reading Strategy: Read and Interpret Math Symbols

Discuss Mathematics is considered an "international language" because the same symbols are used all around the world.

Sometimes there is more than one correct way to translate words into symbols. For example, a sales tax rate of 5% can be written as 5%, 0.05, or $\frac{5}{100}$.

Extend As students work through Chapter 4, point out how symbols make writing some answers (such as domain and range) easier than if they had used only words.

Answers to *Try This*

Possible answers:

1. The value of x is less than or equal to the square root of 10.
2. The sum of the absolute value of x and 2 is greater than 45.
3. The value of x is greater than or equal to negative 5 and is less than 8.
4. Negative 6 minus $\frac{1}{5}$ times x is equal to negative 32.
5. $t < 15$
6. $t = 0.0825c$
7. $a > 100$
8. $22 \leq s \leq 30$

Function Concepts

One-Minute Section Planner

Lesson	Lab Resources	Materials
Lesson 4-1 Graphing Relationships • Match simple graphs with situations. • Graph a relationship. **Review of Grade 7 AF1.5**	***Technology Lab 4-1*** In *Chapter 4 Resource File*	**Optional** graphing calculator
Lesson 4-2 Relations and Functions • Identify functions. • Find the domain and range of relations and functions. **16.0, 17.0, 18.0**		
Lesson 4-3 Writing and Graphing Functions • Write an equation in function notation and evaluate a function for given input values. • Graph functions and determine whether an equation represents a function. **16.0, 17.0, 18.0**	***Algebra Lab 4-3*** In *Chapter 4 Resource File*	
4-3 Technology Lab Connect Equations, Tables, and Graphs • Use a graphing calculator to make the connections among equations, tables, and graphs. **16.0**		**Required** graphing calculator

MK = *Manipulatives Kit*

Notes

Math Background: Teaching the Standards

RELATIONS AND FUNCTIONS

 **16.0, 17.0, 18.0**

Lesson 4-2

Many students have the mistaken belief that relations and functions must be described by equations. It is important to present relations and functions as sets of ordered pairs right from the start to avoid this misconception.

A *relation* is simply a set of ordered pairs. For a given relation, the set of all first values (or *x*-values) is the *domain*. The set of all second values (or *y*-values) is the *range*.

The ordered pairs in a relation may be given as a set. For example, the relation described by the set $\{(-1, 2), (4, 0), (4, 3), (7, -5)\}$ consists of four ordered pairs. The ordered pairs may also be presented in a table, graph, or a mapping diagram. This mapping diagram below describes the same relation as the set of ordered pairs.

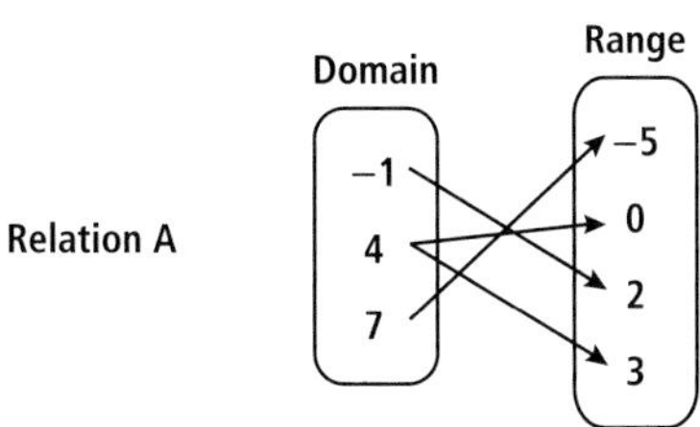

A relation can be described by the way it matches domain and range values. Relation A is *one-to-many*. This means there is at least one domain value (in this case, 4) that is paired with more than one range value (0 and 3).

A relation is *many-to-one* if more than one domain value is paired with a single range value. Relation B, shown below, is many-to-one because the domain values 0 and 9 are both paired with the range value 8.

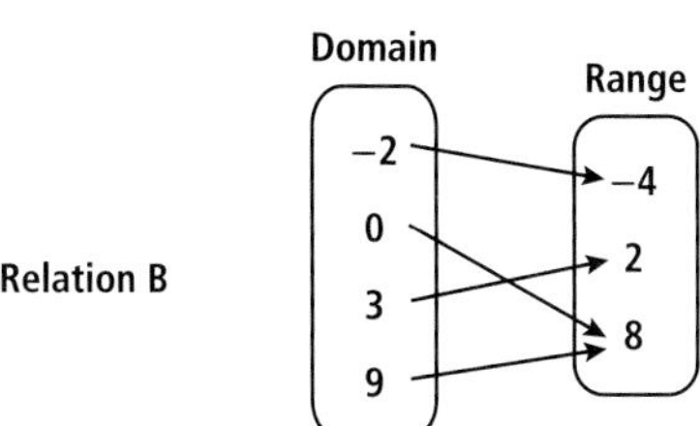

A relation is *one-to-one* if each domain value is paired with a unique range value and each range value is paired with a unique domain value. Relation C is one-to-one.

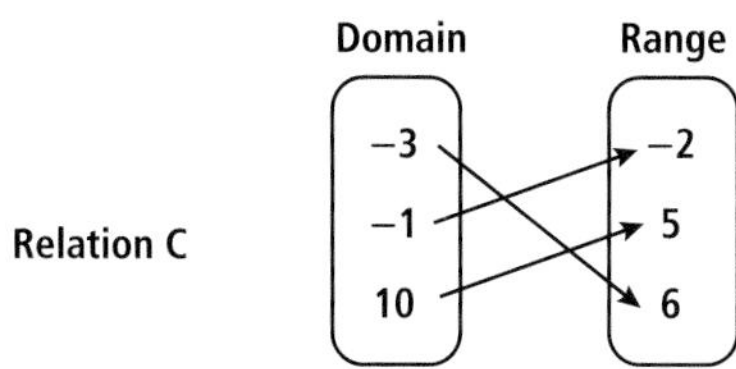

FUNCTIONS 16.0, 17.0, 18.0

Lessons 4-2, 4-3

A *function* is a relation in which each domain value is paired with exactly one range value. Thus, every function is a relation, but not every relation is a function. In the above examples, relations B and C are functions. Relation A is not a function because the domain value 4 is paired with more than one range value.

The definition of *function* may seem somewhat arbitrary to students. It is helpful to explicitly point out the important role that functions play in real-world situations. For example, a meteorologist might study the relation in which each day of the year is paired with the daily high temperature in Los Angeles. It would not make sense if one domain value (a day of the year) were paired with more than one range value (a high temperature). This relation is a function, as are most relations that describe real-world situations. This example illustrates that a function does not have to be defined with an equation or formula; the function above is not described by any formula that we understand.

The real-world example also illustrates why the first value of a function is the *independent variable* and the second value is the *dependent variable*. The second value (e.g., temperature) *depends* on the first value (e.g., day of the year).

Functions may be one-to-one or many-to-one. The function that gives the daily high temperature in Los Angeles is likely to be many-to-one, as there may be several days that are paired with the same temperature. However, by definition a function cannot be one-to-many.

4-1 Organizer

Objectives: Match simple graphs with situations.

Graph a relationship.

Technology Lab
In *Chapter 4 Resource File*

Online Edition
Tutorial Videos

Countdown to Mastery Week 7

Power Presentations with PowerPoint®

Warm Up

State whether each word or phrase represents an amount that is increasing, decreasing, or constant.

1. stays the same constant
2. rises increasing
3. drops decreasing
4. slows down decreasing

Also available on transparency

Q: What do a Math teacher and an English teacher have in common?

A: They can both make a "pair-a-graph."

California Standards

Review of Grade 7 AF1.5

4-1 Graphing Relationships

California Standards

Review of Grade 7 AF1.5 Represent quantitative relationships graphically and interpret the meaning of a specific part of a graph in the situation represented by the graph.

Vocabulary
continuous graph
discrete graph

Who uses this?
Cardiologists can use graphs to analyze their patients' heartbeats. (See Example 2.)

Graphs can be used to illustrate many different situations. For example, trends shown on a cardiograph can help a doctor see how the patient's heart is functioning.

To relate a graph to a given situation, use key words in the description.

EXAMPLE 1 Relating Graphs to Situations

The air temperature was constant for several hours at the beginning of the day and then rose steadily for several hours. It stayed the same temperature for most of the day before dropping sharply at sundown. Choose the graph that best represents this situation.

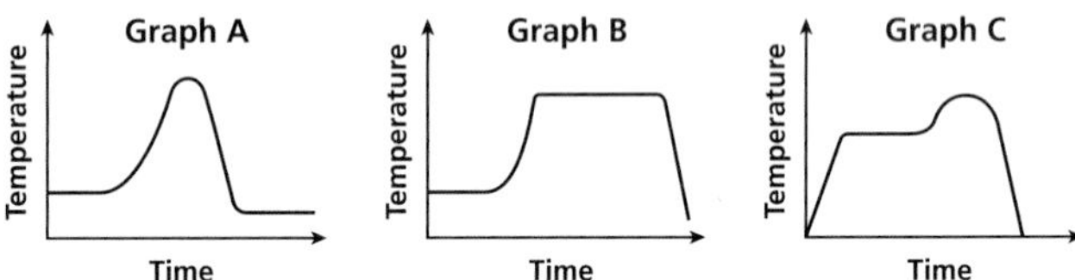

Step 1 Read the graphs from left to right to show time passing.

Step 2 List key words in order and decide which graph shows them.

Key Words	Segment Description...	Graphs...
Was constant	Horizontal	Graphs A and B
Rose steadily	Slanting upward	Graphs A and B
Stayed the same	Horizontal	Graph B
Dropped sharply	Slanting downward	Graph B

Step 3 Pick the graph that shows all the key phrases in order.

horizontal, slanting upward, horizontal, slanting downward

The correct graph is B.

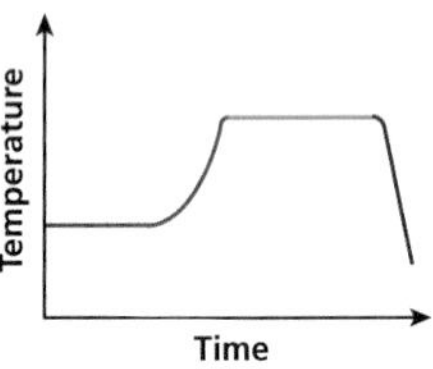

1. The air temperature increased steadily for several hours and then remained constant. At the end of the day, the temperature increased slightly again before dropping sharply. Choose the graph above that best represents this situation. **graph C**

1 Introduce

EXPLORATION

4-1 Graphing Relationships

The sentences below describe the motion of five cars on a highway. Match each sentence with the graph that represents it best.

1. The car's speed remains constant.
2. The car's speed increases slowly but steadily.
3. The car's speed increases sharply.
4. The car's speed decreases gradually.
5. The car's speed decreases suddenly.

Graph A, Graph B, Graph C, Graph D, Graph E (Speed vs. Time)

THINK AND DISCUSS

6. Explain how the graph for the car in Problem 2 would be different if the car started from a complete stop.

Motivate

Have students state what would happen to the height of an ice cube in the following situations.

It is placed in a refrigerator. decrease slowly

It is placed in a hot oven. decrease quickly

It is placed in a freezer. stay the same

Explorations and answers are provided in *Alternate Openers: Explorations Transparencies.*

As seen in Example 1, some graphs are connected lines or curves called **continuous graphs**. Some graphs are only distinct points. These are called **discrete graphs**.

The graph on theme-park attendance is an example of a discrete graph. It consists of distinct points because each year is distinct and people are counted in whole numbers only. The values between the whole numbers are not included, since they have no meaning for the situation.

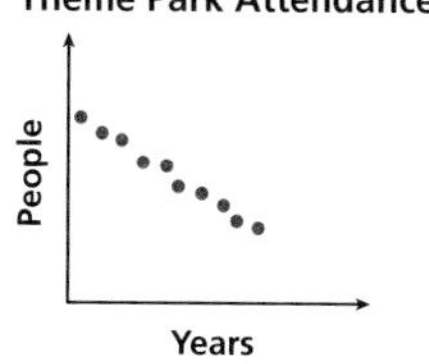

EXAMPLE 2 Sketching Graphs for Situations

Sketch a graph for each situation. Tell whether the graph is continuous or discrete.

A **Simon is selling candles to raise money for the school dance. For each candle he sells, the school will get $2.50. He has 10 candles that he can sell.**

Simon's Earnings

Amount earned ($): 5, 10, 15, 20, 25

Candles sold: 0 1 2 3 4 5 6 7 8 9 10

The amount earned (y-axis) increases by $2.50 for each candle Simon sells (x-axis).

Since Simon can only sell whole candles or none at all, the graph is 11 distinct points.

The graph is discrete.

B **Angelique's heart rate is being monitored while she exercises on a treadmill. While walking, her heart rate remains the same. As she increases her pace, her heart rate rises at a steady rate. When she begins to run, her heart rate increases more rapidly and then remains high while she runs. As she decreases her pace, her heart rate slows down and returns to her normal rate.**

As time passes during her workout (moving left to right along the x-axis), her heart rate (y-axis) does the following:

- remains the same,
- rises at a steady rate,
- increases more rapidly (steeper than previous segment),
- remains high,
- slows down,
- and then returns to her normal rate.

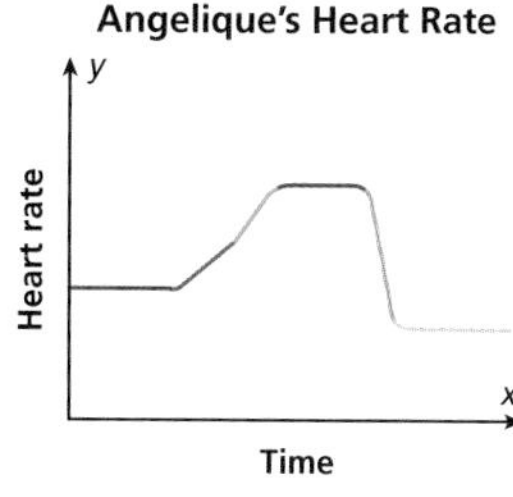

The graph is continuous.

CHECK IT OUT! **Sketch a graph for each situation. Tell whether the graph is continuous or discrete.**

2a. Jamie is taking an 8-week keyboarding class. At the end of each week, she takes a test to find the number of words she can type per minute. She improves each week.

2b. Henry begins to drain a water tank by opening a valve. Then he opens another valve. Then he closes the first valve. He leaves the second valve open until the tank is empty.

Helpful Hint

When sketching or interpreting a graph, pay close attention to the labels on each axis.

2a. discrete;

Keyboarding — Words per minute / Weeks

b. continuous

Water Tank — Water level / Time

Power Presentations with PowerPoint®

Additional Examples

Example 1

Each day several leaves fall from a tree. One day a gust of wind blows off many leaves. Eventually, there are no more leaves on the tree. Choose the graph that best represents this situation. graph B

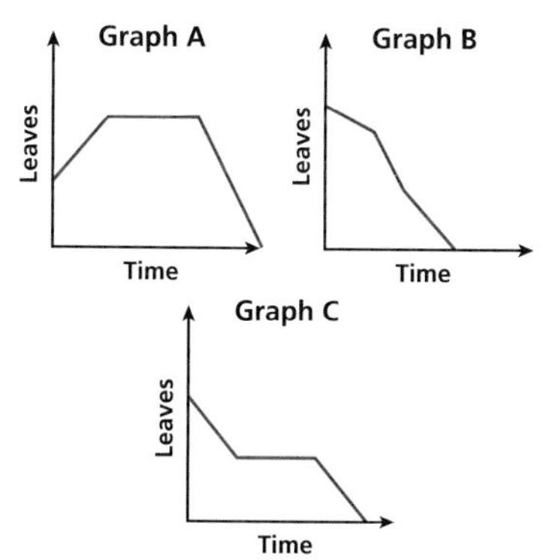

Example 2

Sketch a graph for each situation. Tell whether the graph is continuous or discrete.

A. A truck driver enters a street, drives at a constant speed, stops at a light, and then continues. continuous

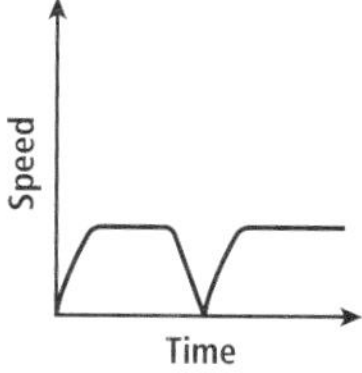

B. A small bookstore sold between 5 and 8 books each day for 7 days. discrete

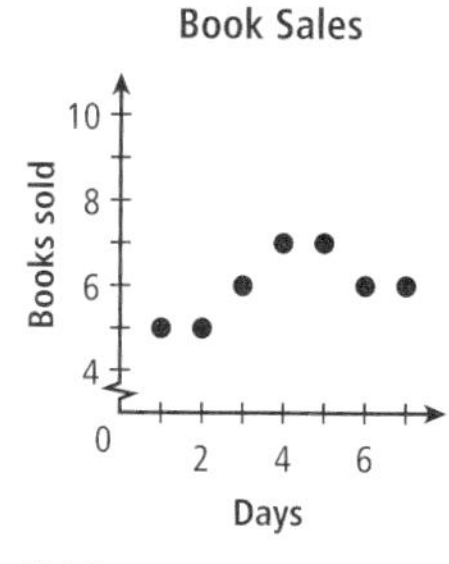

Also available on transparency

2 Teach

Guided Instruction

Explain that all graphs should be read from left to right. Encourage students to write down key phrases from a situation in the order they appear to help with matching graphs. Later in the chapter, students will learn about independent and dependent variables, which will help them identify which label to put on which axis. For now, accept graphs with the axes labeled either way, although you may want to point out that time is usually placed on the horizontal axis.

Universal Access

Through Cooperative Learning

Put students in groups of three or four. Instruct each group to write a situation on one piece of paper and draw a corresponding graph on a separate piece of paper. Collect all graphs and shuffle them; then collect all situations and shuffle. Randomly label graphs A, B, C, . . . , and situations 1, 2, 3, ... Display all graphs and situations on the wall. Have groups match each graph with the correct description.

INTERVENTION

Questioning Strategies

EXAMPLES **1–2**

- What are some phrases used to describe a graph that slants upward? downward? remains constant?
- How do you know when to use discrete points instead of a continuous line?

Teaching Tip **Inclusion** Some students may interpret a horizontal line in a coordinate plane to mean that the x-value is constant. Label some points on the line to show that it is the y-value that is constant.

Power Presentations with PowerPoint®

Additional Examples

Example 3

Write a possible situation for the given graph.

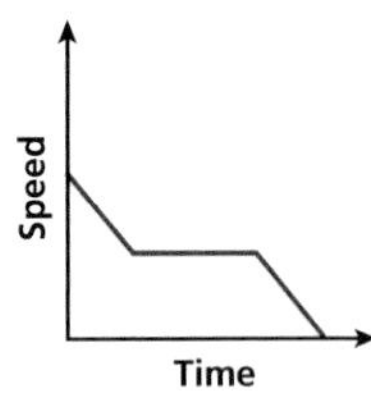

Possible answer: A car approaching traffic slows down, drives at a constant speed, and then slows down until coming to a complete stop.

Also available on transparency 

INTERVENTION

Questioning Strategies

EXAMPLE 3

- What part of the graph shows "increased steadily"? "remained unchanged"? "decreased steadily"?

Both graphs below show a relationship about a child going down a slide. **Graph A** represents the child's *distance from the ground* related to time. **Graph B** represents the child's *speed* related to time.

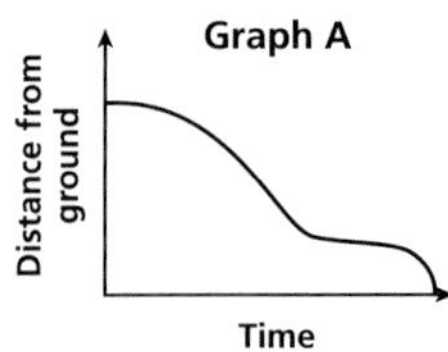

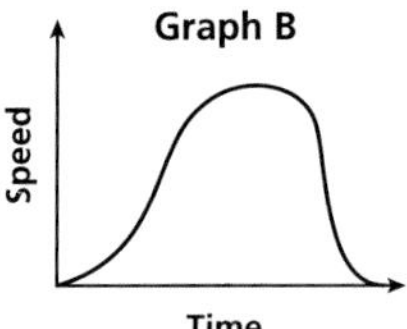

EXAMPLE 3 Writing Situations for Graphs

Write a possible situation for the given graph.

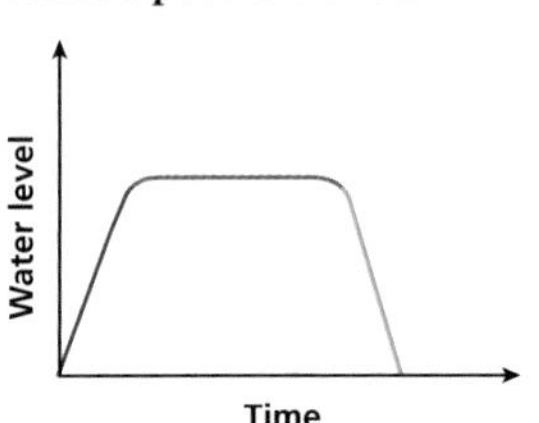

Step 1 Identify labels.
x-axis: time y-axis: water level

Step 2 Analyze sections.
Over time, the water level does the following:
- increases steadily,
- remains unchanged,
- and then decreases steadily.

Possible Situation:

A watering can is filled with water. It sits for a while until the flowers are planted. The water in the can is then emptied on top of the planted flowers.

3. Write a possible situation for the given graph.

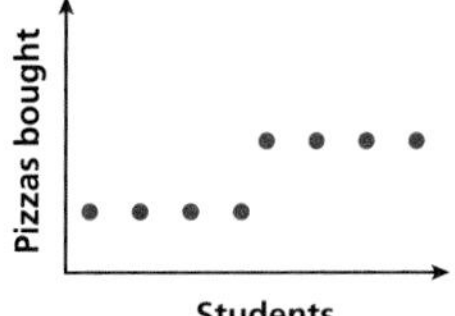

Possible answer: When the number of students reaches a certain point, the number of pizzas bought increases.

THINK AND DISCUSS

1. Should a graph of age related to height be a continuous graph or a discrete graph? Explain.
2. Give an example of a situation that, when graphed, would include a horizontal segment.

3. **GET ORGANIZED** Copy and complete the graphic organizer. Write an example of key words that suggest the given segments on a graph. One example for each segment is given for you.

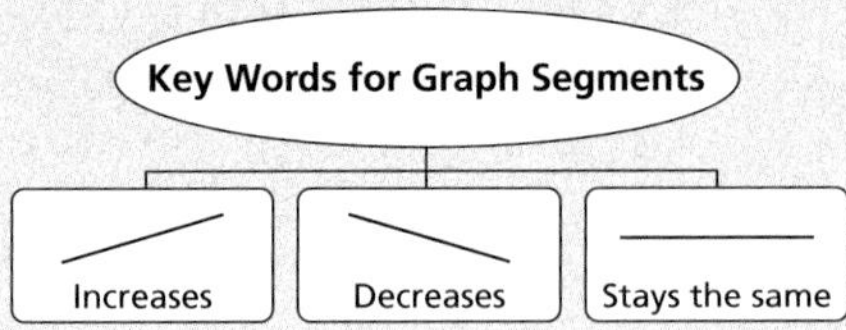

3 Close

Summarize

Be sure students understand what the axes are representing. For example, if a person runs uphill at a *constant* speed, then a speed vs. time graph will be horizontal, but a distance or height vs. time graph will slant upward. Review what a graph of speed vs. time would look like for the following.

Someone is running downhill with an increasing speed. slant upward

Someone is running on a flat path at a decreasing pace. slant downward

FORMATIVE ASSESSMENT and INTERVENTION

***Diagnose Before* the Lesson**
4-1 Warm Up, TE p. 200

***Monitor During* the Lesson**
Check It Out! Exercises, SE pp. 200–202
Questioning Strategies, TE pp. 201–202

***Assess After* the Lesson**
4-1 Lesson Quiz, TE p. 205
Alternative Assessment, TE p. 205

Answers to *Think and Discuss*

1. Continuous; if you plot distinct points, you could always plot more points between any pair of points.
2. Possible answer: Speed related to time—a runner runs a race and keeps a steady pace for part of it.
3. See p. A4.

4-1 Exercises

California Standards Practice
Review of Grade 7 AF1.5

go.hrw.com
Homework Help Online
KEYWORD: MA8CA 4-1
Parent Resources Online
KEYWORD: MA8CA Parent

GUIDED PRACTICE

Vocabulary Apply the vocabulary from this lesson to answer each question.

continuous **1.** A ___?___ graph is made of connected lines or curves. (*continuous* or *discrete*)

discrete **2.** A ___?___ graph is made of only distinct points. (*continuous* or *discrete*)

SEE EXAMPLE 1 p. 200

Choose the graph that best represents each situation.

3. A person alternates between running and walking. graph B

4. A person gradually speeds up to a constant running pace. graph A

5. A person walks, gradually speeds up to a run, and then slows back down to a walk. graph C

Graph A

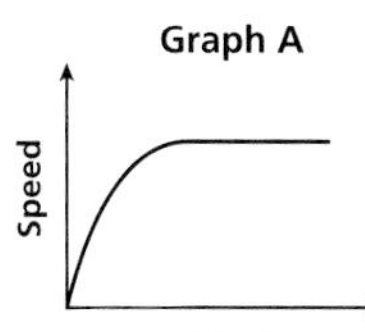

Graph B

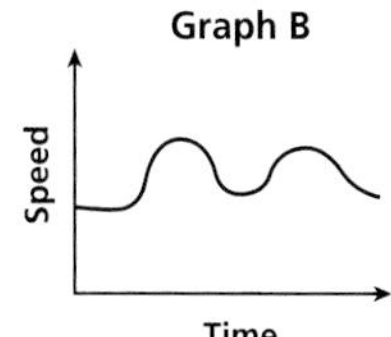

Graph C

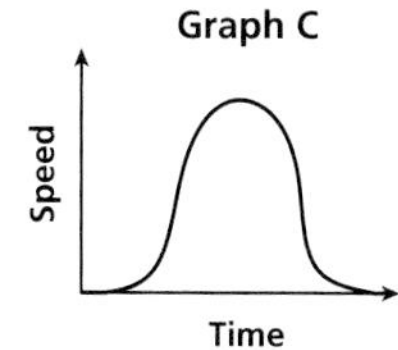

SEE EXAMPLE 2 p. 201

6. Maxine is buying extra pages for her photo album. Each page holds exactly 8 photos. Sketch a graph to show the maximum number of photos she can add to her album if she buys 1, 2, 3, or 4 extra pages. Tell whether the graph is continuous or discrete.

SEE EXAMPLE 3 p. 202

Write a possible situation for each graph.

7.

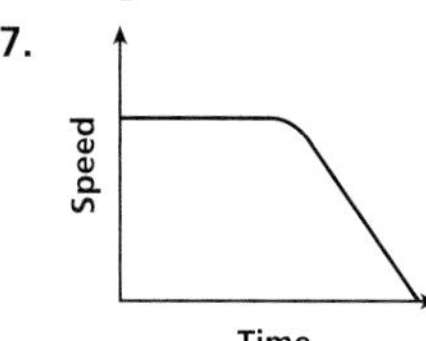

8.

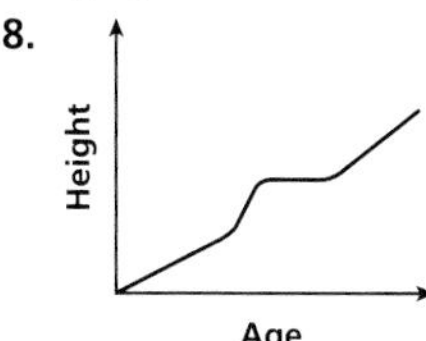

9.

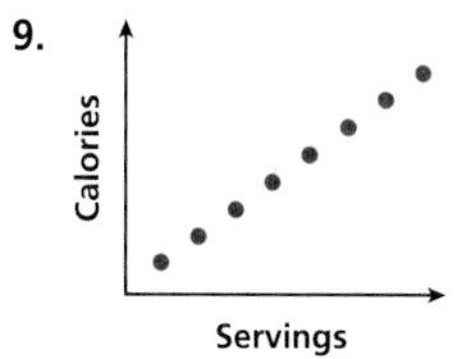

PRACTICE AND PROBLEM SOLVING

Independent Practice	
For Exercises	See Example
10–12	1
13	2
14–16	3

Extra Practice
Skills Practice p. EP8
Application Practice p. EP27

Choose the graph that best represents each situation.

10. A flag is raised up a flagpole quickly at the beginning and then more slowly near the top. graph C

11. A flag is raised up a flagpole in a jerky motion, using a hand-over-hand method. graph A

12. A flag is raised up a flagpole at a constant rate of speed. graph B

Graph A

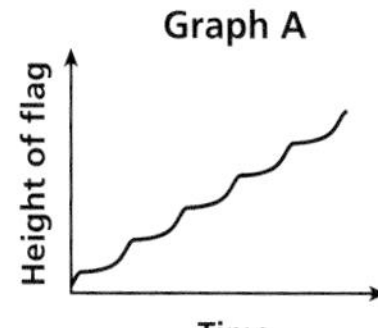

Graph B

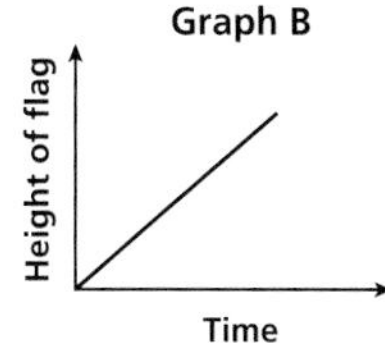

Graph C

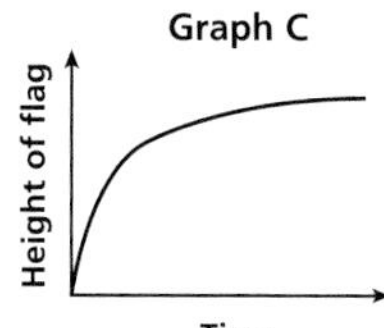

Answers

6. discrete

Photo Album

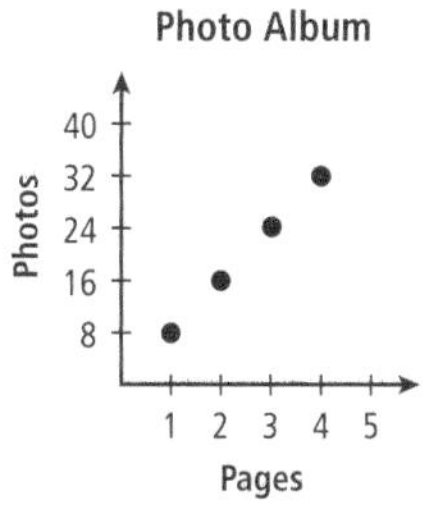

7. Possible answer: A car is moving at a constant speed for several minutes. When it approaches a red light, it slows down and comes to a stop.

8. Possible answer: A plant grows steadily and then has a growth spurt during the rainy season. It remains the same height for a while and then grows steadily again.

9. Possible answer: The more servings you eat, the more Calories you consume.

4-1 Exercises

Assignment Guide

Assign *Guided Practice* exercises as necessary.

If you finished Examples **1–3**
Proficient 10–25, 28–36
Advanced 10–36

Homework Quick Check
Quickly check key concepts.
Exercises: 10, 12, 13, 14, 18

Modeling For **Exercises 3–5,** you may want to have students act out the events happening in the situation to more easily match them to each graph.

Communicating Math Point out to students that some graphs start at (0, 0), like **Exercise 8,** which begins with a height of 0, while some start higher on the vertical axis, like **Exercise 7,** which begins with a positive speed.

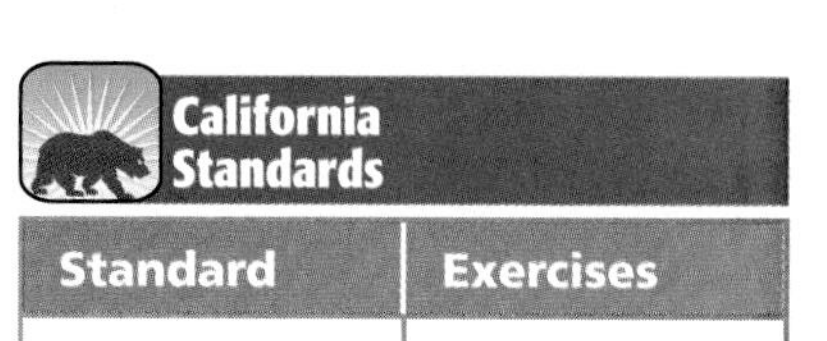

Standard	Exercises
3.0	34–36
7NS1.2	29–31
7AF1.1	32, 33
7AF1.5	3–20, 22–28

Data Collection To help students complete **Exercise 17,** see *Technology Lab Activities.*

CONCEPT CONNECTION **Exercise 22** involves sketching a graph to describe a situation. This exercise prepares students for the Concept Connection on page 222.

Answers

14. Possible answer: A student is driven to school. The distance from home remains constant while the student is at school. Then the distance decreases during the ride back home.

15. Possible answer: The cost of a long-distance phone call increases for the first few minutes and then increases at a slower rate for the remainder of the call.

16. Possible answer: Park attendance steadily declines over the course of a week due to bad weather.

18. Possible answer: The horse starts at the gate, increases speed very quickly, then keeps a fairly steady pace, and then increases speed again at the end of the race. After crossing the finish line the horse slows to a stop.

19–22. See pp. A15–A16.

13. continuous

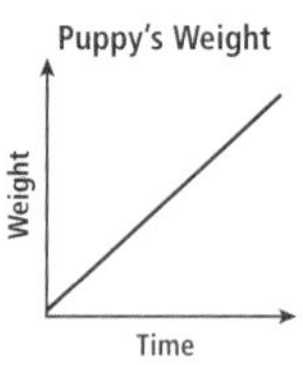

13. For six months, a puppy gained weight at a steady rate. Sketch a graph to illustrate the weight of the puppy during that time period. Tell whether the graph is continuous or discrete.

Write a possible situation for each graph.

14.

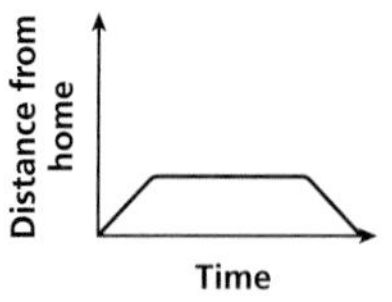

15.

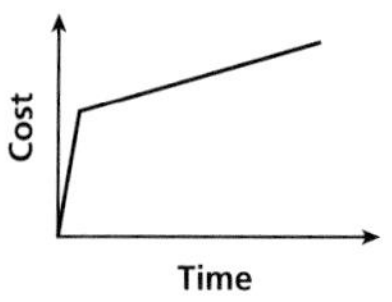

16.

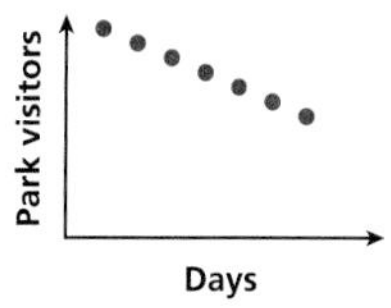

17. Data Collection Use a graphing calculator and motion detector for the following. **17a–c. Check students' work.**

a. On a coordinate plane, draw a graph relating distance away from a starting point walking at various speeds and time.

b. Using the motion detector as the starting point, walk away from the motion detector to make a graph on the graphing calculator that matches the one you drew.

c. Compare your walking speeds to each change in steepness on the graph.

LINK Sports

On November 1, 1938, the underdog Seabiscuit beat the heavily favored Triple-Crown winner War Admiral in a historic horse race at Pimlico Race Course in Baltimore, Maryland.

18. Sports The graph shows the speed of a horse during and after a race. Use it to describe the changing pace of the horse.

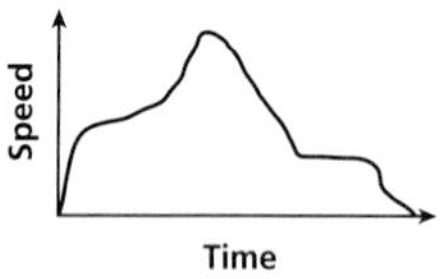

19. Recreation You hike up a mountain path starting at 10 A.M. You camp overnight and then walk back down the same path at the same pace at 10 A.M. the next morning. On the same set of axes, graph the relationship between distance from the top of the mountain and the time of day for both the hike up and the hike down. What does the point of intersection of the graphs represent?

20. Critical Thinking Suppose that you sketched a graph of speed related to time for a brick being dropped from the top of a building. Then you sketched a graph for speed related to time for a ball that was rolled down a hill and then came to rest. How would the graphs be the same? How would they be different?

21. Write About It Describe a real-life situation that could be represented by a graph that has distinct points. Then describe a real-life situation that could be represented by a connected graph.

CONCEPT CONNECTION

22. This problem will prepare you for the Concept Connection on page 222.

A rectangular pool that is 4 feet deep at all places is being filled at a constant rate.

a. Sketch a graph to show the depth of the water as it increases over time.

b. The side view of another swimming pool is shown. If the pool is being filled at a constant rate, sketch a graph to show the depth of the water as it increases over time.

4-1 PRACTICE A

4-1 PRACTICE C

4-1 PRACTICE B

LESSON 4-1 **Practice B**
Graphing Relationships

Choose the graph that best represents each situation.

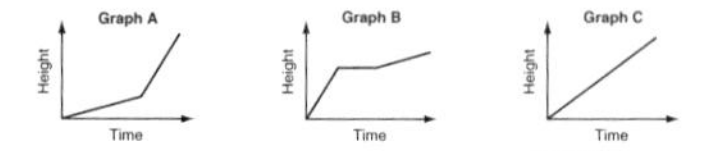

1. A tomato plant grows taller at a steady pace. Graph C
2. A tomato plant grows quickly at first, remains a constant height during a dry spell, then grows at a steady pace. Graph B
3. A tomato plant grows at a slow pace, then grows rapidly with more sun and water. Graph A
4. Lora has $15 to spend on movie rentals for the week. Each rental costs $3. Sketch a graph to show how much money she might spend on movies in a week. Tell whether the graph is continuous or discrete. discrete

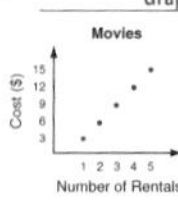

Write a possible situation for each graph.

5.

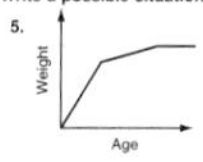

Possible answer: A kitten gains weight quickly after birth, then more slowly, until it reaches its maximum weight.

6.

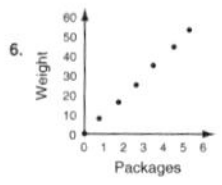

Possible answer: Each package weighs 10 pounds. The box can hold up to 60 pounds.

4-1 READING STRATEGIES

LESSON 4-1 **Reading Strategies**
Use a Model

A relationship between variables is often shown as a continuous graph. Study the segments of the continuous graph below and the common phrases that describe them.

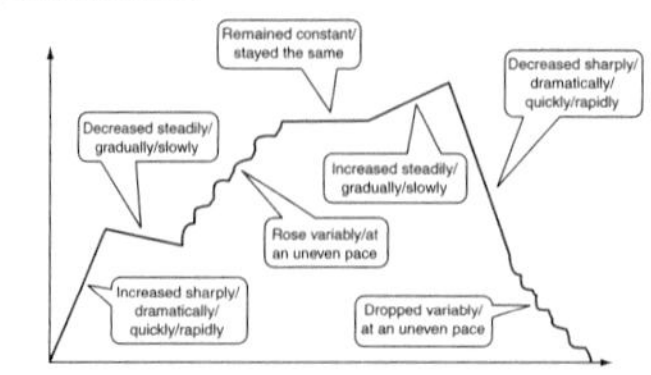

Answer the following.

1. Give two phrases that could describe this graph:

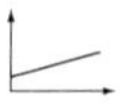

Possible answers: rose slowly; increased gradually

2. Sketch a graph that shows the speed of a car decreased dramatically and then remained constant.

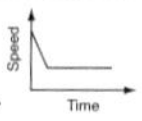

Write the letter of the description that best matches each graph.

A. A baby lost a little weight, then gained weight slowly.
B. A baby gained weight at a rapid pace.
C. A baby gained weight at an uneven pace, then maintained a constant weight.

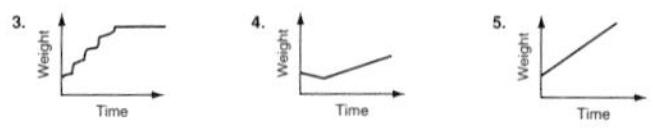

3. C 4. A 5. B

4-1 REVIEW FOR MASTERY

LESSON 4-1 **Review for Mastery**
Graphing Relationships

Graphs are a way to turn words into pictures. Be sure to read the graphs from left to right.

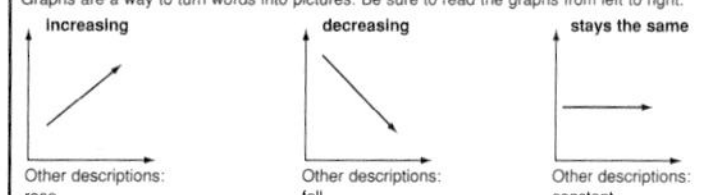

Other descriptions:	Other descriptions:	Other descriptions:
rose	fell	constant
gained	lessened	steady
grew	diminished	continuous

You can divide the graph into sections every time the graph changes directions. Then label each section.

Picture

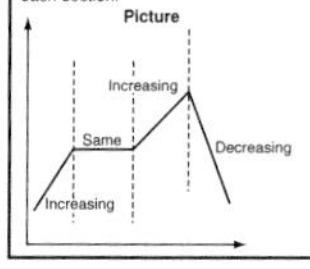

Words

This graph increases, then stays constant, increases again, and finally decreases sharply.

Divide each graph into sections where the graph changes directions. Then label the sections as *increasing, decreasing,* or *same.*

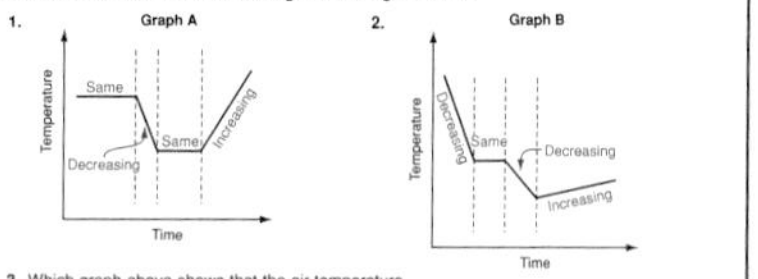

3. Which graph above shows that the air temperature fell steadily, leveled off, fell again, and then increased slightly? Graph B

Multiple Choice For Exercises 23 and 24, choose the best answer.

23. Which situation would NOT be represented by a graph with distinct points?
   - (A) Amount of money earned based on the number of cereal bars sold
   - (B) Number of visitors per day for one week to a grocery store
   - (C) The amount of iced tea in a pitcher at a restaurant during the lunch hour
   - (D) The total cost of buying 1, 2, or 3 CDs at the music store

24. Which situation is best represented by the graph?
   - (A) A snowboarder starts at the bottom of the hill and takes a ski lift to the top.
   - (B) A cruise boat travels at a steady pace from the port to its destination.
   - (C) An object dropped from the top of a building gains speed at a rapid pace before hitting the ground.
   - (D) A marathon runner starts at a steady pace and then runs faster at the end of the race before stopping at the finish line.

Speed
Time

25. **Short Response** Marla participates in a triathlon consisting of swimming, biking, and running. Would a graph of Marla's speed during the triathlon be a connected graph or distinct points? Explain. Possible answer: The graph would be a connected graph because Marla is constantly moving at all times.

CHALLENGE AND EXTEND

Pictured are three vases and graphs representing the height of water as it is poured into each of the vases at a constant rate. Match each vase with the correct graph.

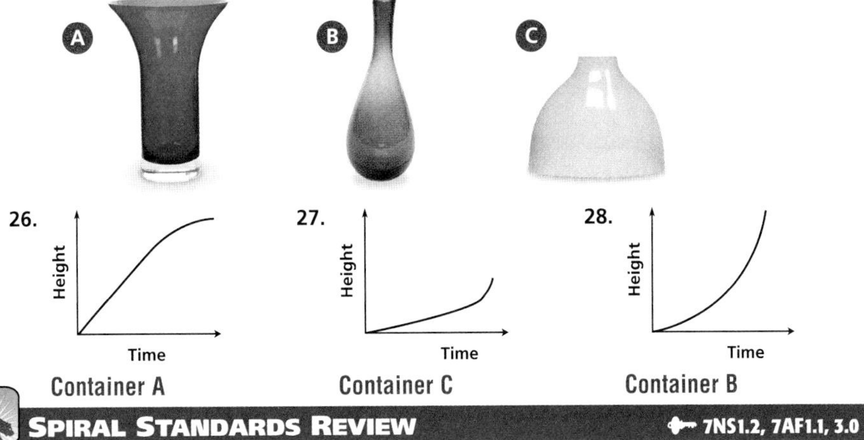

26. Height / Time — Container A

27. Height / Time — Container C

28. Height / Time — Container B

SPIRAL STANDARDS REVIEW

7NS1.2, 7AF1.1, 3.0

Evaluate each expression. *(Lesson 1-4)*

29. -2^3 **−8**
30. 4^4 **256**
31. $\left(\frac{1}{3}\right)^2$ $\frac{1}{9}$

Write and solve an equation to represent each relationship. *(Lesson 2-1)*

32. $n + 11 = 3$; -8

33. $n - 5 = -2$; 3

32. A number increased by 11 is equal to 3.
33. Five less than a number is equal to −2.

Solve each equation. *(Lesson 2-7)*

34. $|x| = 7.2$ **−7.2, 7.2**
35. $19 = |x + 4|$ **−23, 15**
36. $|3x| + 2 = 8$ **−2, 2**

4-1 PROBLEM SOLVING

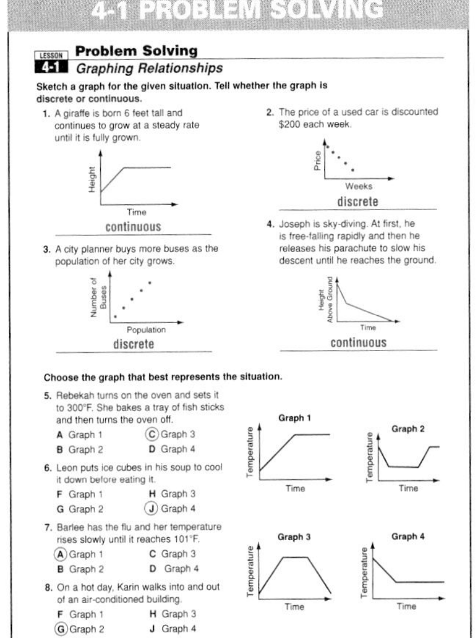

4-1 CHALLENGE

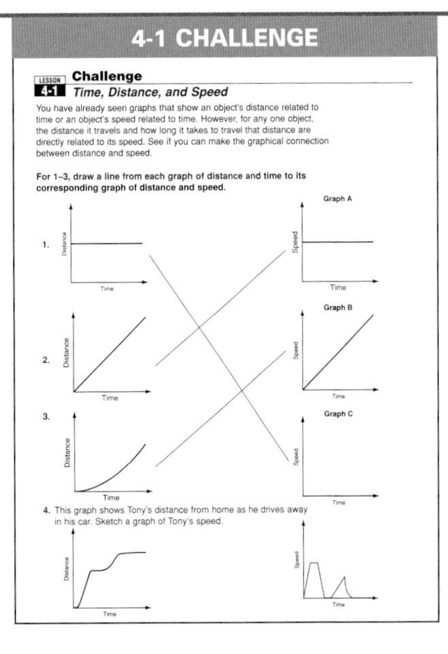

Teaching Tip **Multiple Choice** For **Exercise 23,** students should look for a situation where both units can be broken into fractions. Time and the liquid measurement in choice **C** can both be fractional.

Journal

Write a situation in which the graph would contain either one vertical or one horizontal line. Draw the graph.

ALTERNATIVE ASSESSMENT

Have students write and graph a situation described by distinct points and a situation described by a continuous line.

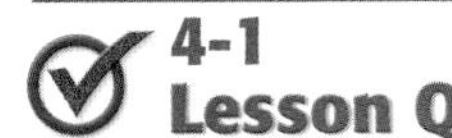

Power Presentations with PowerPoint®

4-1 Lesson Quiz

1. Write a possible situation for the given graph.

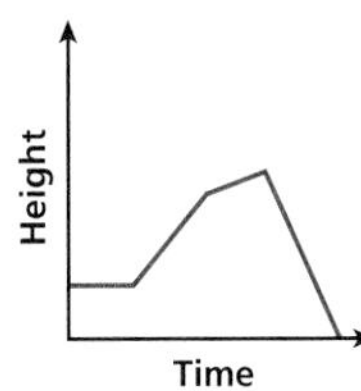

Possible answer: The level of water in a bucket stays constant. A steady rain raises the level. The rain slows down. Someone dumps the bucket.

2. A pet store is selling puppies for $50 each. It has 8 puppies to sell. Sketch a graph for this situation.

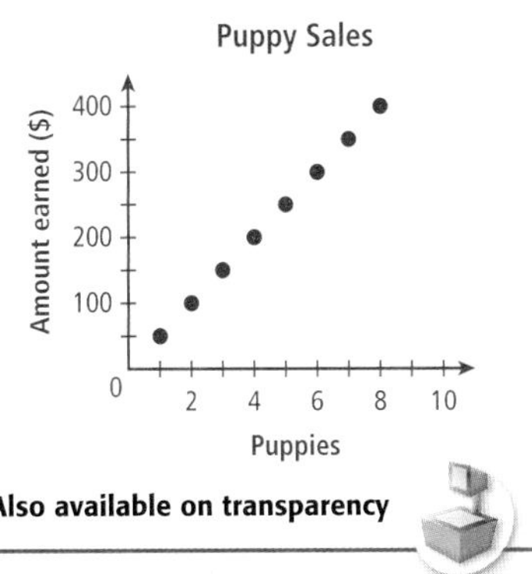

Also available on transparency

4-2 Organizer

Objectives: Identify functions.

Find the domain and range of relations and functions.

Online Edition
Tutorial Videos

Countdown to Mastery Week 7

Power Presentations with PowerPoint®

Warm Up

1. Generate ordered pairs for the function $y = x + 3$ for $x = -2, -1, 0, 1$, and 2. Graph the ordered pairs.
$(-2, 1), (-1, 2), (0, 3), (1, 4), (2, 5)$

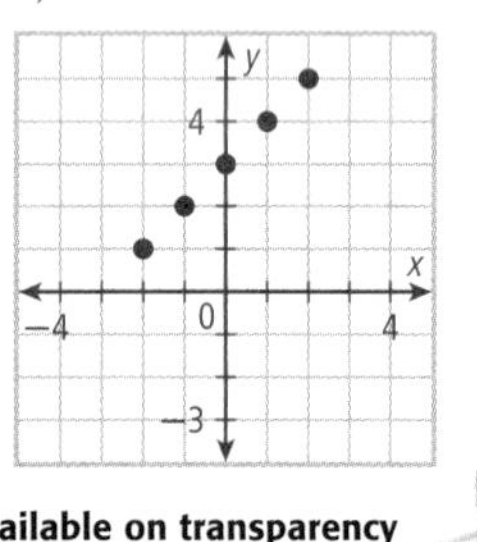

Also available on transparency

Q: Why did the *y*-variable leave the city?

A: He was more at home on the range.

4-2 Relations and Functions

California Standards

16.0 **Students understand the concepts of a relation and a function, determine whether a given relation defines a function, and give pertinent information about given relations and functions.**

Also covered: **17.0, 18.0**

Vocabulary
relation
domain
range
function

Why learn this?

You can use a relation to show finishing positions and scores in a track meet.

In Lesson 4-1, you saw relationships represented by graphs. Relationships can also be represented by a set of ordered pairs, called a **relation**.

In the scoring system of some track meets, for first place you get 5 points, for second place you get 3 points, for third place you get 2 points, and for fourth place you get 1 point. This scoring system is a relation, so it can be shown as ordered pairs, $\{(1, 5), (2, 3), (3, 2), (4, 1)\}$. You can also show relations in other ways, such as tables, graphs, or *mapping diagrams*.

EXAMPLE 1 **Showing Multiple Representations of Relations**

Express the relation for the track meet scoring system, $\{(1, 5), (2, 3), (3, 2), (4, 1)\}$, as a table, as a graph, and as a mapping diagram.

Table

Track Scoring	
Place	**Points**
1	5
2	3
3	2
4	1

Write all x-values under "Place" and all y-values under "Points."

Graph

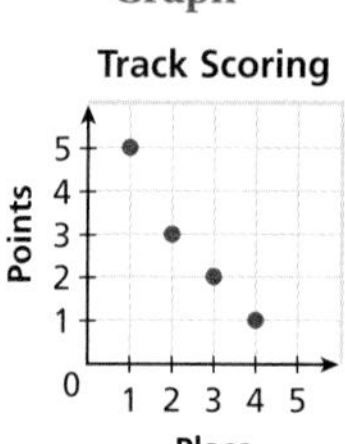

Use the x- and y-values to plot the ordered pairs.

Mapping Diagram

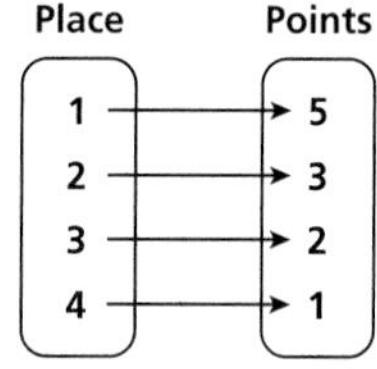

Write all x-values under "Place" and all y-values under "Points." Draw an arrow from each x-value to its corresponding y-value.

Remember!

To review how to plot points in the coordinate plane, see Skills Bank p. SB23.

1. Express the relation $\{(1, 3)\ (2, 4), (3, 5)\}$ as a table, as a graph, and as a mapping diagram.

x	*y*
1	3
2	4
3	5

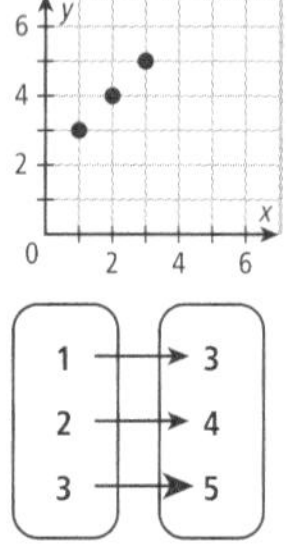

The **domain** of a relation is the set of first coordinates (or *x*-values) of the ordered pairs. The **range** of a relation is the set of second coordinates (or *y*-values) of the ordered pairs. The domain of the track meet scoring system is $\{1, 2, 3, 4\}$. The range is $\{1, 2, 3, 5\}$. Notice that domains and ranges can be written as sets.

1 Introduce

EXPLORATION

4-2 Relations and Functions

Each graph shows the volume of water in a jar over time. Describe a possible situation for each graph or explain why the graph does not make sense.

1. 2. 3. 4. (Graphs: Volume (fl oz) vs. Time (s))

THINK AND DISCUSS

5. Discuss how the graphs in Problems 3 and 4 are different from the graphs in Problems 1 and 2.

Motivate

Display the following chart and have students determine if the examples could contain negative numbers or fractions and decimals.

	Negative Numbers?	Fractions and Decimals?
Ages of Students	No	Yes
Temperatures in Antarctica	Yes	Yes
Number of Desks in Classrooms	No	No

California Standards

Algebra 1 16.0

Also covered:

17.0 Students determine the domain of independent variables **and the range** of dependent variables **defined by a graph, a set of ordered pairs,** or a symbolic expression.

18.0 Students determine whether a relation defined by a graph, a set of ordered pairs, or a symbolic expression **is a function and justify the conclusion.**

EXAMPLE 2 Finding the Domain and Range of a Relation

Writing Math

You can use set-builder notation to write domains and ranges. In Example 2, the domain is $\{x : 1 \le x \le 3\}$. The range is $\{y : 2 \le y \le 4\}$.

Give the domain and range of the relation.

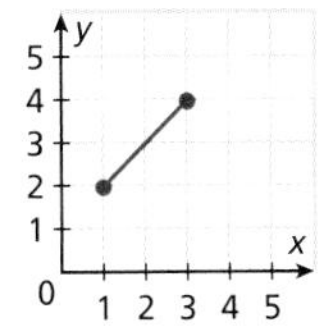

The domain is all x-values from 1 through 3, inclusive.

The range is all y-values from 2 through 4, inclusive.

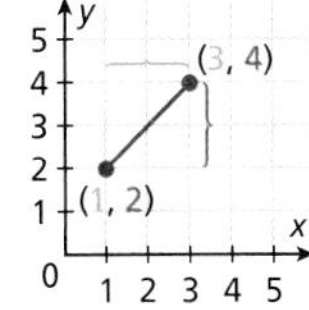

D: $1 \le x \le 3$ R: $2 \le y \le 4$

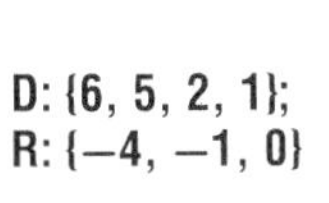

Give the domain and range of each relation.

2a.

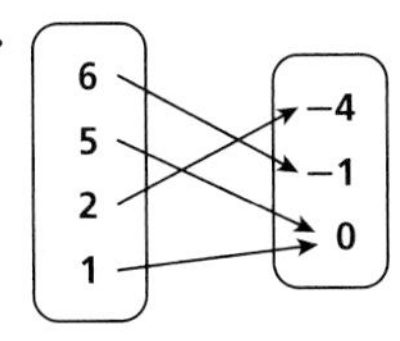

D: {6, 5, 2, 1}; R: {−4, −1, 0}

2b.

x	y
1	1
4	4
8	1

D: {1, 4, 8}; R: {1, 4}

A **function** is a special type of relation that pairs each domain value with exactly one range value.

EXAMPLE 3 Identifying Functions

Give the domain and range of each relation. Tell whether the relation is a function. Explain.

A

Field Trip	
Students x	Buses y
68	2
75	2
125	3

D: {68, 75, 125}
R: {2, 3}

Even though 2 is in the range twice, it is written only once when you are giving the range.

This relation is a function. Each domain value is paired with exactly one range value.

B

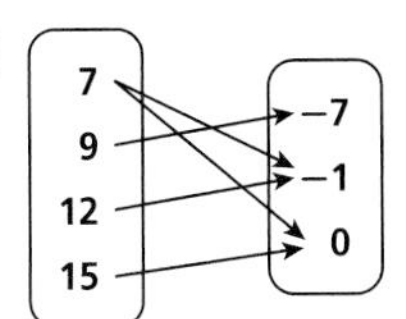

Use the arrows to determine which domain values correspond to each range value.

D: {7, 9, 12, 15}
R: {−7, −1, 0}

This relation is not a function. Each domain value does not have exactly one range value. The domain value 7 is paired with the range values −1 and 0.

COMMON ERROR ALERT

Students may have difficulty remembering how to determine whether a relation is a function. Tell students to think of x as a person and y as a place. A person cannot be in more than one place at a time, but more than one person can be at the same place.

Power Presentations with PowerPoint®

Additional Examples

Example 1

Express the relation {(2, 3), (4, 7), (6, 8)} as a table, as a graph, and as a mapping diagram.

x	y
2	3
4	7
6	8

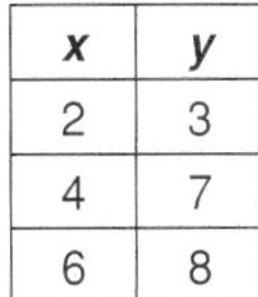

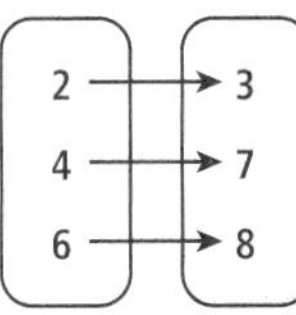

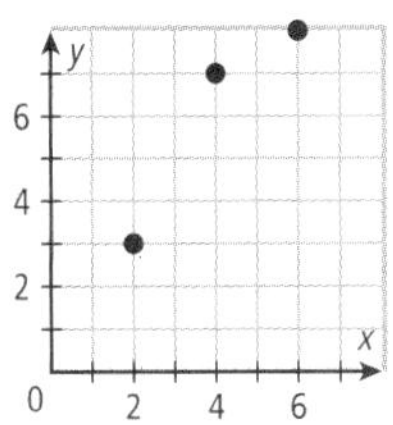

Example 2

Give the domain and range of the relation.

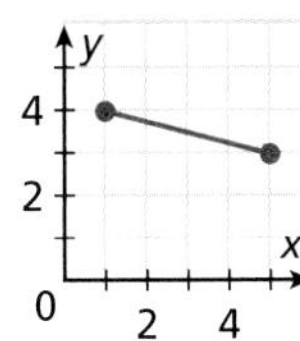

D: $1 \le x \le 5$
R: $3 \le y \le 4$

Also available on transparency

INTERVENTION
Questioning Strategies

EXAMPLE 1

- Which representation do you prefer? Why?

EXAMPLE 2

- When are the domain and range of a relation a continuous interval of values? When are they distinct numbers?

2 Teach

Guided Instruction

Remind students that an ordered pair consists of (x, y). In **Examples 2** and **3,** encourage students to list the ordered pairs when given a mapping diagram, following one arrow at a time.

Communicating Math Remind students how to read set-builder notation. For example, $\{x : 1 \le x \le 3\}$, is read, "the set of all numbers x such that x is greater than or equal to 1 and x is less than or equal to 3."

Universal Access
Through Cognitive Strategies

Show students the following to help them remember which values are in the domain and which are in the range.

- ***x*** and ***y*** are in alphabetical order.
- **D**omain and **r**ange are in alphabetical order.

So the x-values make up the domain, and the y-values make up the range.

Power Presentations with PowerPoint®

Additional Examples

Example 3

Give the domain and range of each relation. Tell whether the relation is a function. Explain.

A. {(3, −2), (5, −1), (4, 0), (3, 1)} D: {3, 5, 4}; R: {−2, −1, 0, 1}; no; 3 is paired with −2 and 1.

B.

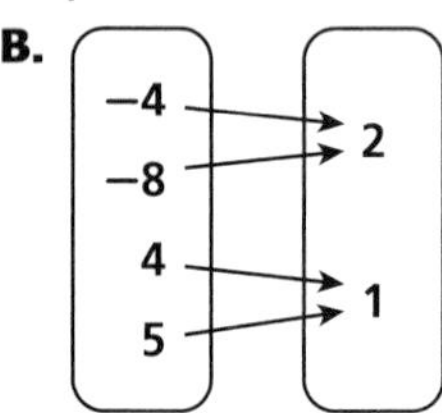

D: {−8, −4, 4, 5}; R: {2, 1}; yes; each domain element is paired with exactly one range element.

C.

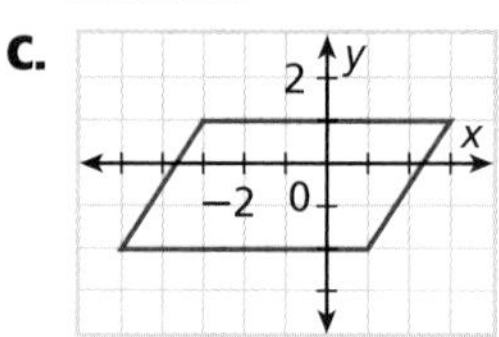

D: $-5 \le x \le 3$; R: $-2 \le y \le 1$; no; nearly all domain values have more than one range value.

Also available on transparency

INTERVENTION
Questioning Strategies

EXAMPLE 3

- Which of the displays (mapping diagram, table, or graph) is easiest for determining if a relation is a function? Why?

Give the domain and range of each relation. Tell whether the relation is a function. Explain.

C

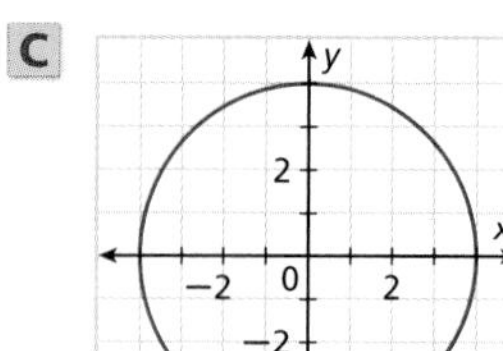

Draw in lines to see the domain and range values.

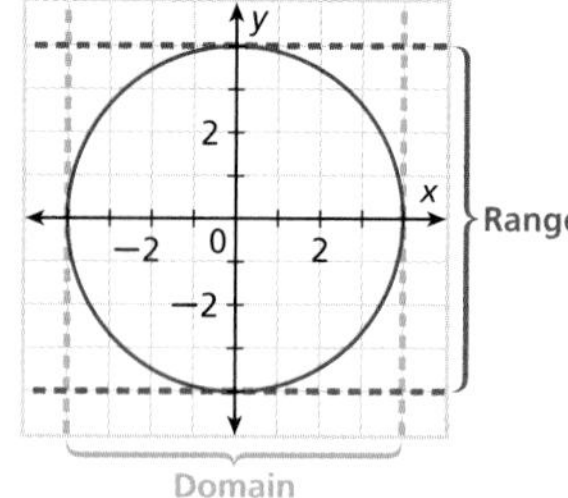

D: $-4 \le x \le 4$ R: $-4 \le y \le 4$

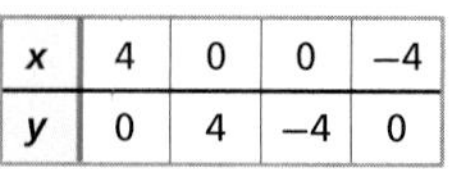

x	4	0	0	−4
y	0	4	−4	0

To compare domain and range values, make a table using points from the graph.

This relation is not a function because there are several domain values that have more than one range value. For example, the domain value 0 is paired with both 4 and −4.

Helpful Hint

To find the domain and range from a graph, it may help to draw lines to see the x- and y-values.

3a. D: {−6, −4, 1, 8}; R: {1, 2, 9}; function; each domain value is paired with exactly one range value.

b. D: {2, 3, 4}; R: {−5, −4, −3}; not a function; the domain value 2 is paired with both −5 and −4.

Give the domain and range of each relation. Tell whether the relation is a function and explain.

3a. $\{(8, 2), (-4, 1), (-6, 2), (1, 9)\}$ **3b.**

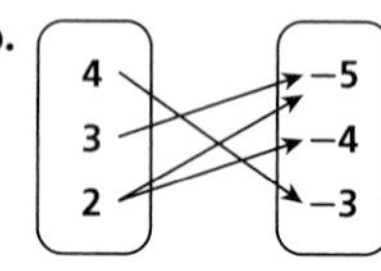

Student to Student

Functions

Eric Dawson
Boone High School

I decide whether a list of ordered pairs is a function by looking at the x-values. If they're all different, then it's a function.

(1, 6), (2, 5), (6, 5), (0, 8)	*(5, 6), (7, 2), (5, 8), (6, 3)*
All different x-values	***Same x-value*** *(with different y-values)*
Function	*Not a function*

THINK AND DISCUSS

1. Describe how to tell whether a set of ordered pairs is a function.
2. Can the graph of a vertical line segment represent a function? Explain.

3. **GET ORGANIZED** Copy and complete the graphic organizer by explaining when a relation is a function and when it is not a function.

A relation is...	
A function if...	Not a function if...

3 Close

Summarize

Ask students to name the four different ways a relation could be represented. list of ordered pairs, table, graph, mapping diagram Write each of the following on the board. Have students find the domain and range and tell whether the relation is a function.

{(1, 4), (2, 4), (3, 5)}
D: {1, 2, 3}; R: {4, 5}; yes

{(1, 4), (2, 5), (2, 6)}
D: {1, 2}; R: {4, 5, 6}; no

FORMATIVE ASSESSMENT

and INTERVENTION

***Diagnose Before* the Lesson**
4-2 Warm Up, TE p. 206

***Monitor During* the Lesson**
Check It Out! Exercises, SE pp. 206–208
Questioning Strategies, TE pp. 207–208

***Assess After* the Lesson**
4-2 Lesson Quiz, TE p. 212
Alternative Assessment, TE p. 212

Answers to *Think and Discuss*

1. A set of ordered pairs is a function if each x-value is assigned exactly one y-value.
2. No; the graph of a vertical line segment cannot represent a function because there is only one element in the domain and it is assigned many different elements in the range.
3. See p. A4.

4-2 Exercises

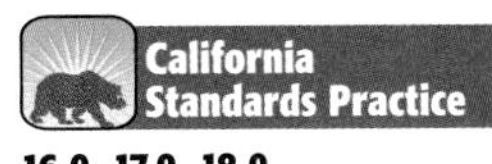

16.0, 17.0, 18.0

go.hrw.com
Homework Help Online
KEYWORD: MA8CA 4-2
Parent Resources Online
KEYWORD: MA8CA Parent

GUIDED PRACTICE

Vocabulary Apply the vocabulary from this lesson to answer each question.

1. Use a mapping diagram to show a relation that is not a *function.*
2. The set of x-values for a relation is also called the __?__. (*domain* or *range*) **domain**

SEE EXAMPLE 1 p. 206

Express each relation as a table, as a graph, and as a mapping diagram.

3. $\{(1, 1), (1, 2)\}$
4. $\left\{(-1, 1), \left(-2, \frac{1}{2}\right), \left(-3, \frac{1}{3}\right), \left(-4, \frac{1}{4}\right)\right\}$
5. $\{(-1, 1), (-3, 3), (5, -5), (-7, 7)\}$
6. $\{(0, 0), (2, -4), (2, -2)\}$

SEE EXAMPLE 2 p. 207

Give the domain and range of each relation.

7. $\{(-5, 7), (0, 0), (2, -8), (5, -20)\}$
8. $\{(1, 2), (2, 4), (3, 6), (4, 8), (5, 10)\}$
9.

x	3	5	2	8	6
y	9	25	4	81	36

10. 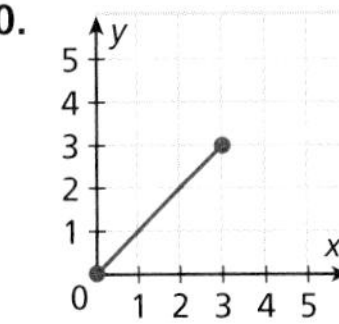

D: $0 \le x \le 3$; R: $0 \le y \le 3$

7. D: {−5, 0, 2, 5}; R: {−20, −8, 0, 7}
8. D: {1, 2, 3, 4, 5}; R: {2, 4, 6, 8, 10}
9. D: {2, 3, 5, 6, 8}; R: { 4, 9, 25, 36, 81}

SEE EXAMPLE 3 p. 207

Multi-Step Give the domain and range of each relation. Tell whether the relation is a function. Explain.

11. $\{(1, 3), (1, 0), (1, -2), (1, 8)\}$
12. $\{(-2, 1), (-1, 2), (0, 3), (1, 4)\}$
13. 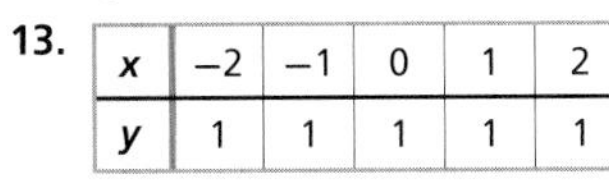

x	−2	−1	0	1	2
y	1	1	1	1	1

14. 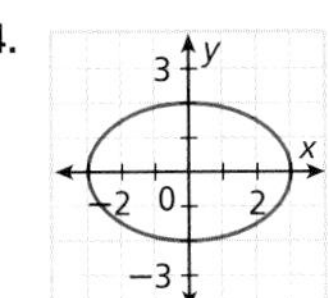

PRACTICE AND PROBLEM SOLVING

Independent Practice	
For Exercises	See Example
15–16	1
17–18	2
19–20	3

Extra Practice
Skills Practice p. EP8
Application Practice p. EP27

Express each relation as a table, as a graph, and as a mapping diagram.

15. $\{(-2, -4), (-1, -1), (0, 0), (1, -1), (2, -4)\}$
16. $\left\{(2, 1), \left(2, \frac{1}{2}\right), (2, 2), \left(2, 2\frac{1}{2}\right)\right\}$

Give the domain and range of each relation.

17. 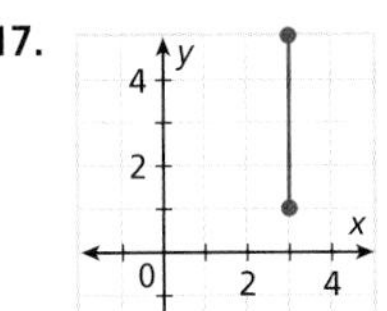

D: {3}; R: $1 \le y \le 5$

18. 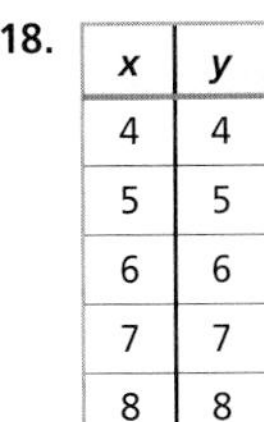

x	y
4	4
5	5
6	6
7	7
8	8

D: {4, 5, 6, 7, 8}; R: {4, 5, 6, 7, 8}

4-2 Exercises

Assignment Guide

Assign *Guided Practice* exercises as necessary.

If you finished Examples **1–3**
Proficient 15–20, 22–24, 27–37, 39–42
Advanced 15–20, 22, 24, 26–29, 31–42

Homework Quick Check
Quickly check key concepts.
Exercises: 16, 18, 20, 22, 24

Visual Encourage students to write out some of the ordered pairs in **Exercise 17** to help them determine the domain and range.

Answers

1. Possible answer:

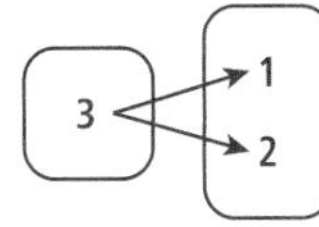

3–6. See p. A16.

11. D: {1}; R: {−2, 0, 3, 8}
Not a function; the domain value 1 is paired with several different range values.

12. D: {−2, −1, 0, 1}; R: {1, 2, 3, 4}
Function; each domain value is paired with exactly one range value.

13. D: {−2, −1, 0, 1, 2}; R: {1}
Function; each element in the domain is paired with exactly one element in the range.

14. D: $-3 \le x \le 3$; R: $-2 \le y \le 2$
Not a function; almost every domain value is paired with 2 range values.

15. 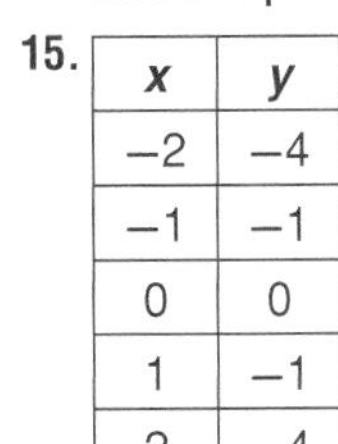

x	y
−2	−4
−1	−1
0	0
1	−1
2	−4

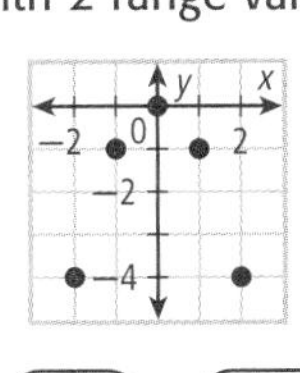

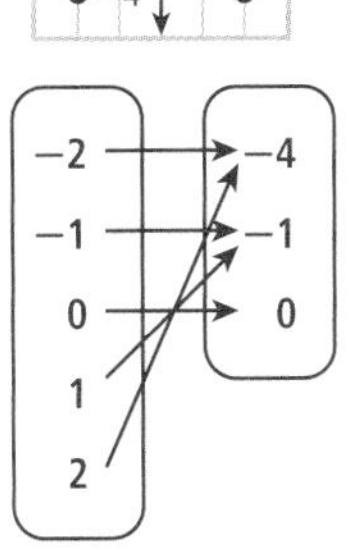

16. 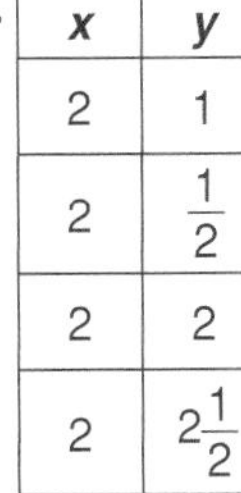

x	y
2	1
2	$\frac{1}{2}$
2	2
2	$2\frac{1}{2}$

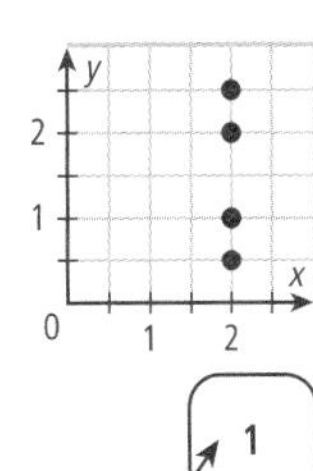

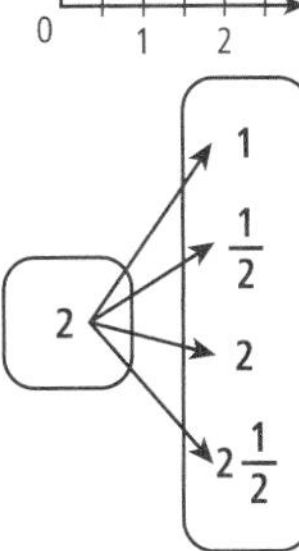

California Standards

Standard	Exercises
5.0	39, 40
16.0	3–6, 15–16, 22, 24a, 25–26a, 27–28, 29c–31, 33, 35a, 36–38c
17.0	7–10, 17–18, 26b, 29a, 35b
18.0	11–14, 19–21, 23, 24b, 26c, 29b, 32, 34, 35c
7SDAP1.2	42

Geometry In **Exercise 22,** remind students that the area of a square with side length s is s^2.

Answers

21. Yes; each domain value is paired with exactly one range value.

x	y
1	125
2	175
3	225
4	275

24a.

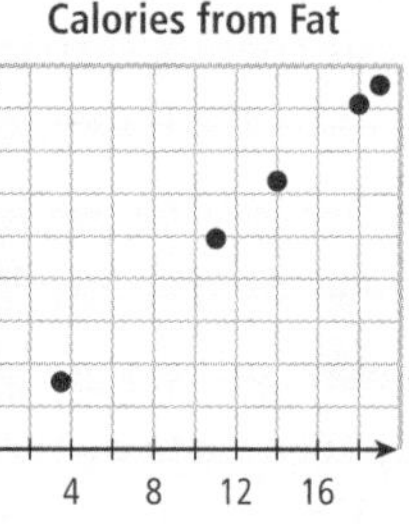

b. Yes; each domain value is paired with exactly one range value.

25.

Hours x	Cost y
1	9
2	11
3	13
4	15
5	15

Yes; each domain value is paired with exactly one range value.

26. See p. A16.

4-2 PRACTICE A

4-2 PRACTICE C

4-2 PRACTICE B

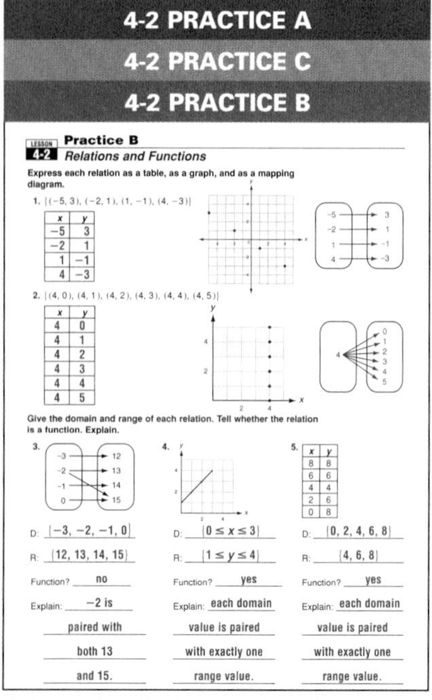

LESSON 4-2 **Practice B**
Relations and Functions

Express each relation as a table, as a graph, and as a mapping diagram.

1. {(−5, 3), (−2, 1), (1, −1), (4, −3)}

x	y
−5	3
−2	1
1	−1
4	−3

2. {(4, 0), (4, 1), (4, 2), (4, 3), (4, 4), (4, 5)}

x	y
4	0
4	1
4	2
4	3
4	4
4	5

Give the domain and range of each relation. Tell whether the relation is a function. Explain.

3. D: {−3, −2, −1, 0} R: {12, 13, 14, 15} Function? no Explain: −2 is paired with both 13 and 15.

4. D: {0 ≤ x ≤ 3} R: {1 ≤ y ≤ 4} Function? yes Explain: each domain value is paired with exactly one range value.

5. D: {0, 2, 4, 6, 8} R: {4, 6, 8} Function? yes Explain: each domain value is paired with exactly one range value.

Multi-Step Give the domain and range of each relation. Tell whether the relation is a function. Explain.

19. D: $-2 \le x \le 2$; R: $0 \le y \le 2$

Function; each domain value is paired with exactly one range value.

20.

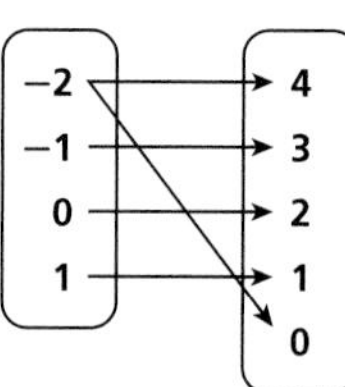

D: {−2, −1, 0, 1}; R: {0, 1, 2, 3, 4};

Not a function; The domain value −2 is paired with 4 and 0.

21. **Consumer Application** An electrician charges a base fee of \$75 plus \$50 for each hour of work. Create a table that shows the amount the electrician charges for 1, 2, 3, and 4 hours of work. Let x represent the number of hours and y represent the amount charged for x hours. Is this relation a function? Explain.

22. **Geometry** Write a relation as a set of ordered pairs in which the x-value represents the length of a side of a square and the y-value represents the area of the square. Use a domain of 2, 4, 6, 9, and 11. **{(2, 4), (4, 16), (6, 36), (9, 81), (11, 121)}**

23. **Multi-Step** Create a mapping diagram to display the numbers of days in 1, 2, 3, and 4 weeks. Is this relation a function? Explain.

23. Yes; each domain value is paired with exactly one range value.

1 → 7, 2 → 14, 3 → 21, 4 → 28

24. **Nutrition** The illustrations list the number of grams of fat and the number of Calories from fat for selected foods.

a. Create a graph for the relation between grams of fat and Calories from fat.

b. Is this relation a function? Explain.

Hamburger
Fat (g): 14
Fat (Cal): 126

Cheeseburger
Fat (g): 18
Fat (Cal): 162

Grilled chicken filet
Fat (g): 3.5
Fat (Cal): 31.5

Breaded chicken filet
Fat (g): 11
Fat (Cal): 99

Taco salad
Fat (g): 19
Fat (Cal): 171

25. **Recreation** A shop rents canoes for a \$7 equipment fee and \$2 per hour, with a maximum cost of \$15 per day. Express the number of hours x and the cost y as a relation in table form, and find the cost to rent a canoe for 1, 2, 3, 4, and 5 hours. Is this relation a function? Explain.

26. **Health** You can burn about 6 Calories a minute bicycling. Let x represent the number of minutes bicycled, and let y represent the number of Calories burned.

a. Write ordered pairs to show the number of Calories burned if you bicycle for 60, 120, 180, 240, or 300 minutes. Graph the ordered pairs.

b. Find the domain and range of the relation.

c. Does this graph represent a function? Explain.

27. **Critical Thinking** For a function, can the number of elements in the range be greater than the number of elements in the domain? Explain.

28. **Reasoning** Tell whether each statement is true or false. Explain your answers.

a. All relations are functions. b. All functions are relations.

27. No; if the number of range values is greater than the number of domain values, then there must be a domain value that is paired with more than one range value.

28a. False; a relation that has several of the same domain values paired with different range values is not a function.

28b. True; a function is defined as a special kind of relation.

4-2 READING STRATEGIES

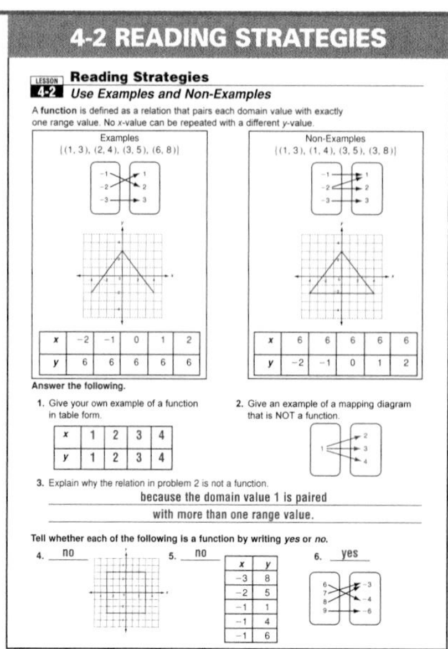

LESSON 4-2 **Reading Strategies**
Use Examples and Non-Examples

A **function** is defined as a relation that pairs each domain value with exactly one range value. No x-value can be repeated with a different y-value.

Examples {(1, 3), (2, 4), (3, 5), (6, 8)}

Non-Examples {(1, 3), (1, 4), (3, 5), (3, 8)}

Answer the following.

1. Give your own example of a function in table form.

2. Give an example of a mapping diagram that is NOT a function.

3. Explain why the relation in problem 2 is not a function. because the domain value 1 is paired with more than one range value.

Tell whether each of the following is a function by writing *yes* or *no*.

4. no 5. no 6. yes

4-2 REVIEW FOR MASTERY

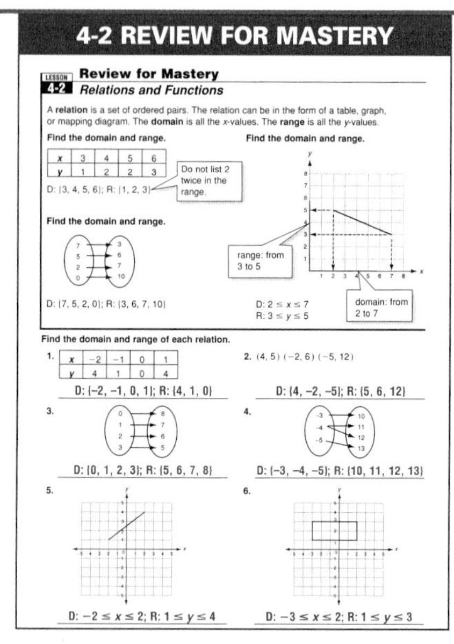

LESSON 4-2 **Review for Mastery**
Relations and Functions

A **relation** is a set of ordered pairs. The relation can be in the form of a table, graph, or mapping diagram. The **domain** is all the x-values. The **range** is all the y-values.

Find the domain and range.

D: {3, 4, 5, 6}; R: {1, 2, 3} — Do not list 2 twice in the range.

Find the domain and range.

D: {7, 5, 2, 0}; R: {3, 6, 7, 10}

D: 2 ≤ x ≤ 7; R: 3 ≤ y ≤ 5 — range: from 3 to 5; domain: from 2 to 7

Find the domain and range of each relation.

1. D: {−2, −1, 0, 1}; R: {4, 1, 0}
2. {(4, 5) (−2, 6) (−5, 12)} D: {4, −2, −5}; R: {5, 6, 12}
3. D: {0, 1, 2, 3}; R: {5, 6, 7, 8}
4. D: {−3, −4, −5}; R: {10, 11, 12, 13}
5. D: −2 ≤ x ≤ 2; R: 1 ≤ y ≤ 4
6. D: −3 ≤ x ≤ 2; R: 1 ≤ y ≤ 3

29. This problem will prepare you for the Concept Connection on page 222.
   a. The graph shows the number of gallons being pumped into a pool over a 5-hour time period. Find the domain and range of the graph.
   b. Does the graph represent a function? Explain.
   c. Give the time and volume as ordered pairs at 2 hours and at 3 hours 30 minutes.

29a. D: $0 \le t \le 5$; R: $0 \le v \le 750$
b. Yes; each x-value is paired with exactly one y-value.
c. (2, 300); (3.5, 525)

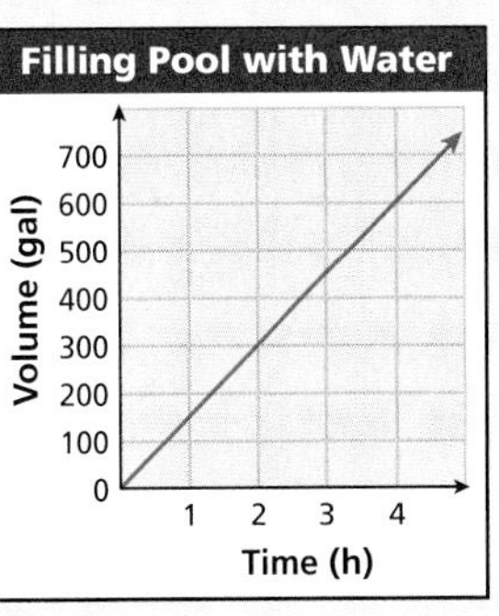

30. **ERROR ANALYSIS** When asked whether the relation $\{(-4, 16), (-2, 4), (0, 0), (2, 4)\}$ is a function, a student stated that the relation is not a function because 4 appears twice. What error did the student make? How would you explain to the student why this relation is a function?

31. **Write About It** Describe a real-world situation using a relation that is NOT a function. Create a mapping diagram to show why the relation is not a function.

Multiple Choice For Exercises 32–34, choose the best answer.

32. Which of the following relations is NOT a function?

Ⓐ $\{(6, 2), (-1, 2), (-3, 2), (-5, 2)\}$

Ⓒ 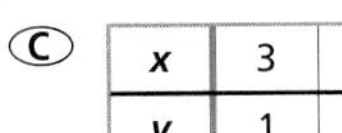

x	3	5	7
y	1	15	30

Ⓑ 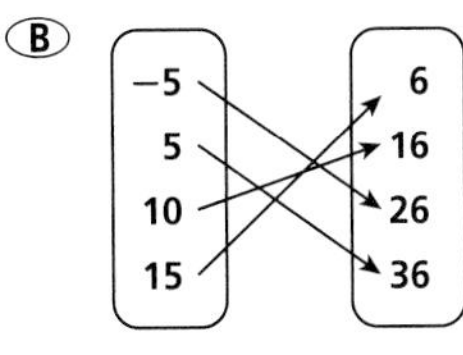

Ⓓ (circled) 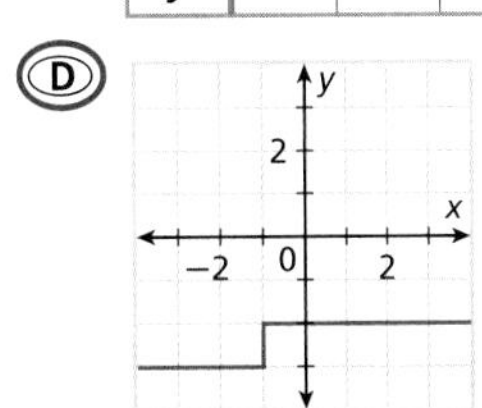

33. Which is NOT a correct way to describe the function $\{(-3, 2), (1, 8), (-1, 5), (3, 11)\}$?

Ⓐ 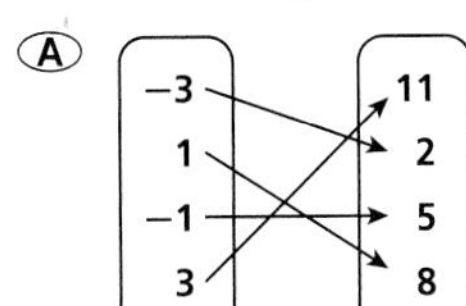

Ⓒ Domain: $\{-3, -1, 1, 3\}$
Range: $\{2, 5, 8, 11\}$

Ⓑ (circled) 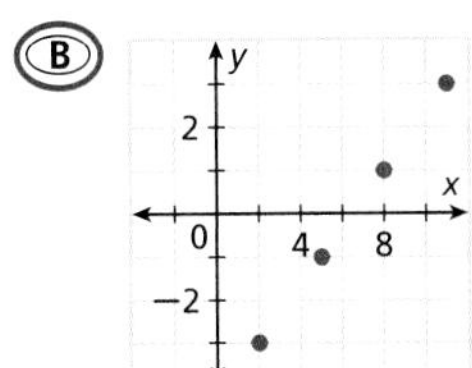

Ⓓ

x	y
−3	2
−1	5
1	8
3	11

Exercise 29 involves finding the domain and range of a graph. This exercise prepares students for the Concept Connection on page 222.

Multiple Choice For **Exercise 32,** choices **A, B,** and **C** can be eliminated because no x-values are repeated.

Students who chose **A** in **Exercise 33** may not understand that in a mapping diagram, the domain and range values can be listed in an order other than that given. Students who chose **C** may not understand that in the domain and range, the x- and y-values can be listed out of order. Remind students that order does not matter.

Answers

30. The student thought that since there are two 4's, one element in the domain is paired with more than one element in the range. The relation is a function because each x-value is paired with exactly one y-value. A relation is a function even if a y-value has more than one x-value paired with it.

31. Possible answer: Packages being sent from a warehouse contain different numbers of items. One package contains 1 item, another package contains 3 items, and yet another package contains 5 items.

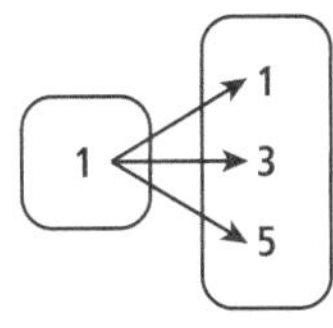

4-2 PROBLEM SOLVING

LESSON 4-2 Problem Solving
Relations and Functions

Give the domain and range of each relation and tell whether it is a function.

1. The mapping diagram shows the ages x and grade level y of four children.

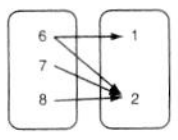

(mapping diagram: 6, 7, 8 → 1, 2)

D: {6, 7, 8}
R: {1, 2}
no

2.

Age x	Shoe Size y
6	8
9	10
12	10
15	10.5
18	11

D: {6, 9, 12, 15, 18}
R: {8, 10, 10.5, 11}
yes

3. The list represents the number of cars sold and the bonus received by the salespeople of a car dealership. {(1, 50), (2, 50), (3, 100), (4, 150)}

D: {1, 2, 3, 4}
R: {50, 100, 150}
yes

4. A 2-inch-tall plant grows at a rate of 2.5 inches every week for 5 weeks. Let x represent the number of weeks and y represent the height of the plant.

D: {0, 1, 2, 3, 4, 5}
R: {2, 4.5, 7, 9.5, 12, 14.5}
yes

Use the graph below to answer questions 5–6. A conservation group has been working to increase the population of a herd of Asian elephants. The graph shows the results of their efforts. Select the correct answer.

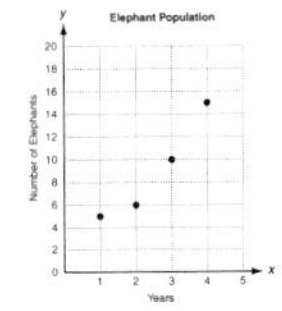

5. Which relation represents the information in the graph?
   A {(1, 4.5), (2, 6), (3, 10), (4, 14.5)}
   Ⓑ {(1, 5), (2, 6), (3, 10), (4, 15)}
   C {(4.5, 1), (6, 2), (10, 3), (14.5, 4)}
   D {(5, 1), (6, 2), (10, 3), (15, 4)}

6. What is the range of the relation shown in the graph?
   F {0, 1, 2, 3, 4, 5}
   G {1, 2, 3, 4}
   H {4.5, 6, 10, 14.5}
   Ⓙ {5, 6, 10, 15}

Elephant Population (graph: Number of Elephants vs. Years)

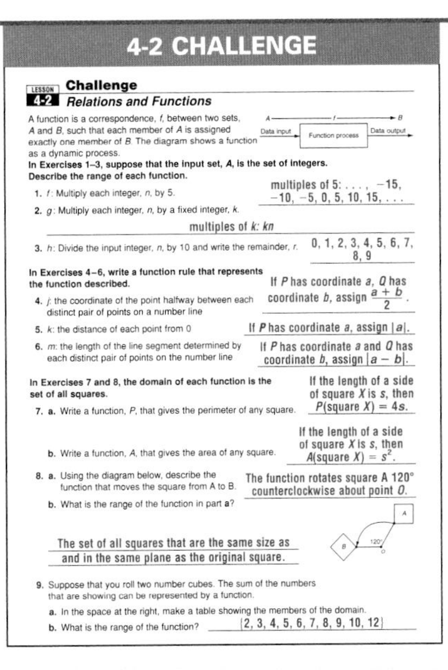

4-2 CHALLENGE

LESSON 4-2 Challenge
Relations and Functions

A function is a correspondence, f, between two sets, A and B, such that each member of A is assigned exactly one member of B. The diagram shows a function as a dynamic process.

(diagram: A —f→ B; Data input → Function process → Data output)

In Exercises 1–3, suppose that the input set, A, is the set of integers. Describe the range of each function.

1. f: Multiply each integer, n, by 5. — multiples of 5: . . . , −15, −10, −5, 0, 5, 10, 15, . . .
2. g: Multiply each integer, n, by a fixed integer, k. — multiples of k: kn
3. h: Divide the input integer, n, by 10 and write the remainder, r. — 0, 1, 2, 3, 4, 5, 6, 7, 8, 9

In Exercises 4–6, write a function rule that represents the function described.

4. j: the coordinate of the point halfway between each distinct pair of points on a number line — If P has coordinate a, Q has coordinate b, assign $\frac{a+b}{2}$.
5. k: the distance of each point from 0 — If P has coordinate a, assign $|a|$.
6. m: the length of the line segment determined by each distinct pair of points on the number line — If P has coordinate a and Q has coordinate b, assign $|a - b|$.

In Exercises 7 and 8, the domain of each function is the set of all squares.

7. a. Write a function, P, that gives the perimeter of any square. — If the length of a side of square X is s, then $P(\text{square } X) = 4s$.
   b. Write a function, A, that gives the area of any square. — If the length of a side of square X is s, then $A(\text{square } X) = s^2$.
8. a. Using the diagram below, describe the function that moves the square from A to B. — The function rotates square A 120° counterclockwise about point O.
   b. What is the range of the function in part **a**? — The set of all squares that are the same size as and in the same plane as the original square.

(diagram: squares A and B, 120°, O)

9. Suppose that you roll two number cubes. The sum of the numbers that are showing can be represented by a function.
   a. In the space at the right, make a table showing the members of the domain.
   b. What is the range of the function? {2, 3, 4, 5, 6, 7, 8, 9, 10, 12}

34. Which graph represents a function?

Ⓐ 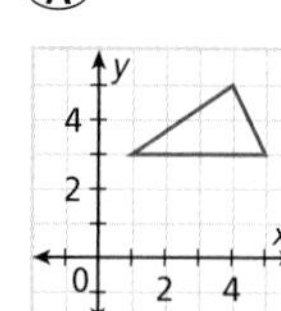

Ⓑ 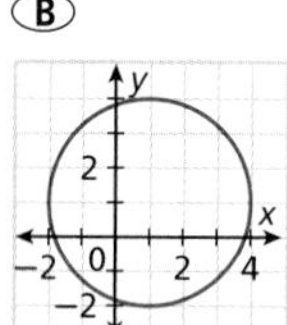

Ⓒ 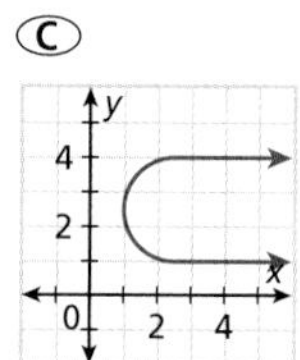

Ⓓ 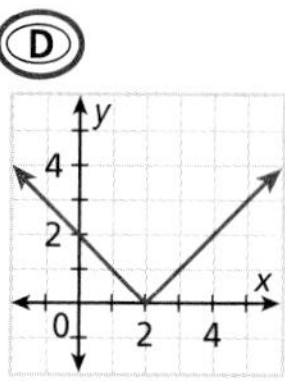

35. **Extended Response** Use the table for the following.

x	−3	−1	0	1	3
y	5	7	9	11	13

a. Express the relation as ordered pairs.

b. Give the domain and range of the relation.

c. Does the relation represent a function? Explain your answer.

35a. {(−3, 5), (−1, 7), (0, 9), (1, 11), (3, 13)}

b. D: {−3, −1, 0, 1, 3}; R: {5, 7, 9, 11, 13}

Yes; each domain value is paired with exactly one range value.

CHALLENGE AND EXTEND

36. What values of a make the relation $\{(a, 1), (2, 3), (4, 5)\}$ a function? Explain.

37. What values of b make the relation $\{(5, 6), (7, 8), (9, b)\}$ a function? Explain.

38. The *inverse* of a relation is created by interchanging the x- and y-coordinates of each ordered pair in the relation.

a. Find the inverse of the following relation: $\{(-2, 5), (0, 4), (3, -8), (7, 5)\}$.

b. Is the original relation a function? Why or why not? Is the inverse of the relation a function? Why or why not?

c. **Reasoning** The statement "If a relation is a function, then the inverse of the relation is also a function" is sometimes true. Give an example of a relation and its inverse that are both functions. Also give an example of a relation and its inverse that are both not functions.

SPIRAL STANDARDS REVIEW
7SDAP1.2, 5.0

39. The ratio of the width of a rectangle to its length is 3:4. The length of the rectangle is 36 cm. Write and solve a proportion to find the rectangle's width. *(Lesson 2-5)* **$\frac{3}{4} = \frac{x}{36}$; 27 cm**

40. A scale drawing of a house is drawn with a scale of 1 in:16 ft. Find the actual length of a hallway that is $\frac{5}{8}$ in. on the scale drawing. *(Lesson 2-5)* **10 ft**

41. Penny wants to drink at least 64 ounces of water today. She has consumed 45 ounces of water so far. Write, solve, and graph an inequality to determine how many more ounces of water Penny must drink to reach her goal. *(Lesson 3-2)*

41. $x + 45 \geq 64$; $x \geq 19$

42. The local pizza parlor sold the following number of pizzas over 10 days. Sketch a graph for the situation. Tell whether the graph is continuous or discrete. *(Lesson 4-1)*

Time (days)	1	2	3	4	5	6	7	8	9	10
Pizzas Sold	5	11	2	4	8	10	3	6	12	1

42. discrete;

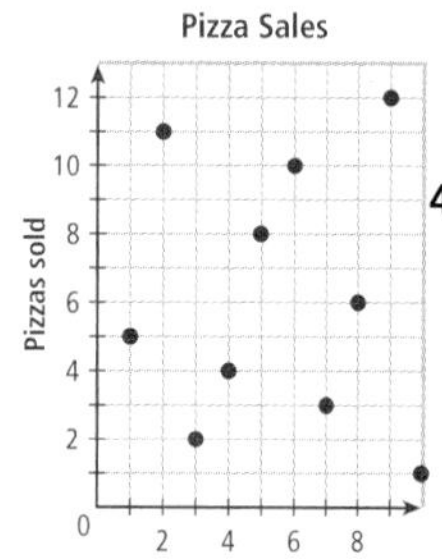

Journal

Have students explain how to determine whether a graphed relation is a function.

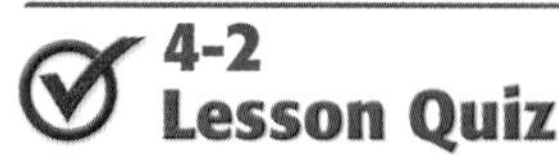

Have students write a list of four ordered pairs. Instruct them to write this relation as a table, a graph, and a mapping diagram. Have them find the domain and range and explain whether their relation is a function.

Power Presentations with PowerPoint®

4-2 Lesson Quiz

1. Express the relation {(−2, 5), (−1, 4), (1, 3), (2, 4)} as a table, as a graph, and as a mapping diagram.

x	y
−2	5
−1	4
1	3
2	4

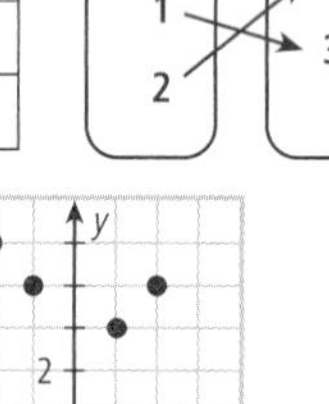

2. Give the domain and range of the relation.

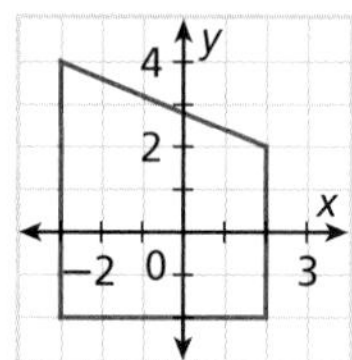

D: $-3 \leq x \leq 2$; R: $-2 \leq y \leq 4$

3. Give the domain and range of the relation. Tell whether the relation is a function. Explain.

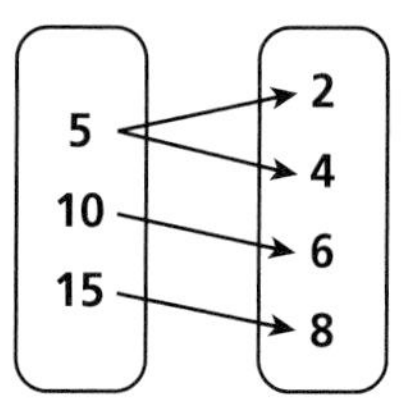

D: {5, 10, 15}; R: {2, 4, 6, 8}; no; 5 is paired with 2 and 4.

Also available on transparency

Answers

36. All real numbers except 2 and 4; values in the domain cannot repeat.

37. All real numbers; values in the range can repeat.

38a. {(5, −2), (4, 0), (−8, 3), (5, 7)}

b. The original relation is a function because each domain value is paired with exactly one range value. The inverse is not a function because a domain value has more than one range value paired with it.

38c. Possible answer: Relation: {(1, 2), (2, 3), (3, 4)}; Inverse: {(2, 1), (3, 2), (4, 3)}; Relation: {(1, 1), (1, 2), (2, 2), (2, 4)}; Inverse: {(1, 1), (2, 1), (2, 2), (4, 2)}

4-3 Writing and Graphing Functions

California Standards

16.0 Students understand the concepts of a relation and a function, determine whether a given relation defines a function, and give pertinent information about given relations and functions.
17.0 Students determine the domain of independent variables and the range of dependent variables defined by a graph, a set of ordered pairs, **or a symbolic expression.**
Also covered: **18.0**

Vocabulary
dependent variable
independent variable
function notation

Why learn this?
You can use a function to calculate how much money you will earn for working specific amounts of time.

Suppose Tasha baby-sits and charges \$5 per hour.

Time Worked (h) x	1	2	3	4
Amount Earned (\$) y	5	10	15	20

The amount of money Tasha earns is \$5 times the number of hours she works. You can write an equation using two variables to show this relationship.

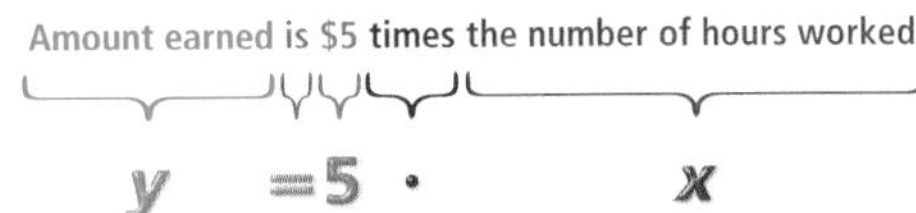

EXAMPLE 1 Using a Table to Write an Equation

Determine a relationship between the x- and y-values. Write an equation.

x	1	2	3	4
y	−2	−1	0	1

Step 1 List possible relationships between the first x- and y-values.

$1 - 3 = -2$ or $1(-2) = -2$

Step 2 Determine whether one relationship works for the remaining values.

$2 - 3 = -1$ ✓ $2(-2) \neq -1$ ✗
$3 - 3 = 0$ ✓ $3(-2) \neq 0$ ✗
$4 - 3 = 1$ ✓ $4(-2) \neq 1$ ✗

The first relationship works. The value of y is 3 less than x.

Step 3 Write an equation.

$y = x - 3$ *The value of y is 3 less than x.*

CHECK IT OUT! 1. Determine a relationship between the x- and y-values in the relation $\{(1, 3), (2, 6), (3, 9), (4, 12)\}$. Write an equation. $y = 3x$

When an equation has two variables, its solutions will be all ordered pairs (x, y) that make the equation true. Since the solutions are ordered pairs, it is possible to represent them on a graph. When you represent all solutions of an equation on a graph, you are *graphing the equation.*

4-3 Organizer

Objectives: Write an equation in function notation and evaluate a function for given input values.

Graph functions and determine whether an equation represents a function.

Algebra Lab
In *Chapter 4 Resource File*

Online Edition
Tutorial Videos

Countdown to Mastery Week 8

Power Presentations with PowerPoint®

Warm Up

Evaluate each expression for $a = 2$, $b = -3$, and $c = 8$.

1. $a + 3c$ 26
2. $ab - c$ −14
3. $\frac{1}{2}c + b$ 1
4. $4c - b$ 35
5. $b^a + c$ 17

Solve for y.

6. $2x + y = 3$ $y = -2x + 3$
7. $-x + 3y = -6$ $y = \frac{1}{3}x - 2$
8. $4x - 2y = 8$ $y = 2x - 4$

Also available on transparency

Math Humor

Q: Why did the x-variable move back home?

A: She was more comfortable in her own domain.

1 Introduce

EXPLORATION

4-3 Writing and Graphing Functions

Dan has \$100 in his savings account. His grandmother promises to deposit \$25 into the account for each day Dan helps her during his summer vacation.

1. Complete the table to show how much money will be in Dan's account for each given number of days Dan works for his grandmother.
2. How much money will be in Dan's account if he works x days?

Days x	Process	Total in Account (\$) y
0		
1	100 + 25(1)	
2	100 + 25(2)	
3		
5		225
10		

3. Write an equation that shows the relationship between x (the number of days Dan works) and y (the total in his account).

THINK AND DISCUSS

4. Discuss whether the above relationship is a function.
5. Explain how you can use your equation to find the total in Dan's account if he works 20 days.

Motivate

ENGLISH LANGUAGE LEARNERS

Have students describe the meaning of the following phrases: Possible answers:

- independently wealthy doesn't need a job
- Independence Day day of freedom
- working independently doesn't need help
- dependent child needs a parent
- insulin dependent needs insulin
- dependent on friends needs friends

Explorations and answers are provided in *Alternate Openers: Explorations Transparencies.*

California Standards

Algebra 1 16.0, 17.0
Also covered:
18.0 Students determine whether a relation defined by a graph, a set of ordered pairs, **or a symbolic expression is a function and justify the conclusion.**

Power Presentations with PowerPoint®

Additional Examples

Example 1

Determine a relationship between the x- and y-values. Write an equation. $y = \frac{x}{5}$

x	5	10	15	20
y	1	2	3	4

Example 2

Graph each equation. Then tell whether the equation represents a function.

A. $-3x + 2 = y$ yes

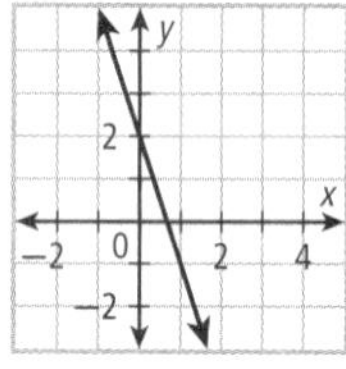

B. $y = |x| + 2$ yes

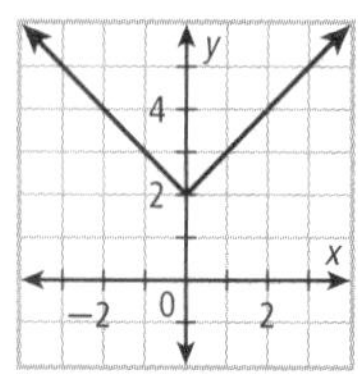

Also available on transparency

INTERVENTION
Questioning Strategies

EXAMPLE 1

- As the x-value is increasing, what is happening to the y-value?
- What situation could this table of numbers represent?

EXAMPLE 2

- When creating the table, what did you notice about the y-values relative to the x-values?

Since the solutions of an equation that has two variables are a set of ordered pairs, they are a relation. One way to tell if this relation is a function is to graph the equation and use the *vertical-line test.*

The Vertical-Line Test

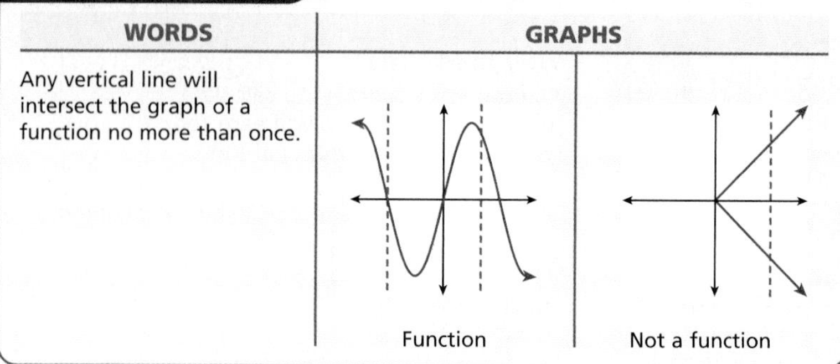

WORDS
GRAPHS
Any vertical line will intersect the graph of a function no more than once.
Function
Not a function

EXAMPLE 2 **Graphing Functions**

Graph each equation. Then tell whether the equation represents a function.

A $2x + 1 = y$

Step 1 Choose several values of x and generate ordered pairs.

x	2x + 1 = y	(x, y)
−3	2(−3) + 1 = −5	(−3, −5)
−2	2(−2) + 1 = −3	(−2, −3)
−1	2(−1) + 1 = −1	(−1, −1)
0	2(0) + 1 = 1	(0, 1)
1	2(1) + 1 = 3	(1, 3)
2	2(2) + 1 = 5	(2, 5)
3	2(3) + 1 = 7	(3, 7)

Step 2 Plot enough points to see a pattern.

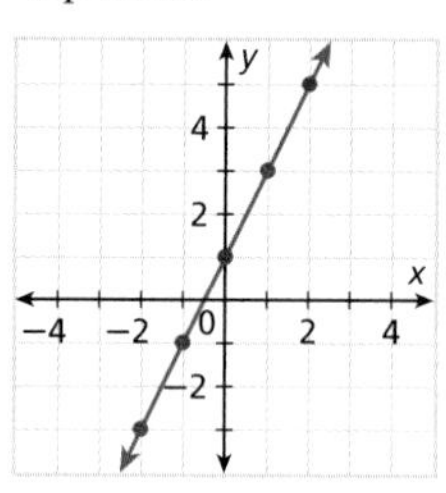

Helpful Hint

When choosing values of x, be sure to choose both positive and negative values.

Step 3 The points appear to form a line. Draw a line through all the points to show all the ordered pairs that satisfy the function. Draw arrowheads on both "ends" of the line.

Step 4 Use the vertical-line test on the graph.

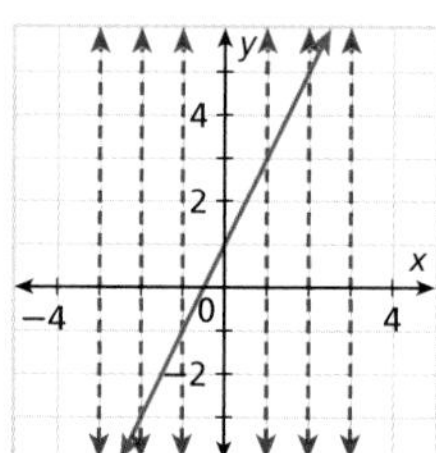

No vertical line will intersect the graph more than once. The equation $y = 2x + 1$ represents a function.

2 Teach

Guided Instruction

If students have a hard time finding a relationship in **Example 1,** have them first test the four basic operations. (Is the same value added to each x, subtracted from each x, etc.?) If those don't work, then it may be a square, square root, or combination of operations. Be sure students can graph ordered pairs before moving on to graphing. Stress the importance of choosing several points (positive, negative, and zero values) when graphing.

Universal Access
Through Communication

Designate a group of four students as the "function machine." This group must create a secret function. Other students give input values to the group, and the group must state the output value. The other students must guess the secret function. Students can explain how they deduced the secret function.

Graph each equation. Then tell whether the equation represents a function.

B $y = x^2$

Step 1 Choose several values of x and generate ordered pairs.

x	$y = x^2$	(x, y)
−3	$y = (-3)^2 = 9$	$(-3, 9)$
−2	$y = (-2)^2 = 4$	$(-2, 4)$
−1	$y = (-1)^2 = 1$	$(-1, 1)$
0	$y = (0)^2 = 0$	$(0, 0)$
1	$y = (1)^2 = 1$	$(1, 1)$
2	$y = (2)^2 = 4$	$(2, 4)$

Step 2 Plot enough points to see a pattern.

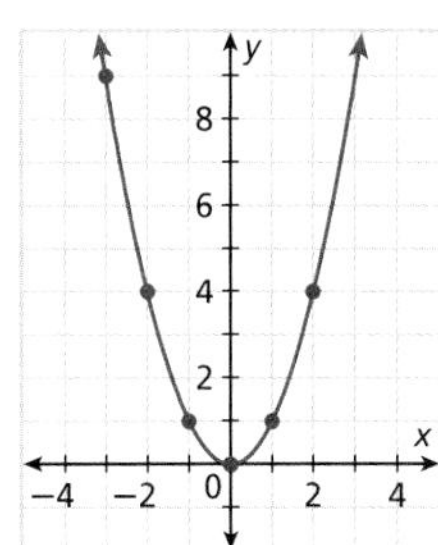

Step 3 The points appear to form an almost U-shaped graph. Draw a smooth curve through the points to show all the ordered pairs that satisfy the function. Draw arrowheads on the "ends" of the curve.

Step 4 Use the vertical-line test on the graph.

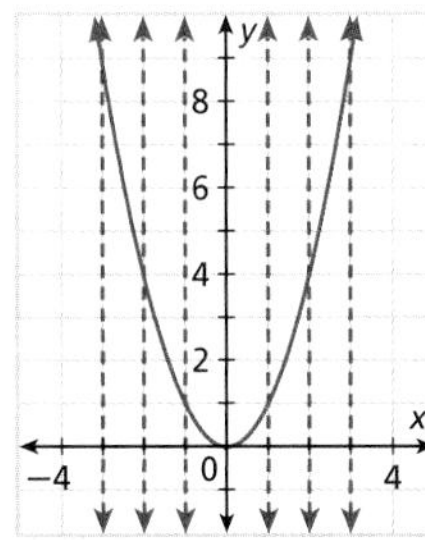

No vertical line will intersect the graph more than once. The equation $y = x^2$ represents a function.

2a. yes

2b. yes

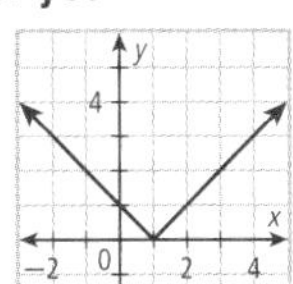

Graph each equation. Then tell whether the equation represents a function.

2a. $y = 3x - 2$ **2b.** $y = |x - 1|$

Looking at the graph of a function can help you determine its domain and range.

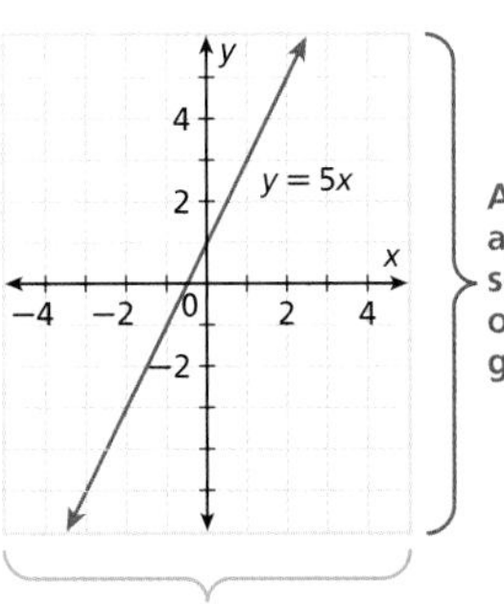

y = 5x
All y-values appear somewhere on the graph.
All x-values appear somewhere on the graph.

For $y = 5x$, the domain is all real numbers and the range is all real numbers.

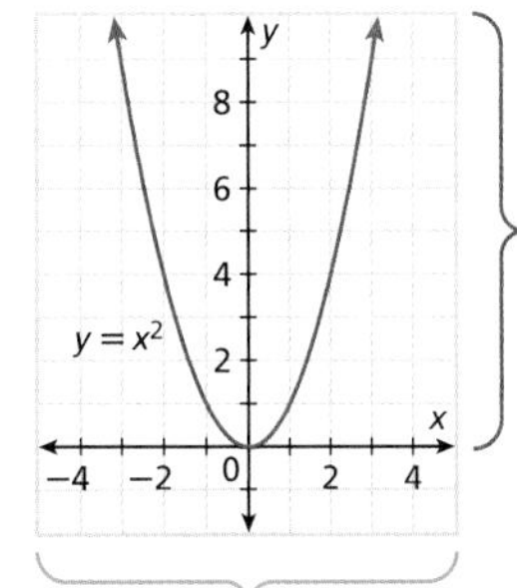

y = x²
Only nonnegative y-values appear on the graph.
All x-values appear somewhere on the graph.

For $y = x^2$, the domain is all real numbers and the range is $y \geq 0$.

Teaching Tip **Inclusion** After seeing the problems in **Example 2,** students may wonder whether all equations represent functions. Tell students that some equations do not represent functions, and that they will study those later. (Refer advanced students to **Exercises 56–60** of this lesson.) For now, they should concentrate on graphing functions and understanding the vertical-line test.

Power Presentations with PowerPoint®

Additional Examples

Example 3

Identify the independent and dependent variables. Write a rule in function notation for each situation.

A. A math tutor charges \$35 per hour. indep.: time; dep.: cost; $f(h) = 35h$

B. A fitness center charges a \$100 initiation fee plus \$40 per month. indep.: number of months; dep.: total cost; $f(m) = 100 + 40m$

Example 4

Evaluate each function for the given input values.

A. For $f(x) = 3x + 2$, find $f(x)$ when $x = 7$ and when $x = -4$. $f(7) = 23$; $f(-4) = -10$

B. For $g(t) = 1.5t - 5$, find $g(t)$ when $t = 6$ and when $t = -2$. $g(6) = 4$; $g(-2) = -8$

C. For $h(r) = \frac{1}{3}r + 2$, find $h(r)$ when $r = 600$ and when $r = -12$. $h(600) = 202$; $h(-12) = -2$

Also available on transparency

INTERVENTION
Questioning Strategies

EXAMPLE 3

- How could you write the rule without using function notation?
- Does $f(x)$ represent domain or range?

EXAMPLE 4

- How is evaluating a function like solving an equation? How is it different?

In a function, one variable (usually denoted by x) is the *independent variable* and the other variable (usually y) is the *dependent variable*. The value of the **dependent variable** *depends* on, or is a function of, the value of the **independent variable.** For Tasha, who earns \$5 per hour, the amount she earns depends on, or is a function of, the amount of time she works.

When an equation represents a function, you can write the equation using *function notation*. If x is independent and y is dependent, the **function notation** for y is $f(x)$, read "f of x," where f names the function.

The dependent variable	is	a function of	the independent variable.
y	is	a function of	x.
y	$=$	f	(x)

Tasha's earnings, $y = 5x$, can be rewritten in function notation by substituting $f(x)$ for y—$f(x) = 5x$. Note that function notation always defines the dependent variable in terms of the independent variable.

EXAMPLE 3 Writing Functions

Identify the independent and dependent variables. Write a rule in function notation for each situation.

A **A lawyer's fee is \$200 per hour for her services.**

The fee for the lawyer depends on how many hours she works.

Dependent: fee Independent: hours

Let h represent the number of hours the lawyer works.

The function for the lawyer's fee is $f(h) = 200h$.

B **Apples cost \$0.99 per pound.**

The cost depends on the number of pounds purchased.

Dependent: cost Independent: pounds

Let p represent the number of pounds of apples purchased.

The function for the cost of the apples is $f(p) = 0.99p$.

C **The admission fee to a local carnival is \$8. Each ride costs \$1.50.**

The total cost depends on the number of rides ridden, plus \$8.

Dependent: total cost Independent: number of rides

Let r represent the number of rides ridden.

The function for the total cost of the carnival is $f(r) = 1.50r + 8$.

CHECK IT OUT! **Identify the independent and dependent variables. Write a rule in function notation for each situation.**

3a. A tutor's fee for music lessons is \$28 per hour for private lessons.

3b. Steven buys lettuce that costs \$1.69/lb.

3c. An amusement park charges a \$6.00 parking fee plus \$29.99 per person.

3a. ind. var.: hours; dep. var.: cost; $f(x) = 28x$
3b. ind. var.: pounds; dep. var.: cost; $f(x) = 1.69x$
3c. ind. var.: people; dep. var.: cost; $f(x) = 6 + 29.99x$

Universal Access
Through Cooperative Learning

Divide students into groups and have them write examples of dependent relationships.

For example:

- I get cranky when I don't eat.
- If I don't work, then I don't get paid.

Then have students exchange papers and rewrite each example in a table.

Independent	Dependent
• when I don't eat • if I don't work	• I get cranky • then I don't get paid

You can think of a function rule as an **input-output** machine. For Tasha's earnings, $f(x) = 5x$, if you input a value x, the output is $5x$.

If Tasha wanted to know how much money she would earn by working 6 hours, she could input 6 for x and find the output. This is called *evaluating the function.*

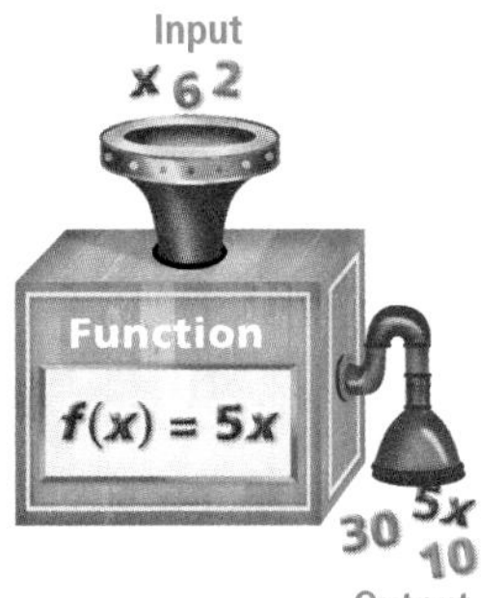

EXAMPLE 4 **Evaluating Functions**

Evaluate each function for the given input values.

A For $f(x) = 5x$, find $f(x)$ when $x = 6$ and when $x = 7.5$.

$f(x) = 5x$

$f(6) = 5(6)$ *Substitute 6 for x.*

$= 30$ *Simplify.*

$f(x) = 5x$

$f(7.5) = 5(7.5)$ *Substitute 7.5 for x.*

$= 37.5$ *Simplify.*

Reading Math

Functions can be named with any letter; f, g, and h are the most common. You read $f(6)$ as "f of 6," and $g(2)$ as "g of 2."

B For $g(t) = 2.30t + 10$, find $g(t)$ when $t = 2$ and when $t = -5$.

$g(t) = 2.30t + 10$

$g(2) = 2.30(2) + 10$

$= 4.6 + 10$

$= 14.6$

$g(t) = 2.30t + 10$

$g(-5) = 2.30(-5) + 10$

$= -11.5 + 10$

$= -1.5$

C For $h(x) = \frac{1}{2}x - 3$, find $h(x)$ when $x = 12$ and when $x = -8$.

$h(x) = \frac{1}{2}x - 3$

$h(12) = \frac{1}{2}(12) - 3$

$= 6 - 3$

$= 3$

$h(x) = \frac{1}{2}x - 3$

$h(-8) = \frac{1}{2}(-8) - 3$

$= -4 - 3$

$= -7$

CHECK IT OUT! **4.** Evaluate $h(c) = 2c - 1$ when $c = 1$ and when $c = -3$.
$h(1) = 1$; $h(-3) = -7$

THINK AND DISCUSS

1. For the function $f(x) = 2x$, what is the domain? What is the range?

2. How do you identify independent and dependent variables?

3. When you input water into an ice machine, the output is ice cubes. Name another real-world object that has an input and an output.

4. GET ORGANIZED Copy and complete the graphic organizer using the equation $y = x + 3$.

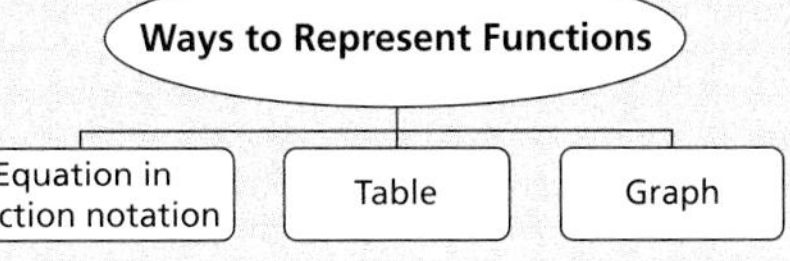

Students might mistake the notation $f(x)$ as meaning f times x. Remind them that $f(x)$ is the notation of a function and is interchangeable with y.

Auditory Tell students that the ***in***put is the ***in***dependent variable. ENGLISH LANGUAGE LEARNERS

Inclusion When students are graphing a function, suggest that they choose simple values for x, such as -2, -1, 0, 1, and 2.

Teaching Tip **Critical Thinking** Help students recognize functions that cannot have negative values. This will help them determine a domain and range.

3 Close

Summarize

Have students name the steps for graphing a function. Choose values for x, generate ordered pairs, graph

Then have students write a rule for the following situations using function notation.

A cable TV service charges \$50 for hookup and \$30 per month. $f(m) = 50 + 30m$

A library charges \$0.25 for every day that a book is late. $f(d) = 0.25d$

FORMATIVE ASSESSMENT and INTERVENTION

***Diagnose Before* the Lesson**
4-3 Warm Up, TE p. 213

***Monitor During* the Lesson**
Check It Out! Exercises, SE pp. 213–216
Questioning Strategies, TE pp. 214–216

***Assess After* the Lesson**
4-3 Lesson Quiz, TE p. 220
Alternative Assessment, TE p. 220

Answers to *Think and Discuss*

1. Both the domain and range are all real numbers.
2. Possible answer: If one data set depends on the other, the first data set represents the dependent variable, and the other data set represents the independent variable.
3. Possible answer: a toaster
4. See p. A4.

4-3 Exercises

Assignment Guide

Assign *Guided Practice* exercises as necessary.

If you finished Examples **1–2**
Proficient 16–26, 37
Advanced 16–26, 37

If you finished Examples **1–4**
Proficient 16–49, 51–55, 57–71
Advanced 16–36, 40–71

Homework Quick Check
Quickly check key concepts.
Exercises: 16, 18, 20, 27, 31

Math Background
For **Exercise 10,** remind students that $-x^2$ is the same as $-(x^2)$.

Answers

5. 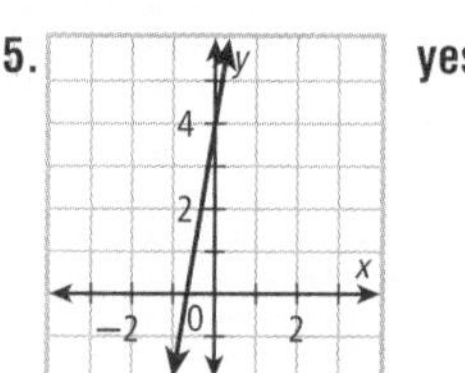 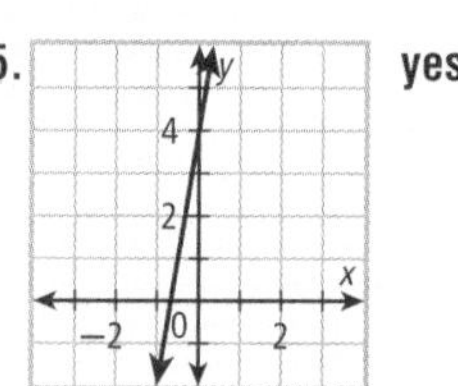 yes

6. 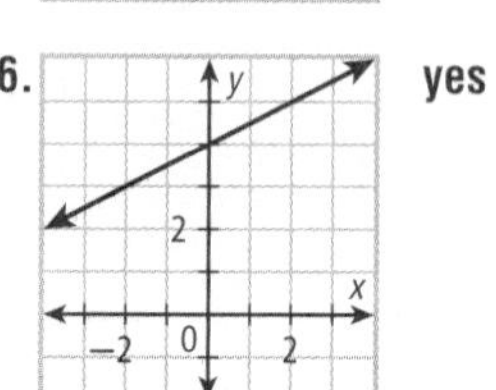 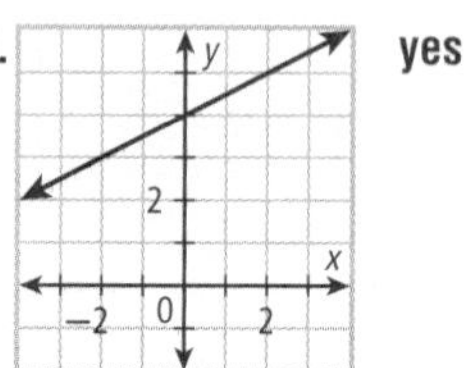 yes

7. 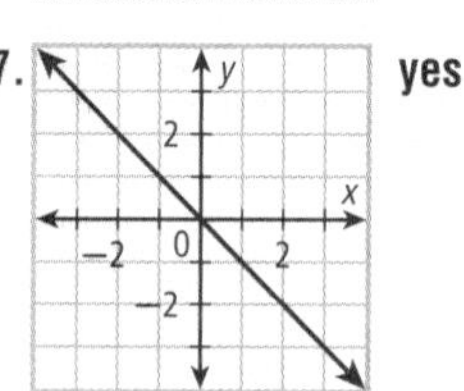 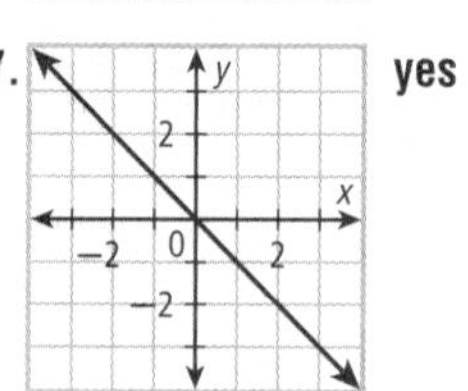 yes

4-3 Exercises

California Standards Practice
16.0, 17.0, 18.0

go.hrw.com
Homework Help Online
KEYWORD: MA8CA 4-3
Parent Resources Online
KEYWORD: MA8CA Parent

GUIDED PRACTICE

Vocabulary Apply the vocabulary from this lesson to answer each question.

1. The output of a function is the ___?___ variable. **dependent**
2. To show that an equation is a function, you can write it using ___?___. **function notation**

SEE EXAMPLE 1 p. 213

Determine a relationship between the x- and y-values. Write an equation.

3.

x	1	2	3	4
y	−1	0	1	2

$y = x - 2$

4. $\{(1, 4), (2, 7), (3, 10), (4, 13)\}$ $y = 3x + 1$

SEE EXAMPLE 2 p. 214

Graph each equation. Then tell whether the equation represents a function.

5. $y = 6x + 4$
6. $y = \frac{1}{2}x + 4$
7. $x + y = 0$
8. $y = |x| - 4$
9. $y = 2x^2 - 7$
10. $y = -x^2 + 5$

SEE EXAMPLE 3 p. 216

Identify the independent and dependent variables. Write a rule in function notation for each situation. **ind. var.: hours; dep. var.: cost; $f(h) = 75h$**

11. An air-conditioning technician charges customers $75 per hour.
ind. var.: hours; dep. var.: cost; $f(x) = 3.50 + 1.25x$
12. An ice rink charges $3.50 for skates and $1.25 per hour.

SEE EXAMPLE 4 p. 217

Evaluate each function for the given input values.

13. For $f(x) = 7x + 2$, find $f(x)$ when $x = 0$ and when $x = 1$. $f(0) = 2$; $f(1) = 9$
14. For $g(x) = 4x - 9$, find $g(x)$ when $x = 3$ and when $x = 5$. $g(3) = 3$; $g(5) = 11$
15. For $h(t) = \frac{1}{3}t - 10$, find $h(t)$ when $t = 27$ and when $t = -15$. $h(27) = -1$; $h(-15) = -15$

PRACTICE AND PROBLEM SOLVING

Independent Practice For Exercises	See Example
16–17	1
18–26	2
27–29	3
30–32	4

Extra Practice
Skills Practice p. EP8
Application Practice p. EP27

Determine a relationship between the x- and y-values. Write an equation.

16.

x	1	2	3	4
y	−2	−4	−6	−8

$y = -2x$

17. $\{(1, -1), (2, -2), (3, -3), (4, -4)\}$ $y = -x$

Graph each equation. Then tell whether the equation represents a function.

18. $y = -3x + 5$
19. $y = 3x$
20. $x + y = 8$
21. $y = 2x + 2$
22. $y = -|x| + 10$
23. $y = -5 + x^2$
24. $y = |x + 1| + 1$
25. $y = (x - 2)^2 - 1$
26. $x^2 + 2 = y$

Identify the independent and dependent variables. Write a rule in function notation for each situation.

27. A movie rental store charges $3.99 to rent a DVD plus $0.99 for every day that it is late. **ind. var.: days late; dep. var.: total cost; $f(x) = 3.99 + 0.99x$**
28. Stephen charges $25 for each lawn he mows.
ind. var.: lawns mowed; dep. var.: amount earned; $f(x) = 25x$
29. A car can travel 28 miles per gallon of gas.
ind. var.: gallons of gas; dep. var.: miles; $f(x) = 28x$

Answers

8. 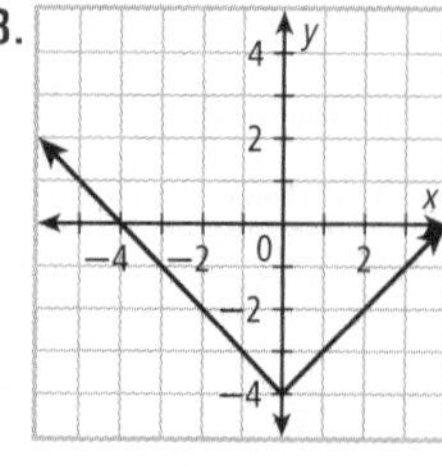 yes

10. 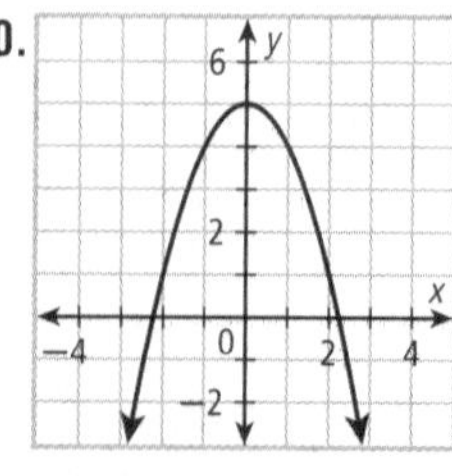 yes

19. 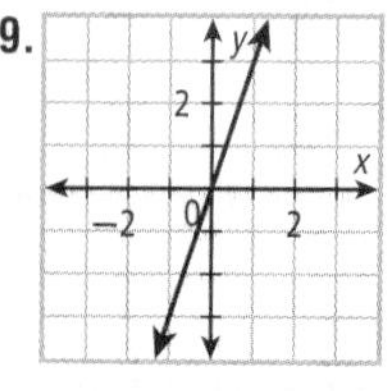 yes

9. yes

18. 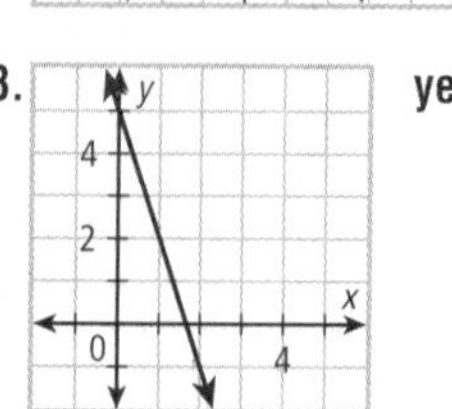 yes

20. 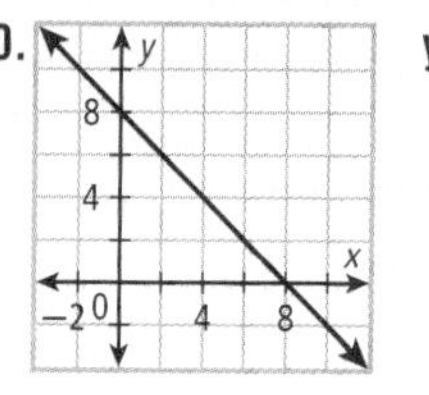 yes

21–26. See p. A16.

California Standards

Standard	Exercises
4.0	62, 64–66, 69
5.0	61–69
16.0	5–12, 18–29, 37, 40–45, 50, 55–60, 70, 71
17.0	40–45, 70, 71
18.0	56, 57, 70, 71

Evaluate each function for the given input values.

30. For $f(x) = x^2 - 5$, find $f(x)$ when $x = 0$ and when $x = 3$. **$f(0) = -5$; $f(3) = 4$**
31. For $g(x) = x^2 + 6$, find $g(x)$ when $x = 1$ and when $x = 2$. **$g(1) = 7$; $g(2) = 10$**
32. For $f(x) = \frac{2}{3}x + 3$, find $f(x)$ when $x = 9$ and when $x = -3$. **$f(9) = 9$; $f(-3) = 1$**

For each function, determine whether the given points are on the graph.

33. $y = 7x - 2$; (1, 5) and (2, 10) **yes; no**
34. $y = |x| + 2$; (3, 5) and (−1, 3) **yes; yes**
35. $y = x^2$; (1, 1) and (−3, −9) **yes; no**
36. $y = \frac{1}{4}x - 2$; $\left(1, -\frac{3}{4}\right)$ and (4, −1) **no; yes**

LINK Transportation

Air Force One refers to two specially configured Boeing 747-200B airplanes. The radio call sign when the president is aboard either aircraft or any Air Force aircraft is "Air Force One."

37. **Transportation** Air Force One can travel 630 miles per hour. Let h be the number of hours traveled. The equation $d = 630h$ gives the distance d in miles that Air Force One travels in h hours.
    a. Is the equation $d = 630h$ a function? If so, identify the independent and dependent variables and write $d = 630h$ in function notation. If not, explain why not. **yes; ind. var.: hours; dep. var.: distance; $f(h) = 630h$**
    b. How far can Air Force One travel in 12 hours? **7560 mi**

38. Complete the table for $h(x) = x^2 + x$.

x	0	1	2	3
$h(x)$	**0**	**2**	**6**	**12**

39. Complete the table for $g(z) = 2z - 5$.

z	1	2	3	4
$g(z)$	**−3**	**−1**	**1**	**3**

Give the domain and range of each function.

40. $-6 = 3x + 2y$
41. $y = 1.1x + 2$
42. $y = \frac{4}{5}x$
43. $y = 3x - 1$
44. $y = |x| + 6$
45. $y = x^2 - 5$
46. Find the value of x so that $(x, 12)$ satisfies $y = 4x + 8$. **1**
47. Find the value of x so that $(x, 6)$ satisfies $y = -x - 4$. **−10**
48. Find the value of y so that $(-2, y)$ satisfies $y = -2x^2$. **−8**
49. ///**ERROR ANALYSIS**/// Rashid saves \$150 each month. He wants to know how much he will have saved in 2 years. He writes the equation $s = m + 150$ to help him figure out how much he will save, where s is the amount saved and m is the number of months he saves. Explain why his equation is incorrect.

49. Rashid must multiply \$150 by the number of months he saves for, not add the number of months to 150.

50. **Write About It** Give a real-life situation that can be described by a function. Explain which is the independent variable and which is the dependent variable.

CONCEPT CONNECTION

51. This problem will prepare you for the Concept Connection on page 222.

The table shows the volume v of water pumped into a pool after t hours.

a. Determine a relationship between the time and the volume of water and write an equation. **$V = 1250t$**
b. Identify the independent and dependent variables. **ind. var.: time; dep. var.: volume**
c. If the pool holds 10,000 gallons, how long will it take to fill? **8 h**

Amount of Water in Pool	
Time (h)	**Volume (gal)**
0	0
1	1250
2	2500
3	3750
4	5000

CONCEPT CONNECTION Exercise 51 involves determining relationships between two variables. This exercise prepares students for the Concept Connection on page 222.

Answers

40. D: all real numbers; R: all real numbers
41. D: all real numbers; R: all real numbers
42. D: all real numbers; R: all real numbers
43. D: all real numbers; R: all real numbers
44. D: all real numbers; R: $y \geq 6$
45. D: all real numbers; R: $y \geq -5$
50. Possible answer: The cost of a hotel room is a function of how many nights you stay. The cost is the dependent variable because it depends on the number of nights; therefore the number of nights is the independent variable.

4-3 READING STRATEGIES

LESSON 4-3 Reading Strategies
Understanding Vocabulary

To read and write functions, you must understand what is meant by an *independent variable* and a *dependent variable*.

domain
x-value — Independent Variable — x
input

range
y-value — Dependent Variable — f(x)
output

Carmen attends a school with a dress code. She went shopping and found acceptable shirts for \$15 each. Her mother has allowed her to buy up to 5 new shirts for the school year.

Independent variable: number of shirts
Dependent variable: total cost
The function that represents this relation is $f(x) = 15x$.
Reasonable domain (x-values): {1, 2, 3, 4, 5}
Reasonable range (y-values): {15, 30, 45, 60, 75}
When $x = 5$, $f(x) = 75$.
So, 5 shirts will cost \$75.

Answer the following based on the situation below.

Molly is making greeting cards for 5 of her friends. Each card is to have 4 ribbons.

1. Identify each as either the independent or the dependent variable.
   "number of ribbons used" **dependent**
   "number of cards made" **independent**
2. Write a function for the relation. **$f(x) = 4x$**
3. What is the reasonable domain for this function? **D: {1, 2, 3, 4, 5}**
4. What is the reasonable range for this function? **R: {4, 8, 12, 16, 20}**
5. Graph the function.

4-3 REVIEW FOR MASTERY

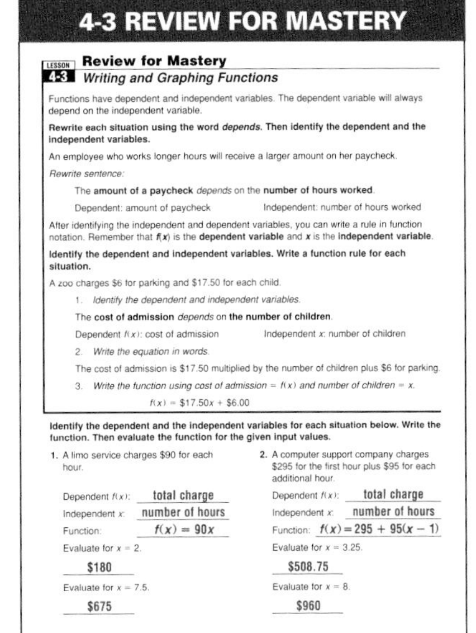

LESSON 4-3 Review for Mastery
Writing and Graphing Functions

Functions have dependent and independent variables. The dependent variable will always depend on the independent variable.

Rewrite each situation using the word *depends*. Then identify the dependent and the independent variables.

An employee who works longer hours will receive a larger amount on her paycheck.

Rewrite sentence:

The **amount of a paycheck** *depends* on the **number of hours worked**.

Dependent: amount of paycheck Independent: number of hours worked

After identifying the independent and dependent variables, you can write a rule in function notation. Remember that $f(x)$ is the **dependent variable** and x is the **independent variable**.

Identify the dependent and independent variables. Write a function rule for each situation.

A zoo charges \$6 for parking and \$17.50 for each child.

1. *Identify the dependent and independent variables.*
   The **cost of admission** *depends* on **the number of children**.
   Dependent $f(x)$: cost of admission Independent x: number of children
2. *Write the equation in words.*
   The cost of admission is \$17.50 multiplied by the number of children plus \$6 for parking.
3. *Write the function using cost of admission = $f(x)$ and number of children = x.*
   $f(x) = \$17.50x + \$6.00$

Identify the dependent and the independent variables for each situation below. Write the function. Then evaluate the function for the given input values.

1. A limo service charges \$90 for each hour.
   Dependent $f(x)$: **total charge**
   Independent x: **number of hours**
   Function: **$f(x) = 90x$**
   Evaluate for $x = 2$. **\$180**
   Evaluate for $x = 7.5$. **\$675**
2. A computer support company charges \$295 for the first hour plus \$95 for each additional hour.
   Dependent $f(x)$: **total charge**
   Independent x: **number of hours**
   Function: **$f(x) = 295 + 95(x - 1)$**
   Evaluate for $x = 3.25$. **\$508.75**
   Evaluate for $x = 8$. **\$960**

4-3 PRACTICE A

4-3 PRACTICE C

4-3 PRACTICE B

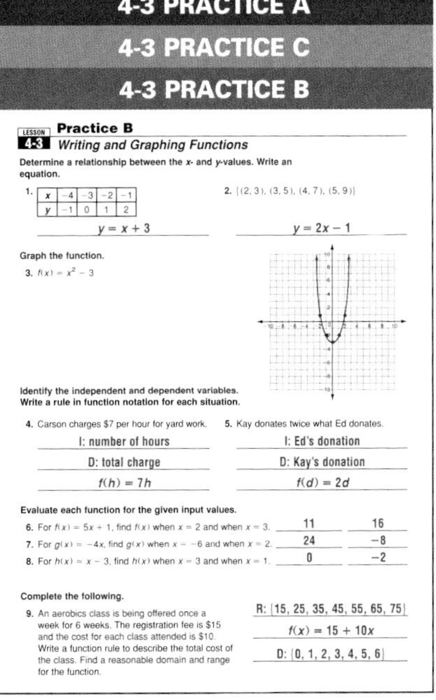

LESSON 4-3 Practice B
Writing and Graphing Functions

Determine a relationship between the x- and y-values. Write an equation.

1.

x	−4	−3	−2	−1
y	−1	0	1	2

$y = x + 3$

2. {(2, 3), (3, 5), (4, 7), (5, 9)} **$y = 2x - 1$**

Graph the function.

3. $f(x) = x^2 - 3$

Identify the independent and dependent variables. Write a rule in function notation for each situation.

4. Carson charges \$7 per hour for yard work.
   I: number of hours
   D: total charge
   $f(h) = 7h$
5. Kay donates twice what Ed donates.
   I: Ed's donation
   D: Kay's donation
   $f(d) = 2d$

Evaluate each function for the given input values.

6. For $f(x) = 5x + 1$, find $f(x)$ when $x = 2$ and when $x = 3$. **11** **16**
7. For $g(x) = -4x$, find $g(x)$ when $x = -6$ and when $x = 2$. **24** **−8**
8. For $h(x) = x - 3$, find $h(x)$ when $x = 3$ and when $x = 1$. **0** **−2**

Complete the following.

9. An aerobics class is being offered once a week for 6 weeks. The registration fee is \$15 and the cost for each class attended is \$10. Write a function rule to describe the total cost of the class. Find a reasonable domain and range for the function.
   R: {15, 25, 35, 45, 55, 65, 75}
   $f(x) = 15 + 10x$
   D: {0, 1, 2, 3, 4, 5, 6}

Multiple Choice Exercise 52 states that one pencil is purchased for \$0.10. Therefore, the function must contain 0.10 as a constant (not multiplied by the variable). This is true only in choice **D**.

Answers

58–60. See p. A16.

Journal

Use $y = x^2 + 1$ to explain how you choose points when graphing a function. Graph the function.

ALTERNATIVE ASSESSMENT

Have students choose a math formula and write the formula in function notation, stating which is the dependent variable and which is the independent variable. Then have them evaluate their function for three appropriate domain values.

Power Presentations with PowerPoint®

4-3 Lesson Quiz

1. Graph $y = |x + 3|$.

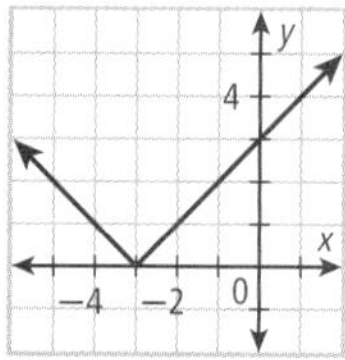

Identify the independent and dependent variables. Write a rule in function notation for each situation.

2. A buffet charges \$8.95 per person. ind.: number of people; dep.: cost; $f(p) = 8.95p$

3. A moving company charges \$130 for weekly truck rental plus \$1.50 per mile. ind.: miles; dep.: cost; $f(m) = 130 + 1.50m$

Evaluate each function for the given input values.

4. For $g(t) = \frac{1}{4}t - 3$, find $g(t)$ when $t = 20$ and when $t = -12$. $g(20) = 2$; $g(-12) = -6$

5. For $f(x) = 6x - 1$, find $f(x)$ when $x = 3.5$ and when $x = -5$. $f(3.5) = 20$; $f(-5) = -31$

Also available on transparency

Multiple Choice For Exercises 52 and 53, choose the best answer.

52. Marsha buys x pens at \$0.70 per pen and one pencil for \$0.10. Which equation gives the total amount c that Marsha spends?

Ⓐ $c = 0.70x + 0.10x$ Ⓒ $c = (0.70 + 0.10)x$
Ⓑ $c = 0.70x + 1$ **Ⓓ** $c = 0.70x + 0.10$

53. Belle is buying pizzas for her daughter's birthday party, using the prices in the table. Which equation best describes the relationship between the total cost c and the number of pizzas p?

Pizzas	Total Cost (\$)
5	26.25
10	52.50
15	78.75

Ⓐ $c = 26.25p$ Ⓒ $c = p + 26.25$
Ⓑ $c = 5.25p$ Ⓓ $c = 6p - 3.75$

54. Gridded Response What is the value of $f(x) = 5 - \frac{1}{2}x$ when $x = 3$? **3.5**

CHALLENGE AND EXTEND

55. Reasoning Complete the following argument, which explains why the vertical-line test can be used to identify functions.

The x-values of all of the points on a vertical line are ___?___. For a relation to be a function, there cannot be a(n) ___?___ that is paired with more than one y-value. If there are two or more points on a vertical line that are also on the graph of a relation, then these points have the same ___?___ but different ___?___. In other words, there is a(n) ___?___ paired with ___?___ y-value. So, the graph cannot represent a function.

55. the same; x-value; x-value; y-values; x-value; more than one

56. Does the equation $x = |y|$ represent a function? Explain.

56. No; possible answer: the x-value 1 corresponds with y-values 1 and −1.

57. Write an equation that does NOT represent a function. **Possible answer: $x = y^2$**

Show that each equation does not represent a function. (*Hint:* **Try to find a domain value that is paired with more than one range value.)**

58. $x^2 + y^2 = 4$ **59.** $y^2 = x^2 + 36$ **60.** $x = |y| + 1$

SPIRAL STANDARDS REVIEW

4.0, 5.0, 16.0, 17.0, 18.0

Solve each equation. Check your answer. *(Lesson 2-3)*

61. $5x + 2 - 7x = -10$ **6** **62.** $3(2 - y) = 15$ **−3** **63.** $\frac{2}{3}p - \frac{1}{2} = \frac{1}{6}$ **1**

Solve each inequality. *(Lesson 3-5)*

64. $21 + 7x \le 7(3 + x)$ **65.** $9(w + 2) < 9w + 17$ $\varnothing$ **66.** $13(r + 1) < 13r - 6$ $\varnothing$

67. $2a - 16 \ge 2a - 17$ **68.** $3t - 12 > 3t + 2$ $\varnothing$ **69.** $2 - 3g + 7 \ge 3(2 - g)$

64. all real numbers
67. all real numbers
69. all real numbers

Give the domain and range of each relation. Tell whether the relation is a function and explain. *(Lesson 4-2)*

70.

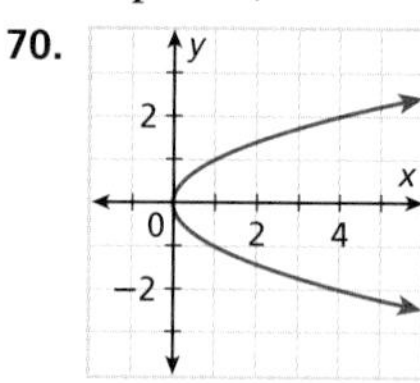

D: $x \ge 0$; R: all real numbers; not a function; some domain values are paired with more than one range value.

71.

x	y
−3	4
−1	2
0	0
1	2
3	−4

D: {−3, −1, 0, 1, 3}; R: {4, 2, 0, −4}; function; each domain value is paired with exactly one range value.

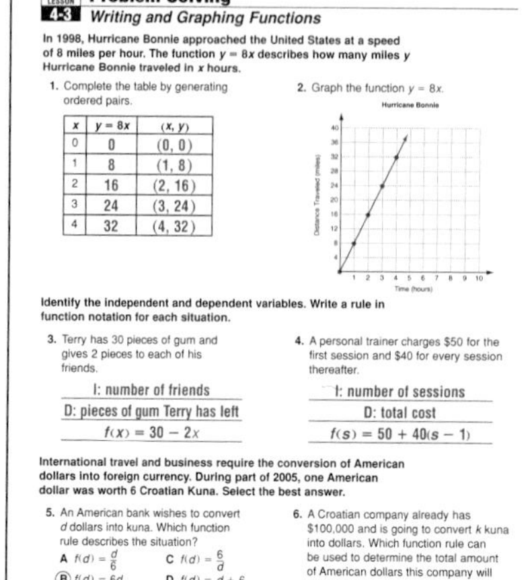

4-3 PROBLEM SOLVING

LESSON 4-3 **Problem Solving**
Writing and Graphing Functions

In 1998, Hurricane Bonnie approached the United States at a speed of 8 miles per hour. The function $y = 8x$ describes how many miles y Hurricane Bonnie traveled in x hours.

1. Complete the table by generating ordered pairs.

x	$y = 8x$	(x, y)
0	0	(0, 0)
1	8	(1, 8)
2	16	(2, 16)
3	24	(3, 24)
4	32	(4, 32)

2. Graph the function $y = 8x$.

Identify the independent and dependent variables. Write a rule in function notation for each situation.

3. Terry has 30 pieces of gum and gives 2 pieces to each of his friends.
I: number of friends
D: pieces of gum Terry has left
$f(x) = 30 - 2x$

4. A personal trainer charges \$50 for the first session and \$40 for every session thereafter.
I: number of sessions
D: total cost
$f(s) = 50 + 40(s - 1)$

International travel and business require the conversion of American dollars into foreign currency. During part of 2005, one American dollar was worth 6 Croatian Kuna. Select the best answer.

5. An American bank wishes to convert d dollars into kuna. Which function rule describes the situation?
A $f(d) = \frac{d}{6}$ C $f(d) = \frac{6}{d}$
Ⓑ $f(d) = 6d$ D $f(d) = d + 6$

6. A Croatian company already has \$100,000 and is going to convert k kuna into dollars. Which function rule can be used to determine the total amount of American dollars this company will have?
F $f(x) = 100{,}000 + 6k$
Ⓖ $f(x) = 100{,}000 + \frac{k}{6}$
H $f(x) = 100{,}000k + 6$
J $f(x) = 100{,}000 + \frac{6}{k}$

7. Macon has \$100 and is thinking about converting some of it into kuna. What is a reasonable range for this situation?
A $0 \le y \le 6$ C $0 \le y \le 100$
Ⓑ $0 \le y \le 16.7$ D $0 \le y \le 600$

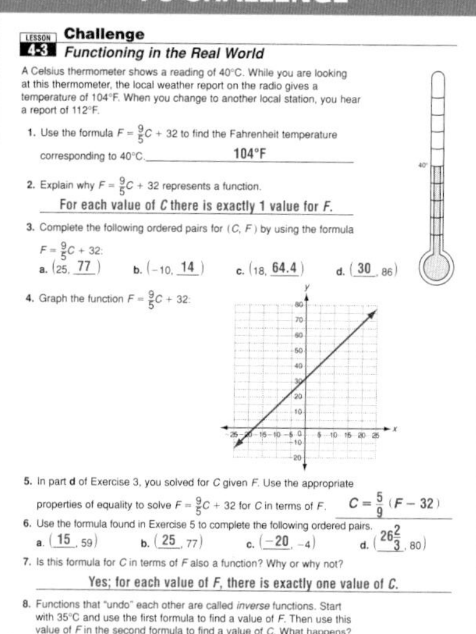

4-3 CHALLENGE

LESSON 4-3 **Challenge**
Functioning in the Real World

A Celsius thermometer shows a reading of 40°C. While you are looking at this thermometer, the local weather report on the radio gives a temperature of 104°F. When you change to another local station, you hear a report of 112°F.

1. Use the formula $F = \frac{9}{5}C + 32$ to find the Fahrenheit temperature corresponding to 40°C. **104°F**

2. Explain why $F = \frac{9}{5}C + 32$ represents a function.
For each value of C there is exactly 1 value for F.

3. Complete the following ordered pairs for (C, F) by using the formula $F = \frac{9}{5}C + 32$:
a. (25, **77**) b. (−10, **14**) c. (18, **64.4**) d. (**30**, 86)

4. Graph the function $F = \frac{9}{5}C + 32$:

5. In part **d** of Exercise 3, you solved for C given F. Use the appropriate properties of equality to solve $F = \frac{9}{5}C + 32$ for C in terms of F. $C = \frac{5}{9}(F - 32)$

6. Use the formula found in Exercise 5 to complete the following ordered pairs.
a. (**15**, 59) b. (**25**, 77) c. (**−20**, −4) d. ($26\frac{2}{3}$, 80)

7. Is this formula for C in terms of F also a function? Why or why not?
Yes; for each value of F, there is exactly one value of C.

8. Functions that "undo" each other are called *inverse* functions. Start with 35°C and use the first formula to find a value of F. Then use this value of F in the second formula to find a value of C. What happens?
The result is the original 35.

Connect Equations, Tables, and Graphs

You can use a graphing calculator to understand the connections among equations, tables, and graphs.

Use with Lesson 4-3

go.hrw.com
Lab Resources Online
KEYWORD: MA8CA Lab4

Activity

Make a table of values for the equation $y = 4x + 3$. Then graph.

1. Press Y= and enter **4x + 3**.

2. Press 2nd WINDOW (TBLSET). Make sure **Indpnt: Auto** and **Depend: Auto** are selected.

3. To view the table, press 2nd GRAPH (TABLE). The x-values and the corresponding y-values appear in table form. Use the up and down arrow keys to scroll through the table.

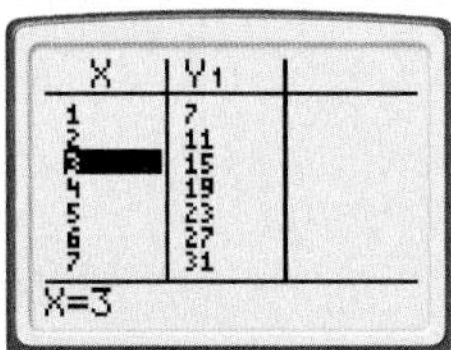

4. To view the table with the graph, press MODE and select **G-T** (Graph-Table) view. Press ENTER. Be sure to use the standard window.

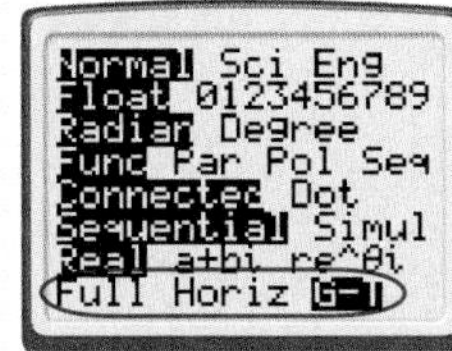

5. Press TRACE to see both the graph and a table of values.

6. Press the left arrow key several times to move the cursor. Notice how the point on the graph and the values in the table correspond.

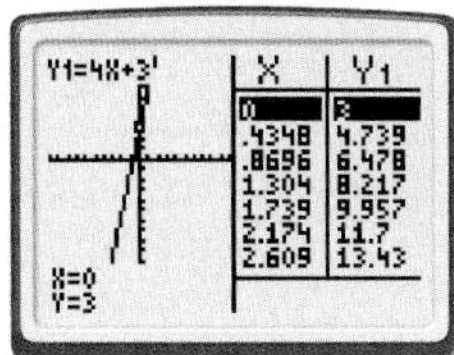

Try This

Make a table of values for each equation. Then graph.

1. $f(x) = 2x - 1$
2. $f(x) = 1.5x$
3. $f(x) = \frac{1}{2}x + 2$
4. Explain the relationship between an equation and its table of values and the graph of the equation. **The table of values and graph show ordered pairs that satisfy the equation.**

Teacher to Teacher

Jack Nunes
Sacramento, CA

I have an activity called *Algebra Walk* in which students become parts of a live function graph. A large coordinate plane is either drawn on or in some way placed on the floor. Eleven students are each given an index card that contains an integer between −5 and 5 inclusive.

The eleven students stand on the x-axis on their given number. Then a function such as $f(x) = x + 3$ is read aloud and displayed. Students mentally evaluate the function for their x-value. Then each student moves and stands on the point that has the appropriate coordinates. If possible, the students who are observing the Algebra Walk stand at an elevated area, such as bleachers, and compare their own graph with the human graph.

Organizer

Use with Lesson 4-3

Objective: Use a graphing calculator to make the connections among equations, tables, and graphs.

Materials: graphing calculator

Online Edition
Graphing Calculator

Countdown to Mastery Week 8

Teach

Discuss

Point out to students that all pairs of decimal values in the table are also ordered pairs.

Close

Key Concept

Equations, tables, and graphs contain the same ordered pairs in different formats.

Assessment

Journal Create an equation. Make a table of values and list three ordered pairs. Then graph the ordered pairs and sketch the graph.

Technology Before beginning, students should check that the tables in their calculator have been cleared. Point out that **TblStart** defines the x-value at which the table values start and that **ΔTbl** defines the increment by which the x-values increase. Have students change these values if they are not already set to 1. After completing the activity, students should return their calculators to **Full** mode.

Answers to *Try This*

1–3. See p. A16.

CHAPTER 4 CONCEPT CONNECTION

SECTION 4A

SECTION 4A CONCEPT CONNECTION

Organizer

Objective: Assess students' ability to apply concepts and skills in Lessons 4-1 through 4-3 in a real-world format

PREMIER Online Edition

Problem	Text Reference
1	Lesson 4-1
2	Lesson 4-2
3	Lesson 4-2
4	Lesson 4-3
5	Lesson 4-3

Function Concepts

Down the Drain The graph shows the relationship between the number of hours that have passed since a pool began to drain and the amount of water in the pool.

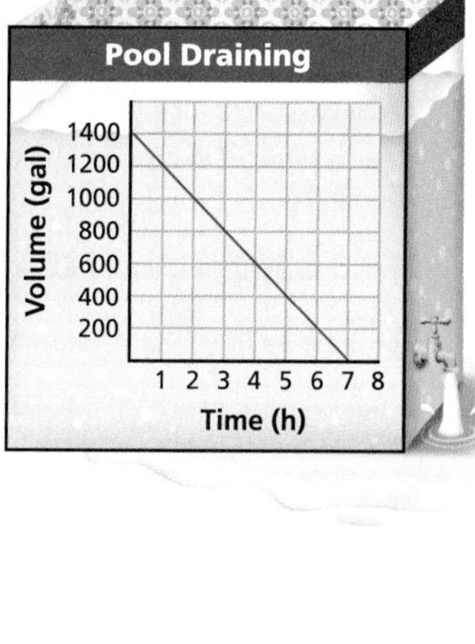

1. Describe in words the relationship between the amount of water in the pool and the number of hours that have passed since the pool began to drain.
2. What are the domain and range for the graph? **$0 \le h \le 7$; $0 \le v \le 1400$**
3. Use the graph to determine how much water is in the pool after 3 hours. How much water is in the pool after $4\frac{1}{2}$ hours? **800 gal; 500 gal**
4. Copy and complete the table.

Draining Pool	
Time (h)	Volume (gal)
0	1400
1	**1200**
2	**1000**
3	**800**
4	**600**
5	**400**
6	**200**
7	**0**

5. Write an equation to describe the relationship between the volume V and the number of hours h. Use the equation to find how much water is in the pool after 5.2 hours. **$v = 1400 - 200h$; 360 gal**

1. Possible answer: The pool begins with 1400 gallons. As time goes on, the volume of water decreases by 200 gallons per hour.

INTERVENTION

Scaffolding Questions

1. When draining the pool, what happens to the volume of the water? As the pool drains, the volume of water decreases.
2. Does the volume depend on time, or does time depend on the volume? Volume depends on time.
3. Which axis is labeled with hours? horizontal Which axis is labeled with the amount of water? vertical
4. At what height is the graph at 1 hour? 1200 at 2 hours? 1000
5. What is the rate at which the water is decreasing per hour as the pool drains? The water is decreasing at 200 gallons per hour.

Extension

Write an equation that describes the relationship between the volume V and the time t for a pool that contains 800 gallons and drains at 100 gallons per hour. Does your equation describe a function?
$V(t) = 800 - 100t$; yes

California Standards

Algebra 1 **17.0**

CHAPTER 4

SECTION 4A

Quiz for Lessons 4-1 Through 4-3

4-1 Graphing Relationships

Choose the graph that best represents each situation.

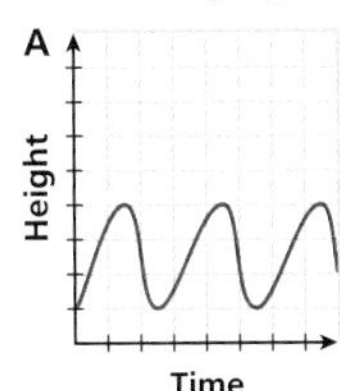

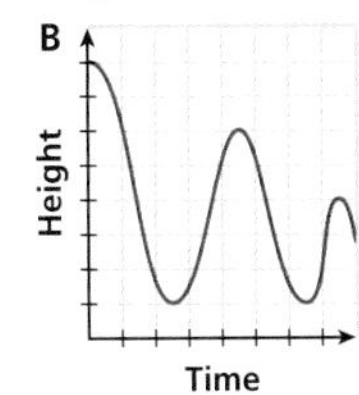

1. A person bungee jumps from a high platform. **B**
2. A person jumps on a trampoline in a steady motion. **A**
3. Xander takes a quiz worth 100 points. Each question is worth 20 points. Sketch a graph to show his possible score if he misses 1, 2, 3, 4, or 5 questions.

4-2 Relations and Functions

Give the domain and range of each relation. Tell whether the relation is a function. Explain.

4. 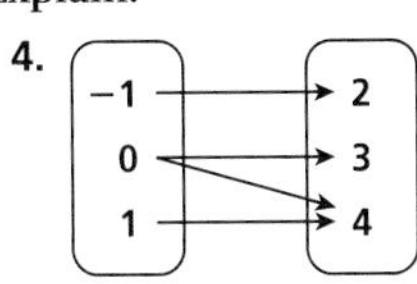

5. 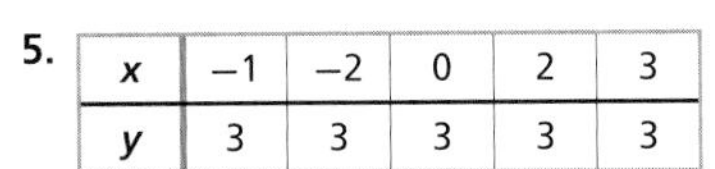

x	–1	–2	0	2	3
y	3	3	3	3	3

6. 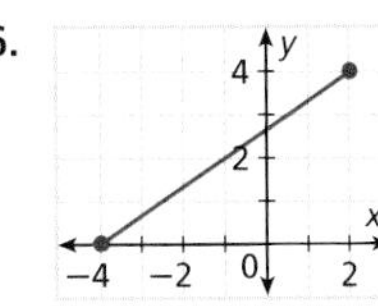

4-3 Writing and Graphing Functions

Determine a relationship between the x- and y-values. Write an equation.

7.

x	y
1	–6
2	–5
3	–4
4	–3

The value of y is 7 less than x; $y = x - 7$.

8.

x	y
1	–3
2	–6
3	–9
4	–12

The value of y is –3 times the value of x; $y = -3x$.

9. A printer can print 8 pages per minute. Identify the dependent and independent variables for the situation. Write a rule in function notation.
ind. var.: minutes; dep. var.: pages; $f(m) = 8m$

Evaluate each function for the given input values.

10. For $f(x) = 3x - 1$, find $f(x)$ when $x = 2$. **5**
11. For $g(x) = x^2 - x$, find $g(x)$ when $x = -2$. **6**

Graph each equation. Then tell whether the equation represents a function.

12. $x + y = 6$ **yes**
13. $y = |x| - 3$ **yes**
14. $y = x^2 + 1$ **yes**

READY TO GO ON?

SECTION 4A

Organizer

Objective: Assess students' mastery of concepts and skills in Lessons 4-1 through 4-3.

Countdown to Mastery Week 8

Resources

Assessment Resources
Section 4A Quiz

Test & Practice Generator
One-Stop Planner®

INTERVENTION 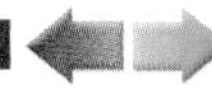

Resources

***Ready to Go On? Intervention and Enrichment* Worksheets**

***Ready to Go On?* CD-ROM**

***Ready to Go On?* Online**

my.hrw.com

Answers

3. See p. A16.
4. D: {–1, 0, 1}; R: {2, 3, 4}; not a function; the x-value 0 is assigned to the y-value 3 and the y-value 4.
5, 6. See p. A16.
12–14. See p. A17.

READY TO GO ON? Diagnose and Prescribe

Ready to Go On? Intervention	*Ready to Go On? Intervention,* Section 4A: Worksheets	CD-ROM	Online
Lesson 4-1 Rev. 7AF1.5	4-1 Intervention	Activity 4-1	Diagnose and Prescribe Online
Lesson 4-2 16.0, 17.0, 18.0	4-2 Intervention	Activity 4-2	
Lesson 4-3 16.0, 17.0, 18.0	4-3 Intervention	Activity 4-3	

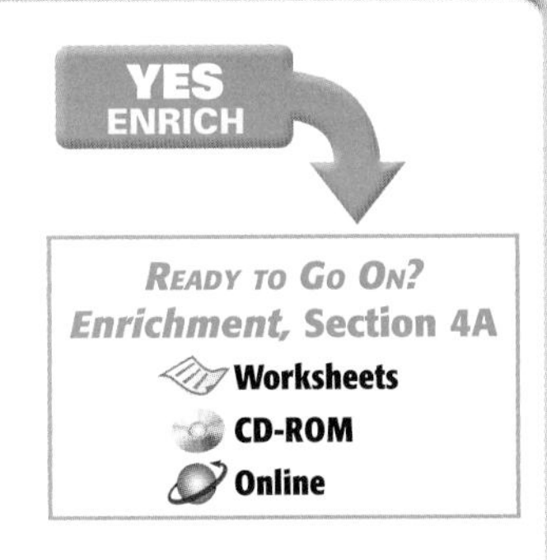

YES
ENRICH
READY TO GO ON? Enrichment, Section 4A
Worksheets
CD-ROM
Online

Applying Functions

One-Minute Section Planner

Lesson	Lab Resources	Materials
Lesson 4-4 Scatter Plots and Trend Lines • Create and interpret scatter plots. • Use trend lines to make predictions. **Review of Grade 7 SDAP1.2**	***Algebra Labs 4-4*** In *Chapter 4 Resource File*	**Optional** uncooked spaghetti, centimeter cubes (MK)
Lesson 4-5 Arithmetic Sequences • Recognize and extend an arithmetic sequence. • Find a given term of an arithmetic sequence. **Preparation for Algebra II 22.0**		

MK = *Manipulatives Kit*

Notes

Math Background: Teaching the Standards

USING RELATIONS AND FUNCTIONS

Lesson 4-5

Scatter plots provide an efficient way to present, analyze, and describe large quantities of data. As such, they are one of the most important applications of relations.

A scatter plot is a graph that shows *bivariate data*; that is, data for which there are two variables for each observation. Each point on the scatter plot represents one data pair. The scatter plot below shows the area and the number of counties for the seven smallest U.S. states. Each point represents the data pair for a single state. Rhode Island has an area of approximately 1500 square miles and 5 counties. This is represented by the ordered pair (1.5, 5).

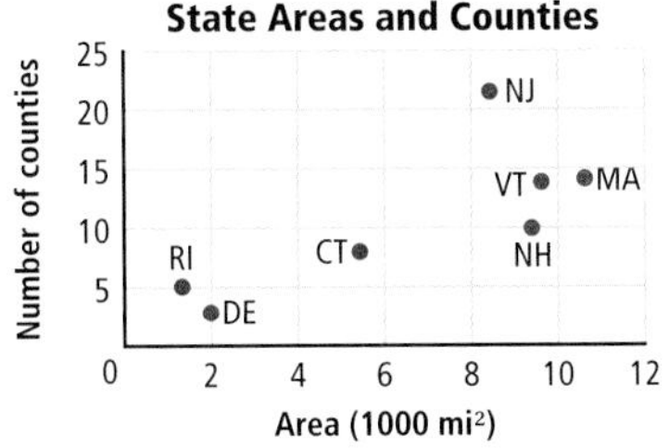

Students are often tempted to connect points on a scatter plot. It is essential that students understand that a scatter plot shows all of the collected data and that a path that is drawn by connecting the points is meaningless.

A *correlation* describes the relationship between the two data sets in a scatter plot. A *positive correlation* means that both sets of data values tend to increase together. The scatter plot of state areas and counties shows a positive correlation. A *negative correlation* means that one set of data values tends to increase as the other decreases. A scatter plot that shows the number of hours a group of people spend reading and the number of hours they spend watching television would likely show a negative correlation.

More specifically, the *correlation coefficient* measures the degree of similarity between two data sets. The correlation coefficient is a value between -1 and 1, where -1 indicates a perfect negative correlation (the data points all fall on a downward slanting line) and 1 indicates a perfect positive coefficient (the data points all fall on an upward-slanting line). The closer the coefficient is to -1 or 1, the stronger the correlation, and the more closely the data points resemble a straight line. A coefficient of 0 means the data show *no correlation*, and in this case the scatter plot's points may appear to be randomly distributed.

ARITHMETIC SEQUENCES

Lesson 4-6

A *sequence* is a type of function whose domain is the natural numbers, {1, 2, 3, ...}. Each natural number is paired with a term of the sequence; hence the range is the terms of the sequence. The figure shows how the natural numbers are paired with the terms of the sequence formed by positive multiples of 3.

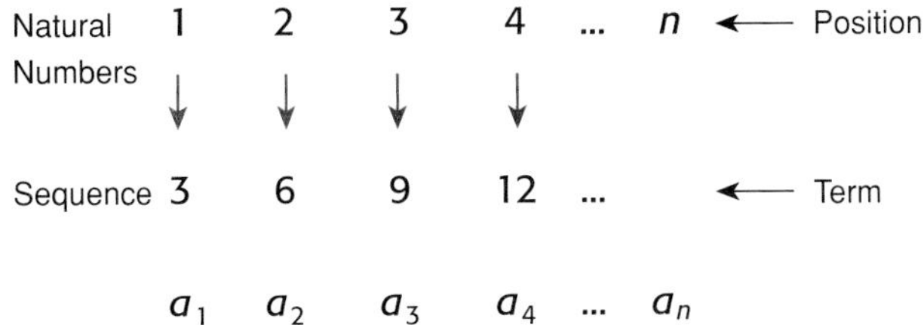

In an *arithmetic sequence*, all pairs of successive terms differ by the same nonzero constant, called the *common difference*. Equivalently, each term is equal to the previous term plus the common difference. The above sequence is arithmetic with common difference 3.

The *n*th term of an arithmetic sequence with common difference d is given by $a_n = a_1 + (n - 1)d$. Students are sometimes puzzled by the use of $n - 1$. Exploring simple cases can help students see why $n - 1$ makes sense. For example, to find the 2nd term of the sequence, start with the first term and add the common difference once. To find the 3rd term, start with the first term and add the common difference twice. Generally, to find the *n*th term, start with the first term and add the common difference $n - 1$ times, as stated in the formula.

4-4 Organizer

Objectives: Create and interpret scatter plots.

Use trend lines to make predictions.

Algebra Labs
In Chapter 4 Resource File

Online Edition
Tutorial Videos, Interactivity, TechKeys

Countdown to Mastery Week 8

Power Presentations with PowerPoint®

Warm Up

Graph each point.

1. $A(3, 2)$ **2.** $B(-3, 3)$

3. $C(-2, -1)$ **4.** $D(0, -3)$

5. $E(1, 0)$ **6.** $F(3, -2)$

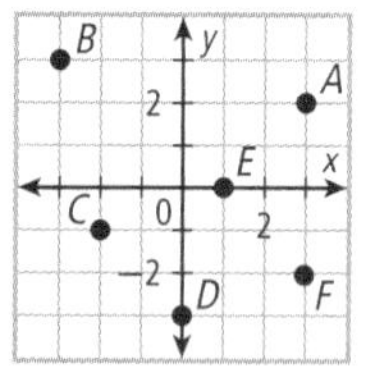

Also available on transparency

Math Humor

Q: What should you title a graph showing the relative diameters and weights of a batch of pancakes?

A: The Batter Plot!

California Standards

Review of Grade 7 **SDAP1.2**

4-4 Scatter Plots and Trend Lines

California Standards

Review of Grade 7
SDAP 1.2 Represent two numerical variables on a scatter plot and informally describe how the data points are distributed and any apparent relationship that exists between the two variables (e.g., between time spent on homework and grade level).

Who uses this?

Ecologists can use scatter plots to help them analyze data about endangered species, such as ocelots. (See Example 1.)

In this chapter, you have examined relationships between sets of ordered pairs, or data. Displaying data visually can help you see relationships.

A **scatter plot** is a graph with points plotted to show a possible relationship between two sets of data. A scatter plot is an effective way to display some types of data.

Vocabulary
scatter plot
correlation
positive correlation
negative correlation
no correlation
trend line

EXAMPLE 1 Graphing a Scatter Plot from Given Data

The table shows the number of species added to the list of endangered and threatened species in the United States during the given years. Graph a scatter plot using the given data.

Increase in List							
Calendar Year	1996	1997	1998	1999	2000	2001	2002
Species Added	91	79	62	11	39	10	9

Source: U.S. Fish and Wildlife Service

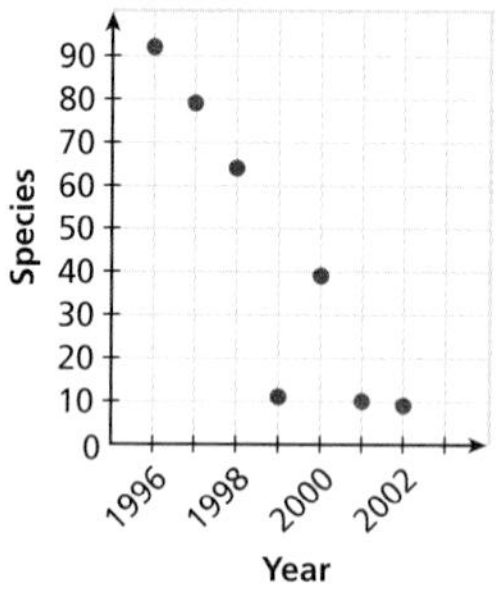

Species Added to List

(Scatter plot: Species 0–90 vs. Year 1996, 1998, 2000, 2002)

Use the table to make ordered pairs for the scatter plot.

The x-value represents the calendar year and the y-value represents the number of species added.

Plot the ordered pairs.

Helpful Hint

The point (2000, 39) tells you that in the year 2000, the list increased by 39 species.

CHECK IT OUT! **1.** The table shows the number of points scored by a high school football team in the first four games of a season. Graph a scatter plot using the given data.

Game	1	2	3	4
Points Scored	6	21	46	34

1. Football Team Scores (scatter plot: Points scored 5–45 vs. Game 1–4)

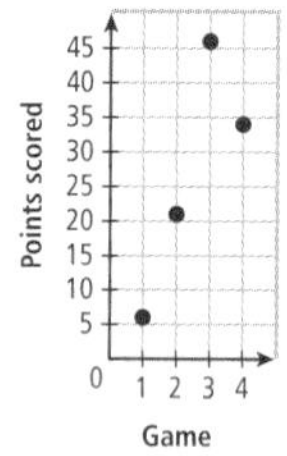

A **correlation** describes a relationship between two data sets. A graph may show the correlation between data. The correlation can help you analyze trends and make predictions. There are three types of correlations between data.

1 Introduce

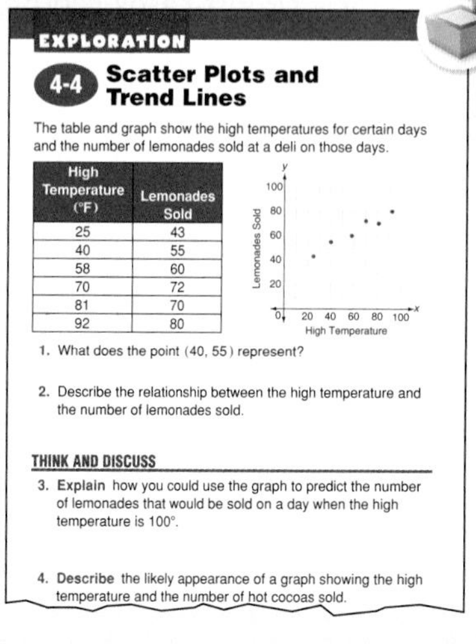

EXPLORATION

4-4 Scatter Plots and Trend Lines

The table and graph show the high temperatures for certain days and the number of lemonades sold at a deli on those days.

High Temperature (°F)	Lemonades Sold
25	43
40	55
58	60
70	72
81	70
92	80

(Graph: Lemonades Sold 20–100 vs. High Temperature 20–100)

1. What does the point (40, 55) represent?
2. Describe the relationship between the high temperature and the number of lemonades sold.

THINK AND DISCUSS

3. **Explain** how you could use the graph to predict the number of lemonades that would be sold on a day when the high temperature is 100°.
4. **Describe** the likely appearance of a graph showing the high temperature and the number of hot cocoas sold.

Motivate

Tell students that when 100 fish were placed in a pond, a fisherman caught 5. The next year, 150 fish were placed in the pond, and the fisherman caught 8. Ask students how many fish they think the fisherman would catch in a year when only 50 fish were placed in the pond. Have students explain their reasoning. Possible answer: 2; the fisherman caught more when there were more fish in the pond, so he should catch fewer when fewer fish are in the pond.

Explorations and answers are provided in *Alternate Openers: Explorations Transparencies.*

Correlations

Positive Correlation	Negative Correlation	No Correlation
Both sets of data values increase.	One set of data values increases as the other set decreases.	There is no relationship between the data sets.
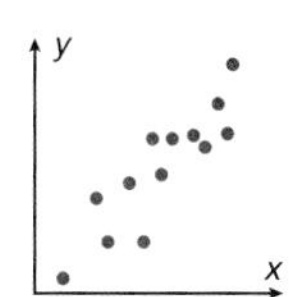	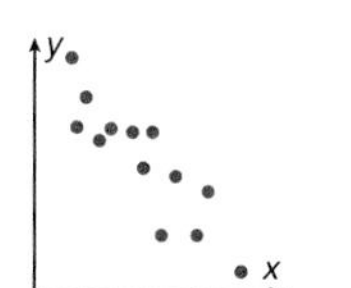	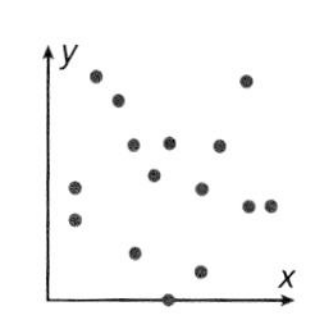

In the endangered species graph, as time increases, the number of new species added decreases. So the correlation between the data is negative.

EXAMPLE 2 Describing Correlations from Scatter Plots

Describe the correlation illustrated by the scatter plot.

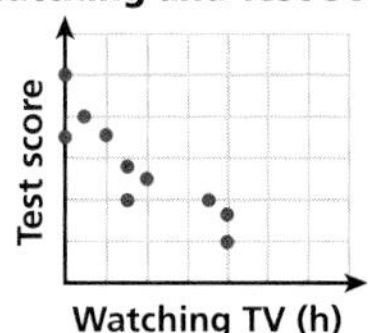

As the number of hours spent watching TV increased, test scores decreased.

There is a negative correlation between the two data sets.

2. Describe the correlation illustrated by the scatter plot.
positive correlation

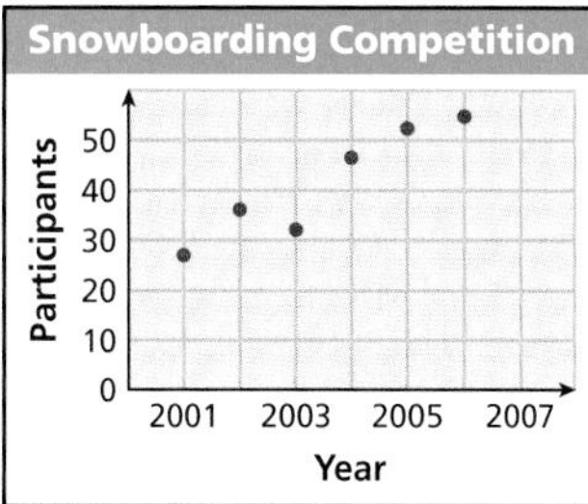

EXAMPLE 3 Identifying Correlations

Identify the correlation you would expect between each pair of data sets. Explain.

A **the number of empty seats in a classroom and the number of students seated in the class**

You would expect a negative correlation. As the number of students increases, the number of empty seats decreases.

B **the number of pets a person owns and the number of books that person read last year**

You would expect no correlation. The number of pets a person owns has nothing to do with how many books the person has read.

2 Teach

Guided Instruction

When working through **Example 2,** show students a graph of a perfect positive correlation (points form a straight line), strong positive correlation (points almost form a straight line), and weak positive correlation (generally going up, but points spread out). Then do the same for negative correlation.

Visual For smaller graphs, a piece of uncooked spaghetti works well when trying to place a trend line.

Universal Access

Through Concrete Manipulatives

Build a tower of centimeter cubes by adding one cube at random time intervals. Centimeter cubes can be found in the Manipulatives Kit (MK). Have a volunteer record how many cubes are in place every second. Have another student graph a scatter plot of the data. Point out the connection between the growing tower of cubes, the passage of time, and the positive correlation in the scatter plot.

Power Presentations with PowerPoint®

Additional Examples

Example 1

The table shows the number of cookies in a jar from the time since they were baked. Graph a scatter plot using the given data.

Cookies in the Jar				
Time Since Baked (d)	1	2	3	4
Cookies	24	16	10	7

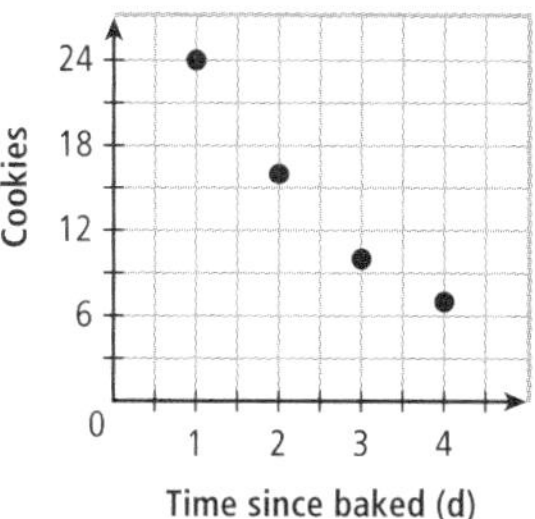

Example 2

Describe the correlation illustrated by the scatter plot.

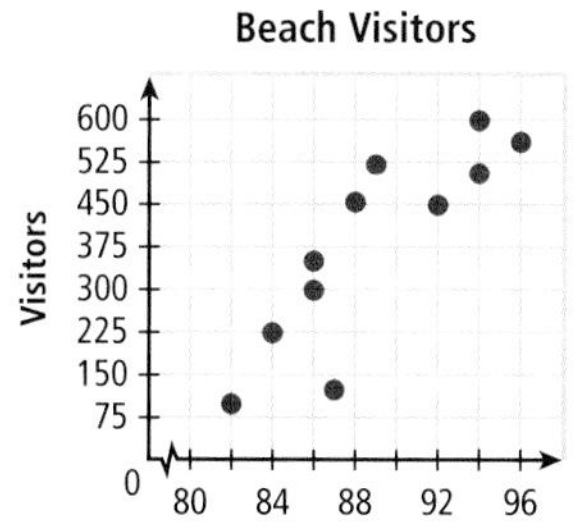

positive correlation

Example 3

Identify the correlation you would expect between each pair of data sets. Explain.

A. The average temperature in a city and the number of speeding tickets given in the city No correlation; the number of speeding tickets has nothing to do with the temperature.

B. The number of people in an audience and ticket sales Positive correlation; as ticket sales increase, the number of people in the audience increases.

C. A runner's time and the distance to the finish line Negative correlation; as a runner's time increases, the distance to the finish line decreases.

Also available on transparency

Power Presentations with PowerPoint®

Additional Examples

Example 4

Choose the scatter plot that best represents the relationship between the age of a car and the amount of money spent each year on repairs. Explain.

Graph A

Yearly Repair Costs

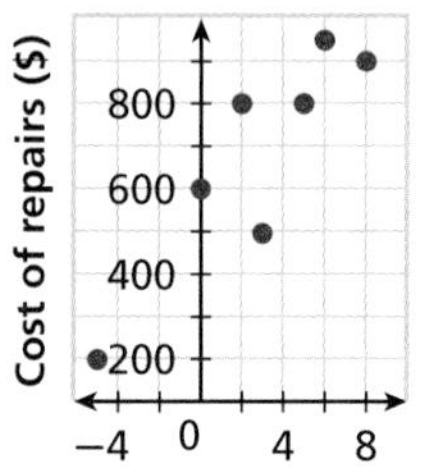

Graph B

Yearly Repair Costs

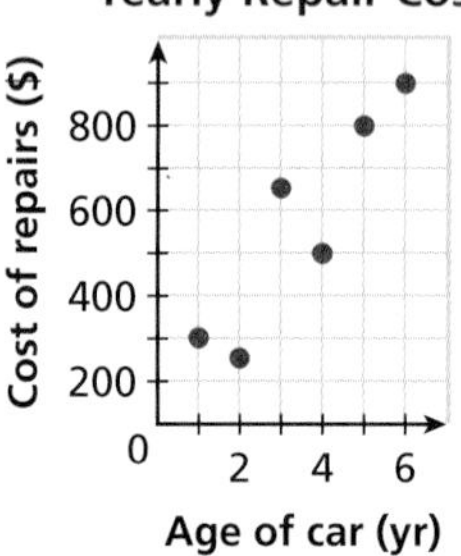

Graph C

Yearly Repair Costs

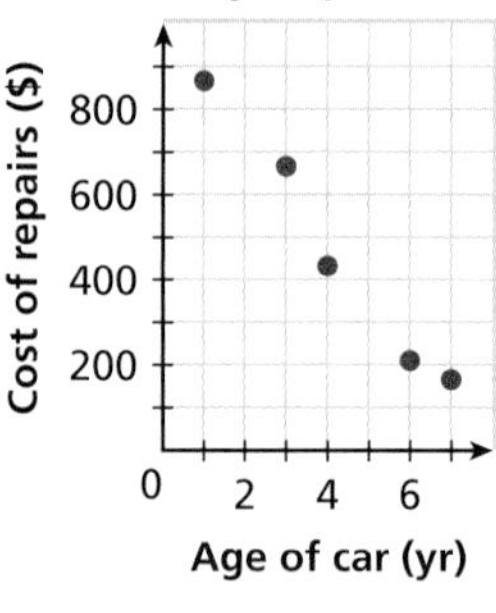

Graph B; graph A shows negative age; graph C shows costs decreasing, a negative correlation.

Also available on transparency

INTERVENTION

Questioning Strategies

EXAMPLE 1

- What do the points being graphed represent?

EXAMPLES 2–4

- What does a scatter plot look like if there is no correlation between the data sets? positive correlation? negative correlation?

3a. No correlation; the temperature in Houston has nothing to do with the number of cars sold in Boston.

b. Positive correlation; as the number of family members increases, more food is needed, so the grocery bill increases too.

4. Graph A; it cannot be graph B because graph B shows negative minutes; it cannot be graph C because graph C shows the temperature of the oven increasing, a positive correlation.

Identify the correlation you would expect between each pair of data sets. Explain.

C **the monthly rainfall and the depth of water in a reservoir**

You would expect a positive correlation. As more rain falls, there is more water in the reservoir.

Identify the correlation you would expect between each pair of data sets. Explain.

3a. the temperature in Houston and the number of cars sold in Boston

3b. the number of members in a family and the size of the family's grocery bill

3c. the number of times you sharpen your pencil and the length of your pencil **Negative correlation; as the number of times you sharpen your pencil increases, the length of the pencil decreases.**

EXAMPLE 4 Matching Scatter Plots to Situations

Choose the scatter plot that best represents the relationship between the number of days since a sunflower seed was planted and the height of the plant. Explain.

Graph A

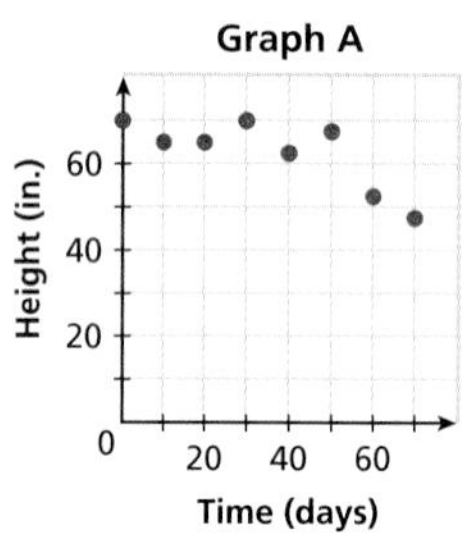

Graph B

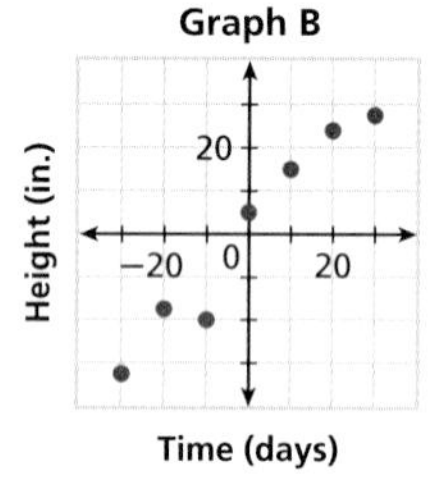

Graph C

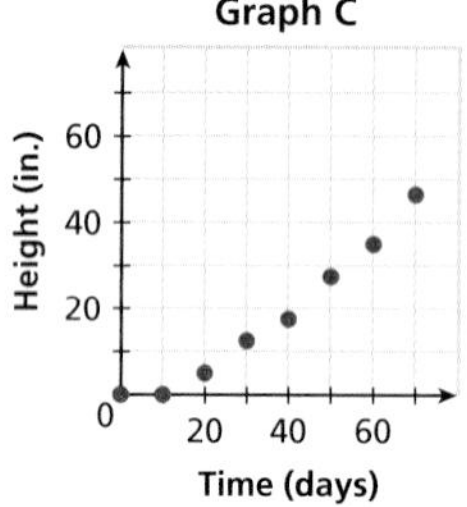

There will be a positive correlation between the number of days and the height because the plant will grow each day.

Neither the number of days nor the plant heights can be negative.

This graph shows all positive coordinates and a positive correlation, so it could represent the data sets.

Graph A has a negative correlation, so it is incorrect.

Graph B shows negative values, so it is incorrect.

Graph C is the correct scatter plot.

4. Choose the scatter plot that best represents the relationship between the number of minutes since an oven was turned off and the temperature of the oven. Explain.

Graph A

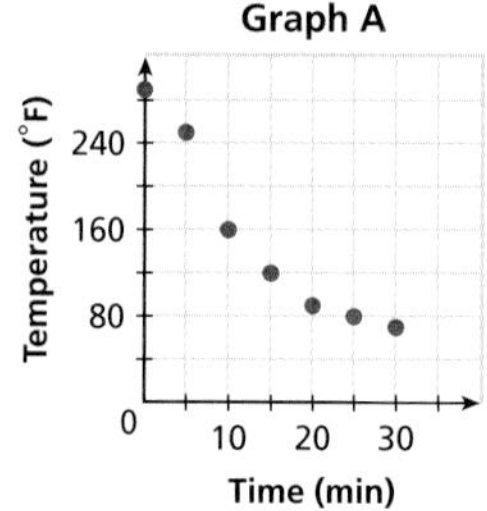

Graph B

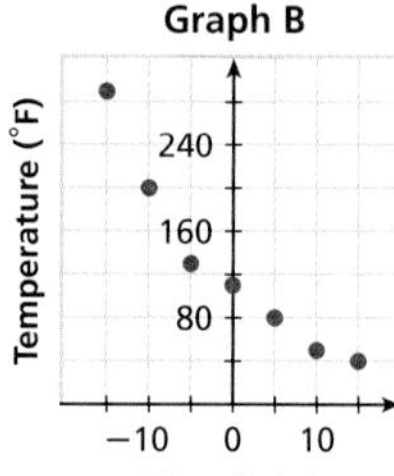

Graph C

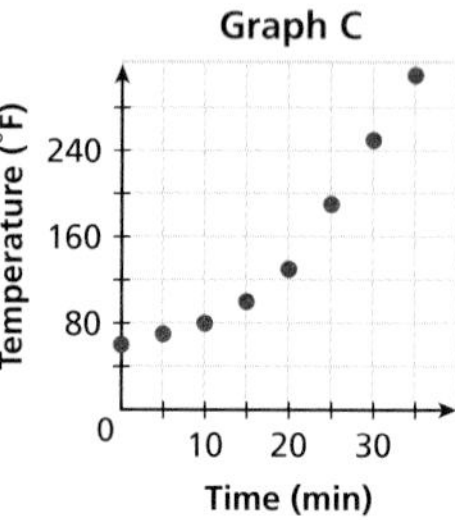

It is often helpful to add a line to better describe a scatter plot. This line, called a **trend line**, helps show the correlation between data sets more clearly. It can also be helpful when making predictions based on the data.

EXAMPLE 5 ***Fund-raising Application***

The scatter plot shows a relationship between the total amount of money collected and the total number of rolls of wrapping paper sold as a school fund-raiser. Based on this relationship, predict how much money will be collected when 175 rolls have been sold.

Fund-raiser

Money raised ($): 200, 400, 600, 800, 1000, 1200

Rolls sold: 50, 100, 150, 200

Draw a trend line and use it to make a prediction.

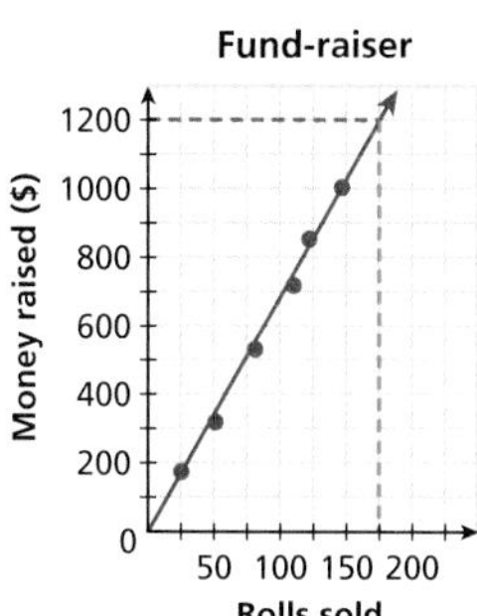

Draw a line that has about the same number of points above and below it. Your line may or may not go through data points.

Find the point on the line whose x-value is 175. The corresponding y-value is 1200.

Based on the data, $1200 is a reasonable prediction of how much money will be collected when 175 rolls have been sold.

5. Based on the trend line above, predict how many wrapping paper rolls need to be sold to raise $500. **about 75 rolls**

THINK AND DISCUSS

1. Is it possible to make a prediction based on a scatter plot with no correlation? Explain your answer.

Know it! Note

2. **GET ORGANIZED** Copy and complete the graphic organizer with either a scatter plot, or a real-world example, or both.

	Graph	Example
Positive Correlation		
Negative Correlation		The amount of water in a watering can and the number of flowers watered
No Correlation		

Power Presentations with PowerPoint®

Additional Examples

Example 5

The scatter plot shows a relationship between the total amount of money collected at the concession stand and the total number of tickets sold at a movie theater. Based on this relationship, predict how much money will be collected at the concession stand when 150 tickets have been sold.
about $750

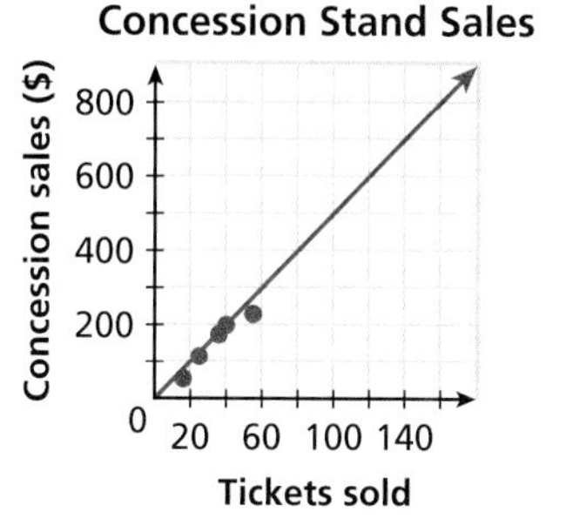

Also available on transparency

INTERVENTION
Questioning Strategies

EXAMPLE 5

- How do you decide where to draw the trend line?
- What factors could affect the accuracy of a prediction?

Language Support Explain to students that in math, *trend* means "tendency," not "fashionable." A *trend* line shows where the data *tend* to lie. A trend line is also called a "line of fit" or "line of best fit."

Close

Summarize

Tell students that in a positive correlation, the values of the variables tend to go in the same direction; that is, as the values of the first variable increase, so do the values of the second variable. In a negative correlation, the opposite is true. As the values of the first variable increase, the values of the second variable tend to decrease. Have students give real-world examples of each type.

FORMATIVE ASSESSMENT

and INTERVENTION

***Diagnose Before* the Lesson**
4-4 Warm Up, TE p. 224

***Monitor During* the Lesson**
Check It Out! Exercises, SE pp. 224–227
Questioning Strategies, TE pp. 226–227

***Assess After* the Lesson**
4-4 Lesson Quiz, TE p. 231
Alternative Assessment, TE p. 231

Answers to *Think and Discuss*

1. No; no correlation means that there is no relationship and the points on the graph show neither a positive nor negative correlation.
2. See p. A4.

4-4 Exercises

Assignment Guide

Assign *Guided Practice* exercises as necessary.

If you finished Examples **1–3**
Proficient 14–18
Advanced 14–18

If you finished Examples **1–5**
Proficient 14–32, 34–41
Advanced 14–24, 26–41

Homework Quick Check
Quickly check key concepts.
Exercises: 14, 16, 18, 20, 21, 22

Answers

2. Possible answer: A graph with a negative correlation shows one set of values decreasing as the other set increases, while a graph with no correlation shows no relationship.

4.

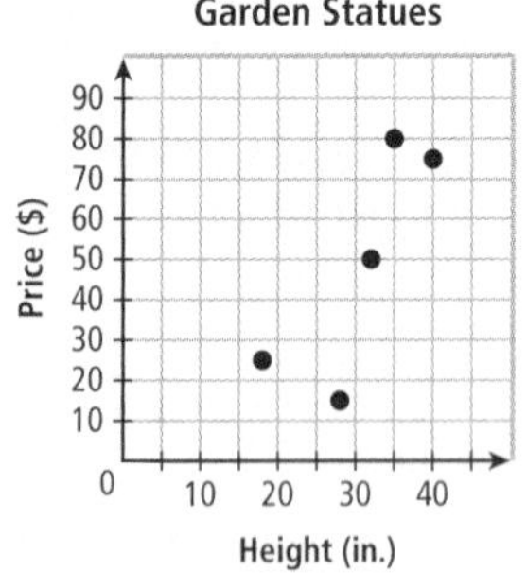

California Standards

Standard	Exercises
4.0	35–38
5.0	34–38
18.0	39–41
7SDAP1.2	4–33

4-4 Exercises

California Standards Practice
Review of Grade 7 **SDAP1.2**

go.hrw.com
Homework Help Online
KEYWORD: MA8CA 4-4
Parent Resources Online
KEYWORD: MA8CA Parent

GUIDED PRACTICE

3. No; a trend line just fits the pattern of data points, so it usually does not pass through every point.

Vocabulary Apply the vocabulary from this lesson to answer each question.

1. Give an example of a graph that is not a *scatter plot.* **Possible answer: a circle graph**
2. How is a scatter plot that shows *no correlation* different from a scatter plot that shows a *negative correlation*?
3. Does a *trend line* always pass through every point on a scatter plot? Explain.

SEE EXAMPLE 1 p. 224

Graph a scatter plot using the given data.

4.

Garden Statue	Cupid	Gnome	Lion	Flamingo	Wishing well
Height (in.)	32	18	35	28	40
Price ($)	50	25	80	15	75

SEE EXAMPLE 2 p. 225

Describe the correlation illustrated by each scatter plot.

5. **positive correlation**

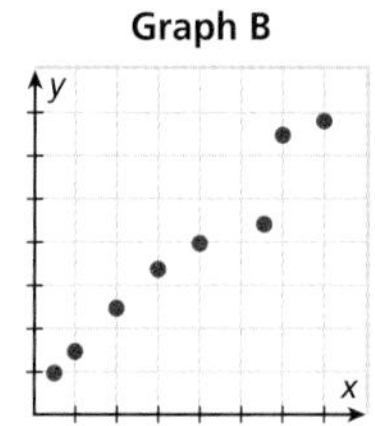

6. **negative correlation**

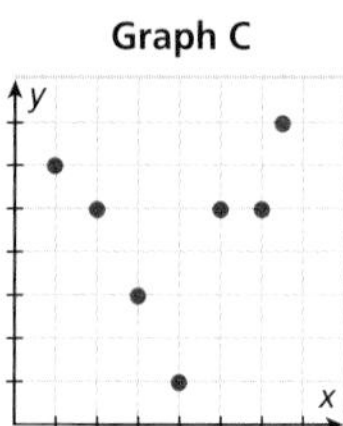

SEE EXAMPLE 3 p. 225

Identify the correlation you would expect between each pair of data sets. Explain.

7. the volume of water poured into a container and the amount of empty space left in the container **Negative correlation; as more water is poured, less space remains.**
8. a person's shoe size and the length of the person's hair **No correlation; there is no relationship.**
9. the outside temperature and the number of people at the beach **Positive correlation; as temperature increases, the number of people at the beach increases.**

SEE EXAMPLE 4 p. 226

Choose the scatter plot that best represents the described relationship. Explain.

10. age of car and number of miles traveled **Graph B; there should be a positive correlation.**
11. age of car and resale value of the car **Graph A; there should be a negative correlation.**
12. age of car and number of states traveled to **Graph C; there should be no correlation.**

Graph A

Graph B

Graph C

Teacher to Teacher

To reinforce the concepts of scatter plots and trend lines, I use an exercise where the students guess the ages of various celebrities. Then students make a scatter plot showing the relationship between their guesses and the actual ages of the celebrities. This helps them to discover the trend line. Because of the topic, students are very involved.

Lendy Jones
Killeen, TX

SEE EXAMPLE 5
p. 227

13. **Transportation** The scatter plot shows the total number of miles passengers flew on U.S. domestic flights in the month of April for the years 1997–2004. Based on this relationship, predict how many miles passengers will fly in April 2008.
Possible answer: 53 million

U.S. Domestic Air Travel in April

Miles (billions): 0, 36, 38, 40, 42, 44, 46, 48
Year: 1998, 2002, 2006

Answer

14.

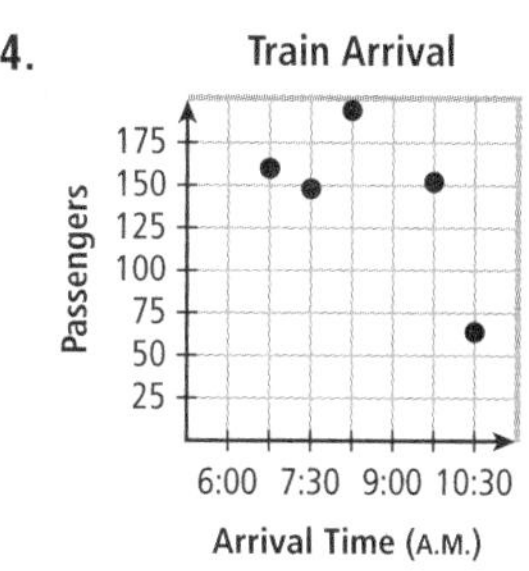

PRACTICE AND PROBLEM SOLVING

Independent Practice

For Exercises	See Example
14	1
15–16	2
17–18	3
19–20	4
21	5

Extra Practice
Skills Practice p. EP9
Application Practice p. EP27

Graph a scatter plot using the given data.

14.

Train Arrival Time	6:45 A.M.	7:30 A.M.	8:15 A.M.	9:45 A.M.	10:30 A.M.
Passengers	160	148	194	152	64

Describe the correlation illustrated by each scatter plot.

15.

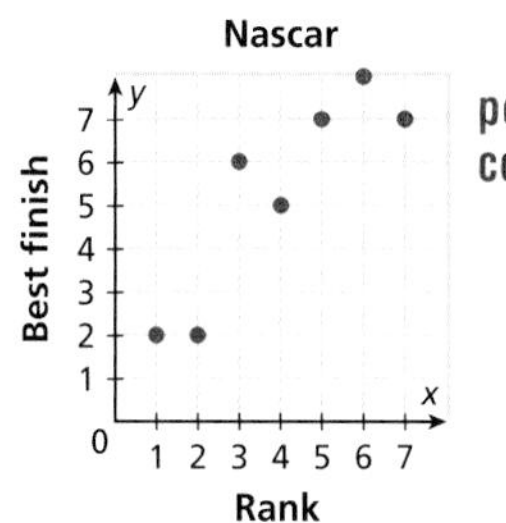

positive correlation

16. **Concert Ticket Costs**

Ticket cost ($): 10, 20, 30, 40, 50, 60, 70
Row: 0, 10, 20, 30

negative correlation

17. Positive correlation; greater speed results in more distance covered in a given time.

Identify the correlation you would expect between each pair of data sets. Explain.

17. the speed of a runner and the distance she can cover in 10 minutes

18. the year a car was made and the total mileage **Negative correlation; cars that are made in higher-numbered years are newer and should have lower mileage.**

Choose the scatter plot that best represents the described relationship. Explain.

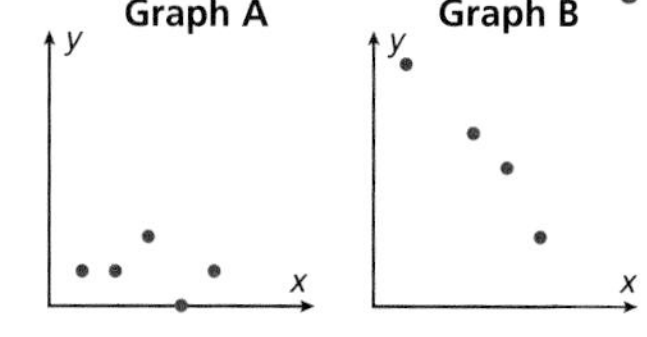

19. the number of college classes taken and the number of roommates **Graph A; there should be no correlation.**

20. the number of college classes taken and the hours of free time. **Graph B; there should be a negative correlation.**

LINK

Ecology

The ocelot population in Texas is dwindling due in part to their habitat being destroyed. The ocelot population at Laguna Atascosa National Wildlife Refuge is monitored by following 5–10 ocelots yearly by radio telemetry.

21. **Ecology** The scatter plot shows a projection of the average ocelot population living in Laguna Atascosa National Wildlife Refuge near Brownsville, Texas. Based on this relationship, predict the number of ocelots living at the wildlife refuge in 2014 if nothing is done to help manage the ocelot population.
Possible answer: 25

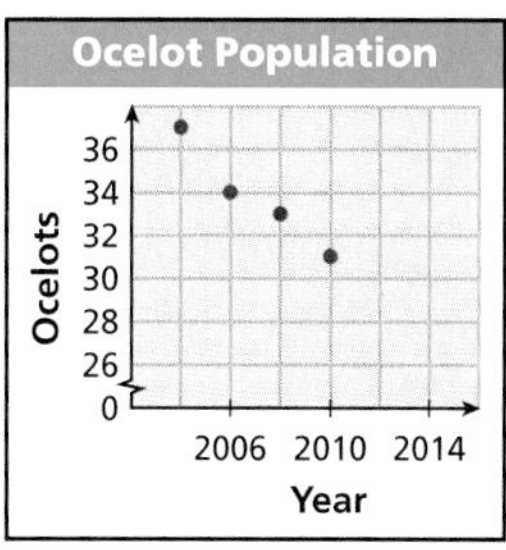

4-4 READING STRATEGIES

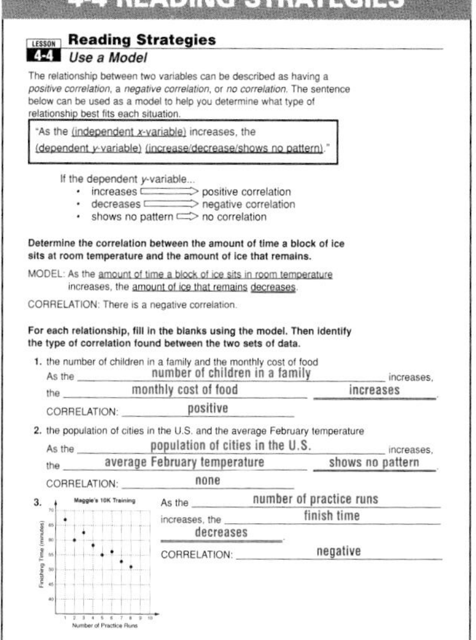

LESSON 4-4 **Reading Strategies**
Use a Model

The relationship between two variables can be described as having a *positive correlation*, a *negative correlation*, or *no correlation*. The sentence below can be used as a model to help you determine what type of relationship best fits each situation.

"As the (independent x-variable) increases, the (dependent y-variable) (increase/decrease/shows no pattern)."

If the dependent y-variable...
- increases ⟹ positive correlation
- decreases ⟹ negative correlation
- shows no pattern ⟹ no correlation

Determine the correlation between the amount of time a block of ice sits at room temperature and the amount of ice that remains.

MODEL: As the amount of time a block of ice sits in room temperature increases, the amount of ice that remains decreases.
CORRELATION: There is a negative correlation.

For each relationship, fill in the blanks using the model. Then identify the type of correlation found between the two sets of data.

1. the number of children in a family and the monthly cost of food
As the number of children in a family increases, the monthly cost of food increases.
CORRELATION: positive

2. the population of cities in the U.S. and the average February temperature
As the population of cities in the U.S. increases, the average February temperature shows no pattern.
CORRELATION: none

3. As the number of practice runs increases, the finish time decreases.
CORRELATION: negative

4-4 REVIEW FOR MASTERY

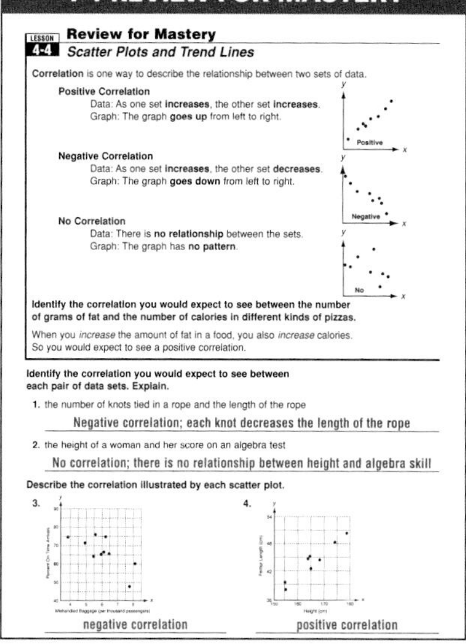

LESSON 4-4 **Review for Mastery**
Scatter Plots and Trend Lines

Correlation is one way to describe the relationship between two sets of data.

Positive Correlation
Data: As one set **increases**, the other set **increases**.
Graph: The graph **goes up** from left to right.

Negative Correlation
Data: As one set **increases**, the other set **decreases**.
Graph: The graph **goes down** from left to right.

No Correlation
Data: There is **no relationship** between the sets.
Graph: The graph has **no pattern**.

Identify the correlation you would expect to see between the number of grams of fat and the number of calories in different kinds of pizzas.

When you *increase* the amount of fat in a food, you also *increase* calories. So you would expect to see a positive correlation.

Identify the correlation you would expect to see between each pair of data sets. Explain.

1. the number of knots tied in a rope and the length of the rope
Negative correlation; each knot decreases the length of the rope

2. the height of a woman and her score on an algebra test
No correlation; there is no relationship between height and algebra skill

Describe the correlation illustrated by each scatter plot.

3. negative correlation
4. positive correlation

4-4 PRACTICE A

4-4 PRACTICE C

4-4 PRACTICE B

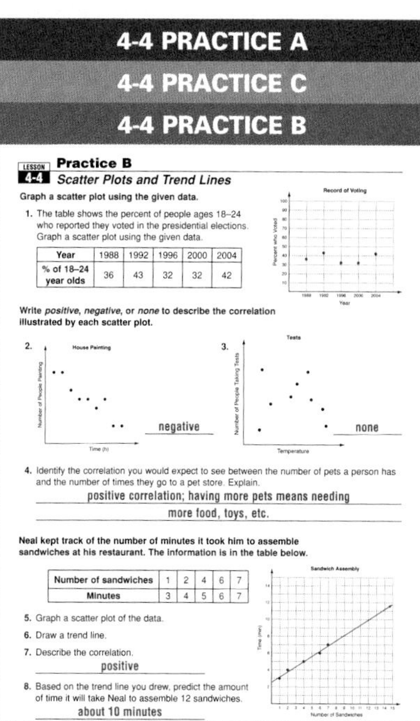

LESSON 4-4 **Practice B**
Scatter Plots and Trend Lines

Graph a scatter plot using the given data.

1. The table shows the percent of people ages 18–24 who reported they voted in the presidential elections. Graph a scatter plot using the given data.

Year	1988	1992	1996	2000	2004
% of 18–24 year olds	36	43	32	32	42

Write *positive*, *negative*, or *none* to describe the correlation illustrated by each scatter plot.

2. negative
3. none

4. Identify the correlation you would expect to see between the number of pets a person has and the number of times they go to a pet store. Explain.
positive correlation; having more pets means needing more food, toys, etc.

Neal kept track of the number of minutes it took him to assemble sandwiches at his restaurant. The information is in the table below.

Number of sandwiches	1	2	4	6	7
Minutes	3	4	5	6	7

5. Graph a scatter plot of the data.
6. Draw a trend line.
7. Describe the correlation.
positive
8. Based on the trend line you drew, predict the amount of time it will take Neal to assemble 12 sandwiches.
about 10 minutes

CONCEPT CONNECTION **Exercise 27** involves using a trend line to make a prediction. This exercise prepares students for the Concept Connection on page 240.

Answers

26. Fewer people will buy an item if the price goes up. So there is a negative correlation between the price of an item and the number of people buying the item.

27a, c.

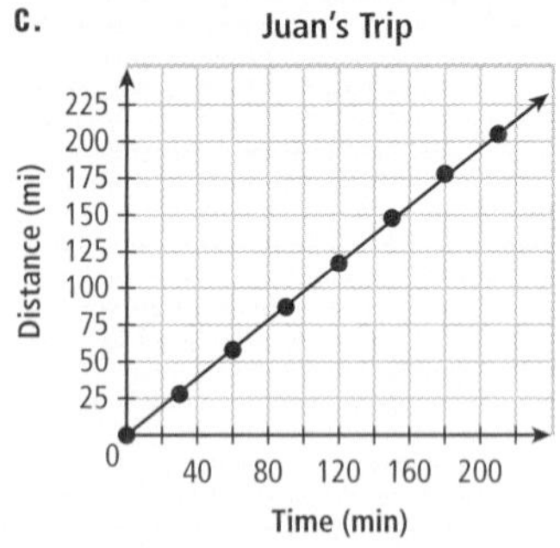

b. Positive correlation; as time increases, the number of miles also increases.

c. Possible answer: about 240 mi

23. Positive correlation; as the number of left shoes sold increases, the number of right shoes sold also increases, because most people need shoes for both feet.

24a, c.

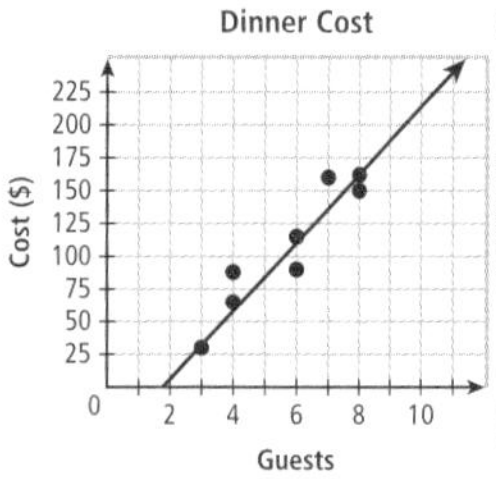

b. Positive correlation; as the number of guests increases, the cost increases.

d. Possible answer: about $230

e. The cost will also increase.

25. B; the bath water is probably hot at first, but then as time passes, the water cools down. The temperature decreases with time.

22. Estimation Angie enjoys putting jigsaw puzzles together. The scatter plot shows the number of puzzle pieces and the time in minutes it took her to complete each of her last six puzzles. Use the trend line to estimate the time in minutes it will take Angie to complete a 1200-piece puzzle. **Possible answer: 600 min**

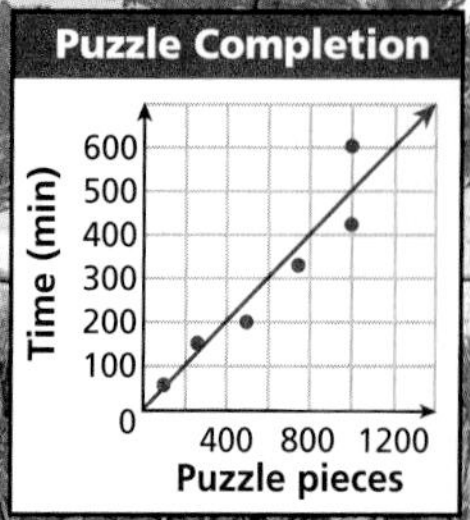

23. Critical Thinking Describe the correlation between the number of left shoes sold and the number of right shoes sold.

24. Roma had guests for dinner at her house eight times and has recorded the number of guests and the total cost for each meal in the table.

Guests	3	4	4	6	6	7	8	8
Cost ($)	30	65	88	90	115	160	150	162

a. Graph a scatter plot of the data.

b. Describe the correlation.

c. Draw a trend line.

d. Based on the trend line you drew, predict the cost of dinner for 11 guests.

e. **What if...?** Suppose that each cost in the table increased by $5. How will this affect the cost of dinner for 11 guests?

25. ///ERROR ANALYSIS/// Students graphed a scatter plot for the temperature of hot bath water over time if no new water is added. Which graph is incorrect? Explain the error.

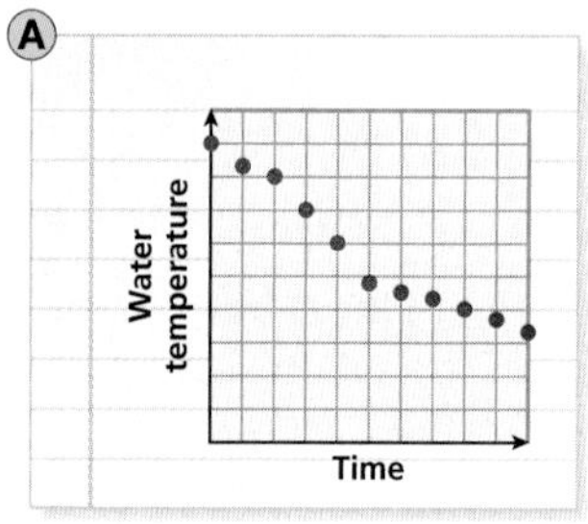

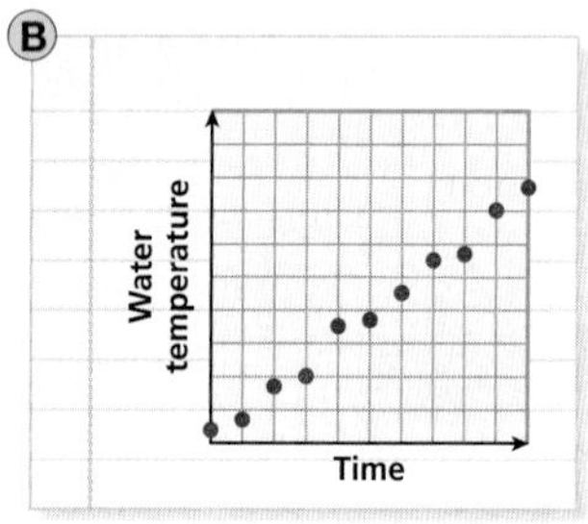

26. Critical Thinking Do you think more people or fewer people will buy an item if the price goes up? Describe the correlation you would expect.

CONCEPT CONNECTION

27. This problem will prepare you for the Concept Connection on page 240.

Juan and his parents are visiting a university 205 miles from their home. As they travel, Juan uses the car odometer and his watch to keep track of the distance.

a. Make a scatter plot for this data set.

b. Describe the correlation. Explain.

c. Draw a trend line for the data and predict the distance Juan would have traveled going to a university 4 hours away.

Time (min)	Distance (mi)
0	0
30	28
60	58
90	87
120	117
150	148
180	178
210	205

4-4 PROBLEM SOLVING

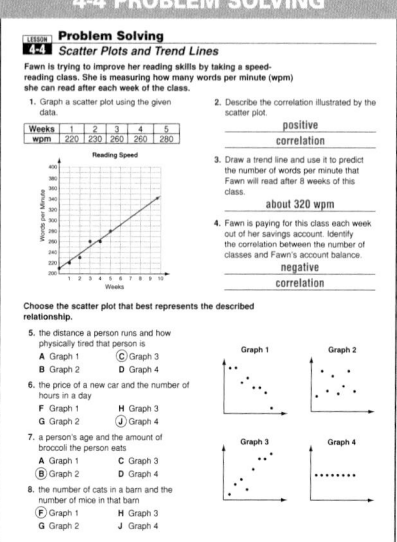

LESSON 4-4 **Problem Solving**
Scatter Plots and Trend Lines

Fawn is trying to improve her reading skills by taking a speed-reading class. She is measuring how many words per minute (wpm) she can read after each week of the class.

1. Graph a scatter plot using the given data.

Weeks	1	2	3	4	5
wpm	220	230	260	260	280

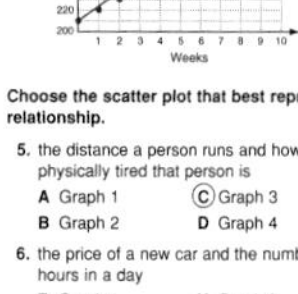

2. Describe the correlation illustrated by the scatter plot.
positive correlation

3. Draw a trend line and use it to predict the number of words per minute that Fawn will read after 8 weeks of this class.
about 320 wpm

4. Fawn is paying for this class each week out of her savings account. Identify the correlation between the number of classes and Fawn's account balance.
negative correlation

Choose the scatter plot that best represents the described relationship.

5. the distance a person runs and how physically tired that person is
A Graph 1 (C) Graph 3
B Graph 2 D Graph 4

6. the price of a new car and the number of hours in a day
F Graph 1 H Graph 3
G Graph 2 (J) Graph 4

7. a person's age and the amount of broccoli the person eats
A Graph 1 C Graph 3
(B) Graph 2 D Graph 4

8. the number of cats in a barn and the number of mice in that barn
(F) Graph 1 H Graph 3
G Graph 2 J Graph 4

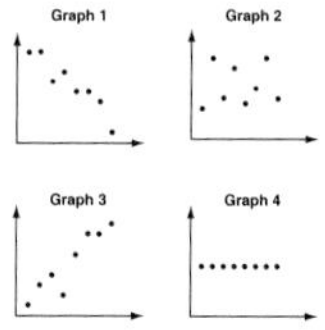

4-4 CHALLENGE

LESSON 4-4 **Challenge**
Bounding Data with Lines

A scatter plot that represents a data set has many advantages. When you visualize the data on the coordinate plane, you can draw an inference about whether there may be a correlation, positive or negative. You may also be able to draw the inference that no correlation is apparent.
In the graph at right, you can see a scatter plot for the data set below.

(1, 1), (2, 3), (2, 4), (3, 4), (4, 3), and (5, 6)

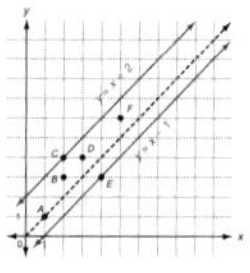

The scatter plot shows a positive correlation between x and y. The points cluster closely to the line $y = x$. The greatest difference in the y-coordinates of the data points and the corresponding y-coordinates of the graph of $y = x$ is 2.

Refer to the graph above.

1. a. On the coordinate grid above, graph $y = x + 2$.
b. On the coordinate grid above, graph $y = x - 1$.
c. Do the graphs that you sketched in parts **a** and **b** bound or enclose all the given data points? Explain your response.
Yes, all the data points are either on the lines or between them.

The graph at right shows a scatter plot and the line $y = x$.

In Exercises 2 and 3, refer to the graph at right.

2. a. Find the greatest difference in the y-coordinates of the data points above the graph of $y = x$ and the corresponding y-coordinates of the graph of $y = x$. 3 units
b. Find the greatest difference in the y-coordinates of the data points below the graph of $y = x$ and the corresponding y-coordinates of the graph of $y = x$. 2 units

3. Using your answers from Exercise 2, sketch lines that are parallel to $y = x$ and that bound all the data points.

4. Explain how you can use bounding lines to analyze a data set with a positive correlation.
The closer together the parallel bounding lines are, the more tightly the data cluster around a line. The farther apart the parallel bounding lines are, the more loosely the data points cluster around a line.

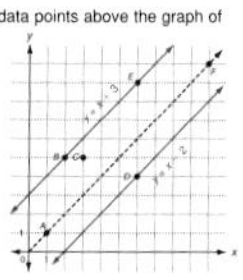

28. **Write About It** Predict whether there will be a positive, negative, or no correlation between the number of siblings a person has and the number of pets that person has. Then conduct a survey of your classmates to find the number of siblings they have and the number of pets they have. Graph the data in a scatter plot. What is the relationship between the two data sets? Was your prediction correct?
Check students' work.

Multiple Choice For Exercises 29 and 30, choose the best answer.

29. Which graph is the best example of a negative correlation?

Ⓐ Ⓑ Ⓒ Ⓓ

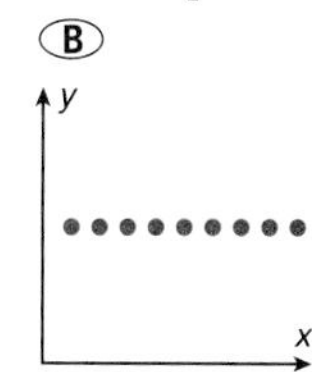

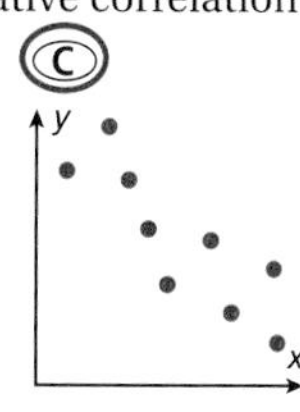

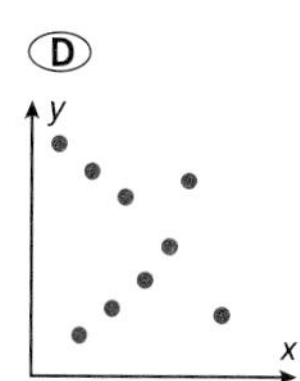

30. Which situation best describes a positive correlation?

Ⓐ The amount of rainfall on Fridays

Ⓑ The height of a candle and the amount of time it stays lit

Ⓒ The price of a pizza and the number of toppings added

Ⓓ The temperature of a cup of hot chocolate and the length of time it sits

31. **Short Response** Write a real-world situation for the graph. Explain your answer.

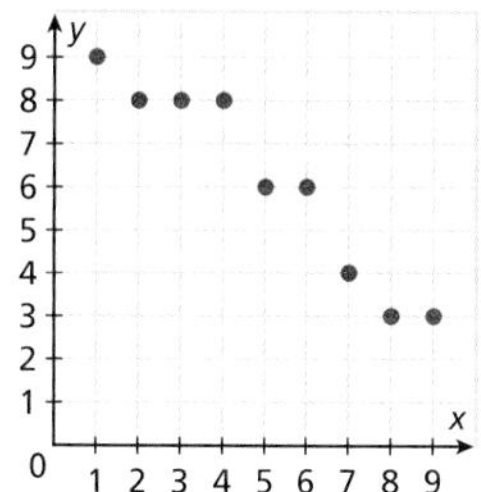

31. Possible answer: The number of milk cartons at the grocery store varies with the number of people who pass by the milk. Each person who passes by either takes milk or does not. If the person does not, the same number of cartons remain.

CHALLENGE AND EXTEND

32. Describe a situation that involves a positive correlation. Gather data on the situation. Make a scatter plot showing the correlation. Use the scatter plot to make a prediction. Repeat for a negative correlation and for no correlation.
Check students' work.

33. Research an endangered or threatened species in your state. Gather information on its population for several years. Make a scatter plot using the data you gather. Is there a positive or negative correlation? Explain. Draw a trend line and make a prediction about the species population over the next 5 years. **Check students' work.**

SPIRAL STANDARDS REVIEW

4.0, 5.0, 18.0

Write an equation to represent each relationship. Then solve the equation. *(Lesson 2-4)*

34. Five times a number increased by 2 is equal to twice the number decreased by 4.
$5n + 2 = 2n - 4$; -2

35. Five times the sum of a number and 2 is equal to 8 less than twice the number.
$5(n + 2) = 2n - 8$; -6

Solve each inequality. *(Lesson 3-5)*

36. $4(6 + x) \geq -2x$ $x \geq -4$

37. $3(x - 1) > 3x$ $\emptyset$

38. $2(3 - x) < 2(1 + x)$ $x > 1$

Graph each equation. Then tell whether the equation represents a function. *(Lesson 4-3)*

39. $y = 2x - 3$

40. $y = -|x| + 3$

41. $y = x^2 - 4$

Answers

39.

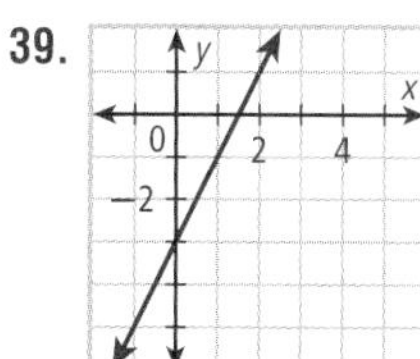

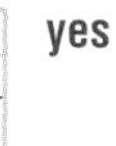

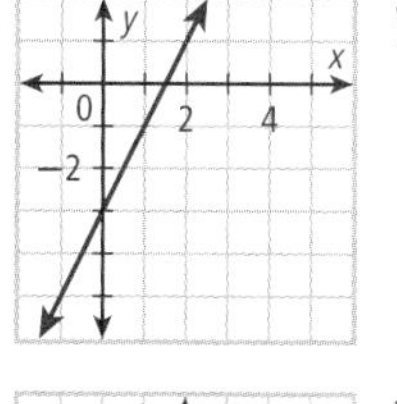

yes

40.

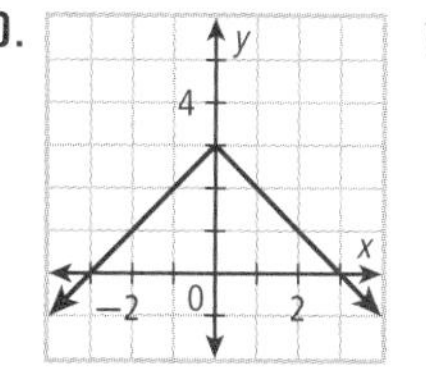

yes

41.

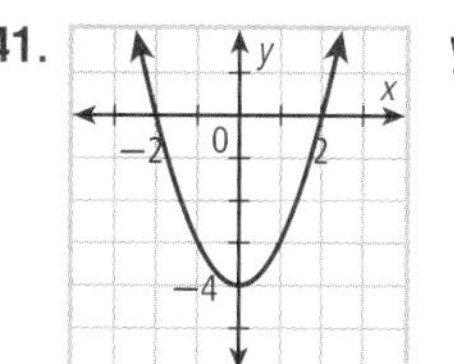

yes

Teaching Tip **Multiple Choice** Students who choose **B** or **D** for **Exercise 29** may be confusing no correlation with negative correlation.

Students who chose **B** or **D** in **Exercise 30** chose situations that describe negative correlations.

Journal

Have students describe how to identify positive and negative correlations from a scatter plot.

ALTERNATIVE ASSESSMENT

Have students create a scatter plot showing population over time for an endangered species and predict its population in 2020.

Power Presentations with PowerPoint®

4-4 Lesson Quiz

For Items 1 and 2, identify the correlation you would expect between each pair of data sets. Explain.

1. The outside temperature in the summer and the cost of the electric bill Positive correlation; as the outside temperature increases, the electric bill increases because of the use of the air conditioner.

2. The price of a car and the number of passengers it seats No correlation; a very expensive car could seat only 2 passengers.

3. The scatter plot shows the number of orders placed for flowers before Valentine's Day at one shop. Based on this relationship, predict the number of flower orders placed on February 12. about 45

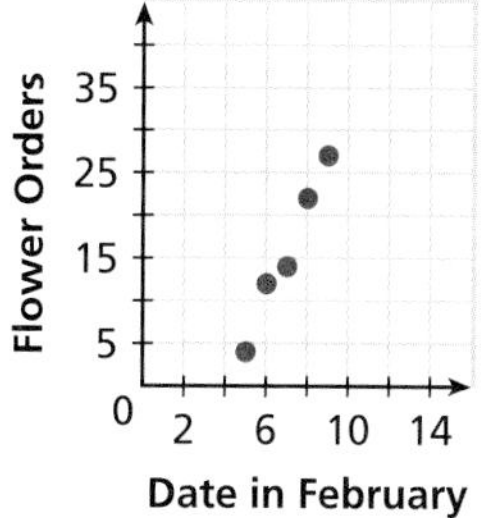

Also available on transparency

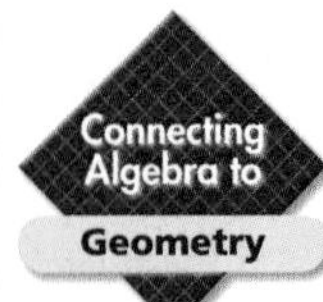

Organizer

See Skills Bank page SB25

Objective: Apply the algebra skills learned in Lesson 4-4 to approximate a median-fit line.

Teach

Remember

Students review the concept of finding the median, plotting points on a coordinate plane, and drawing trend lines.

Point out to students that only one set of data values can be ordered from least to greatest. In this case, x-values are ordered, not y-values.

INTERVENTION For additional review and practice on finding medians, see Skills Bank page SB25.

Close

Assess

Using the data in the example, have students demonstrate finding the median points for the second and third sections.

Reinforcement of 6SDAP1.1
Also covered:
Reinforcement of 7SDAP1.2
Represent two numerical variables on a scatterplot and informally describe how the data points are distributed and any apparent relationship that exists between the two variables (e.g., between time spent on homework and grade level).

Median-Fit Line

You have learned about trend lines. Now you will learn about another line of fit called the median-fit line.

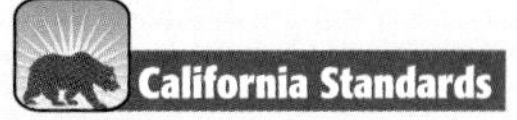

Reinforcement of 6SDAP1.1
Compute the range, mean, **median,** and mode **of data sets.**
Also covered: **Reinforcement of 7SDAP1.2**

Example

At a water raft rental shop, a group of up to four people can rent a single raft. The table shows the number of rafts rented to different groups of people one morning. Find the median-fit line for the data.

People x	1	2	4	5	5	5	7	9	10	11	12	15
Rafts Rented y	1	1	1	3	4	5	4	7	5	3	4	6

1. Plot the points on a coordinate plane.

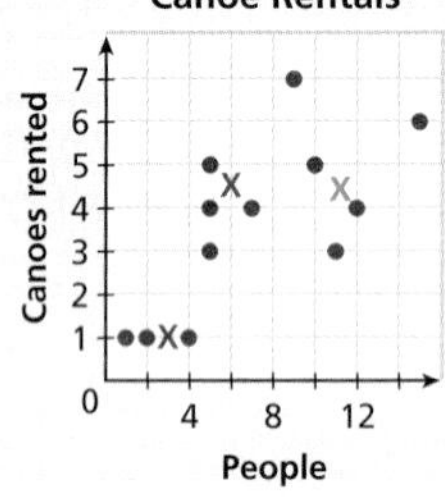

2. Divide the data into three sections of equal size. Find the medians of the x-values and the y-values for each section. Plot the three median points with an X.

1	2	4	5	5	5	7	9	10	11	12	15
1	1	1	3	4	5	4	7	5	3	4	6

Median point: (3, 1) Median point: (6, 4.5) Median point: (11.5, 4.5)

3. Connect the outside, or first and third, median points with a line.

4. Lightly draw a dashed line straight down from the middle median point to the line just drawn. Mark the dashed line to create three equal segments.

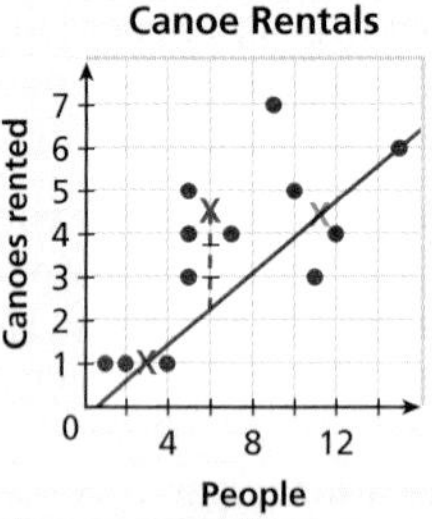

5. Keeping your ruler parallel to the first line you drew, move your ruler to the mark closest to the line. Draw the line. This is the median-fit line.

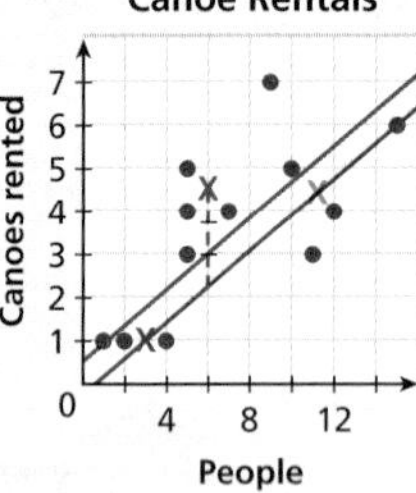

Try This

1. A manager at a restaurant kept track one afternoon of the number of people in a party and the time it took to seat them. Graph the data and find the median-fit line.

People x	3	7	8	8	10	12
Wait Time y (min)	1	5	3	9	6	6

2. Use your median-fit line to predict the time it took to seat a party of 6. **4 min**

Answer to *Try This*

1.

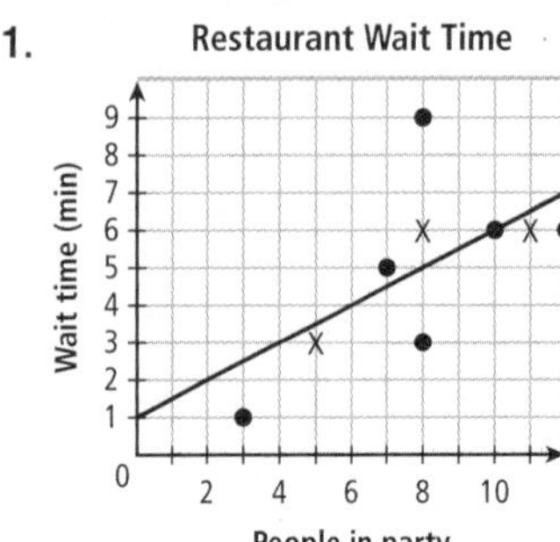

Inductive Reasoning

Inductive reasoning is the process of reasoning that a rule or statement is true because specific cases are true. A common example of inductive reasoning is drawing a conclusion based on a pattern.

A statement you believe to be true based on inductive reasoning is a **conjecture.**

24.1 Students explain the difference between inductive and deductive reasoning and identify and **provide examples** of each.

The diagrams below represent the side views of tables. Each has a tabletop and a base. Copy and complete the chart using the pattern shown in the diagrams.

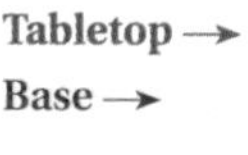
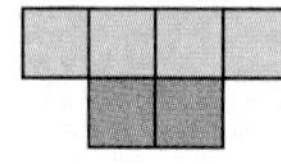
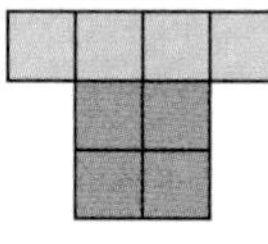
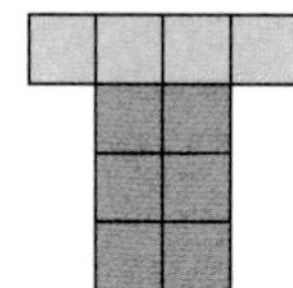

TABLE NUMBER	FIGURE	DESCRIPTION OF FIGURE	NUMBER OF BLOCKS
1		width of table top = 4 height of base = 1	6
2		width of table top = 4 height of base = 2	8
3		width of table top = 4 height of base = 3	10
4		width of tabletop = 4 height of base = 4	12
5		width of tabletop = 4 height of base = 5	14

1. Possible answers: For each row in the table, the number of blocks is 2 more than the previous row; the number of blocks is 2 times the table number plus 4.

1. Explain any patterns you see in the table.
2. **Make a Conjecture** How many blocks do you think there will be in the 25th table? **54**
3. **Make a Conjecture** Write an expression that you think you can use to find the number of blocks in the nth table. Explain why you think your expression is correct.

Answers

3. $4 + 2n$; possible answer: the tabletop has 4 blocks and the number of blocks in the base is twice the table number.

Science In many science experiments, data is collected and a hypothesis is made based on the data. Ask students whether this is an example of inductive reasoning. yes Then have students give specific examples of this type of science experiment. These examples may be experiments they have done in the past, or experiments found in their science textbooks.

Extend

Have students each choose a different number. Then add 11, multiply by 6, subtract 3, divide by 3, add 5, divide by 2, and then subtract the original number. Ask students to use inductive reasoning to make a conjecture. The result is always 13.

Remind students that inductive reasoning cannot be used to prove a conjecture. Challenge them to prove that the result is always 13. (*Hint:* Begin by letting x = the original number.)

Organizer

Objective: Use models to represent algebraic relationships.

Online Edition

Countdown to Mastery Week 8

Teach

Discuss

Begin the discussion with non-mathematical examples of inductive reasoning. For instance, the sun has risen every day in the past, so we use inductive reasoning to predict that the sun will rise tomorrow. We can't be *absolutely* certain this event will happen, but it is a reasonable conjecture based on what we have observed.

Have students think of other instances where people use inductive reasoning to make a prediction about the future. Possible answers: weather forecasts, predictions about population growth

Alternative Approach

Use square tiles to model the pattern.

Close

Key Concept

Inductive reasoning is observing a pattern and making a prediction based on your observations. Unlike conclusions in deductive reasoning, a conclusion drawn from inductive reasoning has not been proven to be true.

Assessment

Journal Sketch a model of a table with a width of 6 and a base of 4 columns. Extend the pattern by three terms by adding rows of blocks to the table's base. Have students write expressions for each term of the pattern.

Algebra 1 24.1

4-5 Organizer

Objectives: Recognize and extend an arithmetic sequence.

Find a given term of an arithmetic sequence.

 **Online Edition**
Tutorial Videos

 **Countdown to Mastery Week 9**

Power Presentations with PowerPoint®

Warm Up

Evaluate.

1. $5 + (-7)$ -2 **2.** $\frac{2}{3} + \frac{1}{3} + \frac{1}{3}$ $\frac{4}{3}$

3. $5.3 + 0.8$ 6.1 **4.** $6(4 - 1)$ 18

5. $-3(2 - 5)$ 9 **6.** $\frac{12}{5}\left(\frac{10}{3} + \frac{5}{4}\right)$ 11

7. $\frac{3}{4} + h$ where $h = -2$ $-\frac{5}{4}$

8. $n - 2.8$ where $n = 5.1$ 2.3

9. $6(x - 1)$ where $x = 5$ 24

10. $10 + (5 - 1)s$ where $s = -4$ -6

Also available on transparency

Math Humor

Teacher: Is something wrong with your printer? Your history paper is covered in dots.

Student: Those are ellipses. After the first paragraph, imagine the rest!

Preparation for Algebra II 22.0

4-5 Arithmetic Sequences

Preparation for Algebra II
22.0 Students find the general term and the sums of arithmetic series and of both finite and infinite geometric series.

Vocabulary
sequence
term
arithmetic sequence
common difference

Why learn this?

The distance between you and a lightning strike can be approximated by using an arithmetic sequence.

During a thunderstorm, you can estimate your distance from a lightning strike by counting the number of seconds from the time you see the lightning until the time you hear the thunder.

When you list the times and distances in order, each list forms a sequence. A **sequence** is a list of numbers that often form a pattern. Each number in a sequence is a **term**.

Time (s)	1	2	3	4	5	6	7	8
Distance (mi)	0.2	0.4	0.6	0.8	1.0	1.2	1.4	1.6

+0.2 +0.2 +0.2 +0.2 +0.2 +0.2 +0.2

Notice that in the distance sequence, you can find the next term by adding 0.2 to the previous term. When the terms of a sequence differ by the same nonzero number d, the sequence is an **arithmetic sequence** and d is the **common difference**. So the distances in the table form an arithmetic sequence with common difference 0.2.

EXAMPLE 1 Identifying Arithmetic Sequences

Determine whether each sequence appears to be an arithmetic sequence. If so, find the common difference and the next three terms in the sequence.

A **12, 8, 4, 0, ...**

Step 1 Find the difference between successive terms.

12, 8, 4, 0, ...
-4 -4 -4

You add −4 to each term to find the next term. The common difference is −4.

Step 2 Use the common difference to find the next 3 terms.

12, 8, 4, 0, -4, -8, -12
-4 -4 -4

The sequence appears to be an arithmetic sequence with a common difference of -4. If so, the next 3 terms would be -4, -8, -12.

B **1, 4, 9, 16, ...**

Find the difference between successive terms.

1, 4, 9, 16, ...
$+3$ $+5$ $+7$

The difference between successive terms is not the same.

This sequence is not an arithmetic sequence.

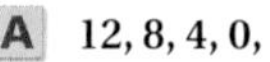

The three dots at the end of a sequence are called an ellipsis. They mean that the sequence continues and can be read as "and so on."

1 Introduce

EXPLORATION

4-5 Arithmetic Sequences

Mei collects postcards. On August 1, she has 10 cards in her collection. She decides to buy three cards every day thereafter for the rest of the month.

1. The table shows the number of postcards in Mei's collection. Complete the table for the first six days of August.

Day of Month	1	2	3	4	5	6
Postcards	10	13	16			

2. How many postcards will Mei have on August 10 (day 10)?
3. How many postcards will Mei have on August 15 (day 15)?
4. Find a shortcut that you can use to find the number of postcards Mei will have at the end of the month (day 31).

THINK AND DISCUSS

5. **Explain** how you found the shortcut to determine the number of postcards Mei will have on day 31.
6. **Describe** a general rule you can use to find the number of postcards Mei will have on day n.

Motivate

Display the following list of numbers. Ask students to find the next 3 numbers.

1, 2, 4, 8, 16, _, _, _

Tell students that this list of numbers is a *sequence*. Explain that in this lesson they will learn about a type of sequence called an arithmetic sequence.

Explorations and answers are provided in *Alternate Openers: Explorations Transparencies.*

Determine whether each sequence appears to be an arithmetic sequence. If so, find the common difference and the next three terms.

1a. $-\frac{3}{4}, -\frac{1}{4}, \frac{1}{4}, \frac{3}{4}, \ldots$ 1b. $\frac{2}{3}, \frac{1}{3}, -\frac{1}{3}, -\frac{2}{3}, \ldots$ 1c. $4, 1, -2, -5, \ldots$

1a. yes; $d = \frac{1}{2}$; $\frac{5}{4}, \frac{7}{4}, \frac{9}{4}$

1b. no

1c. yes; $d = -3$; $-8, -11, -14$

The variable a is often used to represent terms in a sequence. The variable a_9, read "a sub 9," is the ninth term in a sequence. To designate any term, or the nth term, in a sequence, you write a_n, where n can be any number.

1	2	3	4...	n	← Position
↓	↓	↓	↓		
3,	5,	7,	9...		← Term
a_1	a_2	a_3	a_4	a_n	

The sequence above starts with the first term, 3. The common difference d is 2. You can use the first term, 3, and the common difference, 2, to write a rule for finding a_n.

Words	Numbers	Algebra
1st term	3	a_1
2nd term = 1st term plus common difference	$3 + (1)2 = 5$	$a_1 + 1d$
3nd term = 1st term plus 2 common differences	$3 + (2)2 = 7$	$a_1 + 2d$
4th term = 1st term plus 3 common differences	$3 + (3)2 = 9$	$a_1 + 3d$
⋮	⋮	⋮
nth term = 1st term plus $(n - 1)$ common differences	$3 + (n - 1)2$	$a_1 + (n - 1)d$

The pattern in the table shows that to find the nth term, add the first term to the product of $(n - 1)$ and the common difference.

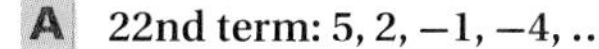

Finding the nth Term of an Arithmetic Sequence

The nth term of an arithmetic sequence with **common difference d** and first term a_1 is

$$a_n = a_1 + (n - 1)d.$$

EXAMPLE 2 **Finding the nth Term of an Arithmetic Sequence**

Find the indicated term of each arithmetic sequence.

A **22nd term: 5, 2, −1, −4, ...**

Step 1 Find the common difference.

5, 2, −1, −4, ... *The common difference is −3.*

−3 −3 −3

Step 2 Write a rule to find the 22nd term.

$a_n = a_1 + (n - 1)d$ *Write the rule to find the nth term.*

$a_{22} = 5 + (22 - 1)(-3)$ *Substitute 5 for a_1, 22 for n, and −3 for d.*

$= 5 + (21)(-3)$ *Simplify the expression in parentheses.*

$= 5 - 63$ *Multiply.*

$= -58$ *Add.*

The 22nd term is −58.

Students sometimes get confused when finding the nth term. Tell students that if they are finding the 6th term, they will be multiplying the difference d by 5, 6 − 1. The reason is that the formula uses the first term of a sequence as a constant. Ask students what number they would multiply the difference by if they were looking for the 20th term. 19

Power Presentations with PowerPoint®

Additional Examples

Example 1

Determine whether each sequence appears to be an arithmetic sequence. If so, find the common difference and the next three terms.

A. 9, 13, 17, 21, . . . arithmetic; 4; 25, 29, 33

B. 10, 8, 5, 1, . . . not arithmetic

Example 2

Find the indicated term of each arithmetic sequence.

A. 16th term: 4, 8, 12, 16, . . . 64

B. 25th term: $a_1 = -5$; $d = -2$ −53

Also available on transparency

2 Teach

English Language Learners

Guided Instruction

Remind students that they had to look for a pattern when they were writing equations earlier in this chapter. Tell them that they will also look for a pattern when identifying an arithmetic sequence. Then review the Distributive Property and the order of operations with students. When teaching the formula for the nth term in an arithmetic sequence, point out that students will need to calculate $n - 1$ first because it is in parentheses.

Universal Access

Through Cognitive Strategies

Challenge students to identify the best way to memorize vocabulary terms and formulas like the one on this page. Suggest the following methods:

- Writing the information over and over again.
- Making up a song or chant.
- Creating flash cards to use with a partner.
- Writing sentences with the vocabulary and working problems with the formula.

INTERVENTION

Questioning Strategies

EXAMPLE 1

- How is identifying an arithmetic sequence similar to identifying a function rule?

EXAMPLE 2

- How do you know what number to substitute for d?
- How do you know what number to substitute for n?

Visual Point out the colors used in the table above **Example 2.** The first term, or a_1, is green. The common difference, or d, is blue, and $n - 1$ is red. Students may want to use these colors in their work.

Power Presentations with PowerPoint®

Additional Examples

Example 3

A bag of cat food weighs 18 pounds. Each day, the cats are fed 0.5 pound of food. How much does the bag of cat food weigh on day 30? 3.5 lb

Also available on transparency

INTERVENTION

Questioning Strategies

EXAMPLE 3

- How can you identify d in a word problem?
- Why is n not the same as the number of days later?

Language Support Point out the words in **Example 3** that will help students put the information in a formula. Tell students that *each* or *every* with a time word such as *day* or *hour* signals that the following number is d. Explain that the number to substitute for n may be indicated by an ordinal number. The first term of the sequence is a number that can be associated with the words *at the start* or *first*. ENGLISH LANGUAGE LEARNERS

Find the indicated term of each arithmetic sequence.

B 15th term: $a_1 = 7; d = 3$

$a_n = a_1 + (n - 1)d$	*Write the rule to find the nth term.*
$a_{15} = 7 + (15 - 1)3$	*Substitute 7 for a_1, 15 for n, and 3 for d.*
$= 7 + (14)3$	*Simplify the expression in parentheses.*
$= 7 + 42$	*Multiply.*
$= 49$	*Add.*

The 15th term is 49.

Find the indicated term of each arithmetic sequence.

2a. 60th term: 11, 5, −1, −7, ... **−343**

2b. 12th term: $a_1 = 4.2; d = 1.4$ **19.6**

EXAMPLE 3 *Travel Application*

The odometer on a car reads 60,473 on day 1. Every day, the car is driven 54 miles. If this pattern continues, what will be the odometer reading on day 20?

Step 1 Determine whether the situation appears to be arithmetic.

The sequence for the situation is arithmetic because the odometer reading will increase by 54 miles per day.

Step 2 Find d, a_1, and n.

Since the odometer reading will increase by 54 miles per day, $d = 54$.
Since the odometer reading on day 1 is 60,473 miles, $a_1 = 60,473$.
Since you want to find the odometer reading on day 20, you will need to find the 20th term of the sequence, so $n = 20$.

Step 3 Find the odometer reading for a_n.

$a_n = a_1 + (n - 1)d$	*Write the rule to find the nth term.*
$a_{21} = 60{,}473 + (20 - 1)54$	*Substitute 60,473 for a_1, 54 for d, and 20 for n.*
$= 60{,}473 + (19)54$	*Simplify the expression in parentheses.*
$= 60{,}473 + 1026$	*Multiply.*
$= 61{,}499$	*Add.*

The odometer will read 61,499 miles on day 20.

3. Each time a truck stops, it drops off 250 pounds of cargo. At stop 1, it started with a load of 2000 pounds. How much does the load weigh on stop 6? **750 lb**

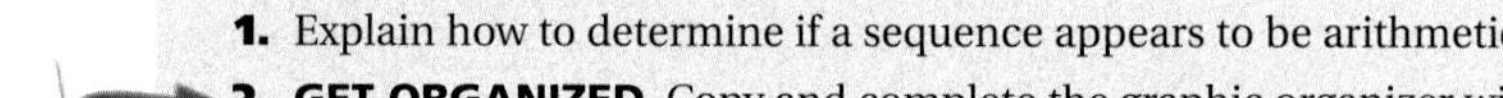

THINK AND DISCUSS

1. Explain how to determine if a sequence appears to be arithmetic.

2. GET ORGANIZED Copy and complete the graphic organizer with steps for finding the nth term of an arithmetic sequence.

Finding the nth Term of an Arithmetic Sequence → 1. → 2.

3 Close

Summarize

Display the formula $a_n = a_1 + (n - 1)d$. Have students define each variable in the formula. Then have them find the value of each variable and the 24th term of the following arithmetic sequence.

10, 4, −2, −8, . . .

In the formula, a_n is the nth term, a_1 is the first term, n is the number of terms, and d is the common difference. $a_1 = 10$, $n = 24$, $d = -6$, $a_{24} = -128$.

FORMATIVE ASSESSMENT and INTERVENTION

***Diagnose Before* the Lesson**
4-5 Warm Up, TE p. 234

***Monitor During* the Lesson**
Check It Out! Exercises, SE pp. 235–236
Questioning Strategies, TE pp. 235–236

***Assess After* the Lesson**
4-5 Lesson Quiz, TE p. 239
Alternative Assessment, TE p. 239

Answers to *Think and Discuss*

Possible answers:

1. If the sequence has a common difference, it could be an arithmetic sequence.
2. See p. A4.

4-5 Exercises

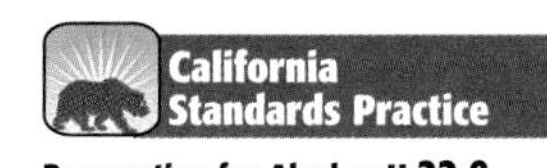

Preparation for Algebra II 22.0

Homework Help Online
KEYWORD: MA8CA 4-5

Parent Resources Online
KEYWORD: MA8CA Parent

GUIDED PRACTICE

1. **Vocabulary** When trying to find the nth term of an arithmetic sequence you must first know the ______?______. (*common difference* or *sequence*) **common difference**

SEE EXAMPLE 1 p. 234

Multi-Step Determine whether each sequence appears to be an arithmetic sequence. If so, find the common difference and the next three terms.

2. 2, 8, 14, 20, ... **yes; $d = 6$; 26, 32, 38**
3. 2.1, 1.4, 0.7, 0, ... **yes; $d = -0.7$; −0.7, −1.4, −2.1**
4. 1, 1, 2, 3, ... **no**
5. 0.1, 0.3, 0.9, 2.7, ... **no**

SEE EXAMPLE 2 p. 235

Find the indicated term of each arithmetic sequence.

6. 21st term: 3, 8, 13, 18, ... **103**
7. 18th term: $a_1 = -2$; $d = -3$ **−53**

SEE EXAMPLE 3 p. 236

8. **Shipping** To package and ship an item, it costs \$5 for shipping supplies and \$0.75 for each pound the package weighs. What is the cost of shipping a 12-pound package? **\$14**

PRACTICE AND PROBLEM SOLVING

Independent Practice

For Exercises	See Example
9–12	1
13–14	2
15	3

Extra Practice
Skills Practice p. EP9
Application Practice p. EP27

Multi-Step Determine whether each sequence appears to be an arithmetic sequence. If so, find the common difference and the next three terms.

9. −1, 10, −100, 1,100, ... **no**
10. 0, −2, −4, −6, ... **yes; $d = -2$; −8, −10, −12**
11. −22, −31, −40, −49, ... **yes; $d = -9$; −58, −67, −76**
12. 0.2, 0.5, 0.9, 1.1, ... **no**

Find the indicated term of each arithmetic sequence.

13. 31st term: 1.40, 1.55, 1.70, ... **5.9**
14. 50th term: $a_1 = 2.2$; $d = 1.1$ **56.1**

15. **Travel** Rachel signed up for a frequent-flier program and received 3000 bonus miles. She earns 1300 frequent-flier miles each time she purchases a round-trip ticket. How many frequent-flier miles will she have after 5 round-trips? **9500 mi**

Find the common difference for each arithmetic sequence.

16. 0, 6, 12, 18, ... **6**
17. $\frac{1}{2}, \frac{3}{4}, 1, \frac{5}{4}, \ldots$ **$\frac{1}{4}$**
18. 107, 105, 103, 101, ... **−2**
19. 7.9, 5.7, 3.5, 1.3, ... **−2.2**
20. $\frac{1}{5}, \frac{2}{5}, \frac{3}{5}, \frac{4}{5}, \ldots$ **$\frac{1}{5}$**
21. 4.25, 4.32, 4.39, 4.46, ... **0.07**

Find the next four terms in each arithmetic sequence.

22. −4, −7, −10, −13, ... **−16, −19, −22, −25**
23. $\frac{1}{8}, 0, -\frac{1}{8}, -\frac{1}{4}, \ldots$ **23. $-\frac{3}{8}, -\frac{1}{2}, -\frac{5}{8}, -\frac{3}{4}$**
24. 505, 512, 519, 526, ... **533, 540, 547, 554**
25. 1.8, 1.3, 0.8, 0.3, ... **−0.2, −0.7, −1.2, −1.7**
26. $\frac{2}{3}, \frac{4}{3}, 2, \frac{8}{3}, \ldots$ **$\frac{10}{3}, 4, \frac{14}{3}, \frac{16}{3}$**
27. −1.1, −0.9, −0.7, −0.5 **−0.3, −0.1, 0.1, 0.3**

Find the given term of each arithmetic sequence.

28. 5, 10, 15, 20, ...; 17th term **85**
29. 121, 110, 99, 88, ...; 10th term **22**
30. −2, −5, −8, −11, ...; 41st term **−122**
31. −30, −22, −14, −6, ...; 20th term **122**

32. **Critical Thinking** For the arithmetic sequence $5a - 1, 3a - 1, a - 1, -a - 1, \ldots$ find the common difference and the next three terms.
(when $a \neq 0$) $d = -2a$; $-3a - 1, -5a - 1, -7a - 1$.

4-5 Exercises

Assignment Guide

Assign *Guided Practice* exercises as necessary.

If you finished Examples **1–3**
Proficient 10–14 even, 15–45, 47–53
Advanced 10–14 even, 15–53

Homework Quick Check
Quickly check key concepts.
Exercises: 10, 14, 15, 20, 30, 36

California Standards

Standard	Exercises
4.0	48, 49
5.0	48–51
7SDAP1.2	52, 53
Prep. for 2A22.0	2–47

CONCEPT CONNECTION Exercise 41 involves using an arithmetic sequence to calculate distance. This exercise prepares students for the Concept Connection on page 250.

Answers

38a. 1, 1, 2, 3, 5, 8, 13, 21, 34, 55; no; there is no common difference.

b. Yes; every 3rd term is divisible by 2; every 3rd term is the sum of 2 odd numbers.

c. Every 4th term is divisible by 3, and every 5th term is divisible by 5.

40. Possible answer: Find the difference between two successive terms. If the terms of the sequence become greater in value, then the common difference is positive. If the terms of the sequence become less in value, then the common difference is negative.

33a. It could be arithmetic because you pay $2 per lap, so the common difference could be 2.

b. $9, $11, $13, $15; $a_n = 2n + 7$

33. **Recreation** The rates for a go-cart course are shown.

JESSIKA'S SPEEDWAY
License: $7
Per Lap: $2

a. Explain why the relationship described on the flyer could be an arithmetic sequence.

b. Find the cost for 1, 2, 3, and 4 laps. Write a rule to find the *n*th term of the sequence.

c. How much would 15 laps cost? **$37**

d. **What if...?** After 9 laps, you get the 10th one free. Will the sequence still be arithmetic? Explain.
No; the sequence will not increase by 2 from the 9th term to the 10th term.

California LINK — Number Theory

The design of the College of Engineering Plaza at California Polytechnic State University is based on the Fibonacci Sequence.

Find the given term of each arithmetic sequence.

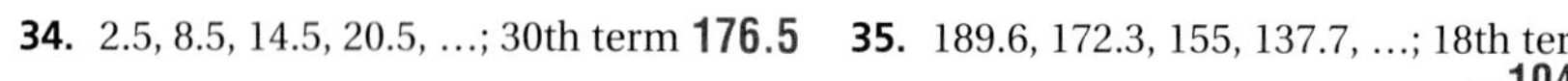

34. 2.5, 8.5, 14.5, 20.5, ...; 30th term **176.5**

35. 189.6, 172.3, 155, 137.7, ...; 18th term **−104.5**

36. $\frac{1}{4}, \frac{3}{4}, \frac{5}{4}, \frac{7}{4}, \ldots$; 15th term $\mathbf{\frac{29}{4}}$

37. $\frac{2}{3}, \frac{11}{12}, \frac{7}{6}, \frac{17}{12}, \ldots$; 25th term $\mathbf{\frac{20}{3}}$

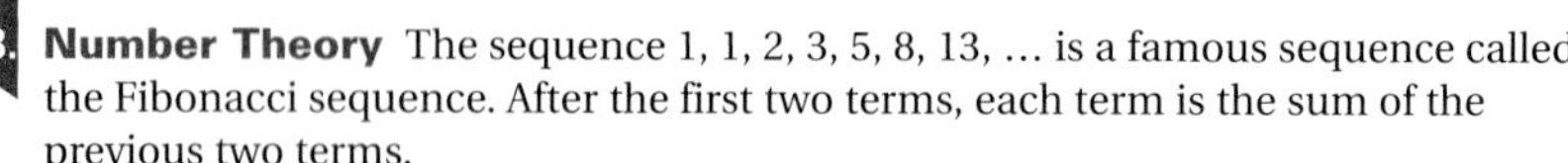

38. **Number Theory** The sequence 1, 1, 2, 3, 5, 8, 13, ... is a famous sequence called the Fibonacci sequence. After the first two terms, each term is the sum of the previous two terms.

a. Write the first 10 terms of the Fibonacci sequence. Is the Fibonacci sequence arithmetic? Explain.

b. Notice that the third term is divisible by 2. Are the 6th and 9th terms also divisible by 2? What conclusion can you draw about every third term? Why is this true?

c. Can you find any other patterns? (*Hint:* Look at every 4th and 5th term.)

39a. $a_n = 6 + 3(n - 1)$

d. $a_n = 7 + 3(n - 1)$; $8200

39. **Entertainment** Seats in a concert hall are arranged in the pattern shown.

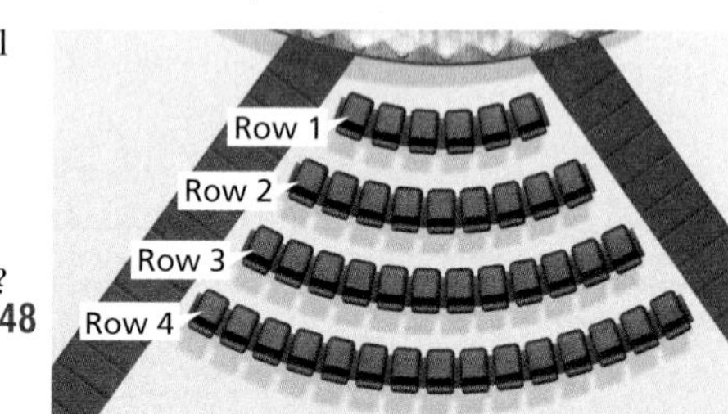

a. The numbers of seats in the rows form an arithmetic sequence. Write a rule for the arithmetic sequence.

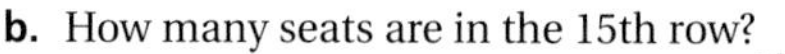

b. How many seats are in the 15th row? **48**

c. A ticket costs $40. Suppose every seat in the first 10 rows is filled. What is the total revenue from those seats? **$7800**

d. **What if...?** An extra chair is added to each row. Write the new rule for the arithmetic sequence and find the new total revenue from the first 10 rows.

40. **Write About It** Explain how to find the common difference of an arithmetic sequence. How can you determine whether the arithmetic sequence has a positive common difference or a negative common difference?

CONCEPT CONNECTION — STATE

41. This problem will prepare you for the Concept Connection on page 240.

Juan is traveling to visit universities. He notices mile markers along the road. He records the mile marker every 10 minutes. His father is driving at a constant speed.

a. Copy and complete the table.

b. Write the rule for the sequence. $a_n = 520 + (n - 1)(-11)$

c. What does the common difference represent? **c. number of miles per interval**

d. If this sequence continues, find the mile marker for time interval 10. **421**

Time Interval	Mile Marker
1	520
2	509
3	498
4	**487**
5	**476**
6	**465**

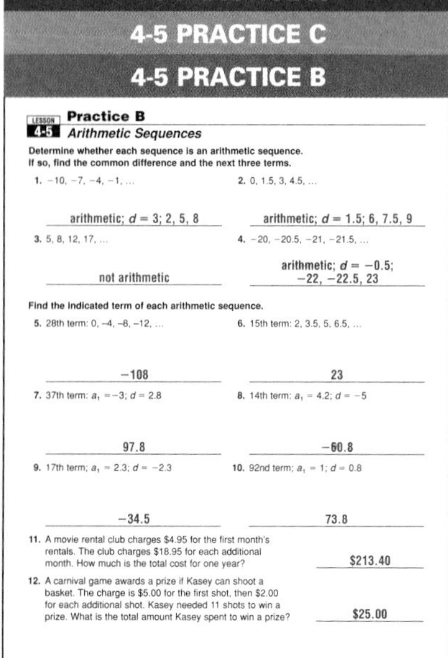

4-5 PRACTICE A
4-5 PRACTICE C
4-5 PRACTICE B

LESSON 4-5 **Practice B**
Arithmetic Sequences

Determine whether each sequence is an arithmetic sequence. If so, find the common difference and the next three terms.

1. −10, −7, −4, −1, ... **arithmetic; $d = 3$; 2, 5, 8**
2. 0, 1.5, 3, 4.5, ... **arithmetic; $d = 1.5$; 6, 7.5, 9**
3. 5, 8, 12, 17, ... **not arithmetic**
4. −20, −20.5, −21, −21.5, ... **arithmetic; $d = -0.5$; −22, −22.5, 23**

Find the indicated term of each arithmetic sequence.

5. 28th term: 0, −4, −8, −12, ... **−108**
6. 15th term: 2, 3.5, 5, 6.5, ... **23**
7. 37th term: $a_1 = -3$; $d = 2.8$ **97.8**
8. 14th term: $a_1 = 4.2$; $d = -5$ **−60.8**
9. 17th term; $a_1 = 2.3$; $d = -2.3$ **−34.5**
10. 92nd term; $a_1 = 1$; $d = 0.8$ **73.8**
11. A movie rental club charges $4.95 for the first month's rentals. The club charges $18.95 for each additional month. How much is the total cost for one year? **$213.40**
12. A carnival game awards a prize if Kasey can shoot a basket. The charge is $5.00 for the first shot, then $2.00 for each additional shot. Kasey needed 11 shots to win a prize. What is the total amount Kasey spent to win a prize? **$25.00**

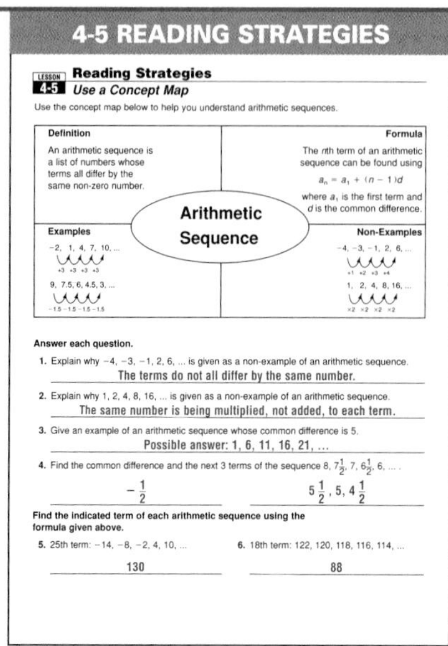

4-5 READING STRATEGIES

LESSON 4-5 **Reading Strategies**
Use a Concept Map

Use the concept map below to help you understand arithmetic sequences.

Arithmetic Sequence

Definition
An arithmetic sequence is a list of numbers whose terms all differ by the same non-zero number.

Formula
The *n*th term of an arithmetic sequence can be found using
$a_n = a_1 + (n - 1)d$
where a_1 is the first term and d is the common difference.

Examples
−2, 1, 4, 7, 10, ... (+3 +3 +3 +3)
9, 7.5, 6, 4.5, 3, ... (−1.5 −1.5 −1.5 −1.5)

Non-Examples
−4, −3, −1, 2, 6, ... (+1 +2 +3 +4)
1, 2, 4, 8, 16, ... (×2 ×2 ×2 ×2)

Answer each question.

1. Explain why −4, −3, −1, 2, 6, ... is given as a non-example of an arithmetic sequence. **The terms do not all differ by the same number.**
2. Explain why 1, 2, 4, 8, 16, ... is given as a non-example of an arithmetic sequence. **The same number is being multiplied, not added, to each term.**
3. Give an example of an arithmetic sequence whose common difference is 5. **Possible answer: 1, 6, 11, 16, 21, ...**
4. Find the common difference and the next 3 terms of the sequence 8, $7\frac{1}{2}$, 7, $6\frac{1}{2}$, 6, ... $\mathbf{-\frac{1}{2}}$ $\mathbf{5\frac{1}{2}, 5, 4\frac{1}{2}}$

Find the indicated term of each arithmetic sequence using the formula given above.

5. 25th term: −14, −8, −2, 4, 10, ... **130**
6. 18th term: 122, 120, 118, 116, 114, ... **88**

4-5 REVIEW FOR MASTERY

LESSON 4-5 **Review for Mastery**
Arithmetic Sequences

An **arithmetic sequence** is a list of numbers (or **terms**) with a **common difference** between each number. After you find the common difference, you can use it to continue the sequence.

Determine whether each sequence is an arithmetic sequence. If so, find the common difference and the next three terms.

1, 2, 4, 8, ... (+1 +2 +4) — Find how much you add or subtract to move from term to term.

The difference between terms is *not* constant.

This sequence is *not* an arithmetic sequence.

0, 6, 12, 18, ... (+6 +6 +6) — Find how much you add or subtract to move from term to term.

The difference between terms is constant.

This sequence is an arithmetic sequence with a common difference of 6.

0, 6, 12, 18, 24, 30, 36 (+6 +6 +6) — Use the difference of 6 to find three more terms.

Fill in the blanks with the differences between terms. State whether each sequence is an arithmetic sequence.

1. 14, 12, 10, 8, ... **−2, −2, −2** Is this an arithmetic sequence? **yes**
2. 0.3, 0.6, 1.0, 1.5, ... **+0.3, +0.4, +0.5** Is this an arithmetic sequence? **no**

Use the common difference to find the next three terms in each arithmetic sequence.

3. 7, 4, 1, −2, **−5**, **−8**, **−11**, ... (−3 −3 −3 −3 −3 −3)
4. −5, 0, 5, 10, **15**, **20**, **25**, ... (+5 +5 +5)

Determine whether each sequence is an arithmetic sequence. If so, find the common difference and the next three terms.

5. −1, 2, −3, 4, ... **no**
6. 1.25, 3.75, 6.25, 8.75, ... **yes; 2.5; 11.25, 13.75, 16.25**

Multiple Choice For Exercises 42–44, choose the best answer.

42. What are the next three terms in the arithmetic sequence −21, −12, −3, 6, ... ?

Ⓐ 9, 12, 15 Ⓑ 15, 24, 33 Ⓒ 12, 21, 27 Ⓓ 13, 20, 27

43. What is the common difference for the data listed in the second column?

Ⓐ −1.8 Ⓒ 2.8

Ⓑ 1.8 Ⓓ −3.6

Altitude (ft)	Boiling Point of Water (°F)
1000	210.2
2000	208.4
3000	206.6

44. Which of the following sequences CANNOT be arithmetic?

Ⓐ −4, 2, 8, 14, ... Ⓑ 9, 4, −1, −6, ... Ⓒ 2, 4, 8, 16, ... Ⓓ $\frac{1}{3}, 1\frac{1}{3}, 2\frac{1}{3}, 3\frac{1}{3}, \ldots$

CHALLENGE AND EXTEND

45. The first term of an arithmetic sequence is 2, and the common difference is 9. Find two consecutive terms of the sequence that have a sum of 355. What positions in the sequence are the terms? **20th and 21st term**

46. The 60th term of an arithmetic sequence is 106.5, and the common difference is 1.5. What is the first term of the sequence? **18**

47. Athletics Verona is training for a marathon. The first part of her training schedule is shown below.

Session	1	2	3	4	5	6
Distance Run (mi)	3.5	5	6.5	8	9.5	11

Session 16; yes; she increases the amount she runs by 1.5 miles each time.

a. If Verona continues this pattern, during which training session will she run 26 miles? Is her training schedule an arithmetic sequence? Explain.

b. If Verona's training schedule starts on a Monday and she runs every third day, on which day will she run 26 miles? **Thursday**

SPIRAL STANDARDS REVIEW

7SDAP1.2, 🔑 4.0, 🔑 5.0

48. Three sides of a triangle are represented by x, $x + 3$ and $x + 5$. The perimeter of the triangle is 35 units. Solve for x. *(Lesson 2-3)* **9**

49. The length of a rectangle is 2 and the width is represented by $x + 4$. The area of the rectangle is 40 square units. Solve for x. *(Lesson 2-3)* **16**

Solve each compound inequality and graph the solutions. *(Lesson 3-6)*

50. $4 < 2n + 6 \leq 20$ **$-1 < n \leq 7$**

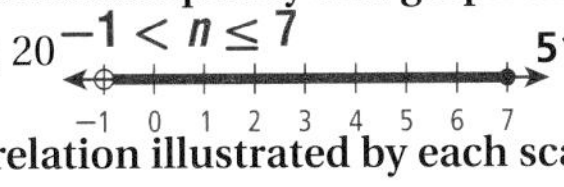

−1 0 1 2 3 4 5 6 7

51. $t + 5 > 7$ OR $2t - 8 < -12$ **$t < -2$ OR $t > 2$**

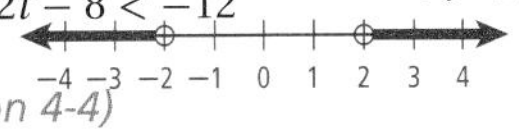

−4 −3 −2 −1 0 1 2 3 4

Describe the correlation illustrated by each scatter plot. *(Lesson 4-4)*

52.

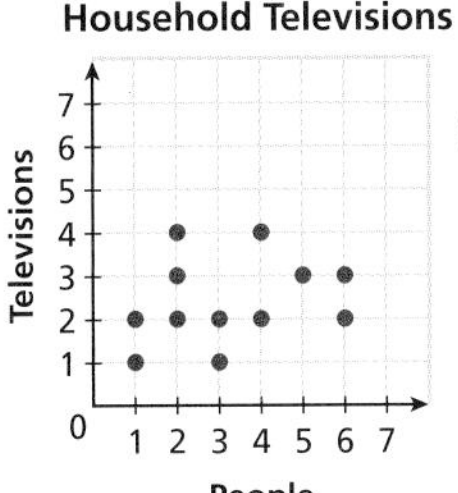

no correlation

53.

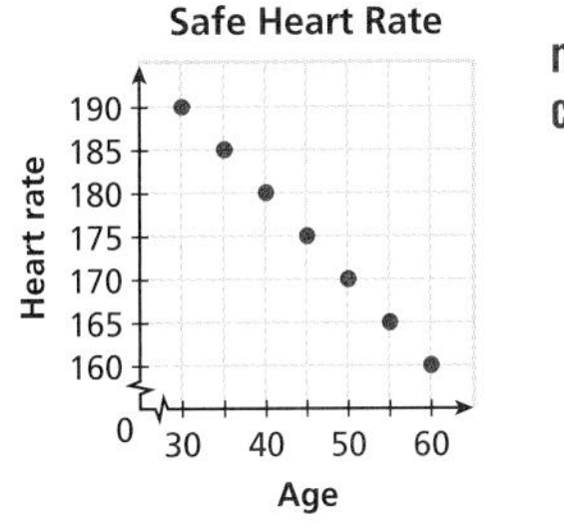

negative correlation

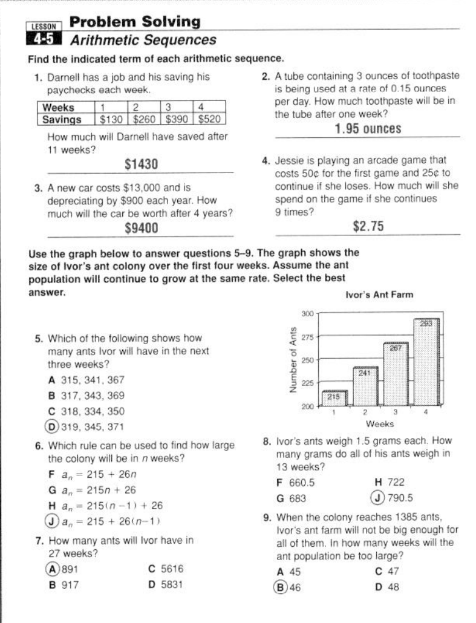

4-5 PROBLEM SOLVING

LESSON 4-5 **Problem Solving**
Arithmetic Sequences

Find the indicated term of each arithmetic sequence.

1. Darnell has a job and his saving his paychecks each week.

Weeks	1	2	3	4
Savings	$130	$260	$390	$520

How much will Darnell have saved after 11 weeks?

$1430

2. A tube containing 3 ounces of toothpaste is being used at a rate of 0.15 ounces per day. How much toothpaste will be in the tube after one week?

1.95 ounces

3. A new car costs $13,000 and is depreciating by $900 each year. How much will the car be worth after 4 years?

$9400

4. Jessie is playing an arcade game that costs 50¢ for the first game and 25¢ to continue if she loses. How much will she spend on the game if she continues 9 times?

$2.75

Use the graph below to answer questions 5–9. The graph shows the size of Ivor's ant colony over the first four weeks. Assume the ant population will continue to grow at the same rate. Select the best answer.

Ivor's Ant Farm (Number of Ants vs. Weeks: 1 – 215, 2 – 241, 3 – 267, 4 – 293)

5. Which of the following shows how many ants Ivor will have in the next three weeks?
A 315, 341, 367
B 317, 343, 369
C 318, 334, 350
Ⓓ 319, 345, 371

6. Which rule can be used to find how large the colony will be in n weeks?
F $a_n = 215 + 26n$
G $a_n = 215n + 26$
H $a_n = 215(n - 1) + 26$
Ⓙ $a_n = 215 + 26(n - 1)$

7. How many ants will Ivor have in 27 weeks?
Ⓐ 891 C 5616
B 917 D 5831

8. Ivor's ants weigh 1.5 grams each. How many grams do all of his ants weigh in 13 weeks?
F 660.5 H 722
G 683 Ⓙ 790.5

9. When the colony reaches 1385 ants, Ivor's ant farm will not be big enough for all of them. In how many weeks will the ant population be too large?
A 45 C 47
Ⓑ 46 D 48

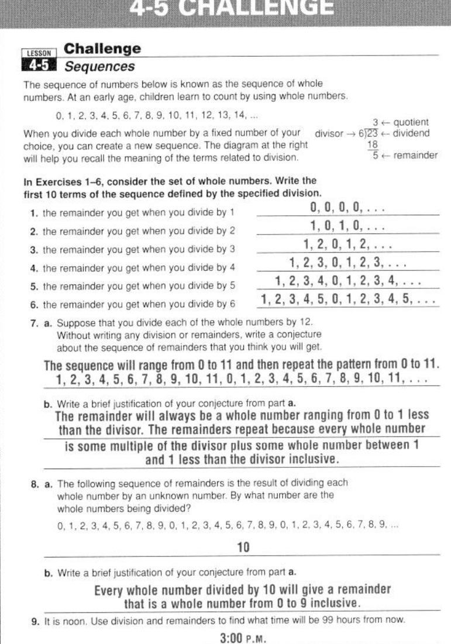

4-5 CHALLENGE

LESSON 4-5 **Challenge**
Sequences

The sequence of numbers below is known as the sequence of whole numbers. At an early age, children learn to count by using whole numbers.

0, 1, 2, 3, 4, 5, 6, 7, 8, 9, 10, 11, 12, 13, 14, ...

When you divide each whole number by a fixed number of your choice, you can create a new sequence. The diagram at the right will help you recall the meaning of the terms related to division.

divisor → 6)23 ← dividend; 3 ← quotient; 18; 5 ← remainder

In Exercises 1–6, consider the set of whole numbers. Write the first 10 terms of the sequence defined by the specified division.

1. the remainder you get when you divide by 1 **0, 0, 0, 0, . . .**
2. the remainder you get when you divide by 2 **1, 0, 1, 0, . . .**
3. the remainder you get when you divide by 3 **1, 2, 0, 1, 2, . . .**
4. the remainder you get when you divide by 4 **1, 2, 3, 0, 1, 2, 3, . . .**
5. the remainder you get when you divide by 5 **1, 2, 3, 4, 0, 1, 2, 3, 4, . . .**
6. the remainder you get when you divide by 6 **1, 2, 3, 4, 5, 0, 1, 2, 3, 4, 5, . . .**

7. a. Suppose that you divide each of the whole numbers by 12. Without writing any division or remainders, write a conjecture about the sequence of remainders that you think you will get.

The sequence will range from 0 to 11 and then repeat the pattern from 0 to 11. 1, 2, 3, 4, 5, 6, 7, 8, 9, 10, 11, 0, 1, 2, 3, 4, 5, 6, 7, 8, 9, 10, 11, . . .

b. Write a brief justification of your conjecture from part **a.**

The remainder will always be a whole number ranging from 0 to 1 less than the divisor. The remainders repeat because every whole number is some multiple of the divisor plus some whole number between 1 and 1 less than the divisor inclusive.

8. a. The following sequence of remainders is the result of dividing each whole number by an unknown number. By what number are the whole numbers being divided?

0, 1, 2, 3, 4, 5, 6, 7, 8, 9, 0, 1, 2, 3, 4, 5, 6, 7, 8, 9, 0, 1, 2, 3, 4, 5, 6, 7, 8, 9, ...

10

b. Write a brief justification of your conjecture from part **a.**

Every whole number divided by 10 will give a remainder that is a whole number from 0 to 9 inclusive.

9. It is noon. Use division and remainders to find what time will be 99 hours from now.

3:00 P.M.

Teaching Tip

Multiple Choice In **Exercise 43,** tell students to note that the data in the second column are decreasing. This means that the difference will be negative. They can eliminate choices **B** and **C.** Students who chose **D** may not understand what the common difference is. Remind them that d is the difference between consecutive terms.

In **Exercise 44,** point out to students that although choice **C** does have a pattern, it is not arithmetic. You cannot add the same number to each term to get the next term.

Journal

Have students compare and contrast determining whether a sequence is arithmetic to determining whether a function is linear.

ALTERNATIVE ASSESSMENT

Have students create three arithmetic sequences. Then have them find the 10th, 25th, and 100th terms for each sequence.

Power Presentations with PowerPoint®

4-5 Lesson Quiz

Determine whether each sequence appears to be an arithmetic sequence. If so, find the common difference and the next three terms in the sequence.

1. 3, 9, 27, 81, . . . not arithmetic

2. 5, 6.5, 8, 9.5, . . . arithmetic; 1.5; 11, 12.5, 14

Find the indicated term of each arithmetic sequence.

3. 23rd term: −4, −7, −10, −13, . . . −70

4. 40th term: 2, 7, 12, 17, . . . 197

5. 7th term: $a_1 = -12$, $d = 2$ 0

6. 34th term: $a_1 = 3.2$, $d = 2.6$ 89

7. Zelle has knitted 61 rows of a scarf. Each day she adds 17 more rows. How many rows total has Zelle knitted on day 17? 333 rows

Also available on transparency

SECTION 4B

CONCEPT CONNECTION

Organizer

Objective: Assess students' ability to apply concepts and skills in Lessons 4-4 and 4-5 in a real-world format.

Problem	Text References
1	Lesson 4-4
2	Lesson 4-4
3	Lesson 4-4
4	Lesson 4-5
5	Lesson 4-5

SECTION 4B

STATE

Applying Functions

College Knowledge Myra is helping her brother plan a college visit 10 hours away from their home. She creates a table listing approximate travel times and distances from their home.

1. Create a scatter plot for the data.
2. Draw a trend line through the data.
3. Based on the trend line, how many miles will they have traveled after 5 hours? **Possible answer: 300 miles**
4. If Myra's brother decided to visit a college 13 hours away from their home, approximately how many miles will they travel? **approximately 800 miles**
5. To find the average speed for the entire trip, find $\frac{\text{change in distance}}{\text{change in time}}$ between the initial ordered pair and the final ordered pair. Include the units. **65.7 mi/h**

Time (h)	Distance (mi)
0	0
2	123
3	190
4	207
6	355
8	472
10	657

1, 2.

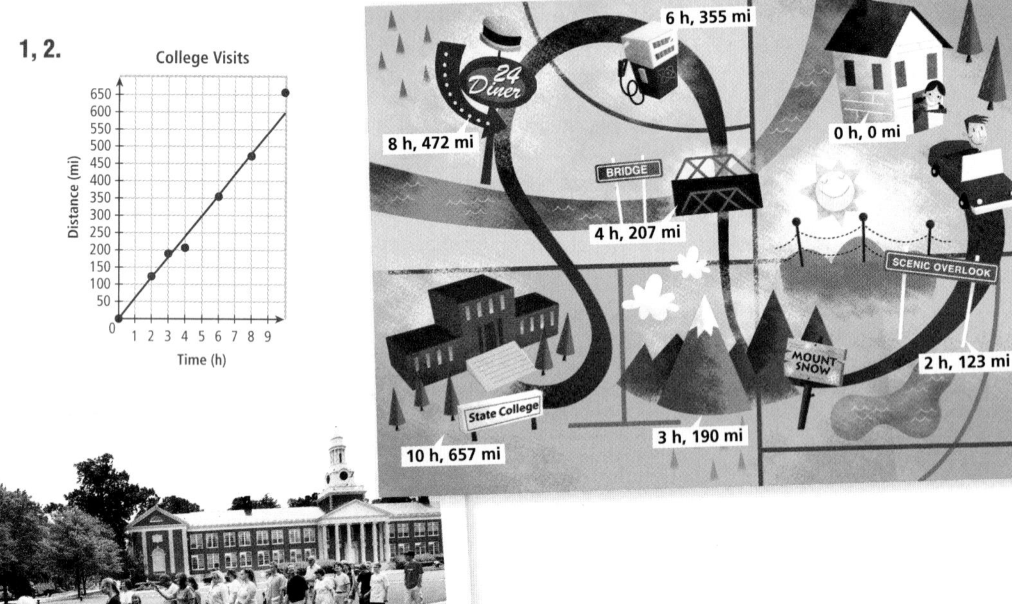

INTERVENTION

Scaffolding Questions

1. What are two points that will be graphed? Possible answer: (0, 0), (4, 207)
2. Does the trend line have to go through all the points? no

3–4. How do you use a trend line to make predictions? Find the point on the graph with the given x-value and use it to identify the corresponding y-value.

5. What is the total change in distance? 657 mi What is the total change in time? 10 h

Extension

How far away would you estimate the college to be if they traveled for 15 hours? about 985 mi

Review of Grade 7 **SDAP1.2**

CHAPTER 4

SECTION 4B

Quiz for Lessons 4-4 and 4-5

1. [Answer scatter plot: Time (min) vs. Pages read]

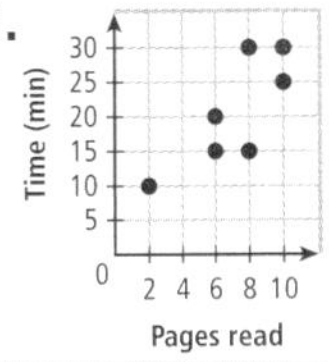

4-4 Scatter Plots and Trend Lines

The table shows the time it takes different people to read a given number of pages.

Pages Read	2	6	6	8	8	10	10
Time (min)	10	15	20	15	30	25	30

1. Graph a scatter plot using the given data.
2. Describe the correlation illustrated by the scatter plot. **positive correlation**

Choose the scatter plot that best represents the described relationship. Explain.

3. number of movie tickets sold and number of empty seats **graph A**
4. number of movie tickets sold and amount of concession sales **graph B**
5. number of movie tickets sold and length of movie **graph C**

Graph A

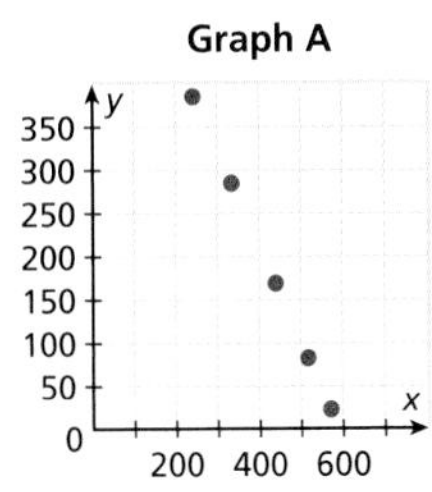

Graph B

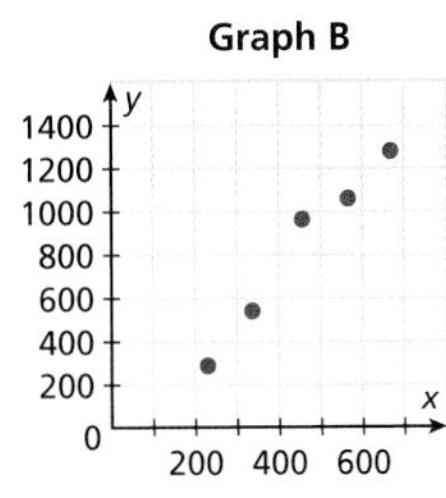

Graph C

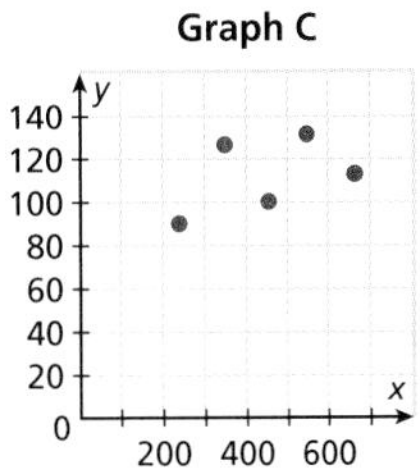

6. The scatter plot shows the estimated annual sales for an electronics and appliance chain of stores for the years 2004–2009. Based on this relationship, predict the annual sales in 2012.
Possible answer: 16.5 million

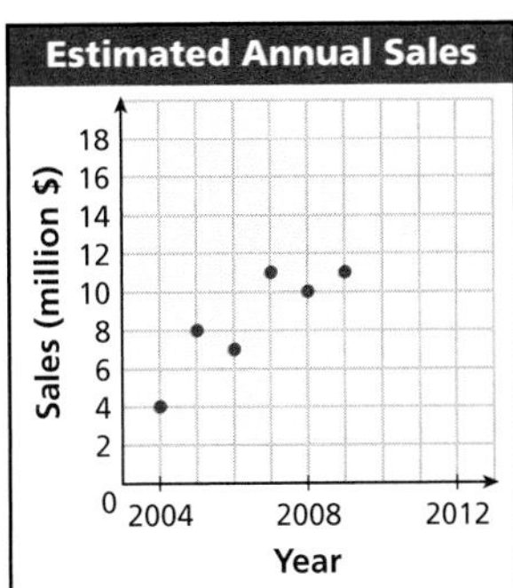

4-5 Arithmetic Sequences

Determine whether each sequence appears to be an arithmetic sequence. If so, find the common difference and the next three terms.

7. 7, 3, −1, −5, … **yes; $d = -4$; −9, −13, −17**
8. 3, 6, 12, 24, … **no**
9. −3.5, −2, −0.5, 1, … **yes; $d = 1.5$; 2.5, 4, 5.5**

Find the indicated term of the arithmetic sequence.

10. 31st term: 12, 7, 2, −3, … **−138**
11. 22nd term: $a_1 = 6$; $d = 4$ **90**
12. With no air resistance, an object would fall 16 feet during the first second, 48 feet during the second second, 80 feet during the third second, 112 feet during the fourth second, and so on. How many feet will the object fall during the ninth second? **272 ft**

READY TO GO ON?

SECTION 4B

Organizer

Objective: Assess students' mastery of concepts and skills in Lessons 4-4 and 4-5.

Countdown to Mastery Week 9

Resources

Assessment Resources

Section 4B Quiz

INTERVENTION 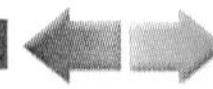

Resources

***Ready to Go On? Intervention and Enrichment* Worksheets**

***Ready to Go On?* CD-ROM**

***Ready to Go On?* Online**

my.hrw.com

READY TO GO ON? Diagnose and Prescribe

Ready to Go On? Intervention	*Ready to Go On?* Intervention, Section 4B		
	Worksheets	CD-ROM	Online
Lesson 4-4 **Rev. 7SDAP1.2**	4-4 Intervention	Activity 4-4	Diagnose and Prescribe Online
Lesson 4-5 **Prep. 2A22.0**	4-5 Intervention	Activity 4-5	

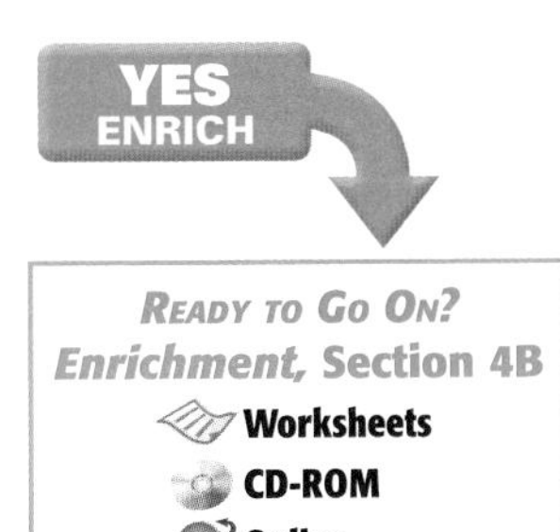

***Ready to Go On?* Enrichment, Section 4B**

Worksheets

CD-ROM

Online

Study Guide: Review

Organizer

Objective: Help students organize and review key concepts and skills presented in Chapter 4.

Online Edition
Multilingual Glossary

Resources

***Multilingual Glossary* Online**
go.hrw.com
KEYWORD: MA8CA Glossary

Tutorial Videos
CD-ROM

Answers

1. domain
2. negative correlation
3. term
4. continuous

5. continuous

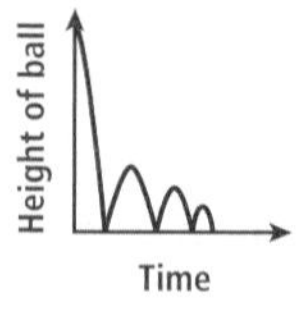

6. continuous

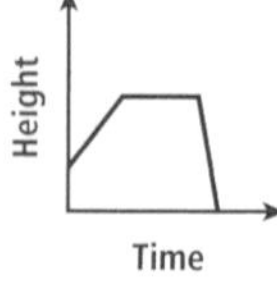

7. Possible answer: A family buys a fish tank and some fish. After two weeks, they buy some more fish. After two more weeks, they buy even more fish.
8. Possible answer: A monkey swings from a high branch to a lower branch. He climbs along the branch. Then he jumps to a higher branch and takes a nap.

CHAPTER 4

Study Guide: Review

Vocabulary

Complete the sentences below with vocabulary words from the list above.

1. The set of x-coordinates of the ordered pairs of a relation is called the ___?___.
2. If one set of data values increases as another set of data values decreases, the relationship can be described as having a(n) ___?___.
3. A sequence is an ordered list of numbers where each number is a(n) ___?___.

4-1 Graphing Relationships *(pp. 200–205)*

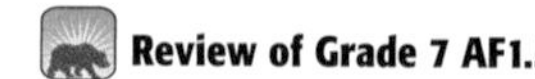

Review of Grade 7 AF1.5

EXAMPLES

Sketch a graph for each situation. Tell whether the graph is continuous or discrete.

- A parking meter has a limit of 1 hour. The cost is \$0.25 per 15 minutes and the meter accepts quarters only.

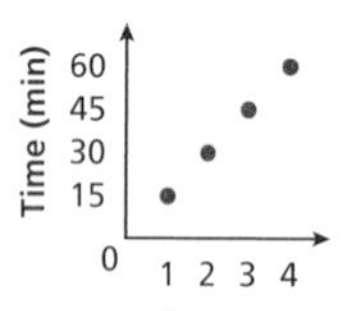

Since only quarters are accepted, the graph is not connected.

The graph is discrete.

- Ian bought a cup of coffee. At first, he sipped slowly. As it cooled, he drank more quickly. The last bit was cold, and he dumped it out.

As time passes the coffee was **sipped slowly, drank more quickly,** and then **dumped out.**

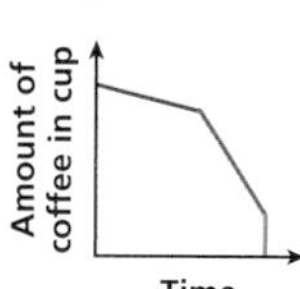

The graph is continuous.

EXERCISES

Sketch a graph for each situation. Tell whether the graph is continuous or discrete.

4. A girl was walking home at a steady pace. Then she stopped to talk to a friend. After her friend left, she jogged the rest of the way home.
5. A ball is dropped from a second story window and bounces to a stop on the patio below.
6. Jason was on the second floor when he got a call to attend a meeting on the sixth floor. He took the stairs. After the meeting, he took the elevator to the first floor.

Write a possible situation for each graph.

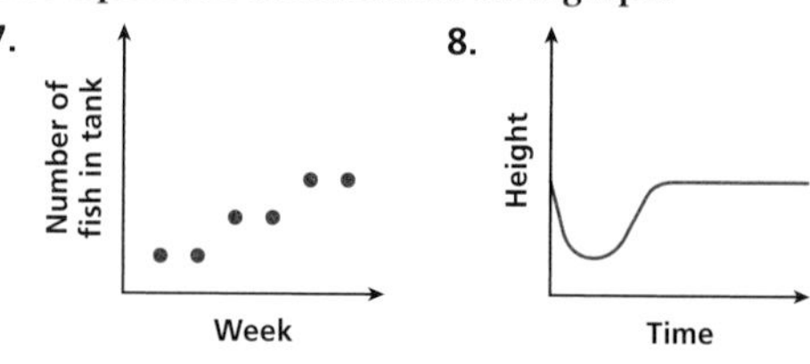

EXAMPLES

- Express the relation $\{(2, 15), (4, 12), (5, 7), (7, 2)\}$ as a table, as a graph, and as a mapping diagram.

Table

x	y
2	15
4	12
5	7
7	2

Graph

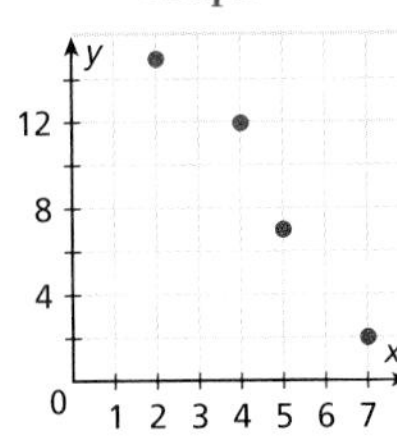

Mapping Diagram

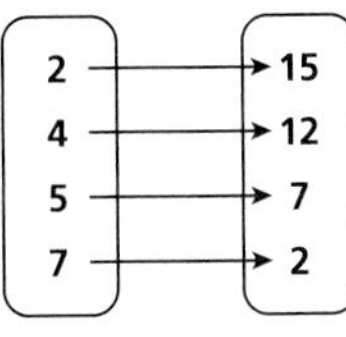

Give the domain and range of each relation. Tell whether the relation is a function. Explain.

-

x	y
−3	0
−2	0
−1	1

D: $\{-3, -2, -1\}$

R: $\{0, 1\}$

The relation is a function because each domain value is paired with exactly one range value.

- 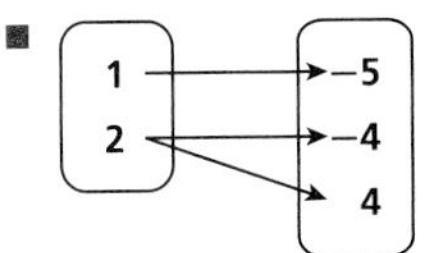

D: $\{1, 2\}$

R: $\{-5, -4, 4\}$

The relation is not a function because one domain value is paired with two range values.

- 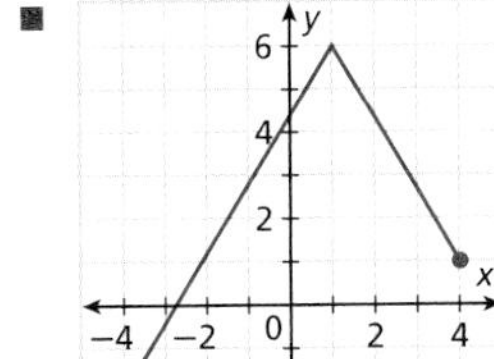

D: $-4 \le x \le 4$

R: $-2 \le y \le 6$

The relation is a function because every x-value is paired with exactly one y-value.

EXERCISES

Express each relation as a table, as a graph, and as a mapping diagram.

9. $\{(-1, 0), (0, 1), (2, 1)\}$
10. $\{(-2, -1), (-1, 1), (2, 3), (3, 4)\}$

Give the domain and range of each relation.

11. $\{(-4, 5), (-2, 3), (0, 1), (2, -1)\}$
12. $\{(-2, -1) (-1, 0), (0, -1), (1, 0), (2, -1)\}$
13.

x	0	1	4	1	4
y	0	−1	−2	1	2

14. 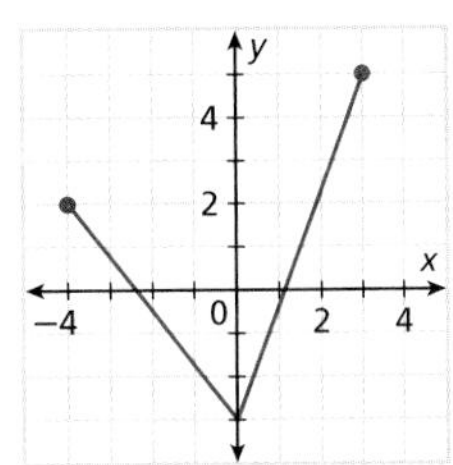

Give the domain and range of each relation. Tell whether the relation is a function. Explain.

15. $\{(-5, -3), (-3, -2), (-1, -1), (1, 0)\}$
16. 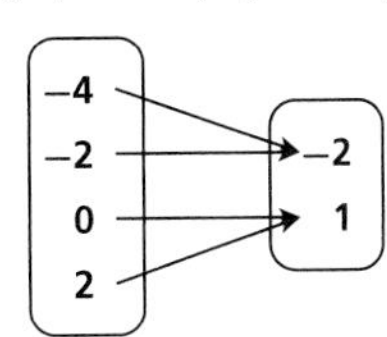

17.

x	1	2	3	4	1
y	3	2	1	0	−1

18. A local parking garage charges $5.00 for the first hour plus $1.50 for each additional hour or part of an hour. Write a relation as a set of ordered pairs in which the x-value represents the number of hours and the y-value represents the cost for x hours. Use a domain of 1, 2, 3, 4, 5. Is this relation a function? Explain.
19. A baseball coach is taking the team for ice cream. Four students can ride in each car. Create a mapping diagram to show the number of cars needed to transport 8, 10, 14, and 16 students. Is this relation a function? Explain.

Answers

9.

x	−1	0	2
y	0	1	1

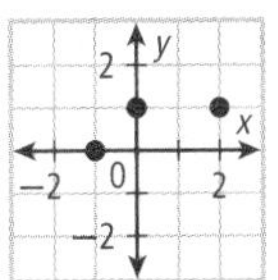

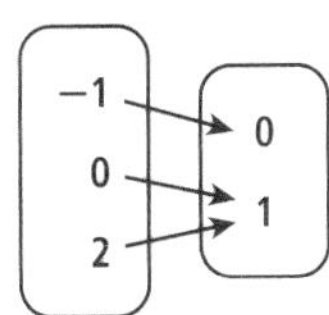

10. 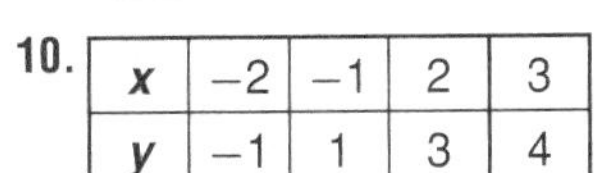

x	−2	−1	2	3
y	−1	1	3	4

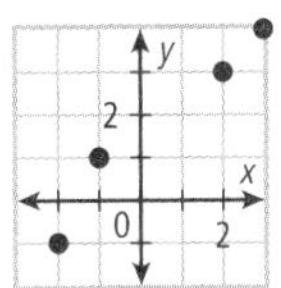

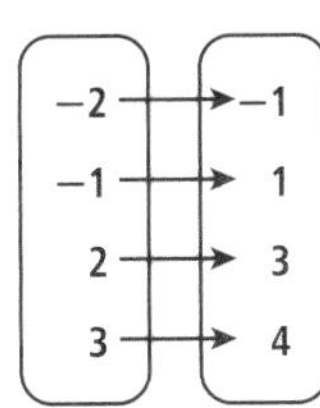

11. D: $\{-4, -2, 0, 2\}$; R: $\{-1, 1, 3, 5\}$
12. D: $\{-2, -1, 0, 1, 2\}$; R: $\{-1, 0\}$
13. D: $\{0, 1, 4\}$; R: $\{-2, -1, 0, 1, 2\}$
14. D: $-4 \le x \le 3$; R: $-3 \le y \le 5$
15. D: $\{-5, -3, -1, 1\}$; R: $\{-3, -2, -1, 0\}$; function; every element of the domain is assigned to exactly one element in the range.
16. D: $\{-4, -2, 0, 2\}$; R: $\{-2, 1\}$; function; each element of the domain is assigned to exactly one element in the range.
17. D: $\{1, 2, 3, 4\}$; R: $\{-1, 0, 1, 2, 3\}$; not a function; the x-value 1 is assigned to the y-value 3 and the y-value −1.
18. $\{(1, 5.00), (2, 6.50), (3, 8.00), (4, 9.50), (5, 11.00)\}$; yes; each x-value has exactly one y-value.
19. 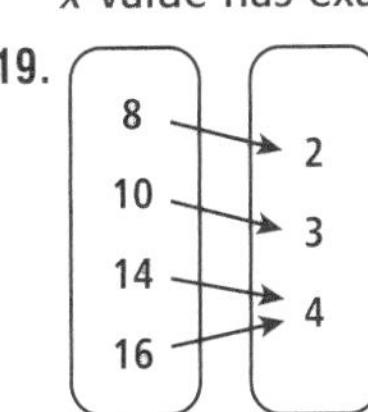

Yes; each element in the domain is assigned to exactly one element in the range.

Answers

20. The value of y is 7 less than x; $y = x - 7$.
21. The value of y is $\frac{1}{2}$ times x; $y = \frac{1}{2}x$.
22. The value of y is 9 times x; $y = 9x$.
23. independent variable: number of cakes; dependent variable: cost; $f(c) = 6c$
24. independent variable: number of CDs Raul will buy; dependent variable: number of CDs Tim will buy; $g(n) = 2n$
25. 14
26. -11
27. 6; -1
28. $k(4) = 15$; $k(-6) = 25$
29. $w(16) = -1.5$; $w(12.25) = -2$
30. 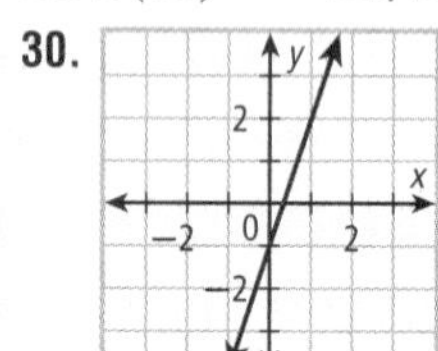 yes
31. 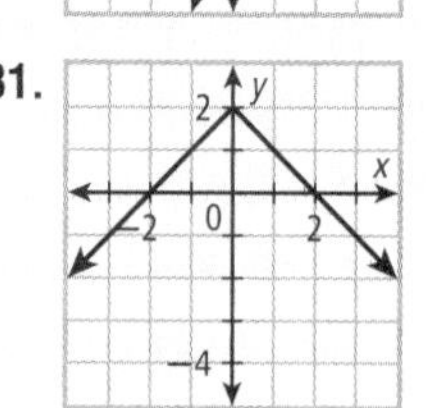 yes
32. 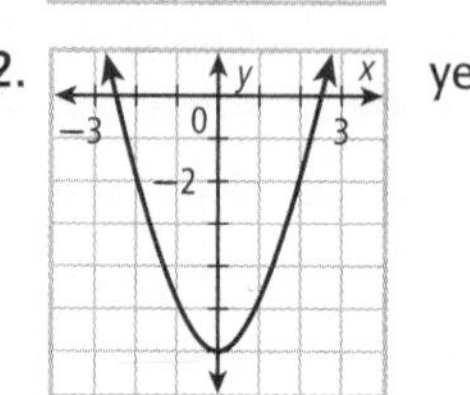 yes
33. 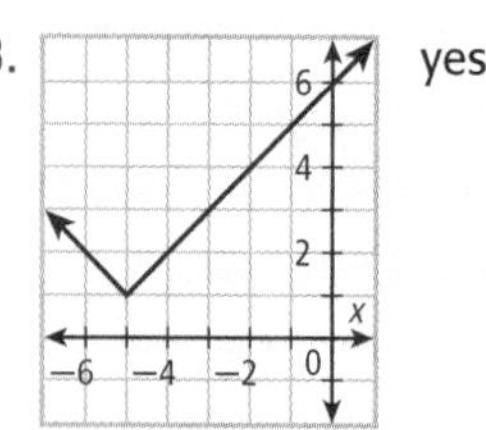 yes
34. D: all real numbers; R: all real numbers
35. D: all real numbers; R: all real numbers
36. D: all real numbers; R: $y \geq -6$
37. D: all real numbers; R: $y \geq 5$

4-3 Writing and Graphing Functions *(pp. 213–220)*

 16.0, 17.0, 18.0

EXAMPLES

■ **Determine a relationship between the x- and y-values in the table. Write an equation.**

x	1	2	3	4
y	-3	-6	-9	-12

What are possible relationships between the x-values and the y-values?

$1 - 4 = -3$ $\quad 1(-3) = -3$

$2 - 4 \neq -6$ ✗ $\quad 2(-3) = -6$ ✓

$3(-3) = -9$ ✓

$4(-3) = -12$ ✓

$y = -3x$ *Write an equation.*

Identify the independent and dependent variables. Write a rule in function notation for the situation.

■ Nia earns $5.25 per hour.
Nia's pay depends on the number of hours she works.
Dependent: pay
Independent: hours

Let h represent the number of hours Nia works. The function for Nia's pay is $f(h) = 5.25h$.

■ **Graph the function $y = 3x - 1$.**

Step 1 Choose several values of x to generate ordered pairs.

x	$y = 3x - 1$	(x, y)
-1	$y = 3(-1) - 1 = -4$	$(-1, -4)$
0	$y = 3(0) - 1 = -1$	$(0, -1)$
1	$y = 3(1) - 1 = 2$	$(1, 2)$
2	$y = 3(2) - 1 = 5$	$(2, 5)$

Step 2 Plot enough points to see a pattern.

Step 3 Draw a line through the points to show all the ordered pairs that satisfy this function.

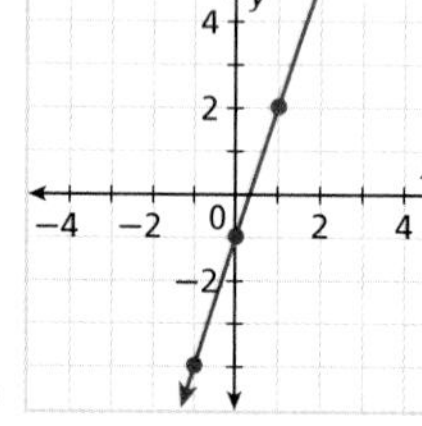

EXERCISES

Determine the relationship between the x- and y-values. Write an equation.

20.

x	y
1	-6
2	-5
3	-4
4	-3

21.

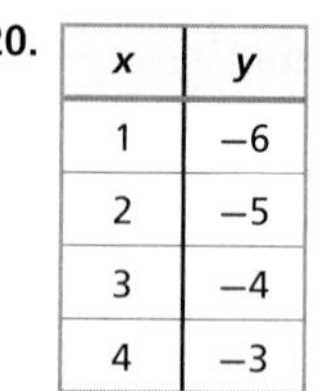

x	y
1	0.5
2	1
3	1.5
4	2

22. $\{(1, 9), (2, 18), (3, 27), (4, 36)\}$

Identify the independent and dependent variables. Write a rule in function notation for each situation.

23. A baker spends $6 on ingredients for each cake he bakes.
24. Tim will buy twice as many CDs as Raul.

Evaluate each function for the given input values.

25. For $f(x) = -2x + 4$, find $f(x)$ when $x = -5$.
26. For $g(n) = -n^2 - 2$, find $g(n)$ when $n = -3$.
27. For $h(t) = 7 - |t + 3|$, find $h(t)$ when $t = -4$ and when $t = 5$.
28. For $k(p) = \frac{1}{2}(p)^2 + 7$, find $k(p)$ when $p = 4$ and $p = -6$
29. For $w(x) = \sqrt{x} - 5.5$, find $w(x)$ when $x = 16$ and $x = 12.25$.

Graph each equation. Then tell whether the equation represents a function.

30. $3x - y = 1$
31. $y = 2 - |x|$
32. $y = x^2 - 6$
33. $y = |x + 5| + 1$

Give the domain and range of each function.

34. $y = 2x + 7$
35. $y = 4x - 5$
36. $y = |x| - 6$
37. $y = x^2 + 5$

4-4 Scatter Plots and Trend Lines *(pp. 224–231)*

Review of Grade 7 SDAP1.2

EXAMPLE

- **The graph shows the amount of money in a savings account. Based on this relationship, predict how much money will be in the account in month 7.**

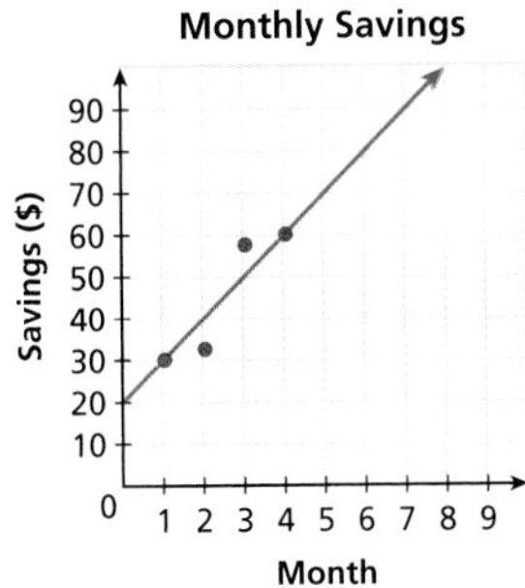

Draw a line that has about the same number of points above and below it. Your line may or may not go through data points.

Find the point on the line whose x-value is 7.

Based on the data, \$90 is a reasonable prediction.

EXERCISES

38. The table shows the value of a car for the given years. Graph a scatter plot using the given data. Describe the correlation illustrated by the scatter plot.

Year	2000	2001	2002	2003
Value (thousand \$)	28	25	23	20

39. The graph shows the results of a 2003–2004 survey on class size at the given grade levels. Based on this relationship, predict the class size for the 9th grade.

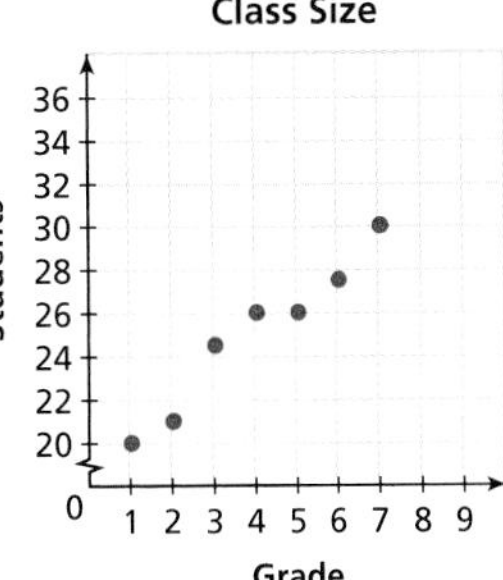

4-5 Arithmetic Sequences *(pp. 234–239)*

Prep for Algebra II 22.0

EXAMPLES

- **Determine whether the sequence appears to be arithmetic. If so, find the common difference and the next three terms.**

  −8, −5 ,−2 , 1,...

  Step 1 Find the difference between successive terms.

  −8, −5, −2, 1,... *The common difference is 3.*

  +3 +3 +3

  Step 2 Use the common difference to find the next 3 terms.

  −8, −5, −2, 1, 4, 7, 10

  +3 +3 +3

- **Find the indicated term of the arithmetic sequence. 18th term: $a_1 = -4$; $d = 6$**

  $a_n = a_1 + (n-1)d$ *Write the rule.*

  $a_{18} = -4 + (18-1)6$ *Substitute.*

  $= -4 + (17)6$ *Simplify.*

  $= -4 + 102$ *Simplify.*

  $= 98$

  The 18th term is 98.

EXERCISES

Determine whether each sequence appears to be arithmetic. If so, find the common difference and the next three terms.

40. 20, 14, 8, 2,...

41. −15, −12, −9, −4,...

42. 5, 4, 2, −1,...

43. −8, −5.5, −3, −0.5,...

Find the indicated term of each arithmetic sequence.

44. 31st term: −15, −11, −7, −3,...

45. 24th term: $a_1 = 7$; $d = -3$

46. 17th term: $a_1 = -20$; $d = 2.5$

47. Marie has \$180 in a savings account. She plans to deposit \$12 per week. Assuming that she does not withdraw any money from her account, what will her balance be at week 20?

48. The table shows the temperature at the given heights above sea level. Find the temperature at 8000 feet above sea level.

Height Above Sea Level (thousand feet)	1	2	3	4
Temperature (°C)	30	23.5	17	10.5

Answers

38.

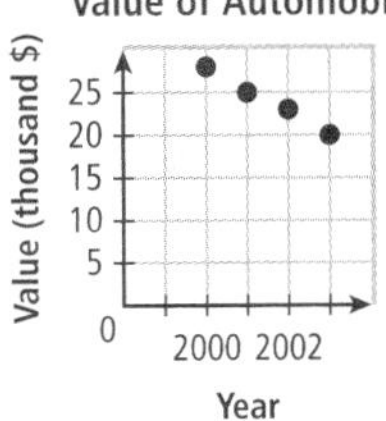

Negative correlation; as the time increases, the value of the automobile decreases.

39. Possible answer: 33

40. appears to be arithmetic; −6; −4, −10, −16

41. not arithmetic

42. not arithmetic

43. appears to be arithmetic; 2.5; 2, 4.5, 7

44. 105

45. −62

46. 20

47. \$420

48. −15.5°C

Study Guide: Review 245

Organizer

Objective: Assess students' mastery of concepts and skills in Chapter 4.

Online Edition

Resources

Assessment Resources

Chapter 4 Tests
- Free Response (Levels A, B, C)
- Multiple Choice (Levels A, B, C)
- Performance Assessment

***IDEA Works!* CD-ROM**

Modified Chapter 4 Test

Answers

8.
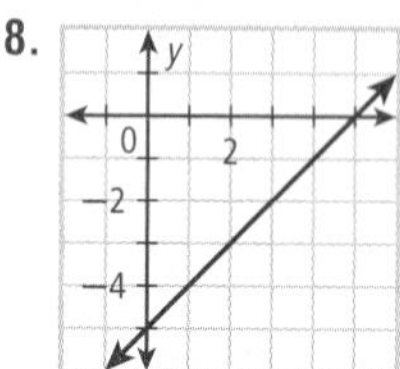

9.
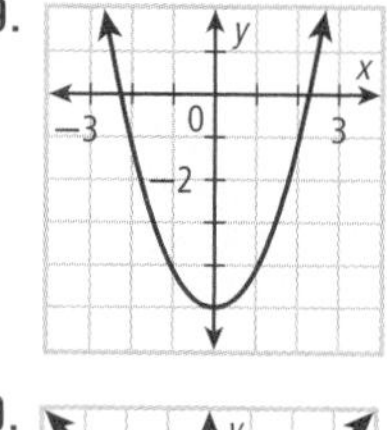

10.
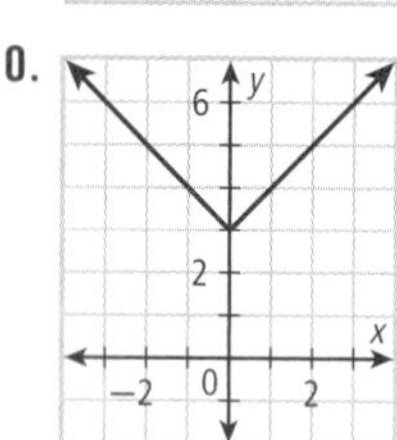

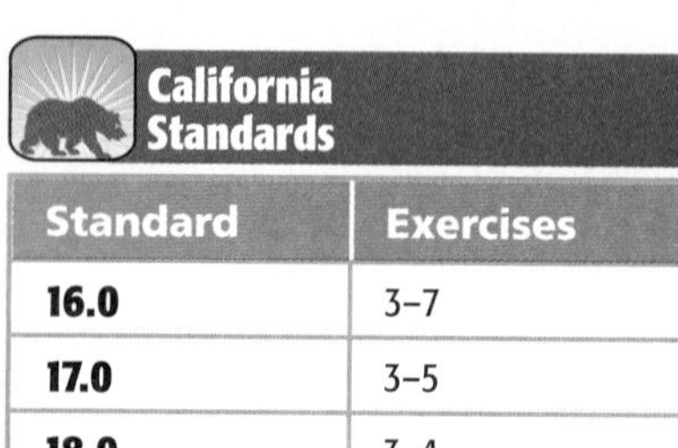

Standard	Exercises
16.0	3–7
17.0	3–5
18.0	3, 4

CHAPTER TEST

Choose the graph that best represents each situation.

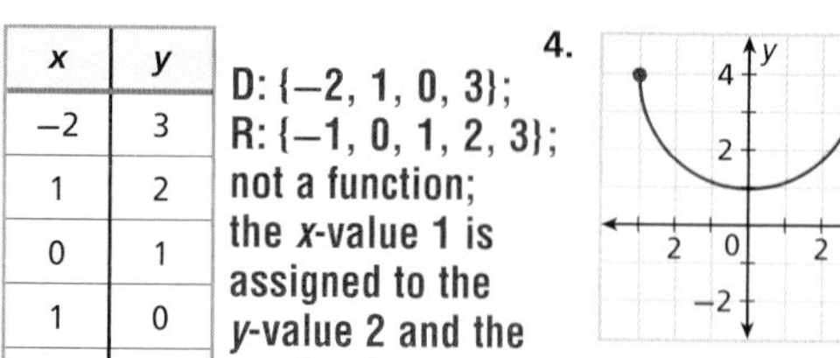

1. A person walks leisurely, stops, and then continues walking. **graph A**
2. A person jogs, then runs, and then jogs again. **graph B**

Give the domain and range for each relation.
Tell whether the relation is a function. Explain.

3.

x	y
−2	3
1	2
0	1
1	0
3	−1

D: {−2, 1, 0, 3}; R: {−1, 0, 1, 2, 3}; not a function; the *x*-value 1 is assigned to the *y*-value 2 and the *y*-value 0.

4.
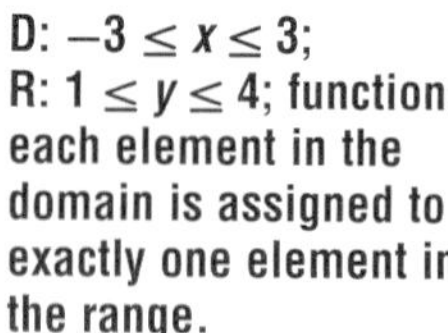

D: $-3 \le x \le 3$; R: $1 \le y \le 4$; function; each element in the domain is assigned to exactly one element in the range.

5. Bowling costs $3 per game plus $2.50 for shoe rental. Identify the independent and dependent variables. Write a rule in function notation for the situation.
independent variable: games played; dependent variable: total cost; $y = 3x + 2.50$

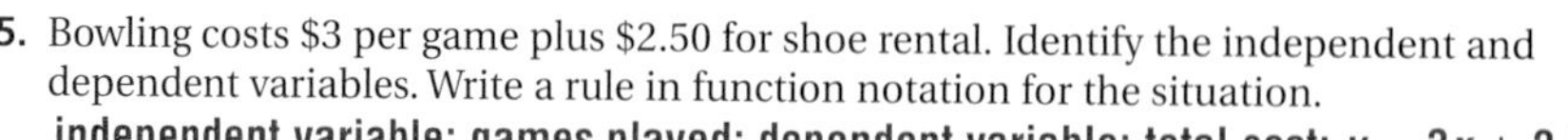

Evaluate each function for the given input values.

6. For $f(x) = -3x + 4$, find $f(x)$ when $x = -2$. **10**
7. For $f(x) = 2x^2$, find $f(x)$ when $x = -3$. **18**

Graph each equation. Then tell whether the equation represents a function.

8. $y = x - 5$ **yes**
9. $y = x^2 - 5$ **yes**
10. $y = |x| + 3$ **yes**

The table shows possible recommendations for the number of hours of sleep that children should get every day.

Age (yr)	1	2	3	4	5	14
Sleep Needed (h)	14	13	12	12	11	9

11. Graph a scatter plot of the given data.
12. Describe the correlation illustrated by the scatter plot.
13. Predict how many hours of sleep are recommended for a 16-year-old. **Possible answer: 7 h**

Determine whether each sequence appears to be an arithmetic sequence. If so, find the common difference and the next three terms.

14. 11, 6, 1, −4,... **yes; $d = -5$; −9, −14, −19**
15. −4, −3, −1, 2,... **no**
16. 7, 21, 30, 45,... **no**

Find the indicated term of each arithmetic sequence.

17. 32nd term: 18, 11, 4, −3,... **−199**
18. 24th term: $a_1 = 4$; $d = 6$ **142**
19. Mandy's new job has a starting salary of $16,000 and annual increases of $800. How much will she earn during her fifth year? **$19,200**

11.
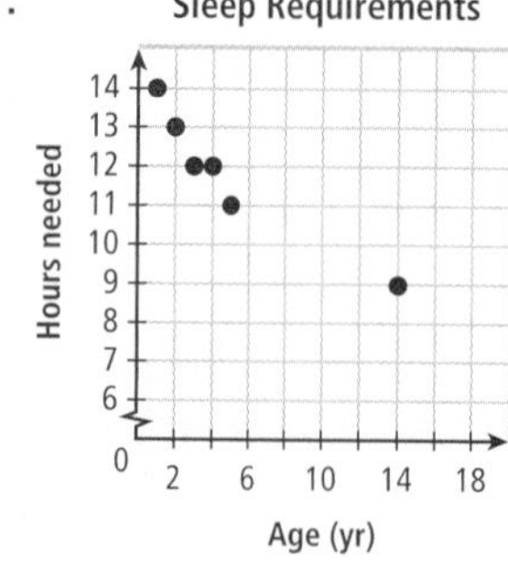

12. Negative correlation: as the child's age increases, the number of hours of sleep needed decreases.

COLLEGE ENTRANCE EXAM PRACTICE

CHAPTER 4

FOCUS ON ACT

Questions on the ACT Mathematics Test do not require the use of a calculator, but you may bring one to use with the test. Make sure that it is a calculator that is on the approved list for the ACT.

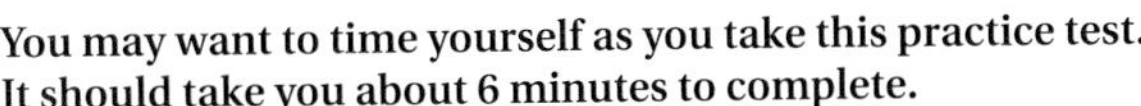

You may want to time yourself as you take this practice test. It should take you about 6 minutes to complete.

When taking the test, you will be more comfortable using a calculator that you are used to. If you already have a calculator, make sure it is one of the permitted calculators. If you plan to use a new one, make sure to practice using it before the test.

1. The soccer team is ordering new uniforms. There is a one-time setup charge of \$50.00, and each uniform costs \$23.50. Which of the following best describes the total cost C for ordering uniforms for p players?

(A) $C = 23.50p$

(B) $C = 50p$

(C) $C = 73.50p$

(D) $C = 23.50p + 50$

(E) $C = 50p + 23.50$

2. In the given relation, what domain value corresponds to the range value -2?
$\{(-1, 2), (-2, 4), (2, 5), (0, -2), (2, 0)\}$

(F) -2

(G) 0

(H) 2

(J) 4

(K) 5

3. Evaluate $h(x) = \frac{1}{2}(5 - 6x) + 9x$ when $x = \frac{2}{3}$.

(A) $\frac{9}{2}$

(B) $\frac{13}{2}$

(C) 7

(D) $\frac{19}{2}$

(E) $\frac{23}{2}$

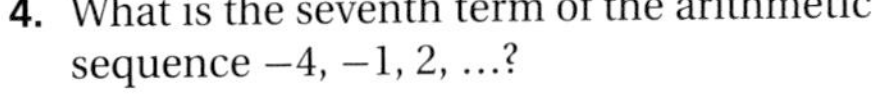

4. What is the seventh term of the arithmetic sequence $-4, -1, 2, \ldots$?

(F) 5

(G) 10

(H) 11

(J) 14

(K) 17

5. The graph of which function is shown below?

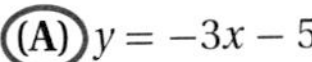

(A) $y = -3x - 5$

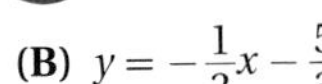
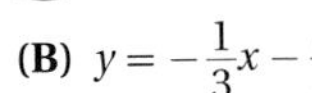

(B) $y = -\frac{1}{3}x - \frac{5}{3}$

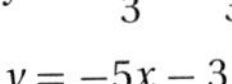
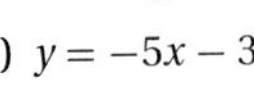

(C) $y = -5x - 3$

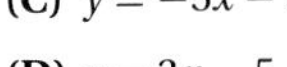

(D) $y = 3x - 5$

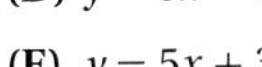

(E) $y = 5x + 3$

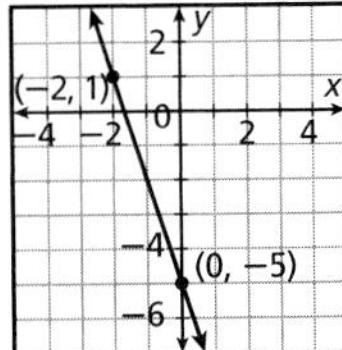
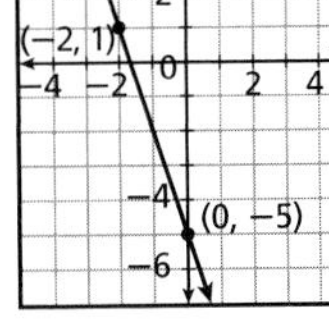

6. Which of the following relations is NOT a function?

(F) $\{(0, 1), (1, 2), (2, 3), (3, 4)\}$

(G) $\{(1, 2), (2, 2), (3, 3), (4, 3)\}$

(H) $\{(0, 2), (2, 4), (4, 1), (1, 3)\}$

(J) $\{(1, 3), (4, 2), (2, 0), (3, 4)\}$

(K) $\{(0, 2), (1, 3), (4, 3), (1, 2)\}$

COLLEGE ENTRANCE EXAM PRACTICE

CHAPTER 4

Organizer

Objective: Provide practice for college entrance exams such as the ACT.

PREMIER **Online Edition**

Resources

College Entrance Exam Practice

Questions on the ACT represent the following content areas:

Pre-Algebra, 23%

Elementary Algebra, 17%

Intermediate Algebra, 15%

Coordinate Geometry, 15%

Plane Geometry, 23%

Trigonometry, 7%

Items on this page focus on:

- Elementary Algebra
- Coordinate Geometry

Text References:

Item	1	2	3	4	5	6
Lesson	4-3	4-2	4-3	4-5	4-3	4-2

Teaching Tip

Multiple Choice

1. Students who chose **A** did not take into account the setup charge for the order. Students who chose **C** added the one-time setup charge to the price for each uniform.

2. Students who chose **J** may not understand the meaning of the terms *domain* and *range*. Students who selected a different incorrect answer may not have read the problem carefully.

3. Students who chose **E** found $h\left(\frac{3}{2}\right)$ instead of $h\left(\frac{2}{3}\right)$. Students who chose **A** may have tried to simplify the expression before evaluating it and may not have applied the distributive property correctly.

4. Students who chose **G** may have incorrectly remembered the formula for finding the *n*th term of an arithmetic sequence as $a_n = a_1 + (d - 1)n$. Suggest to students that when the term to be found is a low-numbered term of the sequence, they can use the common difference repeatedly to find the result.

5. Students who chose **B** reversed the values of x and y in the definition of the function.

6. Students who chose **G** may think that a function is a relation in which each element of the range corresponds to exactly one element of the domain.

Organizer

Objective: Provide opportunities to learn and practice common test-taking strategies.

Teaching Tip **Extended Response** This Strategy for Success explains how extended-response test items are scored and demonstrates how to create a response that is deserving of full credit. Explain to students that extended-response questions are longer and more complex than short-response questions and that the scoring rubric used is based on a 4-point scale rather than a 2-point scale. Use the analogy that these questions are like essay questions in an English class; they require complete explanations to receive full credit.

CHAPTER 4

Extended Response: Understand the Scores

Extended response test items are typically multipart questions that require a high level of thinking. The responses are scored using a 4-point rubric. To receive full credit, you must correctly answer all parts of the question and provide a clear explanation. A partial answer is worth 2 to 3 points, an incorrect solution is worth 1 point, and no response is worth 0 points.

EXAMPLE 1

Extended Response A train traveling from Boston, Massachusetts, to Richmond, Virginia, averages about 55 miles per hour. Define the variables, write an equation, make a table, and draw a graph to show the distance the train travels in 0 to 5 hours.

Here are examples of four different responses and their scores using the rubric shown.

4-point response:

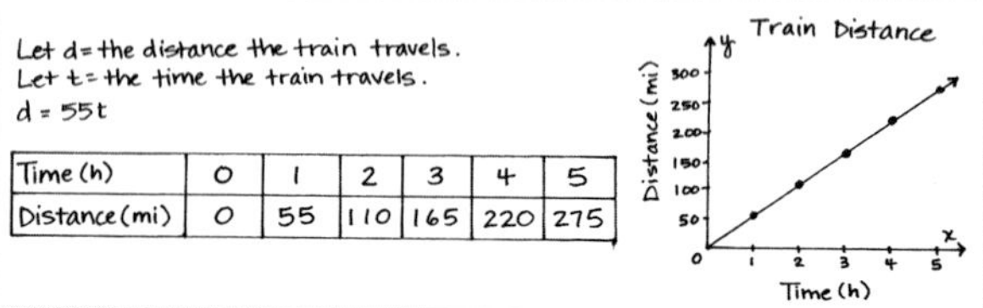

3-point response:

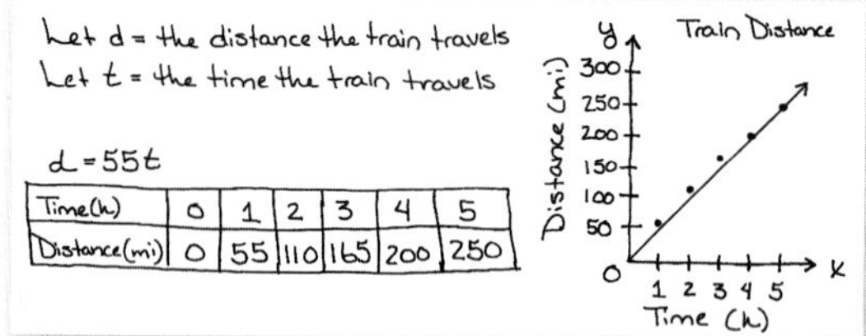

The student shows all of the work, but there are two minor computation errors when $t = 4$ and $t = 5$.

2-point response:

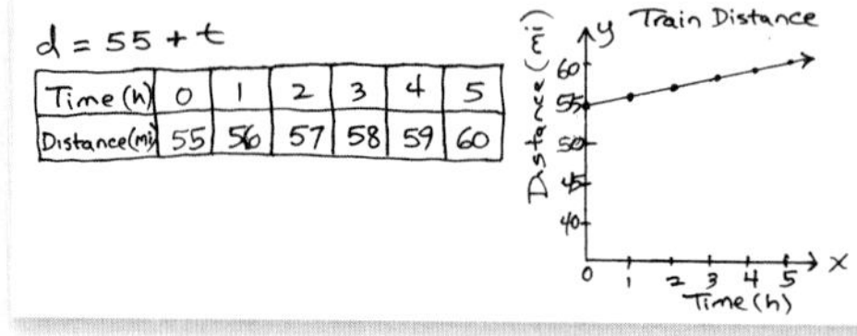

The student writes an incorrect equation and uses it to create an incorrect table and graph. However, the table and graph are correct for the student's equation.

1-point response:

$d = 55t$

The student does not answer two parts of the question.

Teaching Tip **Reading Math** As you read through each test item, ask students to determine how many parts are in each question. Encourage students to underline important words in the question: *List, Explain, Solve,* etc.

Never leave an extended-response test item blank. At least try to define variables or write equations where appropriate. You will get some points just for trying.

Read each test item and answer the questions that follow using the rubric below.

Scoring Rubric:

4 points: The student shows all of the work, correctly answers all parts of the question, and provides a clear explanation.

3 points: The student shows most of the work and provides a clear explanation but has a minor computation error, or the student shows all of the work and arrives at a correct solution but does not provide a clear explanation.

2 points: The student makes major errors resulting in an incorrect solution, or the student gives a correct solution but does not show any work nor provide an explanation.

1 point: The student shows no work and gives an incorrect solution.

0 points: The student gives no response.

Item A

Extended Response Draw a graph that is a function. Explain why it is a function. Then draw a graph that is NOT a function. Explain why it is not a function.

1. What should be included in a 4-point response?
2. Explain how would you score the response below.

Function Not a function

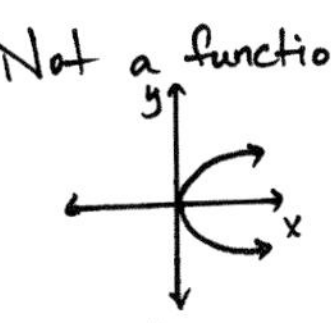

The first graph is a function because each x-value has exactly one y-value. When $x = 1$, $y = 1$. The second graph is not a function because there is more than one y-value for each x-value. When $x = 1$, $y = 1$, and $y = -1$. Therefore, the second graph is not a function.

Item B

Extended Response A car travels at a steady rate of 60 miles per hour. Identify the independent and dependent variables. Describe the domain and range. Write an equation to describe the situation.

3. Ana wrote the response below.

The equation is $y = 60x$. The independent variable is time and the dependent variable is distance. The domain and range are all real numbers.

Explain how would you score Ana's response.

4. If you did not give Ana full credit, what should be added to Ana's response, if anything, so that it receives full credit?

Item C

Extended Response Lara bought 8 notebooks and 4 binders. She spent \$14 total without tax. How much did each notebook cost if each binder cost \$2.50? Write an equation and find the solution.

5. Explain how would you score the response below.

Let s = the cost of each notebook.
Let b = the cost of each binder.
$8s + 4b = 14$
$8s + 4(2.50) = 14$
$8s + 10 = 14$
$8s = 4$
$s = 2$ *The notebooks cost \$2 each*

6. If you did not give the response full credit, what should be added to the response, if anything, so that it receives full credit?

Answers

1. Possible answer: a graph of a function and an explanation of why it is a function; a graph of a relation that is not a function and an explanation of why it is not a function
2. Possible answer: The response is worth 4 points because it has two graphs, one of which is a function and one of which is not a function. The explanations are complete and clearly written.
3. Possible answer: 3; Ana answered 2 of the sections correctly, but the domain and range are not all real numbers.
4. The domain and range should be all real numbers greater than or equal to zero.
5. Possible answer: The response is worth 3 points because the student showed all of the work and completed all parts of the question, but in the last step of the equation, the student divided incorrectly.
6. Change the last step to $s = 0.5$ and then state that the notebooks cost \$0.50.

Answers to Test Items

A. See answer to Problem 2.

B. The equation is $y = 60x$. The independent variable is time and the dependent variable is distance. The domain and range are all real numbers greater than or equal to zero.

C. \$0.50; let $s =$ the cost of each spiral notebook, let $b =$ the cost of each binder purchased, $8s + 4b = 14$

California Standards

Algebra 1 **16.0, 17.0, 18.0**

MASTERING THE STANDARDS

Organizer

Objective: Provide review and practice for Chapters 1–4.

Online Edition

Resources

Assessment Resources

Chapter 4 Cumulative Test

Focus on California Standards Benchmark Tests and Intervention

California Standards Practice CD-ROM

go.hrw.com
KEYWORD: MA8CA Practice

California Standards

Standard	Exercises
1.0	4, 7
3.0	1, 20
4.0 🔑	6, 14, 18
5.0 🔑	2, 5, 8, 13, 16, 18, 19
16.0	10, 12, 21
17.0	11, 17
18.0	9, 10
7AF1.3 🔑	3, 15
7AF1.4	15

MASTERING THE STANDARDS

go.hrw.com
Standards Practice Online
KEYWORD: MA8CA Practice

CUMULATIVE ASSESSMENT, CHAPTERS 1–4

Multiple Choice

1. How many different values of x are solutions of $|x - 2| = 3$?

Ⓐ none
Ⓑ one
Ⓒ two
Ⓓ three

2. Jemma is ordering DVDs. The DVDs cost $14 each and shipping costs $5, no matter how many she buys. Jemma can spend at most $75. Which inequality represents the number of DVDs she can buy?

Ⓐ $14 + 5x \le 75$
Ⓑ $5 + 14x \le 75$
Ⓒ $14(x + 5) \le 75$
Ⓓ $5(x + 14) \le 75$

3. Simplify the expression $2(m - 4) + 7m$.

Ⓐ $-5m - 8$
Ⓑ $2m - 1$
Ⓒ $9m - 4$
Ⓓ $9m - 8$

4. Which property is illustrated by the equation $(x + 4) + y = x + (4 + y)$?

Ⓐ Associative Property of Addition
Ⓑ Closure Property of the Real Numbers
Ⓒ Commutative Property of Addition
Ⓓ Distributive Property

5. Roberto is solving the equation $3(x - 5) + 1 = 10$. As a first step, he rewrites the equation as $3x - 15 + 1 = 10$. Which property justifies this step?

Ⓐ Associative Property of Addition
Ⓑ Closure Property of the Real Numbers
Ⓒ Commutative Property of Addition
Ⓓ Distributive Property

6. For which values of p is the inequality $2(p + 2) < 8$ true?

Ⓐ $p < 1$
Ⓑ $p < 2$
Ⓒ $p < 4$
Ⓓ $p < 6$

7. Which of the following is an example of the Distributive Property?

Ⓐ $3 \cdot 4 \cdot 7 = (3 \cdot 4) \cdot 7$
Ⓑ $7(6 + 1) = 7 \cdot 6 + 7 \cdot 1$
Ⓒ $2 \cdot 9 = 9 \cdot 2$
Ⓓ $(6 + 11) + 4 = 6 + (11 + 4)$

8. Jo Ann needs at least 3 pounds of peaches for a recipe. At the market, she calculates that she has enough money to buy 5 pounds at most. Which graph shows all possible numbers of pounds of peaches Jo Ann can buy so that she has enough for the recipe?

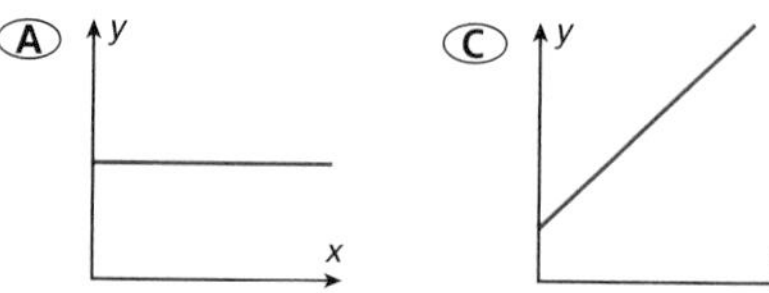

Ⓐ –1 0 1 2 3 4 5 6 7
Ⓑ –1 0 1 2 3 4 5 6 7
Ⓒ –1 0 1 2 3 4 5 6 7
Ⓓ –1 0 1 2 3 4 5 6 7

9. Mr. Jackson drew a graph on the board and said that the graph is an example of a relation that is *not* a function. Which graph could he have drawn?

Ⓐ Ⓒ

Ⓑ
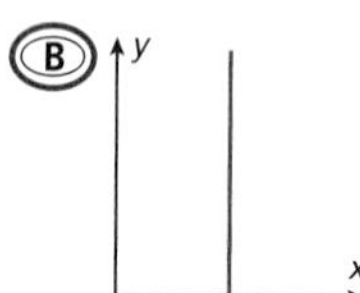

Ⓓ
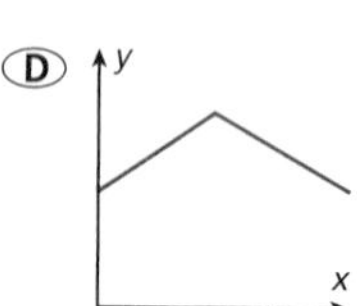

10. Which relation is NOT a function?

Ⓐ $\{(1, -5), (3, 1), (-5, 4), (4, -2)\}$
Ⓑ $\{(2, 7), (3, 7), (4, 7), (5, 8)\}$
Ⓒ $\{(1, -5), (-1, 6), (1, 5), (6, -3)\}$
Ⓓ $\{(3, -2), (5, -6), (7, 7), (8, 8)\}$

Teaching Tip

Multiple Choice Students who chose **C** in **Item 3** may not have distributed 2 over the entire expression in parentheses.

Students who chose **D** in **Item 7** may believe that the Distributive Property always describes an equation that has a sum inside parentheses. Remind them that the Distributive Property also includes multiplication.

Item 8 describes an interval between 3 and 5. Eliminate choices **A** and **B,** and then decide if the endpoints should be included.

Most test problems are written so that they can be solved without lengthy calculations. If you find yourself getting involved in a long, complicated calculation, check the information in the problem again to see if you might have missed something helpful.

11. The graph below shows a function.

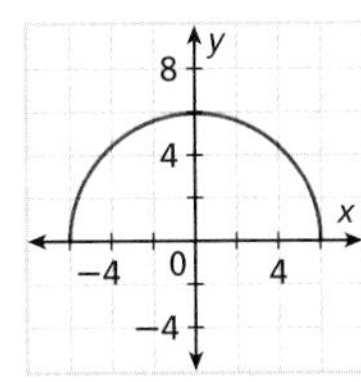

What is the domain of the function?

Ⓐ $x \geq 0$

Ⓑ $x \geq -6$

Ⓒ $0 \leq x \leq 6$

Ⓓ $-6 \leq x \leq 6$ (circled)

12. Which of the following statements is true for every relation that is a function?

Ⓐ The domain is the set of all real numbers.

Ⓑ The range is the set of all real numbers.

Ⓒ Each domain value is paired with exactly one range value. (circled)

Ⓓ Each range value is paired with exactly one domain value.

13. Which of the following is a solution of $x + 1 \leq \frac{3}{2}$ AND $x - 1 \geq -\frac{5}{4}$?

Ⓐ $\frac{3}{2}$ Ⓒ $-\frac{1}{3}$

Ⓑ $\frac{1}{3}$ (circled) Ⓓ $-\frac{3}{2}$

Gridded Response

14. What is the value of x when $3(x + 7) - 6x = 4 - (x + 1)$? **9**

15. Allie simplifies $5(4 + 3x) - 2x$. What value should she use for the coefficient of x in the simplified expression? **13**

16. WalkieTalkie phone company charges $18.00 for basic phone service per month and $0.15 per minute for long distance calls. Arena Calls charges $80.00 per month with no fee for long distance calls. What is the minimum number of minutes of long distance calls for which the cost of WalkieTalkie is more than the cost of Arena Calls? **414**

Short Response

17. A function is graphed below. **D: $-6 \leq x \leq 6$** **R: $3 \leq y \leq 8$**

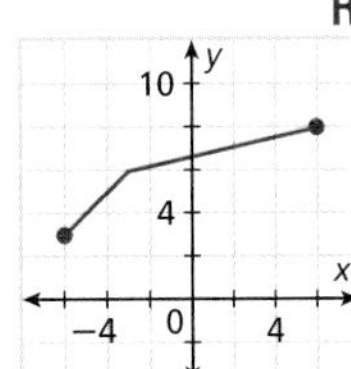

What is the domain and range of the function?

18. The figure gives the dimensions of a rectangular picture frame.

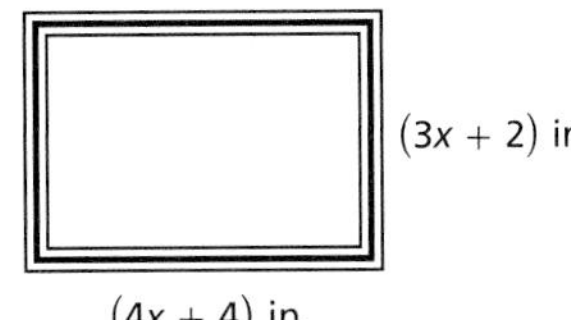

The frame has a perimeter of 40 inches. What is the value of x? Show your work. **2**

19. A company prints custom t-shirts. There is a $25 set-up fee and the shirts cost $9 each. Ray wants to have n shirts printed and he must spend no more than $115. **$25 + 9n \leq 115$**

a. Write an inequality that Ray can use to find the number of shirts he can have printed.

b. Solve the inequality. Show your work. **$n \leq 10$**

20. Consider the inequality $3|x| + 4 > 13$.

a. Solve the inequality. Write the solution as a compound inequality. **$x < -3$ OR $x > 3$**

b. Graph the solutions on a number line.

Extended Response

21. A relation is shown in the table.

a. Express the relation as a mapping diagram.

b. Is the relation a function? Explain why or why not.

c. Write a possible real-life situation for the relation.

x	y
2	12
3	15
3	18
5	40
6	64

Short-Response Rubric

Items 17–20

2 Points = The student's answer is an accurate and complete execution of the task or tasks.

1 Point = The student's answer contains attributes of an appropriate response but is flawed.

0 Points = The student's answer contains no attributes of an appropriate response.

Extended-Response Rubric

Item 21

4 Points = The student draws the correct mapping diagram in part **a,** gives the correct answer and explanation in part **b,** and writes a possible real-world situation in part **c.**

3 Points = The student draws the correct mapping diagram in part **a,** gives the correct answer but not the correct explanation in part **b,** and writes a possible real-world situation in part **c.**

2 Points = The student draws the correct mapping diagram in part **a,** gives the correct answer and an incorrect explanation in part **b,** and writes an incorrect real-world situation in part **c;** or the student attempts to answer all parts and correctly answers one part.

1 Point = The student draws the mapping diagram with a minor error in part **a,** gives the correct answer but no explanation in part **b,** and attempts to write a possible real-world situation in part **c;** or the student attempts to answer all parts of the problem but does not correctly answer any part.

0 Points = The student does not answer correctly and does not attempt all parts of the problem.

Answers

20b.

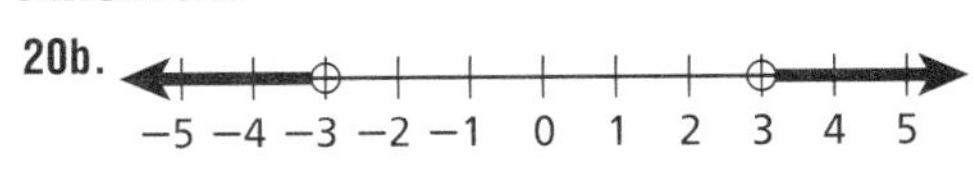

21a.

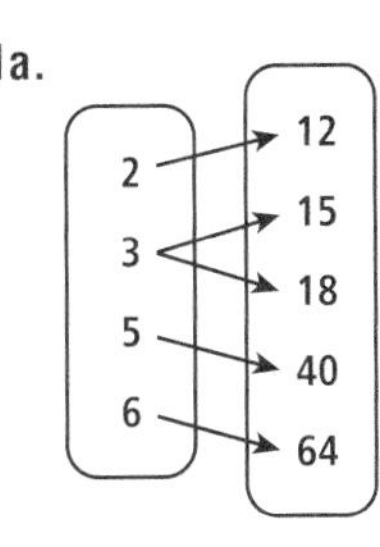

21b. No; 3 is mapped to two different values.

c. Possible answer: There were 5 different field trips. The x-values are the number of chaperones, and the y-values are the number of students on each trip.

Linear Functions

Legend	
✔	Grade-level Standard
◄	Review
►	Beyond the Standards
A	Assessment
O	Optional

Pacing Guide

Calendar Planner
Teacher's **One-Stop** Planner®

Lesson/Lab		California Standards	Time	Advanced Students	Benchmark Students	Strategic Students
5-1	Linear Equations and Functions	6.0, 7.0, 17.0, 18.0	100 min	✔	✔	✔
5-2	Using Intercepts	6.0	50 min	✔	✔	✔
CN	Area in the Coordinate Plane	Reinforcement of Grade 7 MG2.1	25 min	O	◄	◄
LAB	Explore Constant Changes	24.1	25 min	O	✔	✔
5-3	Slope	6.0, Preparation for 8.0	100 min	✔	✔	✔
LR	Conditional Statements	24.1	50 min	✔	✔	✔
5-4	Direct Variation	6.0	50 min	✔	✔	✔
Concept Connection		5.0, 6.0	25 min	A	A	O
Ready to Go On?			25 min	A	A	A
5-5	Slope-Intercept Form	6.0	50 min	✔	✔	✔
5-6	Point-Slope Form	6.0, 7.0	50 min	✔	✔	✔
5-7	Slopes of Parallel and Perpendicular Lines	8.0, 25.1	50 min	✔	✔	✔
LR	Proving Conjectures	24.1, 25.1	50 min	✔	✔	✔
Concept Connection			25 min	A	A	O
Ready to Go On?			25 min	A	A	A
Study Guide: Review			50 min	✔	✔	✔
Chapter Test		6.0, 7.0, 8.0	50 min	A	A	A

* **Benchmark students** are achieving at or near grade level.

** **Strategic students** may be a year or more below grade level, and may require additional time for intervention.

Countdown to Mastery, Weeks 9, 10, 11

ONGOING ASSESSMENT and INTERVENTION

	DIAGNOSE	PRESCRIBE
Assess Prior Knowledge	**Before Chapter 5**	
	Diagnose readiness for the chapter.	Prescribe intervention.
	Are You Ready? SE p. 253	***Are You Ready? Intervention*** Skills 13, 58, 60, 72, 79
Formative Assessment	**Before Every Lesson**	
	Diagnose readiness for the lesson.	Prescribe intervention.
	Warm Up TE, every lesson	**Skills Bank** pp. SB1–SB32 **Review for Mastery** CRF Chapters 1–5
	During Every Lesson	
	Diagnose understanding of lesson concepts.	Prescribe intervention.
	Questioning Strategies TE, every example **Check It Out!** SE, every example **Think and Discuss** SE, every lesson **Write About It** SE, every lesson **Journal** TE, every lesson	**Reading Strategies** CRF, every lesson ***Success for ELL*** pp. 71–86 ***Lesson Tutorial Videos*** Chapter 5
	After Every Lesson	
	Diagnose mastery of lesson concepts.	Prescribe intervention.
	Lesson Quiz TE, every lesson **Alternative Assessment** TE, every lesson **Ready to Go On?** SE pp. 289, 313 ***Test and Practice Generator***	**Review for Mastery** CRF, every lesson **Problem Solving** CRF, every lesson ***Ready to Go On? Intervention*** Chapter 5 ***Homework Help Online***
	Before Chapter 5 Testing	
	Diagnose mastery of concepts in the chapter.	Prescribe intervention.
	Ready to Go On? SE pp. 289, 313 **Concept Connection** SE pp. 288, 312 **Section Quizzes** AR pp. 85–86 ***Test and Practice Generator***	***Ready to Go On? Intervention*** Chapter 5 **Scaffolding Questions** TE pp. 288, 312
	Before Assessment of California Standards	
	Diagnose mastery of California Standards.	Prescribe intervention.
	Focus on California Standards: Benchmark Tests **Mastering the Standards** SE pp. 322–323 ***California Standards Practice* CD-ROM**	***Focus on California Standards: Intervention***
Summative Assessment	**After Chapter 5**	
	Check mastery of chapter concepts.	Prescribe intervention.
	Multiple-Choice Tests (Forms A, B, C) **Free-Response Tests (Forms A, B, C)** **Performance Assessment** AR pp. 99–100 ***Test and Practice Generator***	**Review for Mastery** CRF, every lesson ***Lesson Tutorial Videos*** Chapter 5

KEY: **SE** = *Student Edition* **TE** = *Teacher's Edition* **CRF** = *Chapter Resource File* **AR** = *Assessment Resources* Available online Available on CD-ROM

Supporting the Teacher

Chapter 5 Resource File

Family Involvement
pp. 1–4, 37–40

Practice A, B, C
pp. 5–7, 13–15, 21–23, 29–31, 41–43, 49–51, 57–59

Review for Mastery
pp. 8–9, 16–17, 24–25, 32–33, 44–45, 52–53, 60–61

Challenge
pp. 10, 18, 26, 34, 46, 54, 62

Problem Solving
pp. 11, 19, 27, 35, 47, 55, 63

Reading Strategies ELL
pp. 12, 20, 28, 36, 48, 56, 64

Algebra Lab
pp. 65–66, 70–75

Technology Lab
pp. 67–69

Workbooks

Homework and Practice Workbook SPANISH
Teacher's Edition .... pp. 27–33

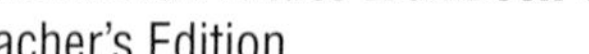

Know-It Notebook SPANISH
Teacher's Guide .... Chapter 5

Review for Mastery Workbook SPANISH
Teacher's Guide .... pp. 53–66

Focus on California Standards: Intervention Workbook SPANISH
Teacher's Guide

Teacher Tools

Power Presentations
Complete PowerPoint® presentations for Chapter 5 lessons

Lesson Tutorial Videos SPANISH
Holt authors Ed Burger and Freddie Renfro present tutorials to support the Chapter 5 lessons.

Teacher's One-Stop Planner SPANISH
Easy access to all Chapter 5 resources and assessments, as well as software for lesson planning, test generation, and puzzle creation

IDEA Works!
Key Chapter 5 resources and assessments modified to address special learning needs

Solutions Key .... Chapter 5

Interactive Answers and Solutions

TechKeys

Lab Resources 

Project Teacher Support

Parent Resources 

Transparencies

Lesson Transparencies, Volume 1 .... Chapter 5
- Teacher Tools
- Warm-ups
- Teaching Transparencies
- Lesson Quizzes

Alternate Openers: Explorations .... pp. 27–33

Countdown to Mastery .... pp. 17–23

Know-It Notebook .... Chapter 5
- Vocabulary
- Key Concepts
- Graphic Organizers
- Chapter Review
- Big Ideas

Technology Highlights for the Teacher

Power Presentations

Dynamic presentations to engage students. Complete PowerPoint® presentations for every lesson in Chapter 5.

2-1 Solving One-Step Equations

Isolate a variable by using inverse operations which "undo" operations on the variable.

An equation is like a balanced scale. To keep the balance, perform the same operation on both sides.

Inverse Operations	
Operation	**Inverse Operation**
Addition	Subtraction
Subtraction	Addition

One-Stop Planner SPANISH

Easy access to Chapter 5 resources and assessments. Includes lesson planning, test generation, and puzzle creation software.

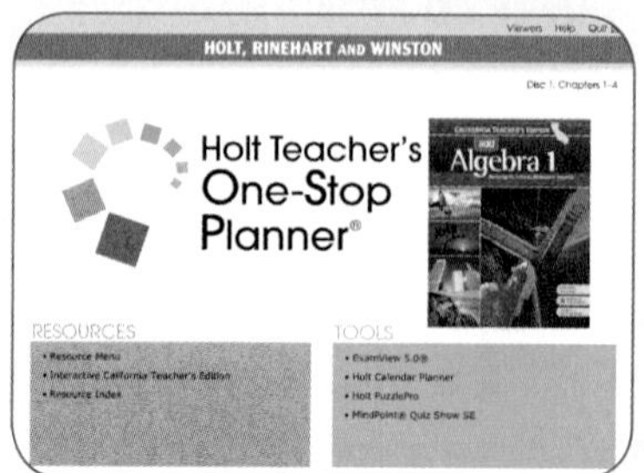

 Premier Online Edition SPANISH

Includes Tutorial Videos, Lesson Activities, Lesson Quizzes, Homework Help, Chapter Project and more.

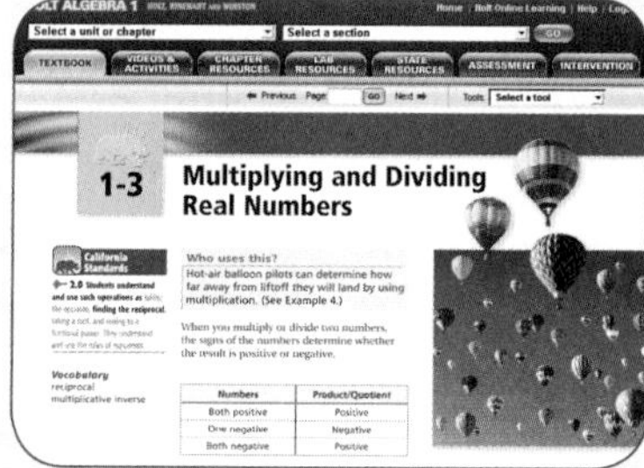

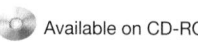

KEY: **SE** = *Student Edition* **TE** = *Teacher's Edition*  ELL English Language Learners  SPANISH Spanish available  Available online Available on CD-ROM

Universal Access

Teaching Tips to help all students appear throughout the chapter. A few that target specific students are included in the lists below.

Strategic Students

Practice A	CRF, every lesson
Review for Mastery	CRF, every lesson
Reading Strategies	CRF, every lesson
Academic Vocabulary Connections	TE p. 254
Modeling	TE p. 291
Questioning Strategies	TE, every example
Ready to Go On? Intervention	Chapter 5
Know-It Notebook SPANISH	Chapter 5
Homework Help Online	
Lesson Tutorial Videos SPANISH	
Online Interactivities SPANISH	

Special Needs Students

Practice A	CRF, every lesson
Review for Mastery	CRF, every lesson
Reading Strategies	CRF, every lesson
Academic Vocabulary Connections	TE p. 254
Inclusion	TE pp. 273, 283, 292, 300
IDEA Works! Modified Resources	Chapter 5
Ready to Go On? Intervention	Chapter 5
Know-It Notebook SPANISH	Chapter 5
Lesson Tutorial Videos SPANISH	
Online Interactivities SPANISH	

English Learners

ENGLISH LANGUAGE LEARNERS

Reading Strategies	CRF, every lesson
Vocabulary Exercises	SE, every exercise set
Academic Vocabulary Connections	TE p. 254
English Language Learners	TE pp. 264, 292
Language Support	TE pp. 259, 264, 292
Success for English Language Learners	Chapter 5
Know-It Notebook SPANISH	Chapter 5
Multilingual Glossary	
Lesson Tutorial Videos SPANISH	

Benchmark Students

Practice B	CRF, every lesson
Problem Solving	CRF, every lesson
Academic Vocabulary Connections	TE p. 254
Questioning Strategies	TE, every example
Ready to Go On? Intervention	Chapter 5
Know-It Notebook SPANISH	Chapter 5
Homework Help Online	
Online Interactivities SPANISH	

Advanced Students

Practice C	CRF, every lesson
Challenge	CRF, every lesson
Reading and Writing Math EXTENSION	TE p. 255
Concept Connection EXTENSION	TE pp. 288, 312
Ready to Go On? Enrichment	Chapter 5

Technology Highlights for Universal Access

Lesson Tutorial Videos SPANISH

Starring Holt authors Ed Burger and Freddie Renfro! Live tutorials to support every lesson in Chapter 5.

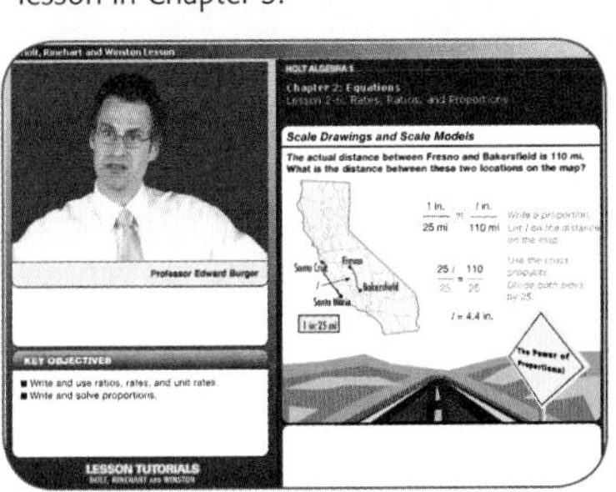

Multilingual Glossary

Searchable glossary includes definitions in English, Spanish, Vietnamese, Chinese, Hmong, Korean, and other languages.

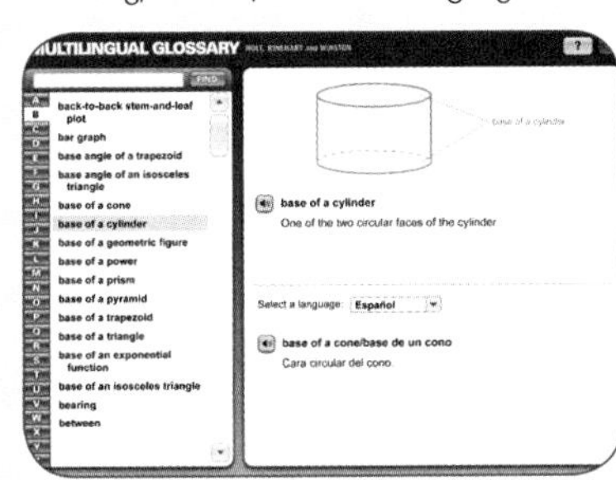

Online Interactivities SPANISH

Interactive tutorials provide visually engaging alternative opportunities to learn concepts and master skills.

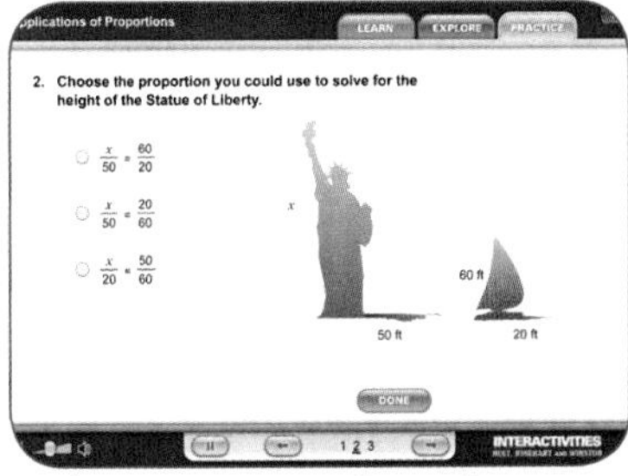

KEY: **SE** = *Student Edition* **TE** = *Teacher's Edition* **CRF** = *Chapter Resource File*  SPANISH Spanish available Available online  Available on CD-ROM

Ongoing Assessment

Assessing Prior Knowledge

Determine whether students have the prerequisite concepts and skills for success in Chapter 5.

Are You Ready? SPANISH .... SE p. 253
Warm Up .... TE, every lesson

Chapter and Standards Assessment

Provide review and practice for Chapter 5 and standards mastery.

Concept Connection .... SE pp. 288, 312
Study Guide: Review .... SE pp. 314–317
Strategies for Success .... SE pp. 320–321
Mastering the Standards .... SE pp. 322–323
College Entrance Exam Practice .... SE p. 319
***Countdown to Mastery* Transparencies** .... pp. 17–23
Focus on California Standards: Benchmark Tests
Focus on California Standards: Intervention Workbook
***California Standards Practice* CD-ROM** SPANISH
IDEA Works! Modified Worksheets and Tests

Alternative Assessment

Assess students' understanding of Chapter 5 concepts and combined problem-solving skills.

Alternative Assessment .... TE, every lesson
Performance Assessment .... AR pp. 87–100
Portfolio Assessment .... AR p. xxxiii
Chapter 5 Project

Daily Assessment

Provide formative assessment for each day of Chapter 5.

Questioning Strategies .... TE, every example
Think and Discuss .... SE, every lesson
Check It Out! Exercises .... SE, every example
Write About It .... SE, every lesson
Journal .... TE, every lesson
Lesson Quiz .... TE, every lesson
Alternative Assessment .... TE, every lesson
IDEA Works! Modified Lesson Quizzes .... Chapter 5

Weekly Assessment

Provide formative assessment for each week of Chapter 5.

Concept Connection .... SE pp. 288, 312
Ready to Go On? .... SE pp. 289, 313
Cumulative Assessment .... SE pp. 322–323
Test and Practice Generator SPANISH .... *One-Stop Planner*

Formal Assessment

Provide summative assessment of Chapter 5 mastery.

Section Quizzes .... AR pp. 85–86
Chapter 5 Test SPANISH .... SE p. 318
Chapter Test (Levels A, B, C) .... AR pp. 87–98
• Multiple Choice • Free Response
Cumulative Test .... AR pp. 161–164
Test and Practice Generator SPANISH .... *One-Stop Planner*

Technology Highlights for Ongoing Assessment

Automatically assess readiness and prescribe intervention for Chapter 5 prerequisite skills.

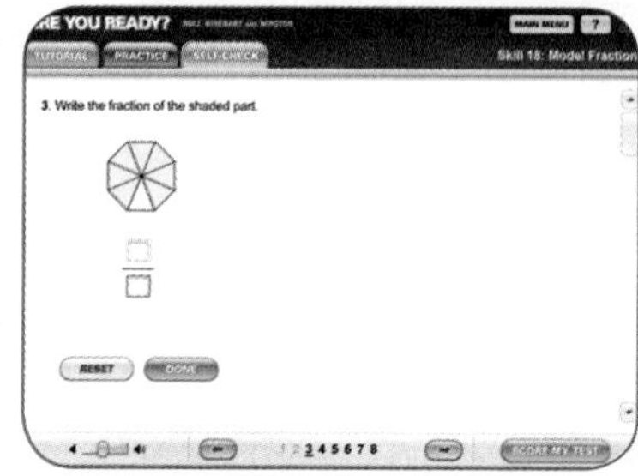

Automatically assess understanding of and prescribe intervention for Sections 5A and 5B.

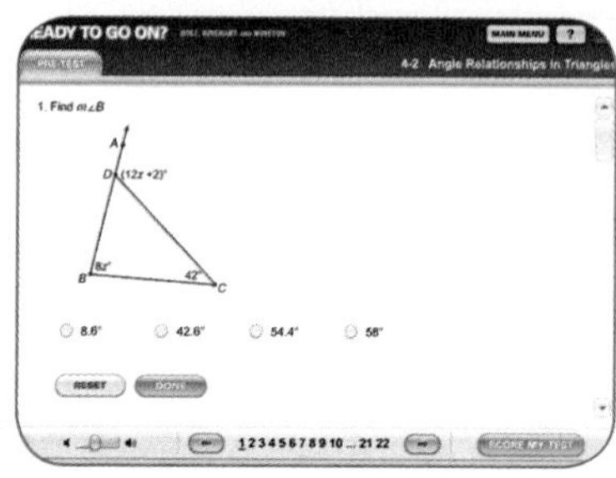

Automatically assess proficiency with California Algebra I Standards and provide intervention.

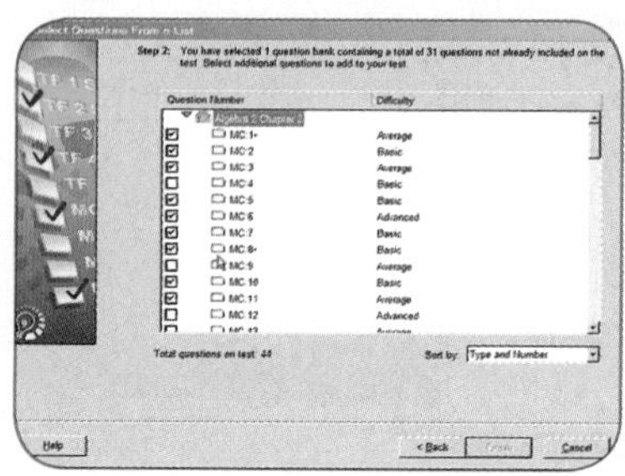

KEY: **SE** = *Student Edition* **TE** = *Teacher's Edition* **AR** = Assessment Resources SPANISH Spanish available · Available online · Available on CD-ROM

Three levels (A, B, C) of multiple-choice and free-response chapter tests are available in the *Assessment Resources.*

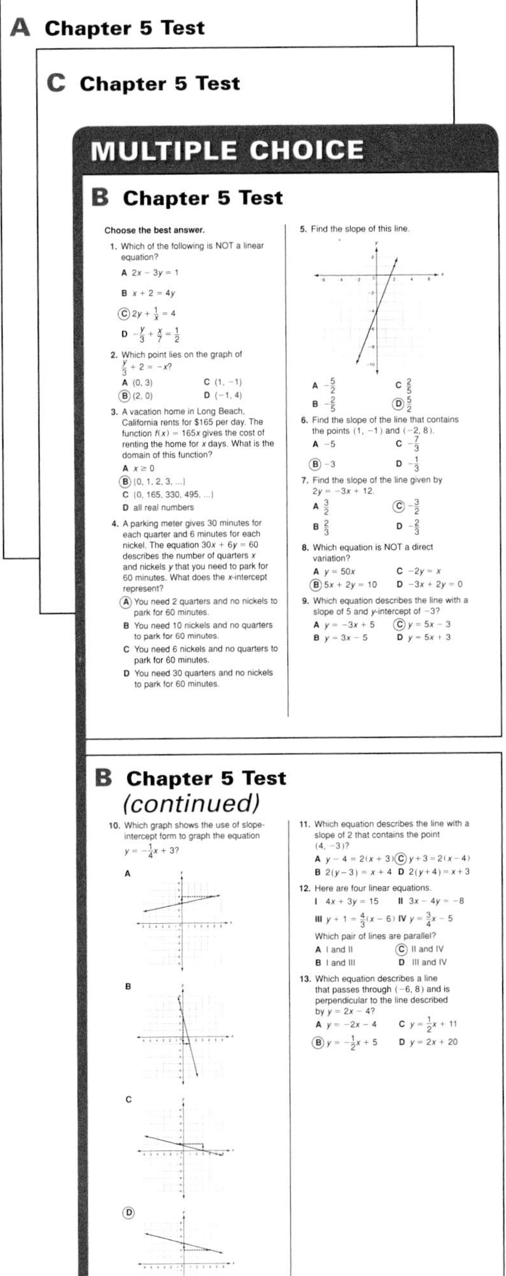

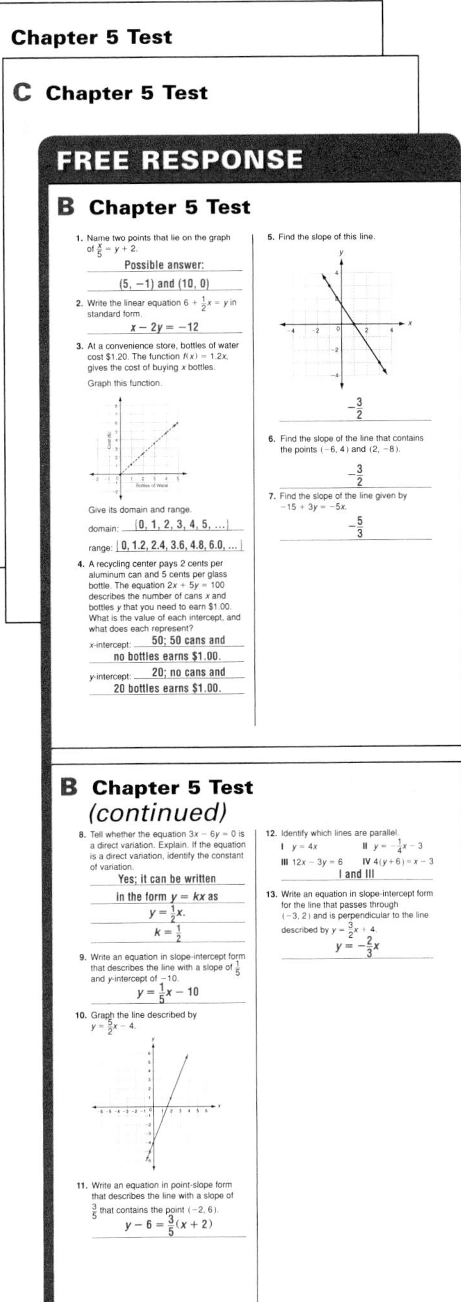

Modified tests and worksheets found in *IDEA Works!*

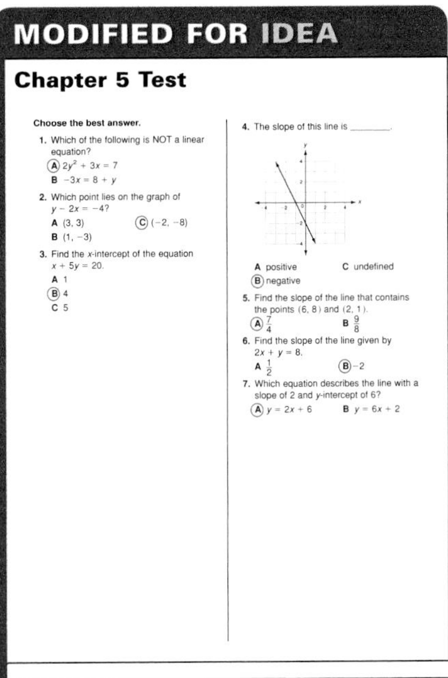

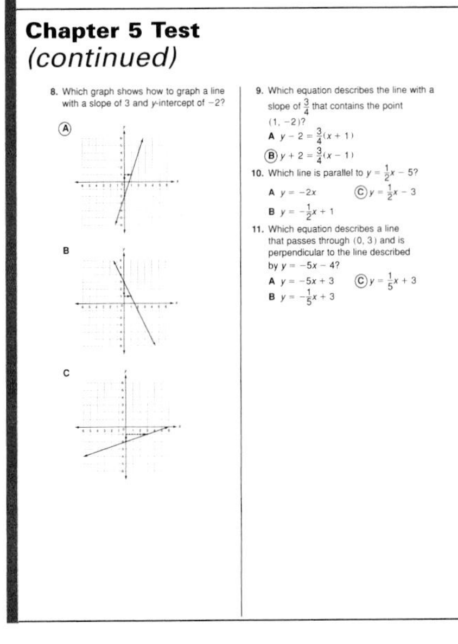

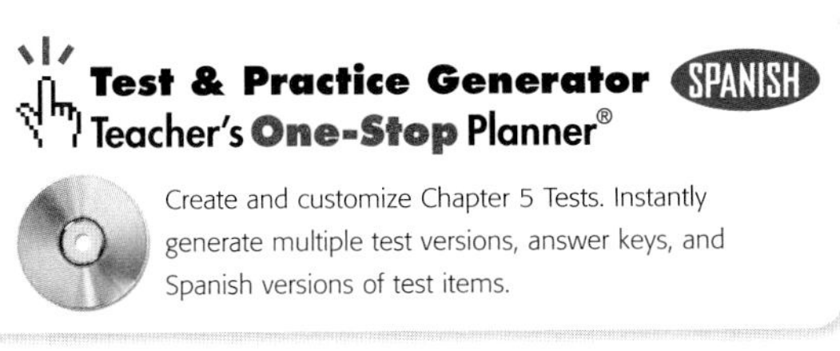

Create and customize Chapter 5 Tests. Instantly generate multiple test versions, answer keys, and Spanish versions of test items.

CHAPTER 5

SECTION 5A
Characteristics of Linear Functions

On page 288, students write, graph, and evaluate algebraic expressions to describe maximum heart rates during exercise.

Exercises designed to prepare students for success on the Concept Connection can be found on pages 261, 268, 279, and 286.

SECTION 5B
Using Linear Functions

On page 312, students use a linear function to model a real-world traffic situation. They describe how changing slope affects the graph of this function.

Exercises designed to prepare students for success on the Concept Connection can be found on pages 295, 302, and 309.

Algebra in *California*

When linear functions are used to model real-world situations, their characteristics (such as slopes and intercepts) represent different parts of the situation. For example, slope may represent the incline of a hill—both its steepness and its direction. Students will study slope in Lesson 5-3 of this chapter.

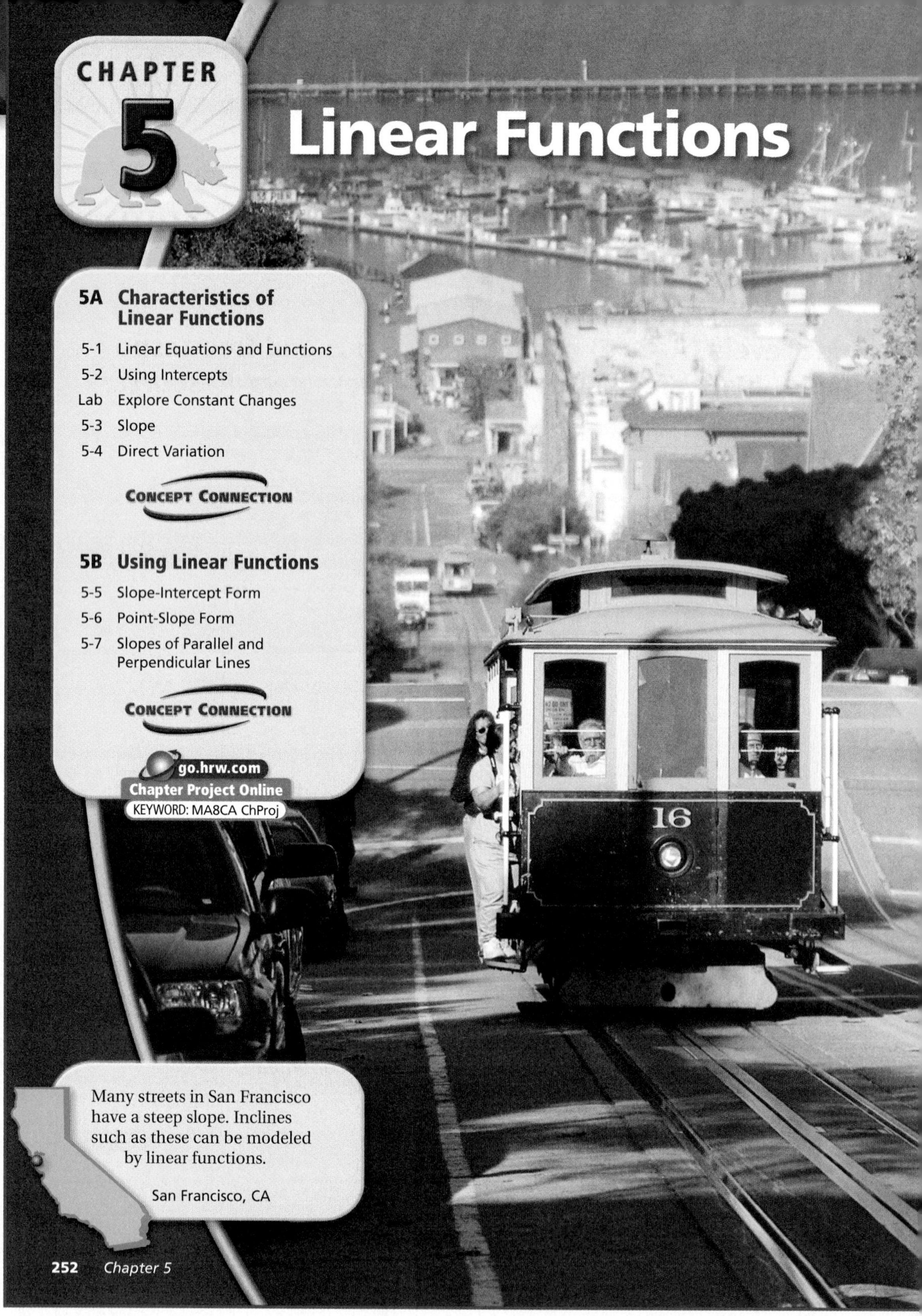

CHAPTER 5

Linear Functions

go.hrw.com
Chapter Project Online
KEYWORD: MA8CA ChProj

Many streets in San Francisco have a steep slope. Inclines such as these can be modeled by linear functions.

San Francisco, CA

252 Chapter 5

About the Project

Take Flight

In the Chapter Project, students research distances and flight times between several locations. Students then graph a scatter plot of the data and analyze a trend line in terms of slopes and intercepts.

Project Resources

All project resources for teachers and students are provided online.

Materials:

- graphing calculator or graph paper

ARE YOU READY?

Vocabulary
Match each term on the left with a definition on the right.

1. coefficient **E**
2. coordinate plane **C**
3. coordinates **D**
4. perpendicular **B**

A. a change in the size or position of a figure
B. forming right angles
C. a two-dimensional system formed by the intersection of a horizontal number line and a vertical number line
D. an ordered pair of numbers that gives the location of a point
E. a number multiplied by a variable

Ordered Pairs
Graph each point on the same coordinate plane.

5. $A(2, 5)$ 6. $B(-1, -3)$ 7. $C(-5, 2)$ 8. $D(4, -4)$
9. $E(-2, 0)$ 10. $F(0, 3)$ 11. $G(8, 7)$ 12. $H(-8, -7)$

Solve for a Variable
Solve each equation for y.

13. $2x + y = 8$ **$y = 8 - 2x$**
14. $5y = 5x - 10$ **$y = x - 2$**
15. $2y = 6x - 8$ **$y = 3x - 4$**
16. $10x + 25 = 5y$ **$y = 2x + 5$**

Evaluate Expressions
Evaluate each expression for the given value of the variable.

17. $4g - 3; g = -2$ **-11**
18. $8p - 12; p = 4$ **20**
19. $4x + 8; x = -2$ **0**
20. $-5t - 15; t = 1$ **-20**

Connect Words and Algebra
21. The value of a stock begins at \$0.05 and increases by \$0.01 each month. Write an equation representing the value of the stock v in any month m. **$v = 0.05 + 0.01m$**
22. Write a situation that could be modeled by the equation $b = 100 - s$.
Possible answer: The amount of money in your bank account equals \$100 minus the amount spent.

Rates and Unit Rates
Find each unit rate.

23. 322 miles on 14 gallons of gas **23 mi/gal**
24. \$14.25 for 3 pounds of deli meat **\$4.75/lb**
25. 32 grams of fat in 4 servings **8 g/serving**
26. 120 pictures on 5 rolls of film **24 pictures/roll**

ARE YOU READY?

CHAPTER 5

Organizer

Objective: Assess students' understanding of prerequisite skills.

Prerequisite Skills
Ordered Pairs
Solve for a Variable
Evaluate Expressions
Connect Words and Algebra
Rates and Unit Rates

Assessing Prior Knowledge
INTERVENTION

Diagnose and Prescribe

Use this page to determine whether intervention is necessary or whether enrichment is appropriate.

Resources
 ***Are You Ready? Intervention and Enrichment* Worksheets**

 ***Are You Ready?* CD-ROM**

 ***Are You Ready?* Online**

my.hrw.com

Answers
5–12. See p. A17.

ARE YOU READY?
Diagnose and Prescribe

Prerequisite Skill	*Are You Ready? Intervention,* Chapter 5 Worksheets	CD-ROM	Online
Ordered Pairs	Skill 79	Activity 79	Diagnose and Prescribe Online
Solve for a Variable	Skill 72	Activity 72	
Evaluate Expressions	Skill 60	Activity 60	
Connect Words and Algebra	Skill 58	Activity 58	
Rates and Unit Rates	Skill 13	Activity 13	

Are You Ready? Enrichment, Chapter 5
Worksheets
CD-ROM
Online

Organizer

Objective: Help students understand the new concepts they will learn in Chapter 5.

Academic Vocabulary Connections

Becoming familiar with the academic vocabulary on this student page will be helpful to students. Discussing some of the vocabulary terms in the chapter also may be helpful.

1. What shape do you think is formed when a **linear function** is graphed on a coordinate plane? Possible answer: a line
2. The meaning of *intercept* is similar to the meaning of *intersect*. What do you think the ***x*-intercept** of a line might be? Possible answer: where it intersects the *x*-axis
3. **Slope** is a word used in everyday life, as well as in mathematics. What is your understanding of the word *slope*? Possible answer: a slant or an incline

CHAPTER 5

Unpacking the Standards

The information below "unpacks" the standards. The Academic Vocabulary is highlighted and defined to help you understand the language of the standards. Refer to the lessons listed after each standard for help with the math terms and phrases. The Chapter Concept shows how the standard is applied in this chapter.

California Standard	Academic Vocabulary	Chapter Concept
6.0 Students graph a linear equation and compute the *x*- and *y*-intercepts (e.g., graph $2x + 6y = 4$). They are also able to sketch the region defined by linear inequalities (e.g., they sketch the region defined by $2x + 6y < 4$). (Lessons **5-1, 5-2, 5-3, 5-4, 5-5, 5-6**)	**graph** to represent data with a diagram **compute** to calculate an answer	You graph an equation of a line using various methods: • plotting points that are solutions of an equation and connecting them with a line. • finding the points where a line will intersect the *x*-axis and the *y*-axis, and then connecting those two points with a line.
7.0 Students verify that a point lies on a line, given an equation of the line. Students are able to derive linear equations by using the point-slope formula. (Lessons **5-1, 5-6**)	**verify** to check whether or not something is true **derive** to reach a conclusion by reasoning	You learn that all points on the graph of a line are solutions to the equation. You also write an equation of a line given a point on the line and its slope.
8.0 Students understand the concepts of parallel lines and perpendicular lines and how their slopes are related. Students are able to find the equation of a line perpendicular to a given line that passes through a given point. (Lesson **5-7**)	**related** connected by similarities **passes through** to move all the way through	You use slope to determine if lines are parallel or perpendicular. You also write equations for perpendicular lines. 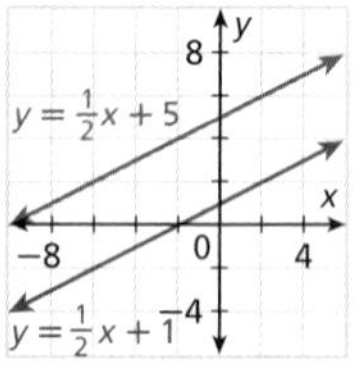 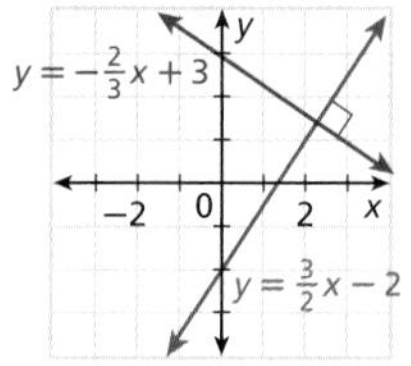

Looking Back

Previously, students

- wrote functions.
- graphed functions.
- described characteristics of functions, such as domain, range, independent variables, and dependent variables.

In This Chapter

Students will study

- writing linear functions.
- graphing linear functions.
- characteristics of linear functions and their graphs, such as the *x*-intercept, *y*-intercept, and slope.

Looking Forward

Students can use these skills

- to write and solve linear inequalities and graph their solutions.
- to graph and solve systems of linear equations.
- to graph and solve systems of linear inequalities.

Study Strategy: Use Multiple Representations

Representing a math concept in more than one way can help you understand it more clearly. As you read the explanations and example problems in your text, note the use of tables, lists, graphs, diagrams, and symbols, as well as words to explain a concept.

From Lesson 4-3:

In this example from Chapter 4, the given function is described using an equation, a table, ordered pairs, and a graph.

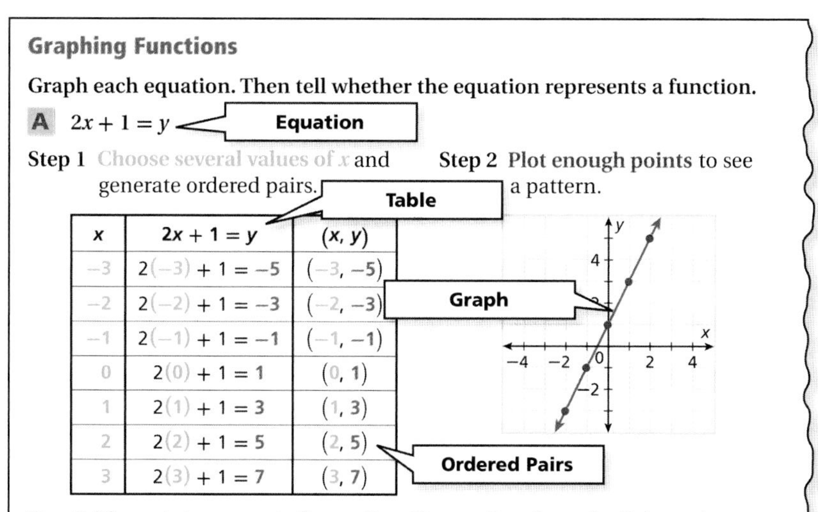

Graphing Functions

Graph each equation. Then tell whether the equation represents a function.

A $2x + 1 = y$ ← **Equation**

Step 1 Choose several values of x and generate ordered pairs. ← **Table**

x	$2x + 1 = y$	(x, y)
−3	$2(-3) + 1 = -5$	$(-3, -5)$
−2	$2(-2) + 1 = -3$	$(-2, -3)$
−1	$2(-1) + 1 = -1$	$(-1, -1)$
0	$2(0) + 1 = 1$	$(0, 1)$
1	$2(1) + 1 = 3$	$(1, 3)$
2	$2(2) + 1 = 5$	$(2, 5)$
3	$2(3) + 1 = 7$	$(3, 7)$

← **Ordered Pairs**

Step 2 Plot enough points to see a pattern. ← **Graph**

Step 3 The points appear to form a line. Draw a line through all the points to show all the ordered pairs that satisfy the function. Draw arrowheads on both "ends" of the line.

Try This

1. If an employee earns $8.00 an hour, $y = 8x$ gives the total pay y the employee will earn for working x hours. For this equation, make a table of ordered pairs and a graph. Explain the relationships between the equation, the table, and the graph. How does each one describe the situation?
2. What situations might make one representation more useful than another?

Reading and Writing Math — Organizer

Objective: Help students apply strategies to understand and retain key concepts.

Resources

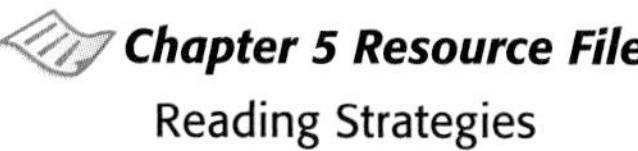

Reading Strategies

Study Strategy: Use Multiple Representations

Discuss Students make key mathematical connections when they see the same concept presented in various formats side by side.

For the example presented, the numbers in the domain of $2x + 1 = y$ appear in green and are also the x-coordinates of the points plotted on the graph. The numbers in the range appear in blue and are also the y-coordinates of the points plotted on the graph.

Extend As students work through the application problems in Chapter 5, have them discuss which representation they think is best for that problem and why.

Answers to *Try This*

1. **Employee's Earnings**

Total pay ($): 8, 16, 24, 32
Hours worked: 0, 2, 4, 6

Hours Worked	Total Pay ($)
0	0
1	8
2	16
3	24
4	32
5	40

The table shows some ordered-pair solutions to the equation. The graph is a visual representation of all ordered-pair solutions to the equation, including those in the table.

2. Possible answer: an equation is useful when you need a rule to calculate how much money you make for working certain hours. A table is useful if you need a list of pay amounts for various amounts of time worked. A graph is useful to see the relationship between hours worked and total pay.

SECTION 5A

Linear Functions

One-Minute Section Planner

Lesson	Lab Resources	Materials
Lesson 5-1 Linear Equations and Functions • Identify and graph linear equations and linear functions. **6.0, 7.0, 18.0**	***Algebra Lab*** **5-1** In *Chapter 5 Resource File*	**Optional** graphing calculator
Lesson 5-2 Using Intercepts • Find *x*- and *y*-intercepts and interpret their meanings in real-world situations. • Use *x*- and *y*-intercepts to graph lines. **6.0**		
5-3 Algebra Lab Explore Constant Changes • Explore the relationship between constant change and the slope of a line.		**Optional** snap cubes or linking cubes
Lesson 5-3 Slope • Find slopes of lines. **Prep for 8.0, 6.0**	***Technology Lab*** **5-3** In *Chapter 5 Resource File*	**Optional** number cubes (MK), CBR or CBL with motion detector
Lesson 5-4 Direct Variation • Identify, write, and graph direct variation. **6.0**		**Optional** graphing calculator, ruler (MK)

MK = *Manipulatives Kit*

Notes

Math Background: Teaching the Standards

LINEAR FUNCTIONS 

Lesson 5-1

A solution of a linear equation in two variables, x and y, is an ordered pair, (a, b), such that when a is substituted for x and b is substituted for y the resulting equation is true. Thus the ordered pair $(2, 5)$ is a solution of $y = 3x - 1$ because $5 = 3(2) - 1$ is a true statement. The ordered pair $(5, 4)$ is not a solution of the equation because $4 \neq 3(5) - 1$.

In contrast to linear equations in one variable, linear equations in two variables have infinitely many solutions. It is important for students to understand the connection between the solutions of a linear equation and the graph of the equation–the graph of an equation is precisely the set of ordered pairs that are solutions of the equation.

A specific example helps to clarify this last point. The graph of $y = 3x - 1$ consists of all ordered pairs (a, b) such that $b = 3a - 1$. In other words, the graph consists of all ordered pairs of the form $(a, 3a - 1)$. As shown above, the point $(2, 5)$ satisfies this relationship and so it must lie on the graph. Conversely, the point $(1, 2)$ lies on the graph, so it must be a solution of the equation, and indeed $2 = 3(1) - 1$. It was also shown above that $(5, 4)$ is *not* a solution of the equation; therefore this point does *not* lie on the graph.

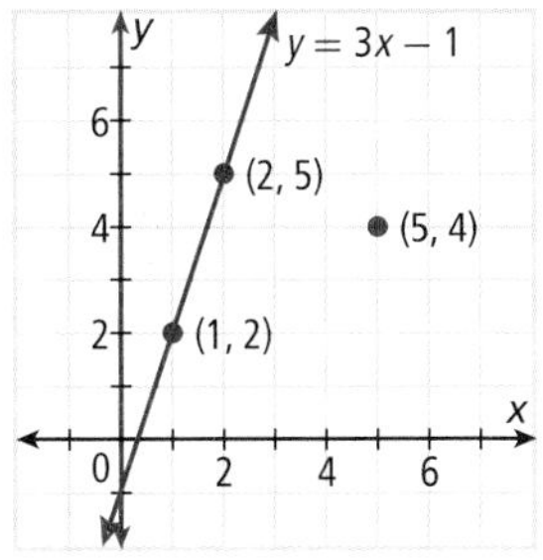

FIRST DIFFERENCES

Lesson 5-1

Given a table of ordered pairs that have equally-spaced x-values, the differences in the y-values are called *first differences,* and these values can be used to determine whether a set of ordered pairs satisfies a linear function.

A set of ordered pairs satisfies a linear function if and only if the first differences are constant. In the table below, the x-values are equally spaced and the first differences are all 3, so the ordered pairs satisfy a linear function. In other words, when graphed, these points will all lie on the same line.

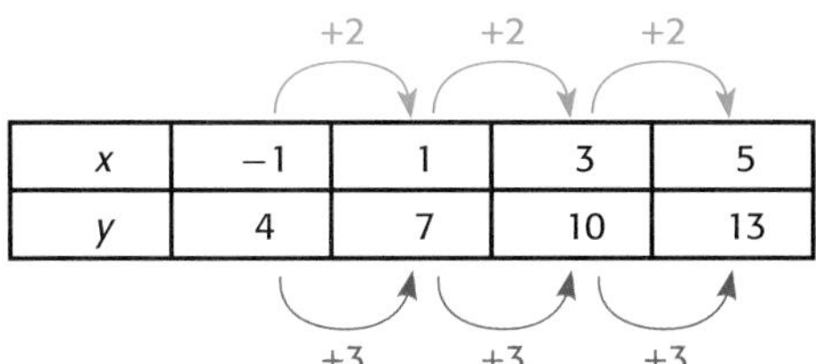

x	−1	1	3	5
y	4	7	10	13

This works because it is equivalent to saying that the function has a constant rate of change, which is true for any linear function. In the above example, the rate of change is $\frac{\text{change in } y}{\text{change in } x} = \frac{3}{2}$.

SLOPE

Lesson 5-3

The slope of a line is defined as the ratio of rise to run for *any pair* of points on the line.

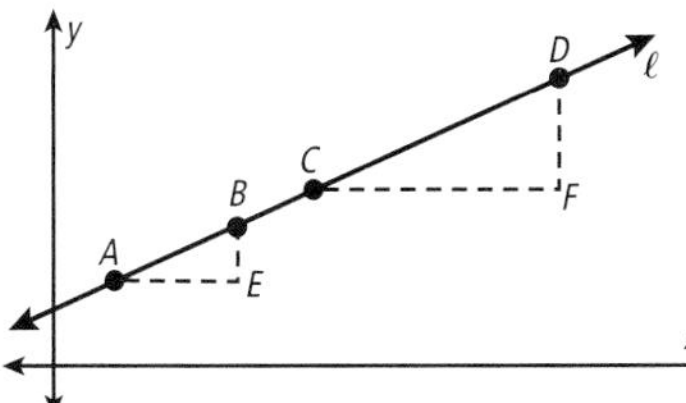

To see why the slope of line ℓ is the same whether points A and B are used or points C and D are used, draw $\overline{AE}$ and $\overline{CF}$ parallel to the x-axis, and $\overline{BE}$ and $\overline{DF}$ parallel to the y-axis. Then $\overline{AE}$ and $\overline{CF}$ are parallel (since they are both parallel to the x-axis) and $\angle A \cong \angle C$, since they are corresponding angles formed by parallel lines cut by a transversal. By a similar argument, $\angle B \cong \angle D$. Thus, $\triangle ABE$ is similar to $\triangle CDF$. Corresponding sides of similar triangles are proportional so $\frac{BE}{DF} = \frac{AE}{CF}$, which can be rewritten as $\frac{BE}{AE} = \frac{DF}{CF}$. This shows that the ratio of rise to run (slope) is the same for both pairs of points.

5-1 Organizer

Objective: Identify and graph linear equations and linear functions.

Algebra Lab
In *Chapter 5 Resource File*

Online Edition
Tutorial Videos, Graphing Calculator

Countdown to Mastery Week 9

Power Presentations with PowerPoint®

Warm Up

1. Solve $2x - 3y = 12$ for y.
   $y = \frac{2}{3}x - 4$
2. Evaluate the function $f(x) = \frac{1}{5}x + 1$ for $x = -10, -5, 0, 5,$ and 10.
   $f(-10) = -1; f(-5) = 0;$
   $f(0) = 1; f(5) = 2; f(10) = 3$

Also available on transparency

Q: How are linear functions similar to Cupid?

A: They have a partner for every number.

5-1 Linear Equations and Functions

California Standards

6.0 Students graph a linear equation and compute the *x*- and *y*-intercepts **(e.g., graph $2x + 6y = 4$).** They are also able to sketch the region defined by linear inequalities (e.g., they sketch the region defined by $2x + 6y < 4$).
Also covered: **7.0, 17.0, 18.0**

Vocabulary
linear equation
linear function

Why learn this?
Linear equations can describe many real-world situations, such as distances traveled at a constant speed.

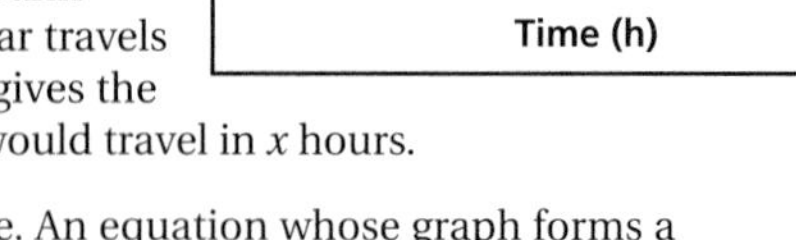

Many stretches on the German autobahn have a speed limit of 120 km/h. If a car travels continuously at this speed, $y = 120x$ gives the number of kilometers y that the car would travel in x hours.

Notice that the graph is a straight line. An equation whose graph forms a straight line is a **linear equation**. Also notice that this is a function. A function represented by a linear equation is a **linear function**.

For any two points, there is exactly one line that can be drawn through them both. This means you need only two ordered pairs to graph a line. However, graphing three points is a good way to check that your line is correct.

EXAMPLE 1 Graphing Linear Equations

Graph each linear equation. Then tell whether it represents a function.

A $y = -x + 4$

Step 1 Choose three values of x and generate ordered pairs.

x	$y = -x + 4$	(x, y)
−1	$y = -(-1) + 4 = 5$	$(-1, 5)$
0	$y = -(0) + 4 = 4$	$(0, 4)$
1	$y = -(1) + 4 = 3$	$(1, 3)$

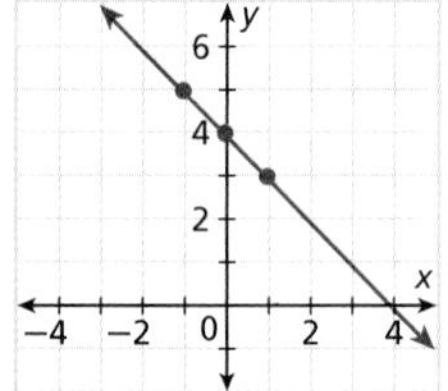

Step 2 Plot the points and connect them with a straight line.
No vertical line will intersect this graph more than once, so $y = -x + 4$ represents a function.

Helpful Hint
Sometimes solving for y first makes it easier to generate ordered pairs using values of x. To review solving for a variable, see Lesson 2-6.

B $y - 2x = -1$

Step 1 Solve for y.

$$\begin{aligned} y - 2x &= -1 \\ +2x \quad &\quad +2x \\ y \quad &= 2x - 1 \end{aligned}$$ *Add 2x to both sides.*

Step 2 Choose three values of x and generate ordered pairs.

x	$y = 2x - 1$	(x, y)
0	$y = 2(0) - 1 = -1$	$(0, -1)$
1	$y = 2(1) - 1 = 1$	$(1, 1)$
2	$y = 2(2) - 1 = 3$	$(2, 3)$

California Standards

Algebra 1 6.0
Also covered:
7.0 Students verify that a point lies on a line, given an equation of the line. Students are able to derive linear equations by using the point-slope formula.
17.0 Students determine the domain of independent variables and the range of dependent variables defined by a graph, a set of ordered pairs, **or a symbolic expression.**
18.0 Students determine whether a relation defined by a graph, a set of ordered pairs, or a symbolic expression **is a function** and justify the conclusion.

1 Introduce

EXPLORATION

5-1 Linear Equations and Functions

The table shows the fees that a DVD rental company charges for movie rentals.

Movies	2	4	6	8	10
Cost ($)	8	12	16	20	24

1. Which is the independent variable and which is the dependent variable?
2. For every increase of two movies, by how much does the cost increase?
3. Make a graph of the data.
4. What do you notice about the points that you plotted?

THINK AND DISCUSS

5. **Explain** how you know this relationship is a function.
6. **Describe** how to use your graph to predict the cost of renting 12 movies.

Motivate

Pose this situation: During a storm, snow fell at a rate of 0.5 in/h. The equation $y = 0.5x$ gives the number of inches of snow y that fell in x hours. Then have students graph ordered-pair solutions for this equation. Ask the following questions:

- What pattern do the points form? a line
- Is the relation a function? yes
- Why? Possible answer: Each x is paired with exactly one y.

Explorations and answers are provided in *Alternate Openers: Explorations Transparencies*.

For more on graphing linear equations, see the Function Builder on page MB2.

1a.

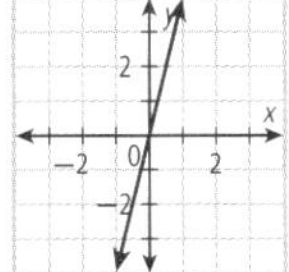

1b.

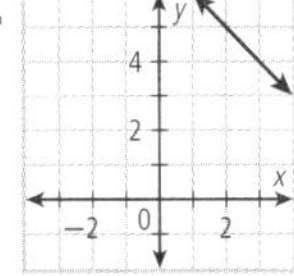

1c.

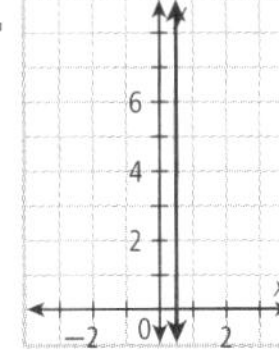

Step 3 Plot the points and connect them with a straight line.

No vertical line will intersect this graph more than once, so $2x + y = 1$ represents a function.

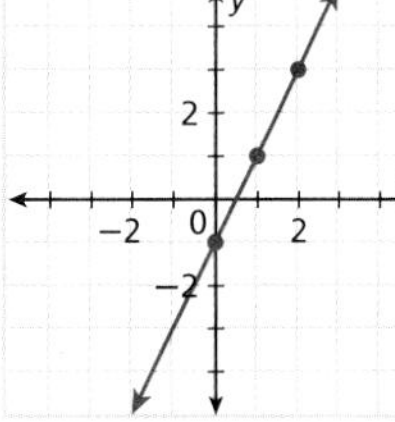

C $y = -3$

Any ordered pair with a y-coordinate of -3 will satisfy this equation.

Plot several points that have a y-coordinate of -3 and connect them with a straight line.

No vertical line will intersect this graph more than once, so $y = -3$ represents a function.

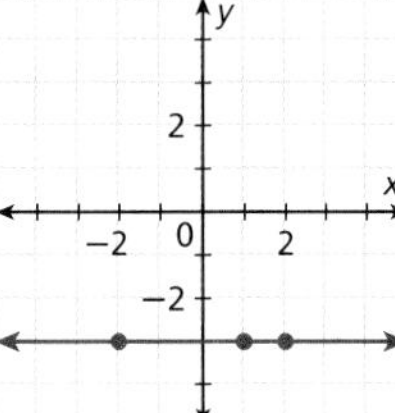

D $x = 2$

Any ordered pair with an x-coordinate of 2 will satisfy this equation.

Plot several points that have an x-coordinate of 2 and connect them with a straight line.

There is a vertical line that intersects this graph more than once, so $x = 2$ does *not* represent a function.

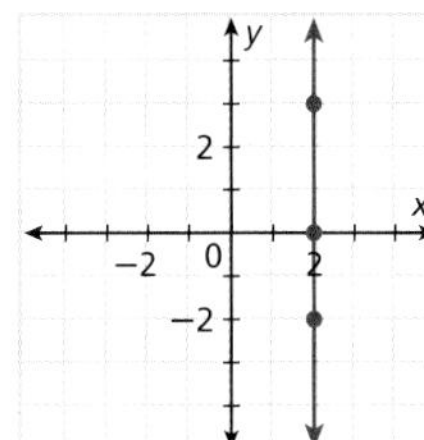

CHECK IT OUT! **Graph each linear equation. Then tell whether it represents a function.**

1a. $y = 4x$ **yes** **1b.** $x + y = 7$ **yes** **1c.** $x = \frac{1}{2}$ **no**

Linear Equations and Their Graphs

For any linear equation in two variables,

- all points on its graph are solutions to the equation.
- all solutions to the equation appear on its graph.

EXAMPLE 2 Determining Whether a Point is on a Graph

Without graphing, tell whether each point is on the graph of $y = -2x + 4$.

A $(1, 2)$

Substitute:

$$y = -2x + 4$$
$$2 \stackrel{?}{=} -2(1) + 4$$
$$2 \stackrel{?}{=} -2 + 4$$
$$2 = 2 \checkmark$$

Since $(1, 2)$ is a solution to $y = -2x + 4$, $(1, 2)$ is on the graph.

B $(-4, 0)$

Substitute:

$$y = -2x + 4$$
$$0 \stackrel{?}{=} -2(-4) + 4$$
$$0 \stackrel{?}{=} -8 + 4$$
$$0 \neq -4 \times$$

Since $(-4, 0)$ is not a solution to $y = -2x + 4$, $(-4, 0)$ is not on the graph.

Power Presentations with PowerPoint®

Additional Examples

Example 1

Graph each linear equation. Then tell whether it represents a function.

A. $y = 2x + 1$ yes

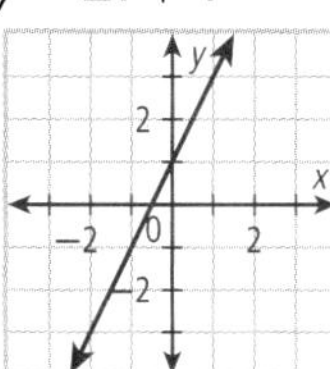

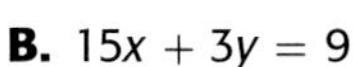
B. $15x + 3y = 9$ yes

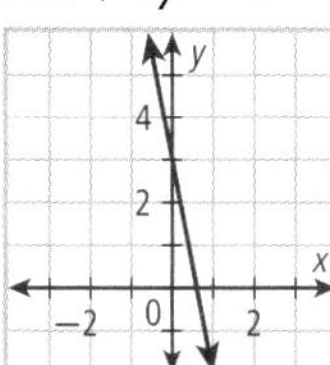

C. $x = -2$ no

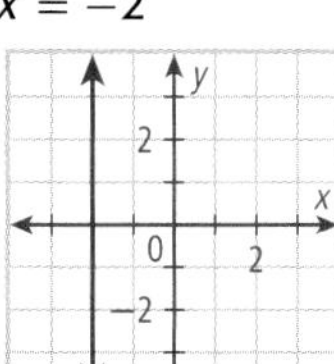

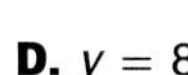
D. $y = 8$ yes

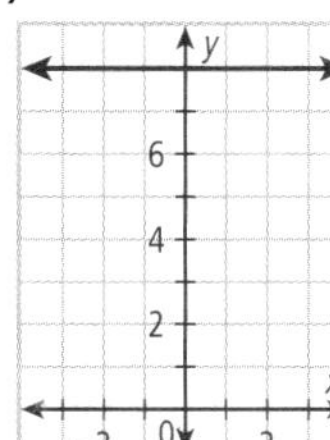

Example 2

Without graphing, tell whether each point is on the graph of $2x + 5y = 16$.

A. $(3, 2)$ yes

B. $(2, 2)$ no

C. $(8, 0)$ yes

Also available on transparency

2 Teach

Guided Instruction

Before working through **Examples 1** and **2,** review how to solve one-step, two-step, and multi-step equations. Encourage students to substitute small whole numbers rather than numbers that are difficult to calculate with when generating ordered pairs.

Reading Math Point out that the word *linear* includes the word *line.* **English Language Learners**

Universal Access

Through Visual Cues

Graph some examples of linear and nonlinear functions on the board. Also draw graphs that are not functions. Have students take turns in choosing which graphs are functions and which are not functions. Then, of the graphs that are functions, have students choose which are linear and which are nonlinear.

INTERVENTION

Questioning Strategies

EXAMPLE 1

- When is the graph of a line a function? When is it not a function?

EXAMPLE 2

- When is it easier to tell if a point is on a graph without graphing? When is it easier to tell if a point is on a graph *with* graphing?

Power Presentations with PowerPoint®

Additional Examples

Example 3

Write each equation in standard form and give the values of *A, B,* and *C*. Then describe the graph.

A. $x = 2y + 4$ $x - 2y = 4$; $A = 1, B = -2, C = 4$, non-horiz., non-vert. line

B. $x = 4$ $x + 0y = 4; A = 1, B = 0, C = 4$; vert. line

Also available on transparency

INTERVENTION

Questioning Strategies

EXAMPLE 3

- What is the standard form of a linear equation?
- If an equation is in standard form, what are the exponents of *x* and *y*?

Technology Have students use a graphing calculator to graph the function in **Example 3** to check their description.

Multiple Representations Students should be aware that there is more than one way (in fact, infinitely many ways) to write a linear equation in standard form. This is because for any linear equation $Ax + By = C$, you can multiply or divide both sides of the equation by any nonzero constant and the resulting equation will be equivalent. For instance, in **Example 3**, you can multiply both sides of $-x + y = 3$ by -1 and get the equivalent equation $x - y = -3$, which is also in standard form.

Without graphing, tell whether each point is on the graph of $x - 3y = 12$.

2a. $(5, 1)$ no **2b.** $(0, -4)$ yes **2c.** $(1.5, -3.5)$ yes

Linear equations can be written in the *standard form* shown below.

Standard Form of a Linear Equation

$Ax + By = C$ where A, B, and C are real numbers and A and B are not both 0

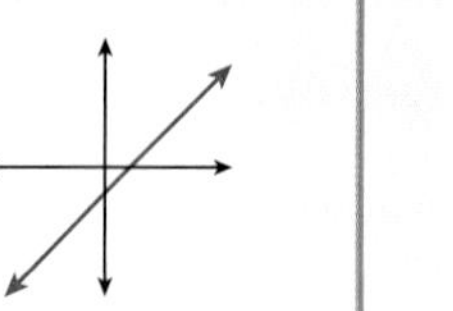	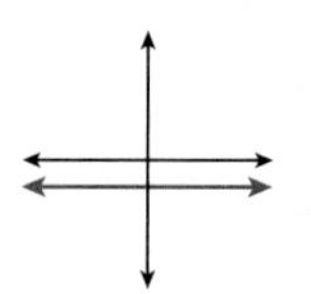	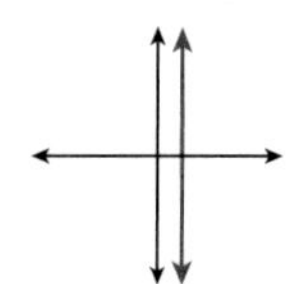
When $A \neq 0$ and $B \neq 0$, the graph is a nonhorizontal, nonvertical line.	When $A = 0$, the graph is a horizontal line.	When $B = 0$, the graph is a vertical line.

Notice that when a linear equation is written in standard form,

- *x* and *y* both have exponents of 1.
- *x* and *y* are not multiplied together.
- *x* and *y* do not appear in denominators, exponents, or radical signs.

Linear		Not Linear	
$3x + 2y = 10$	*Standard form*	$3xy + x = 1$	*x and y are multiplied.*
$y - 2 = 3x$	*Can be written as* $3x - y = -2$	$x^3 + y = -1$	*x has an exponent other than 1.*
$-y = 5x$	*Can be written as* $5x + y = 0$	$x + \frac{6}{y} = 12$	*y is in a denominator.*

EXAMPLE 3 Writing Linear Equations in Standard Form

Write $y = x + 3$ in standard form and give the values of *A, B,* and *C*. Then describe the graph.

$$y = x + 3$$
$$\underline{-x \quad -x}$$ *Subtract x from both sides.*
$$y - x = 3$$
$$-x + y = 3$$ *The equation is in standard form.*

$A = -1, B = 1, C = 3$

The graph is a line that is neither horizontal nor vertical.

Remember!

- $y - x = y + (-x)$
- $y + (-x) = -x + y$
- $-x = -1x$
- $y = 1y$

3a. $5x - y = 9$; $A = 5, B = -1, C = 9$; nonhoriz., nonvert. line

3b. $0x + y = 12$; $A = 0, B = 1, C = 12$; horiz. line

Write each equation in standard form and give the values of *A, B,* and *C*. Then describe the graph.

3a. $y = 5x - 9$ **3b.** $y = 12$ **3c.** $x = 2$

3c. $x + 0y = 2$; $A = 1, B = 0, C = 2$; vert. line

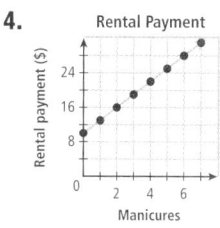

Helpful Hint

For linear functions whose graphs are horizontal, the domain is all real numbers, but the range is only one real number.

For linear functions whose graphs are not horizontal, the domain and range are all real numbers. However, in many real-world situations, the domain and range must be restricted. For example, some quantities cannot be negative, such as distance.

Sometimes domain and range are restricted even further to a set of points. For example, a quantity such as number of people can only be whole numbers. When this happens, the graph is not actually connected because every point on the line is not a solution. However, you may see these graphs shown connected to indicate that the linear pattern, or trend, continues.

EXAMPLE 4 *Career Application*

Sue rents a manicure station in a salon and pays the salon owner $5.50 for each manicure she gives. The amount Sue pays each day, in dollars, is given by $f(x) = 5.50x$, where x is the number of manicures. Graph this function and give its domain and range.

Choose several values of x and make a table of ordered pairs.

x	$f(x) = 5.50x$
0	$f(0) = 5.50(0) = 0$
1	$f(1) = 5.50(1) = 5.50$
2	$f(2) = 5.50(2) = 11.00$
3	$f(3) = 5.50(3) = 16.50$
4	$f(4) = 5.50(4) = 22.00$
5	$f(5) = 5.50(5) = 27.50$

Graph the ordered pairs.

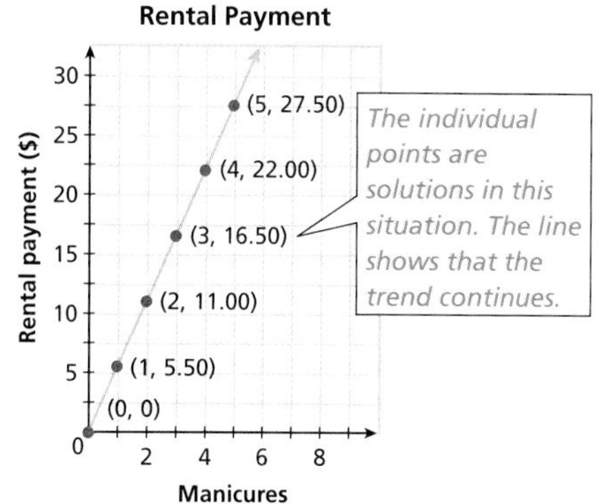

The number of manicures must be a whole number, so the domain is $\{0, 1, 2, 3, \ldots\}$. The range is $\{0, 5.50, 11.00, 16.50, \ldots\}$.

Remember!

$f(x) = y$, so in Example 4, graph the function values (dependent variable) on the y-axis.

4.

D: {0, 1, 2, 3, ...}

R: {$10, $13, $16, $19, ...}

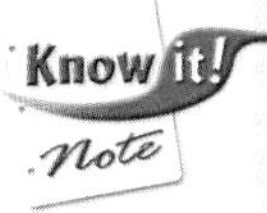

4. **What if...?** At another salon, Sue can rent a station for $10.00 per day plus $3.00 per manicure. The amount she would pay each day is given by $f(x) = 3x + 10$, where x is the number of manicures. Graph this function and give its domain and range.

THINK AND DISCUSS

1. Suppose you are given five ordered pairs. When you graph them, four lie on a straight line, but the fifth does not. Are these ordered pairs solutions to one linear equation? Why or why not?
2. In Example 4, why is every point on the line not a solution?
3. **GET ORGANIZED** Copy and complete the graphic organizer. In each box, describe how to use the information to identify a linear function. Include an example.

Know it! Note

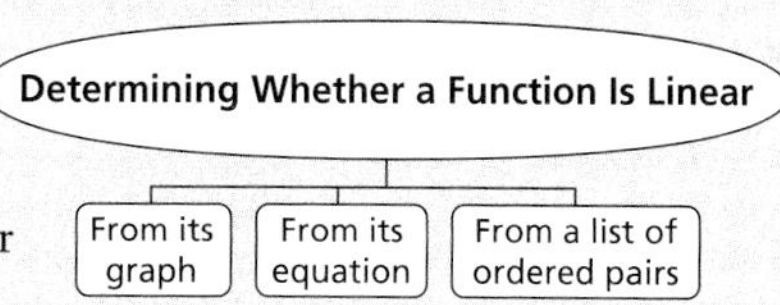

COMMON ERROR ALERT

Students might think that any equation with x and y on the left side is in standard form. Remind them of the other conditions: the exponents of x and y are 1; x and y are not multiplied together; and x and y are not in denominators, exponents, or radical signs.

Language Support Help students understand the use of the word "restricted" in relation to domain and range. It means that all real numbers may not make sense in all situations. Therefore, the real numbers that do not make sense are not in the domain or range.

Power Presentations with PowerPoint®

Additional Examples

Example 4

The relationship between human years and dog years is given by the function $y = 7x$, where x is the number of human years. Graph this function and give its domain and range.

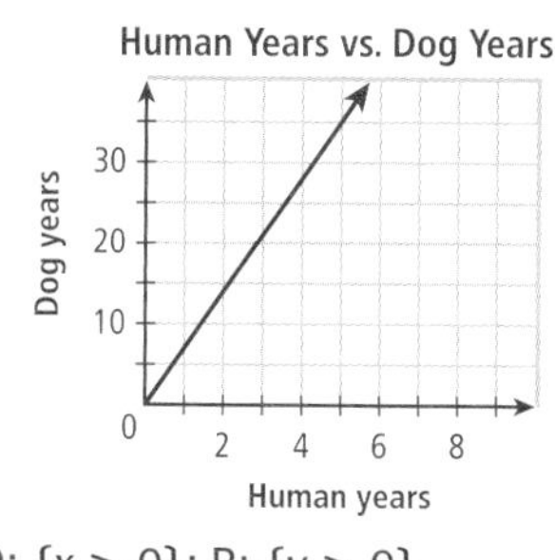

D: $\{x \geq 0\}$; R: $\{y \geq 0\}$

Also available on transparency

INTERVENTION 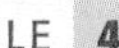

Questioning Strategies

EXAMPLE 4

- How do you decide what a reasonable domain is?

3 Close

Summarize

Review the relationship between a linear equation and its graph: All solutions are on the line and all points on the line are solutions.

Remind students that a linear equation may or may not represent a function.

For example:

- $y = x + 2$ is a linear function.
- $x = 4$ is the graph of a line but is not a function.

FORMATIVE ASSESSMENT

and INTERVENTION 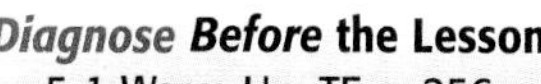

***Diagnose Before* the Lesson**
5-1 Warm Up, TE p. 256

***Monitor During* the Lesson**
Check It Out! Exercises, SE pp. 257–259
Questioning Strategies, TE pp. 257–259

***Assess After* the Lesson**
5-1 Lesson Quiz, TE p. 262
Alternative Assessment, TE p. 262

Answers to *Think and Discuss*

1. No; all the points must lie on a line in order for them to be solutions to a linear equation.
2. It is only possible to do a whole number of manicures, so the points whose x-coordinates are not whole numbers have no meaning in this situation.
3. See p. A4.

Assignment Guide

Assign *Guided Practice* exercises as necessary.

If you finished Examples **1–2**
Proficient 15–27, 34–37, 50–57, 63
Advanced 18–27, 34–37, 50–57, 63, 69–71

If you finished Examples **1–4**
Proficient 18–66 even, 72–84,
Advanced 18–32, 38–56 even, 58–84

Homework Quick Check
Quickly check key concepts.
Exercises: 18, 20, 22, 28, 30, 32

Answers

2–4. For graphs, see p. A17.

11. $2x + 3y = 5$; $A = 2$, $B = 3$, $C = 5$; nonhoriz., nonvert. line
12. $0x + 2y = 8$; $A = 0$, $B = 2$, $C = 8$; horiz., line
13. $x - 5y = -3$; $A = 1$, $B = -5$, $C = -3$; nonhoriz., nonvert. line
14. $3x - 5y = 0$; $A = 3$, $B = -5$, $C = 0$; nonhoriz., nonvert. line

15–16. See p. A17.

17–19. For graphs, see p. A17.

28. $0x + y = 5$; $A = 0$, $B = 1$, $C = 5$; horiz. line
29. $-2x + 4y = 0$; $A = -2$, $B = 4$, $C = 0$; nonhoriz. nonvert. line
30. $0x + 4y = 7$; $A = 0$, $B = 4$, $C = 7$; horiz. line
31. $3x + 0y = 3$; $A = 3$, $B = 0$, $C = 3$; vert. line

33. The equation will be either $Ax = 1$ or $By = 1$; the graph will be either a horizontal or vertical line.

California Standards

Standard	Exercises
3.0	79–84
4.0 🔑	72–78
6.0 🔑	2–4, 15–19, 32, 50–57, 59b, 61a
7.0 🔑	5–10, 20–27, 34–37
17.0	15, 16, 32, 62
18.0	2–4, 17–19, 59c, 64, 68

5-1 Exercises

California Standards Practice
🔑 6.0, 🔑 7.0, 17.0, 18.0

go.hrw.com
Homework Help Online
KEYWORD: MA8CA 5-1
Parent Resources Online
KEYWORD: MA8CA Parent

GUIDED PRACTICE

1. **Vocabulary** Is the *linear equation* $3x - 2 = y$ in standard form? Explain. **No; it is not in the form $Ax + By = C$.**

SEE EXAMPLE 1 p. 256

Graph each linear equation. Then tell whether it represents a function.

2. $y = 2x + 1$ **yes**
3. $x = 5$ **no**
4. $-2x + y = 3$ **yes**

SEE EXAMPLE 2 p. 257

Without graphing, tell whether each point is on the graph of the given line.

5. $-4x + 2y = 8$; $(1, 6)$ **yes**
6. $12x + y = 16$; $\left(\frac{1}{2}, 3\right)$ **no**
7. $5x - 3y = 14$; $(-1, -6)$ **no**
8. $\frac{1}{4}x - 2y = -6$; $(16, 5)$ **yes**
9. $\frac{1}{3}x - 2y = 7$; $(9, -2)$ **yes**
10. $-6x - \frac{1}{4}y = 9$; $(-2, -12)$ **no**

SEE EXAMPLE 3 p. 258

Write each equation in standard form and give the values of *A*, *B*, and *C*. Then describe the graph.

11. $2x + 3y = 5$
12. $2y = 8$
13. $\frac{x + 3}{5} = y$
14. $\frac{x}{5} = \frac{y}{3}$

SEE EXAMPLE 4 p. 259

15. **Transportation** A train travels at a constant speed of 75 mi/h. The function $f(x) = 75x$ gives the distance that the train travels in x hours. Graph this function and give its domain and range.

16. **Entertainment** A movie rental store charges a $6.00 membership fee plus $2.50 for each movie rented. The function $f(x) = 2.50x + 6$ gives the cost of renting x movies. Graph this function and give its domain and range.

PRACTICE AND PROBLEM SOLVING

Independent Practice

For Exercises	See Example
17–19	1
20–27	2
28–31	3
32	4

Extra Practice
Skills Practice p. EP10
Application Practice p. EP28

Graph each linear equation. Then tell whether it represents a function.

17. $3x + 2y = 4$ **yes**
18. $-x + 3 = y$ **yes**
19. $4.8x + 1.2y = 2.4$ **yes**

Without graphing, tell whether each point is on the graph of the given line.

20. $12x + 3y = 6$; $(2, -4)$ **no**
21. $-x + 6y = 24$; $(6, 5)$ **yes**
22. $\frac{1}{2}y = -6x + 1$; $(2, -20)$ **no**
23. $x - 2.7y = 5.4$; $(5.4, 2)$ **no**
24. $\frac{2}{3}x = \frac{1}{3}y - 2$; $(6, 18)$ **yes**
25. $6x + \frac{1}{2}y = -10\frac{1}{3}$; $\left(-\frac{5}{3}, \frac{2}{3}\right)$ **no**
26. $0.35y = 10x - 14$; $(1.4, 0)$ **yes**
27. $x - \frac{4}{5}y = -10$; $(0, 10)$ **no**

Write each equation in standard form and give the values of *A*, *B*, and *C*. Then describe the graph.

28. $y = 5$
29. $4y - 2x = 0$
30. $3 + 4y = 10$
31. $5 + 3x = 8$

32. **Transportation** The gas tank in Tony's car holds 15 gallons, and the car can travel 25 miles for each gallon of gas. When Tony begins with a full tank of gas, the function $f(x) = -\frac{1}{25}x + 15$ gives the amount of gas $f(x)$ that will be left in the tank after traveling x miles (if he does not buy more gas). Graph this function and give its domain and range.

33. **Reasoning** If you know that $AB = 0$ and $A \neq B$, what can you say about the equation $Ax + By = 1$? Describe the graph.

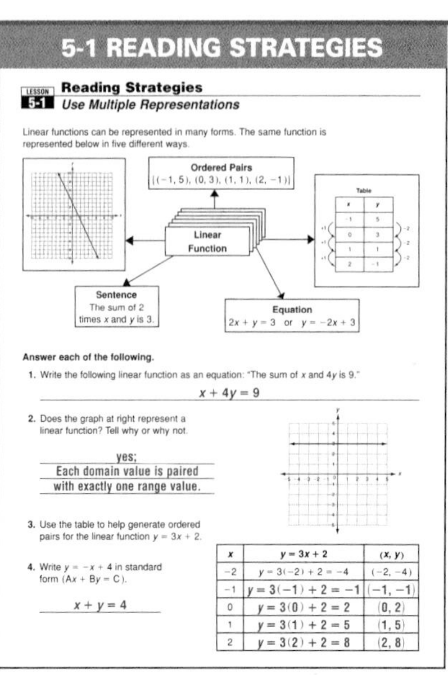

5-1 READING STRATEGIES

LESSON 5-1 **Reading Strategies**
Use Multiple Representations

Linear functions can be represented in many forms. The same function is represented below in five different ways.

x	y
−1	5
0	3
1	1
2	−1

Answer each of the following.

1. Write the following linear function as an equation: "The sum of x and $4y$ is 9." $x + 4y = 9$
2. Does the graph at right represent a linear function? Tell why or why not. yes; Each domain value is paired with exactly one range value.
3. Use the table to help generate ordered pairs for the linear function $y = 3x + 2$.
4. Write $y = -x + 4$ in standard form $(Ax + By = C)$. $x + y = 4$

x	y = 3x + 2	(x, y)
−2	$y = 3(-2) + 2 = -4$	(−2, −4)
−1	$y = 3(-1) + 2 = -1$	(−1, −1)
0	$y = 3(0) + 2 = 2$	(0, 2)
1	$y = 3(1) + 2 = 5$	(1, 5)
2	$y = 3(2) + 2 = 8$	(2, 8)

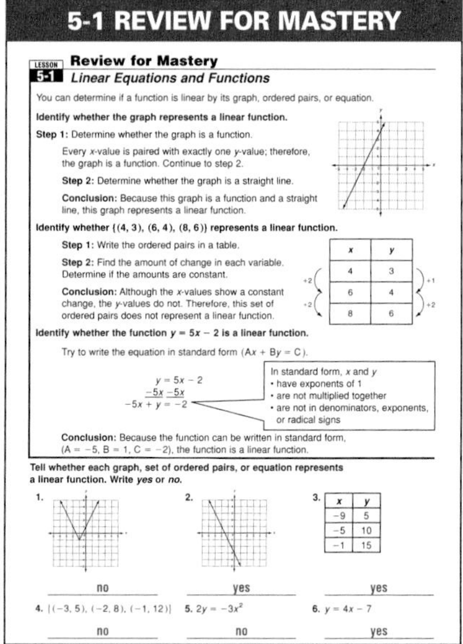

5-1 REVIEW FOR MASTERY

LESSON 5-1 **Review for Mastery**
Linear Equations and Functions

You can determine if a function is linear by its graph, ordered pairs, or equation.

Identify whether the graph represents a linear function.

Step 1: Determine whether the graph is a function.

Every x-value is paired with exactly one y-value; therefore, the graph is a function. Continue to step 2.

Step 2: Determine whether the graph is a straight line.

Conclusion: Because this graph is a function and a straight line, this graph represents a linear function.

Identify whether {(4, 3), (6, 4), (8, 6)} represents a linear function.

Step 1: Write the ordered pairs in a table.

Step 2: Find the amount of change in each variable. Determine if the amounts are constant.

Conclusion: Although the x-values show a constant change, the y-values do not. Therefore, this set of ordered pairs does not represent a linear function.

x	y
4	3
6	4
8	6

Identify whether the function $y = 5x - 2$ is a linear function.

Try to write the equation in standard form $(Ax + By = C)$.

$$y = 5x - 2$$
$$-5x \quad -5x$$
$$-5x + y = -2$$

In standard form, x and y
- have exponents of 1
- are not multiplied together
- are not in denominators, exponents, or radical signs

Conclusion: Because the function can be written in standard form, $(A = -5, B = 1, C = -2)$, the function is a linear function.

Tell whether each graph, set of ordered pairs, or equation represents a linear function. Write *yes* or *no*.

1. no
2. yes
3. yes

x	y
−9	5
−5	10
−1	15

4. $\{(-3, 5), (-2, 8), (-1, 12)\}$ no
5. $2y = -3x^2$ no
6. $y = 4x - 7$ yes

Tell whether the given ordered pairs all lie on the same line.

34. yes

x	2	2	2	2	2
y	5	4	3	2	1

35. yes

x	−8	−6	−4	−2	0
y	2	0	−2	−4	−6

36. no

x	−12	−10	−6	−2	2	4	6
y	−0.25	0	0.25	0.50	0.75	1	1.25

37. yes

x	−5	−1	0	3	5	7	11
y	1	1	1	1	1	1	1

Tell whether each equation is linear. If so, write the equation in standard form and give the values of A, B, and C.

38. $2x - 8y = 16$
39. $y = 4x + 2$
40. $2x = \frac{y}{3} - 4$
41. $\frac{4}{x} = y$ no
42. $\frac{x+4}{2} = \frac{y-4}{3}$
43. $x = 7$
44. $xy = 6$ no
45. $3x - 5 + y = 2y - 4$
46. $y = -x + 2$
47. $5x = 2y - 3$
48. $2y = -6$
49. $y = \sqrt{x}$ no

Graph each linear equation.

50. $y = 3x + 7$
51. $y = x + 25$
52. $y = 8 - x$
53. $y = 2x$
54. $-2y = -3x + 6$
55. $y - x = 4$
56. $y - 2x = -3$
57. $x = 5 + y$

58. Measurement One inch is equal to approximately 2.5 centimeters. Let x represent inches and y represent centimeters. Write an equation in standard form relating x and y. Give the values of A, B, and C. $2.5x - y = 0$; $A = 2.5$, $B = -1$, $C = 0$

59. Wages Molly earns $8.00 an hour at her job.

a. Let x represent the number of hours that Molly works. Write a function using x and $f(x)$ that describes Molly's pay for working x hours. $f(x) = 8x$

b. Graph this function.

c. Is this function a linear function? Explain. Yes; its graph is a line

60. Write About It For $y = 2x - 1$, make a table of ordered pairs and a graph. Describe the relationships between the equation, the table, and the graph.

CONCEPT CONNECTION

61. This problem will prepare you for the Concept Connection on page 288.

Juan is running on a treadmill. The table shows the number of Calories Juan burns as a function of time.

a. Create a graph of the data.

b. How can you tell from the graph that the relationship is linear? The graph forms a line.

Time (min)	Calories
3	27
6	54
9	81
12	108
15	135
18	162
21	189

CONCEPT CONNECTION Exercise 61 involves creating a graph from a table and determining whether the relationship is linear. This exercise prepares students for the Concept Connection on page 288.

Answers

32. D: $0 \le x \le 375$; R: $0 \le y \le 15$

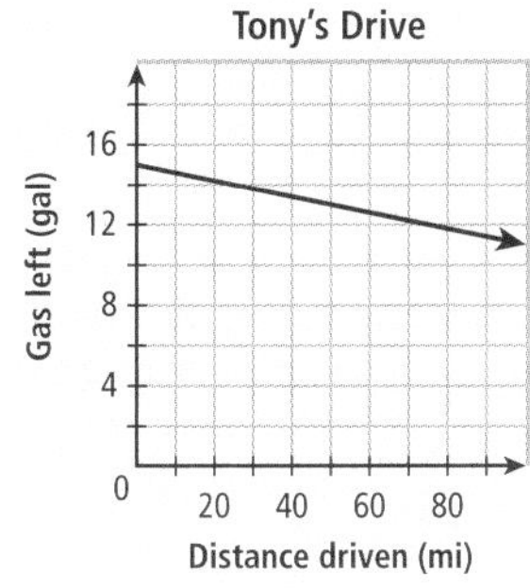

38. yes; $2x - 8y = 16$; $A = 2$; $B = -8$; $C = 16$
39. yes; $-4x + y = 2$; $A = -4$; $B = 1$; $C = 2$
40. yes; $2x - \frac{1}{3}y = -4$; $A = 2$; $B = -\frac{1}{3}$; $C = -4$
42. yes; $3x - 2y = -20$; $A = 3$; $B = -2$; $C = -20$
43. yes; $x = 7$; $A = 1$; $B = 0$; $C = 7$
45. yes; $3x - y = 1$; $A = 3$; $B = -1$; $C = 1$
46. yes; $x + y = 2$; $A = 1$, $B = 1$, $C = 2$
47. yes; $5x - 2y = -3$; $A = 5$, $B = -2$, $C = -3$
48. yes; $2y = -6$; $A = 0$, $B = 2$, $C = -6$

50–57, 59b, 60, 61a. See p. A17.

5-1 PROBLEM SOLVING

LESSON 5-1 **Problem Solving**
Linear Equations and Functions

Write the correct answer.

1. A daycare center charges a $75 enrollment fee plus $100 per week. The function $f(x) = 100x + 75$ gives the cost of daycare for x weeks. Graph this function and give its domain and range.
D: {0, 1, 2, 3, ...}
R: {$75, $175, $275, $375, ...}

2. A family swimming pool holds 60 m^3 of water. The function $f(x) = 60 - 0.18x$ gives the cubic meters of water in the pool, taking into account water lost to evaporation over x days. Graph this function and give its domain and range.
D: $x \ge 0$
R: $0 \le y \le 60$

Elijah is using a rowing machine. The table shows how many Calories he can burn for certain lengths of time. Select the best answer.

Time (min)	Calories
2	24
4	48
6	72
8	96
10	120

3. Which function could be used to describe the number of Calories burned after x minutes?
F $y = 12 + x$ H $xy = 12$
G $x + y = 12$ (J) $y = 12x$

4. What is the domain of the function?
A {0, 1, 2, 3, ...} (C) $x \ge 0$
B {2, 4, 6, ...} D $x \ge 2$

5. What is the range of the function?
F {0, 12, 24, 36, ...} (H) $y \ge 0$
G {24, 48, 72, ...} J $y \ge 24$

6. Elijah graphed the function in problem 4. Which best describes the graph?
(A) It is a line that increases from left to right.
B It is a line that decreases from left to right.
C It forms a U-shape.
D It forms a V-shape.

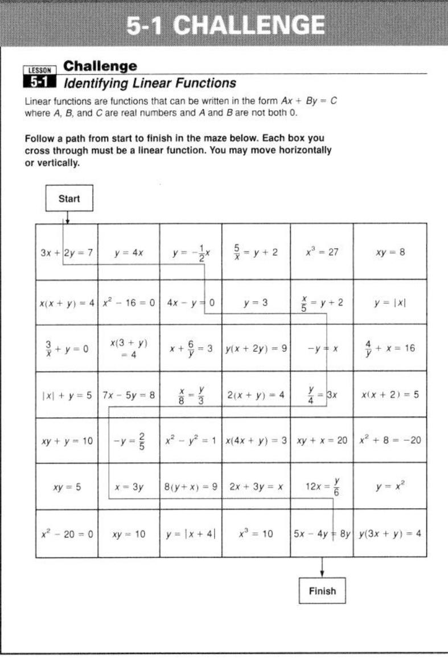

5-1 CHALLENGE

LESSON 5-1 **Challenge**
Identifying Linear Functions

Linear functions are functions that can be written in the form $Ax + By = C$ where A, B, and C are real numbers and A and B are not both 0.

Follow a path from start to finish in the maze below. Each box you cross through must be a linear function. You may move horizontally or vertically.

Start

$3x + 2y = 7$	$y = 4x$	$y = -\frac{1}{2}x$	$\frac{5}{x} = y + 2$	$x^3 = 27$	$xy = 8$
$x(x + y) = 4$	$x^2 - 16 = 0$	$4x - y = 0$	$y = 3$	$\frac{x}{5} = y + 2$	$y = \lvert x \rvert$
$\frac{3}{x} + y = 0$	$x(3 + y) = 4$	$x + \frac{6}{y} = 3$	$y(x + 2y) = 9$	$-y = x$	$\frac{4}{y} + x = 16$
$\lvert x \rvert + y = 5$	$7x - 5y = 8$	$\frac{x}{8} = \frac{y}{3}$	$2(x + y) = 4$	$\frac{y}{4} = 3x$	$x(x + 2) = 5$
$xy + y = 10$	$-y = \frac{2}{5}$	$x^2 - y^2 = 1$	$x(4x + y) = 3$	$xy + x = 20$	$x^2 + 8 = -20$
$xy = 5$	$x = 3y$	$8(y + x) = 9$	$2x + 3y = x$	$12x = \frac{y}{6}$	$y = x^2$
$x^2 - 20 = 0$	$xy = 10$	$y = \lvert x + 4 \rvert$	$x^3 = 10$	$5x - 4y = 8y$	$y(3x + y) = 4$

Finish

5-1 PRACTICE A

5-1 PRACTICE C

5-1 PRACTICE B

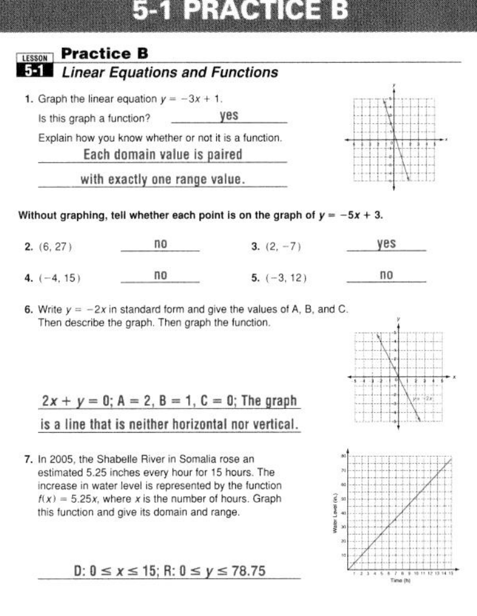

LESSON 5-1 **Practice B**
Linear Equations and Functions

1. Graph the linear equation $y = -3x + 1$.
Is this graph a function? yes
Explain how you know whether or not it is a function.
Each domain value is paired with exactly one range value.

Without graphing, tell whether each point is on the graph of $y = -5x + 3$.

2. (6, 27) no
3. (2, −7) yes
4. (−4, 15) no
5. (−3, 12) no

6. Write $y = -2x$ in standard form and give the values of A, B, and C. Then describe the graph. Then graph the function.
$2x + y = 0$; A = 2, B = 1, C = 0; The graph is a line that is neither horizontal nor vertical.

7. In 2005, the Shabelle River in Somalia rose an estimated 5.25 inches every hour for 15 hours. The increase in water level is represented by the function $f(x) = 5.25x$, where x is the number of hours. Graph this function and give its domain and range.
D: $0 \le x \le 15$; R: $0 \le y \le 78.75$

Multiple Choice Students who did not choose **C** in **Exercise 65** may not understand that in a linear equation, *x* or *y* cannot be in the denominator of a fraction.

Journal

Have students explain how to identify a linear function from its graph and from its equation.

ALTERNATIVE ASSESSMENT

Have students write a real-world problem that can be represented by a linear function. Then have them write the function rule and determine a reasonable domain and range.

Power Presentations with PowerPoint®

5-1 Lesson Quiz

Graph each linear equation. Then tell whether it represents a function.

1. $2y + x = 6$

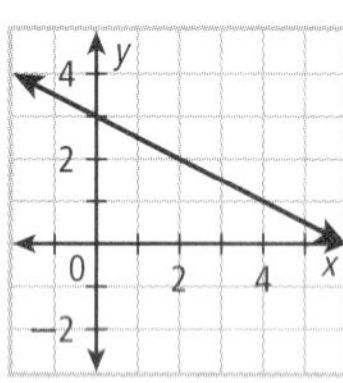

yes

2. $3y = 12$

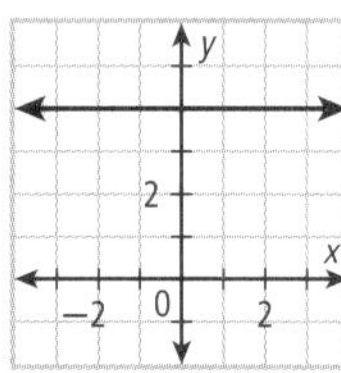

yes

Without graphing, tell whether each point is on the graph of $6x - 2y = 8$.

3. (1, 1) no **4.** (3, 5) yes

5. The cost of a can of iced-tea mix at SaveMore Grocery is \$4.75. The function $f(x) = 4.75x$ gives the cost of *x* cans of iced-tea mix. Graph this function and give its domain and range.

Cost of Iced-Tea Mix

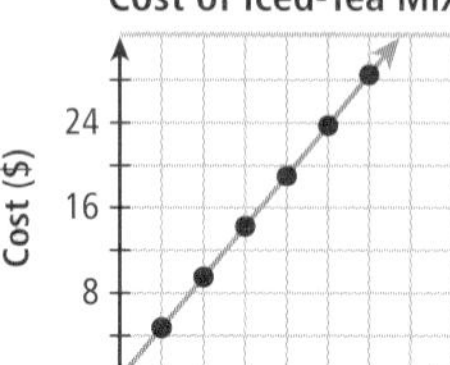

D: {0, 1, 2, 3, . . .}
R: {0, 4.75, 9.50, 14.25, . . .}

Also available on transparency

64. Yes; the equation can be written in stand. form with $A = 1$, $B = 0$, and $C = 9$. No; all solutions are ordered pairs with *x*-value 9. The *x*-value 9 corresponds to more than one *y*-value.

62. Critical Thinking Describe a real-world situation that can be represented by a linear function whose domain and range must be limited. Give your function and its domain and range.

63. Physical Science A ball was dropped from a height of 100 meters. Its height above the ground in meters at different times after its release is given in the table. Are all of these ordered pairs solutions to one linear equation? Explain. No; when graphed, the points do not all lie on the same line.

Time (s)	0	1	2	3
Height (m)	100	90.2	60.8	11.8

64. Critical Thinking Is the equation $x = 9$ a linear equation? Does it describe a linear function? Explain.

Multiple Choice For Exercises 65 and 66, choose the best answer.

65. Which is NOT a linear equation?

Ⓐ $y = 8x$ Ⓑ $y = x + 8$  Ⓒ $y = \frac{8}{x}$ Ⓓ $y = 8 - x$

66. The speed of sound in 0°C air is about 331 feet per second. Which equation could be used to describe the distance in feet *d* that sound will travel in air in *s* seconds?

Ⓐ $d = s + 331$ Ⓑ $d = 331s$ Ⓒ $s = 331d$ Ⓓ $s = 331 - d$

67. Extended Response Write your own linear function. Show that it is a linear function in two different ways.

CHALLENGE AND EXTEND

68. What equation describes the *x*-axis? the *y*-axis? Do these equations represent linear functions?
$y = 0$; $x = 0$; the first describes a linear function, but the second does not.

Geometry Copy and complete each table below. Then tell whether the table shows a linear relationship.

69.

Perimeter of a Square	
Side Length	Perimeter
1	4
2	8
3	12
4	16

linear

70.

Area of a Square	
Side Length	Area
1	1
2	4
3	9
4	16

not linear

71.

Volume of a Cube	
Side Length	Volume
1	1
2	8
3	27
4	64

not linear

SPIRAL STANDARDS REVIEW 3.0, 4.0

Solve each equation. Check your answer. *(Lesson 2-3)*

72. $4(t + 3) = 36$ 6 **73.** $3(2 - x) = 9$ −1 **74.** $k + 3k + 2 = -6$ −2 **75.** $3h - \frac{1}{6} + h = \frac{5}{18}$ $\frac{1}{9}$

Solve each equation. Check your answer. *(Lesson 2-4)*

76. $6m + 5 = 3m - 4$ −3 **77.** $2(t - 4) = 3 - (3t + 1)$ 2 **78.** $9y + 5 - 2y = 2y + 5 - y + 3$ $\frac{1}{2}$

Solve each inequality. *(Lesson 3-7)*

79. $|t| - 9 \leq -10$ ∅ **80.** $|z - 8| + 2 > 4$ $z < 6$ OR $z > 10$ **81.** $|x - 1| - 11 \leq 12$ $-22 \leq x \leq 24$

82. $|x - 5| + 5.6 > 4.7$ all real numbers **83.** $|0.5x| + 7.4 < 4.5$ ∅ **84.** $|x - 7| + \frac{1}{4} \geq \frac{1}{2}$ $x \leq \frac{27}{4}$ OR $x \geq \frac{29}{4}$

Answers

62. Possible answer: The value in cents of *x* dimes is $y = 10x$. Since you can only have a whole number of dimes, the domain and range are restricted to whole numbers.

67. Possible answer: $3x + 2y = 7$; it is a linear equation because it can be written in standard form with $A = 3$, $B = 2$, and $C = 7$. The graph shows a linear function.

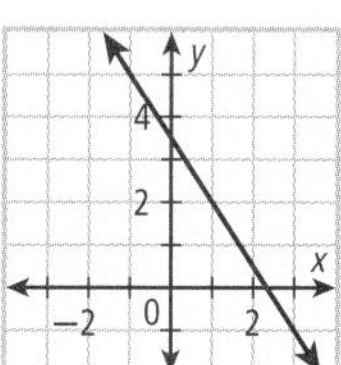

5-2 Using Intercepts

California Standards

6.0 Students graph a linear equation and compute the x- and y-intercepts (e.g., graph 2x + 6y = 4). They are also able to sketch the region defined by linear inequalities (e.g., they sketch the region defined by 2x + 6y < 4).

Vocabulary
y-intercept
x-intercept

Who uses this?
Divers can use intercepts to determine the time a safe ascent will take.

A diver explored the ocean floor 120 feet below the surface and then ascended at a rate of 30 feet per minute. The graph shows the diver's elevation below sea level during the ascent.

A **y-intercept** is the y-coordinate of any point where a graph intersects the y-axis. The x-coordinate of this point is always 0.

An **x-intercept** is the x-coordinate of any point where a graph intersects the x-axis. The y-coordinate of this point is always 0.

The x-intercept is 4. It represents the time that the diver reaches the surface, or when depth = 0.

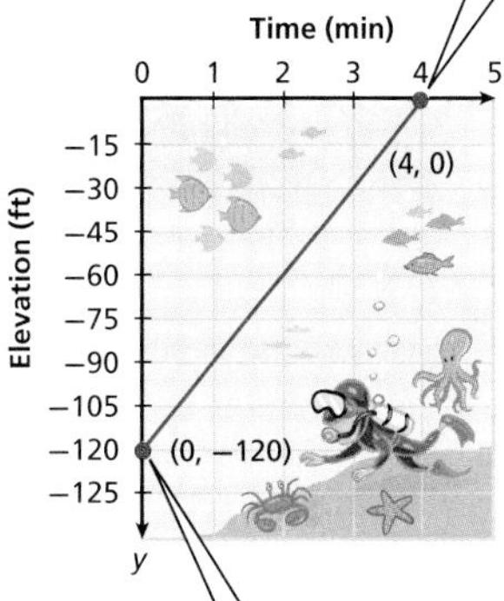

The y-intercept is −120. It represents the diver's elevation at the start of the ascent, or when time = 0.

EXAMPLE **1** **Finding Intercepts**

Find the x- and y-intercepts.

A

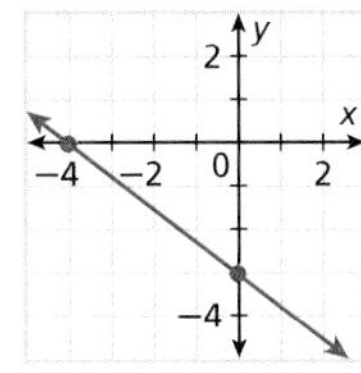

The graph intersects the y-axis at (0, −3).
The y-intercept is -3.

The graph intersects the x-axis at (−4, 0).
The x-intercept is -4.

B $3x - 2y = 12$

To find the x-intercept, replace y with 0 and solve for x.

$$3x - 2y = 12$$
$$3x - 2(0) = 12$$
$$3x - 0 = 12$$
$$3x = 12$$
$$\frac{3x}{3} = \frac{12}{3}$$
$$x = 4$$

The x-intercept is 4.

To find the y-intercept, replace x with 0 and solve for y.

$$3x - 2y = 12$$
$$3(0) - 2y = 12$$
$$0 - 2y = 12$$
$$-2y = 12$$
$$\frac{-2y}{-2} = \frac{12}{-2}$$
$$y = -6$$

The y-intercept is -6.

CHECK IT OUT! **Find the x- and y-intercepts.**

1a. x-int.: −2; y-int.: 3

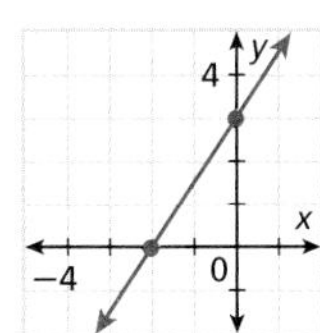

1b. $-3x + 5y = 30$ x-int.: −10; y-int.: 6

1c. $4x + 2y = 16$ x-int.: 4; y-int.: 8

5-2 Organizer

Objectives: Find x- and y-intercepts and interpret their meanings in real-world situations.

Use x- and y-intercepts to graph lines.

Online Edition
Tutorial Videos

Countdown to Mastery Week 9

Power Presentations with PowerPoint®

Warm Up

Solve each equation.

1. $5x + 0 = -10$ -2
2. $33 = 0 + 3y$ 11
3. $\frac{4}{5}x + \frac{1}{10} = \frac{9}{10}$ 1
4. $2x + 14 = -3x + 4$ -2
5. $-5y - 1 = 7y + 5$ $-\frac{1}{2}$

Also available on transparency

Teacher: Where's the graph of your function?

Student: It was intercepted on the way to school.

1 Introduce

EXPLORATION

5-2 Using Intercepts

Katarina's family is traveling from Brownsville, Texas, to their home in Laredo, Texas. The distance from Brownsville to Laredo is 200 miles, and Katarina's mother is driving at a speed of 50 miles per hour.

1. Complete the table.

Time from Start of Trip (h)	0	1	2	3	4
Distance to Laredo (mi)	200	150			

2. Make a graph of the data.
3. What is the starting distance? What point on the graph corresponds to the starting distance? Where is this point located?
4. How long does it take to reach Laredo? What point on the graph corresponds to this time? Where is this point located?

THINK AND DISCUSS

5. **Explain** how you could use a graph to find the time it would take to reach Laredo if Katarina's mother drove at a speed of 40 miles per hour.
6. **Describe** what it means for a point to lie on the y-axis in a graph of distance versus time.

Motivate

Have students graph $3x + 4y = 12$ by generating ordered pairs for x and y using the following table.

x	y
−2	4.5
0	3
2	1.5
4	0

Then have students circle the rows of the table that include 0. Ask students where these points are located on the graph. the axes

Explorations and answers are provided in *Alternate Openers: Explorations Transparencies.*

California Standards

Algebra 1 6.0

Power Presentations with PowerPoint®

Additional Examples

Example 1

Find the *x*- and *y*-intercepts.

A.

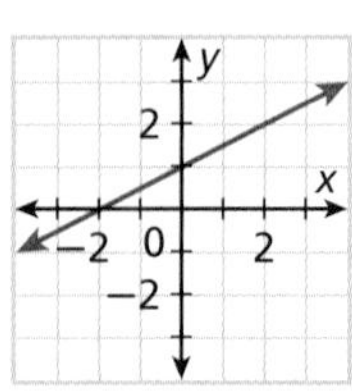

x-int.: −2; *y*-int.: 1

B. $5x - 2y = 10$

x-int.: 2; *y*-int.: −5

Example 2

Trish can run the 200 m dash in 25 s. The function $f(x) = 200 - 8x$ gives the distance remaining to run after *x* seconds. Graph this function and find the intercepts. What does each intercept represent?

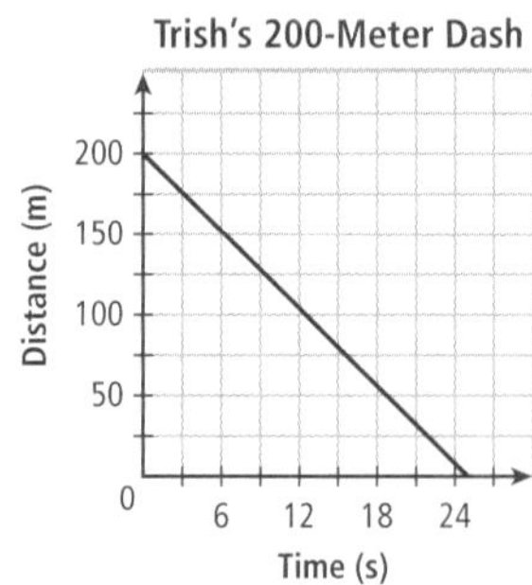

x-int.: 25; *y*-int.: 200

x-int.: the time when Trish finishes the race, when the distance remaining is 0

y-int.: the number of meters Trish has to run at the start of the race, when the time passed is 0

Also available on transparency

INTERVENTION

Questioning Strategies

EXAMPLE 1

- What point on a graph corresponds to the *x*-intercept? the *y*-intercept?
- What intercept do you find by substituting zero for *x*?

EXAMPLE 2

- Why is the graph of only the first quadrant shown?
- What do other points on the graph, such as (5, 160), (10, 120), and so on, represent?

Student to Student

Finding Intercepts

Madison Stewart
Jefferson High School

I use the "cover-up" method to find intercepts. To use this method, make sure the equation is in standard form first.

If I have $4x - 2y = 12$:

First, I cover 4x with my finger and solve the equation I can still see.

$- 2y = 12$
$y = -6$

The y-intercept is −6.

Then I cover −2y with my finger and do the same thing.

$4x = 12$
$x = 3$

The x-intercept is 3.

EXAMPLE 2 *Travel Application*

The Sandia Peak Tramway in Albuquerque, New Mexico, travels a distance of about 4500 meters to the top of Sandia Peak. Its speed is 300 meters per minute. The function $f(x) = 4500 - 300x$ gives the tram's distance in meters from the top of the peak after *x* minutes. Graph this function and find the intercepts. What does each intercept represent?

Neither time nor distance can be negative, so choose several nonnegative values for x. Use the function to generate ordered pairs.

x	0	2	5	10	15
$f(x) = 4500 - 300x$	4500	3900	3000	1500	0

Graph the ordered pairs. Connect the points with a line.

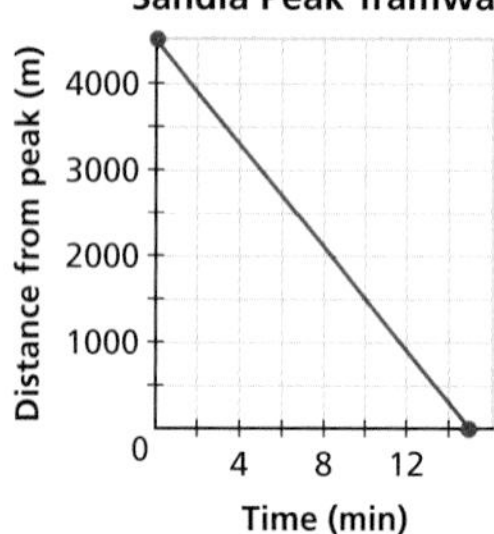

- *y*-intercept: 4500. This is the starting distance from the top (time = 0).
- *x*-intercept: 15. This the time when the tram reaches the peak (distance = 0).

2a.

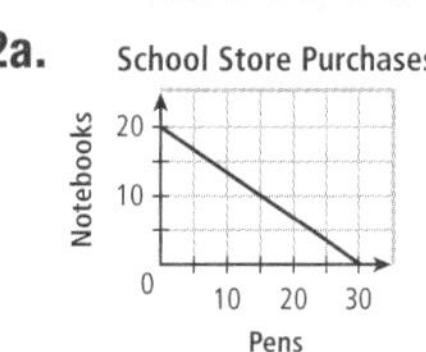

***x*-int.: 30; *y*-int.: 20**

2b. *x*-int.: pens that can be purchased if no notebooks are purchased; *y*-int.: notebooks that can be purchased if no pens are purchased

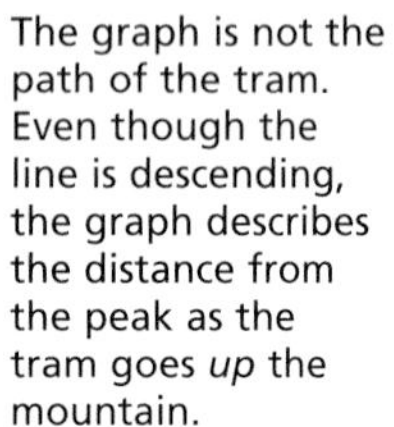

Caution!

The graph is not the path of the tram. Even though the line is descending, the graph describes the distance from the peak as the tram goes *up* the mountain.

2. The school store sells pens for \$2.00 and notebooks for \$3.00. The equation $2x + 3y = 60$ describes the number of pens *x* and notebooks *y* that you can buy for \$60.

a. Graph the function and find its intercepts.

b. What does each intercept represent?

2 Teach

Guided Instruction

Show how to find the intercepts from a graph and then from an equation. Show students the "cover-up" method of finding intercepts from an equation (described in Student to Student) and ask students why it works. The value covered up always becomes zero.

ENGLISH LANGUAGE LEARNERS

Language Support Have students familiar with American football explain the meaning of *interception* in that sport. Then ask the class how it relates to an intercept in math.

Universal Access

Through Number Sense

Give students the following scenario: *You have \$25, and you spend \$5 per week.* Tell students that the function $y = 25 - 5x$ describes the amount of money *y* they will have after *x* weeks. Have them find ordered pairs for $x = 0, 1, 2, 3, 4$, and 5. (0, 25), (1, 20), (2, 15), (3, 10), (4, 5), (5, 0) Graph the ordered pairs, labeling each as follows: (week 1, \$20 left).

Discuss why the value of *y* when $x = 6$ is not reasonable in this situation. You have no money left to spend after the 5th week.

Remember, to graph a line, you need to plot only two ordered pairs. It is often simplest to find the ordered pairs that contain the intercepts.

EXAMPLE 3 Graphing Linear Equations by Using Intercepts

Use intercepts to graph the line given by each equation.

A $2x - 4y = 8$

Step 1 Find the intercepts.

x-intercept:	y-intercept:
$2x - 4y = 8$	$2x - 4y = 8$
$2x - 4(0) = 8$	$2(0) - 4y = 8$
$2x = 8$	$-4y = 8$
$\frac{2x}{2} = \frac{8}{2}$	$\frac{-4y}{-4} = \frac{8}{-4}$
$x = 4$	$y = -2$

Step 2 Graph the line.

Plot (4, 0) and (0, −2).
Connect with a straight line.

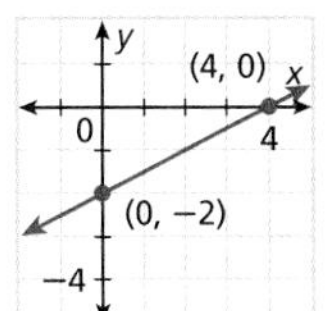

B $\frac{2}{3}y = 4 - \frac{1}{2}x$

Step 1 Write the equation in standard form.

$6\left(\frac{2}{3}y\right) = 6\left(4 - \frac{1}{2}x\right)$ *Multiply both sides by 6, the LCD of the fractions, to clear the fractions.*

$4y = 24 - 3x$

$3x + 4y = 24$ *Write the equation in standard form.*

Step 2 Find the intercepts.

x-intercept:	y-intercept:
$3x + 4y = 24$	$3x + 4y = 24$
$3x + 4(0) = 24$	$3(0) + 4y = 24$
$3x = 24$	$4y = 24$
$\frac{3x}{3} = \frac{24}{3}$	$\frac{4y}{4} = \frac{24}{4}$
$x = 8$	$y = 6$

Step 3 Graph the line.

Plot (8, 0) and (0, 6).
Connect with a straight line.

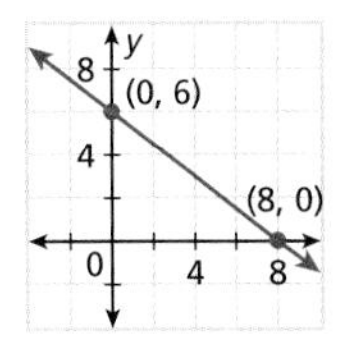

Helpful Hint

You can use a third point to check your line. Either choose a point from your graph and check it in the equation, or use the equation to generate a point and check that it is on your graph.

Use intercepts to graph the line given by each equation.

3a. $-3x + 4y = -12$ **3b.** $y = \frac{1}{3}x - 2$

3a. (graph)

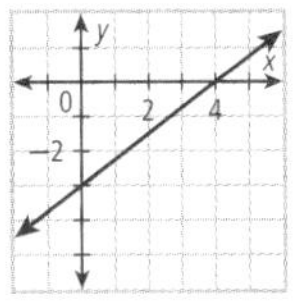

3b. (graph)

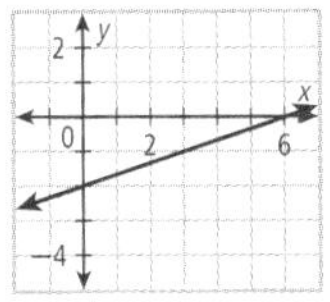

THINK AND DISCUSS

1. A function has x-intercept 4 and y-intercept 2. Name two points on the graph of this function.
2. What is the y-intercept of $2.304x + y = 4.318$? What is the x-intercept of $x - 92.4920y = -21.5489$?

3. **GET ORGANIZED** Copy and complete the graphic organizer.

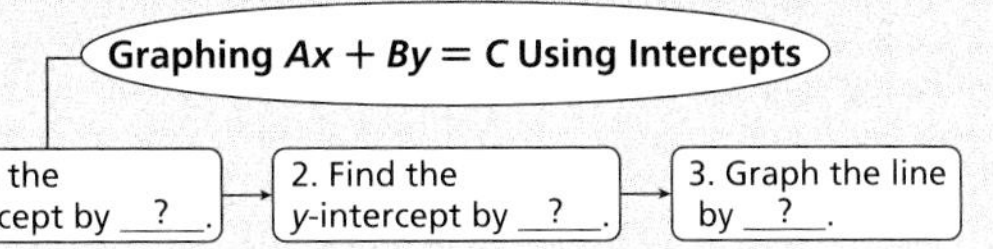

Power Presentations with PowerPoint®

Additional Examples

Example 3

Use intercepts to graph the line given by each equation.

A. $3x - 7y = 21$

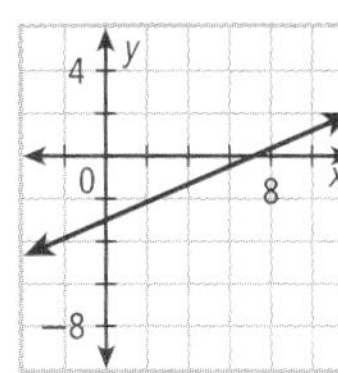

B. $y = -x + 4$

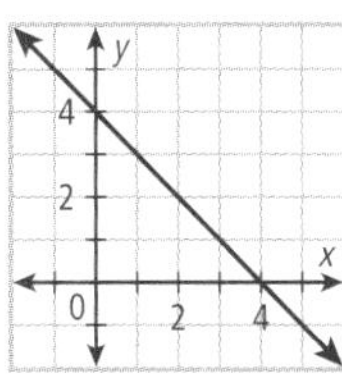

Also available on transparency

INTERVENTION Questioning Strategies

EXAMPLE 3

- What is the difference between graphing a line using intercepts and graphing a line by generating a table of ordered pairs?

3 Close

Summarize

Review how to find the x- and y-intercepts from a graph and from an equation.

Tell students that finding intercepts is especially useful for graphing lines, because it is often quicker than generating ordered pairs, especially when the equation is written in standard form.

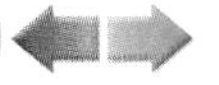

FORMATIVE ASSESSMENT and INTERVENTION

***Diagnose Before* the Lesson**
5-2 Warm Up, TE p. 263

***Monitor During* the Lesson**
Check It Out! Exercises, SE pp. 263–265
Questioning Strategies, TE pp. 264–265

***Assess After* the Lesson**
5-2 Lesson Quiz, TE p. 268
Alternative Assessment, TE p. 268

Answers to *Think and Discuss*

1. (4, 0) and (0, 2)
2. 4.318; −21.5489
3. See p. A4.

5-2 Exercises

Assignment Guide

Assign *Guided Practice* exercises as necessary.

If you finished Examples **1–3**
Proficient 13–33, 38–42, 44, 46–52
Advanced 14–20 even, 22–33, 38–52

Homework Quick Check
Quickly check key concepts.
Exercises: 14, 18, 22, 24, 26, 30

Answers

8a. Refrigeration Tank Temperature

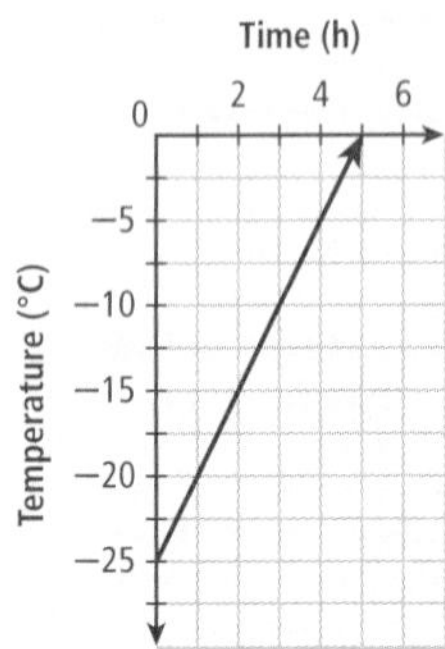

b. *x*-int.: time when temp. = 0°C; *y*-int.: initial temp.

9–12, 22–23. See p. A18.

5-2 Exercises

California Standards Practice
6.0, 24.1, 25.1

go.hrw.com
Homework Help Online
KEYWORD: MA8CA 5-2
Parent Resources Online
KEYWORD: MA8CA Parent

GUIDED PRACTICE

1. **Vocabulary** The ___?___ is the y-coordinate of the point where a graph crosses the y-axis. (x-*intercept* or y-*intercept*) **y-intercept**

SEE EXAMPLE 1 p. 263

Find the x- and y-intercepts.

2. 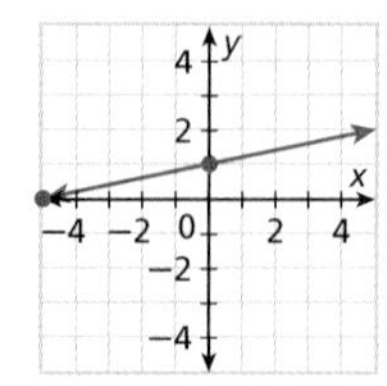

3.

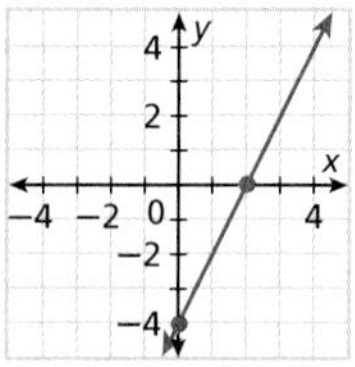

4.

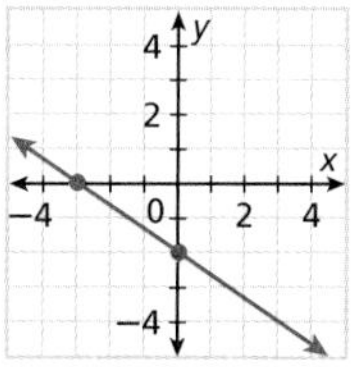

5. $2x - 4y = 4$ **x-int.: 2; y-int.: –1**
6. $-2y = 3x - 6$ **x-int.: 2; y-int.: 3**
7. $4y + 5x = 2y - 3x + 16$ **x-int.: 2; y-int.: 8**

2. *x*-int.: –5; *y*-int.: 1
3. *x*-int.: 2; *y*-int.: –4
4. *x*-int.: –3; *y*-int.: –2

SEE EXAMPLE 2 p. 264

8. **Biology** To thaw a specimen stored at -25°C, the temperature of a refrigeration tank is raised 5°C every hour. The temperature in the tank after x hours can be described by the function $f(x) = -25 + 5x$.
   a. Graph the function and find its intercepts. **x-int.: 5; y-int.: –25**
   b. What does each intercept represent?

SEE EXAMPLE 3 p. 265

Use intercepts to graph the line given by each equation.

9. $4x - 5y = 20$
10. $y = 2x + 4$
11. $\frac{1}{3}x - \frac{1}{4}y = 2$
12. $-5y + 2x = -10$

PRACTICE AND PROBLEM SOLVING

Independent Practice

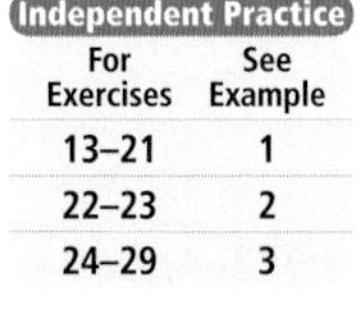

For Exercises	See Example
13–21	1
22–23	2
24–29	3

Extra Practice
Skills Practice p. EP10
Application Practice p. EP28

Find the x- and y-intercepts.

13. **x-int.: –1; y-int.: 3**
14. **x-int.: –5; y-int.: –1**
15. **x-int.: –4; y-int.: 2**

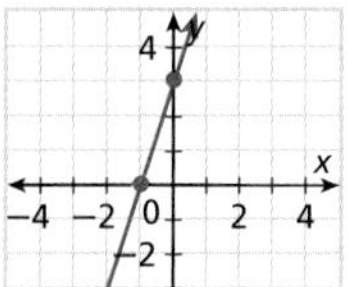

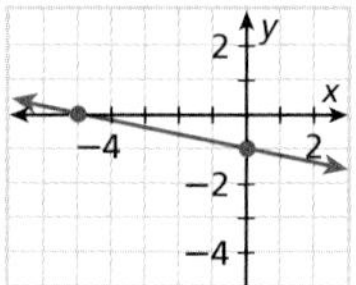

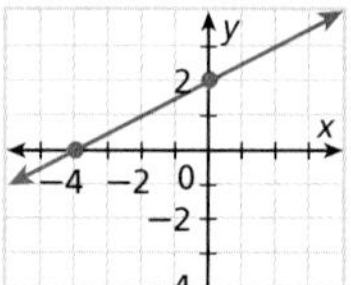

16. $6x + 3y = 12$
17. $4y - 8 = 2x$
18. $-2y + x = 2y - 8$
19. $4x + y = 8$
20. $y - 3x = -15$
21. $2x + y = 10x - 1$

16. *x*-int.: 2; *y*-int.: 4
17. *x*-int.: –4; *y*-int.: 2
18. *x*-int.: –8; *y*-int.: 2
19. *x*-int.: 2; *y*-int.: 8
20. *x*-int.: 5; *y*-int.: –15
21. *x*-int.: $\frac{1}{8}$; *y*-int.: –1

22. **Environmental Science** A fishing lake was stocked with 300 bass. Each year, the population decreases by 25. The population of bass in the lake after x years is represented by the function $f(x) = 300 - 25x$.
   a. Graph the function and find its intercepts.
   b. What does each intercept represent?

23. **Sports** Julie is running a 5-kilometer race. She ran 1 kilometer every 5 minutes. Julie's distance from the finish line after x minutes is represented by the function $f(x) = 5 - \frac{1}{5}x$.
   a. Graph the function and find its intercepts.
   b. What does each intercept represent?

5-2 READING STRATEGIES

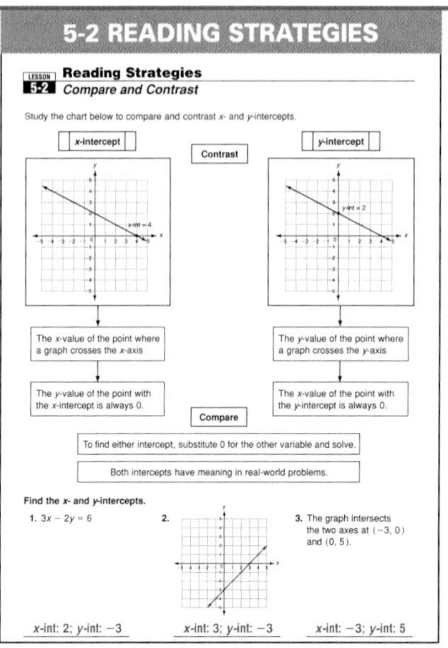

LESSON 5-2 **Reading Strategies**
Compare and Contrast

Study the chart below to compare and contrast x- and y-intercepts.

x-intercept	Contrast	y-intercept
x-int = 4		y-int = 2
The x-value of the point where a graph crosses the x-axis		The y-value of the point where a graph crosses the y-axis
The y-value of the point with the x-intercept is always 0.		The x-value of the point with the y-intercept is always 0.

Compare

To find either intercept, substitute 0 for the other variable and solve.

Both intercepts have meaning in real-world problems.

Find the x- and y-intercepts.

1. $3x - 2y = 6$ — x-int: 2; y-int: -3
2. x-int: 3; y-int: -3
3. The graph intersects the two axes at $(-3, 0)$ and $(0, 5)$. — x-int: -3; y-int: 5

5-2 REVIEW FOR MASTERY

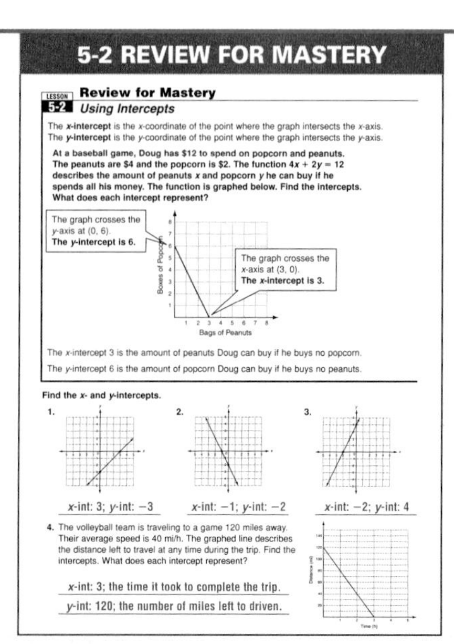

LESSON 5-2 **Review for Mastery**
Using Intercepts

The **x-intercept** is the x-coordinate of the point where the graph intersects the x-axis.
The **y-intercept** is the y-coordinate of the point where the graph intersects the y-axis.

At a baseball game, Doug has \$12 to spend on popcorn and peanuts. The peanuts are \$4 and the popcorn is \$2. The function $4x + 2y = 12$ describes the amount of peanuts x and popcorn y he can buy if he spends all his money. The function is graphed below. Find the intercepts. What does each intercept represent?

The x-intercept 3 is the amount of peanuts Doug can buy if he buys no popcorn.
The y-intercept 6 is the amount of popcorn Doug can buy if he buys no peanuts.

Find the x- and y-intercepts.

1. x-int: 3; y-int: -3
2. x-int: -1; y-int: -2
3. x-int: -2; y-int: 4

4. The volleyball team is traveling to a game 120 miles away. Their average speed is 40 mi/h. The graphed line describes the distance left to travel at any time during the trip. Find the intercepts. What does each intercept represent?

x-int: 3; the time it took to complete the trip.
y-int: 120; the number of miles left to driven.

California Standards

Standard	Exercises
4.0	48–50
6.0	2–8a, 9–12, 13–22a, 23a, 24–29, 30b, 31a, 32a, 32b, 33a, 33b, 38a, 40, 42–45
15.0	47
24.1	33c
25.1	46

Use intercepts to graph the line given by each equation.

24. $4x - 6y = 12$ 25. $2x + 3y = 18$ 26. $\frac{1}{2}x - 4y = 4$

27. $y - x = -1$ 28. $5x + 3y = 15$ 29. $x - 3y = -1$

LINK Biology

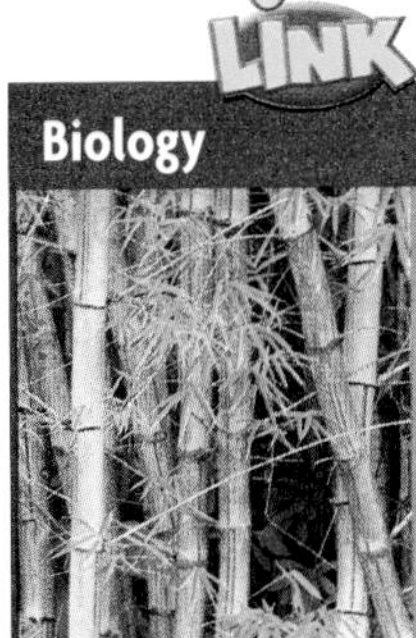

Bamboo is the world's fastest-growing woody plant. Some varieties can grow more than 30 centimeters a day and up to 40 meters tall.

30. **Biology** A bamboo plant is growing 1 foot per day. When you first measure it, it is 4 feet tall.
   a. Write an equation to describe the height y, in feet, of the bamboo plant x days after you measure it. **$y = x + 4$**
   b. What is the y-intercept? **y-int.: 4**
   c. What is the meaning of the y-intercept in this problem? **orig. height of bamboo plant**

31. **Estimation** Look at the scatter plot and trend line. **x-int.: 600; y-int.: 7.5**
   a. Estimate the x- and y-intercepts.
   b. What is the real-world meaning of each intercept?

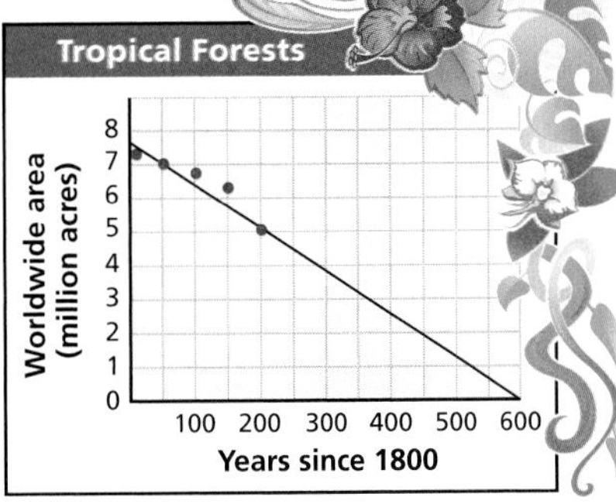

32. **Personal Finance** A bank employee notices an abandoned checking account with a balance of \$412. If the bank charges a \$4 monthly fee for the account, the function $b = 412 - 4m$ shows the balance b in the account after m months.
   a. Graph the function.
   b. Find the intercepts. What does each intercept represent?
   c. When will the bank account balance be 0? **after 103 mo (8 yr 7 mo)**

33. **Reasoning** Complete the following to learn about intercepts of horizontal and vertical lines.
   a. Graph $x = -6$, $x = 1$, and $x = 5$. Find the intercepts.
   b. Graph $y = -3$, $y = 2$, and $y = 7$. Find the intercepts.
   c. Based on your results in parts **a** and **b**, use inductive reasoning to make a conjecture about the intercepts of horizontal lines $x = k$ $(k \neq 0)$ and vertical lines $y = c$ $(c \neq 0)$. What happens when k and c are equal to 0?

For help with inductive reasoning, see p. 233.

33c. Horiz.: For $y = c$, the y-int. is c, and there is no x-int. Vert.: For $x = k$, the x-int. is k, and there is no y-int.

Match each equation with a graph.

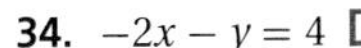

34. $-2x - y = 4$ **D** 35. $y = 4 - 2x$ **A** 36. $2y + 4x = 8$ **A** 37. $4x - 2y = 8$ **B**

A.

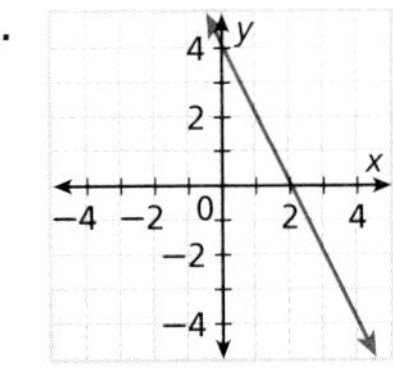

B.

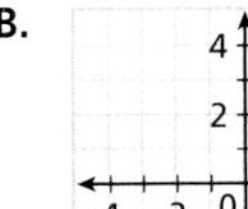

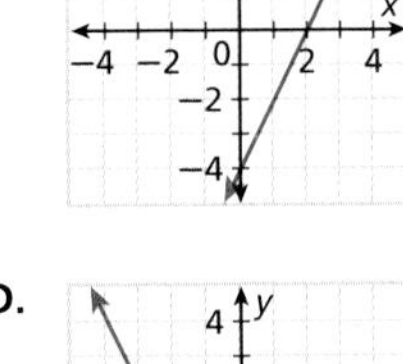

C.

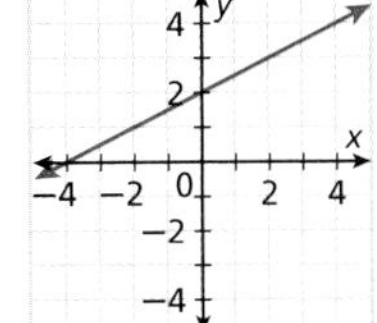

D.

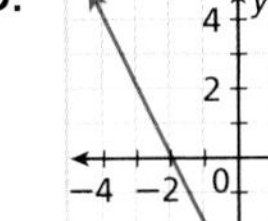

COMMON ERROR ALERT

Students may combine intercepts to form a point. In **Exercise 9,** for example, a student might take the x-intercept (5) and the y-intercept (−4) to form the point (5, −4). Remind students that the intercepts give you two separate points: (5, 0) and (0, −4).

Answers

24.

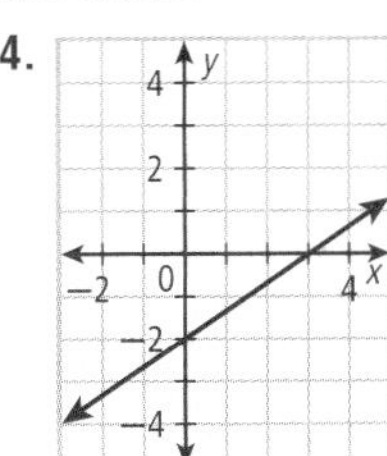

25.

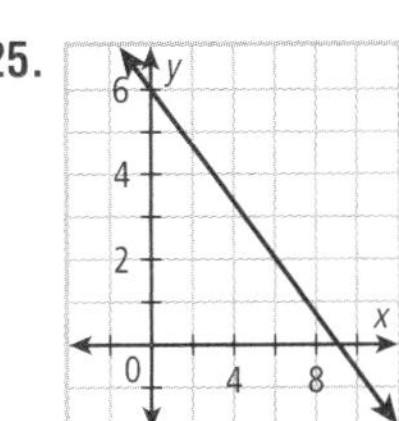

26.

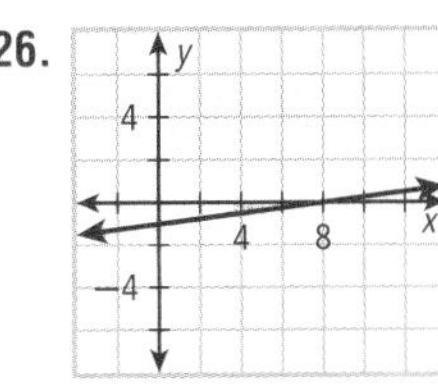

27.

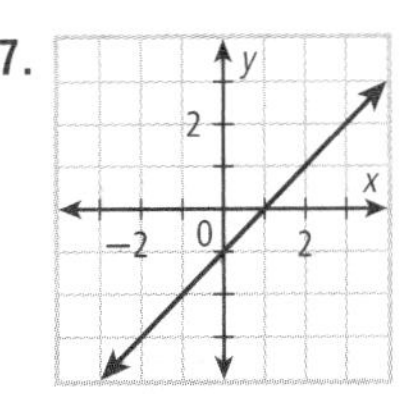

28, 29, 31b, 32a, 32b, 33a, 33b. See p. A18.

5-2 PROBLEM SOLVING

LESSON 5-2 Problem Solving
Using Intercepts

Write the correct answer.

1. Naima has \$40 to spend on refreshments for herself and her friends at the movie theater. The equation $5x + 2y = 40$ describes the number of large popcorns x and small drinks y she can buy. Graph this function and find its intercepts.
   y-int: 20; x-int: 8

2. Turner is reading a 400-page book. He reads 4 pages every 5 minutes. The number of pages Turner has left to read after x minutes is represented by the function $f(x) = 400 - \frac{4}{5}x$. Graph this function and find its intercepts.
   y-int: 400; x-int: 500

The graph shows the distance of an elevator at Chimney Rock, North Carolina, from its destination as a function of time. Use the graph to answer questions 3–6. Select the best answer.

3. What is the x-intercept of this function?
   A 0 (B) 30 C 258 D 300

4. What does the x-intercept represent?
   F the total distance the elevator travels
   G the number of seconds that have passed for any given distance
   (H) the number of seconds it takes the elevator to reach its destination
   J the distance that the elevator has traveled at any given time

5. What is the y-intercept for this function?
   A 0 B 30 (C) 258 D 300

6. What does the y-intercept represent?
   (F) the total distance the elevator travels
   G the number of seconds that have passed for any given distance
   H the number of seconds it takes the elevator to reach its destination
   J the distance that the elevator has traveled at any given time

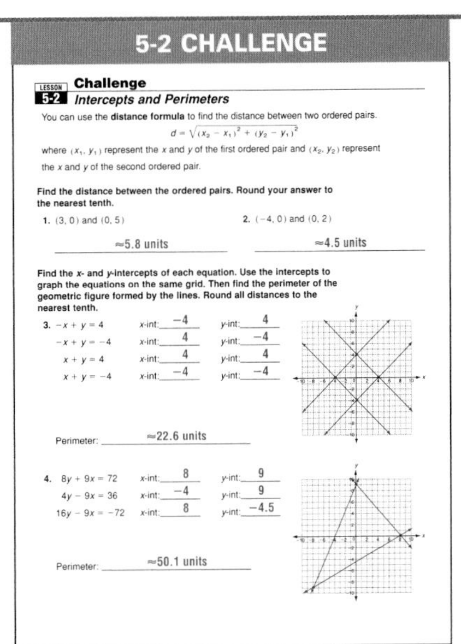

5-2 CHALLENGE

LESSON 5-2 Challenge
Intercepts and Perimeters

You can use the **distance formula** to find the distance between two ordered pairs.

$$d = \sqrt{(x_2 - x_1)^2 + (y_2 - y_1)^2}$$

where (x_1, y_1) represent the x and y of the first ordered pair and (x_2, y_2) represent the x and y of the second ordered pair.

Find the distance between the ordered pairs. Round your answer to the nearest tenth.

1. (3, 0) and (0, 5) **≈5.8 units**
2. (−4, 0) and (0, 2) **≈4.5 units**

Find the x- and y-intercepts of each equation. Use the intercepts to graph the equations on the same grid. Then find the perimeter of the geometric figure formed by the lines. Round all distances to the nearest tenth.

3. $-x + y = 4$ x-int: **−4** y-int: **4**
   $-x + y = -4$ x-int: **4** y-int: **−4**
   $x + y = 4$ x-int: **4** y-int: **4**
   $x + y = -4$ x-int: **−4** y-int: **−4**
   Perimeter: **≈22.6 units**

4. $8y + 9x = 72$ x-int: **8** y-int: **9**
   $4y - 9x = 36$ x-int: **−4** y-int: **9**
   $16y - 9x = -72$ x-int: **8** y-int: **−4.5**
   Perimeter: **≈50.1 units**

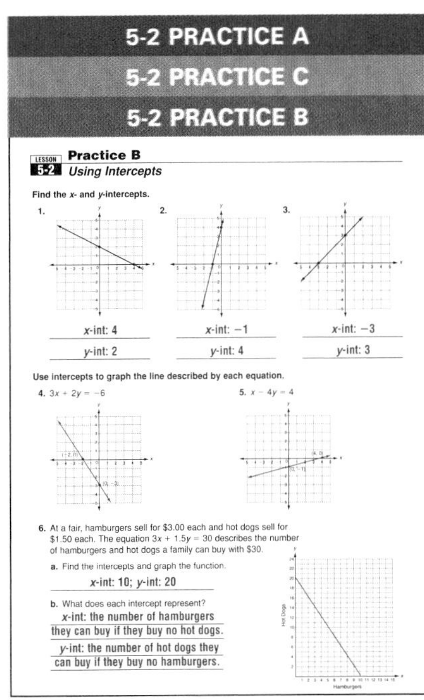

5-2 PRACTICE A
5-2 PRACTICE C
5-2 PRACTICE B

LESSON 5-2 Practice B
Using Intercepts

Find the x- and y-intercepts.

1. **x-int: 4** **y-int: 2**
2. **x-int: −1** **y-int: 4**
3. **x-int: −3** **y-int: 3**

Use intercepts to graph the line described by each equation.

4. $3x + 2y = -6$
5. $x - 4y = 4$

6. At a fair, hamburgers sell for \$3.00 each and hot dogs sell for \$1.50 each. The equation $3x + 1.5y = 30$ describes the number of hamburgers and hot dogs a family can buy with \$30.
   a. Find the intercepts and graph the function. **x-int: 10; y-int: 20**
   b. What does each intercept represent? **x-int: the number of hamburgers they can buy if they buy no hot dogs. y-int: the number of hot dogs they can buy if they buy no hamburgers.**

 **Exercise 38** involves identifying and interpreting x- and y-intercepts. This exercise prepares students for the Concept Connection on page 288.

 **Multiple Choice** Students who chose **B** in **Exercise 40** may have chosen just the coefficient of x. Students who chose **C** found the y-intercept instead of the x-intercept.

Journal

Have students explain how to find the intercepts of $5x - 8y = 40$.

ALTERNATIVE ASSESSMENT

Have students write an equation in standard form, find the intercepts, and then graph the line using the intercepts.

Power Presentations with PowerPoint®

5-2 Lesson Quiz

1. An amateur filmmaker has \$6000 to make a film that costs \$75/h to produce. The function $f(x) = 6000 - 75x$ gives the amount of money left to make the film after x hours of production. Graph this function and find the intercepts. What does each intercept represent?

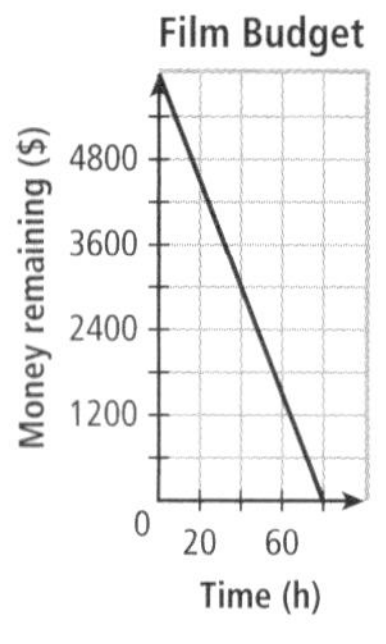

x-int.: 80; when all the money has been spent; y-int.: 6000; the initial amount of money available.

2. Use intercepts to graph the line given by $\frac{1}{4}x = 2 - \frac{1}{3}y$.

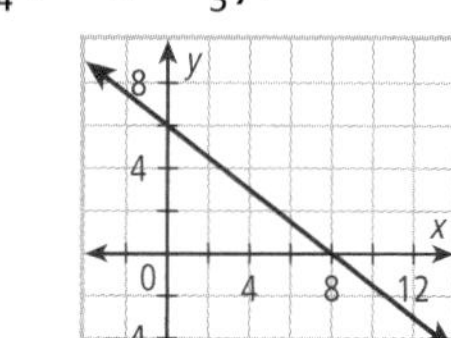

Also available on transparency

38. This problem will prepare you for the Concept Connection on page 288.

Kristyn rode a stationary bike at the gym. She programmed the timer for 20 minutes. The display counted backward to show how much time remained in her workout. It also showed her mileage.

a. What are the intercepts? **x-int.: 20; y-int.: 1.75**

b. What do the intercepts represent?
x-int.: time remaining when Kristyn started her workout; y-int.: total distance Kristyn covered

Time Remaining (min)	Distance Covered (mi)
20	0
16	0.35
12	0.70
8	1.05
4	1.40
0	1.75

39. Write About It Write a real-world problem that could be modeled by a linear function whose x-intercept is 5 and whose y-intercept is 60.

Multiple Choice For Exercises 40 and 41, choose the best answer.

40. Which is the x-intercept of $-2x = 9y - 18$?

Ⓐ -9 Ⓑ -2 Ⓒ 2 Ⓓ 9

41. Which situation could be represented by the graph?

Ⓐ Jamie owed her uncle \$200. Each week for 40 weeks she paid him \$5.

Ⓑ Jamie owed her uncle \$200. Each week for 5 weeks she paid him \$40.

Ⓒ Jamie owed her uncle \$40. Each week for 5 weeks she paid him \$200.

Ⓓ Jamie owed her uncle \$40. Each week for 200 weeks she paid him \$5.

Jamie's Balance

Time (weeks): 0, 10, 20, 30; Debt (\$): −40, −80, −120, −160, −200

42. Gridded Response What is the y-intercept of $60x + 55y = 660$? **12**

CHALLENGE AND EXTEND

Use intercepts to graph the line given by each equation.

43. $\frac{1}{2}x + \frac{1}{5}y = 1$ **44.** $0.5x - 0.2y = 0.75$ **45.** $y = \frac{3}{8}x + 6$

46. Reasoning For any linear equation $Ax + By = C$, where $A \neq 0$ and $B \neq 0$, show that the x-intercept is $\frac{C}{A}$ and the y-intercept is $\frac{C}{B}$.

SPIRAL STANDARDS REVIEW

47. Marlon's fish tank is 80% filled with water. Based on the measurements shown, what volume of the tank is NOT filled with water? *(Lesson 2-5)* **600 in^3**

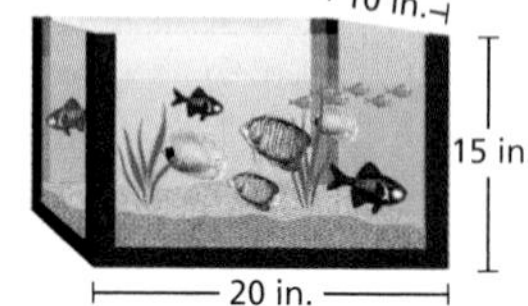

Solve each inequality and graph the solutions. *(Lesson 3-4)*

48. $2(t - 1) + 2 \leq -16$ **$t \leq -8$** **49.** $m + 4 \geq 2(-3 + 2)$ **$m \geq -6$** **50.** $-2(w + 2) > 10$ **$w < -7$**

Tell whether the given ordered pairs all lie on the same line. *(Lesson 5-1)*

51. $\{(-2, 0), (0, 3), (2, 6), (4, 9), (6, 12)\}$ **yes** **52.** $\{(0, 0), (1, 1), (4, 2), (9, 3), (16, 4)\}$ **no**

Answers

39. Possible answer: Jen wants to save \$60. Each week, she will earn \$12. The function shows how much money Jen has left to save each week.

43.

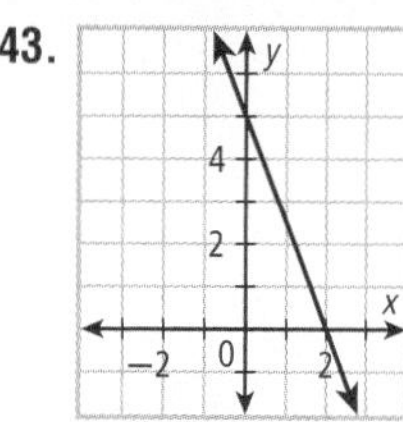

44.

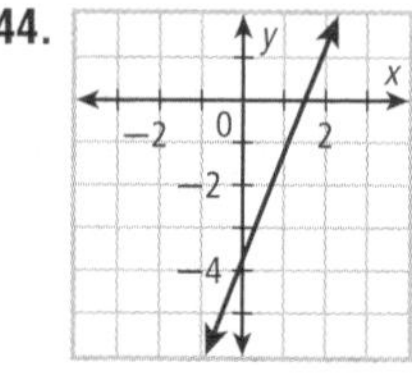

45.

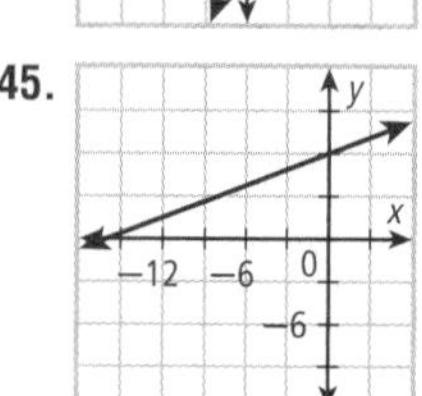

46. Possible answer: To find the x-int., let $y = 0$. Then $Ax = C$ and $x = \frac{C}{A}$. To find the y-int., let $x = 0$. Then $By = C$ and $y = \frac{C}{B}$.

48.

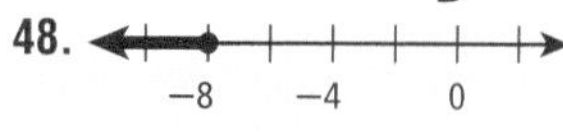

49.

50.

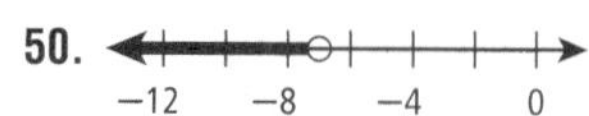

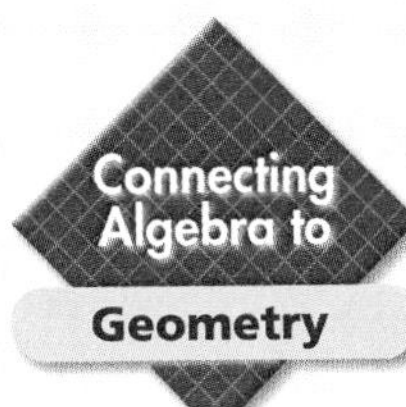

Area in the Coordinate Plane

Lines in the coordinate plane can form the sides of polygons. You can use points on these lines to help you find the areas of these polygons.

California Standards

Reinforcement of **7MG2.1 Use formulas routinely for finding the** perimeter and **area of basic two-dimensional figures** and the surface area and volume of basic three-dimensional figures, **including rectangles,** parallelograms, trapezoids, squares, **triangles,** circles, prisms, and cylinders.

Example

Find the area of the triangle formed by the x-axis, the y-axis, and the line given by $3x + 2y = 18$.

Step 1 Find the intercepts of $3x + 2y = 18$.

x-intercept:	y-intercept:
$3x + 2y = 18$	$3x + 2y = 18$
$3x + 2(0) = 18$	$3(0) + 2y = 18$
$3x = 18$	$2y = 18$
$x = 6$	$y = 9$

Step 2 Use the intercepts to graph the line. The x-intercept is 6, so plot $(6, 0)$. The y-intercept is 9, so plot $(0, 9)$. Connect with a straight line. Then shade the triangle formed by the line and the axes, as described.

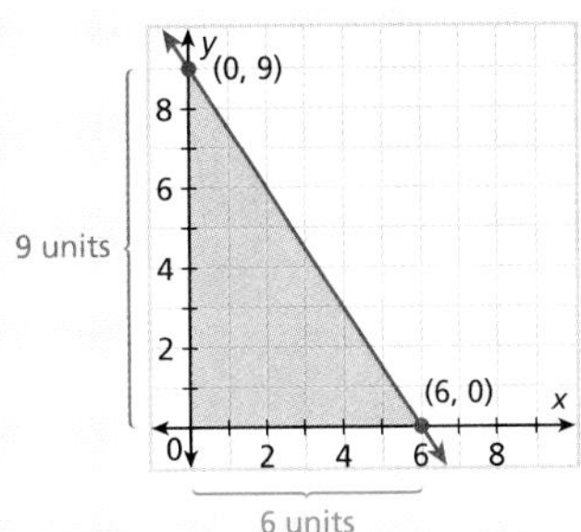

Step 3 Recall that the area of a triangle is given by $A = \frac{1}{2}bh$.

- The length of the base is 6.
- The height is 9.

Step 4 Substitute these values into the formula.

$$A = \frac{1}{2}bh$$

$$A = \frac{1}{2}(6)(9) \quad \textit{Substitute into the area formula.}$$

$$= \frac{1}{2}(54) \quad \textit{Simplify.}$$

$$= 27$$

The area of the triangle is 27 square units.

Try This

1. Find the area of the triangle formed by the x-axis, the y-axis, and the line given by $3x + 2y = 12$. **12 sq. units**
2. Find the area of the triangle formed by the x-axis, the y-axis, and the line given by $y = 6 - x$. **18 sq. units**
3. What polygon is formed by the x-axis, the y-axis, the line given by $y = 6$, and the line given by $x = 4$? What is its area? **rectangle; 24 sq. units**

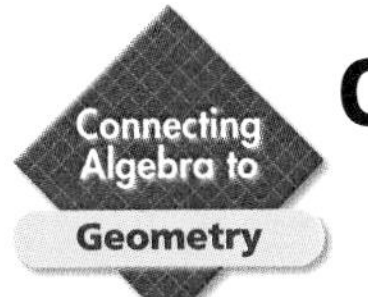

Organizer

See Skills Bank page SB16

Objective: Apply algebra skills to finding areas of geometric figures in the coordinate plane.

Teach

Remember

Students review and apply the formulas for the areas of triangles and rectangles.

INTERVENTION For additional review and practice on finding the area of geometric figures, see Skills Bank page SB16.

Discuss with students how identifying the intercepts of the line determines the base and height of the triangle.

Close

Assess

Use the triangle from the example. Have students change the equation of the line so that the area of the triangle increases. Then have them find the area of the new triangle. Possible answer: $8x + 9y = 72$; 36 square units

California Standards

Reinforcement of 7MG2.1

Organizer

Use with Lesson 5-3

Objective: Explore the relationship between constant change and the slope of a line.

Online Edition

Countdown to Mastery Week 10

Teach

Discuss

For each situation:

- encourage students to identify the independent and dependent variables.
- ask students to explain whether the points in the graph should be connected.

Alternative Approach

Have students write the function rule for each scenario and compare the number multiplied by the independent variable with the amount of constant change.

Answers to *Activity 1*

2. The number of books Janice reads per week; the number of books read increases by 2 each week.
3. 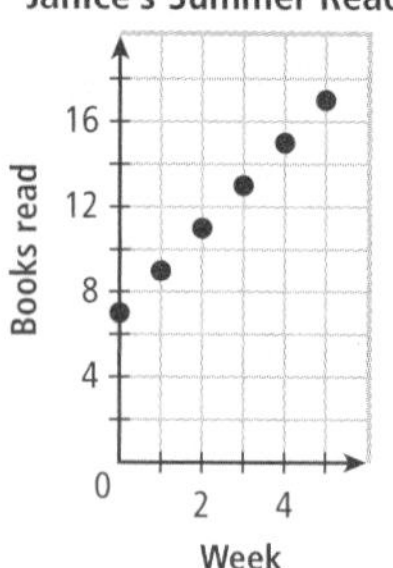

The points lie on a line that ascends from left to right.
4. Possible answer: The y-coordinate of each point is 2 greater than that of the previous point.

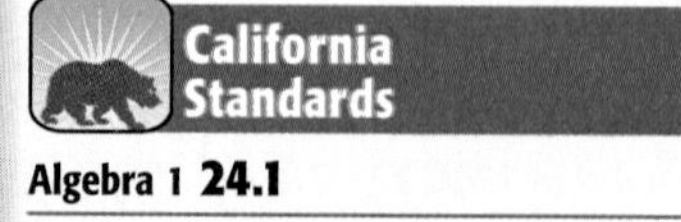
California Standards

Algebra 1 24.1

5-3 Algebra LAB

Explore Constant Changes

Use with Lesson 5-3

There are many real-life situations in which the amount of change is constant. In these activities, you will explore what happens when

- a quantity increases by a constant amount.
- a quantity decreases by a constant amount.

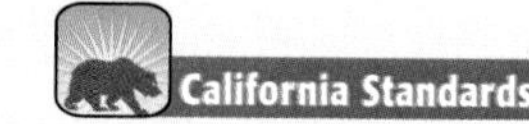
California Standards

24.1 Students explain the difference between inductive and deductive reasoning and identify and **provide examples** of each.

Activity 1

Janice has read 7 books for her summer reading club. She plans to read 2 books each week for the rest of the summer. The table shows the total number of books that Janice will have read after different numbers of weeks have passed.

Janice's Summer Reading	
Week	**Total Books Read**
0	7
1	9
2	11
3	13
4	15
5	17

1. What number is added to the number of books in each row to get the number of books in the next row? **2**
2. What does your answer to Problem 1 represent in Janice's situation? Describe the meaning of the constant change.
3. Graph the ordered pairs from the table. Describe how the points are related.
4. Look again at your answer to Problem 1. Explain how this number affects your graph.

Try This

At a particular college, a full-time student must take at least 12 credit hours per semester and may take up to 18 credit hours per semester. Tuition costs $200 per credit hour.

Tuition Costs	
Credit Hours	**Cost ($)**
12	2400
13	2600
14	2800
15	3000
16	3200
17	3400
18	3600

1. Copy and complete the table by using the information above.
2. What number is added to the cost in each row to get the cost in the next row? **200**
3. What does your answer to Problem 2 above represent in the situation? Describe the meaning of the constant change.
4. Graph the ordered pairs from the table. Describe how the points are related.
5. Look again at your answer to Problem 2. Explain how this number affects the shape of your graph.
6. Compare your graphs from Activity 1 and Problem 4. How are they alike? How are they different?
7. **Reasoning** Make a conjecture about the graph of any situation that involves repeated addition of a positive number. Why do you think your conjecture is correct?

Possible answer: It will be a line that ascends from left to right because the *y*-values will keep increasing by the same amount.

Answers to *Try This*

3. The cost of one credit hour; each additional credit hour increases the cost of tuition by $200.
4. Tuition Costs (graph: Cost ($) 0, 800, 1600, 2400, 3200 vs. Credit hours 4, 8, 12, 16)
The points lie on a line that ascends from left to right.
5. Possible answer: The y-coordinate of each point is 200 greater than that of the previous point.
6. Possible answer: They are both lines that ascend from left to right. The tuition graph forms a steeper line.

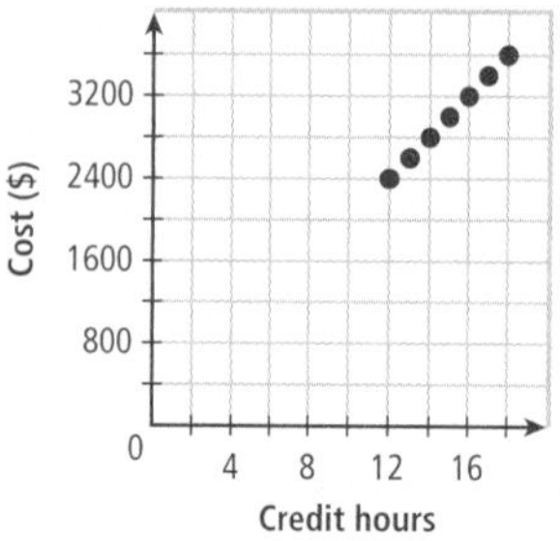

Activity 2

An airplane is 3000 miles from its destination. The plane is traveling at a rate of 540 miles per hour. The table shows how far the plane is from its destination after various amounts of time have passed.

Airplane's Distance	
Time (h)	Distance to Destination (mi)
0	3000
1	2460
2	1920
3	1380
4	840

1. What number is subtracted from the distance in each row to get the distance in the next row? **540**
2. What does your answer to Problem 1 represent in the situation? Describe the meaning of the constant change.
3. Graph the ordered pairs from the table. Describe how the points are related.
4. Look again at your answer to Problem 1. Explain how this number affects your graph.

Try This

A television game show begins with 20 contestants. Each week, the players vote 2 contestants off the show.

Game Show	
Week	Contestants Remaining
0	20
1	**18**
2	**16**
3	**14**
4	**12**
5	**10**
6	**8**

8. Copy and complete the table by using the information above.
9. What number is subtracted from the number of contestants in each row to get the number of contestants in the next row? **2**
10. What does your answer to Problem 9 represent in the situation? Describe the meaning of the constant change.
11. Graph the ordered pairs from the table. Describe how the points are related.
12. Look again at your answer to Problem 9. Explain how this number affects the shape of your graph.
13. Compare your graphs from Activity 2 and Problem 11. How are they alike? How are they different?
14. **Reasoning** Make a conjecture about the graph of any situation that involves repeated subtraction of a positive number. Why do you think your conjecture is correct?
15. Compare your two graphs from Activity 1 with your two graphs from Activity 2. How are they alike? How are they different?
16. **Reasoning** Make a conjecture to describe how the graphs of situations involving repeated subtraction differ from graphs of situations involving repeated addition. Explain your answer.

14. Possible answer: It will be a line that descends from left to right because you will keep decreasing the *y*-values by the same amount.

15. Possible answer: They both form lines. In Act. 1, the lines were ascending from left to right. In Act. 2, the lines were descending from left to right.

16. Possible answer: When situations involve repeated subt., the line is descending. When situations involve repeated add., the line is ascending.

Teacher to Teacher

Pauline Embree
Irvine, CA

Students may benefit from modeling the situations in this Algebra Lab.

Divide students into groups. For Activity 1, assign one group to week 0, one group to week 1, and so on. Using snap cubes or linking cubes, have each group build a figure to represent the total books read during their week. Line up the figures in order by week and ask students to describe how they differ from one to the next. Lead students to see that each consecutive figure differs by the same number of cubes (2). That same number, the constant change, is the slope of the graphed line.

Activity 2 and the Try This problems can be modeled similarly.

Close

Key Concept

If a situation involves a quantity that increases or decreases by a constant amount, the data points will form a straight line. The steepness of the line is determined by the amount of increase or decrease.

Assessment

Journal Create a word problem involving a situation that uses repeated addition or subtraction. Write at least five ordered pairs and graph the line. Explain how the graph is related to the situation.

Answers to *Activity 2*

2. The plane's speed; the distance to the destination is decreasing by 540 mi each hour.
3.

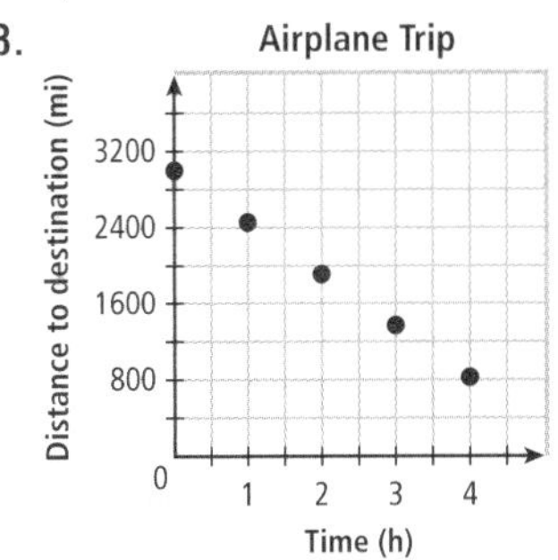

The points lie on a line that descends from left to right.

4. Possible answer: The *y*-coordinate of each point is 540 less than that of the previous point.

Answers to *Try This*

10. The number of contestants voted off each week; the total number of contestants is decreasing by 2 each week.
11.

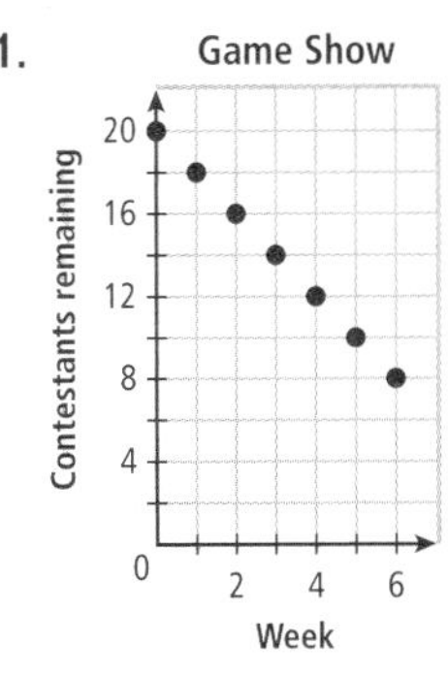

The points lie on a line that descends from left to right.

12. Possible answer: The *y*-coordinate of each point is 2 less than that of the previous point.
13. Possible answer: Both are lines that descend from left to right. The airplane graph is steeper.

5-3 Organizer

Objective: Find slopes of lines.

Technology Lab
In *Chapter 5 Resource File*

Online Edition
Tutorial Videos

Countdown to Mastery Week 10

Power Presentations with PowerPoint®

Warm Up

Add or subtract.

1. $4 + (-6)$ −2 **2.** $-3 + 5$ 2

3. $-7 - 7$ −14 **4.** $2 - (-1)$ 3

5. Find the *x*- and *y*-intercepts of $2x - 5y = 20$. *x*-int.: 10; *y*-int.: −4

Describe the correlation shown by each scatter plot.

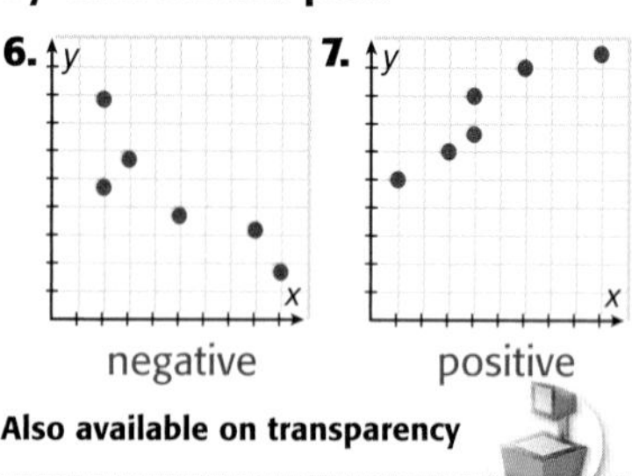

Also available on transparency

Math Humor

Q: Why were the math students getting up and sprinting around the classroom?

A: Their teacher kept saying "rise" and "run".

California Standards

Preparation for 8.0
Also covered:
6.0 Students graph a linear equation and **compute the *x*- and *y*-intercepts** (e.g., graph $2x + 6y = 4$). They are also able to sketch the region defined by linear inequalities (e.g., they sketch the region defined by $2x + 6y < 4$).

5-3 Slope

California Standards

Preparation for 8.0 Students understand the concepts of parallel lines and perpendicular lines and how their slopes are related. Students are able to find the equation of a line perpendicular to a given line that passes through a given point.
Also covered: **6.0**

Vocabulary
rate of change
rise
run
slope

Why learn this?

You can use the slope formula to find how quickly a quantity, such as the amount of water in a reservoir, is changing. (See Example 5.)

A **rate of change** is a ratio that compares the amount of change in a dependent variable to the amount of change in an independent variable.

$$\text{rate of change} = \frac{\text{change in dependent variable } (y)}{\text{change in independent variable } (x)}$$

For any two points on a nonvertical line, this ratio is constant. The constant rate of change of a nonvertical line is called the *slope* of the line.

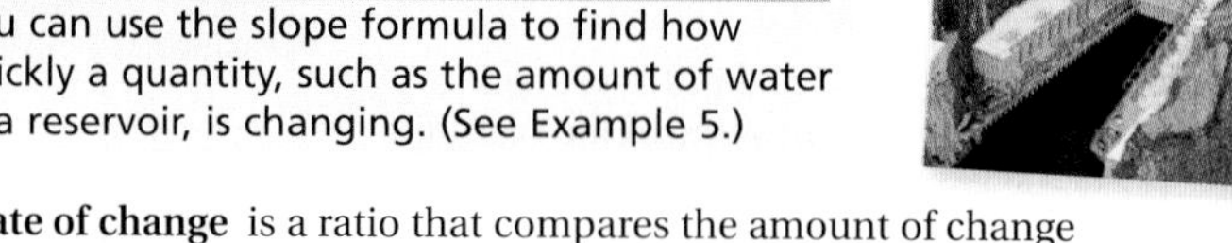

Know it! Note — **Slope of a Line**

The **rise** is the difference in the *y*-values of two points on a line.

The **run** is the difference in the *x*-values of two points on a line.

The **slope** of a line (m) is the ratio of rise to run for any two points on the line. $m = \frac{\text{rise}}{\text{run}}$

If (x_1, y_1) and (x_2, y_2) are two points on a line, then the slope of the line can be found using the slope formula. $m = \frac{y_2 - y_1}{x_2 - x_1}$

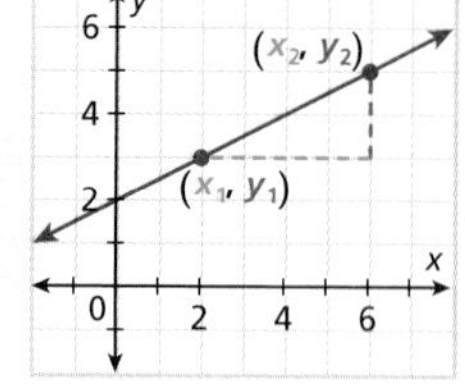

EXAMPLE 1 Finding Slope from a Graph

Find the slope of the line.

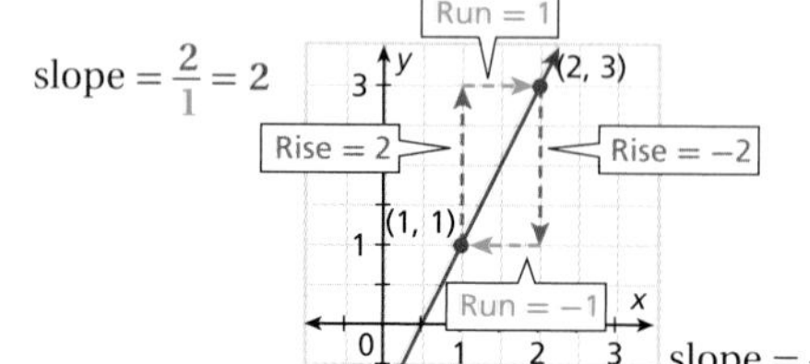

Begin at one point and count vertically to find the rise.

Then count horizontally to the second point to find the run.

Helpful Hint

Notice that it does not matter which point you start at. The slope is the same.

CHECK IT OUT! **1.** Find the slope of the line. $-\frac{1}{2}$

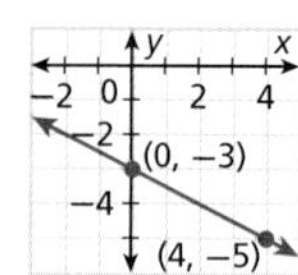

1 Introduce

EXPLORATION

5-3 Slope

In this Exploration, you will investigate a formula for finding the slope of a line.

1. Use the graph to count the vertical change (rise) from point *A* to point *B*.
2. Use the graph to count the horizontal change (run) from point *A* to point *B*.
3. The slope of a line is the ratio $\frac{\text{rise}}{\text{run}}$. What is the slope of the line?
4. Explain how you could have found the rise by using only the *y*-coordinates of the two points, without seeing the graph.
5. Explain how you could have found the run by using only the *x*-coordinates of the two points, without seeing the graph.

THINK AND DISCUSS

6. **Describe** a general method you can use to find the slope of a line if you are given the coordinates of two points on the line.
7. **Explain** how you could use your method to find the slope of the line that contains the points (5, 8) and (10, 18).

Motivate

Instruct students to graph a line with *x*-intercept 3 and *y*-intercept 4. On the same grid, tell them to graph a line with *x*-intercept 5 and *y*-intercept 1. Ask students how the lines are the same. Both are slanting in the same direction. Ask them how the lines are different. One is steeper than the other.

Tell students that in this section they will learn how to describe the steepness and direction of a line.

Explorations and answers are provided in *Alternate Openers: Explorations Transparencies.*

EXAMPLE 2 Finding Slopes of Horizontal and Vertical Lines

Find the slope of each line.

A

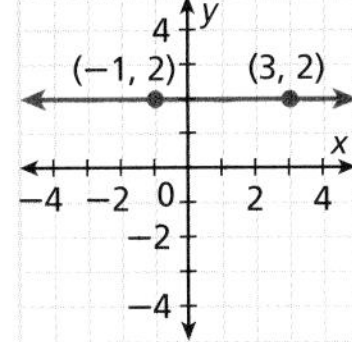

$\frac{\text{rise}}{\text{run}} = \frac{0}{4} = 0$

The slope is 0.

B

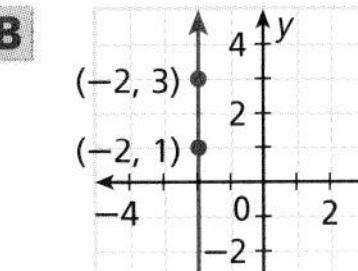

$\frac{\text{rise}}{\text{run}} = \frac{2}{0}$ *You cannot divide by 0.*

The slope is undefined.

CHECK IT OUT! Find the slope of each line.

2a.

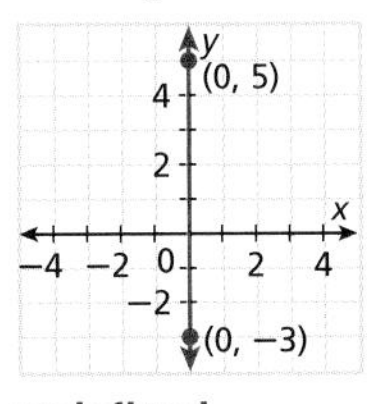

undefined

2b.

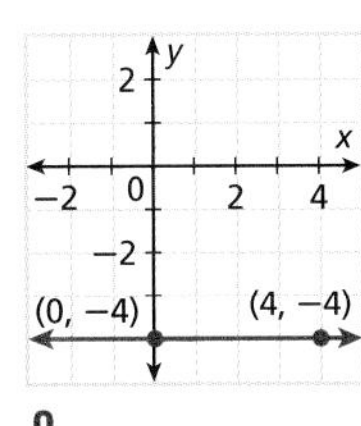

0

If you know 2 different points on a line, you can use the slope formula to find the slope of the line.

EXAMPLE 3 Finding Slope by Using the Slope Formula

Find the slope of the line that contains $(4, -2)$ and $(-1, 2)$.

$m = \frac{y_2 - y_1}{x_2 - x_1}$ *Use the slope formula.*

$= \frac{2 - (-2)}{-1 - 4}$ *Substitute $(4, -2)$ for (x_1, y_1) and $(-1, 2)$ for (x_2, y_2).*

$= \frac{4}{-5} = -\frac{4}{5}$ *Simplify.*

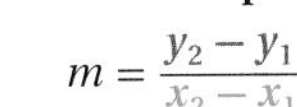

Reading Math

The small numbers to the bottom right of the variables are called subscripts. Read x_1 as "x sub one" and y_2 as "y sub two."

CHECK IT OUT!

3a. Find the slope of the line that contains $(-2, -2)$ and $(7, -2)$. **0**

3b. Find the slope of the line that contains $(5, -7)$ and $(6, -4)$. **3**

As shown in the previous examples, slope can be positive, negative, zero, or undefined.

Know it! Note

Positive Slope	Negative Slope	Zero Slope	Undefined Slope
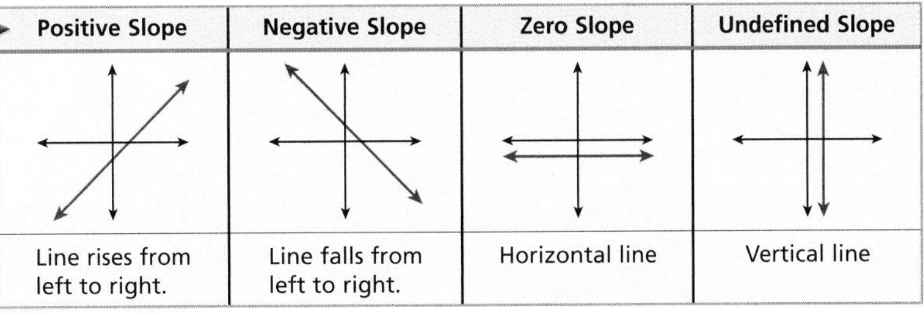			
Line rises from left to right.	Line falls from left to right.	Horizontal line	Vertical line

2 Teach

Guided Instruction

Be sure students understand slope as the ratio of rise to run. Students should also see that both methods—using the slope formula and using a graph to count rise and run—yield the same result.

In **Example 3,** help students see the importance of the order when substituting into the slope formula. Tell them they can choose either point as (x_2, y_2), but must be consistent.

Teaching Tip

Inclusion Point out that in the slope ratio, the rise (y-values) is recorded before the run (x-values). This is the opposite of students' understanding from working in the coordinate plane. Until now, students have been taught to look at the x-values (horizontal) first and then the y-values (vertical) second. Direct students' attention to this difference.

Power Presentations with PowerPoint®

Additional Examples

Example 1

Find the slope of the line.

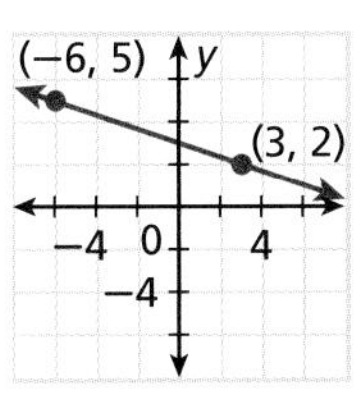

$-\frac{1}{3}$

Example 2

Find the slope of each line.

A. undefined

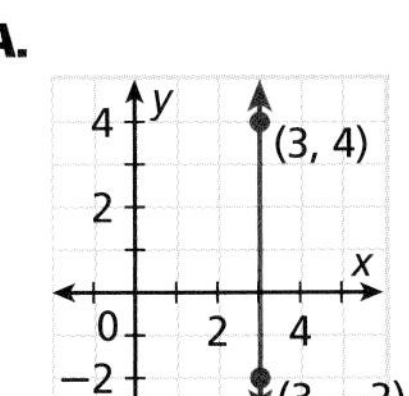

B. 0

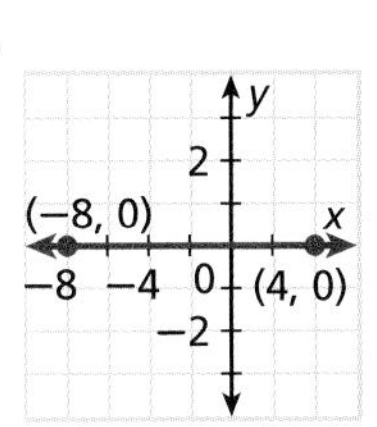

Example 3

Find the slope of the line that contains $(2, 5)$ and $(8, 1)$. $-\frac{2}{3}$

Also available on transparency

INTERVENTION

Questioning Strategies

EXAMPLE 1

- Does it matter which point you start at to find the slope?

EXAMPLE 2

- Why is the slope of a vertical line undefined?

EXAMPLE 3

- If a line has slope 0, what will be true about the y-coordinates of any two points on that line?
- If a line has undefined slope, what will be true about the x-coordinates of any two points on that line?

Power Presentations with PowerPoint®

Additional Examples

Example 4

Tell whether the slope of each line is positive, negative, zero, or undefined.

A.

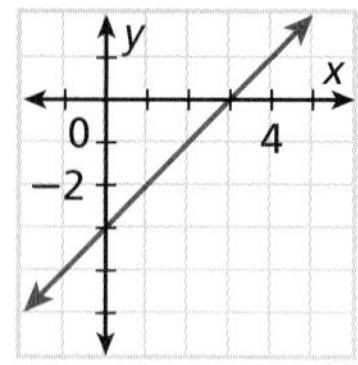

pos.

B.

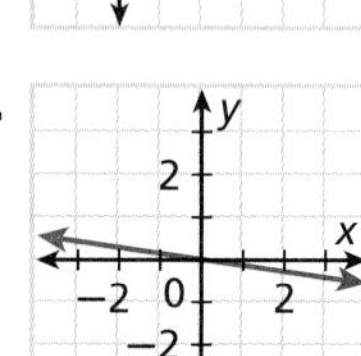

neg.

Also available on transparency

INTERVENTION

Questioning Strategies

EXAMPLE 4

- Why don't you need points to determine whether the slope is positive, negative, zero, or undefined?

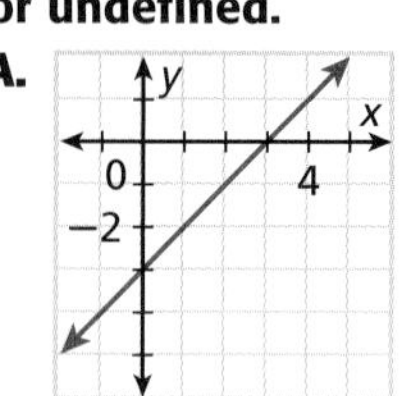

EXAMPLE 4 Describing Slope

Tell whether the slope of each line is positive, negative, zero, or undefined.

A

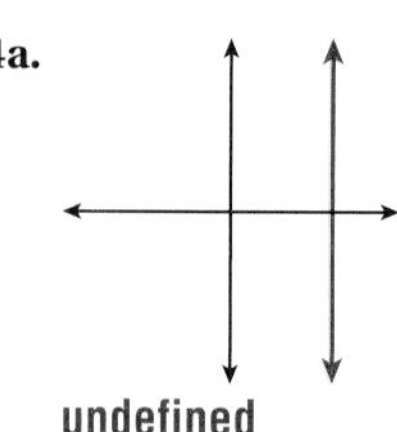

The line falls from left to right.

The slope is negative.

B

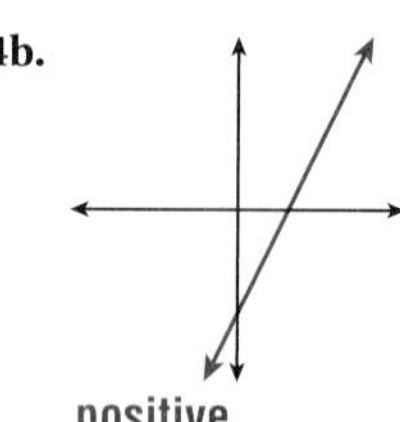

The line is horizontal.

The slope is 0.

CHECK IT OUT! Tell whether the slope of each line is positive, negative, zero, or undefined.

4a. undefined

4b. positive

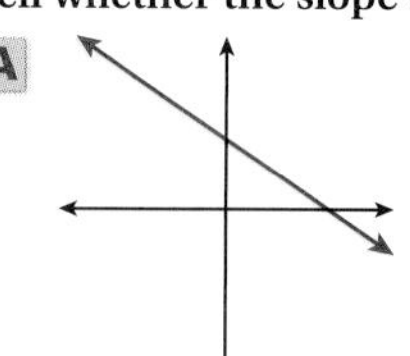

Remember that slope is a rate of change. In real-world problems, finding the slope can give you information about how a quantity is changing.

EXAMPLE 5 *Application*

Water is being released from a reservoir. The graph shows how much water is in the reservoir at different times. Find the slope of the line. Then tell what the slope represents.

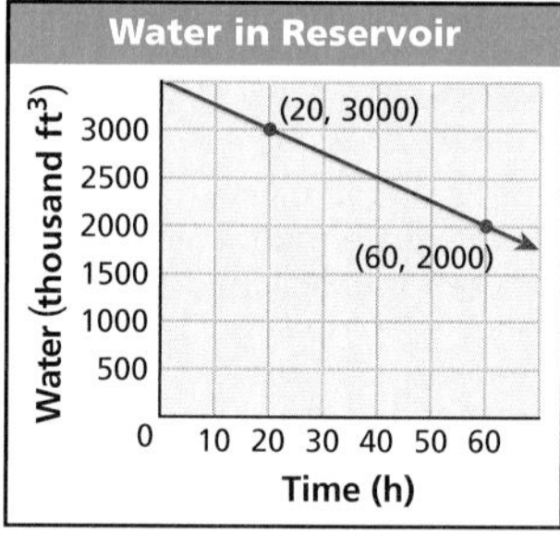

Step 1 Use the slope formula.

$$m = \frac{y_2 - y_1}{x_2 - x_1}$$

$$= \frac{2000 - 3000}{60 - 20}$$

$$= \frac{-1000}{40}$$

$$= -25$$

Step 2 Tell what the slope represents.

In this situation, y represents volume of water and x represents time.

So slope represents $\frac{\text{change in volume}}{\text{change in time}}$ in units of $\frac{\text{thousands of cubic feet}}{\text{hours}}$.

A slope of −25 means the amount of water in the reservoir is decreasing (negative change) at a rate of 25 thousand cubic feet each hour.

Caution!

Pay attention to the scales on the axes. One square on the grid may not represent 1 unit, as in Example 5. Also, one square on the x-axis may not represent the same quantity as one square on the y-axis.

Universal Access

Through Multiple Representations

Show students how to use a "T-Chart" to find the slope.

	x	y	
+1	1	1	+3
+1	2	4	+3
	3	7	

$$\text{Slope} = \frac{\text{change in } y}{\text{change in } x} = \frac{+3}{+1} = 3$$

This method works whether the ordered pairs are given in a table or a list, or selected from a graph.

Through Auditory Cues

To help students interpret the meanings of different slopes, emphasize reading the graph *from left to right.*

Positive slope → y-values increase ***from left to right***

Negative slope → y-values decrease ***from left to right***

Zero slope → y-values have zero change ***from left to right***

Undefined slope → There is ***NO left to right;*** the line is vertical.

Through Cooperative Learning

Divide the class into groups of 3–5 students. Give each group four number cubes. One member of each group rolls the number cubes. All group members then use the rolled numbers to create two ordered pairs and calculate the slope of the line between these two points. The student who finds the steepest slope wins the round and receives 1 point. (Note that a negative slope may be steeper than a positive one.) Play continues until one student reaches 5 points.

5. The graph shows the height of a plant over a period of days. Find the slope of the line. Then tell what the slope represents.

$m = \frac{1}{2}$; the height of the plant is increasing at a rate of 1 cm every 2 days.

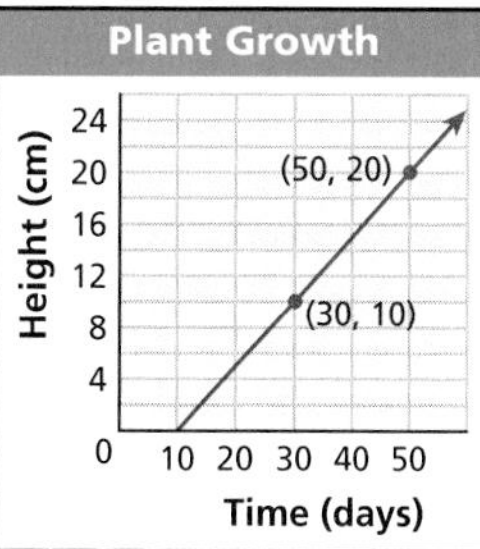

If you know the equation of a line, you can find its slope by using any two ordered-pair solutions. It is often easiest to use the ordered pairs that contain the intercepts.

EXAMPLE 6 Finding Slope from an Equation

Find the slope of the line given by $6x - 5y = 30$.

Step 1 Find the x-intercept.

$$6x - 5y = 30$$
$$6x - 5(0) = 30 \quad \text{Let } y = 0.$$
$$6x = 30$$
$$\frac{6x}{6} = \frac{30}{6}$$
$$x = 5$$

Step 2 Find the y-intercept.

$$6x - 5y = 30$$
$$6(0) - 5y = 30 \quad \text{Let } x = 0.$$
$$-5y = 30$$
$$\frac{-5y}{-5} = \frac{30}{-5}$$
$$y = -6$$

Step 3 The line contains $(5, 0)$ and $(0, -6)$ Use the slope formula.

$$m = \frac{y_2 - y_1}{x_2 - x_1} = \frac{-6 - 0}{0 - 5} = \frac{-6}{-5} = \frac{6}{5}$$

6. Find the slope of the line given by $2x + 3y = 12$. $-\frac{2}{3}$

A line's slope is a measure of its steepness. Some lines are steeper than others. As the absolute value of the slope increases, the line becomes steeper.

Comparing Slopes

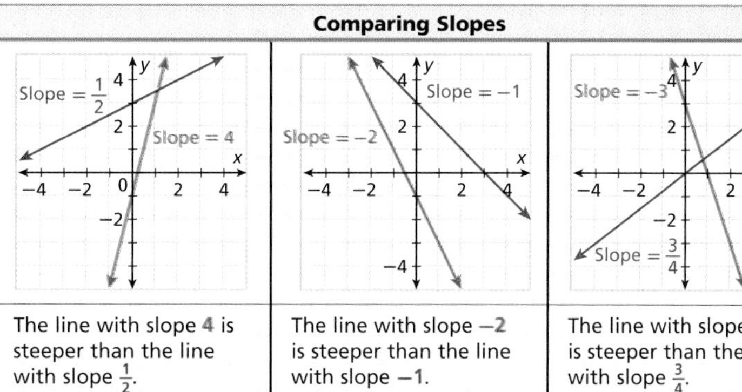

The line with slope 4 is steeper than the line with slope $\frac{1}{2}$.	The line with slope −2 is steeper than the line with slope −1.	The line with slope −3 is steeper than the line with slope $\frac{3}{4}$.
$\lvert 4 \rvert > \left\lvert \frac{1}{2} \right\rvert$	$\lvert -2 \rvert > \lvert -1 \rvert$	$\lvert -3 \rvert > \left\lvert \frac{3}{4} \right\rvert$

Power Presentations with PowerPoint®

Additional Examples

Example 5

The graph shows the average electricity costs in dollars for operating a refrigerator for several months. Find the slope of the line. Then tell what the slope represents.

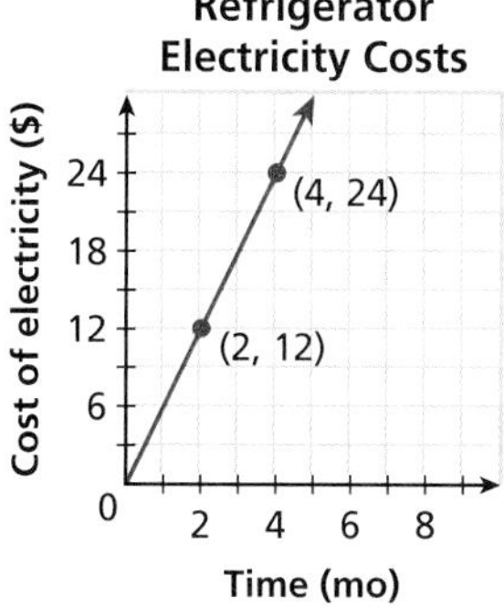

slope = 6; cost to run refrigerator is $6/mo

Example 6

Find the slope of the line given by $4x - 2y = 16$. 2

Also available on transparency

INTERVENTION

Questioning Strategies

EXAMPLE 5

- What kind of slope represents a negative rate of change? a positive rate of change?

EXAMPLE 6

- Do you have to find the x- and y-intercepts to find the slope? Explain why or why not.
- How could you solve this problem by graphing?

3 Close

Summarize

Ask students to give descriptions of lines with the following slopes:

1. $m = 0$ horizontal line
2. $m = \frac{1}{50}$
   line rising from left to right, not steep
3. $m = -10$
   line falling from left to right, steep
4. $m = \frac{2}{0}$ vertical line

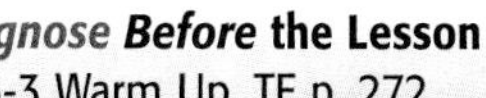

and INTERVENTION

Diagnose ***Before*** **the Lesson**
5-3 Warm Up, TE p. 272

Monitor ***During*** **the Lesson**
Check It Out! Exercises, SE pp. 272–275
Questioning Strategies, TE pp. 273–275

Assess ***After*** **the Lesson**
5-3 Lesson Quiz, TE p. 279
Alternative Assessment, TE p. 279

Answers to *Think and Discuss*

1. 6 units; 5 units; $\frac{6}{5}$
2. vertical line
3. Possible answer: 2.5, because it is less steep.
4. See p. A4.

THINK AND DISCUSS

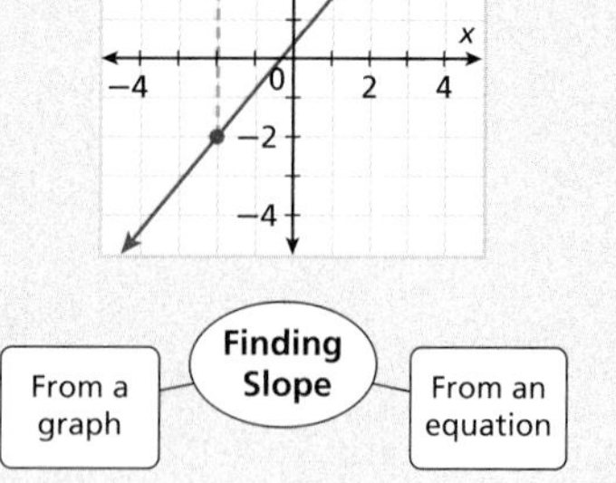

1. What is the rise shown in the graph? What is the run? What is the slope?
2. Two points lie on a line. When you substitute their coordinates into the slope formula, you get 0 in the denominator. Describe the graph of this line.
3. Would you rather climb a hill with a slope of 4 or a hill with a slope of 2.5? Explain your answer.

4. **GET ORGANIZED** Copy and complete the graphic organizer. In each box, show how to find slope using the given method.

From a graph — Finding Slope — From an equation

5-3 Exercises

5-3 Exercises

Preparation for **8.0**; 6.0, 24.1

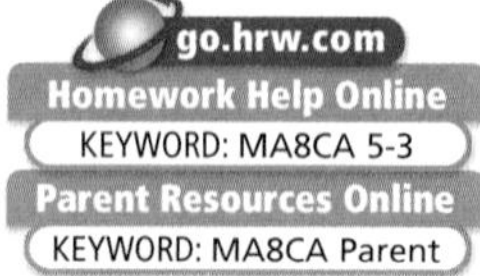

Assignment Guide

Assign *Guided Practice* exercises as necessary.

If you finished Examples **1–3**
Proficient 20–24, 33, 34, 38, 39
Advanced 20–24, 38, 39, 45–50

If you finished Examples **1–6**
Proficient 20–42, 50–58
Advanced 20–32, 35–58

Homework Quick Check
Quickly check key concepts.
Exercises: 20, 21, 24, 26, 28, 32

GUIDED PRACTICE

Vocabulary Apply the vocabulary from this lesson to answer each question.

1. Rise ? is the difference in the *y*-values of two points on a line. (*Rise* or *Run*)
2. The *slope* of any nonvertical line is ___?___. (*positive* or *constant*) **constant**

SEE EXAMPLE 1 p. 272

Find the slope of each line.

3. 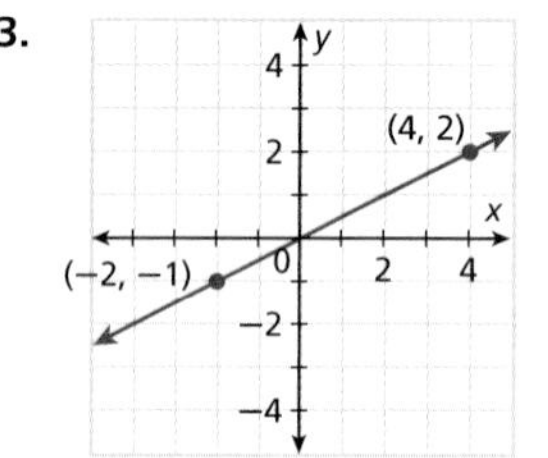

$\frac{1}{2}$

4. 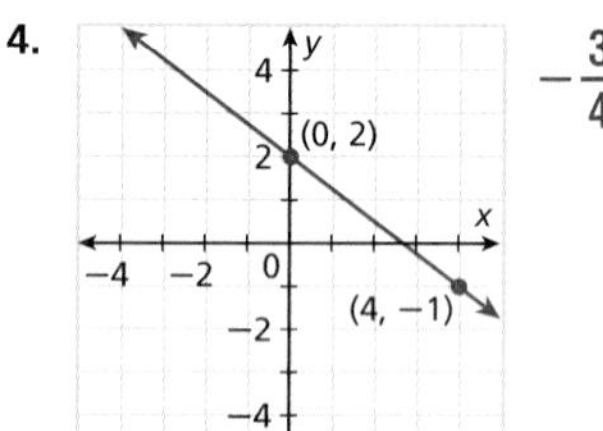

$-\frac{3}{4}$

SEE EXAMPLE 2 p. 273

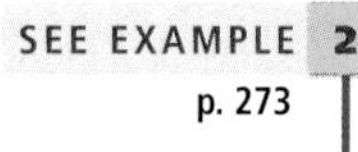

5. 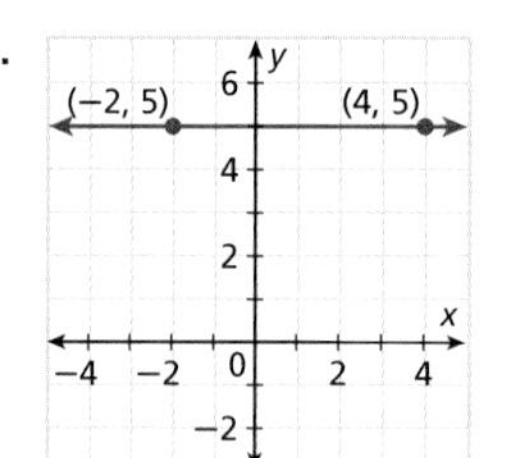

0

6. 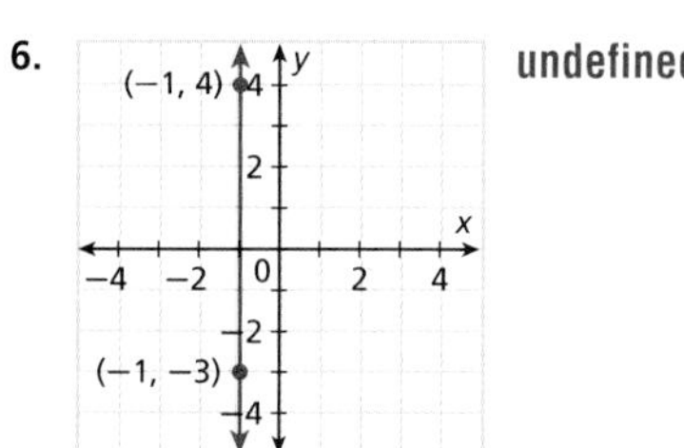

undefined

Teacher to Teacher

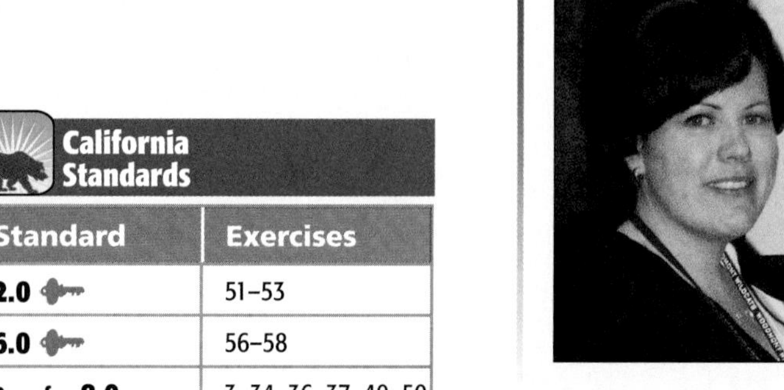

When I introduce slope, I use a motion detector to motivate the lesson. I have a student walk at a normal pace toward the detector while the class watches the graph appear on the overhead panel. We discuss how the axes are labeled (distance-time). Students make and test conjectures about how to make the line more or less steep (walk faster or slower) and about how to change the direction of the graph (walk toward or away from the detector).

We discuss the units of the slope (m/s) and determine that this is speed, a rate of change. This also helps students remember that the slope of a horizontal line is zero (standing still, having zero speed), and that a vertical line has undefined slope, since it cannot be created by the detector. By starting in this fashion, I can always refer back to the motion detector activity as students continue to learn about slope.

Jennifer J. Southers
Piedmont, SC

California Standards

Standard	Exercises
2.0	51–53
6.0	56–58
Prep for **8.0**	3–34, 36, 37, 40–50
24.1	38

SEE EXAMPLE 3
p. 273

Find the slope of the line that contains each pair of points.

7. $(3, 6)$ and $(6, 9)$ **1** **8.** $(2, 7)$ and $(4, 4)$ $-\frac{3}{2}$ **9.** $(-1, -5)$ and $(-9, -1)$ $-\frac{1}{2}$

10. $(5, 3)$ and $(-2, 0.5)$ $\frac{2.5}{7}$ **11.** $\left(\frac{3}{4}, \frac{7}{5}\right)$ and $\left(\frac{1}{4}, \frac{2}{5}\right)$ **2** **12.** $(-2, 3)$ and $(2, -3)$ $-\frac{3}{2}$

SEE EXAMPLE 4
p. 274

Tell whether the slope of each line is positive, negative, zero, or undefined.

13. 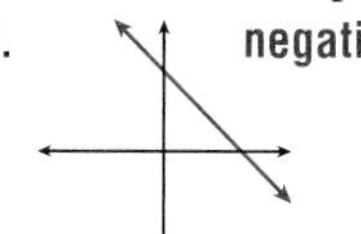 **negative**

14. 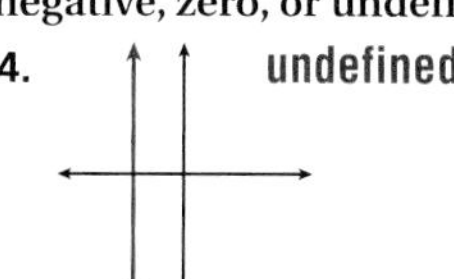 **undefined**

SEE EXAMPLE 5
p. 274

Find the slope of each line. Then tell what the slope represents.

15. 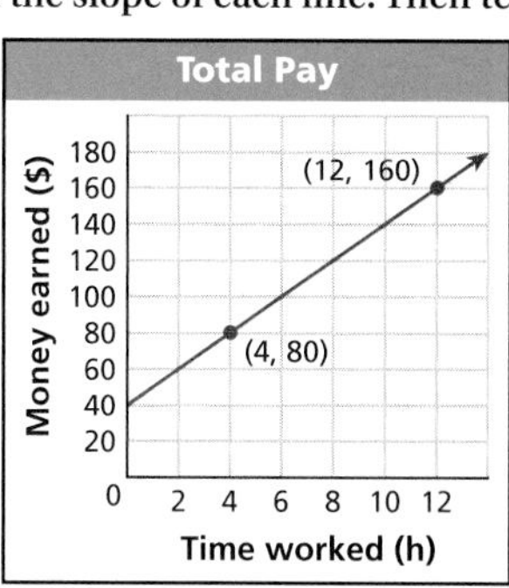

10; the money earned is increasing at a rate of $10/h.

16. 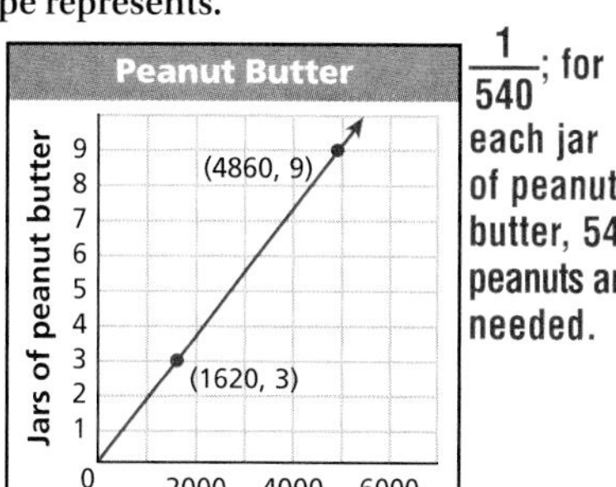

$\frac{1}{540}$**; for each jar of peanut butter, 540 peanuts are needed.**

SEE EXAMPLE 6
p. 275

Find the slope of the line given by each equation.

17. $8x + 2y = 96$ **−4** **18.** $5x = 90 - 9y$ $-\frac{5}{9}$ **19.** $5y = 160 + 9x$ $\frac{9}{5}$

PRACTICE AND PROBLEM SOLVING

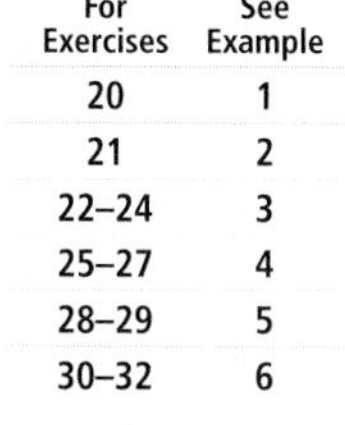

Independent Practice

For Exercises	See Example
20	1
21	2
22–24	3
25–27	4
28–29	5
30–32	6

Extra Practice

Skills Practice p. EP10
Application Practice p. EP28

Find the slope of each line.

20. 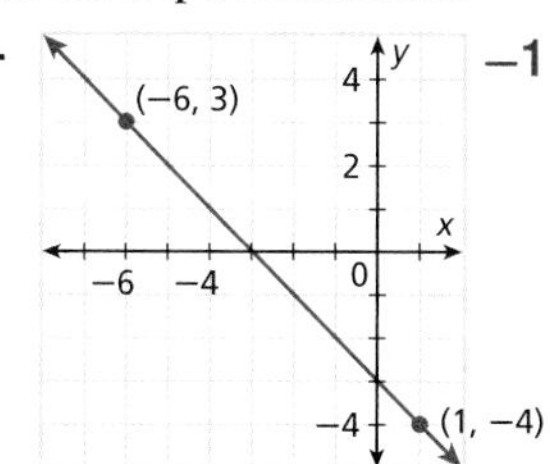

−1

21. 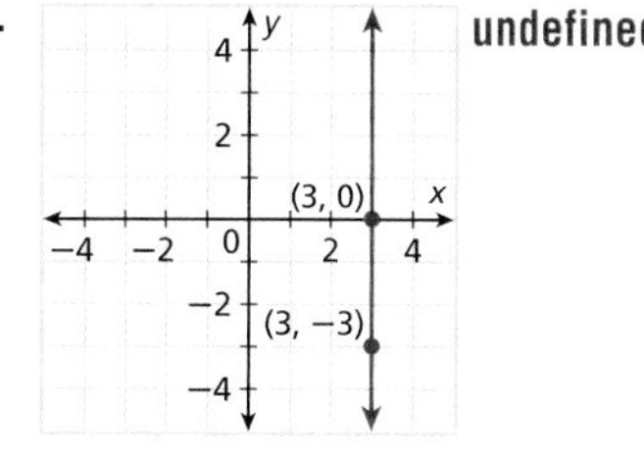

undefined

Find the slope of the line that contains each pair of points.

22. $(2, 5)$ and $(3, 1)$ **−4** **23.** $(-9, -5)$ and $(6, -5)$ **0** **24.** $(3, 4)$ and $(3, -1)$ **undefined**

Tell whether the slope of each line is positive, negative, zero, or undefined.

25. 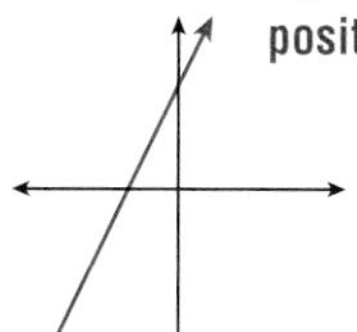 **positive**

26. 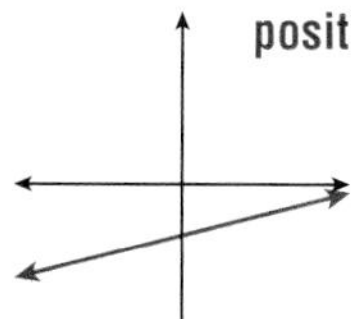 **positive**

27. 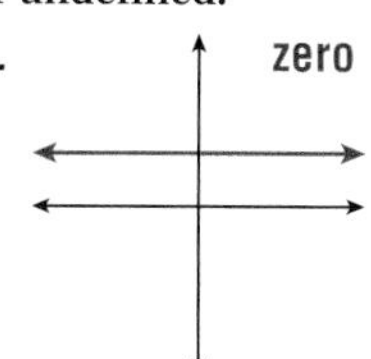 **zero**

COMMON ERROR /// ALERT \\\

In **Exercise 6,** students may write 0 for the slope of a vertical line, thinking that "0" and "undefined" are the same. Remind students that 0 is a real number; it is not undefined.

5-3 PRACTICE A

LESSON 5-3 **Practice A**
Slope

Find the rise and run between each set of points. Then, write the slope of the line.

1. slope = $\frac{1}{3}$ 2. slope = 2 3. slope = $-\frac{3}{2}$

Find the slope of the line that contains each pair of points.

4. $(3, 1)$ and $(9, 2)$
$m = \frac{y_2 - y_1}{x_2 - x_1} = \frac{2 - 1}{9 - 3} = \frac{1}{6}$

5. $(-2, 3)$ and $(2, -1)$
$m = \frac{y_2 - y_1}{x_2 - x_1} = \frac{-1 - 3}{2 - (-2)} = \frac{-4}{4} = -1$

6. $(4, 6)$ and $(0, -2)$
$m = \frac{y_2 - y_1}{x_2 - x_1} = \frac{-2 - 6}{0 - 4} = \frac{-8}{-4} = 2$

Tell whether the slope of each line is positive, negative, zero, or undefined.

7. zero 8. negative 9. undefined

Complete the steps to find the slope of the line described by $2x + 5y = 10$.

9. a. Find the x-intercept.
Let $y = 0$
$2x + 5(0) = -10$
$2x = -10$
$\div 2 \quad \div 2$
$x = -5$

b. Find the y-intercept.
Let $x = 0$
$2(0) + 5y = -10$
$5y = -10$
$\div 5 \quad \div 5$
$y = -2$

c. The line contains $(-5, 0)$ and $(0, -2)$. Use the slope formula.
$m = \frac{y_2 - y_1}{x_2 - x_1} = \frac{-2 - 0}{0 - (-5)} = \frac{-2}{5}$

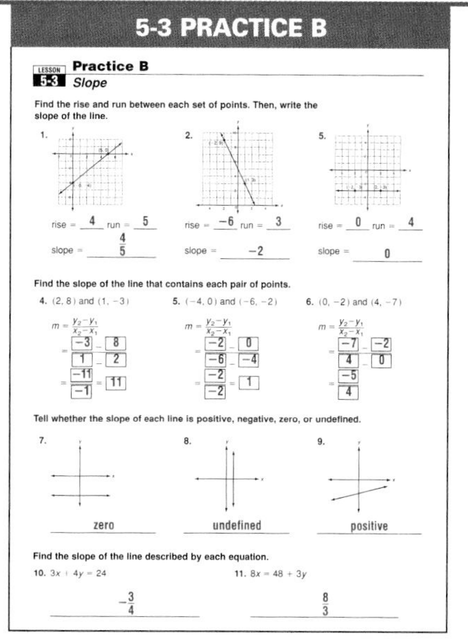

5-3 PRACTICE B

LESSON 5-3 **Practice B**
Slope

Find the rise and run between each set of points. Then, write the slope of the line.

1. rise = 4 run = 5, slope = $\frac{4}{5}$ 2. rise = −6 run = 3, slope = −2 5. rise = 0 run = 4, slope = 0

Find the slope of the line that contains each pair of points.

4. $(2, 8)$ and $(1, -3)$
$m = \frac{y_2 - y_1}{x_2 - x_1} = \frac{-3 - 8}{1 - 2} = \frac{-11}{-1} = 11$

5. $(-4, 0)$ and $(-6, -2)$
$m = \frac{y_2 - y_1}{x_2 - x_1} = \frac{-2 - 0}{-6 - (-4)} = \frac{-2}{-2} = 1$

6. $(0, -2)$ and $(4, -7)$
$m = \frac{y_2 - y_1}{x_2 - x_1} = \frac{-7 - (-2)}{4 - 0} = \frac{-5}{4}$

Tell whether the slope of each line is positive, negative, zero, or undefined.

7. zero 8. undefined 9. positive

Find the slope of the line described by each equation.

10. $3x + 4y = 24$ $-\frac{3}{4}$ 11. $8x = 48 + 3y$ $\frac{8}{3}$

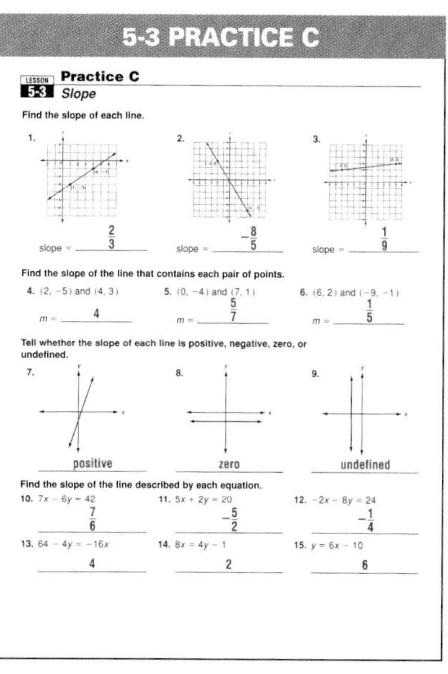

5-3 PRACTICE C

LESSON 5-3 **Practice C**
Slope

Find the slope of each line.

1. slope = $\frac{2}{3}$ 2. slope = $-\frac{8}{5}$ 3. slope = $\frac{1}{9}$

Find the slope of the line that contains each pair of points.

4. $(2, -5)$ and $(4, 3)$ $m = 4$ 5. $(0, -4)$ and $(7, 1)$ $m = \frac{5}{7}$ 6. $(6, 2)$ and $(-9, -1)$ $m = \frac{1}{5}$

Tell whether the slope of each line is positive, negative, zero, or undefined.

7. positive 8. zero 9. undefined

Find the slope of the line described by each equation.

10. $7x - 6y = 42$ $\frac{7}{6}$ 11. $5x + 2y = 20$ $-\frac{5}{2}$ 12. $-2x - 8y = 24$ $-\frac{1}{4}$

13. $64 - 4y = -16x$ 4 14. $8x = 4y - 1$ 2 15. $y = 6x - 10$ 6

Answers

38b. The slope of a vertical line will always be undefined because the x-coordinate of any 2 points will be the same. Therefore, the denominator in the slope formula will always be 0. Because a number can't be divided by 0, the slope will always be undefined.

39. Possible answer: Given the 2 points (x_2, y_2) and (x_2, y_2), you could substitute into the slope formula or graph the 2 points, connect with a line, and count the rise and run.

28. $\frac{5}{9}$; temperature in Celsius is increasing at a rate of 5 degrees Celsius for each 9 degrees Fahrenheit.

29. $-\frac{9}{5{,}000}$; the boiling point is decreasing at a rate of 9°F for each 5000 ft above sea level.

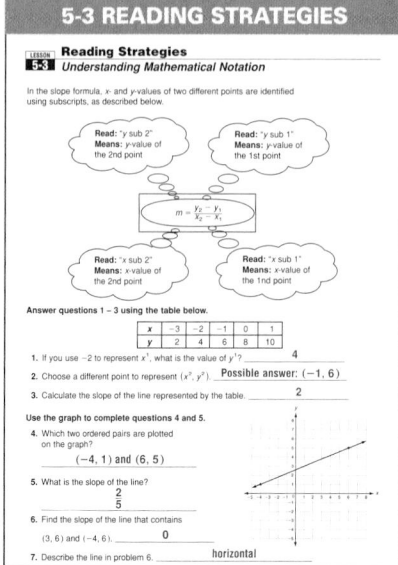

California LINK

Travel

Lombard Street in San Francisco has 8 sharp, hair-pin turns to help make navigating the steep street easier for pedestrians and drivers.

35a. In 16 s, about 420 files were scanned
b. Possible answer: (16, 420)
c. Possible answer: (26, 650)
d. Possible answer: 23

38a. The slope of a horizontal line will always be 0 because the y-coordinates of any 2 points will be the same. Therefore, the numerator in the slope formula will always be 0.

Find the slope of each line. Then tell what the slope represents.

28.

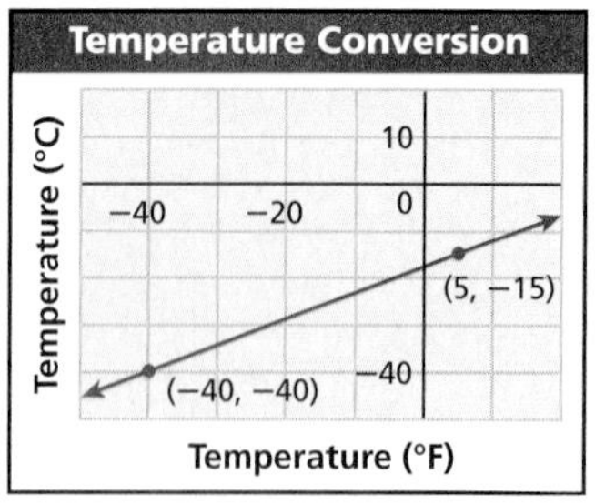

29.

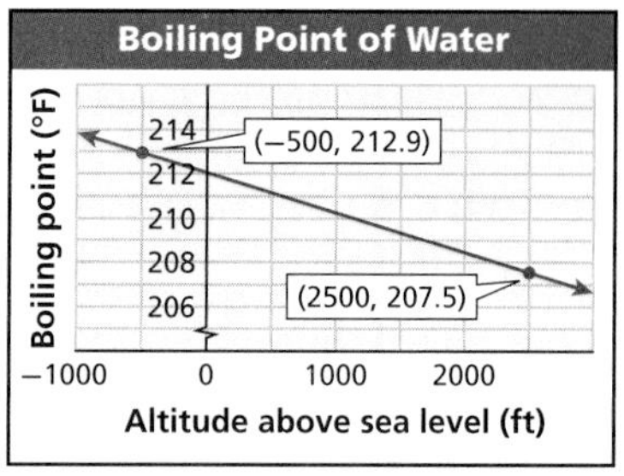

Find the slope of the line given by each equation.

30. $7x + 13y = 91$ $\frac{7}{13}$ 31. $5y = 130 - 13x$ $\frac{13}{5}$ 32. $7 - 3y = 9x$ -3

33. **Construction** Most staircases in use today have 9-inch treads and $8\frac{1}{2}$-inch risers. What is the slope of a staircase with these measurements? $\frac{17}{18}$

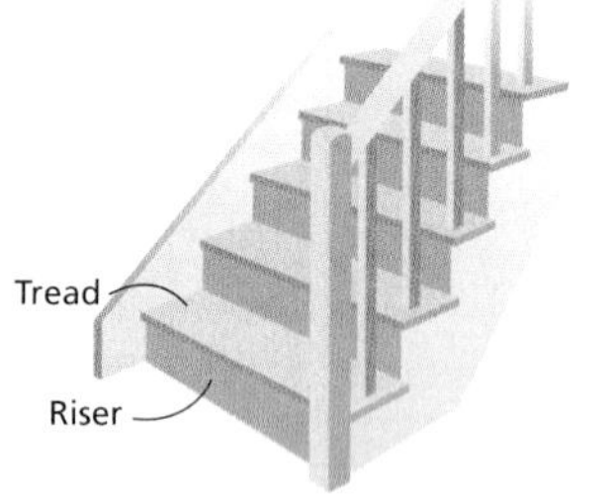

34. **Travel** Filbert Street is one of the steepest streets in San Francisco. Part of Filbert Street has a slope of 0.315. In this part, a vertical change of 1 unit corresponds to a horizontal change of about how many units? Round your answer to the nearest thousandth. **3.174**

35. **Estimation** The graph shows the number of files scanned by a computer virus detection program over time.
   a. What does point A represent?
   b. Estimate the coordinates of point A.
   c. Estimate the coordinates of point B.
   d. Use your answers from parts **b** and **c** to estimate the rate of change (in files per second) between points A and B.

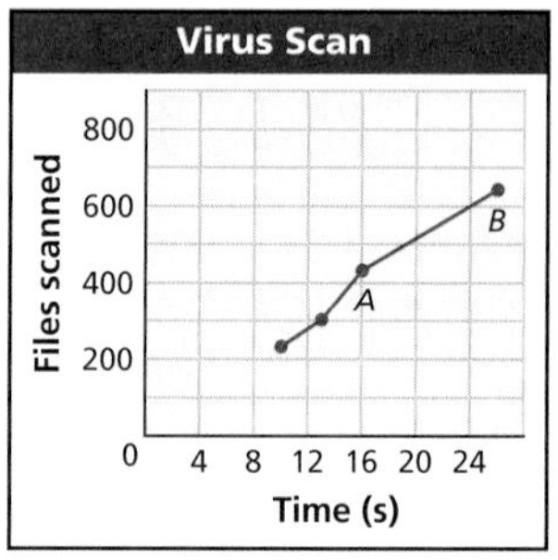

Each table shows a linear relationship. Find the slope.

36. $\frac{7}{2}$

x	y
1	18.5
2	22
3	25.5
4	29

37. **10**

x	y
0	25
2	45
4	65
6	85

38. **Reasoning** Use deductive reasoning and the slope formula to prove that
   a. the slope of any horizontal line is 0.
   b. the slope of any vertical line is undefined.

39. **Write About It** You are given the coordinates of two points on a line. Describe two different ways to find the slope of that line.

40. What is the slope of the line given by $4x = 0$? by $5y = 0$? **undefined; 0**

278 *Chapter 5 Linear Functions*

5-3 READING STRATEGIES

LESSON 5-3 **Reading Strategies**
Understanding Mathematical Notation

In the slope formula, x- and y-values of two different points are identified using subscripts, as described below.

Read: "y sub 2" **Means:** y-value of the 2nd point
Read: "y sub 1" **Means:** y-value of the 1st point

$$m = \frac{y_2 - y_1}{x_2 - x_1}$$

Read: "x sub 2" **Means:** x-value of the 2nd point
Read: "x sub 1" **Means:** x-value of the 1nd point

Answer questions 1 – 3 using the table below.

x	−3	−2	−1	0	1
y	2	4	6	8	10

1. If you use −2 to represent x^1, what is the value of y^1? 4
2. Choose a different point to represent (x^2, y^2). Possible answer: (−1, 6)
3. Calculate the slope of the line represented by the table. 2

Use the graph to complete questions 4 and 5.

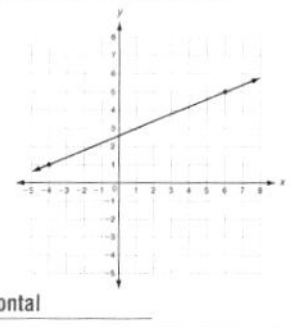

4. Which two ordered pairs are plotted on the graph? (−4, 1) and (6, 5)
5. What is the slope of the line? $\frac{2}{5}$
6. Find the slope of the line that contains (3, 6) and (−4, 6). 0
7. Describe the line in problem 6. horizontal

5-3 REVIEW FOR MASTERY

LESSON 5-3 **Review for Mastery**
Slope

You can find the slope of a line from any two ordered pairs. The ordered pairs can be given to you, or you might need to read them from a table or graph.

Find the slope of the line that contains (–1, 3) and (2, 0).

Step 1: Name the ordered pairs. (It does not matter which is first and which is second.)

first ordered pair (−1, 3) (2, 0) second ordered pair

Step 2: Label each number in the ordered pairs.

(−1, 3) (2, 0)
(x_1, y_1) (x_2, y_2)

Step 3: Substitute the ordered pairs into the slope formula.

$$m = \frac{y_2 - y_1}{x_2 - x_1} = \frac{0 - 3}{2 - (-1)} = \frac{-3}{3} = -1$$

The slope of the line that contains (−1, 3) and (2, 0) is −1.

Find the slope of each linear relationship.

1.

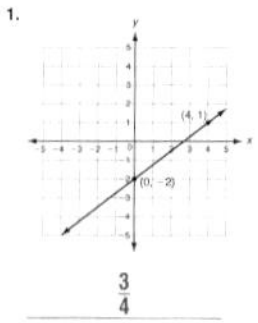

$\frac{3}{4}$

2.

x	y
4	−5
8	−3
12	−1
16	1

$\frac{1}{2}$

3. The line contains (5, −2) and (7, 6). 4

CONCEPT CONNECTION

41. This problem will prepare you for the Concept Connection on page 288.

a. The graph shows a relationship between a person's age and his or her maximum heart rate in beats per minute. Find the slope. Then tell what the slope represents. **−1**

b. Describe the rate of change in this situation. **For each yr that a person ages, the max. heart rate decreases by 1 beat/min.**

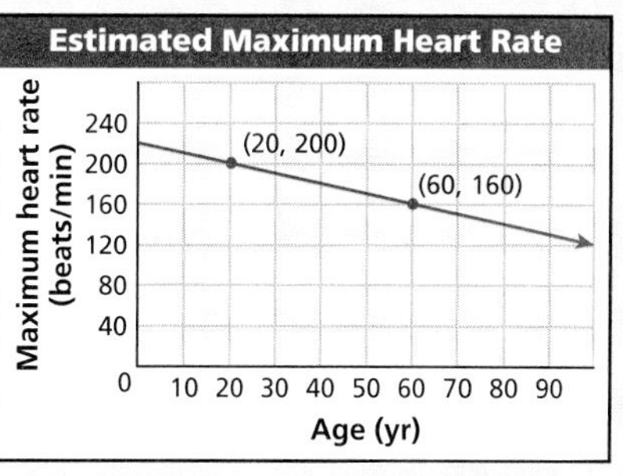

Multiple Choice For Exercises 42–44, choose the best answer.

42. A line with slope $-\frac{1}{3}$ could pass through which of the following pairs of points?

Ⓐ $\left(0, -\frac{1}{3}\right)$ and $(1, 1)$ Ⓒ $(0, 0)$ and $\left(-\frac{1}{3}, -\frac{1}{3}\right)$

Ⓑ $(-6, 5)$ and $(-3, 4)$ Ⓓ $(5, -6)$ and $(4, 3)$

43. The equation $2y + 3x = -6$ describes a line with what slope?

Ⓐ $\frac{3}{2}$ Ⓑ 0 Ⓒ $\frac{1}{2}$ **Ⓓ** $-\frac{3}{2}$

44. What is the slope of a line that passes through the points $(-1, 2)$ and $(1, -3)$?

Ⓐ $-\frac{5}{2}$ Ⓑ $-\frac{2}{5}$ Ⓒ $\frac{2}{5}$ Ⓓ $\frac{5}{2}$

CHALLENGE AND EXTEND

Find the slope of the line that contains each pair of points.

45. $(a, 0)$ and $(0, b)$ $-\frac{b}{a}$ **46.** $(2x, y)$ and $(x, 3y)$ $-\frac{2y}{x}$ **47.** (x, y) and $(x + 2, 3 - y)$ $\frac{3-2y}{2}$

48. Recreation Tara and Jade are hiking together up a hill with a constant slope. Each has a different stride. For Tara's stride, the run is 32 inches and the rise is 8 inches. The run for Jade's stride is 36 inches. What is the rise for Jade's stride? **9 in.**

Find the value of x so that the line that contains each pair of points has the given slope.

49. $(4, x)$ and $(6, 3x)$, $m = \frac{1}{2}$ $\frac{1}{2}$ **50.** $(x, 2)$ and $(-5, 8)$, $m = -1$ **1**

SPIRAL STANDARDS REVIEW

Solve each equation. Check your answer. *(Lesson 2-1)*

51. $k - 3.14 = 1.71$ **4.85** **52.** $-7 = p - 12$ **5** **53.** $25 = f - 16$ **41**

Tell whether the given ordered pairs all lie on the same line. *(Lesson 5-1)*

54. $\{(1, 1), (2, 4), (3, 9), (4, 16)\}$ **no** **55.** $\{(9, 0), (8, -5), (5, -20), (3, -30)\}$ **yes**

Find the x- and y-intercepts. *(Lesson 5-2)*

56. $2x + y = 6$ **x-int.: 3; y-int.: 6** **57.** $y = -3x - 9$ **x-int.: −3; y-int.: −9** **58.** $2y = -4x + 1$ **x-int.:** $\frac{1}{4}$**; y-int.:** $\frac{1}{2}$

CONCEPT CONNECTION **Exercise 41** involves finding the slope from a graph and describing the rate of change. This exercise prepares students for the Concept Connection on page 288.

Teaching Tip **Multiple Choice** In **Exercise 42,** student who chose **A** may have subtracted the coordinates in different orders.

Journal

Have students compare both methods of finding slope—counting the rise and run and using the formula.

ALTERNATIVE ASSESSMENT

Have students graph four lines with different slopes—one positive, one negative, one zero, and one undefined. Students should then label two points on each line and find each slope.

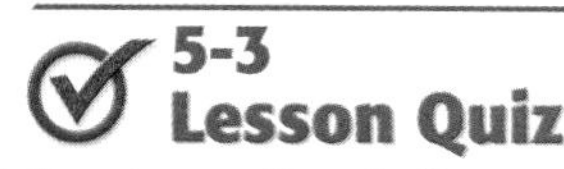

5-3 Lesson Quiz

Find the slope of each line.

1. 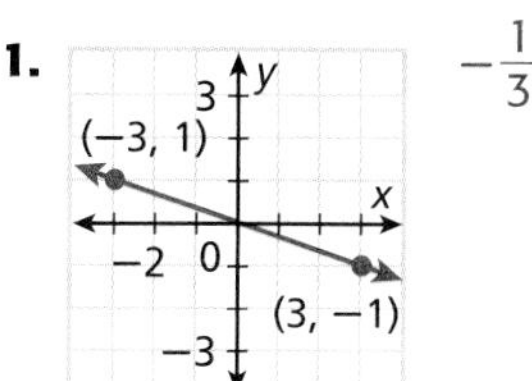

$-\frac{1}{3}$

2. 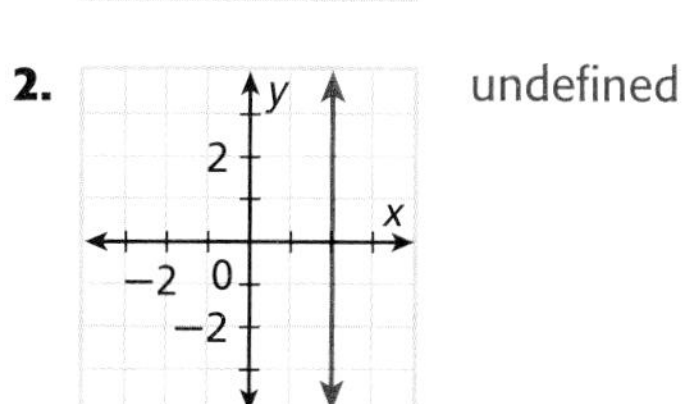

undefined

3. Find the slope of the line that contains $(5, 3)$ and $(-1, 4)$. $-\frac{1}{6}$

4. Find the slope. Then tell what the slope represents.

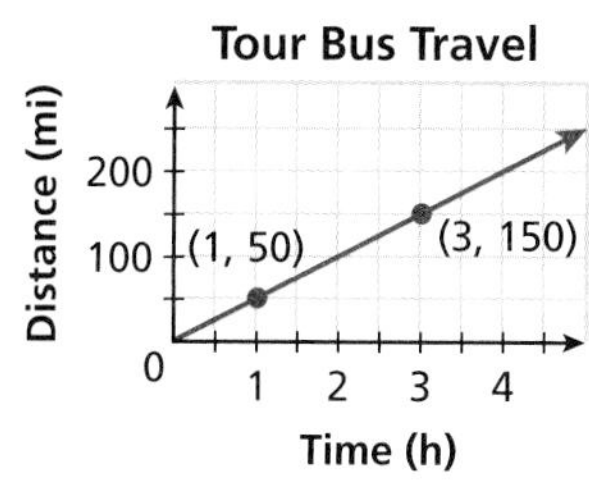

50; speed of bus is 50 mi/h

5. Find the slope of the line given by $x - 2y = 8$. $\frac{1}{2}$

Also available on transparency

5-3 PROBLEM SOLVING

LESSON 5-3 Problem Solving
Slope

Write the correct answer.

1. The graph shows the number of emergency kits assembled by volunteers over a period of days. Find the slope of the line. Then tell what the slope represents. 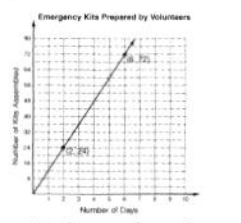
   12; the number of kits assembled per day.

2. The graph shows how much flour is in a bag at different times. Find the slope of the line. Then tell what the slope represents. 
   −0.2; the number of pounds of flour used per day.

3. The function $20x - y = 250$ describes the profit y Bridget can make from selling x pairs of earrings. The graph of this function is a line. Find its slope. **20**

The graph below shows the cost of membership at Fabulously Fit. Use the graph to answer questions 4–7. Select the best answer.

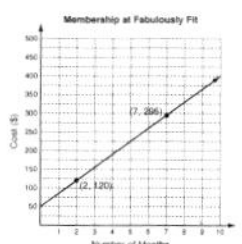

4. What is the slope of the line?
   A 24 C 50
   Ⓑ 35 D 70

5. What does the slope represent?
   F the enrollment fee
   G the late payment fee
   H the total cost of membership
   Ⓙ the monthly membership fee

6. A second line is graphed that shows the cost of membership at The Fitness Studio. The line contains (0, 35) and (5, 85). What is the slope of this line?
   Ⓐ 10 C 45
   B 20 D 50

7. How much greater is the monthly fee at Fabulously Fit than The Fitness Studio?
   F \$15 H \$35
   Ⓖ \$25 J \$40

5-3 CHALLENGE

LESSON 5-3 Challenge
Exploring the Meaning of a Difference Quotient

When two variables x and y are related and (x_1, y_1) and (x_2, y_2) satisfy the relationship, you can write the quotient as shown at right. The quotient is called a *difference quotient*. $\frac{y_2 - y_1}{x_2 - x_1}$

The difference quotient can have different meanings in different situations.

In Exercises 1–5, use the grid at the right.

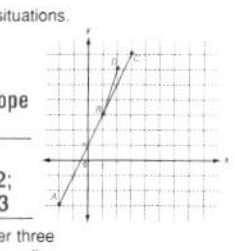

1. Graph and connect $A(-2, -3)$, $B(1, 3)$, and $C(3, 7)$.
2. Calculate the slope of $\overline{AB}$ and of $\overline{BC}$. **Slope of $\overline{AB}$ = Slope of $\overline{BC}$ = 2**
3. On the same grid, graph $D(2, 6)$. Connect A, B and D.
4. Calculate the slope of $\overline{AB}$ and of $\overline{BD}$. **Slope of $\overline{AB}$ = 2; Slope of $\overline{BD}$ = 3**
5. Explain how to use a difference quotient to determine whether three points are collinear, that is, whether three points lie on the same line.
   Points A, B, and C lie on a line if the slopes of $\overline{AB}$, $\overline{BC}$ and $\overline{AC}$ are equal.

Another application of the difference quotient is the measurement of the *grade*, or steepness, of a road. A grade of 3% means that the road surface rises 3 feet for every horizontal run of 100 feet. A roadway that slopes down has a negative grade.

6. If the vertical rise of a highway is 150 feet when the horizontal run is 5000 feet, what is the grade of the road? **3%**
7. If the grade of a road is 5%, what is the vertical rise of the road when the horizontal run is 6000 feet? **300 feet**
8. On a certain stretch of road, the point 420 feet east of point A is 24 feet lower than point A. Point B, 600 feet east of A, is 36 feet lower than point A.
   a. Find the grade of the road surface between points A and B. **6%**
   b. Would a motorist driving along a stretch of road from point B to point A report the same grade for the road as a motorist driving from A to B would report? Explain your response.
   No; the uphill grade is positive and the downhill grade is negative.

In economics, the additional cost to produce one more unit of an item is called the *marginal cost* of the item. Marginal cost is found by computing the difference quotient, or difference in $\frac{\text{manufacturing cost}}{\text{difference in units made}}$.

9. The cost that a manufacturer pays for producing 5 pairs of shoes is \$113. The cost for 12 pairs of shoes is \$127. Use a difference quotient to find the marginal cost, or manufacturing cost, per pair of shoes. **\$2**

Organizer

Objectives: Understand and be able to explain the difference between inductive and deductive reasoning.
Provide examples of inductive and deductive reasoning.

Online Edition
Student Edtion

Countdown to Mastery Week 10

Teach

Discuss

Before discussing Adele's situation, review inductive reasoning with students. (See p. 233.)

Have students explain why Adele has not proven her conjecture. Even though inductive reasoning cannot be used to prove conjectures, it still has an important place in mathematics. By examining several examples, mathematicians look for information with which they can use deductive reasoning to prove or disprove a conjecture.

Students will use deductive reasoning to prove a conjecture later in this chapter. (See p. 311)

California Standards

Algebra 1 24.1

Comparing Deductive and Inductive Reasoning

Use with Lesson 5-3

California Standards

24.1 Students explain the difference between inductive and deductive reasoning and identify and provide examples of each.

Example

While doing her algebra homework, Adele came to the following problem:

Find the slope of the line that contains (2, 3) and (6, 9).

Adele wrote:

Let $(x_1, y_1) = (2, 3)$ and $(x_2, y_2) = (6, 9)$.

$$\frac{y_2 - y_1}{x_2 - x_1} = \frac{9-3}{6-2} = \frac{6}{4} = \frac{3}{2}$$

The slope is $\frac{3}{2}$.

But Adele was not sure of her answer. She had missed class, and she wondered if it was important which point was (x_1, y_1) and which point was (x_2, y_2). She thought, "Maybe the answer is different if I switch the points." She decided to check.

Let $(x_1, y_1) = (6, 9)$ and $(x_2, y_2) = (2, 3)$.

$$\frac{y_2 - y_1}{x_2 - x_1} = \frac{3-9}{2-6} = \frac{-6}{-4} = \frac{3}{2}$$

The slope is $\frac{3}{2}$.

Adele repeated the same process for the next three problems, and she found the same result. Then she said, "It doesn't matter which point is (x_1, y_1) and which point is (x_2, y_2). The slope is the same."

To make her conjecture, Adele used inductive reasoning. Remember that when you use inductive reasoning, you first note a pattern in specific cases and then make a conjecture about every case. Adele noticed something about several specific lines and made a conjecture about every line.

Conjectures based on inductive reasoning may or may not be true. In other words, you cannot use inductive reasoning to prove a statement.

In contrast, a statement reached through deductive reasoning is true. Once you have proven a statement through deductive reasoning, you can apply that statement to specific cases.

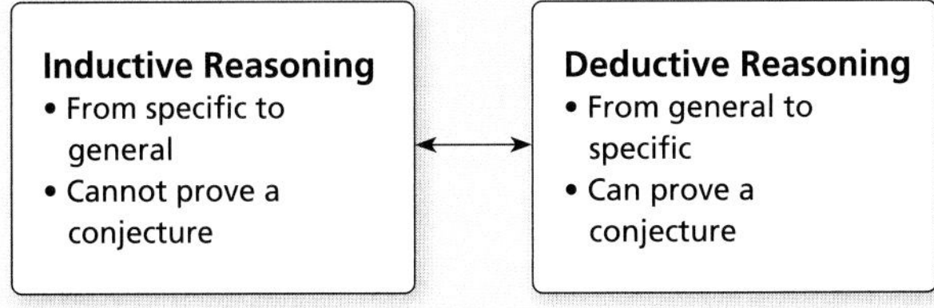

Inductive Reasoning
• From specific to general
• Cannot prove a conjecture
Deductive Reasoning
• From general to specific
• Can prove a conjecture

Try This

For each situation, tell whether the conclusion was reached through inductive or deductive reasoning.

1. It has been raining for three days. Andrew predicts that it will rain again tomorrow. **inductive**
2. All Internal Revenue Service (IRS) workers are federal employees. John is an IRS worker. Carla concludes that John is a federal employee. **deductive**
3. Jennifer is going to the beach this weekend. Her mother says, "I know you will come home with a sunburn because you always get a sunburn when you go to the beach." **inductive**
4. Marc examined the sequence below.

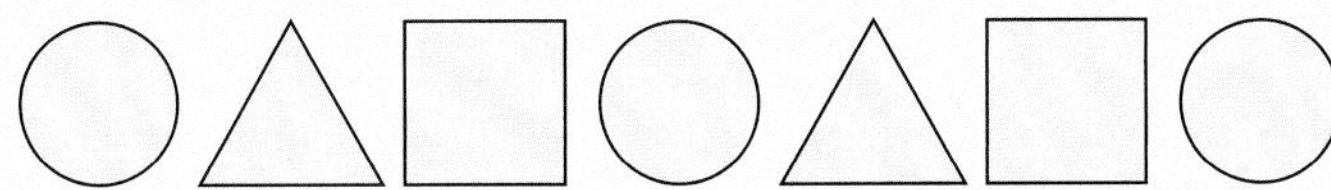

Then he said, "The next shape will be a triangle." **inductive**

5. All numbers that end in 0 are divisible by 10. Therefore, 1,225,610 is divisible by 10. **deductive**
6. All numbers that end in 0 are divisible by 10, and all numbers that are divisible by 10 are also divisible by 5. Therefore 1,225,610 is divisible by 5. **deductive**
7. Morgan noticed that $3 + 5 = 8$, $7 + 15 = 22$, and $25 + 5 = 30$. He concludes that the sum of two odd numbers is always even. **inductive**
8. Rachel looked at the scatter plot and concluded that a student who received a 75 on the math test probably received an 85 on the science test. **inductive**

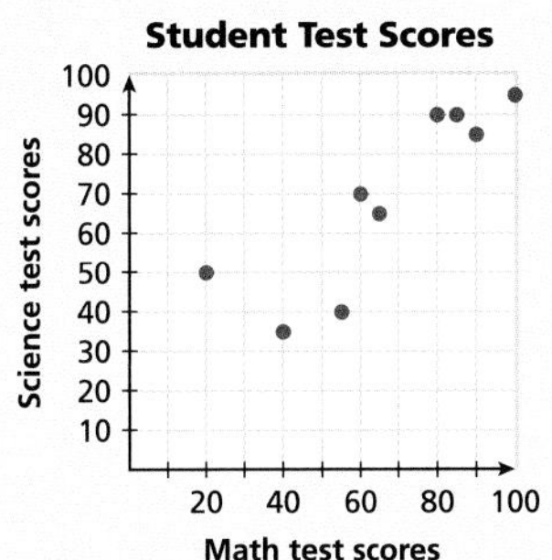

9. Create your own situations that illustrate inductive and deductive reasoning. Describe at least one situation for each type of reasoning. **Check students' work.**
10. In your own words, describe the difference between inductive and deductive reasoning. **Check students' work.**

COMMON ERROR ALERT

Trying to "prove by example" is one of the most common mistakes students make when beginning to write proofs. Emphasize often that giving an example, or 2 examples, or 500 examples only provides evidence for a conjecture. It cannot prove a conjecture true.

Geometry In **Example 2,** students may think the converse of statement 3 is false by reasoning that the shape could be a square. Remind them that a square is also considered a rectangle.

Close

Key Concept

When you examine several specific cases and draw a conclusion about something general, you are using inductive reasoning. When you prove a general case, you are using deductive reasoning.

Assess

Have students make a poster for classroom display that compares inductive and deductive reasoning. The poster should include at least one example of each type of reasoning.

Extend

Present the following equations and conjecture:

$12 \div 4 = 3$ $14 \div 7 = 2$

$20 \div 5 = 4$ $16 \div 2 = 8$

Conjecture: When dividing a number a by a number b, the answer will always be less than a.

Ask students whether they think the conjecture is reasonable based on the equations. Answers will vary. Then ask whether the conjecture is true and why. No; possible counterexample: if $b = 1$, then the answer will be equal to a.

Challenge students to come up with other examples in which several specific examples suggest a conjecture that is not true. Use this activity to reinforce that inductive reasoning cannot be used to prove a conjecture.

5-4 Organizer

Objective: Identify, write, and graph direct variation.

Online Edition
Tutorial Videos

Countdown to Mastery Week 10

Power Presentations with PowerPoint®

Warm Up

Solve for *y*.

1. $3 + y = 2x$ $y = 2x - 3$ **2.** $6x = 3y$ $y = 2x$

Write an equation that describes the relationship.

3.

x	1	2	3	4
y	3	6	9	12

$y = 3x$

Solve for *x*.

4. $\frac{3}{5} = \frac{x}{15}$ 9

5. $\frac{6}{2} = \frac{1.5}{x}$ 0.5

Also available on transparency

Math Humor

Parent: How is your math homework going?

Child: Well, *m* is negative, so at least I'm on the down slope!

California Standards

Algebra 1 6.0

5-4 Direct Variation

California Standards

6.0 Students graph a linear equation and compute the *x*- and *y*-intercepts (e.g., graph $2x + 6y = 4$). They are also able to sketch the region defined by linear inequalities (e.g., they sketch the region defined by $2x + 6y < 4$).

Vocabulary
direct variation
constant of variation

Who uses this?
Chefs can use direct variation to determine ingredients needed for a certain number of servings.

A recipe for paella calls for 1 cup of rice to make 5 servings. In other words, a chef needs 1 cup of rice for every 5 servings.

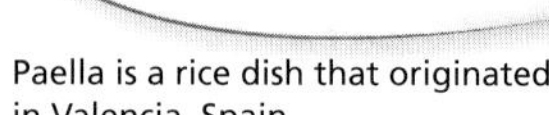
Paella is a rice dish that originated in Valencia, Spain.

Rice (c) x	1	2	3	4
Servings y	5	10	15	20

The equation $y = 5x$ describes this relationship. In this relationship, the number of servings *varies directly* with the number of cups of rice.

A **direct variation** is a special type of linear relationship that can be written in the form $y = kx$, where k is a nonzero constant called the **constant of variation**.

EXAMPLE 1 Identifying Direct Variations from Equations

Tell whether each equation represents a direct variation. If so, identify the constant of variation.

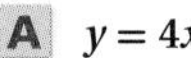

A $y = 4x$

This equation represents a direct variation because it is in the form $y = kx$. The constant of variation is 4.

B $-3x + 5y = 0$

$-3x + 5y = 0$ *Solve the equation for y.*

$+3x \quad\quad +3x$ *Since −3x is added to y, add 3x to both sides.*

$5y = 3x$

$\frac{5y}{5} = \frac{3x}{5}$ *Since y is multiplied by 5, divide both sides by 5.*

$y = \frac{3}{5}x$

This equation represents a direct variation because it can be written in the form $y = kx$. The constant of variation is $\frac{3}{5}$.

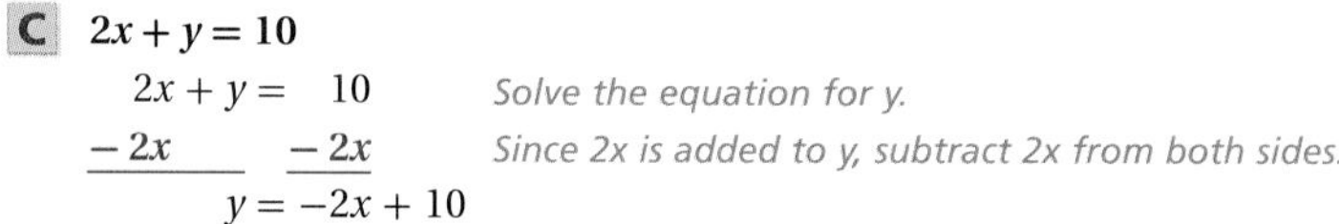

C $2x + y = 10$

$2x + y = 10$ *Solve the equation for y.*

$-2x \quad\quad -2x$ *Since 2x is added to y, subtract 2x from both sides.*

$y = -2x + 10$

This equation does not represent a direct variation because it cannot be written in the form $y = kx$.

1a. no

1b. yes; $-\frac{3}{4}$

1c. yes; -3

CHECK IT OUT! **Tell whether each equation represents a direct variation. If so, identify the constant of variation.**

1a. $3y = 4x + 1$ **1b.** $3x = -4y$ **1c.** $y + 3x = 0$

1 Introduce

EXPLORATION

5-4 Direct Variation

You will need a graphing calculator for this Exploration.

1. Use your calculator to graph the following functions in the same viewing window.
$y = 3x$
$y = \frac{1}{2}x$
$y = 5x$
2. What do you notice about the graphs? What do they all have in common?
3. Make a table for the function $y = 3x$ as follows. Press Y= and delete the functions that have been entered for **Y2** and **Y3**. Then press 2nd GRAPH to view the table for **Y1**.
4. Choose any row of the table except the row for $x = 0$. Divide the *y*-value by the *x*-value. What is the result? Is this true for every row of the table?
5. Follow the same procedure to examine the tables for $y = \frac{1}{2}x$ and $y = 5x$. For each row (except $x = 0$), divide the *y*-value by the *x*-value. Describe the results for each function.

THINK AND DISCUSS

6. **Predict** what would happen if you made a table of values for $y = 7x$ and divided any *y*-value by its corresponding *x*-value (except $x = 0$).
7. **Describe** the graph of an equation that has the form $y = kx$.

Motivate

Have a volunteer count the number of people present in the classroom and multiply the number by 2. Ask what the product could represent in relation to the number of people in the room. Possible answer: number of shoes What could the product represent if you multiplied by 10? Possible answer: number of fingers

Tell students that these are examples of direct variations.

Explorations and answers are provided in *Alternate Openers: Explorations Transparencies*.

What happens if you solve $y = kx$ for k?

$$y = kx$$

$$\frac{y}{x} = \frac{kx}{x} \quad \textit{Divide both sides by } x\ (x \neq 0).$$

$$\frac{y}{x} = k$$

So, in a direct variation, the ratio $\frac{y}{x}$ is equal to the constant of variation. Another way to identify a direct variation is to check whether $\frac{y}{x}$ is the same for each ordered pair (except where $x = 0$).

EXAMPLE 2 Identifying Direct Variations from Ordered Pairs

Tell whether each relationship is a direct variation. Explain.

A

x	1	3	5
y	6	18	30

Method 1 Write an equation.

$y = 6x$ *Each y-value is 6 times the corresponding x-value.*

This is a direct variation because it can be written as $y = kx$, where $k = 6$.

Method 2 Find $\frac{y}{x}$ for each ordered pair.

$\frac{6}{1} = 6$ $\frac{18}{3} = 6$ $\frac{30}{5} = 6$

This is a direct variation because $\frac{y}{x}$ is the same for each ordered pair.

B

x	2	4	8
y	−2	0	4

Method 1 Write an equation.

$y = x - 4$ *Each y-value is 4 less than the corresponding x-value.*

This is not a direct variation because it cannot be written as $y = kx$.

Method 2 Find $\frac{y}{x}$ for each ordered pair.

$\frac{-2}{2} = -1$ $\frac{0}{4} = 0$ $\frac{4}{8} = \frac{1}{2}$

This is not a direct variation because $\frac{y}{x}$ is not the same for all ordered pairs.

Tell whether each relationship is a direct variation. Explain.

2a.

x	y
−3	0
1	3
3	6

2b.

x	y
2.5	−10
5	−20
7.5	−30

2c.

x	y
−2	5
1	3
4	1

2a. No; possible answer: the value of $\frac{y}{x}$ is not the same for each ordered pair.
2b. Yes; possible answer: the value of $\frac{y}{x}$ is the same for each ordered pair.
2c. No; possible answer: the value of $\frac{y}{x}$ is not the same for each ordered pair.

If you know one ordered pair that satisfies a direct variation, you can write the equation. You can also find other ordered pairs that satisfy the direct variation.

COMMON ERROR ALERT

Students may have trouble differentiating between a direct variation and a simple linear relationship like $y = x + 2$. Explain that although both $y = 2x$ and $y = x + 2$ are linear functions, the relationship between x and y in a direct variation contains only multiplication and always has a y-intercept of 0.

Power Presentations with PowerPoint®

Additional Examples

Example 1

Tell whether each equation represents a direct variation. If so, identify the constant of variation.

A. $y = 3x$ yes; 3

B. $3x + y = 8$ no

C. $-4x + 3y = 0$ yes; $\frac{4}{3}$

Example 2

Tell whether each relationship is a direct variation. Explain.

A.

x	2	4	6
y	6	12	18

Yes; possible answer: the value of $\frac{y}{x}$ is the same for each ordered pair.

B.

x	1	3	7
y	−2	0	4

No; possible answer: the value of $\frac{y}{x}$ is not the same for each ordered pair.

Also available on transparency

INTERVENTION 

Questioning Strategies

EXAMPLE 1

- Is the constant of variation always the coefficient of x? Explain.

EXAMPLE 2

- Why does finding $\frac{y}{x}$ tell you whether the relationship is a direct variation?
- If the coefficient of x is 1, can the relationship be a direct variation? Explain.

Inclusion Point out that an equation cannot be a direct variation if it contains numerals other than zero that are not coefficients of x or y.

2 Teach

Guided Instruction

Review writing an equation from a table. Remind students that they are looking for a consistent relationship between x and y in which y is always a constant multiple of x. Before **Example 3,** review solving a proportion by using cross products.

Visual Some students may find a table of values easier to read if the values are written in columns rather than rows.

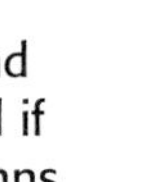

Universal Access

Through Modeling

Have students work in small groups. Using a ruler (MK), each group should measure and record the thickness of one algebra book. Then have them measure and record the height of 2 algebra books, 3 algebra books, and so on, until all group members' books are on the stack. Using these data, ask each group to explain how the relationship between the number of books and the height of the stack models a direct variation.

Power Presentations with PowerPoint®

Additional Examples

Example 3

The value of y varies directly with x, and $y = 3$ when $x = 9$. Find y when $x = 21$. 7

Example 4

A group of people are tubing down a river at an average speed of 2 mi/h. Write a direct variation equation that gives the number of miles y that the people will float in x hours. Then graph.

$y = 2x$

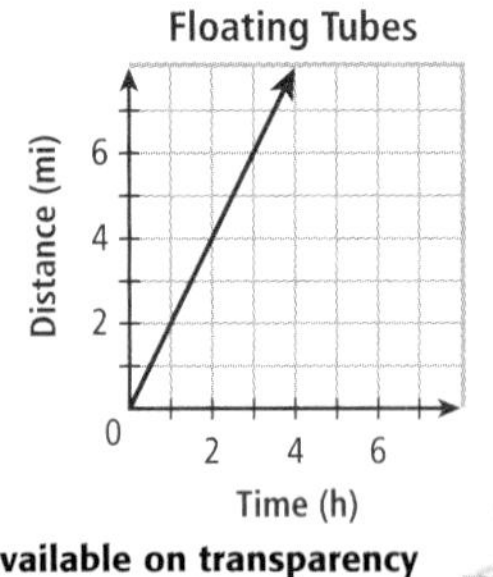

Also available on transparency

INTERVENTION

Questioning Strategies

EXAMPLE 3

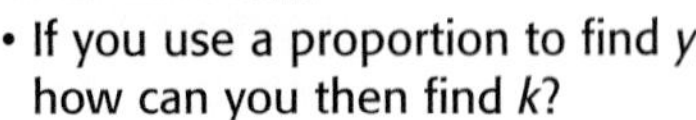

• If you use a proportion to find y, how can you then find k?

EXAMPLE 4

• How can you "see" the constant of variation in the ordered pairs? in the graph?

Critical Thinking Ask students whether the graph in **Example 4** appears to suggest that the three-toed sloth is *not* "an extremely slow animal." Point out that the steep slope represents a rate of 6 ft/min, which is equivalent to $\frac{3}{44}$ mi/h, or about 0.07 mi/h.

EXAMPLE 3 Writing and Solving Direct Variation Equations

The value of y varies directly with x, and $y = 6$ when $x = 12$. Find y when $x = 27$.

Method 1 Find the value of k and then write the equation.

$y = kx$	*Write the equation for a direct variation.*
$6 = k(12)$	*Substitute 6 for y and 12 for x. Solve for k.*
$\frac{1}{2} = k$	*Since k is multiplied by 12, divide both sides by 12.*

The equation is $y = \frac{1}{2}x$. When $x = 27$, $y = \frac{1}{2}(27) = 13.5$.

Method 2 Use a proportion.

$\frac{6}{12} = \frac{y}{27}$	*In a direct variation, $\frac{y}{x}$ is the same for all values of x and y.*
$12y = 162$	*Use cross products.*
$y = 13.5$	*Since y is multiplied by 12, divide both sides by 12.*

3. The value of y varies directly with x, and $y = 4.5$ when $x = 0.5$. Find y when $x = 10$. **90**

EXAMPLE 4 Graphing Direct Variations

The three-toed sloth is an extremely slow animal. On the ground, it travels at a speed of about 6 feet per minute. Write a direct variation equation for the distance y a sloth will travel in x minutes. Then graph.

Step 1 Write a direct variation equation.

distance	=	6 feet per minute	times	number of minutes
y	=	6	•	x

Step 2 Choose values of x and generate ordered pairs.

x	$y = 6x$	(x, y)
0	$y = 6(0) = 0$	$(0, 0)$
1	$y = 6(1) = 6$	$(1, 6)$
2	$y = 6(2) = 12$	$(2, 12)$

Step 3 Graph the points and connect.

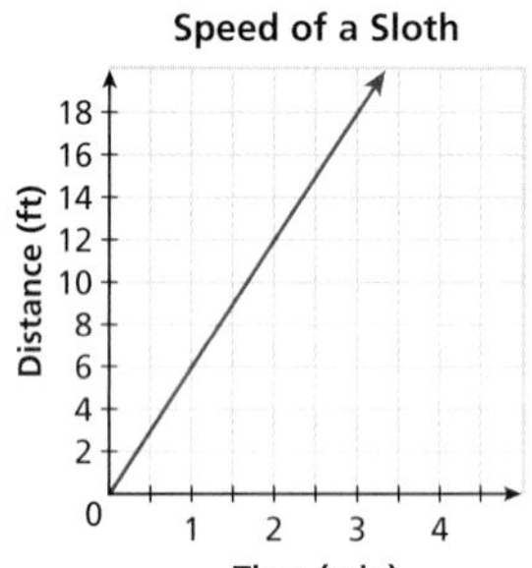

4. $y = 4x$

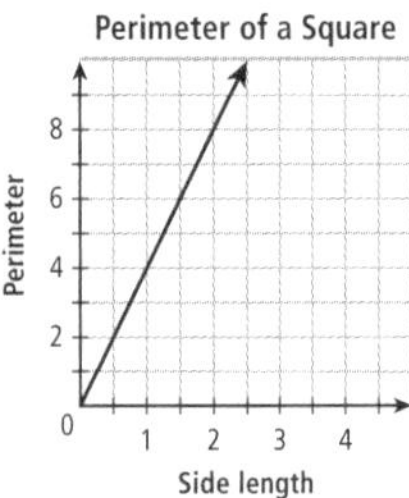

4. The perimeter y of a square varies directly with its side length x. Write a direct variation equation for this relationship. Then graph.

Look at the graph in Example 4. It passes through $(0, 0)$ and has a slope of 6. The graph of any direct variation $y = kx$

• contains $(0, 0)$.
• has a slope of k.

3 Close

Summarize

Ask students if each relationship or equation is a direct variation. If so, have them identify the constant of variation.

x	0	3	6
y	2	8	14

no; $\frac{2}{0} \neq \frac{8}{3} \neq \frac{14}{6}$

$x - 4y = 0$ yes; $\frac{1}{4}$

$5x + 10 = y$ no; cannot be written in the form $y = kx$.

FORMATIVE ASSESSMENT and INTERVENTION

***Diagnose Before* the Lesson**
5-4 Warm Up, TE p. 282

***Monitor During* the Lesson**
Check It Out! Exercises, SE pp. 282–284
Questioning Strategies, TE pp. 283–284

***Assess After* the Lesson**
5-4 Lesson Quiz, TE p. 287
Alternative Assessment, TE p. 287

THINK AND DISCUSS

1. How do you know that a direct variation is linear?
2. Why does the graph of any direct variation contain $(0, 0)$?
3. **GET ORGANIZED** Copy and complete the graphic organizer. In each box, describe how you can use the given information to identify a direct variation.

Recognizing a Direct Variation		
From an Equation	From Ordered Pairs	From a Graph

Answers to *Think and Discuss*

1. It can be written in standard form $kx - y = 0$ with $A = k$, $B = -1$, and $C = 0$.
2. Possible answer: For any value of k, $(0, 0)$ is a solution of $y = kx$.
3. See p. A4.

5-4 Exercises

California Standards Practice
6.0, 24.1

go.hrw.com
Homework Help Online
KEYWORD: MA8CA 5-4
Parent Resources Online
KEYWORD: MA8CA Parent

GUIDED PRACTICE

1. **Vocabulary** If x varies directly with y, then the relationship between the two variables is said to be a __?__. (*direct variation* or *constant of variation*) direct variation

SEE EXAMPLE 1 p. 282

Tell whether each equation represents a direct variation. If so, identify the constant of variation.

2. $y = 4x + 9$ no
3. $2y = -8x$ yes; -4
4. $x + y = 0$ yes; -1

SEE EXAMPLE 2 p. 283

Tell whether each relationship is a direct variation. Explain.

5. no

x	10	5	2
y	12	7	4

6. yes

x	3	−1	−4
y	−6	2	8

SEE EXAMPLE 3 p. 284

7. The value of y varies directly with x, and $y = -3$ when $x = 1$. Find y when $x = -6$. 18
8. The value of y varies directly with x, and $y = 6$ when $x = 18$. Find y when $x = 12$. 4

SEE EXAMPLE 4 p. 284

9. **Wages** Cameron earns \$5 per hour at her after-school job. The total amount of her paycheck varies directly with the amount of time she works. Write a direct variation equation for the amount of money y that she earns for working x hours. Then graph. $y = 5x$

PRACTICE AND PROBLEM SOLVING

Tell whether each equation represents a direct variation. If so, identify the constant of variation.

10. $y = \frac{1}{6}x$ yes; $\frac{1}{6}$
11. $4y = x$ yes; $\frac{1}{4}$
12. $x = 2y - 12$ no

Tell whether each relationship is a direct variation. Explain.

13. yes

x	6	9	17
y	13.2	19.8	37.4

14. yes

x	−6	3	12
y	4	−2	−8

5-4 Exercises

Assignment Guide

Assign *Guided Practice* exercises as necessary.

If you finished Examples **1–2**
Proficient 10–14, 18, 19
Advanced 10–14, 18, 19, 46

If you finished Examples **1–4**
Proficient 10–17, 20–44, 46–54
Advanced 10–17, 20–54

Homework Quick Check
Quickly check key concepts.
Exercises: 10, 14, 16, 17, 22, 36

Answers

5. Possible answer: The value of $\frac{y}{x}$ is not the same for each ordered pair.
6. Possible answer: The value of $\frac{y}{x}$ is the same for each ordered pair.
9. Cameron's Wages

Amount earned (\$) vs. Time worked (h): line from 0 through (2, 10). Axis values: 0, 2, 4, 6, 8; 1, 2, 3, 4.

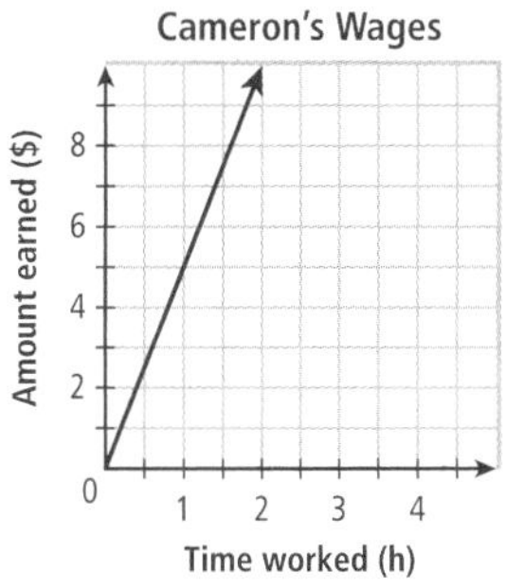

13. Possible answer: The value of $\frac{y}{x}$ is the same for each ordered pair.
14. Possible answer: The value of $\frac{y}{x}$ is the same for each ordered pair.

California Standards

Standard	Exercises
4.0	47–48
6.0	9, 17, 20–35, 37b, 45b
7.0	52–54
17.0	49–51
24.1	46

Exercise 40 involves writing an equation of direct variation and determining the constant of variation. This exercise prepares students for the Concept Connection on page 288.

Answers

17.

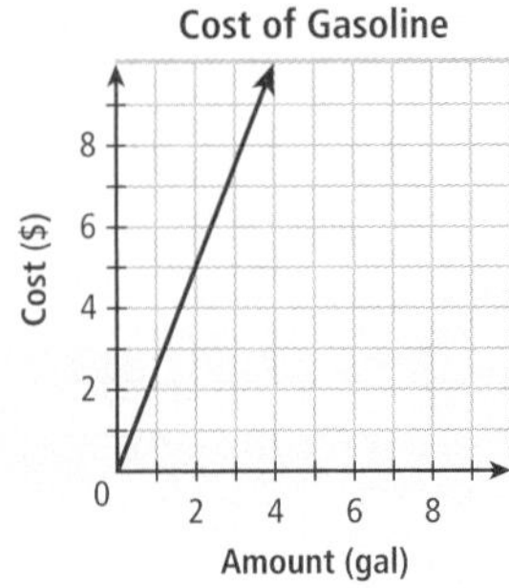

20. $y = 5x$

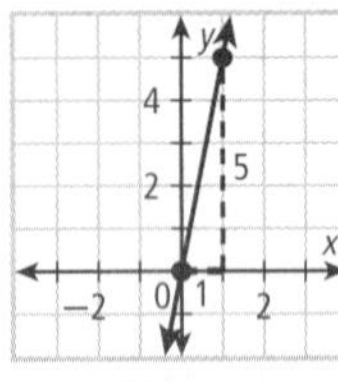

$k = 5$; graph shows slope $= 5$

21. $y = -3x$

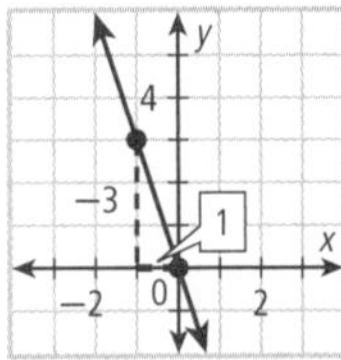

$k = -3$; graph shows slope $= -3$

22–35, 37b, 38. See pp. A18–A19.

39. Possible answer: The ratio $\frac{y}{x}$ is the same for all ordered pairs in a direct var., so you can write a proportion using any two ordered pairs.

Independent Practice

For Exercises	See Example
10–12	1
13–14	2
15–16	3
17	4

Extra Practice

Skills Practice p. EP10
Application Practice p. EP28

15. The value of y varies directly with x, and $y = 8$ when $x = -32$. Find y when $x = 64$. **−16**

16. The value of y varies directly with x, and $y = \frac{1}{2}$ when $x = 3$. Find y when $x = 1$. $\mathbf{\frac{1}{6}}$

17. While on his way to school, Norman saw that the cost of gasoline was \$2.50 per gallon. Write a direct variation equation to describe the cost y of x gallons of gas. Then graph. $\mathbf{y = 2.50x}$

Tell whether each relationship is a direct variation. Explain your answer.

18. The equation $-15x + 4y = 0$ relates the length of a videotape in inches x to its approximate playing time in seconds y. **Yes; it can be written as $y = \frac{15}{4}x$.**

19. The equation $y - 2.00x = 2.50$ relates the cost y of a taxicab ride to distance x of the cab ride in miles. **No; it cannot be written in the form $y = kx$.**

Each ordered pair is a solution of a direct variation. Write the equation of direct variation. Then graph your equation and show that the slope of the line is equal to the constant of variation.

20. (2, 10)	21. (−3, 9)	22. (8, 2)	23. (1.5, 6)
24. (7, 21)	25. (1, 2)	26. (2, −16)	27. $\left(\frac{1}{7}, 1\right)$
28. (−2, 9)	29. (9, −2)	30. (4, 6)	31. (3, 4)
32. (5, 1)	33. (1, −6)	34. $\left(-1, \frac{1}{2}\right)$	35. (7, 2)

LINK Astronomy

The Mars rover *Spirit* landed on Mars in January 2004 and immediately began sending photos of the planet's surface back to Earth.

36. **Astronomy** Weight varies directly with gravity. A Mars lander weighed 767 pounds on Earth but only 291 pounds on Mars. Its accompanying Mars rover weighed 155 pounds on Mars. How much did it weigh on Earth? Round your answer to the nearest pound. **409 lb**

37. **Environment** Mischa bought an energy-efficient washing machine. She will save about 15 gallons of water per wash load.
   a. Write an equation of direct variation to describe how many gallons of water y Mischa saves for x loads of laundry she washes. $\mathbf{y = 15x}$
   b. Graph your direct variation from part **a.** Is every point on the graph a solution in this situation? Why or why not?
   c. If Mischa does 2 loads of laundry per week, how many gallons of water will she have saved at the end of a year? **1560 gal**

For help with deductive reasoning, see pp. 99, 108, and 169.

38. **Reasoning** Use deductive reasoning to show that if you double an x-value in a direct variation, then the corresponding y-value will also double.

39. **Write About It** In a direct variation $y = kx$, k is sometimes called the "constant of proportionality." How are proportions related to direct variations?

CONCEPT CONNECTION

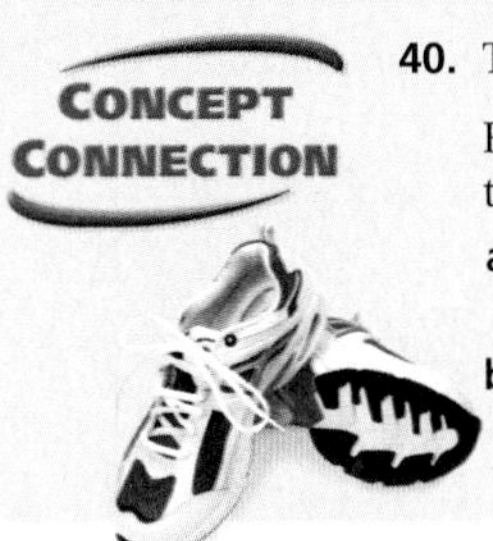

40. This problem will prepare you for the Concept Connection on page 288.

Rhea exercised on a treadmill at the gym. When she was finished, the display showed that she had walked at an average speed of 3 miles per hour.
   a. Write an equation that gives the number of miles y that Rhea would cover in x hours if she walked at this speed. $\mathbf{y = 3x}$
   b. Explain why this is a direct variation and find the value of k. What does this value represent in Rhea's situation? **It is written in the form $y = kx$, where $k = 3$. This value represents the speed at which Rhea is walking.**

5-4 PRACTICE A
5-4 PRACTICE C
5-4 PRACTICE B

LESSON 5-4 **Practice B**
Direct Variation

Tell whether each equation is a direct variation. If so, identify the constant of variation.

1. $y = 3x$ yes; 3
2. $y = 2x - 9$ no
3. $2x + 3y = 0$ yes; $-\frac{2}{3}$
4. $3y = 9x$ yes; 3

Find the value of $\frac{y}{x}$ for each ordered pair. Then, tell whether each relationship is a direct variation.

5.

x	6	15	21
y	2	5	7
$\frac{y}{x}$	$\frac{1}{3}$	$\frac{1}{3}$	$\frac{1}{3}$

yes

6.

x	6	10	25
y	24	40	100
$\frac{y}{x}$	4	4	4

yes

7.

x	10	15	20
y	3	5	9
$\frac{y}{x}$	$\frac{3}{10}$	$\frac{1}{3}$	$\frac{9}{20}$

no

8. The value of y varies directly with x, and $y = -18$ when $x = 6$. Find y when $x = -8$.
Find k: $-3 = k$
Use k to find y: $y = kx$; $y = (-3)(-8)$; $y = 24$

9. The value of y varies directly with x, and $y = \frac{1}{2}$ when $x = 5$. Find y when $x = 30$.
Find k: $\frac{1}{10} = k$
Use k to find y: $y = kx$; $y = \left(\frac{1}{10}\right)(30)$; $y = 3$

10. The amount of interest earned in a savings account varies directly with the amount of money in the account. A certain bank offers a 2% savings rate. Write a direct variation equation for the amount of interest y earned on a balance of x. Then graph.
$y = 0.02x$

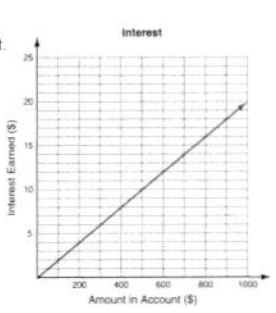

Interest (Interest Earned ($) vs. Amount in Account ($))

11. Another bank offers a different savings rate. If an account with \$400 earns interest of \$6, how much interest is earned by an account with \$1800?
\$27

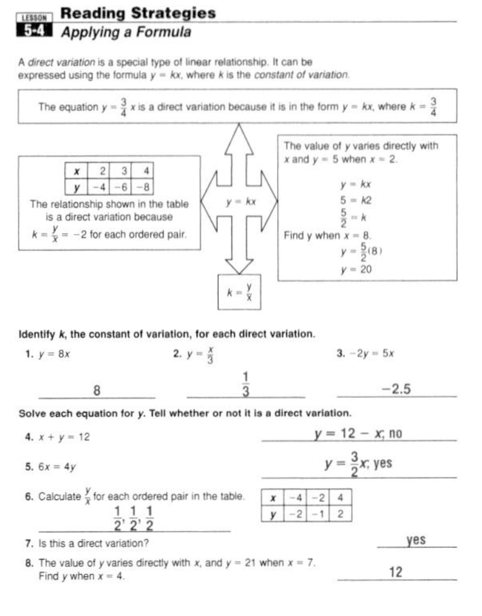
5-4 READING STRATEGIES

LESSON 5-4 **Reading Strategies**
Applying a Formula

A *direct variation* is a special type of linear relationship. It can be expressed using the formula $y = kx$, where k is the *constant of variation*.

The equation $y = \frac{3}{4}x$ is a direct variation because it is in the form $y = kx$, where $k = \frac{3}{4}$

$y = kx$

x	2	3	4
y	−4	−6	−8

The relationship shown in the table is a direct variation because $k = \frac{y}{x} = -2$ for each ordered pair.

The value of y varies directly with x and $y = 5$ when $x = 2$.
$y = kx$
$5 = k2$
$\frac{5}{2} = k$
Find y when $x = 8$.
$y = \frac{5}{2}(8)$
$y = 20$

$k = \frac{y}{x}$

Identify k, the constant of variation, for each direct variation.

1. $y = 8x$ 8
2. $y = \frac{x}{3}$ $\frac{1}{3}$
3. $-2y = 5x$ −2.5

Solve each equation for y. Tell whether or not it is a direct variation.

4. $x + y = 12$ $y = 12 - x$; no
5. $6x = 4y$ $y = \frac{3}{2}x$; yes
6. Calculate $\frac{y}{x}$ for each ordered pair in the table. $\frac{1}{2}, \frac{1}{2}, \frac{1}{2}$

x	−4	−2	4
y	−2	−1	2

7. Is this a direct variation? yes
8. The value of y varies directly with x, and $y = 21$ when $x = 7$. Find y when $x = 4$. 12

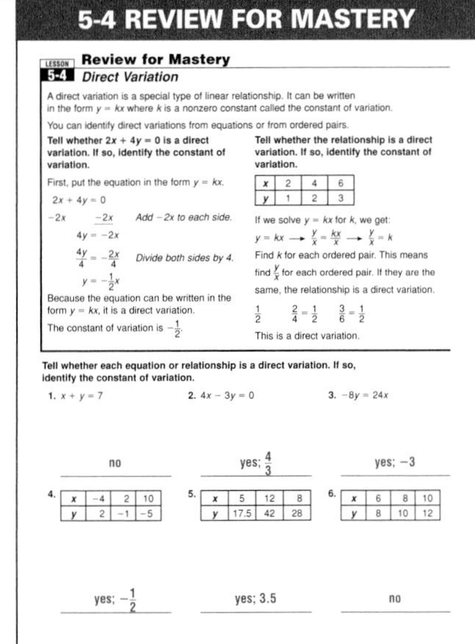
5-4 REVIEW FOR MASTERY

LESSON 5-4 **Review for Mastery**
Direct Variation

A direct variation is a special type of linear relationship. It can be written in the form $y = kx$ where k is a nonzero constant called the constant of variation.

You can identify direct variations from equations or from ordered pairs.

Tell whether $2x + 4y = 0$ is a direct variation. If so, identify the constant of variation.

First, put the equation in the form $y = kx$.
$2x + 4y = 0$
$-2x \quad -2x$ *Add −2x to each side.*
$4y = -2x$
$\frac{4y}{4} = -\frac{2x}{4}$ *Divide both sides by 4.*
$y = -\frac{1}{2}x$
Because the equation can be written in the form $y = kx$, it is a direct variation.
The constant of variation is $-\frac{1}{2}$.

Tell whether the relationship is a direct variation. If so, identify the constant of variation.

x	2	4	6
y	1	2	3

If we solve $y = kx$ for k, we get:
$y = kx \rightarrow \frac{y}{x} = \frac{kx}{x} \rightarrow \frac{y}{x} = k$
Find k for each ordered pair. This means find $\frac{y}{x}$ for each ordered pair. If they are the same, the relationship is a direct variation.
$\frac{1}{2} \quad \frac{2}{4} = \frac{1}{2} \quad \frac{3}{6} = \frac{1}{2}$
This is a direct variation.

Tell whether each equation or relationship is a direct variation. If so, identify the constant of variation.

1. $x + y = 7$ no
2. $4x - 3y = 0$ yes; $\frac{4}{3}$
3. $-8y = 24x$ yes; −3

4.

x	−4	2	10
y	2	−1	−5

yes; $-\frac{1}{2}$

5.

x	5	12	8
y	17.5	42	28

yes; 3.5

6.

x	6	8	10
y	8	10	12

no

Multiple Choice For Exercises 41–43, choose the best answer.

41. Which equation does NOT represent a direct variation?

Ⓐ $y = \frac{1}{3}x$ Ⓑ $y = -2x$ Ⓒ $y = 4x + 1$ (circled) Ⓓ $6x - y = 0$

42. Identify which set of data represents a direct variation.

Ⓐ (circled)

x	1	2	3
y	1	2	3

Ⓒ

x	1	2	3
y	3	5	7

Ⓑ

x	1	2	3
y	0	1	2

Ⓓ

x	1	2	3
y	3	4	5

43. Two yards of fabric cost $13, and 5 yards of fabric cost $32.50. Which equation relates the cost of the fabric c to its length ℓ?

Ⓐ $c = 2.6\ell$ Ⓑ $c = 6.5\ell$ (circled) Ⓒ $c = 13\ell$ Ⓓ $c = 32.5\ell$

44. **Gridded Response** A car is traveling at a constant speed. After 3 hours, the car has traveled 180 miles. If the car continues to travel at the same constant speed, how many hours will it take to travel a total of 270 miles? **4.5**

CHALLENGE AND EXTEND

45b.

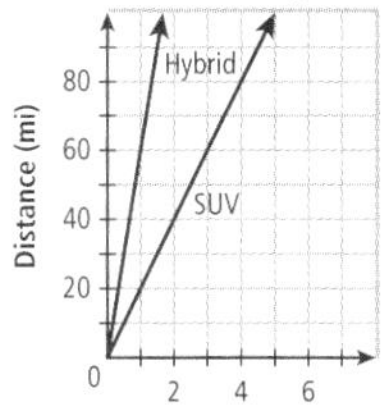

Gas Mileage

(Graph: Distance (mi) vs. Gas used (gal); lines labeled Hybrid and SUV; y-axis 0, 20, 40, 60, 80; x-axis 2, 4, 6)

45. **Transportation** The equation $y = 20x$ gives the number of miles y that a gasoline-powered sport-utility vehicle (SUV) can travel on x gallons of gas. The equation $y = 60x$ gives the number of miles y that a gas-electric hybrid car can travel on x gallons of gas.

a. If you drive 120 miles, how much gas will you save by driving the hybrid instead of the SUV? **4 gal**

b. Graph both equations on the same coordinate plane. Will the lines ever meet? Explain. **No; the lines begin at (0, 0) and then move apart.**

c. **What if...?** Shannon drives 15,000 miles in one year. How many gallons of gas will she use if she drives the SUV? the hybrid? **750 gal; 250 gal**

46. **Reasoning** Suppose $Ax + By = C$, where A, B, and C are real numbers, $A \neq 0$, and $B \neq 0$, describes a direct variation. Use deductive reasoning to show that $C = 0$.

SPIRAL STANDARDS REVIEW

4.0, 7.0, 17.0

Solve each equation. Check your answer. *(Lesson 2-3)*

47. $p(1 + 4) - 2(p + 6) = 6$ **6**

48. $s - (s + 5) + 3(s - 1) = -2$ **2**

Give the domain and range of each relation. Tell whether the relation is a function. *(Lesson 4-2)*

49. D: {1, 2, 3, 4}; R:{−5, −4, −3, −2}; yes

50. D: {1, 2, 3, 4}; R: {−2, −4, −6, −8}; yes

51. D: {−3, −2, −1}; R: {9, 6, 3, 0}; no

49.

x	y
1	−5
2	−4
3	−3
4	−2

50.

x	y
1	−2
2	−4
3	−6
4	−8

51.

x	y
−3	9
−2	6
−1	3
−2	0

Without graphing, tell whether each point is on the graph of $2x - y = 5$. *(Lesson 5-1)*

52. $(3, 1)$ **yes** 53. $(1, -2)$ **no** 54. $(4, -3)$ **no**

Multiple Choice Students might eliminate the correct choice **A** in **Exercise 42** because they do not understand that the constant of variation can be 1.

Journal

Have students explain how a rate of change, a slope, and a constant of variation are related.

ALTERNATIVE ASSESSMENT

Have students write two equations of direct variation involving common proportions, such as 12 inches = 1 foot. Then have them graph the equations and identify the constants of variation.

Answer

46. See p. A19.

Power Presentations with PowerPoint®

5-4 Lesson Quiz

Tell whether each equation represents a direct variation. If so, identify the constant of variation.

1. $2y = 6x$ yes; 3

2. $3x = 4y - 7$ no

Tell whether each relationship is a direct variation. Explain.

3.

x	−4	0	8
y	2	3	5

no; $\frac{2}{-4} \neq \frac{3}{0} \neq \frac{5}{8}$

4.

x	1	3	7
y	4.3	12.9	30.1

yes; $\frac{4.3}{1} = \frac{12.9}{3} = \frac{30.1}{7}$

5. The value of y varies directly with x, and $y = -8$ when $x = 20$. Find y when $x = -4$. 1.6

6. Apples cost $0.80 per pound. The equation $y = 0.8x$ describes the cost y of x pounds of apples. Graph this direct variation.

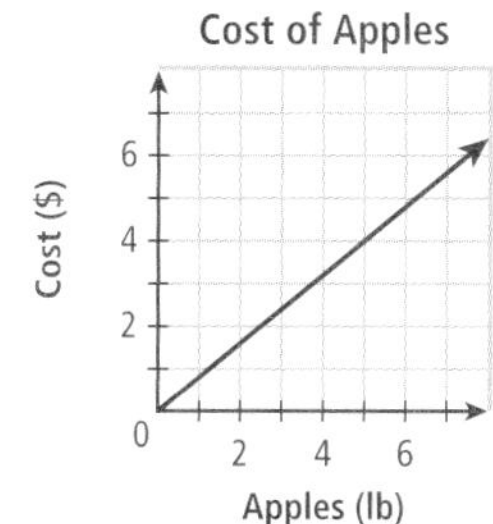

Also available on transparency

5-4 PROBLEM SOLVING

LESSON 5-4 **Problem Solving**
Direct Variation

Write the correct answer.

1. Wesley earns $6.50 per hour at the bookstore. The total amount of his paycheck varies directly with the number of hours he works. Write a direct variation equation for the amount of money y Wesley earns for working x hours.
$y = 6.5x$

2. The equation $-4x + y = 0$ relates the number of pages in a photo album y to the number of pictures in the album x. Tell whether the relationship is a direct variation. Explain your answer.
yes; it can be written as $y = 4x$.

3. The formula $9x - 5y = -160$ relates the temperature in degrees Fahrenheit y to the temperature in degrees Celsius x. Tell whether the relationship is a direct variation. Explain your answer.
no; it cannot be written in the form $y = kx$.

4. The number of miles driven varies directly with the number of gallons of gas used. Erin drove 297 miles on 9 gallons of gas. How far would she be able to drive on 14 gallons of gas?
462 miles

Select the best answer.

5. The table shows the relationship between the number of lemons purchased and their cost.

Lemons x	1	2	3	4
Cost y	0.1	0.2	0.3	0.4

Is the relationship a direct variation?
Ⓐ Yes; it can be written as $y = 0.1x$.
B Yes; it can be written as $y = 10x$.
C No; it cannot be written as $y = kx$.
D No; the relationship is not a function.

6. The table shows the relationship between the hours since sunrise and the temperature in degrees Celsius.

Hour x	1	2	3	4
Temp. y	25	26	28	32

Is the relationship a direct variation?
F Yes; it can be written as $y = 25x$.
G Yes; it can be written as $y = 8x$.
Ⓗ No; it cannot be written as $y = kx$.
J No; the relationship is not a function.

7. The Diaz family is driving at a constant speed on the highway so their distance varies directly with their speed. They traveled 17.5 miles in 15 minutes. How far did they travel in 2 hours?
A 50 miles Ⓒ 140 miles
B 70 miles D 262.5 miles (17.5 times 15)

8. On July 26, 2005, it rained a record 37 inches in Mumbai, India, in a 24-hour period. Which equation of direct variation relates the number of inches of rain y to the number of hours x?
F $y = \frac{24}{37}x$ H $y = 24x$
Ⓖ $y = \frac{37}{24}x$ J $y = 37x$

5-4 CHALLENGE

LESSON 5-4 **Challenge**
Combining Direct-Variation Relationships

In Lesson 5.3, you learned that when y varies directly as x, there is a nonzero number, k, such that $y = kx$. There are many situations in which one variable varies directly with another variable.

A 700-gallon tank contains 500 gallons of a certain liquid. Three pumps feed three different ingredients into the tank at its top. A discharge pump at the base of the tank removes the mixed ingredients. The rates at which the pipes feed and remove liquid are shown at right.

Pump 1:	5 gallons per minute
Pump 2:	10 gallons per minute
Pump 3:	15 gallons per minute
Discharge pump:	35 gallons per minute

(Diagram labels: Pump 1, Pump 2, Pump 3, Discharge)

Let t represent the amount of time for which each pipe is operating.

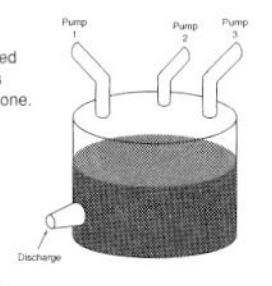

1. Write a direct-variation relationship for the gallons supplied by each pump. Then find the amount of time that it takes for each pump to fill the tank to capacity if each works alone.
a. pump 1 $y = 5t$, 40 minutes
b. pump 2 $y = 10t$, 20 minutes
c. pump 3 $y = 15t$, $13\frac{1}{3}$ minutes

2. On certain occasions, some pumps are turned on at the same time. Write a direct-variation relationship for each combination of pumps operating simultaneously.
a. pump 1 and pump 2 $y = 15t$
b. pump 2 and pump 3 $y = 25t$
c. pump 1, pump 2, and pump 3 $y = 30t$

3. At noon, the tank contains 500 gallons of solution. At noon, all pumps, and the discharge pump, are turned on simultaneously.
a. Write an equation for the quantity, Q, of solution t minutes after noon. $Q = 500 + 30t - 35t$
b. Is the tank filling or emptying? At what rate is this happening? emptying at 5 gallons per minute
c. After how many minutes will the tank be full or empty? after 100 minutes, the tank will be empty

4. At noon, the tank contains 500 gallons of solution and all feeder pumps are turned on. At 12:06 p.m., the discharge pump is turned on.
a. Write an equation or equations for the quantity, Q, of solution t minutes after noon. $Q = 500 + 30(t + 6) - 35t$, or $Q = 680 - 5t$
b. How many minutes after noon will the tank either be full or be empty? after 136 minutes, the tank will be empty

SECTION 5A

CONCEPT CONNECTION

Organizer

Objective: Assess students' ability to apply concepts and skills in Lessons 5-1 through 5-4 in a real-world format.

Online Edition

Problem	Text Reference
1	Lessons 4-3, 5-1
2	Lessons 5-1, 5-2, 5-3
3	Lessons 5-2, 5-3, 5-4
4	Lessons 5-3, 5-4
5	Lessons 5-2, 5-3, 5-4
6	Lesson 1-1
7	Lesson 2-5

Answers

1.

Age (yr)	Maximum Heart Rate (beats/min)
13	205.95
14	205.1
15	204.25
16	203.4
17	202.55
18	201.7

2. x-int.: 255.29; y-int.: 217; slope: -0.85

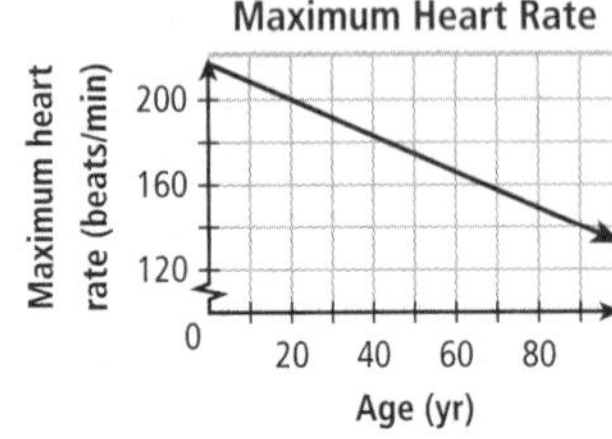

Algebra 1 6.0

CHAPTER 5

SECTION 5A

Characteristics of Linear Functions

Heart Health People who exercise need to be aware of their maximum heart rate.

1. One way to estimate your maximum heart rate m is to subtract 85% of your age in years from 217. Create a table of values that shows the maximum heart rates for people ages 13 to 18. Then write an equation to describe the data in the table. $m = 217 - 0.85a$
2. Use your table from Problem 1 to graph the relationship between age and maximum heart rate. What are the intercepts? What is the slope?
3. What do the intercepts represent in this situation?
4. What does the slope represent? Explain why the slope is negative.
5. Another formula for estimating maximum heart rate is $m = 206.3 - 0.711a$, where a represents age in years. Describe how this equation is different from your equation in Problem 1. Include slope and intercepts in your description.
6. Which equation gives a higher maximum heart rate? the first equation
7. To be exercising in your *aerobic training zone* means that your heart rate is 70% to 80% of your maximum heart rate. Write two equations that someone could use to estimate the range of heart rates that are within his or her aerobic training zone. Use your equation for maximum heart rate from Problem 1.

3. x-int.: the (hypothetical) age at which someone's max. heart rate would be 0 beats/min; y-int.: max. heart rate of someone who is 0 years old.

4. slope: how much max. heart rate decreases for each year that someone ages; because as age increases, max. heart rate decreases

5. The slope is steeper, and the y-int. is less.

7. min.:
$m = 0.7(217 - 0.85a)$
$= 151.9 - 0.595a$
max.:
$m = 0.8(217 - 0.85a)$
$= 173.6 - 0.68a$

INTERVENTION

Scaffolding Questions

1. What are the independent and dependent variables? independent: age; dependent: maximum heart rate
2. How can you find the slope? Possible answer: Once you know the intercepts, use (255.29, 0) and (0, 217) in the slope formula.
3. What does $a = 0$ represent? age of 0 yr What does $m = 0$ represent? max. heart rate of 0 beats/min Are these values reasonable in this situation? no
4. What is the ratio of dependent variable to independent variable? rate/age Does the rate increase or decrease with age? decrease

5–7. Discuss the variables, intercepts, and slopes in the formulas described.

Extension

Find your maximum heart rate using the method given in **Problem 5.** Then find the range of heart rates that are within your aerobic training zone using this method and the information given in **Problem 7.** Possible answer: For age 14, the maximum rate is about 196 beats/min, and the range is about 137–157 beats/min.

CHAPTER 5

SECTION 5A

Quiz for Lessons 5-1 Through 5-4

5-1 Linear Equations and Functions

Graph each linear equation. Then tell whether it represents a function.

1. $x + y = 4$ yes
2. $x = 6$ no
3. $\frac{x}{y} = 6$ yes
4. $y - 2 = -\frac{1}{3}x$ yes

Without graphing, tell whether each point is on the graph of $y = -4x - 1$.

5. $(0, 0)$ no
6. $(-1, 0)$ no
7. $(0, -1)$ yes
8. $\left(-\frac{1}{2}, -1\right)$ no

5-2 Using Intercepts

9. A baby pool that held 120 gallons of water is draining at a rate of 6 gal/min. The function $f(x) = 120 - 6x$ gives the amount of water in the pool after x minutes. Graph the function and find its intercepts. What does each intercept represent?

Use intercepts to graph the line given by each equation.

10. $2x - 4y = 16$
11. $-3y + 6x = -18$
12. $y = -3x + 3$

5-3 Slope

Find the slope of each line. Then tell what the slope represents.

13. 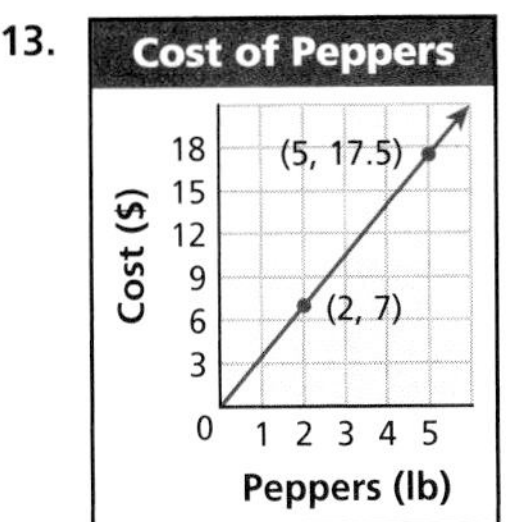

3.5; peppers cost $3.50/lb.

14. 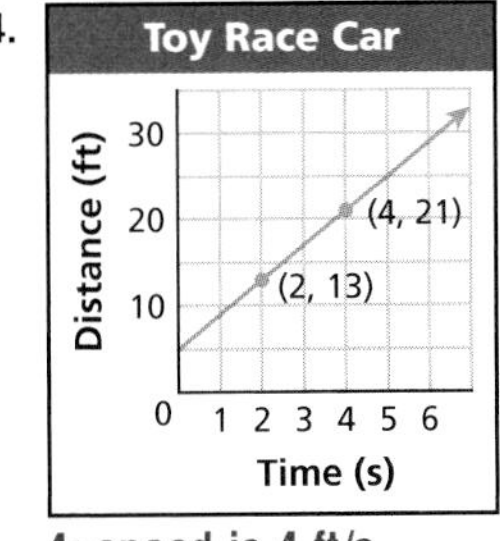

4; speed is 4 ft/s.

15. 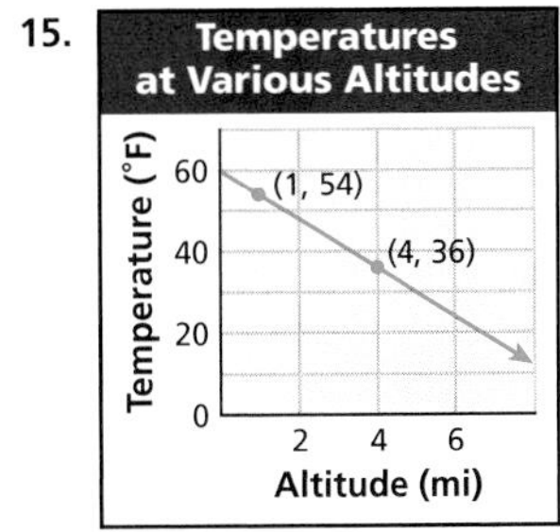

−6; temp. decreases 6°F/mi.

Find the slope of the line given by each equation.

16. $3x + y = 1$ -3
17. $y + 4x = 8$ -4
18. $x - 2y = 2$ $\frac{1}{2}$
19. $4x - 5y = -2$ $\frac{4}{5}$

5-4 Direct Variation

Tell whether each relationship is a direct variation. If so, identify the constant of variation.

20. no

x	1	4	8	12
y	3	6	10	14

21. yes; $\frac{1}{2}$

x	−6	−2	0	3
y	−3	−1	0	1.5

22. The value of y varies directly with x, and $y = 10$ when $x = 4$. Find x when $y = 14$. 5.6

READY TO GO ON? SECTION 5A

Organizer

Objective: Assess students' mastery of concepts and skills in Lessons 5-1 through 5-4.

 Countdown to Mastery Week 11

Resources

 ***Assessment Resources***
Section 5A Quiz

INTERVENTION 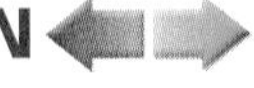

Resources

 ***Ready to Go On? Intervention and Enrichment*** **Worksheets**

 ***Ready to Go On?*** **CD-ROM**

 ***Ready to Go On?*** **Online**

my.hrw.com

Answers

1–4. For graphs, see p. A19.
9–12. See p. A19.

READY TO GO ON? Diagnose and Prescribe

NO INTERVENE

Ready to Go On? Intervention	Ready to Go On? Intervention, Section 5A: Worksheets	CD-ROM	Online
Lesson 5-1 6.0, 7.0	5-1 Intervention	Activity 5-1	Diagnose and Prescribe Online
Lesson 5-2 6.0	5-2 Intervention	Activity 5-2	
Lesson 5-3 6.0	5-3 Intervention	Activity 5-3	
Lesson 5-4 6.0	5-4 Intervention	Activity 5-4	

YES ENRICH

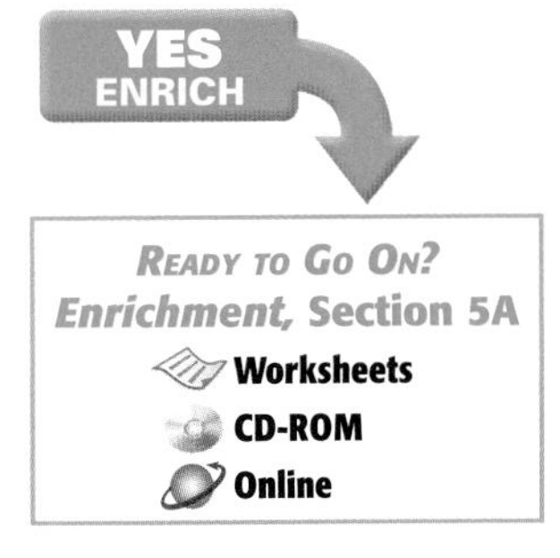

Using Linear Functions

One-Minute Section Planner

Lesson	Lab Resources	Materials
Lesson 5-5 Slope-Intercept Form • Write a linear equation in slope-intercept form. • Graph a line using slope-intercept form. **6.0**	***Algebra Labs*** **5-5** In *Chapter 5 Resource File*	**Optional** graphing calculator, masking tape, rope or string, graph paper
Lesson 5-6 Point-Slope Form • Graph a line and write a linear equation using point-slope form. • Write a linear equation given two points. **6.0, 7.0**		
Lesson 5-7 Slopes of Parallel and Perpendicular Lines • Identify and graph parallel and perpendicular lines. • Write equations to describe lines parallel or perpendicular to a given line. **8.0, 25.1**	***Algebra Lab*** **5-7** In *Chapter 5 Resource File*	**Optional** graphing calculator

MK = *Manipulatives Kit*

Notes

Math Background: Teaching the Standards

Professional Development

MORE ON LINEAR FUNCTIONS

Lessons 5-5, 5-6

Any linear function may be written in slope-intercept form, $y = mx + b$, where m is the slope of the line and b is the y-intercept. It is useful to understand how m and b affect the appearance of the line.

For nonnegative values of m, the graph of $y = mx$ is a *vertical stretch* or *compression* of the graph of $y = x$. The greater the value of m, the steeper the resulting line. The figure shows how $y = 2x$ represents a vertical stretch of $y = x$. When m is negative, the line is reflected across the x-axis, as seen in the graph of $y = -2x$.

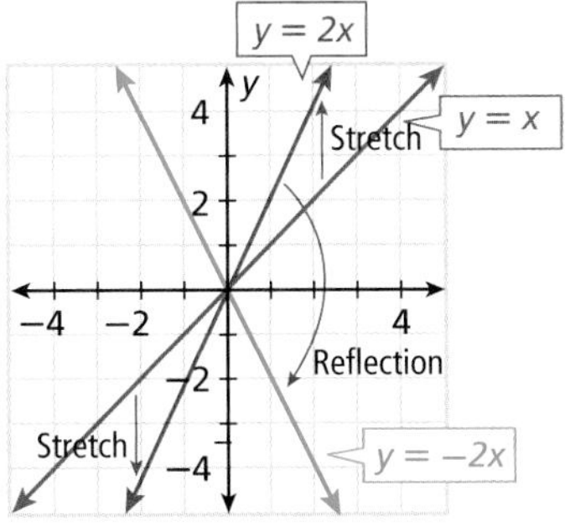

In general, the graph of $y = mx + b$ is a *vertical translation* of the graph of $y = mx$. If b is positive, the translation is upward by b units. If b is negative, the translation is downward by $|b|$ units. Comparing the graphs of $y = x$, $y = x + 3$, $y = x - 2$, and $y = x - 4$ illustrates this.

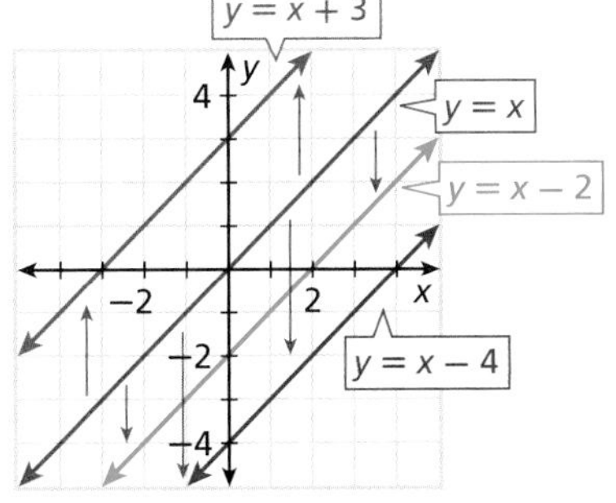

Putting all of these ideas together shows that the graph of every linear function is the result of one or more transformations of the graph of the *parent function* $y = x$. For example, to get the graph of $y = -5x + 3$, the graph of $y = x$ is first stretched vertically by a factor of 5, then reflected across the x-axis, and then translated upward by 3 units.

PERPENDICULAR LINES 8.0

Lesson 5-7

Two nonvertical lines are perpendicular if and only if the product of their slopes is -1 (or, equivalently, if and only if their slopes are opposite reciprocals). Students should understand the logic of the phrase *if and only if*. It means that the statement is true "in both directions": if nonvertical lines are perpendicular, then the product of their slopes is -1; if the product of the slopes is -1, then the lines are perpendicular.

Students should also be aware that they will have to accept this result as true until they are able to prove it in a geometry course. The main steps in the proof that nonvertical perpendicular lines have slopes whose product is -1 are outlined below.

Assume perpendicular lines k and ℓ intersect at P and that line ℓ has positive slope m. Then it is possible to construct a right triangle PQR that has its hypotenuse along line ℓ and has legs of length m and 1 as shown. Extend $\overline{PR}$ through P and mark off a length of m along the line (at point S). Construct a perpendicular at S to form right triangle TPS. Basic facts from geometry and the *ASA* triangle congruence theorem show that $\triangle PQR \cong \triangle TPS$. Thus, $\overline{TS} \cong \overline{PR}$ and so $TS = 1$. The slope of $\overline{TS}$ must be $-\frac{1}{m}$, and $-\frac{1}{m} \cdot m = -1$.

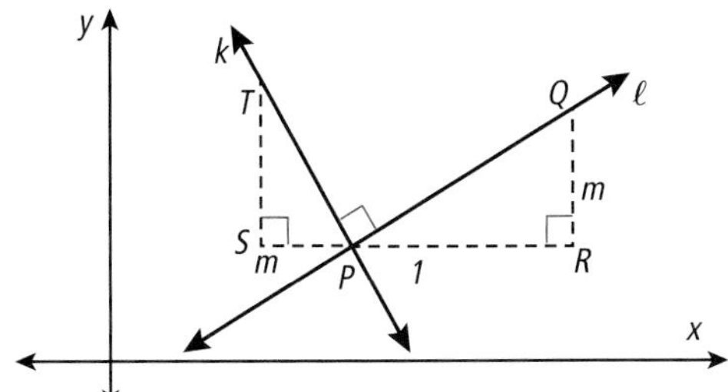

5-5 Organizer

Objectives: Write a linear equation in slope-intercept form.

Graph a line using slope-intercept form.

Algebra Labs
In Chapter 5 Resource File

Online Edition
Tutorial Videos

Countdown to Mastery Week 11

Power Presentations with PowerPoint®

Warm Up

Find each *y*-intercept.

1. $y = 3x + 2$ 2

2. $5x - 3y = 12$ -4

Find each slope.

3. $y = \frac{2}{3}x$ $\frac{2}{3}$

4. $6x + 2y = 6$ -3

Solve each equation for *y*.

5. $4x + 2y = 10$ $y = -2x + 5$

6. $3x + 2 = 6y$ $y = \frac{1}{2}x + \frac{1}{3}$

Also available on transparency

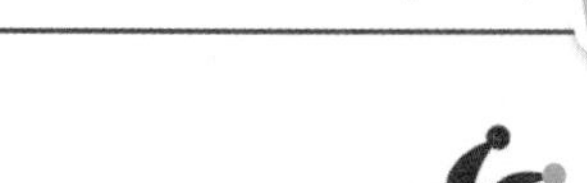

Math Humor

Q: Why was the scientist smiling as he worked?

A: His graph had a great plot!

California Standards

Algebra 1 🔑 **6.0**

5-5 Slope-Intercept Form

California Standards

🔑 **6.0 Students graph a linear equation and compute** the *x*- and ***y*-intercepts** (e.g., graph $2x + 6y = 4$). They are also able to sketch the region defined by linear inequalities (e.g., they sketch the region defined by $2x + 6y < 4$).

Who uses this?

Consumers can use slope-intercept form to model and calculate costs, such as the cost of renting a moving van. (See Example 4.)

You have seen that you can graph a line if you know two points on the line. Another way is to use the point that contains the *y*-intercept and the slope of the line.

EXAMPLE 1 **Graphing by Using Slope and *y*-intercept**

Graph each line given the slope and *y*-intercept.

A slope $= \frac{3}{4}$; *y*-intercept $= -2$

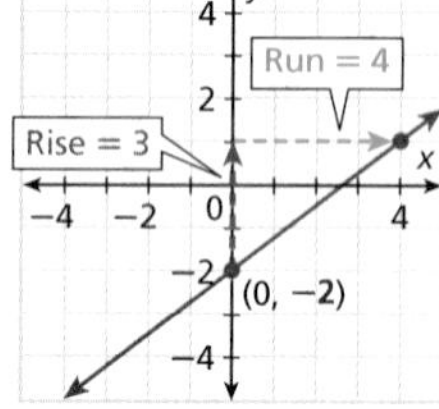

Step 1 The *y*-intercept is -2, so the line contains $(0, -2)$. Plot $(0, -2)$.

Step 2 Slope $= \frac{\text{rise}}{\text{run}} = \frac{3}{4}$. Count 3 units up and 4 units right from $(0, -2)$ and plot another point.

Step 3 Draw the line through the two points.

B slope $= -2$, *y*-intercept $= 4$

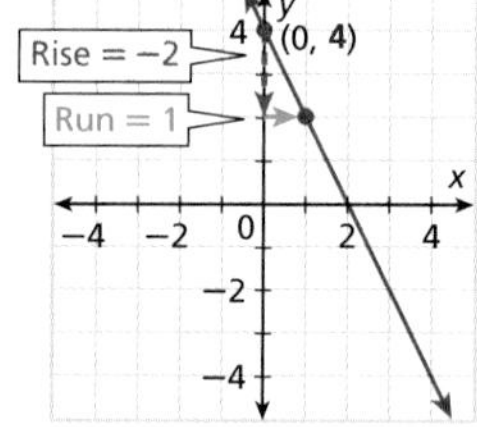

Step 1 The *y*-intercept is 4, so the line contains (0, 4). Plot (0, 4).

Step 2 Slope $= \frac{\text{rise}}{\text{run}} = \frac{-2}{1}$. Count 2 units down and 1 unit right from (0, 4) and plot another point.

Step 3 Draw the line through the two points.

Writing Math

Any integer can be written as a fraction with 1 in the denominator.

$-2 = \frac{-2}{1}$

1a.

1b.

CHECK IT OUT! Graph each line given the slope and *y*-intercept.

1a. slope = 2, *y*-intercept = -3 **1b.** slope $= -\frac{2}{3}$, *y*-intercept = 1

If you know the slope of a line and the *y*-intercept, you can write an equation that describes the line.

Step 1 If a line has slope *m* and the *y*-intercept is *b*, then $(0, b)$ is on the line. Substitute these values into the slope formula.

Slope formula → $m = \frac{y_2 - y_1}{x_2 - x_1}$ $m = \frac{y - b}{x - 0}$ ← *Since you don't know* (x_2, y_2)*, use* (x, y).

1 Introduce

EXPLORATION

5-5 Slope-Intercept Form

You will need graph paper or a graphing calculator for this Exploration.

1. Graph each function in the table. Once you have made each graph, find the slope of the line and the *y*-intercept. Record your results in the table.

Function	Slope	*y*-intercept
$y = 3x + 2$		
$y = -2x - 4$		
$y = \frac{1}{2}x - 3$		
$y = x + 1$		

2. Describe any patterns you notice in the table.
3. Use your results to predict the slope of the line described by $y = -5x + 7$.
4. Use your results to predict the *y*-intercept of the function $y = -3x - 2$.

THINK AND DISCUSS

5. **Predict** what the graph of $y = \frac{2}{3}x + 4$ will look like.
6. **Show** how you could write a linear function whose *y*-intercept is -1 and whose graph has a slope of 3.

Motivate

Ask students how they would graph the function $y = 2x + 3$. Possible answers: generate ordered pairs; use intercepts

Then tell students that in this lesson, they will learn a quick way to graph linear functions. It does not involve generating ordered pairs and uses only one intercept.

Explorations and answers are provided in *Alternate Openers: Explorations Transparencies.*

Step 2 Solve for y: $m = \frac{y - b}{x - 0}$

$$m = \frac{y - b}{x} \quad \text{Simplify the denominator.}$$

$$m \cdot x = \left(\frac{y - b}{x}\right) \cdot x \quad \text{Multiply both sides by } x.$$

$$mx = y - b$$

$$+b \quad +b \quad \text{Add } b \text{ to both sides.}$$

$$mx + b = y, \text{ or } y = mx + b$$

Slope-Intercept Form of a Linear Equation

The slope-intercept form of a linear equation is $y = mx + b$, where m is the slope of the equation's graph and b is the **y-intercept**.

Any linear equation can be written in slope-intercept form by solving for y and simplifying. In this form, you can immediately see the slope and y-intercept. Also, you can quickly graph a line when the equation is written in slope-intercept form.

EXAMPLE 2 Writing Linear Equations in Slope-Intercept Form

Write the equation of each line in slope-intercept form.

> **Remember!**
> Subtraction is the same as addition of the opposite.
> $-12x - \frac{1}{2} =$
> $-12x + \left(-\frac{1}{2}\right)$

A slope $= \frac{1}{3}$, y-intercept $= 6$

$y = mx + b$ — *Substitute the given values for m and b.*

$y = \frac{1}{3}x + 6$ — *Simplify if necessary.*

B slope $= -12$, y-intercept $= -\frac{1}{2}$

$y = mx + b$

$y = -12x + \left(-\frac{1}{2}\right)$

$y = -12x - \frac{1}{2}$

C slope $= 1$, y-intercept $= 0$

$y = mx + b$ — *Substitute the given values for m and b.*

$y = 1x + 0$

$y = x$ — *Simplify.*

D slope $= 0$, y-intercept $= -5$

$y = mx + b$

$y = 0x + (-5)$

$y = -5$

E slope $= 4$, $(2, 5)$ is on the line

Step 1 Find the y-intercept.

$y = mx + b$ — *Write the slope-intercept form.*

$5 = 4(2) + b$ — *Substitute 4 for m, 2 for x, and 5 for y.*

$5 = 8 + b$ — *Solve for b. Since 8 is added to b, subtract 8 from both sides to undo the addition.*

$-8 \quad -8$

$-3 = b$

Step 2 Write the equation.

$y = mx + b$ — *Write the slope-intercept form.*

$y = 4x + (-3)$ — *Substitute 4 for m and −3 for b.*

$y = 4x - 3$

2. A line has slope 8 and $(3, -1)$ is on the line. Write the equation of this line in slope-intercept form. $y = 8x - 25$

Power Presentations with PowerPoint®

Additional Examples

Example 1

Graph each line given the slope and y-intercept.

A. slope $= -\frac{2}{5}$; y-intercept $= 4$

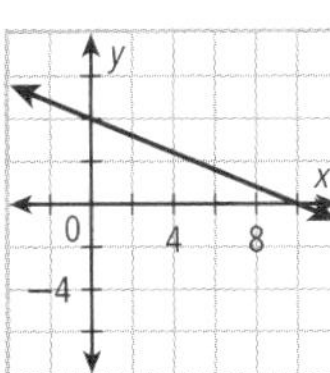

B. slope $= 4$; y-intercept $= -\frac{1}{2}$

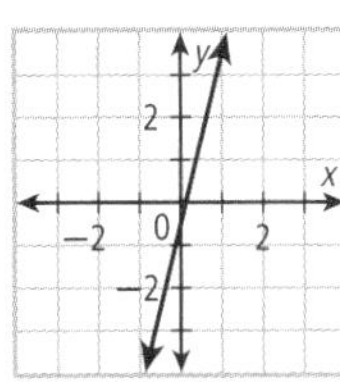

Example 2

Write the equation of each line in slope-intercept form.

A. slope $= \frac{1}{4}$; y-intercept $= 4$

$y = \frac{1}{4}x + 4$

B. slope $= -9$; y-intercept $= -\frac{5}{4}$

$y = -9x - \frac{5}{4}$

C. slope $= 3$; y-intercept $= \frac{1}{2}$

$y = 3x + \frac{1}{2}$

D. slope $= -\frac{1}{4}$; y-intercept $= -6$

$y = -\frac{1}{4}x - 6$

E. slope $= 2$; $(3, 4)$ is on the line

$y = 2x - 2$

Also available on transparency

2 Teach

Guided Instruction

Remind students that slope is the ratio of rise over run. Graph a line such as $y = -\frac{1}{2}x + 2$ in two ways, once using a slope of $\frac{-1}{2}$ and once using a slope of $\frac{1}{-2}$, to show that they result in the same line. In **Example 3,** remind students that they can quickly check that their graph is reasonable by looking at the slope. Lines with positive slopes rise from left to right, and lines with negative slopes fall.

Universal Access

Through Modeling

Use masking tape to outline a coordinate plane on a floor of square tiles. Then give a pair of students a length of rope. Announce an equation in slope-intercept form, and have the two students move around on the plane so that when they hold the rope taut, it represents the line described by the given equation, with each of them as two points on the line. A third student can check that these two points satisfy the equation.

INTERVENTION

Questioning Strategies

EXAMPLE 1

- What is the first step when graphing a line given the slope and y-intercept?

EXAMPLE 2

- What does b represent?
- What do the equation and graph look like if $b = 0$?

Power Presentations with PowerPoint®

Additional Examples

Example 3

Write each equation in slope-intercept form. Then graph the line given by the equation.

A. $y = 3x - 1$ $\quad y = 3x - 1$

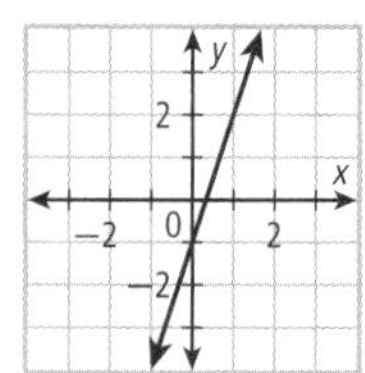

B. $y = 2$ $\quad y = 2$

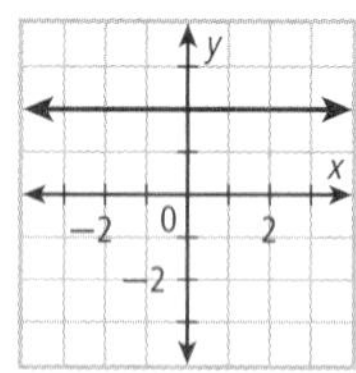

C. $2y + 3x = 6$ $\quad y = -\frac{3}{2}x + 3$

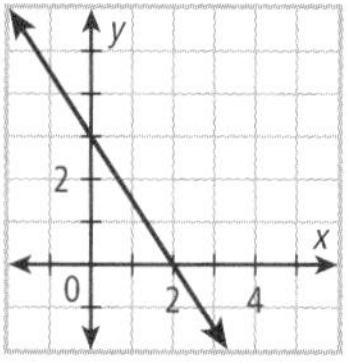

Also available on transparency

INTERVENTION
Questioning Strategies

EXAMPLE 3

- Does the coefficient of x in a linear equation always equal the slope? Explain.

Multiple Representations Remind students that they could use the intercepts to graph the equations in **Example 3.**

Math Builders For more on graphing linear equations, see the Function Builder on page MB2.

3a. $y = \frac{2}{3}x$

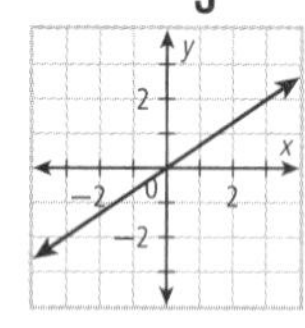

Helpful Hint

To divide $(8 - 3x)$ by 2, you can multiply by $\frac{1}{2}$ and distribute.

$\frac{8-3x}{2} = \frac{1}{2}(8 - 3x)$

$= \frac{1}{2}(8) + \frac{1}{2}(-3x)$

$= 4 - \frac{3}{2}x$

3b. $y = -3x + 5$

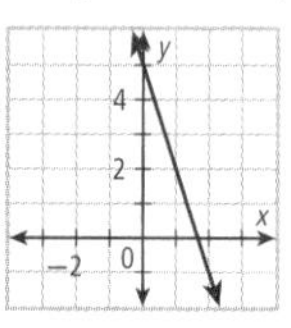

3c. $y = -4$

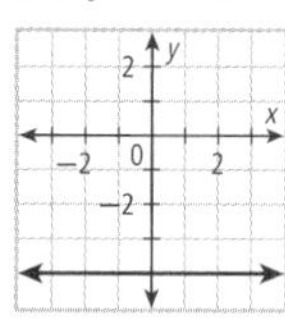

EXAMPLE 3 Using Slope-Intercept Form to Graph

Write each equation in slope-intercept form. Then graph the line given by the equation.

A $y = 4x - 3$

$y = 4x - 3$ is in the form $y = mx + b$.

slope: $m = 4 = \frac{4}{1}$

y-intercept: $b = -3$

Step 1 Plot $(0, -3)$.

Step 2 Count 4 units up and 1 unit right and plot another point.

Step 3 Draw the line connecting the two points.

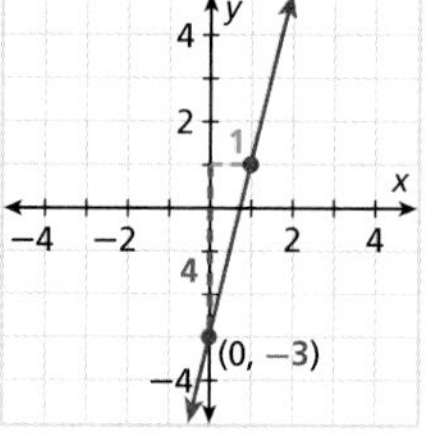

B $y = -\frac{2}{3}x + 2$

$y = -\frac{2}{3}x + 2$ is in the form $y = mx + b$.

slope: $m = -\frac{2}{3} = \frac{-2}{3}$

y-intercept: $b = 2$

Step 1 Plot $(0, 2)$

Step 2 Count 2 units down and 3 units right and plot another point.

Step 3 Draw the line connecting the two points.

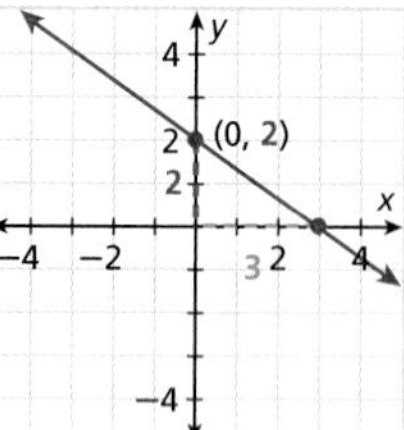

C $3x + 2y = 8$

Step 1 Write the equation in slope-intercept form by solving for y.

$3x + 2y = 8$

$\underline{-3x \qquad -3x}$ *Subtract 3x from both sides.*

$2y = 8 - 3x$

$\frac{2y}{2} = \frac{8-3x}{2}$ *Since y is multiplied by 2, divide both sides by 2.*

$y = 4 - \frac{3}{2}x$ $\quad \frac{3x}{2} = \frac{3}{2}x$

$y = -\frac{3}{2}x + 4$ *Write the equation in the form $y = mx + b$.*

Step 2 Graph the line.

$y = -\frac{3}{2}x + 4$ is in the form $y = mx + b$.

slope: $m = -\frac{3}{2} = \frac{-3}{2}$

y-intercept: $b = 4$

- Plot $(0, 4)$.
- Then count 3 units down and 2 units right and plot another point.
- Draw the line connecting the two points.

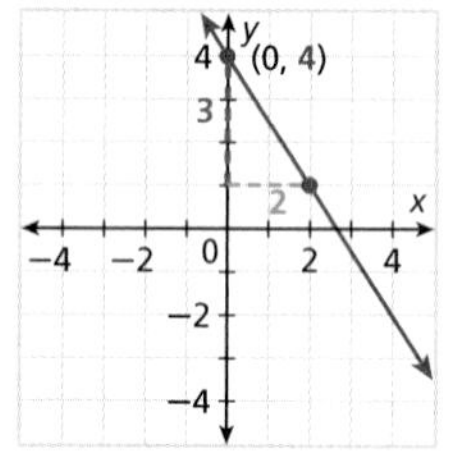

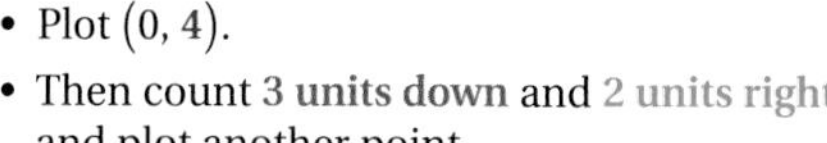

CHECK IT OUT! Write each equation in slope-intercept form. Then graph the line given by the equation.

3a. $y = \frac{2}{3}x$ $\quad$ **3b.** $6x + 2y = 10$ $\quad$ **3c.** $y = -4$

Teaching Tip **Inclusion** Students may confuse rise and run when counting slope on a graph. Draw $\updownarrow$ over $\leftrightarrow$ on the board to help them remember which number goes up or down and which goes left or right.

Teaching Tip **Language Support** In **Example 4,** the term *caterer* may be unfamiliar to some students. Explain that a caterer prepares food that is served at a special event, such as a wedding. **ENGLISH LANGUAGE LEARNERS**

EXAMPLE 4 Consumer Application

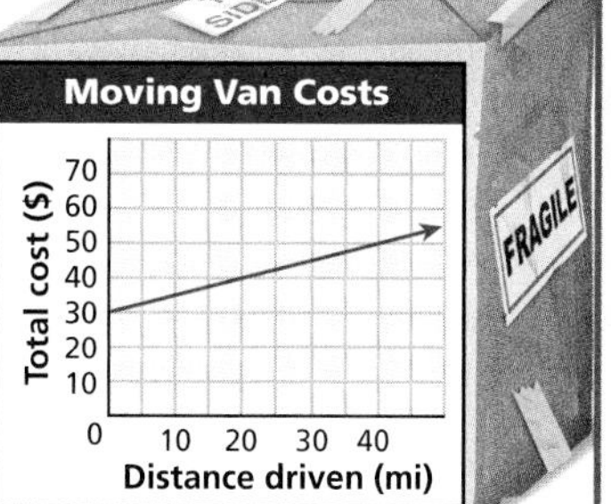

To rent a van, a moving company charges \$30.00 plus \$0.50 per mile. The cost as a function of the number of miles driven is shown in the graph.

a. Write an equation that represents the cost as a function of the number of miles.

Cost	is	\$0.50 per mile	times	miles	plus	\$30.00
y	$=$	0.5	$\cdot$	x	$+$	30

An equation is $y = 0.5x + 30$.

b. Identify the slope and y-intercept and describe their meanings.

The y-intercept is 30. This is the cost for 0 miles, or the initial fee of \$30.00.

The slope is 0.5. This is the rate of change of the cost: \$0.50 per mile.

c. Find the cost of the van for 150 miles.

$y = 0.5x + 30$

$= 0.5(150) + 30 = 105$ *Substitute 150 for x in the equation.*

The cost of the van for 150 miles is \$105.

4. A caterer charges a \$200 fee plus \$18 per person served. The cost as a function of the number of guests is shown in the graph.

a. Write an equation that represents the cost as a function of the number of guests. **$y = 18x + 200$**

b. Identify the slope and y-intercept and describe their meanings.

c. Find the cost of catering an event for 200 guests. **\$3800**

4b. slope: 18; cost per person; y-int: 200; fee

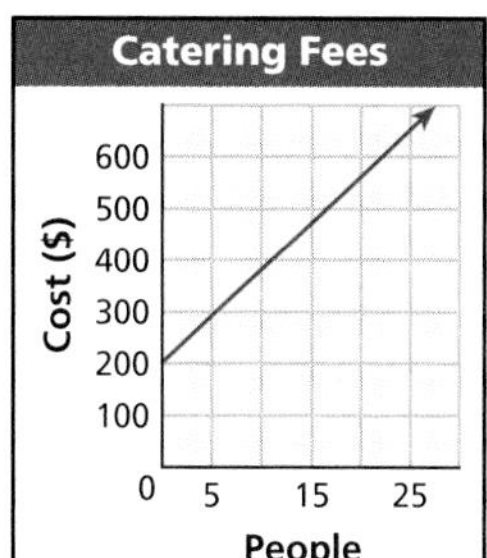

THINK AND DISCUSS

1. If a linear function has a y-intercept of b, at what point does its graph cross the y-axis?

2. Where does the line given by $y = 4.395x - 23.75$ cross the y-axis?

Know it! Note

3. GET ORGANIZED Copy and complete the graphic organizer.

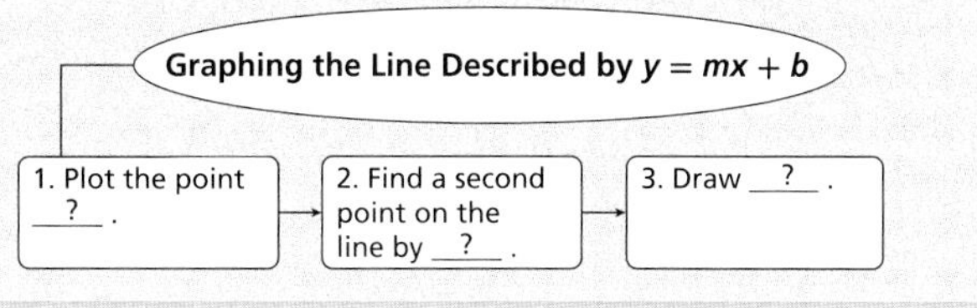

Power Presentations with PowerPoint®

Additional Examples

Example 4

A closet organizer charges a \$100 initial consultation fee plus \$30 per hour. The cost as a function of the number of hours worked is graphed below.

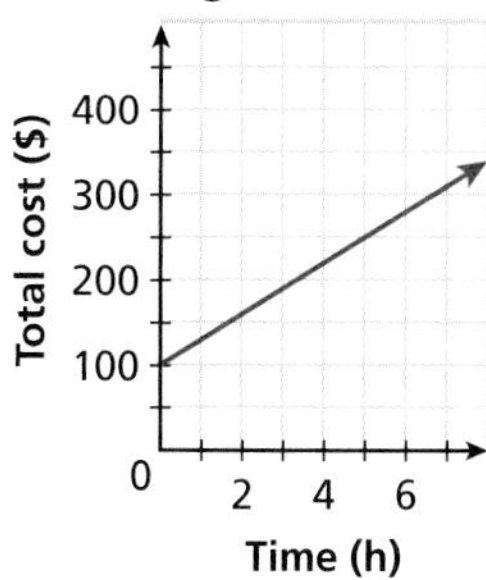

a. Write an equation that represents the cost as a function of the number of hours. $y = 30x + 100$

b. Identify the slope and y-intercept and describe their meanings. y-int.: 100; the cost for 0 h, or the initial fee of \$100. Slope: 30; the rate of change of the cost: \$30/h.

c. Find the cost if the organizer works 12 hours. \$460

Also available on transparency

INTERVENTION

Questioning Strategies

EXAMPLE 4

- Why doesn't the graph start at the origin?
- How can you use the graph to check the slope?

3 Close

Summarize

Review slope-intercept form, reminding students that an integer slope can be written with a denominator of 1. Review how to write an equation of a line in slope-intercept form when given the slope and y-intercept or when given the slope and a point on the line.

FORMATIVE ASSESSMENT and INTERVENTION

***Diagnose Before* the Lesson**
5-5 Warm Up, TE p. 290

***Monitor During* the Lesson**
Check It Out! Exercises, SE pp. 290–293
Questioning Strategies, TE pp. 291–293

***Assess After* the Lesson**
5-5 Lesson Quiz, TE p. 296
Alternative Assessment, TE p. 296

Answers to *Think and Discuss*

1. $(0, b)$
2. $(0, -23.75)$
3. See p. A4.

5-5 Exercises

Assignment Guide

Assign *Guided Practice* exercises as necessary.

If you finished Examples **1–2**
Proficient 13–20, 46
Advanced 13–20, 46

If you finished Examples **1–4**
Proficient 13–35, 39–46, 49–56
Advanced 13–30, 32–35, 39–56

Homework Quick Check
Quickly check key concepts.
Exercises: 14, 18, 20, 24, 26, 27

Answers

1. 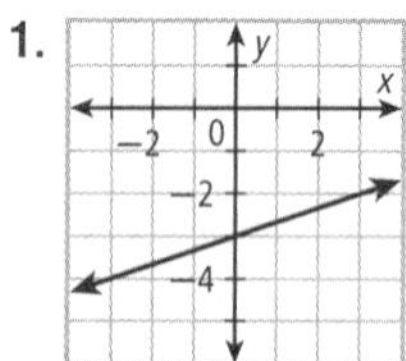

2. 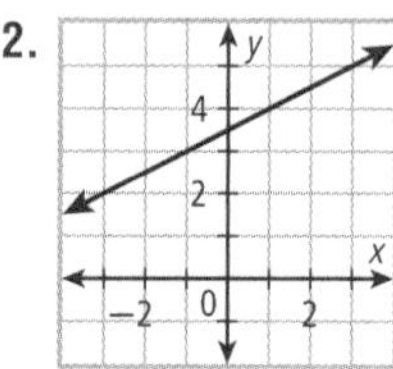

3. 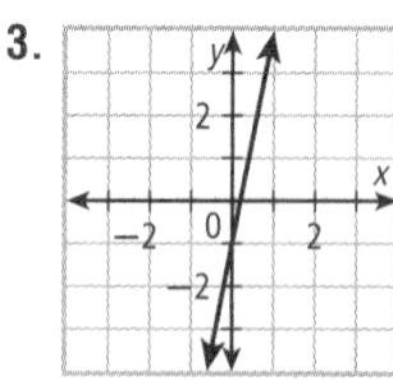

4. 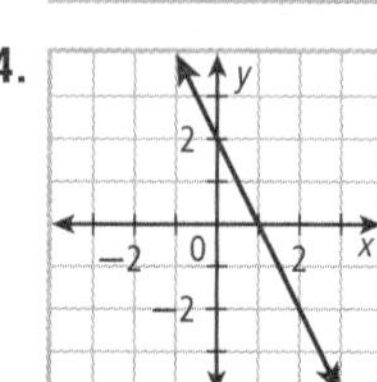

9–11. For graphs, see p. A19.
13–16, 21–29. See pp. A19–A20.

California Standards

Standard	Exercises
4.0	52, 53
5.0	49–53
6.0	1–4, 9–11, 12b, 13–16, 21–29, 30b, 32–35, 40c, 43, 46, 54–56
7.0	8, 19, 20
25.1	48
25.2	31

5-5 Exercises

California Standards Practice 6.0, 7.0, 25.1, 25.2

go.hrw.com
Homework Help Online KEYWORD: MA8CA 5-5
Parent Resources Online KEYWORD: MA8CA Parent

GUIDED PRACTICE

SEE EXAMPLE 1 p. 290

Graph each line given the slope and y-intercept.

1. slope $= \frac{1}{3}$, y-intercept $= -3$
2. slope $= 0.5$, y-intercept $= 3.5$
3. slope $= 5$, y-intercept $= -1$
4. slope $= -2$, y-intercept $= 2$

SEE EXAMPLE 2 p. 291

Write the equation of each line in slope-intercept form.

5. slope $= 8$, y-intercept $= 2$ **$y = 8x + 2$**
6. slope $= \frac{1}{2}$, y-intercept $= -6$ **$y = \frac{1}{2}x - 6$**
7. slope $= 0$, y-intercept $= -3$ **$y = -3$**
8. slope $= 5$, the point $(2, 7)$ is on the line **$y = 5x - 3$**

SEE EXAMPLE 3 p. 292

Write each equation in slope-intercept form. Then graph the line given by the equation.

9. $y = \frac{2}{5}x - 6$ **$y = \frac{2}{5}x - 6$**
10. $3x - y = 1$ **$y = 3x - 1$**
11. $2x + y = 4$ **$y = -2x + 4$**

SEE EXAMPLE 4 p. 293

12. Helen is in a bicycle race. She has already biked 10 miles at a rate of 18 miles per hour. She keeps biking at the same rate throughout the race. Her distance as a function of time is shown in the graph.
   a. Write an equation that represents the distance Helen has biked as a function of time. **$y = 18x + 10$**
   b. Identify the slope and y-intercept and describe their meanings.
   c. How far will Helen have biked after 2 hours? **46 mi**

12b. slope: 18; Helen's speed; y-int.: 10; dist. she has already biked

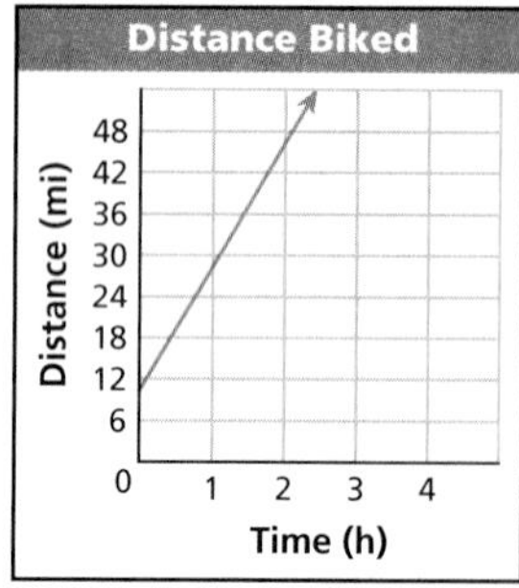

PRACTICE AND PROBLEM SOLVING

Independent Practice

For Exercises	See Example
13–16	1
17–20	2
21–29	3
30	4

Extra Practice
Skills Practice p. EP11
Application Practice p. EP28

Graph each line given the slope and y-intercept.

13. slope $= \frac{1}{4}$, y-intercept $= 7$
14. slope $= -6$, y-intercept $= -3$
15. slope $= 1$, y-intercept $= -4$
16. slope $= -\frac{4}{5}$, y-intercept $= 6$

Write the equation of each line in slope-intercept form.

17. slope $= 5$, y-intercept $= -9$ **$y = 5x - 9$**
18. slope $= -\frac{2}{3}$, y-intercept $= 2$ **$y = -\frac{2}{3}x + 2$**
19. slope $= -\frac{1}{2}$, $(6, 4)$ is on the line **$y = -\frac{1}{2}x + 7$**
20. slope $= 0$, $(6, -8)$ is on the line **$y = -8$**

Write each equation in slope-intercept form. Then graph the line given by the equation.

21. $y = -\frac{1}{2}x + 3$
22. $y = \frac{1}{3}x - 5$
23. $y = x + 6$
24. $6x + 3y = 12$
25. $y = \frac{7}{2}$
26. $4x + y = 9$
27. $-\frac{1}{2}x + y = 4$
28. $\frac{2}{3}x + y = 2$
29. $2x + y = 8$

5-5 READING STRATEGIES

LESSON 5-5 Reading Strategies
Follow a Procedure

The procedure outlined below shows how to graph a line using slope-intercept form.

Graph the line described by $2x + y = 4$.

Step 1: Rewrite in slope-intercept form.
$2x + y = 4$
$-2x \quad -2x$
$y = -2x + 4$

Step 2: Identify the slope and y-intercept.
$y = mx + b$
$m = -2 = \frac{-2}{1}$
$b = 4$

Step 3: Plot the point $(0, b)$.

Step 4: Plot a second point using the slope. (Down 2, Right 1)

Step 5: Draw a line through the points.

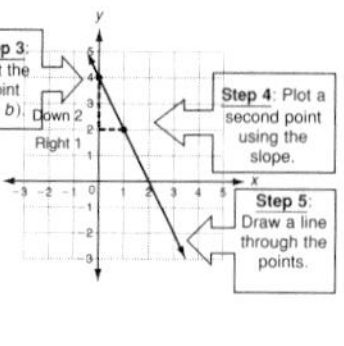

Answer the following.

1. What is the benefit of always writing slope as a fraction?
   With a fraction, you have a "rise" and "run" for graphing.
2. What point would you plot first if $b = -8$? **(0, −8)**

Identify the slope and y-intercept for each equation.

3. $y = 5x + 12$ m: **5** b: **12**
4. $y = -3x$ m: **−3** b: **0**
5. $y = x - 4$ m: **1** b: **−4**
6. $3y = x + 9$ m: **$\frac{1}{3}$** b: **3**

Graph the line described by each equation.

7. $3x + y = 2$ 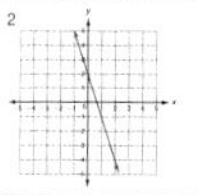
8. $x - 2y = 6$

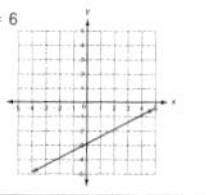

5-5 REVIEW FOR MASTERY

LESSON 5-5 Review for Mastery
Slope-Intercept Form

An equation is in **slope-intercept form** if it is written as:

$y = mx + b.$ (m is the slope. b is the y-intercept.)

A line has a slope of −4 and a y-intercept of 3. Write the equation in slope-intercept form.

$y = mx + b$ *Substitute the given values for m and b.*
$y = -4x + 3$

A line has a slope of 2. The ordered pair (3, 1) is on the line. Write the equation in slope-intercept form.

Step 1: Find the y-intercept.
$y = mx + b$
$y = 2x + b$ *Substitute the given value for m.*
$1 = 2(3) + b$ *Substitute the given values for x and y.*
$1 = 6 + b$ *Solve for b.*
$-6 \quad -6$
$-5 = b$

Step 2: Write the equation.
$y = mx + b$
$y = 2x - 5$ *Substitute the given value for m and the value you found for b.*

Write the equation that describes each line in slope-intercept form.

1. slope $= \frac{1}{4}$, y-intercept $= 3$ **$y = \frac{1}{4}x + 3$**
2. slope $= -5$, y-intercept $= 0$ **$y = -5x$**
3. slope $= 7$, y-intercept $= -2$ **$y = 7x - 2$**
4. slope is 3, (4, 6) is on the line. **$y = 3x - 6$**
5. slope is $\frac{1}{2}$, (−2, 8) is on the line. **$y = \frac{1}{2}x + 9$**
6. slope is −1, (5, −2) is on the line. **$y = -x + 3$**

30. Fitness Pauline's health club has an enrollment fee of $175 and costs $35 per month. Total cost as a function of number of membership months is shown in the graph.

a. Write an equation that represents the total cost as a function of months. **$y = 35x + 175$**

b. Identify the slope and y-intercept and describe their meanings.

c. Find the cost of one year of membership. **$595**

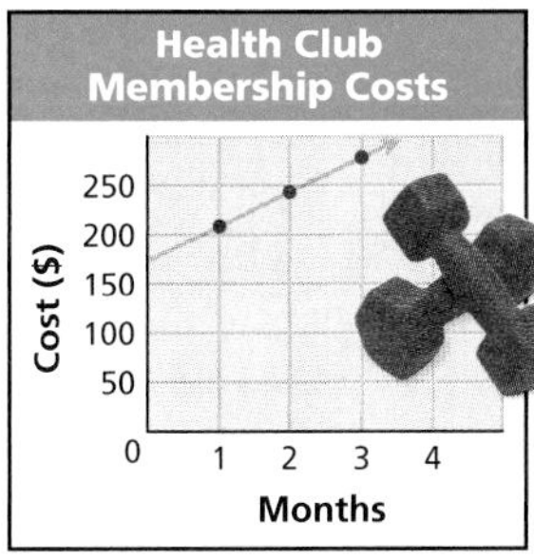

30b. slope: 35; monthly cost; y-int.: 175; enrollment fee

Health Club Membership Costs

Cost ($): 0, 50, 100, 150, 200, 250; Months: 0, 1, 2, 3, 4

31. ///ERROR ANALYSIS/// Two students wrote $3x + 2y = 5$ in slope-intercept form. Who is incorrect? Describe the error.

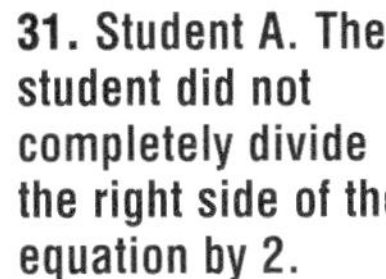

31. Student A. The student did not completely divide the right side of the equation by 2.

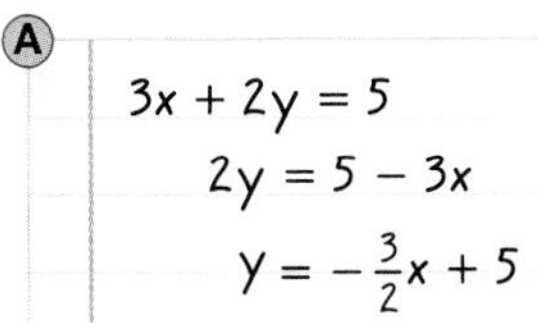

(A)

$3x + 2y = 5$

$2y = 5 - 3x$

$y = -\frac{3}{2}x + 5$

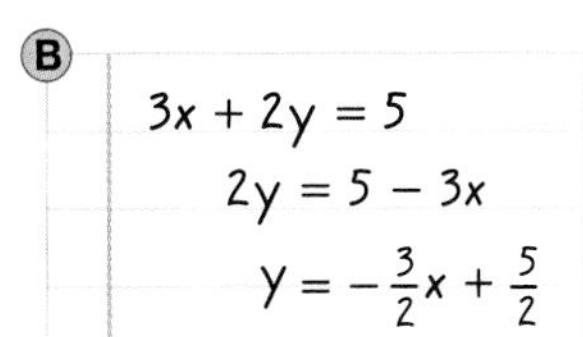

(B)

$3x + 2y = 5$

$2y = 5 - 3x$

$y = -\frac{3}{2}x + \frac{5}{2}$

Reasoning **Tell whether each situation is possible or impossible. If possible, draw a sketch of the graphs. If impossible, explain.**

32. Two different lines have the same slope. **possible**

33. Two different linear functions have the same y-intercept. **possible**

34. Two different intersecting lines have the same slope. **impossible**

35. A linear function does not have a y-intercept. **impossible**

Match each equation with its corresponding graph.

36. $y = 2x - 1$ **C**

37. $y = \frac{1}{2}x - 1$ **A**

38. $y = -\frac{1}{2}x + 1$ **B**

A.

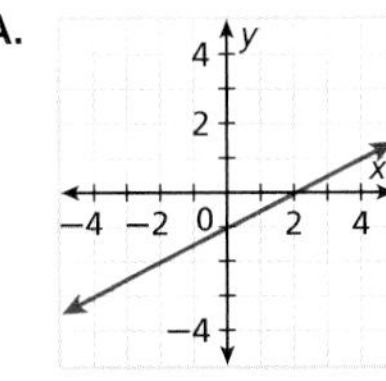

B.

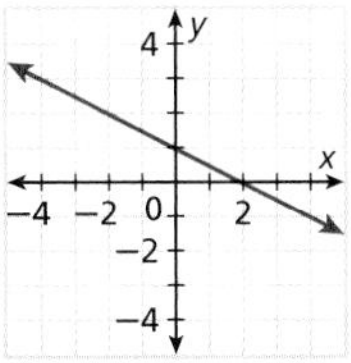

C.

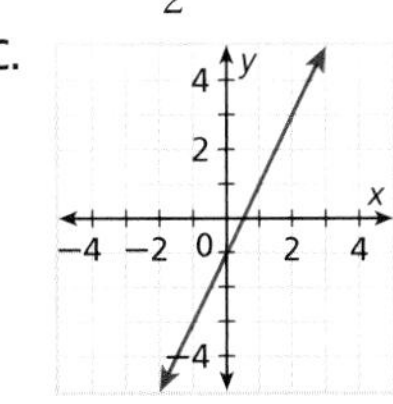

39. Write About It Write an equation for a vertical line. Can you write this equation in slope-intercept form? Why or why not?

Possible answer: $x = -4$; no; because it has an undef. slope and no y-int.

40. This problem will prepare you for the Concept Connection on page 312.

a. Ricardo and Sam walk from Sam's house to school. Sam lives 3 blocks from Ricardo's house. The graph shows their distance from Ricardo's house as they walk to school at specific times. Create a table of these values.

b. Find an equation for the distance as a function of time.

c. Using the equation, what are the slope and y-intercept? What do they represent in this situation?

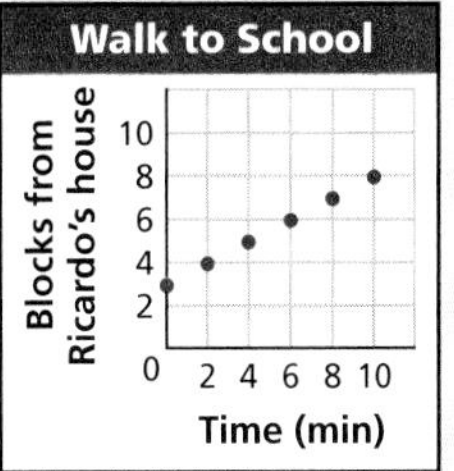

CONCEPT CONNECTION **Exercise 40** involves representing a real-world function relationship with a graph, a table of values, and an equation. This exercise prepares students for the Concept Connection on page 312.

Answers

32.

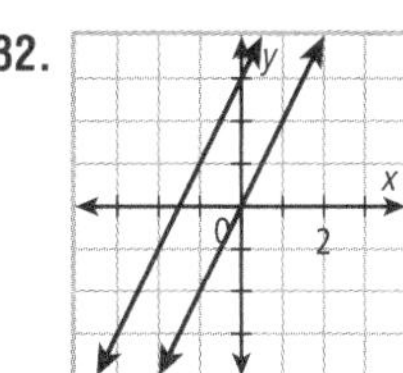

33.

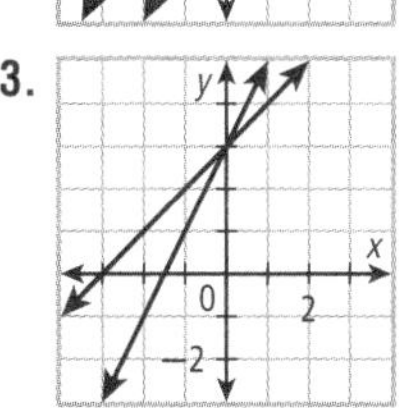

34. Lines with the same slope are par. and therefore cannot intersect.

35. If a lin. func. does not have a y-int., then its graph does not intersect the y-axis. The y-axis is vert. so the only lines that do not intersect the y-axis are also vert. But vert. lines cannot be graphs of functions. All nonvert. lines will intersect the y-axis, so every lin. func. will have a y-int.

40a.

x	y
0	3
2	4
4	5
6	6
8	7
10	8

b. $y = \frac{1}{2}x + 3$

c. slope: $\frac{1}{2}$; boys' walking speed; y-int.: 3; dist. from Sam's house to Ricardo's house

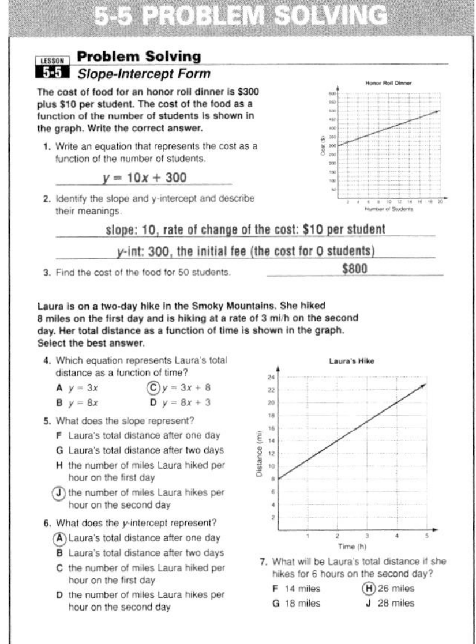

5-5 PROBLEM SOLVING

LESSON 5-5 **Problem Solving**
Slope-Intercept Form

The cost of food for an honor roll dinner is $300 plus $10 per student. The cost of the food as a function of the number of students is shown in the graph. Write the correct answer.

1. Write an equation that represents the cost as a function of the number of students.
$y = 10x + 300$

2. Identify the slope and y-intercept and describe their meanings.
slope: 10, rate of change of the cost: $10 per student
y-int: 300, the initial fee (the cost for 0 students)

3. Find the cost of the food for 50 students. **$800**

Laura is on a two-day hike in the Smoky Mountains. She hiked 8 miles on the first day and is hiking at a rate of 3 mi/h on the second day. Her total distance as a function of time is shown in the graph. Select the best answer.

4. Which equation represents Laura's total distance as a function of time?
A $y = 3x$
(C) $y = 3x + 8$
B $y = 8x$
D $y = 8x + 3$

5. What does the slope represent?
F Laura's total distance after one day
G Laura's total distance after two days
H the number of miles Laura hiked per hour on the first day
(J) the number of miles Laura hikes per hour on the second day

6. What does the y-intercept represent?
(A) Laura's total distance after one day
B Laura's total distance after two days
C the number of miles Laura hiked per hour on the first day
D the number of miles Laura hikes per hour on the second day

7. What will be Laura's total distance if she hikes for 6 hours on the second day?
F 14 miles
(H) 26 miles
G 18 miles
J 28 miles

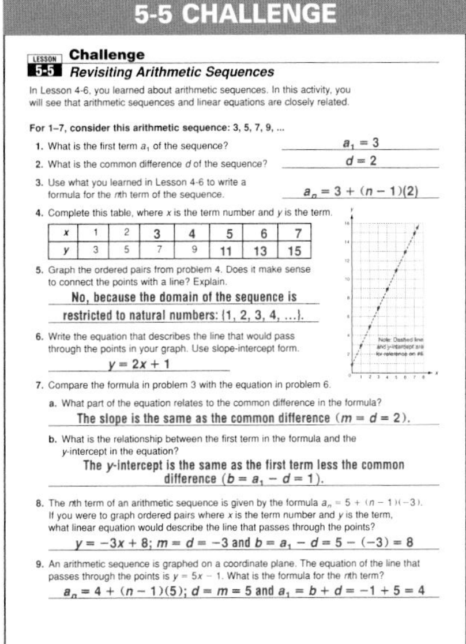

5-5 CHALLENGE

LESSON 5-5 **Challenge**
Revisiting Arithmetic Sequences

In Lesson 4-6, you learned about arithmetic sequences. In this activity, you will see that arithmetic sequences and linear equations are closely related.

For 1–7, consider this arithmetic sequence: 3, 5, 7, 9, ...

1. What is the first term a_1 of the sequence? **$a_1 = 3$**

2. What is the common difference d of the sequence? **$d = 2$**

3. Use what you learned in Lesson 4-6 to write a formula for the nth term of the sequence. **$a_n = 3 + (n - 1)(2)$**

4. Complete this table, where x is the term number and y is the term.

x	1	2	3	4	5	6	7
y	3	5	7	9	11	13	15

5. Graph the ordered pairs from problem 4. Does it make sense to connect the points with a line? Explain.
No, because the domain of the sequence is restricted to natural numbers: {1, 2, 3, 4, ...}.

6. Write the equation that describes the line that would pass through the points in your graph. Use slope-intercept form.
$y = 2x + 1$

7. Compare the formula in problem 3 with the equation in problem 6.
a. What part of the equation relates to the common difference in the formula?
The slope is the same as the common difference ($m = d = 2$).
b. What is the relationship between the first term in the formula and the y-intercept in the equation?
The y-intercept is the same as the first term less the common difference ($b = a_1 - d = 1$).

8. The nth term of an arithmetic sequence is given by the formula $a_n = 5 + (n - 1)(-3)$. If you were to graph ordered pairs where x is the term number and y is the term, what linear equation would describe the line that passes through the points?
$y = -3x + 8$; $m = d = -3$ and $b = a_1 - d = 5 - (-3) = 8$

9. An arithmetic sequence is graphed on a coordinate plane. The equation of the line that passes through the points is $y = 5x - 1$. What is the formula for the nth term?
$a_n = 4 + (n - 1)(5)$; $d = m = 5$ and $a_1 = b + d = -1 + 5 = 4$

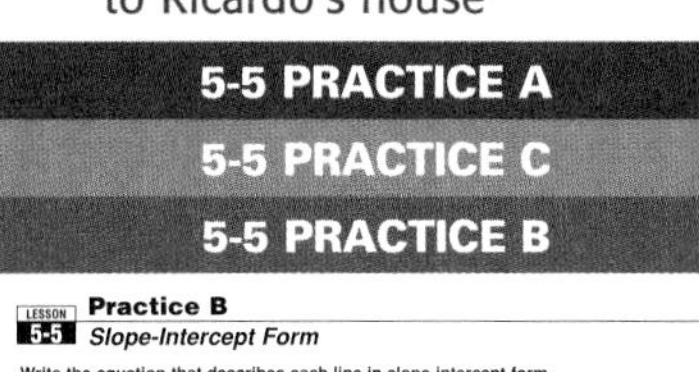

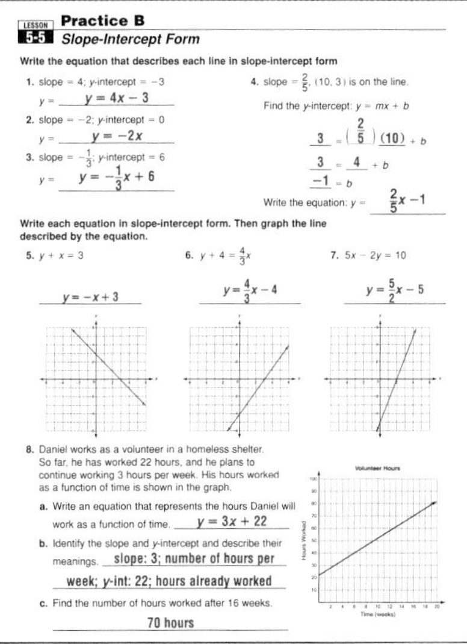

LESSON 5-5 **Practice B**
Slope-Intercept Form

Write the equation that describes each line in slope-intercept form

1. slope = 4; y-intercept = −3
$y =$ **$y = 4x - 3$**

2. slope = −2; y-intercept = 0
$y =$ **$y = -2x$**

3. slope = $-\frac{1}{3}$; y-intercept = 6
$y =$ **$y = -\frac{1}{3}x + 6$**

4. slope = $\frac{2}{5}$, (10, 3) is on the line.
Find the y-intercept: $y = mx + b$
3 = (**$\frac{2}{5}$**)(**10**) + b
3 = **4** + b
−1 = b
Write the equation: $y =$ **$\frac{2}{5}x - 1$**

Write each equation in slope-intercept form. Then graph the line described by the equation.

5. $y + x = 3$ **$y = -x + 3$**

6. $y + 4 = \frac{4}{3}x$ **$y = \frac{4}{3}x - 4$**

7. $5x - 2y = 10$ **$y = \frac{5}{2}x - 5$**

8. Daniel works as a volunteer in a homeless shelter. So far, he has worked 22 hours, and he plans to continue working 3 hours per week. His hours worked as a function of time is shown in the graph.
a. Write an equation that represents the hours Daniel will work as a function of time. **$y = 3x + 22$**
b. Identify the slope and y-intercept and describe their meanings. **slope: 3; number of hours per week; y-int: 22; hours already worked**
c. Find the number of hours worked after 16 weeks. **70 hours**

Multiple Choice In Exercise 41, students who chose **C** chose a function whose graph has the same slope, but this function does not have the same y-intercept. Students who chose **D** may have forgotten to divide by -2.

Journal

Have students describe three different ways to graph a line.

ALTERNATIVE ASSESSMENT

Have students write equations for 4 lines: one whose slope is a positive integer, one whose slope is a negative integer, and two whose slopes are fractions. Three should be in slope-intercept form, and one in standard form. Then have them trade equations with a partner, who will ensure that the above conditions are met and then graph the lines.

Power Presentations with PowerPoint®

5-5 Lesson Quiz

Write the equation of each line in slope-intercept form.

1. slope = 3, y-intercept = -2
$y = 3x - 2$

2. slope = 0, y-intercept = $\frac{1}{2}$
$y = \frac{1}{2}$

3. slope = $\frac{3}{2}$, $(2, 7)$ is on the line
$y = \frac{3}{2}x + 4$

Write each equation in slope-intercept form. Then graph the line given by the equation.

4. $6x + 2y = 10$ $\quad y = -3x + 5$

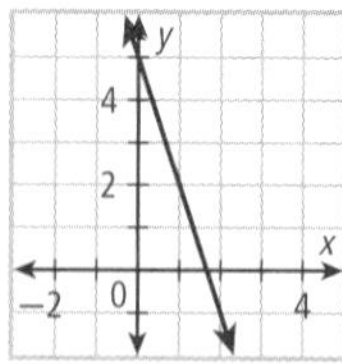

5. $x - y = 6$ $\quad y = x - 6$

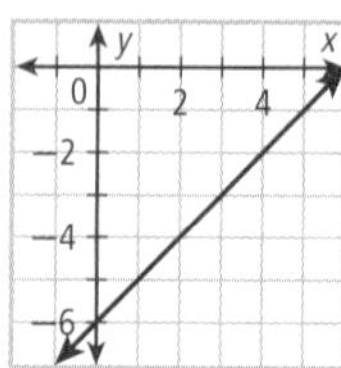

Also available on transparency

Multiple Choice For Exercises 41–43, choose the best answer.

41. Which function has the same y-intercept as $y = \frac{1}{2}x - 2$?

Ⓐ $2x + 3y = 6$ Ⓑ $x + 4y = -8$ (circled) Ⓒ $-\frac{1}{2}x + y = 4$ Ⓓ $\frac{1}{2}x - 2y = -2$

42. What is the slope-intercept form of $x - y = -8$?

Ⓐ $y = -x - 8$ Ⓑ $y = x - 8$ Ⓒ $y = -x + 8$ Ⓓ $y = x + 8$ (circled)

43. Which function has a y-intercept of 3?

Ⓐ $2x - y = 3$ Ⓑ $2x + y = 3$ (circled) Ⓒ $2x + y = 6$ Ⓓ $y = 3x$

44. Gridded Response What is the slope of the line given by $-6x = -2y + 5$? **3**

45. Short Response Write a function whose graph has the same slope as the line given by $3x - 9y = 9$ and the same y-intercept as $8x - 2y = 6$. Show your work.
$y = \frac{1}{3}x - 3$

CHALLENGE AND EXTEND

46. $y = -\frac{A}{B}x + \frac{C}{B}$; slope $= -\frac{A}{B}$; y-int.: $\frac{C}{B}$

46. The standard form of a linear equation is $Ax + By = C$. Rewrite this equation in slope-intercept form. What is the slope? What is the y-intercept?

47. What value of n in the equation $nx + 5 = 3y$ would give a line with slope -2? **-6**

48. Reasoning A line has slope 3 and $(1, 6)$ is on the line. Below are the steps to find the equation of this line. Fill in the missing reasons for each step.

Statements	Reasons
1. $y = mx + b$	a. Slope-intercept form
2. $6 = 3(1) + b$	b. Substitute 1 for x, 6 for y, and 3 for m.
3. $6 = 3 + b$	c. Identity Property of Multiplication
4. $3 = b$	d. Subtraction Property of Equality
5. $y = mx + b$	e. Slope-intercept form
6. $y = 3x + 3$	f. Substitute 3 for m and 3 for b.

SPIRAL STANDARDS REVIEW

Write an inequality for each statement. Solve the inequality and graph the solutions. *(Lesson 3-4)*

49. The sum of three times a number and four is less than or equal to 10.

50. One-half the difference of a number and 150 is greater than or equal to 75.

Solve each inequality. *(Lesson 3-5)*

51. $3n \leq 2n + 8$ **$n \leq 8$**

52. $4x - 4 > 2(x + 5)$ **$x > 7$**

53. $2(2t + 1) > 6t + 8$ **$t < -3$**

Find the x- and y-intercepts. *(Lesson 5-2)*

54. $12x = 3y$ **x-int.: 0; y-int.: 0**

55. $y = -2x + 6$ **x-int.: 3; y-int.: 6**

56. $y = -0.5x - 3.5$ **x-int.: -7; y-int.: -3.5**

Answers

49. $3x + 4 \leq 10$

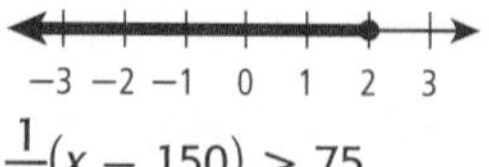

(number line: −3 −2 −1 0 1 2 3)

50. $\frac{1}{2}(x - 150) \geq 75$

(number line: 200 300 400 500 600)

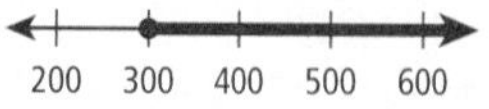

5-6 Point-Slope Form

PIES
old,
ded.
yful!
teer.
KITTENS AVAILABLE
to good home. 2 mo. old, litter trained. Very cute and playful! $10 adoption fee.
DC
8 n
sho
Ve
ha

California Standards

7.0 Students verify that a point lies on a line, given an equation of the line. Students are able to derive linear equations by using the point-slope formula.
Also covered: **6.0**

Why learn this?

You can use point-slope form to represent a cost function, such as the cost of placing a newspaper ad. (See Example 5.)

In Lesson 5-5, you saw that if you know the slope of a line and the y-intercept, you can graph the line. You can also graph a line if you know its slope and any point on the line.

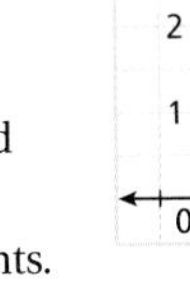

EXAMPLE 1 Using Slope and a Point to Graph

Graph the line with the given slope that contains the given point.

A slope = 3; $(1, 1)$

Step 1 Plot $(1, 1)$.

Step 2 Use the slope to move from $(1, 1)$ to another point.

$$\text{slope} = \frac{\text{rise}}{\text{run}} = 3 = \frac{3}{1}$$

Move 3 units up and 1 unit right and plot another point.

Step 3 Draw the line connecting the two points.

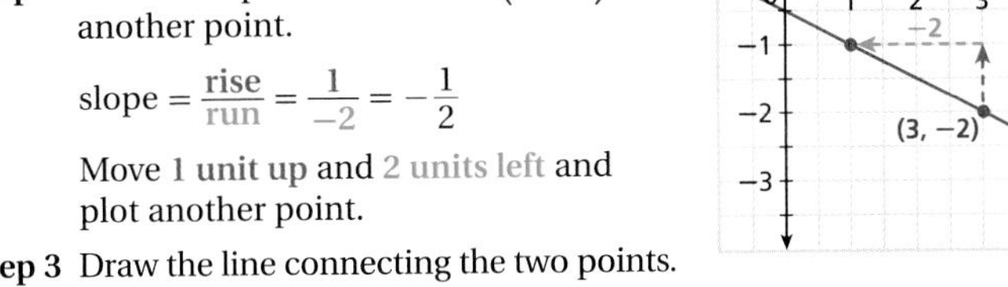

B slope $= -\frac{1}{2}$; $(3, -2)$

Step 1 Plot $(3, -2)$.

Step 2 Use the slope to move from $(3, -2)$ to another point.

$$\text{slope} = \frac{\text{rise}}{\text{run}} = \frac{1}{-2} = -\frac{1}{2}$$

Move 1 unit up and 2 units left and plot another point.

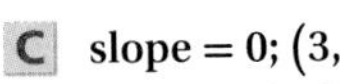

Step 3 Draw the line connecting the two points.

Helpful Hint

For a negative fraction, you can write the negative sign in one of three places.

$$-\frac{1}{2} = \frac{-1}{2} = \frac{1}{-2}$$

C slope = 0; $(3, 2)$

A line with slope of 0 is horizontal.
Draw the horizontal line through $(3, 2)$.

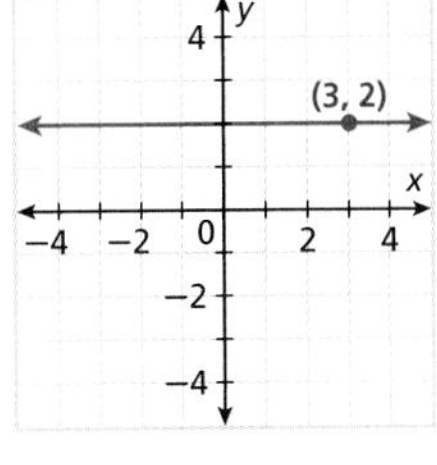

1.

CHECK IT OUT! 1. Graph the line with slope -1 that contains $(2, -2)$.

5-6 Organizer

Objectives: Graph a line and write a linear equation using point-slope form.

Write a linear equation given two points.

Online Edition
Tutorial Videos

Countdown to Mastery Week 11

Power Presentations with PowerPoint®

Warm Up

Find the slope of the line containing each pair of points.

1. $(0, 2)$ and $(3, 4)$ $\frac{2}{3}$
2. $(-2, 8)$ and $(4, 2)$ -1
3. $(3, 3)$ and $(12, -15)$ -2

Write the following equations in slope-intercept form.

4. $y - 5 = 3(x + 2)$ $y = 3x + 11$
5. $3x + 4y + 20 = 0$
$y = -\frac{3}{4}x - 5$

Also available on transparency

Math Humor

Q: What did the horizontal line say to the vertical line?

A: It was nice running into you.

1 Introduce

EXPLORATION

5-6 Point-Slope Form

In this Exploration, you will investigate another way to write linear equations.

1a. Does the line described by $y - 4 = 5(x - 3)$ contain the point $(3, 4)$? How do you know?
b. What is the slope of the line described by $y - 4 = 5(x - 3)$?
2a. Does the line described by $y - 2 = \frac{1}{2}(x - 1)$ contain the point $(1, 2)$? How do you know?
b. What is the slope of the line described by $y - 2 = \frac{1}{2}(x - 1)$?
3a. Does the line described by $y - 6 = -3(x - 12)$ contain the point $(12, 6)$? How do you know?
b. What is the slope of the line described by $y - 6 = -3(x - 12)$?
4. Describe any patterns you notice in Problems 1–3.

THINK AND DISCUSS

5. Explain how you can use the patterns you discovered to make some predictions about the line described by $y + 2 = -2(x + 3)$.
6. Discuss what equation you think describes a line with slope 4 that contains the point $(5, 8)$. Explain your reasoning.

Motivate

Plot the points $(-3, 2)$ and $(1, -6)$ on a coordinate grid. Ask students to find the slope of the line that contains these two points. -2 Then ask if they could write the equation of the line using slope-intercept form. no Ask why not. because you do not know the y-intercept

Tell students that in this lesson, they will learn a new formula to write an equation of a line, using any two points on the line.

Explorations and answers are provided in *Alternate Openers: Explorations Transparencies.*

California Standards

Algebra 1 **7.0**
Also covered:
6.0 Students graph a linear equation and compute the x- and **y-intercepts** (e.g., graph $2x + 6y = 4$). They are also able to sketch the region defined by linear inequalities (e.g., they sketch the region by $2x + 6y = 4$.)

Power Presentations with PowerPoint®

Additional Examples

Example 1

Graph the line with the given slope that contains the given point.

A. slope = 2; (3, 1)

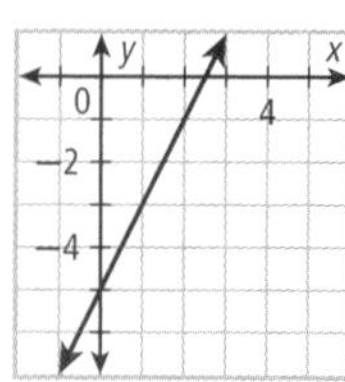

B. slope = $\frac{3}{4}$; (−2, 4)

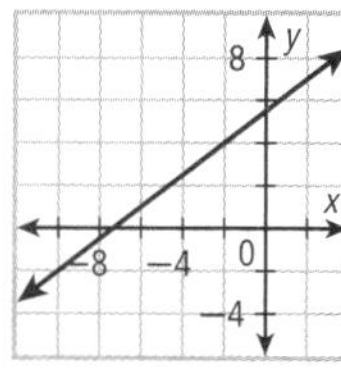

C. slope = 0; (4, −3)

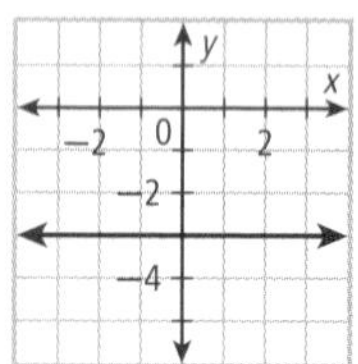

Example 2

Write an equation in point-slope form for the line with the given slope that contains the given point.

A. slope = $\frac{1}{6}$; (5, 1)

$y - 1 = \frac{1}{6}(x - 5)$

B. slope = −4; (0, 3)

$y - 3 = -4(x - 0)$

C. slope = 1; (−1, −4)

$y + 4 = 1(x + 1)$

Also available on transparency

INTERVENTION
Questioning Strategies

EXAMPLE 1

- How could you check that the graph is reasonable?

EXAMPLE 2

- How do you use the point to write the equation?

If you know the slope and any point on the line, you can write an equation of the line by using the slope formula.

$$m = \frac{y_2 - y_1}{x_2 - x_1} \quad \textit{Slope formula}$$

$$m(x_2 - x_1) = \left(\frac{y_2 - y_1}{x_2 - x_1}\right)(x_2 - x_1) \quad \textit{Multiply both sides by } (x_2 - x_1).$$

$$m(x_2 - x_1) = y_2 - y_1 \quad \textit{Simplify.}$$

$$y_2 - y_1 = m(x_2 - x_1)$$

Point-Slope Form of a Linear Equation

The line with slope m that contains the point (x_1, y_1) can be described by the equation $y - y_1 = m(x - x_1)$.

EXAMPLE 2 Writing Linear Equations in Point-Slope Form

Write an equation in point-slope form for the line with the given slope that contains the given point.

A slope = $\frac{5}{2}$; (−3, 0)

$y - y_1 = m(x - x_1)$

$y - 0 = \frac{5}{2}[x - (-3)]$

$y - 0 = \frac{5}{2}(x + 3)$

B slope = −7; (4, 2)

$y - y_1 = m(x - x_1)$

$y - 2 = -7(x - 4)$

C slope = 0; (−2, −3)

$y - y_1 = m(x - x_1)$

$y - (-3) = 0[x - (-2)]$

$y + 3 = 0(x + 2)$

CHECK IT OUT! Write an equation in point-slope form for the line with the given slope that contains the given point.

2a. slope = 2; $\left(\frac{1}{2}, 1\right)$ $y - 1 = 2\left(x - \frac{1}{2}\right)$

2b. slope = 0; (3, −4) $y + 4 = 0(x - 3)$

EXAMPLE 3 Writing Linear Equations in Slope-Intercept Form

Write an equation in slope-intercept form for the line with slope −4 that contains (−1, −2).

Step 1 Write the equation in point-slope form: $y - y_1 = m(x - x_1)$

$y - (-2) = -4[x - (-1)]$

Step 2 Write the equation in slope-intercept form by solving for y.

$y - (-2) = -4[x - (-1)]$

$y + 2 = -4(x + 1)$ *Rewrite subtraction of negative numbers as addition.*

$y + 2 = -4x - 4$ *Distribute −4 on the right side.*

$\quad -2 \qquad -2$ *Subtract 2 from both sides.*

$y = -4x - 6$

CHECK IT OUT! **3.** Write an equation in slope-intercept form for the line with slope $\frac{1}{3}$ that contains (−3, 1). $y = \frac{1}{3}x + 2$

2 Teach

Guided Instruction

Show students that they can graph a line starting at *any* point on the line if they know the slope, by counting vertically and horizontally from that point. Show how point-slope form comes from the slope formula, and show how it also simplifies to slope-intercept form. Ask students why you might want to rewrite an equation that is in point-slope form in slope-intercept form. Possible answer: because you can quickly graph when an equation is written in slope-intercept form

Universal Access
Through Auditory Cues

Have students work in pairs to quiz each other out loud about the various forms of a linear equation. Have one student state a linear equation, such as $3x + y = 8$ or $y = 2x + 2$, and have the other tell which form the equation is in (standard, slope-intercept, or point-slope). Then have students reverse roles. If time permits, reverse the exercise, so that the first student states a form and the second student gives an equation in that form.

EXAMPLE 4 Using Two Points to Write an Equation

Write an equation in slope-intercept form for the line through the two points.

A $(1, -4)$ and $(3, 2)$

Step 1 Find the slope.

$$m = \frac{y_2 - y_1}{x_2 - x_1} = \frac{2 - (-4)}{3 - 1} = \frac{6}{2} = 3$$

Step 2 Substitute the slope and one of the points into the point-slope form.

$$y - y_1 = m(x - x_1)$$

$$y - 2 = 3(x - 3) \quad \text{Choose (3, 2).}$$

Step 3 Write the equation in slope-intercept form.

$$y - 2 = 3(x - 3)$$

$$y - 2 = 3x - 9$$

$$\underline{+2} \quad \underline{+2}$$

$$y = 3x - 7$$

B $(4, -7)$ and $(0, 5)$

Step 1 Find the slope.

$$m = \frac{y_2 - y_1}{x_2 - x_1} = \frac{5 - (-7)}{0 - 4} = \frac{12}{-4} = -3$$

Step 2 Substitute the slope and one of the points into the point-slope form.

$$y - y_1 = m(x - x_1)$$

$$y - (-7) = -3(x - 4) \quad \text{Choose (4, -7).}$$

$$y + 7 = -3(x - 4)$$

Step 3 Write the equation in slope-intercept form.

$$y + 7 = -3(x - 4)$$

$$y + 7 = -3x + 12$$

$$\underline{-7} \quad \underline{-7}$$

$$y = -3x + 5$$

Helpful Hint

After Step 1 of Example 4B, you could have written the equation in slope-intercept form immediately, because one of the given points contained the y-intercept.

CHECK IT OUT! Write an equation in slope-intercept form for the line through the two points.

4a. $(1, -2)$ and $(3, 10)$ $y = 6x - 8$

4b. $(6, 3)$ and $(0, -1)$ $y = \frac{2}{3}x - 1$

EXAMPLE 5 *Problem-Solving Application*

PROBLEM SOLVING

The cost to place an ad in a newspaper for one week is a linear function of the number of lines in the ad. The costs for 3, 5, and 10 lines are shown. Write an equation in slope-intercept form that represents the function. Then find the cost of an ad that is 18 lines long.

City Gazette

Newspaper Ad Costs

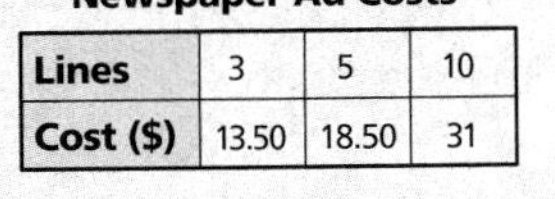

Lines	3	5	10
Cost ($)	13.50	18.50	31

1 Understand the Problem

- The **answer** will have two parts—an equation in slope-intercept form and the cost of an ad that is 18 lines long.
- The ordered pairs given in the table—$(3, 13.50)$, $(5, 18.50)$, and $(10, 31)$—satisfy the equation.

2 Make a Plan

You can use two of the ordered pairs to find the slope. Then use point-slope form to write the equation. Finally, write the equation in slope-intercept form.

COMMON ERROR ALERT

When calculating slope, students may put negative numbers in the y_1 and x_1 positions but forget to change the calculation to addition. Remind them that subtracting a negative number is the same as adding a positive number.

Power Presentations with PowerPoint®

Additional Examples

Example 3

Write an equation in slope-intercept form for the line with slope 3 that contains $(-1, 4)$.

$y = 3x + 7$

Example 4

Write an equation in slope-intercept form for the line through the two points.

A. $(2, -3)$ and $(4, 1)$

$y = 2x - 7$

B. $(0, 1)$ and $(-2, 9)$

$y = -4x + 1$

Also available on transparency

INTERVENTION

Questioning Strategies

EXAMPLE 3

- How do you switch from point-slope form to slope-intercept form?

EXAMPLE 4

- Given two points, what are the steps in writing an equation of the line through those points?

Teaching Tip

Communicating Math Once students have been introduced to multiple methods for graphing a line, discuss with them which method is easiest for different situations.

Power Presentations with PowerPoint®

Additional Examples

Example 5

The cost to stain a deck is a linear function of the deck's area. The costs to stain 100, 250, and 400 square feet are shown in the table. Write an equation in slope-intercept form that represents the function. Then find the cost to stain a deck whose area is 75 square feet.

Area (ft²)	Cost ($)
100	150
250	337.50
400	525

$y = 1.25x + 25$; $118.75

Also available on transparency

INTERVENTION
Questioning Strategies

EXAMPLE 5

- How can you find a point on the line?
- How can you find the slope of the line?

Inclusion Encourage students to look for ways to make problems easier to solve. In **Example 5,** any two points can be used to find the slope, but some pairs may be easier to work with than others.

For more on using ordered pairs to write a linear equation, see the Function Builder on page MB2.

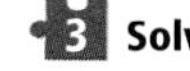

3 Solve

Step 1 Choose any two ordered pairs from the table to find the slope.

$$m = \frac{y_2 - y_1}{x_2 - x_1} = \frac{18.50 - 13.50}{5 - 3} = \frac{5}{2} = 2.5 \quad \textit{Use (3, 13.50) and (5, 18.50).}$$

Step 2 Substitute the slope and any ordered pair from the table into the point-slope form.

$y - y_1 = m(x - x_1)$

$y - 31 = 2.5(x - 10)$ *Use (10, 31).*

Step 3 Write the equation in slope-intercept form by solving for y.

$y - 31 = 2.5(x - 10)$

$y - 31 = 2.5x - 25$ *Distribute 2.5.*

$y = 2.5x + 6$ *Add 31 to both sides.*

Step 4 Find the cost of an ad containing 18 lines by substituting 18 for x.

$y = 2.5x + 6$

$y = 2.5(18) + 6 = 51$

The cost of an ad containing 18 lines is $51.

4 Look Back

If the equation is correct, the ordered pairs that you did not use in Step 2 will be solutions. Substitute (3, 13.50) and (5, 18.50) into the equation.

$y = 2.5x + 6$	
13.50	$2.5(3) + 6$
13.5	$7.5 + 6$
13.5	13.5 ✓

$y = 2.5x + 6$	
18.50	$2.5(5) + 6$
18.5	$12.5 + 6$
18.5	18.5 ✓

5. What if...? At a different newspaper, the costs to place an ad for one week are shown. Write an equation in slope-intercept form that represents this linear function. Then find the cost of an ad that is 21 lines long.

$y = 2.25x + 6$; $53.25

Lines	Cost ($)
3	12.75
5	17.25
10	28.50

THINK AND DISCUSS

1. How are point-slope form and slope-intercept form alike? different?

2. When is point-slope form useful? When is slope-intercept form useful?

3. GET ORGANIZED Copy and complete the graphic organizer. In each box, describe how to find the equation of a line using each method.

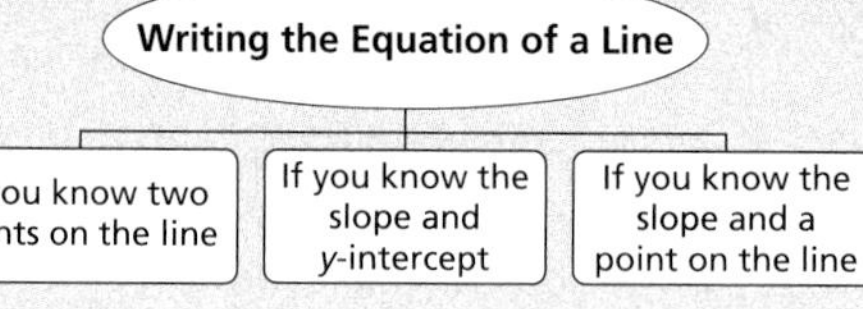

3 Close

Summarize

Ask students what they would need to do *first*, given the following information, before writing an equation in slope-intercept form.

slope and (0, 3)	nothing
slope and (2, 2)	Write the equation in point-slope form.
2 points on the line	Find the slope.
point-slope form	Simplify.

FORMATIVE ASSESSMENT and INTERVENTION

***Diagnose Before* the Lesson**
5-6 Warm Up, TE p. 297

***Monitor During* the Lesson**
Check It Out! Exercises, SE pp. 297–300
Questioning Strategies, TE pp. 298–300

***Assess After* the Lesson**
5-6 Lesson Quiz, TE p. 303
Alternative Assessment, TE p. 303

Answers to *Think and Discuss*

1. Possible answer: Both are based on the slope and a point. However, slope-intercept form uses the point that contains the y-intercept, while point-slope form can use any point.
2. Possible answer: Point-slope form is useful when you know the slope and a point that does not contain the y-intercept, or when you know 2 points. Slope-intercept form is useful when you know the slope and the y-intercept.
3. See p. A5.

California Standards Practice
6.0, 7.0, 25.2

go.hrw.com
Homework Help Online
KEYWORD: MA8CA 5-6
Parent Resources Online
KEYWORD: MA8CA Parent

GUIDED PRACTICE

SEE EXAMPLE 1 p. 297

Graph the line with the given slope that contains the given point.

1. slope = 1; (1, 0)
2. slope = −1; (3, 1)
3. slope = −2; (−4, −2)

SEE EXAMPLE 2 p. 298

Write an equation in point-slope form for the line with the given slope that contains the given point.

4. slope = $\frac{1}{5}$; (2, −6) $y + 6 = \frac{1}{5}(x - 2)$
5. slope = −4; (1, 5) $y - 5 = -4(x - 1)$
6. slope = 0; (3, −7) $y + 7 = 0(x - 3)$

SEE EXAMPLE 3 p. 298

Write an equation in slope-intercept form for the line with the given slope that contains the given point.

7. slope = $-\frac{1}{3}$; (−3, 8) 7. $y = -\frac{1}{3}x + 7$
8. slope = 2; (1, 1) $y = 2x - 1$
9. slope = $\frac{1}{3}$; (−6, −2) $y = \frac{1}{3}x$
10. slope = 2; (−1, 1) $y = 2x + 3$
11. slope = 3; (2, −7) $y = 3x - 13$
12. slope = −4; (4, 2) $y = -4x + 18$

SEE EXAMPLE 4 p. 299

Write an equation in slope-intercept form for the line through the two points.

13. (−2, 2) and (2, −2)
14. (0, −4) and (1, −6)
15. (1, 1) and (−5, 3)
16. (−3, 1) and (0, 10)
17. (7, 8) and (6, 9)
18. (0, −2) and (2, 8)

SEE EXAMPLE 5 p. 299

19. **Measurement** An oil tank is being filled at a constant rate. The depth of the oil is a function of the number of minutes the tank has been filling, as shown in the table. Write an equation in slope-intercept form that represents this linear function. Then find the depth of the oil after one-half hour. $y = \frac{1}{5}x + 3$; 9 ft

Time (min)	Depth (ft)
0	3
10	5
15	6

PRACTICE AND PROBLEM SOLVING

Independent Practice

For Exercises	See Example
20–22	1
23–28	2
29–34	3
35–40	4
41	5

Extra Practice
Skills Practice p. EP11
Application Practice p. EP28

Graph the line with the given slope that contains the given point.

20. slope = $-\frac{1}{2}$; (3, 1)
21. slope = $\frac{3}{5}$; (1, −2)
22. slope = 4; (−1, 0)

Write an equation in point-slope form for the line with the given slope that contains the given point.

23. slope = $\frac{2}{9}$; (−1, 5)
24. slope = 0; (4, −2)
25. slope = 8; (1, 8)
26. slope = $\frac{1}{2}$; (−8, 3)
27. slope = 3; (4, 7)
28. slope = −2; (−1, 3)

Write an equation in slope-intercept form for the line with the given slope that contains the given point.

29. slope = $-\frac{2}{7}$; (14, −3)
30. slope = $\frac{4}{5}$; (−15, 1)
31. slope = $-\frac{1}{4}$; (4, −1)
32. slope = −6; (9, 3)
33. slope = −5; (2, 3)
34. slope = $\frac{1}{5}$; (−5, −2)

Write an equation in slope-intercept form for the line through the two points.

35. (7, 8) and (−7, 6)
36. (2, 7) and (−4, 4)
37. (−1, 2) and (4, −23)
38. (4, −1) and (−8, −10)
39. (0, 11) and (−7, −3)
40. (1, 27) and (−2, 12)

35. $y = \frac{1}{7}x + 7$
36. $y = \frac{1}{2}x + 6$
37. $y = -5x - 3$
38. $y = \frac{3}{4}x - 4$
39. $y = 2x + 11$
40. $y = 5x + 22$

5-6 Exercises

Assignment Guide

Assign *Guided Practice* exercises as necessary.

If you finished Examples **1–3**
Proficient 20–34
Advanced 20–34, 52

If you finished Examples **1–5**
Proficient 20–43, 46–51, 54–60
Advanced 20–43, 46, 45–60

Homework Quick Check
Quickly check key concepts.
Exercises: 22, 24, 30, 36, 42, 43

Answers

1.
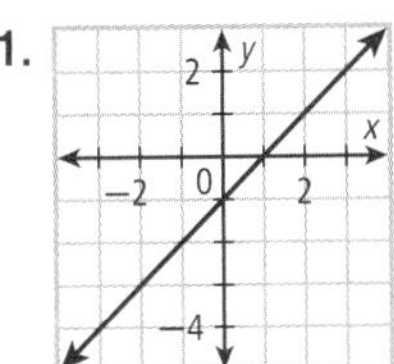

2.
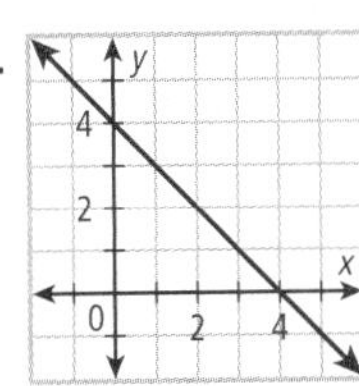

3.
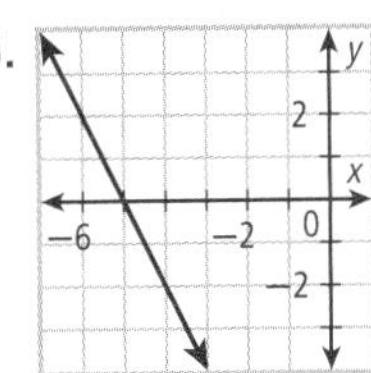

Answers

13. $y = -x$
14. $y = -2x - 4$
15. $y = -\frac{1}{3}x + \frac{4}{3}$
16. $y = 3x + 10$
17. $y = -x + 15$
18. $y = 5x - 2$

20.
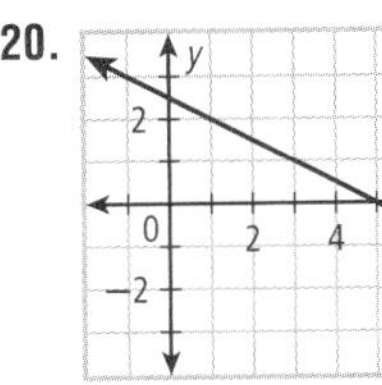

21.
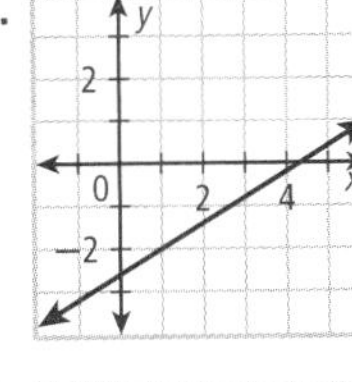

22.
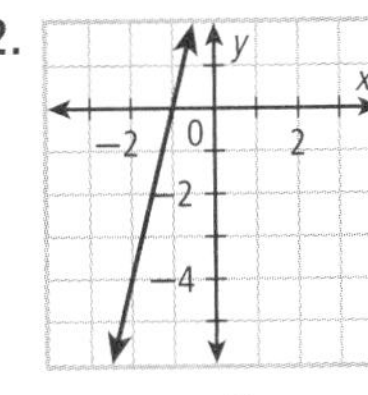

23. $y - 5 = \frac{2}{9}(x + 1)$
24. $y + 2 = 0(x - 4)$
25. $y - 8 = 8(x - 1)$
26. $y - 3 = \frac{1}{2}(x + 8)$
27. $y - 7 = 3(x - 4)$
28. $y - 3 = -2(x + 1)$
29. $y = -\frac{2}{7}x + 1$
30. $y = \frac{4}{5}x + 13$
31. $y = -\frac{1}{4}x$
32. $y = -6x + 57$
33. $y = -5x + 13$
34. $y = \frac{1}{5}x - 1$

California Standards

Standard	Exercises
5.0	54, 55
6.0	1–3, 20–22, 50, 51, 56–58
7.0	4–18, 23–40, 47b, 49, 52, 53, 59–60
25.2	44

Science Link **Exercise 41** involves finding the boiling point of water in degrees Celsius. Students can check their equation by substituting the altitude at sea level (0) into the equation and checking that the answer is 100.

Statistics In **Exercise 47,** remind students that a trend line should have about the same number of points below it as above it.

Exercise 48 involves using two points to write an equation for a line. This exercise prepares students for the Concept Connection on page 312.

Answers

44. Student A is incorrect. Student A incorrectly wrote $x - (-5)$ as $x - 5$ instead of $x + 5$.

47a.

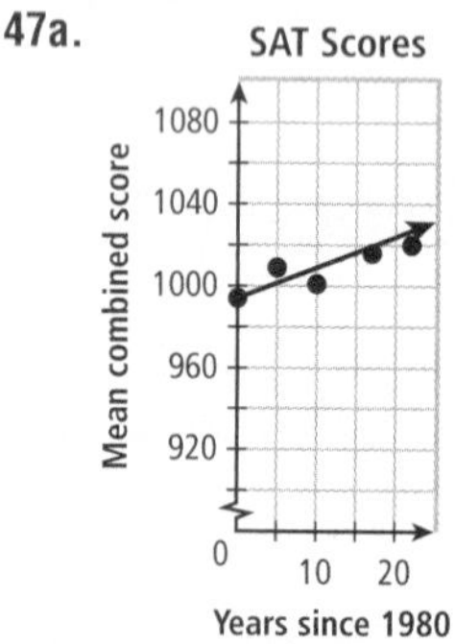

54.

55. −3 −2 −1 0 1 2 3

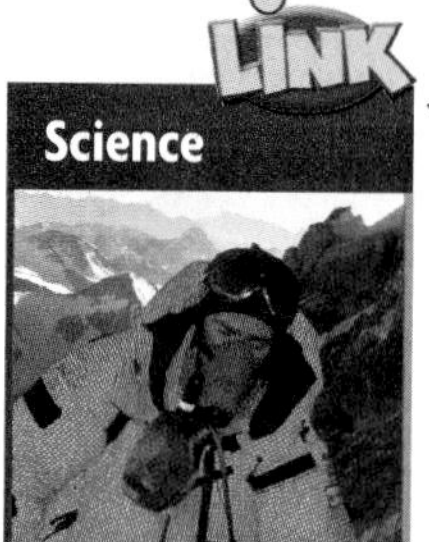

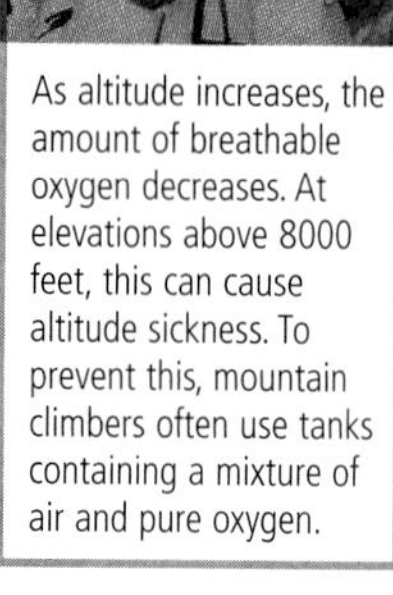

As altitude increases, the amount of breathable oxygen decreases. At elevations above 8000 feet, this can cause altitude sickness. To prevent this, mountain climbers often use tanks containing a mixture of air and pure oxygen.

41. **Science** At higher altitudes, water boils at lower temperatures. This relationship between altitude and boiling point is linear. The table shows some altitudes and the corresponding boiling points. Write an equation in slope-intercept form that represents this linear function. Then find the boiling point at 6000 feet. $y = -\frac{1}{500}x + 212$; 200°F

Boiling Point of Water

Altitude (ft)	Temperature (°F)
1000	210
1500	209
3000	206

The tables show linear relationships between x and y. Copy and complete the tables.

42.

x	−2	0	**4**	7
y	−18	**−8**	12	27

43.

x	−4	1	0	**6**
y	14	4	**6**	−6

44. **///ERROR ANALYSIS///** Two students used point-slope form to find an equation that describes the line with slope −3 through (−5, 2). Who is incorrect? Explain the error.

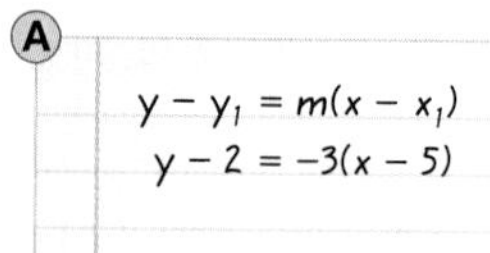

B

$y - y_1 = m(x - x_1)$
$y - 2 = -3[x - (-5)]$
$y - 2 = -3(x + 5)$

45. Possible answer: When you know a point and the slope, you can immediately use point-slope form. When you know 2 points, first use them to find the slope. Then use point-slope form, just as in the first case.

46. Possible answer: Linear equations that describe vert. lines cannot be written in point-slope form because they have undef. slope. All nonvert. lines represent functions, and they can all be written in point-slope form.

45. **Critical Thinking** Compare the methods for finding the equation of a line when you know

- a point on the line and the slope of the line.
- two points on the line.

How are the methods alike? How are they different?

46. **Write About It** Explain why the first statement is false but the second is true.

- All linear equations can be written in point-slope form.
- All linear equations that describe functions can be written in point-slope form.

47. **Multi-Step** The table shows the mean scores on a standardized test for several different years.

Years Since 1980	0	5	10	17	21
Mean Score	994	1009	1001	1016	1020

a. Make a scatter plot of the data and add a trend line to your graph.

b. Use your trend line to estimate the slope and y-intercept, and write an equation in slope-intercept form. **Possible answer: slope: 1.5; y-int.: 994; $y = 1.5x + 994$**

c. What do the slope and y-intercept represent in this situation? **slope: number of points by which mean score is increasing each year; y-int.: mean score in 1980**

48. This problem will prepare you for the Concept Connection on page 312.

a. Stephen is walking from his house to his friend Sharon's house. When he is 12 blocks away, he looks at his watch. He looks again when he is 8 blocks away and finds that 6 minutes have passed. Write two ordered pairs for these data in the form (time, blocks). **(0, 12) and (6, 8)**

b. Write a linear equation for these two points. $y = -\frac{2}{3}x + 12$

c. What is the total amount of time it takes Stephen to reach Sharon's house? **18 min**

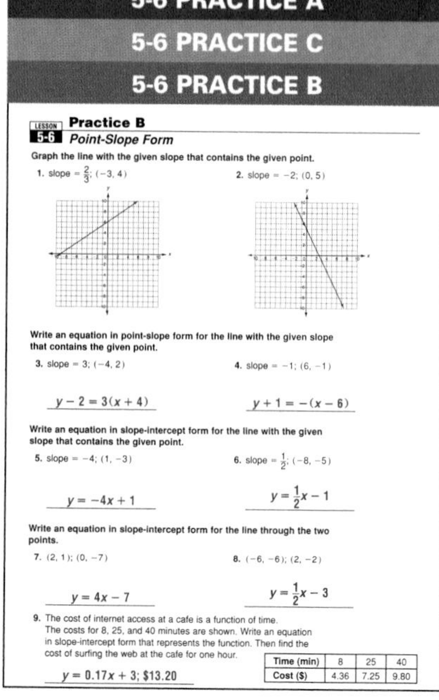

5-6 PRACTICE A
5-6 PRACTICE C
5-6 PRACTICE B

LESSON 5-6 **Practice B**
Point-Slope Form

Graph the line with the given slope that contains the given point.

1. slope = $\frac{2}{3}$; (−3, 4)
2. slope = −2; (0, 5)

Write an equation in point-slope form for the line with the given slope that contains the given point.

3. slope = 3; (−4, 2) — $y - 2 = 3(x + 4)$
4. slope = −1; (6, −1) — $y + 1 = -(x - 6)$

Write an equation in slope-intercept form for the line with the given slope that contains the given point.

5. slope = −4; (1, −3) — $y = -4x + 1$
6. slope = $\frac{1}{2}$; (−8, −5) — $y = \frac{1}{2}x - 1$

Write an equation in slope-intercept form for the line through the two points.

7. (2, 1); (0, −7) — $y = 4x - 7$
8. (−6, −6); (2, −2) — $y = \frac{1}{2}x - 3$

9. The cost of internet access at a cafe is a function of time. The costs for 8, 25, and 40 minutes are shown. Write an equation in slope-intercept form that represents the function. Then find the cost of surfing the web at the cafe for one hour. $y = 0.17x + 3$; $13.20

Time (min)	8	25	40
Cost ($)	4.36	7.25	9.80

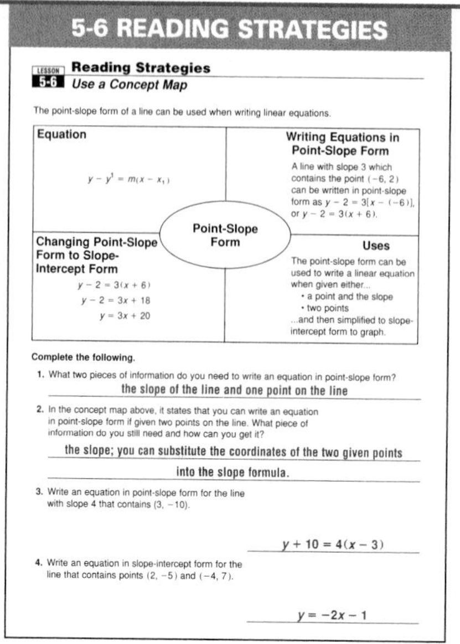

5-6 READING STRATEGIES

LESSON 5-6 **Reading Strategies**
Use a Concept Map

The point-slope form of a line can be used when writing linear equations.

Equation	Writing Equations in Point-Slope Form
$y - y^1 = m(x - x_1)$	A line with slope 3 which contains the point (−6, 2) can be written in point-slope form as $y - 2 = 3[x - (-6)]$, or $y - 2 = 3(x + 6)$.
Changing Point-Slope Form to Slope-Intercept Form	**Uses**
$y - 2 = 3(x + 6)$ $y - 2 = 3x + 18$ $y = 3x + 20$	The point-slope form can be used to write a linear equation when given either... • a point and the slope • two points ...and then simplified to slope-intercept form to graph.

Point-Slope Form

Complete the following.

1. What two pieces of information do you need to write an equation in point-slope form? **the slope of the line and one point on the line**

2. In the concept map above, it states that you can write an equation in point-slope form if given two points on the line. What piece of information do you still need and how can you get it? **the slope; you can substitute the coordinates of the two given points into the slope formula.**

3. Write an equation in point-slope form for the line with slope 4 that contains (3, −10). $y + 10 = 4(x - 3)$

4. Write an equation in slope-intercept form for the line that contains points (2, −5) and (−4, 7). $y = -2x - 1$

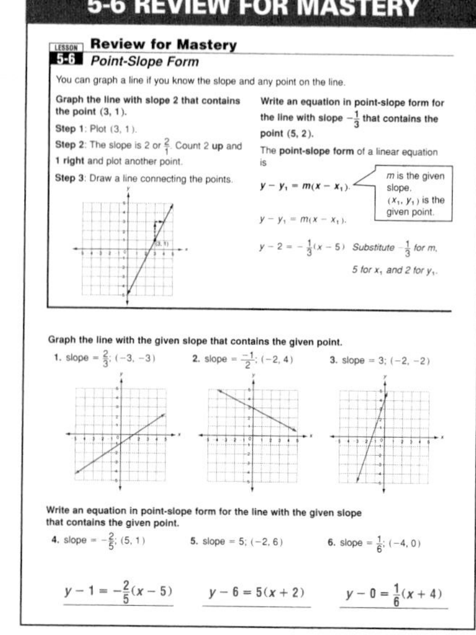

5-6 REVIEW FOR MASTERY

LESSON 5-6 **Review for Mastery**
Point-Slope Form

You can graph a line if you know the slope and any point on the line.

Graph the line with slope 2 that contains the point (3, 1).

Step 1: Plot (3, 1).

Step 2: The slope is 2 or $\frac{2}{1}$. Count 2 **up** and **1 right** and plot another point.

Step 3: Draw a line connecting the points.

Write an equation in point-slope form for the line with slope $-\frac{1}{3}$ that contains the point (5, 2).

The **point-slope form** of a linear equation is

$y - y_1 = m(x - x_1)$. — *m* is the given slope. (x_1, y_1) is the given point.

$y - y_1 = m(x - x_1)$.

$y - 2 = -\frac{1}{3}(x - 5)$ *Substitute $-\frac{1}{3}$ for m, 5 for x_1 and 2 for y_1.*

Graph the line with the given slope that contains the given point.

1. slope = $\frac{2}{3}$; (−3, −3)
2. slope = $\frac{-1}{2}$; (−2, 4)
3. slope = 3; (−2, −2)

Write an equation in point-slope form for the line with the given slope that contains the given point.

4. slope = $-\frac{2}{5}$; (5, 1) — $y - 1 = -\frac{2}{5}(x - 5)$
5. slope = 5; (−2, 6) — $y - 6 = 5(x + 2)$
6. slope = $\frac{1}{6}$; (−4, 0) — $y - 0 = \frac{1}{6}(x + 4)$

Multiple Choice For Exercises 49 and 50, choose the best answer.

49. Which equation describes the line through $(-5, 1)$ with slope of 1?

(A) $y + 1 = x - 5$
(B) $y + 5 = x - 1$
(C) $y - 1 = -5(x - 1)$
(D) $y - 1 = x + 5$

50. A line contains (4, 4) and (5, 2). What are the slope and y-intercept?

(A) slope $= -2$; y-intercept $= 2$
(B) slope $= 1.2$; y-intercept $= -2$
(C) slope $= -2$; y-intercept $= 12$
(D) slope $= 12$; y-intercept $= 1.2$

CHALLENGE AND EXTEND

51. A linear function has the same y-intercept as $x + 4y = 8$ and its graph contains the point $(2, 7)$. Find the slope and y-intercept. **slope: $\frac{5}{2}$; y-int.: 2**

52. Write the equation of a line in slope-intercept form that contains $\left(\frac{3}{4}, \frac{1}{2}\right)$ and has the same slope as the line described by $y + 3x = 6$. **$y = -3x + \frac{11}{4}$**

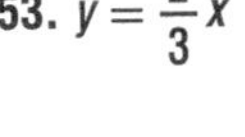

53. Write the equation of a line in slope-intercept form that contains $\left(-\frac{1}{2}, -\frac{1}{3}\right)$ and $\left(1\frac{1}{2}, 1\right)$.

53. $y = \frac{2}{3}x$

SPIRAL STANDARDS REVIEW

5.0, 6.0, 7.0

Solve each compound inequality and graph the solutions. *(Lesson 3-6)*

54. $-4 \le x + 2 \le 1$ **$-6 \le x \le -1$**

55. $m - 5 > -7$ AND $m + 1 < 2$ **$m > -2$ AND $m < 1$**

Graph each function. *(Lesson 4-3)*

56. $y = x - 3$

57. $y = x^2 + 5$

58. $y = |2x|$

Write the equation of each line in slope-intercept form. *(Lesson 5-5)*

59. slope = 3, the point $(3, 4)$ is on the line **$y = 3x - 5$**

60. slope = -2, the point $(2, 4)$ is on the line **$y = -2x + 8$**

Career Path

go.hrw.com
Career Resources Online
KEYWORD: MA8CA Career

Michael Raynor
Data mining major

Q: What math classes did you take in high school?
A: Algebra 1 and 2, Geometry, and Statistics

Q: What math classes have you taken in college?
A: Applied Statistics, Data Mining Methods, Web Mining, and Artificial Intelligence

Q: How do you use math?
A: Once for a class, I used software to analyze basketball statistics. What I learned helped me develop strategies for our school team.

Q: What are your future plans?
A: There are many options for people with data mining skills. I could work in banking, pharmaceuticals, or even the military. But my dream job is to develop game strategies for an NBA team.

Teaching Tip

Multiple Choice In **Exercise 49,** students who chose **B** most likely reversed x_1 and y_1 in the point-slope form. Students who chose **A** probably added x_1 and y_1.

Answers

56–58. See p. A20.

Journal

Have students describe a situation in which the point-slope form is more useful than the slope-intercept form.

ALTERNATIVE ASSESSMENT

Have students choose two points on a coordinate grid and write an equation in slope-intercept form for the line that passes through the points. Then have them graph the line and check their work by making sure their two original points are on the line.

Power Presentations with PowerPoint®

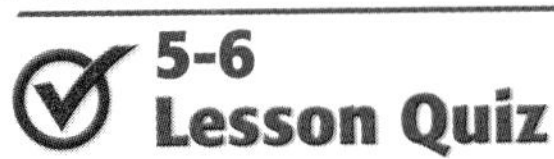

5-6 Lesson Quiz

Write an equation in slope-intercept form for the line with the given slope that contains the given point.

1. slope $= -1$; $(0, 9)$
$y = -x + 9$

2. slope $= -\frac{1}{3}$; $(3, -6)$
$y = -\frac{1}{3}x - 5$

Write an equation in slope-intercept form for the line through the two points.

3. $(-1, 7)$ and $(2, 1)$
$y = -2x + 5$

4. $(0, 4)$ and $(-7, 2)$
$y = \frac{2}{7}x + 4$

5. The cost to take a taxi from the airport is a linear function of the distance driven. The costs for 5, 10, and 20 miles are shown in the table. Write an equation in slope-intercept form that represents the function.

Distance (mi)	Cost ($)
5	14
10	22
20	38

$y = 1.6x + 6$

Also available on transparency

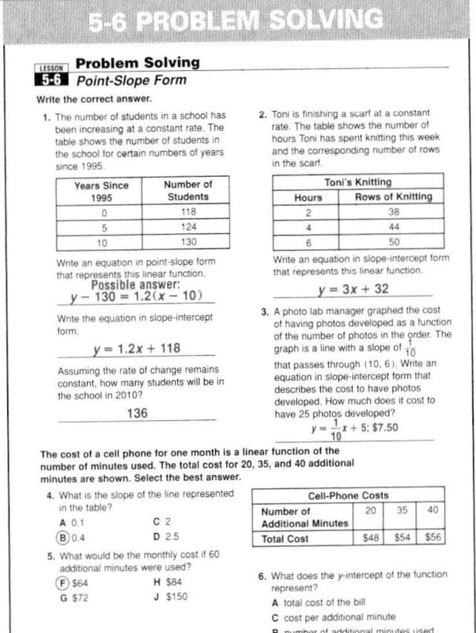

5-6 PROBLEM SOLVING

LESSON 5-6 **Problem Solving**
Point-Slope Form

Write the correct answer.

1. The number of students in a school has been increasing at a constant rate. The table shows the number of students in the school for certain numbers of years since 1995.

Years Since 1995	Number of Students
0	118
5	124
10	130

Write an equation in point-slope form that represents this linear function.
Possible answer: $y - 130 = 1.2(x - 10)$

Write the equation in slope-intercept form.
$y = 1.2x + 118$

Assuming the rate of change remains constant, how many students will be in the school in 2010?
136

2. Toni is finishing a scarf at a constant rate. The table shows the number of hours Toni has spent knitting this week and the corresponding number of rows in the scarf.

Toni's Knitting	
Hours	Rows of Knitting
2	38
4	44
6	50

Write an equation in slope-intercept form that represents this linear function.
$y = 3x + 32$

3. A photo lab manager graphed the cost of having photos developed as a function of the number of photos in the order. The graph is a line with a slope of $\frac{1}{10}$ that passes through (10, 6). Write an equation in slope-intercept form that describes the cost to have photos developed. How much does it cost to have 25 photos developed?
$y = \frac{1}{10}x + 5$; $7.50

The cost of a cell phone for one month is a linear function of the number of minutes used. The total cost for 20, 35, and 40 additional minutes are shown. Select the best answer.

Cell-Phone Costs			
Number of Additional Minutes	20	35	40
Total Cost	$48	$54	$56

4. What is the slope of the line represented in the table?
A 0.1
(B) 0.4
C 2
D 2.5

5. What would be the monthly cost if 60 additional minutes were used?
(F) $64
G $72
H $84
J $150

6. What does the y-intercept of the function represent?
A total cost of the bill
C cost per additional minute
B number of additional minutes used
(D) cost with no additional minutes used

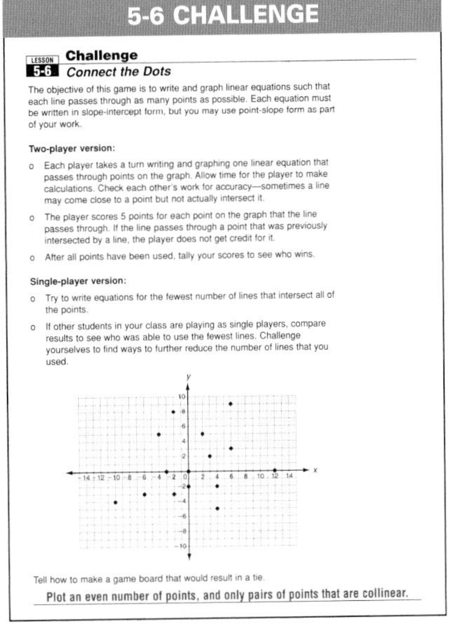

5-6 CHALLENGE

LESSON 5-6 **Challenge**
Connect the Dots

The objective of this game is to write and graph linear equations such that each line passes through as many points as possible. Each equation must be written in slope-intercept form, but you may use point-slope form as part of your work.

Two-player version:

- Each player takes a turn writing and graphing one linear equation that passes through points on the graph. Allow time for the player to make calculations. Check each other's work for accuracy—sometimes a line may come close to a point but not actually intersect it.
- The player scores 5 points for each point on the graph that the line passes through. If the line passes through a point that was previously intersected by a line, the player does not get credit for it.
- After all points have been used, tally your scores to see who wins.

Single-player version:

- Try to write equations for the fewest number of lines that intersect all of the points.
- If other students in your class are playing as single players, compare results to see who was able to use the fewest lines. Challenge yourselves to find ways to further reduce the number of lines that you used.

Tell how to make a game board that would result in a tie.
Plot an even number of points, and only pairs of points that are collinear.

5-7 Organizer

Objectives: Identify and graph parallel and perpendicular lines.

Write equations to describe lines parallel or perpendicular to a given line.

Algebra Lab
In Chapter 5 Resource File

Online Edition
Tutorial Videos, Interactivity

Countdown to Mastery Week 11

Power Presentations with PowerPoint®

Warm Up

Find the reciprocal.

1. 2 $\frac{1}{2}$ **2.** $\frac{1}{3}$ 3

3. $-\frac{3}{4}$ $-\frac{4}{3}$

Find the slope of the line that passes through each pair of points.

4. (2, 2) and (−1, 3) $-\frac{1}{3}$

5. (3, 4) and (4, 6) 2

6. (5, 1) and (0, 0) $\frac{1}{5}$

Also available on transparency

Math Humor

Q: What did the lines do at the gym to avoid each other?

A: They used the parallel bars.

California Standards

Algebra 1 8.0

Also covered:

25.1 Students use properties of numbers to construct simple valid argument (direct and indirect) **for**, or formulate counterexamples to, **claimed assertions.**

5-7 Slopes of Parallel and Perpendicular Lines

California Standards

8.0 Students understand the concepts of parallel lines and perpendicular lines and how those slopes are related. Students are able to find the equation of a line perpendicular to a given line that passes through a given point.
Also covered: **25.1**

Vocabulary
parallel lines
perpendicular lines

Why learn this?

Parallel lines and their equations can be used to model costs, such as the cost of a booth at a farmers' market.

To sell at a particular farmers' market for a year, there is a $100 membership fee. Then you pay $3 for each hour that you sell at the market. However, if you were a member the previous year, the membership fee is reduced to $50.

- The red line shows the total cost if you are a new member.
- The blue line shows the total cost if you are a returning member.

These two lines are *parallel*. **Parallel lines** are lines in the same plane that have no points in common. In other words, they do not intersect.

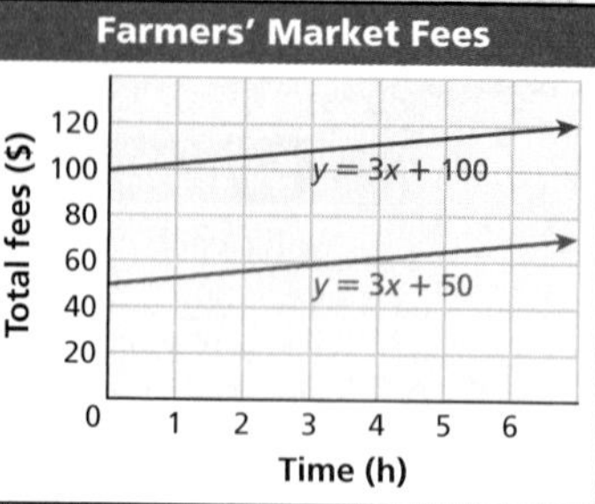

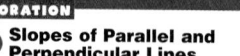

Know it! Note

Parallel Lines

WORDS	Two different nonvertical lines are parallel if and only if they have the same slope.	All different vertical lines are parallel.
GRAPH	$y = \frac{1}{2}x + 5$; $y = \frac{1}{2}x + 1$	$x = 2$; $x = 4$

EXAMPLE 1 Identifying Parallel Lines

Identify which lines are parallel.

A $y = \frac{4}{3}x + 3$; $y = 2$; $y = \frac{4}{3}x - 5$; $y = -3$

The lines described by $y = \frac{4}{3}x + 3$ and $y = \frac{4}{3}x - 5$ both have slope $\frac{4}{3}$. These lines are parallel.The lines described by $y = 2$ and $y = -3$ both have slope 0. These lines are parallel.

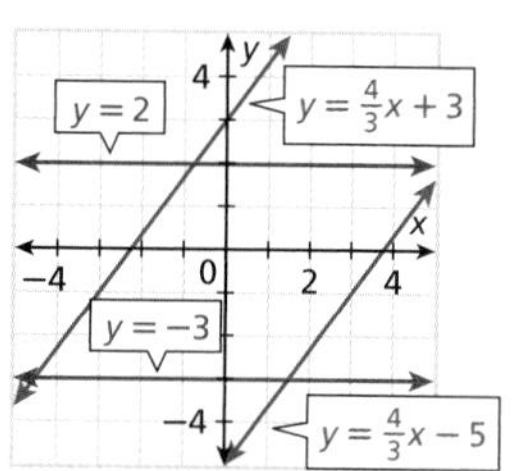

1 Introduce

EXPLORATION

5-7 Slopes of Parallel and Perpendicular Lines

You will need graph paper or a graphing calculator for this Exploration.

1. Graph $y = 2x + 3$ and $y = 2x - 2$ so that you can see both graphs at the same time. What do you notice about the lines?
2. Compare the slopes of the lines.
3. Repeat this process with $y = \frac{1}{3}x + 2$ and $y = \frac{1}{3}x$. What do you notice about the lines? What are the slopes of the lines?

THINK AND DISCUSS

4. **Discuss** any conjectures that you can make based on your findings.
5. **Describe** what you would expect to be true, based on your conjectures, about the graphs of $y = \frac{2}{3}x - 2$ and $y = \frac{2}{3}x - 5$.

Motivate

Have students use a graphing calculator to graph $y = 4x + 3$ and $y = 4x - 1$. Ask students where the lines intersect. They do not intersect.

Have students graph $y = 4x + 3$ and $y = -\frac{1}{4}x + 3$.

Tell students to estimate the measures of the angles at the intersection of the two lines. 90°

Explorations and answers are provided in *Alternate Openers: Explorations Transparencies.*

Identify which lines are parallel.

B $y = 3x + 2$; $y = -\frac{1}{2}x + 4$; $x + 2y = -4$; $y - 5 = 3(x - 1)$

Write all equations in slope-intercept form to determine the slopes.

$y = 3x + 2$ slope-intercept form ✓	$y = -\frac{1}{2}x + 4$ slope-intercept form ✓
$x + 2y = -4$ $-x \quad -x$ $2y = -x - 4$ $\frac{2y}{2} = \frac{-x-4}{2}$ $y = -\frac{1}{2}x - 2$	$y - 5 = 3(x - 1)$ $y - 5 = 3x - 3$ $+5 \quad +5$ $y = 3x + 2$

The lines given by $y = 3x + 2$ and $y - 5 = 3(x - 1)$ have the same slope, but they are not parallel lines. They are the same line.

The lines given by $y = -\frac{1}{2}x + 4$ and $x + 2y = -4$ represent parallel lines. They each have slope $-\frac{1}{2}$.

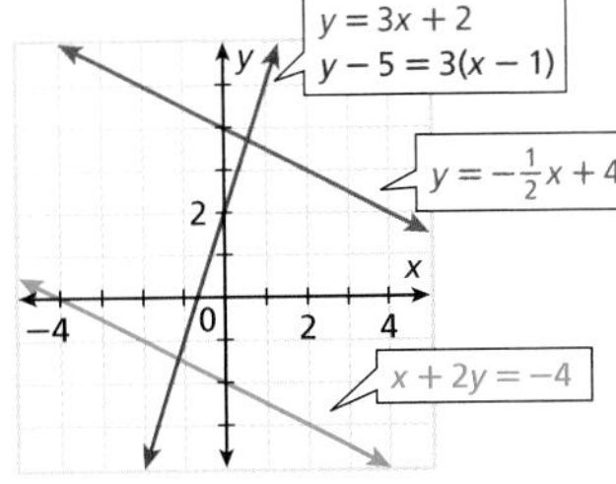

2. slope of $\overline{AB} = 0$; slope of $\overline{BC} = \frac{5}{3}$; slope of $\overline{CD} = 0$; slope of $\overline{AD} = \frac{5}{3}$; $\overline{AB}$ is par. to $\overline{CD}$ because they have the same slope. $\overline{AD}$ is par. to $\overline{BC}$ because they have the same slope. Since opp. sides are par., *ABCD* is a parallelogram.

CHECK IT OUT! **Identify which lines are parallel.**

1a. $y = 2x + 2$; $y = 2x + 1$; $y = -4$; $x = 1$

1b. $y = \frac{3}{4}x + 8$; $-3x + 4y = 32$; $y = 3x$; $y - 1 = 3(x + 2)$

1a. $y = 2x + 2$ and $y = 2x + 1$ **1b.** $y = 3x$ and $y - 1 = 3(x + 2)$

EXAMPLE 2 *Geometry Application*

Reasoning

Remember!

In a parallelogram, opposite sides are parallel.

Show that *ABCD* is a parallelogram.

Use the ordered pairs and the slope formula to find the slopes of $\overline{AB}$ and $\overline{CD}$.

slope of $\overline{AB} = \frac{7 - 5}{4 - (-1)} = \frac{2}{5}$

slope of $\overline{CD} = \frac{3 - 1}{4 - (-1)} = \frac{2}{5}$

$\overline{AB}$ is parallel to $\overline{CD}$ because they have the same slope.

$\overline{AD}$ is parallel to $\overline{BC}$ because they are both vertical.

Therefore, *ABCD* is a parallelogram because both pairs of opposite sides are parallel.

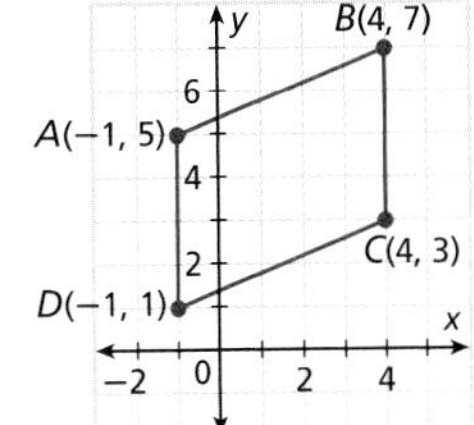

CHECK IT OUT! **2.** Show that the points $A(0, 2)$, $B(4, 2)$, $C(1, -3)$, and $D(-3, -3)$ are the vertices of a parallelogram.

Power Presentations with PowerPoint®

Additional Examples

Example 1

Identify which lines are parallel.

A. $y = \frac{5}{3}x - 2$; $y = x$; $y = \frac{5}{3}x + 4$; $y = x + 1$

$y = \frac{5}{3}x - 2$ and $y = \frac{5}{3} + 4$;

$y = x$ and $y = x + 1$

B. $y = 2x - 3$; $y = -\frac{2}{3}x + 3$; $2x + 3y = 8$; $y + 1 = 3(x - 3)$

$y = -\frac{2}{3}x + 3$ and $2x + 3y = 8$

Example 2

Show that *JKLM* is a parallelogram.

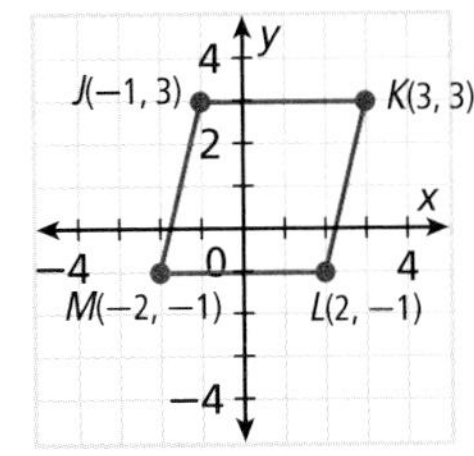

Slope of $\overline{JK} = 0$; slope of $\overline{KL} = 4$; slope of $\overline{ML} = 0$; slope of $\overline{JM} = 4$; $\overline{JK}$ is par. to $\overline{ML}$ because they are both horiz. $\overline{KL}$ is par. to $\overline{JM}$ because they have the same slope. Since opposite sides are par., *JKLM* is a parallelogram.

Also available on transparency

INTERVENTION

Questioning Strategies

EXAMPLE 1

- What is always true about the slopes of parallel lines?
- Can functions whose graphs are parallel lines have the same *y*-intercept? Explain.

EXAMPLE 2

- Why is it not necessary to calculate the slopes of horizontal and vertical lines?

2 Teach

Guided Instruction

Start the lesson by reviewing how to rewrite equations that are in standard and point-slope form in slope-intercept form. Then work through **Examples 1** and **2.** Prior to **Example 3,** remind students that reciprocals, like $\frac{3}{7}$ and $\frac{7}{3}$, have a product of 1. Opposite reciprocals, like $\frac{2}{3}$ and $-\frac{3}{2}$, have a product of -1. Then work through the remaining examples.

Universal Access

Through Communication

Divide the class into small groups. Have the groups develop and present one of the following:

- a 60-second TV commercial about parallel or perpendicular lines
- a two-minute news segment about how to use parallel and perpendicular lines in geometry
- a brief infomercial about the equations of parallel and perpendicular lines

Power Presentations with PowerPoint®

Additional Examples

Example 3

Identify which lines are perpendicular:
$y = 3; x = -2;$
$y = 3x; y = -\frac{1}{3}(x - 4)$. $y = 3$ and $x = -2$; $y = 3x$ and $y = -\frac{1}{3}(x - 4)$

Example 4

Show that ABC is a right triangle.

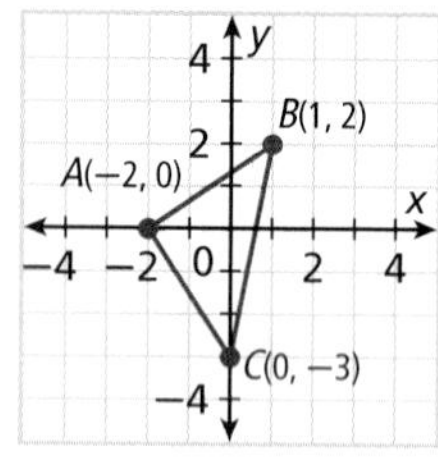

Slope of $\overline{AB} = \frac{2}{3}$; slope of $\overline{AC} = -\frac{3}{2}$; $\overline{AB}$ is perp. to $\overline{AC}$ because the product of their slopes is −1. Since $\triangle ABC$ contains a rt. angle, ABC is a rt. triangle.

Also available on transparency

INTERVENTION

Questioning Strategies

EXAMPLE 3

- What is true about the slopes of perpendicular lines?
- Can perpendicular lines have the same y-intercept? Explain.

EXAMPLE 4

- What is true about the intersection of two perpendicular lines?
- What is the maximum number of right angles a triangle could contain?

Perpendicular lines are lines that intersect to form right angles (90°).

Perpendicular Lines

WORDS	Two nonvertical lines are perpendicular if and only if the product of their slopes is −1.	Vertical lines are perpendicular to horizontal lines.
GRAPH	$y = -\frac{2}{3}x + 3$; $y = \frac{3}{2}x - 2$	$y = 3$; $x = 2$

EXAMPLE 3 Identifying Perpendicular Lines

Identify which lines are perpendicular: $x = -2$; $y = 1$; $y = -4x$; $y + 2 = \frac{1}{4}(x + 1)$.

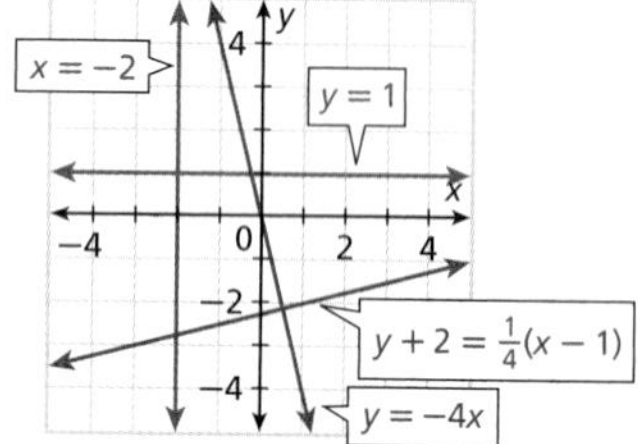

The line given by $x = -2$ is a vertical line, and the line given by $y = 1$ is a horizontal line. These lines are perpendicular.

The slope of the line given by $y = -4x$ is −4. The slope of the line given by $y + 2 = \frac{1}{4}(x - 1)$ is $\frac{1}{4}$.

$$(-4)\left(\frac{1}{4}\right) = -1$$

These lines are perpendicular because the product of their slopes is −1.

3. Identify which lines are perpendicular: $y = -4$; $y - 6 = 5(x + 4)$; $x = 3$; $y = -\frac{1}{5}x + 2$.

$y = -4$ and $x = 3$; $y - 6 = 5(x + 4)$ and $y = -\frac{1}{5}x + 2$

EXAMPLE 4 *Geometry Application*

Reasoning

Show that PQR is a right triangle.

If PQR is a right triangle, $\overline{PQ}$ will be perpendicular to $\overline{QR}$.

$$\text{slope of } \overline{PQ} = \frac{3-1}{3-0} = \frac{2}{3}$$

$$\text{slope of } \overline{QR} = \frac{3-0}{3-5} = \frac{3}{-2} = -\frac{3}{2}$$

$\overline{PQ}$ is perpendicular to $\overline{QR}$ because $\frac{2}{3}\left(-\frac{3}{2}\right) = -1$.

Therefore, PQR is a right triangle because it contains a right angle.

Helpful Hint

A right triangle contains one right angle. In Example 4, $\angle P$ and $\angle R$ are clearly not right angles, so the only possibility is $\angle Q$.

4. slope of $\overline{PQ} = 2$; slope of $\overline{QR} = -1$; slope of $\overline{PR} = -\frac{1}{2}$; $\overline{PQ}$ is perp. to $\overline{PR}$ because the product of their slopes is −1. Since PQR contains a rt. angle, PQR is a rt. triangle.

4. Show that $P(1, 4)$, $Q(2, 6)$, and $R(7, 1)$ are the vertices of a right triangle.

Geometry Have students think of geometric shapes that have parallel or perpendicular lines. Their list could include squares, rhombuses, rectangles, and trapezoids, as well as parallelograms and right triangles.

Technology When using a graphing calculator, lines may not appear perpendicular in the standard window. This is because units on the x-axis are larger than units on the y-axis. To view a more accurate graph, have students use the square window by pressing ZOOM and selecting **5:ZSquare**.

EXAMPLE 5 Writing Equations of Parallel and Perpendicular Lines

A **Write an equation in slope-intercept form for the line that passes through $(4, 5)$ and is parallel to the line given by $y = 5x + 10$.**

Step 1 Find the slope of the line.

$y = 5x + 10$ *The slope is 5.*

The parallel line also has a slope of 5.

Step 2 Write the equation in point-slope form.

$y - y_1 = m(x - x_1)$ *Use point-slope form.*

$y - 5 = 5(x - 4)$ *Substitute 5 for m, 4 for x_1, and 5 for y_1.*

Step 3 Write the equation in slope-intercept form.

$y - 5 = 5(x - 4)$

$y - 5 = 5x - 20$ *Distribute 5 on the right side.*

$y = 5x - 15$ *Add 5 to both sides.*

B **Write an equation in slope-intercept form for the line that passes through $(3, 2)$ and is perpendicular to the line given by $y = 3x - 1$.**

Step 1 Find the slope of the line.

$y = 3x - 1$ *The slope is 3.*

The perpendicular line has a slope of $-\frac{1}{3}$, because $3\left(-\frac{1}{3}\right) = -1$.

Step 2 Write the equation in point-slope form.

$y - y_1 = m(x - x_1)$ *Use point-slope form.*

$y - 2 = -\frac{1}{3}(x - 3)$ *Substitute $-\frac{1}{3}$ for m, 3 for x_1, and 2 for y_1.*

Step 3 Write the equation in slope-intercept form.

$y - 2 = -\frac{1}{3}(x - 3)$

$y - 2 = -\frac{1}{3}x + 1$ *Distribute $-\frac{1}{3}$ on the right side.*

$y = -\frac{1}{3}x + 3$ *Add 2 to both sides.*

If you know the slope of a line, the slope of a perpendicular line will be the "opposite reciprocal."

$\frac{2}{3} \rightarrow -\frac{3}{2}$

$\frac{1}{5} \rightarrow -5$

$-7 \rightarrow \frac{1}{7}$

5a. Write an equation in slope-intercept form for the line that passes through $(5, 7)$ and is parallel to the line given by $y = \frac{4}{5}x - 6$.

5b. Write an equation in slope-intercept form for the line that passes through $(-5, 3)$ and is perpendicular to the line given by $y = 5x$.

5a. $y = \frac{4}{5}x + 3$ **5b.** $y = -\frac{1}{5}x + 2$

THINK AND DISCUSS

1. Are the lines given by $y = \frac{1}{2}x$ and $y = 2x$ perpendicular? Explain.
2. Describe the slopes and y-intercepts when two nonvertical lines are parallel.
3. **GET ORGANIZED** Copy and complete the graphic organizer. In each box, sketch an example and describe the slopes.

Parallel lines	Perpendicular lines

COMMON ERROR ALERT

Students might always use the coefficient of x for slope, regardless of the form of the equation. Tell students to always check the form of the equation first, because the coefficient of x may change when the equation is written in slope-intercept form.

Additional Examples

Example 5

A. Write an equation in slope-intercept form for the line that passes through $(4, 10)$ and is parallel to the line given by $y = 3x + 8$. $y = 3x - 2$

B. Write an equation in slope-intercept form for the line that passes through $(2, -1)$ and is perpendicular to the line given by $y = 2x - 5$. $y = -\frac{1}{2}x$

Also available on transparency

INTERVENTION

Questioning Strategies

EXAMPLE 5

- How do you know what to substitute for m if you are writing an equation for a line parallel to a given line? for a line perpendicular to a given line?

Visual Encourage students to check their work in **Example 5** by graphing.

3 Close

Summarize

Remind students that if two lines are parallel, their slopes are the same. If two lines are perpendicular, their slopes have a product of −1. Tell students that equations can be presented in many ways, and that they may need to rewrite equations in slope-intercept form before deciding on the value of the slope.

FORMATIVE ASSESSMENT and INTERVENTION

***Diagnose Before* the Lesson**
5-7 Warm Up, TE p. 304

***Monitor During* the Lesson**
Check It Out! Exercises, SE pp. 305–307
Questioning Strategies, TE pp. 305–307

***Assess After* the Lesson**
5-7 Lesson Quiz, TE p. 310
Alternative Assessment, TE p. 310

Answers to *Think and Discuss*

1. No; the product of their slopes is 1, not −1.
2. The slopes are the same, and the y-intercepts are different.
3. See p. A5.

Assignment Guide

Assign *Guided Practice* exercises as necessary.

If you finished Examples **1–3**
Proficient 9–15, 18–21, 49
Advanced 9–15, 18–21, 49, 56, 57

If you finished Examples **1–5**
Proficient 9–17, 18–44 even, 46–54, 56–68
Advanced 9–17, 18–44 even, 46–68

Homework Quick Check
Quickly check key concepts.
Exercises: 10, 12, 14, 16, 26, 42

Answers

3. $y = \frac{3}{4}x - 1$ and $y - 3 = \frac{3}{4}(x - 5)$
4. slope of $\overline{AD} = -\frac{3}{2}$
slope of $\overline{BC} = -\frac{3}{2}$
$\overline{AD}$ and $\overline{BC}$ are par. because they have the same slope and $\overline{AB}$ is not parallel to $\overline{CD}$. Therefore, *ABCD* is a trapezoid.
5. $y = \frac{2}{3}x - 4$ and $y = -\frac{3}{2}x + 2$; $y = -1$ and $x = 3$
6. $y = -\frac{3}{7}x - 4$ and $y - 7 = \frac{7}{3}(x - 3)$; $y - 4 = -7(x + 2)$ and $y - 1 = \frac{1}{7}(x - 4)$

5-7 Exercises

California Standards Practice
7.0, 8.0, 25.1

go.hrw.com
Homework Help Online
KEYWORD: MA8CA 5-7
Parent Resources Online
KEYWORD: MA8CA Parent

GUIDED PRACTICE

1. **Vocabulary** ___?___ lines have the same slope. (*Parallel* or *Perpendicular*) **Parallel**

SEE EXAMPLE 1 p. 304

Identify which lines are parallel.

2. $y = 6$; $y = 6x + 5$; $y = 6x - 7$; $y = -8$ **$y = 6x + 5$ and $y = 6x - 7$; $y = 6$ and $y = -8$**
3. $y = \frac{3}{4}x - 1$; $y = -2x$; $y - 3 = \frac{3}{4}(x - 5)$; $y - 4 = -2(x + 2)$

SEE EXAMPLE 2 p. 305

4. **Reasoning** Show that *ABCD* is a trapezoid. (*Hint:* In a trapezoid, exactly one pair of opposite sides is parallel.)

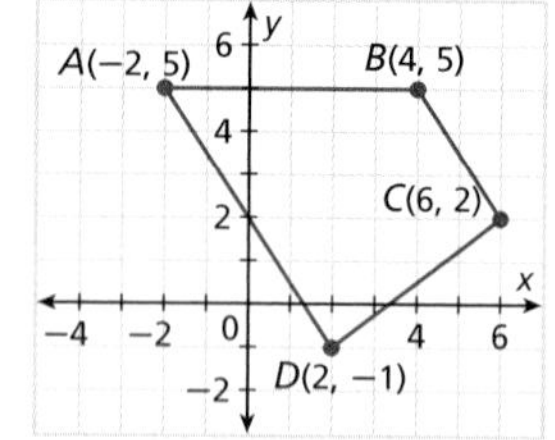

SEE EXAMPLE 3 p. 306

Identify which lines are perpendicular.

5. $y = \frac{2}{3}x - 4$; $y = -\frac{3}{2}x + 2$; $y = -1$; $x = 3$
6. $y = -\frac{3}{7}x - 4$; $y - 4 = -7(x + 2)$; $y - 1 = \frac{1}{7}(x - 4)$; $y - 7 = \frac{7}{3}(x - 3)$

SEE EXAMPLE 4 p. 306

7. **Reasoning** Show that *PQRS* is a rectangle. (*Hint:* In a rectangle, all four angles are right angles.)

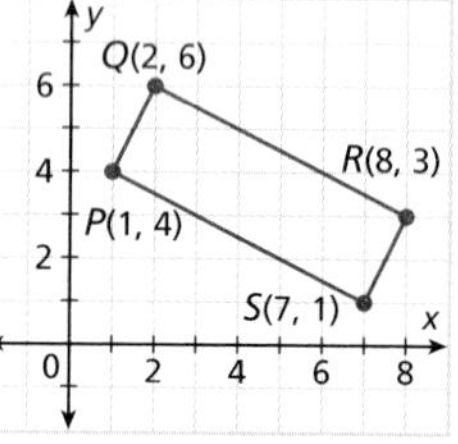

SEE EXAMPLE 5 p. 307

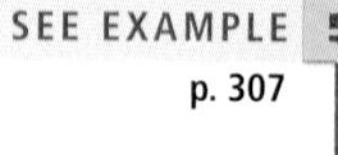

8. Write an equation in slope-intercept form for the line that passes through (5, 0) and is perpendicular to the line given by $y = -\frac{5}{2}x + 6$. **$y = \frac{2}{5}x - 2$**

PRACTICE AND PROBLEM SOLVING

Independent Practice For Exercises	See Example
9–11	1
12	2
13–15	3
16	4
17	5

Extra Practice
Skills Practice p. EP11
Application Practice p. EP28

Identify which lines are parallel.

9. $x = 7$; $y = -\frac{5}{6}x + 8$; $y = -\frac{5}{6}x - 4$; $x = -9$
10. $y = -x$; $y - 3 = -1(x + 9)$; $y - 6 = \frac{1}{2}(x - 14)$; $y + 1 = \frac{1}{2}x$
11. $y = -3x + 2$; $y = \frac{1}{2}x - 1$; $-x + 2y = 17$; $3x + y = 27$
12. **Reasoning** Show that *LMNP* is a parallelogram.

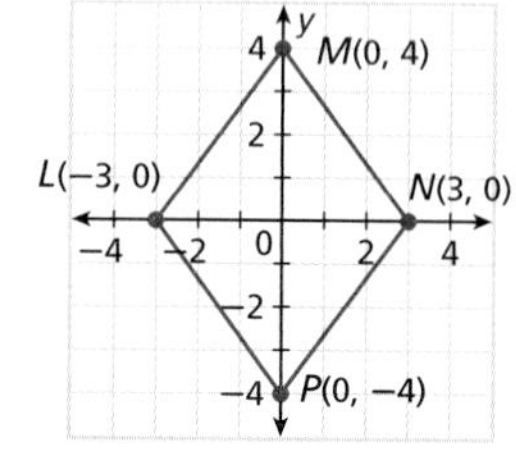

Identify which lines are perpendicular.

13. $y = 6x$; $y = \frac{1}{6}x$; $y = -\frac{1}{6}x$; $y = -6x$
14. $y - 9 = 3(x + 1)$; $y = -\frac{1}{3}x + 5$; $y = 0$; $x = 6$
15. $x - 6y = 15$; $y = 3x - 2$; $y = -3x - 3$; $y = -6x - 8$; $3y = -x - 11$
$x - 6y = 15$ and $y = -6x - 8$; $y = 3x - 2$ and $3y = -x - 11$

Answers

7. slope of $\overline{PQ} = 2$; slope of $\overline{QR} = -\frac{1}{2}$;
slope of $\overline{RS} = 2$; slope of $\overline{PS} = -\frac{1}{2}$
$\overline{PQ}$ is perp. to $\overline{QR}$ because the product of their slopes is −1. $\overline{QR}$ is perp. to $\overline{RS}$ because the product of their slopes is −1. $\overline{RS}$ is perp. to $\overline{PS}$ because the product of their slopes is −1. $\overline{PS}$ is perp. to $\overline{PQ}$ because the product of their slopes is −1. Therefore all the angles are rt. angles, and *PQRS* is a rectangle.
9. $x = 7$ and $x = -9$; $y = -\frac{5}{6}x + 8$ and $y = -\frac{5}{6}x - 4$
10. $y = -x$ and $y - 3 = -1(x + 9)$
11. $y = -3x + 2$ and $3x + y = 27$; $y = \frac{1}{2}x - 1$ and $-x + 2y = 17$
12. slope of $\overline{LM} = \frac{4}{3}$; slope of $\overline{MN} = -\frac{4}{3}$;
slope of $\overline{PN} = \frac{4}{3}$; slope of $\overline{LP} = -\frac{4}{3}$
$\overline{LM}$ is par. to $\overline{PN}$ because they have the same slope. $\overline{MN}$ is par. to $\overline{LP}$ because they have the same slope. Since opp. sides are par., *LMNP* is a parallelogram.
13. $y = 6x$ and $y = -\frac{1}{6}x$; $y = \frac{1}{6}x$ and $y = -6x$
14. $y - 9 = 3(x + 1)$ and $y = -\frac{1}{3}x + 5$; $y = 0$ and $x = 6$

California Standards

Standard	Exercises
5.0	59
6.0	54, 60–62
7.0	54, 63–68
8.0	50, 51b–53, 56–58
25.1	4, 7, 12, 16, 55, 58

22. $y = 3x + 4$
23. $y = \frac{1}{2}x - 5$
24. $y = \frac{1}{4}x - 1$
25. $y = 2x + 5$
26. $y = \frac{5}{2}x - \frac{25}{2}$
27. $y = 3x + 13$
28. $y = 4$
29. $y = -x + 5$
30. $y = -\frac{2}{3}x + \frac{23}{3}$
31. $y = 4x - 23$
32. $y = \frac{1}{2}x - 4$
33. $y = -\frac{3}{4}x$
34. $y = \frac{1}{3}x - 4$
35. $y = -x + 1$
36. $y = -\frac{4}{3}x - 3$
37. $y = \frac{2}{5}x - \frac{31}{5}$
38. $y = \frac{1}{3}x - \frac{14}{3}$
39. $y = -\frac{1}{5}x - \frac{11}{5}$
40. $y = \frac{3}{2}x - 1$
41. $y = -\frac{1}{2}x - \frac{1}{2}$
42. $y = 4x - 11$
43. $y = \frac{1}{2}x + 6$
44. $y = -x + 5$
45. $y = x - 3$

16. **Reasoning** Show that ABC is a right triangle.

17. Write an equation in slope-intercept form for the line that passes through $(0, 0)$ and is parallel to the line given by $y = -\frac{6}{7}x + 1$. $y = -\frac{6}{7}x$

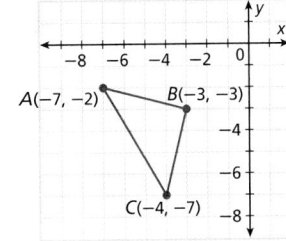

Without graphing, tell whether each pair of lines is parallel, perpendicular, or neither.

18. $x = 2$ and $y = -5$ **perp.**
19. $y = 7x$ and $y - 28 = 7(x - 4)$ **neither**
20. $y = 2x - 1$ and $y = \frac{1}{2}x + 2$ **neither**
21. $y - 3 = \frac{1}{4}(x - 3)$ and $y + 13 = \frac{1}{4}(x + 1)$ **par.**

Write an equation in slope-intercept form for the line that is parallel to the given line and that passes through the given point.

22. $y = 3x - 7$; $(0, 4)$
23. $y = \frac{1}{2}x + 5$; $(4, -3)$
24. $4y = x$; $(4, 0)$
25. $y = 2x + 3$; $(1, 7)$
26. $5x - 2y = 10$; $(3, -5)$
27. $y = 3x - 4$; $(-2, 7)$
28. $y = 7$; $(2, 4)$
29. $x + y = 1$; $(2, 3)$
30. $2x + 3y = 7$; $(4, 5)$
31. $y = 4x + 2$; $(5, -3)$
32. $y = \frac{1}{2}x - 1$; $(0, -4)$
33. $3x + 4y = 8$; $(4, -3)$

Write an equation in slope-intercept form for the line that is perpendicular to the given line and that passes through the given point.

34. $y = -3x + 4$; $(6, -2)$
35. $y = x - 6$; $(-1, 2)$
36. $3x - 4y = 8$; $(-6, 5)$
37. $5x + 2y = 10$; $(3, -5)$
38. $y = 5 - 3x$; $(2, -4)$
39. $-10x + 2y = 8$; $(4, -3)$
40. $2x + 3y = 7$; $(4, 5)$
41. $4x - 2y = -6$; $(3, -2)$
42. $-2x - 8y = 16$; $(4, 5)$
43. $y = -2x + 4$; $(-2, 5)$
44. $y = x - 5$; $(0, 5)$
45. $x + y = 2$; $(8, 5)$

46. Write an equation describing the line that is parallel to the y-axis and that is 6 units to the right of the y-axis. $x = 6$

47. Write an equation describing the line that is perpendicular to the y-axis and that is 4 units below the x-axis. $y = -4$

48. **Critical Thinking** Is it possible for two linear functions whose graphs are parallel lines to have the same y-intercept? Explain.

49. **Estimation** Estimate the slope of a line that is perpendicular to the line through $(2.07, 8.95)$ and $(-1.9, 25.07)$. **Possible answer: about −4**

50. **Write About It** Explain in words how to write an equation in slope-intercept form for a line parallel to $y - 3 = -6(x - 3)$.

CONCEPT CONNECTION

51. This problem will prepare you for the Concept Connection on page 312.
    a. Flora walks from her home to the bus stop at a rate of 50 steps per minute. Write a rule that gives her distance from home (in steps) as a function of time. $y = 50x$
    b. Flora's neighbor Dan lives 30 steps closer to the bus stop. He begins walking at the same time and at the same pace as Flora. Write a rule that gives Dan's distance from *Flora's* house as a function of time. $y = 50x + 30$
    c. Will Flora meet Dan along the walk? Use a graph to help explain your answer.

CONCEPT CONNECTION Exercise 51 involves writing and graphing a function. This exercise prepares students for the Concept Connection on page 312.

Answers

16. slope of $\overline{AB} = -\frac{1}{4}$
slope of $\overline{BC} = 4$
$\overline{AB}$ is perp. to $\overline{BC}$ because the product of their slopes is −1. Since ABC contains a rt. angle, ABC is a rt. triangle.

48. Possible answer: No; par. lines have no points in common. If they had the same y-int., they would both intersect the y-axis at the same place, and they could not be par.

50. Possible answer: First find the slope of $y - 3 = -6(x - 3)$. Since it is written in point-slope form, you can immediately tell that the slope is −6. Then find the y-int. of $y - 3 = -6(x - 3)$ by solving for y: $y = -6x + 21$. So the y-int. is 21. Choose any other y-int. b and write the equation $y = -6x + b$. This line will be par. to $y - 3 = -6(x - 3)$.

51c. No; because the graphs of these lines are par. and never intersect; this means Flora and Dan will never be at the same place at the same time. Since Dan is walking at the same pace as Flora, Flora will not be able to catch up.

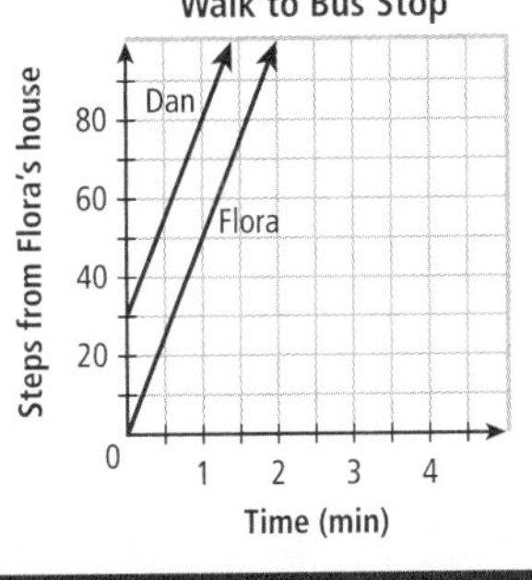

5-7 READING STRATEGIES

LESSON 5-7 Reading Strategies
Compare and Contrast

Parallel Lines | Perpendicular Lines

Contrast
Parallel lines never intersect.
Perpendicular lines intersect to form right angles.

The slopes of parallel lines are the same.
The slopes of perpendicular lines have a product of −1.

Compare
Both parallel and perpendicular lines can be identified by their equations.
Both parallel and perpendicular lines have applications in geometry.

Possible answers are given for 1 and 2.

1. Write an equation of a line parallel to $y = 3x + 4$. $y = 3x + 3$
2. Write an equation of a line perpendicular to $y = 3x + 4$. $y = -\frac{1}{3}x + 3$

$A(9, -4)$, $B(-3, 0)$ and $C(1, 4)$ are the vertices of a triangle.

3. Find the slope of $\overline{AB}$. $-\frac{1}{3}$
4. Find the slope of $\overline{BC}$. 1
5. Find the slope of $\overline{AC}$. −1
6. Is ABC a right triangle? Why? yes; $\overline{BC}$ and $\overline{AC}$ are perpendicular because $1(-1) = -1$.

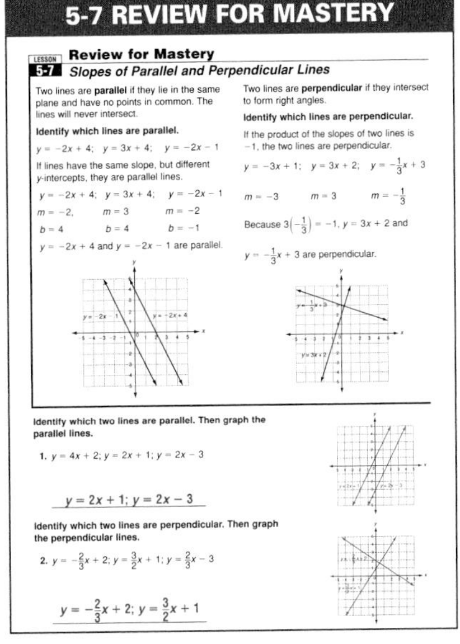

5-7 REVIEW FOR MASTERY

LESSON 5-7 Review for Mastery
Slopes of Parallel and Perpendicular Lines

Two lines are **parallel** if they lie in the same plane and have no points in common. The lines will never intersect.

Identify which lines are parallel.

$y = -2x + 4$; $y = 3x + 4$; $y = -2x - 1$

If lines have the same slope, but different y-intercepts, they are parallel lines.

$y = -2x + 4$; $y = 3x + 4$; $y = -2x - 1$
$m = -2$, $m = 3$, $m = -2$
$b = 4$, $b = 4$, $b = -1$

$y = -2x + 4$ and $y = -2x - 1$ are parallel.

Two lines are **perpendicular** if they intersect to form right angles.

Identify which lines are perpendicular.

If the product of the slopes of two lines is −1, the two lines are perpendicular.

$y = -3x + 1$; $y = 3x + 2$; $y = -\frac{1}{3}x + 3$
$m = -3$, $m = 3$, $m = -\frac{1}{3}$

Because $3\left(-\frac{1}{3}\right) = -1$, $y = 3x + 2$ and $y = -\frac{1}{3}x + 3$ are perpendicular.

Identify which two lines are parallel. Then graph the parallel lines.

1. $y = 4x + 2$; $y = 2x + 1$; $y = 2x - 3$
$y = 2x + 1$; $y = 2x - 3$

Identify which two lines are perpendicular. Then graph the perpendicular lines.

2. $y = -\frac{2}{3}x + 2$; $y = \frac{3}{2}x + 1$; $y = \frac{2}{3}x - 3$
$y = -\frac{2}{3}x + 2$; $y = \frac{3}{2}x + 1$

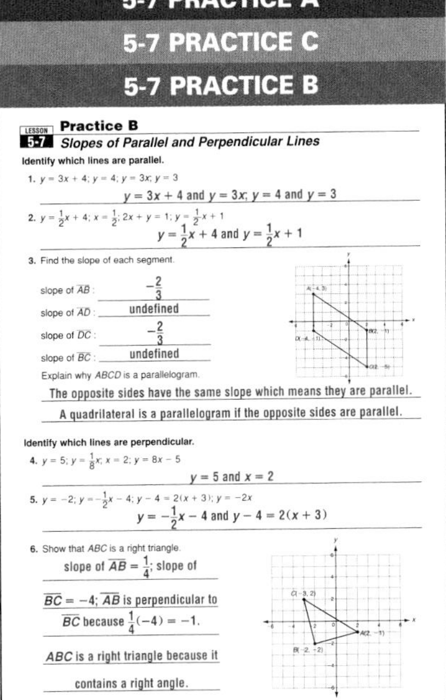

5-7 PRACTICE A
5-7 PRACTICE C
5-7 PRACTICE B

LESSON 5-7 Practice B
Slopes of Parallel and Perpendicular Lines

Identify which lines are parallel.

1. $y = 3x + 4$; $y = 4$; $y = 3x$; $y = 3$
$y = 3x + 4$ and $y = 3x$; $y = 4$ and $y = 3$

2. $y = \frac{1}{2}x + 4$; $x = \frac{1}{2}$; $2x + y = 1$; $y = \frac{1}{2}x + 1$
$y = \frac{1}{2}x + 4$ and $y = \frac{1}{2}x + 1$

3. Find the slope of each segment.
slope of $\overline{AB}$: $-\frac{2}{3}$
slope of $\overline{AD}$: undefined
slope of $\overline{DC}$: $-\frac{2}{3}$
slope of $\overline{BC}$: undefined
Explain why $ABCD$ is a parallelogram.
The opposite sides have the same slope which means they are parallel. A quadrilateral is a parallelogram if the opposite sides are parallel.

Identify which lines are perpendicular.

4. $y = 5$; $y = \frac{1}{8}x$; $x = 2$; $y = 8x - 5$
$y = 5$ and $x = 2$

5. $y = -2$; $y = -\frac{1}{2}x - 4$; $y - 4 = 2(x + 3)$; $y = -2x$
$y = -\frac{1}{2}x - 4$ and $y - 4 = 2(x + 3)$

6. Show that ABC is a right triangle.
slope of $\overline{AB} = \frac{1}{4}$; slope of $\overline{BC} = -4$; $\overline{AB}$ is perpendicular to $\overline{BC}$ because $\frac{1}{4}(-4) = -1$.
ABC is a right triangle because it contains a right angle.

Multiple Choice Students who chose **C** for **Exercise 52** chose the same line, not a parallel line.

Students who chose **A** in **Exercise 53** most likely did not completely distribute the slope when simplifying the point-slope form.

Answers

55, 58, 60–62. See p. A20.

Journal

Have students explain how to write the equation of a line that is perpendicular to a given line, such as $y - 2 = 3(x + 1)$.

ALTERNATIVE ASSESSMENT

Have students write three equations: one in standard form, one in slope-intercept form, and one in point-slope form. Have them write equations parallel to each line. Then have them write equations perpendicular to each line.

Power Presentations with PowerPoint®

5-7 Lesson Quiz

Write an equation in slope-intercept form for the line described.

1. contains the point $(8, -12)$ and is parallel to $y = -\frac{3}{4}x - 9$ $\quad y = -\frac{3}{4}x - 6$
2. contains the point $(4, -3)$ and is perpendicular to $y = 4x + 5$ $\quad y = -\frac{1}{4}x - 2$
3. Show that *WXYZ* is a rectangle.

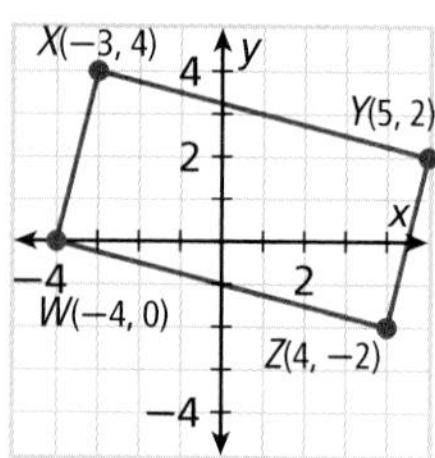

Slope of $\overline{XY} = -\frac{1}{4}$; slope of $\overline{YZ} = 4$; slope of $\overline{WZ} = -\frac{1}{4}$; slope of $\overline{XW} = 4$; the product of the slopes of adjacent sides is -1. Therefore, all angles are rt. angles, and *WXYZ* is a rectangle.

Also available on transparency

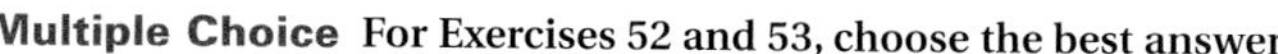

Multiple Choice For Exercises 52 and 53, choose the best answer.

52. Which line is parallel to the line given by $y = -3x + 2$?

    (A) $y = -3x$ (circled) $\quad$ (B) $y = \frac{1}{3}x$ $\quad$ (C) $y = 2 - 3x$ $\quad$ (D) $y = \frac{1}{3}x + 2$

53. Which line passes through $(3, 3)$ and is perpendicular to the line given by $y = \frac{3}{5}x + 2$?

    (A)

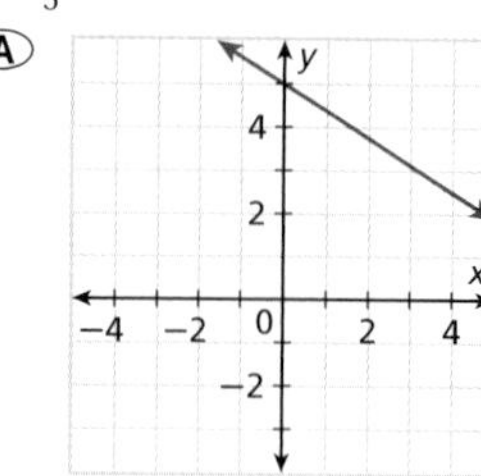

    (C) (circled)

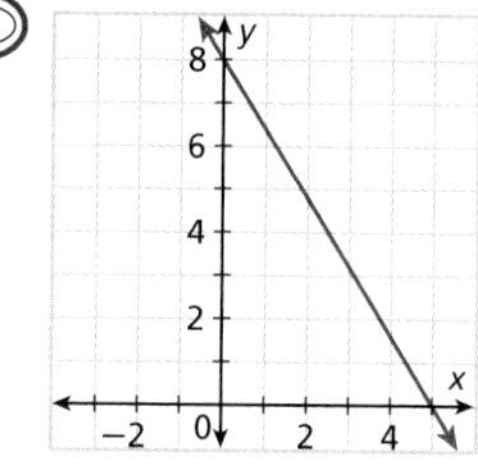

    (B) $y = \frac{5}{3}x - 2$ $\quad$ (D) $y = \frac{3}{5}x + \frac{6}{5}$

54. **Gridded Response** The graph of a linear function $f(x)$ is parallel to the line given by $2x + y = 5$ and contains the point $(6, -2)$. What is the *y*-intercept of $f(x)$? **10**

CHALLENGE AND EXTEND

55. **Reasoning** Three or more points that lie on the same line are called *collinear points*. Show that the points *A*, *B*, and *C* must be collinear if the line containing *A* and *B* has the same slope as the line containing *B* and *C*.
56. The lines given by $y = (a + 12)x + 3$ and $y = 4ax$ are parallel. What is the value of a? **4**
57. The lines given by $y = (5a + 3)x$ and $y = -\frac{1}{2}x$ are perpendicular. What is the value of a? $-\frac{1}{5}$

58. **Geometry** The diagram shows a square in the coordinate plane. Use the diagram and deductive reasoning to show that the diagonals of a square are perpendicular.

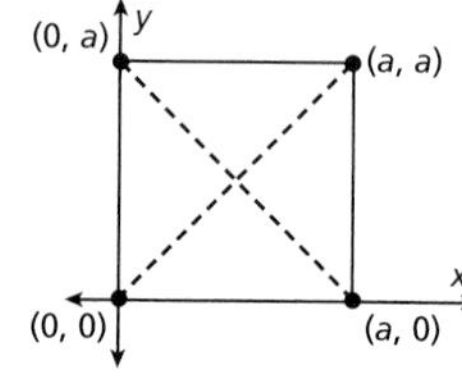

SPIRAL STANDARDS REVIEW

59. The record high temperature for a given city is 112°F + *t*. The morning temperature today was 94°F and the temperature will increase 2*t* degrees. Write and solve an inequality to find all values of *t* that would break the record for the high temperature. *(Lesson 3-4)* $94 + 2t > 112 + t$; $t > 18$

Graph each function. *(Lesson 4-3)*

60. $y = -3x + 5$ $\quad$ 61. $y = x - 1$ $\quad$ 62. $y = x^2 - 3$

Write an equation in slope-intercept form for the line with the given slope that contains the given point. *(Lesson 5-6)*

63. slope $= \frac{2}{3}$; $(6, -1)$ $\quad$ 64. slope $= -5$; $(2, 4)$ $\quad$ 65. slope $= -\frac{1}{2}$; $(-1, 0)$

66. slope $= -\frac{1}{3}$; $(2, 7)$ $\quad$ 67. slope $= 0$; $(-3, 3)$ $\quad$ 68. slope $= \frac{1}{5}$; $(-4, -2)$

63. $y = \frac{2}{3}x - 5$
64. $y = -5x + 14$
65. $y = -\frac{1}{2}x - \frac{1}{2}$
66. $y = -\frac{1}{3}x + \frac{23}{3}$
67. $y = 3$
68. $y = \frac{1}{5}x - \frac{6}{5}$

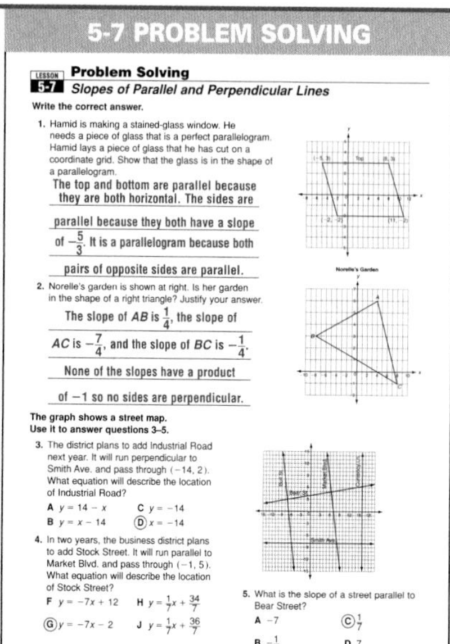

5-7 PROBLEM SOLVING

LESSON 5-7 **Problem Solving**
Slopes of Parallel and Perpendicular Lines

Write the correct answer.

1. Hamid is making a stained-glass window. He needs a piece of glass that is a perfect parallelogram. Hamid lays a piece of glass that he has cut on a coordinate grid. Show that the glass is in the shape of a parallelogram.
   The top and bottom are parallel because they are both horizontal. The sides are parallel because they both have a slope of $-\frac{5}{3}$. It is a parallelogram because both pairs of opposite sides are parallel.
2. Norelle's garden is shown at right. Is her garden in the shape of a right triangle? Justify your answer.
   The slope of *AB* is $\frac{1}{4}$, the slope of *AC* is $-\frac{7}{4}$, and the slope of *BC* is $-\frac{1}{4}$. None of the slopes have a product of -1 so no sides are perpendicular.

Norelle's Garden

The graph shows a street map. Use it to answer questions 3–5.

3. The district plans to add Industrial Road next year. It will run perpendicular to Smith Ave. and pass through $(-14, 2)$. What equation will describe the location of Industrial Road?
   A $y = 14 - x$ $\quad$ C $y = -14$
   B $y = x - 14$ $\quad$ (D) $x = -14$ (circled)
4. In two years, the business district plans to add Stock Street. It will run parallel to Market Blvd. and pass through $(-1, 5)$. What equation will describe the location of Stock Street?
   F $y = -7x + 12$ $\quad$ H $y = \frac{1}{7}x + \frac{34}{7}$
   (G) $y = -7x - 2$ (circled) $\quad$ J $y = \frac{1}{7}x + \frac{36}{7}$
5. What is the slope of a street parallel to Bear Street?
   A -7 $\quad$ (C) $\frac{1}{7}$ (circled)
   B $-\frac{1}{7}$ $\quad$ D 7

5-7 CHALLENGE

LESSON 5-7 **Challenge**
Constructing Polygons Using Parallel and Perpendicular Lines

Two facts about parallel and perpendicular lines are summarized below.

If two nonvertical lines are parallel, then their slopes are equal.

If two nonvertical lines are perpendicular, then their slopes are negative reciprocals of one another.

You can use these facts if you want to construct special polygons on the coordinate plane.

In Exercises 1–4, use the grid and the graph of $y = 2x + 1$.

1. a. Write an equation in slope-intercept form for the line parallel to the graph of $y = 2x + 1$ and having a *y*-intercept of 4. $y = 2x + 4$
   b. Graph your equation on the grid at right above.
2. a. Find the *y*-coordinate of the point on the graph of $y = 2x + 1$ for which $x = -2$. -3
   b. Find an equation for the line containing the point found in Part a and perpendicular to the graph of. $y = 2x + 1$ $\quad y = -\frac{1}{2}x - 4$
   c. Graph your equation from Part b on the grid at right above.
3. a. Find the *y*-coordinate of the point on the graph of $y = 2x + 1$ for which $x = 1$. 3
   b. Find an equation for the line containing the point found in Part a and perpendicular to the graph of $y = 2x + 1$. $y = -\frac{1}{2}x + \frac{7}{2}$
   c. Graph your equation from Part b on the grid at right above.
4. Identify the polygon that you formed. Explain your response.
   It is a rectangle because it has four right angles.

In Exercises 5 and 6, use the grid at right.

5. Suppose that you want to make a square using the graph of $x + y = 4$ to help determine one side of the square.
   Write equations in standard form to determine a square with corners at $(4, 0)$, $(0, 4)$, $(-4, 0)$ and $(0, -4)$. $x - y = -4$; $x + y = -4$; $x - y = 4$; $x + y = 4$
6. On the grid at right, graph each of the equations that you wrote in Exercise 5.

Proving Conjectures

After working several math problems, Adele used inductive reasoning to conclude that when using two points to find the slope of a line, the order in which the points are substituted into the slope formula does not matter. (See pp. 280–281.)

California Standards

25.1 Students use properties of numbers to construct simple, valid arguments (direct and indirect) **for,** or formulate counterexamples to, **claimed assertions.**
Also covered: **24.1**

Example

Inductive reasoning alone cannot prove a statement. However, inductive reasoning often leads to a conjecture that can be proved or disproved using deductive reasoning.

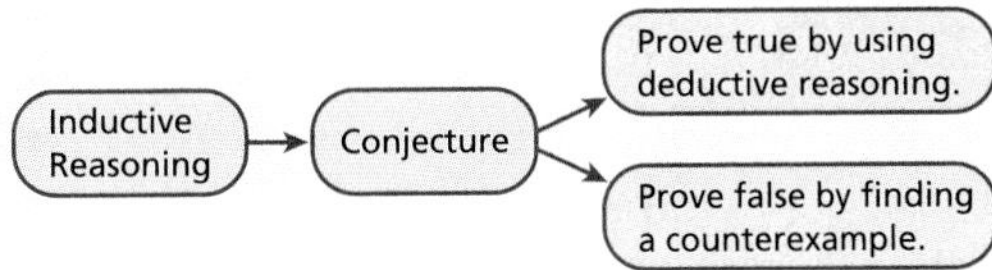

When Adele returned to class, she learned that her conjecture was correct. However, Adele wants to prove that her conjecture is true.

Adele's algebra teacher helped Adele write her conjecture as a conditional statement:

If (x_1, y_1) and (x_2, y_2) are two different points on a line, then $m = \frac{y_2 - y_1}{x_2 - x_1} = \frac{y_1 - y_2}{x_1 - x_2}$.

Try This

Adele wrote a proof of her conjecture, but she did not write reasons for her statements. Complete her proof by giving the reasons.

Statements	Reasons
1. (x_1, y_1) and (x_2, y_2) are two different points on a line.	Given ?
2. $m = \frac{y_2 - y_1}{x_2 - x_1}$	Slope formula ?
3. $= \frac{y_2 - y_1}{x_2 - x_1}(1)$	Identity Property ? of Multiplication
4. $= \frac{y_2 - y_1}{x_2 - x_1}\left(\frac{-1}{-1}\right)$	$\frac{-1}{-1} = 1$?
5. $= \frac{-y_2 + y_1}{-x_2 + x_1}$	Distributive Property (in both numerator and denominator) ?
6. $= \frac{y_1 + (-y_2)}{x_1 + (-x_2)}$	Commutative Property of Addition ?
7. $= \frac{y_1 - y_2}{x_1 - x_2}$	Definition of subtraction as addition of the opposite ?

Organizer

Objective: Use deductive reasoning to prove a conjecture.

Online Edition
Student Edtion

Countdown to Mastery Week 12

Teach

Discuss

Explain that the flow chart on the student page illustrates an important reasoning process that mathematicians often use to prove or disprove statements.

Students may say that Adele's conjecture is correct because it was taught in Lesson 5-3. Explain that we often trust statements given in textbooks to be true, but that is not the same as proving that a statement is true.

Have students identify the hypothesis and conclusion in Adele's conjecture. H: (x_1, y_1) and (x_2, y_2) are two different points on a line; C: $m = \frac{y_2 - y_1}{x_2 - x_1} = \frac{y_1 - y_2}{x_1 - x_2}$

Close

Key Concept

Inductive reasoning can lead to a conjecture that you may be able to prove or disprove using deductive reasoning.

Assess

Have students write a paragraph that explains the process shown in the flow chart on the student page.

Extend

Have students revisit Exercise 33 in Lesson 5-2. (If students did not complete this exercise, have them complete it now.) Challenge them to prove their conjecture from part **c** by using deductive reasoning.

Poss. ans.: For horiz. lines $y = c$ $(c \neq 0)$, all points have the same y-coord. So the line will pass through $(0, c)$ and c is the y-int. When $c \neq 0$, the line $y = c$ is par. to the x-axis. So $y = c$ does not cross the x-axis and there is no x-int. Similar reasoning can be used for vert. lines.

California Standards

25.1 Students use properties of numbers to construct simple, valid arguments (direct and indirect) for, or formulate counterexamples to, claimed assertions.
Also covered:
24.1 Students explain the difference between inductive and deductive reasoning and identify **and provide examples** of each.

Organizer

Objective: Assess students' ability to apply concepts and skills in Lessons 5-5 through 5-7 in a real-world format.

Online Edition

Problem	Text Reference
1	Lesson 4-2
2	Lesson 5-3
3	Lesson 5-1
4	Lesson 5-6
5	Lesson 5-3

Answer

3.

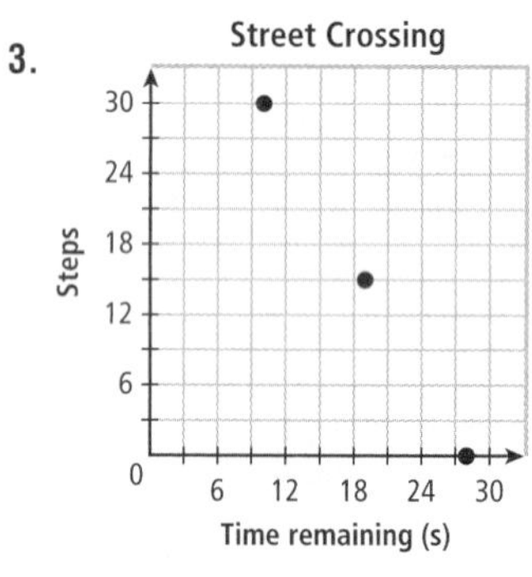

California Standards

Algebra 1 6.0

SECTION 5B

Using Linear Functions

Take a Walk! All intersections in Durango, Colorado, have crossing signals with timers. Once the signal changes to walk, the timer begins at 28 seconds and counts down to show how much time pedestrians have to cross the street.

1. Pauline counted her steps as she crossed the street. She counted 15 steps with 19 seconds remaining. When she reached the opposite side of the street, she had counted a total of 30 steps and had 10 seconds remaining. Copy and complete the table below using these values.

Time Remaining (s)	28	**19**	**10**
Steps Taken	0	**15**	**30**

2. Find the average rate of change for Pauline's walk. $-\frac{5}{3}$, or $-1\frac{2}{3}$, **steps/s**
3. Sketch a graph of the points in the table, or plot them on your graphing calculator.
4. Find an equation for the line through the points. $y = -\frac{5}{3}x + \frac{140}{3}$
5. How would the graph change if Pauline increased her speed? What if she decreased her speed? **The line would become steeper; the line would become less steep.**

INTERVENTION

Scaffolding Questions

1–2. What are the independent and dependent variables? ind.: time remaining; dep.: steps

3–4. Will the points go upward or downward from left to right? Explain. Downward; as time remaining increases, number of steps taken decreases. What does the slope represent? steps per time remaining

5. How can you find the equation for the relationship? Possible answer: Use point-slope form.

In terms of the number of steps, what does it mean to increase or decrease speed? If speed increases, the number of steps increases; if speed decreases, the number of steps decreases.

Extension

At the next intersection, Pauline walked at the same speed, but the distance across the street was longer. How will the graph of this situation compare to the graph of the original situation? It will be shifted up.

READY TO GO ON?

CHAPTER 5

SECTION 5B

Quiz for Lessons 5-5 Through 5-7

5-5 Slope-Intercept Form

Graph each line given the slope and y-intercept.

1. slope $= \frac{1}{4}$
   y-intercept $= 2$
2. slope $= -3$
   y-intercept $= 5$
3. slope $= -1$
   y-intercept $= -6$

Write each equation in slope-intercept form. Then graph the line given by the equation.

4. $2x + y = 5$ **$y = -2x + 5$**
5. $2x - 6y = 6$ 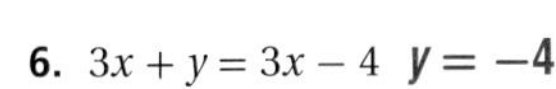 **$y = \frac{1}{3}x - 1$**
6. $3x + y = 3x - 4$ **$y = -4$**
7. **Entertainment** At a chili cook-off, people pay a \$3.00 entrance fee and \$0.50 for each bowl of chili they taste. The graph shows the total cost per person as a function of the number of bowls of chili tasted. **a. $y = 0.5x + 3$**

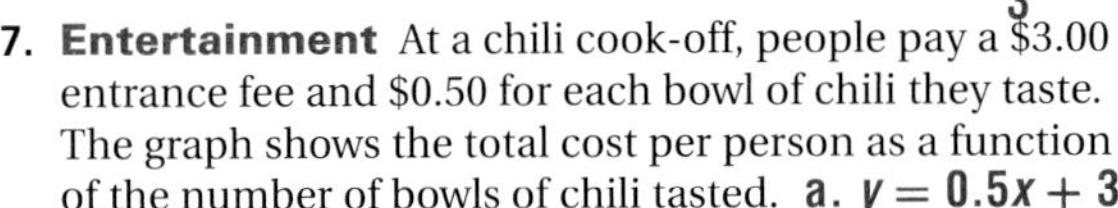

   a. Write a rule that gives the total cost per person as a function of the number of bowls of chili tasted.
   b. Identify the slope and y-intercept and describe their meanings in this situation.
   slope: 0.5; cost per bowl of chili; y-int: 3; entrance fee

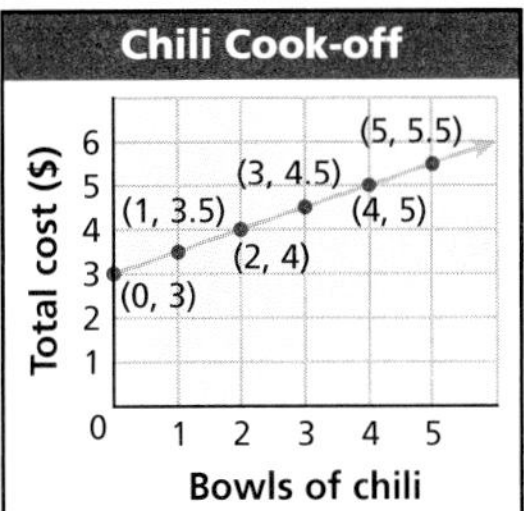

5-6 Point-Slope Form

Graph the line with the given slope that contains the given point.

8. slope $= -3$; $(0, 3)$
9. slope $= -\frac{2}{3}$; $(-3, 5)$
10. slope $= 2$; $(-3, -1)$
11. Write an equation in slope-intercept form for the line with slope -3 that contains $(2, -4)$. **$y = -3x + 2$**

Write an equation in slope-intercept form for the line through the two points.

12. $(3, 1)$ and $(4, 3)$
    $y = 2x - 5$
13. $(-1, -1)$ and $(1, 7)$
    $y = 4x + 3$
14. $(1, -4)$ and $(-2, 5)$
    $y = -3x - 1$

5-7 Slopes of Parallel and Perpendicular Lines

Identify which lines are parallel.

15. $y = -2x$; $y = 2x + 1$; $y = 2x$; $y = 2(x + 5)$ **$y = 2x + 1$, $y = 2x$, and $y = 2(x + 5)$**
16. $-3y = x$; $y = -\frac{1}{3}x + 1$; $y = -3x$; $y + 2 = x + 4$ **$-3y = x$ and $y = -\frac{1}{3}x + 1$**

Identify which lines are perpendicular.

17. $y = -4x - 1$; $y = \frac{1}{4}x$; $y = 4x - 6$; $x = -4$ **$y = -4x - 1$ and $y = \frac{1}{4}x$**
18. $y = -\frac{3}{4}x$; $y = \frac{3}{4}x - 3$; $y = \frac{4}{3}x$; $y = 4$; $x = 3$ **$y = -\frac{3}{4}x$ and $y = \frac{4}{3}x$; $y = 4$ and $x = 3$**
19. Write an equation in slope-intercept form for the line that passes through $(5, 2)$ and is parallel to the line given by $3x - 5y = 15$. **$y = \frac{3}{5}x - 1$**
20. Write an equation in slope-intercept form for the line that passes through $(3, 5)$ and is perpendicular to the line given by $y = -\frac{3}{2}x - 2$. **$y = \frac{2}{3}x + 3$**

READY TO GO ON?

SECTION 5B

Organizer

Objective: Assess students' mastery of concepts and skills in Lessons 5-5 through 5-7.

Countdown to Mastery Week 12

Resources

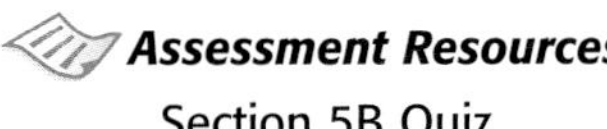

Assessment Resources
Section 5B Quiz

Test & Practice Generator
One-Stop Planner®

INTERVENTION 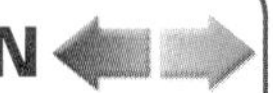

Resources

***Ready to Go On? Intervention and Enrichment* Worksheets**

***Ready to Go On?* CD-ROM**

***Ready to Go On?* Online**

my.hrw.com

Answers

1–3. See p. A20.
4–6. For graphs, see p. A20.
8–10. See p. A20.

READY TO GO ON?
Diagnose and Prescribe

NO INTERVENE

Ready to Go On? Intervention	*Ready to Go On? Intervention*, Section 5B		
	Worksheets	CD-ROM	Online
Lesson 5-5 6.0	5-5 Intervention	Activity 5-5	Diagnose and Prescribe Online
Lesson 5-6 7.0	5-6 Intervention	Activity 5-6	
Lesson 5-7 8.0	5-7 Intervention	Activity 5-7	

YES ENRICH

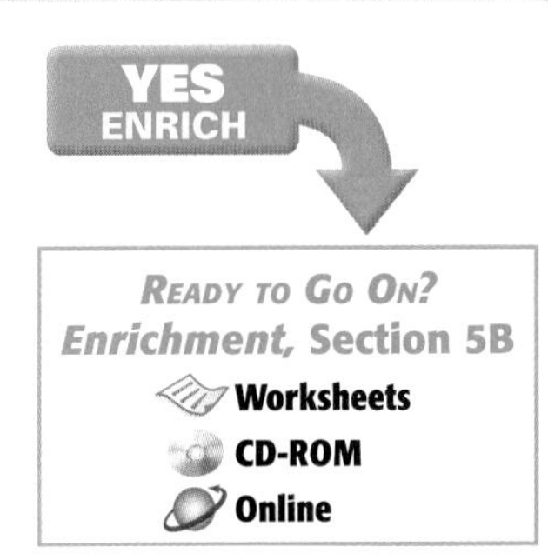

Ready to Go On? Enrichment, Section 5B
Worksheets
CD-ROM
Online

Study Guide: Review

Organizer

Objective: Help students organize and review key concepts and skills presented in Chapter 5.

Online Edition
Multilingual Glossary

Resources

PuzzlePro
One-Stop Planner®

***Multilingual Glossary* Online**
go.hrw.com
KEYWORD: MA8CA Glossary

Lesson Tutorial Videos
CD-ROM

Test & Practice Generator
One-Stop Planner®

Answers

1. direct variation
2. y-intercept
3. slope; y-intercept
4. yes

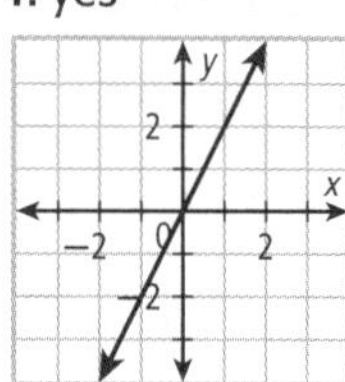

5. yes

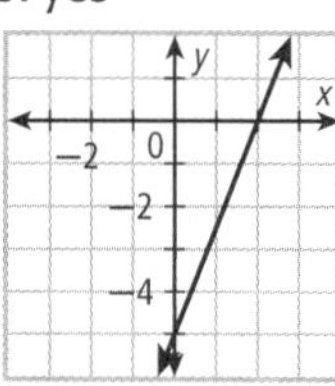

6. yes

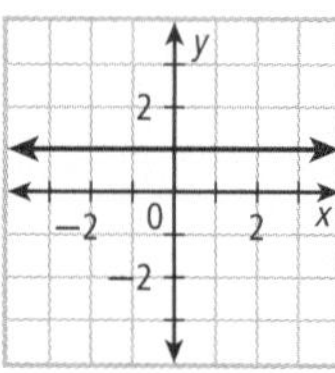

7. yes

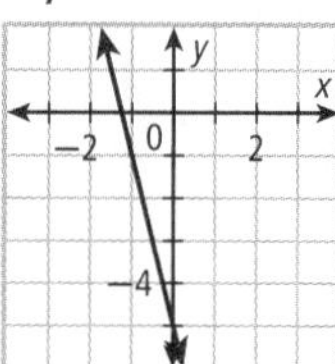

8. no
9. yes
10. yes
11. no
12. $5x + y = 1$; $A = 5$; $B = 1$; $C = 1$; non horiz., non vert. line
13. $x + 6y = -2$; $A = 1$; $B = 6$; $C = -2$; non horiz., non vert. line
14. $7x - 4y = 0$; $A = 7$, $B = -4$, $C = 0$; non horiz., non vert. line
15. $y = 9$; $A = 0$; $B = 1$; $C = 9$; horiz. line

CHAPTER 5

Study Guide: Review

Vocabulary

constant of variation 282	**parallel lines** 304	**run** 272
direct variation 282	**perpendicular lines** 306	**slope** 272
linear equation 256	**rate of change** 272	***x*-intercept** 263
linear function 256	**rise** 272	***y*-intercept** 263

Complete the sentences below with vocabulary words from the list above. Words may be used more than once.

1. An equation that can be written in the form $y = kx$ is a(n) __?__ .
2. The x-coordinate of the point that contains the __?__ is always 0.
3. In the equation $y = mx + b$, the value of m is the __?__ , and the value of b is the __?__ .

5-1 Linear Equations and Functions *(pp. 256–262)*

6.0, 7.0, 17.0, 18.0

EXAMPLES

■ **Graph $y = -3x + 2$. Then tell whether it represents a function.**

Generate ordered pairs.

x	$y = -3x + 2$	(x, y)
-2	$y = -3(-2) + 2 = 8$	$(-2, 8)$
0	$y = -3(0) + 2 = 2$	$(0, 2)$
2	$y = -3(2) + 2 = -4$	$(2, -4)$

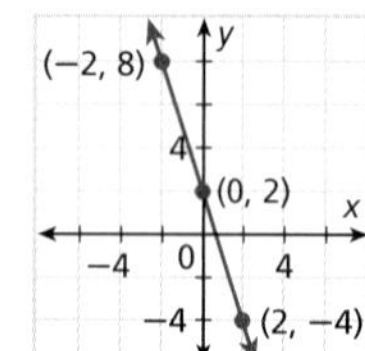

Plot the points and connect them with a straight line.

No vertical line will intersect this graph more than once, so $y = -3x + 2$ represents a function.

■ **Write $y = 2x - 3$ in standard form and give the values of A, B, and C.**

$$\begin{aligned} y &= 2x - 3 \\ -2x \quad & -2x \\ -2x + y &= -3 \end{aligned}$$

Subtract 2x from both sides.

$A = -2 \quad B = 1 \quad C = -3$

EXERCISES

Graph each linear equation. Then tell whether it describes a function.

4. $2x = y$
5. $5x - 2y = 10$
6. $y = 1$
7. $y + 5 = -4x$

Without graphing, tell whether each point is on the graph of $3x + 2y = 1$.

8. $(1, 6)$
9. $\left(0, \frac{1}{2}\right)$
10. $(3, -4)$
11. $(5, 1.5)$

Write each equation in standard form and give the values of A, B, and C. Then describe the graph.

12. $y = -5x + 1$
13. $\frac{x + 2}{2} = -3y$
14. $4y = 7x$
15. $9 = y$

5-2 Using Intercepts (pp. 263–268)

EXAMPLE

■ **Find the x- and y-intercepts of $2x + 5y = 10$.**

Let $y = 0$.	Let $x = 0$.
$2x + 5(0) = 10$	$2(0) + 5y = 10$
$2x + 0 = 10$	$0 + 5y = 10$
$2x = 10$	$5y = 10$
$\frac{2x}{2} = \frac{10}{2}$	$\frac{5y}{5} = \frac{10}{5}$
$x = 5$	$y = 2$
The x-intercept is 5.	The y-intercept is 2.

EXERCISES

Find the x- and y-intercepts.

16.

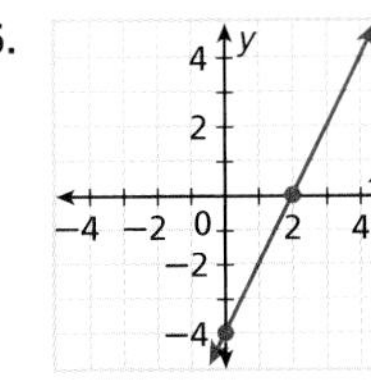

17.

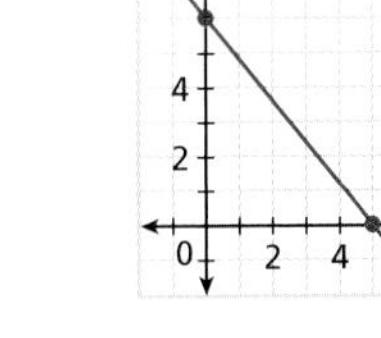

18. $3x - y = 9$
19. $-2x + y = 1$
20. $-x + 6y = 18$
21. $3x - 4y = 1$

5-3 Slope (pp. 272–279)

Prep for 8.0, 6.0

EXAMPLES

■ **Find the slope.**

Conversion of Measurement

Length (ft)

(3, 9)

(2, 6)

(1, 3)

Length (yd)

$$\text{slope} = \frac{\text{change in } y}{\text{change in } x} = \frac{3}{1} = 3$$

■ **Find the slope of the line given by $2x - 3y = 6$.**

Step 1 Identify the x- and y-intercepts.

Let $y = 0$.	Let $x = 0$.
$2x - 3(0) = 6$	$2(0) - 3y = 6$
$2x = 6$	$-3y = 6$
$x = 3$	$y = -2$

The line contains $(3, 0)$ and $(0, -2)$.

Step 2 Use the slope formula.

$$m = \frac{y_2 - y_1}{x_2 - x_1} = \frac{-2 - 0}{0 - 3} = \frac{-2}{-3} = \frac{2}{3}$$

EXERCISES

22. Find the slope of the line graphed below.

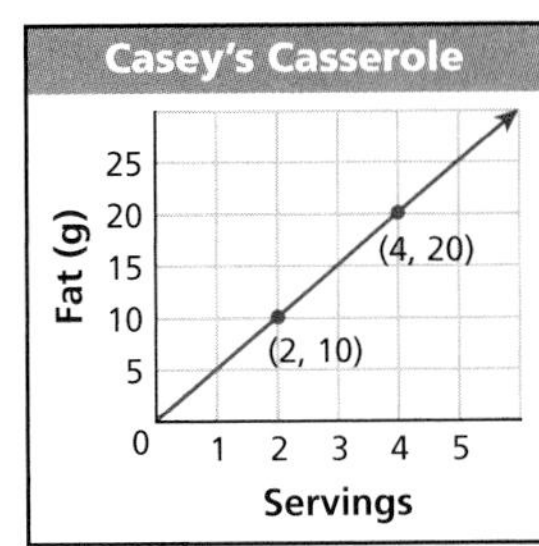

Find the slope of the line described by each equation.

23. $4x + 3y = 24$
24. $y = -3x + 6$
25. $x + 2y = 10$
26. $3x = y + 3$
27. $y + 2 = 7x$
28. $16x = 4y + 1$

Find the slope of the line that contains each pair of points.

29. $(1, 2)$ and $(2, -3)$
30. $(4, -2)$ and $(-5, 7)$
31. $(-3, -6)$ and $(4, 1)$
32. $\left(\frac{1}{2}, 2\right)$ and $\left(\frac{3}{4}, \frac{5}{2}\right)$
33. $(2, 2)$ and $(2, 7)$
34. $(1, -3)$ and $(5, -3)$

Answers

16. x-int.: 2; y-int.: −4
17. x-int.: 5; y-int.: 6
18. x-int.: 3; y-int.: −9
19. x-int.: $-\frac{1}{2}$; y-int.: 1
20. x-int.: −18; y-int.: 3
21. x-int.: $\frac{1}{3}$; y-int.: $-\frac{1}{4}$
22. 5
23. $-\frac{4}{3}$
24. −3
25. $-\frac{1}{2}$
26. 3
27. 7
28. 4
29. −5
30. −1
31. 1
32. 2
33. undefined
34. 0

Study Guide: Review **315**

Answers

35. yes; −6
36. yes; 1
37. no
38. yes; $-\frac{1}{2}$
39. −12
40. Maleka's Baby-sitting Earnings

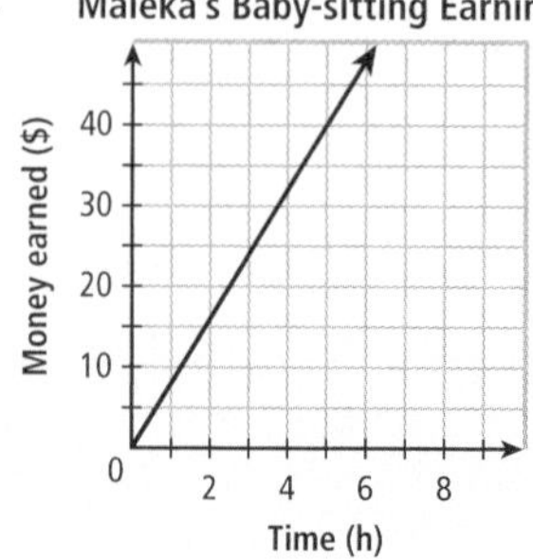

41. 

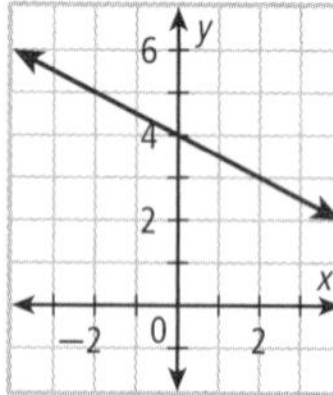

42. 

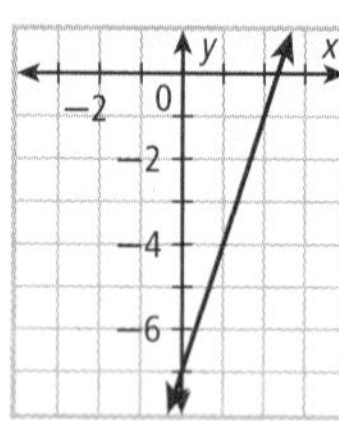

43. $y = \frac{1}{3}x + 5$
44. $y = 4x - 9$
45. 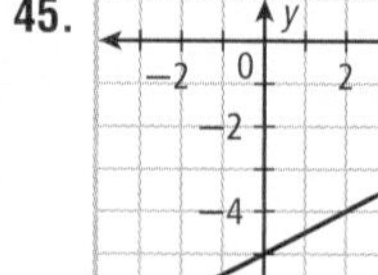

46. 

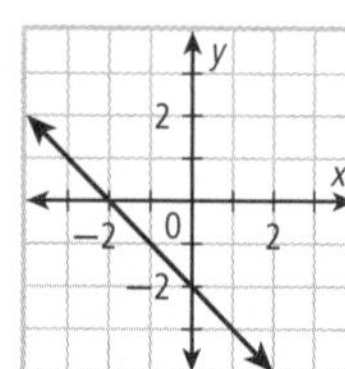

47. $y - 3 = 2(x - 1)$
48. $y - 4 = -5(x + 6)$

5-4 Direct Variation (pp. 282–287)

EXAMPLE

■ **Tell whether $6x = -4y$ is a direct variation. If so, identify the constant of variation.**

$$6x = -4y$$
$$\frac{6x}{-4} = \frac{-4y}{-4} \quad \textit{Solve the equation for y.}$$
$$-\frac{6}{4}x = y$$
$$y = -\frac{3}{2}x \quad \textit{Simplify.}$$

This equation is a direct variation because it can be written in the form $y = kx$, where $k = -\frac{3}{2}$.

EXERCISES

Tell whether each equation is a direct variation. If so, identify the constant of variation.

35. $y = -6x$
36. $x - y = 0$
37. $y + 4x = 3$
38. $2x = -4y$
39. The value of y varies directly with x, and $y = -8$ when $x = 2$. Find y when $x = 3$.
40. Maleka charges $8 per hour for baby-sitting. The amount of money she makes varies directly with the number of hours she baby-sits. The equation $y = 8x$ tells how much she earns y for baby-sitting x hours. Graph this direct variation.

5-5 Slope-Intercept Form (pp. 290–296)

EXAMPLE

■ **Graph the line with slope $= -\frac{4}{5}$ and y-intercept = 8.**

Step 1 Plot $(0, 8)$.

Step 2 For a slope of $\frac{-4}{5}$, count 4 down and 5 right from $(0, 8)$. Plot another point.

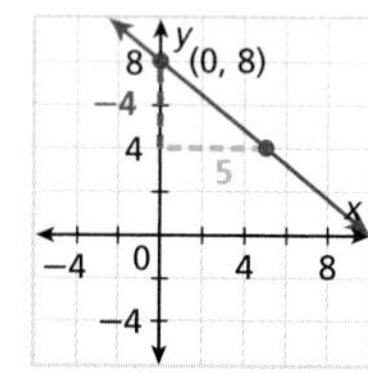

Step 3 Connect the two points with a line.

EXERCISES

Graph each line given the slope and y-intercept.

41. slope $= -\frac{1}{2}$; y-intercept = 4
42. slope = 3; y-intercept = −7

Write the equation of each line in slope-intercept form.

43. slope $= \frac{1}{3}$, y-intercept = 5
44. slope = 4, the point $(1, -5)$ is on the line

5-6 Point-Slope Form (pp. 297–303)

EXAMPLES

■ **Graph the line with slope $\frac{1}{3}$ that passes through $(3, -4)$.**

Step 1 Plot $(3, -4)$.

Step 2 For a slope of $\frac{1}{3}$, count 1 up and 3 right from $(3, -4)$. Plot another point.

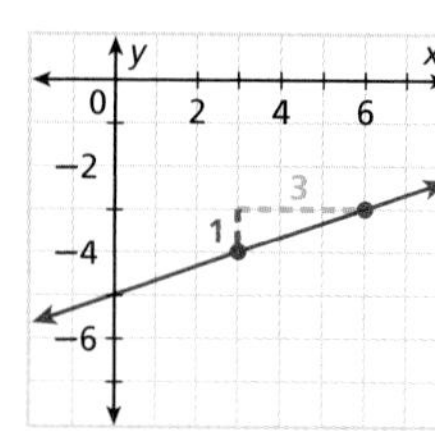

Step 3 Connect the two points with a line.

EXERCISES

Graph the line with the given slope that contains the given point.

45. slope $= \frac{1}{2}$; $(4, -3)$
46. slope = −1; $(-3, 1)$

Write an equation in point-slope form for the line with the given slope that contains the given point.

47. slope = 2; $(1, 3)$
48. slope = −5; $(-6, 4)$

■ Write an equation in slope-intercept form for the line through $(4, -1)$ and $(-2, 8)$.

$m = \frac{y_2 - y_1}{x_2 - x_1}$

$= \frac{8 - (-1)}{-2 - 4} = \frac{9}{-6} = -\frac{3}{2}$ *Find the slope.*

$y - y_1 = m(x - x_1)$ *Substitute into the point-slope form.*

$y - 8 = -\frac{3}{2}[x - (-2)]$

$y - 8 = -\frac{3}{2}(x + 2)$ *Solve for y.*

$y - 8 = -\frac{3}{2}x - 3$

$y = -\frac{3}{2}x + 5$

Write an equation in slope-intercept form for the line through the two points.

49. $(1, 4)$ and $(3, 8)$ **50.** $(0, 3)$ and $(-2, 5)$

51. $(-2, 4)$ and $(-1, 6)$ **52.** $(-3, 2)$ and $(5, 2)$

53. A water tank at an aquarium is losing water. The depth of the water is a linear function of the number of minutes since the leak began, as shown in the table. Write an equation in slope-intercept form that represents this linear function. Then find the depth of the water after 2 hours.

Time (min)	Depth (in.)
0	48
30	38
60	28

5-7 Slopes of Parallel and Perpendicular Lines *(pp. 304–310)*

8.0, 25.1

EXAMPLE

■ Write an equation in slope-intercept form for the line that passes through $(4, -2)$ and is perpendicular to the line given by $y = -4x + 3$.

Step 1 Find the slope of $y = -4x + 3$.
The slope is -4. The perpendicular line has a slope of $\frac{1}{4}$.

Step 2 Write the equation.
The perpendicular line has a slope of $\frac{1}{4}$ and contains $(4, -2)$.

$y - y_1 = m(x - x_1)$

$y - (-2) = \frac{1}{4}(x - 4)$

$y + 2 = \frac{1}{4}(x - 4)$

Step 3 Write the equation in slope-intercept form.

$y + 2 = \frac{1}{4}(x - 4)$

$y + 2 = \frac{1}{4}x - 1$ *Distribute $\frac{1}{4}$.*

$y = \frac{1}{4}x - 3$ *Subtract 2 from both sides.*

EXERCISES

Identify which lines are parallel.

54. $y = -\frac{1}{3}x$; $y = 3x + 2$;
$y = -\frac{1}{3}x - 6$; $y = 3$

55. $y - 2 = -4(x - 1)$; $y = 4x - 4$;
$y = \frac{1}{4}x$; $y = -4x - 2$

Identify which lines are perpendicular.

56. $y - 1 = -5(x - 6)$; $y = \frac{1}{5}x + 2$;
$y = 5$; $y = 5x + 8$

57. $y = 2x$; $y - 2 = 3(x + 1)$;
$y = \frac{2}{3}x - 4$; $y = -\frac{1}{3}x$

58. Show that ABC is a right triangle.

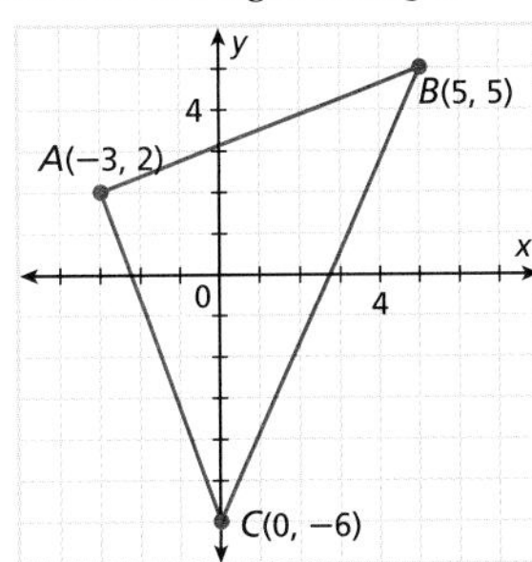

59. Write an equation in slope-intercept form for the line that passes through $(1, -1)$ and is parallel to the line given by $y = 2x - 4$.

Answers

49. $y = 2x + 2$

50. $y = -x + 3$

51. $y = 2x + 8$

52. $y = 2$

53. $y = -\frac{1}{3}x + 48$; 8 in.

54. $y = -\frac{1}{3}x$ and $y = -\frac{1}{3}x - 6$

55. $y - 2 = -4(x - 1)$ and $y = -4x - 2$

56. $y - 1 = -5(x - 6)$ and $y = \frac{1}{5}x + 2$

57. $y - 2 = 3(x + 1)$ and $y = -\frac{1}{3}x$

58. slope of $\overline{AB} = \frac{3}{8}$; slope of $\overline{AC} = -\frac{8}{3}$; $\overline{AB}$ is perp. to $\overline{AC}$ because the product of their slopes is -1. Therefore, ABC is a rt. triangle.

59. $y = 2x - 3$

Organizer

Objective: Assess students' mastery of concepts and skills in Chapter 5.

 Online Edition

Resources

 ***Assessment Resources***

Chapter 5 Tests

- Free Response (Levels A, B, C)
- Multiple Choice (Levels A, B, C)
- Performance Assessment

 ***IDEA Works!*** **CD-ROM**

Modified Chapter 5 Test

Test & Practice Generator

One-Stop Planner®

Answers

3. 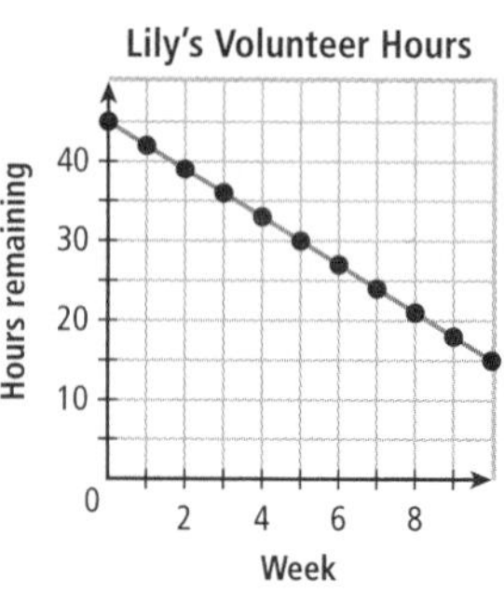

x-int.: 15; y-int.: 45; x-int.: number of weeks that will have passed when Lily has no vol. hours remaining; y-int.: orig. amount of vol. hours

4. 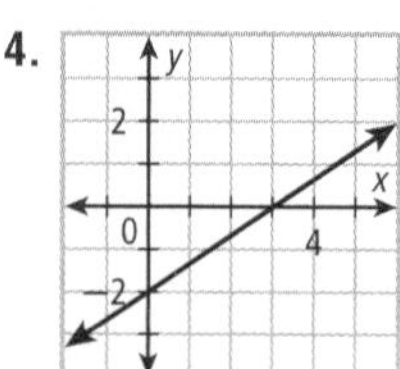

5. slope = 8.5; \$8.50 per ticket
6. slope = −12; height decreases by 12 ft per s
7. slope = 1; temperature increases by 1°F per h
12. 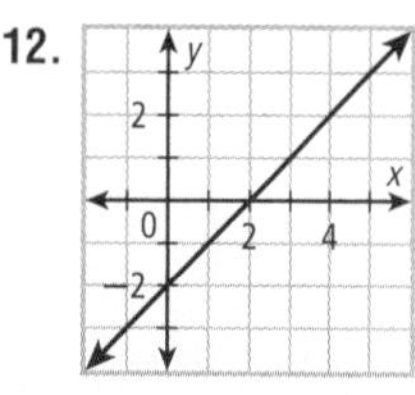
13. 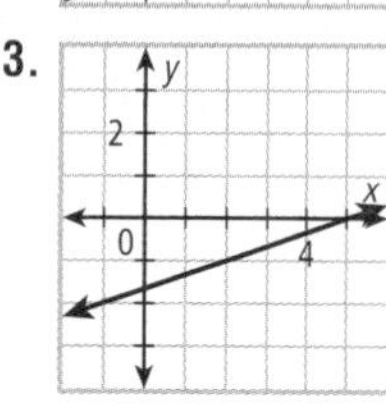
15. $y = -\frac{1}{2}x + 3$ and $x + 2y = 4$
16. $y - 2 = 3x$ and $y = -\frac{1}{3}x + 5$

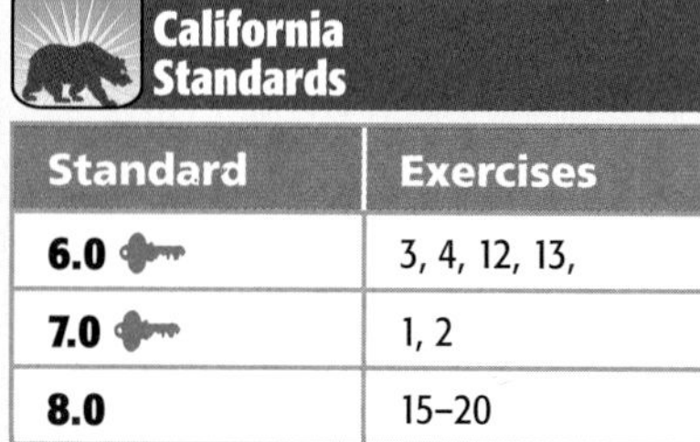

California Standards

Standard	Exercises
6.0	3, 4, 12, 13,
7.0	1, 2
8.0	15–20

CHAPTER TEST

Without graphing, tell whether each point is on the graph of the given line.

1. $-x + 8y = 22$; $(2, -3)$ **no**
2. $5x - 7y = -11$; $(2, 3)$ **yes**
3. Lily plans to volunteer at the tutoring center for 45 hours. She can tutor 3 hours per week. The function $f(x) = 45 - 3x$ gives the number of hours she will have left to tutor after x weeks. Graph the function and find its intercepts. What does each intercept represent?
4. Use intercepts to graph the line given by $2x - 3y = 6$.

Find the slope of each line. Then tell what the slope represents.

5. 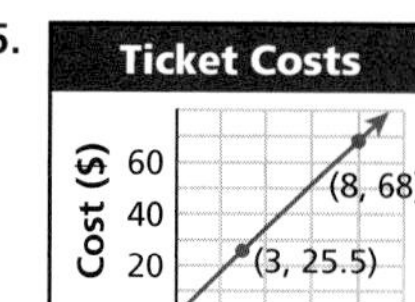

6. 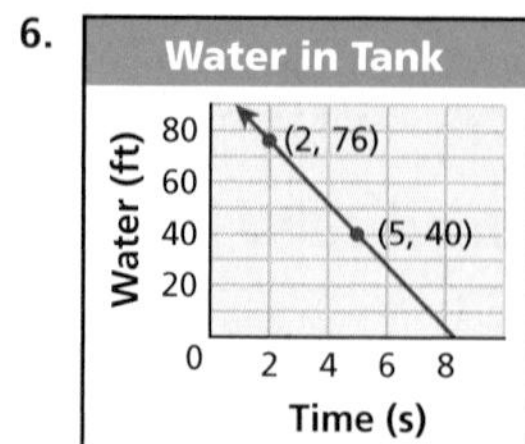

7. 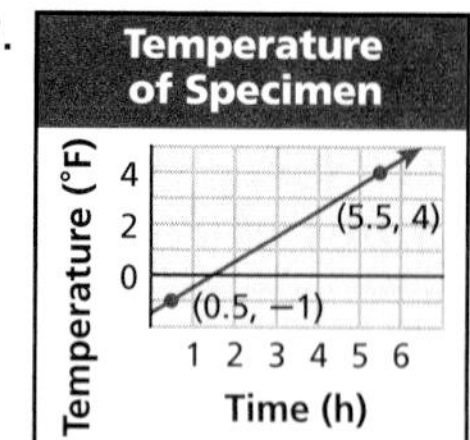

Tell whether each relationship is a direct variation. If so, identify the constant of variation.

8. **no**

x	−1	2	5	9
y	4	7	10	14

9. **yes;** $-\frac{1}{2}$

x	−2	2	6	10
y	1	−1	−3	−5

10. **yes;** $\frac{1}{4}$

x	4	−8	16	−24
y	1	−2	4	−6

11. **no**

x	8	5	1	−2
y	4	2.5	1	−1

12. Write the equation $2x - 2y = 4$ in slope-intercept form. Then graph the line given by the equation. $y = x - 2$
13. Graph the line with slope $\frac{1}{3}$ that contains the point $(-4, -3)$.
14. Write an equation in slope-intercept form for the line through $(-1, 1)$ and $(0, 3)$. $y = 2x + 3$
15. Identify which lines are parallel: $y = -\frac{1}{2}x + 3$; $y = \frac{1}{2}x + 1$; $y = 2x$; $x + 2y = 4$.
16. Identify which lines are perpendicular: $y - 2 = 3x$; $y + 4x = -1$; $y = -\frac{1}{3}x + 5$; $y = \frac{1}{3}x - 4$.
17. Write an equation in slope-intercept form for the line that passes through $(0, 6)$ and is parallel to the line given by $y = 2x + 3$. $y = 2x + 6$
18. Write an equation in slope-intercept form for the line that passes through $(4, 6)$ and is perpendicular to the line given by $y = x - 3$. $y = -x + 10$
19. Write an equation in slope-intercept form for the line parallel to $y = 3x - 4$ that passes through $(0, -1)$. $y = 3x - 1$
20. Write an equation in slope-intercept form for the line perpendicular to $y = \frac{1}{2}x + 7$ that passes through $(-1, 3)$. $y = -2x + 1$

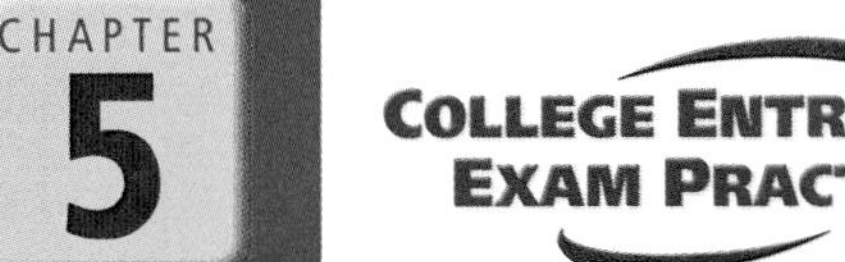

FOCUS ON SAT

SAT scores are based on the total number of items answered correctly minus a fraction of the number of multiple-choice questions answered incorrectly. No points are subtracted for questions unanswered.

On the SAT, there is a penalty for incorrect answers. Guess only when you can eliminate at least one of the answer choices.

You may want to time yourself as you take this practice test. It should take you about 7 minutes to complete.

1. The line through $A(1, -3)$ and $B(-2, d)$ has slope -2. What is the value of d?

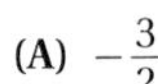

(A) $-\frac{3}{2}$

(B) -1

(C) $\frac{1}{2}$

(D) 3

(E) 5

2. The ordered pairs $\{(0, -3), (4, -1), (6, 0), (10, 2)\}$ satisfy a pattern. Which is NOT true?

(A) The pattern is linear.

(B) The pattern can be described by $2x - 4y = 12$.

(C) The ordered pairs lie on a line.

(D) $(-4, 1)$ satisfies the same pattern.

(E) The set of ordered pairs is a function.

3. If y varies directly as x, what is the value of x when $y = 72$?

x	7	12	
y	28	48	72

(A) 17

(B) 18

(C) 24

(D) 28

(E) 36

4. The line segment between the points $(4, 0)$ and $(2, -2)$ forms one side of a rectangle. Which of the following coordinates could determine another vertex of that rectangle?

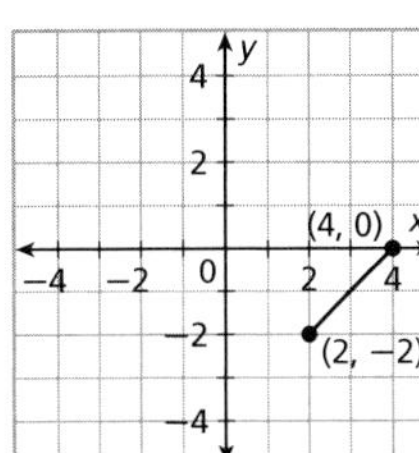

(A) $(-2, 6)$

(B) $(-2, -2)$

(C) $(0, 6)$

(D) $(1, 2)$

(E) $(4, 6)$

5. Which of the following has the same slope as the line given by $2x - 3y = 3$?

(A) $3x - 2y = 2$

(B) $\frac{2}{3}x - y = -2$

(C) $2x - 2y = 3$

(D) $\frac{1}{3}x - 2y = -2$

(E) $-2x - 3y = 2$

COLLEGE ENTRANCE EXAM PRACTICE

CHAPTER 5

Organizer

Objective: Provide practice for college entrance exams such as the SAT.

Resources

College Entrance Exam Practice

Questions on the SAT represent the following math content areas:

Number and Operations, 30–32%

Algebra and Functions, 28–32%

Geometry and Measurement, 27–30%

Data Analysis, Statistics, and Probability, 10–12%

Items on this page focus on:
- Algebra and Functions
- Geometry and Measurement

Text References:

Item	1	2	3	4	5
Lesson	5-3	5-1	5-3	5-6	5-4

Teaching Tip

Multiple Choice

1. Students who chose **A** may have inverted the slope formula. Students who chose **E** most likely used addition in the slope formula instead of subtraction.
2. Students who did not choose **D** should review terminology and properties of linear functions.
3. Students who chose **A** most likely added the difference between $x = 7$ and $x = 12$ (5) to $x = 12$. Remind students to look for a value of k so that the given values satisfy $y = kx$.
4. Students who did not choose **A** may not have verified that the line segments between two pairs of points were perpendicular. Remind students that a rectangle has four right angles.
5. Students who chose **C** selected a function with the same x-coefficient as the given function, but they did not find the slope. Students who chose **A** selected an answer with the same y-intercept as the given function.

Organizer

Objective: Provide opportunities to learn and practice common test-taking strategies.

Teaching Tip **Multiple Choice** This Strategy for Success focuses on how to recognize the distracters given in multiple-choice test items. Tell students that the "wrong" answer choices given in multiple-choice items are not randomly written, but are created based on common student errors.

Multiple Choice: Recognize Distracters

In multiple-choice items, the options that are incorrect are called *distracters*. This is an appropriate name, because these incorrect options can distract you from the correct answer.

Test writers create distracters by using common student errors. Beware! Even if the answer you get when you work the problem is one of the options, it may not be the correct answer.

EXAMPLE 1

What is the y-intercept of $4x + 10 = -2y$?

Ⓐ 10 Ⓒ −2.5

Ⓑ 5 Ⓓ −5

Look at each option carefully.

A This is a distracter. The y-intercept would be 10 if the function was $4x + 10 = y$. A common error is to ignore the coefficient of y.

B This is a distracter. Another common error is to divide by 2 instead of −2 when solving for y.

C This is a distracter. One of the most common errors students make is confusing the x-intercept and the y-intercept. This distracter is actually the *x-intercept* of the given line.

D This is the correct answer.

EXAMPLE 2

What is the equation of a line with a slope of −4 that contains (2, −3)?

Ⓐ $y - 3 = -4(x - 2)$ Ⓒ $y + 3 = -4(x - 2)$

Ⓑ $y - 2 = -4(x + 3)$ Ⓓ $y + 4 = -3(x - 2)$

Look at each option carefully.

A This is a distracter. Students often make errors with positive and negative signs. You would get this answer if you simplified $y - (-3)$ as $y - 3$.

B This is a distracter. You would get this answer if you switched the x-coordinate and the y-coordinate.

C This is the correct answer.

D This is a distracter. You would get this answer if you substituted the given values incorrectly into the point-slope formula.

When you calculate an answer to a multiple-choice test item, try to solve the problem again with a different method to make sure your answer is correct.

Read each test item and answer the questions that follow.

Item A
A line contains $(1, 2)$ and $(-2, 14)$. What are the slope and *y*-intercept?

Ⓐ Slope $= -4$; *y*-intercept $= -2$

Ⓑ Slope $= 4$; *y*-intercept $= 6$

Ⓒ Slope $= -\frac{1}{4}$; *y*-intercept $= 1$

Ⓓ Slope $= -4$; *y*-intercept $= 6$

1. What common error does the slope in choice B represent?
2. The slope given in choice A is correct, but the *y*-intercept is not. What error was made when finding the *y*-intercept?
3. What formula can you use to find the slope of a line? How was this formula used incorrectly to get the slope in choice C?

Item B
Which of these equations has a graph that is NOT parallel to the line given by $y = \frac{1}{2}x + 4$?

Ⓐ $y = 6 - \frac{1}{2}x$

Ⓑ $y = \frac{1}{2}x + 6$

Ⓒ $-2y = -x + 1$

Ⓓ $2y = x$

4. When given two linear equations, describe how to determine whether their graphs are parallel.
5. Which is the correct answer? Describe the errors a student might make to get each of the distracters.

Item C
Which of these lines has a slope of -3?

Ⓐ
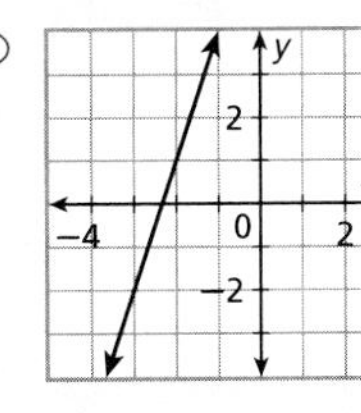

Ⓒ
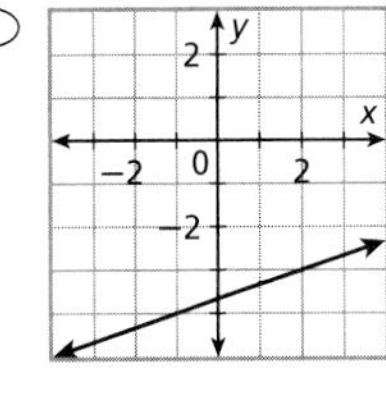

Ⓑ
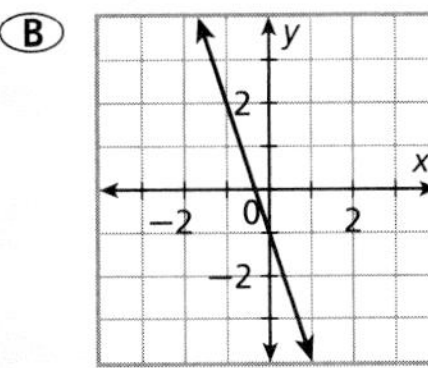

Ⓓ
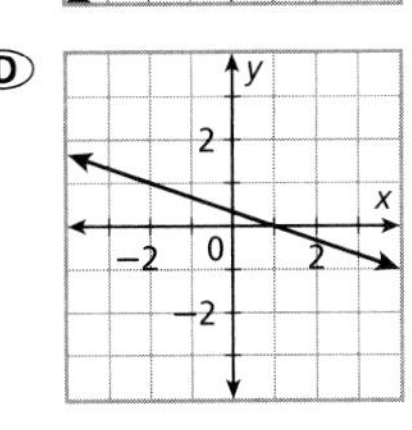

6. Which two answer choices can be eliminated immediately? Why?
7. Decribe how to find the slope of a line from its graph.
8. What common error does choice A represent?
9. What common error does choice D represent?
10. Which is the correct answer?

Item D
Which is NOT a linear function?

Ⓐ $f(x) = 4 + x$

Ⓑ $f(x) = -x - 4$

Ⓒ $f(x) = 4x^2$

Ⓓ $f(x) = \frac{1}{4}x$

11. When given a function, how can you tell if it is linear?
12. What part of the function given in choice B might make someone think it is not linear?
13. What part of the function given in choice D might make someone think it is not linear?
14. What part of the function given in choice C makes it NOT linear?

Inclusion Show students how common errors, such as dropping negative signs or switching the *x*- and *y*-coordinates, will lead to an incorrect answer. Point out instances in which that incorrect answer is given as one of the answer choices. Any error analysis that students can do on a regular basis will help them to recognize distracters. Use **Problems 1, 9,** and **10** to discuss common errors with linear equations.

Answers

1. The slope should be -4 instead of 4. An error was made with the neg. sign.
2. Possible answer: When $y = mx + b$ was solved for b using the point $(1, 2)$, 4 was subtracted from both sides instead of -4.
3. $m = \frac{y_2 - y_1}{x_2 - x_1}$; the formula was incorrectly inverted.
4. They have the same slope.
5. **A** is the correct answer because it is the only option whose slope is not equal to $\frac{1}{2}$.
   Possible answers: You might get **B** or **D** if you do not read the question correctly and think you were looking for a line par. to $y = \frac{1}{2}x + 4$. You might get **C** if you divide by 2 instead of -2 when solving for *y*.
6. **A** and **C**; a line with a negative slope falls from left to right, so the correct answer cannot be **A** or **C**.
7. Possible answer: Locate 2 points on the graph. Begin at one of the points and count the rise and the run to the second point. Divide the rise by the run.
8. The slope of the line in **A** is 3. The line increases from left to right. The question asked for a slope of -3.
9. The slope of the line in **D** is $-\frac{1}{3}$, not -3. The rise is -1 and the run is 3.
10. B
11. When a linear equation is written in standard form, *x* and *y* both have exponents of 1, *x* and *y* are not multiplied together, and *x* and *y* do not appear in denominators or in exponents.
12. the negative sign
13. the fraction
14. *x* has an exponent of 2.

Answers to Test Items

A. D
B. A
C. B
D. C

Algebra I 6.0, 7.0, 8.0

MASTERING THE STANDARDS

Organizer

Objective: Provide review and practice for Chapters 1–5.

Online Edition

Resources

Assessment Resources

Chapter 5 Cumulative Test

Focus on California Standards Benchmark Tests and Intervention

California Standards Practice CD-ROM

go.hrw.com
KEYWORD: MA8CA Practice

CUMULATIVE ASSESSMENT, CHAPTERS 1–5

Multiple Choice

1. Which of the following is an example of the Commutative Property of Multiplication?

(A) $5 \cdot 2 \cdot 7 = (5 \cdot 2) \cdot 7$

(B) $2(4 + 3) = 2 \cdot 4 + 2 \cdot 3$

(C) $6 \cdot 8 = 8 \cdot 6$

(D) $(2 + 4) + 6 = (4 + 2) + 6$

2. Which of these lines has an x-intercept of 4 and a y-intercept of 3?

(A) $y = \frac{3}{4}x + 3$

(B) $y = \frac{4}{3}x + 4$

(C) $y = -\frac{3}{4}x + 3$

(D) $y = -\frac{4}{3}x + 4$

3. Steven claims that the whole numbers are closed under division. Beth disagrees. Which of the following equations could Beth use as a counterexample to show that Steven's claim is false?

(A) $12 \div 3 = 4$

(B) $4 \div 8 = \frac{1}{2}$

(C) $\frac{1}{2} \div \frac{1}{4} = 2$

(D) $-10 \div 5 = -2$

4. The side length of a square s can be determined by the formula $s = \sqrt{A}$ where A represents the area of the square. What is the side length of a square with area 0.09 square meters?

(A) 0.0081 meters

(B) 0.81 meters

(C) 0.03 meters

(D) 0.3 meters

5. What is the value of x when $3x - 4(x + 5) = -18$?

(A) -2

(B) 2

(C) 13

(D) 23

6. Which relationship is a function?

(A)

x	0	2	2	5
y	1	2	4	2

(B)

x	1	1	1	1
y	1	2	3	4

(C)

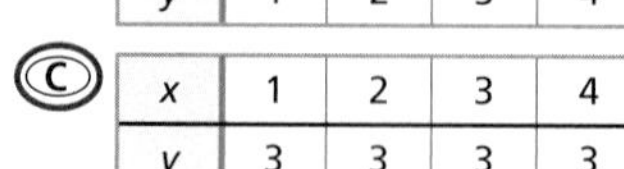

x	1	2	3	4
y	3	3	3	3

(D)

x	0	5	5	5
y	-1	2	3	4

7. Which function has x-intercept -2 and y-intercept 4?

(A) $2x - y = 4$

(B) $2y - x = 4$

(C) $y - 2x = 4$

(D) $x - 2y = 4$

8. Keiko graphs the line $x - 3y + 3 = 0$. Then she plots the point $(4, 2)$. Which of the following describes the location of the point?

(A) The point is below the line.

(B) The point is above the line.

(C) The point is to the left of the line.

(D) The point is on the line.

9. Which graph is described by $x - 3y = -3$?

(A)

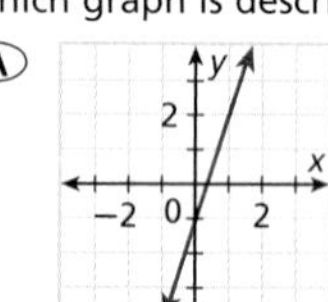

(C)

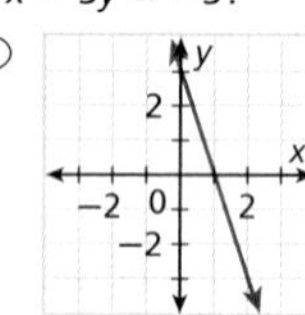

(B)

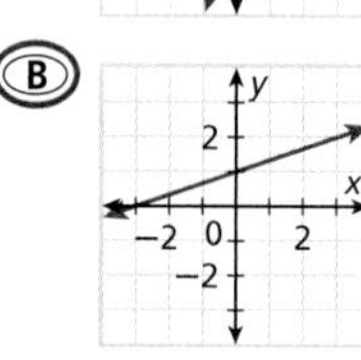

(D)

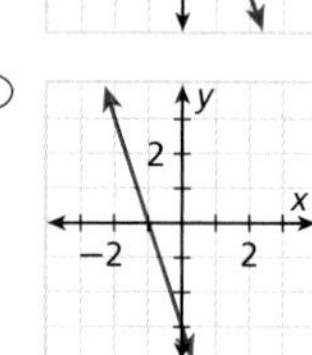

California Standards

Standard	Items
1.0	1, 3
1.1	3
2.0	4
4.0	5
5.0	5
6.0	7, 9, 15, 16, 17a
7.0	8, 10, 18, 20c
8.0	11, 12, 19b, 20b
17.0	17
18.0	6
24.3	3

Teaching Tip

Multiple Choice Students who chose **A** or **B** in **Item 4** are most likely squaring the area rather than taking the square root.

In **Item 9,** solving for y shows that the slope of the line is positive. You can eliminate choices **C** and **D.**

When answering multiple-choice test items, check that the test item number matches the number on your answer sheet, especially if you skip test items that you plan to come back to.

10. Which steps could you use to graph the line that has slope 2 and contains the point $(-1, 3)$?

Ⓐ Plot $(-1, 3)$. Move 1 unit up and 2 units right and plot another point.

Ⓑ Plot $(-1, 3)$. Move 2 units up and 1 unit right and plot another point.

Ⓒ Plot $(-1, 3)$. Move 1 unit up and 2 units left and plot another point.

Ⓓ Plot $(-1, 3)$. Move 2 units up and 1 unit left and plot another point.

11. Which line is parallel to the line described by $2x + 3y = 6$?

Ⓐ $3x + 2y = 6$　Ⓒ $2x + 3y = -6$

Ⓑ $3x - 2y = -6$　Ⓓ $2x - 3y = 6$

12. Which function's graph is NOT perpendicular to the line described by $4x - y = -2$?

Ⓐ $y + \frac{1}{4}x = 0$　Ⓒ $3y = \frac{3}{4}x + 3$

Ⓑ $\frac{1}{2}x = 10 - 2y$　Ⓓ $y = -\frac{1}{4}x + \frac{3}{2}$

13. Brent is solving the inequality $-5x + 3 + 2x > 9$. As a first step, he rewrites the inequality as $-5x + 2x + 3 > 9$. Which property justifies this step?

Ⓐ Associative Property of Addition

Ⓑ Closure Property of the Real Numbers

Ⓒ Commutative Property of Addition

Ⓓ Distributive Property

Gridded Response

14. What is the slope of a line that is perpendicular to the line shown?

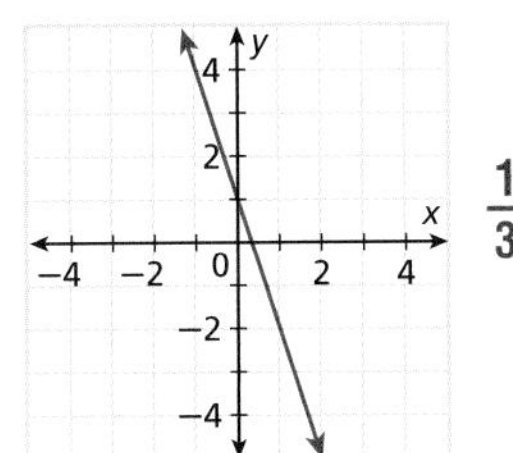

$\frac{1}{3}$

15. What is the x-intercept of $3x - 4y - 12 = 0$? **4**

16. What is the y-intercept of $y - 2 = 3(x + 4)$? **14**

Short Response

17. A video store charges a \$10 membership fee plus \$2 for each movie rental. The total cost for x movie rentals is given by $f(x) = 2x + 10$.

a. Graph this function.

b. Give a reasonable domain and range.

18. a. Write the equation of the line that has an x-intercept of -3 and a y-intercept of 6.

b. Use your equation to help you decide whether or not the point $(-2, 2)$ lies on the line. Explain how you know.

19. a. Find the slope of the line below.

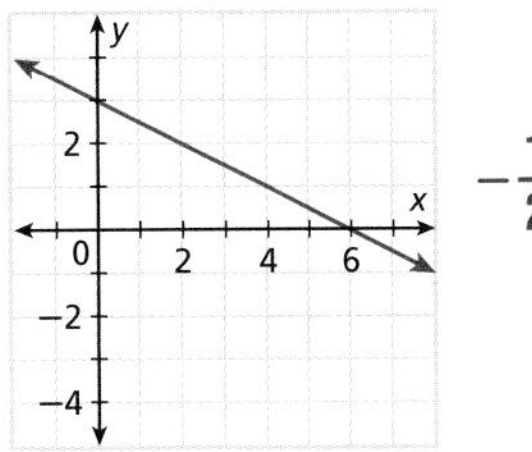

$-\frac{1}{2}$

b. Write an equation in slope-intercept form for a line that is perpendicular to the line in part **a** and has the same y-intercept as the function in part **a**. Show your work and explain how you got your answer. $y = 2x + 3$

Extended Response

20. A regional planner uses the coordinate plane shown below to design roads through the towns of Acorn, Bandon, and Chester.

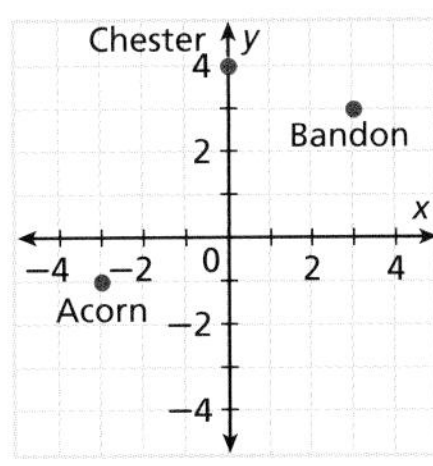

a. Route 1 is a straight road that passes through Acorn and Bandon. Write an equation for Route 1.

b. The planner uses the equation $2x - 3y = -12$ to lay out the path of Highway 205. Does Highway 205 pass through Chester? Why or why not?

c. Show how the planner can use slopes to determine whether Route 1 and Highway 205 intersect.

Short-Response Rubric

Items 17–19

2 Points = The student's answer is an accurate and complete execution of the task or tasks.

1 Point = The student's answer contains attributes of an appropriate response but is flawed.

0 Points = The student's answer contains no attributes of an appropriate response.

Extended-Response

Item 20

4 points = The student writes the correct equation and shows all work in part **a,** gives the correct answer and explanation in part **b,** and determines the correct answer and shows all work in part **c.**

3 points = The student writes the correct equation but does not show all work in part **a,** gives the correct answer and some explanation in part **b,** and determines the correct answer and shows some work in part **c.**

2 points = The student writes the correct equation but shows no work in part **a,** gives the correct answer but no explanation in part **b,** and determines the correct answer and shows some work in part **c;** or the student attempts to answer all parts and correctly answers only two parts.

1 point = The student writes the correct equation but shows no work in part **a,** gives the correct answer but no explanation in part **b,** and determines the correct answer but shows no work in part **c;** or the student attempts to answer all parts of the problem but does not correctly answer any part.

0 points = The student does not answer correctly and does not attempt all parts of the problem.

Answers

17a.

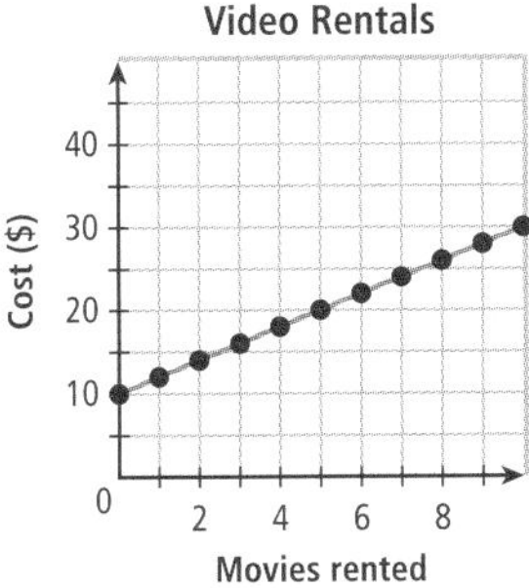

b. D: whole numbers; R: even whole numbers greater than or equal to 10

18a. $y = 2x + 6$

b. The point lies on the line because $(-2, 2)$ is a solution of the equation.

20a. $y = \frac{2}{3}x + 1$

b. Yes, $(0, 4)$ is a solution of $2x - 3y = -12$.

c. The roads do not intersect. They are parallel since both lines have a slope of $\frac{2}{3}$.

Systems of Equations and Inequalities

✔	Grade-level Standard
◀	Review
▶	Beyond the Standards
A	Assessment
O	Optional

Pacing Guide

Calendar Planner
Teacher's One-Stop Planner®

Lesson/Lab		California Standards	Time	Advanced Students	Benchmark Students	Strategic Students
LAB	Solve Linear Equations by Using a Spreadsheet	5.0	25 min	O	✔	✔
6-1	Solving Systems by Graphing	6.0, 9.0	50 min	✔	✔	✔
LAB	Model Systems of Linear Equations	9.0	25 min	✔	✔	✔
6-2	Solving Systems by Substitution	9.0	50 min	✔	✔	✔
6-3	Solving Systems by Elimination	9.0	50 min	✔	✔	✔
6-4	Solving Special Systems	8.0, 9.0	50 min	✔	✔	✔
6-5	Applying Systems	9.0, 15.0	50 min	✔	✔	✔
Concept Connection			25 min	A	A	O
Ready to Go On?			25 min	A	A	A
6-6	Solving Linear Inequalities	6.0	50 min	✔	✔	✔
6-7	Solving Systems of Linear Inequalities	6.0, 9.0	75 min	✔	✔	✔
LAB	Solve Systems of Linear Inequalities	9.0	25 min	O	O	✔
Concept Connection			25 min	A	A	O
Ready to Go On?			25 min	A	A	A
Study Guide: Review			50 min	✔	✔	✔
Chapter Test		6.0, 9.0	50 min	A	A	A

* **Benchmark students** are achieving at or near grade level.

** **Strategic students** may be a year or more below grade level, and may require additional time for intervention.

Countdown to Mastery, Weeks 12, 13, 14

ONGOING ASSESSMENT and INTERVENTION

	DIAGNOSE	PRESCRIBE
Assess Prior Knowledge	**Before Chapter 6**	
	Diagnose readiness for the chapter.	Prescribe intervention.
	Are You Ready? SE p. 325	***Are You Ready? Intervention*** Skills 60, 69, 72, 74, 75
Formative Assessment	**Before Every Lesson**	
	Diagnose readiness for the lesson.	Prescribe intervention.
	Warm Up TE, every lesson	**Skills Bank** pp. SB1–SB32 **Review for Mastery** CRF Chapters 1–6
	During Every Lesson	
	Diagnose understanding of lesson concepts.	Prescribe intervention.
	Questioning Strategies TE, every example **Check It Out!** SE, every example **Think and Discuss** SE, every lesson **Write About It** SE, every lesson **Journal** TE, every lesson	**Reading Strategies** CRF, every lesson ***Success for ELL*** pp. 87–100 ***Lesson Tutorial Videos*** Chapter 6
	After Every Lesson	
	Diagnose mastery of lesson concepts.	Prescribe intervention.
	Lesson Quiz TE, every lesson **Alternative Assessment** TE, every lesson **Ready to Go On?** SE pp. 363, 379 ***Test and Practice Generator***	**Review for Mastery** CRF, every lesson **Problem Solving** CRF, every lesson ***Ready to Go On? Intervention*** Chapter 6 ***Homework Help Online***
	Before Chapter 6 Testing	
	Diagnose mastery of concepts in the chapter.	Prescribe intervention.
	Ready to Go On? SE pp. 363, 379 **Concept Connection** SE pp. 362, 378 **Section Quizzes** AR pp. 105–106 ***Test and Practice Generator***	***Ready to Go On? Intervention*** Chapter 6 **Scaffolding Questions** TE pp. 362, 378
	Before Assessment of California Standards	
	Diagnose mastery of California Standards.	Prescribe intervention.
	Focus on California Standards: Benchmark Tests **Mastering the Standards** SE pp. 388–389 ***California Standards Practice* CD-ROM**	***Focus on California Standards: Intervention***
Summative Assessment	**After Chapter 6**	
	Check mastery of chapter concepts.	Prescribe intervention.
	Multiple-Choice Tests (Forms A, B, C) **Free-Response Tests (Forms A, B, C)** **Performance Assessment** AR pp. 119–120 ***Test and Practice Generator***	**Review for Mastery** CRF, every lesson ***Lesson Tutorial Videos*** Chapter 6

KEY: **SE** = *Student Edition* **TE** = *Teacher's Edition* **CRF** = *Chapter Resource File* **AR** = *Assessment Resources* Available online Available on CD-ROM

Supporting the Teacher

Chapter 6 Resource File

Family Involvement
pp. 1–4, 45–48

Practice A, B, C
pp. 5–7, 13–15, 21–23, 29–31, 37–39, 49–51, 57–59

Review for Mastery
pp. 8–9, 16–17, 24–25, 32–33, 40–41, 52–53, 60–61

Challenge
pp. 10, 18, 26, 34, 42, 54, 62

Problem Solving
pp. 11, 19, 27, 35, 43, 55, 63

Reading Strategies ELL
pp. 12, 20, 28, 36, 44, 56, 64

Algebra Lab
pp. 65–70

Workbooks

Homework and Practice Workbook SPANISH
Teacher's Edition .... pp. 34–40

Know-It Notebook SPANISH
Teacher's Guide .... Chapter 6

Review for Mastery Workbook SPANISH
Teacher's Guide .... pp. 67–80

Focus on California Standards: Intervention Workbook SPANISH
Teacher's Guide

Teacher Tools

Power Presentations
Complete PowerPoint® presentations for Chapter 6 lessons

Lesson Tutorial Videos SPANISH
Holt authors Ed Burger and Freddie Renfro present tutorials to support the Chapter 6 lessons.

Teacher's One-Stop Planner SPANISH
Easy access to all Chapter 6 resources and assessments, as well as software for lesson planning, test generation, and puzzle creation

IDEA Works!
Key Chapter 6 resources and assessments modified to address special learning needs

Solutions Key .... Chapter 6

Interactive Answers and Solutions

TechKeys

Lab Resources

Project Teacher Support

Parent Resources 

Transparencies

Lesson Transparencies, Volume 1 .... Chapter 6
- Teacher Tools
- Warm-ups
- Teaching Transparencies
- Lesson Quizzes

Alternate Openers: Explorations .... pp. 34–40

Countdown to Mastery .... pp. 23–27

Know-It Notebook .... Chapter 6
- Vocabulary
- Key Concepts
- Graphic Organizers
- Chapter Review
- Big Ideas

Technology Highlights for the Teacher

Power Presentations

Dynamic presentations to engage students. Complete PowerPoint® presentations for every lesson in Chapter 6.

2-1 Solving One-Step Equations

Isolate a variable by using inverse operations which "undo" operations on the variable.

An equation is like a balanced scale. To keep the balance, perform the same operation on both sides.

Inverse Operations	
Operation	Inverse Operation
Addition	Subtraction
Subtraction	Addition

One-Stop Planner SPANISH

Easy access to Chapter 6 resources and assessments. Includes lesson planning, test generation, and puzzle creation software.

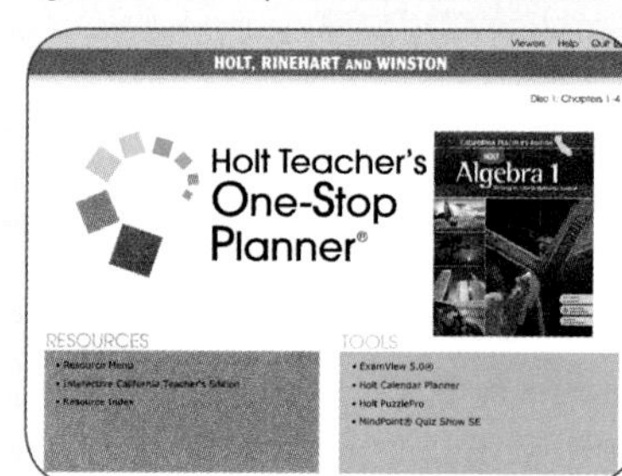

Premier Online Edition SPANISH

Includes Tutorial Videos, Lesson Activities, Lesson Quizzes, Homework Help, Chapter Project and more.

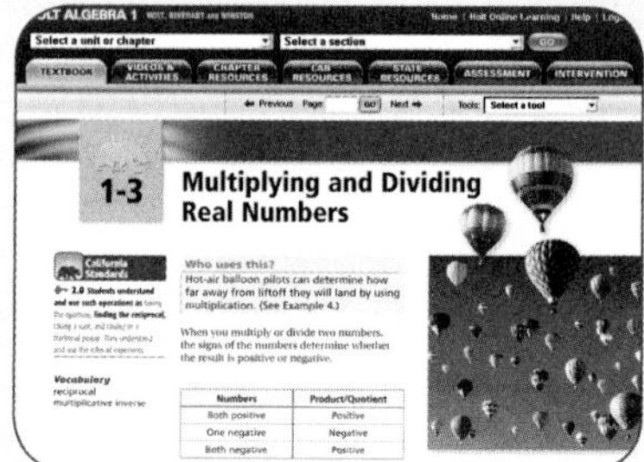

KEY:  **SE** = *Student Edition* **TE** = *Teacher's Edition*  ELL English Language Learners  SPANISH Spanish available 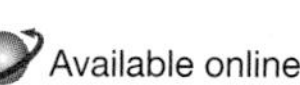 Available online Available on CD-ROM

CHAPTER 6

Universal Access

Teaching Tips to help all students appear throughout the chapter. A few that target specific students are included in the lists below.

Strategic Students

- **Practice A** ... CRF, every lesson
- **Review for Mastery** ... CRF, every lesson
- **Reading Strategies** ... CRF, every lesson
- **Academic Vocabulary Connections** ... TE p. 326
- **Modeling** ... TE p. 372
- **Questioning Strategies** ... TE, every example
- ***Ready to Go On? Intervention*** ... Chapter 6
- ***Know-It Notebook*** SPANISH ... Chapter 6
- ***Homework Help Online***
- ***Lesson Tutorial Videos*** SPANISH
- ***Online Interactivities*** SPANISH

Special Needs Students

- **Practice A** ... CRF, every lesson
- **Review for Mastery** ... CRF, every lesson
- **Reading Strategies** ... CRF, every lesson
- **Academic Vocabulary Connections** ... TE p. 326
- **Inclusion** ... TE pp. 333, 337
- ***IDEA Works! Modified Resources*** ... Chapter 6
- ***Ready to Go On? Intervention*** ... Chapter 6
- ***Know-It Notebook*** SPANISH ... Chapter 6
- ***Lesson Tutorial Videos*** SPANISH
- ***Online Interactivities*** SPANISH

English Learners

ENGLISH LANGUAGE LEARNERS

- **Reading Strategies** ... CRF, every lesson
- **Vocabulary Exercises** ... SE, every exercise set
- **Academic Vocabulary Connections** ... TE p. 326
- **English Language Learners** ... TE pp. 359, 375
- **Language Support** ... TE pp. 359, 375
- ***Success for English Language Learners*** ... Chapter 6
- ***Know-It Notebook*** SPANISH ... Chapter 6
- ***Multilingual Glossary***
- ***Lesson Tutorial Videos*** SPANISH

Benchmark Students

- **Practice B** ... CRF, every lesson
- **Problem Solving** ... CRF, every lesson
- **Academic Vocabulary Connections** ... TE p. 326
- **Questioning Strategies** ... TE, every example
- ***Ready to Go On? Intervention*** ... Chapter 6
- ***Know-It Notebook*** SPANISH ... Chapter 6
- ***Homework Help Online***
- ***Online Interactivities*** SPANISH

Advanced Students

- **Practice C** ... CRF, every lesson
- **Challenge** ... CRF, every lesson
- **Reading and Writing Math** EXTENSION ... TE p. 327
- **Concept Connection** EXTENSION ... TE pp. 362, 378
- ***Ready to Go On? Enrichment*** ... Chapter 6

Technology Highlights for Universal Access

 Lesson Tutorial Videos 

Starring Holt authors Ed Burger and Freddie Renfro! Live tutorials to support every lesson in Chapter 6.

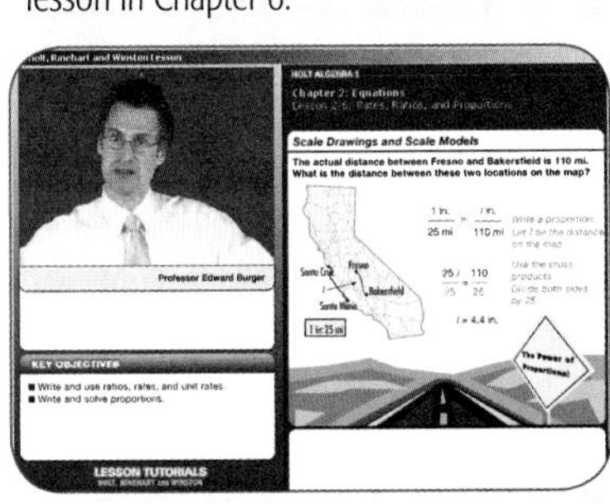

Multilingual Glossary

Searchable glossary includes definitions in English, Spanish, Vietnamese, Chinese, Hmong, Korean, and other languages.

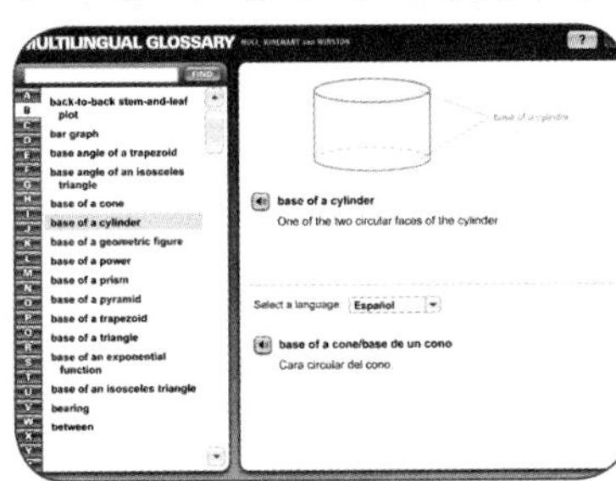

Online Interactivities 

Interactive tutorials provide visually engaging alternative opportunities to learn concepts and master skills.

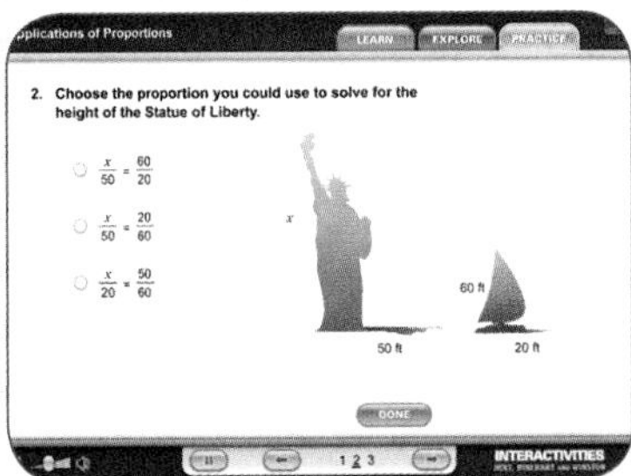

KEY: **SE** = *Student Edition* **TE** = *Teacher's Edition* **CRF** = *Chapter Resource File* SPANISH Spanish available  Available online  Available on CD-ROM

Ongoing Assessment

Assessing Prior Knowledge

Determine whether students have the prerequisite concepts and skills for success in Chapter 6.

Are You Ready? SPANISH .... SE p. 325
Warm Up .... TE, every lesson

Chapter and Standards Assessment

Provide review and practice for Chapter 6 and standards mastery.

Concept Connection .... SE pp. 362, 378
Study Guide: Review .... SE pp. 380–383
Strategies for Success .... SE pp. 386–387
Mastering the Standards .... SE pp. 388–389
College Entrance Exam Practice .... SE p. 385
***Countdown to Mastery* Transparencies** ..pp. 23–27
Focus on California Standards: Benchmark Tests
Focus on California Standards: Intervention Workbook
***California Standards Practice* CD-ROM** SPANISH
IDEA Works! Modified Worksheets and Tests

Alternative Assessment

Assess students' understanding of Chapter 6 concepts and combined problem-solving skills.

Alternative Assessment .... TE, every lesson
Performance Assessment .... AR pp. 119–120
Portfolio Assessment .... AR p. xxxiii
Chapter 6 Project

Daily Assessment

Provide formative assessment for each day of Chapter 6.

Questioning Strategies .... TE, every example
Think and Discuss .... SE, every lesson
Check It Out! Exercises .... SE, every example
Write About It .... SE, every lesson
Journal .... TE, every lesson
Lesson Quiz .... TE, every lesson
Alternative Assessment .... TE, every lesson
IDEA Works! Modified Lesson Quizzes .... Chapter 6

Weekly Assessment

Provide formative assessment for each week of Chapter 6.

Concept Connection .... SE pp. 362, 378
Ready to Go On? .... SE pp. 363, 379
Cumulative Assessment .... SE pp. 388–389
Test and Practice Generator SPANISH .. *One-Stop Planner*

Formal Assessment

Provide summative assessment of Chapter 6 mastery.

Section Quizzes .... AR pp. 105–106
Chapter 6 Test SPANISH .... SE p. 384
Chapter Test (Levels A, B, C) .... AR pp. 107–118
• Multiple Choice • Free Response
Cumulative Test .... AR pp. 121–124
Test and Practice Generator SPANISH .. *One-Stop Planner*

Technology Highlights for Ongoing Assessment

Are You Ready? SPANISH

Automatically assess readiness and prescribe intervention for Chapter 6 prerequisite skills.

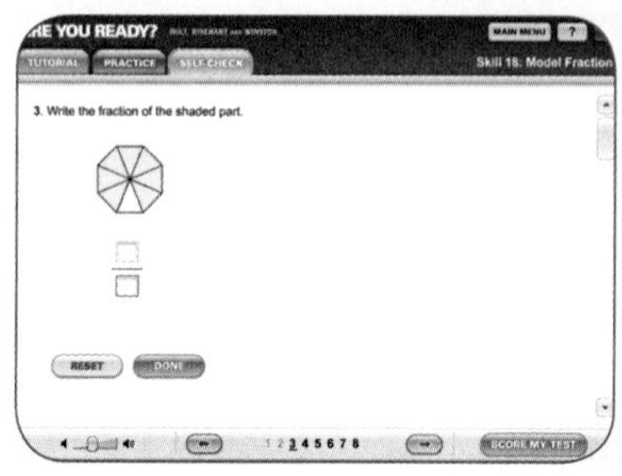

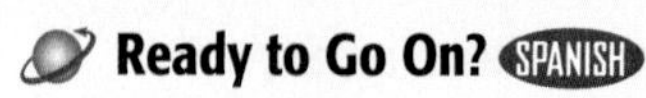

Ready to Go On? SPANISH

Automatically assess understanding of and prescribe intervention for Sections 6A and 6B.

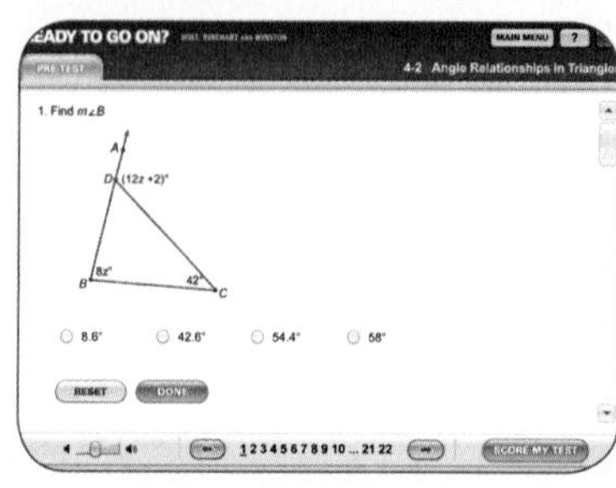

Focus on California Standards: Benchmark Tests and Intervention SPANISH

Automatically assess proficiency with California Algebra I Standards and provide intervention.

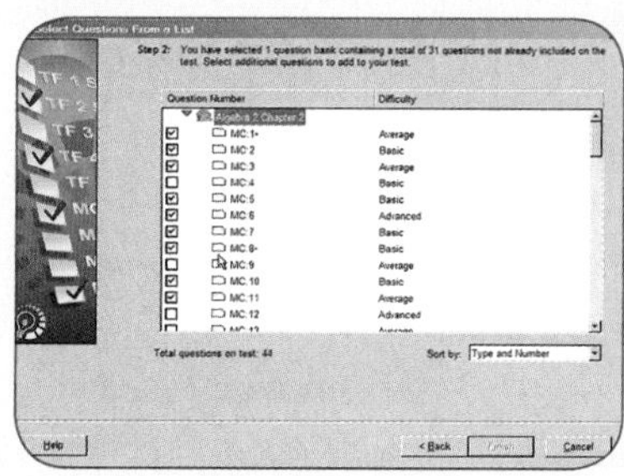

KEY: **SE** = *Student Edition* **TE** = *Teacher's Edition* **AR** = Assessment Resources  Spanish available  Available online 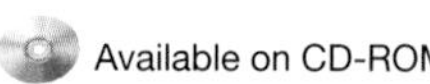 Available on CD-ROM

Three levels (A, B, C) of multiple-choice and free-response chapter tests are available in the *Assessment Resources.*

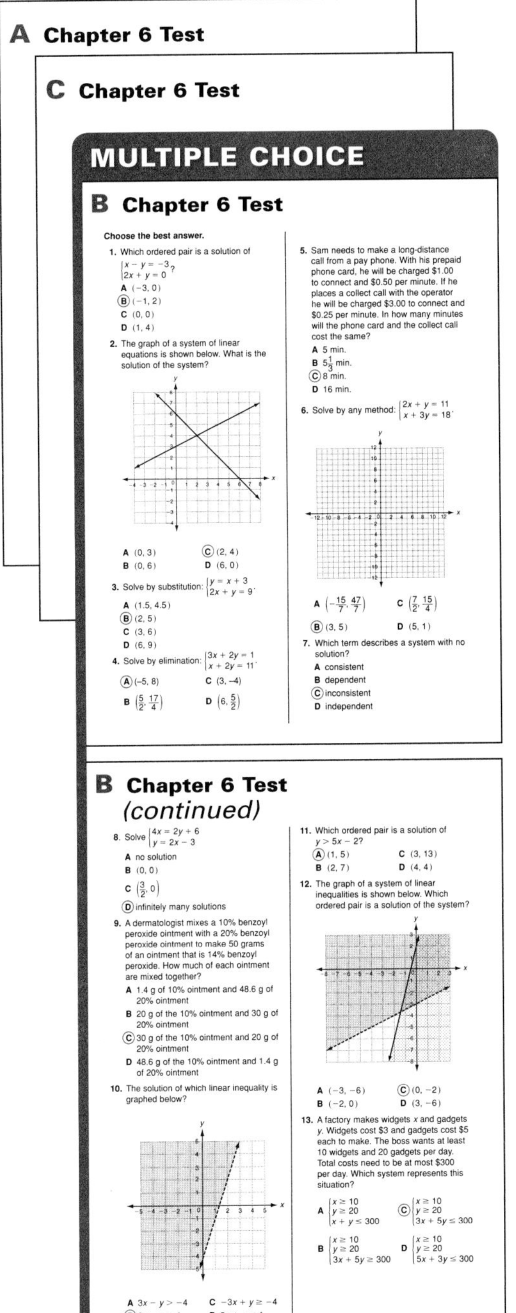

A Chapter 6 Test
C Chapter 6 Test
MULTIPLE CHOICE
B Chapter 6 Test
B Chapter 6 Test (continued)

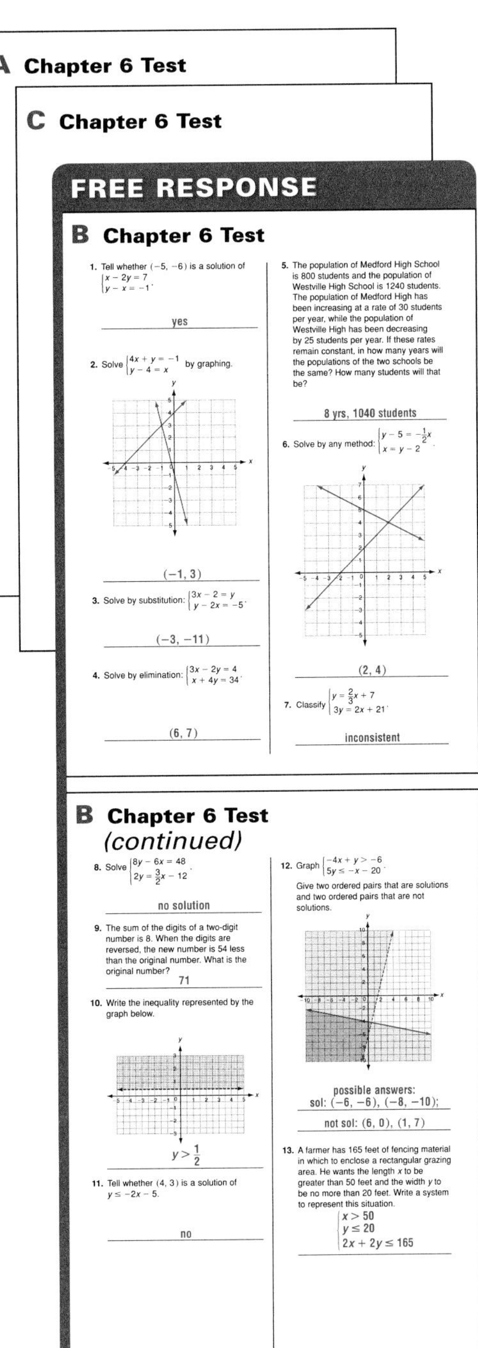

Modified tests and worksheets found in *IDEA Works!*

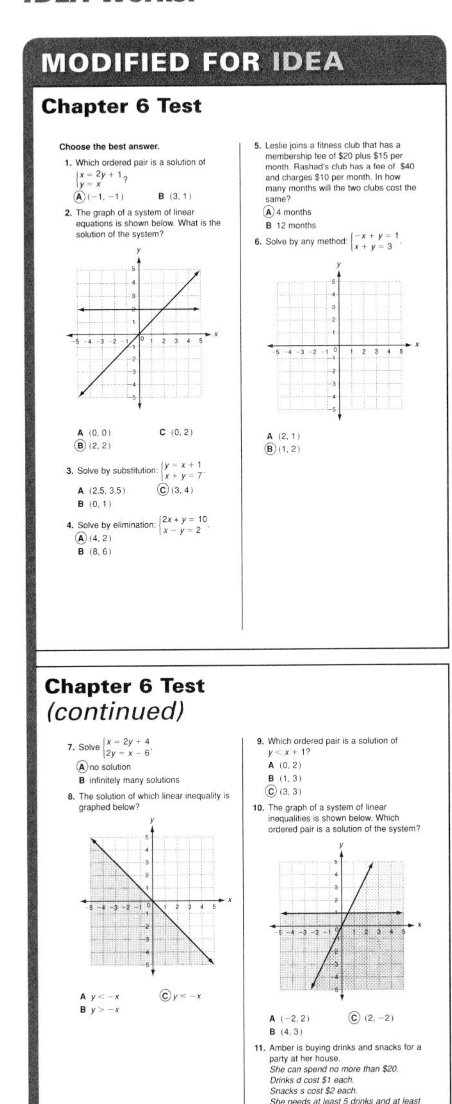

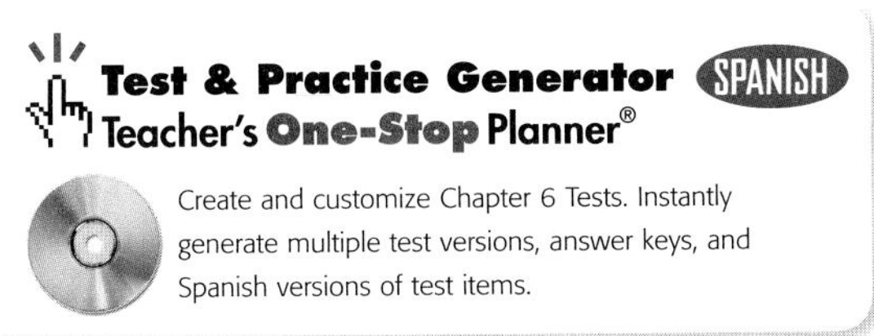

Create and customize Chapter 6 Tests. Instantly generate multiple test versions, answer keys, and Spanish versions of test items.

CHAPTER 6

SECTION 6A
Systems of Linear Equations

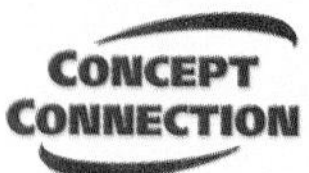

CONCEPT CONNECTION On page 362, students write and solve systems of equations to help them make good business decisions.

Exercises designed to prepare students for success on the Concept Connection can be found on pages 332, 341, 348, 354, and 360.

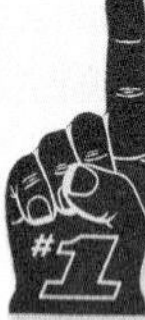

SECTION 6B
Linear Inequalities

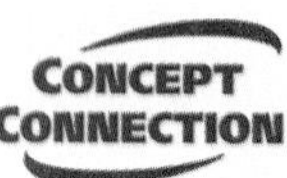

CONCEPT CONNECTION On page 378, students write and graph systems of inequalities to model a real-world sales situation.

Exercises designed to prepare students for success on the Concept Connection can be found on pages 369 and 375.

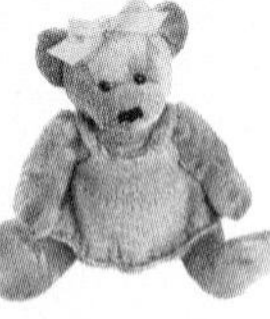

Algebra in *California*

The Staples Center is the home of the WNBA's Los Angeles Sparks. The price of tickets for the lower level of the arena ranges from \$8.50 to \$50.00. Premier seating costs from \$20.00 to \$50.00. Lesson 6-5 of this chapter will show students how to use a system of equations to find the cost of buying tickets for different levels of seating.

CHAPTER 6

Systems of Equations and Inequalities

go.hrw.com
Chapter Project Online
KEYWORD: MA8CA ChProj

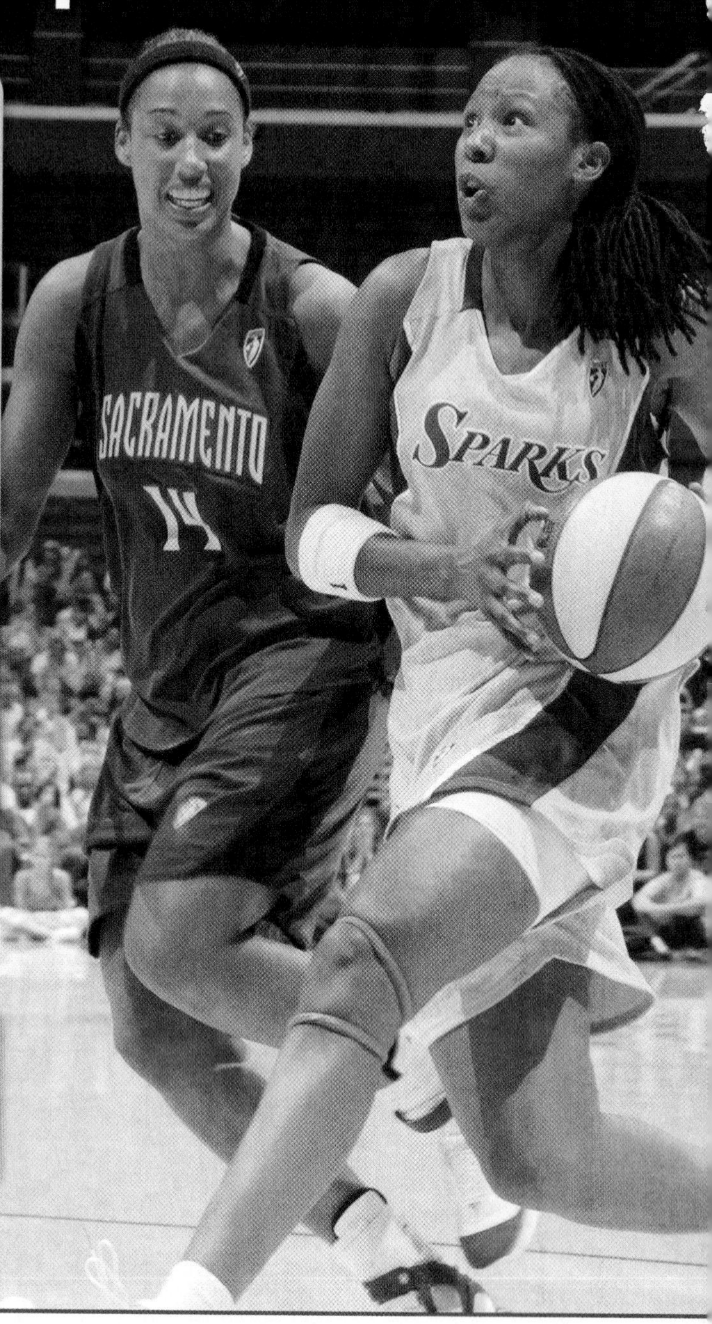

You can solve a system of equations to decide how many basketball game tickets you can buy at different prices.

Staples Center
Los Angeles, CA

324 *Chapter 6*

About the Project

Where's the Money?

In the Chapter Project, students research current salaries for professional athletes. Students then use the data to write a system of equations to determine whether the salaries overlap and where. Students also write a system of equations to determine how many game tickets they can buy at each price level.

Project Resources

All project resources for teachers and students are provided online.

go.hrw.com
Project Teacher Support
KEYWORD: MA8CS ProjectTS

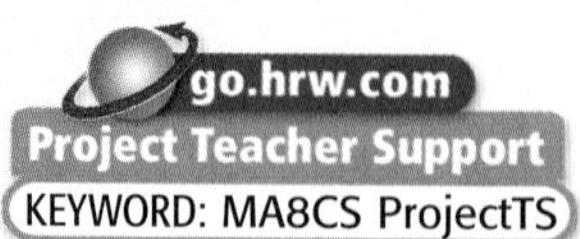

ARE YOU READY?

Vocabulary

Match each term on the left with a definition on the right.

1. inequality **B**
2. linear equation **F**
3. ordered pair **A**
4. slope **E**
5. solution of an equation **D**

A. a pair of numbers (x, y) that represent the coordinates of a point
B. a statement that two quantities are not equal
C. the y-value of the point at which the graph of an equation crosses the y-axis
D. a value of the variable that makes the equation true
E. the ratio of the vertical change to the horizontal change for a nonvertical line
F. an equation whose graph is a straight line

Graph Linear Functions

Graph each function.

6. $y = \frac{3}{4}x + 1$
7. $y = -3x + 5$
8. $y = x - 6$
9. $x + y = 4$
10. $y = -\frac{2}{3}x + 4$
11. $y = -5$

Solve Multi-Step Equations

Solve each equation.

12. $-7x - 18 = 3$ **−3**
13. $12 = -3n + 6$ **−2**
14. $\frac{1}{2}d + 30 = 32$ **4**
15. $-2p + 9 = -3$ **6**
16. $33 = 5y + 8$ **5**
17. $-3 + 3x = 27$ **10**

Solve for a Variable

Solve each equation for y.

18. $7x + y = 4$ $\mathbf{y = -7x + 4}$
19. $y + 2 = -4x$ $\mathbf{y = -4x - 2}$
20. $8 = x - y$ $\mathbf{y = x - 8}$
21. $x + 2 = y - 5$ $\mathbf{y = x + 7}$
22. $2y - 3 = 12x$ $\mathbf{y = 6x + \frac{3}{2}}$
23. $y + \frac{3}{4}x = 4$ $\mathbf{y = -\frac{3}{4}x + 4}$

Evaluate Expressions

Evaluate each expression for the given value of the variable.

24. $t - 5$ for $t = 7$ **2**
25. $9 - 2a$ for $a = 4$ **1**
26. $\frac{1}{2}x - 2$ for $x = 14$ **5**
27. $n + 15$ for $n = 37$ **52**
28. $9c + 4$ for $c = \frac{1}{3}$ **7**
29. $16 + 3d$ for $d = 5$ **31**

Solve and Graph Inequalities

Solve and graph each inequality.

30. $b - 9 \geq 1$ $\mathbf{b \geq 10}$
31. $-2x < 10$ $\mathbf{x > -5}$
32. $3y \leq -3$ $\mathbf{y \leq -1}$
33. $\frac{1}{3}y \leq 5$ $\mathbf{y \leq 15}$

ARE YOU READY?

CHAPTER 6

Organizer

Objective: Assess students' understanding of prerequisite skills.

Prerequisite Skills

Graph Linear Functions
Solve Multi-Step Equations
Solve for a Variable
Evaluate Expressions
Solve and Graph Inequalities

Assessing Prior Knowledge

INTERVENTION 

Diagnose and Prescribe

Use this page to determine whether intervention is necessary or whether enrichment is appropriate.

Resources

 ***Are You Ready? Intervention and Enrichment* Worksheets**

 ***Are You Ready?* CD-ROM**

 ***Are You Ready?* Online**

my.hrw.com

Answers

6–11. See p. A21.

30–33. For graphs, see p. A21.

ARE YOU READY?

Diagnose and Prescribe

NO INTERVENE

Prerequisite Skill	*Are You Ready? Intervention,* Chapter 6 Worksheets	CD-ROM	Online
Graph Linear Functions	Skill 75	Activity 75	Diagnose and Prescribe Online
Solve Multi-Step Equations	Skill 69	Activity 69	
Solve for a Variable	Skill 72	Activity 72	
Evaluate Expressions	Skill 60	Activity 60	
Solve and Graph Inequalities	Skill 74	Activity 74	

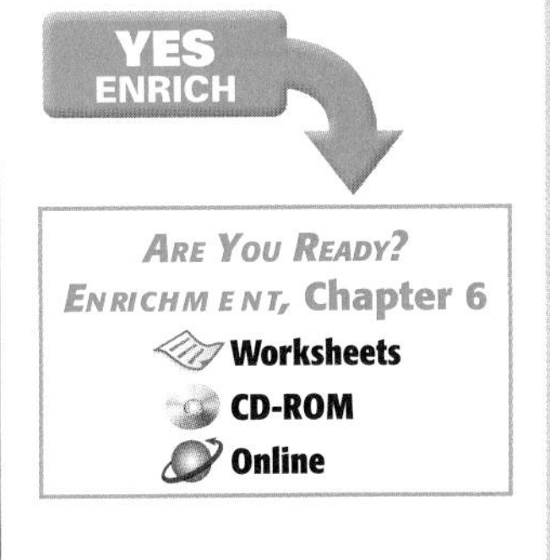
YES ENRICH

Are You Ready? Enrichment, Chapter 6
Worksheets
CD-ROM
Online

Organizer

Objective: Help students understand the new concepts they will learn in Chapter 6.

Academic Vocabulary Connections

Becoming familiar with the academic vocabulary on this student page will be helpful to students. Discussing some of the vocabulary terms in the chapter may also be helpful.

1. The word *system* means "a group." How do you think a **system of linear equations** is different from a linear equation? Possible answer: A system of linear equations is a group of linear equations, rather than just one linear equation.
2. A **consistent system** has *at least one* solution. How many solutions do you think an **inconsistent system** has? none
3. A **dependent system** has infinitely many solutions. Which vocabulary term above means a system with *exactly one* solution? independent system
4. In Chapters 4 and 5, you saw that a solution of a linear equation was the ordered pair that made the equation true. Modify this to define **solution of a linear inequality**. any ordered pair that makes the inequality true

CHAPTER 6 Unpacking the Standards

The information below "unpacks" the standards. The Academic Vocabulary is highlighted and defined to help you understand the language of the standards. Refer to the lessons listed after each standard for help with the math terms and phrases. The Chapter Concept shows how the standard is applied in this chapter.

California Standard	Academic Vocabulary	Chapter Concept
6.0 Students graph a linear equation and compute the x- and y-intercepts (e.g., graph $2x + 6y = 4$). **They are also able to sketch the region defined by linear inequalities (e.g., they sketch the region defined by $2x + 6y < 4$).** (Lessons **6-1, 6-6, 6-7**)	**define** to mark the limits of	You solve a linear inequality that contains two variables and graph the solutions on the coordinate plane.
8.0 Students understand the concepts of parallel lines and perpendicular lines **and how their slopes are related.** Students are able to find the equation of a line perpendicular to a given line that passes through a given point. (Lesson **6-4**)	**concept** idea or meaning	You understand parallel lines and how they are related in the coordinate plane.
9.0 Students solve a system of two linear equations in two variables algebraically and are able to interpret the answer graphically. Students are able to solve a system of two linear inequalities in two variables and to sketch the solution sets. (Lessons **6-1, 6-2, 6-3, 6-4, 6-5, 6-7;** Labs **6-2,** 6-7)	**algebraically** having to do with algebra **interpret** understand **graphically** having to do with a graph or graphs **in two variables** containing two variables	You use algebra to find solutions that satisfy two linear equations or inequalities, and you understand how the solutions are represented in the coordinate plane.
15.0 Students apply algebraic techniques to solve rate problems, work problems, **and percent mixture problems.** (Lesson **6-5**)	**algebraic** having to do with algebra **technique** a way of doing something	You use algebra to solve real-world problems about rates and mixtures.

Standard 5.0 is also covered in this chapter. To see this standard unpacked, go to Chapter 2, p. 70.

Looking Back

Previously, students

- solved one-step and multi-step equations.
- solved one-step and multi-step inequalities.
- graphed linear equations on a coordinate plane.

In This Chapter

Students will study

- how to find a solution that satisfies two linear equations.
- how to find solutions that satisfy two linear inequalities.
- how to graph one or more linear inequalities on a coordinate plane.

Looking Forward

Students can use these skills

- to find a solution that satisfies three or more linear equations.
- to find solutions that satisfy two or more nonlinear equations.
- to graph nonlinear inequalities on a coordinate plane.

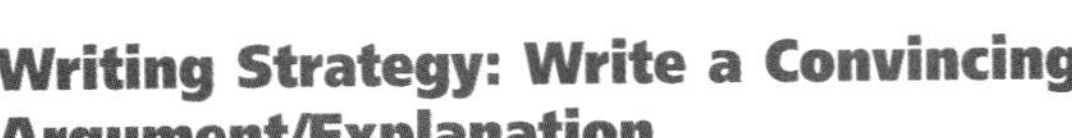

California Standards

English-Language Arts, Writing 8.2.4.b

Writing Strategy: Write a Convincing Argument/Explanation

The Write About It icon appears throughout the book. These icons identify questions that require you to write a complete argument or explanation. Writing a convincing argument or explanation shows that you have a solid understanding of a concept.

To be effective, an argument or explanation should include

- reasoning, evidence, work, or facts.
- a complete response that will answer or explain.

From Lesson 3-7

54. **Write About It** Describe how to use an absolute-value inequality to find all the values on a number line that are within 5 units of −6.

Step 1 **Identify what you need to answer or explain.**
Explain how an absolute-value inequality can help find values on a number line that are within 5 units of −6.

Step 2 **Give evidence, work, or facts that are needed to answer the question.**
The distance between two numbers can be found using subtraction. The inequality $|x| < 5$ describes all real numbers whose distance from 0 is less than 5 units. To find all real numbers whose distance from −6 is less than 5 units, you must subtract −6 from x.

$$|x - (-6)| < 5$$

Step 3 **Write a complete response that answers or explains.**
The difference between a number and −6 must be less than 5.

$$|x - (-6)| < 5$$
$$|x + 6| < 5$$

Try This

Write a convincing argument or explanation.

1. What is the least whole number that is a solution of $12x + 15.4 > 118.92$? Explain.
2. Which equation has an error? Explain the error.

   A. $4(6 \cdot 5) = (4)6 \cdot (4)5$ B. $4(6 \cdot 5) = (4 \cdot 6)5$

Organizer

Objective: Help students apply strategies to understand and retain key concepts.

Resources

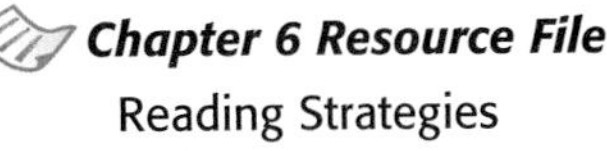

Reading Strategies

Writing Strategy: Write a Convincing Argument/Explanation

Discuss A convincing argument or explanation leaves no doubt in the mind of the reader. There is no point at which the reader can say "Why?" or "How did you get that?"

Extend As students work through the *Write About It* problems in Chapter 6, encourage them to write as thoroughly as possible. Have students check each other's work, checking for adequate evidence and completed work shown.

Answers to *Try This*

Possible answers:

1. Possible answer: The actual answer is $x > 8.62\overline{6}$. The nearest whole number that is greater than $8.62\overline{6}$ is 9.
2. Possible answer: Equation A is the equation with the error. The Distributive Property does not work over multiplication, only over addition or subtraction.

Writing 8.2.4b Present detailed evidence, examples, and reasoning to support arguments, differentiating between fact and opinion.

Systems of Linear Equations

One-Minute Section Planner

Lesson	Lab Resources	Materials
6-1 Technology Lab Solve Linear Equations by Using a Spreadsheet • Use a spreadsheet to model real-world linear relationships. **5.0**		**Required** spreadsheet software
Lesson 6-1 Solving Systems by Graphing • Identify solutions of systems of linear equations in two variables. • Solve systems of linear equations in two variables by graphing. **9.0**		**Required** graph paper, straightedge **Optional** graphing calculator
6-2 Algebra Lab Model Systems of Linear Equations • Use algebra tiles to model and solve systems of linear equations. **9.0**		**Required** algebra tiles (MK)
Lesson 6-2 Solving Systems by Substitution • Solve systems of linear equations in two variables by substitution. **9.0**		**Optional** graphing calculator
Lesson 6-3 Solving Systems by Elimination • Solve systems of linear equations in two variables by elimination. • Compare and choose an appropriate method for solving systems of linear equations. **9.0**	***Algebra Lab 6-3*** In *Chapter 6 Resource File*	**Optional** transparency algebra tiles (MK)
Lesson 6-4 Solving Special Systems • Solve special systems of linear equations in two variables. • Classify systems of linear equations and determine the number of solutions. **8.0, 9.0**	***Algebra Lab 6-4*** In *Chapter 6 Resource File*	**Optional** graphing calculator
Lesson 6-5 Applying Systems • Use systems of equations to solve application problems. **9.0, 15.0**		

MK = *Manipulatives Kit*

Notes

Math Background: Teaching the Standards

Professional Development

SYSTEMS OF LINEAR EQUATIONS  9.0

Lessons 6-1 to 6-5

A *system of linear equations* is a set of two or more linear equations that each contain two or more variables. In this course, the systems consist of two equations that each contain two variables. A *solution* of such a system is an ordered pair that satisfies both equations.

Consider the system $\begin{cases} x + y = 5 \\ y - x = -1 \end{cases}$. The ordered pair (3, 2) is a solution of the system because it satisfies both equations: $3 + 2 = 5$ and $2 - 3 = -1$.

The graph of an equation is the set of all of its solutions. Therefore, if an ordered pair is a solution of two linear equations, it must lie on both graphs. In other words, the solution is the *intersection* of the graphs. The intersection of the graphs of $x + y = 5$ and $y - x = -1$ is (3, 2).

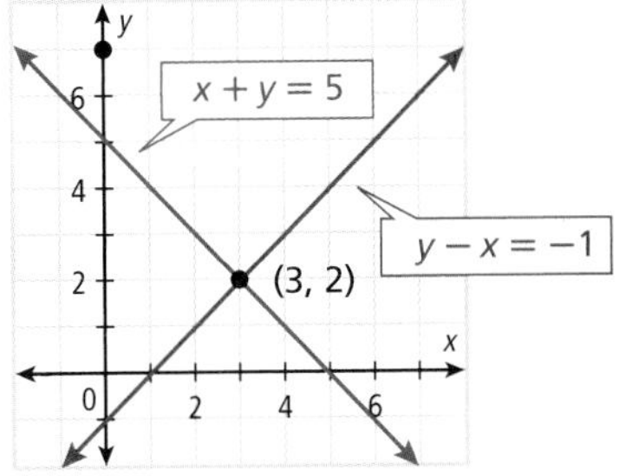

This graphic representation leads naturally to the conclusions that some systems may have no solutions (lines may be parallel) and that some systems may have infinitely many solutions (lines may be coincident).

Graphing is an intuitive way to solve systems, and it visually reinforces the meaning of a solution. Graphing also highlights the connection between algebra and geometry; in particular, it shows that you can solve a problem presented in purely algebraic terms by using geometric methods.

ALGEBRAIC METHODS 9.0

Lessons 6-2 to 6-5

The intersection point of two lines may not have integer coordinates, thereby motivating the need for algebraic methods of solving systems. In general, the goal of algebraic methods is to eliminate a variable so that the techniques for solving single-variable equations may be used.

As an example of an algebraic method, one can solve both equations in a system for y to get two equations that can be set equal to each other. Solving both equations for y in the system discussed earlier gives $y = 5 - x$ and $y = x - 1$. The two expressions for y must be equal, so $5 - x = x - 1$. Solving shows that $x = 3$, and substituting this value of x into either of the original equations gives $y = 2$.

This method is called the *substitution method.* In general, solve either equation for either variable and then substitute into the other equation. This yields an equation that can be solved using previously learned skills. In future math courses, students will see that the substitution method is useful for solving systems when one or more of the equations are not linear.

Although the substitution method works with any system, it may be awkward to use when no variable term has a coefficient of 1. In this case, the *elimination method* may be a better choice.

Students should understand that the elimination method is based on the properties of equality.

For example, to solve $\begin{cases} 2x + 3y = 11 \\ -6x + 5y = -19 \end{cases}$, you can multiply both sides of the first equation by 3 using the Multiplication Property of Equality. To solve the resulting system, $\begin{cases} 6x + 9y = 33 \\ -6x + 5y = -19 \end{cases}$, you can add the two equations together to eliminate the x-terms. This is justified by the Addition Property of Equality since you are adding equal quantities, $-6x + 5y$ and -19, to both sides of the first equation. The result is one equation in one variable, $14y = 14$, that is easy to solve for y. Then substitute to find x.

In general, elimination works well for systems of all linear equations containing any number of variables, and it is a fundamental process in the study of linear algebra.

Organizer

Use with Lesson 6-1

Objective: Use a spreadsheet to model real-world linear relationships.

Materials: spreadsheet software

Countdown to Mastery Week 12

Teach

Discuss

Ask students what the breakeven point represents. Lead them to see that it is when the cost and sales are equal and profit is thus 0.

Close

Key Concept

You can use a spreadsheet to view the expressions evaluated for many values at a time and observe the pattern.

Assessment

Journal Have students explain what a breakeven point is and how, given the cost and sales equations, they can use a spreadsheet to find this point.

Algebra 1 **5.0**

6-1

Use with Lesson 6-1

Solve Linear Equations by Using a Spreadsheet

You can use a spreadsheet to answer "What if...?" questions. By changing one or more values, you can quickly model different scenarios.

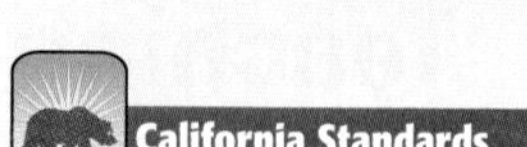

California Standards

5.0 Students solve multistep problems, including word problems involving linear equations and linear inequalities **in one variable** and provide justification for each step.

Activity

Company Z makes DVD players. The company's costs are $400 per week plus $20 per DVD player. Each DVD player sells for $45. How many DVD players must company Z sell in one week to make a profit?

Let n represent the number of DVD players company Z sells in one week.

$c = 400 + 20n$ *The total cost is $400 plus $20 times the number of DVD players made.*

$s = 45n$ *The total sales income is $45 times the number of DVD players sold.*

$p = s - c$ *The total profit is the sales income minus the total cost.*

1. Set up your spreadsheet with columns for number of DVD players, total cost, total income, and profit.

2. Under Number of DVD Players, enter 1 in cell A2.

3. Use the equations above to enter the formulas for total cost, total sales, and total profit in row 2.
   - In cell B2, enter the formula for total cost.
   - In cell C2, enter the formula for total sales income.
   - In cell D2, enter the formula for total profit.

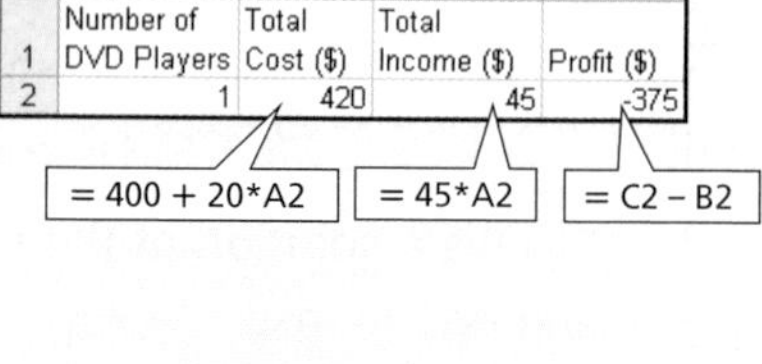

Company Z Profit

	A	B	C	D
1	Number of DVD Players	Total Cost ($)	Total Income ($)	Profit ($)
2	1	420	45	-375

4. Fill columns A, B, C, and D by selecting cells A1 through D1, clicking the small box at the bottom right corner of cell D2, and dragging the box down through several rows.

5. Find the point where the profit is $0. This is known as the breakeven point, where total cost and total income are the same.

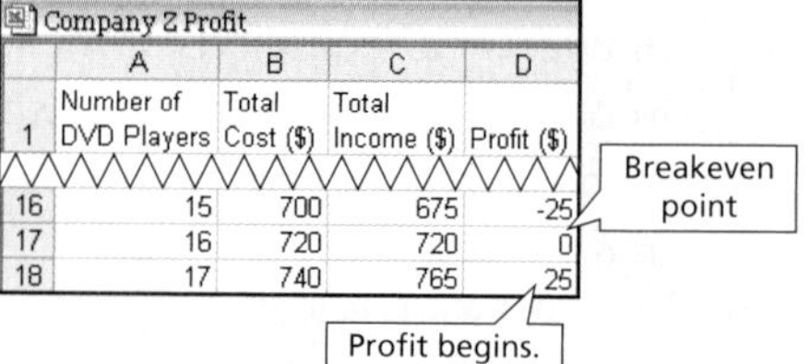

Company Z Profit

	A	B	C	D
1	Number of DVD Players	Total Cost ($)	Total Income ($)	Profit ($)
16	15	700	675	-25
17	16	720	720	0
18	17	740	765	25

Try This

For Exercises 1 and 2, use the spreadsheet from the activity.

1. If company Z sells 10 DVD players, will they make a profit? Explain. What if they sell 16?
2. Company Z makes a profit of $225 dollars. How many DVD players did they sell? **25**

For Exercise 3, make a spreadsheet.

3. Company Y's costs are $400 per week plus $20 per DVD player. They want the breakeven point to occur with sales of 8 DVD players. What should the sales price be? **$70**

Answers to *Try This*

1. Company Z will not make a profit; it will lose $150. If it sells 16 DVD players it still will not make a profit; it will only break even.

6-1 Solving Systems by Graphing

California Standards

9.0 Students solve a system of two linear equations in two variables algebraically **and are able to interpret the answer graphically.** Students are able to solve a system of two linear inequalities in two variables and to sketch the solution sets.
Also covered: **6.0**

Why learn this?
You can compare costs by graphing a system of linear equations.

Sometimes there are different charges for the same service or product at different places. For example, Bowl-o-Rama charges \$2.50 per game plus \$2 for shoe rental while Bowling Pinz charges \$2 per game plus \$4 for shoe rental. A *system of linear equations* can be used to compare these charges.

A **system of linear equations** is a set of two or more linear equations containing two or more variables. A **solution of a system of linear equations** with two variables is an ordered pair that satisfies each equation in the system. So, if an ordered pair is a solution, it will make both equations true.

Vocabulary
system of linear equations
solution of a system of linear equations

EXAMPLE 1 Identifying Solutions of Systems

Tell whether the ordered pair is a solution of the given system.

A $(4, 1); \begin{cases} x + 2y = 6 \\ x - y = 3 \end{cases}$

$x + 2y = 6$	
$4 + 2(1)$	6
$4 + 2$	6
6	$6 \checkmark$

Substitute 4 for x and 1 for y.

$x - y = 3$	
$4 - 1$	3
3	$3 \checkmark$

The ordered pair $(4, 1)$ makes both equations true.

$(4, 1)$ is a solution of the system.

B $(-1, 2); \begin{cases} 2x + 5y = 8 \\ 3x - 2y = 5 \end{cases}$

$2x + 5y = 8$	
$2(-1) + 5(2)$	8
$-2 + 10$	8
8	$8 \checkmark$

Substitute −1 for x and 2 for y.

$3x - 2y = 5$	
$3(-1) - 2(2)$	5
$-3 - 4$	5
-7	$5 \times$

Substitute −1 for x and 2 for y.

The ordered pair $(-1, 2)$ makes one equation true, but not the other.

$(-1, 2)$ is not a solution of the system.

Helpful Hint

If an ordered pair does not satisfy the first equation in the system, there is no need to check the other equations.

CHECK IT OUT! **Tell whether the ordered pair is a solution of the given system.**

1a. $(1, 3); \begin{cases} 2x + y = 5 \\ -2x + y = 1 \end{cases}$ yes **1b.** $(2, -1); \begin{cases} x - 2y = 4 \\ 3x + y = 6 \end{cases}$ no

6-1 Organizer

Objectives: Identify solutions of systems of linear equations in two variables.

Solve systems of linear equations in two variables by graphing.

Online Edition
Tutorial Videos, Interactivity, TechKeys, Graphing Calculator

Countdown to Mastery Week 12

Power Presentations with PowerPoint®

Warm Up

Evaluate each expression for $x = 1$ and $y = -3$.

1. $x - 4y$ 13

2. $-2x + y$ -5

Write each equation in slope-intercept form.

3. $y - x = 1$ $y = x + 1$

4. $2x + 3y = 6$ $y = -\frac{2}{3}x + 2$

5. $0 = 5y + 5x$ $y = -x$

Also available on transparency

Math Humor

Teacher: What is the name of the formula that describes the phases of the moon?

Student: The lunear (linear) equation

1 Introduce

EXPLORATION

6-1 Solving Systems by Graphing

You will need a graphing calculator for this Exploration.

1. Press [Y=] and enter the equations $y = 2x - 5$ and $y = -x + 4$ as **Y1** and **Y2**.

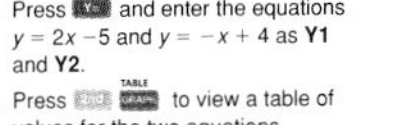

2. Press [2nd] [GRAPH] to view a table of values for the two equations.
3. Use the table to find an x-value that produces the same y-value for both equations. Write this x-value and the corresponding y-value as an ordered pair.

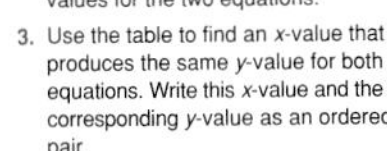

4. Use the arrow keys to scroll up and down the table. Does there appear to be any other x-value that produces the same y-value for both equations?

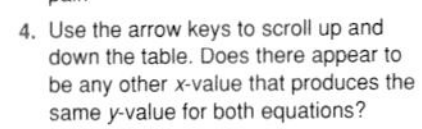

5. Press [GRAPH] to view a graph of the equations.

THINK AND DISCUSS

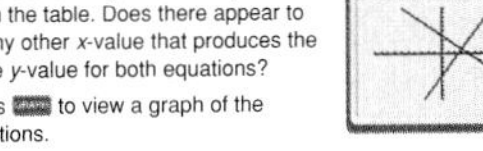

6. **Describe** the graph of the functions.
7. **Explain** what happens on the graph at the point that you found in Step 3.

Motivate

Have students choose an ordered pair that is a solution of $y = x + 1$. Point out that there are infinitely many ordered-pair solutions. Then ask which of the ordered pairs is also a solution of $y = 5 - x$. Let them try several pairs. Tell students that there is only one ordered pair that is a solution of both equations. (2, 3) Then explain that this lesson will show a method for finding that pair.

Explorations and answers are provided in *Alternate Openers: Explorations Transparencies.*

California Standards

Algebra 1 **9.0**
Also covered:
6.0 Students graph a linear equation and compute the x- and y-intercepts (e.g., graph $2x + 6y = 4$). They are also able to sketch the region defined by a linear inequality (e.g., they sketch the region defined by $2x + 6y < 4$).

Power Presentations with PowerPoint®

Additional Examples

Example 1

Tell whether the ordered pair is a solution of the given system.

A. $(5, 2); \begin{cases} \frac{2}{5}x - y = 0 \\ 3x - y = 13 \end{cases}$ yes

B. $(-2, 2); \begin{cases} x + 3y = 4 \\ -x + y = 2 \end{cases}$ no

Example 2

Solve each system by graphing. Check your answer.

A. $\begin{cases} y = x \\ y = -2x - 3 \end{cases}$ $(-1, -1)$

B. $\begin{cases} y = x - 6 \\ y + \frac{1}{3}x = -1 \end{cases}$ $\left(\frac{15}{4}, -\frac{9}{4}\right)$

Also available on transparency

INTERVENTION

Questioning Strategies

EXAMPLE 1

- How do you know when an ordered pair is a solution of a system of linear equations?

EXAMPLE 2

- What does the intersection of the two lines represent?

All solutions of a linear equation are on its graph. To find a solution of a system of linear equations, you need a point that each line has in common. In other words, you need their point of intersection.

$\begin{cases} y = 2x - 1 \\ y = -x + 5 \end{cases}$

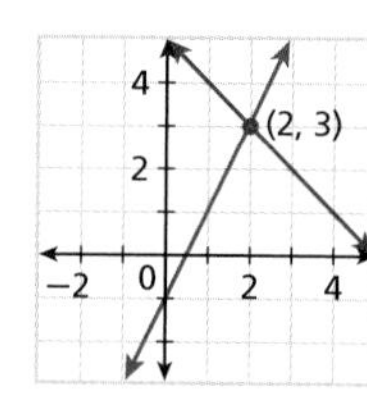

The point $(2, 3)$ is where the two lines intersect and is a solution of both equations, so $(2, 3)$ is the solution of the system.

EXAMPLE 2 Solving a System of Linear Equations by Graphing

Solve each system by graphing. Check your answer.

Helpful Hint

Sometimes it is difficult to tell exactly where the lines cross when you solve by graphing. Check your answer by substituting it into both equations.

A $\begin{cases} y = x - 3 \\ y = -x - 1 \end{cases}$

Graph the system.

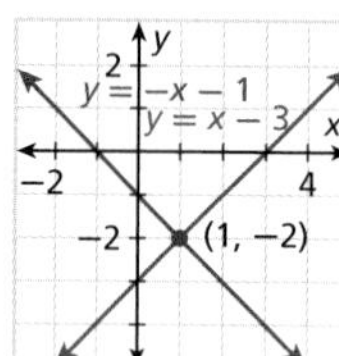

The solution appears to be at $(1, -2)$.

Check

Substitute $(1, -2)$ into the system.

$y = x - 3$	
-2	$1 - 3$
-2	-2 ✓

$y = -x - 1$	
-2	$-(1) - 1$
-2	-2 ✓

The solution is $(1, -2)$.

Math Builders

For more on graphing systems of equations, see the System Builder on page MB4.

B $\begin{cases} x + y = 0 \\ y = -\frac{1}{2}x + 1 \end{cases}$

$$\begin{aligned} x + y &= 0 \\ \underline{-x} \quad & \underline{-x} \\ y &= -x \end{aligned}$$

Rewrite the first equation in slope-intercept form.

Graph the system.

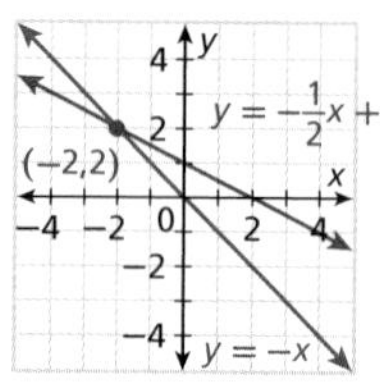

The solution appears to be at $(-2, 2)$.

Check

Substitute $(-2, 2)$ into the system.

$x + y = 0$	
$-2 + 2$	0
0	0 ✓

$y = -\frac{1}{2}x + 1$	
2	$-\frac{1}{2}(-2) + 1$
2	$1 + 1$
2	2 ✓

The solution is $(-2, 2)$.

Solve each system by graphing. Check your answer.

2a. $\begin{cases} y = -2x - 1 \\ y = x + 5 \end{cases}$ **(−2, 3)**

2b. $\begin{cases} y = \frac{1}{3}x - 3 \\ 2x + y = 4 \end{cases}$ **(3, −2)**

2 Teach

Guided Instruction

Before teaching students to solve a system by graphing, review slope-intercept form and how to write an equation in that form.

Communicating Math Warn students that the brace, {, is not always used to indicate a system of equations. A standardized test might omit the symbol and simply say that the equations are a system.

Universal Access

Through Multiple Representations

Have students copy and complete the table for the system of equations.

$\begin{cases} y = -2x + 9 \\ y = x + 3 \end{cases}$

x	$y_1 = -2x + 9$	$y_2 = x + 3$
0	9	3
1	7	4
2	5	5
3	3	6

Graph the system, and discuss similarities between the table and the graph. For example, from the table, you can see that when $x = 0$, the y-value of one equation is 9, and the y-value of the other equation is 3. On the graph you can see that the point $(0, 9)$ is on one line and the point $(0, 3)$ is on the other line.

EXAMPLE 3 Problem-Solving Application

Bowl-o-Rama charges $2.50 per game plus $2 for shoe rental, and Bowling Pinz charges $2 per game plus $4 for shoe rental. For how many games will the cost to bowl be the same at both places? What is that cost?

1 Understand the Problem

The **answer** will be the number of games played for which the total cost is the same at both bowling alleys. **List the important information:**

- Game price: Bowl-o-Rama $2.50 Bowling Pinz: $2
- Shoe-rental fee: Bowl-o-Rama $2 Bowling Pinz: $4

2 Make a Plan

Write a system of equations, one equation to represent the price at each company. Let x be the number of games played and y be the total cost.

	Total cost	is	price per game	times	games	plus	shoe-rental.
Bowl-o-Rama	y	=	2.5	•	x	+	2
Bowling Pinz	y	=	2	•	x	+	4

3 Solve

Graph $y = 2.5x + 2$ and $y = 2x + 4$. The lines appear to intersect at (4, 12). So, the cost at both places will be the same for 4 games bowled and that cost will be $12.

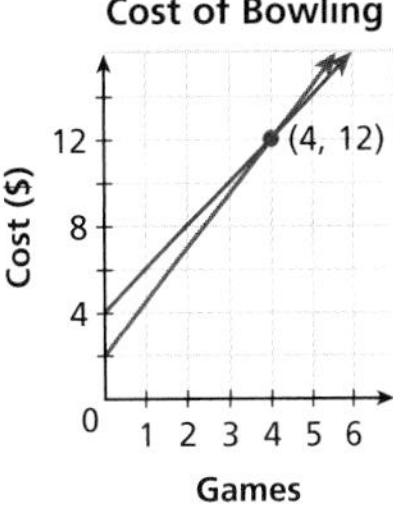

4 Look Back

Check (4, 12) using both equations.
Cost of bowling 4 games at Bowl-o-Rama:
$\$2.5(4) + \$2 = 10 + 2 = 12$ ✓
Cost of bowling 4 games at Bowling Pinz:
$\$2(4) + \$4 = 8 + 4 = 12$ ✓

Writing Math

The solution set for Example 3 is written {(4, 12)}.

CHECK IT OUT! 3. Video club A charges $10 for membership and $3 per movie rental. Video club B charges $15 for membership and $2 per movie rental. For how many movie rentals will the cost be the same at both video clubs? What is that cost? **5 movies; $25**

THINK AND DISCUSS

1. Explain how to use a graph to solve a system of linear equations.
2. Explain how to check a solution of a system of linear equations.

3. **GET ORGANIZED** Copy and complete the graphic organizer. In each box, write a step for solving a linear system by graphing. More boxes may be added.

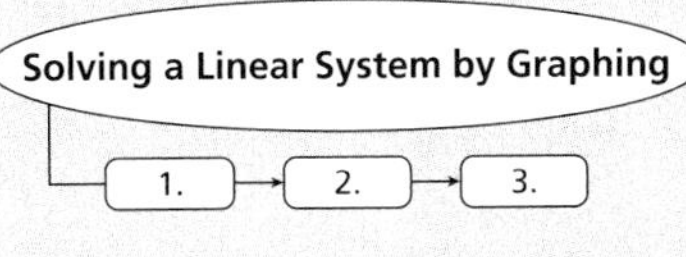

COMMON ERROR ALERT

Students sometimes have difficulty correctly assigning x and y variables in word problems, such as in **Example 3.** Remind them that y usually represents the dependent variable. In this case, y cannot be determined unless the value of x is known. In other words, y is dependent on x.

Power Presentations with PowerPoint®

Additional Examples

Example 3

Wren and Jenni are reading the same book. Wren is on page 14 and reads 2 pages every night. Jenni is on page 6 and reads 3 pages every night. After how many nights will they have read the same number of pages? 8 nights How many pages will that be? 30 pages

INTERVENTION
Questioning Strategies

EXAMPLE 3

- What does the graph show on the left side of the point of intersection?
- What does the graph show on the right side of the point of intersection?

Teaching Tip **Visual Cues** In **Example 3** students may benefit from using a table to organize the information.

	Shoe Rental	Game Price
Bowl-o-Rama	$2.00	$2.50
Bowling Pinz	$4.00	$2.00

3 Close

Summarize

Have students graph the equations below to determine whether each ordered pair is the solution of the given system. Have them check their work by substituting the ordered pair into the system of equations.

1. $(0, -2); \begin{cases} y = x - 2 \\ 4y + \frac{1}{2}x = -8 \end{cases}$ yes

2. $(3, 6); \begin{cases} y + 3x = 9 \\ y = 2x \end{cases}$ no

FORMATIVE ASSESSMENT and INTERVENTION

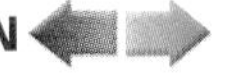

***Diagnose Before* the Lesson**
6-1 Warm Up, TE p. 329

***Monitor During* the Lesson**
Check It Out! Exercises, SE pp. 329–331
Questioning Strategies, TE pp. 330–331

***Assess After* the Lesson**
6-1 Lesson Quiz, TE p. 334
Alternative Assessment, TE p. 334

Answers to *Think and Discuss*

1. Locate the point of intersection. The ordered pair is a solution of the system.
2. Substitute the x- and y-values of the ordered pair. If both equations are true, the solution is correct.
3. See p. A5.

6-1 Exercises

GUIDED PRACTICE

1. **Vocabulary** Describe a *solution of a system of linear equations.* **an ordered pair that satisfies both equations**

SEE EXAMPLE 1 p. 329

Tell whether the ordered pair is a solution of the given system.

2. $(2, -2)$; $\begin{cases} 3x + y = 4 \\ x - 3y = -4 \end{cases}$ **no**
3. $(3, -1)$; $\begin{cases} x - 2y = 5 \\ 2x - y = 7 \end{cases}$ **yes**
4. $(-1, 5)$; $\begin{cases} -x + y = 6 \\ 2x + 3y = 13 \end{cases}$ **yes**

SEE EXAMPLE 2 p. 330

Solve each system by graphing. Check your answer.

5. $\begin{cases} y = \frac{1}{2}x \\ y = -x + 3 \end{cases}$ **(2, 1)**
6. $\begin{cases} y = x - 2 \\ 2x + y = 1 \end{cases}$ **(1, −1)**
7. $\begin{cases} -2x - 1 = y \\ x + y = 3 \end{cases}$ **(−4, 7)**

SEE EXAMPLE 3 p. 331

8. To deliver mulch, Lawn and Garden charges \$30 per cubic yard of mulch plus a \$30 delivery fee. Yard Depot charges \$25 per cubic yard of mulch plus a \$55 delivery fee. For how many cubic yards will the cost be the same? What will that cost be? **5 yd^3; \$180**

PRACTICE AND PROBLEM SOLVING

Independent Practice

For Exercises	See Example
9–11	1
12–15	2
16	3

Extra Practice
Skills Practice p. EP12
Application Practice p. EP29

Tell whether the ordered pair is a solution of the given system.

9. $(1, -4)$; $\begin{cases} x - 2y = 8 \\ 4x - y = 8 \end{cases}$ **no**
10. $(-2, 1)$; $\begin{cases} 2x - 3y = -7 \\ 3x + y = -5 \end{cases}$ **yes**
11. $(5, 2)$; $\begin{cases} 2x + y = 12 \\ -3y - x = -11 \end{cases}$ **yes**

Solve each system by graphing. Check your answer.

12. $\begin{cases} y = \frac{1}{2}x + 2 \\ y = -x - 1 \end{cases}$ **(−2, 1)**
13. $\begin{cases} y = x \\ y = -x + 6 \end{cases}$ **(3, 3)**
14. $\begin{cases} -2x - 1 = y \\ x = -y + 3 \end{cases}$ **(−4, 7)**
15. $\begin{cases} x + y = 2 \\ y = x - 4 \end{cases}$ **(3, −1)**

16. **Multi-Step** Angelo runs 7 miles per week and increases his distance by 1 mile each week. Marc runs 4 miles per week and increases his distance by 2 miles each week. In how many weeks will Angelo and Marc be running the same distance? What will that distance be? **3 weeks; 10 mi**

17. **School** The school band sells carnations on Valentine's Day for \$2 each. They buy the carnations from a florist for \$0.50 each, plus a \$16 delivery charge.
    a. Write a system of equations to describe the situation.
    b. Graph the system. What does the solution represent?
    c. Explain whether the solution shown on the graph makes sense in this situation. If not, give a reasonable solution.

CONCEPT CONNECTION

18. This problem will prepare you for the Concept Connection on page 362.
    a. The Warrior baseball team is selling hats as a fund-raiser. They contacted two companies. Hats Off charges a \$50 design fee and \$5 per hat. Top Stuff charges a \$25 design fee and \$6 per hat. Write an equation for each company's pricing.
    b. Graph the system of equations from part **a.** For how many hats will the cost be the same? What is that cost?
    c. Explain when it is cheaper for the baseball team to use Top Stuff and when it is cheaper to use Hats Off. **fewer than 25 hats: Top Stuff; more than 25 hats: Hats Off**

Assignment Guide

Assign *Guided Practice* exercises as necessary.

If you finished Examples **1–3**
Proficient 9–16, 18–22, 26–42
Advanced 9–16, 18–42

Homework Quick Check
Quickly check key concepts.
Exercises: 10, 14, 16, 18, 22

CONCEPT CONNECTION **Exercise 18** involves writing a system of equations to compare pricing options. This exercise prepares students for the Concept Connection on page 362.

Answers

17a. $\begin{cases} y = 2x \\ y = 16 + 0.50x \end{cases}$

b.

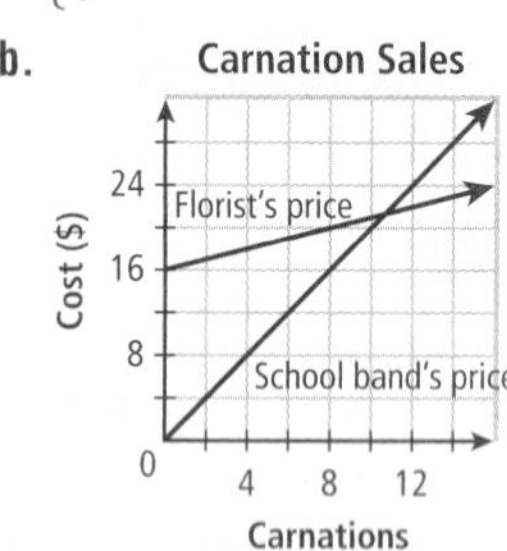

It represents how many carnations need to be sold to break even.

c. No; because the solution is not a whole number of carnations; 11 carnations.

18a. Hats Off: $c = 5h + 50$;
Top Stuff: $c = 6h + 25$

b. 25 hats; \$175

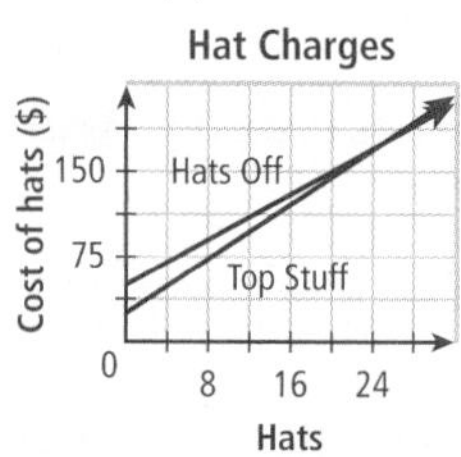

California Standards

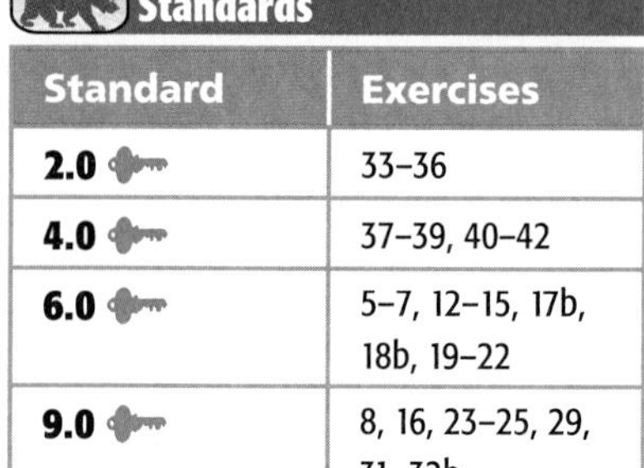

Standard	Exercises
2.0	33–36
4.0	37–39, 40–42
6.0	5–7, 12–15, 17b, 18b, 19–22
9.0	8, 16, 23–25, 29, 31–32b

6-1 READING STRATEGIES

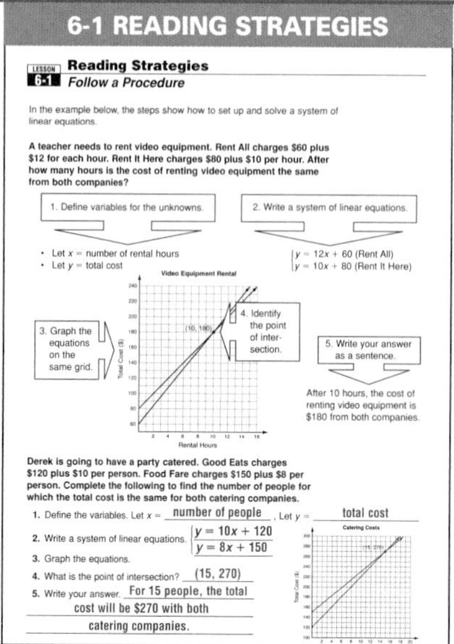

LESSON 6-1 **Reading Strategies**
Follow a Procedure

In the example below, the steps show how to set up and solve a system of linear equations.

A teacher needs to rent video equipment. Rent All charges \$60 plus \$12 for each hour. Rent It Here charges \$80 plus \$10 per hour. After how many hours is the cost of renting video equipment the same from both companies?

1. Define variables for the unknowns.
   - Let x = number of rental hours
   - Let y = total cost

2. Write a system of linear equations.
   $\begin{cases} y = 12x + 60 \text{ (Rent All)} \\ y = 10x + 80 \text{ (Rent It Here)} \end{cases}$

3. Graph the equations on the same grid.

4. Identify the point of intersection.

5. Write your answer as a sentence.
   After 10 hours, the cost of renting video equipment is \$180 from both companies.

Derek is going to have a party catered. Good Eats charges \$120 plus \$10 per person. Food Fare charges \$150 plus \$8 per person. Complete the following to find the number of people for which the total cost is the same for both catering companies.

1. Define the variables. Let x = **number of people**, Let y = **total cost**
2. Write a system of linear equations. $\begin{cases} y = 10x + 120 \\ y = 8x + 150 \end{cases}$
3. Graph the equations.
4. What is the point of intersection? **(15, 270)**
5. Write your answer. **For 15 people, the total cost will be \$270 with both catering companies.**

6-1 REVIEW FOR MASTERY

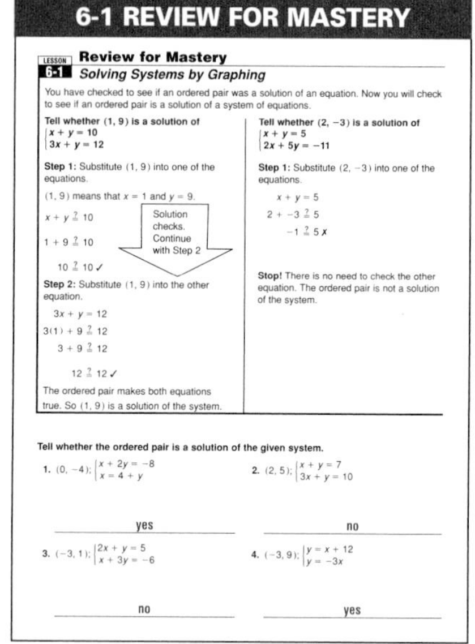

LESSON 6-1 **Review for Mastery**
Solving Systems by Graphing

You have checked to see if an ordered pair was a solution of an equation. Now you will check to see if an ordered pair is a solution of a system of equations.

Tell whether (1, 9) is a solution of $\begin{cases} x + y = 10 \\ 3x + y = 12 \end{cases}$

Step 1: Substitute (1, 9) into one of the equations.

(1, 9) means that $x = 1$ and $y = 9$.

$x + y \stackrel{?}{=} 10$
$1 + 9 \stackrel{?}{=} 10$
$10 \stackrel{?}{=} 10$ ✓

Solution checks. Continue with Step 2

Step 2: Substitute (1, 9) into the other equation.

$3x + y = 12$
$3(1) + 9 \stackrel{?}{=} 12$
$3 + 9 \stackrel{?}{=} 12$
$12 \stackrel{?}{=} 12$ ✓

The ordered pair makes both equations true. So (1, 9) is a solution of the system.

Tell whether (2, −3) is a solution of $\begin{cases} x + y = 5 \\ 2x + 5y = -11 \end{cases}$

Step 1: Substitute (2, −3) into one of the equations.

$x + y = 5$
$2 + -3 \stackrel{?}{=} 5$
$-1 \stackrel{?}{=} 5$ ✗

Stop! There is no need to check the other equation. The ordered pair is not a solution of the system.

Tell whether the ordered pair is a solution of the given system.

1. $(0, -4)$; $\begin{cases} x + 2y = -8 \\ x = 4 + y \end{cases}$ **yes**
2. $(2, 5)$; $\begin{cases} x + y = 7 \\ 3x + y = 10 \end{cases}$ **no**
3. $(-3, 1)$; $\begin{cases} 2x + y = 5 \\ x + 3y = -6 \end{cases}$ **no**
4. $(-3, 9)$; $\begin{cases} y = x + 12 \\ y = -3x \end{cases}$ **yes**

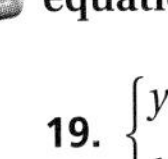

Graphing Calculator Use a graphing calculator to graph and solve the systems of equations in Exercises 19–22. Round your answer to the nearest tenth.

19. $\begin{cases} y = 4.7x + 2.1 \\ y = 1.6x - 5.4 \end{cases}$ **(−2.4, −9.3)**

20. $\begin{cases} 4.8x + 0.6y = 4 \\ y = -3.2x + 2.7 \end{cases}$ **(0.8, 0.1)**

21. $\begin{cases} y = \frac{5}{4}x - \frac{2}{3} \\ \frac{8}{3}x + y = \frac{5}{9} \end{cases}$ **(0.3, −0.3)**

22. $\begin{cases} y = 6.9x + 12.4 \\ y = -4.1x - 5.3 \end{cases}$ **(−1.6, 1.3)**

LINK

Landscaping

Middleton Place Gardens, South Carolina, are the United States' oldest landscaped gardens. The gardens were established in 1741 and opened to the public in the 1920s.

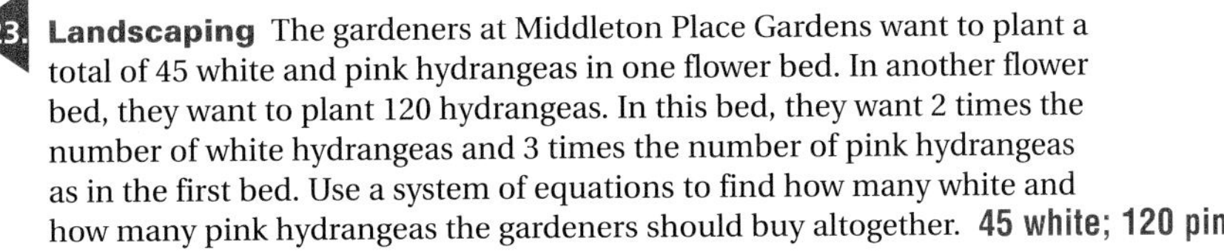

23. **Landscaping** The gardeners at Middleton Place Gardens want to plant a total of 45 white and pink hydrangeas in one flower bed. In another flower bed, they want to plant 120 hydrangeas. In this bed, they want 2 times the number of white hydrangeas and 3 times the number of pink hydrangeas as in the first bed. Use a system of equations to find how many white and how many pink hydrangeas the gardeners should buy altogether. **45 white; 120 pink**

24. **Fitness** Rusty burns 5 Calories per minute swimming and 11 Calories per minute jogging. In the morning, Rusty burns 200 Calories walking and swims for x minutes. In the afternoon, Rusty will jog for x minutes. How many minutes must he jog to burn at least as many Calories y in the afternoon as he did in the morning? Round your answer up to the next whole number of minutes. **34 min**

25. A tree that is 2 feet tall is growing at a rate of 1 foot per year. A 6-foot tall tree is growing at a rate of 0.5 foot per year. In how many years will the trees be the same height? **8 yr**

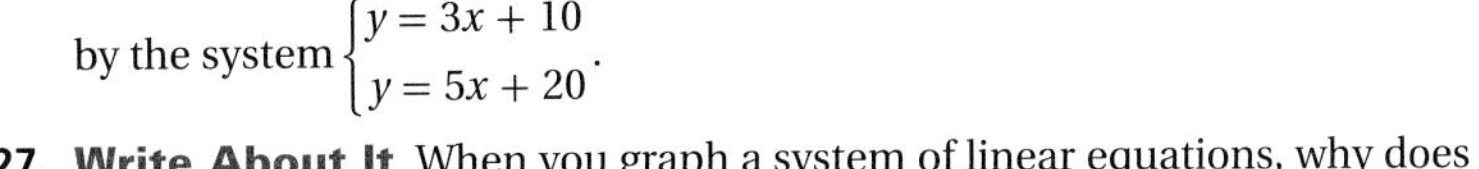

26. **Critical Thinking** Write a real-world situation that could be represented by the system $\begin{cases} y = 3x + 10 \\ y = 5x + 20 \end{cases}$.

27. **Write About It** When you graph a system of linear equations, why does the intersection of the two lines represent the solution of the system?

27. Every point on a line satisfies the related linear equation. A point that is on both lines (the intersection point) satisfies both equations.

Multiple Choice For Exercises 28 and 29, choose the best answer.

28. Taxi company A charges \$4 plus \$0.50 per mile. Taxi company B charges \$5 plus \$0.25 per mile. Which system best represents this problem?

(A) $\begin{cases} y = 4x + 0.5 \\ y = 5x + 0.25 \end{cases}$ (C) $\begin{cases} y = -4x + 0.5 \\ y = -5x + 0.25 \end{cases}$

(B) $\begin{cases} y = 0.5x + 4 \\ y = 0.25x + 5 \end{cases}$ (D) $\begin{cases} y = -0.5x + 4 \\ y = -0.25x + 5 \end{cases}$

29. Which system of equations represents the given graph?

(A) $\begin{cases} y = 2x - 1 \\ y = \frac{1}{3}x + 3 \end{cases}$ **(C)** $\begin{cases} y = 2x + 1 \\ y = \frac{1}{3}x - 3 \end{cases}$

(B) $\begin{cases} y = -2x + 1 \\ y = 2x - 3 \end{cases}$ (D) $\begin{cases} y = -2x - 1 \\ y = 3x - 3 \end{cases}$

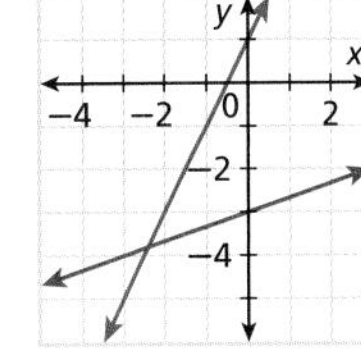

30. **Gridded Response** Which value of b will make the system $y = 2x + 2$ and $y = 2.5x + b$ intersect at the point (2, 6)? **1**

COMMON ERROR ALERT

In **Exercises 5–7** and **12–15,** students may get the wrong answer because of inaccurate graphs. Caution students to use a straightedge when drawing lines.

Teaching Tip **Inclusion** In **Exercise 23,** encourage students to check that they answered the question asked in the problem.

Teaching Tip **Multiple Choice** In **Exercise 28,** choices **C** and **D** can be eliminated because the situation in the problem requires lines with positive slopes.

Choices **B** and **D** can be eliminated in **Exercise 29** because the graph shows two lines with positive slopes.

Answer

26. Possible answer: Store A rents carpet cleaners for a fee of \$10, plus \$3 per day. Store B rents carpet cleaners for a fee of \$20, plus \$5 per day. For how many days rental will the costs be the same?

6-1 PROBLEM SOLVING

LESSON 6-1 Problem Solving
Solving Systems by Graphing

Write the correct answer.

1. Mr. Malone is putting money in two savings accounts. Account A started with \$200 and Account B started with \$300. Mr. Malone deposits \$15 in Account A and \$10 in Account B each month. In how many months will the accounts have the same balance? What will that balance be? **20 months, \$500**

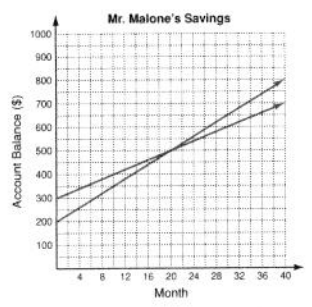

2. Tom currently has 5 comic books in his collection and has subscribed to receive 5 new comic books each month. His uncle has 145 comic books, but sends 5 to each of his 3 nieces each month. In how many months will they have the same number of comic books? How many books will that be? **7 months, 40 books**

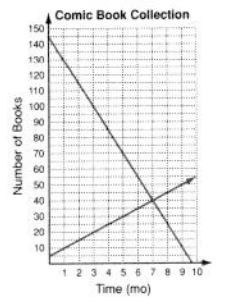

The graph below compares the heights of two trees. Use the graph to answer questions 3–5. Select the best answer.

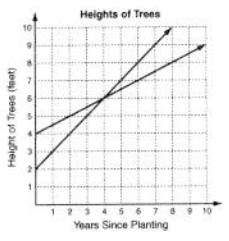

3. How many years after planting will the trees be the same height?
A 1 year **(C) 4 years**
B 2 years D 6 years

4. Which system of equations is represented by the graph?
F $\begin{cases} y = x + 2 \\ y = 0.5x + 2 \end{cases}$ H $\begin{cases} y = 2x + 4 \\ y = x + 4 \end{cases}$
(G) $\begin{cases} y = x + 2 \\ y = 0.5x + 4 \end{cases}$ J $\begin{cases} y = 4x - 2 \\ y = 2x + 2 \end{cases}$

5. How fast does the tree that started at 2 feet tall grow?
A 0.5 ft/yr C 1.5 ft/yr
(B) 1 ft/yr D 2 ft/yr

6. How fast does the tree that started at 4 feet tall grow?
(F) 0.5 ft/yr H 1.5 ft/yr
G 1 ft/yr J 2 ft/yr

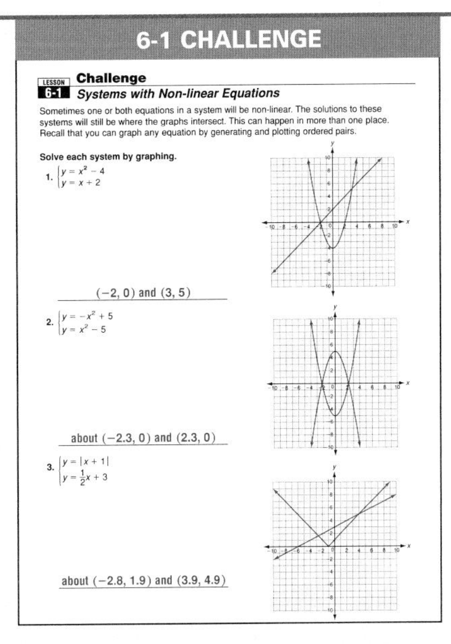

6-1 CHALLENGE

LESSON 6-1 Challenge
Systems with Non-linear Equations

Sometimes one or both equations in a system will be non-linear. The solutions to these systems will still be where the graphs intersect. This can happen in more than one place. Recall that you can graph any equation by generating and plotting ordered pairs.

Solve each system by graphing.

1. $\begin{cases} y = x^2 - 4 \\ y = x + 2 \end{cases}$ **(−2, 0) and (3, 5)**

2. $\begin{cases} y = -x^2 + 5 \\ y = x^2 - 5 \end{cases}$ **about (−2.3, 0) and (2.3, 0)**

3. $\begin{cases} y = \lvert x + 1 \rvert \\ y = \frac{1}{2}x + 3 \end{cases}$ **about (−2.8, 1.9) and (3.9, 4.9)**

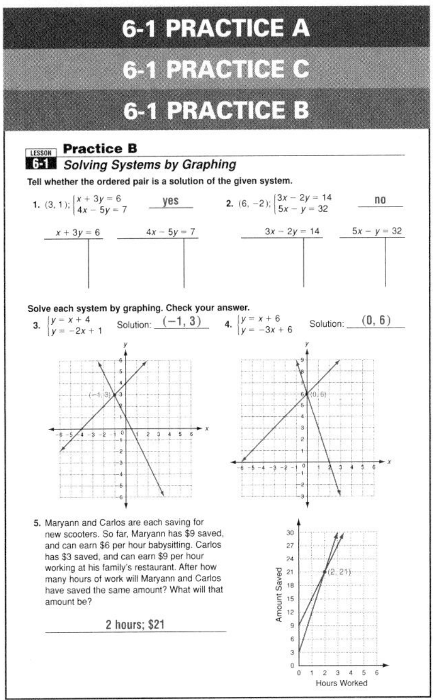

6-1 PRACTICE A

6-1 PRACTICE C

6-1 PRACTICE B

LESSON 6-1 Practice B
Solving Systems by Graphing

Tell whether the ordered pair is a solution of the given system.

1. (3, 1); $\begin{cases} x + 3y = 6 \\ 4x - 5y = 7 \end{cases}$ **yes**

2. (6, −2); $\begin{cases} 3x - 2y = 14 \\ 5x - y = 32 \end{cases}$ **no**

Solve each system by graphing. Check your answer.

3. $\begin{cases} y = x + 4 \\ y = -2x + 1 \end{cases}$ Solution: **(−1, 3)**

4. $\begin{cases} y = x + 6 \\ y = -3x + 6 \end{cases}$ Solution: **(0, 6)**

5. Maryann and Carlos are each saving for new scooters. So far, Maryann has \$9 saved, and can earn \$6 per hour babysitting. Carlos has \$3 saved, and can earn \$9 per hour working at his family's restaurant. After how many hours of work will Maryann and Carlos have saved the same amount? What will that amount be? **2 hours; \$21**

CHALLENGE AND EXTEND

31. **Entertainment** If the pattern in the table continues, in what month will the number of sales of VCRs and DVD players be the same? What will that number be? **month 11; 400**

Total Number Sold				
Month	1	2	3	4
VCRs	500	490	480	470
DVD Players	250	265	280	295

32. Long Distance Inc. charges a \$1.45 connection charge and \$0.03 per minute. Far Away Calls charges a \$1.52 connection charge and \$0.02 per minute.
    a. For how many minutes will a call cost the same from both companies? What is that cost? **7 min; \$1.66**
    b. When is it better to call using Long Distance Inc.? Far Away Calls? Explain.
    c. **What if...?** Long Distance Inc. raised its connection charge to \$1.50 and Far Away Calls decreased its connection charge by 2 cents. How will this affect the graphs? Now which company is better to use for calling long distance? Why?

32b. It is better to use Long Distance Inc. if the call is under 7 minutes because it costs less. If the call is over 7 minutes, it is better to use Far Away Calls because it costs less.

c. The graphs will intersect the y-axis at 1.5. Far Away Calls is cheaper because it costs less per minute.

SPIRAL STANDARDS REVIEW

2.0, 4.0

Solve each equation. Check your answer. *(Lesson 2-1)*

33. $18 = \frac{3}{7}x$ **42**
34. $-\frac{x}{5} = 12$ **−60**
35. $-6y = -13.2$ **2.2**
36. $\frac{2}{5} = \frac{y}{12}$ **$4\frac{4}{5}$**

Solve each equation. Check your answer. *(Lesson 2-3)*

37. $5x + 6x + 5 = 16$ **1**
38. $6(x + 2) = -2(x + 10)$ **−4**
39. $12 - 6z + 5z = 10$**2**

Solve each inequality and graph the solutions. Check your answer. *(Lesson 3-4)*

40. $4(2x + 1) > 28$
41. $3^3 + 9 \leq -4c$
42. $\frac{1}{8}x + \frac{3}{5} \leq \frac{3}{8}$

Career Path

go.hrw.com
Career Resources Online
KEYWORD: MA8CA Career

Ethan Reynolds
Applied Sciences major

Q: What math classes did you take in high school?
A: Career Math, Algebra, and Geometry

Q: What are you studying and what math classes have you taken?
A: I am really interested in aviation. I am taking Statistics and Trigonometry. Next year I will take Calculus.

Q: How is math used in aviation?
A: I use math to interpret aeronautical charts. I also perform calculations involving wind movements, aircraft weight and balance, and fuel consumption. These skills are necessary for planning and executing safe air flights.

Q: What are your future plans?
A: I could work as a commercial or corporate pilot or even as a flight instructor. I could also work toward a bachelor's degree in aviation management, air traffic control, aviation electronics, aviation maintenance, or aviation computer science.

Journal

Have students explain how to determine whether an ordered pair is the solution of a system of equations.

ALTERNATIVE ASSESSMENT

Have students choose a point on the coordinate grid, draw two lines through the point, and write the equations for those lines. Then have students show algebraically that the coordinates of the point of intersection are a solution of both equations they have written.

Power Presentations with PowerPoint®

6-1 Lesson Quiz

Tell whether the ordered pair is a solution of the given system.

1. $(-3, 1)$ $\begin{cases} y = -\frac{1}{3}x \\ 4y + 12 = 3x \end{cases}$ no
2. $(2, -4)$ $\begin{cases} y - 2x = -8 \\ 4y + 13x = 10 \end{cases}$ yes

Solve the system by graphing.

3. $\begin{cases} y + 2x = 9 \\ y = 4x - 3 \end{cases}$ (2, 5)
4. Joy has 5 collectible stamps and will buy 2 more each month. Ronald has 25 collectible stamps and will sell 3 each month. After how many months will they have the same number of stamps? 4 months How many will that be? 13 stamps

Also available on transparency

Answers

40. $x > 3$

−2 −1 0 1 2 3 4

41. $c \leq -9$

−10 −8 −6 −4 −2 0 2

42. $x \leq -1\frac{4}{5}$

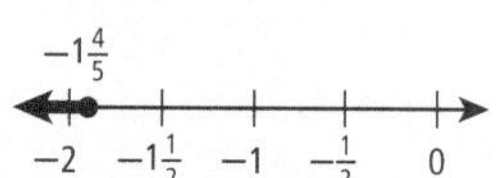

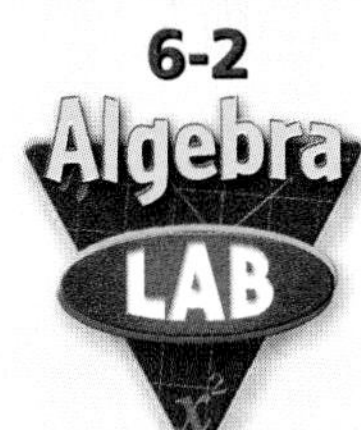

Model Systems of Linear Equations

You can use algebra tiles to model and solve some systems of linear equations.

Use with Lesson 6-2

KEY

 = 1

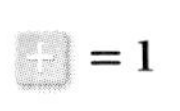 = −1

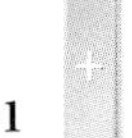 = x 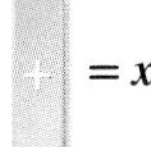 = $-x$

REMEMBER

When two expressions are equal, you can substitute one for the other in any expression or equation.

California Standards

9.0 Students solve a system of two linear equations in two variables algebraically and are able to interpret the answer graphically. Students are able to solve a system of two linear inequalities in two variables and to sketch the solution sets.

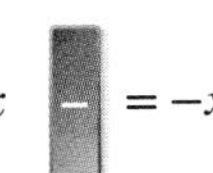

Activity

Use algebra tiles to model and solve $\begin{cases} y = 2x - 3 \\ x + y = 9 \end{cases}$.

MODEL		ALGEBRA
(x, y, 9)	*The first equation is solved for y. Model the second equation, $x + y = 9$, by substituting $2x - 3$ for y.*	$x + y = 9$ $x + (2x - 3) = 9$ $3x - 3 = 9$
	Add 3 yellow tiles on both sides of the mat. This represents adding 3 to both sides of the equation. *Remove zero pairs.*	$3x - 3 = 9$ $+3 \quad +3$ $3x = 12$
	Divide each group into 3 equal groups. Align one x-tile with each group on the right side. One x-tile is equivalent to 4 yellow tiles. $x = 4$	$\frac{3x}{3} = \frac{12}{3}$ $x = 4$

To solve for y, substitute 4 for x in one of the equations: $y = 2x - 3 = 2(4) - 3 = 5$

The solution is (4, 5).

Try This

Use algebra tiles to model and solve each system of equations.

1. $\begin{cases} y = x + 3 \\ 2x + y = 6 \end{cases}$ **2.** $\begin{cases} 2x + 3 = y \\ x + y = 6 \end{cases}$ **3.** $\begin{cases} 2x + 3y = 1 \\ x = -1 - y \end{cases}$ **4.** $\begin{cases} y = x + 1 \\ 2x - y = -5 \end{cases}$

Answers

1. (1, 4)
2. (1, 5)
3. (−4, 3)
4. (−4, −3)

Organizer

Use with Lesson 6-2

Objective: Use algebra tiles to model and solve systems of linear equations.

Materials: algebra tiles

Online Edition
Algebra Tiles

Teach

Discuss

You can represent either x or y with the variable tile. Make sure the variable tile represents the same variable throughout the same system. Algebra tiles can be found in the Manipulatives Kit (MK).

Close

Key Concept

You can solve a system of linear equations by modeling one variable in terms of the other, substituting that value into the other equation, and solving.

Assessment

Journal Have students explain how to use algebra tiles to solve one of the systems in the *Try This* problems.

California Standards

Algebra 1 9.0

6-2 Organizer

Objective: Solve systems of linear equations in two variables by substitution.

Online Edition
Tutorial Videos

Countdown to Mastery Week 12

Power Presentations with PowerPoint®

Warm Up

Solve each equation for *x*.

1. $y = x + 3$ $\quad x = y - 3$

2. $y = 3x - 4$ $\quad x = \dfrac{y + 4}{3}$

Simplify each expression.

3. $2(x - 5)$ $\quad 2x - 10$

4. $12 - 3(x + 1)$ $\quad 9 - 3x$

Evaluate each expression for the given value of *x*.

5. $\frac{2}{3}x + 8$ for $x = 6$ $\quad 12$

6. $3(x - 7)$ for $x = 10$ $\quad 9$

Also available on transparency

Math Humor

Q: Why did the chef throw the unsolved system of equations out of the restaurant?

A: The menu said, "No substitution."

California Standards

Algebra 1 🔑 **9.0**

6-2 Solving Systems by Substitution

California Standards

🔑 **9.0 Students solve a system of two linear equations in two variables algebraically** and are able to interpret the answer graphically. Students are able to solve a system of two linear inequalities in two variables and to sketch the solution sets.

Why learn this?

You can solve systems of equations to help select the best value among high-speed Internet providers. (See Example 3.)

CAMPING OUT FOR THE BEST TICKETS ISN'T WHAT IT USED TO BE...
MARK PARISI

Off the Mark by Mark Parisi. Cartoon copyrighted by Mark Parisi, printed with permission.

Sometimes it is difficult to identify the exact solution to a system by graphing. In this case, you can use a method called *substitution.*

Substitution is used to reduce the system to one equation that has only one variable. Then you can solve this equation by the methods taught in Chapter 2.

Know it! Note

Solving Systems of Equations by Substitution	
Step 1	Solve for one variable in at least one equation, if necessary.
Step 2	Substitute the resulting expression into the other equation.
Step 3	Solve that equation to get the value of the first variable.
Step 4	Substitute that value into one of the original equations and solve for the other variable.
Step 5	Write the values from Steps 3 and 4 as an ordered pair, (*x*, *y*), and check.

EXAMPLE 1 **Solving a System of Linear Equations by Substitution**

Solve each system by substitution.

A $\begin{cases} y = 2x \\ y = x + 5 \end{cases}$

Step 1 $y = 2x$ $\quad$ *Both equations are solved for y.*
$y = x + 5$

Step 2 $y = x + 5$ $\quad$ *Substitute 2x for y in the second equation.*
$2x = x + 5$

Step 3 $\underline{-x \quad -x}$ $\quad$ *Now solve this equation for x. Subtract x from both sides to combine like terms.*
$x = 5$

Step 4 $y = 2x$ $\quad$ *Write one of the original equations.*
$y = 2(5)$ $\quad$ *Substitute 5 for x.*
$y = 10$

Step 5 $(5, 10)$ $\quad$ *Write the solution as an ordered pair.*

Check Substitute $(5, 10)$ into both equations in the system.

$y = 2x$	
10	2(5)
10	10 ✓

$y = x + 5$	
10	5 + 5
10	10 ✓

Helpful Hint

You can substitute the value of one variable into *either* of the original equations to find the value of the other variable.

1 Introduce

EXPLORATION

6-2 Solving Systems by Substitution

You can sometimes use the equations in a system of equations to write a new equation.

1. Consider the two equations shown here. What new equation can you write? Explain. $\quad a = b$, $a = c$
2. Use the idea from Step 1 to write a new equation based on each of the following systems.
   a. $\begin{cases} y = 2x + 1 \\ y = 3x - 4 \end{cases}$
   b. $\begin{cases} x = 3y + 2 \\ x = 5y + 4 \end{cases}$
   c. $\begin{cases} m = -4t + 2 \\ m = t - 8 \end{cases}$
   d. $\begin{cases} 3y = 2x + 7 \\ 3y = -x + 4 \end{cases}$

THINK AND DISCUSS

3. Describe what you notice about all of the equations you wrote in Step 2. (*Hint:* How many variables are in each equation?)
4. Discuss whether it would be possible to use the above method to write a new equation based on this system: $\begin{cases} y = 2x + 6 \\ y + 1 = 4x \end{cases}$

Motivate

In sports, coaches often substitute one player with another who plays the same position. Ask students to suggest other situations in which substitutions are made. Tell them that in a system of equations, you also can make substitutions. You can replace a variable in an equation with an equivalent expression.

Explorations and answers are provided in *Alternate Openers: Explorations Transparencies.*

Solve each system by substitution.

B $\begin{cases} 2x + y = 5 \\ y = x - 4 \end{cases}$

Step 1 $y = x - 4$	*The second equation is solved for y.*
Step 2 $2x + y = 5$	*Write the first equation.*
$2x + (x - 4) = 5$	*Substitute x − 4 for y in the first equation.*
Step 3 $3x - 4 = 5$	*Simplify. Then solve for x.*
$+4 \quad +4$	*Add 4 to both sides.*
$3x = 9$	
$\frac{3x}{3} = \frac{9}{3}$	*Divide both sides by 3.*
$x = 3$	
Step 4 $y = x - 4$	*Write one of the original equations.*
$y = 3 - 4$	*Substitute 3 for x.*
$y = -1$	
Step 5 $(3, -1)$	*Write the solution as an ordered pair.*

C $\begin{cases} x + 4y = 6 \\ x + y = 3 \end{cases}$

Step 1 $x + 4y = 6$	*Solve the first equation for x by subtracting 4y from both sides.*
$-4y \quad -4y$	
$x = 6 - 4y$	
Step 2 $x + y = 3$	
$(6 - 4y) + y = 3$	*Substitute 6 − 4y for x in the second equation.*
Step 3 $6 - 3y = 3$	*Simplify. Then solve for y.*
$-6 \quad -6$	*Subtract 6 from both sides.*
$-3y = -3$	
$\frac{-3y}{-3} = \frac{-3}{-3}$	*Divide both sides by −3.*
$y = 1$	
Step 4 $x + y = 3$	*Write one of the original equations.*
$x + 1 = 3$	*Substitute 1 for y.*
$-1 \quad -1$	*Subtract 1 from both sides.*
$x = 2$	
Step 5 $(2, 1)$	*Write the solution as an ordered pair.*

Helpful Hint

Sometimes neither equation is solved for a variable. You can begin by solving either equation for either x or y.

CHECK IT OUT! Solve each system by substitution. Check your answer.

1a. $\begin{cases} y = x + 3 \\ y = 2x + 5 \end{cases}$ $(-2, 1)$

1b. $\begin{cases} x = 2y - 4 \\ x + 8y = 16 \end{cases}$ $(0, 2)$

1c. $\begin{cases} 2x + y = -4 \\ x + y = -7 \end{cases}$ $(3, -10)$

Sometimes you substitute an expression for a variable that has a coefficient. When solving for the second variable in this situation, you can use the Distributive Property.

COMMON ERROR ALERT

Students often think they have solved a system after finding the value of only one variable. Remind them that the solution is an ordered pair.

Power Presentations with PowerPoint®

Additional Examples

Example 1

Solve each system by substitution. Check your answer.

A. $\begin{cases} y = 3x \\ y = x - 2 \end{cases}$ $(-1, -3)$

B. $\begin{cases} y = x + 1 \\ 4x + y = 6 \end{cases}$ $(1, 2)$

C. $\begin{cases} x + 2y = -1 \\ x - y = 5 \end{cases}$ $(3, -2)$

Also available on transparency

INTERVENTION

Questioning Strategies

EXAMPLE 1

- How is substituting an expression for a variable similar to substituting a number for a variable? How is it different?
- In **Example 1C,** how do you know which variable to isolate?

Teaching Tip **Inclusion** Point out that in **Example 1A** both equations are written in slope-intercept form, so isolating a variable is unnecessary. In **Example 1B,** one equation is in slope-intercept form. The expression containing x from that equation can be substituted into the other equation. In **Example 1C,** neither equation is written in slope-intercept form. First, a variable must be isolated in one or both equations.

2 Teach

Guided Instruction

Review how to apply the Distributive Property and combine like terms to simplify an expression before **Example 2.** Have students practice solving by substitution when at least one equation is in slope-intercept form before having them solve systems where they first need to rewrite an equation. Remind students to check their solutions by substituting the values back into both equations or by graphing both lines and locating their intersection.

Universal Access

Through Cooperative Learning

Have students work in pairs, and give them the system $\begin{cases} 2x - 4y = 10 \\ y + 5x = 3 \end{cases}$. Have one student solve the first equation for y and the other solve the second equation for y. Then have both continue independently to solve by using substitution. Each should arrive at the solution $(1, -2)$. Have them compare their work and discuss which substitution is more efficient.

Power Presentations with PowerPoint®

Additional Examples

Example 2

Solve $\begin{cases} y + 6x = 11 \\ 3x + 2y = -5 \end{cases}$ by substitution. $(3, -7)$

Also available on transparency

INTERVENTION

Questioning Strategies

EXAMPLE 2

- When do you need to use the Distributive Property?
- Why is it important to put the expression you are substituting for a variable in parentheses?

Teaching Tip **Multiple Representations** Allowing students to check their solutions by graphing on a calculator and finding points of intersection will provide a quick check as well as emphasize that there are multiple representations of a system of linear equations.

EXAMPLE 2 **Using the Distributive Property**

Solve $\begin{cases} 4y - 5x = 9 \\ x - 4y = 11 \end{cases}$ by substitution.

Step 1 $x - 4y = 11$ — *Solve the second equation for x by adding 4y to each side.*

$\underline{\quad +4y \quad +4y}$

$x = 4y + 11$

Step 2 $4y - 5x = 9$

$4y - 5(4y + 11) = 9$ — *Substitute 4y + 11 for x in the first equation.*

Step 3 $4y - 5(4y) - 5(11) = 9$ — *Distribute −5 to the expression in the parentheses. Simplify. Solve for y.*

$4y - 20y - 55 = 9$

$-16y - 55 = 9$

$\underline{\quad +55 \quad +55}$ — *Add 55 to both sides.*

$-16y = 64$

$\frac{-16y}{-16} = \frac{64}{-16}$ — *Divide both sides by −16.*

$y = -4$

Step 4 $x - 4y = 11$ — *Write one of the original equations.*

$x - 4(-4) = 11$ — *Substitute −4 for y.*

$x + 16 = 11$ — *Simplify.*

$\underline{\quad -16 \quad -16}$ — *Subtract 16 from both sides.*

$x = -5$

Step 5 $(-5, -4)$ — *Write the solution as an ordered pair.*

Caution!

When you solve one equation for a variable, you must substitute the value or expression into the *other* original equation, not the one that has just been solved.

CHECK IT OUT! 2. Solve $\begin{cases} -2x + y = 8 \\ 3x + 2y = 9 \end{cases}$ by substitution. Check your answer. $(-1, 6)$

Student to Student

Solving Systems by Substitution

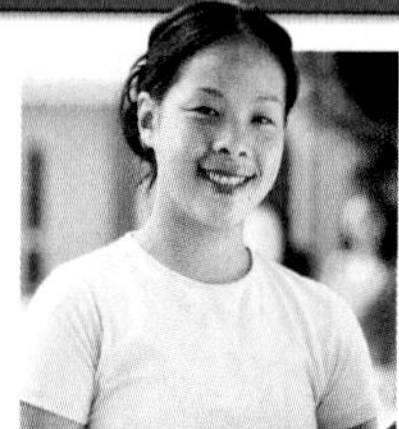

Erika Chu
Terrell High School

I always look for a variable with a coefficient of 1 or −1 when deciding which equation to solve for x or y.

For the system

$\begin{cases} 2x + y = 14 \\ -3x + 4y = -10 \end{cases}$

I would solve the first equation for y because it has a coefficient of 1.

$2x + y = 14$

$y = -2x + 14$

Then I use substitution to find the values of x and y.

$-3x + 4y = -10$

$-3x + 4(-2x + 14) = -10$

$-3x + (-8x) + 56 = -10$

$-11x + 56 = -10$

$-11x = -66$

$x = 6$

$y = -2x + 14$

$y = -2(6) + 14 = 2$

The solution is (6, 2).

EXAMPLE 3 ***Consumer Economics Application***

One high-speed Internet provider has a \$50 setup fee and costs \$30 per month. Another provider has no setup fee and costs \$40 per month.

a. In how many months will both providers cost the same? What will that cost be?

Write an equation for each option. Let t represent the total amount paid and m represent the number of months.

	Total paid	is	setup fee	plus	cost per month	times	months.
Option 1	t	$=$	50	$+$	30	$\cdot$	m
Option 2	t	$=$	0	$+$	40	$\cdot$	m

Step 1 $t = 50 + 30m$ *Both equations are solved for t.*
$t = 40m$

Step 2 $50 + 30m = 40m$ *Substitute 50 + 30m for t in the second equation.*

Step 3 $\underline{-30m \quad -30m}$ *Solve for m. Subtract 30m from both sides to combine like terms.*
$50 = 10m$

$\frac{50}{10} = \frac{10m}{10}$ *Divide both sides by 10.*
$5 = m$

Step 4 $t = 40m$ *Write one of the original equations.*
$= 40(5)$ *Substitute 5 for m.*
$= 200$

Step 5 $(5, 200)$ *Write the solution as an ordered pair.*

In 5 months, the total cost for each option will be the same—\$200.

b. If you plan to cancel in 1 year, which is the cheaper provider? Explain.

Option 1: $t = 50 + 30(12) = 410$ Option 2: $t = 40(12) = 480$

Option 1 is cheaper.

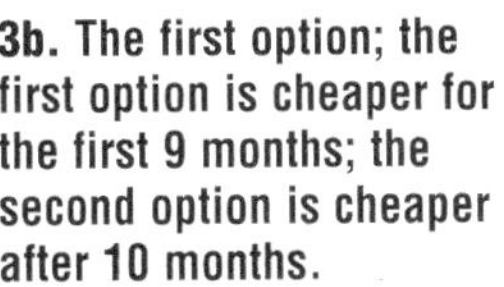

3a. 10 months; \$860

3b. The first option; the first option is cheaper for the first 9 months; the second option is cheaper after 10 months.

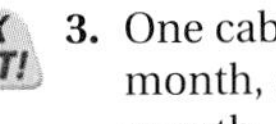

3. One cable television provider has a \$60 setup fee and \$80 per month, and the second has a \$160 equipment fee and \$70 per month.
   a. In how many months will the cost be the same? What will that cost be?
   b. If you plan to move in 6 months, which is the cheaper option? Explain.

THINK AND DISCUSS

1. If you graphed the equations in Example 1A, where would the lines intersect?

2. **GET ORGANIZED** Copy and complete the graphic organizer. In each box, solve the system by substitution using the first step given. Show that each method gives the same solution.

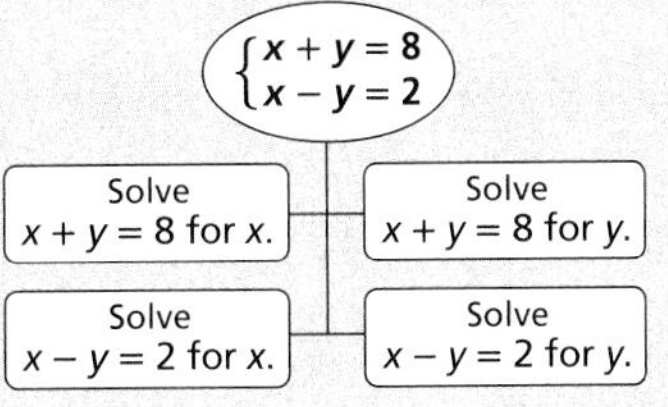
$\begin{cases} x + y = 8 \\ x - y = 2 \end{cases}$
Solve $x + y = 8$ for x.
Solve $x + y = 8$ for y.
Solve $x - y = 2$ for x.
Solve $x - y = 2$ for y.

COMMON ERROR ALERT

Students may "lose" a negative sign when they substitute an expression for a variable. Encourage students to write clearly, even when solving problems on scratch paper. A poorly written minus sign can easily be mistaken for a stray pencil mark.

Power Presentations with PowerPoint®

Additional Examples

Example 3

Jenna is deciding between two cell-phone plans. The first plan has a \$50 sign-up fee and costs \$20 per month. The second plan has a \$30 sign-up fee and costs \$25 per month. After how many months will the total costs be the same? What will the cost be? If Jenna has to sign a one-year contract, which plan will be cheaper? Explain. 4 months; \$130; Jenna should choose the first plan because it costs \$290 for 1 year, and the second plan costs \$330.

Also available on transparency

INTERVENTION

Questioning Strategies

EXAMPLE 3

- What does the graph tell you about each option/plan?
- Why can you set the expressions for each option/plan equal to each other?

Visual In **Example 3,** students may benefit from using a table to organize the information.

	Setup Fee	Monthly Rate
Provider 1	\$50	\$30
Provider 2	\$0	\$40

Answers to *Think and Discuss*

1. at the point (5, 10)
2. See p. A5.

3 Close

Summarize

Have students supply the steps they would need to take to solve the system $\begin{cases} 4x - y = 8 \\ 2x + 3y = 4 \end{cases}$ by substitution. Then have them solve it. Possible answer: Solve the first equation for y, then substitute that expression for y in the second equation. Solve for x. Substitute the value for x into the first equation and solve for y. The solution is (2, 0).

FORMATIVE ASSESSMENT and INTERVENTION

Diagnose Before **the Lesson**
6-2 Warm Up, TE p. 336

Monitor During **the Lesson**
Check It Out! Exercises, SE pp. 337–339
Questioning Strategies, TE pp. 337–339

Assess After **the Lesson**
6-2 Lesson Quiz, TE p. 342
Alternative Assessment, TE p. 342

6-2 Exercises

Assignment Guide

Assign *Guided Practice* exercises as necessary.

If you finished Examples **1–3**
Proficient 8–17, 18–30 even, 33–39, 43–51
Advanced 8–30 even, 31–51

Homework Quick Check
Quickly check key concepts.
Exercises: 10, 12, 16, 20, 26, 30

6-2 Exercises

California Standards Practice
6.0, 9.0

go.hrw.com
Homework Help Online
KEYWORD: MA8CA 6-2
Parent Resources Online
KEYWORD: MA8CA Parent

GUIDED PRACTICE

Solve each system by substitution. Check your answer.

SEE EXAMPLE 1 p. 336

1. $\begin{cases} y = 5x - 10 \\ y = 3x + 8 \end{cases}$ **(9, 35)** **2.** $\begin{cases} 3x + y = 2 \\ 4x + y = 20 \end{cases}$ **(18, −52)** **3.** $\begin{cases} y = x + 5 \\ 4x + y = 20 \end{cases}$ **(3, 8)**

SEE EXAMPLE 2 p. 338

4. $\begin{cases} x - 2y = 10 \\ \frac{1}{2}x - 2y = 4 \end{cases}$ **(12, 1)** **5.** $\begin{cases} y - 2x = 3 \\ 2x - 3y = 21 \end{cases}$ $\left(-\frac{15}{2}, -12\right)$ **6.** $\begin{cases} x = y - 8 \\ -x - y = 0 \end{cases}$ **(−4, 4)**

SEE EXAMPLE 3 p. 339

7. Consumer Economics The Strauss family is deciding between two lawn-care services. Green Lawn charges a \$49 startup fee, plus \$29 per month. Grass Team charges a \$25 startup fee, plus \$37 per month. **3 months; \$136**

a. In how many months will both lawn-care services cost the same? What will that cost be?

b. If the family will use the service for only 6 months, which is the better option? Explain. **Green Lawn; for 6 months, Green Lawn's service costs only \$223, while Grass Team's costs \$247.**

PRACTICE AND PROBLEM SOLVING

Independent Practice	
For Exercises	See Example
8–10	1
11–16	2
17	3

Extra Practice
Skills Practice p. EP12
Application Practice p. EP29

Solve each system by substitution. Check your answer.

8. $\begin{cases} y = x + 3 \\ y = 2x + 4 \end{cases}$ **(−1, 2)** **9.** $\begin{cases} y = 2x + 10 \\ y = -2x - 6 \end{cases}$ **(−4, 2)** **10.** $\begin{cases} x + 2y = 8 \\ x + 3y = 12 \end{cases}$ **(0, 4)**

11. $\begin{cases} 2x + 2y = 2 \\ -4x + 4y = 12 \end{cases}$ **(−1, 2)** **12.** $\begin{cases} y = 0.5x + 2 \\ -y = -2x + 4 \end{cases}$ **(4, 4)** **13.** $\begin{cases} -x + y = 4 \\ 3x - 2y = -7 \end{cases}$ **(1, 5)**

14. $\begin{cases} 3x + y = -8 \\ -2x - y = 6 \end{cases}$ **(−2 −2)** **15.** $\begin{cases} x + 2y = -1 \\ 4x - 4y = 20 \end{cases}$ **(3, −2)** **16.** $\begin{cases} 4x = y - 1 \\ 6x - 2y = -3 \end{cases}$ $\left(\frac{1}{2}, 3\right)$

17. Recreation Casey wants to buy a gym membership. One gym has a \$150 joining fee and costs \$35 per month. Another gym has no joining fee and costs \$60 per month.

a. In how many months will both gym memberships cost the same? What will that cost be? **6 months; \$360**

b. If Casey plans to cancel in 5 months, which is the better option for him? Explain. **the second option; for 5 months, it costs only \$300, while the other option costs \$325.**

Solve each system by substitution. Check your answer.

18. $\begin{cases} x = 5 \\ x + y = 8 \end{cases}$ **(5, 3)** **19.** $\begin{cases} y = -3x + 4 \\ x = 2y + 6 \end{cases}$ **(2, −2)** **20.** $\begin{cases} 3x - y = 11 \\ 5y - 7x = 1 \end{cases}$ **(7, 10)**

21. $\begin{cases} \frac{1}{2}x + \frac{1}{3}y = 6 \\ x - y = 2 \end{cases}$ **(8, 6)** **22.** $\begin{cases} x = 7 - 2y \\ 2x + y = 5 \end{cases}$ **(1, 3)** **23.** $\begin{cases} y = 1.2x - 4 \\ 2.2x + 5 = y \end{cases}$ **(−9, −14.8)**

24. Justin and Lacee are taking a walk. Justin walks at a rate of 6 ft/s, while Lacee walks at 4 ft/s. Lacee starts 10 ft ahead of Justin.

a. After how many seconds will Lacee and Justin be next to each other? What distance will they have walked? **5 s; Justin walked 30 ft, Lacee walked 20 ft**

b. How many seconds will it take for Justin to catch up to Lacee if she starts 32 ft ahead of Justin? **16 s**

6-2 READING STRATEGIES

LESSON 6-2 Reading Strategies
Use a Sequence Chain

Use the sequence chain below to guide you in solving systems of linear equations by the method of substitution.

Sequence Chain: *Solving Systems by Substitution*

Step 1: Isolate one variable in one equation. → **Step 2:** Substitute the expression for that variable into the other equation. → **Step 3:** Solve for the variable remaining in that equation. → **Step 4:** Substitute the value for that variable into either original equation and solve for the other variable. → **Step 5:** Write the found values for x and y as an ordered pair (x, y). → **Step 6:** Check your answer by substituting (x, y) into both equations.

Answer each question.

1. Perform Step 1 for $\begin{cases} x + y = 5 \\ -3x + 5 = \frac{1}{2}y \end{cases}$ by solving the first equation for y.
   $y = 5 - x$ or $y = -x + 5$
2. To solve the system $\begin{cases} y = x + 2 \\ 2x + y = 6 \end{cases}$ by substitution, you can start at Step 2. Explain why.
   The first equation is already solved for y.
3. Why does Step 6 specify substituting into *both* equations?
   The solution of a system must satisfy both equations.

Solve each system of equations by substitution.

4. $\begin{cases} 2x = 3y \\ y = x - 2 \end{cases}$ **(6, 4)**
5. $\begin{cases} x + y = 2 \\ -x = 2y - 7 \end{cases}$ **(−3, 5)**

6-2 REVIEW FOR MASTERY

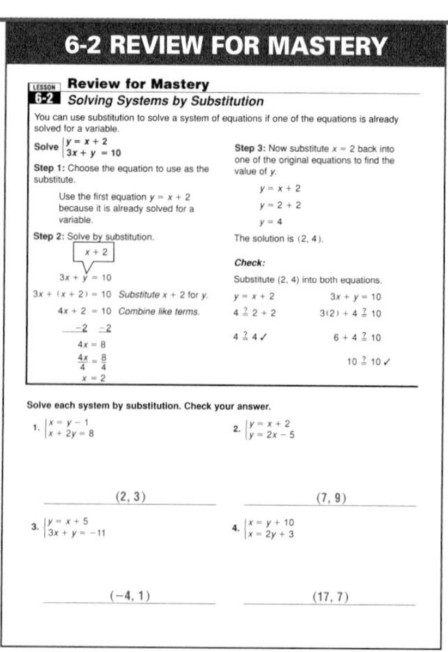

LESSON 6-2 Review for Mastery
Solving Systems by Substitution

You can use substitution to solve a system of equations if one of the equations is already solved for a variable.

Solve $\begin{cases} y = x + 2 \\ 3x + y = 10 \end{cases}$

Step 1: Choose the equation to use as the substitute.

Use the first equation $y = x + 2$ because it is already solved for a variable.

Step 2: Solve by substitution.

$3x + y = 10$ (with $x + 2$ substituted for y)
$3x + (x + 2) = 10$ *Substitute $x + 2$ for y.*
$4x + 2 = 10$ *Combine like terms.*
$\underline{-2 \quad -2}$
$4x = 8$
$\frac{4x}{4} = \frac{8}{4}$
$x = 2$

Step 3: Now substitute $x = 2$ back into one of the original equations to find the value of y.

$y = x + 2$
$y = 2 + 2$
$y = 4$

The solution is $(2, 4)$.

Check:
Substitute $(2, 4)$ into both equations.

$y = x + 2$	$3x + y = 10$
$4 \stackrel{?}{=} 2 + 2$	$3(2) + 4 \stackrel{?}{=} 10$
$4 \stackrel{?}{=} 4$ ✓	$6 + 4 \stackrel{?}{=} 10$
	$10 \stackrel{?}{=} 10$ ✓

Solve each system by substitution. Check your answer.

1. $\begin{cases} x = y - 1 \\ x + 2y = 8 \end{cases}$ **(2, 3)**
2. $\begin{cases} y = x + 2 \\ y = 2x - 5 \end{cases}$ **(7, 9)**
3. $\begin{cases} y = x + 5 \\ 3x + y = -11 \end{cases}$ **(−4, 1)**
4. $\begin{cases} x = y + 10 \\ x = 2y + 3 \end{cases}$ **(17, 7)**

California Standards

Standard	Exercises
6.0	35c, 46–48
7.0	43–45
9.0	1–7a, 8–17a, 18–32, 35b, 39–42, 49–51

25. Ian and Jessica each save their quarters. Ian starts out with 34 quarters and saves 8 quarters a month. Jessica starts out with 2 quarters and saves 16 quarters a month. In how many months will Jessica have the same number of quarters as Ian? How many quarters will each of them have? **4; 66**

26. **Multi-Step** Use the receipts below to write and solve a system of equations to find the cost of a large popcorn and the cost of a small drink. $\begin{cases} 3p + 2d = 21 \\ 2p + 4d = 22 \end{cases}$; **popcorn: \$5; drink: \$3**

CINEMA SNAKSHAK
Customer #3598
3 large popcorn buckets
2 small drinks
Total due: $21.00
CUSTOMER COPY
CINEMA SNAKSHAK
Customer #3599
2 large popcorn buckets
4 small drinks
Total due: $22.00
CUSTOMER COPY
POP CORN
DRINK

27. $\begin{cases} x + y = 1000 \\ 0.05x + 0.06y = 58 \end{cases}$; **\$200 at 5%; \$800 at 6%**

27. **Finance** Helene invested a total of \$1000 in two simple-interest bank accounts. One account paid 5% annual interest; the other paid 6% annual interest. The total amount of interest she earned after one year was \$58. Write and solve a system of equations to find the amount invested in each account. (*Hint:* Change the interest rates into decimals first.)

Geometry **Two angles whose measures have a sum of 90° are called complementary angles. For Exercises 28–31, *x* and *y* represent complementary angles. Find the measure of each angle.**

28. $\begin{cases} x + y = 90 \\ y = 4x - 10 \end{cases}$ $m\angle x = 20°$; $m\angle y = 70°$

29. $\begin{cases} x = 2y \\ x + y = 90 \end{cases}$ $m\angle x = 60°$; $m\angle y = 30°$

30. $\begin{cases} y = 2(x - 15) \\ x + y = 90 \end{cases}$ $m\angle x = 40°$; $m\angle y = 50°$

31. $\begin{cases} x + y = 90 \\ y = 2x + 3 \end{cases}$ $m\angle x = 29°$; $m\angle y = 61°$

32. Tricia and Michael share a cell phone plan. Together, they made a total of 52 calls last month for a total of 620 min. Tricia averaged 15 min for each of her calls, while Michael averaged 10 min.
    a. How many calls did Tricia make last month? Michael? **20; 32**
    b. How many calls did Tricia make if the total number of calls was 60? **4**

33. **Write About It** Explain how to solve a system of equations by substitution.

34. **Critical Thinking** Explain the connection between the solution of a system solved by graphing and the solution to the same system solved by substitution.

35. This problem will prepare you for the Concept Connection on page 362.
    At the school store, Juanita bought 2 books and a backpack for a total of \$26 before tax. Each book cost \$8 less than the backpack.
    a. Write a system of equations that can be used to find the price of each book and the price of the backpack.
    b. Solve this system by substitution.
    c. Solve this system by graphing. Discuss advantages and disadvantages of solving by substitution and solving by graphing.

Exercise 35 involves solving a system of equations by at least two different methods to find prices. This exercise prepares students for the Concept Connection on page 362.

Answers

33. Possible answer: Solve one of the equations for either *x* or *y*. Then substitute the expression equal to *x* or *y* into the other equation. This creates a one-variable equation that can be solved. When you get the value of one variable, substitute it into one of the original equations and solve to find the value of the other variable.

34. The solution of a system solved by graphing is the same as the solution of a system solved by substitution.

35a. $\begin{cases} 2x + y = 26 \\ x = y - 8 \end{cases}$

b. book: \$6; backpack: \$14

c. Check students' graph. Possible answer: Substitution works well since *x* is already isolated. Graphing requires solving both equations for *y*.

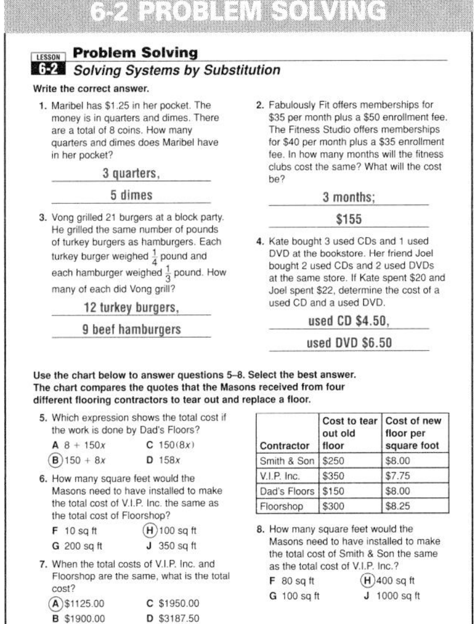

6-2 PROBLEM SOLVING

LESSON 6-2 **Problem Solving**
Solving Systems by Substitution

Write the correct answer.

1. Maribel has \$1.25 in her pocket. The money is in quarters and dimes. There are a total of 8 coins. How many quarters and dimes does Maribel have in her pocket?
   3 quarters,
   5 dimes

2. Fabulously Fit offers memberships for \$35 per month plus a \$50 enrollment fee. The Fitness Studio offers memberships for \$40 per month plus a \$35 enrollment fee. In how many months will the fitness clubs cost the same? What will the cost be?
   3 months;
   \$155

3. Vong grilled 21 burgers at a block party. He grilled the same number of pounds of turkey burgers as hamburgers. Each turkey burger weighed $\frac{1}{4}$ pound and each hamburger weighed $\frac{1}{3}$ pound. How many of each did Vong grill?
   12 turkey burgers,
   9 beef hamburgers

4. Kate bought 3 used CDs and 1 used DVD at the bookstore. Her friend Joel bought 2 used CDs and 2 used DVDs at the same store. If Kate spent \$20 and Joel spent \$22, determine the cost of a used CD and a used DVD.
   used CD \$4.50,
   used DVD \$6.50

Use the chart below to answer questions 5–8. Select the best answer. The chart compares the quotes that the Masons received from four different flooring contractors to tear out and replace a floor.

Contractor	Cost to tear out old floor	Cost of new floor per square foot
Smith & Son	\$250	\$8.00
V.I.P. Inc.	\$350	\$7.75
Dad's Floors	\$150	\$8.00
Floorshop	\$300	\$8.25

5. Which expression shows the total cost if the work is done by Dad's Floors?
   A $8 + 150x$ C $150(8x)$
   (B) $150 + 8x$ D $158x$

6. How many square feet would the Masons need to have installed to make the total cost of V.I.P. Inc. the same as the total cost of Floorshop?
   F 10 sq ft (H) 100 sq ft
   G 200 sq ft J 350 sq ft

7. When the total costs of V.I.P. Inc. and Floorshop are the same, what is the total cost?
   (A) \$1125.00 C \$1950.00
   B \$1900.00 D \$3187.50

8. How many square feet would the Masons need to have installed to make the total cost of Smith & Son the same as the total cost of V.I.P. Inc.?
   F 80 sq ft (H) 400 sq ft
   G 100 sq ft J 1000 sq ft

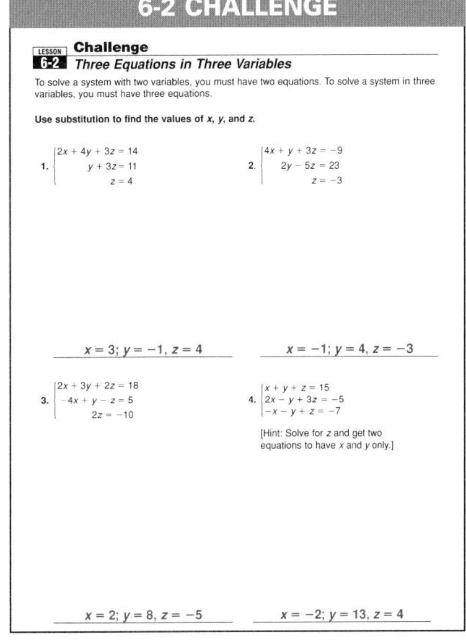

6-2 CHALLENGE

LESSON 6-2 **Challenge**
Three Equations in Three Variables

To solve a system with two variables, you must have two equations. To solve a system in three variables, you must have three equations.

Use substitution to find the values of *x*, *y*, and *z*.

1. $\begin{cases} 2x + 4y + 3z = 14 \\ y + 3z = 11 \\ z = 4 \end{cases}$
   $x = 3; y = -1, z = 4$

2. $\begin{cases} 4x + y + 3z = -9 \\ 2y - 5z = 23 \\ z = -3 \end{cases}$
   $x = -1; y = 4, z = -3$

3. $\begin{cases} 2x + 3y + 2z = 18 \\ -4x + y - z = 5 \\ 2z = -10 \end{cases}$
   $x = 2; y = 8, z = -5$

4. $\begin{cases} x + y + z = 15 \\ 2x - y + 3z = -5 \\ -x - y + z = -7 \end{cases}$
   [Hint: Solve for *z* and get two equations to have *x* and *y* only.]
   $x = -2; y = 13, z = 4$

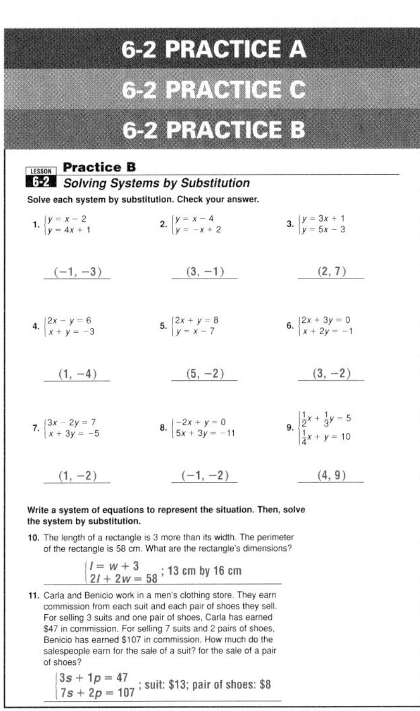

6-2 PRACTICE A
6-2 PRACTICE C
6-2 PRACTICE B

LESSON 6-2 **Practice B**
Solving Systems by Substitution

Solve each system by substitution. Check your answer.

1. $\begin{cases} y = x - 2 \\ y = 4x + 1 \end{cases}$ $(-1, -3)$
2. $\begin{cases} y = x - 4 \\ y = -x + 2 \end{cases}$ $(3, -1)$
3. $\begin{cases} y = 3x + 1 \\ y = 5x - 3 \end{cases}$ $(2, 7)$
4. $\begin{cases} 2x - y = 6 \\ x + y = -3 \end{cases}$ $(1, -4)$
5. $\begin{cases} 2x + y = 8 \\ y = x - 7 \end{cases}$ $(5, -2)$
6. $\begin{cases} 2x + 3y = 0 \\ x + 2y = -1 \end{cases}$ $(3, -2)$
7. $\begin{cases} 3x - 2y = 7 \\ x + 3y = -5 \end{cases}$ $(1, -2)$
8. $\begin{cases} -2x + y = 0 \\ 5x + 3y = -11 \end{cases}$ $(-1, -2)$
9. $\begin{cases} \frac{1}{2}x + \frac{1}{3}y = 5 \\ \frac{1}{4}x + y = 10 \end{cases}$ $(4, 9)$

Write a system of equations to represent the situation. Then, solve the system by substitution.

10. The length of a rectangle is 3 more than its width. The perimeter of the rectangle is 58 cm. What are the rectangle's dimensions?
    $\begin{cases} l = w + 3 \\ 2l + 2w = 58 \end{cases}$; **13 cm by 16 cm**

11. Carla and Benicio work in a men's clothing store. They earn commission from each suit and each pair of shoes they sell. For selling 3 suits and one pair of shoes, Carla has earned \$47 in commission. For selling 7 suits and 2 pairs of shoes, Benicio has earned \$107 in commission. How much do the salespeople earn for the sale of a suit? for the sale of a pair of shoes?
    $\begin{cases} 3s + 1p = 47 \\ 7s + 2p = 107 \end{cases}$; **suit: \$13; pair of shoes: \$8**

Multiple Choice In **Exercise 37,** students who chose **A** may have confused the variables in the second equation. Remind students that the verb *is* or *was* often represents the equal sign in an equation. The second sentence in the exercise indicates that m will equal some expression that contains f, not vice versa.

Journal

Have students write about a price comparison they could make in their own lives and how they could compare the prices with a system of equations.

ALTERNATIVE ASSESSMENT

Have students write and solve a system of linear equations that requires using the Distributive Property in the solution. Then have students write a real-world application problem that can be represented by a system of linear equations in two variables.

Power Presentations with PowerPoint®

6-2 Lesson Quiz

Solve each system by substitution.

1. $\begin{cases} y = 2x \\ y = \frac{1}{2}x - 3 \end{cases}$ $(-2, -4)$

2. $\begin{cases} x = 6y - 11 \\ 3x - 2y = -1 \end{cases}$ $(1, 2)$

3. $\begin{cases} -3x + y = -1 \\ x - y = 4 \end{cases}$ $\left(-\frac{3}{2}, -\frac{11}{2}\right)$

4. Plumber A charges \$60 an hour. Plumber B charges \$40 to visit your home plus \$55 for each hour. For how many hours will the total cost for each plumber be the same? How much will that cost be? If a customer thinks they will need a plumber for 5 hours, which plumber should the customer hire? Explain.
8 hours; \$480; plumber A; plumber A is cheaper for less than 8 hours.

Also available on transparency

36. Estimation Use the graph to estimate the solution to $\begin{cases} 2x - y = 6 \\ x + y = -0.6 \end{cases}$.
Round your answer to the nearest tenth.
Then solve the system by substitution.
Possible estimate: (1.75, −2.5); (1.8, −2.4)

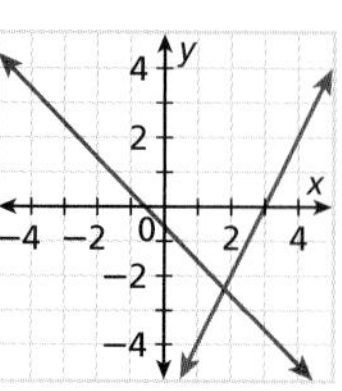

Multiple Choice For Exercises 37 and 38, choose the best answer.

37. Elizabeth met 24 of her cousins at a family reunion. The number of male cousins m was 6 less than twice the number of female cousins f. Which system can be used to find the number of male cousins and female cousins?

Ⓐ $\begin{cases} m + f = 24 \\ f = 2m - 6 \end{cases}$ Ⓑ $\begin{cases} m + f = 24 \\ f = 2m \end{cases}$ Ⓒ $\begin{cases} m = 24 + f \\ m = f - 6 \end{cases}$ **Ⓓ** $\begin{cases} f = 24 - m \\ m = 2f - 6 \end{cases}$

38. Which problem is best represented by the system $\begin{cases} d = n + 5 \\ d + n = 12 \end{cases}$?

Ⓐ Roger has 12 coins in dimes and nickels. There are 5 more dimes than nickels.
Ⓑ Roger has 5 coins in dimes and nickels. There are 12 more dimes than nickels.
Ⓒ Roger has 12 coins in dimes and nickels. There are 5 more nickels than dimes.
Ⓓ Roger has 5 coins in dimes and nickels. There are 12 more nickels than dimes.

CHALLENGE AND EXTEND

39. A car dealership has 378 cars on its lot. The ratio of new cars to used cars is 5:4. Write and solve a system of equations to find the number of new and used cars on the lot.
$\begin{cases} n + u = 378 \\ 4n = 5u \end{cases}$; 210 new cars; 168 used cars

Solve each system by substitution. Check your answer.

40. $\begin{cases} 2r - 3s - t = 12 \\ s + 3t = 10 \\ t = 4 \end{cases}$ $r = 5;\ s = -2;\ t = 4$

41. $\begin{cases} x + y + z = 7 \\ y + z = 5 \\ 2y - 4z = -14 \end{cases}$ $x = 2;\ y = 1;\ z = 4$

42. $\begin{cases} a + 2b + c = 19 \\ -b + c = -5 \\ 3b + 2c = 15 \end{cases}$ $a = 9;\ b = 5;\ c = 0$

SPIRAL STANDARDS REVIEW — 6.0, 7.0, 9.0

Without graphing, tell whether each point is on the graph of $y = 3x - 6x - 9$. (Lesson 5-1)

43. $(0, -9)$ yes **44.** $(3, 0)$ no **45.** $\left(-\frac{1}{3}, -8\right)$ yes

Find the x- and y-intercepts. (Lesson 5-2)

46. $6x - 2y = 12$ x-int: 2; y-int: −6
47. $-3y + x = 15$ x-int: 15; y-int: −5
48. $4y - 40 = -5x$ x-int: 8; y-int: 10

Tell whether each ordered pair is a solution of the given system. (Lesson 6-1)

49. $(3, 0)$; $\begin{cases} 2x - y = -6 \\ x + y = 3 \end{cases}$ no

50. $(-1, 4)$; $\begin{cases} y - 2x = 6 \\ x + 4y = 15 \end{cases}$ yes

51. $(5, 6)$; $\begin{cases} \frac{1}{3}y + x = 7 \\ 2x = 12 \end{cases}$ no

6-3 Solving Systems by Elimination

California Standards

9.0 Students solve a system of two linear equations in two variables algebraically and are able to interpret the answer graphically. Students are able to solve a system of two linear inequalities in two variables and to sketch the solution sets.

Why learn this?

You can solve a system of linear equations to determine how many flowers of each type you can buy to make a bouquet. (See Example 4.)

Another method for solving systems of equations is *elimination*. Like substitution, the goal of elimination is to get one equation that has only one variable.

Remember that an equation stays balanced if you add equal amounts to both sides. Consider the system $\begin{cases} x - 2y = -19 \\ 5x + 2y = 1 \end{cases}$. Since $5x + 2y = 1$, you can add $5x + 2y$ to one side of the first equation and 1 to the other side and the balance is maintained.

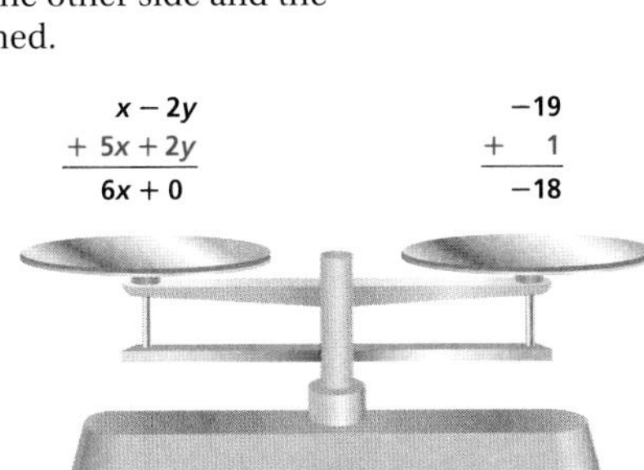

Since $-2y$ and $2y$ have **opposite coefficients**, you can eliminate the y-term by adding the two equations. The result is one equation that has only one variable: $6x = -18$.

Solving Systems of Equations by Elimination	
Step 1	Write the system so that like terms are aligned.
Step 2	Eliminate one of the variables.
Step 3	Solve for the variable not eliminated in Step 2.
Step 4	Substitute the value of the variable into one of the original equations and solve for the other variable.
Step 5	Write the answers from Steps 3 and 4 as an ordered pair, (x, y), and check your answer.

Later in this lesson you will learn how to multiply one or more equations by a number in order to produce opposites that can be eliminated.

6-3 Organizer

Objectives: Solve systems of linear equations in two variables by elimination.

Compare and choose an appropriate method for solving systems of linear equations.

Algebra Lab
In *Chapter 6 Resource File*

Online Edition
Tutorial Videos

Countdown to Mastery Week 13

Power Presentations with PowerPoint®

Warm Up

Simplify each expression.

1. $3x + 2y - 5x - 2y$ $\quad -2x$

2. $5(x - y) + 2x + 5y$ $\quad 7x$

3. $4y + 6x - 3(y + 2x)$ $\quad y$

4. $2y - 4x - 2(4y - 2x)$ $\quad -6y$

Write the least common multiple.

5. 3 and 6 $\quad$ 6 **6.** 4 and 10 $\quad$ 20

7. 6 and 8 $\quad$ 24 **8.** 2 and 5 $\quad$ 10

Also available on transparency

Math Humor

Teacher: What's your solution of the system of equations?

Student: Nothing – I used elimination and got rid of the whole thing!

1 Introduce

EXPLORATION

6-3 Solving Systems by Elimination

In this Exploration, you will investigate another method for solving systems of equations.

1. Consider the following system of equations: $\begin{cases} 2x - y = 5 \\ x + y = 1 \end{cases}$.
   What can you say about the expressions on either side of the equal sign in the equation $x + y = 1$?
2. In general, what happens if you add equal quantities to both sides of an equation?
3. Explain why you can add $x + y$ to the left side of $2x - y = 5$ and add 1 to the right side of $2x - y = 5$.
4. Add $x + y$ to the left side of $2x - y = 5$ and add 1 to the right side of $2x - y = 5$. What is the resulting equation?
5. Solve for x.
6. Use this value of x to find y.

THINK AND DISCUSS

7. **Explain** how you found the value of y once you knew the value of x.
8. **Describe** how you can check your solution to the system of equations.

Motivate

To introduce the term *elimination*, ask students what happens when the expressions below are simplified.

$5x + 2y + x - 2y$ $6x$; the y-terms are *eliminated.*

$2(x - y) - 2x + 7y$ $5y$; the x-terms are *eliminated.*

Tell students that in this lesson, they will eliminate terms to solve a system of equations.

Explorations and answers are provided in *Alternate Openers: Explorations Transparencies*.

California Standards

Algebra 1 9.0

EXAMPLE 1 Elimination Using Addition

Solve $\begin{cases} x - 2y = -19 \\ 5x + 2y = 1 \end{cases}$ by elimination.

Step 1	$x - 2y = -19$	*Write the system so that like terms are aligned.*
Step 2	$+\ \underline{5x + 2y = \quad 1}$	
	$6x \ + 0 = -18$	*Add the equations to eliminate the y-terms.*
Step 3	$6x = -18$	*Simplify and solve for x.*
	$\frac{6x}{6} = \frac{-18}{6}$	*Divide both sides by 6.*
	$x = -3$	
Step 4	$x - 2y = -19$	*Write one of the original equations.*
	$-3 - 2y = -19$	*Substitute −3 for x.*
	$\underline{+3 \qquad\quad +3}$	*Add 3 to both sides.*
	$-2y = -16$	
	$\frac{-2y}{-2} = \frac{-16}{-2}$	*Divide both sides by −2.*
	$y = 8$	
Step 5	$(-3, 8)$	*Write the solution as an ordered pair.*

Helpful Hint

Check your answer.

$x - 2y = -19$	
$-3 - 2(8)$	-19
$-3 - 16$	-19
-19	-19 ✓

$5x + 2y = 1$	
$5(-3) + 2(8)$	1
$-15 + 16$	1
1	1 ✓

CHECK IT OUT! **1.** Solve $\begin{cases} y + 3x = -2 \\ 2y - 3x = 14 \end{cases}$ by elimination. Check your answer. $(-2, 4)$

When two equations each contain the same term, you can subtract one equation from the other to solve the system. To subtract an equation, add the opposite of *each* term.

EXAMPLE 2 Elimination Using Subtraction

Solve $\begin{cases} 3x + 4y = 18 \\ -2x + 4y = 8 \end{cases}$ by elimination.

Step 1	$3x + 4y = 18$	
Step 2	$-\ (-2x + 4y = \ 8)$	
	$3x + 4y = 18$	*Add the opposite of each term in the second equation.*
	$\underline{+\ 2x - 4y = -8}$	
	$5x + \ 0 = 10$	*Eliminate the y-term.*
Step 3	$5x = 10$	*Simplify and solve for x.*
	$x = 2$	
Step 4	$-2x + 4y = \ 8$	*Write one of the original equations.*
	$-2(2) + 4y = \ 8$	*Substitute 2 for x.*
	$-4 + 4y = \ 8$	
	$\underline{+4 \qquad\quad +4}$	*Add 4 to both sides.*
	$4y = 12$	*Simplify and solve for y.*
	$y = 3$	
Step 5	$(2, 3)$	*Write the solution as an ordered pair.*

Remember!

Remember to check by substituting your answer into both original equations.

Teaching Tip **Communicating Math** Some students may recognize the process of combining opposite terms as *cancellation* or *making zero pairs*. Use the word *eliminate* when describing the elimination method, but ask students to think of various names they have used to label this concept. This provides the students with a connection to previous learning. ENGLISH LANGUAGE LEARNERS

Power Presentations with PowerPoint®

Additional Examples

Example 1

Solve $\begin{cases} 3x - 4y = 10 \\ x + 4y = -2 \end{cases}$ by elimination. Check your answer. $(2, -1)$

Example 2

Solve $\begin{cases} 2x + y = -5 \\ 2x - 5y = 13 \end{cases}$ by elimination. Check your answer. $(-1, -3)$

Also available on transparency

INTERVENTION

Questioning Strategies

EXAMPLE 1

- Why is it helpful to write the system so that like terms are aligned?

EXAMPLE 2

- How do you decide what operation to use after you have aligned like terms?

Critical Thinking Challenge students to find two different ways to solve **Example 2** by substitution. One way is to solve each equation for $4y$ and then set the expressions equal to each other. Another is to divide the second equation by -2 and then isolate x.

2 Teach

Guided Instruction

Review combining like terms before **Examples 1** and **2.** Review finding the least common multiple before **Example 3.** Be sure that students are comfortable with solving systems by addition or subtraction before showing them how to solve by multiplication. Discuss when each of the three methods of solving systems of linear equations is most convenient to use. Remind students that a solution is an ordered pair and that they should check their solutions.

Universal Access

Through Concrete Manipulatives

Use transparency algebra tiles (MK) to model $2x + 3y = 6$ and $-2x + y = 10$. Label the x- and y-tiles.

Add the tiles vertically. Remove the zero pairs. This leaves $4y = 16$. Solve for y. Then find x through substitution. $(-3, 4)$

2. Solve $\begin{cases} 3x + 3y = 15 \\ -2x + 3y = -5 \end{cases}$ by elimination. Check your answer. (4, 1)

In some cases, you will first need to multiply one or both of the equations by a number so that one variable has opposite coefficients.

EXAMPLE 3 Elimination Using Multiplication First

Solve each system by elimination.

A $\begin{cases} 2x + y = 3 \\ -x + 3y = -12 \end{cases}$

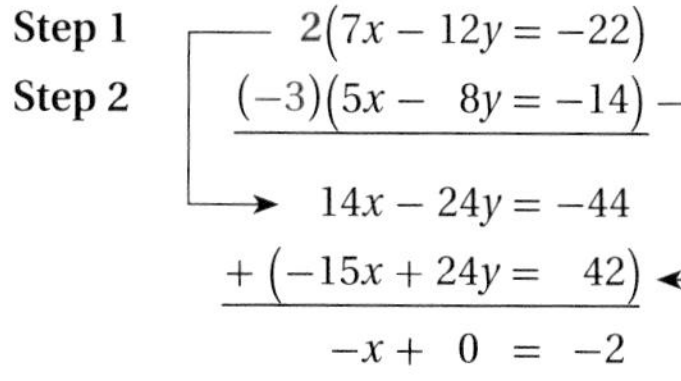

Step 1 $2x + y = 3$

Step 2 $2(-x + 3y = -12)$ — *Multiply each term in the second equation by 2 to get opposite x-coefficients.*

$2x + y = 3$

$+(-2x + 6y = -24)$ — *Add the new equation to the first equation.*

Step 3 $7y = -21$

$y = -3$ — *Simplify and solve for y.*

Step 4 $2x + y = 3$ — *Write one of the original equations.*

$2x - 3 = 3$ — *Substitute −3 for y.*

$+3 \quad +3$ — *Add 3 to both sides.*

$2x = 6$ — *Simplify and solve for x.*

$x = 3$

Step 5 (3, −3) — *Write the solution as an ordered pair.*

B $\begin{cases} 7x - 12y = -22 \\ 5x - 8y = -14 \end{cases}$

Step 1 $2(7x - 12y = -22)$

Step 2 $(-3)(5x - 8y = -14)$ — *Multiply the first equation by 2 and the second equation by −3 to get opposite y-coefficients.*

$14x - 24y = -44$

$+(-15x + 24y = 42)$ — *Add the new equations.*

$-x + 0 = -2$

Step 3 $x = 2$ — *Simplify and solve for x.*

Step 4 $7x - 12y = -22$ — *Write one of the original equations.*

$7(2) - 12y = -22$ — *Substitute 2 for x.*

$14 - 12y = -22$

$-14 \quad -14$ — *Subtract 14 from both sides.*

$-12y = -36$ — *Simplify and solve for y.*

$y = 3$

Step 5 (2, 3) — *Write the solution as an ordered pair.*

Helpful Hint

In Step 1 of Example 3A, you could have also multiplied the first equation by −3 to eliminate the *y*-term.

Helpful Hint

Use the techniques for finding a common denominator when trying to find values to multiply each equation by. To review these techniques, see Skills Bank p. SB8.

CHECK IT OUT! Solve each system by elimination. Check your answer.

3a. $\begin{cases} 3x + 2y = 6 \\ -x + y = -2 \end{cases}$ (2, 0)

3b. $\begin{cases} 2x + 5y = 26 \\ -3x - 4y = -25 \end{cases}$ (3, 4)

COMMON ERROR ALERT

In problems like **Example 3,** students may forget to multiply both sides of the equation by a number when they create an opposite coefficient through multiplication. Remind them that the Multiplication Property of Equality requires both sides of the equation to be multiplied by the same number.

Power Presentations with PowerPoint®

Additional Examples

Example 3

Solve each system by elimination. Check your answer.

A. $\begin{cases} x + 2y = 11 \\ -3x + y = -5 \end{cases}$ (3, 4)

B. $\begin{cases} -5x + 2y = 32 \\ 2x + 3y = 10 \end{cases}$ (−4, 6)

Also available on transparency

Reading Math Be sure students understand that multiplying an equation by a number means to multiply both sides of the equation by that number.

INTERVENTION
Questioning Strategies

EXAMPLE 3

- How do you choose the number to multiply each equation by?

Science Link Systems of linear equations are commonly used in the sciences. A major field of study that uses systems of linear equations is digital signal processing (DSP). DSP has several applications, including weather forecasting, seismic (earth tremor) data processing, and image manipulation.

Number Sense In **Example 4,** students can multiply both equations by 100 before solving. The new system will be equivalent to the original system, but it will be easier to solve because it will not contain decimals.

Visual In **Example 4,** students may benefit from using a table to organize the information.

	Roses	Daises	Total
Number of Flowers	r	d	12
Cost of Flowers	\$2.50r	\$1.75d	\$24.75

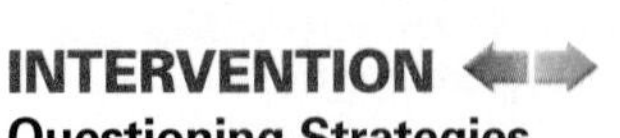

Additional Examples

Example 4

Paige has \$7.75 to buy 12 sheets of felt and card stock for her scrapbook. The felt costs \$0.50 per sheet, and the card stock costs \$0.75 per sheet. How many sheets of each can Paige buy? 5 sheets of felt and 7 sheets of card stock

Also available on transparency

INTERVENTION

Questioning Strategies

EXAMPLE 4

- How do you know which numbers in the problem should be coefficients for the variables?

Consumer Economics Application

Sam spent \$24.75 to buy 12 flowers for his mother. The bouquet contained roses and daisies. How many of each type of flower did Sam buy?

Write a system. Use r for the number of roses and d for the number of daisies.

Step 1 $2.50r + 1.75d = 24.75$ *The cost of roses and daisies totals \$24.75.*

$r + d = 12$ *The total number of roses and daisies is 12.*

Step 2 $2.50r + 1.75d = 24.75$

$(-2.50)(r + d = 12)$ *Multiply the second equation by −2.50 to get opposite r-coefficients.*

$2.50r + 1.75d = 24.75$

$+(-2.50r - 2.50d = -30.00)$ *Add this equation to the first equation to eliminate the r-term.*

Step 3 $-0.75d = -5.25$

$d = 7$ *Simplify and solve for d.*

Step 4 $r + d = 12$ *Write one of the original equations.*

$r + 7 = 12$ *Substitute 7 for d.*

$-7 \quad -7$ *Subtract 7 from both sides.*

$r = 5$

Step 5 $(5, 7)$ *Write the solution as an ordered pair.*

Sam can buy 5 roses and 7 daisies.

4. What if...? Sally spent \$14.85 to buy 13 flowers. She bought lilies, which cost \$1.25 each, and tulips, which cost \$0.90 each. How many of each flower did Sally buy? **9 lilies, 4 tulips**

All systems can be solved in more than one way. For some systems, some methods may be more appropriate than others.

Systems of Linear Equations

METHOD	USE WHEN...	EXAMPLE
Graphing	• Both equations are solved for y. • You want to estimate a solution.	$\begin{cases} y = 3x + 2 \\ y = -2x + 6 \end{cases}$
Substitution	• A variable in either equation has a coefficient of 1 or −1. • Both equations are solved for the same variable. • Either equation is solved for a variable.	$\begin{cases} x + 2y = 7 \\ x = 10 - 5y \end{cases}$ or $\begin{cases} x = 2y + 10 \\ x = 3y + 5 \end{cases}$
Elimination	• Both equations have the same variable with the same or opposite coefficients. • A variable term in one equation is a multiple of the corresponding variable term in the other equation.	$\begin{cases} 3x + 2y = 8 \\ 5x + 2y = 12 \end{cases}$ or $\begin{cases} 6x + 5y = 10 \\ 3x + 2y = 15 \end{cases}$

3 Close

Summarize

Ask students which method they would use to solve each system of equations and why. Possible answers:

$\begin{cases} x + 5y = 28 \\ -x + 2y = 7 \end{cases}$ Elimination using add.; the x-terms are opposites.

$\begin{cases} y = 6 \\ y = 4x - 2 \end{cases}$ Graphing: both in slope-int. form; substitution: both are solved for y.

$\begin{cases} -2x + 5y = -17 \\ 3x - 10y = 28 \end{cases}$ Elimination using mult.; the y-terms are multiples of 5.

FORMATIVE ASSESSMENT and INTERVENTION

***Diagnose Before* the Lesson**
6-3 Warm Up, TE p. 343

***Monitor During* the Lesson**
Check It Out! Exercises, SE pp. 344–346
Questioning Strategies, TE pp. 344–346

***Assess After* the Lesson**
6-3 Lesson Quiz, TE p. 349
Alternative Assessment, TE p. 349

THINK AND DISCUSS

1. Explain how multiplying the second equation in a system by −1 and eliminating by adding is the same as elimination by subtraction. Give an example of a system for which this applies.
2. Explain why it does not matter which variable you solve for first when solving a system by elimination.

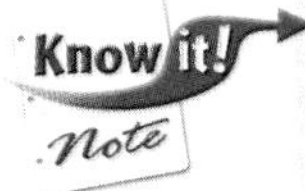

3. **GET ORGANIZED** Copy and complete the graphic organizer. In each box, write an example of a system of equations that you could solve using the given method.

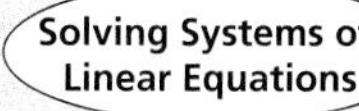
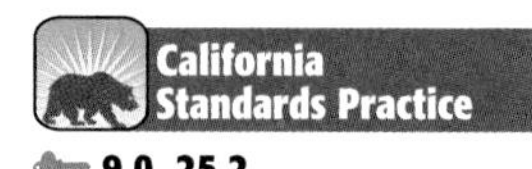

Answers to *Think and Discuss*

1. Multiplying the second equation by −1 and adding is like adding the opposite, which is the same as subtracting; possible answer: $3x + y = 5$; $3x + 2y = 6$.
2. No matter which variable you solve for first, the answer will still be the same.
3. See p. A5.

6-3 Exercises

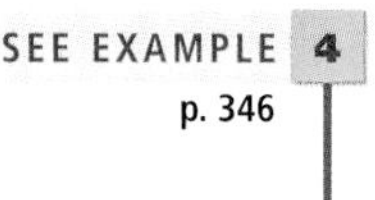

California Standards Practice
9.0, 25.2

go.hrw.com
Homework Help Online
KEYWORD: MA8CA 6-3
Parent Resources Online
KEYWORD: MA8CA Parent

6-3 Exercises

GUIDED PRACTICE

Solve each system by elimination. Check your answer.

SEE EXAMPLE 1 p. 344

1. $\begin{cases} -x + y = 5 \\ x - 5y = -9 \end{cases}$ $(-4, 1)$
2. $\begin{cases} x + y = 12 \\ x - y = 2 \end{cases}$ $(7, 5)$
3. $\begin{cases} 2x + 5y = -24 \\ 3x - 5y = 14 \end{cases}$ $(-2, -4)$

SEE EXAMPLE 2 p. 344

4. $\begin{cases} x - 10y = 60 \\ x + 14y = 12 \end{cases}$ $(40, -2)$
5. $\begin{cases} 5x + y = 0 \\ 5x + 2y = 30 \end{cases}$ $(-6, 30)$
6. $\begin{cases} -5x + 7y = 11 \\ -5x + 3y = 19 \end{cases}$ $(-5, -2)$

SEE EXAMPLE 3 p. 345

7. $\begin{cases} 2x + 3y = 12 \\ 5x - y = 13 \end{cases}$ $(3, 2)$
8. $\begin{cases} -3x + 4y = 12 \\ 2x + y = -8 \end{cases}$ $(-4, 0)$
9. $\begin{cases} 2x + 4y = -4 \\ 3x + 5y = -3 \end{cases}$ $(4, -3)$

SEE EXAMPLE 4 p. 346

10. **Consumer Economics** Each family in a neighborhood is contributing \$20 worth of food to the neighborhood picnic. The Harlin family is bringing 12 packages of buns. The hamburger buns cost \$2.00 per package. The hot-dog buns cost \$1.50 per package. How many packages of each type of bun did they buy?
4 packages of hamburger buns, 8 packages of hot dog buns

PRACTICE AND PROBLEM SOLVING

Solve each system by elimination. Check your answer.

Independent Practice	
For Exercises	See Example
11–13	1
14–16	2
17–19	3
20	4

Extra Practice
Skills Practice p. EP12
Application Practice p. EP29

11. $\begin{cases} -x + y = -1 \\ 2x - y = 0 \end{cases}$ $(-1, -2)$
12. $\begin{cases} -2x + y = -20 \\ 2x + y = 48 \end{cases}$ $(17, 14)$
13. $\begin{cases} 3x - y = -2 \\ -2x + y = 3 \end{cases}$ $(1, 5)$
14. $\begin{cases} x - y = 4 \\ x - 2y = 10 \end{cases}$ $(-2, -6)$
15. $\begin{cases} x + 2y = 5 \\ 3x + 2y = 17 \end{cases}$ $\left(6, -\frac{1}{2}\right)$
16. $\begin{cases} 3x - 2y = -1 \\ 3x - 4y = 9 \end{cases}$ $\left(-\frac{11}{3}, -5\right)$
17. $\begin{cases} x - y = -3 \\ 5x + 3y = 1 \end{cases}$ $(-1, 2)$
18. $\begin{cases} 9x - 3y = 3 \\ 3x + 8y = -17 \end{cases}$
19. $\begin{cases} 5x + 2y = -1 \\ 3x + 7y = 11 \end{cases}$ $(-1, 2)$

18. $\left(-\frac{1}{3}, -2\right)$

20. **Multi-Step** Mrs. Gonzalez bought centerpieces to put on each table at a graduation party. She spent \$31.50. There are 8 tables each requiring either a candle or vase. Candles cost \$3 and vases cost \$4.25. How many of each type did she buy?

20. 2 candles, 6 vases

Assignment Guide

Assign *Guided Practice* exercises as necessary.

If you finished Examples **1–2**
Proficient 11–16, 21, 23
Advanced 11–16, 21, 23

If you finished Examples **1–4**
Proficient 11–21, 24–30 even, 31–48
Advanced 12–20 even, 21, 24–28 even, 31–48

Homework Quick Check
Quickly check key concepts.
Exercises: 12, 14, 18, 20

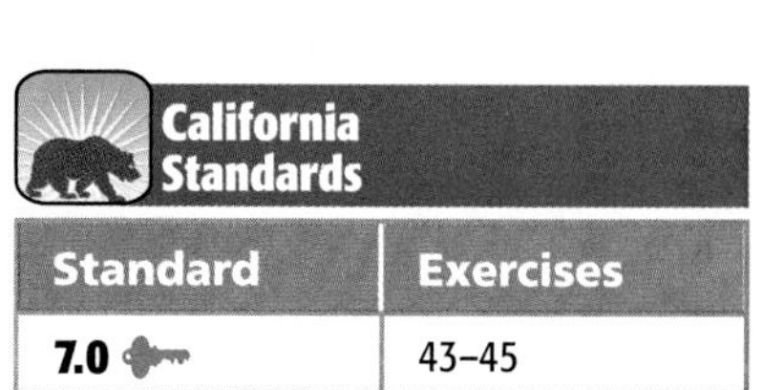

Standard	Exercises
7.0	43–45
9.0	1–21, 23c, 30, 31b, 34, 35b–39, 46–48
16.0	40–42
25.2	22

CONCEPT CONNECTION **Exercise 31** involves writing and solving a system of equations to help calculate savings. This exercise prepares students for the Concept Connection on page 362.

Answers

21. $\begin{cases} \ell - w = 2 \\ 2\ell + 2w = 40 \end{cases}$; length: 11 units; width: 9 units

24. $(40, -2)$; possible answer: elimination using subtraction; coefficients of x-values are the same.

25. $(3, 3)$; possible answer: elimination using multiplication; no variables have the same coefficient, so they cannot be eliminated by addition or subtraction.

26. $(3, -1)$; possible answer: elimination using subtraction; the y-terms have the same coefficients.

27. $\left(\frac{46}{7}, \frac{8}{7}\right)$; possible answer: substitution; the second equation is already solved for a variable.

28. $\left(-\frac{1}{2}, 2\right)$; possible answer: I would use graphing because both equations are in slope-intercept form.

29. $\left(\frac{15}{7}, \frac{9}{7}\right)$; possible answer: I would use elimination, because when the first equation is multiplied by -2 the x-coefficients are opposites.

22. A; the student did not distribute the neg. sign to all values in the parentheses and so mistakenly added 3 to -3.

LINK Math History

In 1247, Qin Jiushao wrote *Mathematical Treatise in Nine Sections*. Its contents included solving systems of equations and the Chinese Remainder Theorem.

31a. $\begin{cases} 3A + 2B = 16 \\ 2A + 3B = 14 \end{cases}$

21. **Geometry** The difference between the length and width of a rectangle is 2 units. The perimeter is 40 units. Write and solve a system of equations to determine the length and width of the rectangle. (*Hint:* The perimeter of a rectangle is $2\ell + 2w$.)

22. **/// ERROR ANALYSIS ///** Which is incorrect? Explain the error.

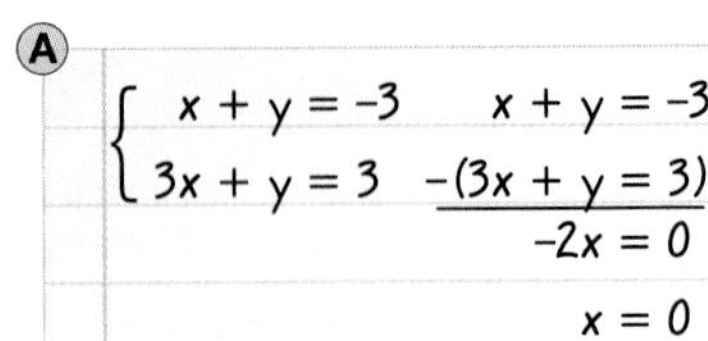

A

$$\begin{cases} x + y = -3 \\ 3x + y = 3 \end{cases} \quad \begin{array}{r} x + y = -3 \\ -(3x + y = 3) \\ \hline -2x = 0 \\ x = 0 \end{array}$$

B

$$\begin{cases} x + y = -3 \\ 3x + y = 3 \end{cases} \quad \begin{array}{r} x + y = -3 \\ -(3x + y = 3) \\ \hline -2x = -6 \\ x = 3 \end{array}$$

23. A music school Terry is interested in is offering a special for new students. If Terry enrolls in 2 classes, he has to pay a fee in addition to the price of classes for a total of \$18. If he decides to take 6 classes, the fee is subtracted from his total for a total of \$38. Follow the steps below to find the cost of each class and the price of the fee.

	Classes	+	Fee	=	Total Price
Price for 2 classes	$2x$	+	y	=	**18**
Price for 6 classes	$6x$	**−**	y	=	38

a. Copy and complete the table.

b. Use the information in the table to write a system of equations. $\begin{cases} 2x + y = 18 \\ 6x - y = 38 \end{cases}$

c. Solve the system of equations to find the price of each class and the price of the fee that Terry has to pay. **7; 4**

Critical Thinking Solve each system. Which method did you use to solve each system? Explain.

24. $\begin{cases} \frac{1}{2}x - 5y = 30 \\ \frac{1}{2}x + 7y = 6 \end{cases}$

25. $\begin{cases} -x + 2y = 3 \\ 4x - 5y = -3 \end{cases}$

26. $\begin{cases} 3x - y = 10 \\ 2x - y = 7 \end{cases}$

27. $\begin{cases} 3y + x = 10 \\ x = 4y + 2 \end{cases}$

28. $\begin{cases} y = -4x \\ y = 2x + 3 \end{cases}$

29. $\begin{cases} 2x + 6y = 12 \\ 4x + 5y = 15 \end{cases}$

30. **Business** A local boys club sold 176 bags of mulch and made a total of \$520. They did not sell any of the expensive cocoa mulch. Use the table to determine how many bags of each type of mulch they sold. **48 bags hardwood mulch; 128 bags pine bark mulch**

Mulch Prices (\$)	
Cocoa	4.75
Hardwood	3.50
Pine Bark	2.75

CONCEPT CONNECTION

31. This problem will prepare you for the Concept Connection on page 362.

a. The school store is running a promotion on school supplies. Different supplies are placed on two shelves. You can purchase 3 items from shelf A and 2 from shelf B for \$16. Or you can purchase 2 items from shelf A and 3 from shelf B for \$14. Write a system of equations that can be used to find the individual prices for the supplies on shelf A and on shelf B.

b. Solve the system of equations by elimination. Check your answer. **$A = 4$; $B = 2$**

c. If the supplies on shelf A are normally \$6 each and the supplies on shelf B are normally \$3 each, how much will you save on each package plan from part **a**? **Buying the first package will save \$8; buying the second package will save \$7.**

6-3 PRACTICE A

6-3 PRACTICE C

6-3 PRACTICE B

LESSON 6-3 Practice B
Solving Systems by Elimination

Follow the steps to solve each system by elimination.

1. $\begin{cases} 2x - 3y = 14 \\ 2x + y = -10 \end{cases}$

Subtract the second equation:

$$\begin{array}{r} 2x - 3y = 14 \\ -(2x + y = -10) \\ \hline -4y = 24 \end{array}$$

Solve the resulting equation:

$y =$ **−6**

Use your answer to find the value of x:

$x =$ **−2**

Solution: (**−2** , **−6**)

2. $\begin{cases} 3x + y = 17 \\ 4x + 2y = 20 \end{cases}$

Multiply the first equation by −2. Then, add the equations:

$$\begin{array}{r} -6x - 2y = -34 \\ +4x + 2y = 20 \\ \hline -2x = -14 \end{array}$$

Solve the resulting equation:

$x =$ **7**

Use your answer to find the value of y:

$y =$ **−4**

Solution: (**7** , **−4**)

Solve each system by elimination. Check your answer.

3. $\begin{cases} x + 3y = -7 \\ -x + 2y = -8 \end{cases}$ **(2, −3)**

4. $\begin{cases} 3x + y = -26 \\ 2x - y = -19 \end{cases}$ **(−9, 1)**

5. $\begin{cases} x + 3y = -14 \\ 2x - 4y = 32 \end{cases}$ **(4, −6)**

6. $\begin{cases} 4x - y = -5 \\ -2x + 3y = 10 \end{cases}$ **$\left(-\frac{1}{2}, 3\right)$**

7. $\begin{cases} y - 3x = 11 \\ 2y - x = 2 \end{cases}$ **(−4, −1)**

8. $\begin{cases} -10x + y = 0 \\ 5x + 3y = -7 \end{cases}$ **$\left(-\frac{1}{5}, -2\right)$**

Solve.

9. Brianna's family spent \$134 on 2 adult tickets and 3 youth tickets at an amusement park. Max's family spent \$146 on 3 adult tickets and 2 youth tickets. What is the price of a youth ticket? **\$22**

10. Carl bought 19 apples of 2 different varieties to make a pie. The total cost of the apples was \$5.10. Granny Smith apples cost \$0.25 each and Gala apples cost \$0.30 each. How many of each type of apple did Carl buy? **7 Gala apples; 12 Granny Smith apples**

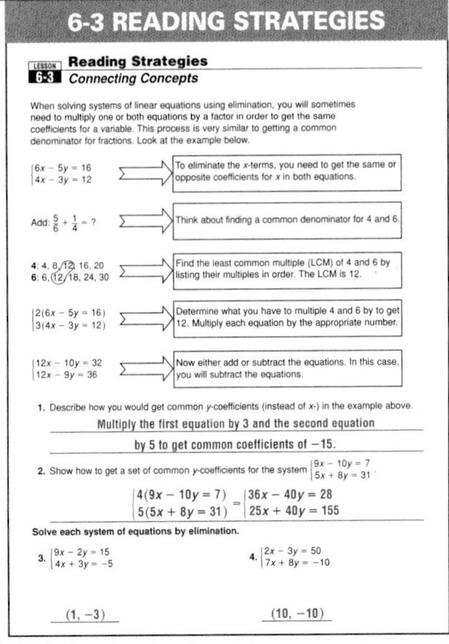

6-3 READING STRATEGIES

LESSON 6-3 Reading Strategies
Connecting Concepts

When solving systems of linear equations using elimination, you will sometimes need to multiply one or both equations by a factor in order to get the same coefficients for a variable. This process is very similar to getting a common denominator for fractions. Look at the example below.

$\begin{cases} 6x - 5y = 16 \\ 4x - 3y = 12 \end{cases}$ ⇒ To eliminate the x-terms, you need to get the same or opposite coefficients for x in both equations.

Add: $\frac{5}{6} + \frac{1}{4} = ?$ ⇒ Think about finding a common denominator for 4 and 6.

4: 4, 8, (12), 16, 20
6: 6, (12), 18, 24, 30 ⇒ Find the least common multiple (LCM) of 4 and 6 by listing their multiples in order. The LCM is 12.

$\begin{cases} 2(6x - 5y = 16) \\ 3(4x - 3y = 12) \end{cases}$ ⇒ Determine what you have to multiple 4 and 6 by to get 12. Multiply each equation by the appropriate number.

$\begin{cases} 12x - 10y = 32 \\ 12x - 9y = 36 \end{cases}$ ⇒ Now either add or subtract the equations. In this case, you will subtract the equations.

1. Describe how you would get common y-coefficients (instead of x-) in the example above.
Multiply the first equation by 3 and the second equation by 5 to get common coefficients of −15.

2. Show how to get a set of common y-coefficients for the system $\begin{cases} 9x - 10y = 7 \\ 5x + 8y = 31 \end{cases}$.
$\begin{cases} 4(9x - 10y = 7) \\ 5(5x + 8y = 31) \end{cases} \Rightarrow \begin{cases} 36x - 40y = 28 \\ 25x + 40y = 155 \end{cases}$

Solve each system of equations by elimination.

3. $\begin{cases} 9x - 2y = 15 \\ 4x + 3y = -5 \end{cases}$ **(1, −3)**

4. $\begin{cases} 2x - 3y = 50 \\ 7x + 8y = -10 \end{cases}$ **(10, −10)**

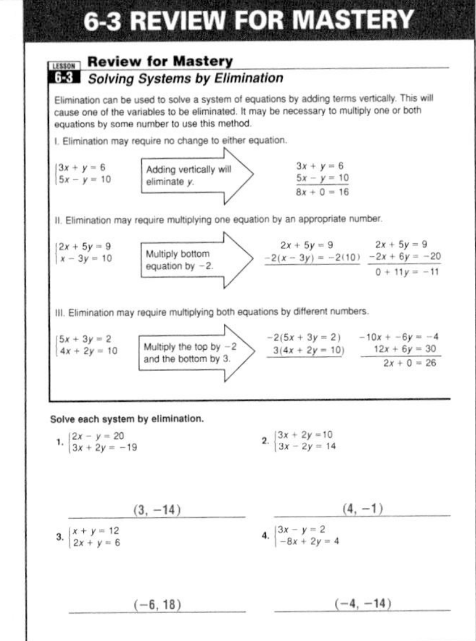

6-3 REVIEW FOR MASTERY

LESSON 6-3 Review for Mastery
Solving Systems by Elimination

Elimination can be used to solve a system of equations by adding terms vertically. This will cause one of the variables to be eliminated. It may be necessary to multiply one or both equations by some number to use this method.

I. Elimination may require no change to either equation.

$\begin{cases} 3x + y = 6 \\ 5x - y = 10 \end{cases}$ ⇒ Adding vertically will eliminate y. ⇒ $\begin{array}{r} 3x + y = 6 \\ 5x - y = 10 \\ \hline 8x + 0 = 16 \end{array}$

II. Elimination may require multiplying one equation by an appropriate number.

$\begin{cases} 2x + 5y = 9 \\ x - 3y = 10 \end{cases}$ ⇒ Multiply bottom equation by −2. ⇒ $\begin{array}{r} 2x + 5y = 9 \\ -2(x - 3y) = -2(10) \end{array}$ $\begin{array}{r} 2x + 5y = 9 \\ -2x + 6y = -20 \\ \hline 0 + 11y = -11 \end{array}$

III. Elimination may require multiplying both equations by different numbers.

$\begin{cases} 5x + 3y = 2 \\ 4x + 2y = 10 \end{cases}$ ⇒ Multiply the top by −2 and the bottom by 3. ⇒ $\begin{array}{r} -2(5x + 3y = 2) \\ 3(4x + 2y = 10) \end{array}$ $\begin{array}{r} -10x + -6y = -4 \\ 12x + 6y = 30 \\ \hline 2x + 0 = 26 \end{array}$

Solve each system by elimination.

1. $\begin{cases} 2x - y = 20 \\ 3x + 2y = -19 \end{cases}$ **(3, −14)**

2. $\begin{cases} 3x + 2y = 10 \\ 3x - 2y = 14 \end{cases}$ **(4, −1)**

3. $\begin{cases} x + y = 12 \\ 2x + y = 6 \end{cases}$ **(−6, 18)**

4. $\begin{cases} 3x - y = 2 \\ -8x + 2y = 4 \end{cases}$ **(−4, −14)**

32. **Write About It** Solve the system $\begin{cases} 3x + y = 1 \\ 2x + 4y = -6 \end{cases}$. Explain how you can check your solution algebraically and graphically.

Multiple Choice For Exercises 33 and 34, choose the best answer.

33. A math test has 25 problems. Some are worth 2 points, and some are worth 3 points. The test is worth 60 points total. Which system can be used to determine the number of 2-point problems and the number of 3-point problems on the test?

    (A) $\begin{cases} x + y = 25 \\ 2x + 3y = 60 \end{cases}$ (circled)   (B) $\begin{cases} x + y = 60 \\ 2x + 3y = 25 \end{cases}$ (C) $\begin{cases} x - y = 25 \\ 2x + 3y = 60 \end{cases}$ (D) $\begin{cases} x - y = 60 \\ 2x - 3y = 25 \end{cases}$

34. An electrician charges $15 plus $11 per hour. Another electrician charges $10 plus $15 per hour. For what amount of time will the cost be the same? What is that cost?

    (A) 1 hour; $25
    (B) $1\frac{1}{4}$ hours; $28.75 (circled)
    (C) $1\frac{1}{2}$ hours; $30
    (D) $1\frac{3}{4}$ hours; $32.50

35. **Short Response** Three hundred and fifty-eight tickets to the school basketball game on Friday were sold. Student tickets were $1.50, and nonstudent tickets were $3.25. The school made $752.25.

    a. Write a system of linear equations that could be used to determine how many student and how many nonstudent tickets were sold. Define the variables you use.

    b. Solve the system you wrote in part **a.** How many student and how many nonstudent tickets were sold? **$s = 235$; $n = 123$; 235 student tickets, 123 nonstudent tickets**

35a. Let s = the number of student tickets sold. Let n = the number of nonstudent tickets sold; $\begin{cases} s + n = 358 \\ 1.50s + 3.25n = 752.25. \end{cases}$

CHALLENGE AND EXTEND

Solve each system by any method. Check your answer.

36. $\begin{cases} x + 16\frac{1}{2} = -\frac{3}{4}y \\ y = \frac{1}{2}x \end{cases}$ **$x = -12$; $y = -6$**

37. $\begin{cases} 2x + y + z = 17 \\ \frac{1}{2}z = 5 \\ x - y = 5 \end{cases}$ **$x = 4$; $y = -1$; $z = 10$**

38. $\begin{cases} x - 2y - z = -1 \\ -x + 2y + 4z = -11 \\ 2x + y + z = 1 \end{cases}$ **$x = 1$; $y = 3$; $z = -4$**

39. Three students participated in a fund-raiser for school. Each sold a combination of pens, notebooks, and bags. The first student sold 2 pens, 7 notebooks, and 3 bags for a total of $73. The second student sold 10 pens, 2 notebooks, and 2 bags for a total of $50. The third student sold 1 pen, 4 notebooks, and 5 bags for a total of $71. Find the price of each item. **pen = $2, notebook = $6, bag = $9**

SPIRAL STANDARDS REVIEW

Determine whether each relation defines a function. Write an equation if possible. *(Lesson 4-3)*

40.

x	1	2	3	4
y	6	7	8	9

yes; $y = x + 5$

41.

x	1	2	3	4
y	3	6	9	12

yes; $y = 3x$

42.

x	1	2	3	4
y	−9	−8	−7	−6

yes; $y = x - 10$

Write an equation in slope-intercept form for the line with the given slope that contains the given point. *(Lesson 5-6)*

43. slope = 2; (5, 1) **$y = 2x - 9$**

44. slope = −4; (3, −1) **$y = -4x + 11$**

45. slope = $\frac{1}{2}$; (−2, 9) **$y = \frac{1}{2}x + 10$**

Solve each system by substitution. Check your answer. *(Lesson 6-2)*

46. $\begin{cases} y = x - 1 \\ x + y = 10 \end{cases}$ **(5.5, 4.5)**

47. $\begin{cases} x = y - 5 \\ 2x + 1 = y \end{cases}$ **(4, 9)**

48. $\begin{cases} y = 2x - 1 \\ x - y = 3 \end{cases}$ **(−2, −5)**

Teaching Tip

Multiple Choice Students who chose **B** or **D** for **Exercise 33** may not have understood how to organize the information. Suggest that students use a table to organize the information into number of problems and number of points.

Answer

32. (1, −2); possible answer: to check the solution algebraically, substitute 1 for x and −2 for y in both equations. If both equations are a true statement, the solution is correct. To check the solution graphically, graph both equations on the same coordinate plane and locate their intersection. If the intersection is (1, −2) then the solution is correct.

Journal

Have students write about which method for solving a system of equations they find the easiest.

ALTERNATIVE ASSESSMENT

Have students write a real-world situation that can be modeled by $\begin{cases} 4x + 8y = 100 \\ x + y = 15 \end{cases}$. Then have them solve the system and tell what the solution means in the context of their problem.

Power Presentations with PowerPoint®

6-3 Lesson Quiz

Solve each system by elimination. Check your answer.

1. $\begin{cases} 2x + y = 25 \\ 3y = 2x - 13 \end{cases}$ (11, 3)

2. $\begin{cases} -3x + 4y = -18 \\ x = -2y - 4 \end{cases}$ (2, −3)

3. $\begin{cases} -2x + 3y = -15 \\ 3x + 2y = -23 \end{cases}$ (−3, −7)

4. Harlan has $44 to buy 7 pairs of socks. Athletic socks cost $5 per pair. Dress socks cost $8 per pair. How many pairs of each can Harlan buy?
   4 pairs of athletic socks and 3 pairs of dress socks

Also available on transparency

6-3 PROBLEM SOLVING

LESSON 6-3 Problem Solving
Solving Systems by Elimination

Write the correct answer.

1. Mr. Nguyen bought a package of 3 chicken legs and a package of 7 chicken wings. Ms. Dawes bought a package of 3 chicken legs and a package of 6 chicken wings. Mr. Nguyen bought 45 ounces of chicken. Ms. Dawes bought 42 ounces of chicken. How much did each chicken leg and each chicken wing weigh?
   chicken leg 8 oz.,
   chicken wing 3 oz.

2. Jayce bought 2 bath towels and returned 3 hand towels. His sister Jayna bought 3 bath towels and 3 hand towels. Jayce's bill was $5. Jayna's bill was $45. What are the prices of a bath towel and a hand towel?
   bath towel $10,
   hand towel $5

3. The Lees spent $31 on movie tickets for 2 adults and 3 children. The Macias spent $26 on movie tickets for 2 adults and 2 children. What are the prices for adult and child movie tickets?
   adult ticket $8,
   child ticket $5

4. Last month Stephanie spent $57 on 4 allergy shots and 1 office visit. This month she spent $9 after 1 office visit and a refund for 2 allergy shots from her insurance company. How much does an office visit cost? an allergy shot?
   office visit $25,
   allergy shot $8

Use the chart below to answer questions 5–6. Select the best answer. The chart shows the price per pound for dried fruit.

Dried Fruit Price List			
Pineapple	Apple	Mango	Papaya
$7.50/lb	$7.00/lb	$8.00/lb	$7.25/lb

5. A customer bought 5 pounds of mango and papaya for $37.75. How many pounds of each fruit did the customer buy?
   (A) 2 lbs mango and 3 lbs papaya (circled)
   B 3 lbs mango and 2 lbs papaya
   C 1 lb mango and 4 lbs papaya
   D 4 lbs mango and 1 lb papaya

6. A store employee made two gift baskets of dried fruit, each costing $100. The first basket had 12 pounds of fruit x and 2 pounds of fruit y. The second basket had 4 pounds of fruit x and 9 pounds of fruit y. Which two fruits did the employee use in the baskets?
   F pineapple and apple
   (G) apple and mango (circled)
   H mango and papaya
   J papaya and pineapple

6-3 CHALLENGE

LESSON 6-3 Challenge
Elimination with Systems of Three Equations

The elimination method can also be used for a system of three equations in three unknowns.

Three camp leaders purchased equipment for a camping trip.
Max bought 10 sleeping bags, 2 tents, and 1 can of bug repellant for $885.
Carlos bought 5 sleeping bags, 4 tents, and 1 can of bug repellant for $865.
Amy bought 9 sleeping bags, 6 tents, and 6 cans of bug repellant for $1410.
If they made their purchases at the same store, how much did each item cost?

1. Write the 3 equations: $\begin{cases} 10x + 2y + z = 885 \\ 5x + 4y + z = 865 \\ 9x + 6y + 6z = 1410 \end{cases}$

2. Subtract the second equation from the first. $5x - 2y = 20$

3. Multiply the second equation by −6 and add the second and third equations. $-21x - 18y = -3780$

4. The equations in steps 2 and 3 form a linear system in two variables. Solve this system for x. $x = 60$

5. Substitute the value of x into the first two equations. Write the resulting system. $\begin{cases} 2y + z = 285 \\ 4y + z = 565 \end{cases}$

6. Solve the system in problem 5 for y and z. $y = 140$, $z = 5$

7. Write the cost of each item. **sleeping bags: $60; tents: $140; bug repellant: $5**

6-4 Organizer

Objectives: Solve special systems of linear equations in two variables.

Classify systems of linear equations and determine the number of solutions.

Algebra Lab
In Chapter 6 Resource File

Online Edition
Tutorial Videos

Countdown to Mastery Week 13

Power Presentations with PowerPoint®

Warm Up

Solve each equation.

1. $2x + 3 = 2x + 4$ no solution
2. $2(x + 1) = 2x + 2$ infinitely many solutions
3. Solve $2y - 6x = 10$ for y. $y = 3x + 5$

Solve by using any method.

4. $\begin{cases} y = 3x + 2 \\ 2x + y = 7 \end{cases}$ (1, 5)
5. $\begin{cases} x - y = 8 \\ x + y = 4 \end{cases}$ (6, −2)

Also available on transparency

California Standards

Algebra 1 9.0

Also covered:

8.0 Students understand the concepts of parallel lines and perpendicular lines **and how their slopes are related.** Students are able to find the equation of a line perpendicular to a given line that passes through a given point.

6-4 Solving Special Systems

California Standards

9.0 Students solve a system of two linear equations in two variables algebraically and are able to interpret the answer graphically. Students are able to solve a system of two linear inequalities in two variables and to sketch the solution sets.
Also covered: **8.0**

Vocabulary
consistent system
inconsistent system
independent system
dependent system

Why learn this?
Linear systems can be used to analyze business growth, such as comic book sales. (See Example 4.)

In Lesson 6-1, you saw that when two lines intersect at a point, there is exactly one solution to the system. Systems with at least one solution are **consistent systems**.

When the two lines in a system do not intersect, they are parallel lines. There are no ordered pairs that satisfy both equations, so there is no solution. A system that has no solution is an **inconsistent system**.

EXAMPLE 1 Systems with No Solution

Solve $\begin{cases} y = x - 1 \\ -x + y = 2 \end{cases}$.

Method 1 Compare slopes and y-intercepts.

$y = x - 1 \rightarrow y = 1x - 1$ *Write both equations in slope-intercept form.*

$-x + y = 2 \rightarrow y = 1x + 2$ *The lines are parallel because they have the same slope and different y-intercepts.*

These lines do not intersect so the system is an inconsistent system.

Method 2 Solve the system algebraically. Use the substitution method because the first equation is solved for y.

$-x + (x - 1) = 2$ *Substitute x − 1 for y in the second equation, and solve.*

$-1 = 2$ ✗ *False statement. The equation has no solutions.*

This system has no solution so it is an inconsistent system.

Remember!
To review slopes of parallel lines, see Lesson 5-7.

Check Graph the system to confirm that the lines are parallel.

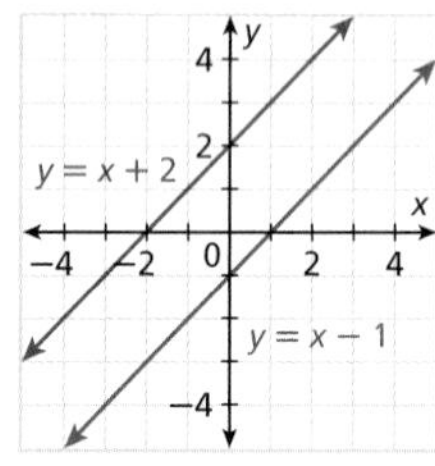

1. Solve $\begin{cases} y = -2x + 5 \\ 2x + y = 1 \end{cases}$. ∅

1 Introduce

EXPLORATION

6-4 Solving Special Systems

You will need a graphing calculator for this Exploration. In this Exploration, you will explore this system of equations: $\begin{cases} y = -\frac{1}{2}x + 3 \\ x + 2y = -4 \end{cases}$.

1. Enter the equations in your calculator as **Y1** and **Y2**. Remember that you must first write each equation in the form $y = \ldots$.
2. Press [2nd] [GRAPH] to view a table of values for the equations.
3. Use the arrow keys to scroll up and down the table. Look for a solution of the system of equations by looking for a value of x for which the two y-values are equal. What do you notice?
4. Press [GRAPH] to view a graph of the functions. What do you notice about the graphs?

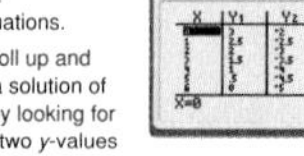

THINK AND DISCUSS

5. **Describe** what happens when you try to solve this system of equations algebraically (by substitution or by elimination).
6. **Explain** why some systems of equations do not have a solution.

Motivate

Review with students equations that have no solution, such as $x + 1 = x + 2$, and equations for which all real numbers are solutions, such as $2(x + 1) = 2x + 2$. Tell students that in this lesson, they will learn about systems of equations that either have no solution or infinitely many solutions.

Explorations and answers are provided in *Alternate Openers: Explorations Transparencies.*

If two linear equations in a system have the same graph, the graphs are coincident lines, or the same line. There are infinitely many solutions of the system because every point on the line represents a solution of both equations.

EXAMPLE 2 Systems with Infinitely Many Solutions

Solve $\begin{cases} y = 2x + 1 \\ 2x - y + 1 = 0 \end{cases}$.

Compare slopes and y-intercepts.

$y = 2x + 1 \rightarrow y = 2x + 1$
$2x - y + 1 = 0 \rightarrow y = 2x + 1$

Write both equations in slope-intercept form. The lines have the same slope and the same y-intercept.

If this system were graphed, the graphs would be the same line. There are infinitely many solutions.

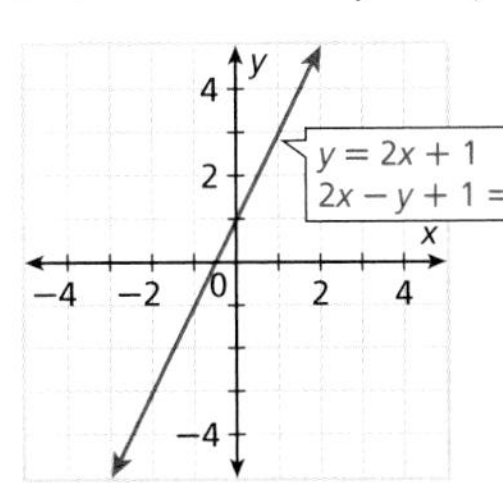

Every point on this line is a solution of the system.

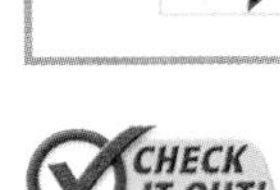

2. Solve $\begin{cases} y = x - 3 \\ x - y - 3 = 0 \end{cases}$. **infinitely many solutions**

Consistent systems can either be independent or dependent.

- An **independent system** has exactly one solution. The graph of an independent system consists of two intersecting lines.
- A **dependent system** has infinitely many solutions. The graph of a dependent system consists of two coincident lines.

Classification of Systems of Linear Equations

CLASSIFICATION	CONSISTENT AND INDEPENDENT	CONSISTENT AND DEPENDENT	INCONSISTENT
Number of Solutions	Exactly one	Infinitely many	None
Description	Different slopes	Same slope, same y-intercept	Same slope, different y-intercepts
Graph	Intersecting lines	Same line	Parallel lines

Students might think that *infinitely many solutions* means that all ordered pairs are solutions. Remind them that the solutions are the infinite number of ordered pairs that make up the line.

Power Presentations with PowerPoint®

Additional Examples

Example 1

Solve $\begin{cases} y = x - 4 \\ -x + y = 3 \end{cases}$. no solution

Example 2

Solve $\begin{cases} y = 3x + 2 \\ 3x - y + 2 = 0 \end{cases}$.

infinitely many solutions

Also available on transparency

INTERVENTION

Questioning Strategies

EXAMPLE 1

- What is true about the graph of a system that is a contradiction when it is solved algebraically?

EXAMPLE 2

- What is true about the graph of a system that is an identity when it is solved algebraically?

Writing Math Remind students that the symbol ∅ (the empty set) can be used to represent the solutions of an inconsistent system. You can use set-builder notation to write the solutions of a dependent system. For example, the solution set for **Example 2** is $\{(x, y): y = 2x + 1\}$ ("the set of all ordered pairs (x, y) such that $y = 2x + 1$").

2 Teach

Guided Instruction

After introducing students to inconsistent systems in **Example 1** and consistent systems in **Example 2,** have students practice classifying systems. Be sure to make connections between the multiple representations of each type of system, as shown in the table on page 351.

Universal Access

Through Cooperative Learning

Have students work in pairs. One student describes either the graph, solution, or classification for a type of system. The other student gives the other two descriptions.

Graph	Solutions	Classification
Intersecting lines	Exactly one	Consistent, independent
Same line	Infinitely many	Consistent, dependent
Parallel lines	None	Inconsistent

Power Presentations with PowerPoint®

Additional Examples

Example 3

Classify each system. Give the number of solutions.

A. $\begin{cases} 3y = x + 3 \\ -\frac{1}{3}x + y = 1 \end{cases}$ consistent and dependent; infinitely many solutions

B. $\begin{cases} x + y = 5 \\ 4 + y = -x \end{cases}$ inconsistent; no solution

C. $\begin{cases} y = 4(x + 1) \\ y - 3 = x \end{cases}$ consistent and independent; one solution

Example 4

Jared and David both started a savings account in January. If the pattern of savings in the table continues, when will the amount in Jared's account equal the amount in David's account?

	Jan	Feb	Mar	Apr	May
Jared	25	30	35	40	45
David	40	45	50	55	60

The amount in Jared's account will never equal the amount in David's account.

Also available on transparency

INTERVENTION
Questioning Strategies

EXAMPLE 3

- How are independent and dependent systems different?
- How are consistent and inconsistent systems different?
- Is it possible for a dependent system to be inconsistent?

EXAMPLE 4

- Why are the values in the first column of the table equal to the constants in the equations?
- How do you determine the rate from the table?
- What would the graph of the system look like?

Multiple Representations Encourage students to check their solutions in **Example 3** by graphing.

EXAMPLE 3 Classifying Systems of Linear Equations

Classify each system. Give the number of solutions.

A $\begin{cases} 2y = x + 2 \\ -\frac{1}{2}x + y = 1 \end{cases}$

$2y = x + 2 \rightarrow y = \frac{1}{2}x + 1$ *Write both equations in slope-intercept form.*

$-\frac{1}{2}x + y = 1 \rightarrow y = \frac{1}{2}x + 1$ *The lines have the same slope and the same y-intercepts. They are the same.*

The system is consistent and dependent. It has infinitely many solutions.

B $\begin{cases} y = 2(x - 1) \\ y = x + 1 \end{cases}$

$y = 2(x - 1) \rightarrow y = 2x - 2$ *Write both equations in slope-intercept form.*

$y = x + 1 \rightarrow y = 1x + 1$ *The lines have different slopes. They intersect.*

The system is consistent and independent. It has one solution.

CHECK IT OUT! Classify each system. Give the number of solutions.

3a. $\begin{cases} x + 2y = -4 \\ -2(y + 2) = x \end{cases}$ **3b.** $\begin{cases} y = -2(x - 1) \\ y = -x + 3 \end{cases}$ **3c.** $\begin{cases} 2x - 3y = 6 \\ y = \frac{2}{3}x \end{cases}$

3a. consistent, dependent; infinitely many solutions

3b. consistent, independent; one solution

3c. inconsistent; no solution

EXAMPLE 4 *Business Application*

The sales manager at Comics Now is comparing its sales with the sales of its competitor, Dynamo Comics. If the sales patterns continue, will the sales for Comics Now ever equal the sales for Dynamo Comics? Explain.

Comic Books Sold per Year (thousands)	2005	2006	2007	2008
Comics Now	130	170	210	250
Dynamo Comics	180	220	260	300

Helpful Hint

The increase in sales is the difference between sales each year.

Use the table to write a system of linear equations. Let y represent the sales total and x represent the increase in sales.

	Sales total	equals	increase in sales per year	times	years	plus	beginning sales.
Comics Now	y	=	40	•	x	+	130
Dynamo Comics	y	=	40	•	x	+	180

$\begin{cases} y = 40x + 130 \\ y = 40x + 180 \end{cases}$

$y = 40x + 130$ *Both equations are in slope-intercept form.*

$y = 40x + 180$ *The lines have the same slope, but different y-intercepts.*

The graphs of the two equations are parallel lines, so there is no solution. If the patterns continue, sales for the two companies will never be equal.

CHECK IT OUT! **4.** Matt has \$100 in a checking account and deposits \$20 per month. Ben has \$80 in a checking account and deposits \$30 per month. Will the accounts ever have the same balance? Explain.

4. Yes; the graphs of the two equations have different slopes so they intersect.

3 Close

Summarize

Give students the system $\begin{cases} y = 3x + 8 \\ \square y = \square x + \square \end{cases}$.

Have them replace the boxes with numbers so that the system has

Possible answers given:

- one solution. 1, 2, 1
- infinitely many solutions. 2, 6, 16
- no solutions. 1, 3, 5

FORMATIVE ASSESSMENT and INTERVENTION

***Diagnose Before* the Lesson**
6-4 Warm Up, TE p. 350

***Monitor During* the Lesson**
Check It Out! Exercises, SE pp. 350–352
Questioning Strategies, TE pp. 351–352

***Assess After* the Lesson**
6-4 Lesson Quiz, TE p. 355
Alternative Assessment, TE p. 355

THINK AND DISCUSS

1. Describe the graph of a system of equations that has infinitely many solutions. Compare the slopes and y-intercepts.
2. What methods can be used to determine the number of solutions of a system of linear equations?

3. **GET ORGANIZED** Copy and complete the graphic organizer. In each box, write the word that describes a system with that number of solutions and sketch a graph.

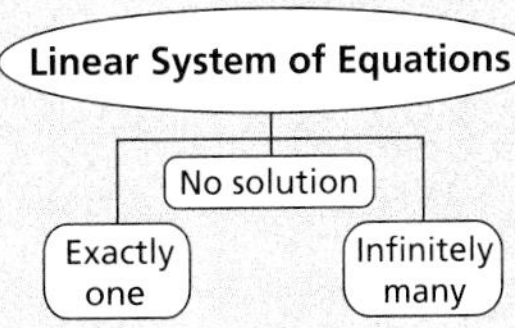

6-4 Exercises

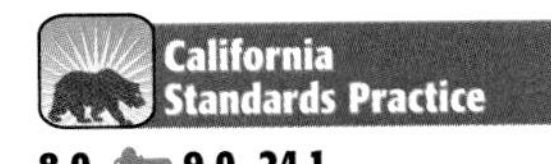

8.0, 9.0, 24.1

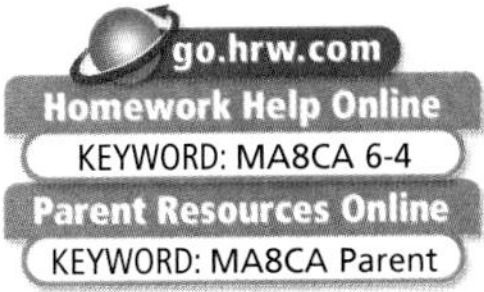

GUIDED PRACTICE

1. **Vocabulary** A ___?___ system can be independent or dependent. (*consistent* or *inconsistent*) consistent

Solve each system of linear equations.

SEE EXAMPLE 1 p. 350

2. $\begin{cases} y = x + 1 \\ -x + y = 3 \end{cases}$ $\varnothing$
3. $\begin{cases} 3x + y = 6 \\ y = -3x + 2 \end{cases}$ $\varnothing$
4. $\begin{cases} -y = 4x + 1 \\ 4x + y = 2 \end{cases}$ $\varnothing$

SEE EXAMPLE 2 p. 351

5. $\begin{cases} y = -x + 3 \\ x + y - 3 = 0 \end{cases}$ inf. many solutions
6. $\begin{cases} y = 2x - 4 \\ 2x - y - 4 = 0 \end{cases}$ inf. many solutions
7. $\begin{cases} -7x + y = -2 \\ 7x - y = 2 \end{cases}$ inf. many solutions

SEE EXAMPLE 3 p. 352

Classify each system. Give the number of solutions.

8. $\begin{cases} y = 2(x + 3) \\ -2y = 2x + 6 \end{cases}$
9. $\begin{cases} y = -3x - 1 \\ 3x + y = 1 \end{cases}$
10. $\begin{cases} 9y = 3x + 18 \\ \frac{1}{3}x - y = -2 \end{cases}$

SEE EXAMPLE 4 p. 352

11. **Athletics** Micah walks on a treadmill at 4 miles per hour. He has walked 2 miles when Luke starts running at 6 miles per hour on the treadmill next to him. If their rates continue, will Luke's distance ever equal Micah's distance? Explain.
Yes; the graphs of the two equations have different slopes so they intersect.

PRACTICE AND PROBLEM SOLVING

Solve each system of linear equations.

12. $\begin{cases} y = 2x - 2 \\ -2x + y = 1 \end{cases}$ $\varnothing$
13. $\begin{cases} x + y = 3 \\ y = -x - 1 \end{cases}$ $\varnothing$
14. $\begin{cases} x + 2y = -4 \\ y = -\frac{1}{2}x - 4 \end{cases}$ $\varnothing$
15. $\begin{cases} -6 + y = 2x \\ y = 2x - 36 \end{cases}$ $\varnothing$
16. $\begin{cases} y = -2x + 3 \\ 2x + y - 3 = 0 \end{cases}$ inf. many solutions
17. $\begin{cases} y = x - 2 \\ x - y - 2 = 0 \end{cases}$ inf. many solutions
18. $\begin{cases} x + y = -4 \\ y = -x - 4 \end{cases}$ inf. many solutions
19. $\begin{cases} -9x - 3y = -18 \\ 3x + y = 6 \end{cases}$

19. inf. many solutions

Answers to *Think and Discuss*

1. The graph is one line. The slopes and y-intercepts are the same.
2. solving algebraically by substitution or elimination, comparing slopes and y-intercepts, or graphing
3. See p. A5.

6-4 Exercises

Assignment Guide

Assign *Guided Practice* exercises as necessary.

If you finished Examples **1–2**
Proficient 12–19, 24–32 even
Advanced 12–19, 25–29 odd

If you finished Examples **1–4**
Proficient 12–23, 24–32 even, 33–34, 37–44
Advanced 12–23, 29–44

Homework Quick Check
Quickly check key concepts.
Exercises: 12, 16, 18, 22, 23

Answers

8. cons., indep.; one sol.
9. inconsis.; no sol.
10. cons., dep.; inf. many solutions

California Standards

Standard	Exercises
3.0	39–41
5.0	37, 38
6.0	42–44
8.0	11, 23, 24, 27, 28c, 29, 31
9.0	2–7, 12–19, 25–26, 30b, 36a, 36b
24.1	36c

Teaching Tip

Critical Thinking There are infinitely many answers to **Exercise 25.** Many students might choose $4 for a DVD and $1 for a video because that solution is easy to see. Encourage students to find decimal solutions, such as $3.50 and $2.

Teaching Tip

Visual In dependent systems, such as in **Exercise 27,** have students substitute solutions of one equation into the other equation to show that the solutions of one equation are also solutions of the other.

Exercise 30 involves writing and solving a system of equations to compare cost. This exercise prepares students for the Concept Connection on page 362.

Answers

24. No; the graphs of the two equations are parallel lines, so there is no solution.
25. There are inf. many answers for the cost of each video game and DVD. The system is consis. and dep.

28b.

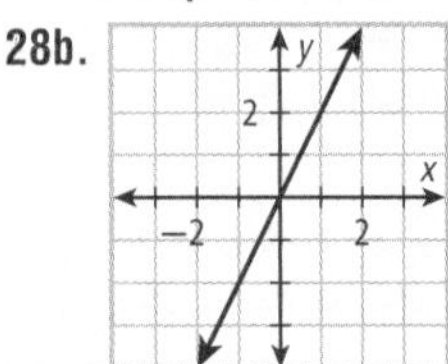

a line

c. The equations are the same.

d. The graph will now have 2 parallel lines. The equations have the same slope but different y-intercepts.

30. See p. A21.

Independent Practice

For Exercises	See Example
12–15	1
16–19	2
20–22	3
23	4

Extra Practice

Skills Practice p. EP12

Application Practice p. EP29

California LINK

Geology

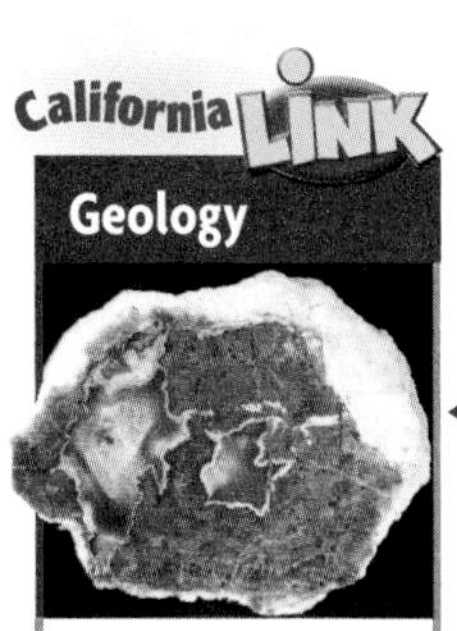

Geodes are rounded, hollow rock formations. Most are partially or completely filled with layers of colored quartz crystals. Geodes have been found at the Hauser Geode Beds near Blythe, CA, since the early 1930s.

Classify each system. Give the number of solutions.

20. $\begin{cases} y = -x + 5 \\ x + y = 5 \end{cases}$ **cons., dep.; inf. many solutions**

21. $\begin{cases} y = -3x + 2 \\ y = 3x \end{cases}$ **cons., indep.; one sol.**

22. $\begin{cases} y - 1 = 2x \\ y = 2x - 1 \end{cases}$ **inconsis.; no sol.**

23. **Sports** Mandy is skating at 5 miles per hour. Nikki is skating at 6 miles per hour and started 1 mile behind Mandy. If their rates stay the same, will Mandy catch up with Nikki? Explain. **Yes; the graphs of the two equations have different slopes, so they intersect.**

24. **Multi-Step** Photocopier A can print 35 copies per minute. Photocopier B can print 35 copies per minute. Copier B is started and makes 10 copies. Copier A is then started. If the copiers continue, will the number of copies from machine A ever equal the number of copies from machine B? Explain.

25. **Entertainment** One week Trey rented 4 DVDs and 2 video games for $18. The next week he rented 2 DVDs and 1 video game for $9. Find the rental costs for each video game and DVD. Explain your answer.

26. Rosa bought 1 pound of cashews and 2 pounds of peanuts for $10. At the same store, Sabrina bought 2 pounds of cashews and 1 pound of peanuts for $11. Find the cost per pound for cashews and peanuts. **cashews: $4/lb; peanuts: $3/lb**

27. **Geology** Pam and Tommy collect geodes. Pam's parents gave her 2 geodes to start her collection, and she buys 4 every year. Tommy has 2 geodes that were given to him for his birthday the same year Pam started her collection. He buys 4 every year. If Pam and Tommy continue to buy the same amount of geodes per year, when will Tommy have as many geodes as Pam? Explain your answer. **They will always have the same amount; both started with 2 and add 4 every year.**

28. Use the data given in the tables.

x	3	4	5	6
y	6	8	10	12

x	12	13	14	15
y	24	26	28	30

a. Write an equation to describe the data in each table. **$y = 2x$; $y = 2x$**

b. Graph the system of equations from part **a**. Describe the graph.

c. How could you have predicted the graph by looking at the equations?

d. **What if...?** Each y-value in the second table increases by 1. How does this affect the graphs of the two equations? How can you tell how the graphs would be affected without actually graphing?

29. **Critical Thinking** Describe the graphs of two equations if the result of solving the system by substitution or elimination is the statement $1 = 3$. **The graph will be 2 parallel lines.**

CONCEPT CONNECTION

30. This problem will prepare you for the Concept Connection on page 362.

The Crusader pep club is selling team buttons that support the sports teams. They contacted Buttons, Etc. which charges $50 plus $1.10 per button, and Logos, which charges $40 plus $1.10 per button.

a. Write an equation for each company's cost.

b. Use the system from part **a** to find when the price for both companies is the same. Explain.

c. What part of the equation should the pep club negotiate to change so that the cost of Buttons, Etc. is the same as Logos? What part of the equation should change in order to get a better price?

6-4 PRACTICE A

6-4 PRACTICE C

6-4 PRACTICE B

LESSON 6-4 Practice B

Solving Special Systems

Solve each system of linear equations.

1. $\begin{cases} y = 2x - 3 \\ y - 2x = -3 \end{cases}$ **infinitely many solutions**

2. $\begin{cases} 3x + y = 4 \\ -3x = y - 7 \end{cases}$ **no solution**

3. $\begin{cases} y = -4x + 1 \\ 4x = -y - 6 \end{cases}$ **no solution**

4. $\begin{cases} y - x + 3 = 0 \\ x = y + 3 \end{cases}$ **infinitely many solutions**

Classify each system. Give the number of solutions.

5. $\begin{cases} y = 3(x - 1) \\ -y + 3x = 3 \end{cases}$ **consistent, dependent; infinitely many solutions**

6. $\begin{cases} y - 2x = 5 \\ x = y - 3 \end{cases}$ **consistent, independent; one solution**

7. Sabina and Lou are reading the same book. Sabina reads 12 pages a day. She had read 36 pages when Lou started the book, and Lou reads at a pace of 15 pages per day. If their reading rates continue, will Sabina and Lou ever be reading the same page on the same day? Explain. **Yes. The graphs of the two equations have different slopes. They will intersect.**

8. Brandon started jogging at 4 miles per hour. After he jogged 1 mile, his friend Anton started jogging along the same path at a pace of 4 miles per hour. If they continue to jog at the same rate, will Anton ever catch up with Brandon? Explain. **No. The graphs of the two equations are parallel lines. They will never intersect.**

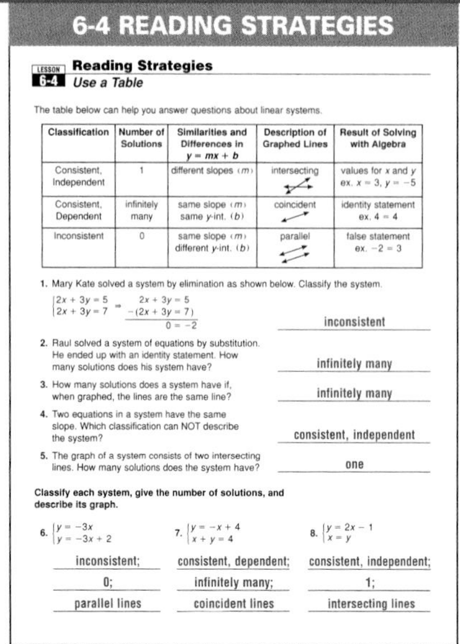

6-4 READING STRATEGIES

LESSON 6-4 Reading Strategies

Use a Table

The table below can help you answer questions about linear systems.

Classification	Number of Solutions	Similarities and Differences in $y = mx + b$	Description of Graphed Lines	Result of Solving with Algebra
Consistent, Independent	1	different slopes (m)	intersecting	values for x and y ex. $x = 3$, $y = -5$
Consistent, Dependent	infinitely many	same slope (m) same y-int. (b)	coincident	identity statement ex. $4 = 4$
Inconsistent	0	same slope (m) different y-int. (b)	parallel	false statement ex. $-2 = 3$

1. Mary Kate solved a system by elimination as shown below. Classify the system.
$\begin{cases} 2x + 3y = 5 \\ 2x + 3y = 7 \end{cases} \Rightarrow \begin{array}{r} 2x + 3y = 5 \\ -(2x + 3y = 7) \\ \hline 0 = -2 \end{array}$ **inconsistent**

2. Raul solved a system of equations by substitution. He ended up with an identity statement. How many solutions does his system have? **infinitely many**

3. How many solutions does a system have if, when graphed, the lines are the same line? **infinitely many**

4. Two equations in a system have the same slope. Which classification can NOT describe the system? **consistent, independent**

5. The graph of a system consists of two intersecting lines. How many solutions does the system have? **one**

Classify each system, give the number of solutions, and describe its graph.

6. $\begin{cases} y = -3x \\ y = -3x + 2 \end{cases}$ **inconsistent; 0; parallel lines**

7. $\begin{cases} y = -x + 4 \\ x + y = 4 \end{cases}$ **consistent, dependent; infinitely many; coincident lines**

8. $\begin{cases} y = 2x - 1 \\ x = y \end{cases}$ **consistent, independent; 1; intersecting lines**

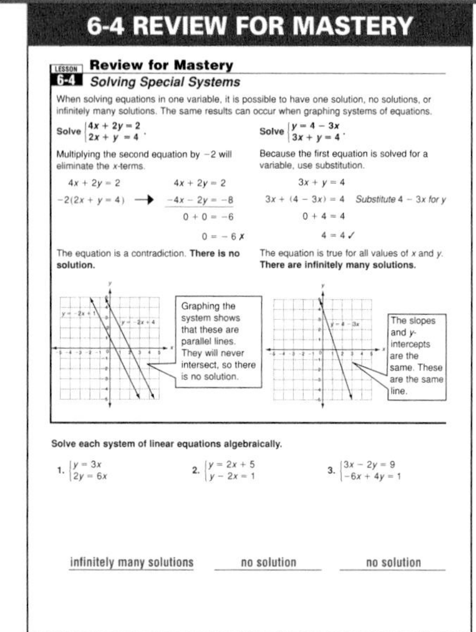

6-4 REVIEW FOR MASTERY

LESSON 6-4 Review for Mastery

Solving Special Systems

When solving equations in one variable, it is possible to have one solution, no solutions, or infinitely many solutions. The same results can occur when graphing systems of equations.

Solve $\begin{cases} 4x + 2y = 2 \\ 2x + y = 4 \end{cases}$.

Multiplying the second equation by -2 will eliminate the x-terms.

$4x + 2y = 2 \qquad\qquad 4x + 2y = 2$

$-2(2x + y = 4) \longrightarrow \underline{-4x - 2y = -8}$

$0 + 0 = -6$

$0 = -6$ ✗

The equation is a contradiction. **There is no solution.**

Solve $\begin{cases} y = 4 - 3x \\ 3x + y = 4 \end{cases}$.

Because the first equation is solved for a variable, use substitution.

$3x + y = 4$

$3x + (4 - 3x) = 4$ *Substitute $4 - 3x$ for y*

$0 + 4 = 4$

$4 = 4$ ✓

The equation is true for all values of x and y. **There are infinitely many solutions.**

y = 4 − 3x
The slopes and y-intercepts are the same. These are the same line.

Solve each system of linear equations algebraically.

1. $\begin{cases} y = 3x \\ 2y = 6x \end{cases}$ **infinitely many solutions**

2. $\begin{cases} y = 2x + 5 \\ y - 2x = 1 \end{cases}$ **no solution**

3. $\begin{cases} 3x - 2y = 9 \\ -6x + 4y = 1 \end{cases}$ **no solution**

31. **ERROR ANALYSIS** Student A says there is no solution to the graphed system of equations. Student B says there is one solution. Which student is incorrect? Explain the error.
Student A; the lines are not parallel, so they will intersect.

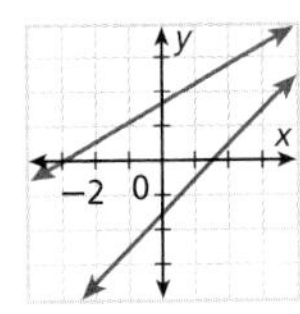

32. **Write About It** Compare the graph of a system that is consistent and independent with the graph of a system that is consistent and dependent.

32. The graph of a system that is consistent and independent shows 2 lines that intersect at 1 point. The graph of a system that is consistent and dependent shows only 1 line.

Multiple Choice **For Exercises 33 and 34, choose the best answer.**

33. Which of the following classifications fit the following system?

$$\begin{cases} 2x - y = 3 \\ 6x - 3y = 9 \end{cases}$$

(A) Inconsistent and independent
(B) Consistent and independent
(C) Inconsistent and dependent
(D) Consistent and dependent

34. Which of the following would be enough information to classify a system of two linear equations?

(A) The graphs have the same slope.
(B) The y-intercepts are the same.
(C) The graphs have different slopes.
(D) The y-intercepts are different.

CHALLENGE AND EXTEND

35. What conditions are necessary for the system $\begin{cases} y = 2x + p \\ y = 2x + q \end{cases}$ to have infinitely many solutions? no solution? **$p = q$; $p \neq q$**

36. **Reasoning** Solve the systems in parts **a** and **b.** Use this information to make a conjecture about all solutions that exist for the system in part **c.**

a. $\begin{cases} 3x + 4y = 0 \\ 4x + 3y = 0 \end{cases}$ **(0, 0)**
b. $\begin{cases} 2x + 5y = 0 \\ 5x + 2y = 0 \end{cases}$ **(0, 0)**
c. $\begin{cases} ax + by = 0 \\ bx + ay = 0 \end{cases}$, for $a > 0$, $b > 0$, $a \neq b$ **(0, 0)**

SPIRAL STANDARDS REVIEW

3.0, 5.0, 6.0

Use the map to find the actual distances between each pair of cities. *(Lesson 2-5)*

37. from Hon to Averly **11 km**
38. from Averly to Lewers **6.25 km**

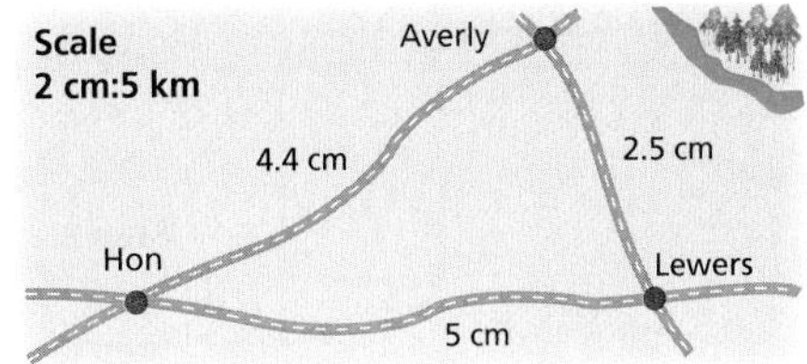

Solve each equation. *(Lesson 2-7)*

39. $|x - 2.5| = 6$ **−3.5, 8.5**
40. $|4x + 6| = -7$ **∅**
41. $|3z + 5| = 8$ **$-\frac{13}{3}$, 1**

Solve each system by graphing. *(Lesson 6-1)*

42. $\begin{cases} y = x - 2 \\ y = -x + 4 \end{cases}$ **(3, 1)**
43. $\begin{cases} y = 2x \\ x + y = -6 \end{cases}$ **(−2, −4)**
44. $\begin{cases} y = -\frac{1}{2}x \\ y - x = 9 \end{cases}$ **(−6, 3)**

Teaching Tip

Multiple Choice In **Exercise 33,** students can eliminate choices **A** and **C** because inconsistent systems are not classified as independent or dependent.

For **Exercise 33,** suggest that students think of the graphs of each answer.

Journal

Have students explain how they can determine the number of solutions of a system of equations by comparing them by writing the equations in slope-intercept form and comparing m and b.

ALTERNATIVE ASSESSMENT

Have students work in pairs to make a poster that describes and classifies all three types of systems of equations. Have them include the result of solving each type algebraically.

Power Presentations with PowerPoint®

6-4 Lesson Quiz

Solve and classify each system.

1. $\begin{cases} y = 5x - 1 \\ 5x - y - 1 = 0 \end{cases}$ infinitely many solutions; consistent, dependent

2. $\begin{cases} y = 4 + x \\ -x + y = 1 \end{cases}$ no solutions; inconsistent

3. $\begin{cases} y = 3(x + 1) \\ y = x - 2 \end{cases}$ $\left(-\frac{5}{2}, -\frac{9}{2}\right)$; consistent, independent

4. If the pattern in the table continues, when will sales for Hats Off equal sales for Tops? never

Hat Sales (thousands)				
Year	2004	2005	2006	2007
Hats Off	6.2	8	9.8	11.6
Tops	3.5	5.3	7.1	8.9

Also available on transparency

6-4 PROBLEM SOLVING

LESSON 6-4 **Problem Solving**
Solving Special Systems

Write the correct answer.

1. Tyra and Charmian are training for a bike race. Tyra has logged 256 miles so far and rides 48 miles per week. Charmian has logged 125 miles so far and rides 48 miles per week. If these rates continue, will Tyra's distance ever equal Charmian's distance? Explain.
No; the graphs are parallel lines so there is no solution.

2. Metroplexpress and Local Express are courier companies. Metroplexpress charges $15 to pick up a package and $0.50 per mile. Local Express charges $10 to pick up a package and $0.55 per mile. Classify this system and find its solution, if any.
consistent and independent; 100 mi and $65

3. The Singhs start savings accounts for their twin boys. The accounts earn 5% annual interest. The initial deposit in each account is $200. Classify this system and find its solution, if any.
consistent and dependent; infinitely many solutions

4. Frank earns $8 per hour. Madison earns $7.50 per hour. Frank started working after Madison had already earned $300. If these rates continue, will Frank's earnings ever equal Madison's earnings? If so, when?
Yes; at 600 hours.

Select the best answer.

5. A studio apartment at The Oaks costs $400 per month plus a $350 deposit. A studio apartment at Crossroads costs $400 per month plus a $300 deposit. How many solutions does this system have?
(A) no solutions
B 1 solution
C 2 solutions
D an infinite number of solutions

6. Jane and Gary are both landscape designers. Jane charges $75 for a consultation plus $25 per hour. Gary charges $50 for a consultation plus $30 per hour. For how many hours will Jane's charges equal Gary's charges?
F never
G after 2 hours
(H) after 5 hours
J always

7. A tank filled with 75 liters of water loses 0.5 liter of water per hour. A tank filled with 50 liters of water loses 0.1 liter of water per hour. How would this system be classified?
A inconsistent
B dependent
(C) consistent and independent
D consistent and dependent

8. Simon is 3 years older than Renata. Five years ago, Renata was half as old as Simon is now. How old are Simon and Renata now?
F Simon is 13 and Renata is 10.
G Simon is 15 and Renata is 10.
H Simon is 16 and Renata is 8.
(J) Simon is 16 and Renata is 13.

6-4 CHALLENGE

LESSON 6-4 **Challenge**
Pick a Path

The puzzle below contains 23 linear equations. You goal is to find paths through the puzzle such that each pair of equations along your path forms a special type of system.

You must begin in the **Start** square, and end in the **Finish** square. Moves can be horizontal, vertical, or diagonal between adjacent squares. Each individual path cannot cross itself, but your answers to 1 and 2 might cross.

Start → ↓ ↘	1: $y = x + 2$	2: $3x = 3y - 6$	3: $3x + y = -1$	4: $8y = 8x + 16$
5: $y = 2x + 3$	6: $y = 3x - 1$	7: $y - x = 2$	8: $\frac{1}{3}x + \frac{1}{3}y = 1$	9: $3x = y + 1$
10: $2y = 6x + 6$	11: $2x - y = -3$	12: $2x + 2y = 4$	13: $2y - 4 = 2x$	14: $x - y = -2$
15: $\frac{1}{2}y = \frac{3}{2}x + \frac{1}{2}$	16: $3y = 2x + 1$	17: $3x - y = 4$	18: $\frac{1}{6}y = \frac{1}{3}x + \frac{1}{2}$	19: $\frac{1}{2}y = \frac{1}{2}x + 1$
20: $10x + 15y = 5$	21: $-12x + 4y = 8$	22: $\frac{1}{2}y = \frac{1}{3}x + \frac{1}{6}$	23: $x = \frac{1}{3}y + 1$	↘ ↓ → **Finish**

Find a path through the puzzle such that each pair of equations forms...

1. ...a consistent and dependent system.
Start – 1 – 2 – 7 – 13 – 14 – 19 – Finish

2. ...an inconsistent system.
Start – 6 – 10 – 15 – 21 – 17 – 23 – Finish

6-5 Organizer

Objective: Use systems of equations to solve application problems.

Countdown to Mastery Week 13

Power Presentations with PowerPoint®

Warm Up

Simplify each expression.

1. $3(10a + 4) - 2$ $\quad 30a + 10$

2. $5(20 - t) + 8t$ $\quad 100 + 3t$

3. $(8m + 2n) - (5m + 3n)$

$3m - n$

Solve by using any method.

4. $\begin{cases} y - 2x = 4 \\ x + y = 7 \end{cases}$ $\quad (1, 6)$

5. $\begin{cases} 2x - y = -1 \\ y = x + 5 \end{cases}$ $\quad (4, 9)$

Also available on transparency

Math Humor

Q: What do you use to solve a math problem about a half-dozen roses?

A: A "six-stem" of equations.

California Standards

Algebra 1 9.0, 15.0

6-5 Applying Systems

California Standards

9.0 Students solve a system of two linear equations in two variables algebraically and are able to interpret the answer graphically. Students are able to solve a system of two linear inequalities in two variables and to sketch the solution sets.

15.0 Students apply algebraic techniques to solve rate problems, work problems, **and percent mixture problems.**

Who uses this?

Kayakers can calculate their rate of speed by solving a system of equations.

When a kayaker paddles downstream, the river's current helps the kayaker move faster, so the speed of the current is added to the kayaker's speed in still water to find the total speed. When a kayaker is going upstream, the speed of the current is subtracted from the kayaker's speed in still water.

You can use these ideas and a system of equations to solve problems about rates of speed.

EXAMPLE 1 **Solving Rate Problems**

Ben paddles his kayak 8 miles upstream in 4 hours. He turns around and paddles downstream to his starting point in 2 hours. What is the rate at which Ben paddles in still water? What is the rate of the river's current?

Let b be the rate at which Ben paddles in still water, and let c be the rate of the current.

Use a table to set up two equations—one for the upstream trip and one for the downstream trip.

Remember!

rate • time = distance

	Rate	•	Time	=	Distance
Upstream	$b - c$	•	4	=	8
Downstream	$b + c$	•	2	=	8

Solve the system $\begin{cases} 4(b - c) = 8 \\ 2(b + c) = 8 \end{cases}$. First write the system as $\begin{cases} 4b - 4c = 8 \\ 2b + 2c = 8 \end{cases}$, and then use elimination.

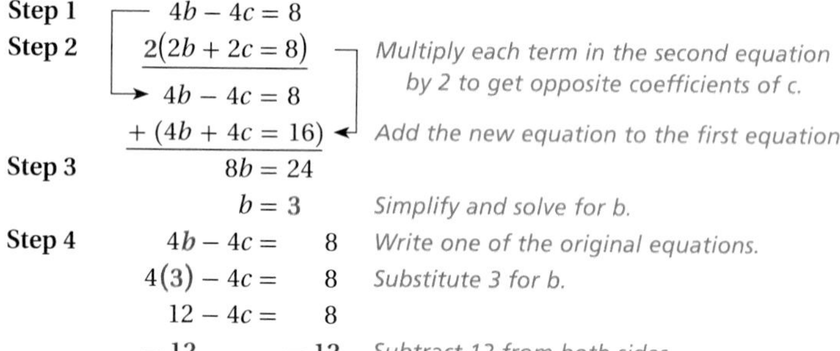

Step 1 $\quad 4b - 4c = 8$

Step 2 $\quad 2(2b + 2c = 8)$ *Multiply each term in the second equation by 2 to get opposite coefficients of c.*

$4b - 4c = 8$

$+ (4b + 4c = 16)$ *Add the new equation to the first equation.*

Step 3 $\quad 8b = 24$

$b = 3$ *Simplify and solve for b.*

Step 4 $\quad 4b - 4c = 8$ *Write one of the original equations.*

$4(3) - 4c = 8$ *Substitute 3 for b.*

$12 - 4c = 8$

$-12 \quad -12$ *Subtract 12 from both sides.*

$-4c = -4$ *Simplify and solve for c.*

$c = 1$

Step 5 $\quad (3, 1)$ *Write the solution as an ordered pair.*

Ben paddles at 3 mi/h in still water. The rate of the current is 1 mi/h.

1 Introduce

EXPLORATION

6-5 Applying Systems

The distance between Los Angeles and New York is 3000 miles. A jet flying from Los Angeles to New York with a tailwind makes the trip in 5 hours. On the return trip, the wind goes against the jet and the trip takes 6 hours.

Los Angeles — 6 hours — 3000 miles — 5 hours — New York

Direction of Wind

1. Suppose the speed of the jet is j and the speed of the wind is w. The overall speed of the jet as it flies with the wind from Los Angeles to New York is the jet's speed plus the wind's speed. Write an expression for the overall speed of the jet from Los Angeles to New York.
2. The overall speed of the jet as it flies against the wind from New York to Los Angeles is the jet's speed minus the wind's speed. Write an expression for the overall speed of the jet as it flies from New York to Los Angeles.
3. Use your expressions from Steps 1 and 2 to complete the *Rate* column of the table. Use numbers to complete the other columns.

	Rate	Time	Distance
LA to NY			
NY to LA			

THINK AND DISCUSS

4. **Show** how you can use the formula rate × time = distance to write equations for each row of the table.

Motivate

Present the following puzzle to the class: The sum of the digits of a two-digit number is 10. When the digits are reversed, the new number is 36 more than the original number. What is the original number? 37

Ask students what strategies they used to solve the problem. Then tell them that they will learn how to use systems of equations to solve these types of puzzles.

Explorations and answers are provided in *Alternate Openers: Explorations Transparencies*.

1. Ben paddles his kayak along a course on a different river. Going upstream, it takes him 6 hours to complete the course. Going downstream, it takes him 2 hours to complete the same course. What is the rate of the current, and how long is the course?
1.5 mi/h; 9 mi

EXAMPLE 2 Solving Mixture Problems

A pharmacist wants to mix an ointment that is 6% zinc oxide with an ointment that is 12% zinc oxide to make 30 grams of an ointment that is 10% zinc oxide. How many grams of each ointment should the pharmacist mix together?

Let s be the number of grams of the 6% ointment, and let t be the number of grams of the 12% ointment.

Use a table to set up two equations—one for the amount of ointment and one for the amount of zinc oxide in the ointment.

	6% Ointment	+	12% Ointment	=	10% Ointment
Amount of Ointment (g)	s	+	t	=	30
Amount of Zinc Oxide (g)	$0.06s$	+	$0.12t$	=	$0.1(30) = 3$

Solve the system $\begin{cases} s + t = 30 \\ 0.06s + 0.12t = 3 \end{cases}$. Use substitution.

Step 1 $s + t = 30$; $\underline{-t \quad -t}$; $s = 30 - t$ — *Solve the first equation for s by subtracting t from both sides.*

Step 2 $0.06s + 0.12t = 3$; $0.06(30 - t) + 0.12t = 3$ — *Substitute 30 − t for s in the second equation.*

$0.06(30) - 0.06t + 0.12t = 3$; $1.8 - 0.06t + 0.12t = 3$ — *Distribute 0.06 to the expression in parentheses.*

Step 3 $1.8 + 0.06t = 3$ — *Simplify. Solve for t.*

$\underline{-1.8 \qquad -1.8}$; $0.06t = 1.2$ — *Subtract 1.8 from both sides.*

$\frac{0.06t}{0.06} = \frac{1.2}{0.06}$; $t = 20$ — *Divide both sides by 0.06.*

Step 4 $s + t = 30$ — *Write one of the original equations.*

$s + 20 = 30$ — *Substitute 20 for t.*

$\underline{-20 \quad -20}$; $s = 10$ — *Subtract 20 from both sides.*

Step 5 $(10, 20)$ — *Write the solution as an ordered pair.*

The pharmacist should use 10 grams of the 6% ointment and 20 grams of the 12% ointment.

2. Suppose the pharmacist wants to get the same result by mixing an ointment that is 9% zinc oxide with an ointment that is 15% zinc oxide. How many grams of each ointment should the pharmacist mix together?
25 g of the 9% solution; 5 g of the 15% solution

2 Teach

Guided Instruction

Remind students that when they use systems of equations to solve a problem, they should always begin by defining the variables. Emphasize that the problems in this lesson require students to write two equations in two variables. After presenting each example, stress that students should check their solution against the information that was presented in the problem.

Universal Access

Through Critical Thinking

Encourage students to use critical thinking to check that their answer to a mixture problem is reasonable. In **Example 2,** when mixing a 6% ointment with a 12% ointment to make a 10% ointment, it makes sense that more of the 12% ointment is needed since the target percentage, 10%, is closer to 12% than to 6%. If the goal had been a 9% ointment, equal amounts of the two ointments would have been blended together.

COMMON ERROR ALERT

Some students may forget to answer the question in the problem after solving the system of equations. Tell students that the solution to the system of equations may not be the final answer, and remind them to make sure they answer the question in the problem.

Power Presentations with PowerPoint®

Additional Examples

Example 1

With a tailwind, an airplane makes a 900-mile trip in 2.25 hours. On the return trip, the plane flies against the wind and makes the trip in 3 hours. What is the plane's speed? What is the wind's speed? 350 mi/h; 50 mi/h

Example 2

A chemist mixes a 20% saline solution and a 40% saline solution to get 60 milliliters of a 25% saline solution. How many milliliters of each saline solution should the chemist use in the mixture?

45 mL of the 20% solution; 15 mL of the 40% solution

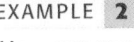

Also available on transparency

INTERVENTION

Questioning Strategies

EXAMPLE 1

- What is the relationship among distance, rate, and time?
- How could you check the solution to this problem?

EXAMPLE 2

- How can you find the total number of grams of zinc oxide in the mixture?
- What other methods could you use to solve the system of equations?

Inclusion Suggest to students that they start their solutions by creating a "dictionary" to identify the variables that they are using in the system. If they get confused, they can look back at their dictionary as a reference.

Power Presentations with PowerPoint®

Additional Examples

Example 3

The sum of the digits of a two-digit number is 10. When the digits are reversed, the new number is 54 more than the original number. What is the original number? 28

Also available on transparency

INTERVENTION

Questioning Strategies

EXAMPLE 3

- Why must you write the number in expanded form?
- How can you translate the first two sentences of the problem into two equations?

Teaching Tip **Number Sense** Once students have set up the variable t to represent the tens digit and u to represent the units digit, some students may be tempted to represent the original number with the expression tu. To explain why this is incorrect, show students an example with a specific number. For example, 63 is not the product of 6 and 3, but rather $6 \bullet 10 + 3$.

EXAMPLE 3 **Solving Number-Digit Problems**

The sum of the digits of a two-digit number is 7. When the digits are reversed, the new number is 45 less than the original number. What is the original number? Check your answer.

Helpful Hint

When you solve a number-digit problem, you must write numbers in expanded form.

Let t represent the tens digit of the original number, and let u represent the units digit. Write the original number and the new number in expanded form.

Original number: $10t + u$ **New number:** $10u + t$

Now set up two equations.

The sum of the digits in the **original number** is 7.

First equation: $t + u = 7$

The **new number** is **45 less than** the **original number.**

Second equation: $10u + t = (10t + u) - 45$

Simplify the second equation, so that the variables are only on the left side.

$$10u + t = 10t + u - 45$$
$$\underline{-10t \quad -10t}$$ *Subtract 10t from both sides.*

$$10u - 9t = u - 45$$
$$\underline{-u \quad -u}$$ *Subtract u from both sides.*

$$9u - 9t = -45$$

$$\frac{9u}{9} - \frac{9t}{9} = \frac{-45}{9}$$ *Divide both sides by 9.*

$$u - t = -5$$

$$-t + u = -5$$ *Write the left side with the variable t first.*

Now solve the system $\begin{cases} t + u = 7 \\ -t + u = -5 \end{cases}$. Use elimination.

Step 1 $t + u = 7$

Step 2 $\underline{-t + u = -5}$

Step 3 $2u = 2$ *Add the equations to eliminate the t-terms.*

$\frac{2u}{2} = \frac{2}{2}$ *Divide both sides by 2.*

$u = 1$

Step 4 $t + u = 7$ *Write one of the original equations.*

$t + 1 = 7$ *Substitute 1 for u.*

$\underline{-1 \quad -1}$ *Subtract 1 from both sides.*

$t = 6$

Step 5 $(6, 1)$ *Write the solution as an ordered pair.*

The original number is 61.

Check Check the solution using the original problem.
The sum of the digits is $6 + 1 = 7$. ✓
When the digits are reversed, the new number is 16, and $61 - 16 = 45$. ✓

CHECK IT OUT! **3.** The sum of the digits of a two-digit number is 17. When the digits are reversed, the new number is 9 more than the original number. What is the original number? Check your answer. **89**

3 Close

Summarize

Revisit the number puzzle that was presented in the Motivate section of the lesson. Ask students to write a system of equations for the problem and to use the system to find the solution.

$\begin{cases} t + u = 10 \\ 10u + t = (10t + u) + 36 \end{cases}$; 37

FORMATIVE ASSESSMENT and INTERVENTION

***Diagnose Before* the Lesson**
6-5 Warm Up, TE p. 356

***Monitor During* the Lesson**
Check It Out! Exercises, SE pp. 357–358
Questioning Strategies, TE pp. 357–358

***Assess After* the Lesson**
6-5 Lesson Quiz, TE p. 361
Alternative Assessment, TE p. 361

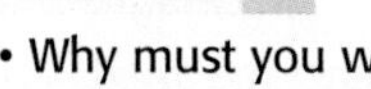

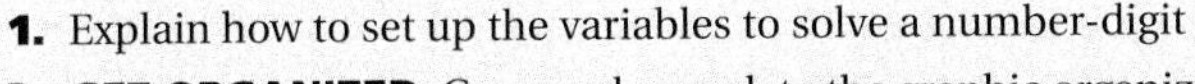

THINK AND DISCUSS

1. Explain how to set up the variables to solve a number-digit problem.

2. **GET ORGANIZED** Copy and complete the graphic organizer. In each box, write an example of each type of problem and find the solution.

Applications of Systems of Equations

Rate Problem | Mixture Problem | Number-Digit Problem

6-5 Exercises

9.0, 15.0, 25.2

Homework Help Online
KEYWORD: MA8CA 6-5
Parent Resources Online
KEYWORD: MA8CA Parent

GUIDED PRACTICE

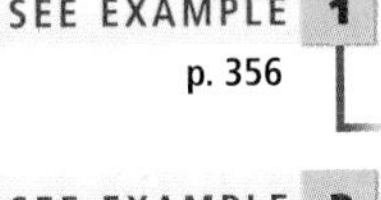
SEE EXAMPLE 1 p. 356

1. **Recreation** It takes Cathy 1.5 hours to paddle her canoe 6 miles upstream. Then she turns her canoe around and paddles 6 miles downstream in 1 hour. What is the rate of the current? What is Cathy's paddling rate in still water? **1 mi/h; 5 mi/h**

SEE EXAMPLE 2 p. 357

2. **Chemistry** A chemist mixed a 15% glucose solution with a 35% glucose solution. This mixture produced 35 liters of a 19% glucose solution. How many liters of each solution did the chemist use in the mixture? **28 L of the 15% solution; 7 L of the 35% solution**

SEE EXAMPLE 3 p. 358

3. The sum of the digits of a two-digit number is 14. When the digits are reversed, the new number is 36 more than the original number. What is the original number? Check your answer. **59**

PRACTICE AND PROBLEM SOLVING

Independent Practice

For Exercises	See Example
4	1
5	2
6	3

Extra Practice

Skills Practice p. EP13
Application Practice p. EP29

4. **Aviation** With a tailwind, a jet flew 2000 miles in 4 hours. The jet's return trip against the same wind required 5 hours. Find the jet's speed and the wind speed. **450 mi/h; 50 mi/h**
5. **Chemistry** A 4% salt solution is mixed with a 16% salt solution. How many milliliters of each solution are needed to obtain 600 milliliters of a 10% salt solution? **300 mL of each**
6. The sum of the digits of a two-digit number is 10. If 18 is added to the number, the digits will be reversed. Find the number. Check your answer. **46**
7. A coin bank contains 250 dimes and quarters worth a total of $39.25.
   a. Let q be the number of quarters, and let d be the number of dimes. Copy and complete the table.

	Quarters	+	Dimes	=	Total
Number of Coins	q	+	d	=	250
Value in Dollars	$0.25q$	+	$0.1d$	=	39.25

   b. Use the information in the table to write a system of equations.
   c. Find the number of quarters and the number of dimes in the bank.

b. $\begin{cases} q + d = 250 \\ 0.25q + 0.1d = 39.25 \end{cases}$

c. 95 quarters; 155 dimes

Answers to *Think and Discuss*

Possible answers:

1. Let one variable represent the tens digit, and let another variable represent the ones digit.
2. See p. A5.

6-5 Exercises

Assignment Guide

Assign *Guided Practice* exercises as necessary.

If you finished Examples **1–3**
Proficient 4–19, 22–32
Advanced 4–6, 10, 11, 13–32

Homework Quick Check
Quickly check key concepts.
Exercises: 4, 5, 6, 10, 11

Language Support For **Exercise 4,** help students understand the term *tailwind.* A tailwind blows in the same direction as the course of the plane. A wind that blows in the direction opposite the course of the plane is called a *headwind.*

ENGLISH LANGUAGE LEARNERS

California Standards

Standard	Exercises
1.1	22–24
3.0	25–28
9.0	3, 6, 7c, 8c, 9c, 11, 13b, 13c, 15, 17, 19, 29–32
15.0	1, 2, 4, 5, 10, 14, 16, 18, 20, 21
25.2	12

Exercise 13 involves writing and solving a system of equations to determine how many T-shirts a pep club should order. This exercise prepares students for the Concept Connection on page 362.

Answers

15. Possible answer: The sum of the digits of a two-digit number is 5. When the digits are reversed, the new number is 27 less than the original number. What is the original number?
Solution:
$\begin{cases} a + b = 5 \\ 10b + a = 10a + c - 27 \end{cases}$
so $a = 4$, $b = 1$, and the original number is 41.

22. $4(x) - 4(1) + x$ (Dist. Prop.);
$4x - 4 + x$ (Multiply.);
$4x + x - 4$ (Comm. Prop. of Add.);
$5x - 4$ (Combine like terms.)

23. $7a - 2(a) - 2(1)$ (Dist. Prop.);
$7a - 2a - 2$ (Multiply.);
$5a - 2$ (Combine like terms.)

24. $4x + 5x - 3x + x^2$ (Comm. Prop. of Add.); $6x + x^2$ (Combine like terms.)

8b. $\begin{cases} p + r = 1 \\ 1.25p + 2.75r = 1.75 \end{cases}$

c. $\frac{2}{3}$ lb peanuts; $\frac{1}{3}$ lb raisins

9a. $f + 4$; $d + 4$

b. $\begin{cases} f = d + 32 \\ f + 4 = 5(d + 4) \end{cases}$

c. father: 36; daughter: 4

13a. $\begin{cases} a + c = 100 \\ 13a + 8c = 1100 \end{cases}$

b. 60 adults'; 40 children's

c. 80 adults'; 20 children's

8. Business A grocery store sells a mixture of peanuts and raisins for \$1.75 per pound. Peanuts cost \$1.25 per pound, and raisins cost \$2.75 per pound. Follow the steps below to find the amount of raisins and peanuts that go into one pound of the mixture.

a. Let p be the amount of peanuts, and let r be the amount of raisins in one pound of the mixture. Copy and complete the table.

	Peanuts	+	Raisins	=	Total
Weight (lb)	p	+	r	=	**1**
Cost (\$)	$1.25p$	+	**$2.75r$**	=	1.75

b. Use the information in the table to write a system of equations.

c. Solve to find the amount of peanuts and raisins in the one-pound mixture.

9. A father is 32 years older than his daughter. In 4 years, the father will be 5 times as old as his daughter. Follow these steps to find their present ages.

a. Let f be the father's present age, and let d be the daughter's present age. Write expressions that give the father's age and the daughter's age in 4 years.

b. Write a system of equations based on the information in the problem.

c. Solve the system to find the present age of the father and daughter.

10. Multi-Step The manager of a food store wants to create a blend of herbs that she can sell for \$1 per ounce. She decides to make 8 ounces of a blend of oregano and sage. What will be the ratio of oregano to sage in the mixture? **3 to 1**

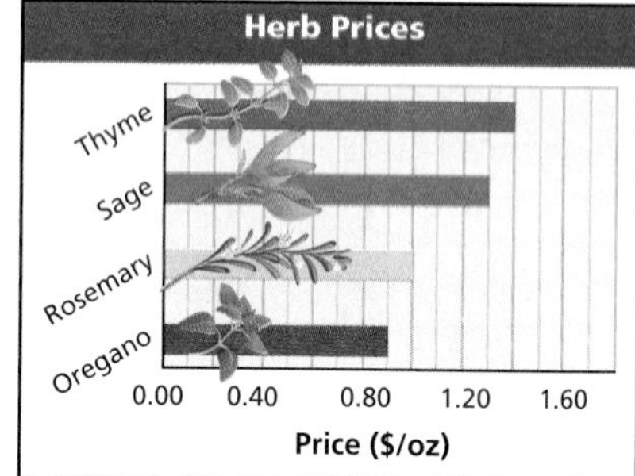

11. The sum of the digits of a two-digit number is 13. Twice the first digit is 1 less than the second digit. What is the two-digit number? **49**

12. ERROR ANALYSIS The sum of Anna's age and Mario's age is 30. Mario is 6 years older than Anna. Two students found Anna's age a as shown. Which solution is incorrect? Explain. **Solution A is incorrect. The second equation in the system should be $a = m - 6$.**

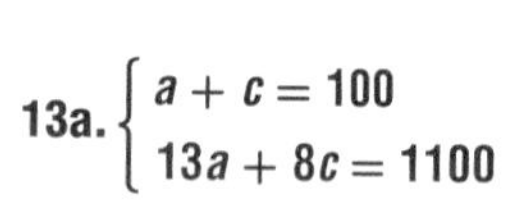

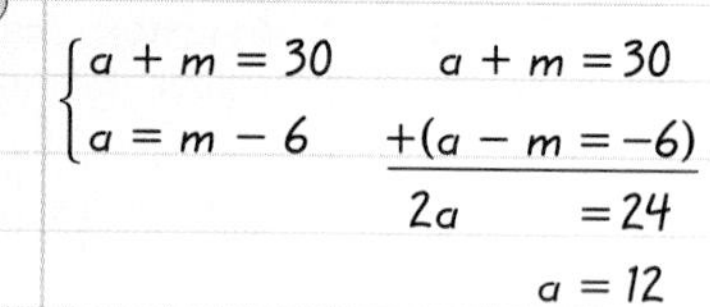

13. This problem will prepare you for the Concept Connection on page 362.

A pep club is planning to sell adults' T-shirts and children's T-shirts as a fund-raiser. The club will order a total of 100 shirts. The club's president wants to raise \$1100 from the sale of the shirts and proposes selling adults' shirts for \$13 each and children's shirts for \$8 each.

a. Write a system of equations that the president could use to determine the number of each type of shirt to order.

b. How many adults' shirts and children's shirts should the club order?

c. How many of each type of shirt should the club order to be able to raise \$1200?

6-5 PRACTICE A

6-5 PRACTICE C

6-5 PRACTICE B

LESSON 6-5 **Practice B**
Applying Systems

Solve each problem.

1. A chemist mixes a 10% saline solution with a 20% saline solution to make 500 milliliters of a 16% saline solution. How many milliliters of each solution does the chemist mix together?
200 mL of the 10% solution; 300 mL of the 20% solution

2. The sum of the digits of a two-digit number is 13. When the digits are reversed, the new number is 27 more than the original number. What is the original number? **58**

3. With a tailwind, a helicopter flies 300 miles in 1.5 hours. When the helicopter flies back against the same wind, the trip takes 3 hours. What is the helicopter's speed? What is the wind's speed?
150 mi/h; 50 mi/h

4. A jar contains 55 quarters and dimes. The total value of the coins is \$8.50. Find the number of quarters and dimes in the jar.
20 quarters; 35 dimes

5. Alex is 6 years older than Frank. The sum of their ages is 50. Find Alex's age and Frank's age.
Alex: 28; Frank: 22

6. Leticia is 21 years older than Katie. In 2 years, Leticia will be twice as old as Katie. Find Leticia's current age and Katie's current age.
Leticia: 40; Katie: 19

7. At the Snack Shack, dried cherries cost \$3.50 per pound. Dried apricots cost \$1.50 per pound. The store's owner wants to make 10 pounds of a cherry-apricot mixture that costs \$2.70 per pound. How many pounds of cherries and apricots should the owner use to make the mixture?
6 pounds of cherries; 4 pounds of apricots

8. The sum of the digits of a two-digit number is 14. The first digit is 4 less than twice the second digit. What is the number? **86**

6-5 READING STRATEGIES

LESSON 6-5 **Reading Strategies**
Recognize Errors

The table can help you recognize common errors in translating word problems into systems of equations.

Word Problem	System of Equations	Error
The sum of the digits of a two-digit number is 10. When the digits are reversed, the new number is 54 less than the original number. What is the original number?	Let t be the tens digit and let u be the units digit. $\begin{cases} t + u = 10 \\ ut = tu - 54 \end{cases}$	You must use expanded form to write the numbers. The correct system is: $\begin{cases} t + u = 10 \\ 10u + t = (10t + u) - 54 \end{cases}$
Jack mixes a 4% saline solution with a 10% saline solution to make 400 mL of an 8% saline solution. How many milliliters of each solution does he use?	Let f be the number of milliliters of the 4% solution and let t be the number of milliliters of the 10% solution. $\begin{cases} f + t = 400 \\ 4f + 10t = 32 \end{cases}$	You must write the percents as decimals. The correct system is: $\begin{cases} f + t = 400 \\ 0.4f + 0.1t = 32 \end{cases}$
A box contains 68 nickels and quarters. The value of the coins is \$13.60. How many nickels and how many quarters are in the box?	Let n be the number of nickels and let q be the number of quarters. $\begin{cases} n + q = 68 \\ 5n + 25q = 13.60 \end{cases}$	You must write the value of coins as decimals. The correct system is: $\begin{cases} n + q = 68 \\ 0.05n + 0.25q = 13.60 \end{cases}$

Tell whether the given system may be used to solve the problem. If not, write a correct system.

1. The sum of the digits of a two-digit number is 9. When the digits are reversed, the new number is 45 more than the original number. What is the original number?
$\begin{cases} t + u = 9 \\ ut = tu + 45 \end{cases}$ **No;** $\begin{cases} t + u = 9 \\ 10u + t = (10t + u) + 45 \end{cases}$

2. A jar contains pennies and dimes. There are 30 coins altogether and the total value of the coins is \$1.74. How many pennies and how many dimes are in the jar?
$\begin{cases} p + d = 30 \\ 1p + 10d = 1.74 \end{cases}$ **No;** $\begin{cases} p + d = 30 \\ 0.01p + 0.1d = 1.74 \end{cases}$

6-5 REVIEW FOR MASTERY

LESSON 6-5 **Review for Mastery**
Applying Systems

When you solve a mixture problem, you can use a table to help you set up the system of equations. Each row of the table gives you one of the equations in the system.

A chemist mixes a 12% alcohol solution with a 20% alcohol solution to make 300 milliliters of an 18% alcohol solution. How many milliliters of each solution does the chemist use?

Let a be the number of milliliters of the 12% solution. Let b be the number of milliliters of the 20% solution.

	12% Solution	+	20% Solution	=	18% Solution
Amount of Solution (mL)	a	+	b	=	300
Amount of Alcohol (mL)	$0.12a$	+	$0.2b$	=	(0.18)300

Write a system of equations by reading each row of the table: $\begin{cases} a + b = 300 \\ 0.12a + 0.2b = 54 \end{cases}$

Now use elimination or substitution to solve the system.

The solution is (75, 225). The chemist uses 75 milliliters of the 12% solution and 225 milliliters of the 20% solution.

Write a system of equations for each mixture problem. Then solve the problem.

1. Jenny mixes a 30% saline solution with a 50% saline solution to make 800 milliliters of a 45% saline solution. How many milliliters of each solution does she use?
$\begin{cases} a + b = 800 \\ 0.3a + 0.5b = 360 \end{cases}$; **200 mL of the 30% solution; 600 mL of the 50% solution**

2. A pharmacist wants to mix a medicine that is 10% aspirin with a medicine that is 25% aspirin to make 10 grams of a medicine that is 16% aspirin. How many grams of each medicine should the pharmacist mix together?
$\begin{cases} a + b = 10 \\ 0.1a + 0.25b = 1.6 \end{cases}$; **6 grams of the 10% medicine; 4 grams of the 25% medicine**

3. Peanuts cost \$1.60 per pound and raisins cost \$2.40 per pound. Brad wants to make 8 pounds of a peanut-raisin mixture that costs \$2.20 per pound. How many pounds of peanuts and raisins should he use?
$\begin{cases} p + r = 8 \\ 1.6p + 2.4r = 17.6 \end{cases}$; **2 pounds of peanuts; 6 pounds of raisins**

14. Poss. ans.: The amount of 10% sol. comes out to be a neg. number. There is no ans. to the problem because it is impossible to mix 2 weaker sol. together to make a stronger one.

15. Possible answer: The sum of the digits of a two-digit number is 5. When the digits are reversed, the new number is 27 less than the original number. What is the original number? Solution:
$\begin{cases} a+b=5 \\ 10b+a=10a+b-27 \end{cases}$
so $a=4$, $b=1$, and the original number is 41.

14. **Critical Thinking** A chemist wants to mix a 10% saline solution with a 15% saline solution to make 20 milliliters of an 18% saline solution. What happens when you try to solve a system of equations to determine the amount of each saline solution that the chemist should use? Why does this happen?

15. **Write About It** Write your own number-digit problem. Include a complete solution to the problem.

Multiple Choice For Exercises 16–18, choose the best answer.

16. With a tailwind, a plane makes a 3000-mile trip in 5 hours. On the return trip, the plane flies against the same wind and covers the 3000 miles in 6 hours. What is the speed of the wind?

Ⓐ 40 mi/h Ⓑ 50 mi/h (circled) Ⓒ 100 mi/h Ⓓ 550 mi/h

17. A jar contains quarters and dimes. There are 15 more quarters than dimes. The total value of the coins is \$23. Which system of equations can be used to find the number of quarters q and the number of dimes d?

Ⓐ $\begin{cases} q=d-15 \\ 0.25q+0.1d=0.23 \end{cases}$ Ⓒ $\begin{cases} d=q+15 \\ 0.25q+0.1d=23 \end{cases}$

Ⓑ $\begin{cases} q=d+15 \\ 0.25q+0.1d=0.23 \end{cases}$ Ⓓ (circled) $\begin{cases} q=d+15 \\ 0.25q+0.1d=23 \end{cases}$

18. Donnell wants to make a 2-pound mixture of cashews and pecans that costs \$2.60 per pound. How many pounds of cashews should he use?

Item	Price per Pound (\$)
Cashews	2.50
Pecans	3.00

Ⓐ 0.4 pound Ⓒ 1.2 pounds
Ⓑ 0.8 pound Ⓓ 1.6 pounds (circled)

CHALLENGE AND EXTEND

19. In 15 years, Maya will be twice as old as David is now. In 15 years, David will be as old as Maya will be 10 years from now. How old are Maya and David now? **Maya: 25; David: 20**

20. To train for a marathon, Mei runs an 18-mile course at a constant speed. If she doubles her usual speed, she can complete the course in an hour and a half less than her usual time. What is Mei's usual speed and her usual time to complete the course? **6 mi/h; 3 h**

21. Write a word problem that can be solved by solving this system of equations.
$\begin{cases} a+b=20 \\ 0.25a+0.5b=6 \end{cases}$
Possible answer: A chemist mixes a 25% acid solution and a 50% acid solution to make 20 mL of a 30% acid solution. How many milliliters of each solution should be used?

SPIRAL STANDARDS REVIEW

1.1, 3.0, 9.0

Use properties and operations to show that the first expression simplifies to the second expression. *(Lesson 1-7)*

22. $4(x-1)+x$, $5x-4$ 23. $7a-2(a+1)$, $5a-2$ 24. $4x+5x+x^2-3x$, $6x+x^2$

Solve each equation. Check your answer. *(Lesson 2-7)*

25. $2|x|+5=11$ **−3, 3** 26. $3+4|x|=3$ **0** 27. $|2x+1|=7$ **−4, 3** 28. $12=3|x+2|$ **−6, 2**

Solve each system of linear equations. Check your answer. *(Lesson 6-4)*

29. $\begin{cases} 2x-y=1 \\ x=\frac{1}{2}y+1 \end{cases}$ **∅** 30. $\begin{cases} -2y=x-1 \\ x+2y=1 \end{cases}$ **inf. many solutions** 31. $\begin{cases} x-y=2 \\ 2x=2y+4 \end{cases}$ **inf. many solutions** 32. $\begin{cases} x+y=3 \\ x+1=-y \end{cases}$ **∅**

COMMON ERROR ALERT

In **Exercise 9,** students may translate the sentence "In 4 years, the father will be 5 times as old as his daughter" by writing the equation $f+4=5d$. Remind students that the daughter will also be 4 years older at this time, and so the correct equation is $f+4=5(d+4)$.

Multiple Choice In **Exercise 17,** since there are 15 more quarters than dimes, one of the equations in the system must be $q=d+15$ or an equivalent equation. Students can use this information to eliminate choices **A** and **C**.

Journal

Have students write a step-by-step guide to solving rate problems, mixture problems, and number-digit problems.

Have students choose one of the three types of problems presented in this lesson. Students should write an original problem of that type, provide a complete solution, and show how to check the answer.

Power Presentations with PowerPoint®

6-5 Lesson Quiz

1. Allyson paddles her canoe 9 miles upstream in 4.5 hours. The return trip downstream takes her 1.5 hours. What is the rate at which Allyson paddles in still water? What is the rate of the current? 4 mi/h; 2 mi/h

2. A pharmacist mixes Lotion A, which is 5% alcohol, with Lotion B, which is 10% alcohol, to make 50 mL of a new lotion that is 8% alcohol. How many milliliters of Lotions A and B go into the mixture? 20 mL of Lotion A and 30 mL of Lotion B

3. The sum of the digits of a two-digit number is 13. When the digits are reversed, the new number is 9 less than the original number. What is the original number? 76

Also available on transparency

6-5 PROBLEM SOLVING

LESSON 6-5 **Problem Solving**
Applying Systems

Write the correct answer.

1. Paula rows a boat 6 miles upstream in 3 hours. She returns 6 miles downstream in 2 hours. What is the rate at which Paula rows in still water? What is the rate of the current?
2.5 mi/h; 0.5 mi/h

2. The sum of the digits of a two-digit number is 10. When the digits are reversed, the new number is 36 less than the original number. What is the original number?
73

3. Jerome mixes a solution that is 8% alcohol with a solution that is 14% alcohol to make 600 milliliters of a solution that is 12% alcohol. How many milliliters of each solution does he mix together?
200 mL of the 8% solution; 400 mL of the 14% solution

4. A jar contains a total of 38 nickels and dimes. The total value of the coins is \$2.75. How many nickels and how many dimes are in the jar?
21 nickels; 17 dimes

The table shows prices of dried beans at a grocery store. Use the table for questions 5 and 6. Select the best answer.

5. Kai bought pinto beans and lima beans. He bought twice as many pounds of pinto beans as lima beans and he spent a total of \$22. Which system can be used to find the number of pounds of each type of bean that Kai bought?

A $\begin{cases} l=2p \\ 1.5l+2.5p=22 \end{cases}$ C $\begin{cases} l=2p \\ 2.5l+1.5p=22 \end{cases}$

Ⓑ (circled) $\begin{cases} p=2l \\ 1.5p+2.5l=22 \end{cases}$ D $\begin{cases} p=2l \\ 2.5l+1.5p=22 \end{cases}$

6. The store's manager wants to make 10 pounds of a mixture consisting of black beans and garbanzo beans. She wants to sell the mixture for \$2.60 per pound. How many pounds of garbanzo beans should she use?

F 2 pounds H 6 pounds
G 4 pounds Ⓙ (circled) 8 pounds

Bean	Price per Pound	Bean	Price per Pound
Black	\$2.00	Lima	\$2.50
Garbanzo	\$2.75	Navy	\$1.75
Kidney	\$2.25	Pinto	\$1.50

6-5 CHALLENGE

LESSON 6-5 **Challenge**
What's the Problem?

Write a word problem that can be solved using each system of equations. Then give the answer to the problem. Possible responses given.

1. $\begin{cases} q+d=40 \\ 0.25q+0.1d=6.25 \end{cases}$

Problem: **Carmen has 40 quarters and dimes. The total value of the coins is \$6.25. How many quarters and how many dimes does she have?**

Answer: **15 quarters; 25 dimes**

2. $\begin{cases} f+t=300 \\ 0.05f+0.1t=(0.08)300 \end{cases}$

Problem: **A chemist mixes a 5% saline solution and a 10% saline solution to make 300 milliliters of an 8% saline solution. How much of each solution does she use?**

Answer: **120 mL of the 5% solution; 180 mL of the 10% solution**

3. $\begin{cases} a+c=75 \\ 6.75a+3.25c=327.75 \end{cases}$

Problem: **Adult tickets cost \$6.75 and children's tickets cost \$3.25. A total of 75 tickets were sold. The total revenue was \$327.75. How many of each type of ticket were sold?**

Answer: **24 adult tickets; 51 children's tickets**

4. $\begin{cases} n=m+14 \\ n+2=2(m+2) \end{cases}$

Problem: **Nick is 14 years older than Mike. In two years, Nick will be twice as old as Mike. What are the current ages of Nick and Mike?**

Answer: **Nick: 26; Mike: 12**

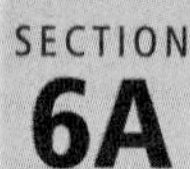

Concept Connection

Organizer

Objective: Assess students' ability to apply concepts and skills in Lessons 6-1 through 6-5 in a real-world format.

Online Edition

Problem	Text Reference
1	Lesson 6-2
2	Lessons 6-1, 6-2, 6-3, 6-4
3	Lessons 6-1, 6-2, 6-3
4	Lessons 6-1, 6-2, 6-3
5	Lessons 6-1, 6-2, 6-3

Concept Connection

SECTION 6A

Systems of Equations

1. Spirit for You; for 100 fingers Spirit charges \$285 and Go Team charges \$320.

We've Got Spirit Some cheerleaders are going to sell spirit bracelets and foam fingers to raise money for traveling to away games.

1. Two companies, Spirit for You and Go Team, are interested in providing the foam fingers. The cheerleaders plan to sell 100 foam fingers. Based on this information, which company should they choose? Explain your reasoning.

Company	Design fee	Cost per item
Spirit for You	\$35	\$2.50
Go Team	\$20	\$3.00

2. The cheerleaders sold foam fingers for \$5 and spirit bracelets for \$4. They sold 40 more foam fingers than bracelets, and they earned \$965. Write a system of equations to describe this situation.

2. $\begin{cases} f = b + 40 \\ 965 = 5f + 4b \end{cases}$

3. Solve this system using at least two different methods. Explain each method. **$f = 125$, $b = 85$; check students' work.**
4. Using the company you chose in Problem 1, how much profit did the cheerleaders make from the foam fingers alone? (*Hint:* profit = amount earned − expenses) **\$277.50**
5. What is the maximum price the cheerleaders could pay for each spirit bracelet in order to make a total profit of \$500? **\$1.38**

362

INTERVENTION 

Scaffolding Questions

1. **What are the variables in this problem situation?** The independent variable is the number of foam fingers. The dependent variable is the total cost.
2. **How do you calculate total sales?** For each item, multiply the number of items by the unit price, and then add the products.
3. **What are the possible ways that you can solve a system of equations?** Substitution, elimination, graphing, using a table
4. **What are expenses?** money spent to create products
5. **Which method is best for this situation? Explain.** Some students may prefer algebraic methods, while others will prefer using a graphing calculator.

Extension

If the cheerleaders needed to make a total profit of \$600, would the maximum price they pay for the spirit bracelets be more or less than the answer in **Problem 5**? Explain. less; because they could not spend as much up front

California Standards

Algebra 1 9.0

CHAPTER 6

SECTION 6A

Quiz for Lessons 6-1 Through 6-5

6-1 Solving Systems by Graphing

Tell whether the ordered pair is a solution of the given system.

1. $(-2, 1);\begin{cases} y = -2x - 3 \\ y = x + 3 \end{cases}$ yes
2. $(9, 2);\begin{cases} x - 4y = 1 \\ 2x - 3y = 3 \end{cases}$ no
3. $(3, -1);\begin{cases} y = -\frac{1}{3}x \\ y + 2x = 5 \end{cases}$ yes

Solve each system by graphing. Check your answer.

4. $\begin{cases} y = x + 5 \\ y = \frac{1}{2}x + 4 \end{cases}$ (−2, 3)
5. $\begin{cases} y = -x - 2 \\ 2x - y = 2 \end{cases}$ (0, −2)
6. $\begin{cases} \frac{2}{3}x + y = -3 \\ 4x + y = 7 \end{cases}$ (3, −5)
7. **Banking** Christiana and Marlena opened their first savings accounts on the same day. Christiana opened her account with $50 and plans to deposit $10 every month. Marlena opened her account with $30 and plans to deposit $15 every month. After how many months will their two accounts have the same amount of money? What will that amount be? 4 mo; $90

6-2 Solving Systems by Substitution

Solve each system by substitution. Check your answer.

8. $\begin{cases} y = -x + 5 \\ 2x + y = 11 \end{cases}$ (6, −1)
9. $\begin{cases} 4x - 3y = -1 \\ 3x - y = -2 \end{cases}$ (−1, −1)
10. $\begin{cases} y = -x \\ y = -2x - 5 \end{cases}$ (−5, 5)

6-3 Solving Systems by Elimination

Solve each system by elimination. Check your answer.

11. $\begin{cases} x + 3y = 15 \\ 2x - 3y = -6 \end{cases}$ (3, 4)
12. $\begin{cases} x + y = 2 \\ 2x + y = -1 \end{cases}$ (−3, 5)
13. $\begin{cases} -2x + 5y = -1 \\ 3x + 2y = 11 \end{cases}$ (3, 1)
14. It takes Akira 10 minutes to make a black and white drawing and 25 minutes for a color drawing. On Saturday he made a total of 9 drawings in 2 hours. Write and solve a system of equations to determine how many drawings of each type Akira made. $10x + 25y = 120$; $x + y = 9$; 7 black and white, 2 color

6-4 Solving Special Systems

Classify each system. Give the number of solutions.

15. $\begin{cases} 3x = -6y + 3 \\ 2y = -x + 1 \end{cases}$ cons., dep.; inf. many solutions
16. $\begin{cases} y = -4x + 2 \\ 4x + y = -2 \end{cases}$ incons.; no sol.
17. $\begin{cases} 4x - 3y = 8 \\ y = 4(x + 2) \end{cases}$ cons., indep.; one sol.

6-5 Applying Systems

18. The sum of the digits of a two-digit number is 6. When the digits are reversed, the new number is 18 more than the original number. What is the original number? Check your answer. 24

READY TO GO ON? SECTION 6A

Organizer

Objective: Assess students' mastery of concepts and skills in Lessons 6-1 through 6-5.

Countdown to Mastery Week 13

Resources

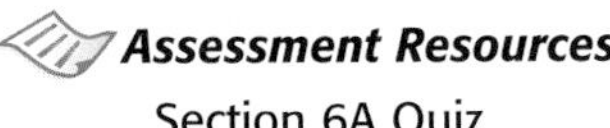
Assessment Resources
Section 6A Quiz

Test & Practice Generator
One-Stop Planner®

INTERVENTION

Resources

Ready to Go On? Intervention and Enrichment Worksheets

Ready to Go On? CD-ROM

Ready to Go On? Online

my.hrw.com

READY TO GO ON? Diagnose and Prescribe

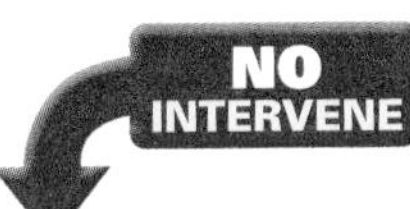
NO INTERVENE

Ready to Go On? Intervention	*Ready to Go On? Intervention,* Section 6A Worksheets	CD-ROM	Online
Lesson 6-1 9.0	6-1 Intervention	Activity 6-1	Diagnose and Prescribe Online
Lesson 6-2 9.0	6-2 Intervention	Activity 6-2	
Lesson 6-3 9.0	6-3 Intervention	Activity 6-3	
Lesson 6-4 9.0	6-4 Intervention	Activity 6-4	
Lesson 6-5 15.0	6-5 Intervention	Activity 6-5	

YES ENRICH

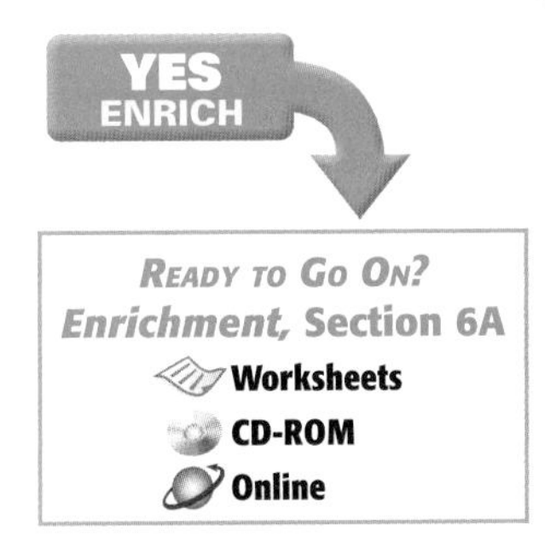
Ready to Go On? Enrichment, Section 6A
Worksheets
CD-ROM
Online

Linear Inequalities

One-Minute Section Planner

Lesson	Lab Resources	Materials
Lesson 6-6 Solving Linear Inequalities • Graph and solve linear inequalities in two variables. **6.0**	***Algebra Lab* 6-6** In *Chapter 6 Resource File*	**Optional** graphing calculator, graph paper
Lesson 6-7 Solving Systems of Linear Inequalities • Graph and solve systems of linear inequalities in two variables. **6.0, 9.0**		**Optional** colored pencils (MK), graphing calculator, transparency grids
6-7 Technology Lab Solve Systems of Linear Inequalities • Use a graphing calculator to view solutions of a system of linear inequalities. **9.0**		**Required** graphing calculator

MK = *Manipulatives Kit*

Notes

Math Background: Teaching the Standards

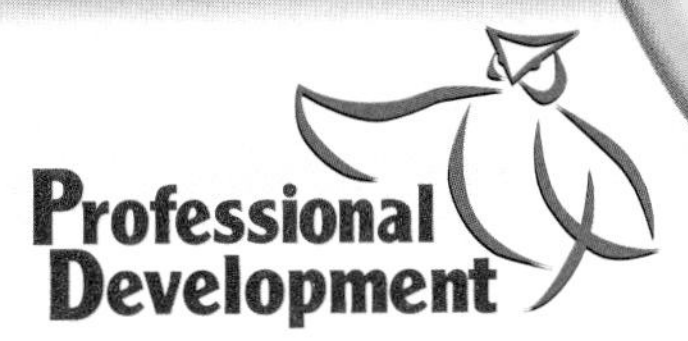

LINEAR INEQUALITIES 6.0

Lesson 6-6

A *linear inequality in two variables* is an inequality that may be written in the form $ax + by < c$, where a and b are not both 0, and where the symbols $\leq$, $>$, or $\geq$ may be used instead of $<$. A *solution* of a linear inequality in two variables is an ordered pair that makes the inequality true. For example, (4, 5) is a solution of the linear inequality $y > \frac{1}{2}x + 1$ because $5 > \frac{1}{2}(4) + 1$ is a true statement.

Students can begin to explore solutions of inequalities in two variables by fixing the value of one variable and then testing values of the other. For $y > \frac{1}{2}x + 1$, when $x = 4$ it is easy to see that any value of y greater than 3 is a solution. That is, the ordered pairs (4, 3.1), (4, 5), and (4, 17) are all solutions of $y > \frac{1}{2}x + 1$. More generally, the solution set when $x = 4$ can be represented by the ray described by $y > 3$. This can be shown on a coordinate plane as the part of the vertical line $x = 4$ where the y-values are greater than 3. Similarly, the solution set when $x = 6$ can be represented by the ray described by $y > 4$. Doing this for other values of x results in a collection of rays.

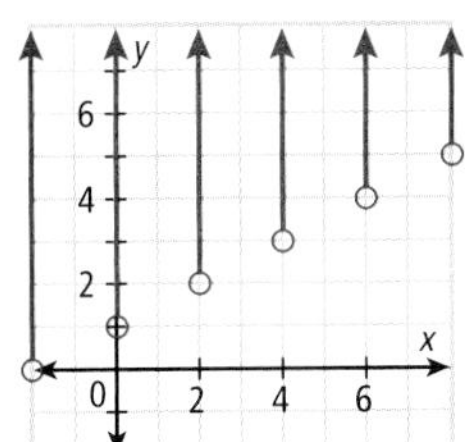

If we imagine doing this for all values of x, we see that the solution set of $y > \frac{1}{2}x + 1$ can be represented by an infinite set of rays similar to those graphed above. These rays fill the part of the coordinate plane that lies above the line $y = \frac{1}{2}x + 1$. That is, the solution set can be represented by a half plane.

The shaded region shows the half plane that represents the solution set of $y > \frac{1}{2}x + 1$. All ordered pairs in this region are solutions of the inequality.

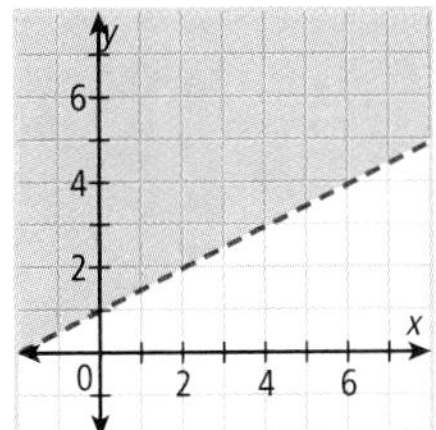

Note that the line $y = \frac{1}{2}x + 1$ is the boundary of the half plane. This boundary is shown with a dotted line because the points on the line are not solutions of the inequality. (For the inequality $y \geq \frac{1}{2}x + 1$, the points on the line *are* solutions and the boundary would be drawn as a solid line.)

Students should know how to check solutions to inequalities by selecting specific points from a graph. In the above graph, the point (4, 6) lies in the shaded region. Therefore, (4, 6) should be a solution of the inequality $y > \frac{1}{2}x + 1$. This is easily verified: $6 > \frac{1}{2}(4) + 1$ is a true statement. The point (5, 2) is *not* in the shaded region and so should *not* be a solution of the inequality. Again, this is easily verified by substituting 2 for x and 5 for y and noting that the resulting inequality is false.

SYSTEMS OF INEQUALITIES 6.0

Lesson 6-7

As discussed above, the solution set of a single inequality in two variables can be represented by a half plane. The solution set of a system of two inequalities in two variables can therefore be represented by the intersection of two half planes. Students should understand that this intersection may be an infinite region, a straight line, or the empty set. As before, specific points inside and outside the solution region should be checked in *both* inequalities to verify that the correct solution region has been identified.

6-6 Organizer

Objective: Graph and solve linear inequalities in two variables.

Algebra Lab
In Chapter 6 Resource File

Online Edition
Tutorial Videos

Countdown to Mastery Week 13

Power Presentations with PowerPoint®

Warm Up

Graph each inequality.

1. $x > -5$

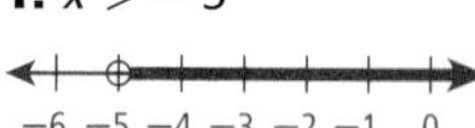

2. $y \leq 0$

3. Write $-6x + 2y = -4$ in slope-intercept form, and graph. $y = 3x - 2$

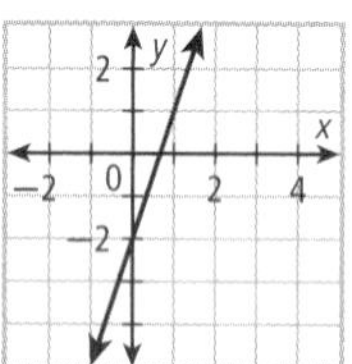

Also available on transparency

Math Humor

Q: Why did the math student name her boundary line Hope?

A: Because it was dashed.

California Standards

Algebra 1 6.0

6-6 Solving Linear Inequalities

California Standards

6.0 Students graph a linear equation and compute the *x*- and *y*-intercepts (e.g., graph $2x + 6y = 4$). **They are also able to sketch the region defined by linear inequality (e.g., they sketch the region defined by $2x + 6y < 4$).**

Vocabulary
linear inequality
solution of a linear inequality

Who uses this?
Consumers can use linear inequalities to determine how much food they can buy for an event. (See Example 3.)

A **linear inequality** is similar to a linear equation, but the equal sign is replaced with an inequality symbol. A **solution of a linear inequality** is any ordered pair that makes the inequality true.

EXAMPLE 1 Identifying Solutions of Inequalities

Tell whether the ordered pair is a solution of the inequality.

A $(7, 3); y < x - 1$

y	$<$	$x - 1$
3		$7 - 1$
3	$<$	6 ✓

Substitute (7, 3) for (x, y).

$(7, 3)$ is a solution.

B $(4, 5); y > 3x + 2$

y	$>$	$3x + 2$
5		$3(4) + 2$
5		$12 + 2$
5	$>$	14 ✗

Substitute (4, 5) for (x, y).

$(4, 5)$ is not a solution.

Tell whether the ordered pair is a solution of the inequality.

1a. $(4, 5); y < x + 1$ no **1b.** $(1, 1); y > x - 7$ yes

A linear inequality describes a region of a coordinate plane called a *half-plane*. All points in the region are solutions of the linear inequality. The boundary line of the region is the graph of the related equation.

When the inequality is written as $y \leq$ or $y \geq$, the points on the boundary line are solutions, and the line is solid.

When the inequality is written as $y <$ or $y >$, the points on the boundary line are not solutions, and the line is dashed.

When the inequality is written as $y >$ or $y \geq$, the points above the boundary line are also solutions.

When the inequality is written as $y <$ or $y \leq$, the points below the boundary line are also solutions.

1 Introduce

EXPLORATION

6-6 Solving Linear Inequalities

You will need graph paper for this Exploration.
You will investigate how to solve linear inequalities.

1. Graph $y = 2x + 1$.
2. Choose three points above the line. Give the coordinates of each point and tell whether y is greater than, less than, or equal to $2x + 1$ at each point.
3. Now choose three points below the line. Give the coordinates of each point and tell whether y is greater than, less than, or equal to $2x + 1$ at each point.
4. Now choose three points on the line. Give the coordinates of each point and tell whether y is greater than, less than, or equal to $2x + 1$ at each point.

THINK AND DISCUSS

5. **Describe** the set of all points on the coordinate plane for which $y > 2x + 1$.
6. **Describe** the set of all points on the coordinate plane for which $y \leq 2x + 1$.

Motivate

Pose some real-world situations that can be represented by linear inequalities in two variables. For example: The cost of 5 pencils and 2 pens must be at most \$4. $5x + 2y \leq 4$ Challenge students to find many possible solutions. Possible answers: $(0.10, 1.50)$ = pencils \$0.10, pens \$1.50; $(0.25, 1.00)$ = pencils \$0.25, pens \$1.00 Ask students if negative numbers are reasonable solutions for this problem. no

Explorations and answers are provided in *Alternate Openers: Explorations Transparencies.*

Graphing Linear Inequalities	
Step 1	Solve the inequality for y (slope-intercept form).
Step 2	Graph the boundary line. Use a solid line for $\le$ or $\ge$. Use a dashed line for $<$ or $>$.
Step 3	Shade the half-plane above the line for $y >$ or $y \ge$. Shade the half-plane below the line for $y <$ or $y \le$. Check your answer.

EXAMPLE 2 Graphing Linear Inequalities in Two Variables

Graph the solutions of each linear inequality. Check your answer.

A $y < 3x + 4$

Step 1 The inequality is already solved for y.

Step 2 Graph the boundary line $y = 3x + 4$. Use a dashed line for $<$.

Step 3 The inequality is $<$, so shade below the line.

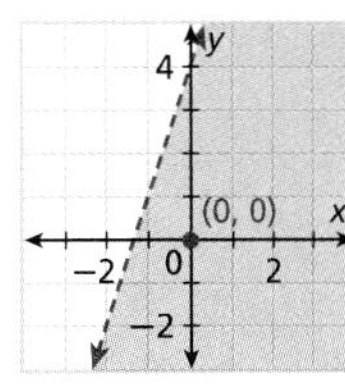

Check

y	$<$	$3x + 4$
0		$3(0) + 4$
0		$0 + 4$
0	$<$	4 ✓

Substitute (0, 0) for (x, y) because it is not on the boundary line.

The point (0, 0) satisfies the inequality, so the graph is shaded correctly.

B $3x + 2y \ge 6$

Step 1 Solve the inequality for y.

$$3x + 2y \ge 6$$
$$\underline{-3x \qquad -3x}$$
$$2y \ge -3x + 6$$
$$y \ge -\frac{3}{2}x + 3$$

Step 2 Graph the boundary line $y = -\frac{3}{2}x + 3$. Use a solid line for $\ge$.

Step 3 The inequality is $\ge$, so shade above the line.

Check

y	$\ge$	$-\frac{3}{2}x + 3$
0		$\frac{3}{2}(0) + 3$
0		$0 + 3$
0	$\ge$	3 ✗

A false statement means that the half-plane containing (0, 0) should NOT be shaded. (0, 0) is not one of the solutions, so the graph is shaded correctly.

Helpful Hint

Use the "test point" method shown in Example 2 to check your answers. The point (0, 0) is a good test point to use if it does not lie on the boundary line. However, be aware that this method will check only that your shading is correct. It will not check the boundary line.

CHECK IT OUT! Graph the solutions of each linear inequality. Check your answer.

2a. $4x - 3y > 12$ **2b.** $2x - y - 4 > 0$ **2c.** $y \ge -\frac{2}{3}x + 1$

2a.

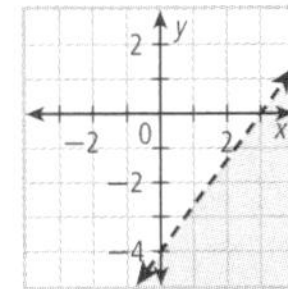

2b.

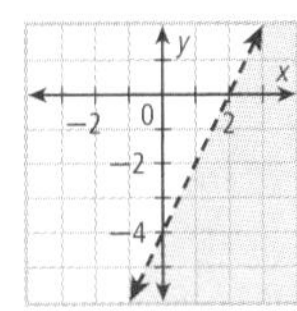

2c.

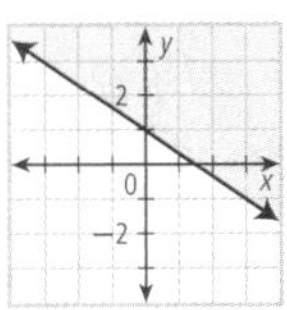

2 Teach

Guided Instruction

Explain to students that graphing an inequality begins with graphing an equation. The inequality symbol determines whether the points on the boundary line are solutions (solid line) or not solutions (dashed line). Ask students to think about what the shaded part will mean before they shade. Have students test several points in the area to be shaded to determine whether they make the inequality true.

Teaching Tip

Writing Math To represent the solutions to **Example 2A** using set-builder notation, write $\{(x, y): y < 3x + 4\}$.

Power Presentations with PowerPoint®

Additional Examples

Example 1

Tell whether the ordered pair is a solution of the inequality.

A. $(-2, 4);\ y < 2x + 1$ no

B. $(3, 1);\ y > x - 4$ yes

Example 2

Graph the solutions of each linear inequality. Check your answer.

A. $y \le 2x - 3$

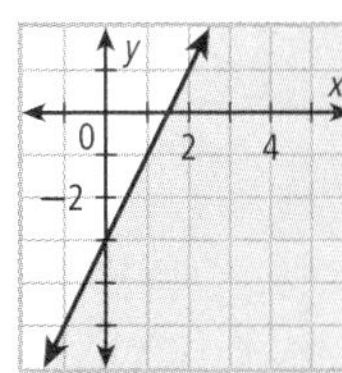

B. $5x + 2y > -8$

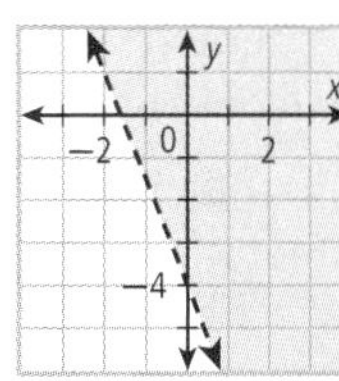

C. $4x - y + 2 \le 0$

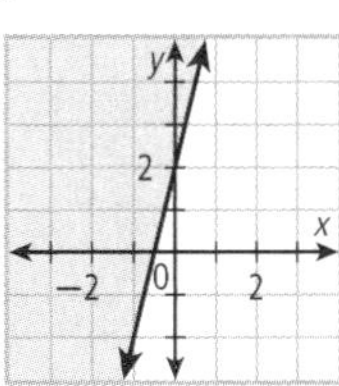

Also available on transparency

INTERVENTION Questioning Strategies

EXAMPLE 1

- How do you know if an ordered pair is not a solution of a linear inequality?

EXAMPLE 2

- How can you check that you shaded the correct half-plane?
- Explain why the point (0, 0) should not be used as a test point if it lies on the boundary line.

Power Presentations with PowerPoint®

Additional Examples

Example 3

Ada has at most 285 beads to make jewelry. A necklace requires 40 beads, and a bracelet requires 15 beads. Write a linear inequality to describe the situation. Graph the solutions, describe reasonable solutions, and then give two combinations of necklaces and bracelets Ada could make.

$40x + 15y \leq 285$

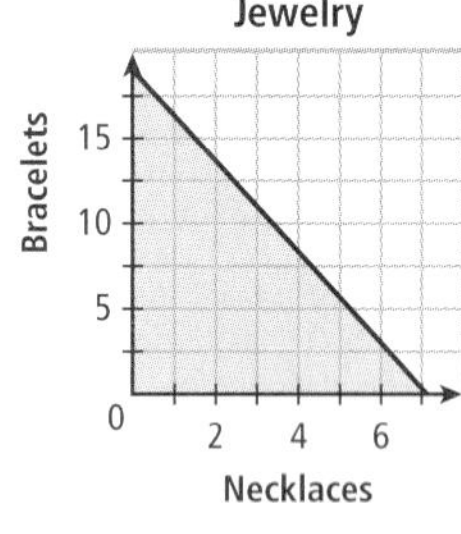

Only whole number solutions are reasonable. Possible answer: (2 necklaces, 8 bracelets), (5 necklaces, 3 bracelets)

Also available on transparency

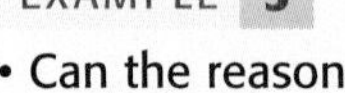

INTERVENTION

Questioning Strategies

EXAMPLE 3

- Can the reasonable solutions of a linear inequality include fractions or decimals? Why or why not?

Number Sense In **Example 3,** discuss with students what numbers are reasonable solutions. In many real-world situations, reasonable solutions are often nonnegative, and sometimes only whole numbers are reasonable.

EXAMPLE 3 *Consumer Economics Application*

Sarah can spend at most \$7.50 on vegetables. Broccoli costs \$1.25 per bunch and carrots cost \$0.75 per package.

a. Write a linear inequality to describe the situation.

Let x represent the number of bunches of broccoli and let y represent the number of packages of carrots.

Write an inequality. Use $\leq$ for "at most."

Cost of broccoli	plus	cost of carrots	is at most	\$7.50.
$1.25x$	$+$	$0.75y$	$\leq$	7.50

Solve the inequality for y.

$$1.25x + 0.75y \leq 7.50$$

$$100(1.25x + 0.75y) \leq 100(7.50)$$ *You can multiply both sides of the inequality by 100 to eliminate the decimals.*

$$125x + 75y \leq 750$$

$$-125x \qquad -125x$$ *Subtract 125x from both sides.*

$$75y \leq 750 - 125x$$

$$\frac{75y}{75} \leq \frac{750 - 125x}{75}$$ *Divide both sides by 75.*

$$y \leq 10 - \frac{5}{3}x$$

b. Graph the solutions.

Step 1 Since Sarah cannot buy a negative amount of vegetables, the system is graphed only in Quadrant I. Graph the boundary line $y = -\frac{5}{3}x + 10$. Use a solid line for $\leq$.

Step 2 Shade below the line. Sarah must buy whole numbers of bunches or packages. All the points on or below the line with whole number coordinates are the different combinations of broccoli and carrots that Sarah can buy.

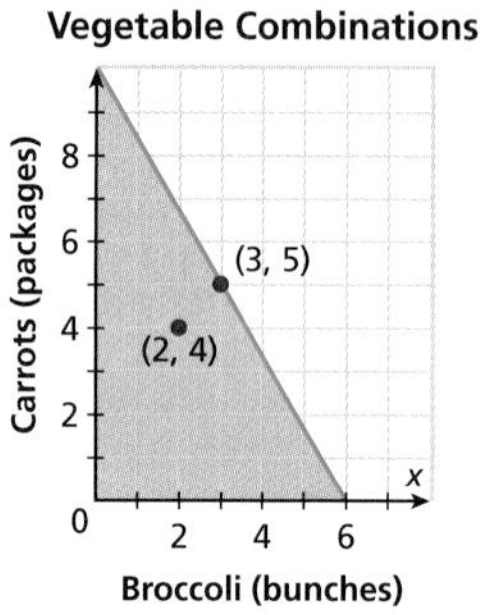

Vegetable Combinations

Carrots (packages) — 2, 4, 6, 8; Broccoli (bunches) — 0, 2, 4, 6, x; points (3, 5), (2, 4)

c. Give two combinations of vegetables that Sarah can buy.

Two different combinations that Sarah could buy for \$7.50 or less are 2 bunches of broccoli and 4 packages of carrots, or 3 bunches of broccoli and 5 packages of carrots.

CHECK IT OUT!

3. **What if...?** Dirk is going to bring two types of olives to the Honor Society induction and can spend no more than \$6. Green olives cost \$2 per pound and black olives cost \$2.50 per pound.
   a. Write a linear inequality to describe the situation.
   b. Graph the solutions.
   c. Give two combinations of olives that Dirk could buy.

3a. $2.5b + 2g \leq 6$

3b.

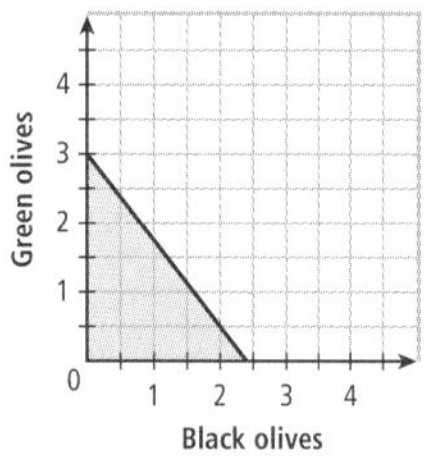

Olive Combinations

Green olives — 1, 2, 3, 4; Black olives — 0, 1, 2, 3, 4

3c. possible answer: (1 lb black, 1 lb green), (0.5 lb black, 2 lb green)

Universal Access

Through Home Connection

Have students search through local advertisements and find two different items (under \$20) they would like to purchase. Tell students they have a maximum of \$125 to purchase different combinations of these two items. Have students write a linear inequality to describe the situation. Possible answer: $13.99x + 17.95y \leq 125$ Then have them graph the solutions of their inequality and give at least two combinations of items they can purchase.

Technology Show students how to graph an inequality on a graphing calculator. Press 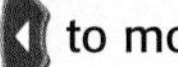 and enter the equation. Press ◀ to move the cursor to the left of Y_1. Press ENTER until the icon that looks like a region above or below a line appears. Press GRAPH. Tell students that the graphing calculator does not distinguish between solid and dashed boundary lines. They will need to decide for themselves if the line should be solid or dashed.

EXAMPLE 4 Writing an Inequality from a Graph

Write an inequality to represent each graph.

A

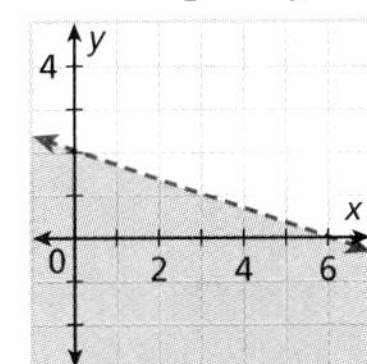

y-intercept: 2; slope: $-\frac{1}{3}$

Write an equation in slope-intercept form.

$y = mx + b \longrightarrow y = -\frac{1}{3}x + 2$

The graph is shaded *below* a *dashed* boundary line.

Replace $=$ with $<$ to write the inequality $y < -\frac{1}{3}x + 2$.

B

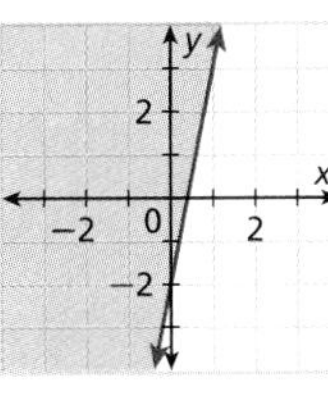

y-intercept: -2; slope: 5

Write an equation in slope-intercept form.

$y = mx + b \longrightarrow y = 5x + (-2)$

The graph is shaded *above* a *solid* boundary line.

Replace $=$ with $\geq$ to write the inequality $y \geq 5x - 2$.

C

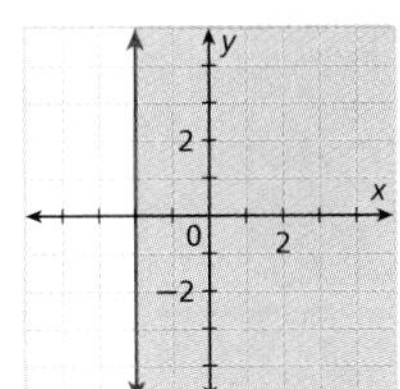

y-intercept: none; slope: undefined

The graph is a vertical line at $x = -2$.

The graph is shaded on the *right* side of a *solid* boundary line.

Replace $=$ with $\geq$ to write the inequality $x \geq -2$.

Write an inequality to represent each graph.

4a.

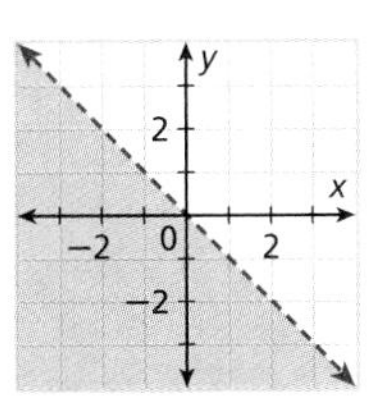

$y < -x$

4b.

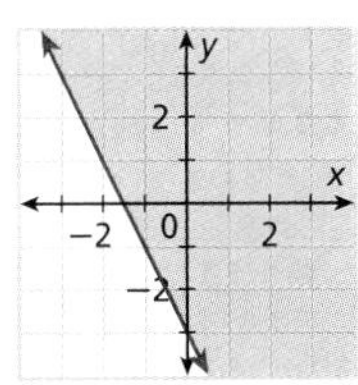

$y \geq -2x - 3$

THINK AND DISCUSS

1. Tell how graphing a linear inequality is the same as graphing a linear equation. Tell how it is different.
2. Explain how you would write a linear inequality from a graph.

3. **GET ORGANIZED** Copy and complete the graphic organizer.

Inequality	$y < 5x + 2$	$y > 7x - 3$	$y \leq 9x + 1$	$y \geq -3x - 2$
Symbol	$<$			
Boundary Line	Dashed			
Shading	Below			

Power Presentations with PowerPoint®

Additional Examples

Example 4

Write an inequality to represent each graph.

A.

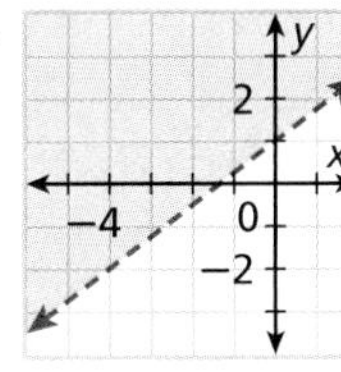

$y > \frac{3}{4}x + 1$

B.

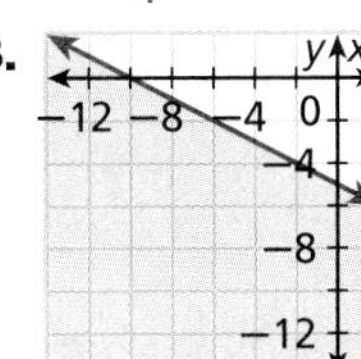

$y \leq -\frac{1}{2}x - 5$

Also available on transparency

INTERVENTION

Questioning Strategies

EXAMPLE 4

- How do you determine which inequality symbol to use?

3 Close

Summarize

For each inequality below, have students describe the boundary line and state which direction should be shaded.

1) $y < 2x + 1$ dashed; below

2) $y \geq -\frac{3}{5}x - 2$ solid; above

3) $2x - 3y \leq 6$ solid; above

4) $y > -3$ dashed; above

5) $x \leq 7$ solid; to the left

FORMATIVE ASSESSMENT

and INTERVENTION

***Diagnose Before* the Lesson**
6-6 Warm Up, TE p. 364

***Monitor During* the Lesson**
Check It Out! Exercises, SE pp. 364–367
Questioning Strategies, TE pp. 365–367

***Assess After* the Lesson**
6-6 Lesson Quiz, TE p. 370
Alternative Assessment, TE p. 370

Answers to *Think and Discuss*

1. Possible answer: In both cases you will always graph a line. They are different because the graph of a linear inequality can be a dashed or solid line, and the graph must be shaded on one side of the line.
2. To write a linear inequality from a graph, find the equation of the boundary line. Use $\geq$ or $\leq$ for a solid boundary line. Use $>$ or $<$ for a dashed boundary line. If the half-plane is shaded above the line, use $>$ or $\geq$, and if it is shaded below, use $<$ or $\leq$.
3. See p. A5.

6-6 Exercises

Assignment Guide

Assign *Guided Practice* exercises as necessary.

If you finished Examples **1–2**
Proficient 12–18, 23–27, 30–36 even
Advanced 12–18, 23–27, 30–36 even

If you finished Examples **1–4**
Proficient 12–21, 30–42 even, 43–48, 51–65
Advanced 12–21, 30–38 even, 39–40, 43–65

Homework Quick Check
Quickly check key concepts.
Exercises: 14, 18, 19, 20, 30, 40

Answers

5.
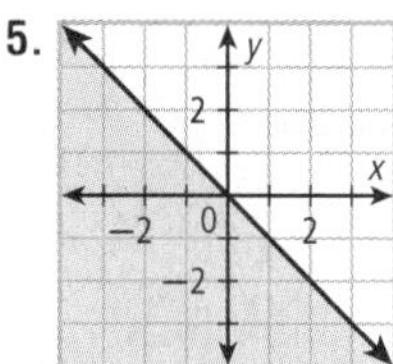

6.
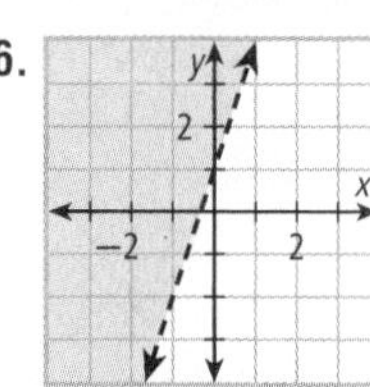

7.
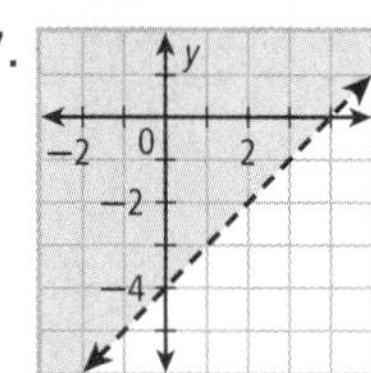

8, 9, 15–19. See p. A21.

California Standards

Standard	Exercises
6.0	5–8, 9b, 15–18, 19b, 22b, 23–26, 27b, 29–37, 40b, 46–48, 51, 53
7.0	54–59
9.0	60–65
18.0	51–53

6-6 Exercises

California Standards Practice
6.0

go.hrw.com
Homework Help Online
KEYWORD: MA8CA 6-6
Parent Resources Online
KEYWORD: MA8CA Parent

GUIDED PRACTICE

1. **Vocabulary** Can a *solution of a linear inequality* lie on a dashed boundary line? Explain. **No; a dashed line means that the ordered pairs are not solutions to the linear inequality.**

SEE EXAMPLE 1 p. 364

Tell whether the ordered pair is a solution of the given inequality.

2. $(0, 3)$; $y \le -x + 3$ **yes**
3. $(2, 0)$; $y > -2x - 2$ **yes**
4. $(-2, 1)$; $y < 2x + 4$ **no**

SEE EXAMPLE 2 p. 365

Graph the solutions of each linear inequality. Check your answer.

5. $y \le -x$
6. $y > 3x + 1$
7. $-y < -x + 4$
8. $-y \ge x + 1$

SEE EXAMPLE 3 p. 366

9. **Multi-Step** Jack is making punch with orange juice and pineapple juice. He can make at most 16 cups of punch.
   a. Write an inequality to describe the situation.
   b. Graph the solutions.
   c. Give two possible combinations of cups of orange juice and pineapple juice that Jack can use in his punch.

SEE EXAMPLE 4 p. 367

Write an inequality to represent each graph.

10. $y < 3$

11.
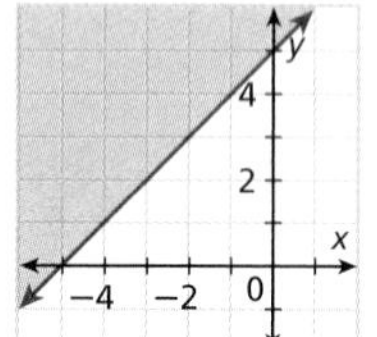
$y \ge x + 5$

PRACTICE AND PROBLEM SOLVING

Independent Practice

For Exercises	See Example
12–14	1
15–18	2
19	3
20–21	4

Extra Practice
Skills Practice p. EP13
Application Practice p. EP29

Tell whether the ordered pair is a solution of the given inequality.

12. $(2, 3)$; $y \ge 2x + 3$ **no**
13. $(1, -1)$; $y < 3x - 3$ **yes**
14. $(0, 7)$; $y > 4x + 7$ **no**

Graph the solutions of each linear inequality. Check your answer.

15. $y > -2x + 6$
16. $-y \ge 2x$
17. $x + y \le 2$
18. $x - y \ge 0$

19. **Multi-Step** Beverly is serving hamburgers and hot dogs at her cookout. Hamburger meat costs \$3 per pound, and hot dogs cost \$2 per pound. She wants to spend no more than \$30.
   a. Write an inequality to describe the situation.
   b. Graph the solutions.
   c. Give two possible combinations of pounds of hamburger and hot dogs that Beverly can buy.

Write an inequality to represent each graph.

20.
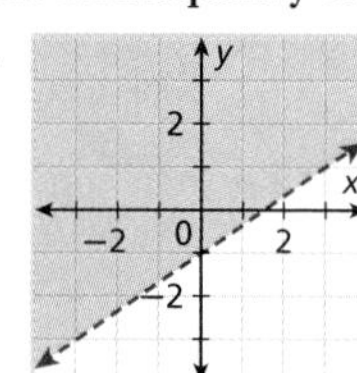
$y > \frac{2}{3}x - 1$

21.
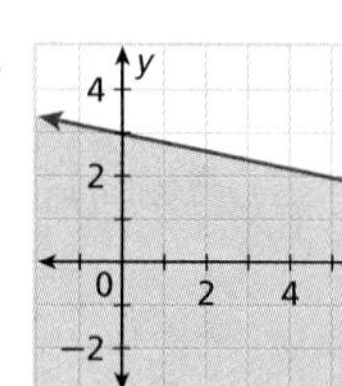
$y \le -\frac{1}{5}x + 3$

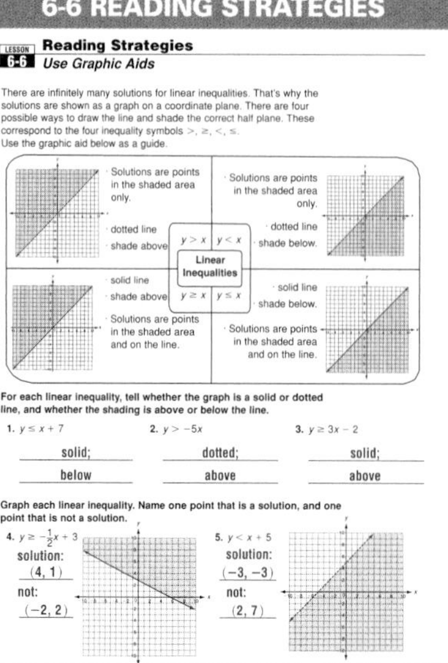

6-6 READING STRATEGIES

LESSON 6-6 **Reading Strategies**
Use Graphic Aids

There are infinitely many solutions for linear inequalities. That's why the solutions are shown as a graph on a coordinate plane. There are four possible ways to draw the line and shade the correct half plane. These correspond to the four inequality symbols >, ≥, <, ≤.
Use the graphic aid below as a guide.

For each linear inequality, tell whether the graph is a solid or dotted line, and whether the shading is above or below the line.

1. $y \le x + 7$ **solid; below**
2. $y > -5x$ **dotted; above**
3. $y \ge 3x - 2$ **solid; above**

Graph each linear inequality. Name one point that is a solution, and one point that is not a solution.

4. $y \ge -\frac{1}{2}x + 3$ solution: **(4, 1)** not: **(−2, 2)**
5. $y < x + 5$ solution: **(−3, −3)** not: **(2, 7)**

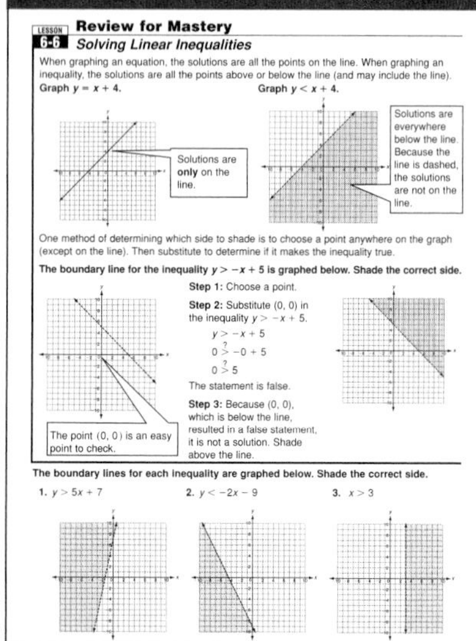

6-6 REVIEW FOR MASTERY

LESSON 6-6 **Review for Mastery**
Solving Linear Inequalities

When graphing an equation, the solutions are all the points on the line. When graphing an inequality, the solutions are all the points above or below the line (and may include the line).

Graph $y = x + 4$. **Graph $y < x + 4$.**

One method of determining which side to shade is to choose a point anywhere on the graph (except on the line). Then substitute to determine if it makes the inequality true.

The boundary line for the inequality $y > -x + 5$ is graphed below. Shade the correct side.

Step 1: Choose a point.

Step 2: Substitute (0, 0) in the inequality $y > -x + 5$.

$y > -x + 5$
$0 \overset{?}{>} -0 + 5$
$0 \overset{?}{>} 5$

The statement is false.

Step 3: Because (0, 0), which is below the line, resulted in a false statement, it is not a solution. Shade above the line.

The boundary lines for each inequality are graphed below. Shade the correct side.

1. $y > 5x + 7$
2. $y < -2x - 9$
3. $x > 3$

22b.

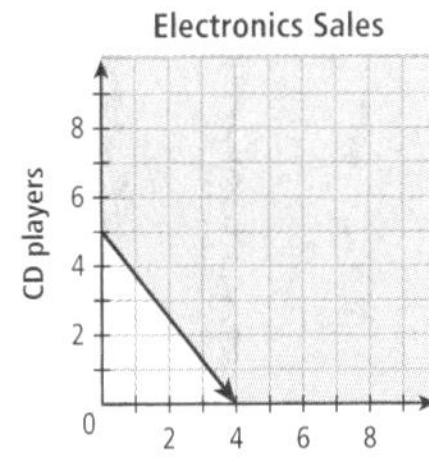

22. **Business** An electronics store makes \$125 profit on every DVD player it sells and \$100 on every CD player it sells. The store owner wants to make a profit of at least \$500 a day selling DVD players and CD players. **$125x + 100y \geq 500$**
 a. Write a linear inequality to determine the number of DVD players x and the number of CD players y that the owner needs to sell to meet his goal.
 b. Graph the linear inequality.
 c. Describe the possible values of x. Describe the possible values of y. **x and y must be whole numbers**
 d. List three possible combinations of DVD players and CD players that the owner could sell to meet his goal. **Possible answer: (5 DVD, 1 CD), (7 DVD, 6 CD), (9 DVD, 2 CD)**

Graph the solutions of each linear inequality. Check your answer.

23. $y \leq 2 - 3x$ 24. $-y < 7 + x$ 25. $2x - y \leq 4$ 26. $3x - 2y > 6$

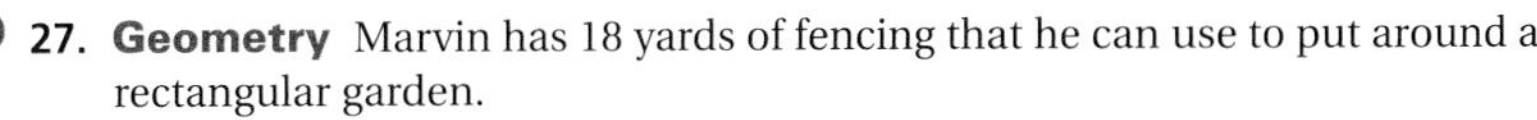

27. **Geometry** Marvin has 18 yards of fencing that he can use to put around a rectangular garden.
 a. Write a linear inequality that describes the possible lengths and widths of the garden. **$2x + 2y \leq 18$**
 b. Graph the inequality and list three possible solutions to the problem.
 c. What are the dimensions of the largest *square* garden that can be fenced in with whole-number dimensions? **4 yd × 4 yd**

28. **Hobbies** Stephen wants to buy yellow tangs and clown fish for his saltwater aquarium. He wants to spend no more than \$77 on fish. At the store, yellow tangs cost \$15 each and clown fish cost \$11 each. Write and graph a linear inequality to find the number of yellow tangs x and the number of clown fish y that Stephen could purchase. Name a solution of your inequality that is not reasonable for the situation. Explain.

Graph each inequality on a coordinate plane.

29. $y > 1$ 30. $-2 < x$ 31. $x \geq -3$ 32. $y \leq 0$

33. $0 \geq x$ 34. $-12 + y > 0$ 35. $x + 7 < 7$ 36. $-4 \geq x - y$

37. **School** At a high school football game, tickets at the gate cost \$7 per adult and \$4 per student. Write a linear inequality to determine the number of adult and student tickets that need to be sold so that the amount of money taken in at the gate is at least \$280. Graph the inequality and list three possible solutions.

38. **Critical Thinking** Why must a region of a coordinate plane be shaded to show all solutions of a linear inequality? **Possible answer: It is not possible to list an infinite number of solutions, so shading is used to show all the solutions in the coordinate plane.**

39. **Write About It** Give a real-world situation that can be described by a linear inequality. Then graph the inequality and give two solutions.
Possible answer: Sammy volunteers at the hospital and the library. The total number of hours he volunteers is more than 5; $h + \ell > 5$; Check students' graphs and solutions.

CONCEPT CONNECTION

40. This problem will prepare you for the Concept Connection on page 378.
 Gloria is making teddy bears. She is making boy and girl bears. She has enough stuffing to create 50 bears. Let x represent the number of girl bears and y represent the number of boy bears.
 a. Write an inequality that shows the possible number of boy and girl bears Jenna can make. **$x + y \leq 50$**
 b. Graph the inequality.
 c. Give three possible solutions for the numbers of boy and girl bears that can be made. **Possible answer: (10, 20), (30, 10), (15, 15)**

Geometry For **Exercise 27,** remind students that the formula for the perimeter of a rectangle is $P = 2\ell + 2w$ and the formula for the perimeter of a square is $P = 4s$.

CONCEPT CONNECTION **Exercise 40** involves writing and graphing an inequality in two variables to determine possible solutions due to constraints on materials. This exercise prepares students for the Concept Connection on page 378.

Answers

23.

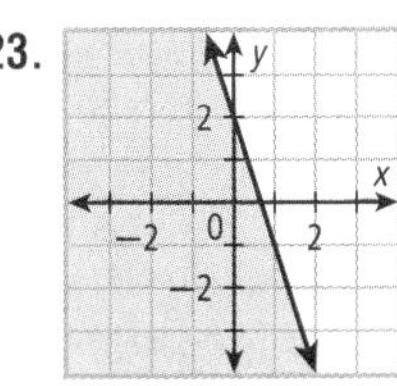

24.

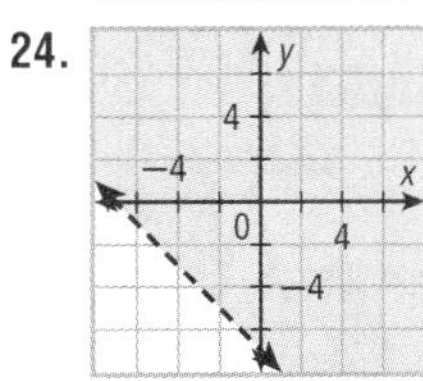

25.

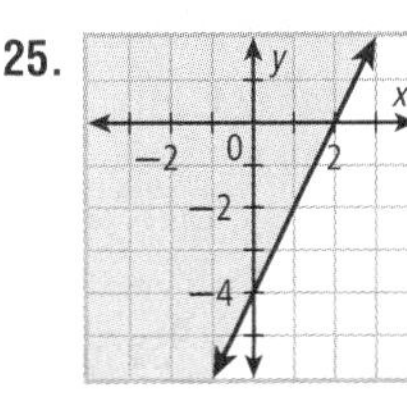

26.

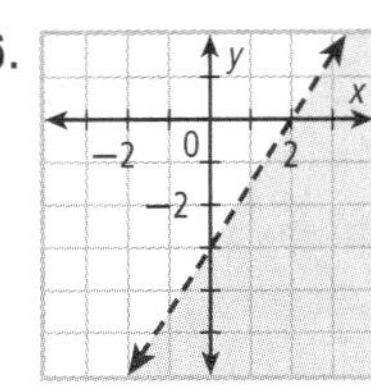

27b, 28–37, 40b. See p. A21.

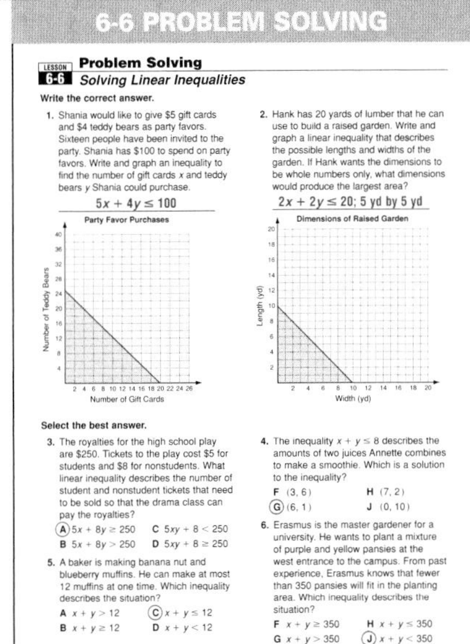

6-6 PROBLEM SOLVING

LESSON 6-6 **Problem Solving**
Solving Linear Inequalities

Write the correct answer.

1. Shania would like to give \$5 gift cards and \$4 teddy bears as party favors. Sixteen people have been invited to the party. Shania has \$100 to spend on party favors. Write and graph an inequality to find the number of gift cards x and teddy bears y Shania could purchase.
 $5x + 4y \leq 100$

2. Hank has 20 yards of lumber that he can use to build a raised garden. Write and graph a linear inequality that describes the possible lengths and widths of the garden. If Hank wants the dimensions to be whole numbers only, what dimensions would produce the largest area?
 $2x + 2y \leq 20$; 5 yd by 5 yd

Select the best answer.

3. The royalties for the high school play are \$250. Tickets to the play cost \$5 for students and \$8 for nonstudents. What linear inequality describes the number of student and nonstudent tickets that need to be sold so that the drama class can pay the royalties?
 Ⓐ $5x + 8y \geq 250$ C $5xy + 8 < 250$
 B $5x + 8y > 250$ D $5xy + 8 \geq 250$

4. The inequality $x + y \leq 8$ describes the amounts of two juices Annette combines to make a smoothie. Which is a solution to the inequality?
 F (3, 6) H (7, 2)
 Ⓖ (6, 1) J (0, 10)

5. A baker is making banana nut and blueberry muffins. He can make at most 12 muffins at one time. Which inequality describes the situation?
 A $x + y > 12$ Ⓒ $x + y \leq 12$
 B $x + y \geq 12$ D $x + y < 12$

6. Erasmus is the master gardener for a university. He wants to plant a mixture of purple and yellow pansies at the west entrance to the campus. From past experience, Erasmus knows that fewer than 350 pansies will fit in the planting area. Which inequality describes the situation?
 F $x + y \geq 350$ H $x + y \leq 350$
 G $x + y > 350$ Ⓙ $x + y < 350$

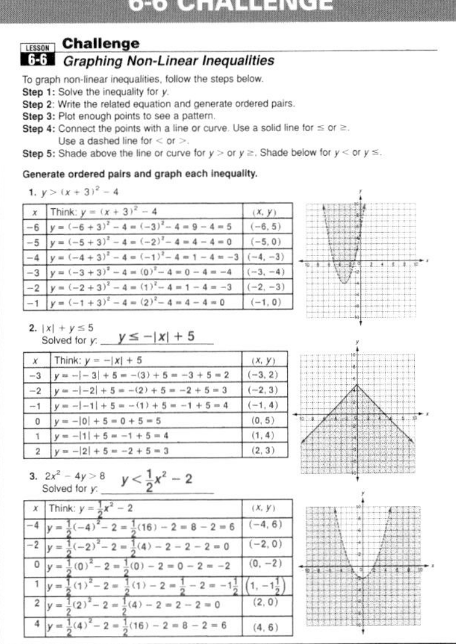

6-6 CHALLENGE

LESSON 6-6 **Challenge**
Graphing Non-Linear Inequalities

To graph non-linear inequalities, follow the steps below.
Step 1: Solve the inequality for y.
Step 2: Write the related equation and generate ordered pairs.
Step 3: Plot enough points to see a pattern.
Step 4: Connect the points with a line or curve. Use a solid line for ≤ or ≥. Use a dashed line for < or >.
Step 5: Shade above the line or curve for $y >$ or $y \geq$. Shade below for $y <$ or $y \leq$.

Generate ordered pairs and graph each inequality.

1. $y > (x + 3)^2 - 4$

x	Think: $y = (x + 3)^2 - 4$	(x, y)
−6	$y = (-6 + 3)^2 - 4 = (-3)^2 - 4 = 9 - 4 = 5$	(−6, 5)
−5	$y = (-5 + 3)^2 - 4 = (-2)^2 - 4 = 4 - 4 = 0$	(−5, 0)
−4	$y = (-4 + 3)^2 - 4 = (-1)^2 - 4 = 1 - 4 = -3$	(−4, −3)
−3	$y = (-3 + 3)^2 - 4 = (0)^2 - 4 = 0 - 4 = -4$	(−3, −4)
−2	$y = (-2 + 3)^2 - 4 = (1)^2 - 4 = 1 - 4 = -3$	(−2, −3)
−1	$y = (-1 + 3)^2 - 4 = (2)^2 - 4 = 4 - 4 = 0$	(−1, 0)

2. $|x| + y \leq 5$
 Solved for y: **$y \leq -|x| + 5$**

x	Think: $y = -\lvert x\rvert + 5$	(x, y)
−3	$y = -\lvert -3\rvert + 5 = -(3) + 5 = -3 + 5 = 2$	(−3, 2)
−2	$y = -\lvert -2\rvert + 5 = -(2) + 5 = -2 + 5 = 3$	(−2, 3)
−1	$y = -\lvert -1\rvert + 5 = -(1) + 5 = -1 + 5 = 4$	(−1, 4)
0	$y = -\lvert 0\rvert + 5 = 0 + 5 = 5$	(0, 5)
1	$y = -\lvert 1\rvert + 5 = -1 + 5 = 4$	(1, 4)
2	$y = -\lvert 2\rvert + 5 = -2 + 5 = 3$	(2, 3)

3. $2x^2 - 4y > 8$
 Solved for y: **$y < \frac{1}{2}x^2 - 2$**

x	Think: $y = \frac{1}{2}x^2 - 2$	(x, y)
−4	$y = \frac{1}{2}(-4)^2 - 2 = \frac{1}{2}(16) - 2 = 8 - 2 = 6$	(−4, 6)
−2	$y = \frac{1}{2}(-2)^2 - 2 = \frac{1}{2}(4) - 2 - 2 - 2 = 0$	(−2, 0)
0	$y = \frac{1}{2}(0)^2 - 2 = \frac{1}{2}(0) - 2 = 0 - 2 = -2$	(0, −2)
1	$y = \frac{1}{2}(1)^2 - 2 = \frac{1}{2}(1) - 2 = \frac{1}{2} - 2 = -1\frac{1}{2}$	$(1, -1\frac{1}{2})$
2	$y = \frac{1}{2}(2)^2 - 2 = \frac{1}{2}(4) - 2 = 2 - 2 = 0$	(2, 0)
4	$y = \frac{1}{2}(4)^2 - 2 = \frac{1}{2}(16) - 2 = 8 - 2 = 6$	(4, 6)

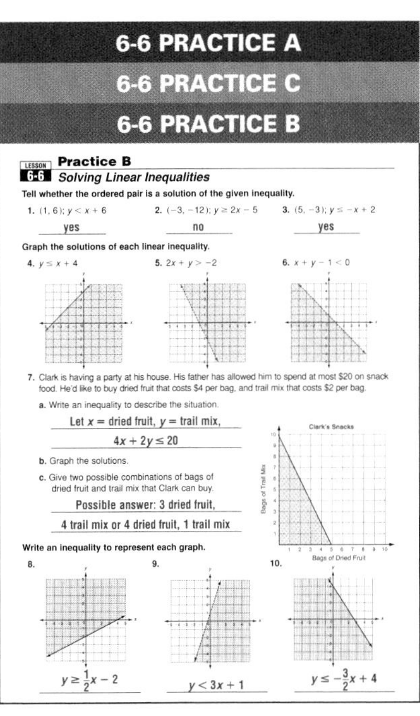

6-6 PRACTICE A
6-6 PRACTICE C
6-6 PRACTICE B

LESSON 6-6 **Practice B**
Solving Linear Inequalities

Tell whether the ordered pair is a solution of the given inequality.

1. (1, 6); $y < x + 6$ **yes** 2. (−3, −12); $y \geq 2x - 5$ **no** 3. (5, −3); $y \leq -x + 2$ **yes**

Graph the solutions of each linear inequality.

4. $y \leq x + 4$ 5. $2x + y > -2$ 6. $x + y - 1 < 0$

7. Clark is having a party at his house. His father has allowed him to spend at most \$20 on snack food. He'd like to buy dried fruit that costs \$4 per bag, and trail mix that costs \$2 per bag.
 a. Write an inequality to describe the situation.
 Let x = dried fruit, y = trail mix,
 $4x + 2y \leq 20$
 b. Graph the solutions.
 c. Give two possible combinations of bags of dried fruit and trail mix that Clark can buy.
 Possible answer: 3 dried fruit, 4 trail mix or 4 dried fruit, 1 trail mix

Write an inequality to represent each graph.

8. **$y \geq \frac{1}{2}x - 2$** 9. **$y < 3x + 1$** 10. **$y \leq -\frac{3}{2}x + 4$**

Multiple Choice In **Exercise 44,** choices **B** and **D** can be eliminated because the boundary line is solid.

Journal

Have students describe the steps for graphing $y \le x + 2$. Have them include how they would decide whether the boundary line is dashed or solid and how they would decide which half-plane to shade.

ALTERNATIVE ASSESSMENT

Have students write an inequality in two variables and graph the solutions. Have them explain what a solid boundary line and a dashed boundary line indicate about the solution set of a linear inequality.

Power Presentations with PowerPoint®

6-6 Lesson Quiz

1. You can spend at most $12.00 for drinks for a picnic. Iced tea costs $1.50 per gallon, and lemonade costs $2.00 per gallon. Write an inequality to describe the situation. Graph the solutions, describe reasonable solutions, and then give two possible combinations of drinks you could buy.
$1.50x + 2.00y \le 12.00$

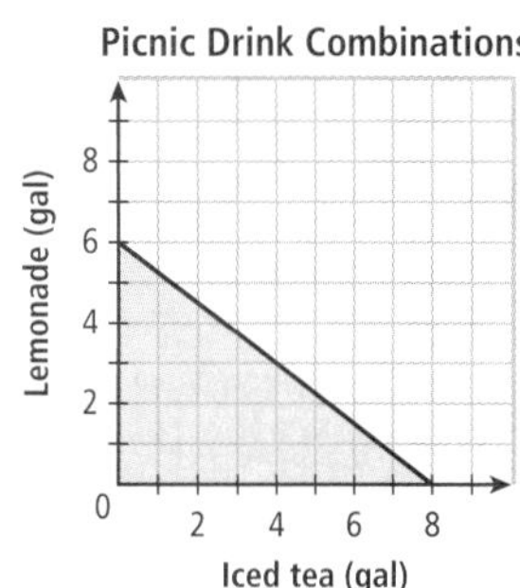

Only whole number solutions are reasonable. Possible answer: (2 gal iced tea, 3 gal lemonade), (4 gal iced tea, 1 gal lemonade)

2. Write an inequality to represent the graph.

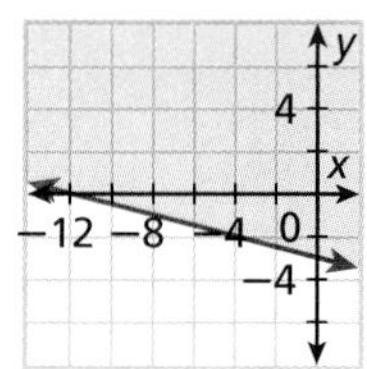

$y \ge -\frac{1}{4}x - 3$

Also available on transparency

41. **ERROR ANALYSIS** Student A wrote $y < 2x - 1$ as the inequality represented by the graph. Student B wrote $y \le 2x - 1$ as the inequality represented by the graph. Which student is incorrect? Explain the error.
Student A; the graph is a solid line.

42. **Write About It** How do you decide to shade above or below an inequality? What does this shading represent?

42. Possible answer: If the inequality is in slope-intercept form, then > or ≥ means you shade above the boundary line, and < or ≤ means you shade below the boundary line. The shading represents all the solutions of the inequality.

Multiple Choice For Exercises 43–45, choose the best answer.

43. Which point is a solution of the inequality $y > -x + 3$?
(A) (0, 3) **(B) (1, 4)** (C) (−1, 4) (D) (0, −3)

44. Which inequality is represented by the graph at right?
(A) $2x + y \ge 3$ **(C) $2x + y \le 3$**
(B) $2x + y > 3$ (D) $2x + y < 3$

45. Which of the following describes the graph of $3 \le x$?
(A) The boundary line is dashed, and the shading is to the right.
(B) The boundary line is dashed, and the shading is to the left.
(C) The boundary line is solid, and the shading is to the right.
(D) The boundary line is solid, and the shading is to the left.

CHALLENGE AND EXTEND

Graph each inequality. Check your answer.

46. $0 \ge -6 - 2x - 5y$ 47. $y > |x|$ 48. $y \ge |x - 3|$

49. A linear inequality has the points (0, 3) and (−3, 1.5) as solutions on the boundary line. Also, the point (1, 1) is not a solution. Write the linear inequality. $y \ge \frac{1}{2}x + 3$

50. Two linear inequalities are graphed on the same coordinate plane. The point (0, 0) is a solution of both inequalities. The entire coordinate plane is shaded except for Quadrant I. What are the two inequalities? $x \le 0$; $y \le 0$

SPIRAL STANDARDS REVIEW

Graph each equation. Then tell whether the equation represents a function. *(Lesson 4-3)*

51. $y = 2x - 4$ **yes** 52. $y = x^2 + 2$ **yes** 53. $y = 3$ **yes**

Write an equation in slope-intercept form for the line through the two points. *(Lesson 5-6)*

54. (0, 9) and (5, 2) 55. (−5, −2) and (7, 7) 56. (0, 0) and (−8, −10)
57. (−1, −2) and (1, 4) 58. (2, 2) and (6, 5) 59. (−3, 2) and (3, −1)

54. $y = -\frac{7}{5}x + 9$
55. $y = \frac{3}{4}x + \frac{7}{4}$
56. $y = \frac{5}{4}x$
57. $y = 3x + 1$
58. $y = \frac{3}{4}x + \frac{1}{2}$
59. $y = -\frac{1}{2}x + \frac{1}{2}$

Solve each system by elimination. Check your answer. *(Lesson 6-3)*

60. $\begin{cases} x + 6y = 14 \\ x - 6y = -10 \end{cases}$ **(2, 2)**
61. $\begin{cases} x + y = 13 \\ 3x + y = 9 \end{cases}$ **(−2, 15)**
62. $\begin{cases} 2x - 4y = 18 \\ 5x - y = 36 \end{cases}$ **(7, −1)**
63. $\begin{cases} 2y + x = 12 \\ y - 2x = 1 \end{cases}$ **(2, 5)**
64. $\begin{cases} 2y - 6x = -8 \\ y = -5x + 12 \end{cases}$ **(2, 2)**
65. $\begin{cases} 2x + 3y = 33 \\ y = \frac{1}{4}x \end{cases}$ **(12, 3)**

Answers

46.

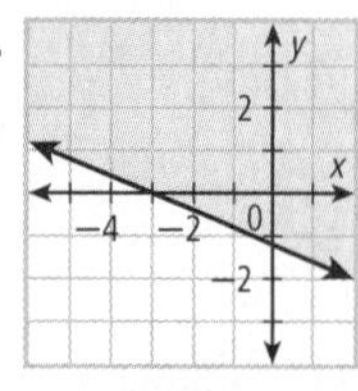

47.

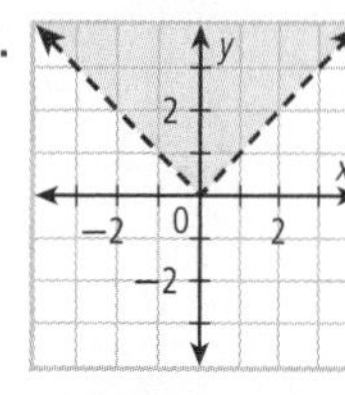

48.

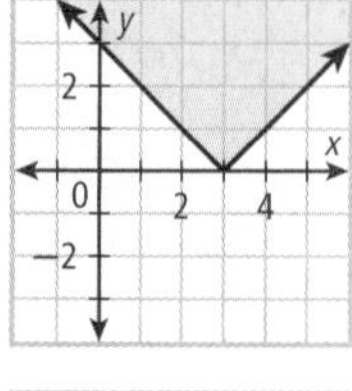

51.

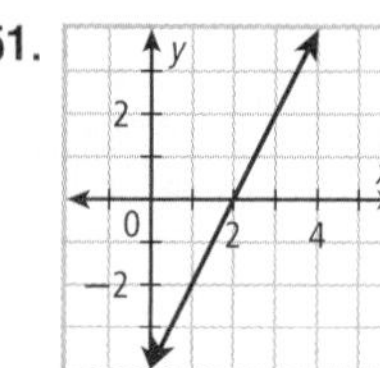

52.

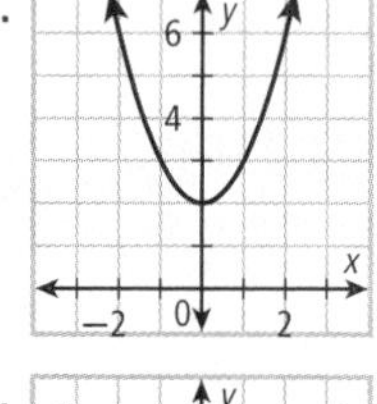

53.

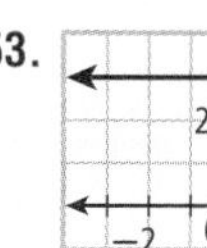

6-7 Solving Systems of Linear Inequalities

California Standards

9.0 Students solve a system of two linear equations in two variables algebraically and are able to interpret the answer graphically. **Students are able to solve a system of two linear inequalities in two variables and to sketch the solution sets.**

Also covered: **6.0**

Vocabulary
system of linear inequalities
solution of a system of linear inequalities

Who uses this?

The owner of a surf shop can use systems of linear inequalities to determine how many surfboards and wakeboards need to be sold to make a certain profit. (See Example 4.)

A **system of linear inequalities** is a set of two or more linear inequalities containing two or more variables. The **solutions of a system of linear inequalities** consists of all the ordered pairs that satisfy all the linear inequalities in the system.

Remember!

An ordered pair must be a solution of all inequalities to be a solution of the system.

EXAMPLE 1 Identifying Solutions of Systems of Linear Inequalities

Tell whether the ordered pair is a solution of the given system.

A $(2, 1); \begin{cases} y < -x + 4 \\ y \le x + 1 \end{cases}$

(2, 1)		
$y < -x + 4$		
1		$-2 + 4$
1	<	2 ✓

(2, 1)		
$y \le x + 1$		
1		$2 + 1$
1	≤	3 ✓

(2, 1) is a solution to the system because it satisfies both inequalities.

B $(2, 0); \begin{cases} y \ge 2x \\ y < x + 1 \end{cases}$

(2, 0)		
$y \ge 2x$		
0		$2(2)$
0	≥	4 ✗

(2, 0)		
$y < x + 1$		
0		$2 + 1$
0	<	3 ✓

(2, 0) is not a solution to the system because it does not satisfy both inequalities.

CHECK IT OUT! Tell whether the ordered pair is a solution of the given system.

1a. $(0, 1); \begin{cases} y < -3x + 2 \\ y \ge x - 1 \end{cases}$ **yes** **1b.** $(0, 0); \begin{cases} y > -x + 1 \\ y > x - 1 \end{cases}$ **no**

To show all the solutions of a system of linear inequalities, graph the solutions of each inequality. The solutions of the system are represented by the overlapping shaded regions. Below are graphs of Examples 1A and 1B.

Math Builders

For more on graphing systems of linear inequalities, see the System Builder on page MB4.

Example 1A

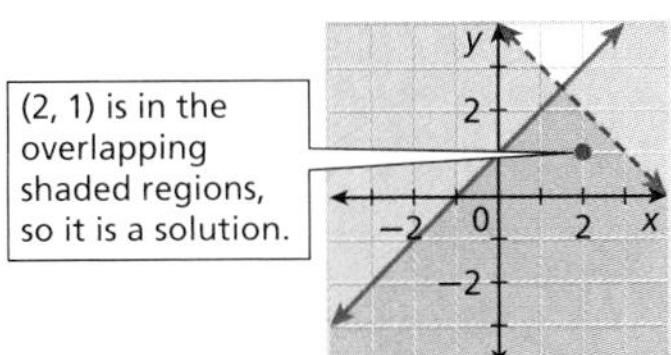

(2, 1) is in the overlapping shaded regions, so it is a solution.
y
2
−2
0
2
x
−2

Example 1B

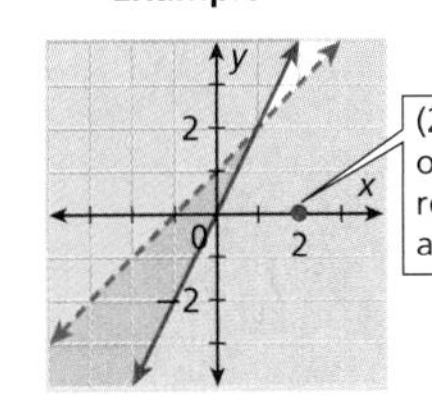

(2, 0) is not in the overlapping shaded regions, so it is not a solution.
y
2
0
2
x
−2

6-7 Organizer

Objective: Graph and solve systems of linear inequalities in two variables.

Online Edition
Tutorial Videos, Interactivity

Countdown to Mastery Week 14

Power Presentations with PowerPoint®

Warm Up

Solve each inequality for *y*.

1. $8x + y < 6$ $y < -8x + 6$

2. $3x - 2y > 10$ $y < \frac{3}{2}x - 5$

3. Graph the solutions of $4x + 3y > 9$.

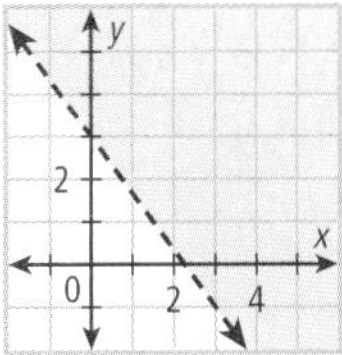

y
2
x
0
2
4

Also available on transparency

Math Humor

Q: Why did the math student wear two pairs of sunglasses?

A: He wanted to have overlapping shades.

1 Introduce

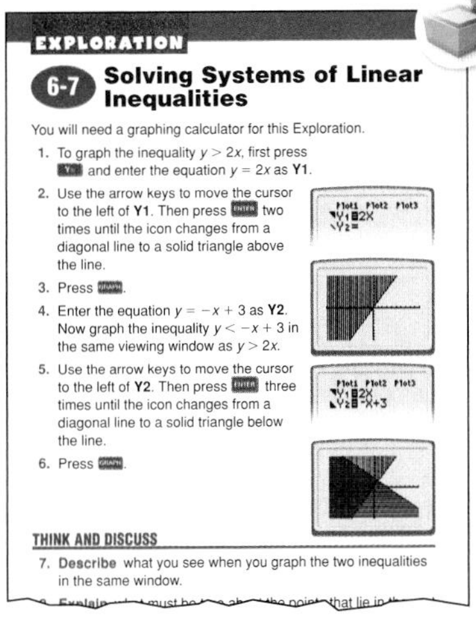

EXPLORATION

6-7 Solving Systems of Linear Inequalities

You will need a graphing calculator for this Exploration.

1. To graph the inequality $y > 2x$, first press Y= and enter the equation $y = 2x$ as **Y1**.
2. Use the arrow keys to move the cursor to the left of **Y1**. Then press ENTER two times until the icon changes from a diagonal line to a solid triangle above the line.
3. Press GRAPH.
4. Enter the equation $y = -x + 3$ as **Y2**. Now graph the inequality $y < -x + 3$ in the same viewing window as $y > 2x$.
5. Use the arrow keys to move the cursor to the left of **Y2**. Then press ENTER three times until the icon changes from a diagonal line to a solid triangle below the line.
6. Press GRAPH.

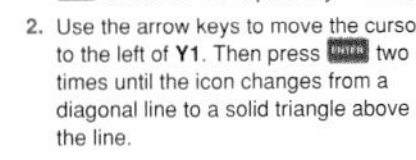

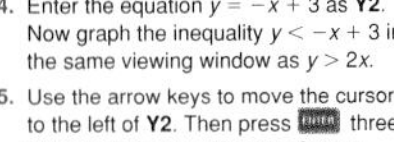

THINK AND DISCUSS

7. **Describe** what you see when you graph the two inequalities in the same window.

Motivate

Have students graph the solutions of the following compound inequality.

$x > 2$ AND $x < 5$ (number line 0 1 2 3 4 5 6)

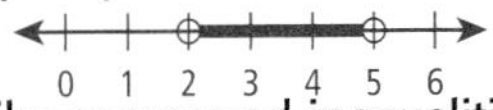

Tell students that, like compound inequalities, systems of inequalites have solutions that are represented by overlapping areas.

Explorations and answers are provided in *Alternate Openers: Explorations Transparencies*.

California Standards

Algebra 1 **9.0**
Also covered:
6.0 Students graph a linear equation and compute the *x*- and *y*-intercepts (e.g., graph $2x + 6y = 4$). **They are also able to sketch the region defined by a linear inequality (e.g., they sketch the region defined by $2x + 6y < 4$).**

Power Presentations with PowerPoint®

Additional Examples

Example 1

Tell whether the ordered pair is a solution of the given system.

A. $(-1, -3)$ $\begin{cases} y \le -3x + 1 \\ y < 2x + 2 \end{cases}$ yes

B. $(-1, 5)$ $\begin{cases} y < -2x - 1 \\ y \ge x + 3 \end{cases}$ no

Example 2

Graph each system of linear inequalities. Give two ordered pairs that are solutions and two that are not solutions.

A. $\begin{cases} y \le 3 \\ y > -x + 5 \end{cases}$

Possible answer: solutions: $(8, 1)$, $(6, 3)$; not solutions: $(-4, 4)$, $(2, 6)$

B. $\begin{cases} -3x + 2y \ge 2 \\ y < 4x + 3 \end{cases}$

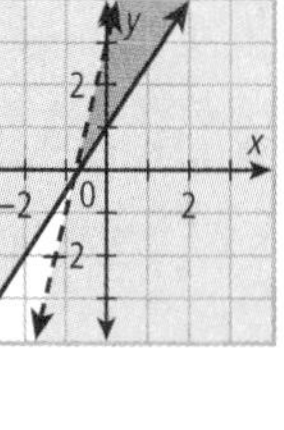

Possible answer: solutions: $(2, 6)$, $(1, 3)$; not solutions: $(0, 0)$, $(-4, 5)$

Example 3

Graph each system of linear inequalities.

A. $\begin{cases} y \le -2x - 4 \\ y > -2x + 5 \end{cases}$

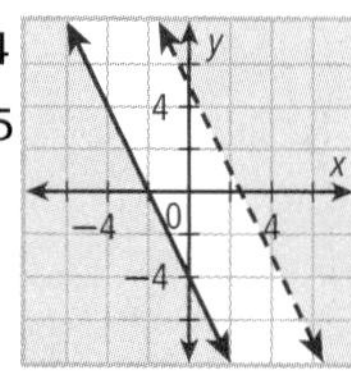

B. $\begin{cases} y > 3x - 2 \\ y < 3x + 6 \end{cases}$

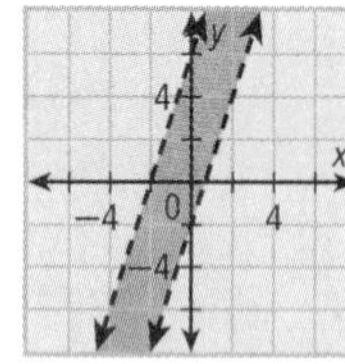

C. $\begin{cases} y \ge 4x + 6 \\ y \ge 4x - 5 \end{cases}$

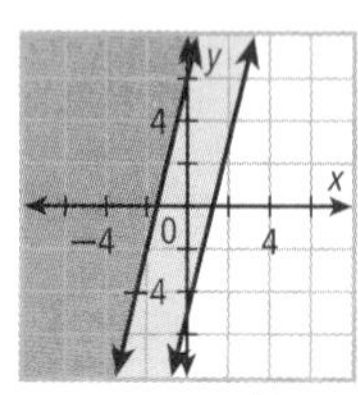

Also available on transparency

EXAMPLE 2 Solving a System of Linear Inequalities by Graphing

Graph the system of linear inequalities. Give two ordered pairs that are solutions and two that are not solutions.

$$\begin{cases} 8x + 4y \le 12 \\ y > \frac{1}{2}x - 2 \end{cases}$$

$8x + 4y \le 12$ *Write the first inequality in slope-intercept form.*

$4y \le -8x + 12$

$y \le -2x + 3$

Graph the system.

$$\begin{cases} y \le -2x + 3 \\ y > \frac{1}{2}x - 2 \end{cases}$$

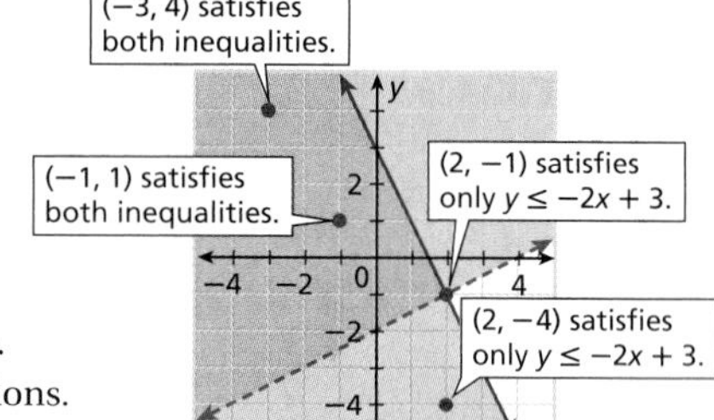
(−3, 4) satisfies both inequalities.
(−1, 1) satisfies both inequalities.
(2, −1) satisfies only y ≤ −2x + 3.
(2, −4) satisfies only y ≤ −2x + 3.

$(-1, 1)$ and $(-3, 4)$ are solutions.
$(2, -1)$ and $(2, -4)$ are not solutions.

CHECK IT OUT! **Graph each system of linear inequalities. Give two ordered pairs that are solutions and two that are not solutions.**

2a. $\begin{cases} y \le x + 1 \\ y > 2 \end{cases}$ **2b.** $\begin{cases} y > x - 7 \\ 3x + 6y \le 12 \end{cases}$

2a.

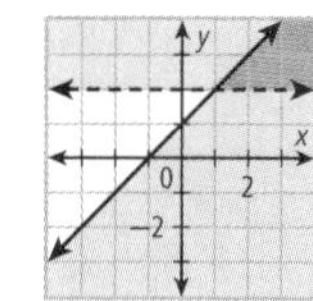

Possible answer: solutions: $(3, 3)$, $(4, 4)$; not solutions: $(-3, 1)$, $(-1, -4)$

2b.

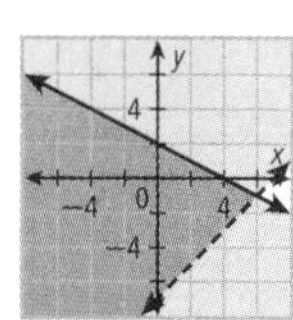

Possible answer: solutions: $(0, 0)$, $(3, -2)$; not solutions: $(4, 4)$, $(1, -6)$

In Lesson 6-4, you saw that in systems of linear equations, if the lines are parallel, there are no solutions. With systems of linear inequalities, that is not always true.

EXAMPLE 3 Graphing Systems with Parallel Boundary Lines

Graph each system of linear inequalities.

A $\begin{cases} y < 2x - 3 \\ y > 2x + 2 \end{cases}$

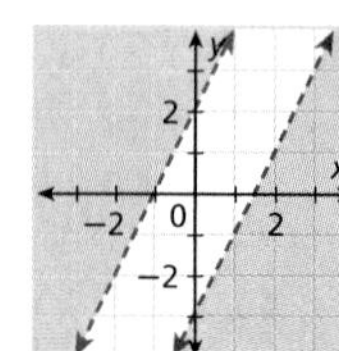

This system has no solution.

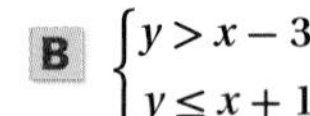

B $\begin{cases} y > x - 3 \\ y \le x + 1 \end{cases}$

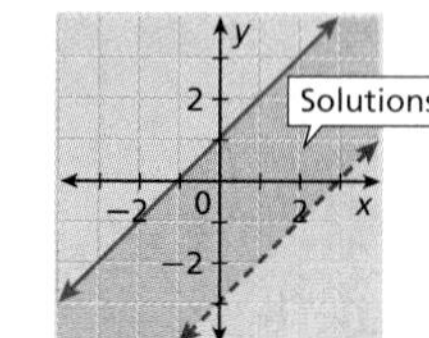
Solutions

The solutions are all points between the parallel lines and on the solid line.

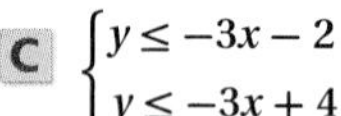

C $\begin{cases} y \le -3x - 2 \\ y \le -3x + 4 \end{cases}$

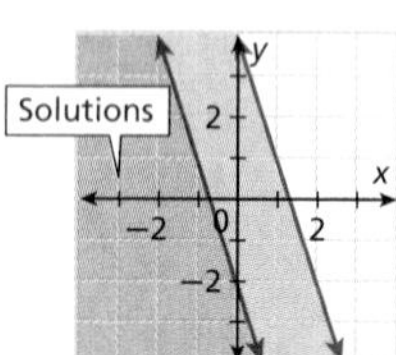
Solutions

The solutions are the same as the solutions of $y \le -3x - 2$.

3a.

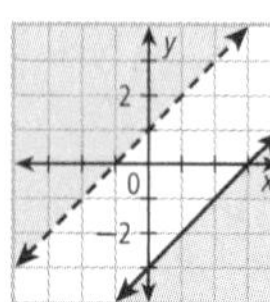

3b.

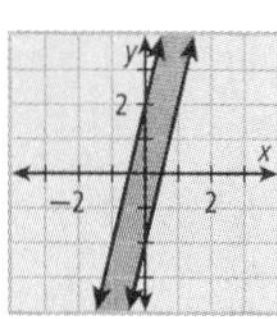

---

2 Teach

Guided Instruction

Tell students that graphing a system of inequalities is just graphing two or more inequalities on the same coordinate plane. The solution is the overlapping region. Encourage students to always use a test point to check that they shaded the correct regions.

Teaching Tip **Visual** Have students shade graphs of inequalities using two different colored pencils (MK). This will make the solution area easier to see.

Universal Access

Through Modeling

Have two students each graph a linear inequality in two variables on different transparencies. Then combine the two graphs by overlapping them, and have students write two ordered pairs that are solutions and two that are not. Repeat with another pair of students until all have taken a turn.

Graph each system of linear inequalities.

3a. $\begin{cases} y > x + 1 \\ y \le x - 3 \end{cases}$ **3b.** $\begin{cases} y \ge 4x - 2 \\ y \le 4x + 2 \end{cases}$ **3c.** $\begin{cases} y > -2x + 3 \\ y > -2x \end{cases}$

3c.

EXAMPLE 4 Business Application

A surf shop makes the profits given in the table. The shop owner sells at least 10 surfboards and at least 20 wakeboards per month. He wants to earn at least \$2000 a month. Show and describe all possible combinations of surfboards and wakeboards that the store owner needs to sell to meet his goals. List two possible combinations.

Profit per Board Sold (\$)	
Surfboard	150
Wakeboard	100

Step 1 Write a system of inequalities.
Let x represent the number of surfboards and y represent the number of wakeboards.

$x \ge 10$ — *He sells at least 10 surfboards.*

$y \ge 20$ — *He sells at least 20 wakeboards.*

$150x + 100y \ge 2000$ — *He wants to earn a total of at least \$2000.*

Step 2 Graph the system.
The graph should be in only the first quadrant because sales are not negative.

Step 3 Describe all possible combinations.
To meet the sales goals, the shop could sell any combination represented by an ordered pair of whole numbers in the solution region. Answers must be whole numbers because the shop cannot sell part of a surfboard or wakeboard.

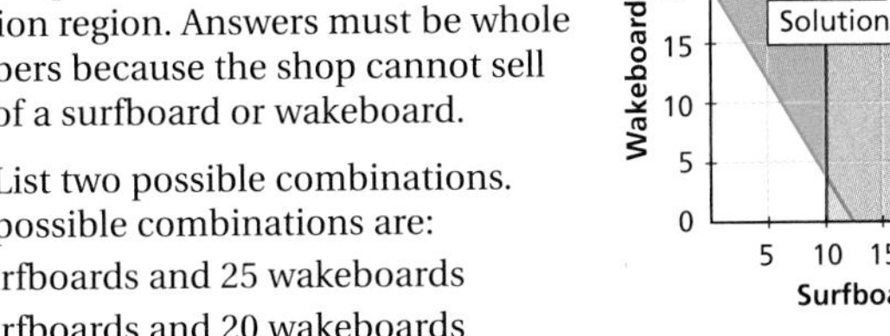

Sales Goals

Step 4 List two possible combinations.
Two possible combinations are:
15 surfboards and 25 wakeboards
25 surfboards and 20 wakeboards

Caution!
An ordered pair solution of the system need not have whole numbers, but answers to many application problems may be restricted to whole numbers.

CHECK IT OUT!

4. At her party, Alice is serving pepper jack cheese and cheddar cheese. She wants to have at least 2 pounds of each. Alice wants to spend at most \$20 on cheese. Show and describe all possible combinations of the two cheeses Alice could buy. List two possible combinations.

Price per Pound (\$)	
Pepper Jack	4
Cheddar	2

4. Cheese Combinations

Possible answer: (3 lb pepper jack, 2 lb cheddar), (2.5 lb pepper jack, 4 lb cheddar)

THINK AND DISCUSS

1. How would you write a system of linear inequalities from a graph?

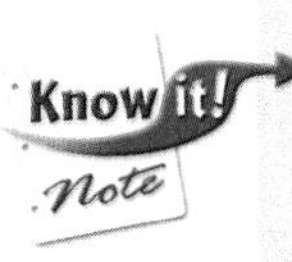

2. GET ORGANIZED Copy and complete each part of the graphic organizer. In each box, draw a graph and list one solution.

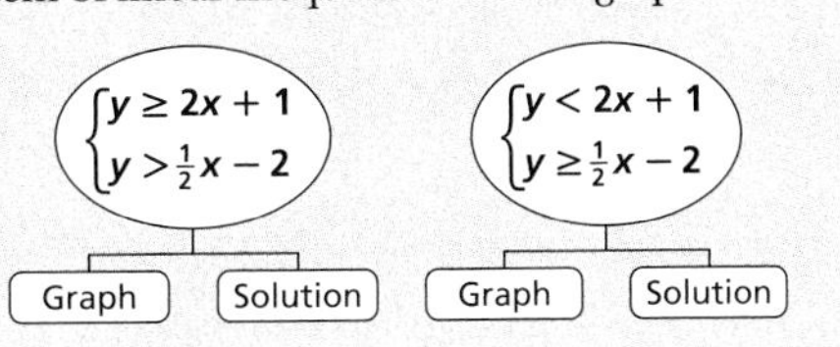

Power Presentations with PowerPoint®

Additional Examples

Example 4

In one week, Ed can mow at most 9 times and rake at most 7 times. He charges \$20 for mowing and \$10 for raking. He needs to earn more than \$125 in one week. Show and describe all the possible combinations of mowing and raking that Ed can do to meet his goal. List two possible combinations.

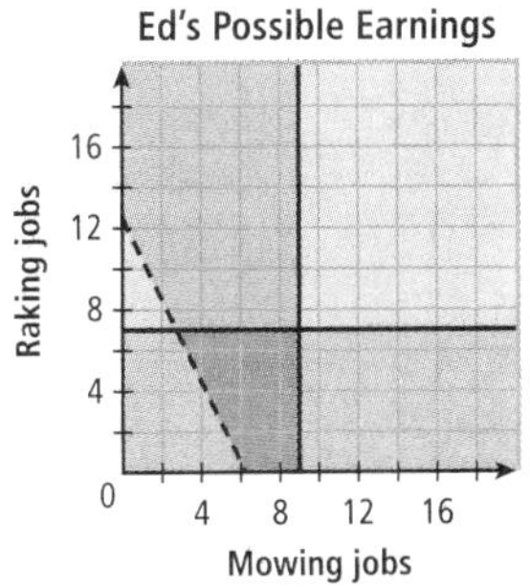

Ed's Possible Earnings

Reasonable answers must be whole numbers. Possible answer: (7 mowing, 4 raking), (8 mowing, 1 raking)

Also available on transparency

INTERVENTION
Questioning Strategies

EXAMPLE 1

- When do you need to check only one inequality? Why?

EXAMPLES 2–3

- How can you check that you shaded the correct areas?

EXAMPLE 4

- How do you choose which region to select the combinations from?

3 Close

Summarize

Emphasize that an ordered pair is a solution of a system of inequalities only if it makes every inequality in that system true. Graphically, the solutions will be in the overlapping shaded regions. Remind students that points on a boundary line are solutions if the line is solid, and are not solutions if the line is dashed. The intersection of boundary lines is a solution only if both lines are solid.

FORMATIVE ASSESSMENT and INTERVENTION

***Diagnose Before* the Lesson**
6-7 Warm Up, TE p. 371

***Monitor During* the Lesson**
Check It Out! Exercises, SE pp. 371–373
Questioning Strategies, TE p. 373

***Assess After* the Lesson**
6-7 Lesson Quiz, TE p. 376
Alternative Assessment, TE p. 376

Answers to *Think and Discuss*

Possible answers:

1. To write a system of linear inequalities from a graph, write the linear inequality for each of the graphs that make up the system.
2. See p. A5.

6-7 Exercises

Assignment Guide

Assign *Guided Practice* exercises as necessary.

If you finished Examples **1–2**
Proficient 16–22, 34, 35
Advanced 16–22, 34, 35

If you finished Examples **1–4**
Proficient 16–29, 30–42 even, 44–47, 51–60
Advanced 16–29, 30, 41–60

Homework Quick Check
Quickly check key concepts.
Exercises: 16, 22, 26, 29, 42

Answers

5.

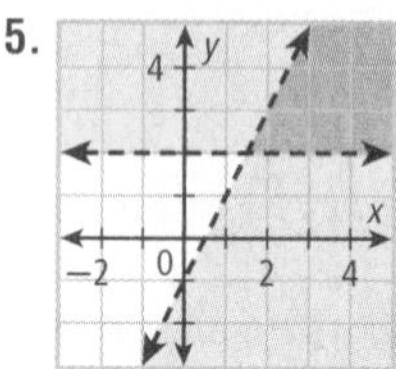

Possible answer: solutions: (3, 3), (4, 3); not solutions: (0, 0), (2, 1)

6.

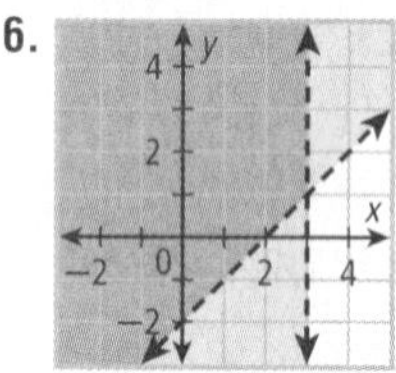

Possible answer: solutions: (0, 0), (1, 1); not solutions: (2, −1), (3, 1)

15.

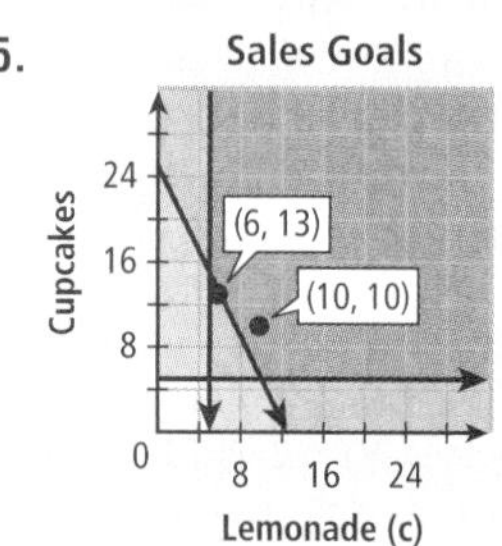

Possible answer:
(6 c lemonade, 13 cupcakes),
(10 c lemonade, 10 cupcakes)

7–14, 19–28. See pp. A21–A22.

California Standards

Standard	Exercises
2.0 🔑	51–53
6.0 🔑	5–14, 19–28, 31–34, 47, 49, 58–60
9.0 🔑	15, 29, 30, 38, 40, 42c, 46

6-7 Exercises

California Standards Practice
🔑 6.0, 🔑 9.0

go.hrw.com
Homework Help Online
KEYWORD: MA8CA 6-7
Parent Resources Online
KEYWORD: MA8CA Parent

GUIDED PRACTICE

1. **Vocabulary** A solution of a system of inequalities is a solution of ___?___ of the inequalities in the system. (*at least one* or *all*) **all**

SEE EXAMPLE 1 p. 371

Tell whether the ordered pair is a solution of the given system.

2. $(0, 0); \begin{cases} y < -x + 3 \\ y < x + 2 \end{cases}$ **yes**
3. $(0, 0); \begin{cases} y < 3 \\ y > x - 2 \end{cases}$ **yes**
4. $(1, 0); \begin{cases} y > 3x \\ y \leq x + 1 \end{cases}$ **no**

SEE EXAMPLE 2 p. 372

Graph each system of linear inequalities. Give two ordered pairs that are solutions and two that are not solutions.

5. $\begin{cases} y < 2x - 1 \\ y > 2 \end{cases}$
6. $\begin{cases} x < 3 \\ y > x - 2 \end{cases}$
7. $\begin{cases} y \geq 3x \\ 3x + y \geq 3 \end{cases}$
8. $\begin{cases} 2x - 4y \leq 8 \\ y > x - 2 \end{cases}$

SEE EXAMPLE 3 p. 372

Graph each system of linear inequalities.

9. $\begin{cases} y > 2x + 3 \\ y < 2x \end{cases}$
10. $\begin{cases} y \leq -3x - 1 \\ y \geq -3x + 1 \end{cases}$
11. $\begin{cases} y > 4x - 1 \\ y \leq 4x + 1 \end{cases}$
12. $\begin{cases} y < -x + 3 \\ y > -x + 2 \end{cases}$
13. $\begin{cases} y > 2x - 1 \\ y > 2x - 4 \end{cases}$
14. $\begin{cases} y \leq -3x + 4 \\ y \leq -3x - 3 \end{cases}$

SEE EXAMPLE 4 p. 373

15. **Business** Sandy makes \$2 profit on every cup of lemonade that she sells and \$1 on every cupcake that she sells. Sandy wants to sell at least 5 cups of lemonade and at least 5 cupcakes per day. She wants to earn at least \$25 per day. Show and describe all the possible combinations of lemonade and cupcakes that Sandy needs to sell to meet her goals. List two possible combinations.

PRACTICE AND PROBLEM SOLVING

Independent Practice

For Exercises	See Example
16–18	1
19–22	2
23–28	3
29	4

Extra Practice
Skills Practice p. EP13
Application Practice p. EP29

Tell whether the ordered pair is a solution of the given system.

16. $(0, 0); \begin{cases} y > -x - 1 \\ y < 2x + 4 \end{cases}$ **yes**
17. $(0, 0); \begin{cases} x + y < 3 \\ y > 3x - 4 \end{cases}$ **yes**
18. $(1, 0); \begin{cases} y > 3x \\ y > 3x + 1 \end{cases}$ **no**

Graph each system of linear inequalities. Give two ordered pairs that are solutions and two that are not solutions.

19. $\begin{cases} y < -3x - 3 \\ y \geq 0 \end{cases}$
20. $\begin{cases} y < -1 \\ y > 2x - 1 \end{cases}$
21. $\begin{cases} y > 2x + 4 \\ 6x + 2y \geq -2 \end{cases}$
22. $\begin{cases} 9x + 3y \leq 6 \\ y > x \end{cases}$

Graph each system of linear inequalities.

23. $\begin{cases} y < 3 \\ y > 5 \end{cases}$
24. $\begin{cases} y < x - 1 \\ y > x - 2 \end{cases}$
25. $\begin{cases} x \geq 2 \\ x \leq 2 \end{cases}$
26. $\begin{cases} y > -4x - 3 \\ y < -4x + 2 \end{cases}$
27. $\begin{cases} y > -1 \\ y > 2 \end{cases}$
28. $\begin{cases} y \leq 2x + 1 \\ y \leq 2x - 4 \end{cases}$

6-7 READING STRATEGIES

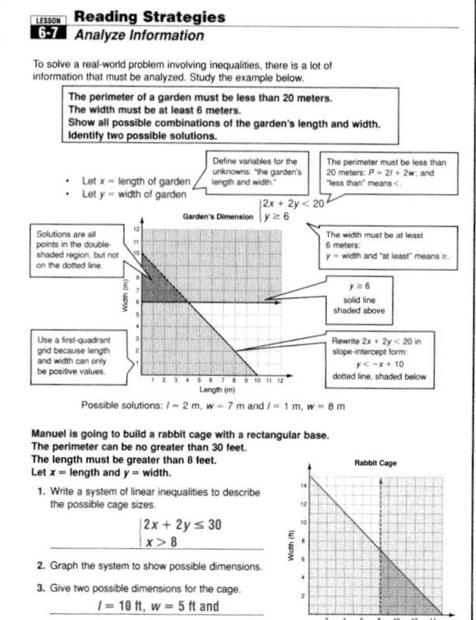

LESSON 6-7 **Reading Strategies**
Analyze Information

To solve a real-world problem involving inequalities, there is a lot of information that must be analyzed. Study the example below.

The perimeter of a garden must be less than 20 meters.
The width must be at least 6 meters.
Show all possible combinations of the garden's length and width.
Identify two possible solutions.

- Let x = length of garden
- Let y = width of garden

Define variables for the unknowns: "the garden's length and width."

The perimeter must be less than 20 meters: $P = 2l + 2w$; and "less than" means <.

Garden's Dimension $\begin{cases} 2x + 2y < 20 \\ y \geq 6 \end{cases}$

The width must be at least 6 meters: y = width and "at least" means ≥.

Solutions are all points in the double-shaded region, but not on the dotted line.

$y \geq 6$ solid line shaded above

Use a first-quadrant grid because length and width can only be positive values.

Rewrite $2x + 2y < 20$ in slope-intercept form: $y < -x + 10$ dotted line, shaded below

Possible solutions: $l = 2$ m, $w = 7$ m and $l = 1$ m, $w = 8$ m

Manuel is going to build a rabbit cage with a rectangular base.
The perimeter can be no greater than 30 feet.
The length must be greater than 8 feet.
Let x = length and y = width.

1. Write a system of linear inequalities to describe the possible cage sizes.
$\begin{cases} 2x + 2y \leq 30 \\ x > 8 \end{cases}$
2. Graph the system to show possible dimensions.
3. Give two possible dimensions for the cage.
$l = 10$ ft, $w = 5$ ft and $l = 11$ ft, $w = 4$ ft

Rabbit Cage

6-7 REVIEW FOR MASTERY

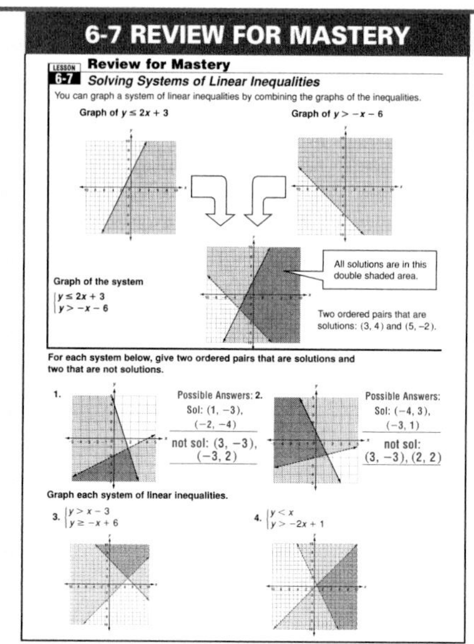

LESSON 6-7 **Review for Mastery**
Solving Systems of Linear Inequalities

You can graph a system of linear inequalities by combining the graphs of the inequalities.

Graph of $y \leq 2x + 3$ Graph of $y > -x - 6$

Graph of the system $\begin{cases} y \leq 2x + 3 \\ y > -x - 6 \end{cases}$

All solutions are in this double shaded area.

Two ordered pairs that are solutions: (3, 4) and (5, −2).

For each system below, give two ordered pairs that are solutions and two that are not solutions.

1. Possible Answers: Sol: (1, −3), (−2, −4) not sol: (3, −3), (−3, 2)
2. Possible Answers: Sol: (−4, 3), (−3, 1) not sol: (3, −3), (2, 2)

Graph each system of linear inequalities.

3. $\begin{cases} y > x - 3 \\ y \geq -x + 6 \end{cases}$
4. $\begin{cases} y < x \\ y > -2x + 1 \end{cases}$

29. **Multi-Step** Linda works at a pharmacy for $15 an hour. She also baby-sits for $10 an hour. Linda needs to earn at least $90 per week, but she does not want to work more than 20 hours per week. Show and describe the number of hours Linda could work at each job to meet her goals. List two possible solutions.

30. **Farming** Tony wants to plant at least 40 acres of corn and at least 50 acres of soybeans. He wants no more than 200 acres of corn and soybeans. Show and describe all the possible combinations of the number of acres of corn and of soybeans Tony could plant. List two possible combinations.

Graph each system of linear inequalities.

31. $\begin{cases} y \geq -3 \\ y \geq 2 \end{cases}$ 32. $\begin{cases} y > -2x - 1 \\ y > -2x - 3 \end{cases}$ 33. $\begin{cases} x \leq -3 \\ x \geq 1 \end{cases}$ 34. $\begin{cases} y < 4 \\ y > 0 \end{cases}$

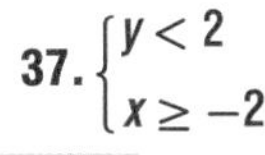
37. $\begin{cases} y < 2 \\ x \geq -2 \end{cases}$

Write a system of linear inequalities to represent each graph.

35. 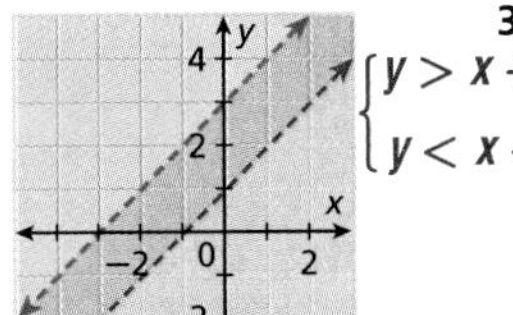

$\begin{cases} y > x + 1 \\ y < x + 3 \end{cases}$

36. 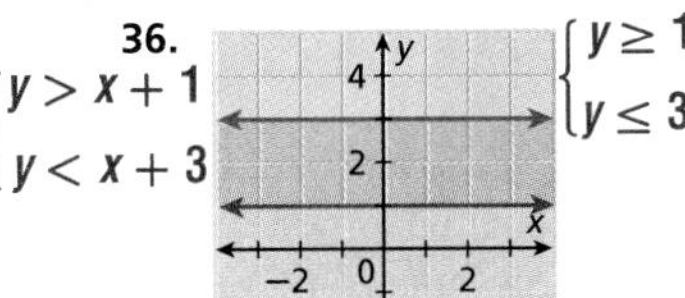

$\begin{cases} y \geq 1 \\ y \leq 3 \end{cases}$

37. 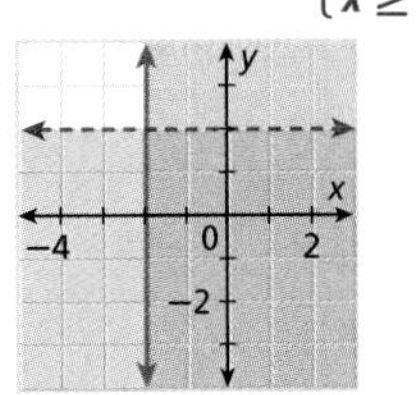

38. **Military** For males to enter the United States Air Force Academy, located in Colorado Springs, CO, they must be at least 17 but less than 23 years of age. Their standing height must be not less than 60 inches and not greater than 80 inches. Graph all possible heights and ages for eligible male candidates. Give three possible combinations.

39. **///ERROR ANALYSIS///** Two students wrote a system of linear inequalities to describe the graph. Which student is incorrect? Explain the error. **Student B; the inequality symbols are incorrect.**

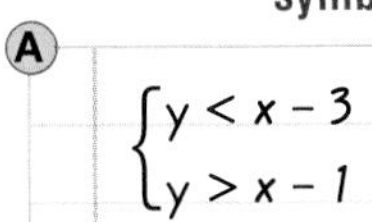
Ⓐ $\begin{cases} y < x - 3 \\ y > x - 1 \end{cases}$

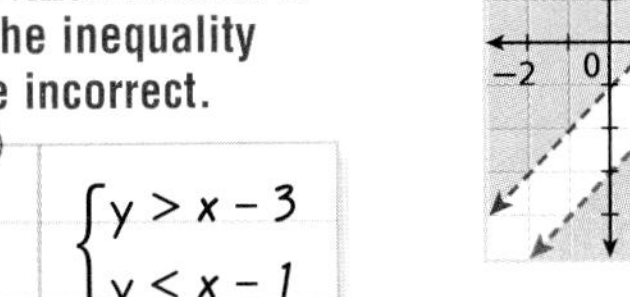
Ⓑ $\begin{cases} y > x - 3 \\ y < x - 1 \end{cases}$

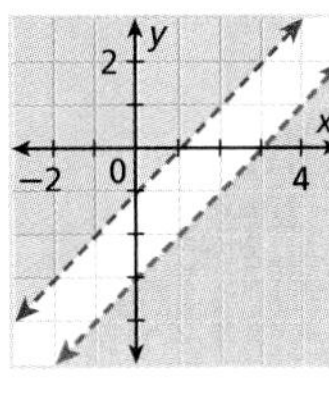

40. **Recreation** Vance wants to fence in a rectangular area for his dog. He wants the length of the rectangle to be at least 30 feet and the perimeter to be no more than 150 feet. Graph all possible dimensions of the rectangle.

41. **Reasoning** Can the solutions of a system of linear inequalities be the points on a line? Explain.

LINK Military

In 1959, the first class graduated from the Air Force Academy. The first class that included women graduated in 1980.

CONCEPT CONNECTION

42. This problem will prepare you for the Concept Connection on page 378.

Gloria is starting her own company making teddy bears. She has enough bear bodies to create 40 bears. She will make girl bears and boy bears.

a. Write an inequality to show this situation.

b. Gloria will charge $15 for girl bears and $12 for boy bears. She wants to earn at least $540 a week. Write an inequality to describe this situation.

c. Graph this situation and locate the solution region.

COMMON ERROR /// ALERT \\\

Students may have trouble graphing systems with horizontal or vertical boundary lines, such as in **Exercises 5 and 6.** Remind them that the line intersects the *x*-axis when *x* is the only variable in the inequality. It intersects the *y*-axis when *y* is the only variable.

Language Support Be sure students understand the meaning of *eligible* in **Exercise 38.** It describes the students who may enter the academy. Students who may not enter the academy are *ineligible.*

ENGLISH LANGUAGE LEARNERS

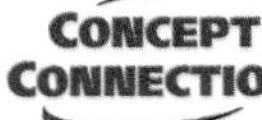
Exercise 42 involves graphing solutions of linear inequalities to determine the number of items that need to be sold to meet earning goals. This exercise prepares students for the Concept Connection on page 378.

Answers

29. 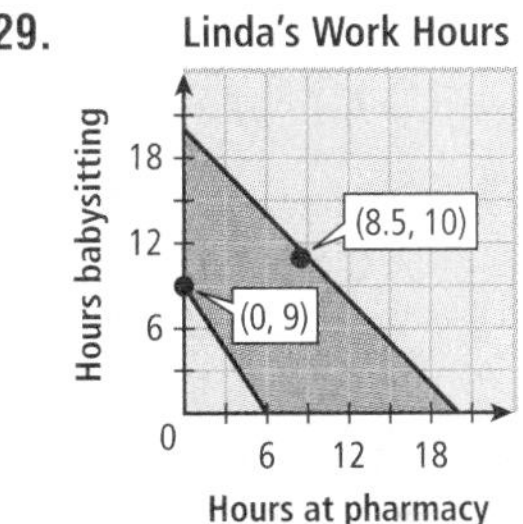

Possible answer: (0 h at pharmacy, 9 h babysitting), (8.5 h at pharmacy, 10 h babysitting)

30–34, 38, 40–42. See p. A22.

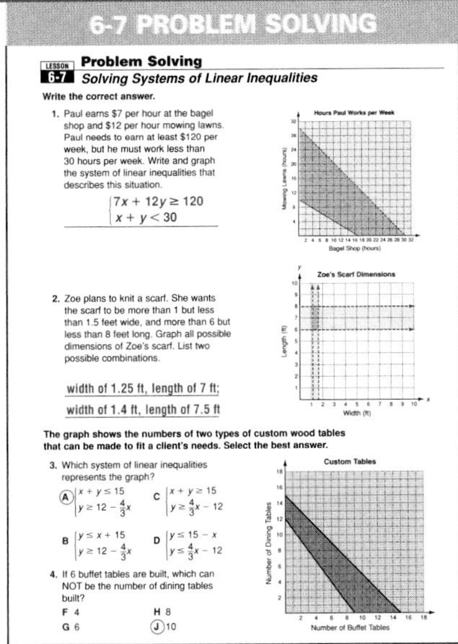

6-7 PROBLEM SOLVING

LESSON 6-7 **Problem Solving**
Solving Systems of Linear Inequalities

Write the correct answer.

1. Paul earns $7 per hour at the bagel shop and $12 per hour mowing lawns. Paul needs to earn at least $120 per week, but he must work less than 30 hours per week. Write and graph the system of linear inequalities that describes this situation.

$\begin{cases} 7x + 12y \geq 120 \\ x + y < 30 \end{cases}$

2. Zoe plans to knit a scarf. She wants the scarf to be more than 1 but less than 1.5 feet wide, and more than 6 but less than 8 feet long. Graph all possible dimensions of Zoe's scarf. List two possible combinations.

width of 1.25 ft, length of 7 ft;
width of 1.4 ft, length of 7.5 ft

The graph shows the numbers of two types of custom wood tables that can be made to fit a client's needs. Select the best answer.

3. Which system of linear inequalities represents the graph?

Ⓐ $\begin{cases} x + y \leq 15 \\ y \geq 12 - \frac{4}{3}x \end{cases}$ C $\begin{cases} x + y \geq 15 \\ y \geq \frac{4}{3}x - 12 \end{cases}$

B $\begin{cases} y \leq x + 15 \\ y \geq 12 - \frac{4}{3}x \end{cases}$ D $\begin{cases} y \leq 15 - x \\ y \leq \frac{4}{3}x - 12 \end{cases}$

4. If 6 buffet tables are built, which can NOT be the number of dining tables built?

F 4 H 8
G 6 Ⓙ 10

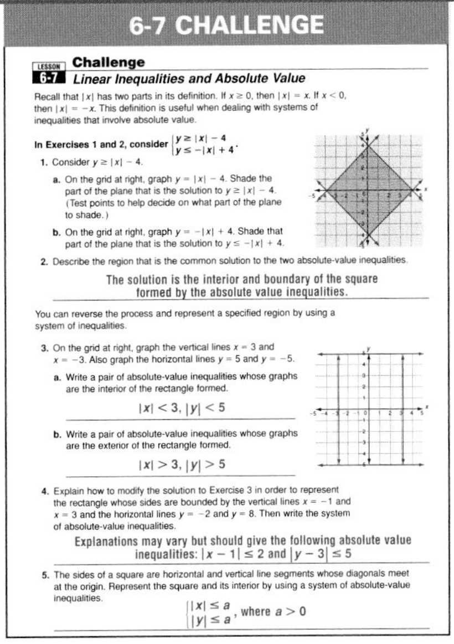

6-7 CHALLENGE

LESSON 6-7 **Challenge**
Linear Inequalities and Absolute Value

Recall that $|x|$ has two parts in its definition. If $x \geq 0$, then $|x| = x$. If $x < 0$, then $|x| = -x$. This definition is useful when dealing with systems of inequalities that involve absolute value.

In Exercises 1 and 2, consider $\begin{cases} y \geq |x| - 4 \\ y \leq -|x| + 4 \end{cases}$.

1. Consider $y \geq |x| - 4$.

a. On the grid at right, graph $y = |x| - 4$. Shade the part of the plane that is the solution to $y \geq |x| - 4$. (Test points to help decide on what part of the plane to shade.)

b. On the grid at right, graph $y = -|x| + 4$. Shade that part of the plane that is the solution to $y \leq -|x| + 4$.

2. Describe the region that is the common solution to the two absolute-value inequalities.

The solution is the interior and boundary of the square formed by the absolute value inequalities.

You can reverse the process and represent a specified region by using a system of inequalities.

3. On the grid at right, graph the vertical lines $x = 3$ and $x = -3$. Also graph the horizontal lines $y = 5$ and $y = -5$.

a. Write a pair of absolute-value inequalities whose graphs are the interior of the rectangle formed.

$|x| < 3, |y| < 5$

b. Write a pair of absolute-value inequalities whose graphs are the exterior of the rectangle formed.

$|x| > 3, |y| > 5$

4. Explain how to modify the solution to Exercise 3 in order to represent the rectangle whose sides are bounded by the vertical lines $x = -1$ and $x = 3$ and the horizontal lines $y = -2$ and $y = 8$. Then write the system of absolute-value inequalities.

Explanations may vary but should give the following absolute value inequalities: $|x - 1| \leq 2$ and $|y - 3| \leq 5$

5. The sides of a square are horizontal and vertical line segments whose diagonals meet at the origin. Represent the square and its interior by using a system of absolute-value inequalities.

$\begin{cases} |x| \leq a \\ |y| \leq a \end{cases}$, where $a > 0$

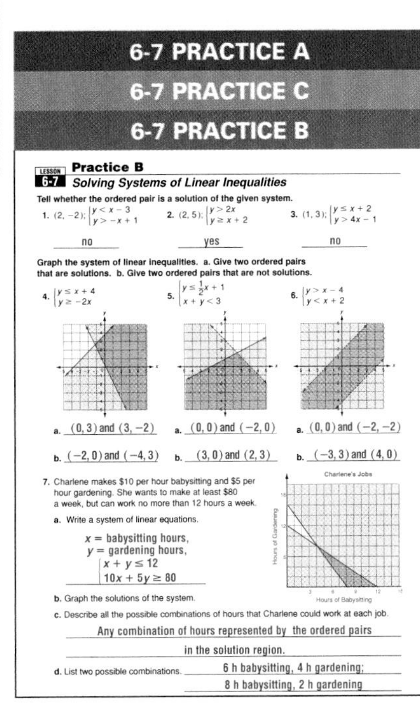

6-7 PRACTICE A
6-7 PRACTICE C
6-7 PRACTICE B

LESSON 6-7 **Practice B**
Solving Systems of Linear Inequalities

Tell whether the ordered pair is a solution of the given system.

1. (2, −2); $\begin{cases} y < x - 3 \\ y > -x + 1 \end{cases}$ no

2. (2, 5); $\begin{cases} y > 2x \\ y \geq x + 2 \end{cases}$ yes

3. (1, 3); $\begin{cases} y \leq x + 2 \\ y > 4x - 1 \end{cases}$ no

Graph the system of linear inequalities. a. Give two ordered pairs that are solutions. b. Give two ordered pairs that are not solutions.

4. $\begin{cases} y \leq x + 4 \\ y \geq -2x \end{cases}$ a. (0, 3) and (3, −2) b. (−2, 0) and (−4, 3)

5. $\begin{cases} y \leq \frac{1}{2}x + 1 \\ x + y < 3 \end{cases}$ a. (0, 0) and (−2, 0) b. (3, 0) and (2, 3)

6. $\begin{cases} y > x - 4 \\ y < x + 2 \end{cases}$ a. (0, 0) and (−2, −2) b. (−3, 3) and (4, 0)

7. Charlene makes $10 per hour babysitting and $5 per hour gardening. She wants to make at least $80 a week, but can work no more than 12 hours a week.

a. Write a system of linear equations.

x = babysitting hours,
y = gardening hours,
$\begin{cases} x + y \leq 12 \\ 10x + 5y \geq 80 \end{cases}$

b. Graph the solutions of the system.

c. Describe all the possible combinations of hours that Charlene could work at each job.

Any combination of hours represented by the ordered pairs in the solution region.

d. List two possible combinations. 6 h babysitting, 4 h gardening; 8 h babysitting, 2 h gardening

Multiple Choice The graph in **Exercise 45** shows solutions between parallel lines. This is not possible when the inequality symbols are both < or both >. Choices **C** and **D** can be eliminated.

Journal

Have students describe a real-world situation that can be modeled by a system of linear inequalities in two variables and in which reasonable solutions must be whole numbers.

ALTERNATIVE ASSESSMENT

Tell students to write and graph a system of inequalities that has solutions, and identify two solutions. Then have students write and graph a system that has no solutions.

Power Presentations with PowerPoint®

6-7 Lesson Quiz

1. Graph $\begin{cases} y < x + 2 \\ 5x + 2y \geq 10 \end{cases}$. Give two ordered pairs that are solutions and two that are not solutions.

Possible answer: solutions: (4, 4), (8, 6); not solutions: (0, 0), (−2, 3)

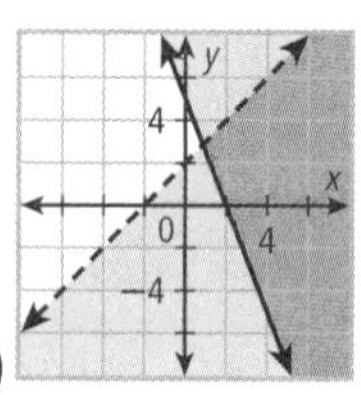

2. Dee has at most \$150 to spend on restocking dolls and trains at her toy store. Dolls cost \$7.50, and trains cost \$5.00. Dee needs no more than 10 trains, and at least 8 dolls. Show and describe all possible combinations of dolls and trains that Dee can buy. List two possible combinations.

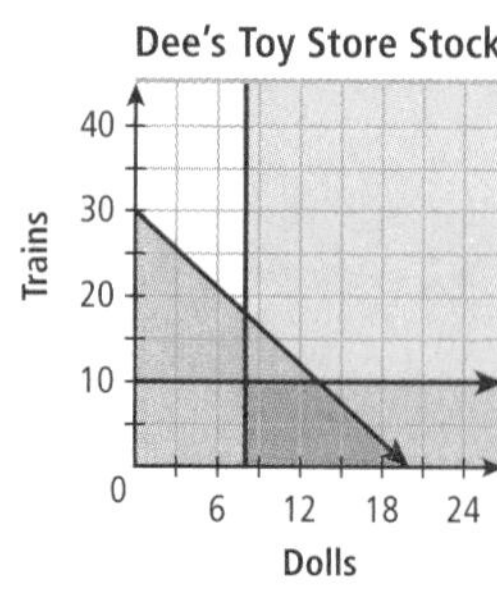

Reasonable answers must be whole numbers. Possible answer: (12 dolls, 6 trains), (16 dolls, 4 trains)

Also available on transparency

43. **Write About It** What must be true of the boundary lines in a system of two linear inequalities if there is no solution of the system? Explain. **The boundary lines must be parallel. If the boundary lines are not parallel, there will be overlap.**

Multiple Choice For Exercises 44 and 45, choose the best answer.

44. Which point is a solution of $\begin{cases} 2x + y \geq 3 \\ y \geq -2x + 1 \end{cases}$?

Ⓐ (0, 0) Ⓑ (0, 1) Ⓒ (1, 0) **Ⓓ (1, 1)**

45. Which system of inequalities best describes the graph?

Ⓐ $\begin{cases} y < 2x - 3 \\ y > 2x + 1 \end{cases}$ Ⓒ $\begin{cases} y < 2x - 3 \\ y < 2x + 1 \end{cases}$

Ⓑ $\begin{cases} y > 2x - 3 \\ y < 2x + 1 \end{cases}$ Ⓓ $\begin{cases} y > 2x - 3 \\ y > 2x + 1 \end{cases}$

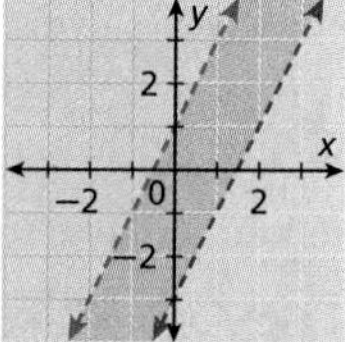

46. **Short Response** Graph and describe $\begin{cases} y + x > 2 \\ y \leq -3x + 4 \end{cases}$. Give two possible solutions of the system.

CHALLENGE AND EXTEND

47. **Estimation** Graph the given system of inequalities. Estimate the area of the overlapping solution regions. **about 12 sq. units**

$\begin{cases} y \geq 0 \\ y \leq x + 3.5 \\ y \leq -x + 3.5 \end{cases}$

48. Write a system of linear inequalities for which (−1, 1) and (1, 4) are solutions and (0, 0) and (2, −1) are not solutions.

49. Graph $|y| < 1$.

50. Write a system of linear inequalities for which the solutions are all the points in the third quadrant. $\begin{cases} x < 0 \\ y < 0 \end{cases}$

SPIRAL STANDARDS REVIEW

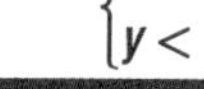

2.0, 6.0

Use the diagram to find each of the following. *(Lesson 1-4)*

51. area of the square **25 cm²**

52. area of the yellow triangle **12.5 cm²**

53. combined area of the blue triangles **12.5 cm²**

5 cm

5 cm

Tell whether the given ordered pairs satisfy a linear function. *(Lesson 5-1)*

54. {(3, 8), (4, 6), (5, 4), (6, 2), (7, 0)} **yes**

55. {(6, 1), (7, 2), (8, 4), (9, 7), (10, 11)} **no**

56. {(2, 10), (7, 9), (12, 8), (17, 7), (22, 6)} **yes**

57. {(1, −9), (3, −7), (5, −5), (7, −3), (9, −1)} **yes**

Graph the solutions of each linear inequality. Check your answer. *(Lesson 6-6)*

58. $y \leq 2x - 1$

59. $-\frac{1}{4}x + y > 6$

60. $5 - x \geq 0$

Answers

46.

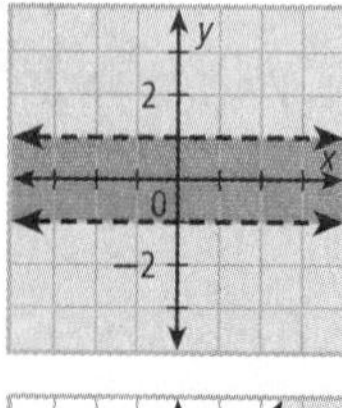

Possible answer: (0, 3), (−2, 6)

48. $\begin{cases} y \geq \frac{3}{2}x + \frac{5}{2} \\ y > -\frac{1}{2}x \end{cases}$

49.

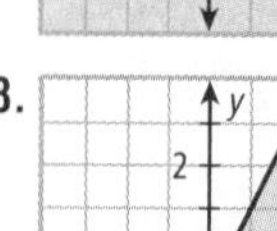

58.

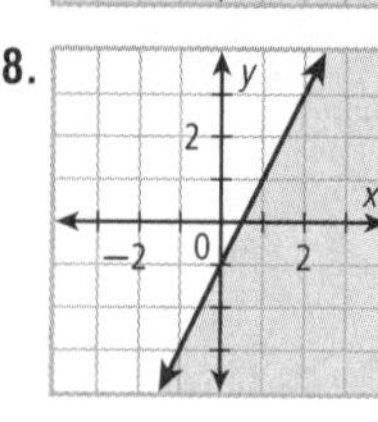

59.

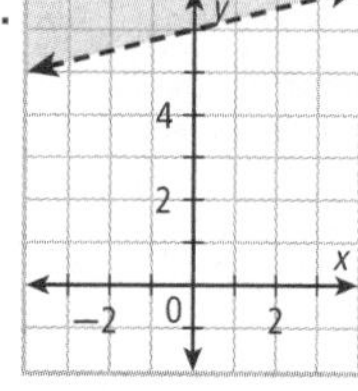

60.

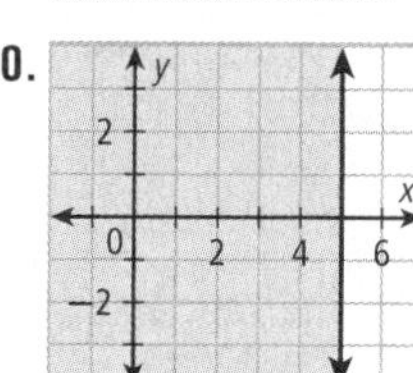

6-7

Solve Systems of Linear Inequalities

A graphing calculator gives a visual solution to a system of linear inequalities.

Use with Lesson 6-7

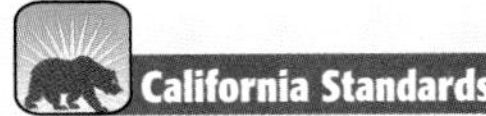

9.0 Students solve a system of two linear equations in two variables algebraically and are able to interpret the answer graphically. **Students are able to solve a system of two linear inequalities in two variables and to sketch the solution sets.**

Graph the system $\begin{cases} y > 2x - 4 \\ 2.75y - x < 6 \end{cases}$. **Give two ordered pairs that are solutions.**

1. Write the first boundary line in slope-intercept form.
   $y > 2x - 4 \quad \rightarrow \quad y = 2x - 4$

2. Press Y= and enter $2x - 4$ for **Y1.**

   Plot1 Plot2 Plot3
   Y1 ■2X-4
   \Y2=

   The inequality contains the symbol >. The solution region is above the boundary line. Press ◄ to move the cursor to the left of **Y1.** Press ENTER until the icon that looks like a region above a line appears. Press GRAPH.

3. Solve the second inequality for y.
   $2.75y - x < 6$
   $2.75y < x + 6$
   $y < \frac{x+6}{2.75} \quad \rightarrow \quad y = \frac{x+6}{2.75}$

4. Press Y= and enter $(x + 6)/2.75$ for **Y2.**

   Plot1 Plot2 Plot3
   Y1 ■2X-4
   Y2 ■(X+6)/2.75

   The inequality contains the symbol <. The solution region is below the boundary line. Press ◄ to move the cursor to the left of **Y2.** Press ENTER until the icon that looks like a region below a line appears. Press GRAPH.

5. The solutions of the system are represented by the overlapping shaded regions. The points (0, 0) and (−1, 0) are in the shaded region.

Check Test (0, 0) in both inequalities.

$y > 2x - 4$		$2.75y - x < 6$	
0	$2(0) - 4$	$2.75(0) - 0$	6
0 >	−4 ✓	0 <	6 ✓

Test (−1, 0) in both inequalities.

$y > 2x - 4$		$2.75y - x < 6$	
0	$2(-1) - 4$	$2.75(0) - (-1)$	6
0 >	−6 ✓	1 <	6 ✓

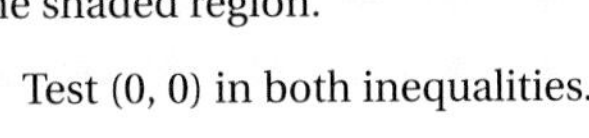

Graph each system. Give two ordered pairs that are solutions.

1. $\begin{cases} x + 5y > -10 \\ x - y < 4 \end{cases}$
2. $\begin{cases} y > x - 2 \\ y \le x + 2 \end{cases}$
3. $\begin{cases} y > x - 2 \\ y \le 3 \end{cases}$
4. $\begin{cases} y < x - 3 \\ y - 3 > x \end{cases}$

Teacher to Teacher

It is important to point out to students that when you graph a linear inequality using a graphing calculator, the boundary line will always appear solid.

Remind students that they will need to consider the points on the boundary line and decide whether or not they are included in the solution set based on the inequality symbol rather than the appearance of the graph.

Larry Ward
Corinth, TX

Organizer

Use with Lesson 6-7

Objective: Use a graphing calculator to view solutions of a system of linear inequalities.

Materials: graphing calculator

Online Edition
Graphing Calculator, TechKeys

Teach

Discuss

After the equation for the boundary line is entered, discuss how to determine whether to shade above or below the line.

Close

Key Concept

You can graph a system of inequalities on a graphing calculator by entering equations for each boundary line and graphing the solutions of each inequality.

Assessment

Journal Have students explain how to use a graphing calculator to solve a system of linear inequalities.

Answers

1. Possible answer: (0, 0), (1, −1)
2. Possible answer: (0, 0), (1, 0)
3. Possible answer: (0, 0), (−2, 2)
4. No solution

Algebra 1 9.0

CONCEPT CONNECTION

SECTION 6B

SECTION 6B CONCEPT CONNECTION

Organizer

Objective: Assess students' ability to apply concepts and skills in Lessons 6-6 through 6-7 in a real-world format.

Problem	Text Reference
1	Lessons 6-6, 6-7
2	Lesson 6-7
3	Lesson 6-7
4	Lesson 4-3
5	Lesson 6-7

Answer

2. 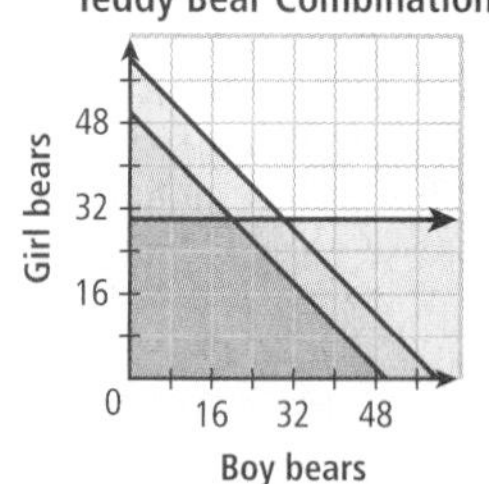

Equations and Formulas

Bearable Sales Gloria makes teddy bears. She dresses some as girl bears with dresses and bows and some as boy bears with bow ties. She is running low on supplies. She has only 100 eyes, 30 dresses, and 60 ties that can be used as bows on the girls and bow ties on the boys.

1. $2x + 2y \leq 100$; $y \leq 30$; $x + y \leq 60$

1. Write the inequalities that describe this situation. Let x represent the number of boy bears and y represent the number of girl bears.
2. Graph the inequalities and locate the region showing the number of boy and girl bears Gloria can make.

3. Possible answer: (5 boys, 20 girls), (10 boys, 15 girls), (30 boys, 5 girls)

3. List at least three combinations of girl and boy bears that Gloria can make.

For 4 and 5, use the table.

4. Using the boundary line in your graph from Problem 2, copy and complete the table with the corresponding number of girl bears.

5. $240; $290; $340; $310; $280; $250

5. Gloria sells the bears for profit. She makes a profit of $8 for the girl bears and $5 for the boy bears. Use the table from Problem 4 to find the profit she makes for each given combination.

6. 20 boy bears and 30 girl bears makes a profit of $340, which is the most; it lies at the intersection of the boundary lines $y \leq 30$ and $2x + 2y \leq 100$.

6. Which combination is the most profitable? Explain. Where does it lie on the graph?

Bear Combinations	
Boy	Girl
0	**30**
10	**30**
20	**30**
30	**20**
40	**10**
50	**0**

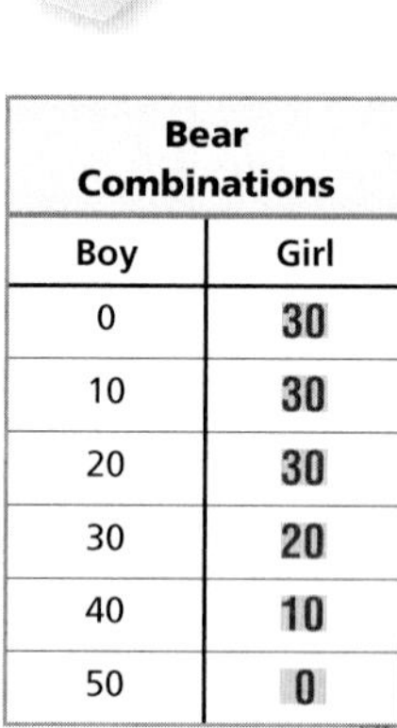

INTERVENTION

Scaffolding Questions

1. How many eyes are there per bear? 2 Which type of bear will use the dresses? girl bears Which type of bear will use the bow? both girl and boy bears
2. Can reasonable solutions be negative? no Explain. Gloria cannot sell a negative number of bears.
3. Can reasonable solutions include fractions or decimals? no Explain. Gloria cannot sell a fraction of a bear.
4. Which lines are included in the solution boundary? $y = 30$, $2x + 2y = 100$
5. What is the formula for Gloria's profit? $P = 5x + 8y$
6. How can you tell which combination is more profitable? the combination that results in the greatest value of P

Extension

What is the most profitable combination if Gloria makes a profit of $5 for girl bears and $8 for boy bears? 30 boy bears and 20 girl bears.

Algebra 1 6.0, 9.0

CHAPTER 6

SECTION 6B

Quiz for Lessons 6-6 Through 6-7

6-6 Solving Linear Inequalities

Tell whether the ordered pair is a solution of the inequality.

1. $(3, -2)$; $y < -2x + 1$ no
2. $(2, 1)$; $y \geq 3x - 5$ yes
3. $(1, -6)$; $y \leq 4x - 10$ yes

Graph the solutions of each linear inequality. Check your answers.

4. $y \geq 4x - 3$
5. $3x - y < 5$
6. $2x + 3y < 9$
7. $y \leq -\frac{1}{2}x$
8. Theo's mother has given him at most \$150 to buy clothes for school. The pants cost \$30 each and the shirts cost \$15 each. How many of each can he buy? Write a linear inequality to describe the situation. Graph the linear inequality and give three possible combinations of pants and shirts Theo could buy.

Write an inequality to represent each graph.

9. 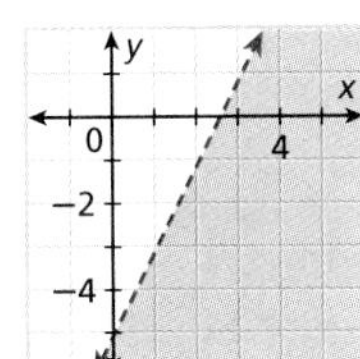
$y < 2x - 5$

10. 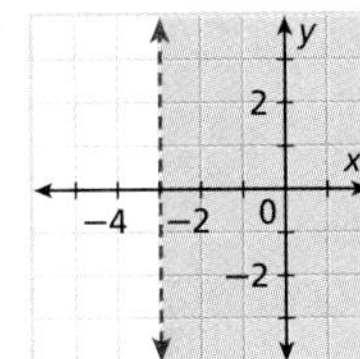
$x > -3$

11. 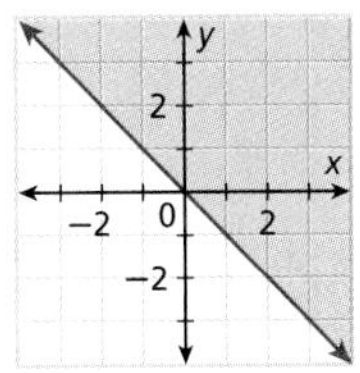
$y \geq -x$

6-7 Solving Systems of Linear Inequalities

Tell whether the ordered pair is a solution of the given system.

12. $(-3, -1)$; $\begin{cases} y > -2 \\ y < x + 4 \end{cases}$ yes
13. $(-3, 0)$; $\begin{cases} y \leq x + 4 \\ y \geq -2x - 6 \end{cases}$ yes
14. $(0, 0)$; $\begin{cases} y \geq 3x \\ 2x + y < -1 \end{cases}$ no

Graph each system of linear inequalities. Give two ordered pairs that are solutions and two that are not solutions.

15. $\begin{cases} y > -2 \\ y < x + 3 \end{cases}$
16. $\begin{cases} x + y \leq 2 \\ 2x + y \geq -1 \end{cases}$
17. $\begin{cases} 2x - 5y \leq -5 \\ 3x + 2y < 10 \end{cases}$

Graph each system of linear inequalities and describe the solutions.

18. $\begin{cases} y \geq x + 1 \\ y \geq x - 4 \end{cases}$
19. $\begin{cases} y \geq 2x - 1 \\ y < 2x - 3 \end{cases}$
20. $\begin{cases} y < -3x + 5 \\ y > -3x - 2 \end{cases}$
21. A grocer sells mangos for \$4/lb and apples for \$3/lb. The grocer starts with 45 lb of mangos and 50 lb of apples each day. The grocer's goal is to make at least \$300 by selling mangos and apples each day. Show and describe all possible combinations of mangos and apples that could be sold to meet the goal. List two possible combinations.

18. The solutions of the system are the solutions of $y \geq x + 1$.
19. The system has no solutions.
20. The solutions are between the graphs of $y = -3x + 5$ and $y = -3x - 2$.

READY TO GO ON? SECTION 6B

Organizer

Objective: Assess students' mastery of concepts and skills in Lessons 6-6 through 6-7.

Countdown to Mastery Week 14

Resources

 ***Assessment Resources***
Section 6B Quiz

INTERVENTION

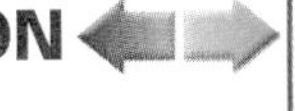

Resources

 ***Ready to Go On? Intervention and Enrichment*** **Worksheets**

 ***Ready to Go On?*** **CD-ROM**

 ***Ready to Go On?*** **Online**

my.hrw.com

Answers

4–8, 15–17, 21. See pp. A22–A23.

READY TO GO ON? Diagnose and Prescribe

Ready to Go On? Intervention	*Ready to Go On? Intervention,* Section 6B: Worksheets	CD-ROM	Online
Lesson 6-6 6.0	6-6 Intervention	Activity 6-6	Diagnose and Prescribe Online
Lesson 6-7 9.0	6-7 Intervention	Activity 6-7	

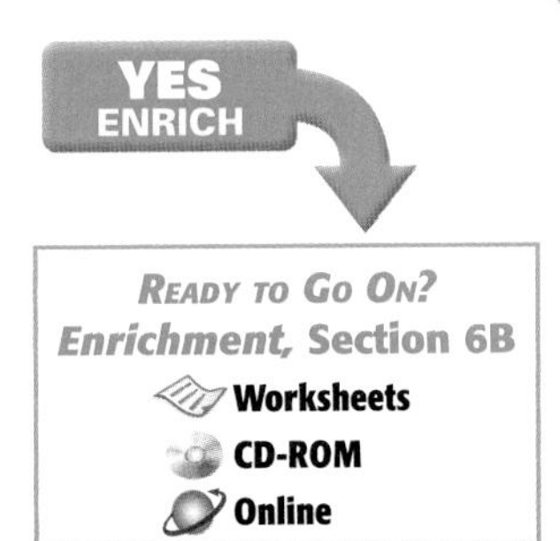

YES ENRICH
READY TO GO ON? Enrichment, Section 6B
Worksheets
CD-ROM
Online

Organizer

Objective: Help students organize and review key concepts and skills presented in Chapter 6.

Online Edition
Multilingual Glossary

Resources

PuzzlePro
One-Stop Planner®

***Multilingual Glossary* Online**

go.hrw.com
KEYWORD: MA8CA Glossary

***Lesson Tutorial Videos* CD-ROM**

Test & Practice Generator
One-Stop Planner®

Answers

1. independent system
2. system of linear equations
3. solution of a system of linear inequalities
4. inconsistent system
5. independent system
6. no
7. yes
8. yes
9. no
10. $(-1, -1)$
11. $(3, 4)$
12. 8 h; $10

CHAPTER 6 Study Guide: Review

Vocabulary

Complete the sentences below with vocabulary words from the list above.

1. A(n) __?__ is a system that has exactly one solution.
2. A set of two or more linear equations that contain the same variable(s) is a(n) __?__.
3. The __?__ consists of all the ordered pairs that satisfy all the inequalities in the system.
4. A system consisting of equations of parallel lines with different y-intercepts is a(n) __?__.
5. A(n) __?__ consists of two intersecting lines.

6-1 Solving Systems by Graphing *(pp. 329–334)*

6.0, 9.0

EXAMPLE

■ Solve $\begin{cases} y = 2x - 2 \\ x + 2y = 16 \end{cases}$ by graphing. Check your answer.

$\begin{cases} y = 2x - 2 \\ y = -\frac{1}{2}x + 8 \end{cases}$ *Write the second equation in slope-intercept form.*

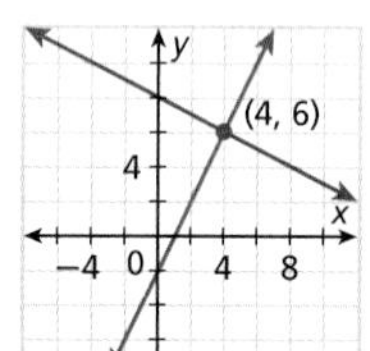

The solution appears to be at $(4, 6)$.

$y = 2x - 2$	
6	$2(4) - 2$
6	6 ✓

$x + 2y = 16$	
$4 + 2(6)$	16
16	16 ✓

The ordered pair $(4, 6)$ makes both equations true, so it is a solution of the system.

EXERCISES

Tell whether the ordered pair is a solution of the given system.

6. $(0, -5); \begin{cases} y = -6x + 5 \\ x - y = 5 \end{cases}$
7. $(4, 3); \begin{cases} x - 2y = -2 \\ y = \frac{1}{2}x + 1 \end{cases}$
8. $\left(1\frac{3}{4}, 7\frac{1}{4}\right); \begin{cases} x + y = 9 \\ 2y = 6x + 4 \end{cases}$
9. $(-1, -1); \begin{cases} y = -2x + 5 \\ 3y = 6x + 3 \end{cases}$

Solve each system by graphing. Check your answer.

10. $\begin{cases} y = 3x + 2 \\ y = -2x - 3 \end{cases}$
11. $\begin{cases} y = -\frac{1}{3}x + 5 \\ 2x - 2y = -2 \end{cases}$
12. Raheel is comparing the cost of two parking garages. Garage A charges a flat fee of $6 per car plus $0.50 per hour. Garage B charges a flat fee of $2 per car plus $1 per hour. After how many hours will the cost at garage A be the same as the cost at garage B? What will that cost be?

6-2 Solving Systems by Substitution *(pp. 336–342)*

 9.0

EXAMPLE

■ Solve $\begin{cases} 2x - 3y = -2 \\ y - 3x = 10 \end{cases}$ by substitution.

Step 1 $y - 3x = 10$; $y = 3x + 10$ — *Solve the second equation for y.*

Step 2 $2x - 3y = -2$; $2x - 3(3x + 10) = -2$ — *Substitute 3x + 10 for y in the first equation.*

Step 3 $2x - 9x - 30 = -2$; $-7x - 30 = -2$; $-7x = 28$; $x = -4$ — *Solve for x.*

Step 4 $y - 3x = 10$; $y - 3(-4) = 10$ — *Substitute −4 for x.*
$y + 12 = 10$; $y = -2$ — *Find the value of y.*

Step 5 $(-4, -2)$ — *Write the solution as an ordered pair.*

To check the solution, substitute $(-4, -2)$ into both equations in the system.

EXERCISES

Solve each system by substitution. Check your answer.

13. $\begin{cases} y = x + 3 \\ y = 2x + 12 \end{cases}$

14. $\begin{cases} y = -4x \\ y = 2x - 3 \end{cases}$

15. $\begin{cases} 2x + y = 4 \\ 3x + y = 3 \end{cases}$

16. $\begin{cases} x + y = -1 \\ y = -2x + 3 \end{cases}$

17. $\begin{cases} x = y - 7 \\ -y - 2x = 8 \end{cases}$

18. $\begin{cases} \frac{1}{2}x + y = 9 \\ 3x - 4y = -6 \end{cases}$

19. The Nash family's car needs repairs. Estimates for parts and labor from two garages are shown below.

Garage	Parts ($)	Labor ($ per hour)
Motor Works	650	70
Jim's Car Care	800	55

For how many hours of labor will the total cost of fixing the car be the same at both garages? What will that cost be? Which garage will be cheaper if the repairs require 8 hours of labor? Explain.

6-3 Solving Systems by Elimination *(pp. 343–349)*

 9.0

EXAMPLE

■ Solve $\begin{cases} 2x - 3y = -8 \\ x + 4y = 7 \end{cases}$ by elimination.

Step 1 $2x - 3y = -8$
Step 2 $(-2)(x + 4y = 7)$ — *Multiply the second equation by −2.*

$2x - 3y = -8$
$+(-2x - 8y = -14)$ — *Eliminate the x-term.*

$0x - 11y = -22$
Step 3 $y = 2$ — *Solve for y.*

Step 4 $2x - 3y = -8$; $2x - 3(2) = -8$; $2x - 6 = -8$; $2x = -2$; $x = -1$ — *Substitute 2 for y. Simplify and solve for x.*

Step 5 $(-1, 2)$ — *Write the solution as an ordered pair.*

To check the solution, substitute $(-1, 2)$ into both equations in the system.

EXERCISES

Solve each system by elimination. Check your answer.

20. $\begin{cases} 4x + y = -1 \\ 2x - y = -5 \end{cases}$

21. $\begin{cases} x + 2y = -1 \\ x + y = 2 \end{cases}$

22. $\begin{cases} x + y = 12 \\ 2x + 5y = 27 \end{cases}$

23. $\begin{cases} 3x - 2y = -6 \\ \frac{1}{3}x + 3y = 9 \end{cases}$

Solve each system by any method. Explain why you chose each method. Check your answer.

24. $\begin{cases} 3x + y = 2 \\ y = -4x \end{cases}$

25. $\begin{cases} y = \frac{1}{3}x - 6 \\ y = -2x + 1 \end{cases}$

26. $\begin{cases} 2y = -3x \\ y = -2x + 2 \end{cases}$

27. $\begin{cases} x - y = 0 \\ 3x + y = 8 \end{cases}$

Answers

13. $(-9, -6)$
14. $\left(\frac{1}{2}, -2\right)$
15. $(-1, 6)$
16. $(4, -5)$
17. $(-5, 2)$
18. $(6, 6)$
19. 10 h; $1350; Motor Works; 8 hours will cost $30 less at Motor Works.
20. $(-1, 3)$
21. $(5, -3)$
22. $(11, 1)$
23. $(0, 3)$
24. $(-2, 8)$; possible answer: substitution; the second equation is already solved for *y*, and *y* has a coefficient of 1 in the first equation.
25. $(3, -5)$; possible answer: graphing; both equations are already in slope-intercept form.
26. $(4, -6)$; possible answer: substitution; the second equation is already solved for *y*.
27. $(2, 2)$; possible answer: elimination; the coefficients of the *y*-terms are opposites.

Answers

28. consistent, independent; one solution
29. inconsistent; no solution
30. consistent, dependent; infinitely many solutions
31. inconsistent; no solution
32. consistent, independent; one solution
33. consistent, dependent; infinitely many solutions
34. inconsistent; no solution
35. Gena: 3 ft/s; walkway: 1 ft/s
36. Blake: 8 yd/min; current: 2 yd/min
37. 30 mL of the 20% sol. and 10 mL of the 60% sol.
38. 29
39. no
40. yes
41. yes
42. no
43. 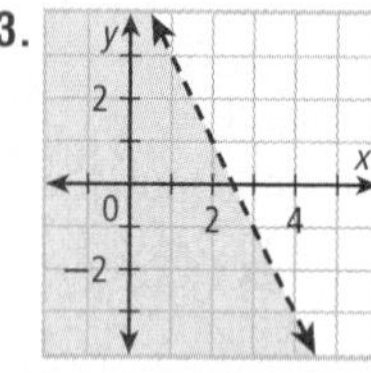

44. 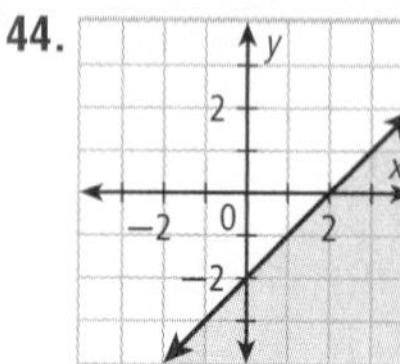

6-4 Solving Special Systems *(pp. 350–355)*

8.0, 9.0

EXAMPLE

■ **Classify the system. Give the number of solutions.**

$$\begin{cases} y = 3x + 4 \\ 6x - 2y = -8 \end{cases}$$

Use the substitution method.

$6x - 2(3x + 4) = -8$ *Substitute 3x + 4 for y in the second equation.*
$6x - 6x - 8 = -8$
$-8 = -8$ ✓ *True.*

The equation is an identity. There are infinitely many solutions.

This system is **consistent** and **dependent**. The two lines are coincident because they have identical slopes and y-intercepts.

If the lines never intersect, the system is **inconsistent**. It has **no solution.** The system is **consistent** and **independent** when there is **one solution.**

EXERCISES

Classify each system. Give the number of solutions.

28. $\begin{cases} y = \frac{1}{2}x + 2 \\ y = \frac{1}{4}x - 8 \end{cases}$

29. $\begin{cases} y = 3x - 7 \\ y = 3x + 2 \end{cases}$

30. $\begin{cases} 2x + y = 2 \\ y - 2 = -2x \end{cases}$

31. $\begin{cases} -3x - y = -5 \\ y = -3x - 5 \end{cases}$

32. $\begin{cases} 2x + 3y = 1 \\ 3x + 2y = 1 \end{cases}$

33. $\begin{cases} x + \frac{1}{2}y = 3 \\ 2x = 6 - y \end{cases}$

34. The two parallel lines graphed below represent a system of equations. Classify the system and give the number of solutions.

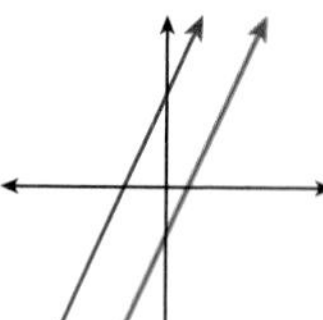

6-5 Applying Systems *(pp. 356–361)*

9.0, 15.0

EXAMPLE

■ **Against the wind, Devin skated 200 meters in 50 seconds. With the wind, he skated the same distance in 25 seconds. What is the rate at which Devin skated? What is the rate of the wind?**

Solve the system $\begin{cases} 50(d - w) = 200 \\ 25(d + w) = 200 \end{cases}$.

Step 1 $50d - 50w = 200$
Step 2 $2(25d + 25w = 200)$ *Multiply each term by 2.*
$50d - 50w = 200$
$+(50d + 50w = 400)$ *Add.*

Step 3 $100d = 600$ *Simplify and solve for d.*
$d = 6$

Step 4 $50d - 50w = 200$
$50(6) - 50w = 200$ *Substitute 6 for d.*
$300 - 50w = 200$ *Subtract 300 from both sides.*
$-300 \quad\quad -300$
$-50w = -100$ *Simplify and solve for w.*
$w = 2$

Step 5 $(6, 2)$ *Write the solution as an ordered pair.*

Devin's skating rate is 6 m/s. The rate of the wind is 2 m/s.

EXERCISES

35. Gena walked 160 feet in 40 seconds on a moving walkway. Against the walkway, she was able to walk the same distance in 80 seconds. What is the rate at which Gena walked, and what is the rate of the walkway?

36. Blake rows his boat against a current 90 yards in 15 minutes. With a current, he rows 90 yards in 9 minutes. What is the rate at which Blake rows, and what is the rate of the current?

37. Cole has a solution that is 20% water and another solution that is 60% water. He wants to mix these to make a 40 mL solution that is 30% water. How many mL of each solution should Cole mix together?

38. The sum of the digits of a two-digit number is 11. When the digits are reversed, the new number is 63 more than the original number. What is the original number?

6-6 Solving Linear Inequalities *(pp. 364–370)*

6.0

EXAMPLE

- **Graph the solutions of $x - 2y < 6$.**

Step 1 Solve the inequality for y.

$$x - 2y < 6$$
$$-2y < -x + 6$$
$$y > \frac{1}{2}x - 3$$

Step 2 Graph $y = \frac{1}{2}x - 3$.
Use a dashed line for $>$.

Step 3 The inequality is $>$, so shade above the boundary line.

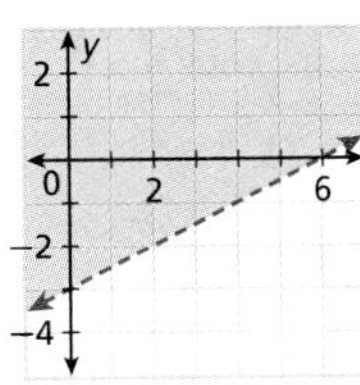

Check Substitute $(0, 0)$ for (x, y) because it is not on the boundary line.

$x - 2y$	< 6
$0 - 2(0)$	6
0	< 6 ✓

(0, 0) satisfies the inequality, so the graph is shaded correctly.

EXERCISES

Tell whether the ordered pair is a solution of the inequality.

39. $(0, -3)$; $y < 2x - 3$

40. $(2, -1)$; $y \geq x - 3$

41. $(6, 0)$; $y > -3x + 4$

42. $(10, 10)$; $y \leq x - 3$

Graph the solutions of each linear inequality.

43. $y < -2x + 5$

44. $x - y \geq 2$

45. $-x + 2y \geq 6$

46. $y > -4x$

47. $x + y + 4 > 0$

48. $5 - y \geq 2x$

49. The Mathematics Club is selling pizza and lemonade to raise money for a trip. They estimate that the trip will cost at least \$450. If they make \$2 on each slice of pizza and \$1 on each bottle of lemonade, how many of each do they need to sell to have enough money for their trip? Write an inequality to describe the situation. Graph and then give two combinations of the number of pizza slices and number of lemonade bottles they need to sell.

6-7 Solving Systems of Linear Inequalities *(pp. 371–376)*

6.0, 9.0

EXAMPLE

- **Graph $\begin{cases} y < -x + 5 \\ y \geq 2x - 3 \end{cases}$. Give two ordered pairs that are solutions and two that are not solutions.**

Graph both inequalities.

The solutions of the system are represented by the overlapping shaded regions.

The points $(0, 0)$ and $(-2, 2)$ are solutions of the system.

The points $(3, -2)$ and $(4, 4)$ are not solutions.

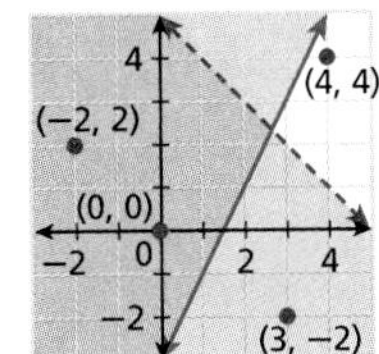

EXERCISES

Tell whether the ordered pair is a solution of the given system.

50. $(3, 3)$; $\begin{cases} y > -2x + 9 \\ y \geq x \end{cases}$

51. $(-1, 0)$; $\begin{cases} 2x - y > -5 \\ y \leq -3x - 3 \end{cases}$

Graph each system of linear inequalities. Give two ordered pairs that are solutions and two that are not solutions.

52. $\begin{cases} y \geq x + 4 \\ y > 6x - 3 \end{cases}$

53. $\begin{cases} y \leq -2x + 8 \\ y > 3x - 5 \end{cases}$

54. $\begin{cases} -x + 2y > 6 \\ x + y < 4 \end{cases}$

55. $\begin{cases} x - y > 7 \\ x + 3y \leq 15 \end{cases}$

Graph each system of linear inequalities.

56. $\begin{cases} y > -x - 6 \\ y < -x + 5 \end{cases}$

57. $\begin{cases} 4x + 2y \geq 10 \\ 6x + 3y < -9 \end{cases}$

Answers

45.

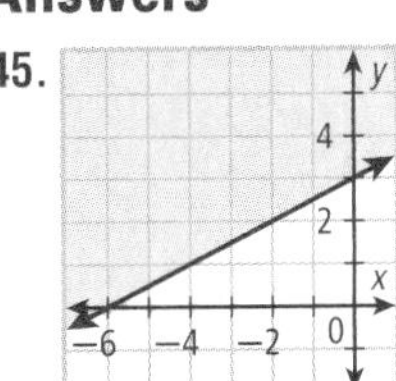

46.

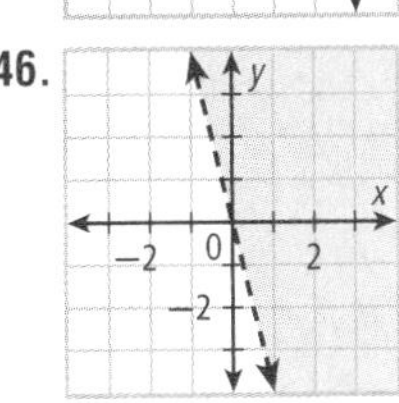

47.

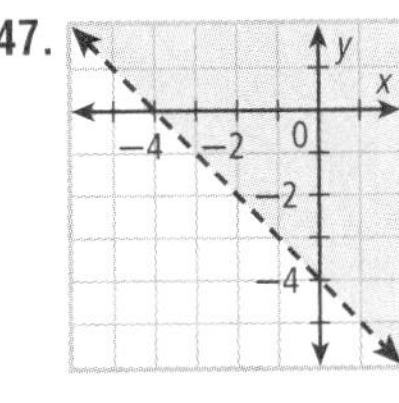

48.

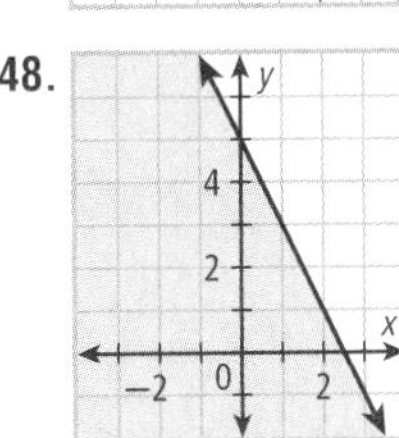

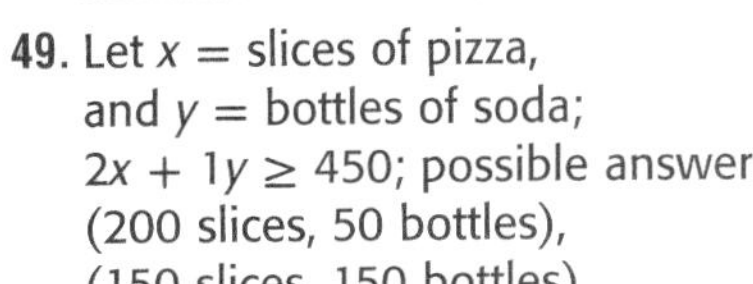

49. Let x = slices of pizza, and y = bottles of soda; $2x + 1y \geq 450$; possible answer: (200 slices, 50 bottles), (150 slices, 150 bottles).

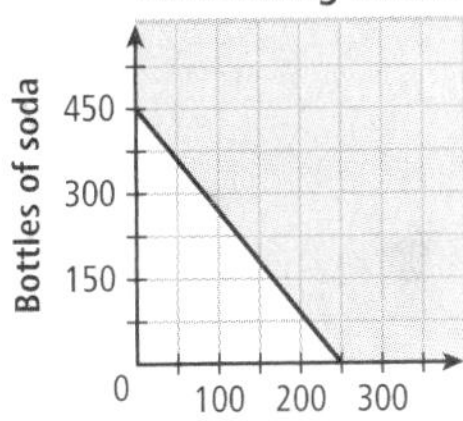

50. no

51. yes

52. Possible answer: solutions: $(-6, 6)$, $(-10, 0)$; not solutions: $(0, 0)$, $(4, -4)$

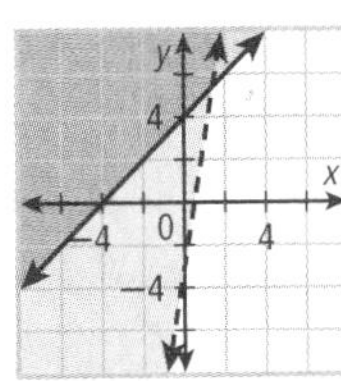

53. Possible answer: solutions: $(0, 0)$, $(-5, 0)$; not solutions: $(8, 0)$, $(3, -3)$

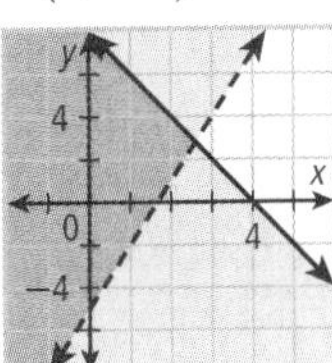

54. Possible answer: solutions: $(-6, 2)$, $(-8, 1)$; not solutions: $(0, 0)$, $(4, 1)$

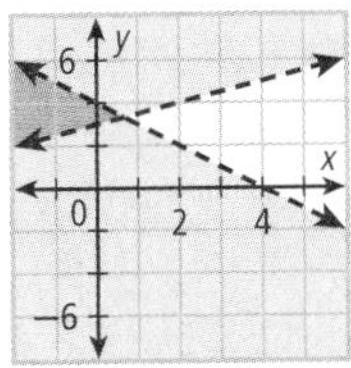

55. Possible answer: solutions: $(8, -8)$, $(9, 0)$; not solutions: $(0, 0)$, $(0, -4)$

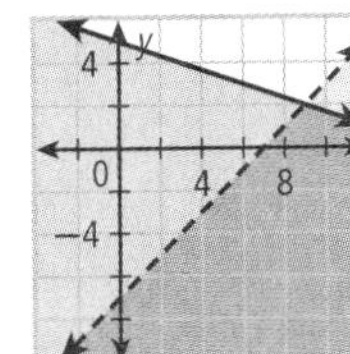

56.

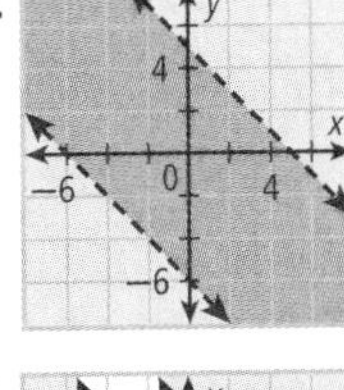

57.

Study Guide: Review 383

CHAPTER 6 **CHAPTER TEST**

Organizer

Objective: Assess students' mastery of concepts and skills in Chapter 6.

Online Edition

Resources

Assessment Resources

Chapter 6 Tests

- Free Response (Levels A, B, C)
- Multiple Choice (Levels A, B, C)
- Performance Assessment

***IDEA Works!* CD-ROM**

Modified Chapter 6 Test

Test & Practice Generator
One-Stop Planner®

Answers

18.

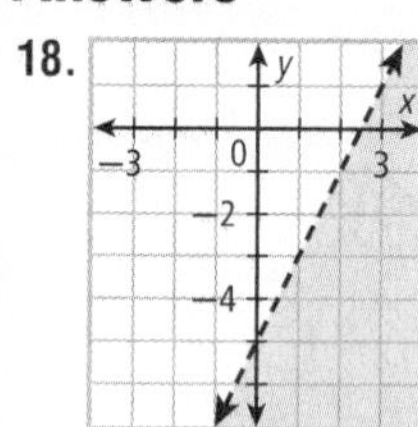

19.

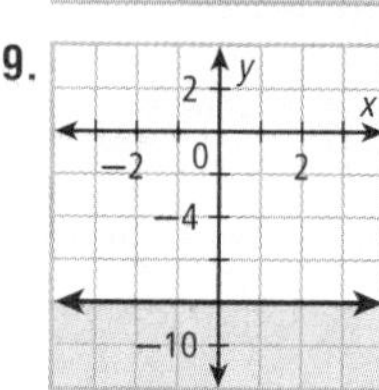

California Standards

Standard	Exercises
6.0	18–20
9.0	4–13, 21–23

CHAPTER 6

CHAPTER TEST

Tell whether the ordered pair is a solution of the given system.

1. $(1, -4); \begin{cases} y = -4x \\ y = 2x - 2 \end{cases}$ **no**

2. $(0, -1); \begin{cases} 3x - y = 1 \\ x + 5y = -5 \end{cases}$ **yes**

3. $(3, 2); \begin{cases} x - 2y = -1 \\ -3x + 2y = 5 \end{cases}$ **no**

Solve each system by graphing.

4. $\begin{cases} y = x - 3 \\ y = -2x - 3 \end{cases}$ **(0, −3)**

5. $\begin{cases} 2x + y = -8 \\ y = \frac{1}{3}x - 1 \end{cases}$ **(−3, −2)**

6. $\begin{cases} y = -x + 4 \\ x = y + 2 \end{cases}$ **(3, 1)**

Solve each system by substitution.

7. $\begin{cases} y = -6 \\ y = -2x - 2 \end{cases}$ **(2, −6)**

8. $\begin{cases} -x + y = -4 \\ y = 2x - 11 \end{cases}$ **(7, 3)**

9. $\begin{cases} x - 3y = 3 \\ 2x = 3y \end{cases}$ **(−3, −2)**

10. The costs for services at two kennels are shown in the table. Joslyn plans to board her dog and have him bathed once during his stay. For what number of days will the cost for boarding and bathing her dog at each kennel be the same? What will that cost be? If Joslyn plans a week-long vacation, which is the cheaper service? Explain. **6; $195; Fido's; it will cost less per day after 6 days.**

Kennel Costs		
	Boarding ($ per day)	Bathing ($)
Pet Care	30	15
Fido's	28	27

Solve each system by elimination.

11. $\begin{cases} 3x - y = 7 \\ 2x + y = 3 \end{cases}$ **(2, −1)**

12. $\begin{cases} 4x + y = 0 \\ x + y = -3 \end{cases}$ **(1, −4)**

13. $\begin{cases} 2x + y = 3 \\ x - 2y = -1 \end{cases}$ **(1, 1)**

Classify each system. Give the number of solutions.

14. $\begin{cases} y = 6x - 1 \\ 6x - y = 1 \end{cases}$ **cons. and dep.; inf. many solutions**

15. $\begin{cases} y = -3x - 3 \\ 3x + y = 3 \end{cases}$ **incons.; no sol.**

16. $\begin{cases} 2x - y = 1 \\ -4x + y = 1 \end{cases}$ **cons. and indep.; one sol.**

17. The sum of the digits of a two-digit number is 13. When the digits are reversed, the new number is 27 less than the original number. What is the original number? **85**

Graph the solutions of each linear inequality.

18. $y < 2x - 5$

19. $-y \geq 8$

20. $y > \frac{1}{3}x$

Graph each system of linear inequalities. Give two ordered pairs that are solutions and two that are not solutions.

21. $\begin{cases} y > \frac{1}{2}x - 5 \\ y \leq 4x - 1 \end{cases}$

22. $\begin{cases} y > -x + 4 \\ 3x - y > 3 \end{cases}$

23. $\begin{cases} y \geq 2x \\ y - 2x < 6 \end{cases}$

24. Ezra and Tava sold at least 150 coupon books. Ezra sold at most 30 books more than twice the number Tava sold. Show and describe all possible combinations of the numbers of coupon books Ezra and Tava sold. List two possible combinations.

Answers

20.

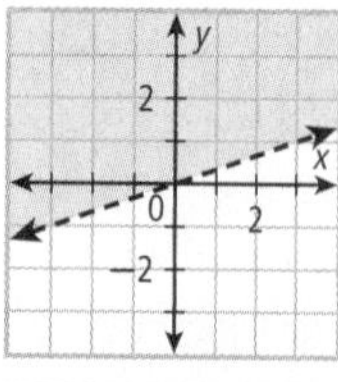

21.

Possible answers: solutions: (2, 0), (4, 0); not solutions: (−2, 0), (−4, 0)

22.

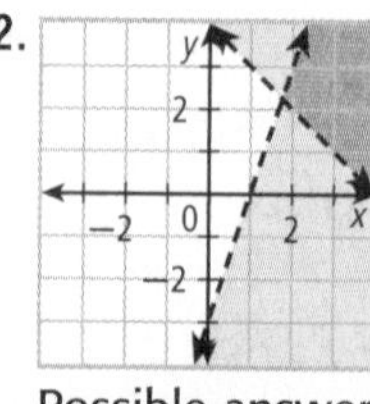

Possible answers: solutions: (6, 4), (9, 0); not solutions: (2, −4), (0, 0)

23.

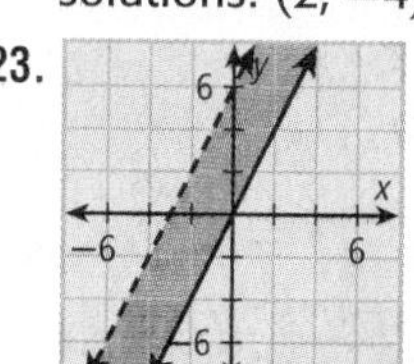

Possible answers: solutions: (0, 1), (0, 2); not solutions: (−6, 0), (4, 1)

24. Ezra and Tava could have sold any combinations represented by an ordered pair of whole numbers in the solutions region.

Possible answers: (Tava: 50, Ezra: 125), (Tava: 65, Ezra: 95)

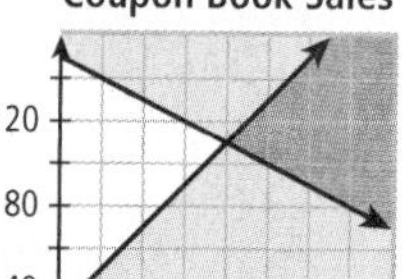

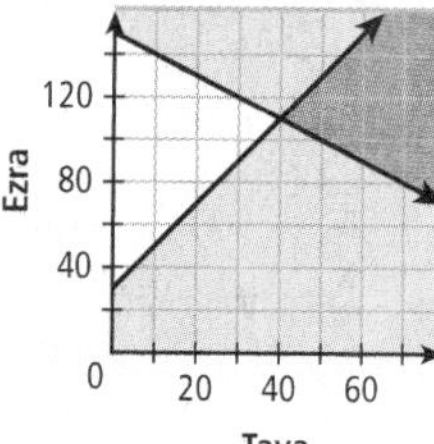

COLLEGE ENTRANCE EXAM PRACTICE

CHAPTER 6

FOCUS ON ACT

Four scores are reported for the ACT Mathematics Test: one score based on all 60 problems and one for each content area. The three content areas are: Pre-Algebra/Elementary Algebra, Intermediate Algebra/Coordinate Geometry, and Plane Geometry/Trigonometry.

Taking classes that cover the content areas on the ACT is a good idea. This way you will have skills from each area of the test. Preparation over a long term is better than cramming at the last minute.

You may want to time yourself as you take this practice test. It should take you about 5 minutes to complete.

1. Which system of inequalities is represented by the graph?

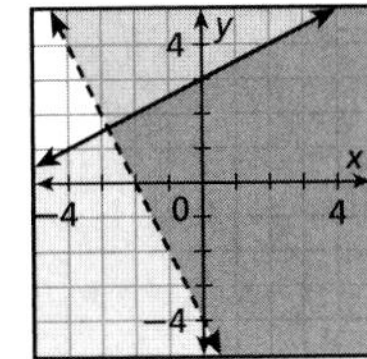

(A) $\begin{cases} -x + 2y < 6 \\ 2x + y > -4 \end{cases}$

(B) $\begin{cases} x - 2y \leq 6 \\ 2x - y \geq 4 \end{cases}$

(C) $\begin{cases} -x + 2y \leq 6 \\ 2x + y \geq 4 \end{cases}$

(D) $\begin{cases} -x + 2y \leq 6 \\ 2x + y > -4 \end{cases}$ (circled)

(E) $\begin{cases} x - 2y \leq 6 \\ 2x - y > 4 \end{cases}$

2. What is the solution for y in the given system?

$\begin{cases} 4x + 3y = 1 \\ -4x + 3y = -7 \end{cases}$

(F) -1 (circled)

(G) 0

(H) 1

(J) 2

(K) 6

3. Wireless phone company A charges \$20 per month plus \$0.12 per minute. Wireless phone company B charges \$50 per month plus \$0.06 per minute. For how many minutes of calls will the monthly bills be the same?

(A) 80 minutes

(B) 100 minutes

(C) 160 minutes

(D) 250 minutes

(E) 500 minutes (circled)

4. Which of the following systems of equations does NOT have a solution?

(F) $\begin{cases} x + 5y = 30 \\ -4x + 5y = 10 \end{cases}$

(G) $\begin{cases} x + 5y = -30 \\ -4x + 5y = 10 \end{cases}$

(H) $\begin{cases} x + 5y = -30 \\ -4x + 5y = -10 \end{cases}$

(J) $\begin{cases} -4x + 5y = -10 \\ -8x + 10y = -20 \end{cases}$

(K) $\begin{cases} -4x + 5y = -10 \\ -4x + 5y = -30 \end{cases}$ (circled)

COLLEGE ENTRANCE EXAM PRACTICE

CHAPTER 6

Organizer

Objective: Provide practice for college entrance exams such as the ACT.

Resources

College Entrance Exam Practice

Questions on the ACT represent the following content areas:

Pre-Algebra, 23%
Elementary Algebra, 17%
Intermediate Algebra, 15%
Coordinate Geometry, 15%
Plane Geometry, 23%
Trigonometry, 7%

Items on this page focus on:

- Elementary Algebra
- Coordinate Geometry

Text References:

Item	1	2	3	4
Lesson	6-7	6-3	6-1 6-2 6-3	6-4

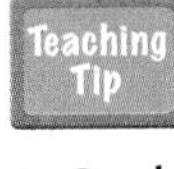

Multiple Choice

1. Students who chose **A** may not have assigned the appropriate inequality symbols to the dashed and solid lines. Remind students of the difference between dashed and solid lines and how they correspond to the solutions of an inequality.
2. Students who chose **H** may have found the solution for x instead of y.
3. Students who chose **A** found the value of the bill for the month, in dollars, instead of the number of minutes.
4. Students who chose **J** may not understand that coinciding lines indicate infinitely many solutions of the system. Remind students that the type of system that has no solution is represented by parallel lines.

Organizer

Objective: Provide opportunities to learn and practice common test-taking strategies.

Teaching Tip **Any Question Type** This Strategy for Success reinforces the importance of reading a test item slowly and carefully, identifying the important information, and being aware of all parts of the question. Explain to students that if they read a question too quickly, they might make assumptions that are not true, answer the wrong question, or not answer all parts of the question. Show students how to read a question for understanding by using the process shown in the example.

Any Question Type: Read the Problem for Understanding

Standardized test questions may vary in format including multiple choice, gridded response, and short or extended response. No matter what format the test uses, read each question carefully and critically. Do not rush. Be sure you completely understand what you are asked to do and what your response should include.

EXAMPLE 1

Extended Response

An interior decorator charges a consultation fee of $50 plus $12 per hour. Another interior decorator charges a consultation fee of $5 plus $22 per hour. Write a system of equations to find the amount of time for which the cost of both decorators will be the same. Graph the system. After how many hours will the cost be the same for both decorators? What will the cost be?

Read the problem again.

What information are you given?

the consultation fees and hourly rates of two decorators

What are you asked to do?

1. Write a system of equations.
2. Graph the system.
3. Interpret the solution to the system.

What should your response include?

1. a system of equations with variables defined
2. a graph of the system
3. the time when the cost is the same for both decorators
4. the cost at that time

Read each test item and answer the questions that follow.

Item A

Short Response Which value of b will make the lines intersect at the point $(-2, 14)$?

$$\begin{cases} y = -6x + 2 \\ y = 4x + b \end{cases}$$

1. What information are you given?
2. What are you asked to do?
3. Ming's answer to this test problem was $y = 4x + 22$. Did Ming answer correctly? Explain.

Item B

Extended Response Solve the system by using elimination. Explain how you can check your solution algebraically and graphically.

$$\begin{cases} 4x + 10y = -48 \\ 6x - 10y = 28 \end{cases}$$

4. What method does the problem ask you to use to solve the system of equations?
5. What methods does the problem ask you to use to check your solution?
6. How many parts are there to this problem? List what needs to be included in your response.

Item C

Gridded Response What is the x-coordinate of the solution to this system? $\begin{cases} y = 6x + 9 \\ y = 12x - 15 \end{cases}$

7. What question is being asked?
8. A student correctly found the solution of the system to be $(4, 33)$. What should the student mark on the grid so that the answer is correct?

After you answer each item, read the item again to be sure your response includes everything that is asked for.

Item D

Short Response Write an inequality to represent the graph below. Give a real-world situation that this inequality could describe.

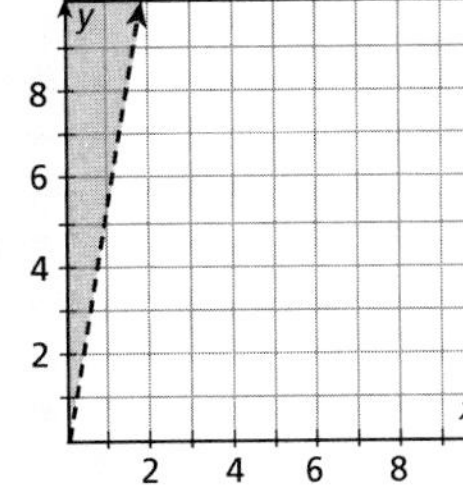

9. As part of his answer, a student wrote the following response:

   The point (1, 5) is not a solution to the inequality because it lies on the line, but (2, 12) is a solution because it lies above the line.

   Is his response appropriate? Explain.

10. What should the response include so that it answers all parts of the problem?

Item E

Multiple Choice Taylor bikes 50 miles per week and increases her distance by 2 miles each week. Josie bikes 30 miles per week and increases her distance by 10 miles each week. In how many weeks will Taylor and Josie be biking the same distance?

(A) 2.5 weeks
(B) 7.5 weeks
(C) 55 weeks
(D) 110 weeks

11. What question is being asked?
12. Carson incorrectly selected option C as his answer. What question did he most likely answer?

Teaching Tip

Reading Math In **Item A,** students are asked for the value of b, not the equation. In **Item B,** a complete answer will show three solution methods. In **Item C,** students are asked for only the x-coordinate of the solution, not the entire ordered pair. In **Item E,** students are asked for only the solution value of the independent variable, number of weeks, not the dependent variable, number of miles.

Answers

1. a system of equations and the point of intersection
2. Find the value of b that makes the system intersect at $(-2, 14)$.
3. No; Ming found the actual equation, which is correct, but the question just asked for the value of b.
4. elimination
5. algebraically and graphically
6. three parts; solving the system using elimination, checking the solution algebraically, and checking the solution graphically
7. What is the x-coordinate of the solution of the system?
8. 4
9. No; the problem did not ask anything about solutions of the inequality.
10. The response should include an inequality that represents the graph and a real-world situation that the inequality could describe.
11. In how many weeks will the girls be biking the same distance?
12. How many miles will the girls bike during the week that they are biking the same distance?

Answers to Test Items

A. 22

B. $(-2, -4)$

C. 4

D. $y > 5x$; Jeff opens a bank account and deposits more than $5 a week.

E. A

California Standards

Algebra 1 6.0, 9.0

MASTERING THE STANDARDS

Organizer

Objective: Provide review and practice for Chapters 1–6.

Online Edition

Resources

Assessment Resources

Chapter 6 Cumulative Test

Focus on California Standards Benchmark Tests and Intervention

***California Standards Practice* CD-ROM**

go.hrw.com
KEYWORD: MA8CA Practice

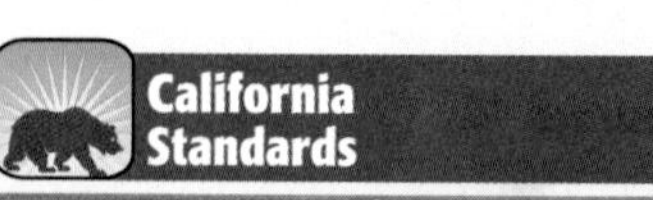

Standard	Items
3.0	11
5.0	17
6.0	1, 4, 9, 12, 16
8.0	3, 12
9.0	2, 6–8, 10, 14, 18–20
15.0	5
17.0	15

go.hrw.com
Standards Practice Online
KEYWORD: MA8CA Practice

CUMULATIVE ASSESSMENT, CHAPTERS 1–6

Multiple Choice

1. What is the x-intercept of $3x + 2y = -6$?

Ⓐ −3 Ⓑ −2 Ⓒ 2 Ⓓ 3

2. Which of the problems below could be solved by finding the solution of this system?

$$\begin{cases} 2x + 2y = 56 \\ y = \frac{1}{3}x \end{cases}$$

Ⓐ The area of a rectangle is 56. The width is one-third the length. Find the length of the rectangle.

Ⓑ The area of a rectangle is 56. The length is one-third the perimeter. Find the length of the rectangle.

Ⓒ The perimeter of a rectangle is 56. The length is one-third more than the width. Find the length of the rectangle.

Ⓓ The perimeter of a rectangle is 56. The width is one-third the length. Find the length of the rectangle.

3. What is the slope of a line perpendicular to a line that passes through (3, 8) and (1, −4)?

Ⓐ $-\frac{1}{6}$ Ⓑ $-\frac{1}{2}$ Ⓒ 2 Ⓓ 6

4. Which inequality is graphed below?

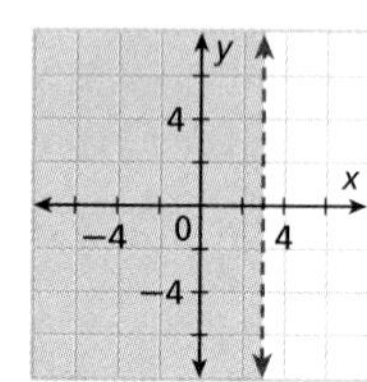

Ⓐ $-x > -3$ Ⓑ $-y > -3$ Ⓒ $2x < -6$ Ⓓ $3y < 9$

5. A chemist has a bottle of a 10% acid solution and a bottle of a 30% acid solution. He mixes the solutions together to get 500 mL of a 25% acid solution. How much of the 30% solution did he use?

Ⓐ 125 mL Ⓑ 150 mL Ⓒ 375 mL Ⓓ 450 mL

6. Which ordered pair is NOT a solution of the system graphed below?

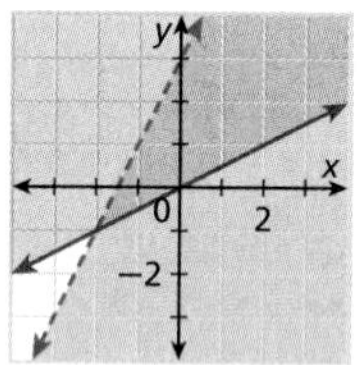

Ⓐ (0, 0) Ⓑ (0, 3) Ⓒ (1, 1) Ⓓ (2, 1)

7. Which of the following best classifies a system of linear equations whose graph is two intersecting lines?

Ⓐ inconsistent and dependent

Ⓑ inconsistent and independent

Ⓒ consistent and dependent

Ⓓ consistent and independent

8. Which ordered pair is a solution of this system?

$$\begin{cases} 2x - y = -2 \\ \frac{1}{3}y = x \end{cases}$$

Ⓐ (0, 2) Ⓑ (1, 3) Ⓒ (2, 6) Ⓓ (3, 8)

9. Where does the graph of $5x - 10y = 30$ cross the y-axis?

Ⓐ (0, −3) Ⓑ $\left(0, \frac{1}{2}\right)$ Ⓒ (6, 0) Ⓓ (0, −6)

Multiple Choice In **Item 2,** the first equation indicates perimeter, so choices **A** and **B** can be eliminated.

Students may not find the slope of the correct line in **Item 3.** For instance, if students chose **D,** they only found the slope of the line that passes through the given points, not the perpendicular line. Encourage students to read carefully and make sure they are answering the correct question. Some questions may take several steps to reach the correct answer.

In **Item 4,** the boundary line graphed is vertical, so choices **B** and **D** can be eliminated.

When answering **Item 6,** students might see that (0, 0) is a solution of the system and stop there. The question asks for an ordered pair that is NOT a solution. Checking the other choices would help them see that there is only one choice that is not a solution.

Most standardized tests allow you to write in your test booklet. Cross out each answer choice you eliminate. This may keep you from accidentally marking an answer other than the one you think is right. However, don't draw in your math book!

10. Hillary needs markers and poster board for a project. The markers are \$0.79 each and the poster board is \$1.89 per sheet. She needs at least 4 sheets of poster board. Hillary has \$15 to spend on project materials. Which system models this information?

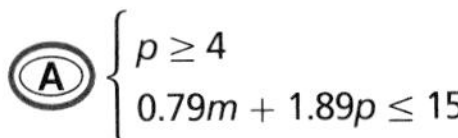

Ⓐ $\begin{cases} p \geq 4 \\ 0.79m + 1.89p \leq 15 \end{cases}$

Ⓑ $\begin{cases} 0.79m \geq 1.89p \\ 4p \leq 15 \end{cases}$

Ⓒ $\begin{cases} 4p \geq 1.89 \\ m + 4p \leq 15 \end{cases}$

Ⓓ $\begin{cases} p + m \leq 15 \\ 0.79m + 1.89p \geq 4 \end{cases}$

11. How many different values of x are solutions of $|x - 2| + 5 = 5$?

Ⓐ 0　　Ⓒ 2

Ⓑ 1　　Ⓓ 3

Gridded Response

12. Kendra graphs the line shown below. Then she finds the equation of the line passing through $(-2, 2)$ that is perpendicular to this line. She writes the equation in slope-intercept form, $y = mx + b$. What is the value of b?

$\frac{4}{3}$

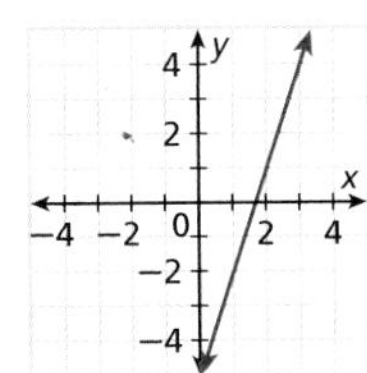

13. What value of y will make the line passing through $(4, -4)$ and $(-8, y)$ have a slope of $-\frac{1}{2}$? 2

14. What value of k will make the system $y - 5x = -1$ and $y = kx + 3$ inconsistent? 5

Short Response

15. What is the domain and range of the function shown in the graph?

D: $-4 \leq x \leq 3$;
R: $-3 \leq y \leq 3$

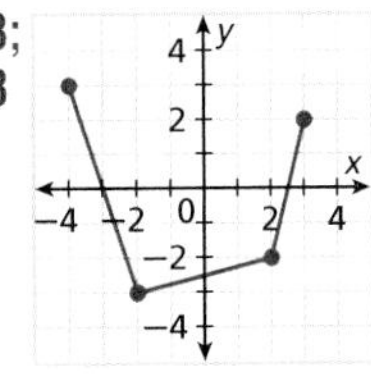

16. Graph $y > \frac{-x}{3} - 1$ on a coordinate plane. Name one point that is a solution of the inequality.

17. Marc and his brother Ty start saving money at the same time. Marc has \$145 and will add \$10 to his savings every week. Ty has \$20 and will add \$15 to his savings every week. After how many weeks will Marc and Ty have the same amount saved? What is that amount? Show your work.
25 weeks; \$395

18. A movie producer is looking for extras to act as office employees in his next movie. The producer needs extras that are at least 40 years old but less than 70 years old. They should be at least 60 inches tall but less than 75 inches tall. Graph all the possible combinations of ages and heights for extras that match the producer's needs. Let x represent age and y represent height. Show your work.

19. Graph the system $\begin{cases} y < -2x + 3 \\ y \geq 6x + 6 \end{cases}$.

a. Is $(0, 0)$ a solution of the system you graphed? Explain why or why not.

b. Is $(-4, 5)$ a solution of the system you graphed? Explain why or why not. **Yes; it is in the overlapping region.**

Extended Response

20. Every year, Erin knits scarves and sells them at the craft fair. This year she used \$6 worth of yarn for each scarf. She also paid \$50 to rent a table at the fair. She sold every scarf for \$10.

a. Write a system of linear equations to represent the amount Erin spent and the amount she collected. Tell what your variables represent. Tell what each equation in the system represents.

b. Use any method to solve the system you wrote in part **a.** Show your work. How many scarves did Erin need to sell to make a profit? Explain.

c. Describe two ways you could check your solution to part **b.** Check your solution by using one of those ways. Show your work.

Short Response Rubric

Items 15–19

2 Points = The student's answer is an accurate and complete execution of the task or tasks.

1 Point = The student's answer contains attributes of an appropriate response but is flawed.

0 Points = The student's answer contains no attributes of an appropriate response.

Extended Response Rubric

Item 20

4 Points = The student correctly writes a system of linear equations, identifying all variables and describes what each equation in the system represents in part **a**, solves the system and gives the correct answer in part **b**, and checks the answer in a method different from how it was solved in part **c.**

3 Points = The student correctly writes a system of equations but does not identify any of the variables in part **a.** The student solves the system and checks the answer in parts **b** and **c.**

2 Points = The student answers all parts correctly but does not show any work or explanation; or the student correctly answers parts **a** and **b** but does not check his or her work as stated in part **c.**

1 Point = The student writes a system of equations in part **a** but does not correctly answer other parts of the problem; or the student attempts to answer all parts of the problem but does not correctly answer any part.

0 Points = The student does not answer correctly and does not attempt all parts of the problem.

Answers

16.

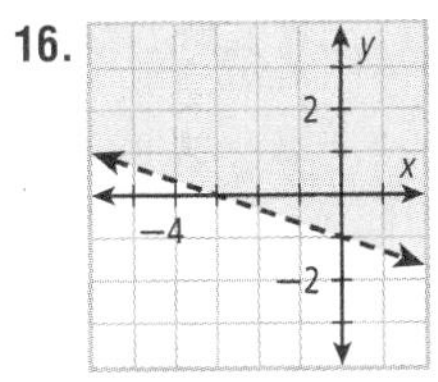

Possible answers: (3, 4)

18.

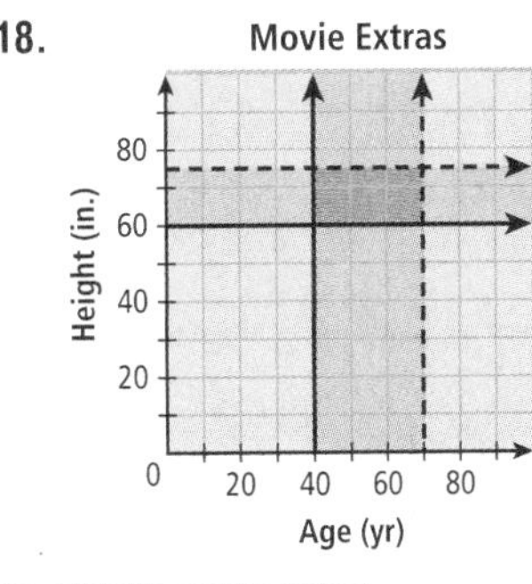

19.

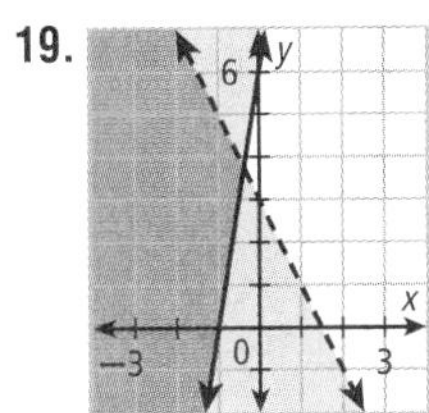

19a. No; possible answer: it is not in the overlapping region.

20a. Let x = the number of scarves and y = the total amount of money.

b. Possible answer: by substitution: $10x = 6x + 50$; $12.5 = x$; 13; Erin can't sell half a scarf, and 12 scarves won't make a profit.

c. Possible answer: Graph the 2 equations and find their point of intersection. Solve for y and then substitute for x and y in both equations. (Check students' work.)

Exponents and Polynomials

✔	Grade-level Standard
◄	Review
►	Beyond the Standards
A	Assessment
O	Optional

Pacing Guide

Calendar Planner
Teacher's **One-Stop** Planner®

Lesson/Lab		California Standards	Time	Advanced Students	Benchmark Students*	Strategic Students**
7-1	Integer Exponents	2.0	50 min	◄	✔	✔
7-2	Powers of 10 and Scientific Notation	2.0	50 min	◄	✔	✔
LR	Inductive Reasoning and Properties of Exponents	2.0, 24.1	50 min	✔	✔	✔
7-3	Multiplication Properties of Exponents	2.0	50 min	✔	✔	✔
7-4	Division Properties of Exponents	2.0	50 min	✔	✔	✔
7-5	Fractional Exponents	9.0, 15.0	100 min	✔	✔	✔
Concept Connection		2.0	25 min	A	A	O
Ready to Go On?			25 min	A	A	A
7-6	Polynomials	Preparation for 10.0	50 min	✔	✔	✔
LAB	Model Polynomial Addition and Subtraction	10.0	25 min	O	✔	✔
7-7	Adding and Subtracting Polynomials	10.0	75 min	✔	✔	✔
LAB	Model Polynomial Multiplication	10.0	25 min	O	✔	✔
7-8	Multiplying Polynomials	10.0	50 min	✔	✔	✔
CN	Volume and Surface Area	Reinforcement of Grade 7 MG2.1	25 min	O	◄	◄
7-9	Special Products of Binomials	10.0	50 min	✔	✔	✔
Concept Connection			25 min	A	A	O
Ready to Go On?			25 min	A	A	A
Study Guide: Review			50 min	✔	✔	✔
Chapter Test		2.0, 10.0	50 min	A	A	A

* **Benchmark students** are achieving at or near grade level.

** **Strategic students** may be a year or more below grade level, and may require additional time for intervention.

Countdown to Mastery, Weeks 14, 15, 16, 17

ONGOING ASSESSMENT and INTERVENTION

	DIAGNOSE	PRESCRIBE
Assess Prior Knowledge	**Before Chapter 7**	
	Diagnose readiness for the chapter.	Prescribe intervention.
	Are You Ready? SE p. 391	***Are You Ready? Intervention*** Skills 6, 7, 8, 45, 57
Formative Assessment	**Before Every Lesson**	
	Diagnose readiness for the lesson.	Prescribe intervention.
	Warm Up TE, every lesson	**Skills Bank** pp. SB1–SB32 **Review for Mastery** CRF Chapters 1–7
	During Every Lesson	
	Diagnose understanding of lesson concepts.	Prescribe intervention.
	Questioning Strategies TE, every example **Check It Out!** SE, every example **Think and Discuss** SE, every lesson **Write About It** SE, every lesson **Journal** TE, every lesson	**Reading Strategies** CRF, every lesson ***Success for ELL*** pp. 101–116 ***Lesson Tutorial Videos*** Chapter 7
	After Every Lesson	
	Diagnose mastery of lesson concepts.	Prescribe intervention.
	Lesson Quiz TE, every lesson **Alternative Assessment** TE, every lesson **Ready to Go On?** SE pp. 429, 463 ***Test and Practice Generator***	**Review for Mastery** CRF, every lesson **Problem Solving** CRF, every lesson ***Ready to Go On? Intervention*** Chapter 7 ***Homework Help Online***
	Before Chapter 7 Testing	
	Diagnose mastery of concepts in the chapter.	Prescribe intervention.
	Ready to Go On? SE pp. 429, 463 **Concept Connection** SE pp. 428, 462 **Section Quizzes** AR pp. 125–126 ***Test and Practice Generator***	***Ready to Go On? Intervention*** Chapter 7 **Scaffolding Questions** TE pp. 428, 462
	Before Assessment of California Standards	
	Diagnose mastery of California Standards.	Prescribe intervention.
	Focus on California Standards: Benchmark Tests **Mastering the Standards** SE pp. 472–473 ***California Standards Practice* CD-ROM**	***Focus on California Standards: Intervention***
Summative Assessment	**After Chapter 7**	
	Check mastery of chapter concepts.	Prescribe intervention.
	Multiple-Choice Tests (Forms A, B, C) **Free-Response Tests (Forms A, B, C)** **Performance Assessment** AR pp. 139–140 ***Test and Practice Generator***	**Review for Mastery** CRF, every lesson ***Lesson Tutorial Videos*** Chapter 7

KEY: **SE** = *Student Edition* **TE** = *Teacher's Edition* **CRF** = *Chapter Resource File* **AR** = *Assessment Resources*  Available online Available on CD-ROM

CHAPTER 7

Supporting the Teacher

Chapter 7 Resource File

Family Involvement
pp. 1–4, 45–48

Practice A, B, C
pp. 5–7, 13–15, 21–23, 29–31, 37–39, 49–51, 57–59, 65–67, 73–75

Review for Mastery
pp. 8–9, 16–17, 24–25, 32–33, 40–41, 52–53, 60–61, 68–69, 76–77

Challenge
pp. 10, 18, 26, 34, 42, 54, 62, 70, 78

Problem Solving
pp. 11, 19, 27, 35, 43, 55, 63, 71, 79

Reading Strategies ELL
pp. 12, 20, 28, 36

Technology Lab
pp. 81, 82

Workbooks

Homework and Practice Workbook SPANISH
Teacher's Edition .... pp. 41–49

Know-It Notebook SPANISH
Teacher's Guide .... Chapter 7

Review for Mastery Workbook SPANISH
Teacher's Guide .... pp. 81–98

Focus on California Standards: Intervention Workbook SPANISH
Teacher's Guide

Teacher Tools

Power Presentations
Complete PowerPoint® presentations for Chapter 7 lessons

Lesson Tutorial Videos SPANISH
Holt authors Ed Burger and Freddie Renfro present tutorials to support the Chapter 7 lessons.

Teacher's One-Stop Planner SPANISH
Easy access to all Chapter 7 resources and assessments, as well as software for lesson planning, test generation, and puzzle creation

IDEA Works!
Key Chapter 7 resources and assessments modified to address special learning needs

Solutions Key .... Chapter 7

Interactive Answers and Solutions

TechKeys

Lab Resources

Project Teacher Support

Parent Resources

Transparencies

Lesson Transparencies, Volume 2 .... Chapter 7
- Teacher Tools
- Warm-ups
- Teaching Transparencies
- Lesson Quizzes

Alternate Openers: Explorations .... pp. 41–49

Countdown to Mastery .... pp. 27–33

Know-It Notebook .... Chapter 7
- Vocabulary
- Key Concepts
- Graphic Organizers
- Chapter Review
- Big Ideas

Technology Highlights for the Teacher

Power Presentations

Dynamic presentations to engage students. Complete PowerPoint® presentations for every lesson in Chapter 7.

2-1 Solving One-Step Equations

Isolate a variable by using inverse operations which "undo" operations on the variable.

An equation is like a balanced scale. To keep the balance, perform the same operation on both sides.

Inverse Operations	
Operation	**Inverse Operation**
Addition	Subtraction
Subtraction	Addition

One-Stop Planner SPANISH

Easy access to Chapter 7 resources and assessments. Includes lesson planning, test generation, and puzzle creation software.

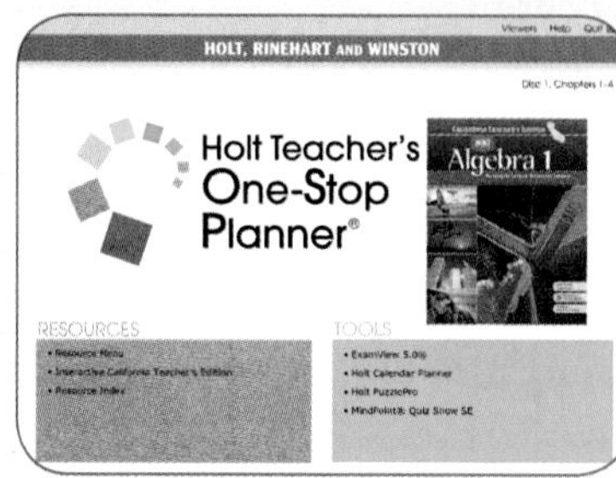

Premier Online Edition SPANISH

Includes Tutorial Videos, Lesson Activities, Lesson Quizzes, Homework Help, Chapter Project and more.

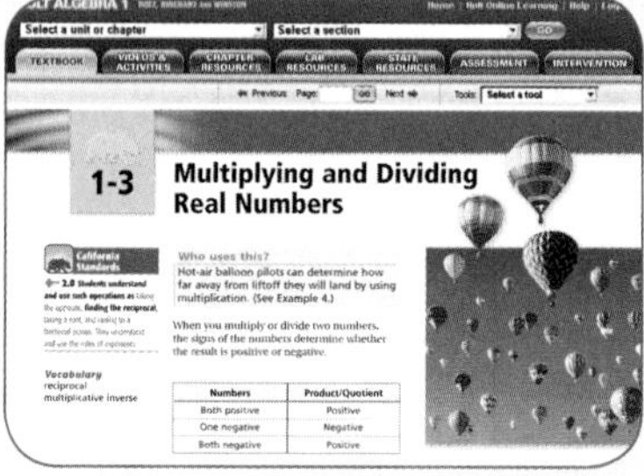

KEY: **SE** = *Student Edition* **TE** = *Teacher's Edition* ELL English Language Learners SPANISH Spanish available Available online Available on CD-ROM

Universal Access

Teaching Tips to help all students appear throughout the chapter. A few that target specific students are included in the lists below.

Strategic Students

Practice A ... CRF, every lesson
Review for Mastery ... CRF, every lesson
Reading Strategies ... CRF, every lesson
Academic Vocabulary Connections ... TE p. 392
Modeling ... TE pp. 431, 448
Questioning Strategies ... TE, every example
Ready to Go On? Intervention ... Chapter 7
Know-It Notebook SPANISH ... Chapter 7
Homework Help Online
Lesson Tutorial Videos SPANISH
Online Interactivities SPANISH

Special Needs Students

Practice A ... CRF, every lesson
Review for Mastery ... CRF, every lesson
Reading Strategies ... CRF, every lesson
Academic Vocabulary Connections ... TE p. 392
Inclusion ... TE pp. 395, 412, 439, 447
IDEA Works! Modified Resources ... Chapter 7
Ready to Go On? Intervention ... Chapter 7
Know-It Notebook SPANISH ... Chapter 7
Lesson Tutorial Videos SPANISH
Online Interactivities SPANISH

English Learners

ENGLISH LANGUAGE LEARNERS

Reading Strategies ... CRF, every lesson
Vocabulary Exercises ... SE, every exercise set
Academic Vocabulary Connections ... TE p. 392
English Language Learners ... TE p. 420
Language Support ... TE pp. 398, 420
Success for English Language Learners ... Chapter 7
Know-It Notebook SPANISH ... Chapter 7
Multilingual Glossary
Lesson Tutorial Videos SPANISH

Benchmark Students

Practice B ... CRF, every lesson
Problem Solving ... CRF, every lesson
Academic Vocabulary Connections ... TE p. 392
Questioning Strategies ... TE, every example
Ready to Go On? Intervention ... Chapter 7
Know-It Notebook SPANISH ... Chapter 7
Homework Help Online
Online Interactivities SPANISH

Advanced Students

Practice C ... CRF, every lesson
Challenge ... CRF, every lesson
Reading and Writing Math EXTENSION ... TE p. 393
Concept Connection EXTENSION ... TE pp. 428, 462
Advanced Learners/GATE ... TE p. 449
Ready to Go On? Enrichment ... Chapter 7

Technology Highlights for Universal Access

Lesson Tutorial Videos 

Starring Holt authors Ed Burger and Freddie Renfro! Live tutorials to support every lesson in Chapter 7.

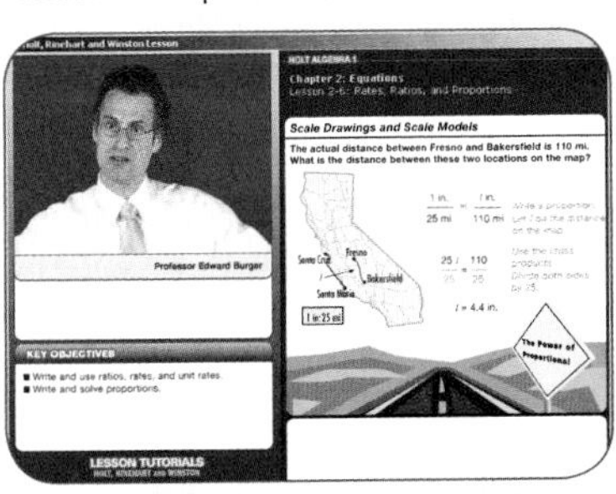

Multilingual Glossary

Searchable glossary includes definitions in English, Spanish, Vietnamese, Chinese, Hmong, Korean, and other languages.

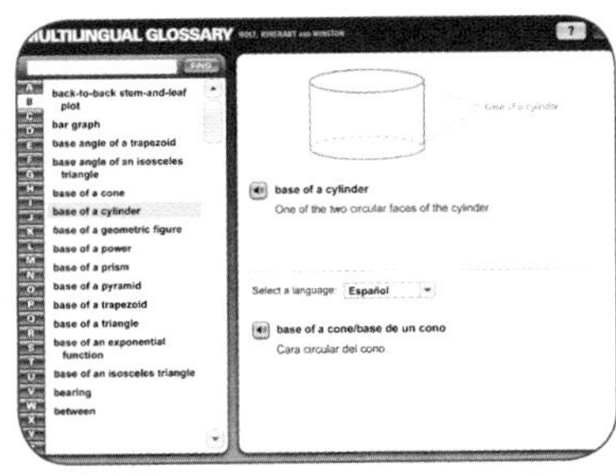

Online Interactivities 

Interactive tutorials provide visually engaging alternative opportunities to learn concepts and master skills.

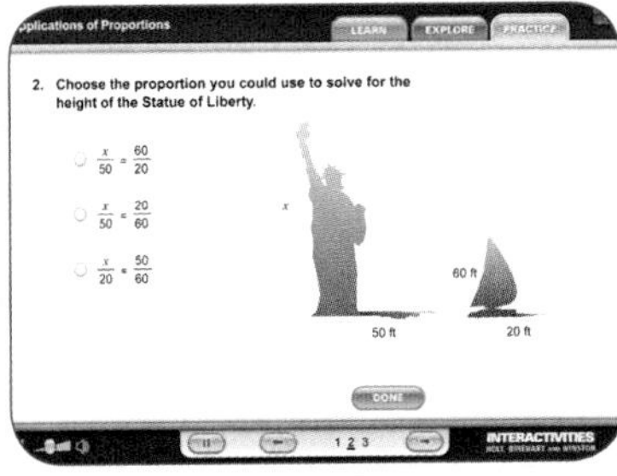

KEY: **SE** = *Student Edition* **TE** = *Teacher's Edition* **CRF** = *Chapter Resource File* SPANISH Spanish available  Available online Available on CD-ROM

Ongoing Assessment

Assessing Prior Knowledge

Determine whether students have the prerequisite concepts and skills for success in Chapter 7.

Are You Ready? SPANISH .... SE p. 391

Warm Up .... TE, every lesson

Chapter and Standards Assessment

Provide review and practice for Chapter 7 and standards mastery.

Concept Connection .... SE pp. 428, 462

Study Guide: Review .... SE pp. 464–467

Strategies for Success .... SE pp. 470–471

Mastering the Standards .... SE pp. 472–473

College Entrance Exam Practice .... SE p. 469

***Countdown to Mastery* Transparencies** .... pp. 27–33

Focus on California Standards: Benchmark Tests

Focus on California Standards: Intervention Workbook

***California Standards Practice* CD-ROM** SPANISH

IDEA Works! Modified Worksheets and Tests

Alternative Assessment

Assess students' understanding of Chapter 7 concepts and combined problem-solving skills.

Alternative Assessment .... TE, every lesson

Performance Assessment .... AR pp. 139–140

Portfolio Assessment .... AR p. xxiii

Chapter 7 Project

Daily Assessment

Provide formative assessment for each day of Chapter 7.

Questioning Strategies .... TE, every example

Think and Discuss .... SE, every lesson

Check It Out! Exercises .... SE, every example

Write About It .... SE, every lesson

Journal .... TE, every lesson

Lesson Quiz .... TE, every lesson

Alternative Assessment .... TE, every lesson

IDEA Works! Modified Lesson Quizzes .... Chapter 7

Weekly Assessment

Provide formative assessment for each week of Chapter 7.

Concept Connection .... SE pp. 428, 462

Ready to Go On? .... SE pp. 429, 463

Cumulative Assessment .... SE pp. 472–473

Test and Practice Generator SPANISH .... *One-Stop Planner*

Formal Assessment

Provide summative assessment of Chapter 7 mastery.

Section Quizzes .... AR pp. 125–126

Chapter 7 Test SPANISH .... SE p. 468

Chapter Test (Levels A, B, C) .... AR pp. 127–138
- Multiple Choice
- Free Response

Cumulative Test .... AR pp. 141–144

Test and Practice Generator SPANISH .... *One-Stop Planner*

Technology Highlights for Ongoing Assessment

Automatically assess readiness and prescribe intervention for Chapter 7 prerequisite skills.

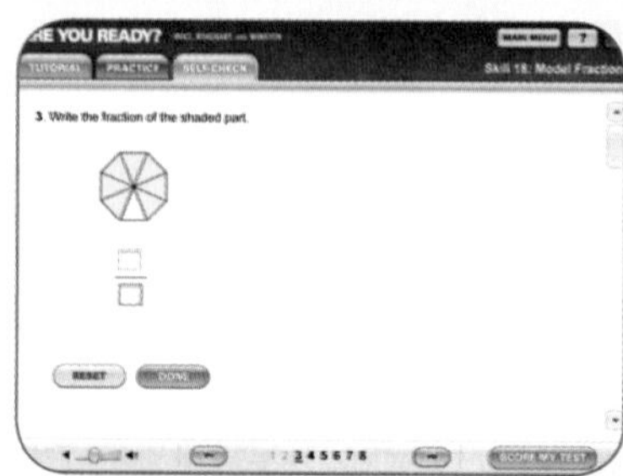

Automatically assess understanding of and prescribe intervention for Sections 7A and 7B.

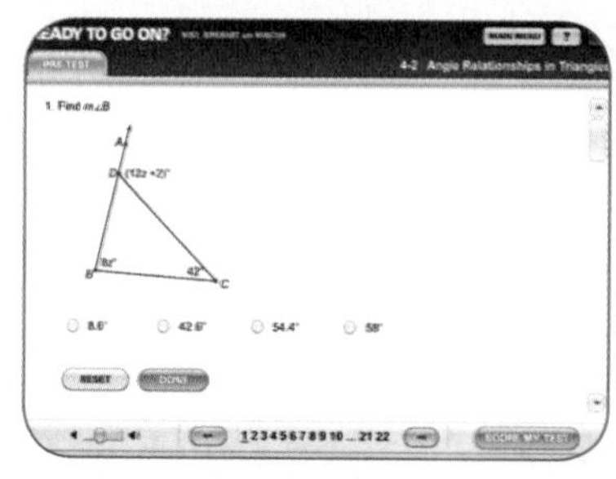

Automatically assess proficiency with California Algebra I Standards and provide intervention.

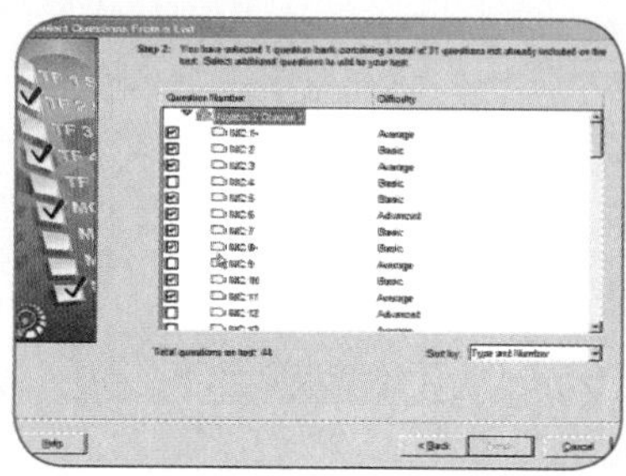

KEY: **SE** = *Student Edition* **TE** = *Teacher's Edition* **AR** = Assessment Resources  Spanish available  Available online Available on CD-ROM

Formal Assessment

Three levels (A, B, C) of multiple-choice and free-response chapter tests are available in the *Assessment Resources.*

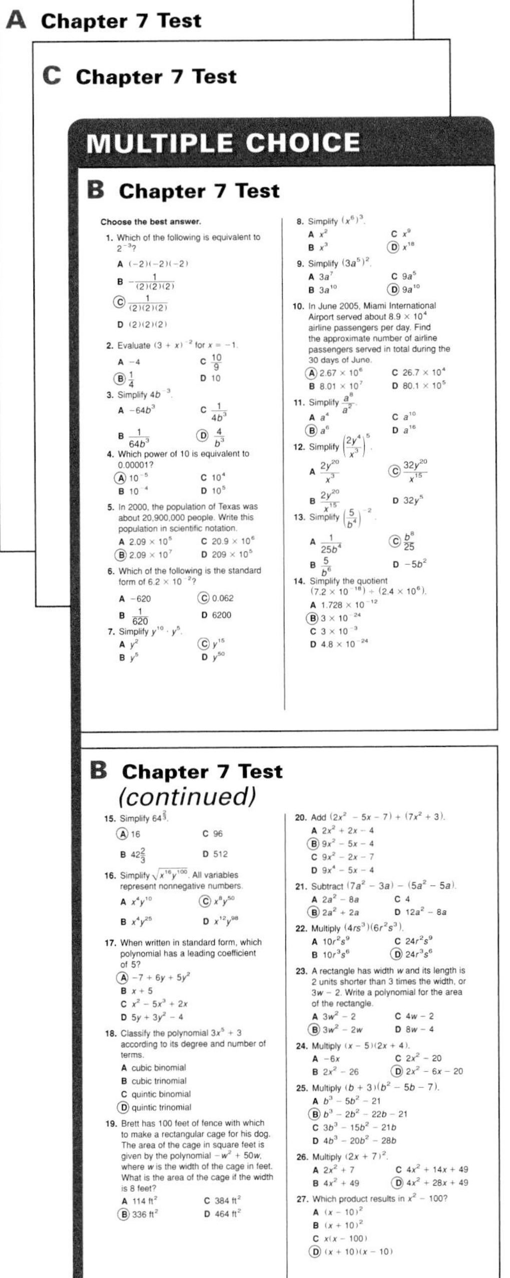

A Chapter 7 Test

C Chapter 7 Test

MULTIPLE CHOICE

B Chapter 7 Test

Choose the best answer.

1. Which of the following is equivalent to 2^{-3}?
A $(-2)(-2)(-2)$
B $-\frac{1}{(2)(2)(2)}$
Ⓒ $\frac{1}{(2)(2)(2)}$
D $(2)(2)(2)$

2. Evaluate $(3 + x)^{-2}$ for $x = -1$.
A -4 C $\frac{10}{9}$
Ⓑ $\frac{1}{4}$ D 10

3. Simplify $4b^{-3}$.
A $-64b^3$ C $\frac{1}{4b^3}$
B $\frac{1}{64b^3}$ Ⓓ $\frac{4}{b^3}$

4. Which power of 10 is equivalent to 0.00001?
Ⓐ 10^{-5} C 10^4
B 10^{-4} D 10^5

5. In 2000, the population of Texas was about 20,900,000 people. Write this population in scientific notation.
A 2.09×10^6 C 20.9×10^6
Ⓑ 2.09×10^7 D 209×10^5

6. Which of the following is the standard form of 6.2×10^{-2}?
A -620 Ⓒ 0.062
B $\frac{1}{620}$ D 6200

7. Simplify $y^{10} \cdot y^5$.
A y^2 Ⓒ y^{15}
B y^5 D y^{50}

8. Simplify $(x^6)^3$.
A x^2 C x^9
B x^3 Ⓓ x^{18}

9. Simplify $(3a^5)^2$.
A $3a^7$ C $9a^5$
B $3a^{10}$ Ⓓ $9a^{10}$

10. In June 2005, Miami International Airport served about 8.9×10^4 airline passengers per day. Find the approximate number of airline passengers served in total during the 30 days of June.
Ⓐ 2.67×10^6 C 26.7×10^4
B 8.01×10^7 D 80.1×10^5

11. Simplify $\frac{a^8}{a^2}$.
A a^4 C a^{10}
Ⓑ a^6 D a^{16}

12. Simplify $\left(\frac{2y^4}{x^3}\right)^5$.
A $\frac{2y^{20}}{x^3}$ Ⓒ $\frac{32y^{20}}{x^{15}}$
B $\frac{2y^{20}}{x^{15}}$ D $32y^9$

13. Simplify $\left(\frac{5}{b^4}\right)^{-2}$.
A $\frac{1}{25b^4}$ Ⓒ $\frac{b^8}{25}$
B $\frac{5}{b^8}$ D $-5b^2$

14. Simplify the quotient $(7.2 \times 10^{-18}) \div (2.4 \times 10^6)$.
A 1.728×10^{-12}
Ⓑ 3×10^{-24}
C 3×10^{-3}
D 4.8×10^{-24}

B Chapter 7 Test (continued)

15. Simplify $64^{\frac{2}{3}}$.
Ⓐ 16 C 96
B $42\frac{2}{3}$ D 512

16. Simplify $\sqrt{x^{16}y^{100}}$. All variables represent nonnegative numbers.
A x^4y^{10} Ⓒ x^8y^{50}
B x^4y^{25} D $x^{12}y^{98}$

17. When written in standard form, which polynomial has a leading coefficient of 5?
Ⓐ $-7 + 6y + 5y^2$
B $x + 5$
C $x^2 - 5x^3 + 2x$
D $5y + 3y^2 - 4$

18. Classify the polynomial $3x^5 + 3$ according to its degree and number of terms.
A cubic binomial
B cubic trinomial
C quintic binomial
Ⓓ quintic trinomial

19. Brett has 100 feet of fence with which to make a rectangular cage for his dog. The area of the cage in square feet is given by the polynomial $-w^2 + 50w$, where w is the width of the cage in feet. What is the area of the cage if the width is 8 feet?
A 114 ft² C 384 ft²
Ⓑ 336 ft² D 464 ft²

20. Add $(2x^2 - 5x - 7) + (7x^2 + 3)$.
A $2x^2 + 2x - 4$
Ⓑ $9x^2 - 5x - 4$
C $9x^2 - 2x - 7$
D $9x^4 - 5x - 4$

21. Subtract $(7a^2 - 3a) - (5a^2 - 5a)$.
A $2a^2 - 8a$ C 4
Ⓑ $2a^2 + 2a$ D $12a^2 - 8a$

22. Multiply $(4rs^3)(6r^2s^3)$.
A $10r^2s^9$ C $24r^2s^9$
B $10r^3s^6$ Ⓓ $24r^3s^6$

23. A rectangle has width w and its length is 2 units shorter than 3 times the width, or $3w - 2$. Write a polynomial for the area of the rectangle.
A $3w^2 - 2$ C $4w - 2$
Ⓑ $3w^2 - 2w$ D $8w - 4$

24. Multiply $(x - 5)(2x + 4)$.
A $-6x$ C $2x^2 - 20$
B $2x^2 - 26$ Ⓓ $2x^2 - 6x - 20$

25. Multiply $(b + 3)(b^2 - 5b - 7)$.
A $b^3 - 5b^2 - 21$
Ⓑ $b^3 - 2b^2 - 22b - 21$
C $3b^3 - 15b^2 - 21b$
D $4b^3 - 20b^2 - 28b$

26. Multiply $(2x + 7)^2$.
A $2x^2 + 7$ C $4x^2 + 14x + 49$
B $4x^2 + 49$ Ⓓ $4x^2 + 28x + 49$

27. Which product results in $x^2 - 100$?
A $(x - 10)^2$
B $(x + 10)^2$
C $x(x - 100)$
Ⓓ $(x + 10)(x - 10)$

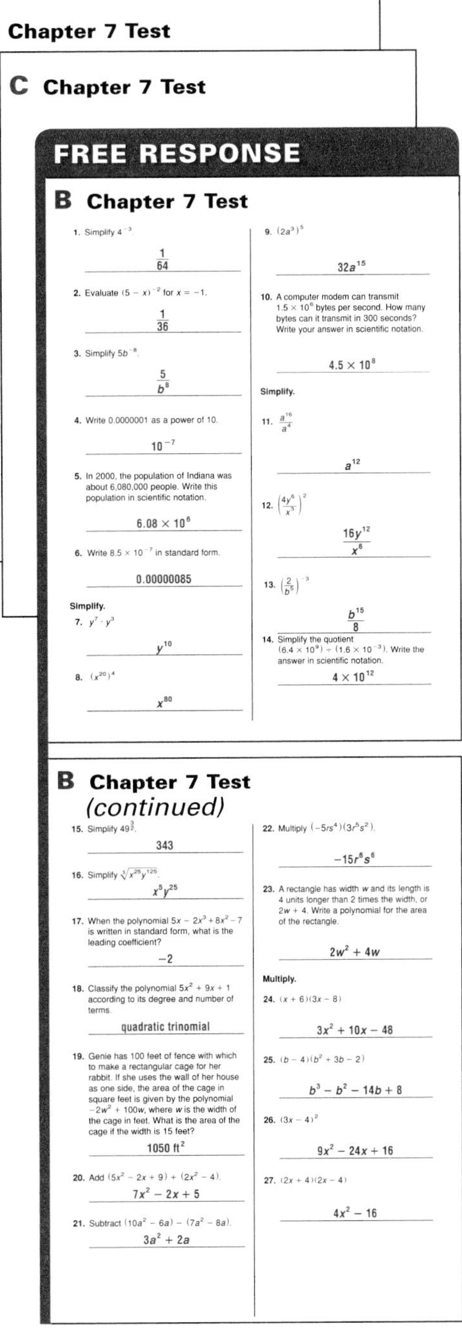

A Chapter 7 Test

C Chapter 7 Test

FREE RESPONSE

B Chapter 7 Test

1. Simplify 4^{-3}.
$\frac{1}{64}$

2. Evaluate $(5 - x)^{-2}$ for $x = -1$.
$\frac{1}{36}$

3. Simplify $5b^{-8}$.
$\frac{5}{b^8}$

4. Write 0.0000001 as a power of 10.
10^{-7}

5. In 2000, the population of Indiana was about 6,080,000 people. Write this population in scientific notation.
6.08×10^6

6. Write 8.5×10^{-7} in standard form.
0.00000085

Simplify.

7. $y^7 \cdot y^3$
y^{10}

8. $(x^{20})^4$
x^{80}

9. $(2a^3)^5$
$32a^{15}$

10. A computer modem can transmit 1.5×10^6 bytes per second. How many bytes can it transmit in 300 seconds? Write your answer in scientific notation.
4.5×10^8

Simplify.

11. $\frac{a^{16}}{a^4}$
a^{12}

12. $\left(\frac{4y^6}{x^3}\right)^2$
$\frac{16y^{12}}{x^6}$

13. $\left(\frac{2}{b^5}\right)^{-3}$
$\frac{b^{15}}{8}$

14. Simplify the quotient $(6.4 \times 10^9) \div (1.6 \times 10^{-3})$. Write the answer in scientific notation.
4×10^{12}

B Chapter 7 Test (continued)

15. Simplify $49^{\frac{3}{2}}$.
343

16. Simplify $\sqrt[5]{x^{25}y^{125}}$.
x^5y^{25}

17. When the polynomial $5x - 2x^3 + 8x^2 - 7$ is written in standard form, what is the leading coefficient?
-2

18. Classify the polynomial $5x^2 + 9x + 1$ according to its degree and number of terms.
quadratic trinomial

19. Genie has 100 feet of fence with which to make a rectangular cage for her rabbit. If she uses the wall of her house as one side, the area of the cage in square feet is given by the polynomial $-2w^2 + 100w$, where w is the width of the cage in feet. What is the area of the cage if the width is 15 feet?
1050 ft²

20. Add $(5x^2 - 2x + 9) + (2x^2 - 4)$.
$7x^2 - 2x + 5$

21. Subtract $(10a^2 - 6a) - (7a^2 - 8a)$.
$3a^2 + 2a$

22. Multiply $(-5rs^4)(3r^3s^2)$.
$-15r^4s^6$

23. A rectangle has width w and its length is 4 units longer than 2 times the width, or $2w + 4$. Write a polynomial for the area of the rectangle.
$2w^2 + 4w$

Multiply.

24. $(x + 6)(3x - 8)$
$3x^2 + 10x - 48$

25. $(b - 4)(b^2 + 3b - 2)$
$b^3 - b^2 - 14b + 8$

26. $(3x - 4)^2$
$9x^2 - 24x + 16$

27. $(2x + 4)(2x - 4)$
$4x^2 - 16$

Modified tests and worksheets found in *IDEA Works!*

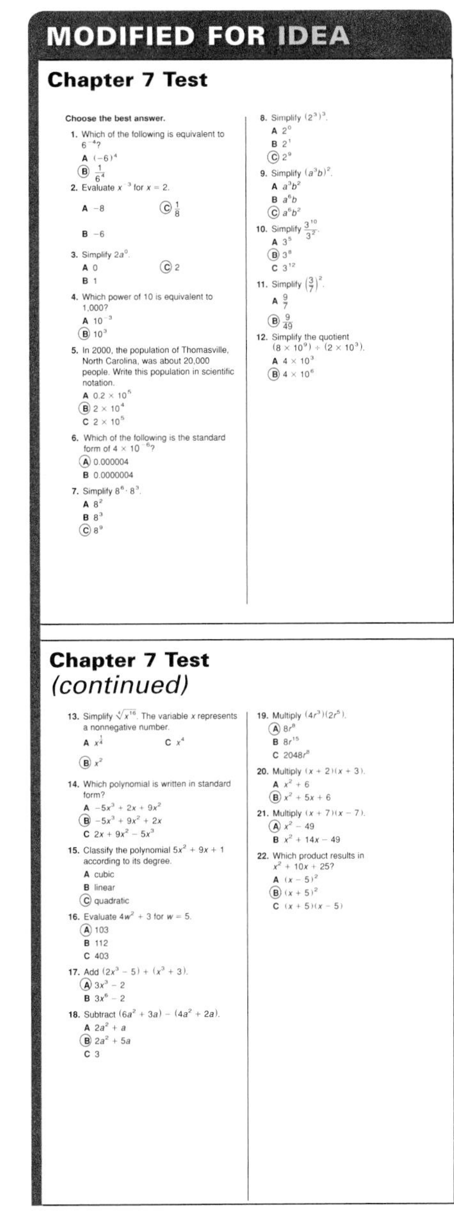

MODIFIED FOR IDEA

Chapter 7 Test

Choose the best answer.

1. Which of the following is equivalent to 6^{-4}?
A $(-6)^4$
Ⓑ $\frac{1}{6^4}$

2. Evaluate x^{-3} for $x = 2$.
A -8 Ⓒ $\frac{1}{8}$
B -6

3. Simplify $2a^0$.
A 0 Ⓒ 2
B 1

4. Which power of 10 is equivalent to 1,000?
A 10^{-3}
Ⓑ 10^3

5. In 2000, the population of Thomasville, North Carolina, was about 20,000 people. Write this population in scientific notation.
A 0.2×10^5
Ⓑ 2×10^4
C 2×10^5

6. Which of the following is the standard form of 4×10^{-6}?
Ⓐ 0.000004
B 0.0000004

7. Simplify $8^6 \cdot 8^3$.
A 8^2
B 8^3
Ⓒ 8^9

8. Simplify $(2^3)^3$.
A 2^0
B 2^1
Ⓒ 2^9

9. Simplify $(a^3b)^2$.
A a^3b^2
B a^6b
Ⓒ a^6b^2

10. Simplify $\frac{3^{10}}{3^2}$.
A 3^5
Ⓑ 3^8
C 3^{12}

11. Simplify $\left(\frac{3}{7}\right)^2$.
A $\frac{9}{7}$
Ⓑ $\frac{9}{49}$

12. Simplify the quotient $(8 \times 10^9) \div (2 \times 10^3)$.
A 4×10^3
Ⓑ 4×10^6

Chapter 7 Test (continued)

13. Simplify $\sqrt[4]{x^{16}}$. The variable x represents a nonnegative number.
A $x^{\frac{1}{4}}$ C x^4
Ⓑ x^2

14. Which polynomial is written in standard form?
A $-5x^3 + 2x + 9x^2$
Ⓑ $-5x^3 + 9x^2 + 2x$
C $2x + 9x^2 - 5x^3$

15. Classify the polynomial $5x^2 + 9x + 1$ according to its degree.
A cubic
B linear
Ⓒ quadratic

16. Evaluate $4w^2 + 3$ for $w = 5$.
Ⓐ 103
B 112
C 403

17. Add $(2x^3 - 5) + (x^3 + 3)$.
Ⓐ $3x^3 - 2$
B $3x^6 - 2$

18. Subtract $(6a^2 + 3a) - (4a^2 + 2a)$.
A $2a^2 + a$
Ⓑ $2a^2 + 5a$
C 3

19. Multiply $(4r^3)(2r^5)$.
Ⓐ $8r^8$
B $8r^{15}$
C $2048r^8$

20. Multiply $(x + 2)(x + 3)$.
A $x^2 + 6$
Ⓑ $x^2 + 5x + 6$

21. Multiply $(x + 7)(x - 7)$.
Ⓐ $x^2 - 49$
B $x^2 + 14x - 49$

22. Which product results in $x^2 + 10x + 25$?
A $(x - 5)^2$
Ⓑ $(x + 5)^2$
C $(x + 5)(x - 5)$

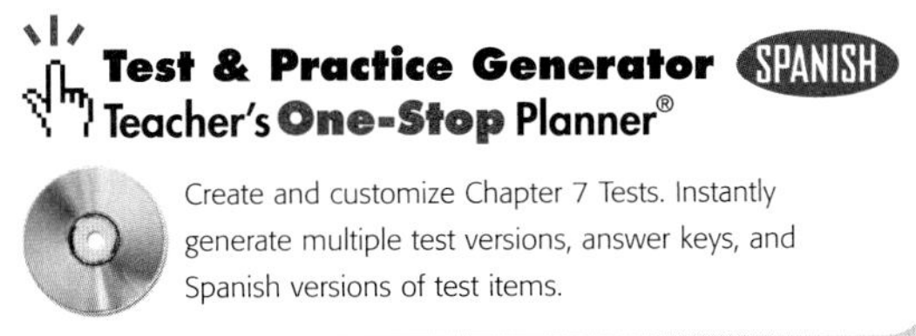

Test & Practice Generator SPANISH
Teacher's One-Stop Planner®

Create and customize Chapter 7 Tests. Instantly generate multiple test versions, answer keys, and Spanish versions of test items.

SECTION 7A Exponents

On page 428, students write, solve, and graph equations to model real-world speed-of-light situations.

Exercises designed to prepare students for success on the Concept Connection can be found on pages 398, 404, 413, 421, and 426.

SECTION 7B Polynomials

On page 462, students multiply polynomials to model a real-world area situation.

Exercises designed to prepare students for success on the Concept Connection can be found on pages 434, 442, 452, and 461.

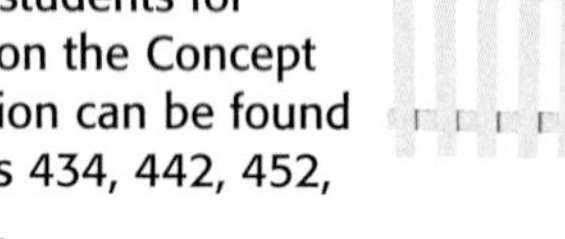

Algebra in *California*

Scientists use exponents and scientific notation to express very large numbers, such as numbers used to express distances in space, and very small numbers, such as numbers used to express the sizes of subatomic particles. Students will learn about exponents and their properties in Lessons 7-1 through 7-5 of this chapter.

CHAPTER 7

Exponents and Polynomials

go.hrw.com
Chapter Project Online
KEYWORD: MA8CA ChProj

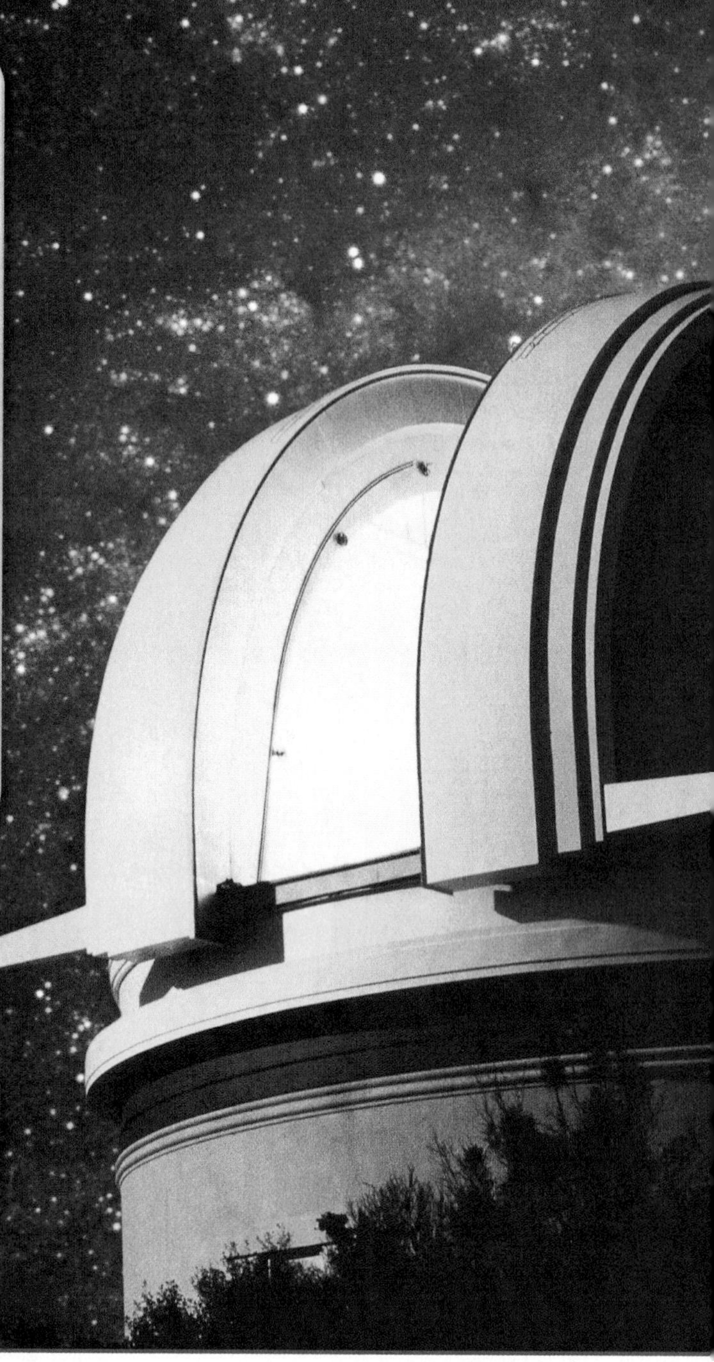

Exponents are used to write very large numbers, such as numbers that describe distances in space.

Palomar Observatory
Palomar Mountain, CA

390 *Chapter 7*

About the Project

Every Second Counts

In the Chapter Project, students consider the passage of time in seconds. First they calculate large numbers of seconds, such as how many seconds they've been alive or how many seconds until graduation. Then they calculate fractions of seconds as they learn about a car's braking distance and driver reaction time. In each case, students use exponents and scientific notation to work with these very large and very small numbers.

Project Resources

All project resources for teachers and students are provided online.

Materials:

- calculators

ARE YOU READY?

Vocabulary

Match each term on the left with a definition on the right.

1. Associative Property F
2. coefficient B
3. Commutative Property C
4. exponent D
5. like terms E

A. a number that is raised to a power
B. a number multiplied by a variable
C. a property of addition and multiplication that states you can add or multiply numbers in any order
D. the number of times a base is used as a factor
E. terms that consist of the same variables raised to the same powers
F. a property of addition and multiplication that states you can group the numbers in any order

Exponents

Write each expression using a base and an exponent.

6. $4 \cdot 4 \cdot 4 \cdot 4 \cdot 4 \cdot 4 \cdot 4$ 4^7
7. $5 \cdot 5$ 5^2
8. $(-10)(-10)(-10)(-10)$ $(-10)^4$
9. $x \cdot x \cdot x$ x^3
10. $k \cdot k \cdot k \cdot k \cdot k$ k^5
11. 9 9^1

Evaluate Powers

Evaluate each expression.

12. 3^4 81
13. -12^2 −144
14. 5^3 125
15. 2^5 32
16. 4^3 64
17. $(-1)^6$ 1

Multiply Decimals

Multiply.

18. 0.006×10 0.06
19. $25{,}250 \times 100$ 2,525,000
20. 2.4×6.5 15.6

Combine Like Terms

Simplify each expression.

21. $6 + 3p + 14 + 9p$ $20 + 12p$
22. $8y - 4x + 2y + 7x - x$ $10y + 2x$
23. $(12 + 3w - 5) + 6w - 3 - 5w$ $4 + 4w$
24. $6n - 14 + 5n$ $11n - 14$

Squares and Square Roots

Tell whether each number is a perfect square. If so, identify its positive square root.

25. 42 no
26. 81 yes; 9
27. 36 yes; 6
28. 50 no
29. 100 yes; 10
30. 4 yes; 2
31. 1 yes; 1
32. 12 no

ARE YOU READY?

CHAPTER 7

Organizer

Objective: Assess students' understanding of prerequisite skills.

Prerequisite Skills

Exponents
Evaluate Powers
Multiply Decimals
Combine Like Terms
Squares and Square Roots

Assessing Prior Knowledge

INTERVENTION 

Diagnose and Prescribe

Use this page to determine whether intervention is necessary or whether enrichment is appropriate.

Resources

 ***Are You Ready? Intervention and Enrichment* Worksheets**

 ***Are You Ready?* CD-ROM**

 ***Are You Ready?* Online**

my.hrw.com

ARE YOU READY? Diagnose and Prescribe

Prerequisite Skill	*Are You Ready? Intervention*, Chapter 7: Worksheets	CD-ROM	Online
Exponents	Skill 7	Activity 7	Diagnose and Prescribe Online
Evaluate Powers	Skill 8	Activity 8	
Multiply Decimals	Skill 45	Activity 45	
Combine Like Terms	Skill 57	Activity 57	
Squares and Square Roots	Skill 6	Activity 6	

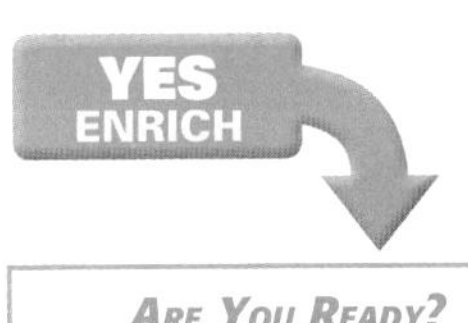

Are You Ready? Enrichment, Chapter 7

 **Worksheets**

 **CD-ROM**

Online

Unpacking the Standards

Organizer

Objective: Help students understand the new concepts they will learn in Chapter 7.

Academic Vocabulary Connections

Becoming familiar with the academic vocabulary on this student page will be helpful to students. Discussing some of the vocabulary terms in the chapter also may be helpful.

1. Very large and very small numbers are often encountered in the sciences. If *notation* means a method of writing something, what might **scientific notation** mean? a method of writing very large and very small numbers
2. A simple definition of **monomial** is "an expression with exactly one term." If the prefix *mono-* means "one" and the prefix *bi-* means "two," define the word **binomial**. an expression with exactly 2 terms
3. What words do you know that begin with the prefix *tri-*? What do they all have in common? Define the word **trinomial** based on the prefix *tri-* and the information given in Problem 2. Possible answers: tricycle, triangle, tripod; they all have 3 of something; an expression with exactly 3 terms.

CHAPTER 7

Unpacking the Standards

The information below "unpacks" the standards. The Academic Vocabulary is highlighted and defined to help you understand the language of the standards. Refer to the lessons listed after each standard for help with the math terms and phrases. The Chapter Concept shows how the standard is applied in this chapter.

California Standard	Academic Vocabulary	Chapter Concept
2.0 Students understand and use such operations as taking the opposite, finding the reciprocal, **taking a root, and raising to a fractional power. They understand and use the rules of exponents.** (Lessons **7-1, 7-2, 7-3, 7-4, 7-5**)	**fractional** having to do with fractions	You evaluate and simplify expressions containing exponents and/or roots. You understand what it means when an exponent is a fraction. ***Example:*** You simplify expressions such as $3^4 \cdot 3^2$. You will evaluate expressions like $16^{\frac{1}{4}}$.
10.0 Students add, subtract, multiply, and divide **monomials and polynomials. Students solve multistep problems, including word problems, by using these techniques.** (Lessons **7-7, 7-8, 7-9**; Labs **7-7, 7-8**)	**multistep** more than one step **technique** a way of doing something	You use your knowledge of exponents to add, subtract, and multiply polynomials, and you use polynomials to solve problems. ***Example:*** You simplify expressions such as $2x^2 - 2x + 5x^2 - 2$ and $x(2x^4 - 5x^3 - x^2)$.

Looking Back

Previously, students:

- wrote and evaluated exponential expressions.
- learned about roots.
- simplified algebraic expressions.

In This Chapter

Students will study:

- properties of exponents and simplifying exponential expressions.
- how to use fractional exponents to express roots.
- how to simplify polynomial expressions.

Looking Forward

Students can use these skills:

- to solve exponential equations and to study exponential functions.
- to solve equations involving roots and to study radical functions.
- to solve polynomial equations.

Reading and Writing Math

Reading Strategy: Read and Understand the Problem

Follow this strategy when solving word problems.
- Read the problem through once.
- Identify exactly what the problem asks you to do.
- Read the problem again, slowly and carefully, to break it into parts.
- Highlight or underline the important information.
- Make a plan to solve the problem.

From Lesson 6-7

29. **Multi-Step** Linda works at a pharmacy for $15 an hour. She also baby-sits for $10 an hour. Linda needs to earn at least $90 per week, but she does not want to work more than 20 hours per week. Show and describe the number of hours Linda could work at each job to meet her goals. List two possible solutions.

Step 1	**Identify exactly what the problem asks you to do.**	• Show and describe the number of hours Linda can work at each job and earn at least $90 per week, without working more than 20 hours per week. • List two possible solutions of the system.
Step 2	**Break the problem into parts. Highlight or underline the important information.**	• Linda has two jobs. She makes **$15 per hour** at one job and **$10 per hour** at the other job. • She wants to earn **at least $90 per week.** • She does **not** want to work **more than 20 hours per week.**
Step 3	**Make a plan to solve the problem.**	• Write a system of inequalities. • Solve the system. • Identify two possible solutions of the system.

Try This

For the problem below,

a. **identify exactly what the problem asks you to do.**

b. **break the problem into parts. Highlight or underline the important information.**

c. **make a plan to solve the problem.**

1. The difference between the length and the width of a rectangle is 14 units. The area is 120 square units. Write and solve a system of equations to determine the length and the width of the rectangle. (*Hint:* The formula for the area of a rectangle is $A = \ell w$.)

Organizer

Objective: Help students apply strategies to understand and retain key concepts.

Online Edition

Resources

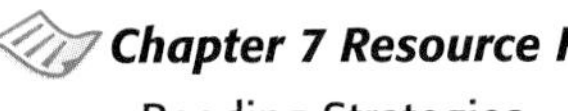

Chapter 7 Resource File

Reading Strategies

ENGLISH LANGUAGE LEARNERS

Reading Strategy: Read and Understand the Problem

Discuss Sometimes students need to read a problem several times before completely understanding it.

Remind students that important information can include more than just numbers. Being aware of words and phrases such as *not, no more than, whole number solutions, inches*, and *two different ways* can be crucial to correctly solving a problem.

Extend As you present word problems in Chapter 7 to the class, ask students what information should be highlighted and why.

As students work through the chapter, have them select at least one word problem from each lesson to break apart and highlight important information.

Answers to *Try This*

1a. Find the length and width of the rectangle.

b. The difference between length and width is 14 units. The area is 120 square units.

c. Write and solve a system of equations.

Exponents

One-Minute Section Planner

Lesson	Lab Resources	Materials
Lesson 7-1 Integer Exponents • Evaluate expressions containing integer exponents. • Simplify expressions containing integer exponents. 2.0		**Optional** graphing calculator
Lesson 7-2 Powers of 10 and Scientific Notation • Evaluate and multiply by powers of 10. • Convert between standard notation and scientific notation. 2.0		**Optional** graphing calculator
Lesson 7-3 Multiplication Properties of Exponents • Use multiplication properties of exponents to evaluate and simplify expressions. 2.0		
Lesson 7-4 Division Properties of Exponents • Use division properties of exponents to evaluate and simplify expressions. 2.0	***Technology Lab 7-4*** In *Chapter 7 Resource File*	
Lesson 7-5 Fractional Exponents • Evaluate and simplify expressions containing fractional exponents. 2.0		**Optional** graphing calculator, number cubes (MK)

MK = *Manipulatives Kit*

Notes

Math Background: Teaching the Standards

EXPONENTS  2.0

Lesson 7-1

Up to this point, students have worked primarily with linear equations and linear inequalities. In Chapter 7, students move toward more complex ideas as they begin to study polynomials. Before beginning this study, students must first have an understanding of exponents.

One common difficulty students have with exponents is the use of zero. For example, students are often puzzled by the fact that any nonzero number raised to the zero power is 1. It makes sense to think of 2^4 as a product where 2 is a factor 4 times ($2^4 = 2 \cdot 2 \cdot 2 \cdot 2$), but when it comes to evaluating 2^0, how does one write a product with 2 as a factor zero times? Students should understand that 2^0 is *defined* to be 1 in order to make it consistent with the rules of exponent arithmetic. For example, in order for the Quotient of Powers Property to work in as many situations as possible, it must be true that $\frac{2^4}{2^4} = 2^{4-4} = 2^0$, but $\frac{2^4}{2^4} = \frac{16}{16} = 1$. Thus, $2^0 = 1$.

This idea of defining certain powers in order to create a system that is as widely consistent as possible also explains why the expression 0^0 is undefined. First, it is clear that $0^1 = 0$, $0^2 = 0$, and $0^{13} = 0$. In fact, for any value of n greater than zero, $0^n = 0$. For this reason, it might make sense to define 0^0 as zero. On the other hand, as shown above, any nonzero number raised to the zero power is 1, so it might also make sense to define 0^0 as 1. Because there is no single real number that works consistently as a definition of 0^0, this expression is considered *indeterminate* and is left undefined.

SCIENTIFIC NOTATION

Lesson 7-2

Scientific notation is an efficient way to write very large and very small numbers, such as numbers used to express distances in space. For example, the distance from the Earth to the Sun is approximately 93 million miles or 93,000,000 miles.

The key step in the translation to scientific notation is to recognize that

$$93{,}000{,}000 = 9.3 \times 10{,}000{,}000$$

and to see that 10,000,000 is a power of 10, namely 10^7. Thus, $93{,}000{,}000 = 9.3 \times 10^7$.

In general, every positive real number may be written in scientific notation, $a \times 10^n$, where $1 \leq a < 10$ and n is an integer. The value of a is called the *coefficient*.

A number line helps to visualize scientific notation. On the number line below, several powers of 10 are graphed.

10^1 10^2 10^3 10^4
10 100 1,000 10,000

The interval between each successive power of 10 is 10 times as large as the preceding interval. When a number is written in scientific notation, such as 6.7×10^3, the power of 10 tells which interval the number lies in and the coefficient tells where the number falls within the interval.

10^1 10^2 10^3 6.7×10^3 10^4
10 100 1,000 10,000

Numbers greater than or equal to 1 but less than 10 are written in scientific notation with an exponent of 0 since, for example,

$$3.8 = 3.8 \times 1$$
$$= 3.8 \times 10^0$$

Numbers greater than 0 but less than 1 are written with negative powers of 10. A specific example shows why this is the case:

$$0.0041 = 4.1 \times 0.001$$
$$= 4.1 \times \frac{1}{1000}$$
$$= 4.1 \times 10^{-3}$$

7-1 Organizer

Objectives: Evaluate expressions containing integer exponents.

Simplify expressions containing integer exponents.

Online Edition
Tutorial Videos

Countdown to Mastery Week 14

Power Presentations with PowerPoint®

Warm Up

Evaluate each expression for the given values of the variables.

1. x^3y^2 for $x = -1$ and $y = 10$ -100
2. $\frac{3x^2}{y^2}$ for $x = 4$ and $y = (-7)$ $\frac{48}{49}$

Write each number as a power of the given base.

3. 64; base 4 4^3
4. -27; base (-3) $(-3)^3$

Also available on transparency

Math Fact !!

The Babylonian number system had no symbol for zero. It was represented by a blank space.

California Standards

Alegbra 1 🔑 2.0

7-1 Integer Exponents

California Standards

🔑 **2.0** Students understand and use such operations as taking the opposite, finding the reciprocal, taking a root, and raising to a fractional power. **They understand and use the rules of exponents.**

Who uses this?
Manufacturers can use negative exponents to express very small measurements.

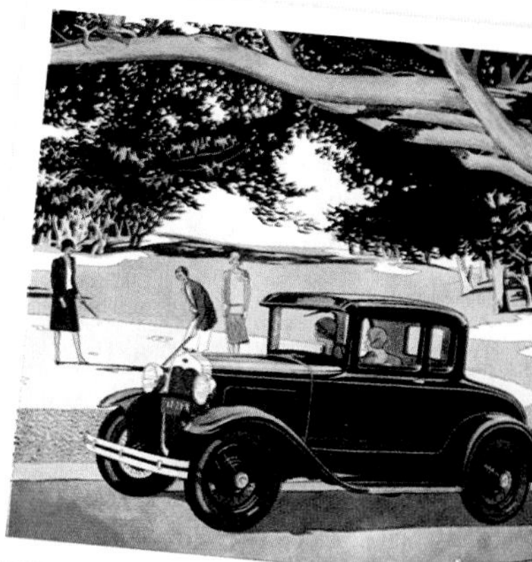

In 1930, the Model A Ford was one of the first cars to boast precise craftsmanship in mass production. The car's pistons had a diameter of $3\frac{7}{8}$ inches; this measurement could vary by at most 10^{-3} inch.

You have seen positive exponents. Recall that to simplify 3^2, use 3 as a factor 2 times: $3^2 = 3 \cdot 3 = 9$.

Remember!

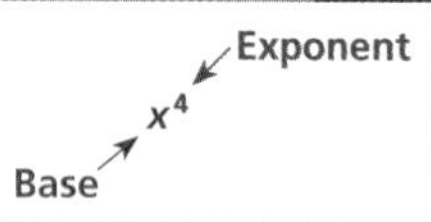

But what does it mean for an exponent to be negative or 0? You can use a table and look for a pattern to make a conjecture.

Power	5^5	5^4	5^3	5^2	5^1	5^0	5^{-1}	5^{-2}
Value	3125	625	125	25	5			

$\div 5$ $\div 5$ $\div 5$ $\div 5$

When the exponent decreases by one, the value of the power is divided by 5. Continue the pattern of dividing by 5:

$$5^0 = \frac{5}{5} = 1 \qquad 5^{-1} = \frac{1}{5} = \frac{1}{5^1} \qquad 5^{-2} = \frac{1}{5} \div 5 = \frac{1}{25} = \frac{1}{5^2}$$

Know it! Note

Integer Exponents

WORDS	NUMBERS	ALGEBRA
Zero exponent—Any nonzero number raised to the zero power is 1.	$3^0 = 1$ $123^0 = 1$ $(-16)^0 = 1$ $\left(\frac{3}{7}\right)^0 = 1$	If $x \neq 0$, then $x^0 = 1$.
Negative exponent—A nonzero number raised to a negative exponent is equal to 1 divided by that number raised to the opposite (positive) exponent.	$3^{-2} = \frac{1}{3^2} = \frac{1}{9}$ $2^{-4} = \frac{1}{2^4} = \frac{1}{16}$	If $x \neq 0$ and n is an integer, then $x^{-n} = \frac{1}{x^n}$.

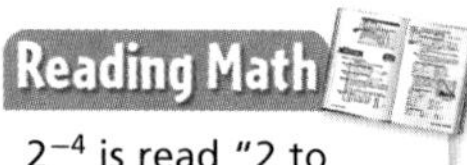

Reading Math

2^{-4} is read "2 to the negative fourth power."

Notice the phrase "nonzero number" in the table above. This is because 0^0 and 0 raised to a negative power are both undefined. For example, if you use the pattern given above the table with a base of 0 instead of 5, you would get $0^0 = \frac{0}{0}$. Also, 0^{-6} would be $\frac{1}{0^6} = \frac{1}{0}$. Since division by 0 is undefined, neither value exists.

1 Introduce

EXPLORATION

7-1 Integer Exponents

A botanist has taken over a study of a plant whose height doubles every day. On the fourth day after he took over the experiment, the plant was 16 inches tall.

1. The botanist can find the height of the plant on previous days by repeatedly dividing by 2. Use this fact to complete the middle column of the table.
2. Use your knowledge of exponents to fill in the right column for days 1 and 2. Then look for patterns to complete the right column.
3. What does day 0 represent? What was the height of the plant on day 0? How can you write the height as a power?
4. What does day -1 represent? What was the height of the plant on day -1? How can you write the height as a power?

Day	Height of Plant (in.)	Height Written as a Power
4	16	2^4
3	8	2^3
2		
1		
0		
-1		
-2		
-3		

THINK AND DISCUSS

5. **Describe** the pattern in the right column of the table.
6. **Show** how you could find the height of the plant on day -4 and then write the height as a power.

Motivate

Show students the following examples and ask them to suggest a rule about the use of negative exponents.

a. $2^{-1} = \frac{1}{2}$ **b.** $2^{-3} = \frac{1}{8}$ **c.** $5^{-2} = \frac{1}{25}$

d. $3^{-2} = \frac{1}{9}$

Possible answer: The negative exponent means that you must use the reciprocal of the base and change the exponent to a positive number.

Explorations and answers are provided in *Alternate Openers: Explorations Transparencies.*

EXAMPLE 1 *Manufacturing Application*

The diameter for the Model A Ford piston could vary by at most 10^{-3} inch. Simplify this expression.

$$10^{-3} = \frac{1}{10^3} = \frac{1}{10 \cdot 10 \cdot 10} = \frac{1}{1000}$$

10^{-3} inch is equal to $\frac{1}{1000}$ inch, or 0.001 inch.

CHECK IT OUT! **1.** A sand fly may have a wingspan up to 5^{-3} m. Simplify this expression. $\frac{1}{125}$ m

EXAMPLE 2 Zero and Negative Exponents

Caution!
In $(-3)^{-4}$, the base is negative because the negative sign is inside the parentheses.
In -3^{-4} the base (3) is positive.

Simplify.

A 2^{-3}

$$2^{-3} = \frac{1}{2^3} = \frac{1}{2 \cdot 2 \cdot 2} = \frac{1}{8}$$

B 5^0

$5^0 = 1$ *Any nonzero number raised to the zero power is 1.*

C $(-3)^{-4}$

$$(-3)^{-4} = \frac{1}{(-3)^4} = \frac{1}{(-3)(-3)(-3)(-3)} = \frac{1}{81}$$

D -3^{-4}

$$-3^{-4} = -\frac{1}{3^4} = -\frac{1}{3 \cdot 3 \cdot 3 \cdot 3} = -\frac{1}{81}$$

CHECK IT OUT! Simplify.
2a. 10^{-4} $\frac{1}{10,000}$ **2b.** $(-2)^{-4}$ $\frac{1}{16}$ **2c.** $(-2)^{-5}$ $-\frac{1}{32}$ **2d.** -2^{-5} $-\frac{1}{32}$

EXAMPLE 3 Evaluating Expressions with Zero and Negative Exponents

Evaluate each expression for the given value(s) of the variable(s).

A x^{-1} for $x = 2$

2^{-1} *Substitute 2 for x.*

$2^{-1} = \frac{1}{2^1} = \frac{1}{2}$ *Use the definition $x^{-n} = \frac{1}{x^n}$.*

B a^0b^{-3} for $a = 8$ and $b = -2$

$8^0 \cdot (-2)^{-3}$ *Substitute 8 for a and −2 for b.*

$1 \cdot \frac{1}{(-2)^3}$ *Evaluate expressions with exponents.*

$1 \cdot \frac{1}{(-2)(-2)(-2)}$ *Write the power in the denominator as a product.*

$1 \cdot \frac{1}{-8}$ *Evaluate the power in the denominator.*

$-\frac{1}{8}$ *Simplify.*

CHECK IT OUT! Evaluate each expression for the given value(s) of the variable(s).
3a. p^{-3} for $p = 4$ **3b.** $8a^{-2}b^0$ for $a = -2$ and $b = 6$

3a. $\frac{1}{64}$
3b. 2

2 Teach

Guided Instruction

Define negative and zero exponents by demonstrating the pattern in the decreasing values of the powers. Use the definition to simplify and evaluate expressions with negative and zero exponents. Then include examples with negative exponents in the denominator. Remind students that factors with negative exponents are not yet simplified.

Universal Access

Through Graphic Organizers

Have students make a chart similar to the one below and let them refer to it during class work and homework.

0^x $(x \leq 0)$	Undefined
x^0 $(x \neq 0)$	1
x^{-2} $(x \neq 0)$	$\frac{1}{x^2}$
$\frac{1}{x^{-2}}$ $(x \neq 0)$	x^2

COMMON ERROR ALERT

Students will sometimes multiply the base by the negative exponent. Have these students reread the definition of a negative exponent. Point out that 10^{-3} means a number less than one, not a number less than zero.

Power Presentations with PowerPoint®

Additional Examples

Example 1

One cup is 2^{-4} gallons. Simplify this expression. $\frac{1}{16}$ gal

Example 2

Simplify.

A. 4^{-3} $\frac{1}{64}$ **B.** 7^0 1

C. $(-5)^{-4}$ $\frac{1}{625}$ **D.** -5^{-4} $-\frac{1}{625}$

Example 3

Evaluate each expression for the given value(s) of the variable(s).

A. x^{-2} for $x = 4$ $\frac{1}{16}$

B. $-2a^0b^{-4}$ for $a = 5$ and $b = -3$ $-\frac{2}{81}$

Also available on transparency

INTERVENTION

Questioning Strategies

EXAMPLES 1–2

- What is the difference between **Examples 2C** and **2D**?
- When will a term with a negative exponent have a negative value?

EXAMPLE 3

- There are no fractions in the problem. Why are there fractions in the answers?
- Why is the value of a variable irrelevant if that variable is raised to the zero power?

Inclusion In **Example 3**, some students may prefer to rewrite the expression with a positive exponent before substituting for the variable.

Technology Students can use the ^ or Y^x keys on their calculators to check their work in **Examples 1–3**.

Power Presentations with PowerPoint®

Additional Examples

Example 4

Simplify.

A. $7w^{-4}$ $\frac{7}{w^4}$ **B.** $\frac{-5}{k^{-2}}$ $-5k^2$

C. $\frac{a^0b^{-2}}{c^{-3}d^6}$ $\frac{c^3}{b^2d^6}$

Also available on transparency

INTERVENTION

Questioning Strategies

EXAMPLE 4

- How do you decide which factors get moved to the other side of the fraction bar?
- What happens to factors with exponents of zero?

What if you have an expression with a negative exponent in a denominator, such as $\frac{1}{x^{-8}}$?

$x^{-n} = \frac{1}{x^n}$, or $\frac{1}{x^n} = x^{-n}$ — *Definition of negative exponent*

$\frac{1}{x^{-8}} = x^{-(-8)}$ — *Substitute −8 for n.*

$= x^8$ — *Simplify the exponent on the right side.*

If a base with a negative exponent is in a denominator, it is equivalent to the same base with the opposite (positive) exponent in the numerator.

An expression that contains negative or zero exponents is not considered to be simplified. Expressions should be rewritten with only positive exponents.

EXAMPLE 4 Simplifying Expressions with Zero and Negative Exponents

Simplify.

A $3y^{-2}$

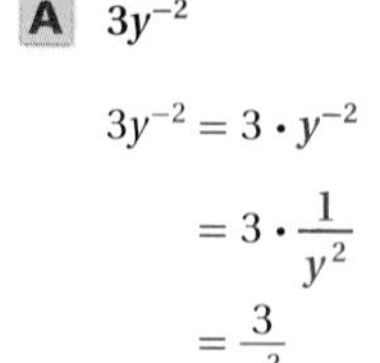

$3y^{-2} = 3 \cdot y^{-2}$

$= 3 \cdot \frac{1}{y^2}$

$= \frac{3}{y^2}$

B $\frac{-4}{k^{-4}}$

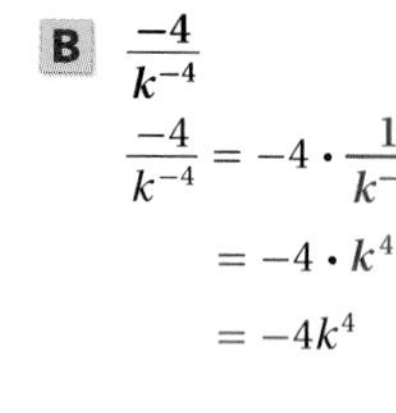

$\frac{-4}{k^{-4}} = -4 \cdot \frac{1}{k^{-4}}$

$= -4 \cdot k^4$

$= -4k^4$

C $\frac{x^{-3}}{a^0y^5}$

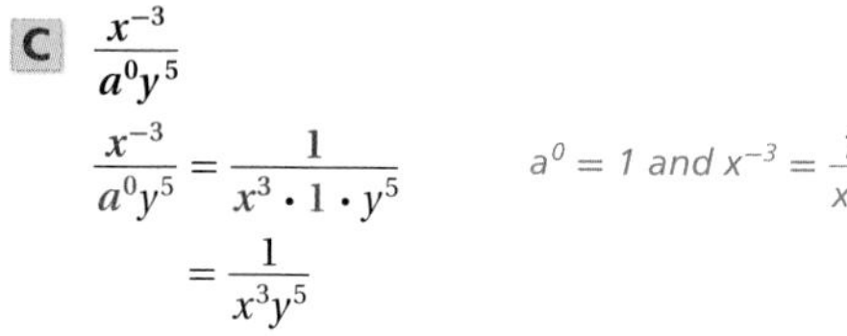

$\frac{x^{-3}}{a^0y^5} = \frac{1}{x^3 \cdot 1 \cdot y^5}$ — *$a^0 = 1$ and $x^{-3} = \frac{1}{x^3}$.*

$= \frac{1}{x^3y^5}$

CHECK IT OUT! Simplify.

4a. $2r^0m^{-3}$ $\frac{2}{m^3}$ **4b.** $\frac{r^{-3}}{7}$ $\frac{1}{7r^3}$ **4c.** $\frac{g^4}{h^{-6}}$ g^4h^6

THINK AND DISCUSS

1. Complete each equation: $2b^? = \frac{2}{b^2}$, $\frac{s^{-3}}{k^?} = \frac{1}{s^3}$, $?^{-2} = \frac{1}{t^2}$

2. GET ORGANIZED Copy and complete the graphic organizer. In each box, describe how to simplify, and give an example.

Simplifying Expressions with Negative Exponents

For a negative exponent in the numerator . . .	For a negative exponent in the denominator . . .

3 Close

Summarize

Remind students that an expression is not yet simplified if it has an exponent that is negative or zero.

Have students state the rules for simplifying expressions with negative exponents in their own words. Accept nontechnical answers such as the following: Make the exponent positive and move the factor to the other side of the fraction bar.

FORMATIVE ASSESSMENT and INTERVENTION

***Diagnose Before* the Lesson**
7-1 Warm Up, TE p. 394

***Monitor During* the Lesson**
Check It Out! Exercises, SE pp. 395–396
Questioning Strategies, TE pp. 395–396

***Assess After* the Lesson**
7-1 Lesson Quiz, TE p. 399
Alternative Assessment, TE p. 399

Answers to *Think and Discuss*

1. −2; 0; *t*
2. See p. A6.

7-1 Exercises

California Standards Practice
2.0, 25.2

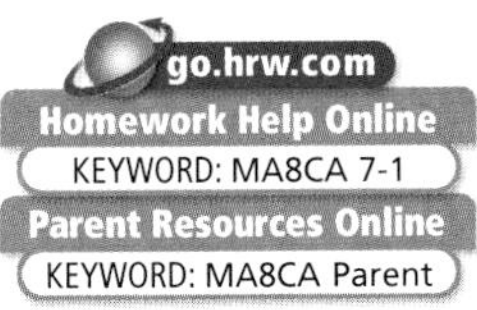
go.hrw.com
Homework Help Online
KEYWORD: MA8CA 7-1
Parent Resources Online
KEYWORD: MA8CA Parent

GUIDED PRACTICE

SEE EXAMPLE 1 p. 395

1. **Medicine** A typical virus is about 10^{-7} m in size. Simplify this expression. $\frac{1}{10{,}000{,}000}$ m

SEE EXAMPLE 2 p. 395

Simplify.

2. 6^{-2} $\frac{1}{36}$ 3. 3^0 1 4. -5^{-2} $-\frac{1}{25}$ 5. 3^{-3} $\frac{1}{27}$ 6. 1^{-8} 1

7. -8^{-3} $-\frac{1}{512}$ 8. 10^{-2} $\frac{1}{100}$ 9. $(4.2)^0$ 1 10. $(-3)^{-3}$ $-\frac{1}{27}$ 11. 4^{-2} $\frac{1}{16}$

SEE EXAMPLE 3 p. 395

Evaluate each expression for the given value(s) of the variable(s).

12. b^{-2} for $b = -3$ $\frac{1}{9}$

13. $(2t)^{-4}$ for $t = 2$ $\frac{1}{256}$

14. $(m-4)^{-5}$ for $m = 6$ $\frac{1}{32}$

15. $2x^0y^{-3}$ for $x = 7$ and $y = -4$ $-\frac{1}{32}$

SEE EXAMPLE 4 p. 396

Simplify.

16. $4m^0$ 4 17. $3k^{-4}$ $\frac{3}{k^4}$ 18. $\frac{7}{r^{-7}}$ $7r^7$ 19. $\frac{x^{10}}{d^{-3}}$ $x^{10}d^3$

20. $2x^0y^{-4}$ $\frac{2}{y^4}$ 21. $\frac{f^{-4}}{g^{-6}}$ $\frac{g^6}{f^4}$ 22. $\frac{c^4}{d^{-3}}$ c^4d^3 23. p^7q^{-1} $\frac{p^7}{q}$

PRACTICE AND PROBLEM SOLVING

Independent Practice	
For Exercises	See Example
24	1
25–36	2
37–42	3
43–57	4

Extra Practice
Skills Practice p. EP14
Application Practice p. EP30

24. **Biology** One of the smallest bats is the northern blossom bat, which is found from Southeast Asia to Australia. This bat weighs about 2^{-1} ounce. Simplify this expression. $\frac{1}{2}$ oz

Simplify.

25. 8^0 1 26. 5^{-4} $\frac{1}{625}$ 27. 3^{-4} $\frac{1}{81}$ 28. -9^{-2} $-\frac{1}{81}$

29. -6^{-2} $-\frac{1}{36}$ 30. 7^{-2} $\frac{1}{49}$ 31. $\left(\frac{2}{5}\right)^0$ 1 32. 13^{-2} $\frac{1}{169}$

33. $(-3)^{-1}$ $-\frac{1}{3}$ 34. $(-4)^2$ 16 35. $\left(\frac{1}{2}\right)^{-2}$ 4 36. -7^{-1} $-\frac{1}{7}$

Evaluate each expression for the given value(s) of the variable(s).

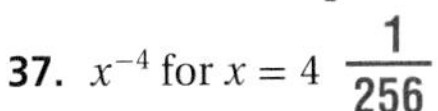

37. x^{-4} for $x = 4$ $\frac{1}{256}$

38. $\left(\frac{2}{3}v\right)^{-3}$ for $v = 9$ $\frac{1}{216}$

39. $(10-d)^0$ for $d = 11$ 1

40. $10m^{-1}n^{-5}$ for $m = 10$ and $n = -2$ $-\frac{1}{32}$

41. $(3ab)^{-2}$ for $a = \frac{1}{2}$ and $b = 8$ $\frac{1}{144}$

42. $4w^vx^v$ for $w = 3$, $v = 0$, and $x = -5$ 4

Simplify.

43. k^{-4} $\frac{1}{k^4}$ 44. $2z^{-8}$ $\frac{2}{z^8}$ 45. $\frac{1}{2b^{-3}}$ $\frac{b^3}{2}$ 46. $c^{-2}d$ $\frac{d}{c^2}$ 47. $-5x^{-3}$ $-\frac{5}{x^3}$

48. $4x^{-6}y^{-2}$ $\frac{4}{x^6y^2}$ 49. $\frac{2f^0}{7g^{-10}}$ $\frac{2g^{10}}{7}$ 50. $\frac{r^{-5}}{s^{-1}}$ $\frac{s}{r^5}$ 51. $\frac{s^5}{t^{-12}}$ s^5t^{12} 52. $\frac{3w^{-5}}{x^{-6}}$ $\frac{3x^6}{w^5}$

53. b^0c^0 1 54. $\frac{2}{3}m^{-1}n^5$ $\frac{2n^5}{3m}$ 55. $\frac{q^{-2}r^0}{s^0}$ $\frac{1}{q^2}$ 56. $\frac{a^{-7}b^2}{c^3d^{-4}}$ $\frac{b^2d^4}{a^7c^3}$ 57. $\frac{h^3k^{-1}}{6m^2}$ $\frac{h^3}{6m^2k}$

7-1 Exercises

Assignment Guide

Assign *Guided Practice* exercises as necessary.

If you finished Examples **1–2**
Proficient 24–36, 77, 86, 88
Advanced 24–36, 77, 100, 101

If you finished Examples **1–4**
Proficient 24–57, 58–74 even, 76–100, 102–111
Advanced 24–57, 58–74 even, 75–111

Homework Quick Check
Quickly check key concepts.
Exercises: 24, 28, 34, 42, 52, 77

California Standards

Standard	Exercises
2.0	1–65, 67–77, 84–93, 94c–99
4.0	102–107
7.0	110, 111
16.0	108, 109
25.2	66

CONCEPT CONNECTION **Exercise 94** involves writing an equation with a negative exponent. This exercise prepares students for the Concept Connection on page 428.

Language Support In **Exercise 77,** students may not understand the word *components*. Explain that a component is a part that makes up a whole.

Answers

77. red blood cell: $\frac{1}{125{,}000}$ m; white blood cell: $\frac{3}{250{,}000}$ m; platelet: $\frac{3}{1{,}000{,}000}$ m
78. def. of neg. exp.
79. A pos. number raised to any power results in a pos. number.
80. true only when $x \neq 0$
81. true only when $x = 1$
82. If $n \geq 0$, 0^{-n} is undefined. If $n < 0$, $0^{-n} = 0$.
83. For example, true when $x > 1$ and $n < -1$, but false when $x = 1$ and $n \neq 0$.
85. Possible answer: Look at the pattern below. As the exponent goes down by 1, the value is half of what it was before.
$2^3 = 8$, $2^2 = 4$,
$2^1 = 2$, $2^0 = 1$,
$2^{-1} = \frac{1}{2}$, $2^{-2} = \frac{1}{4}$,
$2^{-3} = \frac{1}{8} = \frac{1}{2^3}$

Evaluate each expression for $x = 3$, $y = -1$, and $z = 2$.

58. z^{-5} $\frac{1}{32}$
59. $(x + y)^{-4}$ $\frac{1}{16}$
60. $(yz)^0$ 1
61. $(xyz)^{-1}$ $-\frac{1}{6}$
62. $(xy - 3)^{-2}$ $\frac{1}{36}$
63. x^{-y} 3
64. $(yz)^{-x}$ $-\frac{1}{8}$
65. xy^{-4} 3

66. **///ERROR ANALYSIS///** Look at the two equations below. Which is incorrect? Explain the error.

66. Equation A is incorrect because 5 was incorrectly moved to the denom. The neg. exp. applies only to the base x.

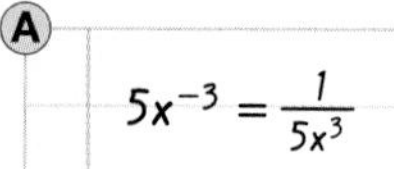

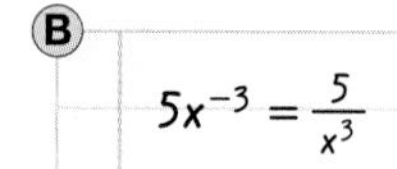

LINK Biology

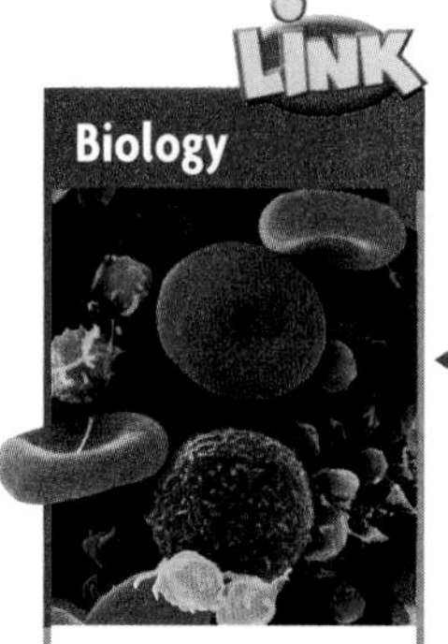

When bleeding occurs, platelets (which appear green in the image above) help to form a clot to reduce blood loss. Calcium and vitamin K are also necessary for clot formation.

Simplify.

67. a^3b^{-2} $\frac{a^3}{b^2}$
68. $c^{-4}d^3$ $\frac{d^3}{c^4}$
69. $v^0w^2y^{-1}$ $\frac{w^2}{y}$
70. $(a^2b^{-7})^0$ 1
71. $-5y^{-6}$ $-\frac{5}{y^6}$
72. $\frac{2a^{-5}}{b^{-6}}$ $\frac{2b^6}{a^5}$
73. $\frac{2a^3}{b^{-1}}$ $2a^3b$
74. $\frac{m^2}{n^{-3}}$ m^2n^3
75. $\frac{x^{-8}}{3y^{12}}$ $\frac{1}{3x^8y^{12}}$
76. $-\frac{20p^{-1}}{5q^{-3}}$ $-\frac{4q^3}{p}$

77. **Biology** Human blood contains red blood cells, white blood cells, and platelets. The table shows the sizes of these components. Simplify each expression.

Blood Components

Part	Size (m)
Red blood cell	$125{,}000^{-1}$
White blood cell	$3(500)^{-2}$
Platelet	$3(1000)^{-2}$

Tell whether each statement is sometimes, always, or never true. Explain.

78. If n is a positive integer, then $x^{-n} = \frac{1}{x^n}$. always
79. If x is positive, then $x^{-n} < 0$. never
80. If n is zero, then x^{-n} is 1. sometimes
81. If n is a negative integer, then $x^{-n} = 1$. sometimes
82. If x is zero, then $x^{-n} = 1$. never
83. If n is an integer, then $x^{-n} > 1$. sometimes

84. **Reasoning** Find the value of $2^3 \cdot 2^{-3}$. Then find the value of $3^2 \cdot 3^{-2}$. Make a conjecture about the value of $a^n \cdot a^{-n}$. 1; 1; $a^n \cdot a^{-n} = 1$

85. **Write About It** Explain in your own words why 2^{-3} is the same as $\frac{1}{2^3}$.

Find the missing value.

86. $\frac{1}{4} = 2^{\blacksquare}$ -2
87. $9^{-2} = \frac{1}{\blacksquare}$ 81
88. $\frac{1}{64} = \blacksquare^{-2}$ 8
89. $\frac{\blacksquare}{3} = 3^{-1}$ 1
90. $7^{-2} = \frac{1}{\blacksquare}$ 49
91. $10^{\blacksquare} = \frac{1}{1000}$ -3
92. $3 \cdot 4^{-2} = \frac{3}{\blacksquare}$ 16
93. $2 \cdot \frac{1}{5} = 2 \cdot 5^{\blacksquare}$ -1

CONCEPT CONNECTION

94. This problem will prepare you for the Concept Connection on page 428.
   a. The product of the frequency f and the wavelength w of light in air is a constant v. Write an equation for this relationship. $fw = v$
   b. Solve this equation for wavelength. Then write this equation as an equation with f raised to a negative exponent. $w = \frac{v}{f}$; $w = vf^{-1}$
   c. The units for frequency are hertz (Hz). One hertz is one cycle per second, which is often written as $\frac{1}{s}$. Rewrite this expression using a negative exponent. s^{-1}

7-1 PRACTICE A

7-1 PRACTICE C

7-1 PRACTICE B

LESSON 7-1 **Practice B**
Integer Exponents

Simplify.

1. $5^{-3} = \frac{1}{5^{3}} = \frac{1}{125}$
2. $2^{-6} = \frac{1}{2^{6}} = \frac{1}{64}$
3. $(-5)^{-2}$ $\frac{1}{25}$
4. $-(4)^{-3}$ $-\frac{1}{64}$
5. -6^0 -1
6. $(7)^{-2}$ $\frac{1}{49}$

Evaluate each expression for the given value(s) of the variable(s).

7. d^{-3} for $d = -2$ $-\frac{1}{8}$
8. a^5b^{-6} for $a = 3$ and $b = 2$ $\frac{243}{64}$
9. $(b - 4)^{-2}$ for $b = 1$ $\frac{1}{9}$
10. $5z^{-x}$ for $z = -3$ and $x = 2$ $\frac{5}{9}$
11. $(5z)^{-x}$ for $z = -3$ and $x = 2$ $\frac{1}{225}$
12. $c^{-3}(16^{-2})$ for $c = 4$ $\frac{1}{16{,}384}$

Simplify.

13. t^{-4} $\frac{1}{t^4}$
14. $3r^{-5}$ $\frac{3}{r^5}$
15. $\frac{s^{-3}}{t^{-5}}$ $\frac{t^5}{s^3}$
16. $\frac{h^0}{3}$ $\frac{1}{3}$
17. $\frac{2x^{-3}y^{-2}}{z^4}$ $\frac{2}{x^3y^2z^4}$
18. $\frac{4fg^{-5}}{5h^{-3}}$ $\frac{4fh^3}{5g^5}$
19. $\frac{14a^{-4}}{20bc^{-1}}$ $\frac{7c}{10a^4b}$
20. $\frac{a^4c^2e^0}{b^{-1}d^{-3}}$ $a^4bc^2d^3$
21. $\frac{-3g^{-2}hk^{-2}}{-6h^0}$ $\frac{h}{2g^2k^2}$
22. A cooking website claims to contain 10^5 recipes. Evaluate this expression. 100,000
23. A ball bearing has diameter 2^{-3} inches. Evaluate this expression. $\frac{1}{8}$ inch or 0.125 inch

7-1 READING STRATEGIES

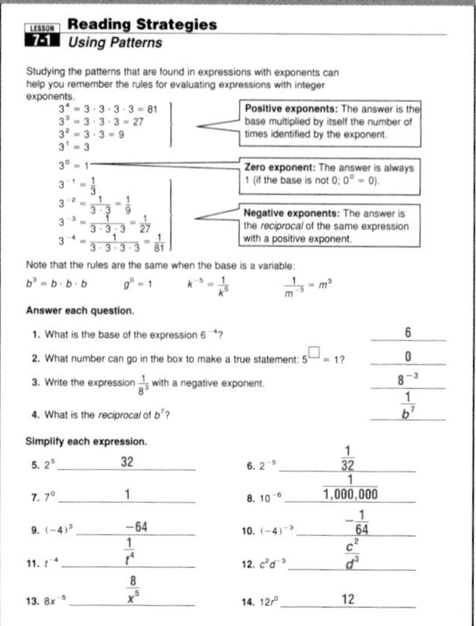

LESSON 7-1 **Reading Strategies**
Using Patterns

Studying the patterns that are found in expressions with exponents can help you remember the rules for evaluating expressions with integer exponents.

$3^4 = 3 \cdot 3 \cdot 3 \cdot 3 = 81$
$3^3 = 3 \cdot 3 \cdot 3 = 27$
$3^2 = 3 \cdot 3 = 9$
$3^1 = 3$

Positive exponents: The answer is the base multiplied by itself the number of times identified by the exponent.

$3^0 = 1$

Zero exponent: The answer is always 1 (if the base is not 0; $0^0 = 0$).

$3^{-1} = \frac{1}{3}$
$3^{-2} = \frac{1}{3 \cdot 3} = \frac{1}{9}$
$3^{-3} = \frac{1}{3 \cdot 3 \cdot 3} = \frac{1}{27}$
$3^{-4} = \frac{1}{3 \cdot 3 \cdot 3 \cdot 3} = \frac{1}{81}$

Negative exponents: The answer is the *reciprocal* of the same expression with a positive exponent.

Note that the rules are the same when the base is a variable:

$b^3 = b \cdot b \cdot b$ $g^0 = 1$ $k^{-5} = \frac{1}{k^5}$ $\frac{1}{m^{-3}} = m^3$

Answer each question.

1. What is the base of the expression 6^{-4}? 6
2. What number can go in the box to make a true statement: $5^{\square} = 1$? 0
3. Write the expression $\frac{1}{8^3}$ with a negative exponent. 8^{-3}
4. What is the *reciprocal* of b^7? $\frac{1}{b^7}$

Simplify each expression.

5. 2^5 32
6. 2^{-5} $\frac{1}{32}$
7. 7^0 1
8. 10^{-6} $\frac{1}{1{,}000{,}000}$
9. $(-4)^3$ -64
10. $(-4)^{-3}$ $-\frac{1}{64}$
11. t^{-4} $\frac{1}{t^4}$
12. c^2d^{-3} $\frac{c^2}{d^3}$
13. $8x^{-5}$ $\frac{8}{x^5}$
14. $12r^0$ 12

7-1 REVIEW FOR MASTERY

LESSON 7-1 **Review for Mastery**
Integer Exponents

Remember that 2^3 means $2 \times 2 \times 2 = 8$. The base is 2, the exponent is positive 3. Exponents can also be 0 or negative.

	Zero Exponents	Negative Exponents	Negative Exponents in the Denominator
Definition	For any nonzero number x, $x^0 = 1$.	For any nonzero number x and any integer n, $x^{-n} = \frac{1}{x^n}$.	For any nonzero number x and any integer n, $\frac{1}{x^{-n}} = x^n$.
Examples	$6^0 = 1$ $\left(\frac{1}{2}\right)^0 = 1$	$5^{-3} = \frac{1}{5^3}$ $2^{-4} = \frac{1}{2^4}$	$\frac{1}{8^{-2}} = 8^2$ $\frac{1}{2^{-4}} = 2^4$
0^0 and 0^{-n} are undefined.			

Simplify 4^{-2}.

4^{-2}
$\frac{1}{4^2}$ *Write without negative exponents.*
$\frac{1}{4 \cdot 4}$ *Write in expanded form.*
$\frac{1}{16}$ *Simplify.*

Simplify $x^2y^{-3}z^0$.

$x^2y^{-3}z^0$
$\frac{x^2z^0}{y^3}$ *Write without negative exponents.*
$\frac{x^2(1)}{y^3}$ $z^0 = 1$.
$\frac{x^2}{y^3}$ *Simplify.*

Fill in the blanks to simplify each expression.

1. 2^{-5}
$2^{-5} = \frac{1}{2^{5}}$
$\frac{1}{2^5} = \frac{1}{2 \cdot 2 \cdot 2 \cdot 2 \cdot 2}$
$= \frac{1}{32}$

2. 10^{-3}
$10^{-3} = \frac{1}{10}$
$\frac{1}{10^3} = \frac{1}{10 \cdot 10 \cdot 10}$
$= \frac{1}{1000}$

3. $\frac{1}{5^{-4}}$
$\frac{1}{5^{-4}} = 5^{4}$
$5^{4} = 5 \cdot 5 \cdot 5 \cdot 5$
$= 625$

Simplify.

4. $5y^{-4}$ $\frac{5}{y^4}$
5. $\frac{8}{a^{-3}}$ $8a^3$
6. $9x^3y^{-2}$ $\frac{9x^3}{y^2}$
7. $\frac{x^3}{x^{-1}y}$ $\frac{x^4}{y}$
8. $\frac{b^2}{a^{-1}b^3}$ $\frac{a}{b}$
9. $5x^{-4}y^2$ $\frac{5y^2}{x^4}$

Multiple Choice For Exercises 95–97, choose the best answer.

95. Which is NOT equivalent to the other three?

Ⓐ $\frac{1}{25}$ Ⓑ 5^{-2} Ⓒ 0.04 **Ⓓ** -25

96. Which is equal to 6^{-2}?

Ⓐ $6(-2)$ Ⓑ $(-6)(-6)$ Ⓒ $-\frac{1}{6 \cdot 6}$ **Ⓓ** $\frac{1}{6 \cdot 6}$

97. Simplify $\frac{a^3b^{-2}}{c^{-1}}$.

Ⓐ $\frac{a^3c}{b^2}$ Ⓑ $\frac{a^3b^2}{-c}$ Ⓒ $\frac{a^3}{-b^2c}$ Ⓓ $\frac{c}{a^3b^2}$

98. **Gridded Response** Simplify $\left[2^{-2} + (6+2)^0\right]$. $\frac{5}{4}$, or 1.25

99. **Short Response** If a and b are real numbers and n is a positive integer, write a simplified expression for the product $a^{-n} \cdot b^0$ that contains only positive exponents. Explain your answer. $\frac{1}{a^n}$; $a^{-n} = \frac{1}{a^n}$ and $b^0 = 1$ for $b \neq 0$. So you have $\frac{1}{a^n} \cdot 1$, or simply $\frac{1}{a^n}$.

CHALLENGE AND EXTEND

100. **Multi-Step** Copy and complete the table of values below. Then graph the ordered pairs and describe the shape of the graph. Possible answer: y increases more rapidly as x increases.

x	−4	−3	−2	−1	0	1	2	3	4
$y = 2^x$	$\frac{1}{16}$	$\frac{1}{8}$	$\frac{1}{4}$	$\frac{1}{2}$	1	2	4	8	16

101. **Reasoning** Copy and complete the table. Then use inductive reasoning to make a conjecture about the values of 1^n and $(-1)^n$ when n is any negative integer.

For help with inductive reasoning, see p. 233.

n	−1	−2	−3	−4	−5
1^n	1	1	1	1	1
$(-1)^n$	−1	1	−1	1	−1

$1^n = 1$; $(-1)^n = -1$ if n is odd, and $(-1)^n = 1$ if n is even.

SPIRAL STANDARDS REVIEW

4.0, 7.0, 16.0

Solve each equation. *(Lesson 2-3)*

102. $2(3x-2) = 8$ 2

103. $-9 = 3(p-1)$ −2

104. $\frac{y}{5} - 6 - 2 = -14 + 2$ −20

105. $1.5h - 5 + 6h = 1 + 6h$ 4

106. $2w + 6 - 3w = -10$ 16

107. $-12 = \frac{1}{2}n + 2 - n$ 28

Identify the independent and dependent variables. Write a rule in function notation for each situation. *(Lesson 4-3)*

108. Pink roses cost $1.50 per stem. ind.: number of roses; dep.: total cost; $f(x) = 1.50x$

109. For dog-sitting, Beth charges a $30 flat fee plus $10 a day. ind.: number of days; dep.: total cost; $f(x) = 10x + 30$

Write an equation in slope-intercept form for the line with the given slope that contains the given point. *(Lesson 5-6)*

110. slope = 3, (3, 5) $y = 3x - 4$

111. slope = $\frac{1}{3}$, (6, 7) $y = \frac{1}{3}x + 5$

Multiple Choice In **Exercise 96,** if students chose **A,** they may have used the negative exponent as a factor. If they chose **B,** they may have made the base negative because the exponent is negative.

If students chose **D** in **Exercise 97,** they probably moved every factor to the opposite side of the fraction bar, even if it had a positive exponent.

Answer

100.

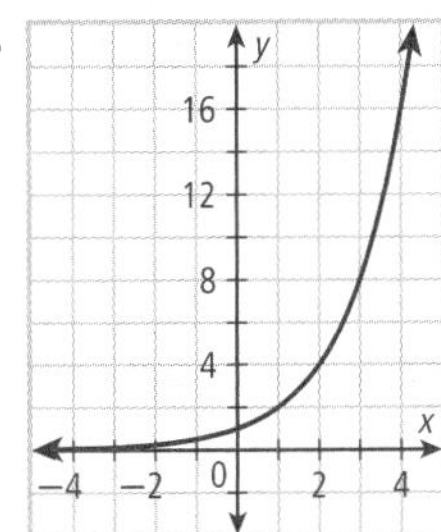

Journal

Have students use patterns to explain why any number raised to the zero power, except zero, is one.

ALTERNATIVE ASSESSMENT

Have students choose three exercises from **Exercises 37–42,** write each expression in words, and then show two different ways to evaluate each expression.

Power Presentations with PowerPoint®

7-1 Lesson Quiz

1. A square foot is 3^{-2} square yards. Simplify this expression. $\frac{1}{9}$ yd²

Simplify.

2. 2^{-6} $\frac{1}{64}$

3. $(-7)^{-3}$ $-\frac{1}{343}$

4. 6^0 1

5. -11^2 −121

Evaluate each expression for the given value(s) of the variable(s).

6. x^{-4} for $x = 10$ $\frac{1}{10{,}000}$

7. $2a^{-1}b^{-3}$ for $a = 6$ and $b = 3$ $\frac{1}{81}$

Simplify.

8. $4y^{-5}$ $\frac{4}{y^5}$

9. $\frac{-3}{y^{-6}}$ $-3y^6$

10. $\frac{x^{-4}}{a^0y^3}$ $\frac{1}{x^4y^3}$

Also available on transparency

7-1 PROBLEM SOLVING

LESSON 7-1 Problem Solving
Integer Exponents

Write the correct answer.

1. At the 2005 World Exposition in Aichi, Japan, tiny mu-chips were embedded in the admissions tickets to prevent counterfeiting. The mu-chip was developed by Hitachi in 2003. Its area is $4^2(10)^{-2}$ square millimeters. Simplify this expression.
   $\frac{4}{25}$ or 0.16 mm²

2. Despite their name, Northern Yellow Bats are commonly found in warm, humid areas in the southeast United States. An adult has a wingspan of about 14 inches and weighs between $3(2)^{-3}$ and $3(2)^{-2}$ ounces. Simplify these expressions.
   $\frac{3}{8}$ and $\frac{3}{4}$ oz

3. Saira is using the formula for the area of a circle to determine the value of π. She is using the expression Ar^{-2} where $A = 50.265$ and $r = 4$. Use a calculator to evaluate Saira's expression to find her approximation of the value of π to the nearest thousandth.
   3.142

4. The volume of a freshwater tank can be expressed in terms of x, y, and z. Expressed in these terms, the volume of the tank is $x^3y^{-2}z$ liters. Determine the volume of the tank if $x = 4$, $y = 3$, and $z = 6$.
   $42\frac{2}{3}$ liters

Alison has an interest in entomology, the study of insects. Her collection of insects from around the world includes the four specimens shown in the table below. Select the best answer.

Insect	Mass
Emperor Scorpion	2^{-5} kg
African Goliath Beetle	11^{-1} kg
Giant Weta	2^{-4} kg
Madagascar Hissing Cockroach	5^{-3} kg

5. Cockroaches have been found on every continent, including Antarctica. What is the mass of Alison's Madagascar Hissing Cockroach expressed as a quotient?
   Ⓐ $-\frac{1}{125}$ kg C $\frac{1}{15}$ kg
   B $\frac{1}{125}$ kg D 125 kg

6. Many Giant Wetas are so heavy that they cannot jump. Which expression is another way to show the mass of the specimen in Alison's collection?
   F $-(2)^4$ kg **Ⓗ** $\frac{1}{2 \cdot 2 \cdot 2 \cdot 2}$ kg
   G $\left(\frac{1}{2}\right)^{-4}$ kg J $4\frac{1}{2}$ kg

7. Scorpions are closely related to spiders and horseshoe crabs. What is the mass of Alison's Emperor Scorpion expressed as a quotient?
   A $-\frac{1}{32}$ kg **Ⓒ** $\frac{1}{32}$ kg
   B $\frac{1}{25}$ kg D 32 kg

7-1 CHALLENGE

LESSON 7-1 Challenge
Exploring Patterns in the Units Digit of x^n

When you write out the first several powers of x^n, where x and n are positive integers, you can discover interesting patterns in the units digits of x^n.

	x^1	x^2	x^3	x^4	x^5	x^6
$x = 2$	$2^1 = 2$	$2^2 = 2(2) = 4$	$2^3 = 2(4) = 8$	$2^4 = 2(8) = 16$	$2^5 = 2(16) = 32$	$2^6 = 2(32) = 64$

Notice that 2^1 and 2^5 have the same units digit and that 2^2 and 2^6 have the same units digit. In the exercises that follow, you can discover other number patterns involving the units digits of x^n.

In Exercises 1–10, find the first nine powers of each value of x. Using the units digit of each result, complete the table. You may find a calculator useful.

		x^1	x^2	x^3	x^4	x^5	x^6	x^7	x^8	x^9
1.	$x = 1$	1	1	1	1	1	1	1	1	1
2.	$x = 2$	2	4	8	6	2	4	8	6	2
3.	$x = 3$	3	9	7	1	3	9	7	1	3
4.	$x = 4$	4	6	4	6	4	6	4	6	4
5.	$x = 5$	5	5	5	5	5	5	5	5	5
6.	$x = 6$	6	6	6	6	6	6	6	6	6
7.	$x = 7$	7	9	3	1	7	9	3	1	7
8.	$x = 8$	8	4	2	6	8	4	2	6	8
9.	$x = 9$	9	1	9	1	9	1	9	1	9
10.	$x = 10$	0	0	0	0	0	0	0	0	0

Refer to the table that you completed in Exercises 1–10. Describe the pattern in the units digits of x^n.

11. 1^n For all n, 1^n has 1 as its units digit.
12. 2^n The pattern is 2, 4, 8, and 6, for $n = 1, 2, 3$, and 4 and then repeats.
13. 3^n The pattern is 3, 9, 7, and 1, for $n = 1, 2, 3$, and 4 and then repeats.
14. 5^n For all $n > 0$, 5^n has 5 as its units digit.
15. Write a rule that determines the units digit of 7^n as a function of n.
    If you divide n by 4, then the units digit is 7, 9, 3, or 1, depending on whether the remainder is 1, 2, 3, or 0, respectively.

7-2 Organizer

Objectives: Evaluate and multiply by powers of 10.

Convert between standard notation and scientific notation.

Online Edition
Tutorial Videos, Interactivity

Countdown to Mastery Week 14

Power Presentations with PowerPoint®

Warm Up

Evaluate each expression.

1. 123×1000 123,000
2. $123 \div 1000$ 0.123
3. 0.003×100 0.3
4. $0.003 \div 100$ 0.00003
5. 10^4 10,000
6. 10^{-4} 0.0001
7. 23^0 1

Also available on transparency

Math Humor

Q: How did the number written in scientific notation feel after he changed into standard form?

A: Powerless.

7-2 Powers of 10 and Scientific Notation

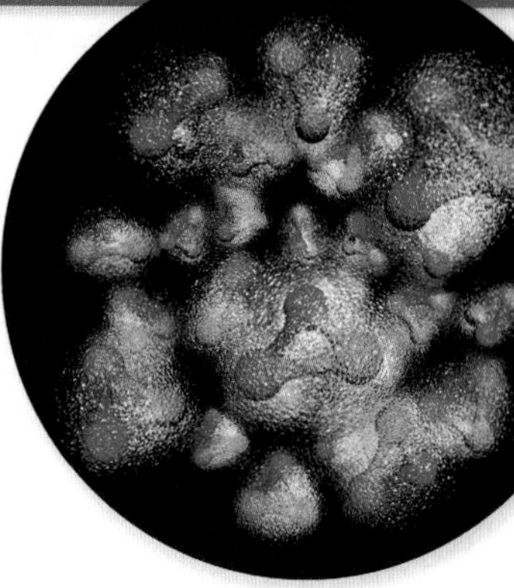

Nucleus of a silicon atom

2.0 Students understand and use such operations as taking the opposite, finding the reciprocal, taking a root, and raising to a fractional power. **They understand and use the rules of exponents.**

Vocabulary
scientific notation

Why learn this?

Powers of 10 can be used to read and write very large and very small numbers, such as the masses of atomic particles. (See Exercise 44.)

The table shows relationships between several powers of 10.

Power	10^3	10^2	10^1	10^0	10^{-1}	10^{-2}	10^{-3}
Value	1000	100	10	1	$\frac{1}{10} = 0.1$	$\frac{1}{100} = 0.01$	$\frac{1}{1000} = 0.001$

(Arrows above the table: $\div 10$ between each pair of adjacent columns, left to right. Arrows below the table: $\times 10$ between each pair of adjacent columns, right to left.)

- Each time you **divide by 10**, the exponent decreases by 1 and the decimal point moves one place to the left.
- Each time you **multiply by 10**, the exponent increases by 1 and the decimal point moves one place to the right.

Know it! Note — **Powers of 10**

WORDS	NUMBERS
Positive Integer Exponent If n is a positive integer, find the value of 10^n by starting with 1 and moving the decimal point n places to the right.	$10^4 = 1\,0,0\,0\,0$ 4 places
Negative Integer Exponent If n is a positive integer, find the value of 10^{-n} by starting with 1 and moving the decimal point n places to the left.	$10^{-6} = \frac{1}{10^6} = 0.0\,0\,0\,0\,0\,1$ 6 places

EXAMPLE 1 Evaluating Powers of 10

Find the value of each power of 10.

A 10^{-3}

Start with 1 and move the decimal point three places to the left.

0.0 0 1

0.001

B 10^2

Start with 1 and move the decimal point two places to the right.

1 0 0

100

C 10^0

Start with 1 and move the decimal point zero places.

1

Writing Math

You may need to add zeros to the right or left of a number in order to move the decimal point in that direction.

1 Introduce

EXPLORATION

7-2 Powers of 10 and Scientific Notation

You will need a calculator for this Exploration.

1. You can use the exponent key, ^, on your calculator to evaluate powers of 10. Use your calculator as needed to complete the table.

Power of 10	Value
10^5	
10^6	
10^7	
10^8	
10^9	

2. Look for patterns in the table. How is the exponent in each power of 10 related to the value of that power of 10?
3. What happens when you try to use your calculator to evaluate larger powers of 10, such as 10^{15}?

THINK AND DISCUSS

4. **Explain** how you could write the value of 10^{15}. How many zeros would you write?
5. **Describe** a general rule you can use to write the value of 10^n, where n is a positive integer.

Motivate

Have students copy the following numbers:

0.0000000000095
2,700,000,000,000,000,000,000

Ask them why the numbers are difficult to copy accurately. They have many zeros.

Say that numbers used in science and technology often contain many zeros. Scientific notation was developed to make these numbers easier to work with.

Explorations and answers are provided in *Alternate Openers: Explorations Transparencies.*

Alegebra 1 2.0

Find the value of each power of 10.

1a. 10^{-2} **0.01** **1b.** 10^{5} **100,000** **1c.** 10^{10} **10,000,000,000**

EXAMPLE 2 Writing Powers of 10

Reading Math

If you do not see a decimal point in a number, it is understood to be at the end of the number.

Write each number as a power of 10.

A 10,000,000

The decimal point is seven places to the right of 1, so the exponent is 7.

10^7

B 0.001

The decimal point is three places to the left of 1, so the exponent is −3.

10^{-3}

C 10

The decimal point is one place to the right of 1, so the exponent is 1.

10^1

Write each number as a power of 10.

2a. 100,000,000 10^8 **2b.** 0.0001 10^{-4} **2c.** 0.1 10^{-1}

You can also move the decimal point to find the product of any number and a power of 10. You start with the number instead of starting with 1.

Know it! Note

Multiplying by Powers of 10	
If the exponent is a positive integer, move the decimal point to the right.	$125 \times 10^5 = 12{,}500{,}000$ (5 places)
If the exponent is a negative integer, move the decimal point to the left.	$36.2 \times 10^{-3} = 0.0362$ (3 places)

EXAMPLE 3 Multiplying by Powers of 10

Find the value of each expression.

A 97.86×10^6

97.8 6 0 0 0 0 — *Move the decimal point 6 places to the right.*

97,860,000

B 19.5×10^{-4}

0 0 1 9.5 — *Move the decimal point 4 places to the left.*

0.00195

Find the value of each expression.

3a. 853.4×10^5 **85,340,000** **3b.** 0.163×10^{-2} **0.00163**

Scientific notation is a method of writing numbers that are very large or very small. A number written in scientific notation has two parts that are multiplied.

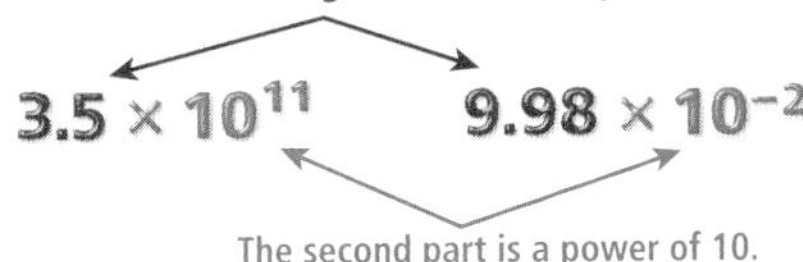
The first part is a number that is greater than or equal to 1 and less than 10.
3.5 × 10¹¹
9.98 × 10⁻²
The second part is a power of 10.

COMMON ERROR ALERT

When writing the powers of 10 in a chart or a list, students will often start at 10, rather than 1. Remind students that $10^0 = 1$.

Power Presentations with PowerPoint®

Additional Examples

Example 1

Find the value of each power of 10.

A. 10^{-6} 0.000001

B. 10^4 10,000

C. 10^9 1,000,000,000

Example 2

Write each number as a power of 10.

A. 1,000,000 10^6

B. 0.0001 10^{-4}

C. 1000 10^3

Example 3

Find the value of each expression.

A. 23.89×10^8 2,389,000,000

B. 467×10^{-3} 0.467

Also available on transparency

INTERVENTION

Questioning Strategies

EXAMPLE 1

- What does a positive exponent represent?
- What does a negative exponent represent?

EXAMPLE 2

- What pattern do you notice when you multiply repeatedly by 10?
- What pattern do you notice when you divide repeatedly by 10?

EXAMPLE 3

- Why does multiplying by a negative power of 10 result in a smaller number?

2 Teach

Guided Instruction

Show students the pattern of powers of 10. First show some with positive exponents:

$10^2 = 10 \times 10 = 100$

$10^3 = 10 \times 10 \times 10 = 1000$

Show how each is the number 1 followed by the same number of zeros as the exponent number. Then work backward for 10 to the first power, zero power, and negative powers. With negative exponents, the number of zeros is one less than the exponent number.

Universal Access

Through Cooperative Learning

Separate students into groups of three. The first student writes a number in standard form. The second student writes that number in scientific notation, and the third student checks/corrects the work. Have students switch roles so that everyone has done each job at least once. Then repeat, having the first student write a number in scientific notation, the second student write that number in standard form, and the third student check/correct the work.

Power Presentations with PowerPoint®

Additional Examples

Example 4

Saturn has a diameter of about 1.2×10^5 km. Its distance from the Sun is about 1,427,000,000 km.

A. Write Saturn's diameter in standard form. 120,000 km

B. Write Saturn's distance from the Sun in scientific notation. 1.427×10^9 km

Example 5

Order the list of numbers from least to greatest.

1.3×10^{-2}, 6.3×10^3, 4.1×10^6, 2.1×10^6, 1×10^{-2}, 5.4×10^{-3}

5.4×10^{-3}, 1×10^{-2}, 1.3×10^{-2}, 6.3×10^3, 2.1×10^6, 4.1×10^6

Also available on transparency

INTERVENTION
Questioning Strategies

EXAMPLE 4

- What does it mean to write a number in standard form?

EXAMPLE 5

- When ordering numbers in scientific notation, why is the power of 10 used to determine the initial order of the numbers?

Teaching Tip **Number Sense** Tell students to associate the direction the decimal point moves with the positive and negative directions on a number line: positive numbers to the right and negative numbers to the left.

EXAMPLE 4 *Astronomy Application*

Jupiter has a diameter of about 143,000 km. Its shortest distance from Earth is about 5.91×10^8 km, and its average distance from the Sun is about 778,400,000 km. Jupiter's orbital speed is approximately 1.3×10^4 m/s.

Reading Math

Standard form refers to the usual way that numbers are written—not in scientific notation.

A Write Jupiter's shortest distance from Earth in standard form.

5.91×10^8

5.9 1 0 0 0 0 0 0 — *Move the decimal point 8 places to the right.*

591,000,000 km

B Write Jupiter's average distance from the Sun in scientific notation.

778,400,000

7 7 8, 4 0 0, 0 0 0 — *Count the number of places you need to move the decimal point to get a number between 1 and 10.*

8 places

7.784×10^8 km — *Use that number as the exponent of 10.*

4a. Use the information above to write Jupiter's diameter in scientific notation. **1.43×10^5 km**

4b. Use the information above to write Jupiter's orbital speed in standard form. **13,000 m/s**

EXAMPLE 5 Comparing and Ordering Numbers in Scientific Notation

Order the list of numbers from least to greatest.

1.2×10^{-1}, 8.2×10^4, 6.2×10^5, 2.4×10^5, 1×10^{-1}, 9.9×10^{-4}

Step 1 List the numbers in order by powers of 10.

9.9×10^{-4}, 1.2×10^{-1}, 1×10^{-1}, 8.2×10^4, 6.2×10^5, 2.4×10^5

Step 2 Order the numbers that have the same power of 10.

9.9×10^{-4}, 1×10^{-1}, 1.2×10^{-1}, 8.2×10^4, 2.4×10^5, 6.2×10^5

5. Order the list of numbers from least to greatest.
5.2×10^{-3}, 3×10^{14}, 4×10^{-3}, 2×10^{-12}, 4.5×10^{30}, 4.5×10^{14}
2×10^{-12}, 4×10^{-3}, 5.2×10^{-3}, 3×10^{14}, 4.5×10^{14}, 4.5×10^{30}

THINK AND DISCUSS

1. Tell why 34.56×10^4 is not correctly written in scientific notation.

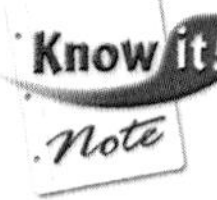

2. GET ORGANIZED Copy and complete the graphic organizer.

Powers of 10 and Scientific Notation
- A negative exponent corresponds to moving the decimal point ___?___.
- A positive exponent corresponds to moving the decimal point ___?___.

3 Close

Summarize

Review with students that to multiply by a positive power of 10, they should move the decimal point to the right, and to multiply by a negative power of 10, they should move the decimal point to the left.

If a number is in scientific notation, it is in the form $x \times 10^y$, with $1 \leq x < 10$ and with y being any integer.

FORMATIVE ASSESSMENT and INTERVENTION

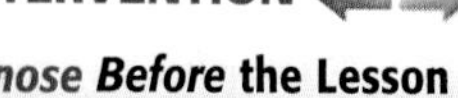

***Diagnose Before* the Lesson**
7-2 Warm Up, TE p. 400

***Monitor During* the Lesson**
Check It Out! Exercises, SE pp. 401–402
Questioning Strategies, TE pp. 401–402

***Assess After* the Lesson**
7-2 Lesson Quiz, TE p. 405
Alternative Assessment, TE p. 405

Answers to *Think and Discuss*

1. 34.56 is not between 1 and 10.
2. See p. A6.

7-2 Exercises

California Standards Practice 2.0

go.hrw.com
Homework Help Online
KEYWORD: MA8CA 7-2
Parent Resources Online
KEYWORD: MA8CA Parent

GUIDED PRACTICE

1. **Vocabulary** Explain how you can tell whether a number is written in *scientific notation.* A number written in sci. notation is a product with 2 parts: a decimal greater than or equal to 1 and less than 10 and a power of 10.

SEE EXAMPLE 1 p. 400

Find the value of each power of 10.

2. 10^6 1,000,000 3. 10^{-5} 0.00001 4. 10^{-4} 0.0001 5. 10^8 100,000,000

SEE EXAMPLE 2 p. 401

Write each number as a power of 10.

6. 10,000 10^4 7. 0.000001 10^{-6} 8. 100,000,000,000,000,000 10^{17}

SEE EXAMPLE 3 p. 401

Find the value of each expression.

9. 650.3×10^6 650,300,000 10. 48.3×10^{-4} 0.00483 11. 92×10^{-3} 0.092

SEE EXAMPLE 4 p. 402

12. **Astronomy** A light-year is the distance that light travels in a year and is equivalent to 9.461×10^{12} km. Write this distance in standard form. 9,461,000,000,000 km

SEE EXAMPLE 5 p. 402

13. Order the list of numbers from least to greatest.
$8.5 \times 10^{-1}, 3.6 \times 10^8, 5.85 \times 10^{-3}, 2.5 \times 10^{-1}, 8.5 \times 10^8$
$5.85 \times 10^{-3}, 2.5 \times 10^{-1}, 8.5 \times 10^{-1}, 3.6 \times 10^8, 8.5 \times 10^8$

PRACTICE AND PROBLEM SOLVING

Independent Practice

For Exercises	See Example
14–17	1
18–20	2
21–24	3
25–26	4
27	5

Extra Practice
Skills Practice p. EP14
Application Practice p. EP30

Find the value of each power of 10.

14. 10^3 1000 15. 10^{-9} 0.000000001 16. 10^{-12} 0.000000000001 17. 10^{14} 100,000,000,000,000

Write each number as a power of 10.

18. 0.01 10^{-2} 19. 1,000,000 10^6 20. 0.000000000000001 10^{-15}

Find the value of each expression.

21. 9.2×10^4 92,000 22. 1.25×10^{-7} 0.000000125 23. 42×10^{-5} 0.00042 24. 0.05×10^7 500,000

25. **Biology** The human body is made of about 1×10^{13} cells. Write this number in standard form. 10,000,000,000,000

26. **Statistics** At the beginning of the twenty-first century, the population of China was about 1,287,000,000. Write this number in scientific notation. 1.287×10^9

27. Order the list of numbers from least to greatest.
$2.13 \times 10^{-1}, 3.12 \times 10^2, 1.23 \times 10^{-3}, 2.13 \times 10^1, 1.32 \times 10^{-3}, 3.12 \times 10^{-3}$
$1.23 \times 10^{-3}, 1.32 \times 10^{-3}, 3.12 \times 10^{-3}, 2.13 \times 10^{-1}, 2.13 \times 10^1, 3.12 \times 10^2$

28. **Health** Donnell is allergic to pollen. The diameter of a grain of pollen is between 1.2×10^{-5} m and 9×10^{-5} m. Donnell's air conditioner has a filter that removes particles larger than 3×10^{-7} m. Will the filter remove pollen? Explain.

28. Yes; the smallest grain of pollen is larger than 3×10^{-7} m.

Grain of pollen, enlarged 1050 times

29. **Entertainment** In the United States, a CD is certified platinum if it sells 1,000,000 copies. A CD that has gone 2 times platinum has sold 2,000,000 copies. How many copies has a CD sold if it has gone 27 times platinum? Write your answer in scientific notation. 2.7×10^7

Write each number in scientific notation.

30. 40,080,000 4.008×10^7 31. 235,000 2.35×10^5 32. 170,000,000,000 1.7×10^{11}

33. 0.0000006 6×10^{-7} 34. 0.000077 7.7×10^{-5} 35. 0.0412 4.12×10^{-2}

7-2 Exercises

Assignment Guide

Assign *Guided Practice* exercises as necessary.

If you finished Examples **1–3**
Proficient 14–24, 53
Advanced 14–24, 53

If you finished Examples **1–5**
Proficient 14–66
Advanced 14–66

Homework Quick Check
Quickly check key concepts.
Exercises: 16, 18, 22, 26, 27, 36

Teaching Tip **Number Sense** In **Exercises 14–17,** have students estimate whether their answer is greater than or less than 10 before finding the value. This will help them if they forget the rules.

Teaching Tip **Technology** For **Exercises 21–24,** students can enter numbers in scientific notation into their calculators by using 2nd EE to indicate the power of 10. For example, to enter 9.2×10^4, press 9.2 2nd EE 4. To enter powers of 10, use ^ or 2nd 10^x LOG. To enter 10^{-5}, press 10 ^ −5 or 2nd 10^x LOG (−5).

California Standards

Standard	Exercises
2.0	2–26, 29–35, 44, 47, 49c–52, 54, 64–66
4.0	55–57
9.0	58–63

Exercise 49 involves writing numbers in scientific notation. This exercise prepares students for the Concept Connection on page 428.

Reading Math For **Exercise 44,** in 1.67×10^{-27}, 1.67 is called the *coefficient.*

Answers

36. no; 5×10^{-4}
37. yes
38. no; 1.2×10^{6}
39. no; 2.5×10^{2}
40. no; 1×10^{-1}
41. yes
42. no; 4.8×10^{4}
43. yes

49b. Possible answer: It would be easy to accidentally omit a 0 or add an extra 0 when writing the number in standard form. You are probably less likely to make an error when using scientific notation.

55.–57.

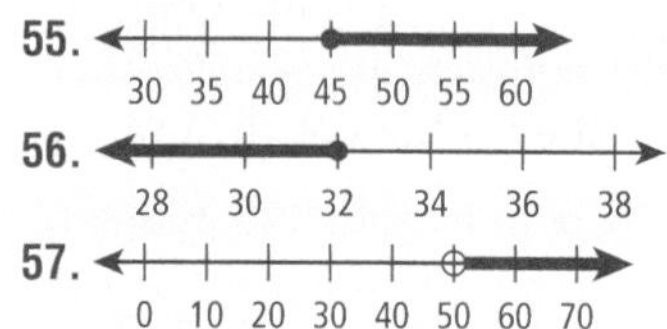

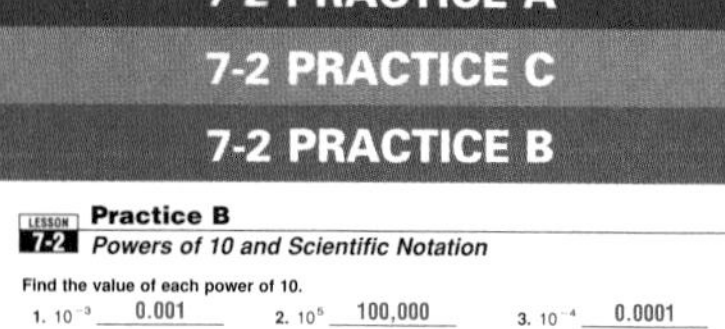

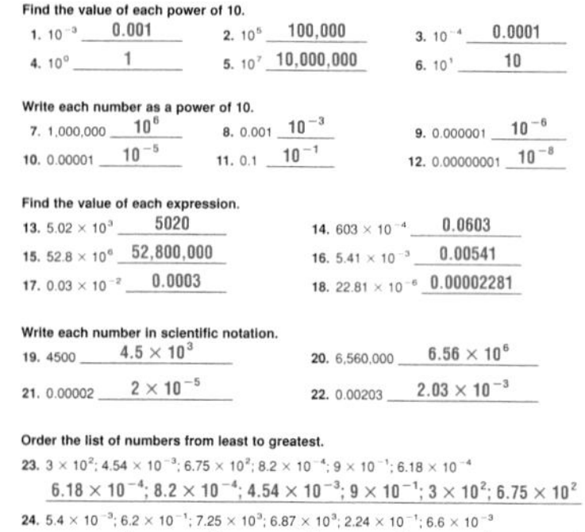

LESSON 7-2 Practice B
Powers of 10 and Scientific Notation

Find the value of each power of 10.

1. 10^{-3} 0.001
2. 10^{5} 100,000
3. 10^{-4} 0.0001
4. 10^{0} 1
5. 10^{7} 10,000,000
6. 10^{1} 10

Write each number as a power of 10.

7. 1,000,000 10^{6}
8. 0.001 10^{-3}
9. 0.000001 10^{-6}
10. 0.00001 10^{-5}
11. 0.1 10^{-1}
12. 0.00000001 10^{-8}

Find the value of each expression.

13. 5.02×10^{3} 5020
14. 603×10^{-4} 0.0603
15. 52.8×10^{6} 52,800,000
16. 5.41×10^{-3} 0.00541
17. 0.03×10^{-2} 0.0003
18. 22.81×10^{-6} 0.00002281

Write each number in scientific notation.

19. 4500 4.5×10^{3}
20. 6,560,000 6.56×10^{6}
21. 0.00002 2×10^{-5}
22. 0.00203 2.03×10^{-3}

Order the list of numbers from least to greatest.

23. 3×10^{2}; 4.54×10^{-3}; 6.75×10^{2}; 8.2×10^{-4}; 9×10^{-1}; 6.18×10^{-4}
6.18×10^{-4}; 8.2×10^{-4}; 4.54×10^{-3}; 9×10^{-1}; 3×10^{2}; 6.75×10^{2}
24. 5.4×10^{-3}; 6.2×10^{-1}; 7.25×10^{3}; 6.87×10^{3}; 2.24×10^{-1}; 6.6×10^{-3}
5.4×10^{-3}; 6.6×10^{-3}; 2.24×10^{-1}; 6.2×10^{-1}; 6.87×10^{3}; 7.25×10^{3}
25. In 1970, the number of televisions sold in the United States was about 1.2×10^{7}. Write this number in standard form. 12,000,000
26. In 1950, about 3,880,000 households in the United States had televisions. Write this number in scientific notation. 3.88×10^{6}
27. Find the volume of the cube shown at right. Write the answer in both standard form and in scientific notation.
64,000,000,000 mm^3;
6.4×10^{10} mm^3

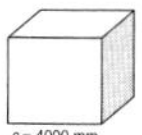

$s = 4000$ mm

State whether each number is written in scientific notation. If not, write it in scientific notation.

36. 50×10^{-5}
37. 8.1×10^{-2}
38. 1,200,000
39. 0.25×10^{3}
40. 0.1
41. 7×10^{8}
42. 48,000
43. 3.5×10^{-6}

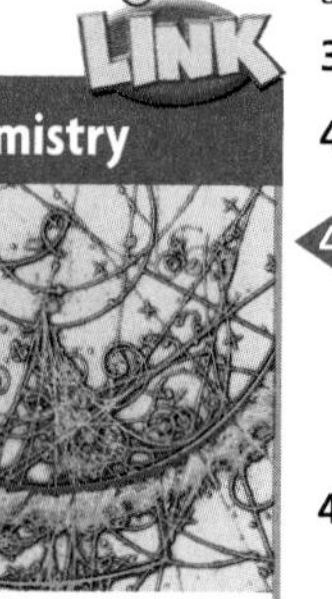

The image above is a colored bubble-chamber photograph. It shows the tracks left by subatomic particles in a particle accelerator.

44. **Chemistry** Atoms are made of three elementary particles: protons, electrons, and neutrons. The mass of a proton is about 1.67×10^{-27} kg. The mass of an electron is about 0.000000000000000000000000000000911 kg. The mass of a neutron is about 1.68×10^{-27} kg. Which particle has the least mass? **electron**

45. **Communication** This bar graph shows the increase of cellular telephone subscribers worldwide.
    a. Write the number of subscribers for the following years in standard form: 1999, 2000, and 2003.
    b. Zorah looks at the bar graph and says, "It looks like the number of cell phone subscribers nearly doubled from 2000 to 2003." Do you agree with Zorah? Use scientific notation to explain.

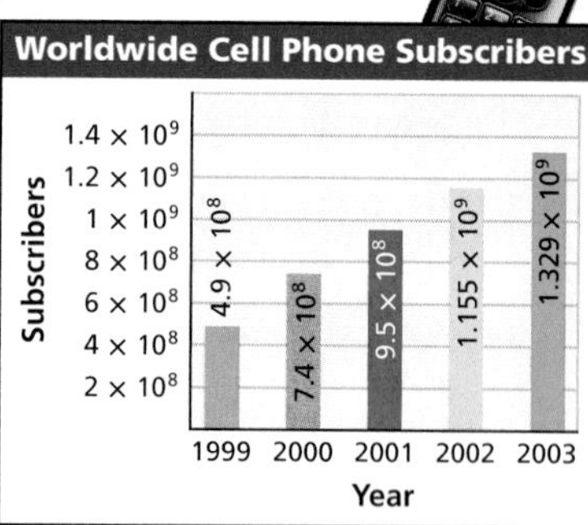

45a. 490,000,000; 740,000,000; 1,329,000,000

b. When you double 7.4×10^{8}, you get approx. 14×10^{8}, or 1.4×10^{9} in sci. notation. 1.4 is close to 1.3, so Zorah's observation is correct.

46. **Measurement** In the metric system, the basic unit for measuring length is the meter (m). Other units for measuring length are based on the meter and powers of 10, as shown in the table.

Selected Metric Lengths	
1 millimeter (mm) = 10^{-3} m	1 dekameter (dam) = 10^{1} m
1 centimeter (cm) = 10^{-2} m	1 hectometer (hm) = 10^{2} m
1 decimeter (dm) = 10^{-1} m	1 kilometer (km) = 10^{3} m

b. $10^{-3} = 0.001$; $10^{-2} = 0.01$; $10^{-1} = 0.1$; $10^{1} = 10$; $10^{2} = 100$; $10^{3} = 1000$

   a. Which lengths in the table are longer than a meter? Which are shorter than a meter? How do you know? **dam, hm, km; mm, cm, dm**
   b. Evaluate each power of 10 in the table to check your answers to part **a.**

47. **Critical Thinking** Recall that $\frac{1}{10^3} = 10^{-3}$. Based on this information, complete the following statement: Dividing a number by 10^{3} is equivalent to multiplying by ▒. **10^{-3}**

48. **Write About It** When you change a number from scientific notation to standard form, explain how you know which way to move the decimal point and how many places to move it. **If the exp. is pos., move the dec. pt. that many places to the right. If the exp. is neg., move the dec. pt. that many places to the left.**

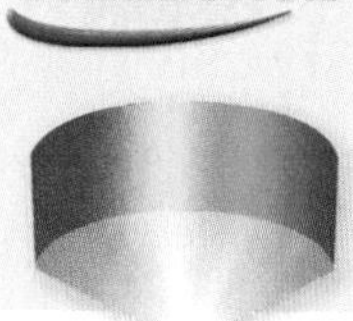

49. This problem will prepare you for the Concept Connection on page 428.
    a. The speed of light is approximately 3×10^{8} m/s. Write this number in standard form. **300,000,000**
    b. Why do you think it would be better to express this number in scientific notation rather than standard form?
    c. The wavelength of a shade of red light is 0.00000068 meters. Write this number in scientific notation. **6.8×10^{-7}**

7-2 READING STRATEGIES

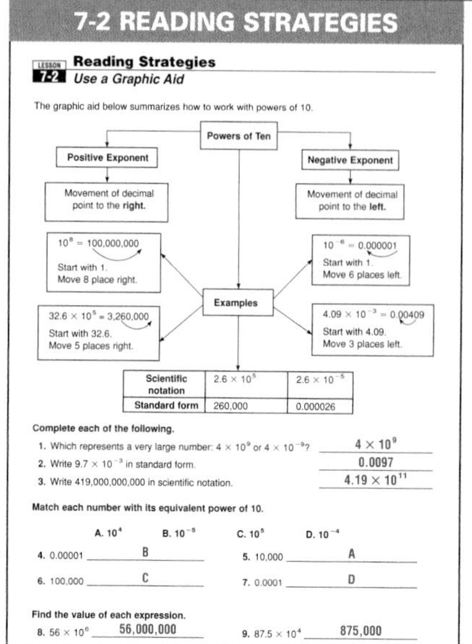

LESSON 7-2 Reading Strategies
Use a Graphic Aid

The graphic aid below summarizes how to work with powers of 10.

Scientific notation	2.6×10^{5}	2.6×10^{-5}
Standard form	260,000	0.000026

Complete each of the following.

1. Which represents a very large number: 4×10^{9} or 4×10^{-9}? 4×10^{9}
2. Write 9.7×10^{-3} in standard form. 0.0097
3. Write 419,000,000,000 in scientific notation. 4.19×10^{11}

Match each number with its equivalent power of 10.

A. 10^{4} B. 10^{-5} C. 10^{5} D. 10^{-4}

4. 0.00001 B
5. 10,000 A
6. 100,000 C
7. 0.0001 D

Find the value of each expression.

8. 56×10^{6} 56,000,000
9. 87.5×10^{4} 875,000

7-2 REVIEW FOR MASTERY

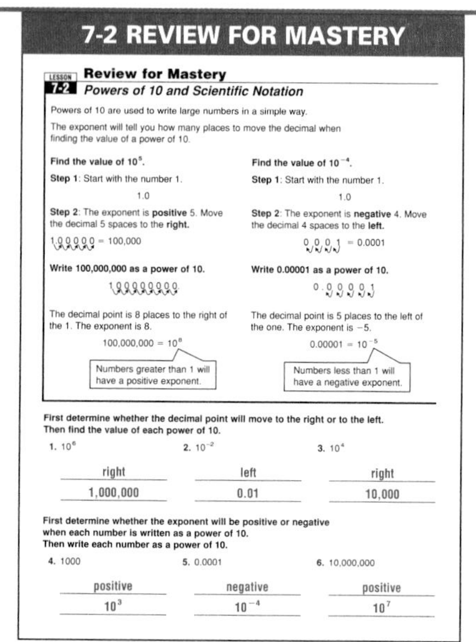

LESSON 7-2 Review for Mastery
Powers of 10 and Scientific Notation

Powers of 10 are used to write large numbers in a simple way.

The exponent will tell you how many places to move the decimal when finding the value of a power of 10.

Find the value of 10^{5}.

Step 1: Start with the number 1.

1.0

Step 2: The exponent is **positive** 5. Move the decimal 5 spaces to the **right.**

1.00000 = 100,000

Write 100,000,000 as a power of 10.

100000000

The decimal point is 8 places to the right of the 1. The exponent is 8.

100,000,000 = 10^{8}

Numbers greater than 1 will have a positive exponent.

Find the value of 10^{-4}.

Step 1: Start with the number 1.

1.0

Step 2: The exponent is **negative** 4. Move the decimal 4 spaces to the **left.**

0001 = 0.0001

Write 0.00001 as a power of 10.

0.00001

The decimal point is 5 places to the left of the one. The exponent is −5.

0.00001 = 10^{-5}

Numbers less than 1 will have a negative exponent.

First determine whether the decimal point will move to the right or to the left. Then find the value of each power of 10.

1. 10^{6} right; 1,000,000
2. 10^{-2} left; 0.01
3. 10^{4} right; 10,000

First determine whether the exponent will be positive or negative when each number is written as a power of 10. Then write each number as a power of 10.

4. 1000 positive; 10^{3}
5. 0.0001 negative; 10^{-4}
6. 10,000,000 positive; 10^{7}

Multiple Choice For Exercises 50–52, choose the best answer.

50. There are about 3.2×10^7 seconds in one year. What is this number in standard form?

(A) 0.000000032
(B) 0.00000032
(C) 32,000,000 (circled)
(D) 320,000,000

51. Which expression is the scientific notation for 82.35?

(A) 8.235×10^1 (circled)   (B) 823.5×10^{-1} (C) 8.235×10^{-1} (D) 0.8235×10^2

52. Which statement is correct for the list of numbers below?
2.35×10^{-8}, 0.000000029, 1.82×10^8, 1,290,000,000, 1.05×10^9

(A) The list is in increasing order.
(B) If 0.000000029 is removed, the list will be in increasing order.
(C) If 1,290,000,000 is removed, the list will be in increasing order. (circled)
(D) The list is in decreasing order.

CHALLENGE AND EXTEND

53. **Technology** The table shows estimates of computer storage. A CD-ROM holds 700 MB. A DVD-ROM holds 4.7 GB. Estimate how many times more storage a DVD has than a CD. Explain how you found your answer.

Computer Storage
1 kilobyte (KB) ≈ 1000 bytes
1 megabyte (MB) ≈ 1 million bytes
1 gigabyte (GB) ≈ 1 billion bytes

53. About 7 times; 4.7 GB, the storage of the DVD, is the same as 4700 MB, which is approx. 7 times 700 MB, the storage of the CD.

54. For parts **a–d,** use what you know about multiplying by powers of 10 and the Commutative and Associative Properties of Multiplication to find each product. Write each answer in scientific notation.

a. $(3 \times 10^2)(2 \times 10^3)$ **6×10^5**   b. $(5 \times 10^8)(1.5 \times 10^{-6})$ **7.5×10^2**
c. $(2.2 \times 10^{-8})(4 \times 10^{-3})$ **8.8×10^{-11}**   d. $(2.5 \times 10^{-12})(2 \times 10^6)$ **5×10^{-6}**
e. **Reasoning** Based on your answers to parts **a–d,** write a rule for multiplying numbers in scientific notation.
f. Does your rule work when you multiply $(6 \times 10^3)(8 \times 10^5)$? Explain.

54e. First multiply the numbers, and then multiply the powers of 10 by adding the exponents.

54f. Yes, but the answer, 48×10^8, is not in sci. notation. After multiplying, you will have to rewrite the answer in sci. notation as 4.8×10^9.

SPIRAL STANDARDS REVIEW

Solve each inequality and graph the solutions. *(Lesson 3-4)*

55. $3(m - 2) \geq 39 + 2m$ 56. $4(p + 12) \leq 80 + 3p$ 57. $n(2 \cdot 7) > 7(100)$

55. $m \geq 45$
56. $p \leq 32$
57. $n > 50$

Solve each system by elimination. Check your answer. *(Lesson 6-3)*

58. $\begin{cases} x + y = 8 \\ x - y = 2 \end{cases}$ **(5, 3)**   59. $\begin{cases} 2x + y = -3 \\ 2x + 3y = -1 \end{cases}$ **(−2, 1)**   60. $\begin{cases} x - 6y = -3 \\ 3x + 4y = 13 \end{cases}$ **(3, 1)**

61. $\begin{cases} 3x + y = -10 \\ 2x - y = -10 \end{cases}$ **(−4, 2)**   62. $\begin{cases} 4x - 3y = 17 \\ -4x + y = -11 \end{cases}$ **(2, −3)**   63. $\begin{cases} x + 5y = 12 \\ 3x + 2y = 23 \end{cases}$ **(7, 1)**

Evaluate each expression for the given value(s) of the variable(s). *(Lesson 7-1)*

64. t^{-4} for $t = 2$ **$\frac{1}{16}$**   65. $(-8m)^0$ for $m = -5$ **1**   66. $3a^{-3}b^0$ for $a = 5$ and $b = 6$ **$\frac{3}{125}$**

Multiple Choice If students chose **A** or **D** in **Exercise 50,** they may have associated the exponent of 10 with the number of zeros in the answer.

In **Exercise 52,** encourage students to write the second and fourth numbers in the list in scientific notation as a first step.

Technology In **Exercise 53,** tell students that metric prefixes are used to describe computer storage. However, bytes do not follow true metric conventions. For example, 1 kilobyte = 1024 bytes, not 1000 bytes.

Journal

Have students explain why 10^5 has 5 zeros, but 10^{-5} has only 4 zeros.

Have students write four numbers in scientific notation, two with positive exponents and two with negative exponents, and then arrange them in ascending order.

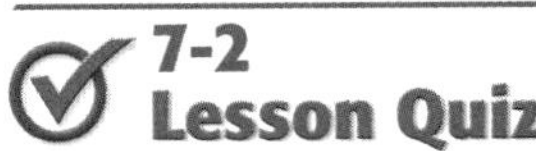

7-2 Lesson Quiz

Find the value of each expression.

1. 37.45×10^5 3,745,000
2. 29.3×10^{-4} 0.00293
3. The Pacific Ocean has an area of about 6.4×10^7 square miles. Its volume is about 170,000,000 cubic miles.
   a. Write the area of the Pacific Ocean in standard form. 64,000,000 mi²
   b. Write the volume of the Pacific Ocean in scientific notation. 1.7×10^8 mi³
4. Order the list of numbers from least to greatest.
3.6×10^{-3}, 1×10^{-5}, 2.7×10^2, 1.3×10^4, 3.1×10^4, 4.1×10^{-3}
1×10^{-5}, 3.6×10^{-3}, 4.1×10^{-3}, 2.7×10^2, 1.3×10^4, 3.1×10^4

Also available on transparency

7-2 PROBLEM SOLVING

LESSON 7-2 Problem Solving
Powers of 10 and Scientific Notation

Write the correct answer.

1. Insects can multiply rapidly during the summer. A pair of houseflies could potentially grow to a population of 1.91×10^{20}. If all the descendants of a female cabbage aphid lived, the population could increase to 1.56×10^{24}. Which population would be larger?
cabbage aphid

2. The graph shows the gross domestic product (GDP) for several countries around the world. Identify the country whose GDP is twice that of another country. Write the GDPs of both countries in standard form.

Gross Domestic Product in 2004
GDP (dollars): 0, 2×10^{11}, 4×10^{11}, 6×10^{11}, 8×10^{11}, 1×10^{12}, 1.2×10^{12}
Country: Afghanistan 2.15×10^{10}; Cambodia 2.7×10^{10}; Ethiopia 5.4×10^{10}; Mexico 1.01×10^{12}; Poland 4.6×10^{11}

Ethiopia: $54,000,000,000; Cambodia: $27,000,000,000

3. The 2005 population estimates of five countries are listed below.

Brazil	1.86×10^8
India	1.08×10^9
Kenya	3.38×10^7
Philippines	8.79×10^7
United Kingdom	6.04×10^7

List the countries in order of population size from least to greatest.
Kenya, UK, Philippines, Brazil, India

The table shows astronomical data about several planets. Use the table to answer questions 4–7. Select the best answer.

4. An AU is an astronomical unit. One AU equals 150,000,000 km. What is that measure in scientific notation?
(A) 1.50×10^8 km (circled)   C 1.50×10^{10} km
B 1.50×10^9 km   D 1.50×10^{11} km

5. Suppose the mass of Mars were written in standard form. How many digits would be to the *left* of the decimal?
F 23   H 25
(G) 24 (circled)   J 26

6. Which of these is the distance from the Sun to Mercury expressed in scientific notation?
A 0.38 AU   (C) 3.8×10^{-1} AU (circled)
B 3.8×10^1 AU   D 38×10^{-2} AU

7. What is the diameter of the Earth in scientific notation?
F 1.28×10^2 km   (H) 1.28×10^4 km (circled)
G 1.28×10^3 km   J 1.28×10^5 km

Astronomical Data for the First Five Planets			
Planet	Avg. Distance from Sun (AU)	Diameter (km)	Mass (kg)
Mercury	0.38	4,880	3.20×10^{23}
Venus	0.72	12,100	4.87×10^{24}
Earth	1	12,800	5.97×10^{24}
Mars	1.52	6,790	6.42×10^{23}
Jupiter	5.20	143,000	1.90×10^{27}

7-2 CHALLENGE

LESSON 7-2 Challenge
Using Scientific Notation to Make Comparisons

The average distance between Earth and the Sun is 93,000,000 miles. The average distance between Jupiter and the Sun is 484,000,000 miles. Using scientific notation, you can answer questions like the one below.

How many times farther from the Sun is Jupiter than Earth?

Answer the following questions.

1. a. Write the distance between Earth and the Sun in scientific notation. **9.3×10^7 miles**
   b. Write the distance between Jupiter and the Sun in scientific notation. **4.84×10^8 miles**
   c. How many times farther from the Sun is Jupiter than Earth? **about 5.2 times**
2. The average distance between Pluto and the Sun is 3,675,000,000 miles.
   a. How many times farther from the Sun is Pluto than Earth? **about 39.5 times**
   b. How many times farther from the Sun is Pluto than Jupiter? **about 7.6 times**
3. The star closest to the Sun is 25,000,000,000,000 miles from the Sun. How many times farther is it from the Sun to the nearest star as it is from Earth to the Sun? **about 269,000 times**

One light-year is the distance light travels in one year. Light travels 186,282 miles in 1 second.

4. How many miles does light travel in a year? Give your answer in scientific notation rounded to the nearest tenth. **5.9×10^{12}**
5. a. One galaxy is 200,000 light-years from the Sun. How many miles from the Sun is the galaxy? **about 1.17×10^{18}**
   b. How many times farther is this galaxy from the Sun than Earth is from the Sun? **about 1.3×10^{10} times**

You can use scientific notation to compare masses of large objects with masses of small objects.

Mass of hydrogen atom:	1.67×10^{-24} grams
Jerry's mass:	6.35×10^1 kilograms
Mass of Earth:	5.97×10^{24} kilograms

6. Write a ratio to compare Jerry's mass with that of a hydrogen atom. **about 3.8×10^{28} to 1.**
7. Write a ratio to compare the mass of Earth with that of a hydrogen atom. **about 3.6×10^{48} to 1.**

Organizer

Objective: Use inductive reasoning to discover multiplication properties of exponents.

Online Edition

Countdown to Mastery Week 15

Teach

Discuss

Remind students that a conjecture is an educated guess that is based on evidence but has not been proven true or false.

Discuss with students what patterns they notice in each activity. Help students represent the patterns in conjectures with words and with algebraic statements. For example, **Activity 3** can be thought of as "distributing" the exponent.

Algebra 1 24.1

Also covered:

2.0 Students understand and use such operations as taking the opposite, finding the reciprocal, taking a root, and raising to a fractional power. **They understand and use the rules of exponents.**

Inductive Reasoning and Properties of Exponents

Use with Lesson 7-3

You can use inductive reasoning to find some properties of exponents.

California Standards

24.1 Students explain the difference between inductive and deductive reasoning and identify and **provide examples** of each.
Also covered: **2.0**

Activity 1

1. Copy and complete the table below.

$3^2 \cdot 3^3 = (3 \cdot 3)(3 \cdot 3 \cdot 3) = 3^5$

$5^4 \cdot 5^2 = (5 \cdot 5 \cdot 5 \cdot 5)(5 \cdot 5) = 5^6$

$4^3 \cdot 4^3 = (4 \cdot 4 \cdot 4)(4 \cdot 4 \cdot 4) = 4^6$

$2^3 \cdot 2^2 = (2 \cdot 2 \cdot 2)(2 \cdot 2) = 2^5$

$6^3 \cdot 6^4 = (\quad)(\quad) =$ **$6 \cdot 6 \cdot 6$; $6 \cdot 6 \cdot 6 \cdot 6$; 6^7**

2. Examine your completed table. Look at the two exponents in each factor and the exponent in the final answer. What pattern do you notice?
The exp. in the final answer is the sum of the exponents of the orig. factors.

3. Use inductive reasoning to make a conjecture: $a^m \cdot a^n = a^{\blacksquare}$. **$m + n$**

Try This

Use your conjecture to write each product below as a single power.

1. $5^3 \cdot 5^5$ **5^8** **2.** $7^2 \cdot 7^2$ **7^4** **3.** $10^8 \cdot 10^4$ **10^{12}** **4.** $8^7 \cdot 8^3$ **8^{10}**

5. Make a table similar to the one above to explore what happens when you multiply more than two powers that have the same base. Then write a conjecture in words to summarize what you find.

Activity 2

1. Copy and complete the table below.

$(2^3)^2 = 2^3 \cdot 2^3 = (2 \cdot 2 \cdot 2)(2 \cdot 2 \cdot 2) = 2^6$

$(2^2)^3 = 2^2 \cdot 2^2 \cdot 2^2 = (2 \cdot 2)(2 \cdot 2)(2 \cdot 2) = 2^6$

$(4^2)^4 = 4^2 \cdot 4^2 \cdot 4^2 \cdot 4^2 = (4 \cdot 4)(4 \cdot 4)(4 \cdot 4)(4 \cdot 4) = 4^8$

$(3^4)^2 = 3^4 \cdot 3^4 = (3 \cdot 3 \cdot 3 \cdot 3)(3 \cdot 3 \cdot 3 \cdot 3) = 3^8$

$(6^3)^4 = 6^3 \cdot 6^3 \cdot 6^3 \cdot 6^3 = (6 \cdot 6 \cdot 6)(6 \cdot 6 \cdot 6)(6 \cdot 6 \cdot 6)(6 \cdot 6 \cdot 6) = 6^{12}$

2. Examine your completed table. Look at the two exponents in the original expression and the exponent in the final answer. What pattern do you notice?
The exp. in the final answer is the product of the exponents in the orig. problem.

3. Use inductive reasoning to make a conjecture: $(a^m)^n = a^{\blacksquare}$. **$mn$**

Answer to *Try This*

5. Possible answer:

$3^2 \cdot 3^3 \cdot 3^4 = (3 \cdot 3) \cdot (3 \cdot 3 \cdot 3) \cdot (3 \cdot 3 \cdot 3 \cdot 3) = 3^9$
$2^2 \cdot 2^2 \cdot 2^3 = (2 \cdot 2) \cdot (2 \cdot 2) \cdot (2 \cdot 2 \cdot 2) = 2^7$
$4^2 \cdot 4^5 \cdot 4^3 = (4 \cdot 4) \cdot (4 \cdot 4 \cdot 4 \cdot 4 \cdot 4) \cdot (4 \cdot 4 \cdot 4) = 4^{10}$
$6^2 \cdot 6^3 \cdot 6^3 \cdot 6^2 = (6 \cdot 6) \cdot (6 \cdot 6 \cdot 6) \cdot (6 \cdot 6 \cdot 6) \cdot (6 \cdot 6) = 6^{10}$

When multiplying powers with the same base, the answer is the base raised to the sum of all the exponents.

Try This

Use your conjecture to write each product below as a single power.

6. $(5^3)^2$ 5^6 7. $(7^2)^2$ 7^4 8. $(3^3)^4$ 3^{12} 9. $(9^7)^3$ 9^{21}

10. Make a table similar to the one in Activity 2 to explore what happens when you raise a power to two powers, for example, $[(4^2)^3]^3$. Then write a conjecture in words to summarize what you find.

Activity 3

❶ Copy and complete the table below.

$(ab)^3 = (ab)(ab)(ab) = (a \cdot a \cdot a)(b \cdot b \cdot b) = a^3 b^3$
$(mn)^4 = (mn)(mn)(mn)(mn) = (m \cdot m \cdot m \cdot m)(n \cdot n \cdot n \cdot n) = m^4 n^4$
$(xy)^2 = (xy)(xy) = (x \cdot x)(y \cdot y) = x^2 y^2$
$(cd)^5 = (cd)(cd)(cd)(cd)(cd) = (c \cdot c \cdot c \cdot c \cdot c)(d \cdot d \cdot d \cdot d \cdot d) = c^5 d^5$
$(pq)^6 = pq \cdot pq \cdot pq \cdot pq \cdot pq \cdot pq$; $(p \cdot p \cdot p \cdot p \cdot p \cdot p)$; $(q \cdot q \cdot q \cdot q \cdot q \cdot q)$; p^6q^6

❷ Examine your completed table. Look at the original expression and the final answer. What pattern do you notice?
To get the final answer, the exp. is "distributed" to each factor in the product.

❸ Use inductive reasoning to make a conjecture: $(ab)^n = a^{\square} b^{\square}$. n; n

Try This

Use your conjecture to write each power below as a product.

11. $(rs)^8$ r^8s^8 12. $(yz)^9$ y^9z^9 13. $(ab)^7$ a^7b^7 14. $(xz)^{12}$ $x^{12}z^{12}$

15. Look at the first row of your table. What property or properties allow you to write $(ab)(ab)(ab)$ as $(a \cdot a \cdot a)(b \cdot b \cdot b)$? Assoc. and Comm. Properties of Mult.

16. Make a table similar to the one above to explore what happens when you raise a product containing more than two factors to a power, for example, $(xyz)^7$. Then write a conjecture in words to summarize what you find. Possible answer:

$(abc)^3 = (abc)(abc)(abc) = (a \cdot a \cdot a)(b \cdot b \cdot b)(c \cdot c \cdot c) = a^3b^3c^3$
$(xyz)^2 = (xyz)(xyz) = (x \cdot x)(y \cdot y)(z \cdot z) = x^2y^2z^2$
$(mnpq)^4 = (mnpq)(mnpq)(mnpq)(mnpq) =$ $(m \cdot m \cdot m \cdot m)(n \cdot n \cdot n \cdot n)(p \cdot p \cdot p \cdot p)(q \cdot q \cdot q \cdot q) = m^4n^4p^4q^4$

When a product is raised to a power, the exp. is "distributed" to each factor in the product.

Close

Key Concepts

The product of two powers with the same base is the base raised to the sum of the exponents.

The power of a power is the base raised to the product of the exponents.

The power of a product is the product of each factor raised to that exponent.

Assess

Journal Have students use numbers to show an example of each property explored.

Extend

Have students write a convincing argument to show that their conjectures from each activity are true.

Answer to *Try This*

10. Possible answer:

$[(3^2)^3]^4 = (3^2)^3 \cdot (3^2)^3 \cdot (3^2)^3 \cdot (3^2)^3 = 3^6 \cdot 3^6 \cdot 3^6 \cdot 3^6 = 3^{24}$
$[(2^2)^2]^3 = (2^2)^2 \cdot (2^2)^2 \cdot (2^2)^2 = 2^4 \cdot 2^4 \cdot 2^4 = 2^{12}$
$[(4^2)^5]^3 = (4^2)^5 \cdot (4^2)^5 \cdot (4^2)^5 = 4^{10} \cdot 4^{10} \cdot 4^{10} = 4^{30}$

When a power is raised to 2 powers, the final answer is the base raised to the product of all the exponents.

7-3 Organizer

Objective: Use multiplication properties of exponents to evaluate and simplify expressions.

Online Edition
Tutorial Videos

Countdown to Mastery Week 15

Power Presentations with PowerPoint®

Warm Up

Write each expression using an exponent.

1. $2 \cdot 2 \cdot 2$ $\quad 2^3$

2. $x \cdot x \cdot x \cdot x$ $\quad x^4$

3. $\frac{1}{4 \cdot 4}$ $\quad 4^{-2}$ or $\frac{1}{4^2}$

Write each expression without using an exponent.

4. 4^3 $\quad 4 \cdot 4 \cdot 4$ $\qquad$ **5.** y^2 $\quad y \cdot y$

6. m^{-4} $\quad \frac{1}{m \cdot m \cdot m \cdot m}$

Also available on transparency

Q: What do you call x^{sun}?

A: Solar power.

Algebra 1 🔑 **2.0**

7-3 Multiplication Properties of Exponents

🔑 **2.0** Students understand and use such operations as taking the opposite, finding the reciprocal, taking a root, and raising to a fractional power. **They understand and use the rules of exponents.**

Who uses this?

Astronomers can multiply expressions with exponents to find the distance between objects in space. (See Example 2.)

You have seen that exponential expressions are useful when writing very small or very large numbers. To perform operations on these numbers, you can use properties of exponents. You can also use these properties to simplify your answer.

In this lesson, you will learn some properties that will help you simplify exponential expressions containing multiplication.

Simplifying Exponential Expressions

An exponential expression is completely simplified if...

- There are no negative exponents.
- The same base does not appear more than once in a product or quotient.
- No powers are raised to powers.
- No products are raised to powers.
- No quotients are raised to powers.
- Numerical coefficients in a quotient do not have any common factor other than 1.

Examples	Nonexamples
$\frac{b}{a}$ $\quad x^3$ $\quad z^{12}$ $\quad a^4b^4$ $\quad \frac{s^5}{t^5}$ $\quad \frac{5a^2}{2b}$	$a^{-2}ba$ $\quad x \cdot x^2$ $\quad (z^3)^4$ $\quad (ab)^4$ $\quad \left(\frac{s}{t}\right)^5$ $\quad \frac{10a^2}{4b}$

Products of powers with the same base can be found by writing each power as repeated multiplication.

$$a^m \cdot a^n = \underbrace{(a \cdot a \cdot \ldots \cdot a)}_{m \text{ factors}} \cdot \underbrace{(a \cdot a \cdot \ldots \cdot a)}_{n \text{ factors}}$$

$$= \underbrace{a \cdot a \cdot \ldots \cdot a}_{m+n \text{ factors}} = a^{m+n}$$

Know it! Note

Product of Powers Property

WORDS	NUMBERS	ALGEBRA
The product of two powers with the same base equals that base raised to the sum of the exponents.	$6^7 \cdot 6^4 = 6^{7+4} = 6^{11}$	If a is any nonzero real number and m and n are integers, then $a^m \cdot a^n = a^{m+n}$.

1 Introduce

EXPLORATION

7-3 Multiplication Properties of Exponents

1. The expression $(x \cdot x \cdot x) \cdot (x \cdot x)$ can be evaluated two ways. As a product of two powers, it can be written as $x^3 \cdot x^2$. As a single power, it can be written as x^5. Use this information to complete the table below.

Expression	Product of Powers	Single Power
$(x \cdot x \cdot x) \cdot (x \cdot x)$	$x^3 \cdot x^2$	x^5
$(y \cdot y \cdot y \cdot y) \cdot (y \cdot y)$		
$(a \cdot a \cdot a \cdot a \cdot a) \cdot (a \cdot a \cdot a \cdot a)$		
$m \cdot (m \cdot m \cdot m \cdot m \cdot m)$		

2. Describe any patterns you see in the table above.
3. Use a similar method to complete the table below.

Expression	Product of Powers	Single Power
$(y \cdot y \cdot y) \cdot (y \cdot y) \cdot (y \cdot y)$	$y^3 \cdot y^2 \cdot y^2$	y^7
$(b \cdot b \cdot b) \cdot (b \cdot b) \cdot (b \cdot b \cdot b \cdot b)$		
$(z \cdot z) \cdot (z \cdot z \cdot z) \cdot (z \cdot z \cdot z \cdot z \cdot z)$		
$x \cdot (x \cdot x) \cdot (x \cdot x \cdot x) \cdot (x \cdot x)$		

THINK AND DISCUSS

4. **Describe** any patterns you see in the second table.
5. **Explain** how you can use your findings to write $x^{10} \cdot x^4$ as a single power.

Motivate

Draw a square on the board. Label one side x^3. Ask students for an expression for the area of the square. $x^3 \cdot x^3$

Show students that this can also be written as $(x^3)^2$, and tell them that the properties in this lesson will show them how to simplify expressions with exponents, such as this one.

Explorations and answers are provided in *Alternate Openers: Explorations Transparencies.*

EXAMPLE 1 **Finding Products of Powers**

Simplify.

A $2^5 \cdot 2^6$

$2^5 \cdot 2^6$

2^{5+6} — *Since the powers have the same base, keep the base and add the exponents.*

2^{11}

B $4^2 \cdot 3^{-2} \cdot 4^5 \cdot 3^6$

$4^2 \cdot 3^{-2} \cdot 4^5 \cdot 3^6$ — *Group powers with the same base together.*

$(4^2 \cdot 4^5) \cdot (3^{-2} \cdot 3^6)$

$4^{2+5} \cdot 3^{-2+6}$ — *Add the exponents of powers with the same base.*

$4^7 \cdot 3^4$

C $a^4 \cdot b^5 \cdot a^2$

$a^4 \cdot b^5 \cdot a^2$

$(a^4 \cdot a^2) \cdot b^5$ — *Group powers with the same base together.*

$a^6 \cdot b^5$ — *Add the exponents of powers with the same base.*

a^6b^5

D $y^2 \cdot y \cdot y^{-4}$

$(y^2 \cdot y^1) \cdot y^{-4}$ — *Group the first two powers.*

$y^3 \cdot y^{-4}$ — *The first two powers have the same base, so add the exponents.*

y^{-1} — *The two remaining powers have the same base, so add the exponents.*

$\frac{1}{y}$ — *Write with a positive exponent.*

Remember!

A number or variable written without an exponent actually has an exponent of 1.

$10 = 10^1$

$y = y^1$

Simplify.

1a. $7^8 \cdot 7^4$ 7^{12}

1b. $3^{-3} \cdot 5^8 \cdot 3^4 \cdot 5^2$ 3×5^{10}

1c. $m \cdot n^{-4} \cdot m^4$ $\frac{m^5}{n^4}$

1d. $x \cdot x^{-1} \cdot x^{-3} \cdot x^{-4}$ $\frac{1}{x^7}$

EXAMPLE 2 ***Astronomy Application***

Light from the Sun travels at about 1.86×10^5 miles per second. It takes about 500 seconds for the light to reach Earth. Find the approximate distance from the Sun to Earth. Write your answer in scientific notation.

distance = rate × time

$= (1.86 \times 10^5) \times 500$

$= (1.86 \times 10^5) \times (5 \times 10^2)$ — *Write 500 in scientific notation.*

$= (1.86 \times 5) \times (10^5 \times 10^2)$ — *Use the Commutative and Associative Properties to group.*

$= 9.3 \times 10^7$ — *Multiply within each group.*

The Sun is about 9.3×10^7 miles from Earth.

2. Light travels at about 1.86×10^5 miles per second. Find the approximate distance that light travels in one hour. Write your answer in scientific notation. 6.696×10^8 mi

Power Presentations with PowerPoint®

Additional Examples

Example 1

Simplify.

A. $3^2 \cdot 3^5$ 3^7

B. $2^4 \cdot 3^4 \cdot 2^{-2} \cdot 3^2$ $2^2 \cdot 3^6$

C. $q^3 \cdot r^2 \cdot q^6$ q^9r^2

D. $n^3 \cdot n^{-4} \cdot n$ 1

Example 2

Light from the Sun travels at about 1.86×10^5 miles per second. It takes about 15,000 seconds for the light to reach Neptune. Find the approximate distance from the Sun to Neptune. Write your answer in scientific notation.

2.79×10^9 mi

Also available on transparency

INTERVENTION

Questioning Strategies

EXAMPLE 1

- How do you know when an expression containing exponents is completely simplified?
- How do you know which powers to group together?

EXAMPLE 2

- What is the formula for distance?
- Why should you write the time in scientific notation?
- If you left the time in standard notation, how would that affect your calculations?

2 Teach

Guided Instruction

Introduce the Product of Powers Property by writing each power in the product in factored form and having students discover the relationship among the exponents. Have students discover the other properties in a similar fashion. In **Example 1,** encourage students to add the exponents of powers with the same base before rewriting negative exponents as positive exponents.

Universal Access

Through Graphic Organizers

Have students create a graphic organizer to show evidence that each property works.

Product of Powers	$3^2 \cdot 3^3$ $9 \cdot 27$ 243	3^5 243
Power of a Power	$(2^3)^4$ 8^4 4096	2^{12} 4096
Power of a Product	$(2 \cdot 4)^3$ 8^3 512	$2^3 \cdot 4^3$ $8 \cdot 64$ 512

Power Presentations with PowerPoint®

Additional Examples

Example 3

Simplify.

A. $(5^2)^4$ 5^8

B. $(4^3)^0$ 1

C. $(x^3)^{-5} \cdot x^4$ $\frac{1}{x^{11}}$

Also available on transparency

INTERVENTION

Questioning Strategies

EXAMPLE 3

- What operation is performed on the exponents when a power is raised to another power?

Teaching Tip **Reading Math** Tell students that the exponent is usually read as an ordinal followed by the word *power*. For example, 7^4 is read "seven to the fourth power." Point out that 2 and 3 are exceptions to this rule. For those exponents, it is customary to say "squared" or "cubed," respectively. If students have trouble with ordinals, suggest that they make a chart with the numbers in the first column and their ordinals in the second column. ENGLISH LANGUAGE LEARNERS

To find a power of a power, you can use the meaning of exponents.

$$(a^m)^n = \underbrace{a^m \cdot a^m \cdot \ldots \cdot a^m}_{n \text{ factors}} = \underbrace{\underbrace{a \cdot a \cdot \ldots \cdot a}_{m \text{ factors}} \cdot \underbrace{a \cdot a \cdot \ldots \cdot a}_{m \text{ factors}} \cdot \ldots \cdot \underbrace{a \cdot a \cdot \ldots \cdot a}_{m \text{ factors}}}_{n \text{ groups of } m \text{ factors}} = a^{mn}$$

Power of a Power Property

WORDS	NUMBERS	ALGEBRA
A power raised to another power equals that base raised to the product of the exponents.	$(6^7)^4 = 6^{7 \cdot 4} = 6^{28}$	If a is any nonzero real number and m and n are integers, then $(a^m)^n = a^{mn}$.

EXAMPLE 3 Finding Powers of Powers

Simplify.

A $(7^4)^3$

$7^{4 \cdot 3}$ *Use the Power of a Power Property.*

7^{12} *Simplify.*

B $(3^6)^0$

$3^{6 \cdot 0}$ *Use the Power of a Power Property.*

3^0 *Zero multiplied by any number is zero.*

1 *Any number raised to the zero power is 1.*

C $(x^2)^{-4} \cdot x^5$

$x^{2 \cdot (-4)}\, x^5$ *Use the Power of a Power Property.*

$x^{-8} \cdot x^5$ *Simplify the exponent of the first term.*

x^{-8+5} *Since the powers have the same base, add the exponents.*

x^{-3}

$\frac{1}{x^3}$ *Write with a positive exponent.*

CHECK IT OUT! Simplify.

3a. $(3^4)^5$ 3^{20} **3b.** $(6^0)^3$ 1 **3c.** $(a^3)^4 \cdot (a^{-2})^{-3}$ a^{18}

Student to Student

Multiplication Properties of Exponents

Briana Tyler
Memorial High School

Sometimes I can't remember when to add exponents and when to multiply them. When this happens, I write everything in expanded form.

For example, I would write $x^2 \cdot x^3$ as $(x \cdot x)(x \cdot x \cdot x) = x^5$. Then $x^2 \cdot x^3 = x^{2+3} = x^5$.

I would write $(x^2)^3$ as $x^2 \cdot x^2 \cdot x^2$, which is $(x \cdot x)(x \cdot x)(x \cdot x) = x^6$.

Then $(x^2)^3 = x^{2 \cdot 3} = x^6$.

This way I get the right answer even if I forget the properties.

Powers of products can be found by using the meaning of an exponent.

$$(ab)^n = \underbrace{ab \cdot ab \cdot \ldots \cdot ab}_{n \text{ factors}} = \underbrace{a \cdot a \cdot \ldots \cdot a}_{n \text{ factors}} \cdot \underbrace{b \cdot b \cdot \ldots \cdot b}_{n \text{ factors}} = a^n b^n$$

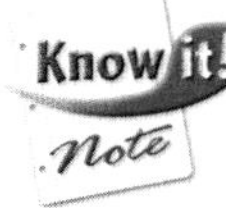

Power of a Product Property

WORDS	NUMBERS	ALGEBRA
A product raised to a power equals the product of each factor raised to that power.	$(2 \cdot 4)^3 = 2^3 \cdot 4^3$	If a and b are any nonzero real numbers and n is any integer, then $(ab)^n = a^n b^n$.

EXAMPLE 4 **Finding Powers of Products**

Simplify.

A $(-3x)^2$

$(-3)^2 \cdot x^2$ — *Use the Power of a Product Property.*

$9x^2$ — *Simplify.*

B $-(3x)^2$

$-(3^2 \cdot x^2)$ — *Use the Power of a Product Property.*

$-(9 \cdot x^2)$ — *Simplify.*

$-9x^2$

C $(x^{-2} \cdot y^0)^3$

$(x^{-2})^3 \cdot (y^0)^3$ — *Use the Power of a Product Property.*

$x^{-2 \cdot 3} \cdot y^{0 \cdot 3}$ — *Use the Power of a Power Property.*

$x^{-6} \cdot y^0$ — *Simplify.*

$x^{-6} \cdot 1$ — *Write y^0 as 1.*

$\frac{1}{x^6}$ — *Write with a positive exponent.*

Caution!

In Example 4B, the negative sign is not part of the base.

$-(3x)^2 = -1 \cdot (3x)^2$

CHECK IT OUT! Simplify.

4a. $(4p)^3$ $64p^3$ **4b.** $(-5t^2)^2$ $25t^4$ **4c.** $(x^2y^3)^4 \cdot (x^2y^4)^{-4}$ $\frac{1}{y^4}$

THINK AND DISCUSS

1. Explain why $(a^2)^3$ and $a^2 \cdot a^3$ are not equivalent expressions.
2. **GET ORGANIZED** Copy and complete the graphic organizer. In each box, give an example for the given property.

Know it! Note

Multiplication Properties of Exponents		
Product of Powers Property	Power of a Power Property	Power of a Product Property

COMMON ERROR ALERT

Students sometimes add exponents when a power is raised to another power. Encourage students to write out the expression in expanded form to help them remember.

Teaching Tip **Communicating Math** Have students write the Product of Powers, Power of a Power, and Power of a Product Properties in their own words. Then have volunteers read their definitions aloud.

Power Presentations with PowerPoint®

Additional Examples

Example 4

Simplify.

A. $-(2y)^2$ $-4y^2$

B. $(-2y)^3$ $-8y^3$

C. $(x^6 \cdot y^{-3})^2$ $\frac{x^{12}}{y^6}$

Also available on transparency

INTERVENTION

Questioning Strategies

EXAMPLE 4

- How does the Power of a Product Property compare with the Distributive Property?
- If a negative number is raised to an even-numbered power, is it positive or negative? Why?

3 Close

Summarize

Have students identify the property they can use to simplify each expression. Then have them simplify the expression.

$(3^2)^3$	Power of a Power; 3^6
$x^2 \cdot x^4$	Product of Powers; x^6
$(4b \cdot c^{-2})^2$	Power of a Product; $\frac{16b^2}{c^4}$

FORMATIVE ASSESSMENT and INTERVENTION

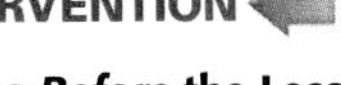

***Diagnose Before* the Lesson**
7-3 Warm Up, TE p. 408

***Monitor During* the Lesson**
Check It Out! Exercises, SE pp. 409–411
Questioning Strategies, TE pp. 409–411

***Assess After* the Lesson**
7-3 Lesson Quiz, TE p. 414
Alternative Assessment, TE p. 414

Answers to *Think and Discuss*

1. $(a^2)^3 = a^{2 \cdot 3} = a^6$, while $a^2 \cdot a^3 = a^{2+3} = a^5$.
2. See p. A6.

7-3 Exercises

Assignment Guide

Assign *Guided Practice* exercises as necessary.

If you finished Examples **1–2**
Proficient 18–22, 53, 68, 84
Advanced 18–22, 53, 68, 84

If you finished Examples **1–4**
Proficient 18–43, 44–52 even, 53, 54, 56–64 even, 66–83, 84–96 even, 98–105
Advanced 18–42 even, 44–54, 56–105

Homework Quick Check
Quickly check key concepts.
Exercises: 18, 22, 28, 32, 40, 42, 46

Inclusion Students may not see the difference between Exercises **15** and **16** and Exercises **32** and **33**. Help students understand why the answers for **15** and **16** are the same while the answers for **32** and **33** are different.

California Standards

Standard	Exercises
2.0 🔑	1–54, 56–64, 66, 69–75b, 76–97, 102–105
3.0	100, 101
4.0 🔑	98, 99
25.2	55

7-3 Exercises

California Standards Practice
🔑 2.0, 25.2

go.hrw.com
Homework Help Online
KEYWORD: MA8CA 7-3
Parent Resources Online
KEYWORD: MA8CA Parent

GUIDED PRACTICE

SEE EXAMPLE 1 p. 409

Simplify.

1. $2^2 \cdot 2^3$ 2^5 2. $5^3 \cdot 5^3$ 5^6 3. $n^6 \cdot n^2$ n^8 4. $x^2 \cdot x^{-3} \cdot x^4$ x^3

SEE EXAMPLE 2 p. 409

5. **Physical Science** If you traveled in space at a speed of 1000 miles per hour, how far would you travel in 7.5×10^5 hours? Write your answer in scientific notation. 7.5×10^8 mi

SEE EXAMPLE 3 p. 410

Simplify.

6. $(x^2)^5$ x^{10} 7. $(y^4)^8$ y^{32} 8. $(p^3)^3$ p^9
9. $(3^{-2})^2$ $\frac{1}{3^4}$, or $\frac{1}{81}$ 10. $(a^{-3})^4 \cdot (a^7)^2$ a^2 11. $xy \cdot (x^2)^3 \cdot (y^3)^4$ x^7y^{13}

SEE EXAMPLE 4 p. 411

12. $(2t)^5$ $32t^5$ 13. $(6k)^2$ $36k^2$ 14. $(r^2s)^7$ $r^{14}s^7$
15. $(-2x^5)^3$ $-8x^{15}$ 16. $-(2x^5)^3$ $-8x^{15}$ 17. $(a^2b^2)^5 \cdot (a^{-5})^2$ b^{10}

PRACTICE AND PROBLEM SOLVING

Independent Practice

For Exercises	See Example
18–21	1
22	2
23–28	3
29–34	4

Extra Practice
Skills Practice p. EP14
Application Practice p. EP30

Simplify.

18. $3^3 \cdot 2^3 \cdot 3$ $2^3 \cdot 3^4$ 19. $6 \cdot 6^2 \cdot 6^3 \cdot 6^2$ 6^8 20. $a^5 \cdot a^0 \cdot a^{-5}$ 1 21. $x^7 \cdot x^{-6} \cdot y^{-3}$ $\frac{x}{y^3}$

22. **Geography** Rhode Island is the smallest state in the United States. Its land area is about 2.9×10^{10} square feet. Alaska, the largest state, is about 5.5×10^2 times as large as Rhode Island. What is the land area of Alaska in square feet? Write your answer in scientific notation. 1.595×10^{13} ft^2

Simplify.

23. $(2^3)^3$ 2^9, or 512 24. $(3^6)^0$ 1 25. $(x^2)^{-1}$ $\frac{1}{x^2}$
26. $(b^4)^6 \cdot b$ b^{25} 27. $b \cdot (a^3)^4 \cdot (b^{-2})^3$ $\frac{a^{12}}{b^5}$ 28. $(x^4)^2 \cdot (x^{-1})^{-4}$ x^{12}
29. $(3x)^3$ $27x^3$ 30. $(5w^8)^2$ $25w^{16}$ 31. $(p^4q^2)^7$ $p^{28}q^{14}$
32. $(-4x^3)^4$ $256x^{12}$ 33. $-(4x^3)^4$ $-256x^{12}$ 34. $(x^3y^4)^3 \cdot (xy^3)^{-2}$ x^7y^6

Find the missing exponent in each expression.

35. $a^{\square}a^4 = a^{10}$ 6 36. $(a^{\square})^4 = a^{12}$ 3 37. $(a^2b^{\square})^4 = a^8b^{12}$ 3
38. $(a^3b^6)^{\square} = \frac{1}{a^9b^{18}}$ −3 39. $(b^2)^{-4} = \frac{1}{b^{\square}}$ 8 40. $a^{\square} \cdot a^6 = a^6$ 0

Geometry Write an expression for the area of each figure.

41. $2x^3$

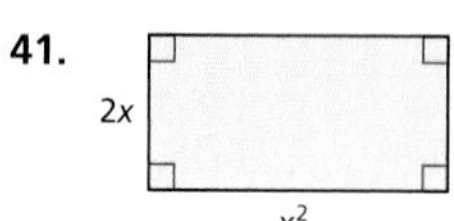

42. a^2b^4

43. $2m^{10}n^6$

(mn)²
(2m⁴n²)²

Simplify, if possible.

44. x^6y^5 x^6y^5 45. $(2x^2)^2 \cdot (3x^3)^3$ $108x^{13}$ 46. $x^2 \cdot y^{-3} \cdot x^{-2} \cdot y^{-3}$ $\frac{1}{y^6}$
47. $(5x^2)(5x^2)^2$ $125x^6$ 48. $-(x^2)^4(-x^2)^4$ $-x^{16}$ 49. $a^3 \cdot a^0 \cdot 3a^3$ $3a^6$
50. $(ab)^3(ab)^{-2}$ ab 51. $10^2 \cdot 10^{-4} \cdot 10^5$ 10^3, or 1000 52. $(x^2y^2)^2(x^2y)^{-2}$ y^2

7-3 READING STRATEGIES

LESSON 7-3 **Reading Strategies**
Use a Table

The table below summarizes the multiplication properties that are needed to simplify expressions with powers.

Product of a Power	To multiply powers with the same base, keep the base and **add the exponents.**	$4^3 \cdot 4^5 = 4^{3+5} = 4^8$ $3^8 \cdot 5^6 \cdot 3^{-6} = 3^{8+(-6)} \cdot 5^6 = 3^2 \cdot 5^6$ $x^{-5} \cdot x^4 \cdot y^7 = x^{-5+4} \cdot y^7 = x^{-1}y^7 = \frac{y^7}{x}$	In general, $a^m \cdot a^n = a^{m+n}$
Power of a Power	To find the power of a power, keep the base and **multiply the exponents.**	$(4^3)^5 = 4^{3 \cdot 5} = 4^{15}$ $(8^9)^0 = 8^{9 \cdot 0} = 8^0 = 1$ $(x^2)^{-6} = x^{2 \cdot -6} = x^{-12} = \frac{1}{x^{12}}$	In general, $(a^m)^n = a^{m \cdot n}$
Power of a Product	To find the power of a product, **apply the exponent** to each factor.	$(5 \cdot 3)^2 = 5^2 \cdot 3^2 = 25 \cdot 9 = 225$ $(-4b)^3 = (-4)^3 \cdot b^3 = -64b^3$ $(x^0 \cdot y^{-1})^5 = (x^0)^5 \cdot (y^{-1})^5 = x^0 \cdot y^{-5} = \frac{1}{y^5}$	In general, $(ab)^n = a^nb^n$

Complete each of the following.

1. What do you do with the exponents to simplify $(c^4)^{-2}$? multiply
2. What do you do with the exponents to simplify $6^4 \cdot 6^8$? add
3. What is the name of the property that can be used to simplify $(6t)^{-9}$? Power of a Product
4. $3(x + 4) = 3x + 12$ shows how the Distributive Property of Multiplication is used to simplify an expression. Which property of exponents is similar to the Distributive Property? Why? Power of a Product; with both properties, a number is applied to all parts.

Simplify each expression.

5. $(m^3)^8$ m^{24} 6. $8^4 \cdot 8^4$ 8^8 7. $(3v^5)^2$ $9v^{10}$
8. $c^{-2} \cdot d^8 \cdot c^{-3}$ $\frac{d^8}{c^5}$ 9. $(2 \cdot 9)^3$ 5832 10. $-(4y^7)^2$ $-16y^{14}$

7-3 REVIEW FOR MASTERY

LESSON 7-3 **Review for Mastery**
Multiplication Properties of Exponents

You can multiply a power by a power by expanding each factor.

Simplify $(4^3)(4^5)$.

$(4^3)(4^5)$
$(4 \cdot 4 \cdot 4)(4 \cdot 4 \cdot 4 \cdot 4 \cdot 4)$ *Expand each factor.*
4^8 *Count the number of factors. The number of factors is the exponent.*

Or you can use the **Product of Powers Property**:

$a^m \cdot a^n = a^{m+n}$ ($a \neq 0$, m and n are integers.)

Simplify $(4^3)(4^5)$.
$(4^3)(4^5)$
4^{3+5}
4^8

Simplify $a^4 \cdot b^5 \cdot a^{-2}$.
$a^{4+(-2)} \cdot b^5$
$a^2 \cdot b^5$
a^2b^5

You can use the **Power of a Power Property** to find a power raised to another power.

$(a^m)^n = a^{mn}$ ($a \neq 0$, m and n are integers.)

Simplify $(2^3)^2$.
$(2^3)^2$
$2^{3 \cdot 2}$
2^6

Simplify $(x^5)^4 \cdot y$.
$x^{5 \cdot 4} \cdot y$
$x^{20}y$

Simplify.

1. $2^3 \cdot 2^4$ 2^7 2. $8^{-2} \cdot 5^3 \cdot 8^6$ $8^4 \cdot 5^3$ 3. $2^4 \cdot 3^5 \cdot 2^8 \cdot 3^{-2}$ $2^{12} \cdot 3^3$
4. $m^8 \cdot n^4 \cdot m^7$ $m^{15}n^4$ 5. $(6^4)^2$ 6^8 6. $(4^{-3})^2$ $\frac{1}{4^6}$
7. $(5^{-3})^3 \cdot 4^0$ $\frac{1}{5^9}$ 8. $(x^2)^{-4} \cdot y^{-3}$ $\frac{1}{x^8y^3}$ 9. $(u^5)^{-2} \cdot (v^3)^4$ $\frac{v^{12}}{u^{10}}$

53. Earth: 9.3×10^7 mi; Mars: 1.4136×10^8 mi; Jupiter: 4.836×10^8 mi; Saturn: 8.928×10^8 mi

53. **Astronomy** The graph shows the approximate time it takes light from the Sun, which travels at a speed of 1.86×10^5 miles per second, to reach several planets. Find the approximate distance from the Sun to each planet in the graph. Write your answers in scientific notation. (*Hint:* Remember $d = rt$.)

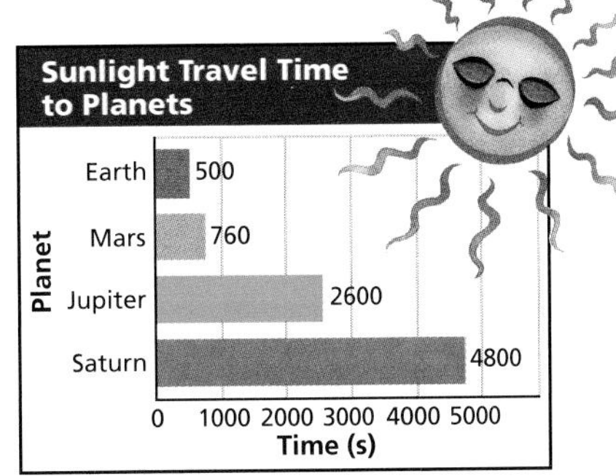

54. **Geometry** The volume of a rectangular prism can be found by using the formula $V = \ell wh$ where ℓ, w, and h represent the length, width, and height of the prism. Find the volume of a rectangular prism whose dimensions are $3a^2$, $4a^5$, and $4a^2b^2$. **$48a^9b^2$**

55. **/// ERROR ANALYSIS ///** Explain the error in each simplification below. What is the correct answer in each case?

a. $x^2 \cdot x^4 = x^8$ b. $(x^4)^5 = x^9$ c. $(x^2)^3 = x^{2^3} = x^8$

Simplify.

56. $(-3x^2)(5x^{-3})$ **$-\frac{15}{x}$** 57. $(a^4b)(a^3b^{-6})$ **$\frac{a^7}{b^5}$** 58. $(6w^5)(2v^2)(w^6)$ **$12v^2w^{11}$**

59. $15m^{12}n^9$

59. $(3m^7)(m^2n)(5m^3n^8)$ 60. $(b^2)^{-2}(b^4)^5$ **b^{16}** 61. $(3st)^2t^5$ **$9s^2t^7$**

62. $(2^2)^2(x^5y)^3$ **$16x^{15}y^3$** 63. $(-t)(-t)^2(-t^4)$ **t^7** 64. $(2m^2)(4m^4)(8n)^2$ **$512m^6n^2$**

65. **Estimation** Estimate the value of each expression. Explain how you estimated.

a. $[(-3.031)^2]^3$ b. $(6.2085 \times 10^2) \times (3.819 \times 10^{-5})$

66. **Physical Science** The speed of sound at sea level is about 344 meters per second. The speed of light is about 8.7×10^5 times faster than the speed of sound. What is the speed of light in meters per second? Write your answer in scientific notation and in standard form. **2.9928×10^8 m/s; 299,280,000 m/s**

67. Yes; because of the Comm. Prop. of Mult., they are both equal to x^6.

67. **Write About It** Is $(x^2)^3$ equal to $(x^3)^2$? Explain.

68. **Biology** A newborn baby has about 26,000,000,000 cells. An adult has about 1.9×10^3 times as many cells as a baby. About how many cells does an adult have? Write your answer in scientific notation. **4.94×10^{13}**

Simplify.

69. $(-4k)^2 + k^2$ **$17k^2$** 70. $-3z^3 + (-3z)^3$ **$-30z^3$** 71. $(2x^2)^2 + 2(x^2)^2$ **$6x^4$**

72. $(2r)^2s^2 + 6(rs)^2 + 1$ **$10r^2s^2 + 1$** 73. $(3a)^2b^3 + 3(ab)^2(2b)$ **$15a^2b^3$** 74. $(x^2)(x^2)(x^2) + 3x^2$ **$x^6 + 3x^2$**

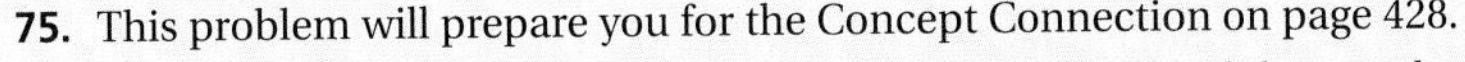

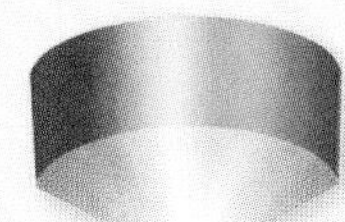

75. This problem will prepare you for the Concept Connection on page 428.

a. The speed of light v is the product of the frequency f and the wavelength w: ($v = fw$). Wavelengths are often measured in *nanometers*. *Nano* means 10^{-9}, so 1 nanometer $= 10^{-9}$ meters. What is 600 nanometers in meters? Write your answer in scientific notation. **6×10^{-7} m**

b. Use your answer from part **a** to find the speed of light in meters per second if $f = 5 \times 10^{14}$ Hz. **3×10^8 m/s**

c. Explain why you can rewrite $(6 \times 10^{-7})(5 \times 10^{14})$ as $(6 \times 5)(10^{-7})(10^{14})$.

Teaching Tip **Science Link** For **Exercise 53,** you can explain to students that a planet's distance from the Sun varies at different points in its orbit. This is because the planets have elliptical orbits. At a point called *perihelion*, a planet is closest to the Sun. At *aphelion*, it is farthest from the Sun. The root in both words, *helion*, comes from the Greek word for Sun.

CONCEPT CONNECTION **Exercise 75** involves using the formula for the speed of light. This exercise prepares students for the Concept Connection on page 428.

Answers

55a. Exponents are multiplied but should be added; x^6.

b. Exponents are added but should be multiplied; x^{20}.

c. Exponent is written as a power but should be multiplied; x^6.

65a. 9^3, or 729; possible answer: Round −3.031 to −3.

b. 0.024; possible answer: Round 6.2085 to 6 and round 3.819 to 4.

75c. Assoc. and Comm. Properties of Mult.

7-3 PROBLEM SOLVING

LESSON 7-3 **Problem Solving**
Multiplication Properties of Exponents

Write the correct answer.

1. In the mid-nineteenth century, several landowners in Australia released domestic rabbits into the wild. Suppose 100 rabbits were released. By 1950, the population had increased about 6×10^6 times. Determine the wild rabbit population in 1950.
about 600,000,000

2. Barnard's star is the fifth closest star to the Earth, after the Sun and the stars in the Alpha Centauri system. It takes 1.86×10^8 seconds for light from Barnard's star to reach the Earth. Light travels at a speed of 1.86×10^5 miles per second. Calculate the distance from Barnard's star to the Earth.
3.46×10^{13} miles

3. Saturn's smallest moon, Tethys, has a diameter of about 6.5×10^2 miles. The diameter of Jupiter's largest moon, Ganymede, is 5 times that of Tethys. Determine the diameter of Ganymede. Write your answer in standard form and in scientific notation.
about 3250 mi or 3.25×10^3 mi

4. Delaware and Montana have roughly the same population. Delaware's area is 2.49×10^3 square miles. Montana is 59 times larger. Determine the area of Montana. Write your answer in standard form and in scientific notation.
147,000 sq mi or 1.47×10^5 sq mi

Select the best answer.

5. The formula for the volume of a cylinder is $V = 2\pi r^2h$ where r is the radius and h is the height. What is the volume of the cylinder shown below?
3y 2x
A $12\pi xy$ cm³ C $24\pi x^2y$ cm³
B $12\pi xy^2$ cm³ **(D) $36\pi xy^2$ cm³**

6. What is the volume of the cube shown below?
$4n^3$ $4n^3$ $4n^3$
F $12n^6$ in³ **(H) $64n^9$ in³**
G $12n^9$ in³ J $256n^9$ in³

7. Belize borders Mexico and Guatemala in Central America. It has an area of 2.30×10^4 square kilometers. Russia borders fourteen countries and is 7.43×10^2 times larger than Belize. What is the area of Russia?
A 1.71×10^6 sq km C 1.71×10^8 sq km
(B) 1.71×10^7 sq km D 1.71×10^9 sq km

8. In 1989, Voyager 2 discovered six moons that orbit Neptune. The smallest of these is Naiad, which orbits Neptune in a brief 7.2 hours, or 8.22×10^{-4} years. Neptune's orbit of the Sun takes 2×10^5 times longer than Naiad's. How long does Neptune's orbit take?
F 10.2 years H 102 years
G 16.4 years **(J) 164 years**

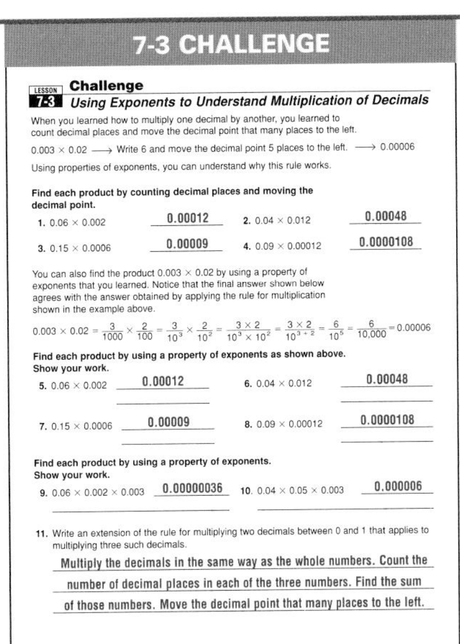

7-3 CHALLENGE

LESSON 7-3 **Challenge**
Using Exponents to Understand Multiplication of Decimals

When you learned how to multiply one decimal by another, you learned to count decimal places and move the decimal point that many places to the left.

0.003 × 0.02 ⟶ Write 6 and move the decimal point 5 places to the left. ⟶ 0.00006

Using properties of exponents, you can understand why this rule works.

Find each product by counting decimal places and moving the decimal point.

1. 0.06 × 0.002 **0.00012** 2. 0.04 × 0.012 **0.00048**
3. 0.15 × 0.0006 **0.00009** 4. 0.09 × 0.00012 **0.0000108**

You can also find the product 0.003 × 0.02 by using a property of exponents that you learned. Notice that the final answer shown below agrees with the answer obtained by applying the rule for multiplication shown in the example above.

$$0.003 \times 0.02 = \frac{3}{1000} \times \frac{2}{100} = \frac{3}{10^3} \times \frac{2}{10^2} = \frac{3 \times 2}{10^3 \times 10^2} = \frac{3 \times 2}{10^{3+2}} = \frac{6}{10^5} = \frac{6}{10{,}000} = 0.00006$$

Find each product by using a property of exponents as shown above. Show your work.

5. 0.06 × 0.002 **0.00012** 6. 0.04 × 0.012 **0.00048**
7. 0.15 × 0.0006 **0.00009** 8. 0.09 × 0.00012 **0.0000108**

Find each product by using a property of exponents. Show your work.

9. 0.06 × 0.002 × 0.003 **0.00000036** 10. 0.04 × 0.05 × 0.003 **0.000006**

11. Write an extension of the rule for multiplying two decimals between 0 and 1 that applies to multiplying three such decimals.
Multiply the decimals in the same way as the whole numbers. Count the number of decimal places in each of the three numbers. Find the sum of those numbers. Move the decimal point that many places to the left.

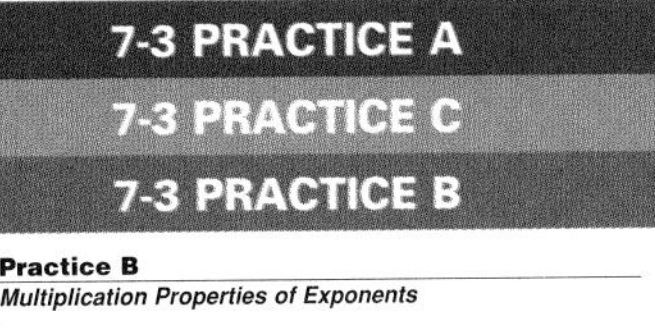

LESSON 7-3 **Practice B**
Multiplication Properties of Exponents

Simplify.

1. $3^4 \cdot 3^2$ **3^6 or 729** 2. $2^5 \cdot 2^4$ **2^9 or 512** 3. $2^3 \cdot 2^5 \cdot 2^1$ **2^9 or 512**

4. $q^{-6} \cdot q^{-1}$ **$\frac{1}{q^7}$** 5. $r^{-3} \cdot r^4 \cdot s^{-4}$ **$\frac{r}{s^4}$** 6. $j^{-2} \cdot j^{-4} \cdot j^2$ **$\frac{1}{j^4}$**

7. $c^5 \cdot b^{-2} \cdot c^3$ **$\frac{c^8}{b^2}$** 8. $(h^2)^5$ **h^{10}** 9. $(g^4)^{-2}$ **$\frac{1}{g^8}$**

10. $(w^6)^0$ **1** 11. $(v^2)^5 \cdot v^4$ **v^{14}** 12. $(w^5)^{-2} \cdot w^{-3}$ **$\frac{1}{w^{13}}$**

13. $(f^6)^{-4} \cdot (f^{-2})^{-3}$ **$\frac{1}{f^{18}}$** 14. $(a^{-2})^{-3} \cdot (a^5)^2$ **a^{16}** 15. $(3b)^4$ **$81b^4$**

16. $(-5k)^2$ **$25k^2$** 17. $-(4m)^3$ **$-64m^3$** 18. $(-3p)^{-2}$ **$\frac{1}{9p^2}$**

19. $(s^4t)^3 \cdot (s^4t^3)^2$ **$s^{20}t^9$** 20. $(a^2b^4)^2 \cdot (a^{-2}b^3)^{-1} \cdot a^4$ **$a^{10}b^5$** 21. $(x^3y^2)^{-4} \cdot (x^2y^{-3})^{-2}$ **$\frac{1}{x^{16}y^2}$**

22. The pitch of a sound is determined by the number of vibrations produced per second. The note "middle C" produces 2.62×10^2 vibrations per second. If a pianist plays middle C for 5×10^{-1} seconds, how many vibrations will occur?
1.31×10^2 or 131 vibrations

Teaching Tip **Multiple Choice** Students who chose **B** for **Exercise 80** may have recalled that any nonzero number raised to the zero power is one, but they may have forgotten to multiply by x^2.

In **Exercise 82,** 4 must be cubed because it is a factor of an expression that is being cubed. Students can eliminate choices **A** and **B** immediately because 4^3 is 64.

Journal

Have students explain how parentheses affect the expressions ab^3c^2, $(ab^3c)^2$ and $(ab)^3c^2$.

ALTERNATIVE ASSESSMENT

Have students work in small groups to create a presentation that explains the properties learned in this lesson. The presentation should include visual aids as needed.

Power Presentations with PowerPoint®

7-3 Lesson Quiz

Simplify.

1. $3^2 \cdot 3^4$ 3^6 **2.** $z^4 \cdot z^{-2} \cdot z$ z^3

3. $(x^3)^2$ x^6 **4.** $-(t^{-3})^5$ $-\frac{1}{t^{15}}$

5. $(5g)^3$ $125g^3$ **6.** $(-3f^{-4})^2$ $\frac{9}{f^8}$

7. $(x^2y)^3 \cdot (x^3y^2)^{-2}$ $\frac{1}{y}$

8. The islands of Samoa have an approximate area of 2.9×10^3 square kilometers. The area of Texas is about 2.3×10^2 times as great as that of the islands. What is the approximate area of Texas? Write your answer in scientific notation.
6.67×10^5 km²

Also available on transparency

Critical Thinking Rewrite each expression so that it has only one exponent. (*Hint:* You may use parentheses.)

76. c^3d^3 $(cd)^3$ **77.** $36a^2b^2$ $(6ab)^2$ **78.** $\frac{8a^3}{b^3}$ $\left(\frac{2a}{b}\right)^3$ **79.** $\frac{k^{-2}}{4m^2n^2}$ $\left(\frac{1}{2kmn}\right)^2$

Multiple Choice For Exercises 80–83, choose the best answer.

80. Which of the following is equivalent to $x^2 \cdot x^0$?
Ⓐ 0 Ⓑ 1 Ⓒ x^2 Ⓓ x^{20}

81. Which of the following is equivalent to $(3 \times 10^5)(4 \times 10^2)$?
Ⓐ 7×10^7 Ⓑ 7×10^{10} Ⓒ 1.2×10^8 Ⓓ 1.2×10^{11}

82. What is the value of n^3 when $n = 4 \times 10^5$?
Ⓐ 1.2×10^9 Ⓑ 1.2×10^{16} Ⓒ 6.4×10^9 Ⓓ 6.4×10^{16}

83. Which represents the area of the triangle?
Ⓐ $6x^2$ Ⓒ $7x^2$
Ⓑ $12x^2$ Ⓓ $24x^2$

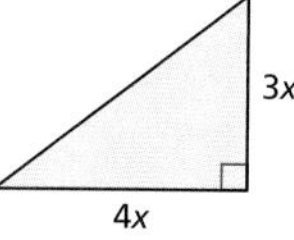

CHALLENGE AND EXTEND

Simplify.

84. $3^2 \cdot 3^x$ 3^{2+x} **85.** $(3^2)^x$ 3^{2x} **86.** $(x^yz)^2$ $x^{2y}z^2$

87. $(x+1)^{-2}(x+1)^3$ $x+1$ **88.** $(x+1)^2(x+1)^{-3}$ $\frac{1}{x+1}$ **89.** $(x^y \cdot x^z)^3$ x^{3y+3z}

90. $(4^x)^x$ 4^{x^2} **91.** $(x^x)^x$ x^{x^2} **92.** $(3x)^{2y}$ 9^yx^{2y}

Find the value of x.

93. $5^x \cdot 5^4 = 5^8$ 4 **94.** $7^3 \cdot 7^x = 7^{12}$ 9

95. $(4^x)^3 = 4^{12}$ 4 **96.** $(6^2)^x = 6^{16}$ 8

97. **Multi-Step** The edge of a cube measures 1.2×10^{-2} m. What is the volume of the cube in cubic centimeters? **1.728 cm³**

SPIRAL STANDARDS REVIEW

2.0, 3.0, 4.0

Write an equation to represent each relationship. Then solve. *(Lesson 2-3)*

98. Three times the sum of a number and nine plus one equals 24. $3(x+9)+1=24; -\frac{4}{3}$

99. Eight increased by 6 times a number equals 71 plus three. $8+6x=71+3; 11$

100. Keenan sets up the sound for his band. He uses a tool to keep the sound level of his amplifiers within 15 decibels of 95 decibels. Write and solve an absolute-value equation to find the maximum and minimum decibel levels. *(Lesson 2-7)*
$|x-95|=15$; 80 dB; 110 dB

101. Jimmy is making dinner for his family and is keeping his soup at a warm temperature. He has the stove set to keep the soup at 120°F. Jimmy needs to make sure the temperature stays within 12°F of its current temperature. Write and solve an absolute-value equation to find the maximum and minimum temperatures. *(Lesson 2-7)*
$|x-120|=12$; 108°F; 132°F

Write each number in standard form. *(Lesson 7-2)*

102. 7.8×10^6 **7,800,000** **103.** 4.95×10^{-4} **0.000495**

104. 983×10^{-1} **98.3** **105.** 0.06×10^8 **6,000,000**

7-4 Division Properties of Exponents

California Standards

2.0 Students understand and use such operations as taking the opposite, finding the reciprocal, taking a root, and raising to a fractional power. **They understand and use the rules of exponents.**

Who uses this?

Economists can use expressions with exponents to calculate national debt statistics. (See Example 3.)

A quotient of powers with the same base can be found by writing the powers in factored form and dividing out common factors.

$$\frac{a^m}{a^n} = \frac{\overbrace{\not{a}\cdot\not{a}\cdot\ \ldots\ \cdot a}^{m \text{ factors}}}{\underbrace{\not{a}\cdot\not{a}\cdot\ \ldots\ \cdot a}_{n \text{ factors}}} = a^{m-n}$$

Quotient of Powers Property

WORDS	NUMBERS	ALGEBRA
The quotient of two nonzero powers with the same base equals the base raised to the difference of the exponents.	$\frac{6^7}{6^4} = 6^{7-4} = 6^3$	If a is a nonzero real number and m and n are integers, then $\frac{a^m}{a^n} = a^{m-n}$.

EXAMPLE 1 **Finding Quotients of Powers**

Simplify.

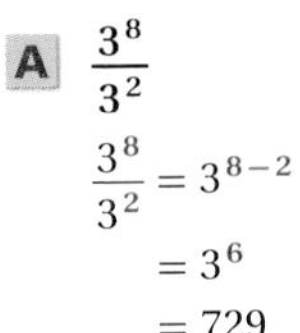

A $\frac{3^8}{3^2}$

$\frac{3^8}{3^2} = 3^{8-2}$

$= 3^6$

$= 729$

B $\frac{x^5}{x^5}$

$\frac{x^5}{x^5} = x^{5-5}$

$= x^0$

$= 1$

Helpful Hint

$3^6 = 729$
Both 3^6 and 729 are considered to be simplified.

C $\frac{a^5b^9}{(ab)^4}$

$\frac{a^5b^9}{(ab)^4} = \frac{a^5b^9}{a^4b^4}$

$= a^{5-4} \cdot b^{9-4}$

$= a^1 \cdot b^5$

$= ab^5$

D $\frac{2^3 \cdot 3^2 \cdot 5^7}{2 \cdot 3^4 \cdot 5^5}$

$\frac{2^3 \cdot 3^2 \cdot 5^7}{2 \cdot 3^4 \cdot 5^5} = 2^{3-1} \cdot 3^{2-4} \cdot 5^{7-5}$

$= 2^2 \cdot 3^{-2} \cdot 5^2$

$= \frac{2^2 \cdot 5^2}{3^2}$

$= \frac{4 \cdot 25}{9}$

$= \frac{100}{9}$

CHECK IT OUT! Simplify.

1a. $\frac{2^9}{2^7}$ 4 1b. $\frac{y}{y^4}$ $\frac{1}{y^3}$ 1c. $\frac{m^5n^4}{(m^5)^2n}$ $\frac{n^3}{m^5}$ 1d. $\frac{3^5 \cdot 2^4 \cdot 4^3}{3^4 \cdot 2^2 \cdot 4^6}$ $\frac{3}{16}$

7-4 Organizer

Objective: Use division properties of exponents to evaluate and simplify expressions.

Technology Lab
In *Chapter 7 Resource File*

PREMIER **Online Edition**
Tutorial Videos

Countdown to Mastery Week 15

Power Presentations with PowerPoint®

Warm Up

Simplify.

1. $(x^2)^3$ x^6
2. 2^{-3} $\frac{1}{2^3}$ or $\frac{1}{8}$
3. $3^2 \cdot x^{-1}$ $\frac{9}{x}$
4. $(v^{-2}w^3)^{-3}$ $\frac{v^6}{w^9}$
5. $3^8 \cdot 3^{-2}$ 3^6
6. $\left(\frac{y}{z}\right)^3$ $\frac{y^3}{z^3}$

Write in scientific notation.

7. 30×10^{-3} 3×10^{-2}
8. 0.16×10^7 1.6×10^6

Also available on transparency

Math Humor

Q: Why does $\frac{(xy)^2}{x^2y^2}$ refuse to be simplified?

A: One is the loneliest number.

1 Introduce

EXPLORATION

7-4 Division Properties of Exponents

1. The expression $\frac{x^5}{x^2}$ can be simplified by expanding the powers and dividing out common factors: $\frac{x^5}{x^2} = \frac{x \cdot x \cdot \not{x} \cdot \not{x} \cdot x}{\not{x} \cdot \not{x}} = x \cdot x \cdot x = x^3$. Use this information to complete the table.
2. Describe any patterns you see in the table.
3. You can use a similar method when the exponent in the denominator is greater than the exponent in the numerator. For example, $\frac{x^2}{x^5} = \frac{\not{x} \cdot \not{x}}{x \cdot \not{x} \cdot \not{x} \cdot x \cdot x} = \frac{1}{x \cdot x \cdot x} = \frac{1}{x^3} = x^{-3}$. Use this information to complete this table.

Expression	Simplified Form
$\frac{x^5}{x^2}$	x^3
$\frac{a^4}{a^2}$	
$\frac{y^7}{y^5}$	
$\frac{x^6}{x^5}$	

Expression	Simplified Form
$\frac{x^2}{x^5}$	x^{-3}
$\frac{m^3}{m^7}$	
$\frac{a^2}{a^8}$	
$\frac{x^6}{x^7}$	

THINK AND DISCUSS

4. **Explain** how the results in the second table compare to those in the first table.
5. **Describe** how you can use your findings to simplify $\frac{z^{10}}{z^{15}}$

Motivate

Have students write out the factors in $\frac{4^9}{4^6}$. $\frac{4 \cdot 4 \cdot 4 \cdot 4 \cdot 4 \cdot 4 \cdot 4 \cdot 4 \cdot 4}{4 \cdot 4 \cdot 4 \cdot 4 \cdot 4 \cdot 4}$ Ask them how to simplify this quotient of powers. $4^3 = 64$ Explain that in this lesson they will learn properties for division of powers.

Explorations and answers are provided in *Alternate Openers: Explorations Transparencies.*

California Standards

Algebra 1 2.0

Power Presentations with PowerPoint®

Additional Examples

Example 1

Simplify.

A. $\frac{2^7}{2^2}$ 2^5, or 32 **B.** $\frac{x^4}{x^3}$ x

C. $\frac{d^4e^3}{(de)^2}$ d^2e

D. $\frac{3 \cdot 4^3 \cdot 5^5}{3^2 \cdot 4^4 \cdot 5^3}$ $\frac{25}{12}$

Example 2

Simplify $(3 \times 10^{10}) \div (6 \times 10^6)$ and write the answer in scientific notation. 5×10^3

Example 3

The Colorado Department of Education spent about 4.408×10^9 dollars in fiscal year 2004–05 on public schools. There were about 7.6×10^5 students enrolled in public school. What was the average spending per student? Write your answer in standard form. \$5800

Also available on transparency

INTERVENTION
Questioning Strategies

EXAMPLE 1

- Why can the Quotient of Powers Property not be used to simplify $\frac{x^4}{y^3}$?
- Is the smaller exponent always subtracted from the larger exponent? Explain.

EXAMPLE 2

- How do you know if your answer is in scientific notation?

EXAMPLE 3

- How do you know which number is the divisor?
- What mathematical operations are needed to answer the question? How do you know?

Writing Math

You can "split up" a quotient of products into a product of quotients:

$\frac{a \times c}{b \times d} = \frac{a}{b} \times \frac{c}{d}$

Example:

$\frac{3 \times 4}{5 \times 7} = \frac{3}{5} \times \frac{4}{7} = \frac{12}{35}$

EXAMPLE 2 **Dividing Numbers in Scientific Notation**

Simplify $(2 \times 10^8) \div (8 \times 10^5)$ and write the answer in scientific notation.

$(2 \times 10^8) \div (8 \times 10^5) = \frac{2 \times 10^8}{8 \times 10^5}$

$= \frac{2}{8} \times \frac{10^8}{10^5}$ *Write as a product of quotients.*

$= 0.25 \times 10^{8-5}$ *Simplify each quotient.*

$= 0.25 \times 10^3$ *Simplify the exponent.*

$= 2.5 \times 10^{-1} \times 10^3$ *Write 0.25 in scientific notation as 2.5×10^{-1}.*

$= 2.5 \times 10^{-1+3}$ *The second two terms have the same base, so add the exponents.*

$= 2.5 \times 10^2$ *Simplify the exponent.*

2. Simplify $(3.3 \times 10^6) \div (3 \times 10^8)$ and write the answer in scientific notation. 1.1×10^{-2}

EXAMPLE 3 ***Economics Application***

In the year 2000, the United States public debt was about 5.6×10^{12} dollars. The population of the United States in that year was about 2.8×10^8 people. What was the average debt per person? Give your answer in standard form.

To find the average debt per person, divide the total debt by the number of people.

$\frac{\text{total debt}}{\text{number of people}} = \frac{5.6 \times 10^{12}}{2.8 \times 10^8}$

$= \frac{5.6}{2.8} \times \frac{10^{12}}{10^8}$ *Write as a product of quotients.*

$= 2 \times 10^{12-8}$ *Simplify each quotient.*

$= 2 \times 10^4$ *Simplify the exponent.*

$= 20{,}000$ *Write in standard form.*

The average debt per person was about \$20,000.

3. In 1990, the United States public debt was about 3.2×10^{12} dollars. The population of the United States in 1990 was about 2.5×10^8 people. What was the average debt per person? Write your answer in standard form. **\$12,800**

A power of a quotient can be found by first writing factors and then writing the numerator and denominator as powers.

$$\left(\frac{a}{b}\right)^n = \underbrace{\frac{a}{b} \cdot \frac{a}{b} \cdot \ldots \cdot \frac{a}{b}}_{n \text{ factors}}$$

$$= \frac{\overbrace{a \cdot a \cdot \ldots \cdot a}^{n \text{ factors}}}{\underbrace{b \cdot b \cdot \ldots \cdot b}_{n \text{ factors}}} = \frac{a^n}{b^n}$$

2 Teach

Guided Instruction

Review the multiplication properties of exponents because some problems in this lesson use both multiplication and division properties. Introduce the division properties in this lesson by examining the powers written in factored form first.

$3 \cdot 3 = 3^2$

Universal Access
Through Graphic Organizers

Have students create a graphic organizer to show evidence that each property works.

Quotient of Powers Property	$\frac{6^7}{6^4} = \frac{279{,}936}{1296}$ 216	$6^{7-4} = 6^3$ 216
Power of a Quotient Property	$\left(\frac{3}{5}\right)^4 = (0.6)^4$ 0.1296	$\frac{3^4}{5^4} = \frac{81}{625}$ 0.1296

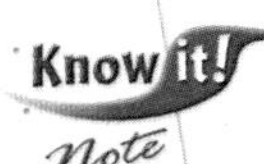

Positive Power of a Quotient Property

WORDS	NUMBERS	ALGEBRA
A quotient raised to a positive power equals the quotient of each base raised to that power.	$\left(\frac{3}{5}\right)^4 = \frac{3}{5} \cdot \frac{3}{5} \cdot \frac{3}{5} \cdot \frac{3}{5} = \frac{3 \cdot 3 \cdot 3 \cdot 3}{5 \cdot 5 \cdot 5 \cdot 5} = \frac{3^4}{5^4}$	If a and b are nonzero real numbers and n is a positive integer, then $\left(\frac{a}{b}\right)^n = \frac{a^n}{b^n}$.

EXAMPLE 4 **Finding Positive Powers of Quotients**

Simplify.

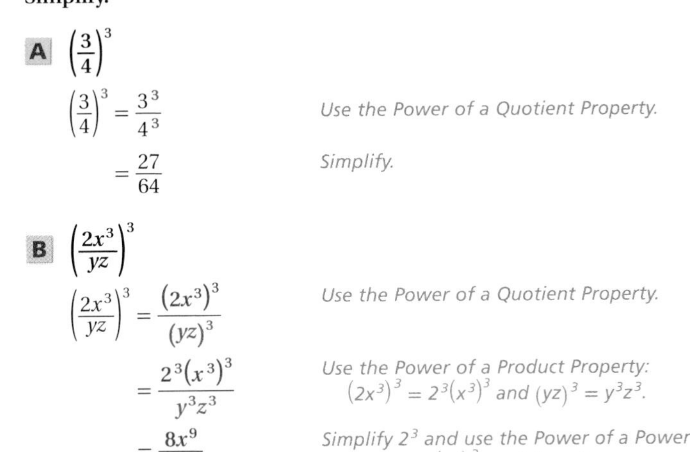

A $\left(\frac{3}{4}\right)^3$

$\left(\frac{3}{4}\right)^3 = \frac{3^3}{4^3}$ *Use the Power of a Quotient Property.*

$= \frac{27}{64}$ *Simplify.*

B $\left(\frac{2x^3}{yz}\right)^3$

$\left(\frac{2x^3}{yz}\right)^3 = \frac{(2x^3)^3}{(yz)^3}$ *Use the Power of a Quotient Property.*

$= \frac{2^3(x^3)^3}{y^3z^3}$ *Use the Power of a Product Property: $(2x^3)^3 = 2^3(x^3)^3$ and $(yz)^3 = y^3z^3$.*

$= \frac{8x^9}{y^3z^3}$ *Simplify 2^3 and use the Power of a Power Property: $(x^3)^3 = x^{3 \cdot 3} = x^9$.*

Simplify.

4a. $\left(\frac{2^3}{3^2}\right)^2$ $\frac{2^6}{3^4}$, or $\frac{64}{81}$ **4b.** $\left(\frac{ab^4}{c^2d^3}\right)^5$ $\frac{a^5b^{20}}{c^{10}d^{15}}$ **4c.** $\left(\frac{a^3b}{a^2b^2}\right)^3$ $\frac{a^3}{b^3}$

Remember that $x^{-n} = \frac{1}{x^n}$. What if x is a fraction?

$\left(\frac{a}{b}\right)^{-n} = \frac{1}{\left(\frac{a}{b}\right)^n} = 1 \div \left(\frac{a}{b}\right)^n$ *Write the fraction as division.*

$= 1 \div \frac{a^n}{b^n}$ *Use the Power of a Quotient Property.*

$= 1 \cdot \frac{b^n}{a^n}$ *Multiply by the reciprocal.*

$= \frac{b^n}{a^n}$ *Simplify.*

$= \left(\frac{b}{a}\right)^n$ *Use the Power of a Quotient Property.*

Therefore, $\left(\frac{a}{b}\right)^{-n} = \left(\frac{b}{a}\right)^n$.

COMMON ERROR ALERT

When using the Power of a Product Property in **Example 4B,** students might forget to apply the power to the coefficients of terms. Remind students to apply the power to each factor in the product, including variables and coefficients.

Power Presentations with PowerPoint®

Additional Examples

Example 4

Simplify.

A. $\left(\frac{4}{7}\right)^2$ $\frac{16}{49}$ **B.** $\left(\frac{3d^2}{ef}\right)^4$ $\frac{81d^8}{e^4f^4}$

C. $\left(\frac{2x^3}{(xy)^3}\right)^2$ $\frac{4}{y^6}$

Also available on transparency

INTERVENTION
Questioning Strategies

EXAMPLE 4

- What happened to a variable if it was in the original expression, but not in the simplified expression?

Auditory The names of the properties in this lesson sound a lot alike. Help students differentiate between the two:

Say "Quotient," and then write $\frac{\square}{\square}$.

Say "of Powers," and then write $\frac{\boxed{x^3}}{\boxed{x^2}}$.

Say "Power," and then write $(\ )^3$.

Say "of a Quotient," and then write $\left(\frac{x}{y}\right)^3$.

Power Presentations with PowerPoint®

Additional Examples

Example 5

Simplify.

A. $\left(\frac{3}{4}\right)^{-3}$ $\frac{64}{27}$

B. $\left(\frac{2x^2}{y^3}\right)^{-2}$ $\frac{y^6}{4x^4}$

C. $\left(\frac{2}{3}\right)^{-2}\left(\frac{6m}{2n}\right)^{-3}$ $\frac{n^3}{12m^3}$

Also available on transparency

INTERVENTION

Questioning Strategies

EXAMPLE 5

- How can you make a negative exponent positive?
- What is the value of $\left(\frac{1}{5}\right)^{-3}$?

Multiple Representations Discuss with students the advantages or disadvantages of different methods of simplifying. For example, in **Example 5A,** students could use the Power of a Quotient Property first: $\left(\frac{2}{5}\right)^{-3} = \frac{2^{-3}}{5^{-3}} = \frac{5^3}{2^3} = \frac{125}{8}$.

Negative Power of a Quotient Property

WORDS	NUMBERS	ALGEBRA
A quotient raised to a negative power equals the reciprocal of the quotient raised to the opposite (positive) power.	$\left(\frac{2}{3}\right)^{-4} = \left(\frac{3}{2}\right)^4 = \frac{3^4}{2^4}$	If a and b are nonzero real numbers and n is a positive integer, then $\left(\frac{a}{b}\right)^{-n} = \left(\frac{b}{a}\right)^n = \frac{b^n}{a^n}$.

EXAMPLE 5 Finding Negative Powers of Quotients

Simplify.

A $\left(\frac{2}{5}\right)^{-3}$

$\left(\frac{2}{5}\right)^{-3} = \left(\frac{5}{2}\right)^3$ *Rewrite with a positive exponent.*

$= \frac{5^3}{2^3}$ *Use the Power of a Quotient Property.*

$= \frac{125}{8}$ *$5^3 = 125$ and $2^3 = 8$.*

B $\left(\frac{3x}{y^2}\right)^{-3}$

$\left(\frac{3x}{y^2}\right)^{-3} = \left(\frac{y^2}{3x}\right)^3$ *Rewrite with a positive exponent.*

$= \frac{(y^2)^3}{(3x)^3}$ *Use the Power of a Quotient Property.*

$= \frac{y^6}{3^3x^3}$ *Use the Power of a Power Property: $(y^2)^3 = y^{2 \cdot 3} = y^6$. Use the Power of a Product Property: $(3x)^3 = 3^3x^3$.*

$= \frac{y^6}{27x^3}$ *Simplify the denominator.*

C $\left(\frac{3}{4}\right)^{-1}\left(\frac{2x}{3y}\right)^{-2}$

$\left(\frac{3}{4}\right)^{-1}\left(\frac{2x}{3y}\right)^{-2} = \left(\frac{4}{3}\right)^1\left(\frac{3y}{2x}\right)^2$ *Rewrite each fraction with a positive exponent.*

$= \frac{4}{3} \cdot \frac{(3y)^2}{(2x)^2}$ *Use the Power of a Quotient Property.*

$= \frac{4}{3} \cdot \frac{3^2y^2}{2^2x^2}$ *Use the Power of a Product Property: $(3y)^2 = 3^2y^2$ and $(2x)^2 = 2^2x^2$.*

$= \frac{{}^1\cancel{4}}{{}_1\cancel{3}} \cdot \frac{\cancel{9}^3y^2}{{}_1\cancel{4}x^2}$ *Divide out common factors.*

$= \frac{3y^2}{x^2}$

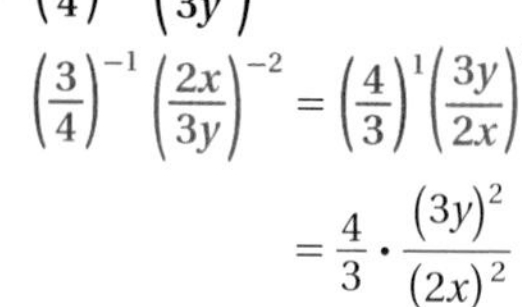

Helpful Hint

Whenever all of the factors in the numerator or the denominator divide out, replace them with 1.

Simplify.

5a. $\left(\frac{4}{3^2}\right)^{-3}$ $\frac{9^3}{4^3}$, or $\frac{729}{64}$ 5b. $\left(\frac{2a}{b^2c^3}\right)^{-4}$ $\frac{b^8c^{12}}{16a^4}$ 5c. $\left(\frac{s}{3}\right)^{-2}\left(\frac{9s^2}{t}\right)^{-1}$ $\frac{t}{s^4}$

3 Close

Summarize

Have students give an example of the Quotient of Powers Property and the Power of a Quotient Property.

Possible answers:

Quotient of Powers: $\frac{x^5}{x^3} = x^{5-3} = x^2$

Power of a Quotient : $\left(\frac{x}{y}\right)^3 = \frac{x^3}{y^3}$

FORMATIVE ASSESSMENT and INTERVENTION

***Diagnose Before* the Lesson**
7-4 Warm Up, TE p. 415

***Monitor During* the Lesson**
Check It Out! Exercises, SE pp. 415–418
Questioning Strategies, TE pp. 416–418

***Assess After* the Lesson**
7-4 Lesson Quiz, TE p. 421
Alternative Assessment, TE p. 421

THINK AND DISCUSS

1. Compare the Quotient of Powers Property and the Product of Powers Property. Then compare the Power of a Quotient Property and the Power of a Product Property.

2. **GET ORGANIZED** Copy and complete the graphic organizer. In each cell, supply the missing information. Then give an example for each property.

If *a* and *b* are nonzero real numbers and *m* and *n* are integers, then...		
$\frac{a^m}{a^n} =$ 	$\left(\frac{a}{b}\right)^n =$	 $\left(\frac{a}{b}\right)^{-n} =$

Answers to *Think and Discuss*

1. Possible answer: Both the Quotient of Powers Property and the Product of Powers Property require that the bases be the same. For quotients, you subtract the exponents. For products, you add the exponents. In the Power of a Quotient Property, each term is raised to the same power. In the Power of a Product Property, each factor is raised to the same power.
2. See p. A6.

7-4 Exercises

California Standards Practice
2.0, 25.1

go.hrw.com
Homework Help Online
KEYWORD: MA8CA 7-4
Parent Resources Online
KEYWORD: MA8CA Parent

GUIDED PRACTICE

SEE EXAMPLE 1 p. 415

Simplify.

1. $\frac{5^8}{5^6}$ **25**
2. $\frac{2^2 \cdot 3^4 \cdot 4^4}{2^9 \cdot 3^5}$ $\mathbf{\frac{2}{3}}$
3. $\frac{15x^6}{5x^6}$ **3**
4. $\frac{a^5b^6}{a^3b^7}$ $\mathbf{\frac{a^2}{b}}$

SEE EXAMPLE 2 p. 416

Simplify each quotient and write the answer in scientific notation.

5. $(2.8 \times 10^{11}) \div (4 \times 10^8)$ $\mathbf{7 \times 10^2}$
6. $(5.5 \times 10^3) \div (5 \times 10^8)$ $\mathbf{1.1 \times 10^{-5}}$
7. $(1.9 \times 10^4) \div (1.9 \times 10^4)$ **1**

SEE EXAMPLE 3 p. 416

8. **Sports** A star baseball player earns an annual salary of $\$8.1 \times 10^6$. There are 162 games in a baseball season. How much does this player earn per game? Write your answer in standard form. **$50,000**

SEE EXAMPLE 4 p. 417

Simplify.

9. $\left(\frac{2}{5}\right)^2$ $\mathbf{\frac{4}{25}}$
10. $\left(\frac{x^2}{xy^3}\right)^3$ $\mathbf{\frac{x^3}{y^9}}$
11. $\left(\frac{a^3}{(a^3b)^2}\right)^2$ $\mathbf{\frac{1}{a^6b^4}}$
12. $\frac{y^{10}}{y}$ $\mathbf{y^9}$

SEE EXAMPLE 5 p. 418

13. $\left(\frac{3}{4}\right)^{-2}$ $\mathbf{\frac{16}{9}}$
14. $\left(\frac{2x}{y^3}\right)^{-4}$ $\mathbf{\frac{y^{12}}{16x^4}}$
15. $\left(\frac{2}{3}\right)^{-1}\left(\frac{3a}{2b}\right)^{-2}$ $\mathbf{\frac{2b^2}{3a^2}}$
16. $\left(\frac{x^3}{y^2}\right)^{-4}$ $\mathbf{\frac{y^8}{x^{12}}}$

PRACTICE AND PROBLEM SOLVING

Simplify.

17. $\frac{3^9}{3^6}$ **27**
18. $\frac{5^4 \cdot 3^3}{5^2 \cdot 3^2}$ **75**
19. $\frac{x^8y^3}{x^3y^3}$ $\mathbf{x^5}$
20. $\frac{x^8y^4}{x^9yz}$ $\mathbf{\frac{y^3}{xz}}$

Simplify each quotient and write the answer in scientific notation.

21. $(4.7 \times 10^{-3}) \div (9.4 \times 10^3)$ $\mathbf{5 \times 10^{-7}}$
22. $(8.4 \times 10^9) \div (4 \times 10^{-5})$ $\mathbf{2.1 \times 10^{14}}$
23. $(4.2 \times 10^{-5}) \div (6 \times 10^{-3})$ $\mathbf{7 \times 10^{-3}}$
24. $(2.1 \times 10^2) \div (8.4 \times 10^5)$ $\mathbf{2.5 \times 10^{-4}}$

7-4 Exercises

Assignment Guide

Assign *Guided Practice* exercises as necessary.

If you finished Examples **1–3**
Proficient 17–25, 34–37, 47, 59
Advanced 17–25, 34–37, 47, 59

If you finished Examples **1–5**
Proficient 17–49, 54–60, 62–71
Advanced 17–49, 54–71

Homework Quick Check
Quickly check key concepts.
Exercises: 18, 22, 25, 28, 30, 48

California Standards

Standard	Exercises
2.0	1–46, 49–60, 62–65, 68–71
4.0	66, 67
25.1	46, 61

Social Studies Link For **Exercise 47,** students might be interested to know that the population density of the United States is actually rather low. Some cities are dense, but there is a lot of open land as well. In comparison, Puerto Rico has a population density of 428 people/km^2. Bermuda's population density is even higher, at 1225 people/km^2.

Language Support Students may be unfamiliar with the use of *concentration* in **Exercise 48.** Explain that *concentration* sometimes means "the act of thinking hard," but in this case, the word refers to the amount of hydrogen ions in a substance.

ENGLISH LANGUAGE LEARNERS

Answers

47. 2000: 3×10^1
  1995: 2.84×10^1
  1990: 2.65×10^1

49. Possible answer: The bases are the same, so subtract the exponent of the denominator from the exponent of the numerator: $\frac{4^5}{4^2} = 4^3 = 64$.
When simplifying $\frac{4^2}{4^5}$, subtracting the exponents gives a negative exponent: $\frac{4^2}{4^5} = 4^{-3} = \frac{1}{4^3} = \frac{1}{64}$.

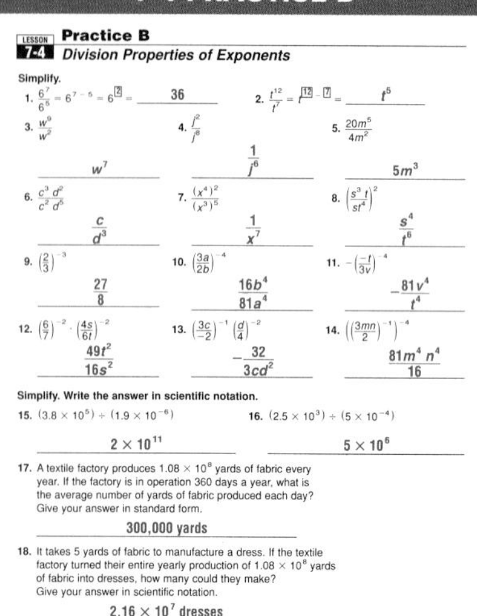

7-4 PRACTICE A

7-4 PRACTICE C

7-4 PRACTICE B

LESSON 7-4 **Practice B**
Division Properties of Exponents

Simplify.

1. $\frac{6^7}{6^5} = 6^{7-5} = 6^{\boxed{2}} =$ 36
2. $\frac{t^{12}}{t^7} = t^{\boxed{12}-\boxed{7}} =$ t^5
3. $\frac{w^9}{w^2}$ w^7
4. $\frac{j^2}{j^8}$ $\frac{1}{j^6}$
5. $\frac{20m^5}{4m^2}$ $5m^3$
6. $\frac{c^3d^2}{c^2d^5}$ $\frac{c}{d^3}$
7. $\frac{(x^4)^2}{(x^3)^5}$ $\frac{1}{x^7}$
8. $\left(\frac{s^3t}{st^4}\right)^2$ $\frac{s^4}{t^6}$
9. $\left(\frac{2}{3}\right)^{-3}$ $\frac{27}{8}$
10. $\left(\frac{3a}{2b}\right)^{-4}$ $\frac{16b^4}{81a^4}$
11. $-\left(\frac{-t}{3v}\right)^{-4}$ $-\frac{81v^4}{t^4}$
12. $\left(\frac{6}{7}\right)^{-2} \cdot \left(\frac{4s}{6t}\right)^{-2}$ $\frac{49t^2}{16s^2}$
13. $\left(\frac{3c}{-2}\right)^{-1}\left(\frac{d}{4}\right)^{-2}$ $-\frac{32}{3cd^2}$
14. $\left(\left(\frac{3mn}{2}\right)^{-1}\right)^{-4}$ $\frac{81m^4n^4}{16}$

Simplify. Write the answer in scientific notation.

15. $(3.8 \times 10^5) \div (1.9 \times 10^{-6})$ 2×10^{11}
16. $(2.5 \times 10^3) \div (5 \times 10^{-4})$ 5×10^6
17. A textile factory produces 1.08×10^8 yards of fabric every year. If the factory is in operation 360 days a year, what is the average number of yards of fabric produced each day? Give your answer in standard form. 300,000 yards
18. It takes 5 yards of fabric to manufacture a dress. If the textile factory turned their entire yearly production of 1.08×10^8 yards of fabric into dresses, how many could they make? Give your answer in scientific notation. 2.16×10^7 dresses

Independent Practice	
For Exercises	See Example
17–20	1
21–24	2
25	3
26–29	4
30–33	5

Extra Practice
Skills Practice p. EP14
Application Practice p. EP30

25. **Astronomy** The mass of Earth is about 3×10^{-3} times the mass of Jupiter. The mass of Earth is about 6×10^{24} kg. What is the mass of Jupiter? Give your answer in scientific notation. 2×10^{27} kg

Simplify.

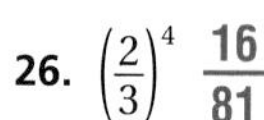

26. $\left(\frac{2}{3}\right)^4$ $\frac{16}{81}$
27. $\left(\frac{a^4}{b^2}\right)^3$ $\frac{a^{12}}{b^6}$
28. $\left(\frac{a^3b^2}{ab^3}\right)^6$ $\frac{a^{12}}{b^6}$
29. $\left(\frac{xy^2}{x^3y}\right)^3$ $\frac{y^3}{x^6}$
30. $\left(\frac{1}{7}\right)^{-3}$ 343
31. $\left(\frac{x^2}{y^5}\right)^{-5}$ $\frac{y^{25}}{x^{10}}$
32. $\left(\frac{8w^7}{16}\right)^{-1}$ $\frac{2}{w^7}$
33. $\left(\frac{1}{4}\right)^{-2}\left(\frac{6x}{7}\right)^{-2}$ $\frac{196}{9x^2}$

Simplify, if possible.

34. $\frac{x^6}{x^5}$ x
35. $\frac{8d^5}{4d^3}$ $2d^2$
36. $\frac{x^2y^3}{a^2b^3}$ $\frac{x^2y^3}{a^2b^3}$
37. $\frac{(3x^3)^3}{(6x^2)^2}$ $\frac{3x^5}{4}$
38. $\frac{(5x^2)^3}{5x^2}$ $25x^4$
39. $\left(\frac{c^2a^3}{a^5}\right)^2$ $\frac{c^4}{a^4}$
40. $\left(\frac{3a}{a^3 \cdot a^0}\right)^3$ $\frac{27}{a^6}$
41. $\left(\frac{-p^4}{-5p^3}\right)^{-2}$ $\frac{25}{p^2}$
42. $\left(\frac{b^{-2}}{b^3}\right)^2$ $\frac{1}{b^{10}}$
43. $\left(\frac{10^2}{10^{-5} \cdot 10^5}\right)^{-1}$ 43. $\frac{1}{100}$
44. $\left(\frac{x^2y^2}{x^2y}\right)^{-3}$ $\frac{1}{y^3}$
45. $\frac{(-x^2)^4}{-(x^2)^4}$ -1

46. **Reasoning** Use the Quotient of a Power Property to explain the definition of x^{-n}. (*Hint:* Think of $\frac{1}{x^n}$ as $\frac{x^0}{x^n}$.) $\frac{1}{x^n} = \frac{x^0}{x^n} = x^{0-n} = x^{-n}$

47. **Geography** *Population density* is the number of people per unit of area. The area of the United States is approximately 9.37×10^6 square kilometers. The table shows population data from the U. S. Census Bureau.

United States Population	
Year	Population (to nearest million)
2000	2.81×10^8
1995	2.66×10^8
1990	2.48×10^8

Write the approximate population density (people per square kilometer) for each of the given years in scientific notation. Round decimals to the nearest hundredth.

48. **Chemistry** The pH of a solution is a number that describes the concentration of hydrogen ions in that solution. For example, if the concentration of hydrogen ions in a solution is 10^{-4}, that solution has a pH of 4.

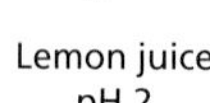

Lemon juice
pH 2

Apples
pH 3

Water
pH 7

Ammonia
pH 11

a. What is the concentration of hydrogen ions in lemon juice? 10^{-2}
b. What is the concentration of hydrogen ions in water? 10^{-7}
c. How many times more concentrated are the hydrogen ions in lemon juice than in water? 10^5, or 100,000, times more concentrated

49. **Write About It** Explain how to simplify $\frac{4^5}{4^2}$. How is it different from simplifying $\frac{4^2}{4^5}$?

Find the missing exponent(s).

50. $\frac{x^{\square}}{x^4} = x^2$ 6
51. $\frac{x^7}{x^{\square}} = x^4$ 3
52. $\left(\frac{a^2}{b^{\square}}\right)^4 = \frac{a^8}{b^{12}}$ 3
53. $\left(\frac{x^4}{y^{\square}}\right)^{-1} = \frac{y^3}{x^{\square}}$ 3; 4

7-4 READING STRATEGIES

LESSON 7-4 **Reading Strategies**
Use a Table

The table below summarizes the division properties that are needed to simplify expressions with powers.

Quotient of Powers	To divide powers with the same base, keep the base and **subtract the exponents.**	$\frac{4^5}{4^3} = 4^{5-3} = 4^2 = 16$ $\frac{x^{12}y^4}{xy^6} = x^{12-1} \cdot y^{4-6} = x^{11}y^{-2} = \frac{x^{11}}{y^2}$	In general, $\frac{a^m}{a^n} = a^{m-n}$
Positive Power of a Quotient	To find the positive power of a quotient, **apply the exponent** to the numerator and denominator.	$\left(\frac{2}{3}\right)^5 = \frac{2^5}{3^5} = \frac{32}{243}$ $\left(\frac{x^2y^5}{y}\right)^3 = \frac{(x^2y^5)^3}{(y)^3} = \frac{x^6y^{15}}{y^3} = x^6y^{12}$	In general, $\left(\frac{a}{b}\right)^n = \frac{a^n}{b^n}$
Negative Power of a Quotient	To find the negative power of a quotient, **apply the positive exponent** to the numerator and denominator of the **reciprocal.**	$\left(\frac{2}{3}\right)^{-5} = \left(\frac{3}{2}\right)^5 = \frac{3^5}{2^5} = \frac{243}{32}$ $\left(\frac{x^3y}{x^5}\right)^{-4} = \left(\frac{x^5}{x^3y}\right)^4 = \frac{x^{20}}{x^{12}y^4} = \frac{x^8}{y^4}$	In general, $\left(\frac{a}{b}\right)^{-n} = \left(\frac{b}{a}\right)^n = \frac{b^n}{a^n}$

Complete each of the following.

1. What do you do with the exponents to simplify $\frac{b^{13}}{b^8}$? subtract
2. Rewrite the expression $\left(\frac{5}{8}\right)^{-4}$ using a positive exponent. $\left(\frac{8}{5}\right)^4$
3. What is the name of the property that can be used to simplify the expression $\left(\frac{4t}{9}\right)^3$? Positive Power of a Quotient

Simplify each expression.

4. $\frac{12^{10}}{12^8}$ 144
5. $\left(\frac{2}{5}\right)^4$ $\frac{16}{625}$
6. $\left(\frac{9}{8}\right)^{-2}$ $\frac{64}{81}$
7. $\frac{f^3g^4}{f^7gh^5}$ $\frac{g^3}{f^4h^5}$
8. $\left(\frac{st}{t^4}\right)^{-6}$ $\frac{t^{18}}{s^6}$
9. $\left(\frac{2c^2}{c^4d}\right)^5$ $\frac{32}{c^{10}d^5}$
10. $\left(\frac{3}{2}\right)^{-3}$ $\frac{8}{27}$
11. $\left(\frac{x^3y}{xy^3}\right)^2$ $\frac{x^4}{y^4}$
12. $\left(\frac{5f^3}{g^7}\right)^{-2}$ $\frac{g^{14}}{25f^6}$

7-4 REVIEW FOR MASTERY

LESSON 7-4 **Review for Mastery**
Division Properties of Exponents

The **Quotient of Powers Property** can be used to divide terms with exponents.

$$\frac{a^m}{a^n} = a^{m-n} \ (a \neq 0,\ m \text{ and } n \text{ are integers.})$$

Simplify $\frac{7^5}{7^2}$.

$\frac{7^5}{7^2} = 7^{5-2}$
$= 7^3$

Simplify $\frac{x^7y}{x^3}$.

$\frac{x^7y}{x^3} = x^{7-3} \cdot y$
$= x^4y$

The **Positive Power of a Quotient Property** can be used to raise quotients to positive powers.

$$\left(\frac{a}{b}\right)^n = \frac{a^n}{b^n} \ (a \neq 0,\ b \neq 0,\ n \text{ is a positive integer.})$$

Simplify $\left(\frac{2}{5}\right)^4$.

$\left(\frac{2}{5}\right)^4 = \frac{2^4}{5^4}$ *Use the Positive Power of a Quotient Property.*
$= \frac{16}{625}$ *Simplify.*

Simplify $\left(\frac{2x^5}{y^4}\right)^3$.

$\left(\frac{2x^5}{y^4}\right)^3 = \frac{(2x^5)^3}{(y^4)^3}$ *Use the Positive Power of a Quotient Property.*
$= \frac{2^3(x^5)^3}{(y^4)^3}$ *Use the Power of a Product Property.*
$= \frac{8x^{15}}{y^{12}}$ *Simplify.*

Simplify.

1. $\frac{5^6}{5^4}$ 25
2. $\frac{x^6y^5}{y^3}$ x^6y^2
3. $\frac{a^2b^4}{(ab)^3}$ $\frac{b}{a}$
4. $\left(\frac{2}{5}\right)^3$ $\frac{2^3}{5^3}$ or $\frac{8}{125}$
5. $\left(\frac{x^3}{y^2}\right)^6$ $\frac{x^{18}}{y^{12}}$
6. $\left(\frac{3m^3}{n^2}\right)^2$ $\frac{9m^6}{n^4}$
7. $\left(\frac{a}{b^2}\right)^3$ $\frac{a^3}{b^6}$
8. $\left(\frac{x^3}{xy}\right)^2$ $\frac{x^4}{y^2}$
9. $\left(\frac{30}{20}\right)^2$ $\frac{9}{4}$

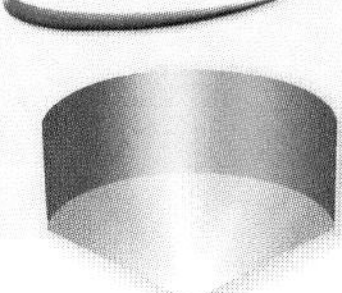

54. This problem will prepare you for the Concept Connection on page 428.

a. Yellow light has a wavelength of 589 nm. A nanometer (nm) is 10^{-9} m. What is 589 nm in meters? Write your answer in scientific notation. 5.89×10^{-7} m

b. The speed of light in air, v, is 3×10^8 m/s, and $v = fw$, where f represents the frequency in hertz (Hz) and w represents the wavelength in meters. What is the frequency of yellow light? about 5.09×10^{14} Hz

Multiple Choice For Exercises 55–57, choose the best answer.

55. Which of the following is equivalent to $(8 \times 10^6) \div (4 \times 10^2)$?

Ⓐ 2×10^3 (B) 2×10^4 Ⓒ 4×10^3 Ⓓ 4×10^4

56. Which of the following is equivalent to $\left(\frac{x^{12}}{3xy^4}\right)^{-2}$?

(A) $\frac{9y^8}{x^{22}}$ Ⓑ $\frac{3y^8}{x^{22}}$ Ⓒ $\frac{3y^6}{x^{12}}$ Ⓓ $\frac{6y^8}{x^{26}}$

57. Which of the following is equivalent to $\frac{(-3x)^4}{-(3x)^4}$?

(A) -1 Ⓑ 1 Ⓒ $-81x^4$ Ⓓ $\frac{1}{81x^4}$

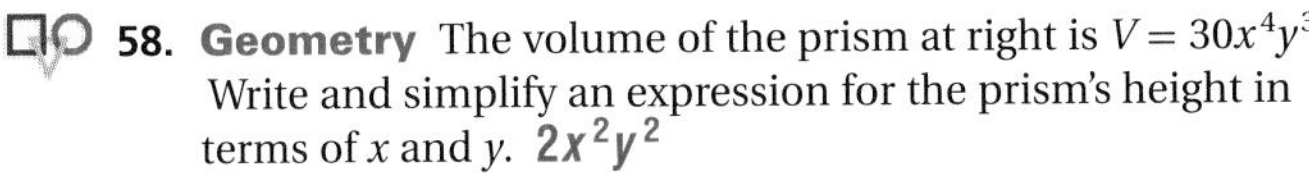

58. Geometry The volume of the prism at right is $V = 30x^4y^3$. Write and simplify an expression for the prism's height in terms of x and y. $2x^2y^2$

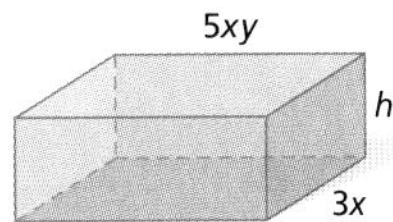

59. Simplify $\frac{3^{2x}}{3^{2x-1}}$. 3 **60.** Simplify $\frac{(x+1)^2}{(x+1)^3}$. $\frac{1}{x+1}$

61. Reasoning Copy and complete the table below to show how the Quotient of Powers Property can be found by using the Product of Powers Property.

	Statements	Reasons
1.	$a^{m-n} = a^{\square + \square}$	Subtraction is addition of the opposite.
2.	$= a^m \cdot a^{-n}$	Product of Powers Property
3.	$= a^m \cdot \frac{1}{a^n}$	Def. of neg. exp.
4.	$= \frac{a^m}{a^n}$	Multiplication can be written as division.

m; $-n$

SPIRAL STANDARDS REVIEW

2.0, 4.0

Find each square root. *(Lesson 1-5)*

62. $\sqrt{36}$ 6 **63.** $\sqrt{1}$ 1 **64.** $-\sqrt{49}$ -7 **65.** $\sqrt{144}$ 12

Solve each equation. Check your answer. *(Lesson 2-4)*

66. $-2(x-1) + 4x = 5x + 3$ $-\frac{1}{3}$ **67.** $x - 1 - (4x + 3) = 5x$ $-\frac{1}{2}$

Simplify. *(Lesson 7-3)*

68. $3^2 \cdot 3^3$ 3^5, or 243 **69.** $k^5 \cdot k^{-2} \cdot k^{-3}$ 1 **70.** $(4t^5)^2$ $16t^{10}$ **71.** $-(5x^4)^3$ $-125x^{12}$

Exercise 54 involves dividing numbers written in scientific notation. This exercise prepares students for the Concept Connection on page 428.

Multiple Choice Students who chose **C** or **D** for **Exercise 55** may have subtracted 4 from 8 instead of dividing.

For **Exercise 56,** remind students that the exponent outside the parentheses applies to every factor inside them, including 3.

In **Exercise 57,** point out that the negative sign in the denominator will be unaffected by the exponent because it is outside the parentheses.

Journal

Have students compare and contrast multiplying and dividing two numbers that are each written in scientific notation.

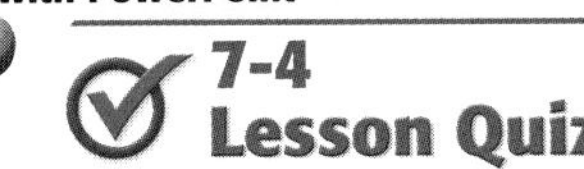

Have students simplify $(5x^2y)^3 \cdot \left(\frac{2xy}{z^4}\right)^{-3}$ and explain at each step which property or definition they used.

Power Presentations with PowerPoint®

7-4 Lesson Quiz

Simplify.

1. $\frac{4^8}{4^3}$ 4^5
2. $\frac{x^5y^2}{(xy)^3}$ $\frac{x^2}{y}$
3. $\left(\frac{2xy^2}{x^3y}\right)^3$ $\frac{8y^3}{x^6}$
4. $\left(\frac{4m}{n^3}\right)^{-2}$ $\frac{n^6}{16m^2}$
5. $\left(\frac{3}{c}\right)^2 \left(\frac{9d^2}{2c}\right)^{-3}$ $\frac{8c}{81d^6}$
6. Simplify $(3 \times 10^{12}) \div (5 \times 10^5)$ and write the answer in scientific notation. 6×10^6
7. The Republic of Botswana has an area of 6×10^5 square kilometers. Its population is about 1.62×10^6. What is the population density of Botswana? Write your answer in standard form. 2.7 people/km²

Also available on transparency

7-4 PROBLEM SOLVING

LESSON 7-4 **Problem Solving**
Division Properties of Exponents

Write the correct answer.

1. Kudzu is a fast-growing vine that has become a nuisance in the southeastern United States. It covers 2.5×10^5 acres in Alabama. In 2004 the population of Alabama was estimated to be 4.45×10^6 people. How many acres of kudzu are there for each person in Alabama? 0.056 acres

2. A cylindrical water tank has a volume of $6\pi x^2y^4$ cubic meters. The formula for the volume of a cylinder is πr^2h. The water tank has a radius of xy meters. What is its height? $6y^2$ meters

3. Voyager 2 was launched in 1979 to explore the planets of the outer solar system. The spacecraft travels an average of 4.68×10^8 kilometers in one year. Determine the speed of Voyager 2 in kilometers per hour. (*Hint*: 1 year = 8760 hours) 5.34×10^4 km/hr

4. The population of Laos is 6.22×10^6. In 2004 its gross domestic product (GDP) was $\$1.13 \times 10^{10}$. The population of Norway is 4.59×10^6. In 2004 its GDP was $\$1.83 \times 10^{11}$. What is the GDP per capita, or per person, of Laos and Norway? Laos: \$1817 Norway: \$39,869

Select the best answer.

5. A rectangular parking lot has an area of $10a^3b^6$ square yards. What is the width of the parking lot? (rectangle: $2a^3$, ?)

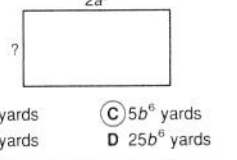

A $5b^2$ yards (C) $5b^6$ yards
B $5b^3$ yards D $25b^6$ yards

6. A storage chest is shaped like a cube. What is the volume of the storage chest? (cube edges: $\frac{x}{4}$)

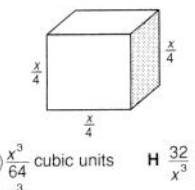

(F) $\frac{x^3}{64}$ cubic units H $\frac{32}{x^3}$ cubic units
G $\frac{x^3}{32}$ cubic units J $64x^3$ cubic units

7. The wavelengths of electromagnetic radiation vary greatly. Green light has a wavelength of about 5.1×10^{-7} meters. The wavelength of a U-band radio wave is 2.0×10^{-2} meters. About how much greater is the wavelength of a U-band radio wave than that of green light?

A 2.55×10^{-9} (C) 3.92×10^4
B 2.55×10^{-5} D 3.92×10^5

8. Puerto Rico has an area of 5.32×10^3 square miles and a population of 3.89×10^6. What is the population density of Puerto Rico in persons per square mile?

F 1.37×10^{-3} H 7.31×10^2
G 1.37×10^{-2} (J) 7.31×10^3

7-4 CHALLENGE

LESSON 7-4 **Challenge**
Applying Properties of Exponents to Rational Numbers

You can use the following three facts to discover a new and interesting fact about rational numbers:

- A rational number is the quotient of two integers with a nonzero denominator.
- Every integer can be written as a product of powers of prime numbers, called the *prime factorization* of the given number. For example, $120 = 2^3 3^1 5^1$.
- When dividing two powers with the same base, subtract the exponents. $\frac{10^5}{10^3} = 10^2$ and $\frac{10^3}{10^5} = \frac{1}{10^2}$

Write the prime factorization of each integer.

1. 24 $2^3 \times 3^1$
2. 108 $2^2 \times 3^3$
3. 452 $2^2 \times 113^1$
4. 1800 $2^3 \times 3^2 \times 5^2$

For each rational number, write the numerator and denominator by using the prime factorization of each. Then use the Quotient-of-Powers Property to simplify the result. Do not multiply out the powers of prime numbers that remain.

5. $\frac{18}{24}$ $\frac{2 \cdot 3^2}{2^3 \cdot 3} = \frac{3}{2^2}$
6. $\frac{48}{180}$ $\frac{2^4 \cdot 3}{2^2 \cdot 3^2 \cdot 5} = \frac{2^2}{3 \cdot 5}$
7. $\frac{250}{288}$ $\frac{2 \cdot 5^3}{2^5 \cdot 3^2} = \frac{5^3}{2^4 \cdot 3^2}$
8. $\frac{540}{1800}$ $\frac{2^2 \cdot 3^3 \cdot 5}{2^3 \cdot 3^2 \cdot 5^2} = \frac{3}{2 \cdot 5}$
9. Examine the final quotients that you wrote in Exercises 5–8. Explain why a prime-number base that appears in a numerator does not appear in the denominator and why a prime-number base that appears in a denominator does not appear in the numerator.
If a prime number base b appear in the numerator (or denominator), it cannot occur in the denominator (or numerator) as well because then the rational number is not fully simplified.
ex: $\frac{b^n a}{b^m c} = \left(\frac{b^m}{b^m}\right)\frac{b^{n-m}a}{c} = \frac{b^{n-m}a}{c}$
10. Let $\frac{a}{b}$ be a rational number. Write a generalization about the representation of $\frac{a}{b}$ as the quotient of prime numbers raised to powers. Illustrate your generalization by using $\frac{54}{120} = \frac{2^1 3^3}{2^3 3^1 5^1}$.
Every rational number can be written as a quotient whose numerator is 1 or the product of prime numbers raised to positive integer exponents and whose denominator can be written as 1 or the product of prime numbers raised to positive integer exponents, and there are no prime bases common to the numerator and the denominator.

7-5 Organizer

Objective: Evaluate and simplify expressions containing fractional exponents.

Online Edition

Countdown to Mastery Week 15

Power Presentations with PowerPoint®

Warm Up

Simplify each expression.

1. $\sqrt{36}$ 6
2. $\sqrt[5]{0}$ 0
3. $\sqrt[3]{64}$ 4
4. $\sqrt[4]{1}$ 1
5. $\sqrt[5]{100{,}000}$ 10
6. $-\sqrt[3]{27}$ −3

Also available on transparency

Math Humor

Q: What do $\sqrt[3]{7}$ and this textbook have in common?

A: Both have an index.

California Standards

Algebra 1 2.0

7-5 Fractional Exponents

California Standards

2.0 Students understand and use such operations as taking the opposite, finding the reciprocal, taking a root, and **raising to a fractional power. They understand and use the rules of exponents.**

Vocabulary
index

Why learn this?

You can use fractional exponents to find the number of Calories animals need to consume each day to maintain health. (See Example 3.)

Recall that the radical symbol $\sqrt{}$ is used to indicate roots. The **index** is the small number to the left of the radical symbol that tells which root to take. For example, $\sqrt[3]{}$ represents a cube root. Since $2^3 = 2 \cdot 2 \cdot 2 = 8$, $\sqrt[3]{8} = 2$.

Another way to write nth roots is by using fractional exponents. For example, for $b > 1$, suppose $\sqrt{b} = b^k$.

$$\sqrt{b} = b^k$$

$$\left(\sqrt{b}\right)^2 = \left(b^k\right)^2 \quad \textit{Square both sides.}$$

$$b^1 = b^{2k} \quad \textit{Power of a Power Property}$$

$$1 = 2k \quad \textit{If } b^m = b^n, \textit{ then } m = n.$$

$$\frac{1}{2} = k \quad \textit{Divide both sides by 2.}$$

So for all $b > 1$, $\sqrt{b} = b^{\frac{1}{2}}$.

Helpful Hint

When $b = 0$, $\sqrt[n]{b} = 0$.
When $b = 1$, $\sqrt[n]{b} = 1$.

Know it! Note

Definition of $b^{\frac{1}{n}}$

WORDS	NUMBERS	ALGEBRA
A number raised to the power of $\frac{1}{n}$ is equal to the nth root of that number.	$3^{\frac{1}{2}} = \sqrt{3}$ $5^{\frac{1}{4}} = \sqrt[4]{5}$ $2^{\frac{1}{7}} = \sqrt[7]{2}$	If $b > 1$ and n is an integer, where $n \geq 2$, then $b^{\frac{1}{n}} = \sqrt[n]{b}$. $b^{\frac{1}{2}} = \sqrt{b}$, $b^{\frac{1}{3}} = \sqrt[3]{b}$, $b^{\frac{1}{4}} = \sqrt[4]{b}$, and so on.

EXAMPLE 1 **Simplifying $b^{\frac{1}{n}}$**

Simplify each expression.

A $125^{\frac{1}{3}}$

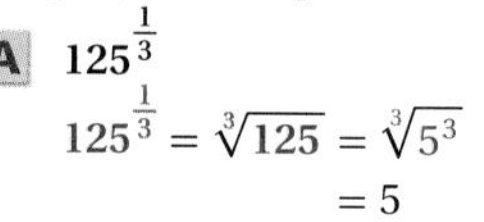

$$125^{\frac{1}{3}} = \sqrt[3]{125} = \sqrt[3]{5^3} = 5 \quad \textit{Use the definition of } b^{\frac{1}{n}}.$$

B $64^{\frac{1}{6}} + 25^{\frac{1}{2}}$

$$64^{\frac{1}{6}} + 25^{\frac{1}{2}} = \sqrt[6]{64} + \sqrt{25} \quad \textit{Use the definition of } b^{\frac{1}{n}}.$$

$$= \sqrt[6]{2^6} + \sqrt{5^2}$$

$$= 2 + 5 = 7$$

Remember!

$\sqrt{}$ is equivalent to $\sqrt[2]{}$.
See Lesson 1-5.

1 Introduce

EXPLORATION

7-5 Fractional Exponents

You will need a graphing calculator for this Exploration.

Recall that whole-number exponents mean repeated multiplication. For example, $3^4 = 3 \cdot 3 \cdot 3 \cdot 3 = 81$. You use a radical to show the inverse operation: $\sqrt[4]{81} = 3$.

1. You can use your calculator to evaluate radicals. To find $\sqrt[3]{4096}$, enter 3 and then press MATH. Select 5: $\sqrt[x]{}$, enter 4096, and press ENTER.
2. Use your calculator to help you complete the table.

Radical	Value
$\sqrt{4096}$	
$\sqrt[3]{4096}$	16
$\sqrt[4]{4096}$	
$\sqrt[6]{4096}$	

3. You can also use your calculator to explore fractional exponents. To evaluate $4096^{\frac{1}{3}}$, first enter 4096. Then press ^ (1 ÷ 3) and press ENTER.
4. Use your calculator to help you complete the table.

Power	Value
$4096^{\frac{1}{2}}$	
$4096^{\frac{1}{3}}$	16
$4096^{\frac{1}{4}}$	
$4096^{\frac{1}{6}}$	

Motivate

Write 4^2 and 4^3 on the board and have students simplify both expressions. 16 and 64

Then write $4^{2\frac{1}{2}}$ on the board. Ask students to guess the value of this expression and explain their thinking. Possible answer: 32; the value should be between 16 and 64.

Tell students that in this lesson they will learn why $4^{2\frac{1}{2}} = 32$.

Explorations and answers are provided in *Alternate Openers: Explorations Transparencies.*

Simplify each expression.

1a. $81^{\frac{1}{4}}$ **3** **1b.** $121^{\frac{1}{2}} + 256^{\frac{1}{4}}$ **15**

A fractional exponent can have a numerator other than 1, as in the expression $b^{\frac{2}{3}}$. You can write the exponent as a product in two different ways.

$$b^{\frac{2}{3}} = b^{\frac{1}{3}\cdot 2} \qquad\qquad b^{\frac{2}{3}} = b^{2\cdot\frac{1}{3}}$$

$$= \left(b^{\frac{1}{3}}\right)^2 \quad \text{Power of a Power Property} \quad = \left(b^2\right)^{\frac{1}{3}}$$

$$= \left(\sqrt[3]{b}\right)^2 \quad \text{Definition of } b^{\frac{1}{n}} \quad = \sqrt[3]{b^2}$$

Definition of $b^{\frac{m}{n}}$

WORDS	NUMBERS	ALGEBRA
A number raised to the power of $\frac{m}{n}$ is equal to the nth root of the number raised to the mth power.	$8^{\frac{2}{3}} = \left(\sqrt[3]{8}\right)^2 = 2^2 = 4$ $8^{\frac{2}{3}} = \sqrt[3]{8^2} = \sqrt[3]{64} = 4$	If $b > 1$ and m and n are integers, where $m \geq 1$ and $n \geq 2$, then $b^{\frac{m}{n}} = \left(\sqrt[n]{b}\right)^m = \sqrt[n]{b^m}$.

EXAMPLE 2 Simplifying Expressions with Fractional Exponents

Simplify each expression.

A $216^{\frac{2}{3}}$

$$216^{\frac{2}{3}} = \left(\sqrt[3]{216}\right)^2 \quad \text{Definition of } b^{\frac{m}{n}}$$
$$= \left(\sqrt[3]{6^3}\right)^2$$
$$= (6)^2 = 36$$

B $32^{\frac{4}{5}}$

$$32^{\frac{4}{5}} = \left(\sqrt[5]{32}\right)^4$$
$$= \left(\sqrt[5]{2^5}\right)^4$$
$$= (2)^4 = 16$$

Simplify each expression.

2a. $16^{\frac{3}{4}}$ **8** **2b.** $1^{\frac{2}{5}}$ **1** **2c.** $27^{\frac{4}{3}}$ **81**

EXAMPLE 3 *Biology Application*

The approximate number of Calories C that an animal needs each day is given by $C = 72m^{\frac{3}{4}}$, where m is the animal's mass in kilograms. Find the number of Calories that a 16 kg dog needs each day.

$$C = 72m^{\frac{3}{4}}$$
$$= 72(16)^{\frac{3}{4}} \quad \text{Substitute 16 for } m.$$
$$= 72 \cdot \left(\sqrt[4]{16}\right)^3 \quad \text{Definition of } b^{\frac{m}{n}}$$
$$= 72 \cdot \left(\sqrt[4]{2^4}\right)^3$$
$$= 72 \cdot (2)^3$$
$$= 72 \cdot 8 = 576$$

The dog needs 576 Calories per day to maintain health.

3. Find the number of Calories that an 81 kg panda needs each day. **1944**

COMMON ERROR ALERT

With fractional exponents with a numerator other than 1, as in **Example 2,** students may confuse the index with the power. Write base$^{\frac{\text{power}}{\text{index}}}$ on the board for students to use as a reference.

Power Presentations with PowerPoint®

Additional Examples

Example 1

Simplify each expression.

A. $343^{\frac{1}{3}}$ 7

B. $32^{\frac{1}{5}} + 9^{\frac{1}{2}}$ 5

Example 2

Simplify each expression.

A. $81^{\frac{5}{4}}$ 243

B. $3125^{\frac{2}{5}}$ 25

Example 3

Given a cube with surface area S, the volume V of the cube can be found by using the formula $V = \left(\frac{S}{6}\right)^{\frac{3}{2}}$. Find the volume of a cube with surface area 54 m^2.
27 m^3

Also available on transparency

INTERVENTION

Questioning Strategies

EXAMPLE **1**

- How do you change a fractional exponent to an nth root?

EXAMPLE **2**

- Will you get the same answer if you raise the number to the power before taking the root?

EXAMPLE **3**

- How can you use the order of operations to solve this problem?

Multiple Representations In **Example 2,** the power can also be placed under the radical sign: $216^{\frac{2}{3}} = \sqrt[3]{216^2}$. However, it is usually more convenient to evaluate the root and then evaluate the power.

2 Teach

Guided Instruction

Review powers and roots by writing $5^3 = 5 \bullet 5 \bullet 5 = 125$ and $\sqrt[3]{125} = 5$. Have students practice writing several of these examples. Then present the definition of $b^{\frac{1}{n}}$ and discuss **Example 1**. Show students two special cases: $1^{\frac{1}{n}} = 1$ and $0^{\frac{1}{n}} = 0$ for all natural-number values of n. Continue with the definition of $b^{\frac{m}{n}}$ and the remaining examples. Remind students of the properties of exponents before presenting **Example 4**.

Universal Access

Through Cooperative Learning

Have students work in pairs. Students take turns rolling both a red (r) and a blue (b) number cube. After each roll, the student uses the numbers shown on the cubes to complete the expression $64^{\frac{r}{b}}$. Then the student simplifies the expression or states that it cannot be simplified. The other student checks the answer and then rolls the number cubes to decide the next expression.

Power Presentations with PowerPoint®

Additional Examples

Example 4

Simplify. All variables represent nonnegative numbers.

A. $\sqrt[4]{a^4b^{20}}$ ab^5

B. $\left(x^6y^4\right)^{\frac{1}{2}}\sqrt{y^2}$ x^3y^3

Also available on transparency

INTERVENTION

Questioning Strategies

EXAMPLE 4

- How do you use properties of exponents to simplify expressions?
- How can you check your answer after you have simplified an expression?

Remember that $\sqrt{\ }$ always indicates a nonnegative square root. When you simplify variable expressions that contain $\sqrt{\ }$, such as $\sqrt{x^2}$, the answer cannot be negative. But x may be negative. Therefore you simplify $\sqrt{x^2}$ as $|x|$ to ensure the answer is nonnegative.

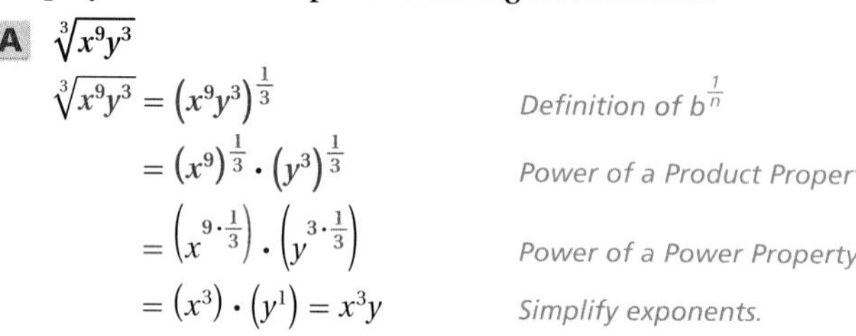

When x is...	and n is...	x^n is...	and $\sqrt[n]{x^n}$ is...
Positive	Even	Positive	Positive
Negative	Even	Positive	Positive
Positive	Odd	Positive	Positive
Negative	Odd	Negative	Negative

When n is even, you must simplify $\sqrt[n]{x^n}$ to $|x|$, because you do not know whether x is positive or negative. When n is odd, simplify $\sqrt[n]{x^n}$ to x.

EXAMPLE 4 Using Properties of Exponents to Simplify Expressions

Simplify. All variables represent nonnegative numbers.

A $\sqrt[3]{x^9y^3}$

$\sqrt[3]{x^9y^3} = \left(x^9y^3\right)^{\frac{1}{3}}$	*Definition of $b^{\frac{1}{n}}$*
$= \left(x^9\right)^{\frac{1}{3}} \cdot \left(y^3\right)^{\frac{1}{3}}$	*Power of a Product Property*
$= \left(x^{9\cdot\frac{1}{3}}\right) \cdot \left(y^{3\cdot\frac{1}{3}}\right)$	*Power of a Power Property*
$= \left(x^3\right) \cdot \left(y^1\right) = x^3y$	*Simplify exponents.*

B $\left(x^2y^{\frac{1}{2}}\right)^4\sqrt[3]{y^3}$

$\left(x^2y^{\frac{1}{2}}\right)^4\sqrt[3]{y^3} = \left(x^2y^{\frac{1}{2}}\right)^4 \cdot y$	$\sqrt[3]{y^3} = y$
$= \left(x^{2\cdot4}\right) \cdot \left(y^{\frac{1}{2}\cdot4}\right) \cdot y$	*Power of a Product Property*
$= \left(x^8\right) \cdot \left(y^2\right) \cdot y$	*Simplify exponents.*
$= x^8 \cdot y^{2+1} = x^8y^3$	*Product of Powers Property*

Helpful Hint

When you are told that all variables represent non-negative numbers, you do not need to use absolute values in your answers.

CHECK IT OUT! Simplify. All variables represent nonnegative numbers.

4a. $\sqrt[4]{x^4y^{12}}$ xy^3

4b. $\dfrac{\left(xy^{\frac{1}{2}}\right)^2}{\sqrt[5]{x^5}}$ xy

THINK AND DISCUSS

1. Explain how to find the value of $\left(\sqrt[10]{25}\right)^5$.

2. GET ORGANIZED Copy and complete the graphic organizer. In each cell, provide the definition and a numerical example of each type of fractional exponent.

Fractional Exponent	Definition	Numerical Example
$b^{\frac{1}{n}}$		
$b^{\frac{m}{n}}$		

Answers to *Think and Discuss*

1. $\left(\sqrt[10]{25}\right)^5 = 25^{\frac{5}{10}} = 25^{\frac{1}{2}} = \sqrt{25} = 5$
2. See p. A6.

3 Close

Summarize

Have students give an equivalent expression with fractional exponents for each expression below. Then have them simplify the expression.

1. $\sqrt[4]{81}$ $81^{\frac{1}{4}}$; 3
2. $\left(\sqrt{25}\right)^3$ $25^{\frac{3}{2}}$; 125
3. $\left(\sqrt[4]{256}\right)^3$ $256^{\frac{3}{4}}$; 64

FORMATIVE ASSESSMENT

and INTERVENTION

***Diagnose Before* the Lesson**
7-5 Warm Up, TE p. 422

***Monitor During* the Lesson**
Check It Out! Exercises, SE pp. 422–424
Questioning Strategies, TE pp. 423–424

***Assess After* the Lesson**
7-5 Lesson Quiz, TE p. 427
Alternative Assessment, TE p. 427

7-5 Exercises

California Standards Practice
2.0, 25.1, 25.2

go.hrw.com
Homework Help Online
KEYWORD: MA8CA 7-5
Parent Resources Online
KEYWORD: MA8CA Parent

GUIDED PRACTICE

1. **Vocabulary** In the expression $\sqrt[5]{3x}$, what is the *index*? 5

SEE EXAMPLE 1 p. 422

Simplify each expression.

2. $8^{\frac{1}{3}}$ 2
3. $16^{\frac{1}{2}}$ 4
4. $0^{\frac{1}{6}}$ 0
5. $27^{\frac{1}{3}}$ 3
6. $81^{\frac{1}{2}}$ 9
7. $216^{\frac{1}{3}}$ 6
8. $1^{\frac{1}{9}}$ 1
9. $625^{\frac{1}{4}}$ 5
10. $36^{\frac{1}{2}} + 1^{\frac{1}{3}}$ 7
11. $8^{\frac{1}{3}} + 64^{\frac{1}{2}}$ 10
12. $81^{\frac{1}{4}} + 8^{\frac{1}{3}}$ 5
13. $25^{\frac{1}{2}} - 1^{\frac{1}{4}}$ 4

SEE EXAMPLE 2 p. 423

14. $81^{\frac{3}{4}}$ 27
15. $8^{\frac{5}{3}}$ 32
16. $125^{\frac{2}{3}}$ 25
17. $25^{\frac{3}{2}}$ 125
18. $36^{\frac{3}{2}}$ 216
19. $64^{\frac{4}{3}}$ 256
20. $1^{\frac{3}{4}}$ 1
21. $0^{\frac{2}{3}}$ 0

SEE EXAMPLE 3 p. 423

22. **Geometry** Given a square with area a, you can use the formula $P = 4a^{\frac{1}{2}}$ to find the perimeter P of the square. Find the perimeter of a square that has an area of 64 m^2. 32 m

SEE EXAMPLE 4 p. 424

Simplify. All variables represent nonnegative numbers.

23. $\sqrt{x^4y^2}$ x^2y
24. $\sqrt[4]{z^4}$ z
25. $\sqrt{x^6y^6}$ x^3y^3
26. $\sqrt[3]{a^{12}b^6}$ a^4b^2
27. $\left(a^{\frac{1}{2}}\right)^2\sqrt{a^2}$ a^2
28. $\left(x^{\frac{1}{3}}\right)^6\sqrt[4]{y^4}$ x^2y
29. $\dfrac{\left(z^{\frac{1}{3}}\right)^3}{\sqrt{z^2}}$ 1
30. $\dfrac{\sqrt[3]{x^6y^9}}{x^2}$ y^3

PRACTICE AND PROBLEM SOLVING

Independent Practice

For Exercises	See Example
31–42	1
43–50	2
51	3
52–59	4

Extra Practice
Skills Practice p. EP15
Application Practice p. EP30

Simplify each expression.

31. $100^{\frac{1}{2}}$ 10
32. $1^{\frac{1}{5}}$ 1
33. $512^{\frac{1}{3}}$ 8
34. $729^{\frac{1}{2}}$ 27
35. $32^{\frac{1}{5}}$ 2
36. $196^{\frac{1}{2}}$ 14
37. $256^{\frac{1}{8}}$ 2
38. $400^{\frac{1}{2}}$ 20
39. $125^{\frac{1}{3}} + 81^{\frac{1}{2}}$ 14
40. $25^{\frac{1}{2}} - 81^{\frac{1}{4}}$ 2
41. $121^{\frac{1}{2}} - 243^{\frac{1}{5}}$ 8
42. $256^{\frac{1}{4}} + 0^{\frac{1}{3}}$ 4
43. $4^{\frac{3}{2}}$ 8
44. $27^{\frac{2}{3}}$ 9
45. $256^{\frac{3}{4}}$ 64
46. $64^{\frac{5}{6}}$ 32
47. $100^{\frac{3}{2}}$ 1000
48. $1^{\frac{5}{3}}$ 1
49. $9^{\frac{5}{2}}$ 243
50. $243^{\frac{2}{5}}$ 9

51. **Biology** Biologists use a formula to estimate the mass of a mammal's brain. For a mammal with a mass of m grams, the approximate mass B of the brain, also in grams, is given by $B = \frac{1}{8}m^{\frac{2}{3}}$. Find the approximate mass of the brain of a mouse that has a mass of 64 grams. 2g

Simplify. All variables represent nonnegative numbers.

52. $\sqrt[3]{a^6c^9}$ a^2c^3
53. $\sqrt[3]{8m^3}$ $2m$
54. $\sqrt[4]{x^{16}y^4}$ x^4y
55. $\sqrt[3]{27x^6}$ $3x^2$
56. $\left(x^{\frac{1}{2}}y^3\right)^2\sqrt{x^2}$ x^2y^6
57. $(a^2b^4)^{\frac{1}{2}}\sqrt[3]{b^6}$ ab^4
58. $\dfrac{\sqrt[3]{x^6y^6}}{yx^2}$ y
59. $\dfrac{\left(a^2b^{\frac{1}{2}}\right)^4}{\sqrt{b^2}}$ a^8b

Fill in the boxes to make each statement true.

60. $256^{\frac{\square}{4}} = 4$ 1
61. $\square^{\frac{1}{5}} = 1$ 1
62. $225^{\frac{1}{\square}} = 15$ 2
63. $\square^{\frac{1}{6}} = 0$ 0
64. $64^{\frac{\square}{3}} = 16$ 2
65. $\square^{\frac{3}{4}} = 125$ 625
66. $27^{\frac{4}{\square}} = 81$ 3
67. $36^{\frac{\square}{2}} = 216$ 3

7-5 Exercises

Assignment Guide

Assign *Guided Practice* exercises as necessary.

If you finished Examples **1–2**
Proficient 32–50 even, 60–78 even, 98–107
Advanced 32–50 even, 60–78 even, 86–88, 91–93, 98–107

If you finished Examples **1–4**
Proficient 32–58 even, 60–90, 92–96 even, 98–107
Advanced 32–80 even, 81–107

Homework Quick Check
Quickly check key concepts.
Exercises: 34, 40, 44, 51, 52, 56

California Standards

Standard	Exercises
2.0	1–97
3.0	98–100
6.0	101–103
17.0	104–107
25.1	82, 83, 86
25.2	84

CONCEPT CONNECTION **Exercise 85** involves using fractional exponents to model a real-world situation related to light. This exercise prepares students for the Concept Connection on page 428.

Answers

86. $4^{\frac{3}{2}} = 4^{3 \cdot \frac{1}{2}} = (4^3)^{\frac{1}{2}} = 64^{\frac{1}{2}} = 8$; $4^{\frac{3}{2}} = 4^{\frac{1}{2} \cdot 3} = \left(4^{\frac{1}{2}}\right)^3 = 2^3 = 8$. It is often easier to take the square root first so that the remaining numbers in the calculation are smaller.

101. $n < 3$

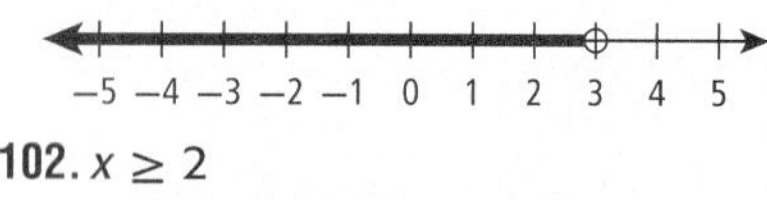

102. $x \geq 2$

103. $y \leq -2$

104. D: {2}; R: {3, 4, 5, 6}; Not a function; the domain value 2 is paired with several different range values.

105. D: {−2, −1, −0, 1}; R: {0, 1, 2, 3}; Function; each domain value is paired with exactly one range value.

106. D: {5, 7, 9, 11}; R: {2}; Function; each domain value is paired with exactly one range value.

107. D: $1 \leq x \leq 4$; R: $2 \leq y \leq 4$; Function; each domain value is paired with exactly one range value.

Simplify each expression.

68. $\left(\frac{81}{169}\right)^{\frac{1}{2}}$ **$\frac{9}{13}$**
69. $\left(\frac{8}{27}\right)^{\frac{1}{3}}$ **$\frac{2}{3}$**
70. $\left(\frac{256}{81}\right)^{\frac{1}{4}}$ **$\frac{4}{3}$**
71. $\left(\frac{1}{16}\right)^{\frac{1}{2}}$ **$\frac{1}{4}$**
72. $\left(\frac{9}{16}\right)^{\frac{3}{2}}$ **$\frac{27}{64}$**
73. $\left(\frac{8}{27}\right)^{\frac{2}{3}}$ **$\frac{4}{9}$**
74. $\left(\frac{16}{81}\right)^{\frac{3}{4}}$ **$\frac{8}{27}$**
75. $\left(\frac{4}{49}\right)^{\frac{3}{2}}$ **$\frac{8}{343}$**
76. $\left(\frac{4}{25}\right)^{\frac{3}{2}}$ **$\frac{8}{125}$**
77. $\left(\frac{1}{81}\right)^{\frac{3}{4}}$ **$\frac{1}{27}$**
78. $\left(\frac{27}{64}\right)^{\frac{2}{3}}$ **$\frac{9}{16}$**
79. $\left(\frac{8}{125}\right)^{\frac{4}{3}}$ **$\frac{16}{625}$**

80. **Multi-Step** Scientists have found that the life span of a mammal living in captivity is related to the mammal's mass. The life span in years L can be approximated by the formula $L = 12m^{\frac{1}{5}}$, where m is the mammal's mass in kilograms. How much longer is the life span of a lion compared with that of a wolf? **12 years**

Typical Mass of Mammals	
Mammal	**Mass (kg)**
Koala	8
Wolf	32
Lion	243
Giraffe	1024

81. **Geometry** Given a sphere with volume V, the formula $r = 0.62V^{\frac{1}{3}}$ may be used to approximate the sphere's radius r. Find the approximate radius of a sphere that has a volume of 27 in³. **1.86 in.**

82. **Reasoning** Show that a number raised to the power $\frac{1}{3}$ is the same as the cube root of that number. (*Hint:* Use properties of exponents to find the cube of $b^{\frac{1}{3}}$. Then compare this with the cube of $\sqrt[3]{b}$. Use the fact that if two numbers have the same cube, then they are equal.)

83. **Critical Thinking** Compare $n^{\frac{2}{3}}$ and $n^{\frac{3}{2}}$ for values of n greater than 1. When simplifying each of these expressions, will the result be greater than n or less than n? Explain.

84. **/// ERROR ANALYSIS ///** Two students simplified $64^{\frac{3}{2}}$. Which solution is incorrect? Explain the error.

Ⓐ
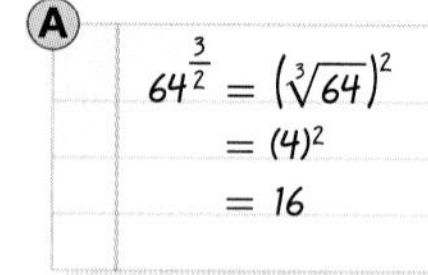

Ⓑ
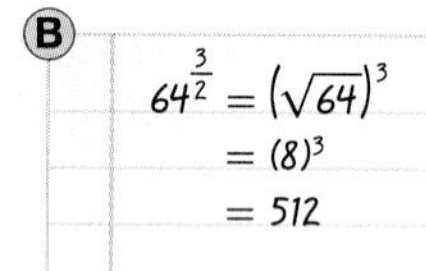

82. $\left(b^{\frac{1}{3}}\right)^3 = b^{\frac{1}{3} \cdot 3} = b^1 = b$. **Also, by definition** $\left(\sqrt[3]{b}\right)^3 = b$. **Therefore,** $b^{\frac{1}{3}} = \sqrt[3]{b}$.

83. $n^{\frac{2}{3}}$ **will be less than** n **because** $\frac{2}{3} < 1$. $n^{\frac{3}{2}}$ **will be greater than** n **because** $\frac{3}{2} > 1$.

84. Solution A is incorrect. The first line should be $64^{\frac{3}{2}} = \left(\sqrt{64}\right)^3$.

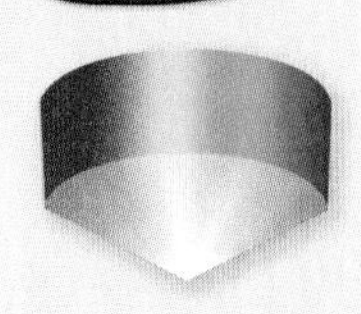

85. This problem will prepare you for the Concept Connection on page 428. You can estimate an object's distance in inches from a light source by using the formula $d = \left(0.8\frac{L}{B}\right)^{\frac{1}{2}}$, where L is the light's luminosity in lumens and B is the light's brightness in lumens per square inch.

a. Find an object's distance to a light source with a luminosity of 4000 lumens and a brightness of 32 lumens per square inch. **10 in.**

b. Suppose the brightness of this light source decreases to 8 lumens per square inch. How does the object's distance from the source change? **The distance doubles (20 in.)**

7-5 PRACTICE A

7-5 PRACTICE C

7-5 PRACTICE B

LESSON 7-5 **Practice B**
Fractional Exponents

Simplify each expression. All variables represent nonnegative numbers.

1. $27^{\frac{1}{3}}$ **3**
2. $121^{\frac{1}{2}}$ **11**
3. $0^{\frac{1}{3}}$ **0**
4. $64^{\frac{1}{2}} + 27^{\frac{1}{3}}$ **11**
5. $16^{\frac{1}{4}} + 8^{\frac{1}{3}}$ **4**
6. $100^{\frac{1}{2}} - 64^{\frac{1}{6}}$ **8**
7. $1^{\frac{1}{5}} + 49^{\frac{1}{2}}$ **8**
8. $25^{\frac{3}{2}}$ **125**
9. $32^{\frac{3}{5}}$ **8**
10. $16^{\frac{3}{4}}$ **8**
11. $1^{\frac{5}{6}}$ **1**
12. $121^{\frac{3}{2}}$ **1331**
13. $\sqrt[5]{y^5}$ **y**
14. $\sqrt{x^4y^{12}}$ **x^2y^6**
15. $\sqrt[3]{a^6b^3}$ **a^2b**
16. $\left(x^{\frac{1}{2}}\right)^4\sqrt{x^6}$ **x^5**
17. $\left(x^{\frac{1}{3}}y\right)^3\sqrt{x^2y^2}$ **x^2y^4**
18. $\frac{\left(x^{\frac{1}{4}}\right)^8}{\sqrt[3]{x^3}}$ **x**

19. Given a cube with volume V, you can use the formula $P = 4V^{\frac{1}{3}}$ to find the perimeter of one of the cube's square faces. Find the perimeter of a face of a cube that has volume 125 m³. **20 m²**

7-5 READING STRATEGIES

LESSON 7-5 **Reading Strategies**
Use a Table

The table below summarizes the definitions you need when you work with fractional exponents.

Definition of $b^{\frac{1}{n}}$	A number raised to the power of $\frac{1}{n}$ is equal to the nth root of that number.	$9^{\frac{1}{2}} = \sqrt{9} = 3$ $32^{\frac{1}{5}} = \sqrt[5]{32} = 2$ $125^{\frac{1}{3}} = \sqrt[3]{125} = 5$	In general, if $b > 1$ and n is an integer where $n \geq 2$, then $b^{\frac{1}{n}} = \sqrt[n]{b}$.
Definition of $b^{\frac{m}{n}}$	A number raised to the power of $\frac{m}{n}$ is equal to the nth root of the number raised to the mth power.	$16^{\frac{3}{4}} = (\sqrt[4]{16})^3 = 2^3 = 8$ $100^{\frac{3}{2}} = (\sqrt{100})^3 = 10^3 = 1000$	In general, if $b > 1$ and m and n are integers where $m \geq 1$ and $n \geq 2$, then $b^{\frac{m}{n}} = (\sqrt[n]{b})^m = \sqrt[n]{b^m}$.

Complete each of the following.

1. The expression $27^{\frac{1}{3}}$ is equal to the **3rd or cube** root of 27.
2. The expression $9^{\frac{5}{2}}$ is equal to the square root of 9 raised to the **5th** power.
3. The expression $32^{\frac{4}{5}}$ is equal to the **5th** root of 32 raised to the **4th** power.

Simplify each expression.

4. $8^{\frac{1}{3}}$ **2**
5. $81^{\frac{1}{2}}$ **9**
6. $16^{\frac{1}{4}}$ **2**
7. $400^{\frac{1}{2}}$ **20**
8. $32^{\frac{2}{5}}$ **4**
9. $81^{\frac{3}{4}}$ **27**
10. $4^{\frac{3}{2}}$ **8**
11. $16^{\frac{5}{2}}$ **1024**
12. $256^{\frac{3}{4}}$ **64**

7-5 REVIEW FOR MASTERY

LESSON 7-5 **Review for Mastery**
Fractional Exponents

To simplify a number raised to the power of $\frac{1}{n}$, write the nth root of the number.

Simplify $216^{\frac{1}{3}}$.

$216^{\frac{1}{3}} = \sqrt[3]{216} = 6$

Think: What number, when taken as a factor 3 times, is equal to 216?
$6^3 = 6 \times 6 \times 6 = 216$, so $\sqrt[3]{216} = 6$.

When an expression contains two or more expressions with fractional exponents, evaluate the expressions with the exponents first, then add or subtract.

Simplify $81^{\frac{1}{2}} + 32^{\frac{1}{5}}$.

$81^{\frac{1}{2}} + 32^{\frac{1}{5}} = \sqrt{81} + \sqrt[5]{32} = 9 + 2 = 11$

Simplify each expression.

1. $64^{\frac{1}{2}}$ **8**
2. $1000^{\frac{1}{3}}$ **10**
3. $1^{\frac{1}{5}}$ **1**
4. $256^{\frac{1}{4}}$ **4**
5. $32^{\frac{1}{5}}$ **2**
6. $49^{\frac{1}{2}}$ **7**
7. $8^{\frac{1}{3}} + 16^{\frac{1}{2}}$ **6**
8. $121^{\frac{1}{2}} + 27^{\frac{1}{3}}$ **14**
9. $32^{\frac{1}{5}} + 1^{\frac{1}{2}}$ **3**
10. $81^{\frac{1}{4}} - 16^{\frac{1}{4}}$ **1**
11. $144^{\frac{1}{2}} - 125^{\frac{1}{3}}$ **7**
12. $625^{\frac{1}{4}} - 0^{\frac{1}{2}}$ **5**

86. **Write About It** You can write $4^{\frac{3}{2}}$ as $4^{3 \cdot \frac{1}{2}}$ or as $4^{\frac{1}{2} \cdot 3}$. Use the Power of a Power Property to show that both expressions are equal. Is one method easier than the other? Explain.

Multiple Choice For Exercises 87–90, choose the best answer.

87. What is $9^{\frac{1}{2}} + 8^{\frac{1}{3}}$?

Ⓐ 4 　 **(B)** 5 　 Ⓒ 6 　 Ⓓ 10

88. Which expression is equal to 8?

(A) $4^{\frac{3}{2}}$ 　 Ⓑ $16^{\frac{1}{2}}$ 　 Ⓒ $32^{\frac{4}{5}}$ 　 Ⓓ $64^{\frac{3}{2}}$

89. Which expression is equivalent to $\sqrt[3]{a^9b^3}$?

Ⓐ a^2b 　 Ⓑ a^3 　 **(C)** a^3b 　 Ⓓ a^3b^3

90. Which of the following is NOT equal to $16^{\frac{3}{2}}$?

Ⓐ $\left(\sqrt{16}\right)^3$ 　 Ⓑ 4^3 　 **(C)** $\left(\sqrt[3]{16}\right)^2$ 　 Ⓓ $\sqrt{16^3}$

CHALLENGE AND EXTEND

Use properties of exponents to simplify each expression.

91. $\left(a^{\frac{1}{3}}\right)\left(a^{\frac{1}{3}}\right)\left(a^{\frac{1}{3}}\right)$ **a** 　 92. $\left(x^{\frac{1}{2}}\right)^5\left(x^{\frac{3}{2}}\right)$ **x^4** 　 93. $\left(x^{\frac{1}{3}}\right)^4\left(x^5\right)^{\frac{1}{3}}$ **x^3**

You can use properties of exponents to help you solve equations. For example, to solve $x^3 = 64$, raise both sides to the $\frac{1}{3}$ power to get $(x^3)^{\frac{1}{3}} = 64^{\frac{1}{3}}$. Simplifying both sides gives $x = 4$. Use this method to solve each equation. Check your answer.

94. $y^5 = 32$ **2** 　 95. $27x^3 = 729$ **3** 　 96. $1 = \frac{1}{8}x^3$ **2**

97. **Geometry** The formula for the surface area of a sphere S in terms of its volume V is $S = (4\pi)^{\frac{1}{3}}(3V)^{\frac{2}{3}}$. What is the surface area of a sphere that has a volume of 36π cm^3? Leave the symbol π in your answer. What do you notice? **36π cm^2; both volume and surface area are described by 36π (although the units are different).**

SPIRAL STANDARDS REVIEW 　 3.0, 6.0, 17.0

Solve each equation. *(Lesson 2-7)*

98. $|x + 6| = 2$ **−8, −4** 　 99. $|5x + 5| = 0$ **−1** 　 100. $|2x - 1| = 3$ **−1, 2**

Solve each inequality and graph the solutions. *(Lesson 3-4)*

101. $3n + 5 < 14$ 　 102. $4 \le \frac{1}{2}x + 3$ 　 103. $7 \ge 2y + 11$

Give the domain and range of each relation. Tell whether the relation is a function. Explain. *(Lesson 4-2)*

104. $\{(2, 3), (2, 4), (2, 5), (2, 6)\}$ 　 105. $\{(-2, 0), (-1, 1), (0, 2), (1, 3)\}$

106.

x	y
5	2
7	2
9	2
11	2

107.

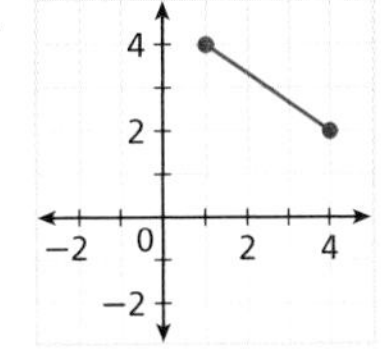

COMMON ERROR ALERT

In **Exercise 80,** students might multiply by 12 before evaluating the fifth root of m. Remind students of the order of operations: grouping symbols, exponents, multiply/divide, add/subtract. Remind them that radical signs are grouping symbols.

Multiple Choice If students answer **B** for **Exercise 89,** they may think that $\sqrt[3]{b^3} = 1$ or $(b^3)^{\frac{1}{3}} = 1$. Remind them that cubing a number and taking the cube root are inverse operations that "undo" each other, so $\sqrt[3]{b^3} = (b^3)^{\frac{1}{3}} = b$

Journal

Have students write the steps they would use to simplify $729^{\frac{5}{6}}$.

Have students write a quiz on fractional exponents. The quiz should include five problems about simplifying expressions of various types. The quiz should also include answers.

Power Presentations with PowerPoint®

7-5 Lesson Quiz

Simplify each expression.

1. $16^{\frac{1}{4}}$ 　 2
2. $144^{\frac{1}{2}} - 27^{\frac{1}{3}}$ 　 9
3. $81^{\frac{3}{2}}$ 　 729
4. $64^{\frac{7}{6}}$ 　 128
5. In an experiment, the approximate population P of a bacteria colony is given by $P = 15t^{\frac{5}{3}}$, where t is the number of days since the start of the experiment. Find the population of the colony on the 8th day. 480

Simplify. All variables represent nonnegative numbers.

6. $\sqrt[5]{x^{10}z^5}$ 　 x^2z
7. $\left(a^4 b^{\frac{1}{4}}\right)^4 \sqrt[3]{b^3}$ 　 $a^{16}b^2$

Also available on transparency

7-5 PROBLEM SOLVING

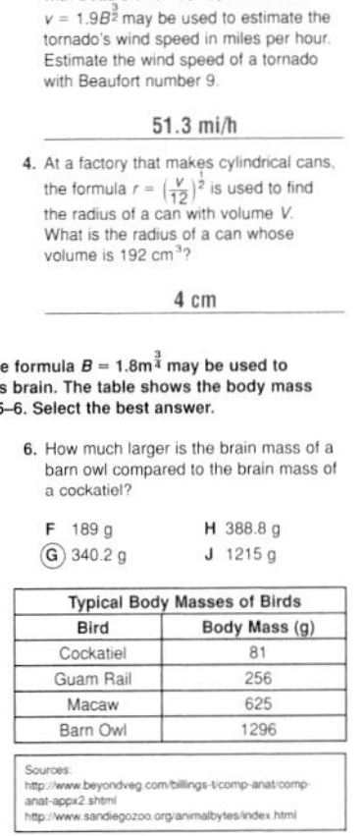

LESSON 7-5 Problem Solving
Fractional Exponents

Write the correct answer.

1. For a pendulum with a length of L meters, the time in seconds that it takes the pendulum to swing back and forth is approximately $2L^{\frac{1}{2}}$. About how long does it take a pendulum that is 9 meters long to swing back and forth?
6 s

2. The Beaufort Scale is used to measure the intensity of tornados. For a tornado with Beaufort number B, the formula $v = 1.9B^{\frac{3}{2}}$ may be used to estimate the tornado's wind speed in miles per hour. Estimate the wind speed of a tornado with Beaufort number 9.
51.3 mi/h

3. Given a cube whose faces each have area A, the volume of the cube is given by the formula $V = A^{\frac{3}{2}}$. Find the volume of a cube whose faces each have an area of 64 in^2.
512 in^3

4. At a factory that makes cylindrical cans, the formula $r = \left(\frac{V}{12}\right)^{\frac{1}{2}}$ is used to find the radius of a can with volume V. What is the radius of a can whose volume is 192 cm^3?
4 cm

Given an animal's body mass m, in grams, the formula $B = 1.8m^{\frac{3}{4}}$ may be used to estimate the mass b, in grams, of the animal's brain. The table shows the body mass of several birds. Use the table for questions 5–6. Select the best answer.

5. Which is the best estimate for the brain mass of a macaw?
A 9 g 　 C 125 g
B 45 g 　 **(D)** 225 g

6. How much larger is the brain mass of a barn owl compared to the brain mass of a cockatiel?
F 189 g 　 H 388.8 g
(G) 340.2 g 　 J 1215 g

7. An animal has a body mass given by the expression x^4. Which expression can be used to estimate the animal's brain mass?
(A) $B = 1.8x^3$ 　 C $B = 1.8x^{12}$
B $B = 1.8x^{\frac{3}{4}}$ 　 D $B = 1.8x$

Typical Body Masses of Birds	
Bird	**Body Mass (g)**
Cockatiel	81
Guam Rail	256
Macaw	625
Barn Owl	1296

Sources:
http://www.beyondveg.com/billings-t/comp-anat/comp-anat-appx2.shtml
http://www.sandiegozoo.org/animalbytes/index.html

7-5 CHALLENGE

LESSON 7-5 Challenge
Keep Growing!

Find a path from start to finish in the maze below. Each box that you pass through must have a value that is *greater than or equal to* the value in the previous box. You may only move horizontally or vertically to go from one box to the next.

START (above the third box of the first row)

$16^{\frac{1}{4}}$	$4^{\frac{1}{2}} - 27^{\frac{1}{3}}$	$0^{\frac{1}{5}}$	$1^{\frac{2}{3}} - 8^{\frac{1}{3}}$	$216^{\frac{2}{3}}$	$8^{\frac{1}{3}} + 9^{\frac{3}{2}}$
$36^{\frac{1}{2}} - 216^{\frac{1}{3}}$	$25^{\frac{1}{2}} - 32^{\frac{2}{5}}$	$9^{\frac{1}{2}} - 8^{\frac{1}{3}}$	$1^{\frac{3}{5}}$	$64^{\frac{1}{6}}$	$100^{\frac{1}{2}} + 27^{\frac{2}{3}}$
$1^{\frac{1}{2}} - 9^{\frac{3}{2}}$	$125^{\frac{2}{3}}$	$81^{\frac{3}{4}}$	$1000^{\frac{2}{3}}$	$16^{\frac{1}{2}} - 16^{\frac{1}{4}}$	$32^{\frac{1}{5}} + 0^{\frac{3}{4}}$
$512^{\frac{2}{9}}$	$9^{\frac{1}{2}} + 3^{\frac{4}{4}}$	$32^{\frac{2}{5}}$	$27^{\frac{1}{3}}$	$121^0 + 1^{\frac{1}{2}}$	$9^{\frac{1}{2}} - 3^0$
$49^{\frac{1}{2}} + 0^{\frac{1}{2}}$	$16^{\frac{3}{4}}$	$16^{\frac{1}{4}} - 1^{\frac{3}{2}}$	$1024^{\frac{1}{10}}$	$81^{\frac{1}{4}} + 49^{\frac{1}{2}}$	$243^{\frac{4}{5}}$
$16^{\frac{3}{4}} + 32^{\frac{1}{5}}$	$100^{\frac{1}{2}}$	$625^{\frac{1}{4}}$	$128^{\frac{2}{7}}$	$144^{\frac{1}{2}} - 81^{\frac{1}{2}}$	$64^{\frac{1}{3}}$
$125^{\frac{1}{3}} - 2^0$	$81^{\frac{3}{4}} - 32^{\frac{4}{5}}$	$256^{\frac{1}{2}}$	$16^{\frac{3}{4}} + 4^{\frac{3}{2}}$	$64^{\frac{2}{3}}$	$32^{\frac{1}{5}} + 100^{\frac{1}{2}}$
$625^{\frac{1}{4}}$	$64^{\frac{5}{6}} - 125^{\frac{2}{3}}$	$243^{\frac{2}{5}}$	$125^{\frac{2}{3}}$	$128^{\frac{3}{7}}$	$243^{\frac{1}{5}}$

FINISH (below the fourth box of the last row)

CONCEPT CONNECTION

Organizer

Objective: Assess students' ability to apply concepts and skills in Lessons 7-1 through 7-5 in a real-world format.

Problem	Text Reference
1	Lesson 7-1
2	Lesson 7-2
3	Lesson 7-3
4	Lesson 7-3
5	Lesson 7-4

Answer

2. 1×10^{15}

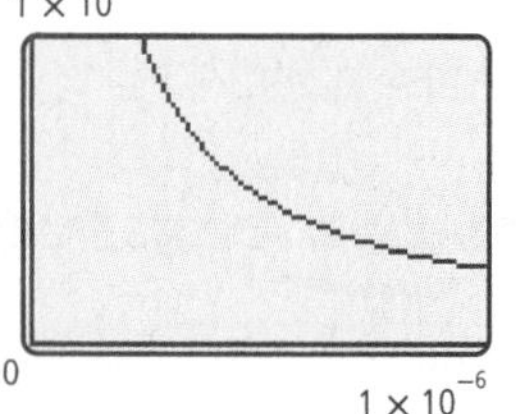

As the wavelength increases, the frequency decreases.

CONCEPT CONNECTION

SECTION 7A

Exponents

I See the Light! The speed of light is the product of its frequency f and its wavelength w. In air, the speed of light is 3×10^8 m/s.

1. $f = \frac{3 \times 10^8}{w}$; $f = (3 \times 10^8)w^{-1}$

1. Write an equation for the relationship described above, and then solve this equation for frequency. Write this equation as an equation with w raised to a negative exponent.
2. Wavelengths of visible light range from 400 to 700 nanometers (10^{-9} meters). Use a graphing calculator and the relationship you found in Problem 1 to graph frequency as a function of wavelength. Sketch the graph with the axes clearly labeled. Describe your graph.
3. The speed of light in water is $\frac{3}{4}$ of its speed in air. Find the speed of light in water. **2.25×10^8 m/s**
4. When light enters water, some colors bend more than others. How much the light bends depends on its wavelength. This is what creates a rainbow. The frequency of green light is about 5.9×10^{14} cycles per second. Find the wavelength of green light in water. **about 3.81×10^{-7} m**
5. When light enters water, colors with shorter wavelengths bend more than colors with longer wavelengths. Violet light has a frequency of 7.5×10^{14} cycles per second, and red light has a frequency of 4.6×10^{14} cycles per second. Which of these colors of light will bend more when it enters water? Justify your answer.

Violet light will bend more. Students can justify by using the inverse relationship, by using the graph, or by finding the wavelength for each color and comparing them.

INTERVENTION 

Scaffolding Questions

1. What does it mean to "solve for frequency"? Isolate the variable that represents frequency.
2. What are a reasonable domain and range? Possible answer: D: 380 to 760; R: 3×10^{14} to 9×10^{14}
3. How do you enter numbers in scientific notation into a calculator? Possible answer: 3×10^{14} is entered as 3 [2nd] [EE] 14 or 3 [×] [2nd] [10^x] 14.
4. What information do you need for this problem? speed of light in water Where can you find this information? answer to Problem 3
5. How does wavelength change as frequency changes? As one increases, the other decreases.

Extension

When you choose an FM radio station, you are choosing the frequency in MHz, or millions of waves per second (90 MHz = 90,000,000 waves per second). Find the wavelength for your favorite FM radio station. Possible answer: Using $w = (3 \times 10^8) f^{-1}$, FM 93.7 has an approximate wavelength of 3.2 m.

Algebra 1 2.0

CHAPTER 7

SECTION 7A

Quiz for Lessons 7-1 Through 7-5

7-1 Integer Exponents

Evaluate each expression for the given value(s) of the variable(s).

1. t^{-6} for $t = 2$ $\frac{1}{64}$
2. n^{-3} for $n = -5$ $-\frac{1}{125}$
3. $r^0 s^{-2}$ for $r = 8$ and $s = 10$ $\frac{1}{100}$

Simplify.

4. $5k^{-3}$ $\frac{5}{k^3}$
5. $\frac{x^4}{y^{-6}}$ x^4y^6
6. $8f^{-4}g^0$ $\frac{8}{f^4}$
7. $\frac{a^{-3}}{b^{-2}}$ $\frac{b^2}{a^3}$
8. **Measurement** Metric units can be written in terms of a base unit. The table shows some of these equivalencies. Simplify each expression.

Selected Metric Prefixes					
Milli-	Centi-	Deci-	Deka-	Hecto-	Kilo-
10^{-3}	10^{-2}	10^{-1}	10^1	10^2	10^3

7-2 Powers of 10 and Scientific Notation

9. Find the value of 10^4. **10,000**
10. Write 0.0000001 as a power of 10. 10^{-7}
11. Write 100,000,000,000 as a power of 10. 10^{11}
12. Find the value of 82.1×10^4. **821,000**
13. **Measurement** The lead in a mechanical pencil has a diameter of 0.5 mm. Write this number in scientific notation. 5×10^{-1}

7-3 Multiplication Properties of Exponents

Simplify.

14. $2^2 \cdot 2^5$ 2^7
15. $3^5 \cdot 3^{-3}$ 3^2, or 9
16. $p^4 \cdot p^5$ p^9
17. $a^3 \cdot a^{-6} \cdot a^{-2}$ $\frac{1}{a^5}$
18. **Biology** A swarm of locusts was estimated to contain 2.8×10^{10} individual insects. If each locust weighs about 2.5 grams, how much did this entire swarm weigh? Write your answer in scientific notation. 7×10^{10} g

Simplify.

19. $(3x^4)^3$ $27x^{12}$
20. $(m^3n^2)^5$ $m^{15}n^{10}$
21. $(-4d^7)^2$ $16d^{14}$
22. $(cd^6)^3 \cdot (c^5d^2)^2$ $c^{13}d^{22}$

7-4 Division Properties of Exponents

Simplify.

23. $\frac{6^9}{6^7}$ 36
24. $\frac{12a^5}{3a^2}$ $4a^3$
25. $\left(\frac{3}{5}\right)^3$ $\frac{27}{125}$
26. $\left(\frac{4p^3}{2pq^4}\right)^2$ $\frac{4p^4}{q^8}$

Simplify each quotient and write the answer in scientific notation.

27. $(8 \times 10^9) \div (2 \times 10^6)$ 4×10^3
28. $(3.5 \times 10^5) \div (7 \times 10^8)$ 5×10^{-4}
29. $(1 \times 10^4) \div (4 \times 10^4)$ 2.5×10^{-1}

7-5 Fractional Exponents

Simplify each expression. All variables represent nonnegative numbers.

30. $81^{\frac{1}{2}}$ 9
31. $125^{\frac{1}{3}}$ 5
32. $4^{\frac{3}{2}}$ 8
33. $0^{\frac{2}{9}}$ 0
34. $\sqrt{x^8y^4}$ x^4y^2
35. $\sqrt[3]{r^9}$ r^3
36. $\sqrt[6]{z^{12}}$ z^2
37. $\sqrt[3]{p^3q^{12}}$ pq^4

READY TO GO ON?

SECTION 7A

Organizer

Objective: Assess students' mastery of concepts and skills in Lessons 7-1 through 7-5.

Countdown to Mastery Week 16

Resources

Assessment Resources

Section 7A Quiz

Test & Practice Generator
One-Stop Planner®

INTERVENTION

Resources

***Ready to Go On? Intervention and Enrichment* Worksheets**

***Ready to Go On?* CD-ROM**

***Ready to Go On?* Online**

my.hrw.com

Answer

8. $10^{-3} = \frac{1}{1000}$, or 0.001;
$10^{-2} = \frac{1}{100}$, or 0.01;
$10^{-1} = \frac{1}{10}$, or 0.1;
$10^1 = 10$; $10^2 = 100$;
$10^3 = 1000$

READY TO GO ON?
Diagnose and Prescribe

NO
INTERVENE

Ready to Go On? Intervention	*Ready to Go On? Intervention,* Section 7A		
	Worksheets	CD-ROM	Online
Lesson 7-1 2.0	7-1 Intervention	Activity 7-1	Diagnose and Prescribe Online
Lesson 7-2 2.0	7-2 Intervention	Activity 7-2	
Lesson 7-3 2.0	7-3 Intervention	Activity 7-3	
Lesson 7-4 2.0	7-4 Intervention	Activity 7-4	
Lesson 7-5 2.0	7-5 Intervention	Activity 7-5	

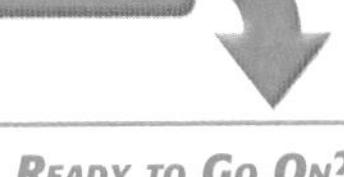

YES
ENRICH

***Ready to Go On? Enrichment,* Section 7A**

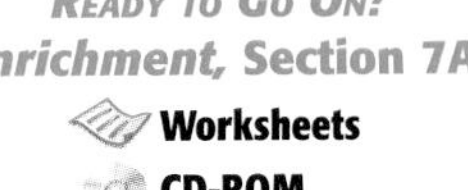

Worksheets
CD-ROM
Online

Polynomials

One-Minute Section Planner

Lesson	Lab Resources	Materials
Lesson 7-6 Polynomials • Classify polynomials and write polynomials in standard form. • Evaluate polynomial expressions. **Preparation for 10.0**		**Optional** index cards, scissors, tape, ruler (MK), 8.5-by-11 inch paper
7-7 Algebra Lab Model Polynomial Addition and Subtraction • Use algebra tiles to model polynomial addition and subtraction. **10.0**		**Required** algebra tiles (MK)
Lesson 7-7 Adding and Subtracting Polynomials • Add and subtract polynomials. **10.0**	***Technology Lab 7-7*** In *Chapter 7 Resource File*	**Optional** books, pencils, slips of paper
7-8 Algebra Lab Model Polynomial Multiplication • Use algebra tiles to model polynomial multiplication. **10.0**		**Required** algebra tiles (MK)
Lesson 7-8 Multiplying Polynomials • Multiply polynomials. **10.0**		**Optional** graphing calculator
Lesson 7-9 Special Products of Binomials • Find special products of binomials **10.0**		

MK = *Manipulatives Kit*

Notes

Math Background: Teaching the Standards

Professional Development

TERMINOLOGY

Lesson 7-6

In order to discuss polynomials, we must agree on terminology. The basic unit is the *monomial*. A monomial is a product of a real number and one or more variables with whole-number exponents. (The real number is usually rational, particularly within the scope of Algebra 1, but this is not a requirement.)

A *polynomial* is a sum of monomials. For example, the polynomial $8x^4 - 3x - 1$ may be written as $8x^4 + (-3x) + (-1)$, which is the sum of the monomials $8x^4$, $-3x$, and -1.

POLYNOMIALS 10.0

Lesson 7-6

Polynomials are in many ways analogous to counting numbers. Because our number system is base 10, all counting numbers can be written in expanded form in terms of powers of 10. For example, consider the expanded form of 653.

$$\begin{aligned} 653 &= 6 \cdot 100 + 5 \cdot 10 + 3 \cdot 1 \\ &= 6 \cdot 10^2 + 5 \cdot 10^1 + 3 \cdot 10^0 \end{aligned}$$

You can create a polynomial by replacing each of the 10s by a variable, such as x.

$$\begin{array}{ccccc} 6 \cdot 10^2 & + & 5 \cdot 10^1 & + & 3 \cdot 10^0 \\ \downarrow & & \downarrow & & \downarrow \\ 6 \cdot x^2 & + & 5 \cdot x^1 & + & 3 \cdot x^0 \end{array}$$

This polynomial is usually written in the more familiar form $6x^2 + 5x + 3$. For counting numbers, the only permissible multipliers of the powers of 10 are the digits 0 through 9, inclusive. For polynomials, any real number can be a multiplier of the variable terms.

The goal of this analogy is not to suggest that there is a correspondence between counting numbers and polynomials but to demonstrate that diverse mathematical concepts sometimes share underlying structures. As such, it makes sense to pose some of the same questions about polynomials that one might pose about counting numbers. For example, can we add, subtract, multiply, and divide polynomials? How?

POLYNOMIAL OPERATIONS  10.0

Lessons 7-7 to 7-9

Adding and subtracting polynomials is fairly straightforward because the process is nothing more than combining like terms.

$$(3x^2 + 7x + 5) + (2x + 6) = 3x^2 + 9x + 11$$

Polynomial multiplication can present greater difficulty for students, so it is essential to build gradually. Multiplication of two monomials is a natural starting point. You can use the Commutative and Associative Properties to show that $(4x)(2x) = 8x^2$.

Use the Distributive Property when multiplying a monomial and a binomial:

$$5x(2x + 3) = (5x)(2x) + (5x)(3) = 10x^2 + 15x$$

The Distributive Property is used repeatedly when multiplying a binomial by a binomial:

$$\begin{aligned} (3x + 2)(7x + 4) &= (3x)(7x + 4) + (2)(7x + 4) \\ &= 21x^2 + 12x + 14x + 8 \\ &= 21x^2 + 26x + 8 \end{aligned}$$

In fact, the Distributive Property can be used to multiply any two polynomials, regardless of the number of terms. The product will have one term for each product of a term from the first polynomial and a term from the second polynomial. So, the product of a binomial (2 terms) and a trinomial (3 terms) will have $2 \cdot 3 = 6$ terms before simplifying:

$$\begin{aligned} &(x + 2)(x^2 + 6x + 8) \\ &= (x + 2)(x^2) + (x + 2)(6x) + (x + 2)(8) \\ &= (x)(x^2) + 2(x^2) + x(6x) + 2(6x) + x(8) + 2(8) \end{aligned}$$

It is important to remember that this rule is true before the product is simplified. Clearly, some of the terms above are like terms and will be combined; the final answer will have fewer than 6 terms.

In general, the product of a polynomial with m terms and a polynomial with n terms has mn terms before simplifying.

7-6 Organizer

Objectives: Classify polynomials and write polynomials in standard form.

Evaluate polynomial expressions.

 **Online Edition**
Tutorial Videos

 **Countdown to Mastery Week 16**

Power Presentations with PowerPoint®

Warm Up

Evaluate each expression for the given value of *x*.

1. $2x + 3; x = 2$ 7
2. $x^2 + 4; x = -3$ 13
3. $-4x - 2; x = -1$ 2
4. $7x^2 + 2x; x = 3$ 69

Identify the coefficient in each term.

5. $4x^3$ 4
6. y^3 1
7. $2n^7$ 2
8. $-s^4$ −1

Also available on transparency 

Math Humor

Q: What happened to the quadratic polynomial when it fell asleep on the beach?

A: It got second-degree burns.

7-6 Polynomials

California Standards

Preparation for 10.0 Students add, subtract, multiply, and divide monomials and polynomials. Students solve multistep problems, including word problems, by using these techniques.

Vocabulary
monomial
degree of a monomial
polynomial
degree of a polynomial
standard form of a polynomial
leading coefficient
quadratic
cubic
binomial
trinomial
root

Who uses this?
Pyrotechnicians can use polynomials to plan complex fireworks displays. (See Example 4.)

A **monomial** is a number, a variable, or a product of numbers and variables with whole-number exponents. A monomial may be a constant or a single variable.

Monomials	Not Monomials
$5 \quad x \quad -7xy \quad 0.5x^4$	$-0.3x^{-2} \quad 4x - y \quad \frac{2}{x^3}$

The **degree of a monomial** is the sum of the exponents of the variables. A constant has degree 0.

EXAMPLE 1 Finding the Degree of a Monomial

Find the degree of each monomial.

A $-2a^2b^4$
The degree is 6. *Add the exponents of the variables: 2 + 4 = 6*

B 4
$4x^0$ *There is no variable, but you can write 4 as $4x^0$.*
The degree is 0.

C $8y$
$8y^1$ *A variable written without an exponent has exponent 1.*
The degree is 1.

Remember!
The *terms* of an expression are the parts being added or subtracted. See Lesson 1-7.

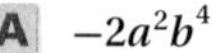

CHECK IT OUT! Find the degree of each monomial.
1a. $1.5k^2m$ 3 **1b.** $4x$ 1 **1c.** $2c^3$ 3

A **polynomial** is a monomial or a sum or difference of monomials. The **degree of a polynomial** is the degree of the term with the greatest degree.

The terms of a polynomial may be written in any order. However, polynomials that contain only one variable are usually written in *standard form.*

The **standard form of a polynomial** that contains one variable is written with the terms in order from greatest degree to least degree. When written in standard form, the coefficient of the first term is called the **leading coefficient**.

1 Introduce

EXPLORATION

7-6 Polynomials

1. The table shows examples of expressions that are and are not *polynomials.* What are some characteristics that the polynomials have in common? Describe some ways in which the polynomials are different from the expressions that are not polynomials.

Polynomials	Not Polynomials
$4x^2 - 5x + 1$	3^x
$3y^8 - 0.5y$	$0.6x^{-1} + 7$
$\frac{1}{2}z^5 - 2z^4 + 8z^2 + \frac{3}{4}z + \frac{1}{3}$	$\frac{4}{x^2}$
$-9x^2$	$-2z^3 + 3z^2 + \frac{1}{z}$
$1.7xy$	$3xy^{-5} + 3x^2y^{-8}$
$4x^2y - x^3y^2$	$\frac{1}{xy^2} + 2$

2. What do you notice about the exponents in the polynomials?
3. Do you think $16x^2 + 2xy + 8y^{-2}$ is a polynomial? Why or why not?

THINK AND DISCUSS

4. **Show** your own examples of expressions that are and are not polynomials.
5. **Describe** how you can tell whether an expression is a polynomial.

Motivate

Write $m^3 + n^2 + p + 5$ on the board. Ask students how many terms are in the expression. 4

Then have students identify the exponent of each variable.

m: 3

n: 2

p: 1

Ask students to identify the greatest exponent. 3

Explorations and answers are provided in *Alternate Openers: Explorations Transparencies.*

Preparation for 10.0

EXAMPLE 2 Writing Polynomials in Standard Form

Write each polynomial in standard form. Then give the leading coefficient.

A $20x - 4x^3 + 2 - x^2$

Find the degree of each term. Then arrange them in descending order.

$$\underbrace{20x}_{1}\ \underbrace{-4x^3}_{3}\ \underbrace{+2}_{0}\ \underbrace{-x^2}_{2} \longrightarrow \underbrace{-4x^3}_{3}\ \underbrace{-x^2}_{2}\ \underbrace{+20x}_{1}\ \underbrace{+2}_{0}$$

Degree: 1 3 0 2 → 3 2 1 0

The standard form is $-4x^3 - x^2 + 20x + 2$. The leading coefficient is -4.

B $y^3 + y^5 + 4y$

Find the degree of each term. Then arrange them in descending order.

$$\underbrace{y^3}_{3}\ \underbrace{+y^5}_{5}\ \underbrace{+4y}_{1} \longrightarrow \underbrace{y^5}_{5}\ \underbrace{+y^3}_{3}\ \underbrace{+4y}_{1}$$

Degree: 3 5 1 → 5 3 1

The standard form is $y^5 + y^3 + 4y$. The leading coefficient is 1.

Remember!

A variable written without a coefficient has a coefficient of 1.

$y^5 = 1y^5$

Write each polynomial in standard form. Then give the leading coefficient.

2a. $16 - 4x^2 + x^5 + 9x^3$ **$x^5 + 9x^3 - 4x^2 + 16$; 1**

2b. $18y^5 - 3y^8 + 14y$ **$-3y^8 + 18y^5 + 14y$; -3**

Some polynomials have special names based on their degree and the number of terms they have.

Degree	Name
0	Constant
1	Linear
2	**Quadratic**
3	**Cubic**
4	Quartic
5	Quintic
6 or more	6th degree, 7th degree, and so on

Terms	Name
1	Monomial
2	**Binomial**
3	**Trinomial**
4 or more	Polynomial

EXAMPLE 3 Classifying Polynomials

Classify each polynomial according to its degree and number of terms.

A $5x - 6$
Degree: 1 Terms: 2 $5x - 6$ is a linear binomial.

B $y + y^2 + 4$
Degree: 2 Terms: 3 $y + y^2 + 4$ is a quadratic trinomial.

C $6x^7 + 9x^2 - x + 3$
Degree: 7 Terms: 4 $6x^7 + 9x^2 - x + 3$ is a 7th-degree polynomial.

D n^3
Degree: 3 Terms: 1 n^3 is a cubic monomial.

Classify each polynomial according to its degree and number of terms.

3a. $x^3 + x^2 - x + 2$ **cubic polynomial**

3b. 6 **constant monomial**

3c. $-3y^8 + 18y^5 + 14y$ **8th-degree trinomial**

COMMON ERROR ALERT

Students often confuse the degree of a polynomial with the number of terms. Students may be less likely to confuse the two if they equate the word *degree* with an exponent-related phrase such as "maximum power."

Power Presentations with PowerPoint®

Additional Examples

Example 1

Find the degree of each monomial.

A. $4p^4q^3$ 7

B. $7ed$ 2

C. 3 0

Example 2

Write each polynomial in standard form. Then give the leading coefficient.

A. $6x - 7x^5 + 4x^2 + 9$
$-7x^5 + 4x^2 + 6x + 9$; -7

B. $y^2 + y^6 - 3y$
$y^6 + y^2 - 3y$; 1

Example 3

Classify each polynomial according to its degree and number of terms.

A. $5n^3 + 4n$ cubic binomial

B. $-2x$ linear monomial

Also available on transparency

2 Teach

Guided Instruction

Discuss with students examples and non-examples of monomials. Explain how to find the degree of a monomial and the degree of a polynomial. Be sure students get plenty of exposure to the new vocabulary in this lesson—it will be used often throughout the remainder of this chapter and Chapter 8.

Universal Access

Through Modeling

Divide students into groups of five, and have each write a monomial on an index card in large print. They may write a constant or a monomial with a variable. Tell them the variable must be *x*, but it can be raised to any power between 1 and 4, and can have any coefficient. Then call out classifications such as *quadratic trinomial* and *quartic binomial.* Have students in each group stand and arrange themselves to form that polynomial, holding their monomial in front of them for the rest of the class to see.

INTERVENTION

Questioning Strategies

EXAMPLE 1

- If a monomial has more than one variable with an exponent, how do you determine its degree?
- Why is the degree of a constant always zero?

EXAMPLE 2

- Do coefficients affect the degree of the polynomial? Explain.
- When is the coefficient of the first term also the leading coefficient of the polynomial?

EXAMPLE 3

- Why will a constant polynomial always be a monomial?
- How does writing a polynomial in standard form help you classify the polynomial?

Power Presentations with PowerPoint®

Additional Examples

Example 4

A tourist accidentally drops her lip balm off the Golden Gate Bridge. The bridge is 220 feet from the water of the bay. The height of the lip balm is given by the polynomial $-16t^2 + 220$, where t is time in seconds. How far above the water will the lip balm be after 3 seconds? 76 ft

Example 5

Tell whether each number is a root of $3x^2 - 48$.

A. 4 yes **B.** 0 no **C.** -4 yes

Also available on transparency

INTERVENTION
Questioning Strategies

EXAMPLE 4

- What step in the order of operations will never be used when evaluating a polynomial in standard form? Why?

EXAMPLE 5

- What does it mean for a number to be a root of a polynomial?
- Can 0 be a root of a polynomial? Is it a root of every polynomial?

EXAMPLE 4 *Physical Science Application*

A firework is launched from a platform 6 feet above the ground at a speed of 200 feet per second. The firework has a 5-second fuse. The height of the firework in feet is given by the polynomial $-16t^2 + 200t + 6$, where t is the time in seconds. How high will the firework be when it explodes?

Substitute the time for t to find the firework's height.

$-16t^2 + 200t + 6$

$-16(5)^2 + 200(5) + 6$ *The time is 5 seconds.*

$-16(25) + 200(5) + 6$

$-400 + 1000 + 6$ *Evaluate the polynomial by using the order of operations.*

606

When the firework explodes, it will be 606 feet above the ground.

4. What if...? Another firework with a 5-second fuse is launched from the same platform at a speed of 400 feet per second. Its height is given by $-16t^2 + 400t + 6$. How high will this firework be when it explodes? **1606 ft**

A **root** of a polynomial in one variable is a value of the variable for which the polynomial is equal to 0.

EXAMPLE 5 Identifying Roots of Polynomials

Tell whether each number is a root of $2k^2 - k - 3$.

A 4		**B** -1
$2k^2 - k - 3$		$2k^2 - k - 3$
$2(4)^2 - 4 - 3$	*Substitute for k.*	$2(-1)^2 - (-1) - 3$
$2(16) - 4 - 3$		$2(1) + 1 - 3$
$32 - 4 - 3$	*Simplify.*	$2 + 1 - 3$
25 ✗		0 ✓
$25 \neq 0$, so 4 is not a root of $2k^2 - k - 3$.		-1 is a root of $2k^2 - k - 3$.

5. Tell whether 1 is a root of $3x^3 + x - 4$. **yes**

THINK AND DISCUSS

1. Explain why each expression is not a polynomial: $2x^2 + 3x^{-3}$; $1 - \frac{a}{b}$.

2. GET ORGANIZED Copy and complete the graphic organizer. In each circle, write an example of the given type of polynomial.

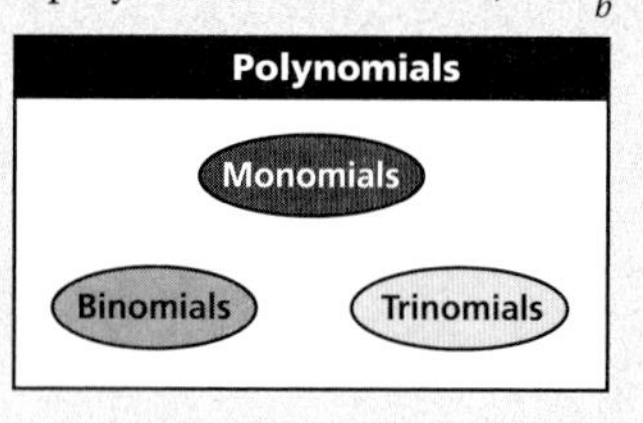

3 Close

Summarize

Have students give examples of monomials, binomials, trinomials, and polynomials of fourth and fifth degree. Write their examples on the board as they say them. For each, have students state whether the polynomial is in standard form, and if not, rewrite it in standard form.

FORMATIVE ASSESSMENT

and INTERVENTION

***Diagnose Before* the Lesson**
7-6 Warm Up, TE p. 430

***Monitor During* the Lesson**
Check It Out! Exercises, SE pp. 430–432
Questioning Strategies, TE pp. 431–432

***Assess After* the Lesson**
7-6 Lesson Quiz, TE p. 435
Alternative Assessment, TE p. 435

Answers to *Think and Discuss*

1. Possible answer: $2x^2 + 3x^{-3}$ contains an expression with a negative exponent. $1 - \frac{a}{b}$ contains a variable within a denominator.
2. See p. A6.

7-6 Exercises

California Standards Practice
Preparation for 10.0; 25.2

go.hrw.com
Homework Help Online
KEYWORD: MA8CA 7-6
Parent Resources Online
KEYWORD: MA8CA Parent

GUIDED PRACTICE

Vocabulary Match each polynomial on the left with its classification on the right.

1. $2x^3 + 6$ **d**
2. $3x^3 + 4x^2 - 7$ **c**
3. $5x^2 - 2x + 3x^4 - 6$ **a**

a. quartic polynomial
b. quadratic polynomial
c. cubic trinomial
d. cubic binomial

SEE EXAMPLE 1 p. 430

Find the degree of each monomial.

4. 10^6 **0**
5. $-7xy^2$ **3**
6. $0.4n^8$ **8**
7. 2 **0**

SEE EXAMPLE 2 p. 431

Write each polynomial in standard form. Then give the leading coefficient.

8. $-2b + 5 + b^2$ **$b^2 - 2b + 5$; 1**
9. $9a^8 - 8a^9$ **$-8a^9 + 9a^8$; −8**
10. $5s^2 - 3s + 3 - s^7$ **$-s^7 + 5s^2 - 3s + 3$; −1**
11. $2x + 3x^2 - 1$ **$3x^2 + 2x - 1$; 3**
12. $5g - 7 + g^2$ **$g^2 + 5g - 7$; 1**
13. $3c^2 + 5c^4 + 5c^3 - 4$ **$5c^4 + 5c^3 + 3c^2 - 4$; 5**

SEE EXAMPLE 3 p. 431

Classify each polynomial according to its degree and number of terms.

14. $x^2 + 2x + 3$ **quadratic trinomial**
15. $7 - x$ **linear binomial**
16. $8 + k + 5k^4$ **quartic trinomial**
17. $q^2 + 6 - q^3 + 3q^4$ **quartic polynomial**
18. $7k^3 + 5k^2$ **cubic binomial**
19. $2a^3 + 4a^2 - a^4$ **quartic trinomial**

SEE EXAMPLE 4 p. 432

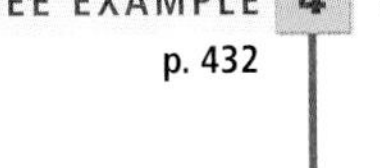

20. **Geometry** The surface area of a cone is approximated by the polynomial $3.14r^2 + 3.14r\ell$, where r is the radius and ℓ is the slant height. Find the approximate surface area of this cone. **301.44 cm²**

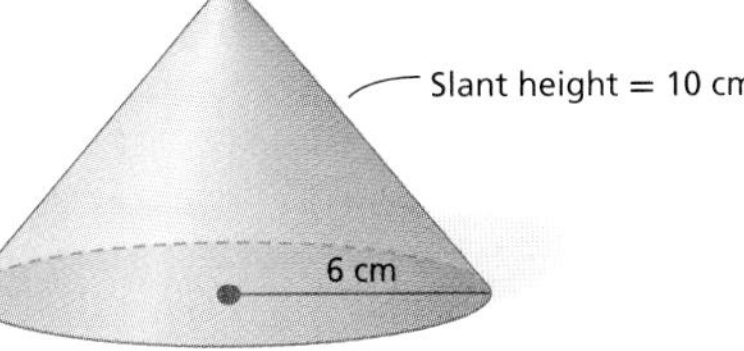

SEE EXAMPLE 5 p. 432

Tell whether each number is a root of the polynomial.

21. $4x^2 + 3$; 0 **no**
22. $-2n + 4$; −2 **no**
23. $a^2 + 6a + 9$; −3 **yes**
24. $m^3 + 2m - 1$; 1 **no**
25. $x^2 - 4x + 3$; 3 **yes**
26. $x^2 - 4x + 3$; 1 **yes**

PRACTICE AND PROBLEM SOLVING

Independent Practice

For Exercises	See Example
27–34	1
35–43	2
44–51	3
52	4
53–58	5

Extra Practice
Skills Practice p. EP15
Application Practice p. EP30

Find the degree of each monomial.

27. $3y^4$ **4**
28. $6k$ **1**
29. $2a^3b^2c$ **6**
30. 325 **0**
31. $2y^4z^3$ **7**
32. $9m^5$ **5**
33. p **1**
34. 5 **0**

Write each polynomial in standard form. Then give the leading coefficient.

35. $2.5 + 4.9t^3 - 4t^2 + t$ **$4.9t^3 - 4t^2 + t + 2.5$; 4.9**
36. $8a - 10a^2 + 2$ **$-10a^2 + 8a + 2$; −10**
37. $x^7 - x + x^3 - x^5 + x^{10}$ **$x^{10} + x^7 - x^5 + x^3 - x$; 1**
38. $-m + 7 - 3m^2$ **$-3m^2 - m + 7$; −3**
39. $3x^2 + 5x - 4 + 5x^3$ **$5x^3 + 3x^2 + 5x - 4$; 5**
40. $-2n + 1 - n^2$ **$-n^2 - 2n + 1$; −1**
41. $4d + 3d^2 - d^3 + 5$ **$-d^3 + 3d^2 + 4d + 5$; −1**
42. $3s^2 + 12s^3 + 6$ **$12s^3 + 3s^2 + 6$; 12**
43. $4x^2 - x^5 - x^3 + 1$ **$-x^5 - x^3 + 4x^2 + 1$; −1**

Classify each polynomial according to its degree and number of terms.

44. 12 **constant monomial**
45. $6k$ **linear monomial**
46. $3.5x^3 - 4.1x - 6$ **cubic trinomial**
47. $4g + 2g^2 - 3$ **quadratic trinomial**
48. $2x^2 - 6x$ **quadratic binomial**
49. $6 - s^3 - 3s^4$ **quartic trinomial**
50. $c^2 + 7 - 2c^3$ **cubic trinomial**
51. $-y^2$ **quadratic monomial**

7-6 Exercises

Assignment Guide

Assign *Guided Practice* exercises as necessary.

If you finished Examples **1–3**
Proficient 27–51
Advanced 27–51

If you finished Examples **1–5**
Proficient 27–79, 81–89
Advanced 27–74, 76–89

Homework Quick Check
Quickly check key concepts.
Exercises: 26, 32, 36, 42, 52, 58

Teacher to Teacher

For many students it is easier to identify the degree of each term in a polynomial when each term is written with the variables and their exponents. For example:

$5x^2y + 25xy + 75$
$= 5x^2y^1 + 25x^1y^1 + 75x^0y^0$
$5x^2y^1 \longrightarrow$ degree $2 + 1 = 3$
$25x^1y^1 \longrightarrow$ degree $1 + 1 = 2$
$75x^0y^0 \longrightarrow$ degree $0 + 0 = 0$

The highest degree is 3, so the polynomial $5x^2y + 25xy + 75$ has degree 3.

Arlane Frederick
Buffalo, NY

California Standards

Standard	Exercises
2.0	86–89
5.0	81, 82
Prep for 10.0	4–58, 63–80
25.2	75

Exercise 74 involves expressing the area and perimeter of a rectangle as a polynomial. This exercise prepares students for the Concept Connection on page 462.

Concrete Manipulatives Have students make (or attempt to make) the boxes for parts **a, b,** and **c** of **Exercise 63.** Give students scissors and tape and make sure they have a ruler and 8.5-by-11-inch paper (standard size of notebook or copy paper). The ruler can be found in the Manipulatives Kit (MK).

Answers

59. A monomial is defined to be a polynomial with one term.
60. Possible answer: $x^3 + 2x + 6$ is a 3rd-degree trinomial, but $x^2 + x - 1$ is a 2nd-degree trinomial.
61. A binomial has 2 terms and a trinomial has 3 terms.
62. A monomial is polynomial with one term. Other polynomials have two or more terms.
73. Possible answer: First identify the degree of each term. From left to right, the degrees are 3, 0, 2, 4, and 1. Arrange the terms in order of decreasing degree, and move the plus or minus sign in front of each term with it: $-2x^4 + 4x^3 + 5x^2 - x - 3$.
78.

Time (s)	Height (ft)
1	59
2	86
3	81
4	44

The rocket will be highest after 2 s.

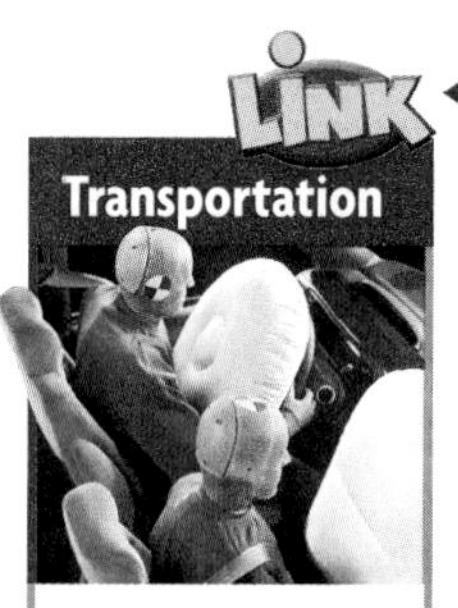

Transportation

Hybrid III is the crash test dummy used by the Insurance Institute for Highway Safety. During a crash test, sensors in the dummy's head, neck, chest, legs, and feet measure and record forces. Engineers study this data to help design safer cars.

52. **Transportation** The polynomial $3.675v + 0.096v^2$ is used by transportation officials to estimate the stopping distance in feet for a car whose speed is v miles per hour on flat, dry pavement. What is the stopping distance for a car traveling at 30 miles per hour? **196.65 ft**

Tell whether each number is a root of the polynomial.

53. $6x$; 0 **yes**
54. $-r^3 + 2r - 2$; 1 **no**
55. $3x^4 - 48$; 2 **yes**
56. $125 - d^3$; 5 **yes**
57. $2n^2 - 3n$; 3 **no**
58. $5t^2 + 3t - 4$; -2 **no**

Tell whether each statement is sometimes, always, or never true. Explain.

59. A monomial is a polynomial. **always**
60. A trinomial is a 3rd-degree polynomial. **sometimes**
61. A binomial is a trinomial. **never**
62. A polynomial has two or more terms. **sometimes**

63. **Geometry** A piece of 8.5-by-11-inch cardboard has identical squares cut from its corners. It is then folded into a box with no lid. The volume of the box in cubic inches is $4c^3 - 39c^2 + 93.5c$, where c is the side length of the missing squares in inches.
   a. What is the volume of the box if $c = 1$ in.? **58.5 in³**
   b. What is the volume of the box if $c = 1.5$ in.? **66 in³**
   c. What is the volume of the box if $c = 4.25$ in.? **0**
   d. **Critical Thinking** Does your answer to part **c** make sense? Explain why or why not. **Yes; the width of the cardboard is 8.5 in., so 4.25 in. cuts will meet, leaving nothing to fold up.**

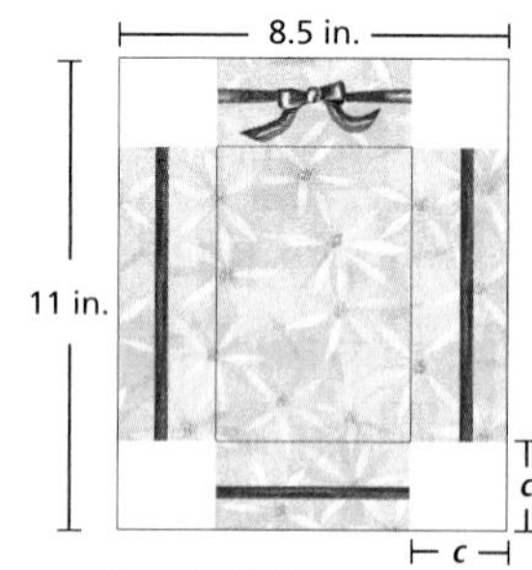

Copy and complete the table by evaluating each polynomial for the given values of x.

	Polynomial	$x = -2$	$x = 0$	$x = 5$
64.	$5x - 6$	$5(-2) - 6 = -16$	$5(0) - 6 = -6$	**19**
65.	$x^5 + x^3 + 4x$	**−48**	**0**	**3270**
66.	$-10x^2$	**−40**	**0**	**−250**

Give one example of each type of polynomial. Possible answers given.

67. quadratic trinomial **$x^2 + 3x - 6$**
68. linear binomial **$5x - 2$**
69. constant monomial **5**
70. cubic monomial **$6x^3$**
71. quintic binomial **$x^5 - 3$**
72. 12th-degree trinomial **$2x^{12} - x + 15$**
73. **Write About It** Explain the steps you would follow to write the polynomial $4x^3 - 3 + 5x^2 - 2x^4 - x$ in standard form.

74. This problem will prepare you for the Concept Connection on page 462.
   a. The perimeter of the rectangle shown is $12x + 6$. What is the degree of this polynomial? **1**
   b. The area of the rectangle is $8x^2 + 12x$. What is the degree of this polynomial? **2**

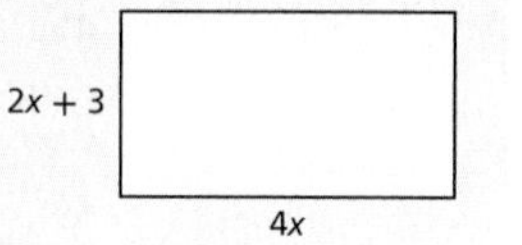

$2x + 3$ (side), $4x$ (base)

7-6 PRACTICE A

7-6 PRACTICE C

7-6 PRACTICE B

LESSON 7-6 **Practice B**
Polynomials

Find the degree of each monomial.

1. $14h^3$ 3
2. $7y$ 1
3. $2a^2$ 2

Write each polynomial in standard form. Then, give the leading coefficient.

4. $3x^2 - 2 + 4x^8 - x$ — $4x^8 + 3x^2 - x - 2$ — 4
5. $7 + 50j - 3j^3 - 4j^2$ — $-3j^3 - 4j^2 + 50j + 7$ — −3
6. $6k + 5k^4 - 4k^3 + 3k^2$ — $5k^4 - 4k^3 + 3k^2 + 6k$ — 5

Classify each polynomial by its degree and number of terms.

7. $-5t^2 + 10$ quadratic binomial
8. $8w + 32 + 9w^4$ quartic trinomial
9. $b - b^3 - 2b^2 + 5b^4$ quartic polynomial

Evaluate each polynomial for the given value.

10. $3m + 8 - 2m^3$ for $m = -1$ 7
11. $4y^5 - 6y + 8y^2 - 1$ for $y = -1$ 9
12. $2w + w^3 - \frac{1}{2}w^2$ for $w = 2$ 10
13. An egg is thrown off the top of a building. Its height in meters above the ground can be approximated by the polynomial $300 + 2t - 4.9t^2$, where t is the time since it was thrown in seconds.
   a. How high is the egg above the ground after 5 seconds? 187.5 m
   b. How high is the egg above the ground after 6 seconds? 135.6 m

Tell whether each number is a root of the polynomial.

14. $2x^3 - 2x + 2$; 1 no
15. $3x^2 - 2x - 8$; 2 yes

7-6 READING STRATEGIES

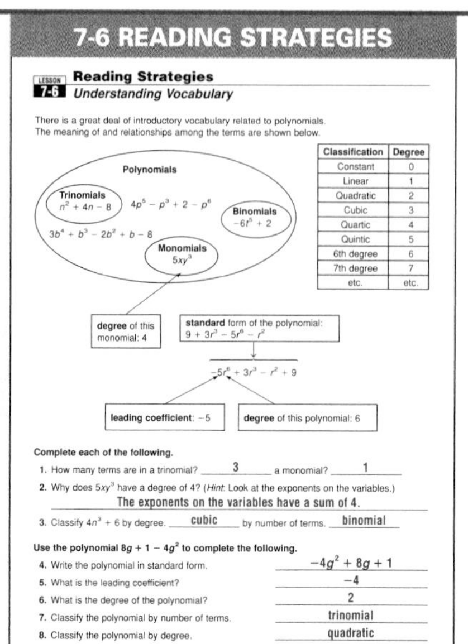
LESSON 7-6 **Reading Strategies**
Understanding Vocabulary

There is a great deal of introductory vocabulary related to polynomials. The meaning of and relationships among the terms are shown below.

Classification	Degree
Constant	0
Linear	1
Quadratic	2
Cubic	3
Quartic	4
Quintic	5
6th degree	6
7th degree	7
etc.	etc.

Complete each of the following.

1. How many terms are in a trinomial? 3 a monomial? 1
2. Why does $5xy^3$ have a degree of 4? (*Hint*: Look at the exponents on the variables.) The exponents on the variables have a sum of 4.
3. Classify $4n^3 + 6$ by degree. cubic by number of terms. binomial

Use the polynomial $8g + 1 - 4g^2$ to complete the following.

4. Write the polynomial in standard form. $-4g^2 + 8g + 1$
5. What is the leading coefficient? −4
6. What is the degree of the polynomial? 2
7. Classify the polynomial by number of terms. trinomial
8. Classify the polynomial by degree. quadratic

7-6 REVIEW FOR MASTERY

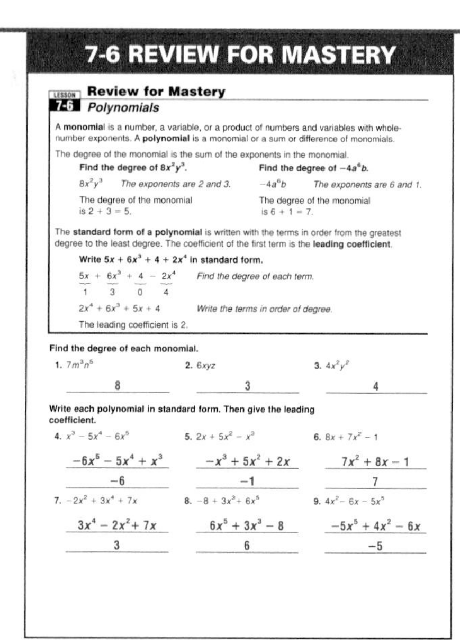
LESSON 7-6 **Review for Mastery**
Polynomials

A **monomial** is a number, a variable, or a product of numbers and variables with whole-number exponents. A **polynomial** is a monomial or a sum or difference of monomials.

The degree of the monomial is the sum of the exponents in the monomial.

Find the degree of $8x^2y^3$.
$8x^2y^3$ *The exponents are 2 and 3.*
The degree of the monomial is $2 + 3 = 5$.

Find the degree of $-4a^6b$.
$-4a^6b$ *The exponents are 6 and 1.*
The degree of the monomial is $6 + 1 = 7$.

The **standard form of a polynomial** is written with the terms in order from the greatest degree to the least degree. The coefficient of the first term is the **leading coefficient**.

Write $5x + 6x^3 + 4 + 2x^4$ in standard form.
$5x + 6x^3 + 4 - 2x^4$ (degrees 1, 3, 0, 4) *Find the degree of each term.*
$2x^4 + 6x^3 + 5x + 4$ *Write the terms in order of degree.*
The leading coefficient is 2.

Find the degree of each monomial.

1. $7m^3n^5$ 8
2. $6xyz$ 3
3. $4x^2y^2$ 4

Write each polynomial in standard form. Then give the leading coefficient.

4. $x^3 - 5x^4 - 6x^5$ — $-6x^5 - 5x^4 + x^3$ — −6
5. $2x + 5x^2 - x^3$ — $-x^3 + 5x^2 + 2x$ — −1
6. $8x + 7x^2 - 1$ — $7x^2 + 8x - 1$ — 7
7. $-2x^2 + 3x^4 + 7x$ — $3x^4 - 2x^2 + 7x$ — 3
8. $-8 + 3x^3 + 6x^5$ — $6x^5 + 3x^3 - 8$ — 6
9. $4x^2 - 6x - 5x^5$ — $-5x^5 + 4x^2 - 6x$ — −5

75. **ERROR ANALYSIS** Two students evaluated $4x - 3x^5$ for $x = -2$. Which is incorrect? Explain the error.

75. A is incorrect. The student incorrectly multiplied −3 by −2 before evaluating the power.

Ⓐ
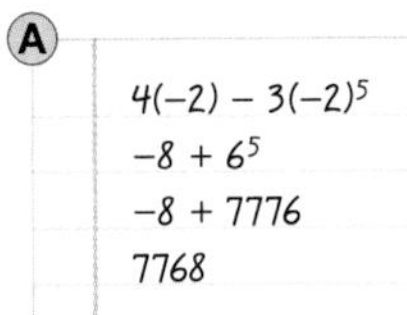

Ⓑ
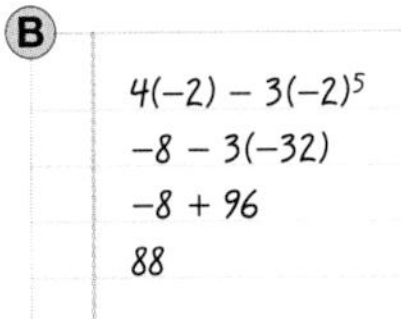

Multiple Choice For Exercises 76 and 77, choose the best answer.

76. Which polynomial has the highest degree?

Ⓐ $3x^8 - 2x^7 + x^6$ Ⓑ $5x - 100$ Ⓒ $25x^{10} + 3x^5 - 15$ Ⓓ $134x^2$

77. Which is NOT a root of $x^3 - x^2 - 2x$?

Ⓐ -1 Ⓑ 0 Ⓒ 1 Ⓓ 2

78. **Short Response** A toy rocket is launched from the ground at 75 feet per second. The polynomial $-16t^2 + 75t$ gives the rocket's height in feet after t seconds. Make a table showing the rocket's height after 1 second, 2 seconds, 3 seconds, and 4 seconds. At which of these times will the rocket be the highest?

CHALLENGE AND EXTEND

79. **Medicine** Doctors and nurses use growth charts and formulas to tell whether a baby is developing normally. The polynomial $0.016m^3 - 0.390m^2 + 4.562m + 50.310$ gives the average length in centimeters of a baby boy between 0 and 10 months of age, where m is the baby's age in months.

a. What is the average length of a 2-month-old baby boy? a 5-month-old baby boy? Round your answers to the nearest centimeter. **58 cm; 65 cm**

b. What is the average length of a newborn (0-month-old) baby boy? **50.310 cm**

c. How could you find the answer to part **b** without doing any calculations?

79c. The first 3 terms of the polynomial will equal 0, so just look at the constant.

80. Consider the binomials $4x^5 + x$, $4x^4 + x$, and $4x^3 + x$.

a. Without calculating, which binomial has the greatest value for $x = 5$? **$4x^5 + x$**

b. Are there any values of x for $4x^3 + x$ which will have the greatest value? Explain.

SPIRAL STANDARDS REVIEW

2.0, 5.0

81. Jordan is allowed 90 minutes of screen time per week. He used m minutes yesterday, and today he has already used $2m$ minutes, leaving 45 minutes for the week. Write and solve an equation for the number of minutes Jordan used yesterday. *(Lesson 2-3)* **$90 - m - 2m = 45$; 15 min**

82. Blue pens cost \$0.50 each and red pens cost \$0.75 each. Giselle bought the same number of each color pen p and an eraser for \$0.45, for a total of \$6.70. Write and solve an equation for the number of pens of each color that Giselle bought. *(Lesson 2-3)* **$0.50p + 0.75p + 0.45 = 6.70$; 5**

Classify each system. Give the number of solutions. *(Lesson 6-4)*

83. $\begin{cases} y = -4x + 5 \\ 4x + y = 2 \end{cases}$

84. $\begin{cases} 2x + 8y = 10 \\ 4y = -x + 5 \end{cases}$

85. $\begin{cases} y = 3x + 2 \\ y = -5x - 6 \end{cases}$

83. incons.; no sol.

84. cons. and dep.; inf. many solutions

85. cons. and indep.; one sol.

Simplify. *(Lesson 7-4)*

86. $\frac{4^7}{4^4}$ **4^3, or 64**

87. $\frac{x^6y^4}{x^4y^9}$ **$\frac{x^2}{y^5}$**

88. $\left(\frac{2v^4}{vw^5}\right)^2$ **$\frac{4v^6}{w^{10}}$**

89. $\left(\frac{2p}{p^3}\right)^{-4}$ **$\frac{p^8}{16}$**

7-6 PROBLEM SOLVING

LESSON 7-6 **Problem Solving**
Polynomials

Write the correct answer.

1. The surface area of a cylinder is given by the polynomial $2\pi r^2 + 2\pi rh$. A cylinder has a radius of 2 centimeters and a height of 5 centimeters. Find the surface area of the cylinder. Use 3.14 for π.

87.92 square centimeters

2. A firework is launched from the ground at a velocity of 180 feet per second. Its height after t seconds is given by the polynomial $-16t^2 + 180t$. Find the height of the firework after 2 seconds and after 5 seconds.

2 s: 296 feet
5 s: 500 feet

3. In the United Kingdom, transportation authorities use the polynomial $\frac{1}{20}v^2 + v$ for calculating the number of feet needed to stop on dry pavement. In the United States, many use the polynomial $0.096v^2$. Both formulas are based on speed v in miles per hour. Calculate the stopping distances for a car traveling 45 miles per hour in both the U.S. and the UK.

UK: 146.25 feet
US: 194.4 feet

4. A piece of cardboard that measures 2 feet by 3 feet can be folded into a box if notches are cut out of the corners. The length of the side of the notch will be the same as the height h of the resulting box. The volume of the box is given by $4h^3 - 10h^2 + 6h$. Find the volume of the box for $h = 0.25$ and $h = 0.5$.

$h = 0.25$: 0.9375 cubic feet
$h = 0.5$: 1 cubic foot

The height of a rocket in meters t seconds after it is launched is approximated by the polynomial $0.5at^2 + vt + h$ where a is always −9.8, v is the initial velocity, and h is the initial height. Use this information with the data in the chart for questions 5 – 7. Select the best answer.

Model Number	Initial Velocity (m/s)
300X	250
Q99	90
4400*i*	125

5. A 300X was launched from a height of 10 meters. What was its height after 3 seconds?

Ⓐ 715.9 m C 755.5 m
B 745.3 m D 760 m

6. Marie and Bob launched their rockets at the same time from a platform 5 meters above the ground. Marie launched the 4400*i* and Bob launched the Q99. How much higher was Marie's rocket after 2 seconds?

F 35 meters H 140 meters
Ⓖ 70 meters J 320 meters

7. The 4400*i* was launched from the ground at the same time the Q99 was launched from 175 meters above the ground. After how many seconds were the rockets at the same height?

A 2 s Ⓒ 5 s
B 4 s D 6 s

7-6 CHALLENGE

LESSON 7-6 **Challenge**
Pick the Polynomial

Match each polynomial with the correct clue. Each polynomial can be used only once. Not every polynomial will be used.

Use these polynomials for 1 – 7.

$x^5 + x^3 + x$	$2x^4y^4 + 3x^2y^5$
$2x^4$	$x^5y - 3x^2y + xy$
$3x + 3y + 3z$	$-3xy^4$
$2xy + 5xy$	$2x^2y + 5xy^2$
$4x^2 - 3x^5 + x$	$4xyz^2 + xyz$

Use these polynomials for 8 – 14.

$4xy + 3x^2y$	$x^3 + x^2 + x$
$x^2 + x - 3$	$x^4 + x^3 + x^2$
$-3 + x + 4x^2$	$2x^2 - 3x^3 + 1$
$x^3y - 3xyz + z$	$x - 3$
$-x + 3$	$x^2 + y^2 + z^2 + w^2$

1. I am a monomial with degree 5. Who am I? **$-3xy^4$**

2. I am a sum of monomials with degree 8. Who am I? **$2x^4y^4 + 3x^2y^5$**

3. I am a trinomial with degree 5. Who am I? **$x^5 + x^3 + x$**

4. I am a binomial. Both of my terms have degree 2. Who am I? **$2xy + 5xy$**

5. I am a monomial with degree 4. Who am I? **$2x^4$**

6. I am a binomial with degree 4. Who am I? **$4xyz^2 + xyz$**

7. I am a trinomial. When you put me in standard form, my leading coefficient is −3. Who am I? **$4x^2 - 3x^5 + x$**

8. I am a linear expression. My constant is −3. Who am I? **$x - 3$**

9. I am a quartic trinomial. I have three different variables. Who am I? **$x^3y - 3xyz + z$**

10. I am a cubic binomial. Who am I? **$4xy + 3x^2y$**

11. I am a quadratic polynomial. I have no constants. Who am I? **$x^2 + y^2 + z^2 + w^2$**

12. I am a cubic trinomial with one variable. Who am I? **$x^3 + x^2 + x$**

13. I am a quadratic trinomial. When you put me in standard form, my leading coefficient is 4. Who am I? **$-3 + x + 4x^2$**

14. I am a quartic trinomial. Who am I? **$x^4 + x^3 + x^2$**

Teaching Tip **Multiple Choice** In **Exercise 76,** students who chose **A** may have confused degree with number of terms. Students who chose **D** may think that the coefficients are significant when determining degree.

Answer

80b. yes; $0 < x < 1$; raising a number between 0 and 1 to a higher power results in a lesser number. So if x is between 0 and 1, the binomial with the least degree will have the greatest value.

Journal

Have students explain how to classify a polynomial according to its degree and number of terms.

ALTERNATIVE ASSESSMENT

Have students write a linear binomial and a quadratic trinomial, each with only x as a variable. Then have them evaluate each polynomial for $x = 3$.

Power Presentations with PowerPoint®

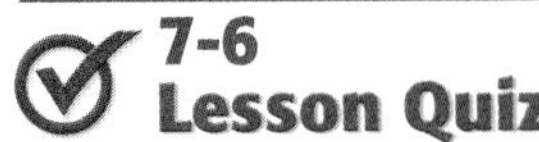

7-6 Lesson Quiz

Find the degree of each polynomial.

1. $7a^3b^2 - 2a^4 + 4b - 15$ 5

2. $25x^2 - 3x^4$ 4

Write each polynomial in standard form. Then give the leading coefficient.

3. $24g^3 + 10 + 7g^5 - g^2$
$7g^5 + 24g^3 - g^2 + 10$; 7

4. $14 - x^4 + 3x^2$ $-x^4 + 3x^2 + 14$; -1

Classify each polynomial according to its degree and number of terms.

5. $18x^2 - 12x + 5$
quadratic trinomial

6. $2x^4 - 1$ quartic binomial

7. The polynomial $3.675v + 0.096v^2$ is used to estimate the stopping distance in feet for a car whose speed is v miles per hour on flat, dry pavement. What is the stopping distance for a car traveling at 70 miles per hour?
727.65 ft

Tell whether each number is a root of $3p^2 - 8p + 4$.

8. 2 yes 9. −2 no

Also available on transparency

Organizer

Use with Lesson 7-7

Objective: Use algebra tiles to model polynomial addition and subtraction.

Materials: algebra tiles

Online Edition
Algebra Tiles

Countdown to Mastery Week 16

Teach

Discuss

Compare like terms and like tiles. In like terms, the same variables are raised to the same powers, but the coefficients may differ. In like tiles, the size and shape are the same, but the color of the tile (whether it is positive or negative) may differ.

In **Activity 2,** remind students to add the opposite of every term in the second expression.

Encourage students to always arrange their tiles and write their answers in standard form. This will help prevent careless errors.

California Standards

Algebra 1 🔑 **10.0**

7-7

Use with Lesson 7-7

Model Polynomial Addition and Subtraction

You can use algebra tiles to model polynomial addition and subtraction.

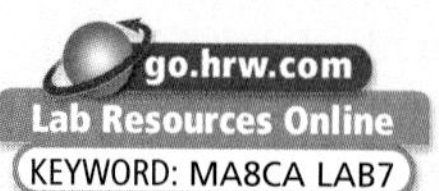

KEY

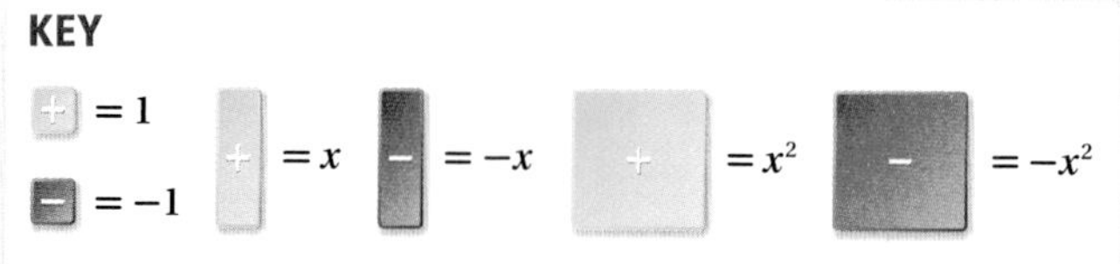

California Standards

🔑 **10.0 Students add, subtract,** multiply, and divide **monomials and polynomials.** Students solve multistep problems, including word problems, by using these techniques.

Activity 1

Use algebra tiles to find $(2x^2 - x) + (x^2 + 3x - 1)$.

MODEL		ALGEBRA
	Use tiles to represent all terms from both expressions.	$(2x^2 - x) + (x^2 + 3x - 1)$
	Rearrange tiles so that like tiles are together. Like tiles are the same size and shape.	$(2x^2 + x^2) + (-x + 3x) - 1$
	Remove any zero pairs.	$3x^2 - x + x + 2x - 1$
	The remaining tiles represent the sum.	$3x^2 + 2x - 1$

Try This

Use algebra tiles to find each sum.

1. $(-2x^2 + 1) + (-x^2)$ $\mathbf{-3x^2 + 1}$
2. $(3x^2 + 2x + 5) + (x^2 - x - 4)$ $\mathbf{4x^2 + x + 1}$
3. $(x - 3) + (2x - 2)$ $\mathbf{3x - 5}$
4. $(5x^2 - 3x - 6) + (x^2 + 3x + 6)$ $\mathbf{6x^2}$
5. $-5x^2 + (2x^2 + 5x)$ $\mathbf{-3x^2 + 5x}$
6. $(x^2 - x - 1) + (6x - 3)$ $\mathbf{x^2 + 5x - 4}$

Use algebra tiles to find $(2x^2 + 6) - 4x^2$.

MODEL		ALGEBRA
	Use tiles to represent the terms in the first expression.	$2x^2 + 6$
To subtract $4x^2$, you would remove 4 yellow x^2-tiles, but there are not enough to do this. Remember that subtraction is the same as adding the opposite, so rewrite $(2x^2 + 6) - 4x^2$ as $(2x^2 + 6) + (-4x^2)$.		
	Add 4 red x^2-tiles.	$2x^2 + 6 + (-4x^2)$
	Rearrange tiles so that like tiles are together.	$2x^2 + (-4x^2) + 6$
	Remove zero pairs.	$2x^2 + (-2x^2) + (-2x^2) + 6$
	The remaining tiles represent the difference.	$-2x^2 + 6$

Try This

Use algebra tiles to find each difference.

7. $(6x^2 + 4x) - 3x^2$ **8.** $(2x^2 + x - 7) - 5x$ **9.** $(3x + 6) - 6$

10. $(8x + 5) - (-2x)$ **11.** $(x^2 + 2x) - (-4x^2 + x)$ **12.** $(3x^2 - 4) - (x^2 + 6x)$

13. [+] [−] represents a zero pair. Use algebra tiles to model two other zero pairs.

14. When is it not necessary to "add the opposite" for polynomial subtraction using algebra tiles? when you have enough tiles to actually remove them to model the subtraction

Close

Key Concept

Polynomial addition is the same as combining like terms. Polynomial subtraction can be written as polynomial addition by adding the opposite.

Assessment

Journal Have students explain how to use algebra tiles to find $(3x^2 - 4x + 1) - 5x$.

Answers to *Try This*

7. $3x^2 + 4x$
8. $2x^2 - 4x - 7$
9. $3x$
10. $10x + 5$
11. $5x^2 + x$
12. $2x^2 - 6x - 4$
13.

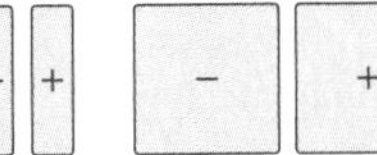

7-7 Organizer

Objective: Add and subtract polynomials.

Technology Lab
In *Chapter 7 Resource File*

Online Edition
Tutorial Videos

Countdown to Mastery Week 16

Power Presentations with PowerPoint®

Warm Up

Simplify each expression by combining like terms.

1. $4x + 2x$ $6x$
2. $3y + 7y$ $10y$
3. $8p - 5p$ $3p$
4. $5n + 6n^2$ not like terms

Simplify each expression.

5. $3(x + 4)$ $3x + 12$
6. $-2(t + 3)$ $-2t - 6$
7. $-1(x^2 - 4x - 6)$
$-x^2 + 4x + 6$

Also available on transparency

Teacher: What is $b + b$?
Shakespeare: Is it $2b$ or not $2b$?

Algebra 1 10.0

7-7 Adding and Subtracting Polynomials

10.0 Students add, subtract, multiply, and divide **monomials and polynomials. Students solve multistep problems, including word problems, by using these techniques.**

Who uses this?
Business owners can add and subtract polynomials that model profit. (See Example 4.)

Just as you can perform operations on numbers, you can perform operations on polynomials. To add or subtract polynomials, combine like terms.

Remember!
Like terms are constants or terms with the same variable(s) raised to the same power(s). To review combining like terms, see Lesson 1-7.

EXAMPLE 1 Adding and Subtracting Monomials

Add or subtract.

A $15m^3 + 6m^2 + 2m^3$
$15m^3 + 6m^2 + 2m^3$ *Identify like terms.*
$15m^3 + 2m^3 + 6m^2$ *Rearrange terms so that like terms are together.*
$17m^3 + 6m^2$ *Combine like terms.*

B $3x^2 + 5 - 7x^2 + 12$
$3x^2 + 5 - 7x^2 + 12$ *Identify like terms.*
$3x^2 - 7x^2 + 5 + 12$ *Rearrange terms so that like terms are together.*
$-4x^2 + 17$ *Combine like terms.*

C $0.9y^5 - 0.4y^5 + 0.5x^5 + y^5$
$0.9y^5 - 0.4y^5 + 0.5x^5 + y^5$ *Identify like terms.*
$0.9y^5 - 0.4y^5 + y^5 + 0.5x^5$ *Rearrange terms so that like terms are together.*
$1.5y^5 + 0.5x^5$ *Combine like terms.*

D $2x^2y - x^2y - x^2y$
$2x^2y - x^2y - x^2y$ *All terms are like terms.*
0 *Combine like terms.*

CHECK IT OUT! Add or subtract.

1a. $2s^2 + 3s^2 + s$ $\mathbf{5s^2 + s}$ **1b.** $4z^4 - 8 + 16z^4 + 2$ $\mathbf{20z^4 - 6}$
1c. $2x^8 + 7y^8 - x^8 - y^8$ $\mathbf{x^8 + 6y^8}$ **1d.** $9b^3c^2 + 5b^3c^2 - 13b^3c^2$ $\mathbf{b^3c^2}$

Polynomials can be added in either vertical or horizontal form.

In vertical form, align the like terms and add:

$$\begin{array}{r} 5x^2 + 4x + 1 \\ +\ 2x^2 + 5x + 2 \\ \hline 7x^2 + 9x + 3 \end{array}$$

In horizontal form, use the Associative and Commutative Properties to regroup and combine like terms:

$$(5x^2 + 4x + 1) + (2x^2 + 5x + 2)$$
$$= (5x^2 + 2x^2) + (4x + 5x) + (1 + 2)$$
$$= 7x^2 + 9x + 3$$

1 Introduce

EXPLORATION

7-7 Adding and Subtracting Polynomials

An ecologist is studying frogs and toads in a wetlands habitat. She finds that the polynomial $3x^2 + x$ models the frog population and that the polynomial $7x^2 - x$ models the toad population. In both cases, x represents the number of months.

1. Complete the table. For each month, evaluate the two polynomials to find the population of frogs and toads. Then add these values to find the total population.

Month, x	Population of Frogs, $3x^2 + x$	Population of Toads, $7x^2 - x$	Total Population
1	4	6	10
2			
3			
4			
5			
6			

2. Look for a pattern in the last column. Write a simplified polynomial that gives the total population in month x.

THINK AND DISCUSS

3. **Show** how to find the sum of the polynomials $3x^2 + x$ and $7x^2 - x$.
4. **Describe** how you could find the sum using the terms of the two polynomials that are being added.

Motivate

Display the following items: 4 books, 3 pencils, 2 books, and 5 pencils.

Ask students for a sensible way to group the items. a group of 6 books and a group of 8 pencils

Explain to students that adding and subtracting monomials is done in a similar way.

Explorations and answers are provided in *Alternate Openers: Explorations Transparencies*.

EXAMPLE **2** **Adding Polynomials**

Add.

A $(2x^2 - x) + (x^2 + 3x - 1)$

$(2x^2 - x) + (x^2 + 3x - 1)$ *Identify like terms.*

$(2x^2 + x^2) + (-x + 3x) + (-1)$ *Group like terms together.*

$3x^2 + 2x - 1$ *Combine like terms.*

B $(-2ab + b) + (2ab + a)$

$(-2ab + b) + (2ab + a)$ *Identify like terms.*

$(-2ab + 2ab) + b + a$ *Group like terms together.*

$0 + b + a$ *Combine like terms.*

$b + a$ *Simplify.*

C $(4b^5 + 8b) + (3b^5 + 6b - 7b^5 + b)$

$(4b^5 + 8b) + (3b^5 + 6b - 7b^5 + b)$ *Identify like terms.*

$(4b^5 + 8b) + (-4b^5 + 7b)$ *Combine like terms in the second polynomial.*

$$\begin{array}{r} 4b^5 + 8b \\ + -4b^5 + 7b \\ \hline 0 \quad + 15b \end{array}$$ *Use the vertical method.* *Combine like terms.*

$15b$ *Simplify.*

D $(20.2y^2 + 6y + 5) + (1.7y^2 - 8)$

$(20.2y^2 + 6y + 5) + (1.7y^2 - 8)$ *Identify like terms.*

$$\begin{array}{r} 20.2y^2 + 6y + 5 \\ + 1.7y^2 + 0y - 8 \\ \hline 21.9y^2 + 6y - 3 \end{array}$$

Use the vertical method.

Write 0y as a placeholder in the second polynomial.

Combine like terms.

Writing Math

When you use the Associative and Commutative Properties to rearrange the terms, the sign in front of each term must stay with that term.

2. Add $(5a^3 + 3a^2 - 6a + 12a^2) + (7a^3 - 10a)$. **$12a^3 + 15a^2 - 16a$**

To subtract polynomials, remember that subtracting is the same as adding the opposite. To find the opposite of a polynomial, you must write the opposite of *each* term in the polynomial:

$$-(2x^3 - 3x + 7) = -2x^3 + 3x - 7$$

EXAMPLE **3** **Subtracting Polynomials**

Subtract.

A $(2x^2 + 6) - (4x^2)$

$(2x^2 + 6) + (-4x^2)$ *Rewrite subtraction as addition of the opposite.*

$(2x^2 + 6) + (-4x^2)$ *Identify like terms.*

$(2x^2 - 4x^2) + 6$ *Group like terms together.*

$-2x^2 + 6$ *Combine like terms.*

B $(a^4 - 2a) - (3a^4 - 3a)$

$(a^4 - 2a) + (-3a^4 + 3a)$ *Rewrite subtraction as addition of the opposite.*

$(a^4 - 2a) + (-3a^4 + 3a)$ *Identify like terms.*

$(a^4 - 3a^4) + (-2a + 3a)$ *Group like terms together.*

$-2a^4 + a$ *Combine like terms.*

2 Teach

Guided Instruction

Review like terms before beginning this lesson. When rearranging terms, remind students to pay close attention to the sign in front of each term. Point out that in **Example 2C,** like terms in the second polynomial were simplified before the polynomials were added. Students will be less likely to make mistakes when the individual polynomials are simplified first.

Visual Cues Draw different marks around like terms so they stand out.

Universal Access

Through Cooperative Learning

Prepare a bag with several small slips of paper (at least four times the number of students in class), each with one of the following: x, $2x$, $-3x$, y, $4y$, $-6y$. Have each student randomly select three or four slips of paper. Have students combine, and simplify if possible, their terms and write the resulting polynomial on a piece of paper. Then have students pair up to find the sums and differences of their polynomials. Have students pair up with as many others as time allows.

COMMON ERROR ALERT

Students often think the terms xy^2 and x^2y are like terms. Write out all factors to show students how they are different: $xy^2 = xyy$, and $x^2y = xxy$.

Power Presentations with PowerPoint®

Additional Examples

Example 1

Add or subtract.

A. $12p^3 + 11p^2 + 8p^3$ $20p^3 + 11p^2$

B. $5x^2 - 6 - 3x + 8$ $5x^2 - 3x + 2$

C. $t^2 + 2s^2 - 4t^2 - s^2$ $-3t^2 + s^2$

D. $10m^2n + 4m^2n - 8m^2n$ $6m^2n$

Example 2

Add.

A. $(4m^2 + 5) + (m^2 - m + 6)$ $5m^2 - m + 11$

B. $(10xy + x) + (-3xy + y)$ $7xy + x + y$

C. $(6x^2 - 4y) + (3x^2 + 3y - 8x^2 - 2y)$ $x^2 - 3y$

D. $\left(\frac{1}{2}a^2 + b + 2\right) + \left(\frac{3}{2}a^2 - 4b + 5\right)$ $2a^2 - 3b + 7$

Also available on transparency

INTERVENTION

Questioning Strategies

EXAMPLE **1**

- How do you identify like terms?

EXAMPLE **2**

- When using a vertical format to add polynomials, what is a placeholder? How is it helpful?

Teaching Tip

Inclusion Remind students that the Commutative Property of Addition states that you can add numbers in any order. The Associative Property of Addition states that you can group any of the numbers together.

Multiple Representations Finding the opposite of a polynomial can be thought of as distributing -1 over the polynomial.

Power Presentations with PowerPoint®

Additional Examples

Example 3

Subtract.

A. $(x^3 + 4y) - (2x^3)$ $\quad -x^3 + 4y$

B. $(7m^4 - 2m^2) - (5m^4 - 5m^2 + 8)$
$2m^4 + 3m^2 - 8$

C. $(-10x^2 - 3x + 7) - (x^2 - 9)$
$-11x^2 - 3x + 16$

D. $(9q^2 - 3q) - (q^2 - 5)$
$8q^2 - 3q + 5$

Example 4

A farmer must add the areas of two plots of land to determine the amount of seed to plant. The area of plot A can be represented by $3x^2 + 7x - 5$, and the area of plot B can be represented by $5x^2 - 4x + 11$. Write a polynomial that represents the total area of both plots of land.
$8x^2 + 3x + 6$

Also available on transparency

INTERVENTION
Questioning Strategies

EXAMPLE **3**

- What is the first step in subtracting polynomials?
- Why are parentheses used when subtracting polynomials?

EXAMPLE **4**

- What is the purpose of aligning terms before adding or subtracting polynomials?

Subtract.

C $(3x^2 - 2x + 8) - (x^2 - 4)$

$(3x^2 - 2x + 8) + (-x^2 + 4)$ — *Rewrite subtraction as addition of the opposite.*

$(3x^2 - 2x + 8) + (-x^2 + 4)$ — *Identify like terms.*

$3x^2 - 2x + 8$ — *Use the vertical method.*

$+ -x^2 + 0x + 4$ — *Write 0x as a placeholder.*

$2x^2 - 2x + 12$ — *Combine like terms.*

D $(11z^3 - 2z) - (z^3 - 5)$

$(11z^3 - 2z) + (-z^3 + 5)$ — *Rewrite subtraction as addition of the opposite.*

$(11z^3 - 2z) + (-z^3 + 5)$ — *Identify like terms.*

$11z^3 - 2z + 0$ — *Use the vertical method.*

$+ -z^3 + 0z + 5$ — *Write 0 and 0z as placeholders.*

$10z^3 - 2z + 5$ — *Combine like terms.*

3. Subtract $(2x^2 - 3x^2 + 1) - (x^2 + x + 1)$. $\mathbf{-2x^2 - x}$

EXAMPLE 4 *Business Application*

The profits of two different manufacturing plants can be modeled as shown, where x is the number of units produced at each plant.

Eastern: $-0.03x^2 + 25x - 1500$

Southern: $-0.02x^2 + 21x - 1700$

Write a polynomial that represents the difference of the profits at the eastern plant and the profits at the southern plant.

$(-0.03x^2 + 25x - 1500)$ — *Eastern plant profits*

$-(-0.02x^2 + 21x - 1700)$ — *Southern plant profits*

$(-0.03x^2 + 25x - 1500)$

$+(+0.02x^2 - 21x + 1700)$ — *Write subtraction as addition of the opposite.*

$-0.01x^2 + 4x + 200$ — *Combine like terms.*

4. Use the information above to write a polynomial that represents the total profits from both plants.
$\mathbf{-0.05x^2 + 46x - 3200}$

THINK AND DISCUSS

1. Identify the like terms in the following list: $-12x^2$, $-4.7y$, $\frac{1}{5}x^2y$, y, $3xy^2$, $-9x^2$, $5x^2y$, $-12x$

2. Describe how to find the opposite of $9t^2 - 5t + 8$.

3. GET ORGANIZED Copy and complete the graphic organizer. In each box, write an example that shows how to perform the given operation.

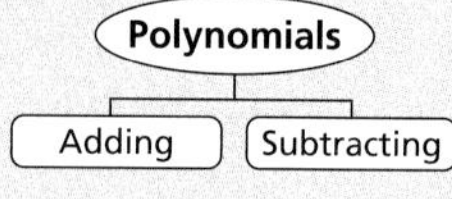

3 Close

Summarize

Have students list the steps for adding and subtracting polynomials.

1. Rewrite subtraction as addition if necessary.
2. Identify like terms.
3. Rearrange terms so that like terms are together.
4. Combine like terms.
5. Simplify if necessary.

FORMATIVE ASSESSMENT and INTERVENTION

***Diagnose Before* the Lesson**
7-7 Warm Up, TE p. 438

***Monitor During* the Lesson**
Check It Out! Exercises, SE pp. 438–440
Questioning Strategies, TE pp. 439–440

***Assess After* the Lesson**
7-7 Lesson Quiz, TE p. 443
Alternative Assessment, TE p. 443

Answers to *Think and Discuss*

1. $-12x^2$ and $-9x^2$; $-4.7y$ and y; $\frac{1}{5}x^2y$ and $5x^2y$
2. Take the opposite of each term: $-9t^2 + 5t - 8$.
3. See p. A6.

7-7 Exercises

California Standards Practice 10.0, 25.2

go.hrw.com
Homework Help Online KEYWORD: MA8CA 7-7
Parent Resources Online KEYWORD: MA8CA Parent

GUIDED PRACTICE

SEE EXAMPLE 1 p. 438

Add or subtract.

1. $7a^2 - 10a^2 + 9a$ **$-3a^2 + 9a$**
2. $13x^2 + 9y^2 - 6x^2$ **$7x^2 + 9y^2$**
3. $0.07r^4 + 0.32r^3 + 0.19r^4$ **$0.26r^4 + 0.32r^3$**
4. $\frac{1}{4}p^3 + \frac{2}{3}p^3$ **$\frac{11}{12}p^3$**
5. $5b^3c + b^3c - 3b^3c$ **$3b^3c$**
6. $-8m + 5 - 16 + 11m$ **$3m - 11$**

SEE EXAMPLE 2 p. 439

Add.

7. $(5n^3 + 3n + 6) + (18n^3 + 9)$
8. $(3.7q^2 - 8q + 3.7) + (4.3q^2 - 2.9q + 1.6)$
9. $(-3x + 12) + (9x^2 + 2x - 18)$
10. $(9x^4 + x^3) + (2x^4 + 6x^3 - 8x^4 + x^3)$

SEE EXAMPLE 3 p. 439

Subtract.

11. $(6c^4 + 8c + 6) - (2c^4)$ **$4c^4 + 8c + 6$**
12. $(16y^2 - 8y + 9) - (6y^2 - 2y + 7y)$ **$10y^2 - 13y + 9$**
13. $(2r + 5) - (5r - 6)$ **$-3r + 11$**
14. $(-7k^2 + 3) - (2k^2 + 5k - 1)$ **$-9k^2 - 5k + 4$**

SEE EXAMPLE 4 p. 440

15. **Geometry** Write a polynomial that represents the measure of angle ABD. **$8a^2 + 5a + 9$**

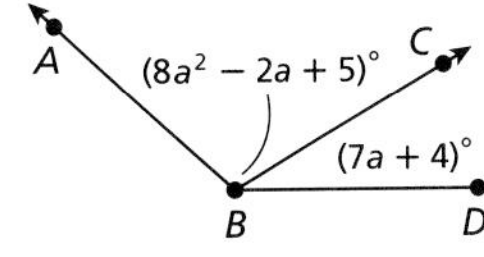

PRACTICE AND PROBLEM SOLVING

Independent Practice	
For Exercises	See Example
16–24	1
25–28	2
29–32	3
33–34	4

Extra Practice
Skills Practice p. EP15
Application Practice p. EP30

Add or subtract.

16. $4k^3 + 6k^2 + 9k^3$
17. $5m + 12n^2 + 6n - 8m$
18. $2.5a^4 - 8.1b^4 - 3.6b^4$
19. $2d^5 + 1 - d^5$
20. $7xy - 4x^2y - 2xy$
21. $-6x^3 + 5x + 2x^3 + 4x^3$
22. $x^2 + x + 3x + 2x^2$
23. $3x^3 - 4 - x^3 - 1$
24. $3b^3 - 2b - 1 - b^3 - b$

Add.

25. $(2t^2 - 8t) + (8t^2 + 9t)$ **$10t^2 + t$**
26. $(-7x^2 - 2x + 3) + (4x^2 - 9x)$ **$-3x^2 - 11x + 3$**
27. $(x^5 - x) + (x^4 + x)$ **$x^5 + x^4$**
28. $(-2z^3 + z + 2z^3 + z) + (3z^3 - 5z^2)$ **$3z^3 - 5z^2 + 2z$**

Subtract.

29. $(t^3 + 8t^2) - (3t^3)$ **$-2t^3 + 8t^2$**
30. $(3x^2 - x) - (x^2 + 3x - x)$ **$2x^2 - 3x$**
31. $(5m + 3) - (6m^3 - 2m^2)$ **$-6m^3 + 2m^2 + 5m + 3$**
32. $(3s^2 + 4s) - (-10s^2 + 6s)$ **$13s^2 - 2s$**
33. **Photography** The measurements of a photo and its frame are shown in the diagram. Write a polynomial that represents the width of the photo. **$4w^2 + 6w + 4$**

34. **Geometry** The length of a rectangle is represented by $4a + 3b$, and its width is represented by $7a - 2b$. Write a polynomial for the perimeter of the rectangle. **$22a + 2b$**

7-7 Exercises

Assignment Guide

Assign *Guided Practice* exercises as necessary.

If you finished Examples **1–2**
Proficient 16–28, 58
Advanced 16–28, 58

If you finished Examples **1–4**
Proficient 16–56, 58, 63–72
Advanced 16–44, 52–72

Homework Quick Check
Quickly check key concepts.
Exercises: 24, 28, 30, 32, 33, 48

Teaching Tip **Auditory** For **Exercises 1–6,** suggest to students that they say each term out loud as they do their homework to hear the difference between like and unlike terms.

Answers

7. $23n^3 + 3n + 15$
8. $8q^2 - 10.9q + 5.3$
9. $9x^2 - x - 6$
10. $3x^4 + 8x^3$
16. $13k^3 + 6k^2$
17. $12n^2 + 6n - 3m$
18. $2.5a^4 - 11.7b^4$
19. $d^5 + 1$
20. $-4x^2y + 5xy$
21. $5x$
22. $3x^2 + 4x$
23. $2x^3 - 5$
24. $2b^3 - 3b - 1$

California Standards

Standard	Exercises
2.0	69–72
6.0	63–68
10.0	1–42, 46–51, 53b, 54–56a, 57–62
25.2	45

Exercise 53 involves writing expressions for the dimensions of a rectangle. This exercise prepares students for the Concept Connection on page 462.

Answers

52. No; polynomial addition simply involves combining like terms. No matter what order the terms are combined in, the sum will be the same. Yes; in polynomial subtraction, the subtraction sign is distributed among all terms in the second polynomial, changing all the signs to their opposites.

53a. (rectangle with length $x + 4$ and width $x - 3$)

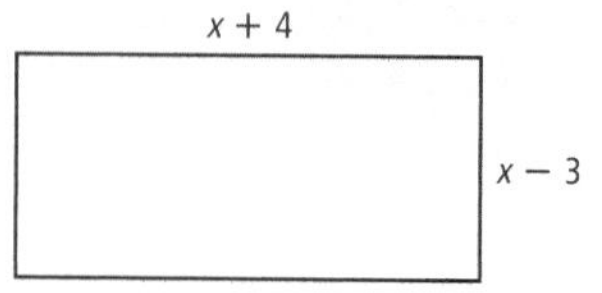

Add or subtract.

35. $(2t - 7) + (-t + 2)$ **$t - 5$**
36. $(4m^2 + 3m) + (-2m^2)$ **$2m^2 + 3m$**
37. $(4n - 2) - 2n$ **$2n - 2$**
38. $(-v - 7) - (-2v)$ **$v - 7$**
39. $(4x^2 + 3x - 6) + (2x^2 - 4x + 5)$ **$6x^2 - x - 1$**
40. $(2z^2 - 3z - 3) + (2z^2 - 7z - 1)$ **$4z^2 - 10z - 4$**
41. $(5u^2 + 3u + 7) - (u^3 + 2u^2 + 1)$ **$-u^3 + 3u^2 + 3u + 6$**
42. $(-7h^2 - 4h + 7) - (7h^2 - 4h + 11)$ **$-14h^2 - 4$**

43. **Geometry** The length of a rectangle is represented by $2x + 3$, and its width is represented by $3x + 7$. The perimeter of the rectangle is 35 units. Find the value of x.

43. $\frac{3}{2}$, or 1.5

44. **Write About It** If the parentheses are removed from $(3m^2 - 5m) + (12m^2 + 7m - 10)$, is the new expression equivalent to the original? If the parentheses are removed from $(3m^2 - 5m) - (12m^2 + 7m - 10)$, is the new expression equivalent to the original? Explain.

44. Yes; the simplified form of both expressions is $15m^2 + 2m - 10$. No; the simplified form of the orig. expression is $-9m^2 - 12m + 10$, and the simplified form of the new expression is $-9m^2 + 2m - 10$.

45. **///ERROR ANALYSIS///** Two students found the sum of the polynomials $(-3n^4 + 6n^3 + 4n^2)$ and $(8n^4 - 3n^2 + 9n)$. Which is incorrect? Explain the error.

A

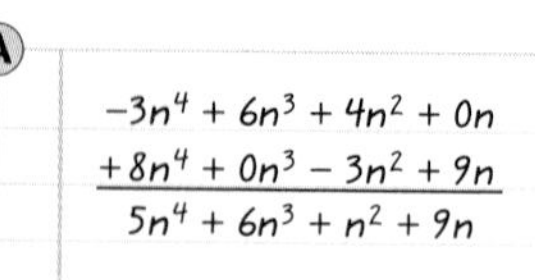

B

$-3n^4 + 6n^3 + 4n^2$
$+8n^4 - 3n^2 + 9n$
$5n^4 + 3n^3 + 13n^2$

45. B is incorrect. The student incorrectly tried to combine $6n^3$ and $-3n^2$, which are not like terms, and $4n^2$ and $9n$, which are not like terms.

Copy and complete the table by finding the missing polynomials.

	Polynomial 1	Polynomial 2	Sum
46.	$x^2 - 6$	$3x^2 - 10x + 2$	**$4x^2 - 10x - 4$**
47.	$12x + 5$	**$3x + 6$**	$15x + 11$
48.	**$x^4 - 3x^2 - 9$**	$5x^4 + 8$	$6x^4 - 3x^2 - 1$
49.	$7x^3 - 6x - 3$	**$6x + 14$**	$7x^3 + 11$
50.	$2x^3 + 5x^2$	$7x^3 - 5x^2 + 1$	**$9x^3 + 1$**
51.	**$2x^2 + x - 5$**	$x + x^2 + 6$	$3x^2 + 2x + 1$

52. **Critical Thinking** Does the order in which you add polynomials affect the sum? Does the order in which you subtract polynomials affect the difference? Explain.

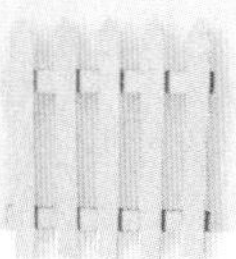

53. This problem will prepare you for the Concept Connection on page 462.
   a. Ian plans to build a fenced dog pen. At first, he planned for the pen to be a square of length x on each side, but then he decided that a square may not be best. He added 4 to the length and subtracted 3 from the width. Draw a diagram to show the dimensions of the new pen.
   b. Write a polynomial that represents the amount of fencing that Ian will need for the new dog pen. **$4x + 2$**
   c. How much fencing will Ian need if $x = 15$? **62 ft**

7-7 PRACTICE A

7-7 PRACTICE C

7-7 PRACTICE B

LESSON 7-7 **Practice B**
Adding and Subtracting Polynomials

Add or subtract.

1. $3m^3 + 8m^3 - 3 + m^3 - 2m^2$ **$12m^3 - 2m^2 - 3$**
2. $2pg - p^5 - 12pg + 5g - 6p^5$ **$-7p^5 - 10pg + 5g$**

Add.

3. $3k^2 - 2k + 7$ + $k - 2$ **$3k^2 - k + 5$**
4. $5x^2 - 2x + 3y$ + $6x^2 + 5x + 6y$ **$11x^2 + 3x + 9y$**
5. $11hz^3 + 3hz^2 + 8hz$ + $9hz^3 + hz^2 - 3hz$ **$20hz^3 + 4hz^2 + 5hz$**
6. $(ab^2 + 13b - 4a) + (3ab^2 + a + 7b)$ **$4ab^2 + 20b - 3a$**
7. $(4x^3 - x^2 + 4x) + (x^3 - x^2 - 4x)$ **$5x^3 - 2x^2$**

Subtract.

8. $12d^2 + 3dx + x$ $-(-4d^2 + 2dx - 8x)$ **$16d^2 + dx + 9x$**
9. $2v^5 - 3v^4 - 8$ $-(3v^5 + 2v^4 - 8)$ **$-v^5 - 5v^4$**
10. $-y^4 + 6ay^2 - y + a$ $-(-6y^4 - 2ay^2 + y)$ **$5y^4 + 8ay^2 - 2y + a$**
11. $(-r^2 + 8pr - p) - (-12r^2 - 2pr + 8p)$ **$11r^2 + 10pr - 9p$**
12. $(un - n^2 + 2un^3) - (3un^3 + n^2 + 4un)$ **$-3un - 2n^2 - un^3$**

13. Antoine is making a banner in the shape of a triangle. He wants to line the banner with a decorative border. How long will the border be? (triangle with sides $12b - 8$, $9b + 8$, $12b - 8$) **$33b - 8$**

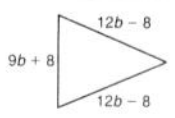

14. Darnell and Stephanie have competing refreshment stand businesses. Darnell's profit can be modeled with the polynomial $c^2 + 8c - 100$, where c is the number of items sold. Stephanie's profit can be modeled with the polynomial $2c^2 - 7c - 200$.
   a. Write a polynomial that represents the difference between Stephanie's profit and Darnell's profit. **$c^2 - 15c - 100$**
   b. Write a polynomial to show how much they can expect to earn if they decided to combine their businesses. **$3c^2 + c - 300$**

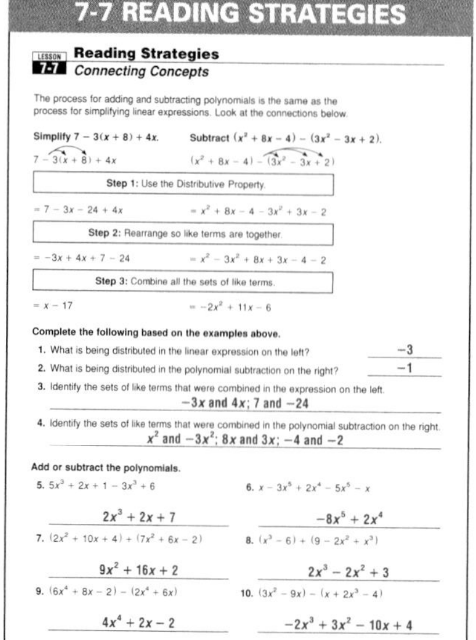

7-7 READING STRATEGIES

LESSON 7-7 **Reading Strategies**
Connecting Concepts

The process for adding and subtracting polynomials is the same as the process for simplifying linear expressions. Look at the connections below.

Simplify $7 - 3(x + 8) + 4x$.	Subtract $(x^2 + 8x - 4) - (3x^2 - 3x + 2)$.
$7 - 3(x + 8) + 4x$	$(x^2 + 8x - 4) - (3x^2 - 3x + 2)$
Step 1: Use the Distributive Property.	
$= 7 - 3x - 24 + 4x$	$= x^2 + 8x - 4 - 3x^2 + 3x - 2$
Step 2: Rearrange so like terms are together.	
$= -3x + 4x + 7 - 24$	$= x^2 - 3x^2 + 8x + 3x - 4 - 2$
Step 3: Combine all the sets of like terms.	
$= x - 17$	$= -2x^2 + 11x - 6$

Complete the following based on the examples above.

1. What is being distributed in the linear expression on the left? **-3**
2. What is being distributed in the polynomial subtraction on the right? **-1**
3. Identify the sets of like terms that were combined in the expression on the left. **$-3x$ and $4x$; 7 and -24**
4. Identify the sets of like terms that were combined in the polynomial subtraction on the right. **x^2 and $-3x^2$; $8x$ and $3x$; -4 and -2**

Add or subtract the polynomials.

5. $5x^3 + 2x + 1 - 3x^3 + 6$ **$2x^3 + 2x + 7$**
6. $x - 3x^5 + 2x^4 - 5x^5 - x$ **$-8x^5 + 2x^4$**
7. $(2x^2 + 10x + 4) + (7x^2 + 6x - 2)$ **$9x^2 + 16x + 2$**
8. $(x^3 - 6) + (9 - 2x^2 + x^3)$ **$2x^3 - 2x^2 + 3$**
9. $(6x^4 + 8x - 2) - (2x^4 + 6x)$ **$4x^4 + 2x - 2$**
10. $(3x^2 - 9x) - (x + 2x^3 - 4)$ **$-2x^3 + 3x^2 - 10x + 4$**

7-7 REVIEW FOR MASTERY

LESSON 7-7 **Review for Mastery**
Adding and Subtracting Polynomia

You can add or subtract polynomials by combining like terms.

The following are like terms: $4y$ and $7y$ $8x^2$ and $2x^2$ $7m^5$ and m^5 — same variables raised to same power

The following are not like terms: $3x^2$ and $3x$ (same variable, different exponent) $4y$ and 7 (one with variable, one constant) $8m$ and $3n$ (same power, but different variable)

Add $3x^2 + 4x + 5x^2 + 6x$.

$3x^2 + 4x + 5x^2 + 6x$ *Identify like terms.*
$3x^2 + 5x^2 + 4x + 6x$ *Rearrange terms so that like terms are together.*
$8x^2 + 10x$ *Combine like terms.*

Add $(5y^2 + 7y + 2) + (4y^2 + y + 8)$.

$(5y^2 + 7y + 2) + (4y^2 + y + 8)$ *Identify like terms.*
$(5y^2 + 4y^2) + (7y + y) + (2 + 8)$ *Rearrange terms so that like terms are together.*
$9y^2 + 8y + 10$ *Combine like terms.*

Determine whether the following are like terms. Explain.

1. $4x$ and x^4 **no; same variable raised to different power**
2. $5y$ and $7y$ **yes; same variable raised to same power**
3. $2z^3$ and $4x^3$ **no; different variable raised to same power**

Add.

4. $2y^2 + 3y + 7y + y^2$ **$3y^2 + 10y$**
5. $8m^4 + 3m - 4m^4$ **$4m^4 + 3m$**
6. $12x^5 + 10x^4 + 8x^4$ **$12x^5 + 18x^4$**
7. $(6x^2 + 3x) + (2x^2 + 6x)$ **$8x^2 + 9x$**
8. $(m^2 - 10m + 5) + (8m + 2)$ **$m^2 - 2m + 7$**
9. $(6x^3 + 5x) + (4x^3 + x^2 - 2x + 9)$ **$10x^3 + x^2 + 3x + 9$**
10. $(2y^5 - 6y^3 + 1) + (y^5 + 8y^4 - 2y^3 - 1)$ **$3y^5 + 8y^4 - 8y^3$**

Multiple Choice For Exercises 54 and 55, choose the best answer.

54. What is the missing term?

$(-14y^2 + 9y^2 - 12y + 3) + (2y^2 + \square - 6y - 2) = (-3y^2 - 15y + 1)$

Ⓐ $-6y$ Ⓑ $-3y$ **Ⓒ $3y$** (circled) Ⓓ $6y$

55. Which is NOT equivalent to $-5t^3 - t$?

Ⓐ $-(5t^3 + t)$ Ⓒ $(t^3 + 6t) - (6t^3 + 7t)$

Ⓑ $(2t^3 - 4t) - (-7t - 3t)$ (circled) Ⓓ $(2t^3 - 3t^2 + t) - (7t^3 - 3t^2 + 2t)$

56. **Extended Response** Tammy plans to put a wallpaper border around the perimeter of her room. She will not put the border across the doorway, which is 3 feet wide.

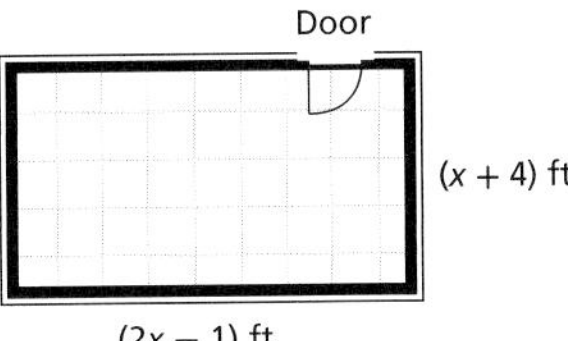

a. Write a polynomial that represents the number of feet of wallpaper border that Tammy will need. **$6x + 3$**

b. A local store has 50 feet of the border that Tammy has chosen. What is the greatest whole-number value of x for which this amount would be enough for Tammy's room? Justify your answer.

c. Determine the dimensions of Tammy's room for the value of x that you found in part **b.** **13 ft × 11 ft**

56b. 7; If $x = 7$, Tammy will need $6(7) + 3 = 45$ feet of wallpaper border. However, if $x = 8$, Tammy will need $6(8) + 3 = 51$ feet of wallpaper border, which is more than the store has.

CHALLENGE AND EXTEND

57. **Geometry** The legs of the isosceles triangle at right measure $(x^3 + 5)$ units. The perimeter of the triangle is $(2x^3 + 3x^2 + 8)$ units. Write a polynomial that represents the measure of the base of the triangle. **$3x^2 - 2$**

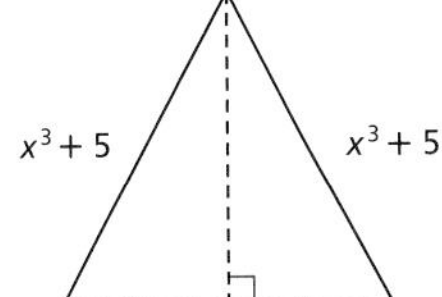

58. Write two polynomials whose sum is $4m^3 + 3m$.

59. Write two polynomials whose difference is $4m^3 + 3m$.

60. Write three polynomials whose sum is $4m^3 + 3m$.

61. Write three trinomials whose sum is $4m^3 + 3m$. **61. $(2m^3 + m^2 + m) + (m^3 + m^2 + m) + (m^3 - 2m^2 + m)$**

62. Write two monomials whose sum is $4m^3 + 3m$. **$4m^3 + 3m$**

58–61. Possible answers given.

58. $(2m^3 + 2m) + (2m^3 + m)$

59. $(5m^3 + 2m) - (m^3 - m)$

60. $(2m^3 + m) + (m^3 + m) + (m^3 + m)$

SPIRAL STANDARDS REVIEW

Solve each inequality and graph the solutions. Check your answer. *(Lesson 3-2)*

63. $d + 5 \geq -2$ **$d \geq -7$** 64. $15 < m - 11$ **$m > 26$** 65. $-6 + t < -6$ **$t < 0$**

Write each equation in slope-intercept form. Then graph the line described by each equation. *(Lesson 5-6)*

66. $3x + y = 8$ **$y = -3x + 8$** 67. $2y = \frac{1}{2}x + 6$ **$y = \frac{1}{4}x + 3$** 68. $y = 4(-x + 1)$ **$y = -4x + 4$**

Simplify. *(Lesson 7-3)*

69. $b^4 \cdot b^7$ **b^{11}** 70. $cd^4 \cdot (c^{-5})^3$ **$\frac{d^4}{c^{14}}$** 71. $(-3z^6)^2$ **$9z^{12}$** 72. $(j^3k^{-5})^3 \cdot (k^2)^4$ **$\frac{j^9}{k^7}$**

Teaching Tip **Multiple Choice** In **Exercise 54,** after determining that the missing term is a y-term, encourage students to write and solve an algebraic equation to find the coefficient: $-12 + x - 6 = -15$.

Answers

63. [number line: −8 −7 −6 −5 −4 −3 −2 −1 0]

64. [number line: 6 16 26 36 46 56 66]

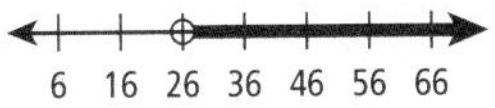

65. [number line: −3 −2 −1 0 1 2 3]

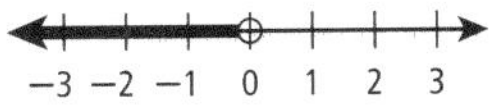

66–68. For graphs, see p. A23.

Journal

Have students describe two different ways of adding polynomials, using examples in their descriptions.

ALTERNATIVE ASSESSMENT

Have students write four different polynomials, using any of the following as the variable part of the terms: x, y, x^2, y^2. Instruct students to pick any two of the polynomials and find the sum. Then have them find the difference of the remaining two polynomials.

Power Presentations with PowerPoint®

7-7 Lesson Quiz

Add or subtract.

1. $7m^2 + 3m + 4m^2$ **$11m^2 + 3m$**
2. $(r^2 + s^2) - (5r^2 + 4s^2)$ **$-4r^2 - 3s^2$**
3. $(10pq + 3p) + (2pq - 5p + 6pq)$ **$18pq - 2p$**
4. $(14d^2 - 8) + (6d^2 - 2d + 1)$ **$20d^2 - 2d - 7$**
5. $(2.5ab + 14b) - (-1.5ab + 4b)$ **$4ab + 10b$**
6. A painter must add the areas of two walls to determine the amount of paint needed. The area of the first wall is modeled by $4x^2 + 12x + 9$, and the area of the second wall is modeled by $36x^2 - 12x + 1$. Write a polynomial that represents the total area of the two walls. **$40x^2 + 10$**

Also available on transparency

7-7 PROBLEM SOLVING

LESSON 7-7 **Problem Solving**
Adding and Subtracting Polynomials

Write the correct answer.

1. There are two boxes in a storage unit. The volume of the first box is $4x^3 + 4x^2$ cubic units. The volume of the second box is $6x^3 - 18x^2$ cubic units. Write a polynomial for the total volume of the two boxes.

$10x^3 - 14x^2$ cubic units

2. The recreation field at a middle school is shaped like a rectangle with a length of $15x$ yards and a width of $10x - 3$ yards. Write a polynomial for the perimeter of the field. Then calculate the perimeter if $x = 2$.

$50x - 6$; 94 yards

3. Two cabins on opposite banks of a river are $12x^2 - 7x + 5$ feet apart. One cabin is $9x + 1$ feet from the river. The other cabin is $3x^2 + 4$ feet from the river. Write the polynomial that represents the width of the river where it passes between the two cabins. Then calculate the width if $x = 3$.

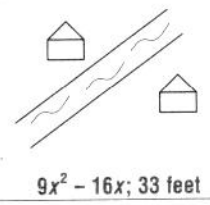

$9x^2 - 16x$; 33 feet

The circle graph represents election results for the president of the math team. Use the graph for questions 4–6. Select the best answer.

Math Team Election Results

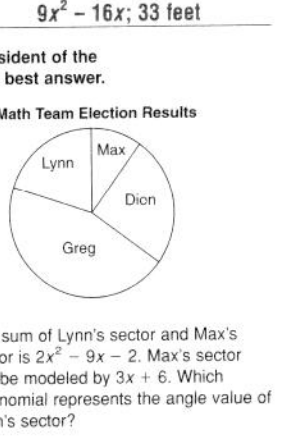

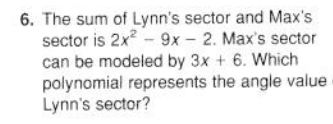

4. The angle value of Greg's sector can be modeled by $x^2 + 6x + 2$. The angle value of Dion's sector can be modeled by $7x + 20$. Which polynomial represents both sectors combined?

A $x^2 + x + 18$ C $6x^2 + 7x + 18$
Ⓑ $x^2 + 13x + 22$ (circled) D $7x^2 + 6x + 22$

5. The sum of Greg and Lynn's sectors is $2x^2 + 4x - 6$. The sum of Max and Dion's sectors is $10x + 26$. Which polynomial represents how much greater Greg and Lynn's combined sectors are than Max and Dion's?

F $2x^2 + 6x + 32$ **Ⓗ $2x^2 - 6x - 32$** (circled)
G $2x^2 - 6x + 20$ J $2x^2 + 14x + 20$

6. The sum of Lynn's sector and Max's sector is $2x^2 - 9x - 2$. Max's sector can be modeled by $3x + 6$. Which polynomial represents the angle value of Lynn's sector?

A $2x^2 - 6x + 4$ C $2x^2 - 12x + 8$
B $2x^2 - 6x - 4$ **Ⓓ $2x^2 - 12x - 8$** (circled)

7-7 CHALLENGE

LESSON 7-7 **Challenge**
Polynomial Functions

A **polynomial function** is a function whose rule is a polynomial. For example, $P(x) = 2x^3 - 4x^2 + 3x - 2$ is a polynomial function.

Like other functions, polynomial functions can be evaluated by substituting a value for the variable and simplifying.

1. For $P(x) = 2x^3 - 4x^2 + 3x - 2$, find $P(2)$. **4**

A variable, or variable expression, can be substituted for the variable in a function as well. For example, if $P(x) = 5x + 3$, then $P(a) = 5a + 3$.

2. For $P(x) = -4x^3 + x - 6$, find $P(b)$. **$-4b^3 + b - 6$**

Suppose $P(x) = 3x - 2$. Then $P(c) + P(c + 1) = 3c - 2 + 3(c + 1) - 2$
$= 3c - 2 + 3c + 3 - 2$
$= 6c - 1$

3. For $P(x) = 10 - 4x$, find $P(d) + P(2d) - P(3)$.

$22 - 12d$

4. For $P(x) = -3x^4 - 7x^3 + 2x^2 - x + 8$, find $P(g^2) + P(g)$.

$-3g^8 - 7g^6 - g^4 - 7g^3 + g^2 - g + 16$

Give an example of $Q(x)$ and $S(x)$ for each situation.

5. $Q(x)$ is a quartic binomial. $S(x)$ is a quartic trinomial. $Q(x) + S(x)$ is a quartic trinomial.
$Q(x) = x^4 + 1$; $S(x) = x^4 + x^3 + 1$

6. $Q(x)$ is a cubic trinomial. $S(x)$ is a cubic binomial. $Q(x) - S(x)$ is a quadratic monomial.
$Q(x) = x^3 + x^2 + 1$; $S(x) = x^3 + 1$

7. $Q(x)$ is a cubic trinomial. $S(x)$ is a cubic trinomial. $Q(x) + S(x)$ is a quadratic binomial.
$Q(x) = x^3 + x^2 + 1$; $S(x) = -x^3 + x^2 + 1$

8. $Q(x)$ is a quintic trinomial. $S(x)$ is a quartic trinomial. $Q(x) + S(x)$ is a quintic polynomial with five terms.
$Q(x) = x^5 + x^4 + 1$; $S(x) = x^4 + x^3 + x^2$

Organizer

Use with Lesson 7-8

Objective: Use algebra tiles to model polynomial multiplication.

Materials: algebra tiles

Online Edition

Countdown to Mastery Week 16

Teach

Discuss

In **Activity 1,** show students that they would get the same product if they placed the first factor along the top and the second factor along the left side. This is because multiplication is commutative.

In **Activity 3,** remind students that zero pairs are only those whose size and shape are the same, but whose colors are different.

Alternative Approach

Use the transparency mat and transparency algebra tiles (MK).

California Standards

Algebra 1 10.0

7-8

Use with Lesson 7-8

Model Polynomial Multiplication

You can use algebra tiles to multiply polynomials. Use the length and width of a rectangle to represent the factors. The area of the rectangle represents the product.

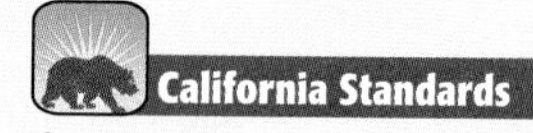

California Standards

10.0 Students add, subtract, **multiply,** and divide **monomials and polynomials.** Students solve multistep problems, including word problems, by using these techniques.

KEY

 $= 1$

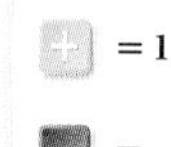 $= -1$

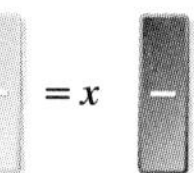 $= x$

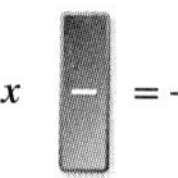 $= -x$

 $= x^2$

REMEMBER

- The product of two values with the same sign is positive.
- The product of two values with different signs is negative.

Activity 1

Use algebra tiles to find $2(x + 1)$.

MODEL		ALGEBRA
$x + 1$; × ; 2	*Place the first factor in a column along the left side of the grid. This will be the width of the rectangle.* *Place the second factor across the top of the grid. This will be the length of the rectangle.*	$2(x + 1)$
×	*Fill in the grid with tiles that have the same width as the tiles in the left column and the same length as the tiles in the top row.*	
×	*The area of the rectangle inside the grid represents the product.*	$x + x + 1 + 1$ $2x + 2$

The rectangle has an area of $2x + 2$, so $2(x + 1) = 2x + 2$. Notice that this is the same product you would get by using the Distributive Property to multiply $2(x + 1)$.

Try This

Use algebra tiles to find each product.

1. $3(x + 2)$ **$3x + 6$**
2. $2(2x + 1)$ **$4x + 2$**
3. $3(x + 1)$ **$3x + 3$**
4. $3(2x + 2)$ **$6x + 6$**

Activity 2

Use algebra tiles to find $2x(x - 3)$.

MODEL		ALGEBRA
$x - 3$; x; $2x$	*Place tiles to form the length and width of a rectangle and fill in the rectangle. The product of two values with the same sign (same color) is positive (yellow). The product of two values with different signs (different colors) is negative (red).*	$2x(x - 3)$
x	*The area of the rectangle inside the grid represents the product. The rectangle has an area of $2x^2 - 6x$, so $2x(x - 3) = 2x^2 - 6x$.*	$x^2 + x^2 - x - x - x - x - x - x$ $2x^2 - 6x$

Try This

Use algebra tiles to find each product.

5. $3x(x - 2)$ **$3x^2 - 6x$**
6. $x(2x - 1)$ **$2x^2 - x$**
7. $x(x + 1)$ **$x^2 + x$**
8. $(8x + 5)(-2x)$ **$-16x^2 - 10x$**

Activity 3

Use algebra tiles to find $(x + 1)(x - 2)$.

MODEL		ALGEBRA
$x - 2$; x; $x + 1$	*Place tiles for each factor to form the length and width of a rectangle. Fill in the grid and remove any zero pairs.*	$(x + 1)(x - 2)$ $x^2 - x - x + x - 1 - 1$
x	*The area inside the grid represents the product. The remaining area is $x^2 - x - 2$, so $(x + 1)(x - 2) = x^2 - x - 2$.*	$x^2 - x - 1 - 1$ $x^2 - x - 2$

Try This

Use algebra tiles to find each product.

9. $(x + 2)(x - 3)$ **$x^2 - x - 6$**
10. $(x - 1)(x + 3)$ **$x^2 + 2x - 3$**
11. $(x - 2)(x - 3)$ **$x^2 - 5x + 6$**
12. $(x + 1)(x + 2)$ **$x^2 + 3x + 2$**

Close

Key Concept

When multiplication is being modeled with algebra tiles, the dimensions of a rectangle represent the factors, and the area of the rectangle represents the product. The area of the rectangle can sometimes be simplified by removing zero pairs.

Assessment

Journal When using algebra tiles to model polynomial multiplication, have students explain how to determine which tiles should be placed inside the multiplication grid to form the rectangle (product). Explanations should include how to determine sizes, shapes, and colors of tiles.

Teacher to Teacher

Before using tiles to multiply polynomials, I like to address a common error that occurs when using the Distributive Property, namely not distributing to all terms.

I distribute something to students, emphasizing that I am distributing to *all* of the students. Later I distribute something else but intentionally omit one or two students and wait for the response. Usually the entire class corrects me, which leads to a good class discussion that helps students understand symbolic examples.

David Mattoon
Fallbrook, CA

7-8 Organizer

Objective: Multiply polynomials.

Online Edition
Tutorial Videos, Interactivity

Countdown to Mastery Week 17

Power Presentations with PowerPoint®

Warm Up

Evaluate.

1. 3^2 9 **2.** 2^4 16

3. 10^2 100

Simplify.

4. $2^3 \cdot 2^4$ 2^7 **5.** $y^5 \cdot y^4$ y^9

6. $(5^3)^2$ 5^6 **7.** $(x^2)^4$ x^8

8. $-4(x - 7)$ $-4x + 28$

Also available on transparency

Math Humor

Student A: What is u times r times r?

Student B: ur^2.

Student A: No, I'm not!

California Standards

Algebra 1 🔑 **10.0**

7-8 Multiplying Polynomials

California Standards

🔑 **10.0 Students** add, subtract, **multiply,** and divide **monomials and polynomials. Students solve multistep problems, including word problems, by using these techniques.**

Why learn this?

You can multiply polynomials to write expressions for areas, such as the area of a dulcimer. (See Example 5.)

To multiply monomials and polynomials, you will use some of the properties of exponents that you learned earlier in this chapter.

Remember!

When multiplying powers with the same base, keep the base and add the exponents.

$x^2 \cdot x^3 = x^{2+3} = x^5$

EXAMPLE 1 Multiplying Monomials

Multiply.

A $(5x^2)(4x^3)$

$(5x^2)(4x^3)$

$(5 \cdot 4)(x^2 \cdot x^3)$ *Group factors with like bases together.*

$20x^5$ *Multiply.*

B $(-3x^3y^2)(4xy^5)$

$(-3x^3y^2)(4xy^5)$

$(-3 \cdot 4)(x^3 \cdot x)(y^2 \cdot y^5)$ *Group factors with like bases together.*

$-12x^4y^7$ *Multiply.*

C $\left(\frac{1}{2}a^3b\right)(a^2c^2)(6b^2)$

$\left(\frac{1}{2}a^3b\right)(a^2c^2)(6b^2)$

$\left(\frac{1}{2} \cdot 6\right)(a^3 \cdot a^2)(b \cdot b^2)(c^2)$ *Group factors with like bases together.*

$3a^5b^3c^2$ *Multiply.*

CHECK IT OUT! Multiply.

1a. $(3x^3)(6x^2)$ $18x^5$ **1b.** $(2r^2t)(5t^3)$ $10r^2t^4$ **1c.** $\left(\frac{1}{3}x^2y\right)(12x^3z^2)(y^4z^5)$ $4x^5y^5z^7$

To multiply a polynomial by a monomial, use the Distributive Property.

EXAMPLE 2 Multiplying a Polynomial by a Monomial

Multiply.

A $5(2x^2 + x + 4)$

$5(2x^2 + x + 4)$

$(5)2x^2 + (5)x + (5)4$ *Distribute 5.*

$10x^2 + 5x + 20$ *Multiply.*

1 Introduce

EXPLORATION

7-8 Multiplying Polynomials

You will need a graphing calculator for this Exploration. As you work through the Exploration, try to find a rule for multiplying a monomial and a polynomial.

1. You can use your calculator to explore the relationship between $x(2x^2 + 3)$ and $2x^3 + 3x$. Press Y= and enter $x(2x^2 + 3)$ as **Y1**. Then enter $2x^3 + 3x$ as **Y2**.
2. Press 2nd TABLE to view a table of values for the two expressions. Use the arrow keys to scroll up and down the table. What do you notice about the values of **Y1** and **Y2** for each value of x? Use this information to make a conjecture about $x(2x^2 + 3)$ and $2x^3 + 3x$.

Use a calculator to predict whether each equation is true.

3. $2x(5x + 9) = 10x^2 + 18x$
4. $3x^3(2x + 9) = 6x^4 + 9$
5. $4x^2(3x - 5) = 12x^3 - 20x^2$
6. $10x^3(3x^2 - 2x) = 30x^5 - 20x^4$

THINK AND DISCUSS

7. **Describe** how to multiply a monomial and a polynomial based on your answers to Problems 3–6.

Motivate

Ask students to explain how to find the area of a rectangle with length 5 cm and width 7 cm.
$A = \ell w$, so $A = (5)(7) = 35$ cm^2

Have students explain how to find the area of a rectangle with length x and width 10.
$A = \ell w$, so $A = (x)(10) = 10x$ cm^2

Explain to students that in this lesson they will learn to describe area when the dimensions are polynomials.

Explorations and answers are provided in *Alternate Openers: Explorations Transparencies.*

Multiply.

B $2x^2y(3x - y)$

$(2x^2y)(3x - y)$

$(2x^2y)3x + (2x^2y)(-y)$ — *Distribute $2x^2y$.*

$(2 \cdot 3)(x^2 \cdot x)y + 2(-1)(x^2)(y \cdot y)$ — *Group like bases together.*

$6x^3y - 2x^2y^2$ — *Multiply.*

C $4a(a^2b + 2b^2)$

$4a(a^2b + 2b^2)$

$(4a)a^2b + (4a)2b^2$ — *Distribute 4a.*

$(4)(a \cdot a^2)(b) + (4 \cdot 2)(a)(b^2)$ — *Group like bases together.*

$4a^3b + 8ab^2$ — *Multiply.*

CHECK IT OUT! Multiply.

2a. $2(4x^2 + x + 3)$ **$8x^2 + 2x + 6$**
2b. $3ab(5a^2 + b)$ **$15a^3b + 3ab^2$**
2c. $5r^2s^2(r - 3s)$ **$5r^3s^2 - 15r^2s^3$**

To multiply a binomial by a binomial, you can apply the Distributive Property more than once:

$(x + 3)(x + 2) = x(x + 2) + 3(x + 2)$ — *Distribute x and 3.*

$= x(x + 2) + 3(x + 2)$

$= x(x) + x(2) + 3(x) + 3(2)$ — *Distribute x and 3 again.*

$= x^2 + 2x + 3x + 6$ — *Multiply.*

$= x^2 + 5x + 6$ — *Combine like terms.*

Another method for multiplying binomials is called the FOIL method.

1. Multiply the **F**irst terms. (F) $(x + 3)(x + 2) \rightarrow x \cdot x = x^2$
2. Multiply the **O**uter terms. (O) $(x + 3)(x + 2) \rightarrow x \cdot 2 = 2x$
3. Multiply the **I**nner terms. (I) $(x + 3)(x + 2) \rightarrow 3 \cdot x = 3x$
4. Multiply the **L**ast terms. (L) $(x + 3)(x + 2) \rightarrow 3 \cdot 2 = 6$

$(x + 3)(x + 2) = x^2 + 2x + 3x + 6 = x^2 + 5x + 6$

F O I L

2 Teach

Guided Instruction

Review the multiplication properties of exponents before beginning this lesson. Encourage students to write each step carefully to avoid making mistakes when distributing. Arrows can be drawn to help keep track of the terms that have been multiplied. Remind students that all of the methods presented in this lesson will give correct answers. Students should choose the method they are most comfortable with.

Universal Access

Through Visual Cues

Show students the "FOIL face" to help them keep track of which terms to multiply.

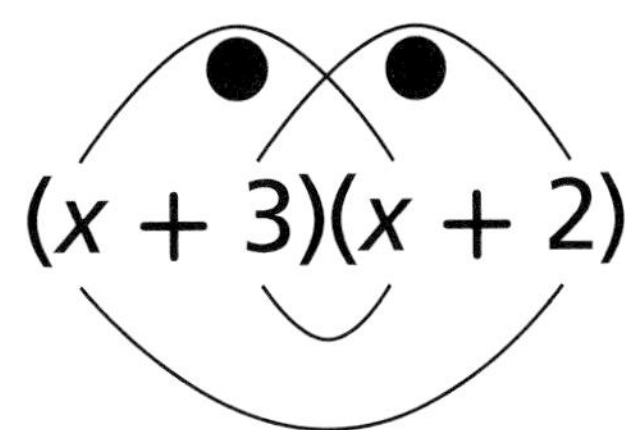

COMMON ERROR ALERT

When a binomial is raised to a power, many students make the following mistake: $(x + 4)^2 = x^2 + 4^2$. Encourage students to write the expression as the product of two binomials first and then multiply. For example, $(x + 4)^2 = (x + 4)(x + 4) = x^2 + 4x + 4x + 16 = x^2 + 8x + 16$.

Power Presentations with PowerPoint®

Additional Examples

Example 1

Multiply.

A. $(6y^3)(3y^5)$ $18y^8$

B. $(3mn^2)(9m^2n)$ $27m^3n^3$

C. $\left(\frac{1}{4}s^2t^2\right)(st)(-12st^2)$ $-3s^4t^5$

Example 2

Multiply.

A. $4(3x^2 + 4x - 8)$
$12x^2 + 16x - 32$

B. $6pq(2p - q)$ $12p^2q - 6pq^2$

C. $\frac{1}{2}x^2y(6xy + 8x^2y^2)$
$3x^3y^2 + 4x^4y^3$

Also available on transparency

INTERVENTION

Questioning Strategies

EXAMPLE 1

- How is multiplying monomials different from adding monomials?
- When multiplying monomials with exponents, why do you add the exponents?

EXAMPLE 2

- Will a monomial times a binomial always be a binomial?
- Will a monomial times a trinomial always be a trinomial? Explain.

Inclusion When using the FOIL method, encourage students to write the product after drawing each arrow rather than drawing all of the arrows at once. State: "Draw the F arrow and write the product, draw the O arrow and write the product," and so on.

Power Presentations with PowerPoint®

Additional Examples

Example 3

Multiply.

A. $(s + 4)(s - 2)$ $s^2 + 2s - 8$

B. $(x - 4)^2$ $x^2 - 8x + 16$

C. $(8m^2 - n)(m^2 - 3n)$
$8m^4 - 25m^2n + 3n^2$

Also available on transparency

INTERVENTION

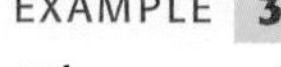

Questioning Strategies

EXAMPLE 3

- What terms from FOIL can often be combined?
- What do the signs from the last terms in each binomial tell you about the signs in the answer?

Math Background In **Example 3C,** remind students that the terms $6a^2b$ and $-ba^2$ are like terms due to the Commutative Property of Multiplication.

EXAMPLE 3 Multiplying Binomials

Multiply.

A $(x + 2)(x - 5)$

$(x + 2)(x - 5)$	
$x(x - 5) + 2(x - 5)$	*Distribute x and 2.*
$x(x) + x(-5) + 2(x) + 2(-5)$	*Distribute x and 2 again.*
$x^2 - 5x + 2x - 10$	*Multiply.*
$x^2 - 3x - 10$	*Combine like terms.*

Helpful Hint

In the expression $(x + 5)^2$, the base is $(x + 5)$.
$(x + 5)^2 =$
$(x + 5)(x + 5)$

B $(x + 5)^2$

$(x + 5)(x + 5)$	*Write as a product of two binomials.*
$(x \cdot x) + (x \cdot 5) + (5 \cdot x) + (5 \cdot 5)$	*Use the FOIL method.*
$x^2 + 5x + 5x + 25$	*Multiply.*
$x^2 + 10x + 25$	*Combine like terms.*

C $(3a^2 - b)(a^2 - 2b)$

$3a^2(a^2) + 3a^2(-2b) - b(a^2) - b(-2b)$	*Use the FOIL method.*
$3a^4 - 6a^2b - a^2b + 2b^2$	*Multiply.*
$3a^4 - 7a^2b + 2b^2$	*Combine like terms.*

CHECK IT OUT! **3a.** $(a + 3)(a - 4)$ **$a^2 - a - 12$**   **3b.** $(x - 3)^2$ **$x^2 - 6x + 9$**   **3c.** $(2a - b^2)(a + 4b^2)$ **$2a^2 + 7ab^2 - 4b^4$**

To multiply polynomials with more than two terms, you can use the Distributive Property several times. Multiply $(5x + 3)$ by $(2x^2 + 10x - 6)$:

$$\begin{aligned}(5x + 3)(2x^2 + 10x - 6) &= 5x(2x^2 + 10x - 6) + 3(2x^2 + 10x - 6)\\ &= 5x(2x^2 + 10x - 6) + 3(2x^2 + 10x - 6)\\ &= 5x(2x^2) + 5x(10x) + 5x(-6) + 3(2x^2) + 3(10x) + 3(-6)\\ &= 10x^3 + 50x^2 - 30x + 6x^2 + 30x - 18\\ &= 10x^3 + 56x^2 - 18\end{aligned}$$

You can also use a rectangle model to multiply polynomials with more than two terms. This is similar to finding the area of a rectangle with length $(2x^2 + 10x - 6)$ and width $(5x + 3)$:

	$2x^2$	$+ 10x$	$- 6$
$5x$	$10x^3$	$50x^2$	$-30x$
$+ 3$	$6x^2$	$30x$	-18

Write the product of the monomials in each row and column.

To find the product, add all of the terms inside the rectangle by combining like terms and simplifying if necessary.

$$10x^3 + 6x^2 + 50x^2 + 30x - 30x - 18$$
$$10x^3 + 56x^2 - 18$$

Universal Access

Through Modeling

A rectangle model can also be used to display the FOIL method.

	x	$+3$
x	x^2	$3x$
$+2$	$2x$	6

This model shows that $(x + 2)(x + 3) = x^2 + 3x + 2x + 6 = x^2 + 5x + 6$.

This rectangle model is useful because it can also be used in the next chapter for factoring polynomials.

Another method that can be used to multiply polynomials with more than two terms is the vertical method. This is similar to methods used to multiply whole numbers.

$$\begin{array}{rrl} & 2x^2 + 10x - 6 & \\ \times & 5x + 3 & \\ \hline & 6x^2 + 30x - 18 & \text{Multiply each term in the top polynomial by 3.} \\ + & 10x^3 + 50x^2 - 30x & \text{Multiply each term in the top polynomial by 5x, and align like terms.} \\ \hline & 10x^3 + 56x^2 + 0x - 18 & \text{Combine like terms by adding vertically.} \\ & 10x^3 + 56x^2 - 18 & \text{Simplify.} \end{array}$$

EXAMPLE 4 Multiplying Polynomials

Helpful Hint

A polynomial with *m* terms multiplied by a polynomial with *n* terms has a product that, before simplifying, has *mn* terms. In Example 4A, there are 2 · 3, or 6, terms before simplifying.

Multiply.

A $(x + 2)(x^2 - 5x + 4)$

$(x + 2)(x^2 - 5x + 4)$

$x(x^2 - 5x + 4) + 2(x^2 - 5x + 4)$ — *Distribute x and 2.*

$x(x^2) + x(-5x) + x(4) + 2(x^2) + 2(-5x) + 2(4)$ — *Distribute x and 2 again.*

$x^3 + 2x^2 - 5x^2 - 10x + 4x + 8$ — *Simplify.*

$x^3 - 3x^2 - 6x + 8$ — *Combine like terms.*

B $(3x - 4)(-2x^3 + 5x - 6)$

$(3x - 4)(-2x^3 + 5x - 6)$

$$\begin{array}{rrl} & -2x^3 + 0x^2 + 5x - 6 & \text{Add } 0x^2 \text{ as a placeholder.} \\ \times & 3x - 4 & \\ \hline & 8x^3 + 0x^2 - 20x + 24 & \text{Multiply each term in the top polynomial by } -4. \\ + & -6x^4 + 0x^3 + 15x^2 - 18x & \text{Multiply each term in the top polynomial by 3x, and align like terms.} \\ \hline & -6x^4 + 8x^3 + 15x^2 - 38x + 24 & \text{Combine like terms by adding vertically.} \end{array}$$

C $(x - 2)^3$

$[(x - 2)(x - 2)](x - 2)$ — *Write as the product of three binomials.*

$[x \cdot x + x(-2) - 2 \cdot x - 2(-2)](x - 2)$ — *Use the FOIL method on the first two factors.*

$(x^2 - 2x - 2x + 4)(x - 2)$ — *Multiply.*

$(x^2 - 4x + 4)(x - 2)$ — *Combine like terms.*

$(x - 2)(x^2 - 4x + 4)$ — *Use the Commutative Property of Multiplication.*

$x(x^2 - 4x + 4) + (-2)(x^2 - 4x + 4)$ — *Distribute x and −2.*

$x(x^2) + x(-4x) + x(4) + (-2)(x^2) + (-2)(-4x) + (-2)(4)$ — *Distribute x and −2 again.*

$x^3 - 4x^2 + 4x - 2x^2 + 8x - 8$ — *Simplify.*

$x^3 - 6x^2 + 12x - 8$ — *Combine like terms.*

Power Presentations with PowerPoint®

Additional Examples

Example 4

Multiply.

A. $(x - 5)(x^2 + 4x - 6)$ $x^3 - x^2 - 26x + 30$

B. $(2x - 5)(-4x^2 - 10x + 3)$ $-8x^3 + 56x - 15$

C. $(x + 3)^3$ $x^3 + 9x^2 + 27x + 27$

D. $(3x + 1)(x^3 + 4x^2 - 7)$ $3x^4 + 13x^3 + 4x^2 - 21x - 7$

Also available on transparency

INTERVENTION Questioning Strategies

EXAMPLE 4

- How is multiplying a polynomial by a binomial similar to multiplying a binomial by a binomial? How is it different?

Advanced Learners/GATE Ask students to find similarities between polynomials and real numbers. Discuss the types of operations you can use with each.

Power Presentations with PowerPoint®

Additional Examples

Example 5

The width of a rectangular prism is 3 feet less than the height, and the length of the prism is 4 feet more than the height.

A. Write a polynomial that represents the area of the base of the prism.
$h^2 + h - 12$

B. Find the area of the base when the height is 5 feet.
18 ft^2

Also available on transparency

INTERVENTION

Questioning Strategies

EXAMPLE 5

- What types of polynomials did you multiply?

Multiply.

D $(2x + 3)(x^2 - 6x + 5)$

	x^2	$-6x$	$+5$
$2x$	$2x^3$	$-12x^2$	$10x$
$+3$	$3x^2$	$-18x$	15

Write the product of the monomials in each row and column.

$2x^3 + 3x^2 - 12x^2 - 18x + 10x + 15$ *Add all terms inside the rectangle.*

$2x^3 - 9x^2 - 8x + 15$ *Combine like terms.*

Multiply. $x^3 - x^2 - 6x + 18$

4a. $(x + 3)(x^2 - 4x + 6)$

4b. $(3x + 2)(x^2 - 2x + 5)$

$3x^3 - 4x^2 + 11x + 10$

EXAMPLE 5 *Music Application*

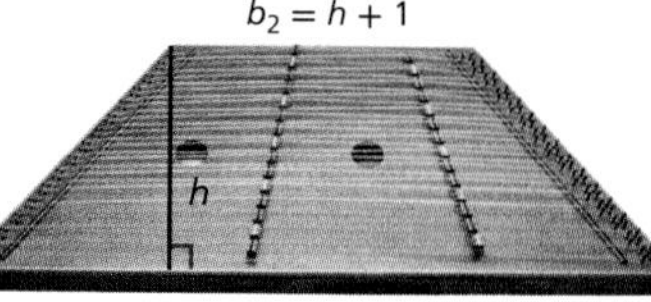

A dulcimer is a musical instrument that is sometimes shaped like a trapezoid.

A **Write a polynomial that represents the area of the dulcimer shown.**

$A = \frac{1}{2}h(b_1 + b_2)$ *Write the formula for area of a trapezoid.*

$= \frac{1}{2}h[(2h - 1) + (h + 1)]$ *Substitute 2h − 1 for b_1 and h + 1 for b_2.*

$= \frac{1}{2}h(3h)$ *Combine like terms.*

$= \frac{3}{2}h^2$ *Simplify.*

The area is represented by $\frac{3}{2}h^2$.

B **Find the area of the dulcimer when the height is 22 inches.**

$A = \frac{3}{2}h^2$ *Use the polynomial from part a.*

$= \frac{3}{2}(22)^2$ *Substitute 22 for h.*

$= \frac{3}{2}(484) = 726$

The area is 726 square inches.

5a. $x^2 - 4x$

5b. 12 m^2

5. The length of a rectangle is 4 meters shorter than its width.

a. Write a polynomial that represents the area of the rectangle.

b. Find the area of the rectangle when the width is 6 meters.

THINK AND DISCUSS

1. Compare the vertical method for multiplying polynomials with the vertical method for multiplying whole numbers.

2. GET ORGANIZED Copy and complete the graphic organizer. In each box, multiply two polynomials using the given method.

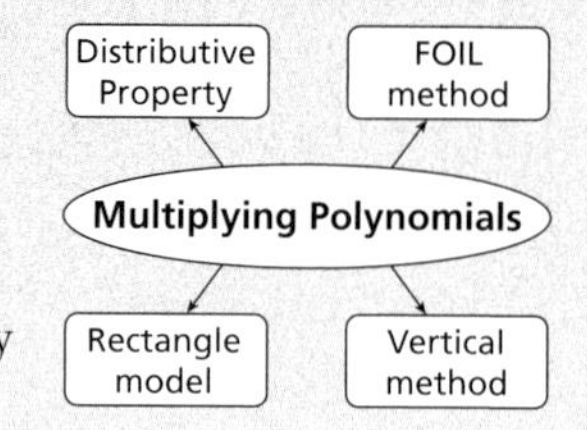

3 Close

Summarize

Ask students to multiply the following using any of the methods learned in this lesson.

$(5r^2s)(9rs)$ $45r^3s^2$

$3x^2(x^3 - 10)$ $3x^5 - 30x^2$

$(y + 2)(y - 5)$ $y^2 - 3y - 10$

$(x + 5y)(xy + 4x + 7y)$

$x^2y + 4x^2 + 27xy + 5xy^2 + 35y^2$

FORMATIVE ASSESSMENT

and INTERVENTION

***Diagnose Before* the Lesson**
7-8 Warm Up, TE p. 446

***Monitor During* the Lesson**
Check It Out! Exercises, SE pp. 446–450
Questioning Strategies, TE pp. 447–450

***Assess After* the Lesson**
7-8 Lesson Quiz, TE p. 453
Alternative Assessment, TE p. 453

Answers to *Think and Discuss*

1. Possible answer: Both numbers and polynomials are set up in 2 rows and require you to multiply each item in the top row by an item in the bottom row. In the end, you add vertically to get the answer. When you are multiplying polynomials, the items are monomial terms. When you are multiplying numbers, the items are digits.
2. See p. A6.

7-8 Exercises

California Standards Practice 10.0

go.hrw.com
Homework Help Online
KEYWORD: MA8CA 7-8
Parent Resources Online
KEYWORD: MA8CA Parent

GUIDED PRACTICE

Multiply.

SEE EXAMPLE 1 p. 446

1. $(2x^2)(7x^4)$
2. $(-5mn^3)(4m^2n^2)$
3. $(6rs^2)(s^3t^2)\left(\frac{1}{2}r^4t^3\right)$
4. $\left(\frac{1}{3}a^5\right)(12a)$
5. $(-3x^4y^2)(-7x^3y)$
6. $(-2pq^3)(5p^2q^2)(-3q^4)$

SEE EXAMPLE 2 p. 446

7. $4(x^2 + 2x + 1)$
8. $3ab(2a^2 + 3b^3)$
9. $2a^3b(3a^2b + ab^2)$
10. $-3x(x^2 - 4x + 6)$
11. $5x^2y(2xy^3 - y)$
12. $5m^2n^3 \cdot mn^2(4m - n)$

SEE EXAMPLE 3 p. 448

13. $(x + 1)(x - 2)$
14. $(x + 1)^2$
15. $(x - 2)^2$
16. $(y - 3)(y - 5)$
17. $(4a^3 - 2b)(a - 3b^2)$
18. $(m^2 - 2mn)(3mn + n^2)$

SEE EXAMPLE 4 p. 449

19. $(x + 5)(x^2 - 2x + 3)$
20. $(3x + 4)(x^2 - 5x + 2)$
21. $(2x - 4)(-3x^3 + 2x - 5)$
22. $(-4x + 6)(2x^3 - x^2 + 1)$
23. $(x - 5)(x^2 + x + 1)$
24. $(a + b)(a - b)(b - a)$

SEE EXAMPLE 5 p. 450

25. **Photography** The length of a rectangular photograph is 3 inches less than twice the width. $2x^2 - 3x$
    a. Write a polynomial that represents the area of the photograph.
    b. Find the area of the photograph when the width is 4 inches. **20 in²**

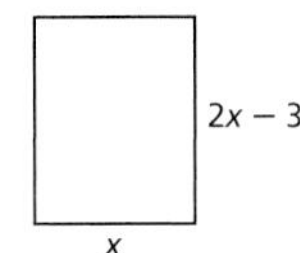

PRACTICE AND PROBLEM SOLVING

Independent Practice

For Exercises	See Example
26–34	1
35–43	2
44–52	3
53–61	4
62	5

Extra Practice
Skills Practice p. EP15
Application Practice p. EP30

Multiply.

26. $(3x^2)(8x^5)$
27. $(-2r^3s^4)(6r^2s)$
28. $(15xy^2)\left(\frac{1}{3}x^2z^3\right)(y^3z^4)$
29. $(-2a^3)(-5a)$
30. $(6x^3y^2)(-2x^2y)$
31. $(-3a^2b)(-2b^3)(-a^3b^2)$
32. $(7x^2)(xy^5)(2x^3y^2)$
33. $(-4a^3bc^2)(a^3b^2c)(3ab^4c^5)$
34. $(12mn^2)(2m^2n)(mn)$
35. $9s(s + 6)$
36. $9(2x^2 - 5x)$
37. $3x(9x^2 - 4x)$
38. $3(2x^2 + 5x + 4)$
39. $5s^2t^3(2s - 3t^2)$
40. $x^2y^3 \cdot 5x^2y(6x + y^2)$
41. $-5x(2x^2 - 3x - 1)$
42. $-2a^2b^3(3ab^2 - a^2b)$
43. $-7x^3y \cdot x^2y^2(2x - y)$
44. $(x + 5)(x - 3)$
45. $(x + 4)^2$
46. $(m - 5)^2$
47. $(5x - 2)(x + 3)$
48. $(3x - 4)^2$
49. $(5x + 2)(2x - 1)$
50. $(x - 1)(x - 2)$
51. $(x - 8)(7x + 4)$
52. $(2x + 7)(3x + 7)$
53. $(x + 2)(x^2 - 3x + 5)$
54. $(x^2 - 4x + 3)(2x + 5)$
55. $(5x - 1)(-2x^3 + 4x - 3)$
56. $(x - 3)(x^2 - 5x + 6)$
57. $(4x^3 - x^2 + 7)(2x^2 - 3)$
58. $(x - 4)^3$
59. $(x - 2)(x^2 + 2x + 1)$
60. $(2x + 10)(4 - x + 6x^3)$
61. $(1 - x)^3$
62. **Geometry** The length of the rectangle at right is 3 feet longer than its width. $x^2 + 3x$
    a. Write a polynomial that represents the area of the rectangle.
    b. Find the area of the rectangle when the width is 5 feet. **40 ft²**

x + 3
x

63. A square tabletop has side lengths of $(4x - 6)$ units. Write a polynomial that represents the area of the tabletop. $16x^2 - 48x + 36$

7-8 Exercises

Assignment Guide

Assign *Guided Practice* exercises as necessary.

If you finished Examples **1–3**
Proficient 26–52, 70–78
Advanced 26–52, 70–78, 90

If you finished Examples **1–5**
Proficient 26–65, 70–80 even, 82–93, 98–105
Advanced 26–64, 70–80 even, 82–105

Homework Quick Check
Quickly check key concepts.
Exercises: 30, 42, 46, 52, 56, 62, 69

Answers

1. $14x^6$
2. $-20m^3n^5$
3. $3r^5s^5t^5$
4. $4a^6$
5. $21x^7y^3$
6. $30p^3q^9$
7. $4x^2 + 8x + 4$
8. $6a^3b + 9ab^4$
9. $6a^5b^2 + 2a^4b^3$
10. $-3x^3 + 12x^2 - 18x$
11. $10x^3y^4 - 5x^2y^2$
12. $20m^4n^5 - 5m^3n^6$
13. $x^2 - x - 2$
14. $x^2 + 2x + 1$
15. $x^2 - 4x + 4$
16. $y^2 - 8y + 15$
17. $4a^4 - 2ab - 12a^3b^2 + 6b^3$
18. $3m^3n - 5m^2n^2 - 2mn^3$
19. $x^3 + 3x^2 - 7x + 15$
20. $3x^3 - 11x^2 - 14x + 8$
21. $-6x^4 + 12x^3 + 4x^2 - 18x + 20$
22. $-8x^4 + 16x^3 - 6x^2 - 4x + 6$
23. $x^3 - 4x^2 - 4x - 5$
24. $-a^3 + a^2b + ab^2 - b^3$
26. $24x^7$
27. $-12r^5s^5$
28. $5x^3y^5z^7$
29. $10a^4$
30. $-12x^5y^3$
31. $-6a^5b^6$
32. $14x^6y^7$
33. $-12a^7b^7c^8$
34. $24m^4n^4$
35. $9s^2 + 54s$
36. $18x^2 - 45x$
37. $27x^3 - 12x^2$
38. $6x^2 + 15x + 12$
39. $10s^3t^3 - 15s^2t^5$
40. $30x^5y^4 + 5x^4y^6$
41. $-10x^3 + 15x^2 + 5x$
42. $-6a^3b^5 + 2a^4b^4$
43. $-14x^6y^3 + 7x^5y^4$
44. $x^2 + 2x - 15$
45. $x^2 + 8x + 16$
46. $m^2 - 10m + 25$
47. $5x^2 + 13x - 6$
48. $9x^2 - 24x + 16$
49. $10x^2 - x - 2$
50. $x^2 - 3x + 2$
51. $7x^2 - 52x - 32$
52. $6x^2 + 35x + 49$
53. $x^3 - x^2 - x + 10$
54. $2x^3 - 3x^2 - 14x + 15$
55. $-10x^4 + 2x^3 + 20x^2 - 19x + 3$
56. $x^3 - 8x^2 + 21x - 18$
57. $8x^5 - 2x^4 - 12x^3 + 17x^2 - 21$
58. $x^3 - 12x^2 + 48x - 64$
59. $x^3 - 3x - 2$
60. $12x^4 + 60x^3 - 2x^2 - 2x + 40$
61. $-x^3 + 3x^2 - 3x + 1$

Standard	Exercises
2.0	98, 102–105
6.0	99–101
10.0	1–24, 26–62a, 63, 64b, 65a–c, 66–69a, 70–81, 82c, 84, 86–88, 90–93b, 95

Exercise 64 involves multiplying polynomials. This exercise prepares students for the Concept Connection on page 462.

Answers

64a.

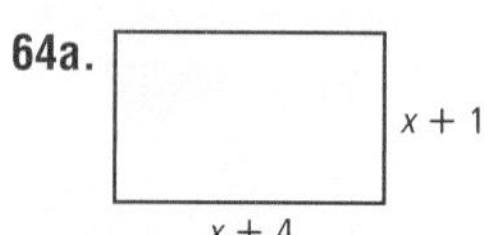

65b. $x^4 - x^3 + 2x^2 - 2x$

c. $x^4 - 5x^3 + 6x^2 + x - 3$

70. $6a^9$

71. $2x^2 - 7x - 30$

72. $3g^2 + 14g - 5$

73. $8x^2 - 16xy + 6y^2$

74. $x^2 - 9$

75. $6x^2 - 9x - 6$

76. $x^2 - 6x - 40$

77. $x^3 + 3x^2$

78. $x^3 + 3x^2 + 2x$

79. $2x^3 - 7x^2 - 10x + 24$

80. $a^3 - a^2b - ab^2 + b^3$

81. $8p^3 - 36p^2q + 54pq^2 - 27q^3$

82a.

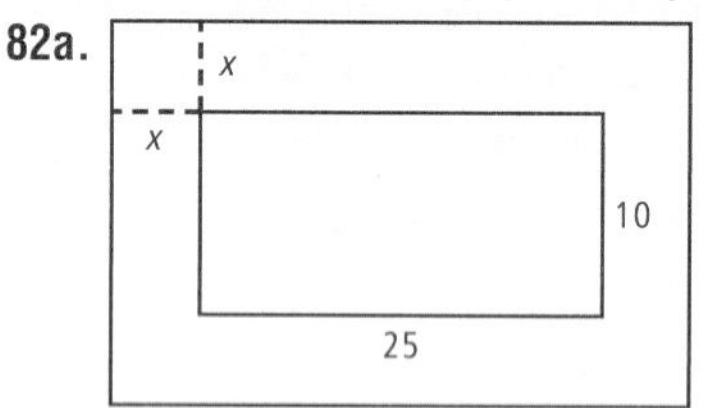

83. Possible answer: Each letter in FOIL represents a pair of terms in a certain position within the factors. The letters must account for every pairing of terms while describing first, outside, inside, and last positions. This is only possible with 2 binomials.

7-8 PRACTICE A

7-8 PRACTICE C

7-8 PRACTICE B

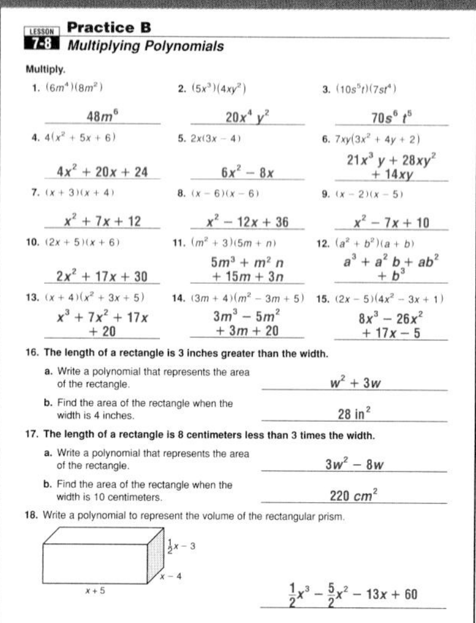

LESSON 7-8 **Practice B**
Multiplying Polynomials

Multiply.

1. $(6m^4)(8m^2)$ — $48m^6$
2. $(5x^3)(4xy^2)$ — $20x^4y^2$
3. $(10s^5t)(7st^4)$ — $70s^6t^5$
4. $4(x^2 + 5x + 6)$ — $4x^2 + 20x + 24$
5. $2x(3x - 4)$ — $6x^2 - 8x$
6. $7xy(3x^2 + 4y + 2)$ — $21x^3y + 28xy^2 + 14xy$
7. $(x + 3)(x + 4)$ — $x^2 + 7x + 12$
8. $(x - 6)(x - 6)$ — $x^2 - 12x + 36$
9. $(x - 2)(x - 5)$ — $x^2 - 7x + 10$
10. $(2x + 5)(x + 6)$ — $2x^2 + 17x + 30$
11. $(m^2 + 3)(5m + n)$ — $5m^3 + m^2n + 15m + 3n$
12. $(a^2 + b^2)(a + b)$ — $a^3 + a^2b + ab^2 + b^3$
13. $(x + 4)(x^2 + 3x + 5)$ — $x^3 + 7x^2 + 17x + 20$
14. $(3m + 4)(m^2 - 3m + 5)$ — $3m^3 - 5m^2 + 3m + 20$
15. $(2x - 5)(4x^2 - 3x + 1)$ — $8x^3 - 26x^2 + 17x - 5$

16. The length of a rectangle is 3 inches greater than the width.

a. Write a polynomial that represents the area of the rectangle. $w^2 + 3w$

b. Find the area of the rectangle when the width is 4 inches. 28 in^2

17. The length of a rectangle is 8 centimeters less than 3 times the width.

a. Write a polynomial that represents the area of the rectangle. $3w^2 - 8w$

b. Find the area of the rectangle when the width is 10 centimeters. 220 cm^2

18. Write a polynomial to represent the volume of the rectangular prism.

$\frac{1}{2}x - 3$; $x - 4$; $x + 5$

$\frac{1}{2}x^3 - \frac{5}{2}x^2 - 13x + 60$

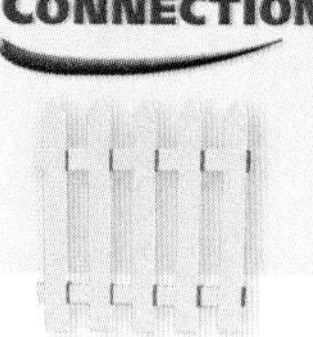

64. This problem will prepare you for the Concept Connection on page 462.

a. Marie is creating a garden. She designs a rectangular garden with a length of $(x + 4)$ feet and a width of $(x + 1)$ feet. Draw a diagram of Marie's garden with the length and width labeled.

b. Write a polynomial that represents the area of Marie's garden. $x^2 + 5x + 4$

c. What is the area when $x = 4$? **40 ft²**

65. Copy and complete the table below.

	A	Degree of A	B	Degree of B	A • B	Degree of A • B
	$2x^2$	2	$3x^5$	5	$6x^7$	7
a.	$5x^3$	3	$2x^2 + 1$	2	$10x^5 + 5x^3$	5
b.	$x^2 + 2$	2	$x^2 - x$	2		4
c.	$x - 3$	1	$x^3 - 2x^2 + 1$	3		4

d. Use the results from the table to complete the following: The product of a polynomial of degree m and a polynomial of degree n has a degree of ___. $m + n$

Geometry Write a polynomial that represents the area of each rectangle.

66. $2x + 3$; $4x$ — $8x^2 + 12x$

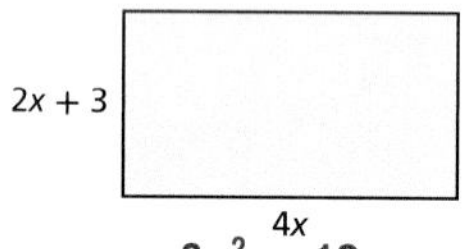

67.

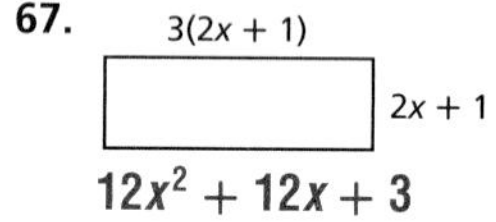

$12x^2 + 12x + 3$

68. $x - 5$; $x - 5$ — $x^2 - 10x + 25$

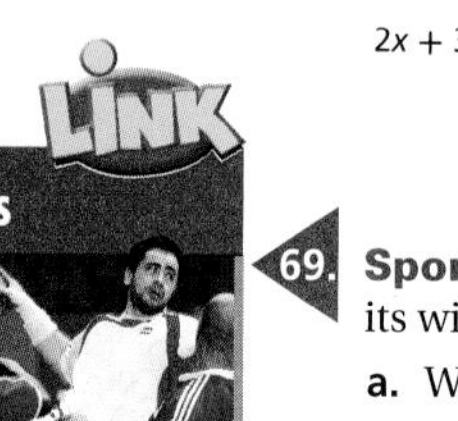

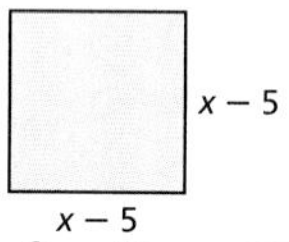

LINK Sports

Team handball is a game with elements of soccer and basketball. It originated in Europe in the 1900s and was first played at the Olympics in 1936 with teams of 11 players. Today, a handball team consists of seven players—six court players and one goalie.

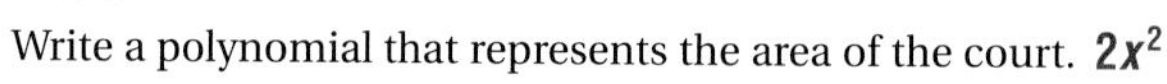

69. Sports The length of a regulation team handball court is twice its width.

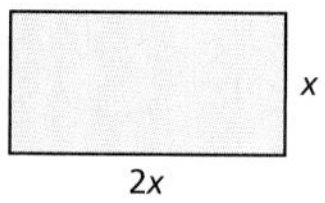

x; $2x$

a. Write a polynomial that represents the area of the court. $2x^2$

b. The width of a team handball court is 20 meters. Find the area of the court. **800 m²**

Multiply.

70. $(1.5a^3)(4a^6)$
71. $(2x + 5)(x - 6)$
72. $(3g - 1)(g + 5)$
73. $(4x - 2y)(2x - 3y)$
74. $(x + 3)(x - 3)$
75. $(1.5x - 3)(4x + 2)$
76. $(x - 10)(x + 4)$
77. $x^2(x + 3)$
78. $(x + 1)(x^2 + 2x)$
79. $(x - 4)(2x^2 + x - 6)$
80. $(a + b)(a - b)^2$
81. $(2p - 3q)^3$

82. Multi-Step A rectangular swimming pool is 25 feet long and 10 feet wide. It is surrounded by a fence that is x feet from each side of the pool.

a. Draw a diagram of this situation.

b. Write expressions for the length and width of the fenced region. (*Hint:* How much longer is one side of the fenced region than the corresponding side of the pool?) $2x + 25$; $2x + 10$

c. Write an expression for the area of the fenced region. $4x^2 + 70x + 250$

83. Write About It Explain why the FOIL method can be used to multiply only two binomials at a time.

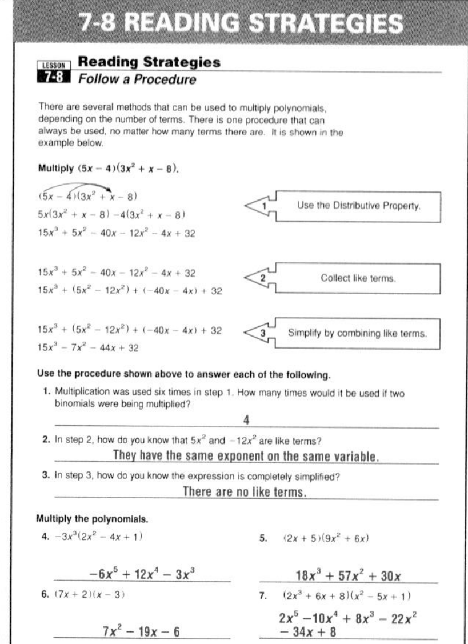

7-8 READING STRATEGIES

LESSON 7-8 **Reading Strategies**
Follow a Procedure

There are several methods that can be used to multiply polynomials, depending on the number of terms. There is one procedure that can always be used, no matter how many terms there are. It is shown in the example below.

Multiply $(5x - 4)(3x^2 + x - 8)$.

$(5x - 4)(3x^2 + x - 8)$
$5x(3x^2 + x - 8) - 4(3x^2 + x - 8)$
$15x^3 + 5x^2 - 40x - 12x^2 - 4x + 32$

1 Use the Distributive Property.

$15x^3 + 5x^2 - 40x - 12x^2 - 4x + 32$
$15x^3 + (5x^2 - 12x^2) + (-40x - 4x) + 32$

2 Collect like terms.

$15x^3 + (5x^2 - 12x^2) + (-40x - 4x) + 32$
$15x^3 - 7x^2 - 44x + 32$

3 Simplify by combining like terms.

Use the procedure shown above to answer each of the following.

1. Multiplication was used six times in step 1. How many times would it be used if two binomials were being multiplied? 4
2. In step 2, how do you know that $5x^2$ and $-12x^2$ are like terms? They have the same exponent on the same variable.
3. In step 3, how do you know the expression is completely simplified? There are no like terms.

Multiply the polynomials.

4. $-3x^3(2x^2 - 4x + 1)$ — $-6x^5 + 12x^4 - 3x^3$
5. $(2x + 5)(9x^2 + 6x)$ — $18x^3 + 57x^2 + 30x$
6. $(7x + 2)(x - 3)$ — $7x^2 - 19x - 6$
7. $(2x^3 + 6x + 8)(x^2 - 5x + 1)$ — $2x^5 - 10x^4 + 8x^3 - 22x^2 - 34x + 8$

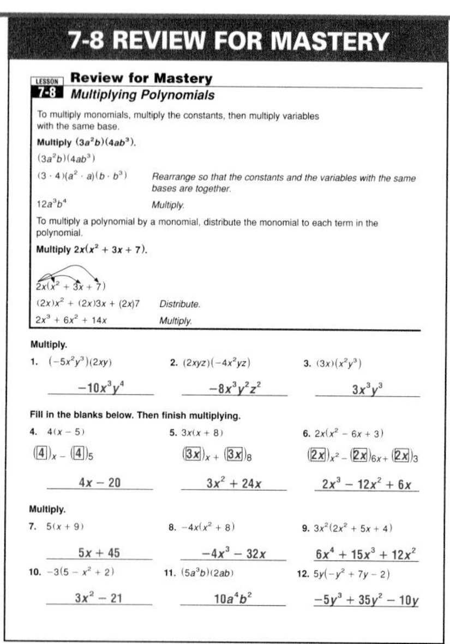

7-8 REVIEW FOR MASTERY

LESSON 7-8 **Review for Mastery**
Multiplying Polynomials

To multiply monomials, multiply the constants, then multiply variables with the same base.

Multiply $(3a^2b)(4ab^3)$.

$(3a^2b)(4ab^3)$
$(3 \cdot 4)(a^2 \cdot a)(b \cdot b^3)$ — *Rearrange so that the constants and the variables with the same bases are together.*
$12a^3b^4$ — *Multiply.*

To multiply a polynomial by a monomial, distribute the monomial to each term in the polynomial.

Multiply $2x(x^2 + 3x + 7)$.

$2x(x^2 + 3x + 7)$
$(2x)x^2 + (2x)3x + (2x)7$ — *Distribute.*
$2x^3 + 6x^2 + 14x$ — *Multiply.*

Multiply.

1. $(-5x^2y^3)(2xy)$ — $-10x^3y^4$
2. $(2xyz)(-4x^2yz)$ — $-8x^3y^2z^2$
3. $(3x)(x^2y^3)$ — $3x^3y^3$

Fill in the blanks below. Then finish multiplying.

4. $4(x - 5)$ — $(4)x - (4)5$ — $4x - 20$
5. $3x(x + 8)$ — $(3x)x + (3x)8$ — $3x^2 + 24x$
6. $2x(x^2 - 6x + 3)$ — $(2x)x^2 - (2x)6x + (2x)3$ — $2x^3 - 12x^2 + 6x$

Multiply.

7. $5(x + 9)$ — $5x + 45$
8. $-4x(x^2 + 8)$ — $-4x^3 - 32x$
9. $3x^2(2x^2 + 5x + 4)$ — $6x^4 + 15x^3 + 12x^2$
10. $-3(5 - x^2 + 2)$ — $3x^2 - 21$
11. $(5a^3b)(2ab)$ — $10a^4b^2$
12. $5y(-y^2 + 7y - 2)$ — $-5y^3 + 35y^2 - 10y$

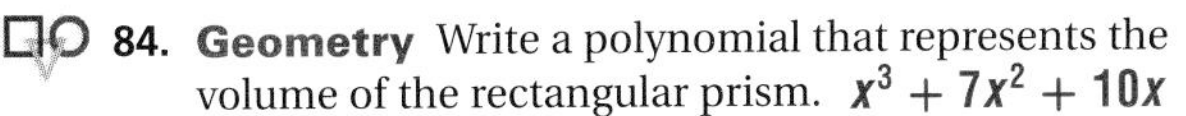

84. **Geometry** Write a polynomial that represents the volume of the rectangular prism. $x^3 + 7x^2 + 10x$

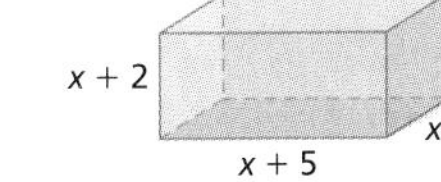

85. **Critical Thinking** Is there any value for x that would make the statement $(x + 3)^3 = x^3 + 3^3$ true? Give an example to justify your answer. **Yes; $x = 0$**

86. **Estimation** The length of a rectangle is 1 foot more than its width. Write a polynomial that represents the area of the rectangle. Estimate the width of the rectangle if its area is 25 square feet. $x^2 + x$; **4.5 ft**

Multiple Choice **For Exercises 87–89, choose the best answer.**

87. Which of the following products is equal to $a^2 - 5a - 6$?

   Ⓐ $(a - 1)(a - 5)$ Ⓑ $(a - 2)(a - 3)$ **(C)** $(a + 1)(a - 6)$ Ⓓ $(a + 2)(a - 3)$

88. Which of the following is equal to $2a(a^2 - 1)$?

   Ⓐ $2a^2 - 2a$ Ⓑ $2a^3 - 1$ **(C)** $2a^3 - 2a$ Ⓓ $2a^2 - 1$

89. What is the degree of the product of $3x^3y^2z$ and x^2yz?

   Ⓐ 5 Ⓑ 6 Ⓒ 7 **(D)** 10

CHALLENGE AND EXTEND

Simplify.

90. $6x^2 - 2(3x^2 - 2x + 4)$ $4x - 8$
91. $x^2 - 2x(x + 3)$ $-x^2 - 6x$
92. $x(4x - 2) + 3x(x + 1)$ $7x^2 + x$

93. The diagram shows a sandbox and the frame that surrounds it.

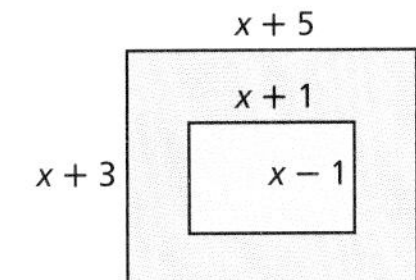

   a. Write a polynomial that represents the area of the sandbox. $x^2 - 1$
   b. Write a polynomial that represents the area of the frame that surrounds the sandbox. $8x + 16$

94. **Geometry** The side length of a square is $(8 + 2x)$ units. The area of this square is the same as the perimeter of another square with a side length of $(x^2 + 48)$ units. Find the value of x. $x = 4$

95. Write a polynomial that represents the product of three consecutive integers. Let x represent the first integer. $x^3 + 3x^2 + 2x$

96. Find m and n so that $x^m(x^n + x^{n-2}) = x^5 + x^3$. **Possible answer: $m = 2$; $n = 3$**

97. Find a so that $2x^a(5x^{2a-3} + 2x^{2a+2}) = 10x^3 + 4x^8$ $a = 2$

SPIRAL STANDARDS REVIEW

2.0, 6.0

98. A stop sign is 2.5 meters tall and casts a shadow that is 3.5 meters long. At the same time, a flagpole casts a shadow that is 28 meters long. If the height of each object is proportional to the length of its shadow, how tall is the flagpole? *(Lesson 2-5)* **20 m**

Graph the solutions of each linear inequality. *(Lesson 6-6)*

99. $y \le x - 2$
100. $4x - 2y < 10$
101. $-y \ge -3x + 1$

Simplify. All variables represent nonnegative numbers. *(Lesson 7-5)*

102. $\sqrt{x^6y^{12}}$ x^3y^6
103. $\left(x^{\frac{1}{2}}\right)^8 \sqrt[3]{y^9}$ x^4y^3
104. $\dfrac{\sqrt{x^4y^{10}}}{x^2}$ y^5
105. $\sqrt[4]{a^{16}b^{24}}$ a^4b^6

Teaching Tip

Multiple Choice Because the last term of the polynomial in **Exercise 87** is negative, the signs of the second terms in the binomials must be different. Eliminate choices **A** and **B.**

Multiplying the first terms in **Exercise 88** gives $2a^3$, so choices **A** and **D** cannot be correct. Students who chose **B** probably did not distribute fully.

Answers

99–101. See p. A23.

Journal

Have students explain how to multiply $(2x + 3)$ by $(x + 4)$ using the method of their choice.

ALTERNATIVE ASSESSMENT

Have students count off by fours. Have the 1's write a monomial, the 2's write a binomial, the 3's write a trinomial, and the 4's write a polynomial of degree four. Rearrange the class into new groups of four, so that each new group has a monomial, a binomial, a trinomial, and a 4th-degree polynomial. (Make some groups of five students if needed.) Have students multiply pairs of their polynomials together. Each group must turn in as many pairs as possible, with work shown for each answer.

Power Presentations with PowerPoint®

7-8 Lesson Quiz

Multiply.

1. $(6s^2t^2)(3st)$ $18s^3t^3$
2. $4xy^2(x + y)$ $4x^2y^2 + 4xy^3$
3. $(x + 2)(x - 8)$ $x^2 - 6x - 16$
4. $(2x - 7)(x^2 + 3x - 4)$
   $2x^3 - x^2 - 29x + 28$
5. $6mn(m^2 + 10mn - 2)$
   $6m^3n + 60m^2n^2 - 12mn$
6. $(2x - 5y)(3x + y)$
   $6x^2 - 13xy - 5y^2$
7. A triangle has a base that is 4 cm longer than its height.
   a. Write a polynomial that represents the area of the triangle. $\frac{1}{2}h^2 + 2h$
   b. Find the area when the height is 8 cm. 48 cm^2

Also available on transparency

7-8 PROBLEM SOLVING

LESSON 7-8 Problem Solving
Multiplying Polynomials

Write the correct answer.

1. A bedroom has a length of $x + 3$ feet and a width of $x - 1$ feet. Write a polynomial to express the area of the bedroom. Then calculate the area if $x = 10$.
   $x^2 + 2x - 3$;
   117 square feet

2. The length of a classroom is 4 feet longer than its width. Write a polynomial to express the area of the classroom. Then calculate the area if the width is 22 feet.
   $w^2 + 4w$;
   572 square feet

3. Nicholas is determining if he can afford to buy a car. He multiplies the number of months m by $i + p + 30f$ where i represents the monthly cost of insurance, p represents the monthly car payment, and f represents the number of times he fills the gas tank each month. Write the polynomial that Nicholas can use to determine how much it will cost him to own a car both for one month and for one year.
   $i + p + 30f$; $12i + 12p + 360f$

4. A seat cushion is shaped like a trapezoid. The shorter base of the cushion is 3 inches greater than the height. The longer base is 2 inches shorter than twice the height. Write the polynomial that can be used to find the area of the cushion. (The area of a trapezoid is represented by $\frac{1}{2}h(b_1 + b_2)$.)
   $\frac{3}{2}h^2 + \frac{1}{2}h$

The volume of a pyramid can be found by using $\frac{1}{3}Bh$ where B is the area of the base and h is the height of the pyramid. The Great Pyramid of Giza has a square base, and each side is about 300 feet longer than the height of the pyramid. Select the best answer.

5. Which polynomial represents the approximate area of the base of the Great Pyramid?
   A $h^2 + 90{,}000$
   B $2h + 90{,}000$
   (C) $h^2 + 600h + 90{,}000$
   D $2h^2 + 600h + 90{,}000$

6. Which polynomial represents the approximate volume of the Great Pyramid?
   (F) $\frac{1}{3}h^3 + 200h^2 + 30{,}000h$
   G $\frac{1}{3}h^2 + 200h + 30{,}000$
   H $h^3 + 600h^2 + 90{,}000h$
   J $3h^3 + 600h^2 + 90{,}000h$

7. The original height of the Great Pyramid was 485 feet. Due to erosion, it is now about 450 feet. Find the approximate volume of the Great Pyramid today.
   A $562{,}500 \text{ ft}^3$ **(C)** $84{,}375{,}000 \text{ ft}^3$
   B $616{,}225 \text{ ft}^3$ D $99{,}623{,}042 \text{ ft}^3$

7-8 CHALLENGE

LESSON 7-8 Challenge
The Missing Binomial

Determine the missing binomial. Choose from the table below. Each binomial is used once.

$x + 4$	$x + 3$	$x - 3$
$x + 1$	$x + 6$	$x - 4$
$x + 2$	$x - 2$	$x - 6$

1. $(\underline{x + 4})(x + 2) = x^2 + 2x + 4x + 8 = x^2 + 6x + 8$
2. $(\underline{x + 1})(x + 5) = x^2 + 5x + x + 5 + = x^2 + 6x + 5$
3. $(\underline{x + 2})(x - 3) = x^2 - 3x + 2x - 6 = x^2 - x - 6$
4. $(\underline{x + 3})(x - 5) = x^2 - 2x - 15$
5. $(\underline{x + 6})(x + 1) = x^2 + 7x + 6$
6. $(\underline{x - 2})(x + 4) = x^2 + 2x - 8$
7. $(\underline{x - 3})(x + 6) = x^2 + 3x - 18$
8. $(\underline{x - 4})(x + 2) = x^2 - 2x - 8$
9. $(\underline{x - 6})(x - 5) = x^2 - 11x + 30$

The binomials missing from the following equations are not all listed in the table. Determine the missing binomials.

10. $(\underline{x + 2})(x + 7) = x^2 + 9x + 14$
11. $(\underline{x + 3})(x + 4) = x^2 + 7x + 12$
12. $(\underline{x - 6})(x - 2) = x^2 - 8x + 12$
13. $(\underline{x - 4})(x - 10) = x^2 - 14x + 40$
14. $(\underline{x + 6})(\underline{x + 3}) = x^2 + 9x + 18$
15. $(\underline{x + 1})(\underline{x - 4}) = x^2 - 3x - 4$
16. $(\underline{x - 2})(\underline{x - 2}) = x^2 - 4x + 4$
17. $(\underline{3x - 1})(x + 2) = 3x^2 + 5x - 2$
18. $(\underline{x - 7})(2x + 3) = 2x^2 - 11x - 21$
19. $(\underline{2x - 3})(\underline{3x + 4}) = 6x^2 - x - 12$

Organizer

See Skills Bank pages SB21–SB22

Objective: Apply polynomial operations to finding areas of geometric figures.

PREMIER **Online Edition**

Teach

Remember

Students review and apply volume and surface area formulas for geometric figures.

INTERVENTION For additional review and practice on finding the volumes and surface areas of geometric figures, see Skills Bank pages SB21–SB22.

Close

Assess

The volume of any prism equals the area of the base times the height. Have students explain how to find the volume of the triangular prism in **Problem 6.** Find the area of the base. It is $2y^2 + y$. Multiply this by the height, which is $3y$. The volume is $6y^3 + 3y^2$.

California Standards

Reinforcement of 7MG2.1

Connecting Algebra to Geometry

Volume and Surface Area

The volume V of a three-dimensional figure is the amount of space it occupies. The surface area S is the total area of the two-dimensional surfaces that make up the figure.

California Standards

Reinforcement of 7MG2.1 Use formulas routinely for finding the perimeter and area of basic two-dimensional figures and **the surface area and volume of basic three-dimensional figures, including** rectangles, parallelograms, trapezoids, squares, triangles, circles, **prisms, and cylinders.**

Rectangular Prism

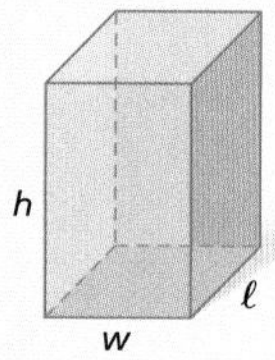

$V = \ell wh$
$S = 2(\ell w + \ell h + wh)$

Cylinder

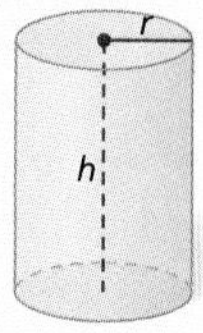

$V = \pi r^2 h$
$S = 2\pi r^2 + 2\pi rh$

Cone

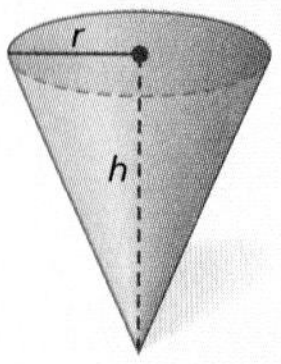

$V = \frac{1}{3}\pi r^2 h$

Pyramid

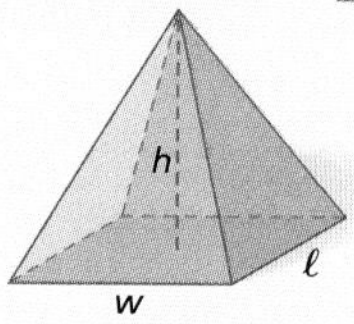

$V = \frac{1}{3}\ell wh$

Example

Write and simplify a polynomial expression for the volume of the cone. Leave the symbol π in your answer.

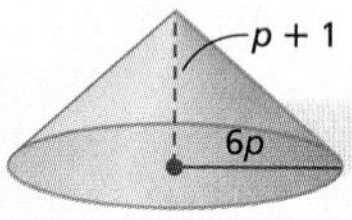

$V = \frac{1}{3}\pi r^2 h$	*Choose the correct formula.*
$= \frac{1}{3}\pi(6p)^2(p+1)$	*Substitute 6p for r and p + 1 for h.*
$= \frac{1}{3}\pi(36p^2)(p+1)$	*Use the Power of a Product Property.*
$= \frac{1}{3}(36)\pi[p^2(p+1)]$	*Use the Associative Property of Multiplication.*
$= 12\pi p^2(p+1)$	*Distribute $12\pi p^2$.*
$= 12\pi p^3 + 12\pi p^2$	

Try This

Write and simplify a polynomial expression for the volume of each figure.

1.

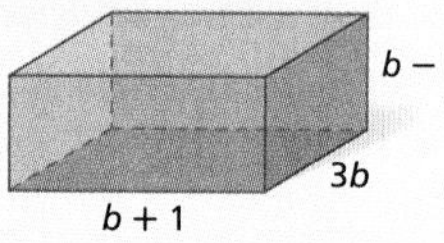

$3b^3 - 12b^2 - 15b$

2.

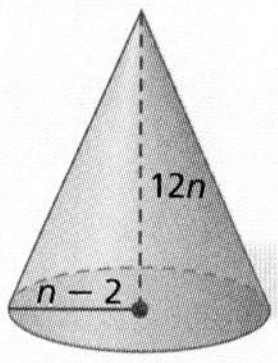

$4\pi n^3 - 16\pi n^2 + 16\pi n$

3. **$2k^3 - k^2 - 6k$**

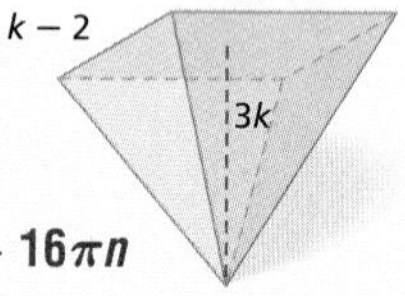

Write and simplify a polynomial expression for the surface area of each figure.

4.

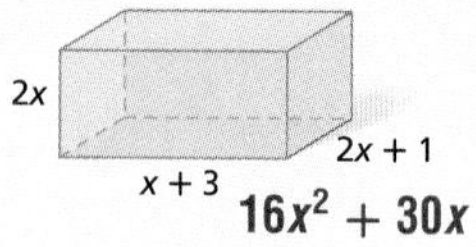

$16x^2 + 30x + 6$

5. **$4\pi w^2 - 4\pi$**

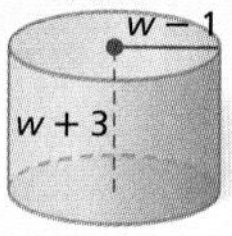

6. **$19y^2 + 14y$**

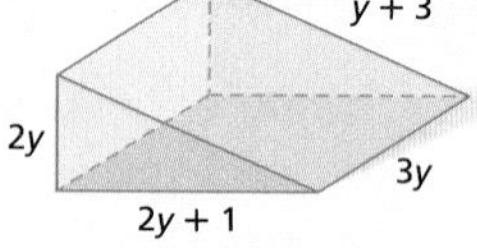

7-9 Special Products of Binomials

California Standards

🔑 **10.0 Students add, subtract, multiply,** and divide **monomials and polynomials. Students solve multistep problems, including word problems, by using these techniques.**

Vocabulary
perfect-square trinomial
difference of two squares

Why learn this?
You can use special products to find areas, such as the area of a path around a pond. (See Example 4.)

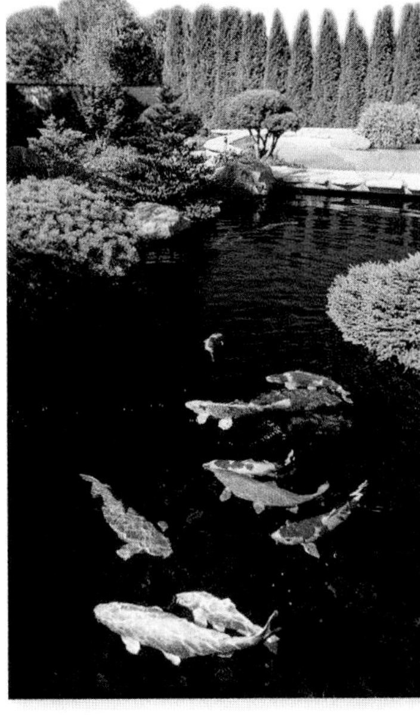

Imagine a square with sides of length $(a + b)$:

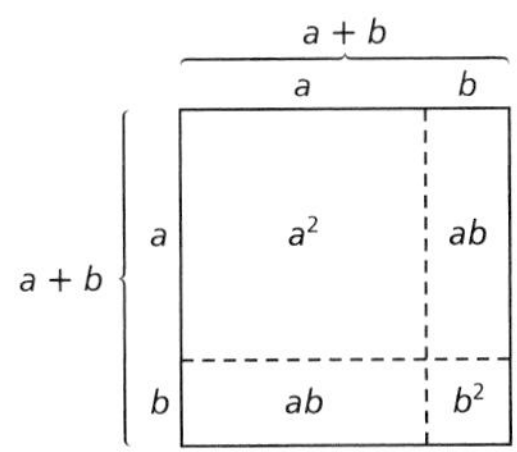

The area of this square is $(a + b)(a + b)$, or $(a + b)^2$. The area of this square can also be found by adding the areas of the smaller squares and rectangles inside. The sum of the areas inside is $a^2 + ab + ab + b^2$.

This means that $(a + b)^2 = a^2 + 2ab + b^2$.

You can use the FOIL method to verify this:

$$(a + b)^2 = (a + b)(a + b) = a^2 + ab + ab + b^2$$

F L I O

$$= a^2 + 2ab + b^2$$

A trinomial of the form $a^2 + 2ab + b^2$ is called a *perfect-square trinomial.* A **perfect-square trinomial** is a trinomial that is the result of squaring a binomial.

EXAMPLE 1 Finding Products in the Form $(a + b)^2$

Multiply.

A $(x + 4)^2$

$(a + b)^2 = a^2 + 2ab + b^2$	*Use the rule for $(a + b)^2$.*
$(x + 4)^2 = x^2 + 2(x)(4) + 4^2$	*Identify a and b: a = x and b = 4.*
$= x^2 + 8x + 16$	*Simplify.*

B $(3x + 2y)^2$

$(a + b)^2 = a^2 + 2ab + b^2$	*Use the rule for $(a + b)^2$.*
$(3x + 2y)^2 = (3x)^2 + 2(3x)(2y) + (2y)^2$	*Identify a and b: a = 3x and b = 2y.*
$= 9x^2 + 12xy + 4y^2$	*Simplify.*

7-9 Organizer

Objective: Find special products of binomials.

Online Edition
Tutorial Videos

Countdown to Mastery Week 17

Power Presentations with PowerPoint®

Warm Up

Simplify.

1. 4^2 16 **2.** 7^2 49

3. $(-2)^2$ 4 **4.** $(x)^2$ x^2

5. $-(5y^2)$ $-5y^2$ **6.** $(m^2)^2$ m^4

7. $2(6xy)$ $12xy$ **8.** $2(8x^2)$ $16x^2$

Also available on transparency

Math Humor

Parent: What happened in math class today?

Student: When the teacher said to look for perfect squares, everyone looked at me.

1 Introduce

EXPLORATION

7-9 Special Products of Binomials

You can use the FOIL method to find the square of a binomial. For example, to find $(a + 1)^2$, first write the product as $(a + 1)(a + 1)$. Then use the FOIL method.

$$(a + 1)^2 = (a + 1)(a + 1)$$
$$= a^2 + a \cdot 1 + 1 \cdot a + 1^2$$
$$= a^2 + a + a + 1$$
$$= a^2 + 2a + 1$$

1. Use the FOIL method to complete the table.

Power	Expanded Form	Product
$(a + 1)^2$	$(a + 1)(a + 1)$	$a^2 + 2a + 1$
$(a + 2)^2$		
$(a + 3)^2$		
$(a + 4)^2$		

2. Look for a pattern in the right column of the table. Use the pattern to find $(a + 5)^2$ without using the FOIL method.
3. Find $(a + 9)^2$ without using the FOIL method.

THINK AND DISCUSS

4. **Describe** a general rule you can use to find $(a + b)^2$.
5. **Show** how you can apply your rule to find $(7 + x)^2$.

Motivate

Have students find the products of the following:

$(x + 3)(x + 3)$ $x^2 + 6x + 9$
$(x + 4)(x + 4)$ $x^2 + 8x + 16$
$(x + 5)(x + 5)$ $x^2 + 10x + 25$

Discuss with students any patterns they see. Lead them to recognize that the middle term of the trinomial is two times the product of the first and last terms of the binomial.

$(a + b)(a + b) = a^2 + 2ab + b^2$

Explorations and answers are provided in *Alternate Openers: Explorations Transparencies.*

California Standards
Algebra 1 🔑 **10.0**

Power Presentations with PowerPoint®

Additional Examples

Example 1

Multiply.

A. $(x + 3)^2$ $x^2 + 6x + 9$

B. $(4s + 3t)^2$ $16s^2 + 24st + 9t^2$

C. $(5 + m^2)^2$ $25 + 10m^2 + m^4$

Example 2

Multiply.

A. $(x - 6)^2$ $x^2 - 12x + 36$

B. $(4m - 10)^2$ $16m^2 - 80m + 100$

C. $(2x - 5y)^2$ $4x^2 - 20xy + 25y^2$

D. $(7 - r^3)^2$ $49 - 14r^3 + r^6$

Also available on transparency

INTERVENTION

Questioning Strategies

EXAMPLE 1

- How do you find the middle term?
- In which position could a perfect-square trinomial have a term with an odd exponent?

EXAMPLE 2

- How are these examples different from those in **Example 1**? What causes the differences? How are they the same?
- Why is the last term of any perfect-square trinomial always positive?

Multiply.

C $(4 + s^2)^2$

$(a + b)^2 = a^2 + 2ab + b^2$ *Use the rule for $(a + b)^2$.*

$(4 + s^2)^2 = (4)^2 + 2(4)(s^2) + (s^2)^2$ *Identify a and b: $a = 4$ and $b = s^2$.*

$= 16 + 8s^2 + s^4$ *Simplify.*

D $(-m + 3)^2$

$(a + b)^2 = a^2 + 2ab + b^2$ *Use the rule for $(a + b)^2$.*

$(-m + 3)^2 = (-m)^2 + 2(-m)(3) + 3^2$ *Identify a and b: $a = -m$ and $b = 3$.*

$= m^2 - 6m + 9$ *Simplify.*

CHECK IT OUT! Multiply.

1a. $(x + 6)^2$ **1b.** $(5a + b)^2$ **1c.** $(1 + c^3)^2$

$x^2 + 12x + 36$ $25a^2 + 10ab + b^2$ $1 + 2c^3 + c^6$

You can use the FOIL method to find products in the form $(a - b)^2$:

$$(a - b)^2 = (a - b)(a - b) = a^2 - ab - ab + b^2$$
$$= a^2 - 2ab + b^2$$

A trinomial of the form $a^2 - 2ab + b^2$ is also a perfect-square trinomial because it is the result of squaring the binomial $(a - b)$.

EXAMPLE 2 Finding Products in the Form $(a - b)^2$

Multiply.

A $(x - 5)^2$

$(a - b)^2 = a^2 - 2ab + b^2$ *Use the rule for $(a - b)^2$.*

$(x - 5)^2 = x^2 - 2(x)(5) + 5^2$ *Identify a and b: $a = x$ and $b = 5$.*

$= x^2 - 10x + 25$ *Simplify.*

B $(6a - 1)^2$

$(a - b)^2 = a^2 - 2ab + b^2$ *Use the rule for $(a - b)^2$.*

$(6a - 1)^2 = (6a)^2 - 2(6a)(1) + (1)^2$ *Identify a and b: $a = 6a$ and $b = 1$.*

$= 36a^2 - 12a + 1$ *Simplify.*

C $(4c - 3d)^2$

$(a - b)^2 = a^2 - 2ab + b^2$ *Use the rule for $(a - b)^2$.*

$(4c - 3d)^2 = (4c)^2 - 2(4c)(3d) + (3d)^2$ *Identify a and b: $a = 4c$ and $b = 3d$.*

$= 16c^2 - 24cd + 9d^2$ *Simplify.*

D $(3 - x^2)^2$

$(a - b)^2 = (a)^2 - 2ab + b^2$ *Use the rule for $(a - b)^2$.*

$(3 - x^2)^2 = (3)^2 - 2(3)(x^2) + (x^2)^2$ *Identify a and b: $a = 3$ and $b = x^2$.*

$= 9 - 6x^2 + x^4$ *Simplify.*

CHECK IT OUT! Multiply.

2a. $(x - 7)^2$ **2b.** $(3b - 2c)^2$ **2c.** $(a^2 - 4)^2$

2a. $x^2 - 14x + 49$
2b. $9b^2 - 12bc + 4c^2$
2c. $a^4 - 8a^2 + 16$

2 Teach

Guided Instruction

Review how to multiply any two binomials before starting this section. Show the FOIL method for $(a + b)^2$ and $(a - b)^2$ next to each other, so students can better visualize the similarities and differences. Tell students that the binomials in this lesson could be multiplied using any of the methods they already know, but that certain types of binomials can be multiplied more quickly knowing these rules.

Universal Access

Through Auditory Cues

Have students learn the "verbal rules" for the special products.

$(a + b)^2 = a^2 + 2ab + b^2$

$(a - b)^2 = a^2 - 2ab + b^2$

- first term squared
- plus (or minus) two times the product of both terms
- plus last term squared

Have students create a similar verbal rule for $(a + b)(a - b) = a^2 - b^2$.

You can use an area model to see that $(a + b)(a - b) = a^2 - b^2$.

1

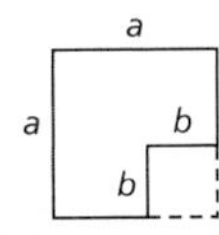

Begin with a square with area a^2. Remove a square with area b^2. The area of the new figure is $a^2 - b^2$.

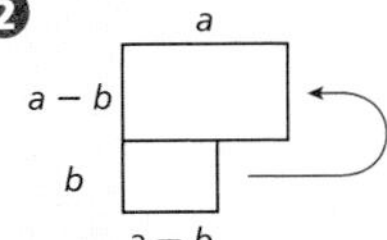

Then remove the smaller rectangle on the bottom. Turn it 90° and slide it up next to the top rectangle.

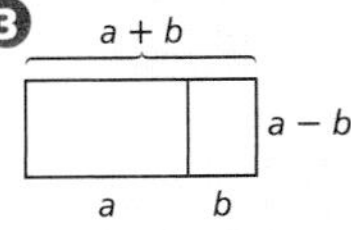

The new arrangement is a rectangle with length $a + b$ and width $a - b$. Its area is $(a + b)(a - b)$.

So $(a + b)(a - b) = a^2 - b^2$. A binomial of the form $a^2 - b^2$ is called a **difference of two squares**.

EXAMPLE 3 Finding Products in the Form $(a + b)(a - b)$

Multiply.

A $(x + 6)(x - 6)$

$(a + b)(a - b) = a^2 - b^2$	*Use the rule for $(a + b)(a - b)$.*
$(x + 6)(x - 6) = x^2 - 6^2$	*Identify a and b: $a = x$ and $b = 6$.*
$= x^2 - 36$	*Simplify.*

B $(x^2 + 2y)(x^2 - 2y)$

$(a + b)(a - b) = a^2 - b^2$	*Use the rule for $(a + b)(a - b)$.*
$(x^2 + 2y)(x^2 - 2y) = (x^2)^2 - (2y)^2$	*Identify a and b: $a = x^2$ and $b = 2y$.*
$= x^4 - 4y^2$	*Simplify.*

C $(7 + n)(7 - n)$

$(a + b)(a - b) = a^2 - b^2$	*Use the rule for $(a + b)(a - b)$.*
$(7 + n)(7 - n) = 7^2 - n^2$	*Identify a and b: $a = 7$ and $b = n$.*
$= 49 - n^2$	*Simplify.*

Multiply.

3a. $(x + 8)(x - 8)$ **3b.** $(3 + 2y^2)(3 - 2y^2)$ **3c.** $(9 + r)(9 - r)$

$x^2 - 64$ $9 - 4y^4$ $81 - r^2$

EXAMPLE 4 *Problem-Solving Application*

A square koi pond is surrounded by a gravel path. Write an expression that represents the area of the path.

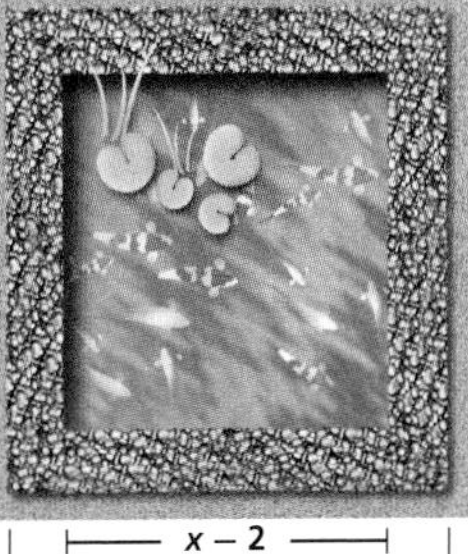

Understand the Problem

The **answer** will be an expression that represents the area of the path.

List the important information:

- The pond is a square with a side length of $x - 2$.
- The path has a side length of $x + 2$.

COMMON ERROR ALERT

When finding the product of $(a - b)^2$, some students might believe that the middle term and the last term will both be negative numbers. Remind them that the last term comes from a number being squared, and thus will never be a negative.

Power Presentations with PowerPoint®

Additional Examples

Example 3

Multiply.

A. $(x + 4)(x - 4)$ $x^2 - 16$

B. $(p^2 + 8q)(p^2 - 8q)$ $p^4 - 64q^2$

C. $(10 + b)(10 - b)$ $100 - b^2$

Also available on transparency

INTERVENTION

Questioning Strategies

EXAMPLE 3

- Why is there no middle term in the product $(a + b)(a - b)$?
- Why does the product $(a + b)(a - b)$ always have a minus sign between the terms?

Teaching Tip **Multiple Representations** In addition to the geometric presentation on this page, students can use FOIL to verify that $(a + b)(a - b) = a^2 - b^2$.

Teaching Tip **Math Background** The binomials $(a + b)$ and $(a - b)$ are called *conjugates*. Conjugates are used in many situations because of the special property that their product is always a difference of squares.

Power Presentations with PowerPoint®

Additional Examples

Example 4

Write a polynomial that represents the area of the yard around the pool shown below. $10x + 29$

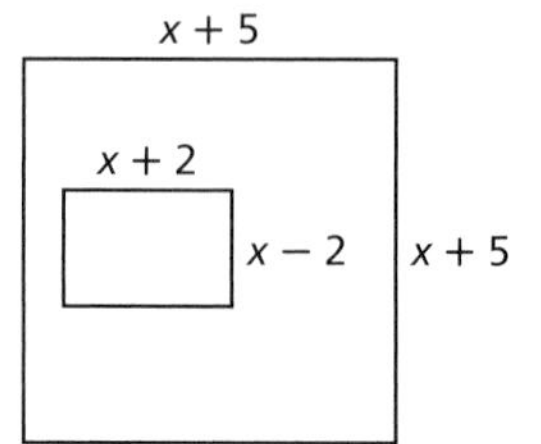

Also available on transparency

INTERVENTION

Questioning Strategies

EXAMPLE 4

- What are you finding when you are multiplying the binomials?
- What area are you asked to find?
- What operation would you need to perform to get this result?

California LINK

Gardens

The Huntington Botanical Gardens in San Marino, CA, include a Japanese garden, several other theme gardens, and a botanical conservatory. The Huntington Botanical Gardens have approximately 15,000 plants from all over the world.

2 Make a Plan

The area of the pond is $(x - 2)^2$. The total area of the path plus the pond is $(x + 2)^2$. You can subtract the area of the pond from the total area to find the area of the path.

3 Solve

Step 1 Find the total area.

$$(x + 2)^2 = x^2 + 2(x)(2) + 2^2$$
$$= x^2 + 4x + 4$$

Use the rule for $(a + b)^2$: $a = x$ and $b = 2$.

Step 2 Find the area of the pond.

$$(x - 2)^2 = x^2 - 2(x)(2) + 2^2$$
$$= x^2 - 4x + 4$$

Use the rule for $(a - b)^2$: $a = x$ and $b = 2$.

Step 3 Find the area of the path.

area of path	=	total area	−	area of pond
a	=	$x^2 + 4x + 4$	−	$(x^2 - 4x + 4)$

$= x^2 + 4x + 4 - x^2 + 4x - 4$ *Identify like terms.*

$= (x^2 - x^2) + (4x + 4x) + (4 - 4)$ *Group like terms together.*

$= 8x$

The area of the path is $8x$. *Combine like terms.*

4 Look Back

Suppose that $x = 10$. Then one side of the path is 12, and the total area is 12^2, or 144. Also, if $x = 10$, one side of the pond is 8, and the area of the pond is 8^2, or 64. This means the area of the path is $144 - 64 = 80$.

According to the solution above, the area of the path is $8x$. If $x = 10$, then $8x = 8(10) = 80$. ✓

CHECK IT OUT! **4.** Write an expression that represents the area of the swimming pool at right. **25**

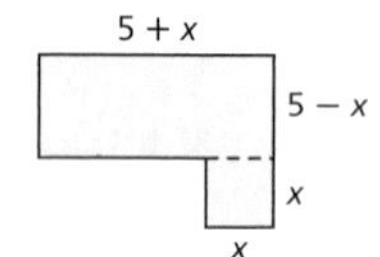

Special Products of Binomials

Perfect-Square Trinomials

$(a + b)^2 = (a + b)(a + b) = a^2 + 2ab + b^2$

$(a - b)^2 = (a - b)(a - b) = a^2 - 2ab + b^2$

Difference of Two Squares

$(a + b)(a - b) = a^2 - b^2$

3 Close

Summarize

Have students state whether each product is a perfect-square trinomial or a difference of two squares, and then find the product.

$(2x + 3y)^2$ perfect-square trinomial; $4x^2 + 12xy + 9y^2$

$(5m + 7)(5m - 7)$ difference of two squares; $25m^2 - 49$

$(4s - t)^2$ perfect-square trinomial; $16s^2 - 8st + t^2$

Tell students that recognizing special products will greatly help them with factoring in the next chapter.

FORMATIVE ASSESSMENT and INTERVENTION

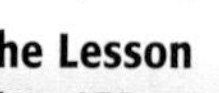

***Diagnose Before* the Lesson**
7-9 Warm Up, TE p. 455

***Monitor During* the Lesson**
Check It Out! Exercises, SE pp. 456–458
Questioning Strategies, TE pp. 456–458

***Assess After* the Lesson**
7-9 Lesson Quiz, TE p. 461
Alternative Assessment, TE p. 461

THINK AND DISCUSS

1. Use the FOIL method to verify that $(a + b)(a - b) = a^2 - b^2$.
2. When a binomial is squared, the middle term of the resulting trinomial is twice the ___?___ of the first and last terms.

3. **GET ORGANIZED** Copy and complete the graphic organizer. Complete the special product rules and give an example of each.

Special Products of Binomials		
Perfect-Square Trinomials		Difference of Two Squares
$(a + b)^2 = ?$	$(a - b)^2 = ?$	$(a + b)(a - b) = ?$

Answers to *Think and Discuss*

1. $(a + b)(a - b) = a^2 - ab + ab - b^2 = a^2 - b^2$
2. product
3. See p. A6.

7-9 Exercises

10.0, 25.2

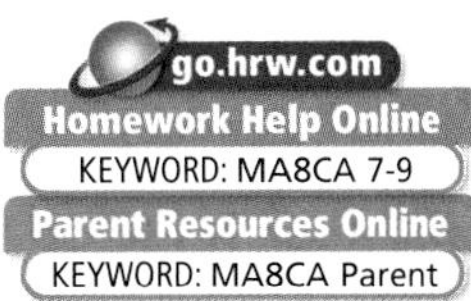

GUIDED PRACTICE

1. **Vocabulary** In your own words, describe a *perfect-square trinomial*. **Possible answer: a trinomial that is the result of squaring a binomial**

SEE EXAMPLE 1 p. 455

Multiply.

2. $(x + 7)^2$ 3. $(2 + x)^2$ 4. $(x + 1)^2$
5. $(2x + 6)^2$ 6. $(5x + 9)^2$ 7. $(2a + 7b)^2$

SEE EXAMPLE 2 p. 456

8. $(x - 6)^2$ 9. $(x - 2)^2$ 10. $(2x - 1)^2$
11. $(8 - x)^2$ 12. $(6p - q)^2$ 13. $(7a - 2b)^2$

SEE EXAMPLE 3 p. 457

14. $(x + 5)(x - 5)$ 15. $(x + 6)(x - 6)$ 16. $(5x + 1)(5x - 1)$
17. $(2x^2 + 3)(2x^2 - 3)$ 18. $(9 - x^3)(9 + x^3)$ 19. $(2x - 5y)(2x + 5y)$

SEE EXAMPLE 4 p. 457

20. **Geometry** Write a polynomial that represents the area of the figure. $\mathbf{2x^2 + 8x + 10}$

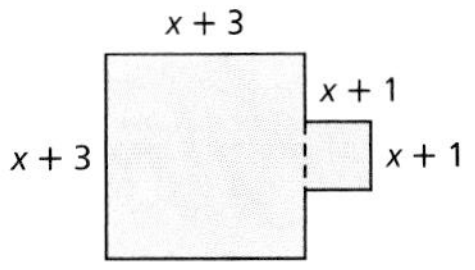

(Figure labels: $x + 3$, $x + 3$, $x + 1$, $x + 1$)

Assignment Guide

Assign *Guided Practice* exercises as necessary.

If you finished Examples **1–2**
Proficient 21–32, 53–57
Advanced 21–32, 41, 44–48 even, 54, 56

If you finished Examples **1–4**
Proficient 21–40, 42–52 even, 53–73, 75–82
Advanced 21–52, 58–62, 64–82

Homework Quick Check
Quickly check key concepts.
Exercises: 22, 28, 36, 39, 42

PRACTICE AND PROBLEM SOLVING

Independent Practice	
For Exercises	See Example
21–26	1
27–32	2
33–38	3
39	4

Extra Practice
Skills Practice p. EP15
Application Practice p. EP30

Multiply.

21. $(x + 3)^2$ 22. $(4 + z)^2$ 23. $(x^2 + y^2)^2$
24. $(p + 2q^3)^2$ 25. $(2 + 3x)^2$ 26. $(r^2 + 5t)^2$
27. $(s^2 - 7)^2$ 28. $(2c - d^3)^2$ 29. $(a - 8)^2$
30. $(5 - w)^2$ 31. $(3x - 4)^2$ 32. $(1 - x^2)^2$
33. $(a - 10)(a + 10)$ 34. $(y + 4)(y - 4)$ 35. $(7x + 3)(7x - 3)$
36. $(x^2 - 2)(x^2 + 2)$ 37. $(5a^2 + 9)(5a^2 - 9)$ 38. $(x^3 + y^2)(x^3 - y^2)$

Answers

2. $x^2 + 14x + 49$
3. $4 + 4x + x^2$
4. $x^2 + 2x + 1$
5. $4x^2 + 24x + 36$
6. $25x^2 + 90x + 81$
7. $4a^2 + 28ab + 49b^2$
8. $x^2 - 12x + 36$
9. $x^2 - 4x + 4$
10. $4x^2 - 4x + 1$
11. $64 - 16x + x^2$
12. $36p^2 - 12pq + q^2$
13. $49a^2 - 28ab + 4b^2$
14. $x^2 - 25$
15. $x^2 - 36$
16. $25x^2 - 1$
17. $4x^4 - 9$
18. $81 - x^6$
19. $4x^2 - 25y^2$
21. $x^2 + 6x + 9$
22. $16 + 8z + z^2$
23. $x^4 + 2x^2y^2 + y^4$
24. $p^2 + 4pq^3 + 4q^6$
25. $4 + 12x + 9x^2$
26. $r^4 + 10r^2t + 25t^2$
27. $s^4 - 14s^2 + 49$
28. $4c^2 - 4cd^3 + d^6$
29. $a^2 - 16a + 64$
30. $25 - 10w + w^2$
31. $9x^2 - 24x + 16$
32. $1 - 2x^2 + x^4$
33. $a^2 - 100$
34. $y^2 - 16$
35. $49x^2 - 9$
36. $x^4 - 4$
37. $25a^4 - 81$
38. $x^6 - y^4$

California Standards

Standard	Exercises
2.0	75
6.0	76–78
10.0	2–39, 41–52, 64b, 67, 68, 71, 72, 79–82
25.2	63

Answers

64a.

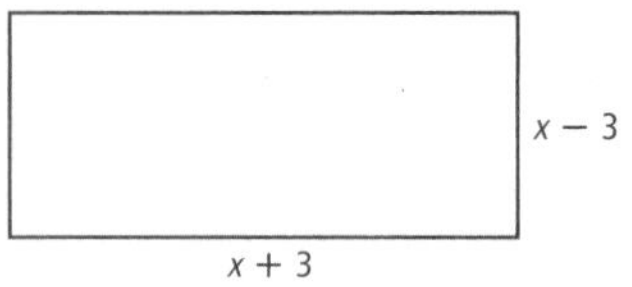

(rectangle with sides $x - 3$ and $x + 3$)

73. Since $x^2 + bx + c$, then $x^2 + bx + c = (x + y)(x + y)$, where y is an integer. After using FOIL, $(x + y)(x + y) = x^2 + (2y)x + y^2$ and $x^2 + (2y)x + y^2 = x^2 + (b)x + c$. You can see that $c = y^2$, or $\sqrt{c} = \pm y$, and $b = 2y$, or $b = \pm 2\sqrt{c}$.

76.

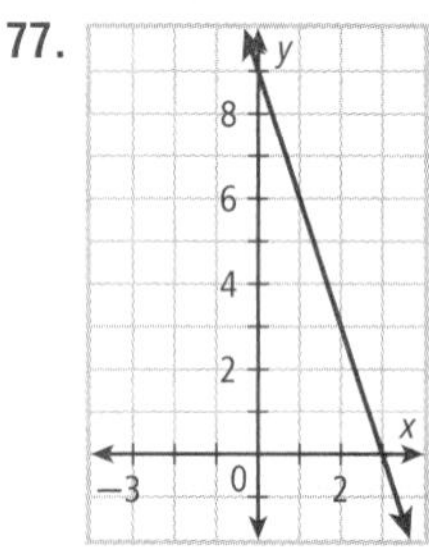

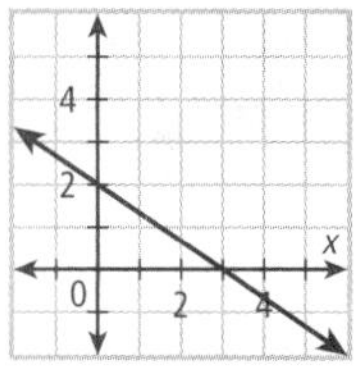

77.

78.

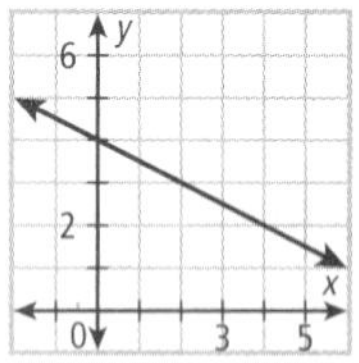

39. $\pi x^2 + 8\pi x + 16\pi$

40a. $x > 2$; values less than or equal to 2 cause the width of the rectangle to be zero or neg., which does not make sense.

49. $x^6 - 2a^3x^3 + a^6$

39. **Entertainment** Write a polynomial that represents the area of the circular puzzle. Remember that the formula for area of a circle is $A = \pi r^2$, where r is the radius of the circle. Leave the symbol π in your answer.

40. **Multi-Step** A square has sides that are $(x - 1)$ units long and a rectangle has a length of x units and a width of $(x - 2)$ units.
   a. What are the possible values of x? Explain.
   b. Which has the greater area, the square or the rectangle? **square**
   c. What is the difference in the areas? **1 sq. unit**

Multiply.

41. $(x + y)^2$ $x^2 + 2xy + y^2$
42. $(x - y)^2$ $x^2 - 2xy + y^2$
43. $(x^2 + 4)(x^2 - 4)$ $x^4 - 16$
44. $(x^2 + 4)^2$ $x^4 + 8x^2 + 16$
45. $(x^2 - 4)^2$ $x^4 - 8x^2 + 16$
46. $(1 - x)^2$ $1 - 2x + x^2$
47. $(1 + x)^2$ $1 + 2x + x^2$
48. $(1 - x)(1 + x)$ $1 - x^2$
49. $(x^3 - a^3)(x^3 - a^3)$
50. $(5 + n)(5 + n)$ $25 + 10n + n^2$
51. $(6a - 5b)(6a + 5b)$ $36a^2 - 25b^2$
52. $(r - 4t^4)(r - 4t^4)$ $r^2 - 8rt^4 + 16t^8$

Copy and complete the tables to verify the special products of binomials.

	a	b	$(a - b)^2$	$a^2 - 2ab + b^2$
	1	4	$(1 - 4)^2 = 9$	$1^2 - 2(1)(4) + 4^2 = 9$
53.	2	4	4	4
54.	3	2	1	1

	a	b	$(a + b)^2$	$a^2 + 2ab + b^2$
55.	1	4	25	25
56.	2	5	49	49
57.	3	0	9	9

	a	b	$(a + b)(a - b)$	$a^2 - b^2$
58.	1	4	−15	−15
59.	2	3	−5	−5
60.	3	2	5	5

LINK

Math History

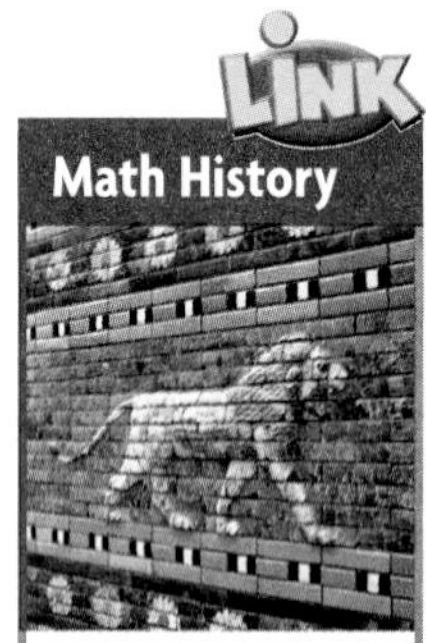

Beginning about 3000 B.C.E., the Babylonians lived in what is now Iraq and Turkey. Around 575 B.C.E., they built the Ishtar Gate to serve as one of eight main entrances into the city of Babylon. The image above is a relief sculpture from a restoration of the Ishtar Gate.

61. **Math History** The Babylonians used tables of squares and the formula $ab = \frac{(a + b)^2 - (a - b)^2}{4}$ to multiply two numbers. Use this formula to find the product $35 \cdot 24$. **840**

62. **Critical Thinking** Find a value of c that makes $16x^2 - 24x + c$ a perfect-square trinomial. **$c = 9$**

63. **ERROR ANALYSIS** Explain the error below. What is the correct product? $(a - b)^2 = a^2 - b^2$ **Possible answer: The square of a diff. is not the same as a diff. of squares; $a^2 - 2ab + b^2$.**

7-9 PRACTICE A
7-9 PRACTICE C
7-9 PRACTICE B

LESSON 7-9 Practice B
Special Products of Binomials

Multiply.

1. $(x + 2)^2$ $x^2 + 4x + 4$
2. $(m + 4)^2$ $m^2 + 8m + 16$
3. $(3 + a)^2$ $9 + 6a + a^2$
4. $(2x + 5)^2$ $4x^2 + 20x + 25$
5. $(3a + 2)^2$ $9a^2 + 12a + 4$
6. $(6 + 5b)^2$ $36 + 60b + 25b^2$
7. $(b - 3)^2$ $b^2 - 6b + 9$
8. $(8 - y)^2$ $64 - 16y + y^2$
9. $(a - 10)^2$ $a^2 - 20a + 100$
10. $(3x - 7)^2$ $9x^2 - 42x + 49$
11. $(4m - 9)^2$ $16m^2 - 72m + 81$
12. $(6 - 3n)^2$ $36 - 36n + 9n^2$
13. $(x + 3)(x - 3)$ $x^2 - 9$
14. $(8 + y)(8 - y)$ $64 - y^2$
15. $(x + 6)(x - 6)$ $x^2 - 36$
16. $(5x + 2)(5x - 2)$ $25x^2 - 4$
17. $(10x + 7y)(10x - 7y)$ $100x^2 - 49y^2$
18. $(x^2 + 3y)(x^2 - 3y)$ $x^4 - 9y^2$

19. Write a simplified expression that represents the...
   a. area of the large rectangle. $36 - x^2$
   b. area of the small rectangle. $4 - x^2$
   c. area of the shaded area. 32

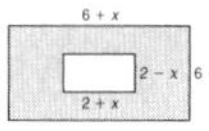

20. The small rectangle is made larger by adding 2 units to the length and 2 units to the width.
   a. What is the new area of the smaller rectangle? $16 - x^2$
   b. What is the area of the new shaded area? 20

7-9 READING STRATEGIES

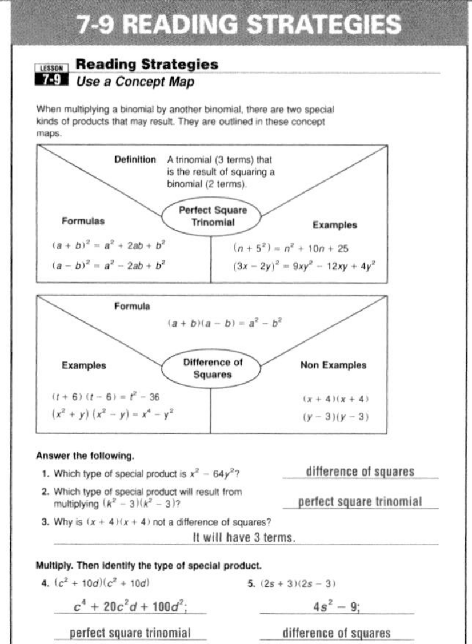

LESSON 7-9 Reading Strategies
Use a Concept Map

When multiplying a binomial by another binomial, there are two special kinds of products that may result. They are outlined in these concept maps.

Perfect Square Trinomial — Definition: A trinomial (3 terms) that is the result of squaring a binomial (2 terms).
Formulas: $(a + b)^2 = a^2 + 2ab + b^2$; $(a - b)^2 = a^2 - 2ab + b^2$
Examples: $(n + 5)^2 = n^2 + 10n + 25$; $(3x - 2y)^2 = 9x^2 - 12xy + 4y^2$

Difference of Squares — Formula: $(a + b)(a - b) = a^2 - b^2$
Examples: $(t + 6)(t - 6) = t^2 - 36$; $(x^2 + y)(x^2 - y) = x^4 - y^2$
Non Examples: $(x + 4)(x + 4)$; $(y - 3)(y - 3)$

Answer the following.
1. Which type of special product is $x^2 - 64y^2$? difference of squares
2. Which type of special product will result from multiplying $(k^2 - 3)(k^2 - 3)$? perfect square trinomial
3. Why is $(x + 4)(x + 4)$ not a difference of squares? It will have 3 terms.

Multiply. Then identify the type of special product.
4. $(c^2 + 10d)(c^2 + 10d)$ $c^4 + 20c^2d + 100d^2$; perfect square trinomial
5. $(2s + 3)(2s - 3)$ $4s^2 - 9$; difference of squares

7-9 REVIEW FOR MASTERY

LESSON 7-9 Review for Mastery
Special Products of Binomials

A **perfect-square trinomial** is a trinomial that is the result of squaring a binomial.

$(a + b)^2 = a^2 + 2ab + b^2$ — Square a. Add product of 2, a, and b. Square b.

$(a - b)^2 = a^2 - 2ab + b^2$ — Square a. Subtract product of 2, a, and b. Square b.

Multiply $(x + 4)^2$.
$(x + 4)^2$ a: x, b: 4
$x^2 + 2(x)(4) + 4^2$ Middle term is added.
$x^2 + 8x + 16$ Simplify.

Multiply $(4x - 3)^2$.
$(4x - 3)^2$ a: 4x, b: 3
$16x^2 - 2(4x)(3) + 3^2$ Middle term is subtracted.
$16x^2 - 24x + 9$ Simplify.

State whether each product will result in a perfect-square trinomial.
1. $(x + 5)(x + 5)$ yes
2. $(x + 2)(x - 2)$ no
3. $(5x - 6)(5x - 6)$ yes

Fill in the blanks. Then write the perfect-square trinomial.
4. $(x + 7)^2$ Square a: x^2; 2(a)(b): 14x; Square b: 49; $x^2 + 14x + 49$
5. $(x - 1)^2$ Square a: x^2; 2(a)(b): 2x; Square b: 1; $x^2 - 2x + 1$
6. $(2x + 10)^2$ Square a: $4x^2$; 2(a)(b): 40x; Square b: 100; $4x^2 + 40x + 100$

Multiply.
7. $(x - 8)^2$ $x^2 - 16x + 64$
8. $(x + 2)^2$ $x^2 + 4x + 4$
9. $(7x - 5)^2$ $49x^2 - 70x + 25$

64. This problem will prepare you for the Concept Connection on page 462.

a. Michael is fencing part of his yard. He started with a square of length x on each side. He then added 3 feet to the length and subtracted 3 feet from the width. Make a sketch to show the fenced area with the length and width labeled.

b. Write a polynomial that represents the area of the fenced region. **$x^2 - 9$**

c. Michael bought a total of 48 feet of fencing. What is the area of his fenced region? **135 ft^2**

65. **Critical Thinking** The polynomial $ax^2 - 49$ is a difference of two squares. Find all possible values of a between 1 and 100 inclusive. **1, 4, 9, 16, 25, 36, 49, 64, 81, 100**

66. **Write About It** When is the product of two binomials also a binomial? Explain and give an example. **When 1 binomial is in the form $a + b$ and the other is in the form $a - b$; $(x + 2)(x - 2) = x^2 - 4$**

Multiple Choice For Exercises 67–70, choose the best answer.

67. What is $(5x - 6y)(5x - 6y)$?

Ⓐ $25x^2 - 22xy + 36y^2$ Ⓒ $25x^2 + 22xy + 36y^2$

(B) $25x^2 - 60xy + 36y^2$ Ⓓ $25x^2 + 60xy + 36y^2$

68. Which product is represented by the model?

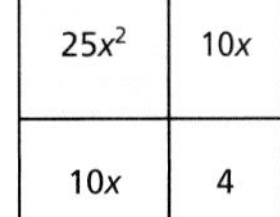

Ⓐ $(2x + 5)(2x + 5)$ Ⓒ $(5x + 2)(5x - 2)$

Ⓑ $(5x - 2)(5x - 2)$ **(D)** $(5x + 2)(5x + 2)$

69. If $a + b = 12$ and $a^2 - b^2 = 96$ what is the value of a?

Ⓐ 2 Ⓑ 4 Ⓒ 8 **(D)** 10

70. If $rs = 15$ and $(r + s)^2 = 64$, what is the value of $r^2 + s^2$?

Ⓐ 25 Ⓑ 30 **(C)** 34 Ⓓ 49

CHALLENGE AND EXTEND

71. $x^3 + 4x^2 - 16x - 64$
72. $x^3 - 4x^2 - 16x + 64$

71. Multiply $(x + 4)(x + 4)(x - 4)$. 72. Multiply $(x + 4)(x - 4)(x - 4)$.

73. **Reasoning** If $x^2 + bx + c$ is a perfect-square trinomial, show that $b = \pm 2\sqrt{c}$.

74. You can multiply two numbers by rewriting the numbers as the difference of two squares. For example:

$$36 \cdot 24 = (30 + 6)(30 - 6) = 30^2 - 6^2 = 900 - 36 = 864$$

Use this method to multiply $27 \cdot 19$. Explain how you rewrote the numbers. **513; rewrite 27 as 23 + 4 and 19 as 23 − 4.**

SPIRAL STANDARDS REVIEW

75. The square paper that Yuki is using to make an origami frog has an area of 165 cm^2. Find the side length of the paper to the nearest centimeter. *(Lesson 1-5)* **13 cm**

Use intercepts to graph the line described by each equation. *(Lesson 5-2)*

76. $2x + 3y = 6$ 77. $y = -3x + 9$ 78. $\frac{1}{2}x + y = 4$

Add or subtract. *(Lesson 7-7)*

79. $3x^2 + 8x - 2x + 9x^2$ 80. $(8m^4 + 2n - 3m^3 + 6) + (9m^3 + 5 - 4m^4)$

81. $(2p^3 + p) - (5p^3 + 9p)$ 82. $(12t - 3t^2 + 10) - (-5t^2 - 7 - 4t)$

79. $12x^2 + 6x$
80. $4m^4 + 6m^3 + 2n + 11$
81. $-3p^3 - 8p$
82. $2t^2 + 16t + 17$

CONCEPT CONNECTION **Exercise 64** involves finding area using polynomials. This exercise prepares students for the Concept Connection on page 462.

Multiple Choice When multiplying binomials of the form $(a - b)(a - b)$ in **Exercise 67,** the middle term of the product is negative. Choices **C** and **D** can be eliminated.

For **Exercise 69,** $a^2 - b^2 = 96$ is the difference of two squares, so $(a + b)(a - b) = 96$, and by substitution, $12(a - b) = 96$. After dividing both sides by 12, $a - b = 8$. This equation and $a + b = 12$ form a system of linear equations, easily solved by elimination.

Journal

Have students describe three ways to find the product of $(x + 2)(x + 2)$; one method must use the special products rule.

ALTERNATIVE ASSESSMENT

Have students create binomials of the form $(a + b)^2$, $(a - b)^2$, and $(a + b)(a - b)$; find each product; and describe how the special products rule is illustrated.

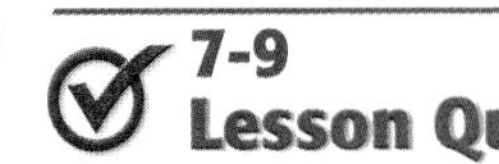

7-9 Lesson Quiz

Multiply.

1. $(x + 7)^2$ $x^2 + 14x + 49$
2. $(x - 2)^2$ $x^2 - 4x + 4$
3. $(5x + 2y)^2$ $25x^2 + 20xy + 4y^2$
4. $(2x - 9y)^2$ $4x^2 - 36xy + 81y^2$
5. $(4x + 5y)(4x - 5y)$ $16x^2 - 25y^2$
6. $(m^2 + 2n)(m^2 - 2n)$ $m^4 - 4n^2$
7. Write a polynomial that represents the shaded area of the figure below. $14x - 85$

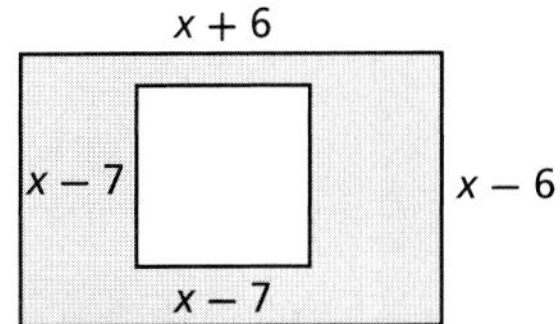

Also available on transparency

7-9 PROBLEM SOLVING

LESSON 7-9 Problem Solving
Special Products of Binomials

Write the correct answer.

1. This week Kyara worked $x + 4$ hours. She is paid $x - 4$ dollars per hour. Write a polynomial for the amount that Kyara earned this week. Then calculate her pay if $x = 12$.
$x^2 - 16$;
\$128

2. A museum set aside part of a large gallery for a special exhibit.
(diagram labels: $x + 8$; $x - 8$; $0.5x + 1$; $0.5x + 1$; Exhibit) 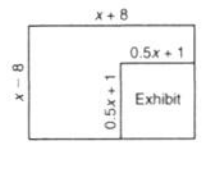
Write a polynomial for the area of the gallery that is not part of the exhibit. Then calculate the area of that section if $x = 60$.
$0.75x^2 - x - 65$;
2575 square feet

3. Gary is building a square table for a kitchen. In his initial sketch, each side measured x inches. After rearranging some furniture, he realized he would have to add one foot to the length and remove one foot from the width and have a rectangular table instead. Write a polynomial to represent the area of the rectangular table.
$x^2 - 144$ in^2

A fountain is in the center of a square garden. The radius of the fountain is $x - 2$ feet. The length of the garden is $2x + 4$ feet. Use this information and the diagram for questions 4 – 7. Select the best answer.

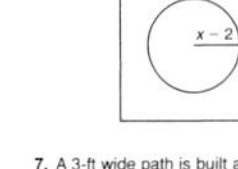

4. Which polynomial represents the area of the fountain?
A $2\pi x - 4\pi$ C $\pi x^2 - 4\pi$
B $\pi x^2 - 4\pi x - 4\pi$ **(D)** $\pi x^2 - 4\pi x + 4\pi$

5. Which polynomial represents the area of the garden, including the fountain?
F $4x^2 + 8$ H $4x^2 + 16$
(G) $4x^2 + 16x + 16$ J $4x^2 + 8x + 16$

6. Which polynomial represents the area of the garden *outside* the fountain? (Use 3.14 for π.)
(A) $0.86x^2 + 28.56x + 3.44$
B $0.86x^2 + 3.44x + 28.56$
C $7.14x^2 + 28.56x + 3.44$
D $7.14x^2 + 3.44x + 28.56$

7. A 3-ft wide path is built around the garden. Which expression represents the area of the path?
F $12x + 33$ H $4x^2 + 28x + 49$
(G) $24x^2 + 84$ J $4x^2 + 40x + 100$

7-9 CHALLENGE

LESSON 7-9 Challenge
Patterns in Special Products

The expansions of $(a + b)^2$, $(a - b)^2$, and $(a + b)(a - b)$ show patterns involving a and b. You can discover other patterns involving a and b when you combine these special products.

In Exercises 1–5, use the given values of a and b to complete the table below.

	a	b	$(a + b)^2$	$(a - b)^2$	$(a + b)^2 - (a - b)^2$	ab
1.	−3	5	4	64	−60	−15
2.	−2	−4	36	4	32	8
3.	3	6	81	9	72	18
4.	4	7	121	9	112	28
5.	5	−8	9	169	−160	−40

6. a. From the table, how are the values of $(a + b)^2 - (a - b)^2$ and ab related?
The difference $(a + b)^2 - (a - b)^2$ is four times the product ab.

b. Based on your work in Exercises 1–5 and your answer to part **a**, write a simplification of $(a + b)^2 - (a + b)^2$. $4ab$

c. Use algebra to show that your response to part **b** is true.
$(a^2 + 2ab + b^2) - (a^2 - 2ab + b^2) = 4ab$

7. Using a table like the one that you completed in Exercises 1–5 and the values of a and b used there, write a simplification of $(a + b)^2 + (a - b)^2$. $(a + b)^2 + (a - b)^2 = 2a^2 + 2b^2$

Write a conjecture for the simplification of each sum or difference. Try to do as much of the simplification as you can mentally.

8. $[(a^2 + b^2) + (a^2 - b^2)]^2$ $4a^4$

9. $[(a^2 + b^2) - (a^2 - b^2)]^2$ $4b^4$

Simplify each expression.

10. $[(a^2 + b^2) + (a^2 - b^2)]^2$
$[(a^2 + b^2) + (a^2 - b^2)]^2 = (a^2 + a^2 + b^2 - b^2)^2 = (2a^2)^2 = 2^2a^4 = 4a^4$

11. $[(a^2 + b^2) - (a^2 - b^2)]^2$
$[(a^2 + b^2) - (a^2 - b^2)]^2 = (a^2 - a^2 + b^2 + b^2)^2 = (2b^2)^2 = 2^2b^4 = 4b^4$

SECTION 7B

Organizer

Objective: Assess students' ability to apply concepts and skills in Lessons 7-6 through 7-9 in a real-world format.

Online Edition

Problem	Text Reference
1	Lesson 7-7
2	Lesson 7-6
3	Lesson 7-8
4	Lesson 7-9
5	Lesson 7-9
6	Lesson 7-9

Polynomials

Don't Fence Me In James has 500 feet of fencing to enclose a rectangular region on his farm for some sheep.

1. Make a sketch of three possible regions that James could enclose and give the corresponding areas.
2. If the length of the region is x, find an expression for the width. **$250 - x$**
3. Use your answer to Problem 2 to write an equation for the area of the region. **$A = x(250 - x)$**
4. Graph your equation from Problem 3 on your calculator. Sketch the graph.
5. James wants his fenced region to have the largest area possible using 500 feet of fencing. Find this area using the graph or a table of values. **15,625 ft^2**
6. What are the length and width of the region with the area from Problem 5? Describe this region. **125 ft × 125 ft; square**

1. Possible answers:

$A = 15{,}625$ ft^2

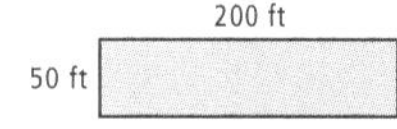

$A = 10{,}000$ ft^2

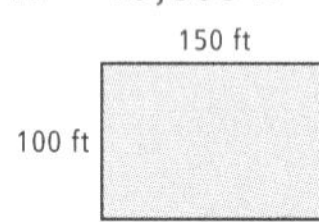

$A = 15{,}000$ ft^2

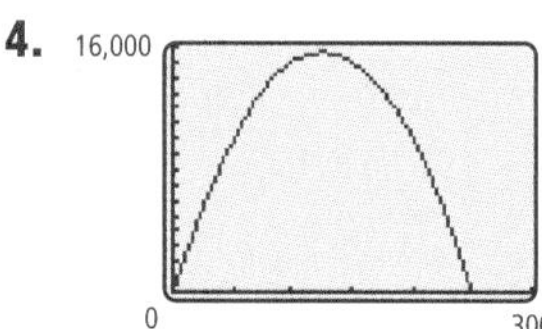

4.

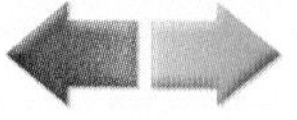

INTERVENTION

Scaffolding Questions

1. What is the perimeter of a rectangle? distance around the rectangle How is it calculated? $P = 2\ell + 2w$
2. What are some possible values for ℓ and w? Possible answers: $\ell = 40, w = 210$; $\ell = 30, w = 220$; $\ell = 45, w = 205$
3. What is the area of a rectangle? number of square units inside the rectangle How is it calculated? $A = \ell w$
4. What is an appropriate viewing window? Possible answer: $0 < x < 250$ and $0 < y < 16{,}000$
5. How can you find the greatest area from the graph or table? Graph: find the y-coordinate of the highest point; Table: find the greatest y-value.
6. How can you find the dimensions from the graph or table? Graph: find the x-coordinate of the highest point; Table: look for the greatest y-value and find its corresponding x-value.

Extension

Now James will use his fencing to create three sides of a rectangular region and build a wall for the fourth side. Now what is the greatest possible area? Describe this region. What is the minimum length of the wall? 31,250 ft^2; 125 ft × 250 ft rectangle; 250 ft

California Standards

Algebra 1 10.0

CHAPTER 7

SECTION 7B

Quiz for Lessons 7-6 Through 7-9

1. $2r^6 + 4r^2 - 3r$; 2
2. $-8y^3 + y^2 + 2y + 7$; -8
3. $t^4 - 12t^3 - 4t$; 1

7-6 Polynomials

Write each polynomial in standard form. Then give the leading coefficient.

1. $4r^2 + 2r^6 - 3r$ 2. $y^2 + 7 - 8y^3 + 2y$ 3. $-12t^3 - 4t + t^4$

Classify each polynomial according to its degree and number of terms.

4. $5b^2$ quadratic monomial
5. $-2x^3 - 5 + x - 2x^7$ 7th-deg. polynomial
6. $5 - 6b^2 + b - 4b^4$ quartic polynomial

Tell whether the number is a root of the polynomial.

7. $3x^2 - 27$; 3 yes
8. $g^2 - 2g - 8$; 4 yes
9. $6x^3 - 49$; 2 no

10. **Business** The function $C(x) = x^3 - 15x + 14$ gives the cost to manufacture x units of a product. What is the cost to manufacture 900 units? **\$728,986,514**

7-7 Adding and Subtracting Polynomials

Add or subtract.

11. $(10m^3 + 4m^2) + (7m^2 + 3m)$
12. $(3t^2 - 2t) + (9t^2 + 4t - 6)$
13. $(12d^6 - 3d^2) + (2d^4 + 1)$
14. $(6y^3 + 4y^2) - (2y^2 + 3y)$
15. $(7n^2 - 3n) - (5n^2 + 5n)$
16. $(b^2 - 10) - (-5b^3 + 4b)$

17. **Geometry** The measures of the sides of a triangle are shown as polynomials. Write a polynomial to represent the perimeter of the triangle. $2s^3 + 4s^2 + 5s + 5$

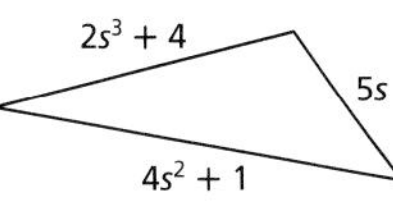

7-8 Multiplying Polynomials

Multiply.

18. $2h^3 \cdot 5h^5$ $10h^8$
19. $(s^8t^4)(-6st^3)$ $-6s^9t^7$
20. $2ab(5a^3 + 3a^2b)$ $10a^4b + 6a^3b^2$
21. $(3k + 5)^2$
22. $(2x^3 + 3y)(4x^2 + y)$
23. $(p^2 + 3p)(9p^2 - 6p - 5)$

24. **Geometry** Write a polynomial expression for the area of a parallelogram whose base is $(x + 7)$ units and whose height is $(x - 3)$ units. $(x^2 + 4x - 21)$ square units

7-9 Special Products of Binomials

Multiply.

25. $(d + 9)^2$
26. $(3 + 2t)^2$
27. $(2x + 5y)^2$
28. $(m - 4)^2$
29. $(a - b)^2$
30. $(3w - 1)^2$
31. $(c + 2)(c - 2)$
32. $(5r + 6)(5r - 6)$

33. **Sports** A child's basketball has a radius of $(x - 5)$ inches. Write a polynomial that represents the surface area of the basketball. (The formula for the surface area of a sphere is $S = 4\pi r^2$, where r represents the radius of the sphere.) Leave the symbol π in your answer. $(4\pi x^2 - 40\pi x + 100\pi)$ in^2

READY TO GO ON? SECTION 7B

Organizer

Objective: Assess students' mastery of concepts and skills in Lessons 7-6 through 7-9.

Countdown to Mastery Week 17

Resources

Assessment Resources
Section 7B Quiz

Test & Practice Generator
One-Stop Planner®

INTERVENTION

Resources

Ready to Go On? Intervention and Enrichment **Worksheets**

Ready to Go On? **CD-ROM**

Ready to Go On? **Online**

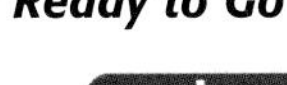
my.hrw.com

Answers

11. $10m^3 + 11m^2 + 3m$
12. $12t^2 + 2t - 6$
13. $12d^6 + 2d^4 - 3d^2 + 1$
14. $6y^3 + 2y^2 - 3y$
15. $2n^2 - 8n$
16. $5b^3 + b^2 - 4b - 10$

21–23, 25–32. See p. A23.

READY TO GO ON? Diagnose and Prescribe

NO INTERVENE

Ready to Go On? Intervention	*Ready to Go On? Intervention*, Section 7B: Worksheets	CD-ROM	Online
Lesson 7-6 Prep for 10.0	7-6 Intervention	Activity 7-6	Diagnose and Prescribe Online
Lesson 7-7 10.0	7-7 Intervention	Activity 7-7	
Lesson 7-8 10.0	7-8 Intervention	Activity 7-8	
Lesson 7-9 10.0	7-9 Intervention	Activity 7-9	

YES ENRICH

Ready to Go On? Enrichment, Section 7B

Worksheets

CD-ROM
Online

Study Guide: Review

Organizer

Objective: Help students organize and review key concepts and skills presented in Chapter 7.

Online Edition
Multilingual Glossary

Resources

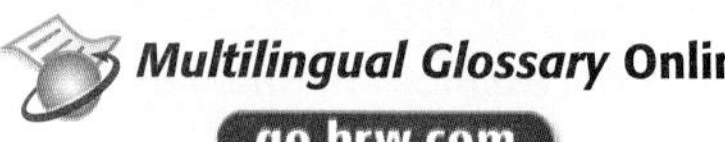

go.hrw.com
KEYWORD: MA8CA Glossary

***Lesson Tutorial Videos* CD-ROM**

Answers

1. cubic
2. standard form of a polynomial
3. monomial
4. trinomial
5. scientific notation
6. $\frac{1}{32}$ in.
7. 1
8. 1
9. $\frac{1}{125}$
10. $\frac{1}{10{,}000}$, or 0.0001
11. $\frac{1}{16}$
12. $\frac{1}{256}$
13. $\frac{27}{4}$
14. $\frac{1}{m^2}$
15. b
16. $-\frac{1}{2x^2y^4}$
17. $2b^6c^4$
18. $\frac{3a^2}{4c^2}$
19. $\frac{s^3}{qr^2}$

CHAPTER 7

Study Guide: Review

Vocabulary

Complete the sentences below with vocabulary words from the list above.

1. A(n) __?__ polynomial is a polynomial of degree 3.
2. When a polynomial is written with the terms in order from highest to lowest degree, it is in __?__.
3. A(n) __?__ is a number, a variable, or a product of numbers and variables with whole-number exponents.
4. A(n) __?__ is a polynomial with three terms.
5. __?__ is a method of writing numbers that are very large or very small.

7-1 Integer Exponents *(pp. 394–399)*

2.0

EXAMPLES

Simplify.

- -2^{-4}

$$-2^{-4} = -\frac{1}{2^4} = -\frac{1}{2 \cdot 2 \cdot 2 \cdot 2} = -\frac{1}{16}$$

- 3^0

$3^0 = 1$ *Any nonzero number raised to the zero power is 1.*

- **Evaluate r^3s^{-4} for $r = -3$ and $s = 2$.**

r^3s^{-4}

$$(-3)^3(2)^{-4} = \frac{(-3)(-3)(-3)}{2 \cdot 2 \cdot 2 \cdot 2} = -\frac{27}{16}$$

- **Simplify $\frac{a^{-3}b^4}{c^{-2}}$.**

$$\frac{a^{-3}b^4}{c^{-2}} = \frac{b^4c^2}{a^3}$$

EXERCISES

6. The diameter of a certain bearing is 2^{-5} in. Evaluate this expression.

Simplify.

7. $(3.6)^0$
8. $(-1)^{-4}$
9. 5^{-3}
10. 10^{-4}

Evaluate each expression for the given value(s) of the variable(s).

11. b^{-4} for $b = 2$
12. $\left(\frac{2}{5}b\right)^{-4}$ for $b = 10$
13. $-2p^3q^{-3}$ for $p = 3$ and $q = -2$

Simplify.

14. m^{-2}
15. bc^0
16. $-\frac{1}{2}x^{-2}y^{-4}$
17. $\frac{2b^6}{c^{-4}}$
18. $\frac{3a^2c^{-2}}{4b^0}$
19. $\frac{q^{-1}r^{-2}}{s^{-3}}$

7-2 Powers of 10 and Scientific Notation *(pp. 400–405)*

EXAMPLES

- **Write 1,000,000 as a power of 10.**

  1,000,000 — *The decimal point is 6 places to the right of 1.*
  $1{,}000{,}000 = 10^6$

- **Find the value of 386.21×10^5.**

  386.2 1 0 0 0 — *Move the decimal point 5 places to the right.*
  38,621,000

- **Write 0.000000041 in scientific notation.**

  0.0 0 0 0 0 0 0 4 1 — *Move the decimal point 8 places to the right to get a number between 1 and 10.*
  4.1×10^{-8}

EXERCISES

Find the value of each power of 10.

20. 10^7 **21.** 10^{-5}

Write each number as a power of 10.

22. 100 **23.** 0.00000000001

Find the value of each expression.

24. 3.25×10^5 **25.** 0.18×10^4

26. 17×10^{-2} **27.** 299×10^{-6}

28. Order the list of numbers from least to greatest. 6.3×10^{-3}, 1.2×10^4, 5.8×10^{-7}, 2.2×10^2

29. In 2003, the average daily value of shares traded on the New York Stock Exchange was about $\$3.85 \times 10^{10}$. Write this amount in standard form.

7-3 Multiplication Properties of Exponents *(pp. 408–414)*

EXAMPLES

Simplify.

- $5^3 \cdot 5^{-2}$

  $5^3 \cdot 5^{-2}$ — *The powers have the same base.*
  $5^{3+(-2)}$ — *Add the exponents.*
  5^1
  5

- $a^4 \cdot b^{-3} \cdot b \cdot a^{-2}$

  $a^4 \cdot b^{-3} \cdot b \cdot a^{-2}$ — *Use properties to group factors.*
  $(a^4 \cdot a^{-2}) \cdot (b^{-3} \cdot b)$
  $a^2 \cdot b^{-2}$ — *Add the exponents of powers with the same base.*
  $\frac{a^2}{b^2}$ — *Write with a positive exponent.*

- $(a^{-3}b^2)^{-2}$

  $(a^{-3})^{-2} \cdot (b^2)^{-2}$ — *Power of a Product Property*
  $a^6 \cdot b^{-4}$ — *Power of a Power Property*
  $\frac{a^6}{b^4}$ — *Write with a positive exponent.*

EXERCISES

Simplify.

30. $5^3 \cdot 5^6$ **31.** $2^6 \cdot 3 \cdot 2^{-3} \cdot 3^3$

32. $b^2 \cdot b^8$ **33.** $r^4 \cdot r$

34. $(x^3)^4$ **35.** $(s^3)^0$

36. $(2^3)^{-1}$ **37.** $(5^2)^{-2}$

38. $(4b^3)^{-2}$ **39.** $(g^3h^2)^4$

40. $(-x^2y)^2$ **41.** $-(x^2y)^2$

42. $(x^2y^3)(xy^3)^4$ **43.** $(j^2k^3)(j^4k^6)$

44. $(5^3 \cdot 5^{-2})^{-1}$ **45.** $(mn^3)^5(mn^5)^3$

46. $(4 \times 10^8)(2 \times 10^3)$ **47.** $(3 \times 10^2)(3 \times 10^5)$

48. $(5 \times 10^3)(2 \times 10^6)$ **49.** $(7 \times 10^5)(4 \times 10^9)$

50. $(3 \times 10^{-4})(2 \times 10^5)$ **51.** $(3 \times 10^{-8})(6 \times 10^{-1})$

52. In 2003, Wyoming's population was about 5.0×10^5. California's population was about 7.1×10 times as large as Wyoming's. What was the approximate population of California? Write your answer in scientific notation.

Answers

20. 10,000,000
21. 0.00001
22. 10^2
23. 10^{-11}
24. 325,000
25. 1800
26. 0.17
27. 0.000299
28. 5.8×10^{-7}, 6.3×10^{-3}, 2.2×10^2, 1.2×10^4
29. $38,500,000,000
30. 5^9
31. $2^3 \cdot 3^4$
32. b^{10}
33. r^5
34. x^{12}
35. 1
36. $\frac{1}{2^3}$, or $\frac{1}{8}$
37. $\frac{1}{5^4}$, or $\frac{1}{625}$
38. $\frac{1}{16b^6}$
39. $g^{12}h^8$
40. x^4y^2
41. $-x^4y^2$
42. x^6y^{15}
43. j^6k^9
44. $\frac{1}{5}$
45. m^8n^{30}
46. 8×10^{11}
47. 9×10^7
48. 1×10^{10}
49. 2.8×10^{15}
50. 6×10^1
51. 1.8×10^{-8}
52. 3.55×10^7

Answers

53. 64
54. m^5
55. $\frac{7}{32}$
56. $6b$
57. t^3v^4
58. 16
59. 5×10^1
60. 2.5×10^7
61. 9
62. 7
63. 16
64. 8
65. z^2
66. $5x^2$
67. x^4y^3
68. m^2n^4
69. 0
70. 4
71. 6
72. 1
73. $3n^2 + 2n - 4$; 3
74. $-a^6 - a^4 + 3a^3 + 2a$; -1
75. linear binomial
76. quintic monomial
77. quartic trinomial
78. constant monomial

7-4 Division Properties of Exponents *(pp. 415–421)*

2.0

EXAMPLE

■ Simplify $\frac{x^9}{x^2}$.

$\frac{x^9}{x^2} = x^{9-2} = x^7$ *Subtract the exponents.*

EXERCISES

Simplify.

53. $\frac{2^8}{2^2}$
54. $\frac{m^6}{m}$
55. $\frac{2^6 \cdot 4 \cdot 7^3}{2^5 \cdot 4^4 \cdot 7^2}$
56. $\frac{24b^6}{4b^5}$
57. $\frac{t^4v^5}{tv}$
58. $\left(\frac{1}{2}\right)^{-4}$

Simplify each quotient and write the answer in scientific notation.

59. $(2.5 \times 10^8) \div (0.5 \times 10^7)$
60. $(2 \times 10^{10}) \div (8 \times 10^2)$

7-5 Fractional Exponents *(pp. 422–427)*

2.0

EXAMPLE

■ Simplify $\sqrt[3]{r^6s^{12}}$.

$\sqrt[3]{r^6s^{12}} = (r^6s^{12})^{\frac{1}{3}}$ *Definition of $b^{\frac{1}{n}}$*

$= (r^6)^{\frac{1}{3}} \cdot (s^{12})^{\frac{1}{3}}$ *Power of a Product Property*

$= \left(r^{6 \cdot \frac{1}{3}}\right) \cdot \left(s^{12 \cdot \frac{1}{3}}\right)$ *Power of a Power Property*

$= (r^2) \cdot (s^4)$ *Simplify exponents.*

$= r^2s^4$

EXERCISES

Simplify each expression.

61. $81^{\frac{1}{2}}$
62. $343^{\frac{1}{3}}$
63. $64^{\frac{2}{3}}$
64. $(2^6)^{\frac{1}{2}}$

Simplify each expression. All variables represent nonnegative numbers.

65. $\sqrt[5]{z^{10}}$
66. $\sqrt[3]{125x^6}$
67. $\sqrt{x^8y^6}$
68. $\sqrt[3]{m^6n^{12}}$

7-6 Polynomials *(pp. 430–435)*

Prep for 10.0

EXAMPLES

■ Find the degree of the polynomial $3x^2 + 8x^5$.

$3x^2 + 8x^5$ *$8x^5$ has the highest degree.*

The degree is 5.

■ Classify the polynomial $y^3 - 2y$ according to its degree and number of terms.

Degree: 3
Terms: 2

The polynomial $y^3 - 2y$ is a cubic binomial.

EXERCISES

Find the degree of each monomial.

69. 5
70. $8st^3$
71. $3z^6$
72. $6h$

Write each polynomial in standard form. Then give the leading coefficient.

73. $2n - 4 + 3n^2$
74. $2a - a^4 - a^6 + 3a^3$

Classify each polynomial according to its degree and number of terms.

75. $2s - 6$
76. $-8p^5$
77. $-m^4 - m^2 - 1$
78. 2

7-7 Adding and Subtracting Polynomials *(pp. 438–443)*

10.0

EXAMPLES

Add.

■ $(h^3 - 2h) + (3h^2 + 4h) - 2h^3$

$(h^3 - 2h) + (3h^2 + 4h) - 2h^3$

$(h^3 - 2h^3) + (3h^2) + (4h - 2h)$

$-h^3 + 3h^2 + 2h$

Subtract.

■ $(n^3 + 5 - 6n^2) - (3n^2 - 7)$

$(n^3 + 5 - 6n^2) + (-3n^2 + 7)$

$(n^3 + 5 - 6n^2) + (-3n^2 + 7)$

$n^3 + (-6n^2 - 3n^2) + (5 + 7)$

$n^3 - 9n^2 + 12$

EXERCISES

Add or subtract.

79. $3t + 5 - 7t - 2$

80. $4x^5 - 6x^6 + 2x^5 - 7x^5$

81. $-h^3 - 2h^2 + 4h^3 - h^2 + 5$

82. $(3m - 7) + (2m^2 - 8m + 6)$

83. $(12 + 6p) - (p - p^2 + 4)$

84. $(3z - 9z^2 + 2) + (2z^2 - 4z + 8)$

85. $(10g - g^2 + 3) - (-4g^2 + 8g - 1)$

86. $(-5x^3 + 2x^2 - x + 5) - (-5x^3 + 3x^2 - 5x - 3)$

7-8 Multiplying Polynomials *(pp. 446–453)*

10.0

EXAMPLES

Multiply.

■ $(2x - 4)(3x + 5)$

$2x(3x) + 2x(5) - 4(3x) - 4(5)$

$6x^2 + 10x - 12x - 20$

$6x^2 - 2x - 20$

■ $(b - 2)(b^2 + 4b - 5)$

$b(b^2) + b(4b) - b(5) - 2(b^2) - 2(4b) - 2(-5)$

$b^3 + 4b^2 - 5b - 2b^2 + (-8b) + 10$

$b^3 + 2b^2 - 13b + 10$

EXERCISES

Multiply.

87. $(2r)(4r)$

88. $(3a^5)(2ab)$

89. $(-3xy)(-6x^2y)$

90. $(3s^3t^2)(2st^4)\left(\frac{1}{2}s^2t^8\right)$

91. $2(x^2 - 4x + 6)$

92. $-3ab(ab - 2a^2b + 5a)$

93. $(a + 3)(a - 6)$

94. $(b - 9)(b + 3)$

95. $(x - 10)(x - 2)$

96. $(t - 1)(t + 1)$

97. $(2q + 6)(4q + 5)$

98. $(5g - 8)(4g - 1)$

7-9 Special Products of Binomials *(pp. 455–461)*

10.0

EXAMPLES

Multiply.

■ $(2h - 6)^2$

$(2h - 6)^2 = (2h)^2 + 2(2h)(-6) + (-6)^2$

$4h^2 - 24h + 36$

■ $(4x - 3)(4x + 3)$

$(4x - 3)(4x + 3) = (4x)^2 - 3^2$

$16x^2 - 9$

EXERCISES

Multiply.

99. $(p - 4)^2$

100. $(x + 12)^2$

101. $(m + 6)^2$

102. $(3c + 7)^2$

103. $(2r - 1)^2$

104. $(3a - b)^2$

105. $(2n - 5)^2$

106. $(h - 13)^2$

107. $(x - 1)(x + 1)$

108. $(z + 15)(z - 15)$

109. $(c^2 - d)(c^2 + d)$

110. $(3k^2 + 7)(3k^2 - 7)$

Answers

79. $-4t + 3$
80. $-6x^6 - x^5$
81. $3h^3 - 3h^2 + 5$
82. $2m^2 - 5m - 1$
83. $p^2 + 5p + 8$
84. $-7z^2 - z + 10$
85. $3g^2 + 2g + 4$
86. $-x^2 + 4x + 8$
87. $8r^2$
88. $6a^6b$
89. $18x^3y^2$
90. $3s^6t^{14}$
91. $2x^2 - 8x + 12$
92. $-3a^2b^2 + 6a^3b^2 - 15a^2b$
93. $a^2 - 3a - 18$
94. $b^2 - 6b - 27$
95. $x^2 - 12x + 20$
96. $t^2 - 1$
97. $8q^2 + 34q + 30$
98. $20g^2 - 37g + 8$
99. $p^2 - 8p + 16$
100. $x^2 + 24x + 144$
101. $m^2 + 12m + 36$
102. $9c^2 + 42c + 49$
103. $4r^2 - 4r + 1$
104. $9a^2 - 6ab + b^2$
105. $4n^2 - 20n + 25$
106. $h^2 - 26h + 169$
107. $x^2 - 1$
108. $z^2 - 225$
109. $c^4 - d^2$
110. $9k^4 - 49$

Organizer

Objective: Assess students' mastery of concepts and skills in Chapter 7.

Resources

Assessment Resources

Chapter 7 Tests

- Free Response (Levels A, B, C)
- Multiple Choice (Levels A, B, C)
- Performance Assessment

***IDEA Works!* CD-ROM**

Modified Chapter 7 Test

California Standards

Standard	Exercises
2.0	1–23, 25–28
10.0	29–38

Evaluate each expression for the given value(s) of the variable(s).

1. $\left(\frac{1}{3}b\right)^{-2}$ for $b = 12$ $\mathbf{\frac{1}{16}}$
2. $\left(14 - a^0b^2\right)^{-3}$ for $a = -2$ and $b = 4$ $\mathbf{-\frac{1}{8}}$

Simplify.

3. $2r^{-3}$ $\mathbf{\frac{2}{r^3}}$
4. $-3f^0g^{-1}$ $\mathbf{-\frac{3}{g}}$
5. m^2n^{-3} $\mathbf{\frac{m^2}{n^3}}$
6. $\frac{1}{2}s^{-5}t^3$ $\mathbf{\frac{t^3}{2s^5}}$

Write each number as a power of 10.

7. 0.0000001 $\mathbf{10^{-7}}$
8. 10,000,000,000,000 $\mathbf{10^{13}}$
9. 1 $\mathbf{10^{0}}$

Find the value of each expression.

10. 1.25×10^{-5} **0.0000125**
11. $10^8 \times 10^{-11}$ **0.001**
12. 325×10^{-2} **3.25**

13. **Technology** In 2002, there were approximately 544,000,000 Internet users worldwide. Write this number in scientific notation. $\mathbf{5.44 \times 10^8}$

Simplify.

14. $\left(f^4\right)^3$ $\mathbf{f^{12}}$
15. $\left(4b^2\right)^0$ **1**
16. $\left(a^3b^6\right)^6$ $\mathbf{a^{18}b^{36}}$
17. $-\left(x^3\right)^5 \cdot \left(x^2\right)^6$ $\mathbf{-x^{27}}$

Simplify each quotient and write the answer in scientific notation.

18. $\left(3.6 \times 10^9\right) \div \left(6 \times 10^4\right)$ $\mathbf{6 \times 10^4}$
19. $\left(3 \times 10^{12}\right) \div \left(9.6 \times 10^{16}\right)$ $\mathbf{3.125 \times 10^{-5}}$

Simplify.

20. $\frac{y^4}{y}$ $\mathbf{y^3}$
21. $\frac{d^2f^5}{\left(d^3\right)^2f^{-4}}$ $\mathbf{\frac{f^9}{d^4}}$
22. $\frac{2^5 \cdot 3^3 \cdot 5^4}{2^8 \cdot 3^2 \cdot 5^4}$ $\mathbf{\frac{3}{8}}$
23. $\left(\frac{4s}{3t}\right)^{-2} \cdot \left(\frac{2s}{6t}\right)^2$ $\mathbf{\frac{1}{16}}$

24. **Geometry** The surface area of a cone is approximated by the polynomial $3.14r^2 + 3.14r\ell$, where r is the radius and ℓ is the slant height. Find the approximate surface area of a cone when $\ell = 5$ cm and $r = 3$ cm. $\mathbf{75.36\ cm^2}$

Simplify each expression. All variables represent nonnegative numbers.

25. $\left(\frac{27}{125}\right)^{\frac{1}{3}}$ $\mathbf{\frac{3}{5}}$
26. $\sqrt[3]{43^3}$ **43**
27. $\sqrt{25y^8}$ $\mathbf{5y^4}$
28. $\sqrt[5]{3^5t^{10}}$ $\mathbf{3t^2}$

Add or subtract.

29. $3a - 4b + 2a$ $\mathbf{5a - 4b}$
30. $\left(2b^2 - 4b^3\right) - \left(6b^3 + 8b^2\right)$ $\mathbf{-10b^3 - 6b^2}$
31. $-9g^2 + 3g - 4g^3 - 2g + 3g^2 - 4$ $\mathbf{-4g^3 - 6g^2 + g - 4}$

Multiply.

32. $-5\left(r^2s - 6\right)$ $\mathbf{-5r^2s + 30}$
33. $(2t - 7)(t + 4)$ $\mathbf{2t^2 + t - 28}$
34. $(4g - 1)\left(4g^2 - 5g - 3\right)$ $\mathbf{16g^3 - 24g^2 - 7g + 3}$
35. $(m + 6)^2$ $\mathbf{m^2 + 12m + 36}$
36. $(3t - 7)(3t + 7)$ $\mathbf{9t^2 - 49}$
37. $\left(3x^2 - 7\right)^2$ $\mathbf{9x^4 - 42x^2 + 49}$

38. **Carpentry** Carpenters use a tool called a *speed square* to help them mark right angles. A speed square is a right triangle.
   a. Write a polynomial that represents the area of the speed square shown. $\mathbf{x^2 - x - 12}$
   b. Find the area when $x = 4.5$ in. $\mathbf{3.75\ in^2}$

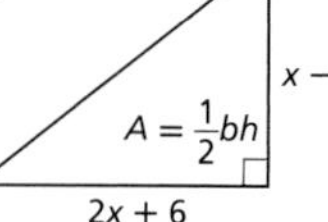

College Entrance Exam Practice

FOCUS ON SAT

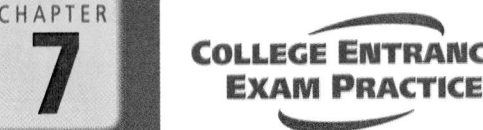

When you receive your SAT scores, you will find a percentile for each score. The percentile tells you what percent of students scored lower than you on the same test. Your percentile at the national and state levels may differ because of the different groups being compared.

You may use some types of calculators on the math section of the SAT. For about 40% of the test items, a graphing calculator is recommended. Bring a calculator that you are comfortable using. You won't have time to figure out how a new calculator works.

You may want to time yourself as you take this practice test. It should take you about 7 minutes to complete.

1. If $(x + 1)(x + 4) - (x - 1)(x - 2) = 0$, what is the value of x?

   (A) -1

   (B) $-\frac{1}{4}$

   (C) 0

   (D) $\frac{1}{4}$

   (E) 1

2. Which of the following is equal to 4^5?

   I. $3^5 \times 1^5$

   II. 2^{10}

   III. $4^0 \times 4^5$

   (A) I only

   (B) II only

   (C) I and II only

   (D) II and III only

   (E) I, II, and III

3. If $x^{-4} = 81$, then $x =$

   (A) -3

   (B) $\frac{1}{4}$

   (C) $\frac{1}{3}$

   (D) 3

   (E) 9

4. What is the value of $2x^3 - 4x^2 + 3x + 1$ when $x = -2$?

   (A) -37

   (B) -25

   (C) -5

   (D) 7

   (E) 27

5. What is the area of a rectangle with a length of $x - a$ and a width of $x + b$?

   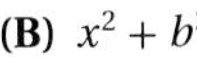

   (A) $x^2 - a^2$

   (B) $x^2 + b^2$

   (C) $x^2 - abx + ab$

   (D) $x^2 - ax - bx - ab$

   (E) $x^2 + bx - ax - ab$

6. For integers greater than 0, define the following operations.

   $a \square b = 2a^2 + 3b$

   $a \triangle b = 5a^2 - 2b$

   What is $(a \square b) + (a \triangle b)$?

   (A) $7a^2 + b$

   (B) $-3a^2 + 5b$

   (C) $7a^2 - b$

   (D) $3a^2 - 5b$

   (E) $-3a^2 - b$

College Entrance Exam Practice

CHAPTER 7

Organizer

Objective: Provide practice for college entrance exams such as the SAT.

PREMIER **Online Edition**

Resources

College Entrance Exam Practice

Questions on the SAT represent the following math content areas:

Number and Operations, 30–32%

Algebra and Functions, 28–32%

Geometry and Measurement, 27–30%

Data Analysis, Statistics, and Probability, 10–12%

Items on this page focus on:
- Algebra and Functions
- Geometry and Measurement

Text References:

Item	1	2	3	4	5	6
Lesson	7-8	7-1, 7-3	7-1	7-6	7-8	7-7

Multiple Choice

1. Students who chose **A** or **E** may have made a sign error in the second term. Suggest that students use parentheses around each product of binomials until the multiplication is complete and then distribute the negative sign from the subtraction of the terms.
2. Students who chose **A, C,** or **E** may have added the bases in choice **I** and kept the exponent the same. Remind students that if the bases are the same when powers are multiplied, then they can add the exponents.
3. Students who chose **D** found the value of x if $x^4 = 81$. Suggest that students rewrite x^{-4} with a positive exponent and try again.
4. Students who chose **C** probably made a sign error in the first or second term. Remind students to be careful when using exponents with negative numbers. Be sure they understand when the negative sign is part of the base, and when it is not.
5. Students who did not choose **E** should review multiplying binomials. Remind students to be cautious of signs.
6. Students who chose **B** subtracted the two binomials instead of adding them. Remind students to read each test item carefully.

Organizer

Objective: Provide opportunities to learn and practice common test-taking strategies.

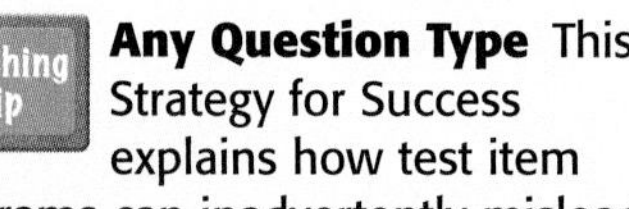

Any Question Type This Strategy for Success explains how test item diagrams can inadvertently mislead students.

If students assume that visual information from a diagram is correct, they will likely misinterpret the information. Advise students that diagrams are not always drawn to scale and that they should not rely solely on the appearance of the drawing to answer the test item. Instead they should look closely at a drawing's labels. They may even need to redraw the diagram to scale in order to better represent the problem.

Explain that even though a test item may not include a diagram, it may be beneficial for students to make a quick sketch. Show students the importance of labeling their sketch with the information in the test item.

Any Question Type: Use a Diagram

When a test item includes a diagram, use it to help solve the problem. Gather as much information from the drawing as possible. However, keep in mind that diagrams are not always drawn to scale and can be misleading.

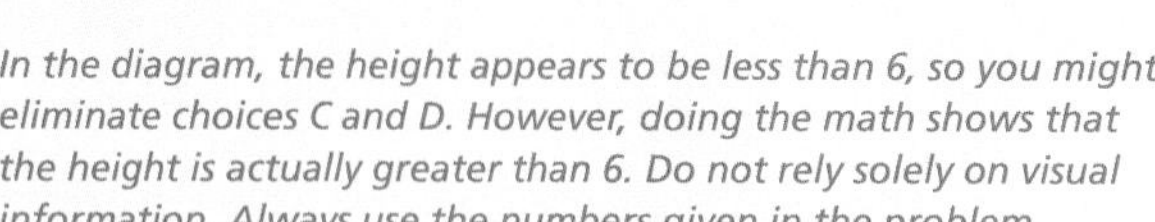

Multiple Choice **What is the height of the triangle when $x = 4$ and $y = 1$?**

Ⓐ 2 Ⓒ 8

Ⓑ 4 Ⓓ 16

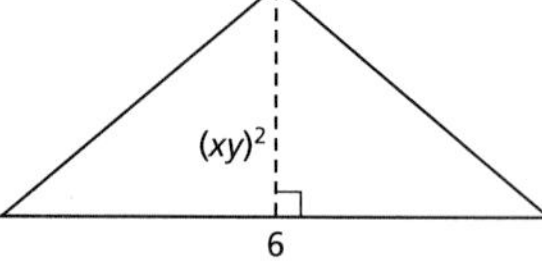

In the diagram, the height appears to be less than 6, so you might eliminate choices C and D. However, doing the math shows that the height is actually greater than 6. Do not rely solely on visual information. Always use the numbers given in the problem.

The height of the triangle is $(xy)^2$.
When $x = 4$ and $y = 1$, $(xy)^2 = (4 \cdot 1)^2 = (4)^2 = 16$.
Choice D is the correct answer.

If a test item does not have a diagram, draw a quick sketch of the problem situation. Label your diagram with the data given in the problem.

EXAMPLE 2

Short Response **A square placemat is lying in the middle of a rectangular table. The side length of the placemat is $\left(\frac{x}{2}\right)$. The length of the table is $12x$, and the width is $8x$. Write a polynomial to represent the area of the placemat. Then write a polynomial to represent the area of the table that surrounds the placemat.**

Use the information in the problem to draw and label a diagram. Then write the polynomials.

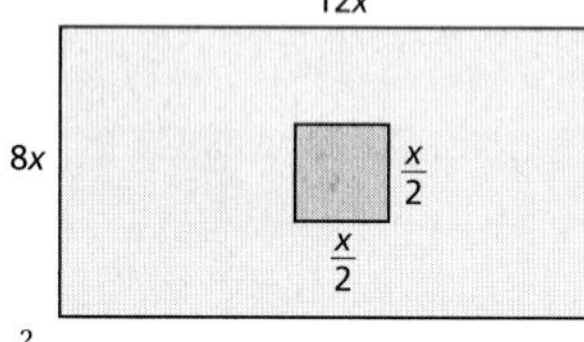

area of placemat $= s^2 = \left(\frac{x}{2}\right)^2 = \left(\frac{x}{2}\right)\left(\frac{x}{2}\right) = \frac{x^2}{4}$

area of table $= \ell w = (12x)(8x) = 96x^2$

area of table − area of placemat $= 96x^2 - \frac{x^2}{4} = \frac{384x^2 - x^2}{4} = \frac{383x^2}{4}$

The area of the placemat is $\frac{x^2}{4}$.

The area of the table that surrounds the placemat is $\frac{383x^2}{4}$.

If a given diagram does not reflect the problem, draw a sketch that is more accurate. If a test item does not have a diagram, use the given information to sketch your own. Try to make your sketch as accurate as possible.

Read each test item and answer the questions that follow.

Item A
Short Response The width of a rectangle is 1.5 feet more than 4 times its length. Write a polynomial expression for the area of the rectangle. What is the area when the length is 16.75 feet?

1. What is the unknown measure in this problem?
2. How will drawing a diagram help you solve the problem?
3. Draw and label a sketch of the situation.

Item B
Multiple Choice Rectangle *ABDC* is similar to rectangle *MNPO*. If the width of rectangle *ABDC* is 8, what is its length?

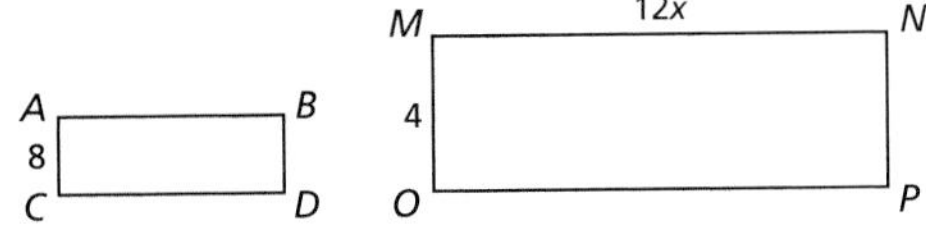

Ⓐ 2

Ⓑ $2x$

Ⓒ $24x$

Ⓓ 24

4. Look at the dimensions in the diagram. Do you think that the length of rectangle *ABDC* is greater or less than the length of rectangle *MNPO*?
5. Do you think the drawings reflect the information in the problem accurately? Why or why not?
6. Draw your own sketch to match the information in the problem.

Item C
Short Response Write a polynomial expression for the area of triangle *QRP*. Write a polynomial expression for the area of triangle *MNP*. Then use these expressions to write a polynomial expression for the area of *QRNM*.

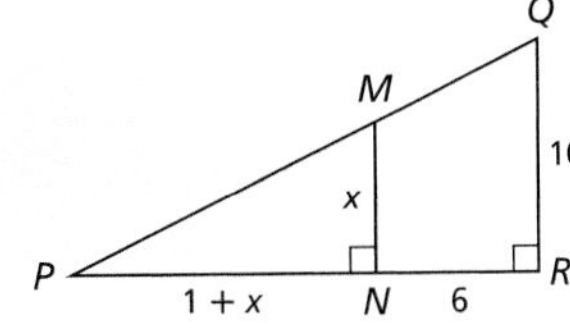

7. Describe how redrawing the figure can help you better understand the information in the problem.
8. After reading this test item, a student redrew the figure as shown below. Is this a correct interpretation of the original figure? Explain.

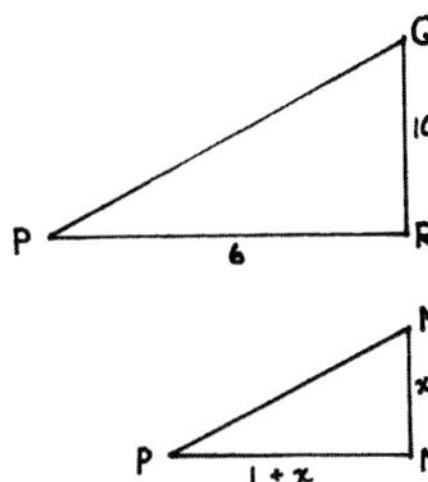

Item D
Multiple Choice The measure of angle *XYZ* is $(x^2 + 10x + 15)^\circ$. What is the measure of angle *XYW*?

Ⓐ $(6x + 15)^\circ$

Ⓑ $(2x^2 + 14x + 15)^\circ$

Ⓒ $(14x + 15)^\circ$

Ⓓ $(6x^2 + 15)^\circ$

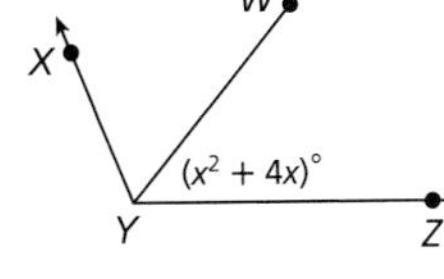

9. What information does the diagram provide that the problem does not?
10. Will the measure of angle *XYW* be less than or greater than the measure of angle *XYZ*? Explain.

Answers

1. the width
2. Possible answer: By drawing a rectangle and labeling each dimension, you will have a better understanding of what should be substituted into the area formula for length and width.
3.

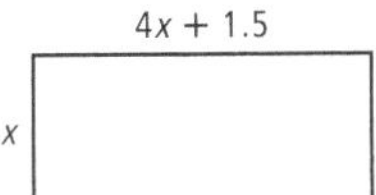

4. greater
5. No; it appears that the length of rectangle *ABDC* is less than the length of rectangle *MNPO*, and this is not consistent with the dimensions that are given.
6. Possible answer:

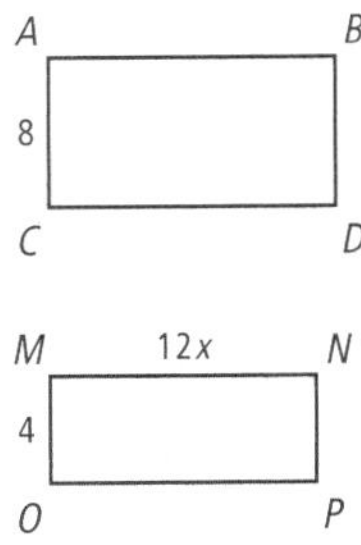

7. Possible answer: By redrawing the figures into 2 separate triangles, you can better see the base and height measures, which will help you correctly set up the area formula for each triangle.
8. No, it is not correct. The student mislabeled the base of triangle *QRP*. It should be labeled $7 + x$.
9. the measure of angle *WYZ*
10. Less than; angle *XYW* lies within angle *XYZ*, so angle *XYW* must be smaller.

Answers to Test Items

A. $4x^2 + 1.5x$; 1147.375 ft^2

B. C

C. $5x + 35$; $\frac{1}{2}(x^2 + x)$; $-\frac{1}{2}x^2 + \frac{9}{2}x + 35$

D. A

California Standards

Algebra 1 10.0

Organizer

Objective: Provide review and practice for Chapters 1–7.

PREMIER Online Edition

Resources

Assessment Resources

Chapter 7 Cumulative Test

Focus on California Standards Benchmark Tests and Intervention

***California Standards Practice* CD-ROM**

go.hrw.com
KEYWORD: MA8CA Practice

CUMULATIVE ASSESSMENT, CHAPTERS 1–7

Multiple Choice

1. A negative number is raised to a power. The result is a negative number. What do you know about the power?

Ⓐ It is an even number.
Ⓑ It is an odd number.
Ⓒ It is zero.
Ⓓ It is a whole number.

2. Which polynomial is the product of $2x + 3$ and $x - 4$?

Ⓐ $2x^2 - 12$
Ⓑ $2x^2 - 5x - 12$
Ⓒ $2x^2 - 8x - 12$
Ⓓ $2x^2 - 11x - 12$

3. Which ordered pair is a solution of this system of equations?

$$\begin{cases} \frac{1}{2}x + y = 4 \\ x - 2y = -12 \end{cases}$$

Ⓐ (4, 2)
Ⓑ (−6, 7)
Ⓒ (0, 4)
Ⓓ (−2, 5)

4. Which is a solution of the inequality $7 - 3(x - 3) > 2(x + 3)$?

Ⓐ 0
Ⓑ 2
Ⓒ 5
Ⓓ 12

5. One dose of Ted's medication contains 0.625 milligram, or $\frac{5}{8}$ milligram, of a drug. Which expression is equivalent to 0.625?

Ⓐ $5(4)^{-2}$
Ⓑ $5(2)^{-4}$
Ⓒ $5(-2)^{3}$
Ⓓ $5(2)^{-3}$

6. A restaurant claims to have served 352×10^6 hamburgers. What is this number in scientific notation?

Ⓐ 3.52×10^6
Ⓑ 3.52×10^8
Ⓒ 3.52×10^4
Ⓓ 352×10^6

7. The solutions of which system of inequalities can be represented by the shaded region?

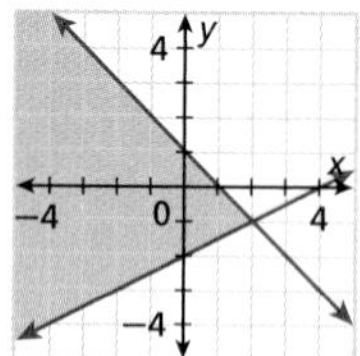

Ⓐ $\begin{cases} y \le -x + 1 \\ y \le \frac{1}{2}x - 2 \end{cases}$

Ⓑ $\begin{cases} y \ge -x + 1 \\ y \ge \frac{1}{2}x - 2 \end{cases}$

Ⓒ $\begin{cases} y \le -x + 1 \\ y \ge \frac{1}{2}x - 2 \end{cases}$

Ⓓ $\begin{cases} y \ge -x + 1 \\ y \le \frac{1}{2}x - 2 \end{cases}$

8. Which equation describes a line parallel to $y = 5 - 2x$?

Ⓐ $y = -2x + 8$
Ⓑ $y = 2x - 5$
Ⓒ $y = 5 + \frac{1}{2}x$
Ⓓ $y = 5 - \frac{1}{2}x$

9. A square has sides of length $x - 4$. A rectangle has a length of $x + 2$ and a width of $2x - 1$. What is the total combined area of the square and the rectangle?

Ⓐ $10x - 14$
Ⓑ $4x - 3$
Ⓒ $3x^2 - 5x + 14$
Ⓓ $3x^2 + 3x - 18$

California Standards

Standard	Exercises
2.0	1, 5, 6, 11–13, 15, 20
4.0	4
6.0	7, 14
7.0	17a
8.0	8, 17a
9.0	3, 17b
10.0	2, 9, 10, 16, 18, 19, 21

Multiple Choice Choice **D** in **Item 6** can be eliminated immediately because the first number is greater than 10.

Students who chose **C** in **Item 8** chose a line perpendicular to the given line. Remind students that parallel lines have the same slope.

When solving **Item 9,** remind students that $A = \ell w$. Therefore, the combined area must have an x^2 in the expression. Eliminate choices **A** and **B.**

Test writers develop multiple-choice test options with distracters. Distracters are incorrect options that are based on common student errors. Be cautious! Even if the answer you calculated is one of the options, it may not be the correct answer. Always check your work carefully.

10. Jennifer has a pocketful of change, all in nickels and quarters. There are 11 coins with a total value of $1.15. Which system of equations can you use to find the number of each type of coin?

(A) $\begin{cases} n + q = 11 \\ n + q = 1.15 \end{cases}$

(B) $\begin{cases} n + q = 11 \\ 5n + 25q = 1.15 \end{cases}$

(C) $\begin{cases} 5n + 25q = 11 \\ n + q = 1.15 \end{cases}$

(D) $\begin{cases} n + q = 11 \\ 0.05n + 0.25q = 1.15 \end{cases}$

11. Which of the following is a true statement?

(A) $\left[(a^m)^n\right]^p = a^{m+n+p}$

(B) $\left[(a^m)^n\right]^p = a^{mn+p}$

(C) $\left[(a^m)^n\right]^p = a^{mnp}$

(D) $\left[(a^m)^n\right]^p = (a^{m+n})^p$

12. In 1867, the United States purchased the Alaska Territory from Russia for $\$7.2 \times 10^6$. The total area was about 6×10^5 square miles. What was the price per square mile?

(A) About $0.12 per square mile

(B) About $1.20 per square mile

(C) About $12.00 per square mile

(D) About $120.00 per square mile

Gridded Response

13. Evaluate the expression $3b^{-2}c^0$ for $b = 2$ and $c = -3$. $\frac{3}{4}$, or 0.75

14. What is the y-intercept of $5x + 6y - 4 = 0$? $\frac{2}{3}$

15. The quotient $(5.6 \times 10^8) \div (8 \times 10^3)$ is written in scientific notation as (7×10^n). What is the value of n? 4

16. Jared multiplies the polynomials $2x - 1$ and $x^2 + 3x - 5$ and simplifies the product. What is the coefficient of the x^2-term? 5

Short Response

17. Line p is given by the equation $x + 2y = -6$. Point A has coordinates $(3, -2)$.

a. Line q passes through point A and is perpendicular to line p. Write the equation of line q. Show your work. $y = 2x - 8$

b. Find the intersection of lines p and q. Show your work. $(2, -4)$

18. A set of positive integers (a, b, c) is called a *Pythagorean triple* if $a^2 + b^2 = c^2$.

a. Find a^2, b^2, and c^2 when $a = 2x$, $b = x^2 - 1$, and $c = x^2 + 1$. Show your work.

b. Is $(2x, x^2 - 1, x^2 + 1)$ a Pythagorean triple? Explain your reasoning.

19. Ron is making an ice sculpture. The block of ice is in the shape of a rectangular prism with a length of $(x + 2)$ inches, a width of $(x - 2)$ inches, and a height of $2x$ inches.

a. Write and simplify a polynomial expression for the volume of the block of ice. Show your work.

b. The final volume of the ice sculpture is $(x^3 + 4x^2 - 10x + 1)$ cubic inches. Write an expression for the volume of ice that Ron carved away. Show your work.

20. Simplify the expression $(3 \cdot a^2 \cdot b^{-4} \cdot a \cdot b^{-3})^{-3}$ using two different methods. Show that the results are the same. $\frac{b^{21}}{27a^9}$

Extended Response

21. Look at the pentagon below.

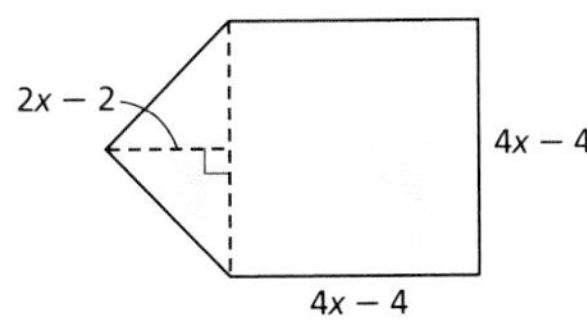

a. Write and simplify an expression that represents the area of the pentagon. Show your work or explain your answer.

b. Show one method of checking that your expression in part **a** is correct.

c. The triangular part of the pentagon can be rearranged to form a square. Write the area of this square as the square of a binomial.

d. Expand the product that you wrote in part **c**. What type of polynomial is this?

e. Is the square of a binomial ever a binomial? Explain your reasoning.

Short-Response Rubric

Items 17–20

2 Points = The student's answer is an accurate and complete execution of the task or tasks.

1 Point = The student's answer contains attributes of an appropriate response but is flawed.

0 Points = The student's answer contains no attributes of an appropriate response.

Extended-Response Rubric

Item 21

4 Points = The student writes the correct expression with full work or explanation in part **a,** shows one method of checking the previous answer in part **b,** writes the correct area as a binomial square in part **c,** expands the product correctly and identifies the type of polynomial in part **d,** and answers correctly with explanation in part **e.**

3 Points = The student writes the correct expression with minimal work or explanation in part **a,** shows one method of checking the previous answer in part **b,** writes the area as a binomial square with minor errors in part **c,** expands the product with minor errors and identifies the type of polynomial in part **d,** and answers correctly with explanation in part **e.**

2 Points = The student answers parts **a, b,** and **e** correctly with attempted explanation; or the student answers parts **c, d,** and **e** correctly with attempted explanation.

1 Point = The student answers one part correctly but does not attempt all parts; or the student attempts to answer all parts of the problem but does not correctly answer any part.

0 Points = The student does not answer correctly and does not attempt all parts of the problem.

Answers

18a. $a^2 = (2x)^2 = 4x^2$

$b^2 = (x^2 - 1)^2 = x^4 - 2x^2 + 1$

$c^2 = (x^2 + 1)^2 = x^4 + 2x^2 + 1$

b. Yes; $(2x)^2 + (x^2 - 1)^2 = 4x^2 + x^4 - 2x^2 + 1 = x^4 + 2x^2 + 1$ and $(x^2 + 1)^2 = x^4 + 2x^2 + 1$.
Because $(2x)^2 + (x^2 - 1)^2 = (x^2 + 1)^2$, the expressions form a Pythagorean triple.

19a. $(2x^3 - 8x)$ in^3

b. $(x^3 - 4x^2 + 2x - 1)$ in^3

20. $(3 \cdot a^2 \cdot b^{-4} \cdot a \cdot b^{-3})^{-3} = (3 \cdot a^3 \cdot b^{-7})^{-3} = 3^{-3} \cdot a^{-9} \cdot b^{21} = \frac{b^{21}}{27a^9}$;
$(3 \cdot a^2 \cdot b^{-4} \cdot a \cdot b^{-3})^{-3} = 3^{-3} \cdot a^{-6} \cdot b^{12} \cdot a^{-3} \cdot b^9 = 3^{-3} \cdot a^{-9} \cdot b^{21} = \frac{b^{21}}{27a^9}$

21a. $20x^2 - 40x + 20$

b. Possible answer: Substitute 5 for x in the diagram. Then the side lengths of the square are 16 units, and the height of the triangle is 8 units. The area of the square is 256 sq. units, and the area of the triangle is 64 sq. units. 256 + 64 is the area of the pentagon, 320 sq. units. Then substitute 5 for x in the simplified expression. It also simplifies to 320.

c. $(2x - 2)^2$

d. $4x^2 - 8x + 4$; trinomial

e. No; for any a and b, $(a + b)^2 = a^2 + 2ab + b^2$ and $(a - b)^2 = a^2 - 2ab + b^2$. These are always trinomials.

Factoring Polynomials

✔	Grade-level Standard
◄	Review
►	Beyond the Standards
A	Assessment
O	Optional

Pacing Guide

Calendar Planner
Teacher's **One-Stop** Planner®

Lesson/Lab	California Standards	Time	Advanced Students	Benchmark Students	Strategic Students
8-1 Factors and Greatest Common Factors	**Preparation for 11.0**	50 min	O	◄	◄
LR Indirect Proofs	**25.1**	25 min	✔	✔	✔
LAB Model Factorization by GCF	**11.0**	25 min	✔	✔	✔
8-2 Factoring by GCF	**11.0**	50 min	✔	✔	✔
LAB Model Factorization of $x^2 + bx + c$	**11.0**	25 min	✔	✔	✔
8-3 Factoring $x^2 + bx + c$	**11.0**	50 min	✔	✔	✔
LAB Model Factorization of $ax^2 + bx + c$	**11.0**	25 min	✔	✔	✔
8-4 Factoring $ax^2 + bx + c$	**11.0**	50 min	✔	✔	✔
Concept Connection	**5.0, 11.0, 15.0**	25 min	A	A	O
Ready to Go On?		25 min	A	A	A
8-5 Factoring Special Products	**11.0**	75 min	✔	✔	✔
CN Mental Math		25 min	O	O	O
8-6 Choosing a Factoring Method	**11.0**	50 min	✔	✔	✔
Concept Connection	**11.0**	25 min	A	A	O
Ready to Go On?		25 min	A	A	A
Study Guide: Review		25 min	✔	✔	✔
Chapter Test	**11.0**	50 min	A	A	A

* **Benchmark students** are achieving at or near grade level.
** **Strategic students** may be a year or more below grade level, and may require additional time for intervention.

Countdown to Mastery, Weeks 17, 18, 19

ONGOING ASSESSMENT and INTERVENTION

	DIAGNOSE	PRESCRIBE

Assess Prior Knowledge

Before Chapter 8

DIAGNOSE

Diagnose readiness for the chapter.

- ***Are You Ready?*** SE p. 475

PRESCRIBE

Prescribe intervention.

- ***Are You Ready? Intervention*** Skills 1, 3, 5, 62, 64

Formative Assessment

Before Every Lesson

DIAGNOSE

Diagnose readiness for the lesson.

- **Warm Up** TE, every lesson

PRESCRIBE

Prescribe intervention.

- **Skills Bank** pp. SB1–SB32
- **Review for Mastery** CRF Chapters 1–8

During Every Lesson

DIAGNOSE

Diagnose understanding of lesson concepts.

- **Questioning Strategies** TE, every example
- **Check It Out!** SE, every example
- **Think and Discuss** SE, every lesson
- **Write About It** SE, every lesson
- **Journal** TE, every lesson

PRESCRIBE

Prescribe intervention.

- **Reading Strategies** CRF, every lesson
- ***Success for ELL*** pp. 117–130
- ***Lesson Tutorial Videos*** Chapter 8

After Every Lesson

DIAGNOSE

Diagnose mastery of lesson concepts.

- **Lesson Quiz** TE, every lesson
- **Alternative Assessment** TE, every lesson
- **Ready to Go On?** SE pp. 513, 529
- ***Test and Practice Generator***

PRESCRIBE

Prescribe intervention.

- **Review for Mastery** CRF, every lesson
- **Problem Solving** CRF, every lesson
- ***Ready to Go On? Intervention*** Chapter 8
- ***Homework Help Online***

Before Chapter 8 Testing

DIAGNOSE

Diagnose mastery of concepts in the chapter.

- **Ready to Go On?** SE pp. 513, 529
- **Concept Connection** SE pp. 512, 528
- **Section Quizzes** AR pp. 145–146
- ***Test and Practice Generator***

PRESCRIBE

Prescribe intervention.

- ***Ready to Go On? Intervention*** Chapter 8
- **Scaffolding Questions** TE pp. 512, 528

Before Assessment of California Standards

DIAGNOSE

Diagnose mastery of California Standards.

- ***Focus on California Standards: Benchmark Tests***
- **Mastering the Standards** SE pp. 538–539
- ***California Standards Practice* CD-ROM**

PRESCRIBE

Prescribe intervention.

- ***Focus on California Standards: Intervention***

Summative Assessment

After Chapter 8

DIAGNOSE

Check mastery of chapter concepts.

- **Multiple-Choice Tests (Forms A, B, C)**
- **Free-Response Tests (Forms A, B, C)**
- **Performance Assessment** AR pp. 159–160
- ***Test and Practice Generator***

PRESCRIBE

Prescribe intervention.

- **Review for Mastery** CRF, every lesson
- ***Lesson Tutorial Videos*** Chapter 8

KEY: **SE** = *Student Edition* **TE** = *Teacher's Edition* **CRF** = *Chapter Resource File* **AR** = *Assessment Resources* Available online Available on CD-ROM

Supporting the Teacher

Chapter 8 Resource File

Family Involvement
pp. 1–4, 37–40

Practice A, B, C
pp. 5–7, 13–15, 21–23, 29–31, 41–43, 49–51

Review for Mastery
pp. 8–9, 16–17, 24–25, 32–33, 44–45, 52–53

Challenge
pp. 10, 18, 26, 34, 46, 54

Problem Solving
pp. 11, 19, 27, 35, 47, 55

Reading Strategies ELL
pp. 12, 20, 28, 36, 48, 56

Algebra Lab
pp. 70–71

Workbooks

Homework and Practice Workbook SPANISH
Teacher's Edition .... pp. 50–55

Know-It Notebook SPANISH
Teacher's Guide .... Chapter 8

Review for Mastery Workbook SPANISH
Teacher's Guide .... pp. 99–110

Focus on California Standards: Intervention Workbook SPANISH
Teacher's Guide

Teacher Tools

Power Presentations
Complete PowerPoint® presentations for Chapter 8 lessons

Lesson Tutorial Videos  SPANISH
Holt authors Ed Burger and Freddie Renfro present tutorials to support the Chapter 8 lessons.

Teacher's One-Stop Planner SPANISH
Easy access to all Chapter 8 resources and assessments, as well as software for lesson planning, test generation, and puzzle creation

IDEA Works!
Key Chapter 8 resources and assessments modified to address special learning needs

Solutions Key .... Chapter 8

Interactive Answers and Solutions

TechKeys

Lab Resources 

Project Teacher Support 

Parent Resources

Transparencies

Lesson Transparencies, Volume 2 .... Chapter 8
- Teacher Tools
- Warm-ups
- Teaching Transparencies
- Lesson Quizzes

Alternate Openers: Explorations .... pp. 50–55

Countdown to Mastery .... pp. 33–38

Know-It Notebook .... Chapter 8
- Vocabulary
- Key Concepts
- Graphic Organizers
- Chapter Review
- Big Ideas

Technology Highlights for the Teacher

 Power Presentations

Dynamic presentations to engage students. Complete PowerPoint® presentations for every lesson in Chapter 8.

2-1 Solving One-Step Equations

Isolate a variable by using inverse operations which "undo" operations on the variable.

An equation is like a balanced scale. To keep the balance, perform the same operation on both sides.

Inverse Operations	
Operation	Inverse Operation
Addition	Subtraction
Subtraction	Addition

 One-Stop Planner SPANISH

Easy access to Chapter 8 resources and assessments. Includes lesson planning, test generation, and puzzle creation software.

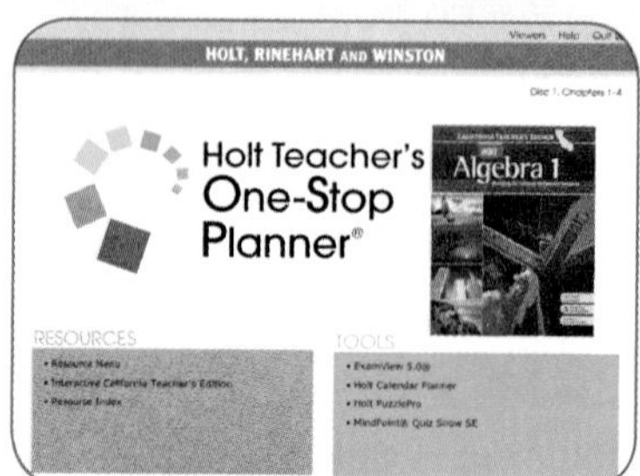

Premier Online Edition SPANISH

Includes Tutorial Videos, Lesson Activities, Lesson Quizzes, Homework Help, Chapter Project and more.

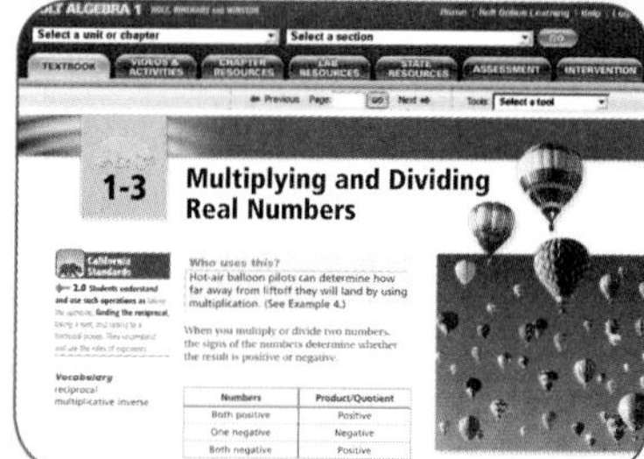

KEY: **SE** = *Student Edition* **TE** = *Teacher's Edition* ELL English Language Learners SPANISH Spanish available — Available online — Available on CD-ROM

Universal Access

Teaching Tips to help all students appear throughout the chapter. A few that target specific students are included in the lists below.

Strategic Students

Practice A .... CRF, every lesson
Review for Mastery .... CRF, every lesson
Reading Strategies .... CRF, every lesson
Academic Vocabulary Connections .... TE p. 476
Concrete Manipulatives .... TE pp. 480, 490
Questioning Strategies .... TE, every example
Ready to Go On? Intervention .... Chapter 8
Know-It Notebook SPANISH .... Chapter 8
Homework Help Online
Lesson Tutorial Videos SPANISH
Online Interactivities SPANISH

Special Needs Students

Practice A .... CRF, every lesson
Review for Mastery .... CRF, every lesson
Reading Strategies .... CRF, every lesson
Academic Vocabulary Connections .... TE p. 476
Inclusion .... TE pp. 484, 488, 498, 506, 516, 525
IDEA Works! Modified Resources .... Chapter 8
Ready to Go On? Intervention .... Chapter 8
Know-It Notebook SPANISH .... Chapter 8
Lesson Tutorial Videos SPANISH
Online Interactivities SPANISH

English Learners

ENGLISH LANGUAGE LEARNERS

Reading Strategies .... CRF, every lesson
Vocabulary Exercises .... SE, every exercise set
Academic Vocabulary Connections .... TE p. 476
English Language Learners .... TE p. 477
Language Support .... TE p. 485
Success for English Language Learners .... Chapter 8
Know-It Notebook SPANISH .... Chapter 8
Multilingual Glossary
Lesson Tutorial Videos SPANISH

Benchmark Students

Practice B .... CRF, every lesson
Problem Solving .... CRF, every lesson
Academic Vocabulary Connections .... TE p. 476
Questioning Strategies .... TE, every example
Ready to Go On? Intervention .... Chapter 8
Know-It Notebook SPANISH .... Chapter 8
Homework Help Online
Online Interactivities SPANISH

Advanced Students

Practice C .... CRF, every lesson
Challenge .... CRF, every lesson
Reading and Writing Math EXTENSION .... TE p. 477
Concept Connection EXTENSION .... TE pp. 512, 528
Advanced Learners/GATE .... TE p. 506
Ready to Go On? Enrichment .... Chapter 8

Technology Highlights for Universal Access

Lesson Tutorial Videos 

Starring Holt authors Ed Burger and Freddie Renfro! Live tutorials to support every lesson in Chapter 8.

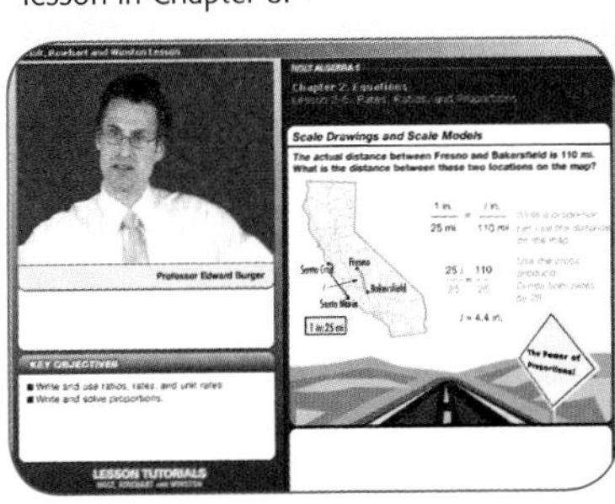

Multilingual Glossary

Searchable glossary includes definitions in English, Spanish, Vietnamese, Chinese, Hmong, Korean, and other languages.

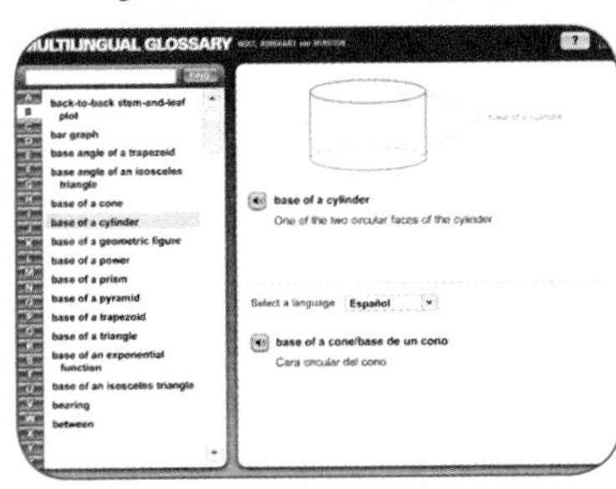

Online Interactivities 

Interactive tutorials provide visually engaging alternative opportunities to learn concepts and master skills.

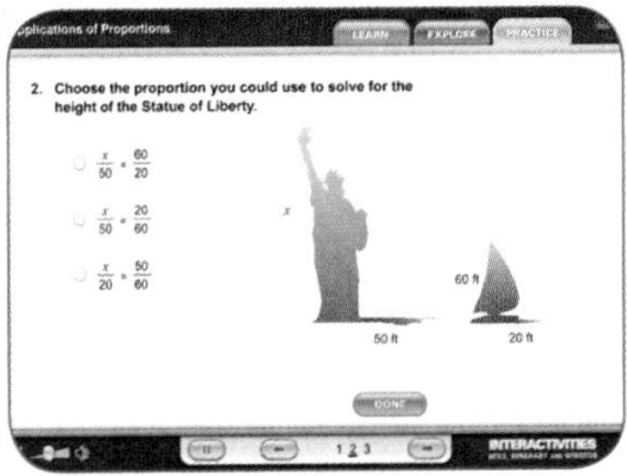

KEY: **SE** = *Student Edition* **TE** = *Teacher's Edition* **CRF** = *Chapter Resource File* SPANISH Spanish available · Available online · Available on CD-ROM

Assessing Prior Knowledge

Determine whether students have the prerequisite concepts and skills for success in Chapter 8.

Are You Ready? SPANISH .... SE p. 475
Warm Up .... TE, every lesson

Chapter and Standards Assessment

Provide review and practice for Chapter 8 and standards mastery.

Concept Connection .... SE pp. 512, 528
Study Guide: Review .... SE pp. 530–533
Strategies for Success .... SE pp. 536–537
Mastering the Standards .... SE pp. 538–539
College Entrance Exam Practice .... SE p. 535
***Countdown to Mastery* Transparencies** .... pp. 1–4
Focus on California Standards: Benchmark Tests
Focus on California Standards: Intervention Workbook
***California Standards Practice* CD-ROM** SPANISH
IDEA Works! Modified Worksheets and Tests

Alternative Assessment

Assess students' understanding of Chapter 8 concepts and combined problem-solving skills.

Alternative Assessment .... TE, every lesson
Performance Assessment .... AR pp. 159–160
Portfolio Assessment .... AR p. xxxiii
Chapter 8 Project

Daily Assessment

Provide formative assessment for each day of Chapter 8.

Questioning Strategies .... TE, every example
Think and Discuss .... SE, every lesson
Check It Out! Exercises .... SE, every example
Write About It .... SE, every lesson
Journal .... TE, every lesson
Lesson Quiz .... TE, every lesson
Alternative Assessment .... TE, every lesson
IDEA Works! Modified Lesson Quizzes .... Chapter 8

Weekly Assessment

Provide formative assessment for each week of Chapter 8.

Concept Connection .... SE pp. 512, 528
Ready to Go On? .... SE pp. 513, 529
Cumulative Assessment .... SE pp. 538–539
Test and Practice Generator SPANISH .... *One-Stop Planner*

Formal Assessment

Provide summative assessment of Chapter 8 mastery.

Section Quizzes .... AR pp. 145–146
Chapter 8 Test SPANISH .... SE p. 534
Chapter Test (Levels A, B, C) .... AR pp. 147–158
• Multiple Choice • Free Response
Cumulative Test .... AR pp. 161–164
Test and Practice Generator SPANISH .... *One-Stop Planner*

Technology Highlights for Ongoing Assessment

Automatically assess readiness and prescribe intervention for Chapter 8 prerequisite skills.

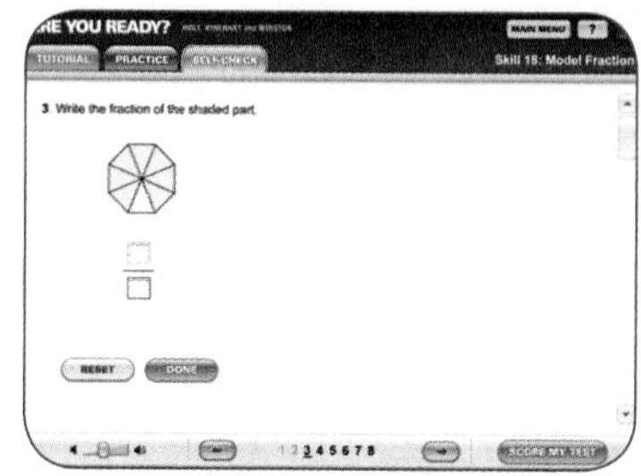

Automatically assess understanding of and prescribe intervention for Sections 8A and 8B.

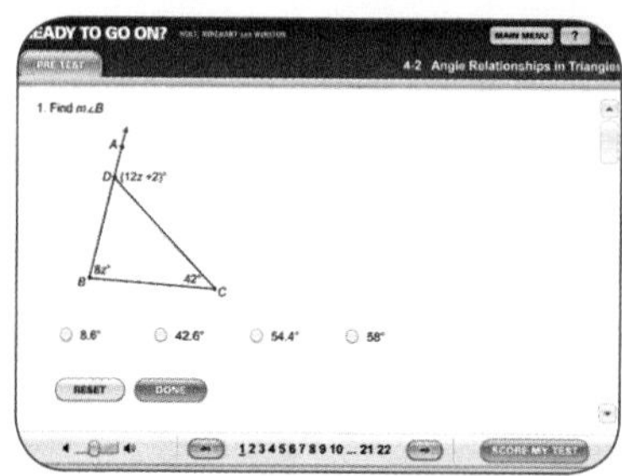

Focus on California Standards: Benchmark Tests and Intervention SPANISH

Automatically assess proficiency with California Algebra I Standards and provide intervention.

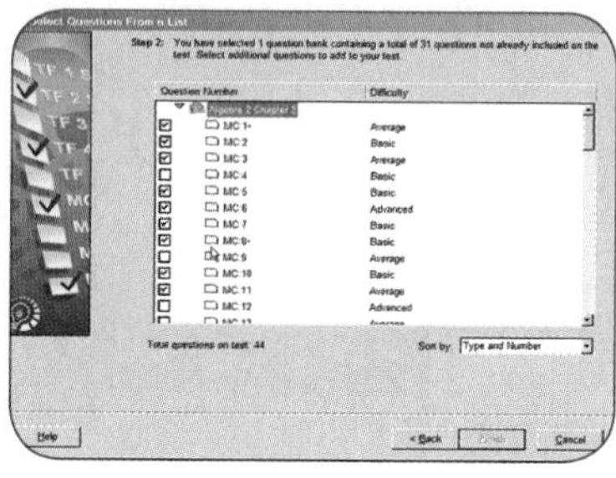

KEY: **SE** = *Student Edition* **TE** = *Teacher's Edition* **AR** = Assessment Resources  Spanish available  Available online  Available on CD-ROM

Three levels (A, B, C) of multiple-choice and free-response chapter tests are available in the *Assessment Resources.*

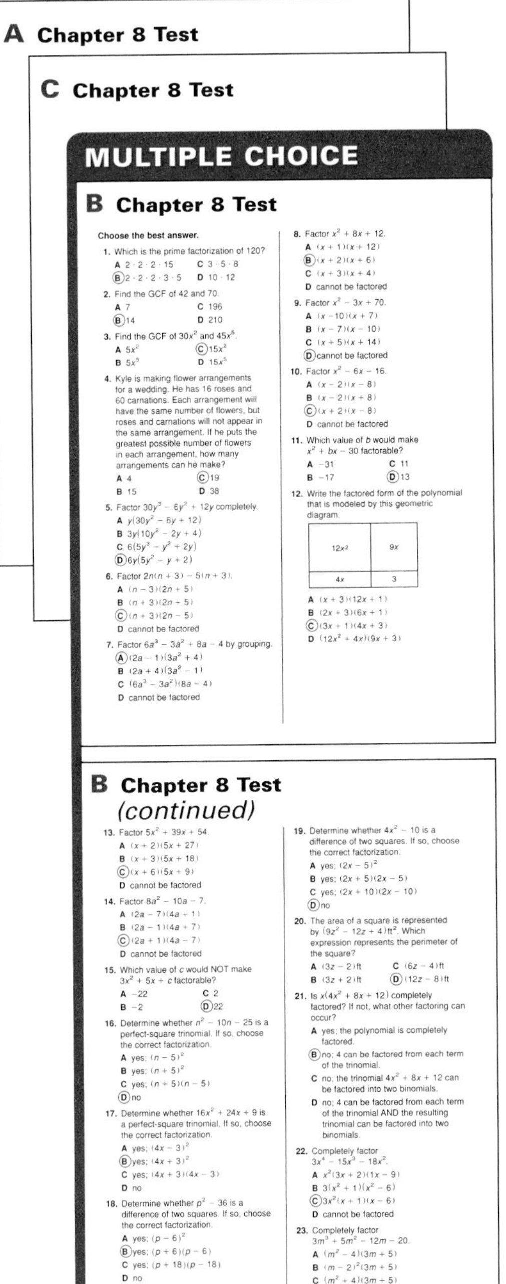

A Chapter 8 Test

C Chapter 8 Test

MULTIPLE CHOICE

B Chapter 8 Test

Choose the best answer.

1. Which is the prime factorization of 120?
   A $2 \cdot 2 \cdot 2 \cdot 15$ (B) $2 \cdot 2 \cdot 2 \cdot 3 \cdot 5$ C $3 \cdot 5 \cdot 8$ D $10 \cdot 12$
2. Find the GCF of 42 and 70.
   A 7 (B) 14 C 196 D 210
3. Find the GCF of $30x^2$ and $45x^5$.
   A $5x^2$ B $5x^5$ (C) $15x^2$ D $15x^5$
4. Kyle is making flower arrangements for a wedding. He has 16 roses and 60 carnations. Each arrangement will have the same number of flowers, but roses and carnations will not appear in the same arrangement. If he puts the greatest possible number of flowers in each arrangement, how many arrangements can he make?
   A 4 B 15 (C) 19 D 38
5. Factor $30y^3 - 6y^2 + 12y$ completely.
   A $y(30y^2 - 6y + 12)$
   B $3y(10y^2 - 2y + 4)$
   C $6(5y^3 - y^2 + 2y)$
   (D) $6y(5y^2 - y + 2)$
6. Factor $2n(n + 3) - 5(n + 3)$.
   A $(n - 3)(2n + 5)$
   B $(n + 3)(2n + 5)$
   (C) $(n + 3)(2n - 5)$
   D cannot be factored
7. Factor $6a^3 - 3a^2 + 8a - 4$ by grouping.
   (A) $(2a - 1)(3a^2 + 4)$
   B $(2a + 4)(3a^2 - 1)$
   C $(6a^3 - 3a^2)(8a - 4)$
   D cannot be factored
8. Factor $x^2 + 8x + 12$.
   A $(x + 1)(x + 12)$
   (B) $(x + 2)(x + 6)$
   C $(x + 3)(x + 4)$
   D cannot be factored
9. Factor $x^2 - 3x + 70$.
   A $(x - 10)(x + 7)$
   B $(x - 7)(x - 10)$
   C $(x + 5)(x + 14)$
   (D) cannot be factored
10. Factor $x^2 - 6x - 16$.
   A $(x - 2)(x - 8)$
   B $(x - 2)(x + 8)$
   (C) $(x + 2)(x - 8)$
   D cannot be factored
11. Which value of b would make $x^2 + bx - 30$ factorable?
   A -31 B -17 C 11 (D) 13
12. Write the factored form of the polynomial that is modeled by this geometric diagram.

$12x^2$	$9x$
$4x$	3

   A $(x + 3)(12x + 1)$
   B $(2x + 3)(6x + 1)$
   (C) $(3x + 1)(4x + 3)$
   D $(12x^2 + 4x)(9x + 3)$

B Chapter 8 Test *(continued)*

13. Factor $5x^2 + 39x + 54$.
   A $(x + 2)(5x + 27)$
   B $(x + 3)(5x + 18)$
   (C) $(x + 6)(5x + 9)$
   D cannot be factored
14. Factor $8a^2 - 10a - 7$.
   A $(2a - 7)(4a + 1)$
   B $(2a - 1)(4a + 7)$
   (C) $(2a + 1)(4a - 7)$
   D cannot be factored
15. Which value of c would NOT make $3x^2 + 5x + c$ factorable?
   A -22 B -2 C 2 (D) 22
16. Determine whether $n^2 - 10n - 25$ is a perfect-square trinomial. If so, choose the correct factorization.
   A yes; $(n - 5)^2$
   B yes; $(n + 5)^2$
   C yes; $(n + 5)(n - 5)$
   (D) no
17. Determine whether $16x^2 + 24x + 9$ is a perfect-square trinomial. If so, choose the correct factorization.
   A yes; $(4x - 3)^2$
   (B) yes; $(4x + 3)^2$
   C yes; $(4x + 3)(4x - 3)$
   D no
18. Determine whether $p^2 - 36$ is a difference of two squares. If so, choose the correct factorization.
   A yes; $(p - 6)^2$
   (B) yes; $(p + 6)(p - 6)$
   C yes; $(p + 18)(p - 18)$
   D no
19. Determine whether $4x^2 - 10$ is a difference of two squares. If so, choose the correct factorization.
   A yes; $(2x - 5)^2$
   B yes; $(2x + 5)(2x - 5)$
   C yes; $(2x + 10)(2x - 10)$
   (D) no
20. The area of a square is represented by $(9z^2 - 12z + 4)\text{ft}^2$. Which expression represents the perimeter of the square?
   A $(3z - 2)$ft B $(3z + 2)$ft C $(6z - 4)$ft (D) $(12z - 8)$ft
21. Is $x(4x^2 + 8x + 12)$ completely factored? If not, what other factoring can occur?
   A yes; the polynomial is completely factored.
   (B) no; 4 can be factored from each term of the trinomial.
   C no; the trinomial $4x^2 + 8x + 12$ can be factored into two binomials.
   D no; 4 can be factored from each term of the trinomial AND the resulting trinomial can be factored into two binomials.
22. Completely factor $3x^4 - 15x^3 - 18x^2$.
   A $x^2(3x + 2)(1x - 9)$
   B $3(x^2 + 1)(x^2 - 6)$
   (C) $3x^2(x + 1)(x - 6)$
   D cannot be factored
23. Completely factor $3m^3 + 5m^2 - 12m - 20$.
   A $(m^2 - 4)(3m + 5)$
   B $(m - 2)^2(3m + 5)$
   C $(m^2 + 4)(3m + 5)$
   (D) $(m + 2)(m - 2)(3m + 5)$

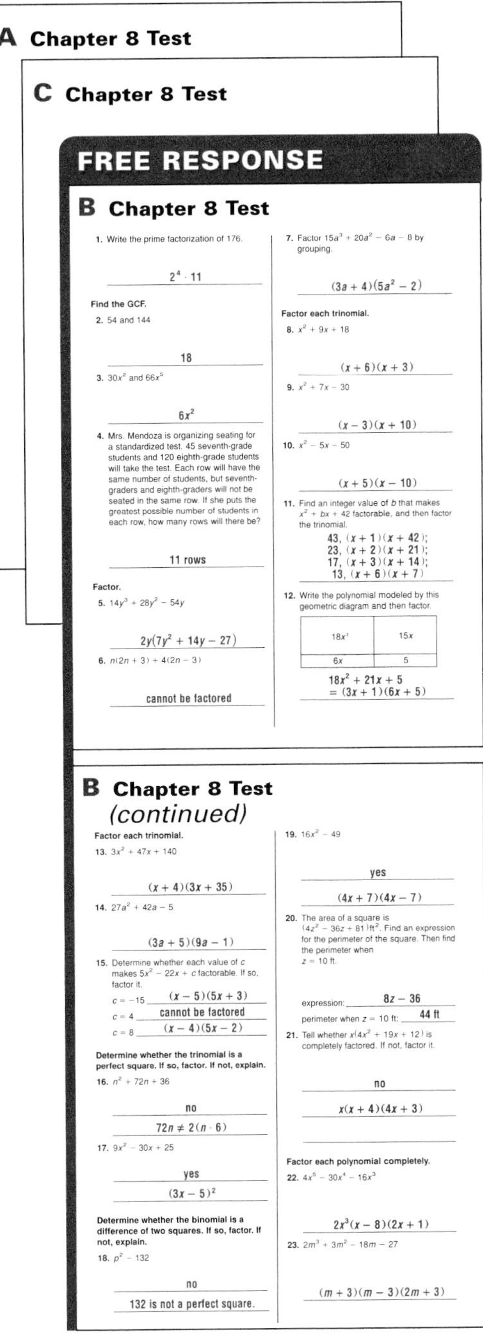

A Chapter 8 Test

C Chapter 8 Test

FREE RESPONSE

B Chapter 8 Test

1. Write the prime factorization of 176. **$2^4 \cdot 11$**

Find the GCF.

2. 54 and 144 **18**
3. $30x^2$ and $66x^5$ **$6x^2$**
4. Mrs. Mendoza is organizing seating for a standardized test. 45 seventh-grade students and 120 eighth-grade students will take the test. Each row will have the same number of students, but seventh-graders and eighth-graders will not be seated in the same row. If she puts the greatest possible number of students in each row, how many rows will there be? **11 rows**

Factor.

5. $14y^3 + 28y^2 - 54y$ **$2y(7y^2 + 14y - 27)$**
6. $n(2n + 3) + 4(2n - 3)$ **cannot be factored**
7. Factor $15a^3 + 20a^2 - 6a - 8$ by grouping. **$(3a + 4)(5a^2 - 2)$**

Factor each trinomial.

8. $x^2 + 9x + 18$ **$(x + 6)(x + 3)$**
9. $x^2 + 7x - 30$ **$(x - 3)(x + 10)$**
10. $x^2 - 5x - 50$ **$(x + 5)(x - 10)$**
11. Find an integer value of b that makes $x^2 + bx + 42$ factorable, and then factor the trinomial. **43, $(x + 1)(x + 42)$; 23, $(x + 2)(x + 21)$; 17, $(x + 3)(x + 14)$; 13, $(x + 6)(x + 7)$**
12. Write the polynomial modeled by this geometric diagram and then factor.

$18x^2$	$15x$
$6x$	5

$18x^2 + 21x + 5 = (3x + 1)(6x + 5)$

B Chapter 8 Test *(continued)*

Factor each trinomial.

13. $3x^2 + 47x + 140$ **$(x + 4)(3x + 35)$**
14. $27a^2 + 42a - 5$ **$(3a + 5)(9a - 1)$**
15. Determine whether each value of c makes $5x^2 - 22x + c$ factorable. If so, factor it.
   $c = -15$ **$(x - 5)(5x + 3)$**
   $c = 4$ **cannot be factored**
   $c = 8$ **$(x - 4)(5x - 2)$**

Determine whether the trinomial is a perfect square. If so, factor. If not, explain.

16. $n^2 + 72n + 36$ **no** **$72n \neq 2(n \cdot 6)$**
17. $9x^2 - 30x + 25$ **yes** **$(3x - 5)^2$**

Determine whether the binomial is a difference of two squares. If so, factor. If not, explain.

18. $p^2 - 132$ **no** **132 is not a perfect square.**
19. $16x^2 - 49$ **yes** **$(4x + 7)(4x - 7)$**
20. The area of a square is $(4z^2 - 36z + 81)\text{ft}^2$. Find an expression for the perimeter of the square. Then find the perimeter when $z = 10$ ft.
   expression: **$8z - 36$**
   perimeter when $z = 10$ ft: **44 ft**
21. Tell whether $x(4x^2 + 19x + 12)$ is completely factored. If not, factor it. **no** **$x(x + 4)(4x + 3)$**

Factor each polynomial completely.

22. $4x^5 - 30x^4 - 16x^3$ **$2x^3(x - 8)(2x + 1)$**
23. $2m^3 + 3m^2 - 18m - 27$ **$(m + 3)(m - 3)(2m + 3)$**

Modified tests and worksheets found in *IDEA Works!*

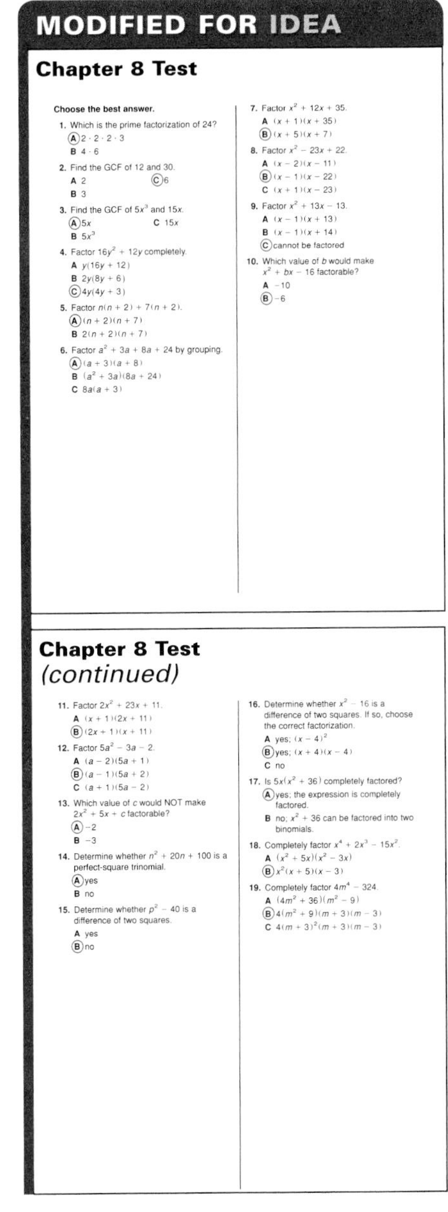

MODIFIED FOR IDEA

Chapter 8 Test

Choose the best answer.

1. Which is the prime factorization of 24?
   (A) $2 \cdot 2 \cdot 2 \cdot 3$
   B $4 \cdot 6$
2. Find the GCF of 12 and 30.
   A 2 B 3 (C) 6
3. Find the GCF of $5x^3$ and $15x$.
   (A) $5x$ B $5x^3$ C $15x$
4. Factor $16y^2 + 12y$ completely.
   A $y(16y + 12)$
   B $2y(8y + 6)$
   (C) $4y(4y + 3)$
5. Factor $n(n + 2) + 7(n + 2)$.
   (A) $(n + 2)(n + 7)$
   B $2(n + 2)(n + 7)$
6. Factor $a^2 + 3a + 8a + 24$ by grouping.
   (A) $(a + 3)(a + 8)$
   B $(a^2 + 3a)(8a + 24)$
   C $8a(a + 3)$
7. Factor $x^2 + 12x + 35$.
   A $(x + 1)(x + 35)$
   (B) $(x + 5)(x + 7)$
8. Factor $x^2 - 23x + 22$.
   A $(x - 2)(x - 11)$
   (B) $(x - 1)(x - 22)$
   C $(x + 1)(x - 23)$
9. Factor $x^2 + 13x - 13$.
   A $(x - 1)(x + 13)$
   B $(x - 1)(x + 14)$
   (C) cannot be factored
10. Which value of b would make $x^2 + bx - 16$ factorable?
   A -10
   (B) -6

Chapter 8 Test *(continued)*

11. Factor $2x^2 + 23x + 11$.
   A $(x + 1)(2x + 11)$
   (B) $(2x + 1)(x + 11)$
12. Factor $5a^2 - 3a - 2$.
   A $(a - 2)(5a + 1)$
   (B) $(a - 1)(5a + 2)$
   C $(a + 1)(5a - 2)$
13. Which value of c would NOT make $2x^2 + 5x + c$ factorable?
   (A) -2
   B -3
14. Determine whether $n^2 + 20n + 100$ is a perfect-square trinomial.
   (A) yes
   B no
15. Determine whether $p^2 - 40$ is a difference of two squares.
   A yes
   (B) no
16. Determine whether $x^2 - 16$ is a difference of two squares. If so, choose the correct factorization.
   A yes; $(x - 4)^2$
   (B) yes; $(x + 4)(x - 4)$
   C no
17. Is $5x(x^2 + 36)$ completely factored?
   (A) yes; the expression is completely factored.
   B no; $x^2 + 36$ can be factored into two binomials.
18. Completely factor $x^4 + 2x^3 - 15x^2$.
   A $(x^2 + 5x)(x^2 - 3x)$
   (B) $x^2(x + 5)(x - 3)$
19. Completely factor $4m^4 - 324$.
   A $(4m^2 + 36)(m^2 - 9)$
   (B) $4(m^2 + 9)(m + 3)(m - 3)$
   C $4(m + 3)^2(m + 3)(m - 3)$

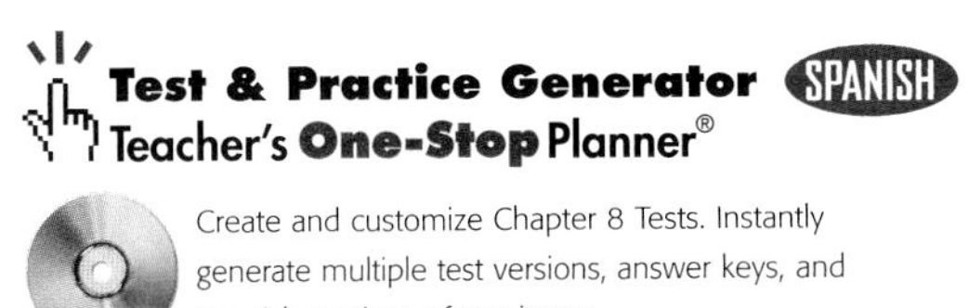

Create and customize Chapter 8 Tests. Instantly generate multiple test versions, answer keys, and Spanish versions of test items.

CHAPTER 8

SECTION **8A**
Factoring Methods

CONCEPT CONNECTION On page 512, students write and factor polynomials to model the distance traveled by an automobile.

Exercises designed to prepare students for success on the Concept Connection can be found on pages 483, 492, 501, and 510.

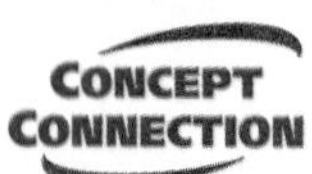

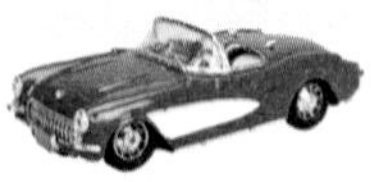

SECTION **8B**
Applying Factoring Methods

CONCEPT CONNECTION On page 528, students factor polynomials to model the dimensions of a garden.

Exercises designed to prepare students for success on the Concept Connection can be found on pages 519 and 526.

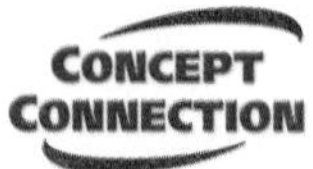

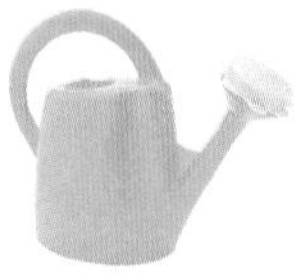

Algebra in *California*

Polynomials can be used to model areas. These polynomials can often be factored to find dimensions. Students will factor polynomials in Lessons 8-2 through 8-6 of this chapter.

CHAPTER 8

Factoring Polynomials

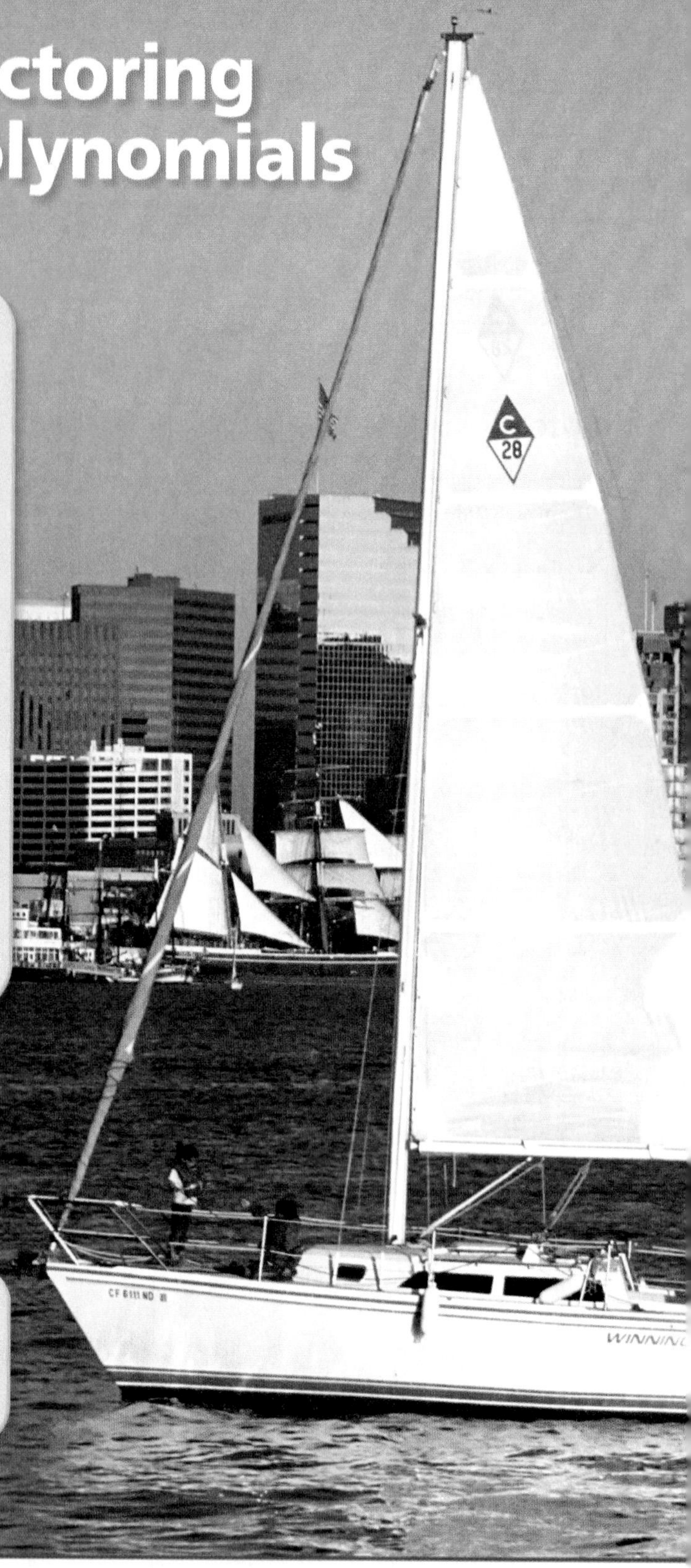

go.hrw.com
Chapter Project Online
KEYWORD: MA8CA ChProj

You can use polynomials to model area. When given the area of a sail as a polynomial, you can sometimes factor to find the sail's dimensions.

San Diego, CA

About the Project

High Fliers

In the Chapter Project, students use polynomials to model the area of kites and flags. When given an area expressed as a polynomial, students factor to find the dimensions of the kite or flag.

Project Resources

All project resources for teachers and students are provided online.

go.hrw.com
Project Teacher Support
KEYWORD: MA8CA ProjectTS

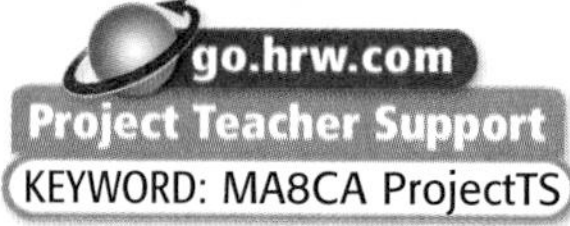

ARE YOU READY?

Vocabulary

Match each term on the left with a definition on the right.

1. binomial **B**
2. composite number **A**
3. factor **F**
4. multiple **C**
5. prime number **E**

A. a whole number greater than 1 that has more than two whole-number factors
B. a polynomial with two terms
C. the product of any number and a whole number
D. a number written as the product of its prime factors
E. a whole number greater than 1 that has exactly two positive factors, itself and 1
F. a number that is multiplied by another number to get a product

Multiples

Write the first four multiples of each number.

6. 3 **3, 6, 9, 12**
7. 4 **4, 8, 12, 16**
8. 8 **8, 16, 24, 32**
9. 15 **15, 30, 45, 60**

Factors

Tell whether the second number is a factor of the first number.

10. 20, 5 **yes**
11. 50, 6 **no**
12. 120, 8 **yes**
13. 245, 7 **yes**

Prime and Composite Numbers

Tell whether each number is prime or composite. If the number is composite, write it as the product of two numbers.

14. 2 **prime**
15. 7 **prime**
16. 10 **comp.; 10 = 2 • 5**
17. 38 **comp.; 38 = 2 • 19**
18. 115 **comp.; 115 = 5 • 23**
19. 147 **comp.; 147 = 21 • 7**
20. 151 **prime**
21. 93 **comp.; 93 = 3 • 31**

Multiply Monomials and Polynomials

Simplify.

22. $2(x + 5)$ **$2x + 10$**
23. $3h(h + 1)$ **$3h^2 + 3h$**
24. $xy(x^2 - xy^3)$ **$x^3y - x^2y^4$**
25. $6m(m^2 - 4m - 1)$ **$6m^3 - 24m^2 - 6m$**

Multiply Binomials

Find each product.

26. $(x + 3)(x + 8)$ **$x^2 + 11x + 24$**
27. $(b - 7)(b + 1)$ **$b^2 - 6b - 7$**
28. $(2p - 5)(p - 1)$ **$2p^2 - 7p + 5$**
29. $(3n + 4)(2n + 3)$ **$6n^2 + 17n + 12$**

ARE YOU READY? CHAPTER 8

Organizer

Objective: Assess students' understanding of prerequisite skills.

Prerequisite Skills

Multiples
Factors
Prime and Composite Numbers
Multiply Monomials and Polynomials
Multiply Binomials

Assessing Prior Knowledge

INTERVENTION

Diagnose and Prescribe

Use this page to determine whether intervention is necessary or whether enrichment is appropriate.

Resources

***Are You Ready? Intervention and Enrichment* Worksheets**

***Are You Ready?* CD-ROM**

***Are You Ready?* Online**

my.hrw.com

ARE YOU READY?
Diagnose and Prescribe

NO INTERVENE

Prerequisite Skill	*Are You Ready? Intervention,* Chapter 8: Worksheets	CD-ROM	Online
Multiples	Skill 1	Activity 1	Diagnose and Prescribe Online
Factors	Skill 3	Activity 3	
Prime and Composite Numbers	Skill 5	Activity 5	
Multiply Monomials and Polynomials	Skill 62	Activity 62	
Multiply Binomials	Skill 64	Activity 64	

YES ENRICH

Are You Ready? Enrichment, Chapter 8

Worksheets

CD-ROM

Online

Unpacking the Standards

Organizer

Objective: Help students understand the new concepts they will learn in Chapter 8.

Academic Vocabulary Connections

Becoming familiar with the academic vocabulary on this student page will be helpful to students. Discussing some of the vocabulary terms in the chapter also may be helpful.

1. List some words that end with the suffixes *-ize* or *-ization*. What does the ending *-ization* seem to mean? What do you think **factorization** means? Possible answers: civilize/civilization, optimize/optimization; the result of an action; the result when something is factored
2. The words *prime*, *primary*, and *primitive* all come from the same root word. What are the meanings of these words? How can their meanings help you understand what a **prime factor** is? The main part; fundamental; early stage of development; a prime factor is a basic building block of the product.
3. What does the word *common* mean? How can you use this meaning to understand the term **greatest common factor**? *Common* means "alike." The greatest common factor of 2 or more numbers is the greatest factor that the numbers share.

CHAPTER 8

Unpacking the Standards

The information below "unpacks" the standards. The Academic Vocabulary is highlighted and defined to help you understand the language of the standards. Refer to the lessons listed after each standard for help with the math terms and phrases. The Chapter Concept shows how the standard is applied in this chapter.

California Standard	Academic Vocabulary	Chapter Concept
11.0 Students apply basic factoring techniques to second- and simple third-degree polynomials. These techniques include finding a common factor for all terms in a polynomial, recognizing the difference of two squares, and recognizing perfect squares of binomials. (Lessons **8-2, 8-3, 8-5, 8-6;** Labs **8-2, 8-3**)	**apply** use **technique** a way of doing something **common** shared among all members of a group	You learn several ways to rewrite polynomials as products. ***Example:*** $x^2 + 3x$ Both terms in the polynomial contain the common term x, so the polynomial can be factored. $x^2 + 3x = x(x + 3)$
25.1 Students use properties of numbers to construct simple, valid arguments (direct and **indirect**) for, or formulate counterexamples to, **claimed assertions.** (pp. 484–485)	**construct** make or prepare **valid** true and correct **assertion** a statement that is made without proof	You learn a new method, indirect proof, for proving a mathematical statement.

Looking Back

Previously, students

- found factors and greatest common factors of numbers.
- added, subtracted, and multiplied polynomials.

In This Chapter

Students will study

- factors and greatest common factors of polynomials.
- how to write a polynomial as a product.

Looking Forward

Students can use these skills

- when solving quadratic equations by factoring.
- when dividing polynomials.

Reading Strategy: Read a Lesson for Understanding

To help you learn new concepts, you should read each lesson with a purpose. As you read a lesson, make notes. Include the main ideas of the lesson and any questions you have. In class, listen for explanations of the vocabulary, clarification of the examples, and answers to your questions.

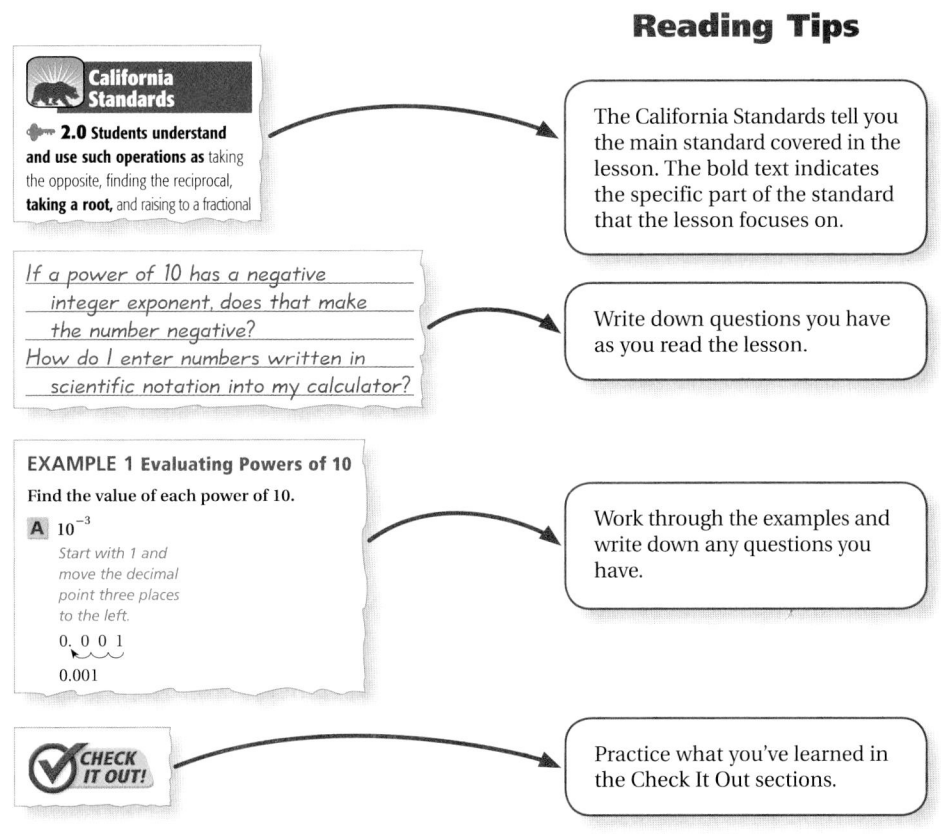

Reading Tips

California Standards

2.0 Students understand and use such operations as taking the opposite, finding the reciprocal, **taking a root,** and raising to a fractional

The California Standards tell you the main standard covered in the lesson. The bold text indicates the specific part of the standard that the lesson focuses on.

If a power of 10 has a negative integer exponent, does that make the number negative?
How do I enter numbers written in scientific notation into my calculator?

Write down questions you have as you read the lesson.

EXAMPLE 1 Evaluating Powers of 10

Find the value of each power of 10.

A 10^{-3}

Start with 1 and move the decimal point three places to the left.

0. 0 0 1

0.001

Work through the examples and write down any questions you have.

Practice what you've learned in the Check It Out sections.

Read Lesson 8-1 prior to your next class. Then answer the questions below.

1. What vocabulary, formulas, and symbols are new?
2. Which examples, if any, are unclear?
3. What questions do you have about the lesson?

Reading and Writing Math CHAPTER 8

Organizer

Objective: Help students apply strategies to understand and retain key concepts.

Resources

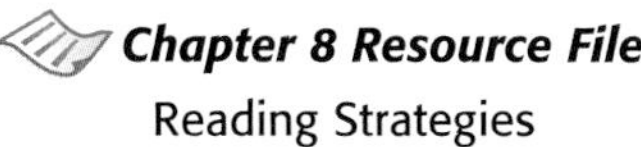

Reading Strategies

ENGLISH LANGUAGE LEARNERS

Reading Strategy: Read a Lesson for Understanding

Discuss Tell students that they may actually save themselves time in the long run because they won't struggle as much with the next day's homework.

Discuss with students what options they have if there is not enough time during class to ask a question. Students may need to ask a classmate or talk to the teacher after class or after school.

Extend Before each lesson in Chapter 8, students should read the lesson and make notes similar to those shown on this page. Tell students to make sure that all their questions are answered before they start their homework.

Answers to *Try This*

1. prime factorization, greatest common factor
2. Check students' work.
3. Check students' work.

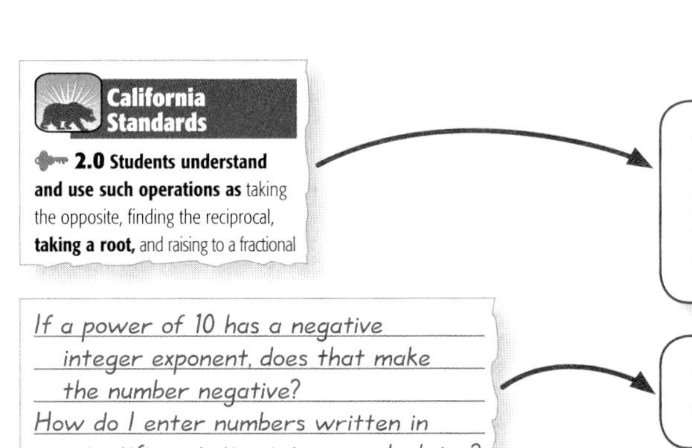

Factoring Methods

One-Minute Section Planner

Lesson	Lab Resources	Materials
Lesson 8-1 Factors and Greatest Common Factors • Write the prime factorization of numbers. • Find the GCF of monomials. **Preparation for 11.0**		**Optional** colored counters (MK)
8-2 Algebra Lab Model Factorization by GCF • Use algebra tiles to model and factor polynomials. **11.0**		**Required** algebra tiles (MK)
Lesson 8-2 Factoring by GCF • Factor polynomials by using the greatest common factor. **11.0**		**Optional** algebra tiles (MK)
8-3 Algebra Lab Model Factorization of $x^2 + bx + c$ • Model and factor trinomials of the form $x^2 + bx + c$. **11.0**		**Required** algebra tiles (MK) **Optional** transparency mat, transparency algebra tiles (MK)
Lesson 8-3 Factoring $x^2 + bx + c$ • Factor quadratic trinomials of the form $x^2 + bx + c$. **11.0**		
8-4 Algebra Lab Model Factorization of $ax^2 + bx + c$ • Model and factor trinomials of the form $ax^2 + bx + c$. **11.0**		**Required** algebra tiles (MK) **Optional** transparency mat, transparency algebra tiles (MK)
Lesson 8-4 Factoring $ax^2 + bx + c$ • Factor quadratic trinomials of the form $ax^2 + bx + c$. **11.0**		**Optional** algebra tiles (MK)

MK = *Manipulatives Kit*

Notes

Math Background: Teaching the Standards

FACTORING NUMBERS  11.0

Lesson 8-1

Understanding factoring begins with an understanding of prime numbers. We define a *prime number* as a whole number greater than 1 that has exactly two whole numbers as factors, itself and 1. The first few prime numbers form the familiar sequence 2, 3, 5, 7, 11, ...

More than 2000 years ago, Euclid proved that there are infinitely many prime numbers. His proof went as follows: Suppose there were a finite number of primes. Then they could be listed in their entirety as $p_1, p_2, ..., p_n$. Consider the number that is the product of all the primes plus one; that is, $p_1 \cdot p_2 \cdot ... \cdot p_n + 1$. This number is not divisible by any of the primes in the list since division by any of these primes would result in a remainder of 1. This means that the number itself must be prime. However, it is greater than any of the primes in the list, so it cannot be one of the primes in the list. This contradicts the assumption that the list includes all of the primes. Thus, the original assumption that there is a finite number of primes must be false.

THE FUNDAMENTAL THEOREM OF ARITHMETIC

Lesson 8-1

The Fundamental Theorem of Arithmetic (also known as the Unique Factorization Theorem) states that every whole number greater than 1 is either a prime number or may be written as a unique product of prime numbers. For example, the number 495 may be written as the product $3 \cdot 3 \cdot 5 \cdot 11$ (or $3^2 \cdot 5 \cdot 11$), and the Fundamental Theorem of Arithmetic asserts that this is the *only* prime factorization, with the exception of different orderings of the factors. One result of this theorem is that when finding the prime factorization of the same number, two students may use very different methods, but in the end they will always arrive at the same prime factors.

The proof of the theorem has two parts: showing that every whole number greater than 1 may be written as a product of primes and showing that this factorization is unique.

The first part is straightforward. Suppose there were one or more whole numbers greater than 1 that could not be written as a product of prime numbers. Let k be the least of all such numbers. Then k cannot be prime, since every prime number is the product of a single prime (namely, itself). Thus, k must be composite and so $k = ab$ where a and b are whole numbers less than k. Since k was taken to be the least whole number that cannot be written as a product of primes, we know that a and b can be written as a product of primes: $a = p_1 \cdot p_2 \cdot ... \cdot p_m$ and $b = q_1 \cdot q_2 \cdot ... \cdot q_n$. So $k = p_1 \cdot p_2 \cdot ... \cdot p_m \cdot q_1 \cdot q_2 \cdot ... \cdot q_n$, which contradicts the initial assumption that k cannot be written as a product of prime numbers. Thus, every whole number greater than 1 must have a prime factorization.

The proof that the prime factorization is unique requires some basic number theory and will not be provided here, but it is worth noting that the standard proof is once again an indirect proof (proof by contradiction).

Students sometimes wonder why 1 is not considered prime. One reason is the fact that including 1 among the prime numbers would mean that prime factorizations are no longer unique. For example, we could write $495 = 1 \cdot 3^2 \cdot 5 \cdot 11$, $495 = 1^2 \cdot 3^2 \cdot 5 \cdot 11$, and so on.

However, it *is* possible to consider negative factors, and in fact, students must consider negative factors when factoring polynomials. From this perspective, a prime number p has exactly four factors (p, $-p$, 1, and -1) and integers such as -5 and -17 would be considered prime. The Fundamental Theorem of Arithmetic would no longer hold, however. For example, the number 18 could be written as a product of primes as $2 \cdot 3^2$ or $2 \cdot (-3)^2$.

Finally, prime factorization gives a convenient method of identifying *all* whole number factors of a number. For example, any factor of 495 must have the form $3^k \cdot 5^m \cdot 11^n$, where $k = 0$, 1, or 2, $m = 0$ or 1, and $n = 0$ or 1. Taking the various combinations shows that the whole number factors of 495 are 1, 3, 5, 9, 11, 15, 33, 45, 55, 99, 165, and 495.

8-1 Organizer

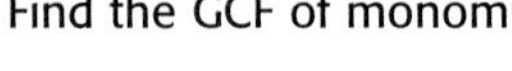

Objectives: Write the prime factorization of numbers.

Find the GCF of monomials.

Online Edition
Tutorial Videos

Countdown to Mastery Week 17

Power Presentations with PowerPoint®

Warm Up

Tell whether the second number is a factor of the first number.

1. 50, 6 no **2.** 105, 7 yes

3. List the factors of 28. ±1, ±2, ±4, ±7, ±14, ±28

Tell whether each number is prime or composite. If the number is composite, write it as the product of two numbers.

4. 11 prime

5. 98 composite; 49 • 2

Also available on transparency

Math Humor

Q: Why couldn't 2 get along with the odd numbers?

A: They had nothing in common.

8-1 Factors and Greatest Common Factors

California Standards

Preparation for 11.0 Students apply basic factoring techniques to second- and simple third-degree polynomials. These techniques include **finding a common factor** for all terms in a polynomial, recognizing the difference of two squares, and recognizing perfect squares of binomials.

Vocabulary
prime factorization
greatest common factor

Who uses this?
Web site designers who sell electronic greeting cards can use greatest common factors to design their Web sites. (See Example 4.)

The numbers that are multiplied to find a product are called *factors* of that product. A number is divisible by its factors.

Remember that a *prime number* is a whole number that has exactly two positive factors, itself and 1. The number 1 is not prime because it has only one factor.

You can use the factors of a number to write the number as a product. The number 12 can be factored several ways.

The order of the factors does not change the product, but there is only one example that cannot be factored further. The circled factorization is the **prime factorization** because all the factors are prime numbers. The prime factors can be written in any order, and, except for changes in the order, there is only one way to write the prime factorization of a number.

Factorizations of 12

1 • 12
2 • 6
3 • 4
1 • 4 • 3
(2 • 2 • 3)

EXAMPLE 1 Writing Prime Factorizations

Write the prime factorization of 60.

Method 1 Factor tree

Choose any two factors of 60 to begin. Keep finding factors until each branch ends in a prime factor.

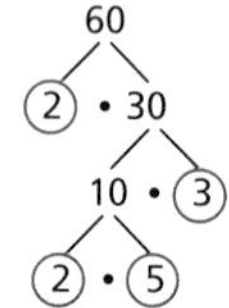

$60 = 2 \cdot 2 \cdot 5 \cdot 3$

Method 2 Ladder diagram

Choose a prime factor of 60 to begin. Keep dividing by prime factors until the quotient is 1.

2 | 60
3 | 30
2 | 10
5 | 5
1

$60 = 2 \cdot 3 \cdot 2 \cdot 5$

The prime factorization of 60 is $2 \cdot 2 \cdot 3 \cdot 5$ or $2^2 \cdot 3 \cdot 5$.

Write the prime factorization of each number.

1a. 40 $2^3 \cdot 5$ **1b.** 33 $3 \cdot 11$ **1c.** 49 7^2 **1d.** 19 19

1 Introduce

EXPLORATION

8-1 Factors and Greatest Common Factors

An artist is planning to create two large rectangular paintings for the lobby of a museum.

1. One of the paintings is to have an area of 24 ft². The height and width of the painting will be whole numbers. List all the possible heights and widths. (You may not need all of the columns of the table.)

Height (ft)	1	2							
Width (ft)	24	12							

2. The other painting is to have an area of 18 ft². The height and width of the painting will be whole numbers. List all the possible heights and widths. (You may not need all of the columns of the table.)

Height (ft)									
Width (ft)									

3. The artist wants the two paintings to have the same height. What are the possible heights?
4. The artist decides to make the two paintings the same height and as tall as possible. What should the height of the paintings be?

THINK AND DISCUSS

5. **Explain** how the heights in the tables are related to the areas of the paintings.
6. **Explain** whether it is possible to make both paintings 12 feet

Motivate

Ask students what it means for two people to have something in common (e.g., to have the same hair color, belong to the same club, etc.). Then ask students what it means for two numbers to have a common factor. What would the greatest common factor of two numbers be? Tell students that in this lesson, they will learn how to find the greatest common factor of numbers and monomials.

Explorations and answers are provided in *Alternate Openers: Explorations Transparencies*.

California Standards

Preparation for 11.0

Factors that are shared by two or more whole numbers are called common factors. The greatest of these common factors is called the **greatest common factor**, or GCF.

Factors of 12: 1, 2, 3, 4, 6, 12
Factors of 32: 1, 2, 4, 8, 16, 32
Common factors: 1, 2, (4)
The greatest of the common factors is 4.

EXAMPLE 2 Finding the GCF of Numbers

Find the GCF of each pair of numbers.

A 24 and 60

Method 1 List the factors.

factors of 24: 1, 2, 3, 4, 6, 8, (12), 24 — *List all the factors.*
factors of 60: 1, 2, 3, 4, 5, 6, 10, (12), 15, 20, 30, 60 — *Circle the GCF.*

The GCF of 24 and 60 is 12.

B 18 and 27

Method 2 Use prime factorization.

$18 = 2 \cdot \boxed{3} \cdot \boxed{3}$ — *Write the prime factorization of each number.*
$27 = \boxed{3} \cdot \boxed{3} \cdot 3$ — *Align the common factors.*
$3 \cdot 3 = 9$

The GCF of 18 and 27 is 9.

CHECK IT OUT! Find the GCF of each pair of numbers.
2a. 12 and 16 **4** **2b.** 15 and 25 **5**

You can also find the GCF of monomials that include variables. To find the GCF of monomials, write the prime factorization of each coefficient and write all powers of variables as products. Then find the product of the common factors.

EXAMPLE 3 Finding the GCF of Monomials

Find the GCF of each pair of monomials.

A $3x^3$ and $6x^2$

$3x^3 = \boxed{3} \cdot \boxed{x} \cdot \boxed{x} \cdot x$ — *Write the prime factorization of each coefficient and write powers as products.*
$6x^2 = 2 \cdot \boxed{3} \cdot \boxed{x} \cdot \boxed{x}$ — *Align the common factors.*
$3 \cdot x \cdot x = 3x^2$ — *Find the product of the common factors.*

The GCF of $3x^3$ and $6x^2$ is $3x^2$.

B $4x^2$ and $5y^3$

$4x^2 = 2 \cdot 2 \cdot x \cdot x$ — *Write the prime factorization of each coefficient and write powers as products.*
$5y^3 = 5 \cdot y \cdot y \cdot y$ — *Align the common factors. There are no common factors other than 1.*

The GCF of $4x^2$ and $5y^3$ is 1.

Helpful Hint

If two terms contain the same variable raised to different powers, the GCF will contain that variable raised to the lower power.

CHECK IT OUT! Find the GCF of each pair of monomials.
3a. $18g^2$ and $27g^3$ $9g^2$ **3b.** $16a^6$ and $9b$ **1** **3c.** $8x$ and $7v^2$ **1**

2 Teach

Guided Instruction

Review prime and composite numbers. Show students that different factor trees can be drawn for some numbers, but they all give the same prime factorization. Show that the GCF of two numbers or monomials is the largest term that divides into both of the numbers or monomials.

Universal Access

Through Number Sense

Discuss with students how to quickly find the GCF of two numbers. If one number is a factor of the greater number, it is the GCF of the two numbers. If not, then check the factors of the smaller number from largest to smallest until one is a factor of the greater number. This is the GCF of the two numbers.

COMMON ERROR ALERT

In **Example 1,** when using a ladder diagram to find the prime factorization of a number, students might include 1 as a prime factor. Remind students that 1 is not a prime number.

Power Presentations with PowerPoint®

Additional Examples

Example 1

Write the prime factorization of 98. $2 \cdot 7^2$

Example 2

Find the GCF of each pair of numbers.

A. 100 and 60 20

B. 26 and 52 26

Example 3

Find the GCF of each pair of monomials.

A. $15x^3$ and $9x^2$ $3x^2$

B. $8x^2$ and $7y^3$ 1

Also available on transparency

INTERVENTION

Questioning Strategies

EXAMPLE 1

- Is the order of the prime factors important?
- How can you check your answer?

EXAMPLE 2

- How can you determine whether you have found all the factors of a number when using Method 1?
- Can the GCF of two numbers be one of the numbers? Explain.

EXAMPLE 3

- If two terms contain the same variable raised to different powers, what power of the variable will the GCF include? Explain.
- What happens if the monomials do not contain the same variable?

Power Presentations with PowerPoint®

Additional Examples

Example 4

A cafeteria has 18 chocolate-milk cartons and 24 regular-milk cartons. The cook wants to arrange the cartons with the same number of cartons in each row. Chocolate and regular milk will not be in the same row. How many rows will there be if the cook puts the greatest possible number of cartons in each row?

7

Also available on transparency

INTERVENTION

Questioning Strategies

EXAMPLE 4

- Is the GCF the answer to the problem? Explain.

Teaching Tip **Concrete Manipulatives** Suggest that students use different colored counters to model the items in **Example 4.** These can be found in the Manipulatives Kit (MK).

EXAMPLE 4 ***Technology Application***

Garrison is creating a Web page that offers electronic greeting cards. He has 24 special occasion designs and 42 birthday designs. The cards will be displayed with the same number of designs in each row. Special occasion and birthday designs will not appear in the same row. How many rows will there be if Garrison puts the greatest possible number of designs in each row?

The 24 special occasion designs and 42 birthday designs must be divided into groups of equal size. The number of designs in each row must be a common factor of 24 and 42.

factors of 24: 1, 2, 3, 4, (6), 8, 12, 24
factors of 42: 1, 2, 3, (6), 7, 14, 21, 42

Find the common factors of 24 and 42.

The GCF of 24 and 42 is 6.

The greatest possible number of designs in each row is 6. Find the number of rows of each group of designs when there are 6 designs in each row.

$$\frac{24 \text{ special occasion designs}}{6 \text{ designs per row}} = 4 \text{ rows}$$

$$\frac{42 \text{ birthday designs}}{6 \text{ designs per row}} = 7 \text{ rows}$$

When the greatest possible number of designs is in each row, there are 11 rows in total.

4. Adrianne is shopping for a CD storage unit. She has 36 CDs by pop music artists and 48 CDs by country music artists. She wants to put the same number of CDs on each shelf without putting pop music and country music CDs on the same shelf. If Adrianne puts the greatest possible number of CDs on each shelf, how many shelves does her storage unit need? 7

THINK AND DISCUSS

1. Describe two ways you can find the prime factorization of a number.

2. GET ORGANIZED Copy and complete the graphic organizer. Show how to write the prime factorization of $100x^2$ by filling in each box.

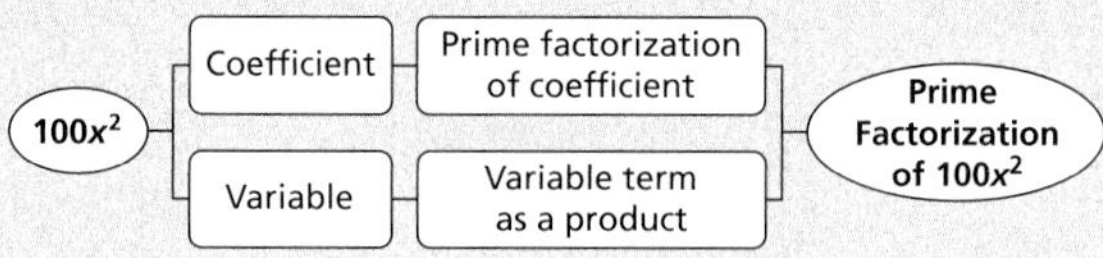

3 Close

Summarize

Have students find the GCF of the following.

56 and 70 14
15 and 30 15
35 and 24 1
$36x^3$ and $50x$ $2x$
$10x^2$ and $25x^4y^2$ $5x^2$

FORMATIVE ASSESSMENT and INTERVENTION

***Diagnose Before* the Lesson**
8-1 Warm Up, TE p. 478

***Monitor During* the Lesson**
Check It Out! Exercises, SE pp. 478–480
Questioning Strategies, TE pp. 479–480

***Assess After* the Lesson**
8-1 Lesson Quiz, TE p. 483
Alternative Assessment, TE p. 483

Answers to *Think and Discuss*

1. Use a factor tree or divide the number by prime factors until the quotient is 1.
2. See p. A6.

8-1 Exercises

California Standards Practice
10.0, Prep for 11.0, 15.0, 25.1

go.hrw.com
Homework Help Online
KEYWORD: MA8CA 8-1
Parent Resources Online
KEYWORD: MA8CA Parent

GUIDED PRACTICE

1. **Vocabulary** Define the term *greatest common factor* in your own words.
Possible answer: the greatest number that is a factor of two given numbers

SEE EXAMPLE 1 p. 478

Write the prime factorization of each number.

2. 20 $2^2 \cdot 5$
3. 36 $3^2 \cdot 2^2$
4. 27 3^3
5. 54 $3^3 \cdot 2$
6. 96 $2^5 \cdot 3$
7. 7 **7**
8. 100 $2^2 \cdot 5^2$
9. 75 $3 \cdot 5^2$

SEE EXAMPLE 2 p. 479

Find the GCF of each pair of numbers.

10. 12 and 60 **12**
11. 14 and 49 **7**
12. 55 and 121 **11**
13. 21 and 14 **7**
14. 13 and 40 **1**
15. 72 and 18 **18**

SEE EXAMPLE 3 p. 479

Find the GCF of each pair of monomials.

16. $15y^3$ and $-20y$ $5y$
17. $6x^2$ and $5x^2$ x^2
18. $12r$ and $30r^2$ $6r$
19. $2x^3$ and 6 **2**
20. $35a^2$ and $6a^3$ a^2
21. $13q^4$ and $2p^2$ **1**

SEE EXAMPLE 4 p. 480

22. Samantha is making beaded necklaces using 54 glass beads and 18 clay beads. She wants each necklace to have the same number of beads, but each necklace will have only one type of bead. If she puts the greatest possible number of beads on each necklace, how many necklaces can she make? **4**

PRACTICE AND PROBLEM SOLVING

Independent Practice

For Exercises	See Example
23–30	1
31–36	2
37–42	3
43	4

Extra Practice
Skills Practice p. EP16
Application Practice p. EP31

Write the prime factorization of each number.

23. 18 $2 \cdot 3^2$
24. 64 2^6
25. 12 $2^2 \cdot 3$
26. 150 $2 \cdot 3 \cdot 5^2$
27. 17 **17**
28. 226 $2 \cdot 113$
29. 49 7^2
30. 63 $3^2 \cdot 7$

Find the GCF of each pair of numbers.

31. 36 and 63 **9**
32. 14 and 15 **1**
33. 30 and 40 **10**
34. 15 and 75 **15**
35. 18 and 22 **2**
36. 16 and 99 **1**

Find the GCF of each pair of monomials.

37. $9s$ and $63s^3$ $9s$
38. $8a^2$ and 11 **1**
39. $-36w^3$ and $15w^2$ $3w^2$
40. $5b^2$ and $3b$ b
41. $3x^2$ and $9x$ $3x$
42. $-64n^4$ and $24n^2$ $8n^2$

43. José is making fruit-filled tart shells for a party. He has 72 raspberries and 108 blueberries. The tarts will each have the same number of berries. Raspberries and blueberries will not be in the same tart. If he puts the greatest possible number of berries in each tart, how many tarts can he make? **5**

Find the GCF of each pair of products.

44. $3 \cdot 5 \cdot t$ and $2 \cdot 2 \cdot 5 \cdot t \cdot t$ $5t$
45. $-1 \cdot 2 \cdot 2 \cdot x \cdot x$ and $2 \cdot 2 \cdot 7 \cdot x \cdot x \cdot x$ $4x^2$
46. $2 \cdot 2 \cdot 2 \cdot 11 \cdot x \cdot x \cdot x$ and $3 \cdot 11$ **11**
47. $2 \cdot 5 \cdot n \cdot n \cdot n$ and $-1 \cdot 2 \cdot 3 \cdot n$ $2n$

48. **Write About It** Explain why the number 2 is the only even prime number.
49. **Reasoning** Show that the following statement is true or provide a counterexample to show it is false. If the GCF of two numbers is 1, then the two numbers are prime.

48. Possible answer: Even numbers greater than 2 all have 2 as a factor and thus are not prime.

49. No; 2 comp. numbers could share no common factors other than 1.

8-1 Exercises

Assignment Guide

Assign *Guided Practice* exercises as necessary.

If you finished Examples **1–2**
Proficient 23–36, 52–58, 62–67, 81
Advanced 23–36, 52–58, 62–67, 81

If you finished Examples **1–4**
Proficient 23–58, 69–72, 74–80 even, 81–85
Advanced 23–51, 52–58 even, 69–85

Homework Quick Check
Quickly check key concepts.
Exercises: 26, 32, 42, 43, 44, 50

California Standards

Standard	Exercises
8.0	82, 83
10.0	85
Prep for 11.0	10–22, 31–47, 50, 51, 68, 69, 73–81
15.0	69
25.1	49

Teaching Tip

Multiple Representations Suggest to students that they put the information in **Exercise 50** in a table to better organize their work, listing the lengths in increasing order.

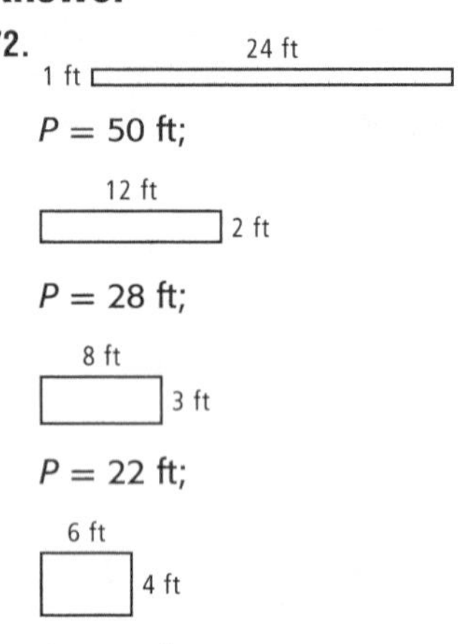

ℓ	w	P
1	84	170
2		
3		

Answer

72. 1 ft × 24 ft

$P = 50$ ft;

12 ft × 2 ft

$P = 28$ ft;

8 ft × 3 ft

$P = 22$ ft;

6 ft × 4 ft

$P = 20$ ft;

Patricia should make the pen 4 ft × 6 ft because these dimensions give the shortest perimeter and she will need to buy the least fencing.

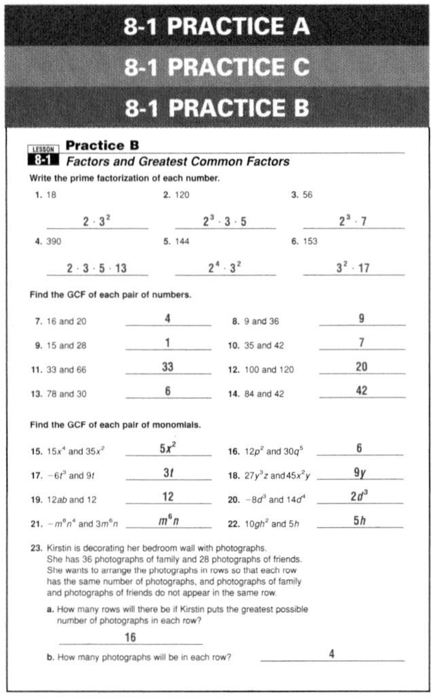

8-1 PRACTICE A

8-1 PRACTICE C

8-1 PRACTICE B

LESSON 8-1 **Practice B**
Factors and Greatest Common Factors

Write the prime factorization of each number.

1. 18 $2 \cdot 3^2$
2. 120 $2^3 \cdot 3 \cdot 5$
3. 56 $2^3 \cdot 7$
4. 390 $2 \cdot 3 \cdot 5 \cdot 13$
5. 144 $2^4 \cdot 3^2$
6. 153 $3^2 \cdot 17$

Find the GCF of each pair of numbers.

7. 16 and 20 4
8. 9 and 36 9
9. 15 and 28 1
10. 35 and 42 7
11. 33 and 66 33
12. 100 and 120 20
13. 78 and 30 6
14. 84 and 42 42

Find the GCF of each pair of monomials.

15. $15x^4$ and $35x^2$ $5x^2$
16. $12p^2$ and $30q^5$ 6
17. $-6t^3$ and $9t$ $3t$
18. $27y^3z$ and $45x^3y$ $9y$
19. $12ab$ and 12 12
20. $-8d^3$ and $14d^4$ $2d^3$
21. $-m^4n^4$ and $3m^6n$ m^4n
22. $10gh^2$ and $5h$ $5h$

23. Kirstin is decorating her bedroom wall with photographs. She has 36 photographs of family and 28 photographs of friends. She wants to arrange the photographs in rows so that each row has the same number of photographs, and photographs of family and photographs of friends do not appear in the same row.

a. How many rows will there be if Kirstin puts the greatest possible number of photographs in each row? 16

b. How many photographs will be in each row? 4

LINK

Music

DCI is a nonprofit organization that oversees drum and bugle corps performances and competitions for youths between the ages of 14 and 21.

50a. 1×84, 2×42, 3×28, 4×21, 6×14, 7×12

50. Multi-Step Angelo is making a rectangular floor for a clubhouse with an area of 84 square feet. The length of each side of the floor is a whole number of feet.

a. What are the possible lengths and widths for Angelo's clubhouse floor?

b. What is the minimum perimeter for the clubhouse floor? **38 ft**

c. What is the maximum perimeter for the clubhouse floor? **170 ft**

51. Music The Cavaliers and the Blue Devils are two of the marching bands that are members of Drum Corps International (DCI). DCI bands are made up of percussionists, brass players, and color guard members who use flags and other props.

In 2004, there were 35 color guard members in the Cavaliers and 40 in the Blue Devils. The two color guards will march in rows with the same number of people in each row without mixing the guards together. If the greatest possible number of people are in each row, how many rows will there be? **15 rows**

For each set of numbers, determine which two numbers have a GCF greater than 1, and find that GCF.

52. 11, 12, 14 **12 and 14; 2**
53. 8, 20, 63 **8 and 20; 4**
54. 16, 21, 27 **21 and 27; 3**
55. 32, 63, 105 **63 and 105; 21**
56. 25, 35, 54 **25 and 35; 5**
57. 35, 54, 72 **54 and 72; 18**

58. Number Sense The prime factorization of 24 is $2^3 \cdot 3$. Without performing any calculations or using a diagram, write the prime factorization of 48. Explain your reasoning. **$2^4 \cdot 3$; possible answer: because $48 = 2 \cdot 24$ and $24 = 2^3 \cdot 3$, $48 = 2 \cdot 2^3 \cdot 3 = 2^4 \cdot 3$.**

Fill in each diagram. Then write the prime factorization of the number.

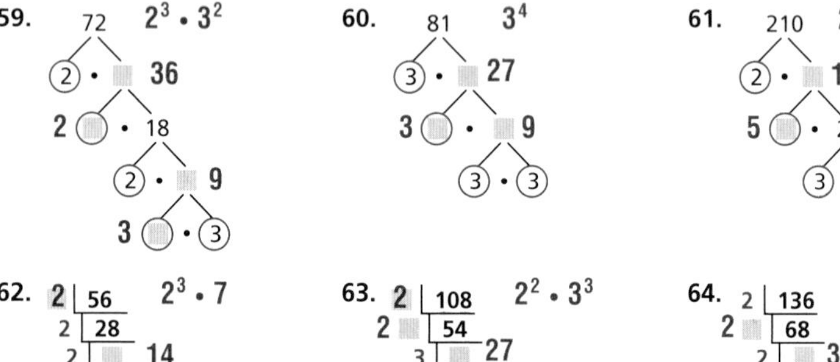

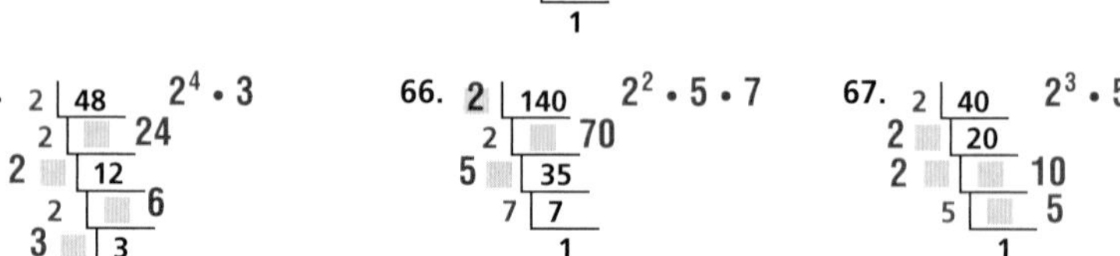

65. 2 | 48 $2^4 \cdot 3$
2 | 24
2 | 12
2 | 6
3 | 3
1

66. 2 | 140 $2^2 \cdot 5 \cdot 7$
2 | 70
5 | 35
7 | 7
1

67. 2 | 40 $2^3 \cdot 5$
2 | 20
2 | 10
5 | 5
1

68. Kate has $12a^2$ raffle tickets and Henry has $18a$ raffle tickets. Kate makes equal piles using all of her tickets. Henry makes equal piles using all of his tickets. Henry and Kate have the same number of piles.

a. Write an expression for the greatest number of piles that Kate and Henry can have. **$6a$**

b. How many tickets will be in each of Kate's piles? in each of Henry's? **$2a$; 3**

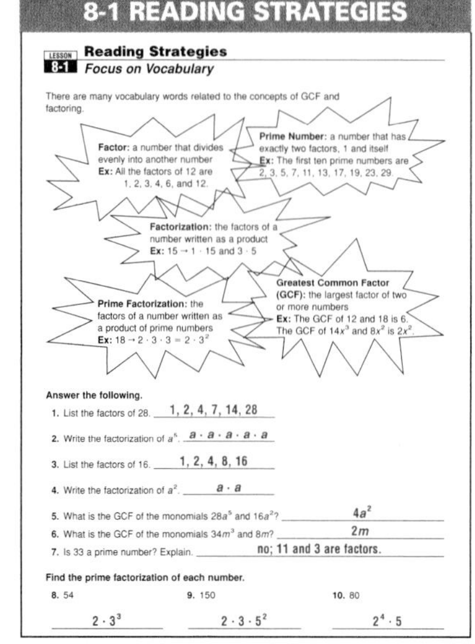

8-1 READING STRATEGIES

LESSON 8-1 **Reading Strategies**
Focus on Vocabulary

There are many vocabulary words related to the concepts of GCF and factoring.

Factor: a number that divides evenly into another number Ex: All the factors of 12 are 1, 2, 3, 4, 6, and 12.
Prime Number: a number that has exactly two factors, 1 and itself Ex: The first ten prime numbers are 2, 3, 5, 7, 11, 13, 17, 19, 23, 29.
Factorization: the factors of a number written as a product Ex: 15 → 1 · 15 and 3 · 5
Prime Factorization: the factors of a number written as a product of prime numbers Ex: 18 → 2 · 3 · 3 → 2 · 3²
Greatest Common Factor (GCF): the largest factor of two or more numbers Ex: The GCF of 12 and 18 is 6. The GCF of 14x³ and 8x² is 2x².

Answer the following.

1. List the factors of 28. 1, 2, 4, 7, 14, 28
2. Write the factorization of a^5. $a \cdot a \cdot a \cdot a \cdot a$
3. List the factors of 16. 1, 2, 4, 8, 16
4. Write the factorization of a^2. $a \cdot a$
5. What is the GCF of the monomials $28a^5$ and $16a^2$? $4a^2$
6. What is the GCF of the monomials $34m^3$ and $8m$? $2m$
7. Is 33 a prime number? Explain. no; 11 and 3 are factors.

Find the prime factorization of each number.

8. 54 $2 \cdot 3^3$
9. 150 $2 \cdot 3 \cdot 5^2$
10. 80 $2^4 \cdot 5$

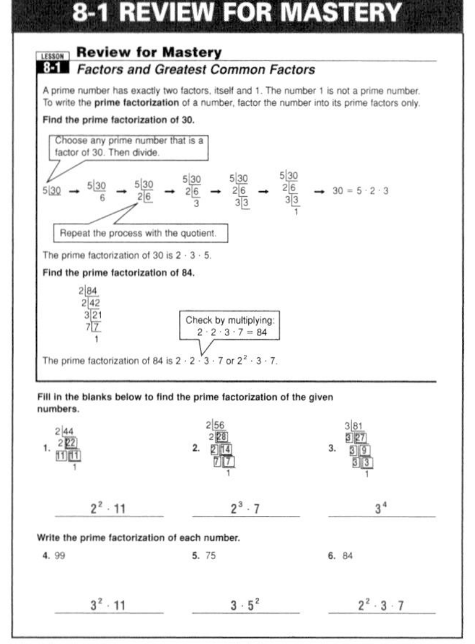

8-1 REVIEW FOR MASTERY

LESSON 8-1 **Review for Mastery**
Factors and Greatest Common Factors

A prime number has exactly two factors, itself and 1. The number 1 is not a prime number. To write the **prime factorization** of a number, factor the number into its prime factors only.

Find the prime factorization of 30.

Choose any prime number that is a factor of 30. Then divide.

5|30 → 5|30, 6 → 5|30, 2|6 → 5|30, 2|6, 3 → 5|30, 2|6, 3|3 → 5|30, 2|6, 3|3, 1 → 30 = 5 · 2 · 3

Repeat the process with the quotient.

The prime factorization of 30 is 2 · 3 · 5.

Find the prime factorization of 84.

2|84
2|42
3|21
7|7
1

Check by multiplying: 2 · 2 · 3 · 7 = 84

The prime factorization of 84 is 2 · 2 · 3 · 7 or $2^2 \cdot 3 \cdot 7$.

Fill in the blanks below to find the prime factorization of the given numbers.

1. 2|44, 2|22, 11|11, 1 $2^2 \cdot 11$
2. 2|56, 2|28, 2|14, 7|7, 1 $2^3 \cdot 7$
3. 3|81, 3|27, 3|9, 3|3, 1 3^4

Write the prime factorization of each number.

4. 99 $3^2 \cdot 11$
5. 75 $3 \cdot 5^2$
6. 84 $2^2 \cdot 3 \cdot 7$

69. This problem will prepare you for the Concept Connection on page 512.

The equation for the motion of an object with constant acceleration is $d = vt + \frac{1}{2}at^2$ where d is distance traveled in feet, v is starting velocity in ft/s, a is acceleration in ft/s^2, and t is time in seconds.

a. A toy car begins with a velocity of 2 ft/s and accelerates at 2 ft/s^2. Write an expression for the distance the toy car travels after t seconds. **$2t + t^2$**

b. What is the GCF of the terms of your expression from part **a**? ***t***

Multiple Choice For Exercises 70 and 71, choose the best answer.

70. Which set of numbers has a GCF greater than 6?

A 18, 24, 36   B 30, 35, 40   C 11, 29, 37   (D) 16, 24, 48

71. The slope of a line is the GCF of 48 and 12. The y-intercept is the GCF of the slope and 8. Which equation describes the line?

(A) $y = 12x + 4$ B $y = 6x + 2$ C $y = 4x + 4$ D $y = 3x + 1$

72. Extended Response Patricia is making a dog pen in her back yard. The pen will be rectangular and have an area of 24 square feet. Draw and label a diagram that shows all possible whole-number dimensions for the pen. Find the perimeter of each rectangle you drew. Which dimensions should Patricia use in order to spend the least amount of money on fencing materials? Explain your reasoning.

CHALLENGE AND EXTEND

Find the GCF of each set.

73. $4n^3, 16n^2, 8n$ **$4n$**

74. $27y^3, 18y^2, 81y$ **$9y$**

75. $100, 25s^5, 50s$ **25**

76. $2p^4r, 8p^3r^2, 16p^2r^3$ **$2p^2r$**

77. $2x^3y, 8x^2y^2, 17xy^3$ **xy**

78. $8a^4b^3, 4a^3b^3, 12a^2b^3$ **$4a^2b^3$**

79. Geometry The area of a triangle is 10 in^2. What are the possible whole-number dimensions for the base and height of the triangle? **1×20; 2×10; 4×5; 20×1; 10×2; 5×4**

80. Number Sense The GCF of three different numbers is 7. The sum of the three numbers is 105. What are the three numbers? **Possible answer: 21, 35, 49**

81. Critical Thinking Find three different *composite* numbers whose GCF is 1. (*Hint:* A composite number has factors other than 1 and itself.) **Possible answer: 6, 35, 143**

SPIRAL STANDARDS REVIEW 8.0, 10.0

Identify which lines are parallel. (Lesson 5-7)

82. $y = 2x + 6$; $y = 5x + 2$; $y = 2x$; $y = 2$ **$y = 2x + 6$ and $y = 2x$**

83. $y = 4x - 2$; $y = 9$; $y = 9x$; $y = 8$ **$y = 9$ and $y = 8$**

84. At a local grocery store, grapes cost $2/lb and cherries cost $3/lb. How many pounds of each should be used to make a 10 lb mixture that costs $2.30/lb? (Lesson 6-5) **7 lb grapes; 3 lb cherries**

85. Write a simplified polynomial expression for the perimeter of the triangle. (Lesson 7-7) **$3x^2 + 14x - 3$**

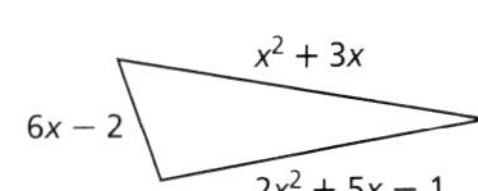

Exercise 69 involves finding the GCF of terms in an expression for constant acceleration. This exercise prepares students for the Concept Connection on page 512.

Multiple Choice In **Exercise 70,** choice **C** can be eliminated because it lists only prime numbers.

Journal

Have students explain how to use the prime factorization of 36 to find *all* of the factors of 36.

ALTERNATIVE ASSESSMENT

Have students create pairs of numbers or monomials that have the following GCFs: 15, 1, 7, $3x^2$, $2xy$, and $8b$.

Power Presentations with PowerPoint®

8-1 Lesson Quiz

Write the prime factorization of each number.

1. 50 $2 \cdot 5^2$

2. 84 $2^2 \cdot 3 \cdot 7$

Find the GCF of each pair of numbers.

3. 18 and 75   3

4. 20 and 36   4

Find the GCF of each pair of monomials.

5. $12x$ and $28x^3$ $4x$

6. $27x^2$ and $45x^3y^2$ $9x^2$

7. Cindi is planting a rectangular flower bed with 40 orange flowers and 28 yellow flowers. She wants to plant them so that each row will have the same number of plants but of only one color. How many rows will Cindi need if she puts the greatest possible number of plants in each row? 17

Also available on transparency

8-1 PROBLEM SOLVING

LESSON 8-1 Problem Solving
Factors and Greatest Common Factors

Write the correct answer.

1. Eloise saved all her awards from school. She has 18 athletic awards and 27 academic awards. Eloise wants to display the two types separately but in rows of equal length. Determine the greatest number of awards Eloise can put in each row. Then determine the total number of rows.
9 awards in each row; total of 5 rows

2. Parker is preparing snacks for the children at a day camp. He has 48 carrot sticks and 36 apple slices. Find the number of identical snacks he can prepare if he puts as much food into each snack as possible without any leftovers. Then describe the snack.
12 snacks of 4 carrot sticks and 3 apple slices

3. Matías and Hannah are responsible for the centerpieces on the buffet tables at the school dance. They have 6 dozen carnations, 80 lilies, and 64 rosebuds. All the centerpieces must be identical. Determine the greatest number of centerpieces Matías and Hannah can make if they use all the flowers. Then describe the centerpiece.
8 centerpieces; 9 carnations, 10 lilies, 8 rosebuds

4. Ms. Thompson has 120 same-sized tiles with which to make a rectangular design on her patio floor. 54 of the tiles are green; the rest are blue. To keep the rectangular shape, all rows must have the same number of tiles. If she wants each row to have the same number of blue and green tiles, how many rows will there be if she wants to use all the tiles and wants the rows to be as long as possible?
6 rows

Part of an ad for interlocking foam squares is shown below. Use it to answer questions 5–7. Select the best answer.

Each package comes with 36 foam squares that interlock for a safe, colorful floor mat!
You can make a ...
square   rectangle   or any shape you want!

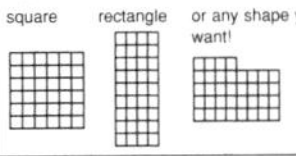

5. A class arranges one package into a rectangle with dimensions other than those shown. Which could have been the dimensions?
(A) 2×18 B 3×16 C 4×8 D 5×6

6. A teacher has 2 packages of red, 6 packages of blue, and half a package of yellow squares. He wants to build a rectangle so that each row is the same color. What can be the maximum number of squares per row?
F 2   G 6   (H) 18   J 36

7. In problem 6, how many rows will be blue?
A 2   B 3   C 6   (D) 12

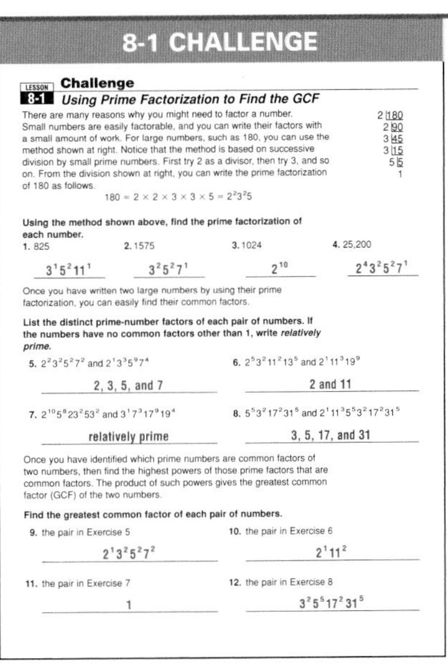

8-1 CHALLENGE

LESSON 8-1 Challenge
Using Prime Factorization to Find the GCF

There are many reasons why you might need to factor a number. Small numbers are easily factorable, and you can write their factors with a small amount of work. For large numbers, such as 180, you can use the method shown at right. Notice that the method is based on successive division by small prime numbers. First try 2 as a divisor, then try 3, and so on. From the division shown at right, you can write the prime factorization of 180 as follows.

2 | 180
2 | 90
3 | 45
3 | 15
5 | 5
1

$$180 = 2 \times 2 \times 3 \times 3 \times 5 = 2^2 3^2 5$$

Using the method shown above, find the prime factorization of each number.

1. 825   **$3^1 5^2 11^1$**
2. 1575   **$3^2 5^2 7^1$**
3. 1024   **2^{10}**
4. 25,200   **$2^4 3^2 5^2 7^1$**

Once you have written two large numbers by using their prime factorization, you can easily find their common factors.

List the distinct prime-number factors of each pair of numbers. If the numbers have no common factors other than 1, write *relatively prime*.

5. $2^2 3^2 5^2 7^2$ and $2^1 3^3 5^9 7^4$ **2, 3, 5, and 7**
6. $2^5 3^2 11^2 13^5$ and $2^1 11^3 19^9$ **2 and 11**
7. $2^{10} 5^8 23^2 53^2$ and $3^1 7^3 17^9 19^4$ **relatively prime**
8. $5^5 3^2 17^2 31^5$ and $2^1 11^3 5^5 3^2 17^2 31^5$ **3, 5, 17, and 31**

Once you have identified which prime numbers are common factors of two numbers, then find the highest powers of those prime factors that are common factors. The product of such powers gives the greatest common factor (GCF) of the two numbers.

Find the greatest common factor of each pair of numbers.

9. the pair in Exercise 5   **$2^1 3^2 5^2 7^2$**
10. the pair in Exercise 6   **$2^1 11^2$**
11. the pair in Exercise 7   **1**
12. the pair in Exercise 8   **$3^2 5^5 17^2 31^5$**

Organizer

Objective: Use indirect proof to prove statements.

Online Edition
Student Edition

Countdown to Mastery Week 17

Teach

Discuss

Begin by introducing contradictions. One way to define *contradiction* is "two or more things that cannot all be true at the same time."

- Today is Tuesday and today is Wednesday.
- Jesse is 14 years old and Blake is 12 years old. Blake is older than Jesse.
- A number is both even and odd.

Ask students to provide examples of contradictions.

To help students understand indirect proof, use a non-mathematical example. One common use of indirect proof is when investigators eliminate someone as a crime suspect because that person has an alibi. For example, assume an individual committed a robbery, but witnesses saw this individual in another city when the robbery took place. So this person was in two places at once, which is impossible. Therefore, he or she did not commit the robbery.

California Standards

Algebra 1 25.1

Use with Lesson 8-1

Indirect Proofs

In Chapter 1, you learned that some numbers are irrational. You now have enough knowledge to *prove* that some numbers are irrational by using deductive reasoning.

25.1 Students use properties of numbers to construct simple, valid arguments (direct and **indirect**) **for,** or formulate counterexamples to, **claimed assertions.**

Prove that if a prime number p is a factor of x^2, then p is also a factor of x.

Statements	Reasons
1. $x = p_1p_2p_3...p_n$ where $p_1, p_2, p_3, ..., p_n$ are prime.	Every number can be written as the product of primes.
2. $x^2 = x \cdot x = (p_1p_2p_3 \cdots p_n)(p_1p_2p_3 \cdots p_n)$	Substitute $p_1p_2p_3...p_n$ for x in Step 1.

The expression $(p_1p_2p_3...p_n)(p_1p_2p_3...p_n)$ contains only prime numbers, so it is the prime factorization of x^2. Since it contains only prime numbers that are factors of x, all prime numbers that are factors of x^2 are factors of x.

In other words, if a prime number is a factor of x^2, then it is also a factor of x.

Proving that some numbers are irrational often requires an *indirect proof.* In an **indirect proof,** first assume that the statement you want to prove is false—in other words, assume that the opposite of the statement is true.

Then use deductive reasoning to find a **contradiction**—two statements that cannot both be true at the same time.

An assumption that leads to a contradiction is false. Therefore, if you assume the opposite of a statement is true, and this leads to a contradiction, the assumption is false. This means the original statement must be true.

Try This

Write the opposite of each statement.

1. Susie is an only child. **Susie has at least one sibling.**
2. All squares have four sides. **There is at least one square that does not have 4 sides.**
3. The sum of two even numbers is always even. **There are at least 2 even numbers whose sum is not even.**

Find the two statements in each set that cannot both be true at the same time.

4. a and b are opposites.
   a and b are both negative.
   a and b are integers.
5. Angles A and B are both acute.
   Angles A and B are adjacent.
   Angles A and B are supplementary.

Teaching Tip

Inclusion Illustrate the statement proved in **Example 1** by giving examples. For instance, let $x = 6$ and let $p = 3$. Then 3 is a factor of x^2 (36) and a factor of x. Note that p must be prime: When $x = 6$ and $p = 4$, the statement does not hold (4 is a factor of 36, but not a factor of 6).

Example 2

Use an indirect proof to show that all prime numbers have irrational square roots.

Statements	Reasons
1. Suppose there were a number p that is prime and $\sqrt{p}$ is rational.	Assume the opposite of the statement you want to prove. In other words, assume the statement you want to prove is false.
2. $\sqrt{p} = \frac{a}{b}$ for integers a and b, $b \neq 0$. Assume a and b have no common factors besides 1; in other words, $\frac{a}{b}$ is in simplest form.	Definition of rational number; every rational number can be written in simplest form.
3. $p = \left(\frac{a}{b}\right)^2$	Definition of square root
4. $p = \frac{a^2}{b^2}$	Power of a Quotient Property
5. $pb^2 = a^2$	Multiplication Property of Equality (Multiply both sides by b^2.)
6. p is a factor of a^2.	Definition of factor
7. p is a factor of a.	Example 1
8. a can be written as the product of p and some number n: $a = pn$	Definition of factor
9. $pb^2 = (pn)^2$	Substitute pn for a in Statement 5.
10. $pb^2 = p^2n^2$	Product of a Power Property
12. $b^2 = pn^2$	Division Property of Equality (Divide both sides by p, $p \neq 0$.)
13. p is a factor of b^2.	Definition of factor
14. p is a factor of b.	Example 1
15. p is a factor of both a and b.	Statements 7 and 14

Once you have proven a statement, you can use that statement in other proofs.

Statement 15 contradicts Statement 2. Therefore, the original statement, Statement 1, is false. There are no prime numbers that have rational square roots. In other words, all prime numbers have irrational square roots.

Try This

6. Complete the following indirect proof to show that there are infinitely many prime numbers.

Assume that there is a finite number of **a.** ___?___.

Then there is a prime number p that is the greatest prime number. Let n be the product of all prime numbers. In other words, $n = 2 \cdot 3 \cdot 5 \cdot \ldots \cdot p$. Then $n + 1 =$ **b.** ___?___. Since all numbers have a unique prime factorization, $n + 1$ must have a(n) **c.** ___?___.

However, 2 is not a factor of $n + 1$ because $n + 1$ is 1 greater than a multiple of **d.** ___?___. Also, 3 is not a factor of **e.** ___?___ because $n + 1$ is **f.** ___?___. There is no prime number that is a factor of $n + 1$ because $n + 1$ is 1 greater than a multiple of **g.** ___?___. So, $n + 1$ does not have a prime factorization. This is a contradiction.

Therefore, the original assumption is false and **h.** ___?___.

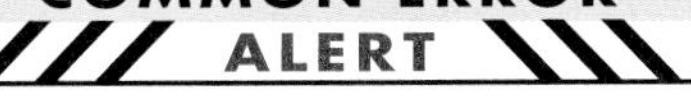

In **Example 2,** students may think that the opposite of "All prime numbers have irrational square roots" is "No prime numbers have irrational square roots" or "All prime numbers have rational square roots." Use a non-mathematical situation to help them understand that the opposite of "all" is "there is at least one:"

Statement: All of my friends have brown hair.

For the above statement to be false, all that is needed is one friend without brown hair, not necessarily all friends without brown hair.

Teaching Tip **Multiple Representations** Although the two-column proof has been emphasized in this text, proofs may be written in other formats. **Try This Exercise 6** is an example of a *paragraph proof.* This style of proof presents statements and their corresponding reasons as sentences in a paragraph. Students should understand that, as long as logical reasoning is used correctly, the format of a proof is not important, and they should choose the one they are most comfortable with.

Close

Key Concept

Indirect proof is based on three ideas:

1. A mathematical statement must be either true or false, but not both.
2. If a statement is true, its opposite is false, and vice versa.
3. If a statement causes a contradiction, the statement must be false.

Assess

Have students create a list of the steps in writing an indirect proof.

Answers

6a. prime numbers

b. $2 \cdot 3 \cdot 5 \cdot \ldots \cdot p + 1$

c. unique prime factorization

d. 2

e. $n + 1$

f. 1 greater than a multiple of 3

g. any prime number

h. there are infinitely many prime numbers

Teaching Tip **Language Support** Because indirect proof relies on finding a contradiction, it is sometimes called *proof by contradiction*.

Algebra LAB Organizer

Use with Lesson 8-2

Objective: Use algebra tiles to model and factor polynomials.

Materials: algebra tiles

PREMIER **Online Edition**

Teach

Discuss

If the algebra tiles (MK) modeling a polynomial cannot be arranged into a rectangle, then the polynomial cannot be factored.

Ask students if they see another way to make a rectangle for $4x + 8$.

Tell students that they can check their answers by multiplying the factors, using the methods taught in Chapter 7. If the answer is correct, the product will be the original polynomial.

Close

Key Concept

You can factor polynomials by arranging tiles into a rectangle and finding expressions for the rectangle's length and width.

Assessment

Journal Have students explain how to model and factor polynomials with algebra tiles.

California Standards

Algebra 1 11.0

8-2 Algebra LAB

Model Factorization by GCF

You can use algebra tiles to write a polynomial as the product of its factors. This process is called factoring. Factoring is the reverse of multiplying.

Use with Lesson 8-2

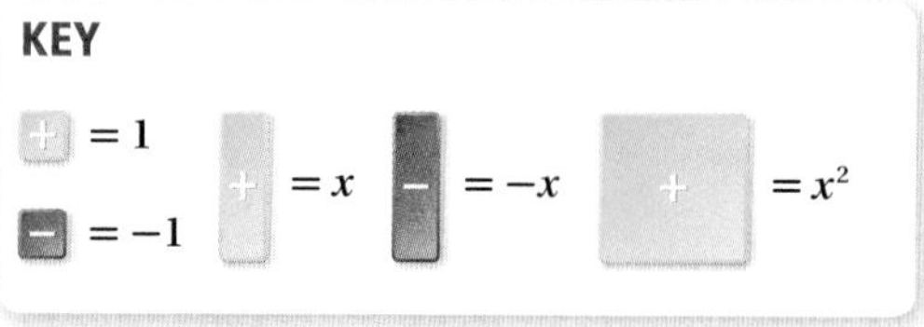

California Standards

11.0 Students apply basic factoring techniques to second- and simple third-**degree polynomials.** These techniques include finding a common factor for all terms in a polynomial, recognizing the difference of two squares, and recognizing perfect squares of binomials.

Activity

Use algebra tiles to factor $4x + 8$.

MODEL		ALGEBRA
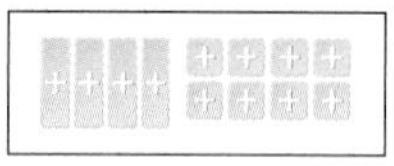	*Model $4x + 8$.*	$4x + 8$
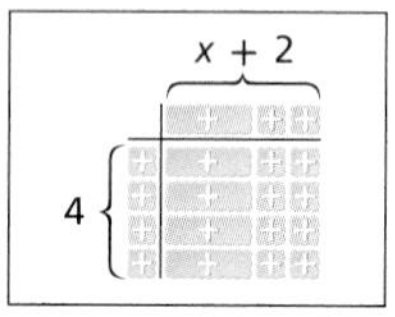	*Arrange the tiles into a rectangle. The total area represents $4x + 8$. The length and width represent the factors. The rectangle has a width of $x + 2$ and a length of 4.*	$4x + 8 = 4(x + 2)$

Use algebra tiles to factor $x^2 - 2x$.

MODEL		ALGEBRA
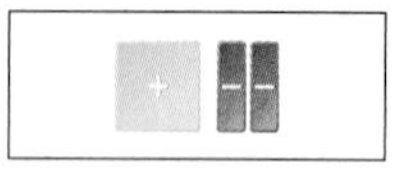	*Model $x^2 - 2x$.*	$x^2 - 2x$
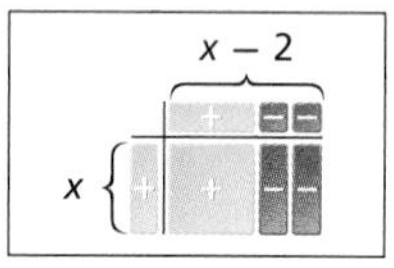	*Arrange the tiles into a rectangle. The total area represents $x^2 - 2x$. The length and width represent the factors. The rectangle has a width of $x - 2$ and a length of x.*	$x^2 - 2x = x(x - 2)$

Try This

Use algebra tiles to factor each polynomial.

1. $3x + 9$ **$3(x + 3)$**
2. $2x + 8$ **$2(x + 4)$**
3. $4x - 12$ **$4(x - 3)$**
4. $3x - 12$ **$3(x - 4)$**
5. $2x^2 + 2x$ **$2x(x + 1)$**
6. $x^2 + 4x$ **$x(x + 4)$**
7. $x^2 - 3x$ **$x(x - 3)$**
8. $2x^2 - 4x$ **$2x(x - 2)$**

Teacher to Teacher

When we factor polynomials using algebra tiles, I emphasize that x-sides can touch only other x-sides, and unit-sides can touch only other unit-sides.

After this lab, I ask students, "What happens if I cannot form a rectangle?" This question helps students realize that not all expressions are factorable.

Donna Phair
Fremont, CA

8-2 Factoring by GCF

California Standards

11.0 Students apply basic factoring techniques to second- and simple third-degree polynomials. These techniques include finding a common factor for all terms in a polynomial, recognizing the difference of two squares, and recognizing perfect squares of binomials.

Why learn this?

You can determine the dimensions of a solar panel by factoring an expression representing the panel's area. (See Example 2.)

Recall the Distributive Property: $ab + ac = a(b + c)$. The Distributive Property allows you to "factor" out the GCF of the terms in a polynomial.

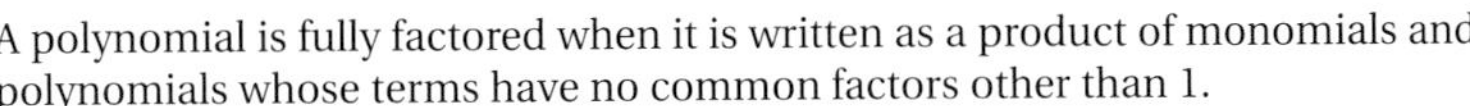

A polynomial is fully factored when it is written as a product of monomials and polynomials whose terms have no common factors other than 1.

Fully Factored	$2(3x - 4)$	Neither 2 nor $3x - 4$ can be factored.
Not Fully Factored	$2(3x - 4x)$	$3x - 4x$ can be factored. The terms have a common factor of x.

Writing Math

Aligning common factors can help you find the greatest common factor of two or more terms.

EXAMPLE 1 Factoring by Using the GCF

Factor each polynomial. Check your answer.

A $4x^2 - 3x$

$4x^2 = 2 \cdot 2 \cdot \boxed{x} \cdot x$ — *Find the GCF.*
$3x = 3 \cdot \boxed{x}$

x — *The GCF of $4x^2$ and $3x$ is x.*

$4x(x) - 3(x)$ — *Write terms as products using the GCF as a factor.*

$x(4x - 3)$ — *Use the Distributive Property to factor out the GCF.*

Check $x(4x - 3)$ — *Multiply to check your answer.*

$4x^2 - 3x$ ✓ — *The product is the original polynomial.*

B $10y^3 + 20y^2 - 5y$

$10y^3 = 2 \cdot \boxed{5} \cdot \boxed{y} \cdot y \cdot y$ — *Find the GCF.*
$20y^2 = 2 \cdot 2 \cdot \boxed{5} \cdot \boxed{y} \cdot y$
$5y = \boxed{5} \cdot \boxed{y}$

$5 \cdot y = 5y$ — *The GCF of $10y^3$, $20y^2$, and $5y$ is $5y$.*

$2y^2(5y) + 4y(5y) - 1(5y)$ — *Write terms as products using the GCF as a factor.*

$5y(2y^2 + 4y - 1)$ — *Use the Distributive Property to factor out the GCF.*

Check $5y(2y^2 + 4y - 1)$ — *Multiply to check your answer.*

$10y^3 + 20y^2 - 5y$ ✓ — *The product is the original polynomial.*

8-2 Organizer

Objective: Factor polynomials by using the greatest common factor.

Online Edition
Tutorial Videos

Countdown to Mastery Week 18

Power Presentations with PowerPoint®

Warm Up

Simplify.

1. $2(w + 1)$ $2w + 2$

2. $3x(x^2 - 4)$ $3x^3 - 12x$

Find the GCF of each pair of monomials.

3. $4h^2$ and $6h$ $2h$

4. $13p$ and $26p^5$ $13p$

Also available on transparency

Math Fact !!!

Around 300 B.C.E., Euclid developed a way of finding the GCF of two numbers by writing the smaller number and the difference of the two numbers as a pair and repeating this process until the two numbers are equal. The GCF of 36 and 60 is found by writing (36, 60); (36, 24); (24, 12); (12, 12). The GCF is 12.

1 Introduce

EXPLORATION

8-2 Factoring by GCF

In this Exploration, you will need to use the Distributive Property. Recall that the Distributive Property states that $a(b + c) = ab + ac$.

1. The table shows the factored form of several polynomials. Use the Distributive Property to multiply the factors and write the resulting polynomial in the middle column of the table.

Factored Form	Polynomial	GCF of Terms
$3(x + 2)$		
$x^2(x - 5)$		
$ab(a + 2b)$		
$5y^2(y^3 - 8)$		
$3a(a^2 + b + 1)$		

2. For each polynomial in the table, find the GCF of the terms. Write the GCF of the terms in the right-hand column of the table.

THINK AND DISCUSS

3. **Describe** what you notice about the GCF of the terms and the factored form of each polynomial.
4. **Explain** whether you think $2(x^2 + x)$ is the factored form of the polynomial $2x^2 + 2x$.

Motivate

Write 6 + 8 on the board. Ask students what the greatest common factor of 6 and 8 is. 2 Then rewrite 6 + 8 with 6 and 8 as products of 2 and one other factor: $2 \cdot 3 + 2 \cdot 4$. Show how to use the Distributive Property to write $2(3 + 4)$.

Explorations and answers are provided in *Alternate Openers: Explorations Transparencies.*

California Standards

Algebra 1 11.0

Power Presentations with PowerPoint®

Additional Examples

Example 1

Factor each polynomial. Check your answer.

A. $2x^2 - 4$ $2(x^2 - 2)$

B. $8x^3 - 4x^2 - 16x$
$4x(2x^2 - x - 4)$

C. $-14x - 12x^2$ $-2x(7 + 6x)$

D. $3x^3 + 2x^2 - 10$ cannot be factored

Example 2

The area of a court for the game squash is $9x^2 + 6x$ m². Factor this polynomial to find possible expressions for the dimensions of the squash court. Possible answer: $3x$ m and $(3x + 2)$m

Also available on transparency

INTERVENTION

Questioning Strategies

EXAMPLE 1

- How do you find a common factor?

EXAMPLE 2

- How could factoring a binomial help you with a problem about area?

Inclusion In **Example 1C,** students either factor out -1 or -1 and another positive factor. Remind them that in either case, they need to change the sign of the terms in the parentheses.

When you factor out -1 as the first step, be sure to include it in all the other steps as well.

Factor each polynomial. Check your answer.

C $-12x - 8x^2$

$-1(12x + 8x^2)$ *Both coefficients are negative. Factor out -1.*

$12x = \boxed{2} \cdot \boxed{2} \cdot 3 \cdot \boxed{x}$
$8x^2 = \boxed{2} \cdot \boxed{2} \cdot 2 \cdot \boxed{x} \cdot x$ *Find the GCF.*

$2 \cdot 2 \cdot \quad x = 4x$ *The GCF of $12x$ and $8x^2$ is $4x$.*

$-1[3(4x) + 2x(4x)]$ *Write each term as a product using the GCF.*

$-1[4x(3 + 2x)]$ *Use the Distributive Property to factor out the GCF.*

$-1(4x)(3 + 2x)$

$-4x(3 + 2x)$

Check

$-4x(3 + 2x) = -12x - 8x^2$ ✓   *Multiply to check your answer.*

D $5x^2 + 7$

$5x^2 = 5 \quad \cdot x \cdot x$
$7 = \quad 7$ *Find the GCF.*

$5x^2 + 7$ *There are no common factors other than 1.*

The polynomial cannot be factored further.

Factor each polynomial. Check your answer.

1a. $5b + 9b^3$ $b(5 + 9b^2)$
1b. $9d^2 - 8^2$ **cannot be factored**
1c. $-18y^3 - 7y^2$ $-y^2(18y + 7)$
1d. $8x^4 + 4x^3 - 2x^2$ $2x^2(4x^2 + 2x - 1)$

To write expressions for the length and width of a rectangle with area expressed by a polynomial, you need to write the polynomial as a product. You can write a polynomial as a product by factoring it.

EXAMPLE 2 ***Science Application***

Mandy's calculator is powered by solar energy. The area of the solar panel is $(7x^2 + x)$ cm². Factor this polynomial to find possible expressions for the dimensions of the solar panel.

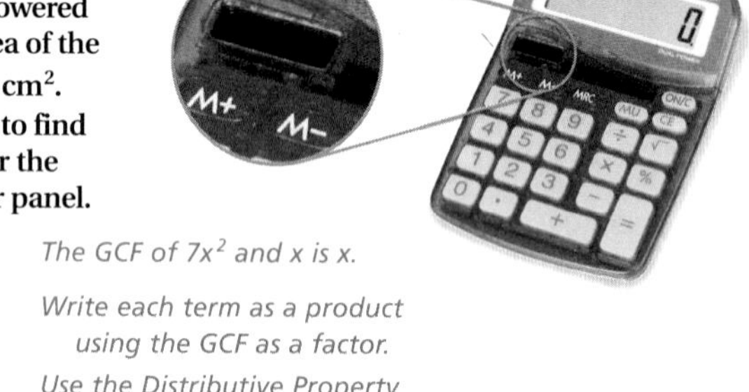

$A = 7x^2 + x$ *The GCF of $7x^2$ and x is x.*

$= 7x(x) + 1(x)$ *Write each term as a product using the GCF as a factor.*

$= x(7x + 1)$ *Use the Distributive Property to factor out the GCF.*

Possible expressions for the dimensions of the solar panel are x cm and $(7x + 1)$ cm.

2. What if...? The area of the solar panel on another calculator is $(2x^2 + 4x)$ cm². Factor this polynomial to find possible expressions for the dimensions of the solar panel.
$2x$ cm; $(x + 2)$ cm

2 Teach

Guided Instruction

Show students how the Distributive Property can be used to write $a(b + c)$ as $ab + ac$ and $ab + ac$ as $a(b + c)$. When factoring out common monomials and determining the remaining factors, have students determine the coefficient part first and then the variable part. Encourage students to check their work at each step, mentally "redistributing" the common factor to see if it matches the line in the previous step.

Universal Access

Through Cognitive Strategies

In **Example 5,** students learn to factor with opposites. To help students learn to recognize opposite binomials, work through the first row of the following chart with students. Then have students complete the chart on their own.

	Opposites		
$x - 3$	$-1(x - 3)$ →	$-x + 3$ →	$3 - x$
$8 - a$	$-1(8 - a)$	$-8 + a$	$a - 8$
$m - n$	$-1(m - n)$	$-m + n$	$n - m$
$y^2 - 6$	$-1(y^2 - 6)$	$-y^2 + 6$	$6 - y^2$

Sometimes the GCF of terms is a binomial. This GCF is called a *common binomial factor*. You factor out a common binomial factor the same way you factor out a monomial factor.

EXAMPLE 3 Factoring Out a Common Binomial Factor

Factor each expression.

A $7(x-3)-2x(x-3)$

$7(x-3)-2x(x-3)$ — *The terms have a common binomial factor of $(x-3)$.*

$(x-3)(7-2x)$ — *Factor out $(x-3)$.*

B $-t(t^2+4)+(t^2+4)$

$-t(t^2+4)+(t^2+4)$ — *The terms have a common binomial factor of (t^2+4).*

$-t(t^2+4)+1(t^2+4)$ — *$(t^2+4)=1(t^2+4)$*

$(t^2+4)(-t+1)$ — *Factor out (t^2+4).*

C $9x(x+4)-5(4+x)$

$9x(x+4)-5(4+x)$ — *$(x+4)=(4+x)$, so the terms have a common binomial factor of $(x+4)$.*

$9x(x+4)-5(x+4)$

$(x+4)(9x-5)$ — *Factor out $(x+4)$.*

D $-3x^2(x+2)+4(x-7)$

$-3x^2(x+2)+4(x-7)$ — *There are no common factors.*

The expression cannot be factored.

CHECK IT OUT! Factor each expression.

3a. $4s(s+6)-5(s+6)$ — $(4s-5)(s+6)$

3b. $7x(2x+3)+(2x+3)$ — $(7x+1)(2x+3)$

3c. $3x(y+4)-2y(x+4)$ — cannot be factored

3d. $5x(5x-2)-2(5x-2)$ — $(5x-2)^2$

You may be able to factor a polynomial by grouping. When a polynomial has four terms, you can sometimes make two groups and factor out the GCF from each group.

EXAMPLE 4 Factoring by Grouping

Factor each polynomial by grouping. Check your answer.

A $12a^3-9a^2+20a-15$

$(12a^3-9a^2)+(20a-15)$ — *Group terms that have a common number or variable as a factor.*

$3a^2(4a-3)+5(4a-3)$ — *Factor out the GCF of each group.*

$3a^2(4a-3)+5(4a-3)$ — *$(4a-3)$ is another common factor.*

$(4a-3)(3a^2+5)$ — *Factor out $(4a-3)$.*

Check $(4a-3)(3a^2+5)$ — *Multiply to check your solution.*

$4a(3a^2)+4a(5)-3(3a^2)-3(5)$

$12a^3+20a-9a^2-15$

$12a^3-9a^2+20a-15$ ✓ — *The product is the original polynomial.*

COMMON ERROR ALERT

Students may forget that a binomial written without a coefficient actually has a coefficient of 1. Suggest that students write in the coefficient of 1 so that they don't forget it is there.

Power Presentations with PowerPoint®

Additional Examples

Example 3

Factor each expression.

A. $5(x+2)+3x(x+2)$
$(x+2)(5+3x)$

B. $-2b(b^2+1)+(b^2+1)$
$(b^2+1)(-2b+1)$

C. $4z(z^2-7)+9(2z^3+1)$
cannot be factored

Example 4

Factor each polynomial by grouping. Check your answer.

A. $6h^4-4h^3+12h-8$
$(3h-2)(2h^3+4)$

B. $5y^4-15y^3+y^2-3y$
$(y-3)(5y^3+y)$

Also available on transparency

INTERVENTION
Questioning Strategies

EXAMPLE 3

- How is the Distributive Property used in these examples?

EXAMPLE 4

- How do you determine which terms to group?
- How can you check your answer?

Power Presentations with PowerPoint®

Additional Examples

Example 5

Factor $2x^3 - 12x^2 + 18 - 3x$.
$(x - 6)(2x^2 - 3)$

Also available on transparency

INTERVENTION

Questioning Strategies

EXAMPLE 5

- How can you recognize opposite binomials?
- Does it matter which pair of terms has -1 as a factor? Explain.

Concrete Manipulatives Students can check their answers using algebra tiles (MK). If an expression is not factored fully, each row of the model can be rearranged into a smaller rectangle.

If $4x + 8$ is factored as $2(2x + 4)$, then each row can still form another rectangle:

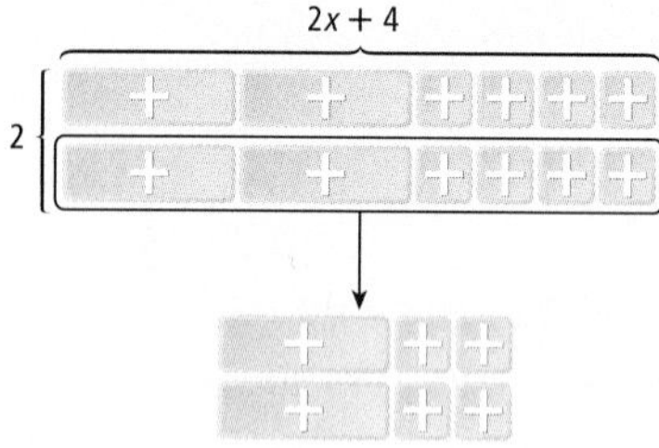

When $4x + 8$ is completely factored as $4(x + 2)$, the rows cannot form another rectangle:

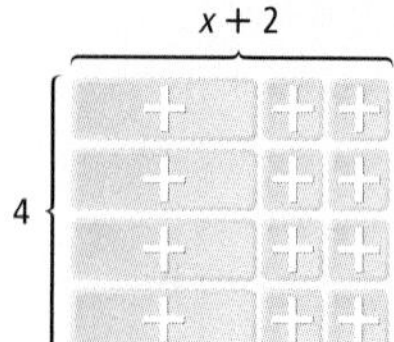

Factor each polynomial by grouping. Check your answer.

B $9x^3 + 18x^2 + x + 2$

$(9x^3 + 18x^2) + (x + 2)$	*Group terms.*
$9x^2(x + 2) + 1(x + 2)$	*Factor out the GCF of each group.*
$9x^2(x + 2) + 1(x + 2)$	*(x + 2) is a common factor.*
$(x + 2)(9x^2 + 1)$	*Factor out (x + 2).*
Check $(x + 2)(9x^2 + 1)$	*Multiply to check your solution.*
$x(9x^2) + x(1) + 2(9x^2) + 2(1)$	
$9x^3 + x + 18x^2 + 2$	
$9x^3 + 18x^2 + x + 2$ ✓	*The product is the original polynomial.*

CHECK IT OUT! Factor each polynomial by grouping. Check your answer.

4a. $6b^3 + 8b^2 + 9b + 12$ **$(2b^2 + 3)(3b + 4)$**

4b. $4r^3 + 24r + r^2 + 6$ **$(4r + 1)(r^2 + 6)$**

Helpful Hint

If two quantities are opposites, their sum is 0.
$(5 - x) + (x - 5)$
$5 - x + x - 5$
$-x + x + 5 - 5$
$0 + 0$
0

Recognizing opposite binomials can help you factor polynomials. The binomials $(5 - x)$ and $(x - 5)$ are opposites. Notice $(5 - x)$ can be written as $-1(x - 5)$.

$-1(x - 5) = (-1)(x) + (-1)(-5)$	*Distributive Property*
$= -x + 5$	*Simplify.*
$= 5 - x$	*Commutative Property of Addition*
So, $(5 - x) = -1(x - 5)$.	

EXAMPLE 5 Factoring with Opposites

Factor $3x^3 - 15x^2 + 10 - 2x$.

$(3x^3 - 15x^2) + (10 - 2x)$	*Group terms.*
$3x^2(x - 5) + 2(5 - x)$	*Factor out the GCF of each group.*
$3x^2(x - 5) + 2(-1)(x - 5)$	*Write (5 − x) as −1(x − 5).*
$3x^2(x - 5) - 2(x - 5)$	*Simplify. (x − 5) is a common factor.*
$(x - 5)(3x^2 - 2)$	*Factor out (x − 5).*

CHECK IT OUT! Factor each polynomial. Check your answer.

5a. $15x^2 - 10x^3 + 8x - 12$ **$(5x^2 - 4)(3 - 2x)$**

5b. $8y - 8 - x + xy$ **$(8 + x)(y - 1)$**

THINK AND DISCUSS

1. Explain how finding the GCF of monomials helps you factor a polynomial.
2. **GET ORGANIZED** Copy and complete the graphic organizer.

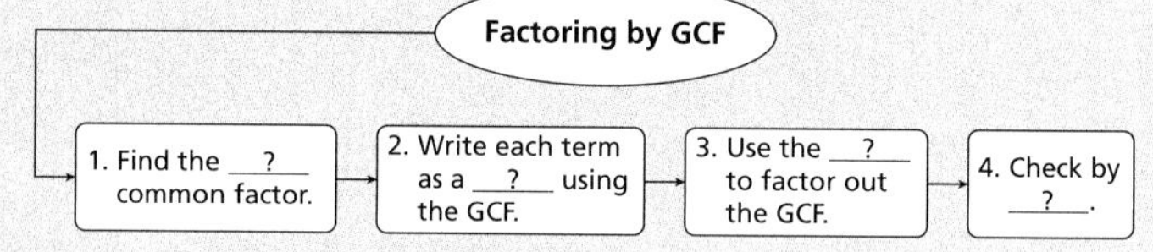

3 Close

Summarize

Ask students whether each of the following can be factored further. If yes, have them factor the polynomial.

$2x^5 - 7x^3$ yes; $x^3(2x^2 - 7)$
$3x^4 + 13y^4 + 3z^4$ no
$p(2p - 1) - 2(p - 1)$ no
$g^2(g - 8) + 6(8 - g)$
yes; $(g - 8)(g^2 - 6)$
$14y^5 + 21$ yes; $7(2y^5 + 3)$

FORMATIVE ASSESSMENT and INTERVENTION

***Diagnose Before* the Lesson**
8-2 Warm Up, TE p. 487

***Monitor During* the Lesson**
Check It Out! Exercises, SE pp. 488–490
Questioning Strategies, TE pp. 488–489

***Assess After* the Lesson**
8-2 Lesson Quiz, TE p. 493
Alternative Assessment, TE p. 493

Answers to *Think and Discuss*

Possible answers:

1. When you know the GCF of the monomials in a polynomial, you can factor out the GCF from each monomial to factor the polynomial.
2. See p. A6.

Multiple Representations Some factorizations may be written differently but still be correct. For instance, **Check It Out 5a** could also be written as $(4 - 5x^2)(2x - 3)$.

8-2 Exercises

California Standards Practice
11.0, 25.1, 25.2

go.hrw.com
Homework Help Online
KEYWORD: MA8CA 8-2
Parent Resources Online
KEYWORD: MA8CA Parent

GUIDED PRACTICE

SEE EXAMPLE 1 p. 487

Factor each polynomial. Check your answer.

1. $15a - 5a^2$ $5a(3 - a)$
2. $10g^3 - 3g$ $g(10g^2 - 3)$
3. $-35x + 42$ $7(-5x + 6)$
4. $-4x^2 - 6x$ $-2x(2x + 3)$
5. $12h^4 + 8h^2 - 6h$
6. $3x^2 - 9x + 3$
7. $9m^2 + m$
8. $14n^3 + 7n + 7n^2$
9. $36f + 18f^2 + 3$

SEE EXAMPLE 2 p. 488

10. **Physical Science** A model rocket is fired vertically into the air at 320 ft/s. The expression $-16t^2 + 320t$ gives the rocket's height after t seconds. Factor this expression. $16t(-t + 20)$

SEE EXAMPLE 3 p. 489

Factor each expression.

11. $2b(b + 3) + 5(b + 3)$ $(2b + 5)(b + 3)$
12. $5(m - 2) - m(m - 2)$ $(5 - m)(m - 2)$
13. $4(x - 3) - x(y + 2)$ cannot be factored

SEE EXAMPLE 4 p. 489

Factor each polynomial by grouping. Check your answer.

14. $6x^3 + 4x^2 + 3x + 2$
15. $x^3 + 4x^2 + 2x + 8$
16. $10a^3 + 4a^2 + 5a + 2$
17. $7r^3 - 35r^2 + 6r - 30$
18. $2m^3 + 4m^2 + 6m + 12$
19. $4b^3 - 6b^2 + 10b - 15$

SEE EXAMPLE 5 p. 490

20. $6b^2 - 3b + 4 - 8b$
21. $2r^2 - 6r + 12 - 4r$
22. $6a^3 - 9a^2 - 12 + 8a$
23. $2m^3 - 6m^2 + 9 - 3m$
24. $3r - r^2 + 2r - 6$
25. $14q^2 - 21q + 6 - 4q$

PRACTICE AND PROBLEM SOLVING

Independent Practice

For Exercises	See Example
26–34	1
35	2
36–41	3
42–47	4
48–53	5

Extra Practice
Skills Practice p. EP16
Application Practice p. EP31

Factor each polynomial. Check your answer.

26. $36d^3 + 24$ $12(3d^3 + 2)$
27. $9y^2 + 45y$ $9y(y + 5)$
28. $14x^3 + 63x^2 - 7x$ $7x(2x^2 + 9x - 1)$
29. $-4d^4 + d^3 - 3d^2$
30. $-15f - 10f^2$
31. $-14x^4 + 5x^2$
32. $33d^3 + 22d + 11$
33. $21c^2 + 14c$
34. $-5g^3 - 15g^2$
35. **Finance** After t years, the amount of money in a savings account that earns simple interest is $P + Prt$, where P is the starting amount and r is the yearly interest rate. Factor this expression. $P(1 + rt)$

Factor each expression.

36. $-4x(x + 2) + 9(x + 2)$
37. $6a(a - 2) - 5b(b + 4)$
38. $5(3x - 2) + x(3x - 2)$
39. $-3(2 + b) + 4b(b + 2)$ $(-3 + 4b)(b + 2)$
40. $a(x - 3) + 2b(x - 3)$ $(a + 2b)(x - 3)$
41. $6y(y - 7) + (y - 7)$ $(6y + 1)(y - 7)$

Factor each polynomial by grouping. Check your answer.

42. $x^3 + 3x^2 + 5x + 15$
43. $2a^3 - 8a^2 + 3a - 12$
44. $10b^3 - 16b^2 + 25b - 40$
45. $n^3 - 2n^2 + 5n - 10$
46. $7x^3 + 2x^2 + 28x + 8$
47. $6x^3 + 18x^2 + x + 3$
48. $2d^3 - d^2 - 3 + 6d$
49. $2m^3 - 2m^2 + 3 - 3m$
50. $20 - 15x - 6x^2 + 8x$
51. $b^3 - 2b - 8 + 4b^2$
52. $5k^2 - k^3 + 3k - 15$
53. $6f^3 - 8f^2 + 20 - 15f$
54. **Art** Factor the expression for the area of the mural shown at right. $x(12x + 1)$

8-2 Exercises

Assignment Guide

Assign *Guided Practice* exercises as necessary.

If you finished Examples **1–3**
Proficient 26–41, 59, 61, 76, 78
Advanced 26–41, 59, 61, 76, 78

If you finished Examples **1–5**
Proficient 26–41, 42–56 even, 59–79, 81–88
Advanced 26–34 even, 35, 36–54 even, 59–88

Homework Quick Check
Quickly check key concepts.
Exercises: 30, 35, 36, 46, 50, 63

Answers

5. $2h(6h^3 + 4h - 3)$
6. $3(x^2 - 3x + 1)$
7. $m(9m + 1)$
8. $7n(2n^2 + 1 + n)$
9. $3(12f + 6f^2 + 1)$
14. $(2x^2 + 1)(3x + 2)$
15. $(x^2 + 2)(x + 4)$
16. $(2a^2 + 1)(5a + 2)$
17. $(7r^2 + 6)(r - 5)$
18. $2(m + 2)(m^2 + 3)$
19. $(2b^2 + 5)(2b - 3)$
20. $(3b - 4)(2b - 1)$
21. $2(r - 2)(r - 3)$
22. $(3a^2 + 4)(2a - 3)$
23. $(2m^2 - 3)(m - 3)$
24. $(2 - r)(r - 3)$
25. $(7q - 2)(2q - 3)$
29. $-d^2(4d^2 - d + 3)$
30. $-5f(3 + 2f)$
31. $x^2(-14x^2 + 5)$
32. $11(3d^3 + 2d + 1)$
33. $7c(3c + 2)$
34. $-5g^2(g + 3)$
36. $(-4x + 9)(x + 2)$
37. cannot be factored
38. $(5 + x)(3x - 2)$
42. $(x^2 + 5)(x + 3)$
43. $(2a^2 + 3)(a - 4)$
44. $(2b^2 + 5)(5b - 8)$
45. $(n^2 + 5)(n - 2)$
46. $(x^2 + 4)(7x + 2)$
47. $(6x^2 + 1)(x + 3)$
48. $(d^2 + 3)(2d - 1)$
49. $(2m^2 - 3)(m - 1)$
50. $(5 + 2x)(4 - 3x)$
51. $(b^2 - 2)(b + 4)$
52. $(k^2 - 3)(5 - k)$
53. $(2f^2 - 5)(3f - 4)$

California Standards

Standard	Exercises
2.0	85–88
8.0	81
9.0	82–84
11.0	1–62, 63c–66, 70–80a
25.1	69, 81
25.2	70

CONCEPT CONNECTION **Exercise 68** involves discovering the Zero Product Property. This exercise prepares students for the Concept Connection on page 512.

Answers

65. $(3a - 3b) - (4a - 4b)$
$3(a - b) - 4(a - b)$
$(3 - 4)(a - b)$
$-1(a - b)$
$(b - a)$;
$(3a - 4a) - (3b - 4b)$
$a(3 - 4) - b(3 - 4)$
$(a - b)(3 - 4)$
$(a - b)(-1)$
$(b - a)$

68a. Either a, b, or both must equal 0.
b. The product of t and $(3 - t)$ is 0, so at least one of the factors must be 0.

Fill in the missing part of each factorization.

55. $16v + 12v^2 = 4v(4 + \mathbf{3v})$
56. $15x - 25x^2 = 5x(3 - \mathbf{5x})$
57. $-16k^3 - 24k^2 = -8k^2(\mathbf{2k} + 3)$
58. $-x - 10 = -1(\mathbf{x} + 10)$

Copy and complete the table.

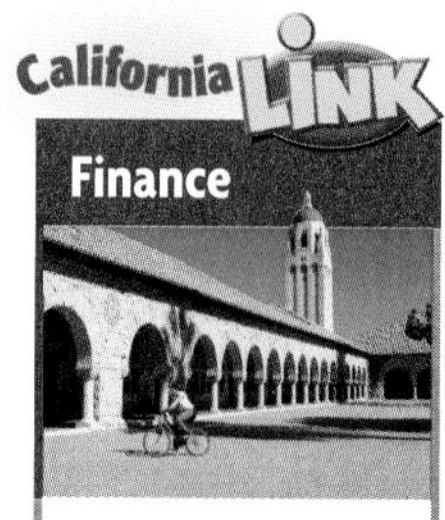

About 76% of undergraduate students at Stanford University receive some form of financial aid to help with their college costs.
Source: Stanford University

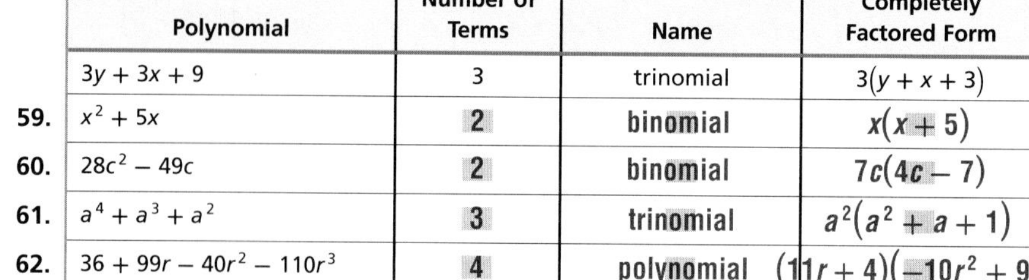

	Polynomial	Number of Terms	Name	Completely Factored Form
	$3y + 3x + 9$	3	trinomial	$3(y + x + 3)$
59.	$x^2 + 5x$	**2**	**binomial**	$x(x + 5)$
60.	$28c^2 - 49c$	**2**	**binomial**	$7c(4c - 7)$
61.	$a^4 + a^3 + a^2$	**3**	**trinomial**	$a^2(a^2 + a + 1)$
62.	$36 + 99r - 40r^2 - 110r^3$	**4**	**polynomial**	$(11r + 4)(-10r^2 + 9)$

63. **Personal Finance** The final amount of money in a certificate of deposit (CD) after n years can be represented by the expression Px^n, where P is the original amount contributed and x is the interest rate.

Year	Original Amount
2004	\$100.00
2005	\$200.00
2006	\$400.00

Justin's aunt purchased CDs to help him pay for college. The table shows the amount of the CD she purchased each year. In 2007, she will pay \$800.00 directly to the college.

a. Each CD has the same interest rate x. Write expressions for the value of the CDs purchased in 2004, 2005, and 2006 when Justin starts college in 2007.
b. Write a polynomial to represent the total value of the CDs purchased in 2004, 2005, and 2006 plus the amount paid to the college in 2007.
c. Factor the polynomial in part **c** by grouping. Evaluate the factored form of the polynomial when the interest rate is 1.09. **$100(x^2 + 4)(x + 2)$; \$1603.12**

63a. $100x^3$; $200x^2$; $400x$
63b. $100x^3 + 200x^2 + 400x + 800$

64. **Write About It** Describe how to find the area of the figure shown. Show each step and write your answer in factored form. **$5x(x + 4)$**

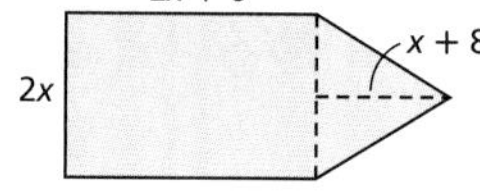

65. **Critical Thinking** Show two methods of factoring the expression $3a - 3b - 4a + 4b$.

66. **Geometry** The area of the triangle is represented by the expression $\frac{1}{2}(x^3 - 2x + 2x^2 - 4)$. The height of the triangle is $x + 2$. Write an expression for the base of the triangle. (*Hint:* The formula for the area of a triangle is $A = \frac{1}{2}bh$.) **$x^2 - 2$**

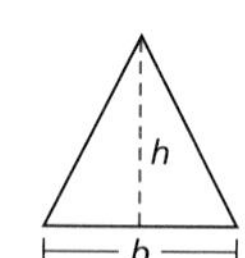

67. **Write About It** Explain how you know when two binomials are opposites.
The sum of opposite binomials is 0.

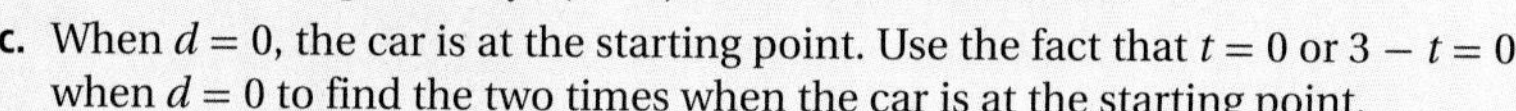

CONCEPT CONNECTION

68. This problem will prepare you for the Concept Connection on page 512.
a. What must be true about either a or b if $ab = 0$?
b. A toy car's distance in feet from the starting point is given by the equation $d = t(3 - t)$. Explain why $t(3 - t) = 0$ means that either $t = 0$ or $3 - t = 0$.
c. When $d = 0$, the car is at the starting point. Use the fact that $t = 0$ or $3 - t = 0$ when $d = 0$ to find the two times when the car is at the starting point.
$t = 0$ and $t = 3$

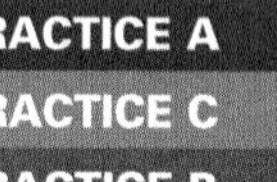

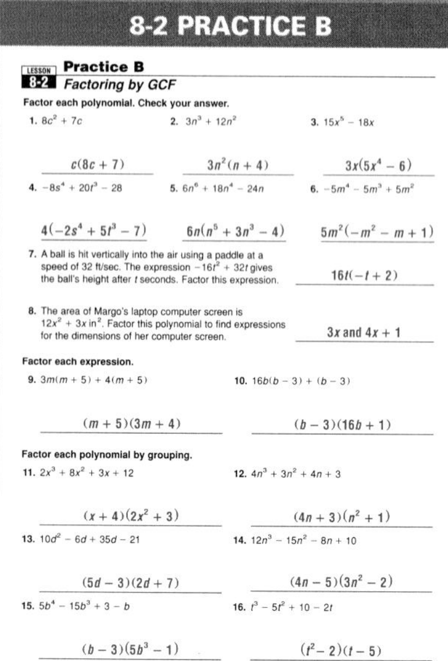

8-2 PRACTICE A
8-2 PRACTICE C
8-2 PRACTICE B

LESSON 8-2 **Practice B**
Factoring by GCF

Factor each polynomial. Check your answer.

1. $8c^2 + 7c$ — $c(8c + 7)$
2. $3n^3 + 12n^2$ — $3n^2(n + 4)$
3. $15x^5 - 18x$ — $3x(5x^4 - 6)$
4. $-8s^4 + 20t^3 - 28$ — $4(-2s^4 + 5t^3 - 7)$
5. $6n^6 + 18n^4 - 24n$ — $6n(n^5 + 3n^3 - 4)$
6. $-5m^4 - 5m^3 + 5m^2$ — $5m^2(-m^2 - m + 1)$
7. A ball is hit vertically into the air using a paddle at a speed of 32 ft/sec. The expression $-16t^2 + 32t$ gives the ball's height after t seconds. Factor this expression. — $16t(-t + 2)$
8. The area of Margo's laptop computer screen is $12x^2 + 3x$ in². Factor this polynomial to find expressions for the dimensions of her computer screen. — $3x$ and $4x + 1$

Factor each expression.

9. $3m(m + 5) + 4(m + 5)$ — $(m + 5)(3m + 4)$
10. $16b(b - 3) + (b - 3)$ — $(b - 3)(16b + 1)$

Factor each polynomial by grouping.

11. $2x^3 + 8x^2 + 3x + 12$ — $(x + 4)(2x^2 + 3)$
12. $4n^3 + 3n^2 + 4n + 3$ — $(4n + 3)(n^2 + 1)$
13. $10d^2 - 6d + 35d - 21$ — $(5d - 3)(2d + 7)$
14. $12n^3 - 15n^2 - 8n + 10$ — $(4n - 5)(3n^2 - 2)$
15. $5b^4 - 15b^3 + 3 - b$ — $(b - 3)(5b^3 - 1)$
16. $t^3 - 5t^2 + 10 - 2t$ — $(t^2 - 2)(t - 5)$

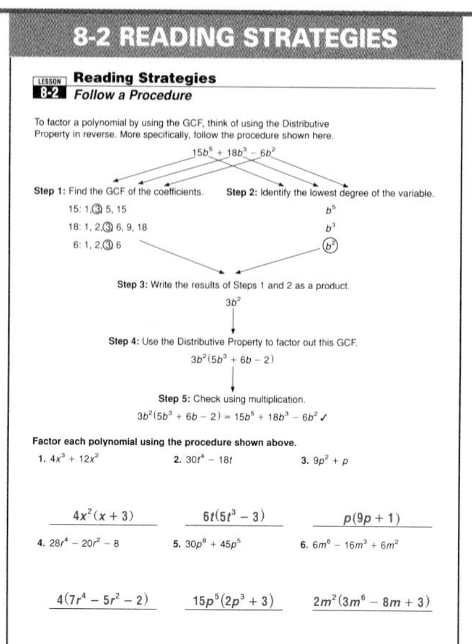

8-2 READING STRATEGIES

LESSON 8-2 **Reading Strategies**
Follow a Procedure

To factor a polynomial by using the GCF, think of using the Distributive Property in reverse. More specifically, follow the procedure shown here.

$15b^5 + 18b^3 - 6b^2$

Step 1: Find the GCF of the coefficients.
15: 1, (3), 5, 15
18: 1, 2, (3), 6, 9, 18
6: 1, 2, (3), 6

Step 2: Identify the lowest degree of the variable.
b^5
b^3
(b^2)

Step 3: Write the results of Steps 1 and 2 as a product.
$3b^2$

Step 4: Use the Distributive Property to factor out this GCF.
$3b^2(5b^3 + 6b - 2)$

Step 5: Check using multiplication.
$3b^2(5b^3 + 6b - 2) = 15b^5 + 18b^3 - 6b^2$ ✓

Factor each polynomial using the procedure shown above.

1. $4x^3 + 12x^2$ — $4x^2(x + 3)$
2. $30t^4 - 18t$ — $6t(5t^3 - 3)$
3. $9p^2 + p$ — $p(9p + 1)$
4. $28r^4 - 20r^2 - 8$ — $4(7r^4 - 5r^2 - 2)$
5. $30p^8 + 45p^5$ — $15p^5(2p^3 + 3)$
6. $6m^8 - 16m^3 + 6m^2$ — $2m^2(3m^6 - 8m + 3)$

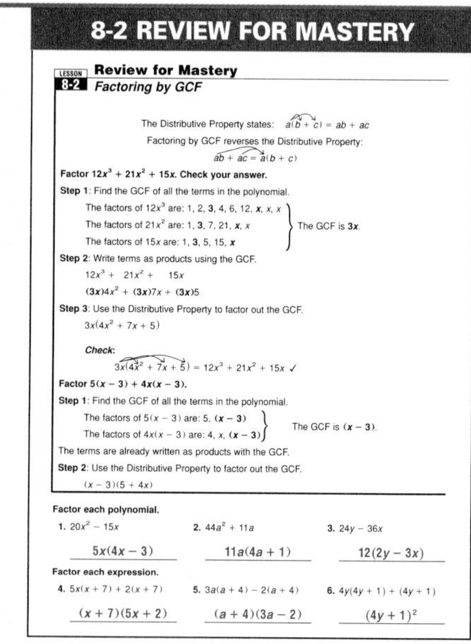

8-2 REVIEW FOR MASTERY

LESSON 8-2 **Review for Mastery**
Factoring by GCF

The Distributive Property states: $a(b + c) = ab + ac$
Factoring by GCF reverses the Distributive Property:
$ab + ac = a(b + c)$

Factor $12x^3 + 21x^2 + 15x$. Check your answer.

Step 1: Find the GCF of all the terms in the polynomial.
The factors of $12x^3$ are: 1, 2, **3**, 4, 6, 12, ***x***, x, x
The factors of $21x^2$ are: 1, **3**, 7, 21, ***x***, x
The factors of $15x$ are: 1, **3**, 5, 15, ***x***
The GCF is **3*x***.

Step 2: Write terms as products using the GCF.
$12x^3 + 21x^2 + 15x$
$(3x)4x^2 + (3x)7x + (3x)5$

Step 3: Use the Distributive Property to factor out the GCF.
$3x(4x^2 + 7x + 5)$

Check:
$3x(4x^2 + 7x + 5) = 12x^3 + 21x^2 + 15x$ ✓

Factor $5(x - 3) + 4x(x - 3)$.

Step 1: Find the GCF of all the terms in the polynomial.
The factors of $5(x - 3)$ are: 5, $(x - 3)$
The factors of $4x(x - 3)$ are: 4, x, $(x - 3)$
The GCF is $(x - 3)$.
The terms are already written as products with the GCF.

Step 2: Use the Distributive Property to factor out the GCF.
$(x - 3)(5 + 4x)$

Factor each polynomial.

1. $20x^2 - 15x$ — $5x(4x - 3)$
2. $44a^2 + 11a$ — $11a(4a + 1)$
3. $24y - 36x$ — $12(2y - 3x)$

Factor each expression.

4. $5x(x + 7) + 2(x + 7)$ — $(x + 7)(5x + 2)$
5. $3a(a + 4) - 2(a + 4)$ — $(a + 4)(3a - 2)$
6. $4y(4y + 1) + (4y + 1)$ — $(4y + 1)^2$

69. **Reasoning** Fill in each blank with a property or definition that justifies the step.

$7x^3 + 2x + 21x^2 + 6 = 7x^3 + 21x^2 + 2x + 6$ a. ____?____

$= (7x^3 + 21x^2) + (2x + 6)$ b. ____?____

$= 7x^2(x + 3) + 2(x + 3)$ c. ____?____

$= (x + 3)(7x^2 + 2)$ d. ____?____

69a. Comm. Prop. of Add.
b. Assoc. Prop. of Add.
c. Dist. Prop.
d. Dist. Prop.

70. **ERROR ANALYSIS** Which factorization of $3n^3 - n^2$ is incorrect? Explain.

A
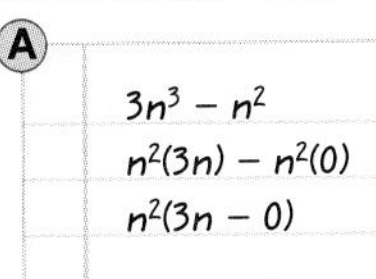

B
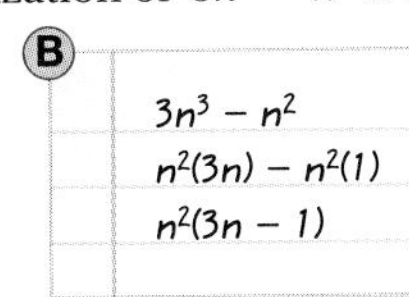

A is incorrect because $n^2 \neq n^2 \cdot 0$.

Multiple Choice For Exercises 71–73, choose the best answer.

71. Which is the complete factorization of $24x^3 - 12x^2$?

(A) $6(4x^3 - 2x^2)$ (B) $12(2x^3 - x^2)$ (C) $12x(2x^2 - x)$ **(D)** $12x^2(2x - 1)$

72. Which is NOT a factor of $18x^2 + 36x$?

(A) 1 **(B)** $4x$ (C) $x + 2$ (D) $18x$

73. The area of a rectangle is represented by the polynomial $x^2 + 3x - 6x - 18$. Which of the following could represent the length and width of the rectangle?

(A) Length: $x + 3$; width: $x + 6$
(C) Length: $x + 3$; width: $x - 6$
(B) Length: $x - 3$; width: $x - 6$
(D) Length: $x - 3$; width: $x + 6$

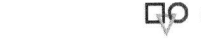

CHALLENGE AND EXTEND

Factor each polynomial. Check your answer.

74. $6ab^2 - 24a^2$ 75. $-72a^2b^2 - 45ab$ $-9ab(8ab + 5)$ 76. $-18a^2b^2 + 21ab$ $-3ab(6ab - 7)$

77. $ab + bc + ad + cd$ 78. $4y^2 + 8ay - y - 2a$ 79. $x^3 - 4x^2 + 3x - 12$

74. $6a(b^2 - 4a)$
77. $(a + c)(b + d)$
78. $(4y - 1)(y + 2a)$
79. $(x^2 + 3)(x - 4)$

80. **Geometry** The area between two concentric circles is called an *annulus*. The formula for area of an annulus is $A = \pi R^2 - \pi r^2$, where R is the radius of the larger circle and r is the radius of the smaller circle. $A = \pi(R^2 - r^2)$

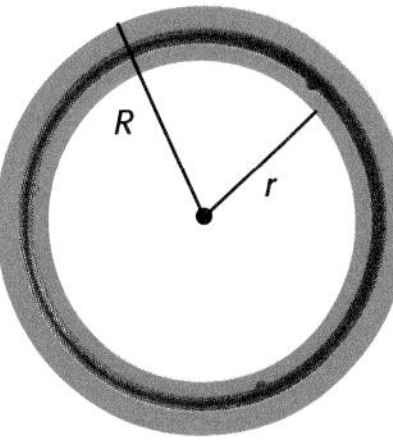

a. Factor the formula for area of an annulus by using the GCF.

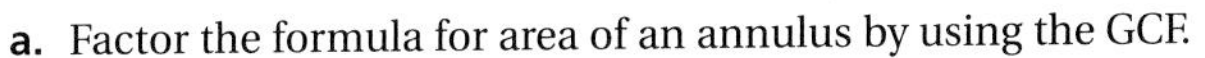

b. Use the factored form to find the area of an annulus with $R = 12$ cm and $r = 5$ cm. $A \approx 374$ cm^2

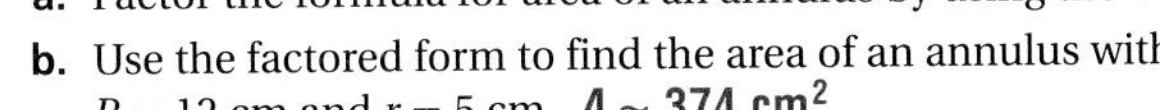

SPIRAL STANDARDS REVIEW

2.0, 8.0, 9.0, 25.1

81. The coordinates of the vertices of a quadrilateral are $A(-2, 5)$, $B(6, 5)$, $C(4, -3)$, and $D(-4, -3)$. Use slope to show that $ABCD$ is a parallelogram. *(Lesson 5-7)*

81. $\overline{AB}$ and $\overline{CD}$ are both horiz., so they have the same slope and are par. The slope of both $\overline{AD}$ and $\overline{BC}$ is 4, so they are par. Two pairs of par. sides define a parallelogram.

Solve each system by elimination. *(Lesson 6-3)*

82. $\begin{cases} x + 2y = 11 \\ 2x - y = 2 \end{cases}$ (3, 4) 83. $\begin{cases} -2x + 2y = 14 \\ x - 3y = -19 \end{cases}$ (−1, 6) 84. $\begin{cases} 3x + 3y = 12 \\ x - 7y = -12 \end{cases}$ (2, 2)

Simplify. *(Lesson 7-4)*

85. $\frac{5^6}{5^4}$ 5^2 86. $\frac{4^5 \cdot 4^2}{4^6}$ 4 87. $\frac{x^5y^3z}{y^3z^4}$ $\frac{x^5}{z^3}$ 88. $\frac{x^8y^3z^7}{x^2y^4z}$ $\frac{x^6z^6}{y}$

Teaching Tip

Multiple Choice If students have difficulty with **Exercise 71,** remind them that a complete factorization means that the terms *inside* the parentheses have no common factors. That eliminates all options except **D.**

If students chose **C** for **Exercise 72,** they may have forgotten that a binomial can be a factor of a binomial. Remind them that $ab + ac = a(b + c)$. Then point out that 4 is not a factor of 18, which means that **B** is the correct answer.

Journal

Have students use examples to describe how to determine whether a polynomial with four terms can be factored into two binomial expressions.

ALTERNATIVE ASSESSMENT

Have students write three polynomial expressions such that one expression cannot be factored, another has a monomial GCF, and the third has a binomial GCF.

Power Presentations with PowerPoint®

8-2 Lesson Quiz

Factor each polynomial. Check your answer.

1. $16x + 20x^3$ $4x(4 + 5x^2)$
2. $4m^4 - 12m^2 + 8m$ $4m(m^3 - 3m + 2)$

Factor each expression.

3. $7k(k - 3) + 4(k - 3)$ $(k - 3)(7k + 4)$
4. $3y(2y + 3) - 5(2y + 3)$ $(2y + 3)(3y - 5)$

Factor each polynomial by grouping. Check your answer.

5. $2x^3 + x^2 - 6x - 3$ $(2x + 1)(x^2 - 3)$
6. $7p^4 - 2p^3 + 63p - 18$ $(7p - 2)(p^3 + 9)$
7. A rocket is fired vertically into the air at 40 m/s. The expression $-5t^2 + 40t + 20$ gives the rocket's height after t seconds. Factor this expression. $-5(t^2 - 8t - 4)$

Also available on transparency

8-2 PROBLEM SOLVING

LESSON 8-2 **Problem Solving**
Factoring by GCF

Write the correct answer.

1. The area of a rug, which is shaped like a rectangle, is $4x^2 + 4x$ square feet. Factor this polynomial to find expressions for the dimensions of the rug.
$4x$ ft; $(x + 1)$ ft

2. The number of customers visiting a local museum since the year 2000 can be modeled by the expression $-3x^2 - 27x + 825$, where x is the number of years since 2000. Factor this polynomial.
$-3(x^2 + 9x - 275)$

3. The perimeter of a rhombus is $12x + 28$ feet. Factor this expression. Then find the length of one side if $x = 8$. (*Hint:* A rhombus is a parallelogram with four congruent sides.)
$4(3x + 7)$; 31 feet

4. The foundation for a new high school building is rectangular in shape, and the area is $5x^3 + 4x^2 - 10x - 8$ square meters. Factor by grouping to find expressions for the dimensions of the building.
$(5x + 4)$ m; $(x^2 - 2)$ m

The diagram shows four sections of an herb garden. Use the figure to answer questions 5–8. Select the best answer.

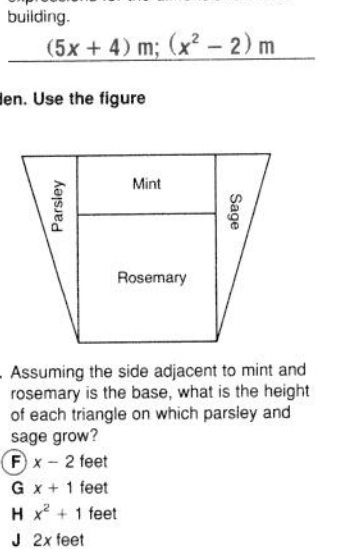
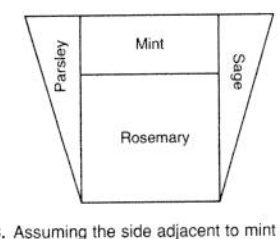

5. The section where rosemary grows is square and has an area of $4x^2$ square feet. What is the length of one side?
A x feet **(C)** $2x$ feet
B x^2 feet D $4x$ feet

6. Rosemary and mint cover $6x^2 - 2x$ square feet. Assuming the length is adjacent to rosemary, what is the width of the mint section?
F $2x$ feet H $2x - 2$ feet
(G) $x - 1$ feet J $3x - 1$ feet

7. The parsley and sage sections each have an area of $\frac{1}{2}(3x^2 - 6x - x + 2)$ square feet. Factor $3x^2 - 6x - x + 2$. What are the base and height of each triangular section?
A $2x - 3$ feet; $x + 1$ feet
B $2x - 3$ feet; $x^2 + 1$ feet
(C) $3x - 1$ feet; $x - 2$ feet
D $3x - 1$ feet; $x^2 - 2$ feet

8. Assuming the side adjacent to mint and rosemary is the base, what is the height of each triangle on which parsley and sage grow?
(F) $x - 2$ feet
G $x + 1$ feet
H $x^2 + 1$ feet
J $2x$ feet

8-2 CHALLENGE

LESSON 8-2 **Challenge**
More Factoring by Grouping

Factoring by grouping requires 4 or more terms. When a polynomial has 3 terms, it is possible to divide the middle term into two terms and factor by grouping. When deciding on which two terms to use, think of terms that will have a common factor with the first and last terms. If that pair doesn't work, change the order of the pairs, or try another pair.

$x^2 + \mathbf{10x} + 21$
$x^2 + \mathbf{3x} + \mathbf{7x} + 21$
$(x^2 + 3x) + (7x + 21)$
$x(x + 3) + 7(x + 3)$
$(x + 3)(x + 7)$

Divide the *b* term into two separate terms. Then factor by grouping.

1. $x^2 + 8x + 12$ $(x + 6)(x + 2)$
2. $x^2 - 13x + 42$ $(x - 6)(x - 7)$
3. $2x^2 + 13x + 21$ $(2x + 7)(x + 3)$
4. $10x^2 + 19x + 6$ $(5x + 2)(2x + 3)$
5. $5x^2 + 19x + 12$ $(5x + 4)(x + 3)$
6. $4x^2 - 16x + 15$ $(2x - 5)(2x - 3)$

When a polynomial has more than 4 terms, it is sometimes possible to factor by grouping.

$(x^3 + 4x^2) + (x^2 + 4x) + (3x + 12)$
$x^2(x + 4) + x(x + 4) + 3(x + 4)$
$(x + 4)(x^2 + x + 3)$

Factor by grouping.

7. $(x^3 + x^2) + (x^2 + x) + (x + 1)$ $(x + 1)(x^2 + x + 1)$
8. $(3x^3 - 6x^2) + (4x^2 - 8x) + (5x - 10)$ $(x - 2)(3x^2 + 4x + 5)$

Factor by grouping in groups of three. You may need to rearrange the terms.

9. $x^6 + 5x^5 + 7x^4 + 3x^2 + 15x + 21$ $(x^4 + 3)(x^2 + 5x + 7)$
10. $6x^{10} + 24x^9 + 48x^8 + 7x^6 + 28x^5 + 56x^4 + 3x^2 + 12x + 24$ $(6x^8 + 7x^4 + 3)(x^2 + 4x + 8)$

Organizer

Use with Lesson 8-3

Objective: Model and factor trinomials of the form $x^2 + bx + c$.

Materials: algebra tiles

Online Edition

Countdown to Mastery Week 18

Teach

Discuss

Remind students that a square is a rectangle, so their algebra tile (MK) arrangements may form a square.

In **Activity 2,** additional x-tiles were used because there were originally not enough to fill the empty spaces.

Tell students to check their answers by multiplying the factors.

Alternative Approach

Use the transparency mat and transparency algebra tiles (MK).

8-3

Model Factorization of $x^2 + bx + c$

You can use algebra tiles to express a trinomial as a product of two binomials. This is called factoring a trinomial.

Use with Lesson 8-3

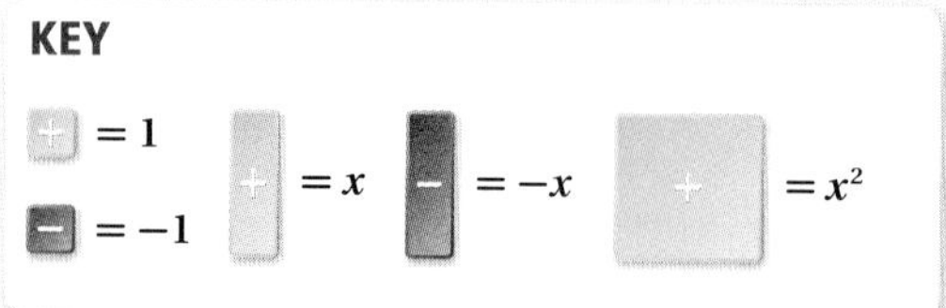

California Standards

11.0 Students apply basic factoring techniques to second- and simple third-**degree polynomials.** These techniques include finding a common factor for all terms in a polynomial, recognizing the difference of two squares, and recognizing perfect squares of binomials.

Activity 1

Use algebra tiles to factor $x^2 + 7x + 6$.

MODEL		ALGEBRA
	Model $x^2 + 7x + 6$.	$x^2 + 7x + 6$
	Try to arrange all of the tiles in a rectangle. Start by placing the x^2-tile in the upper left corner. *Arrange the unit tiles in a rectangle so that the top left corner of this rectangle touches the bottom right corner of the x^2-tile.* *Arrange the x-tiles so that all the tiles together make one large rectangle.* *This arrangement does not work because two x-tiles are left over.*	$x^2 + 7x + 6 \neq (x + 2)(x + 3)$
	Rearrange the unit tiles to form another rectangle.	
$x + 6$ $x + 1$	*Fill in the empty spaces with x-tiles. All 7 x-tiles fit. This is the correct arrangement.* *The total area represents the trinomial. The length and width represent the factors.*	$x^2 + 7x + 6 = (x + 1)(x + 6)$

The rectangle has width $x + 1$ and length $x + 6$. So $x^2 + 7x + 6 = (x + 1)(x + 6)$.

Answers to *Try This*

1. $(x + 1)(x + 1)$
2. $(x + 1)(x + 2)$
3. $(x + 1)(x + 5)$
4. $(x + 3)(x + 3)$
5. $(x + 1)(x + 4)$
6. $(x + 2)(x + 4)$
7. $(x + 2)(x + 3)$
8. $(x + 2)(x + 6)$

California Standards

Algebra 1 11.0

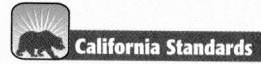

Try This

Use algebra tiles to factor each trinomial.

1. $x^2 + 2x + 1$
2. $x^2 + 3x + 2$
3. $x^2 + 6x + 5$
4. $x^2 + 6x + 9$
5. $x^2 + 5x + 4$
6. $x^2 + 6x + 8$
7. $x^2 + 5x + 6$
8. $x^2 + 8x + 12$

Activity 2

Use algebra tiles to factor $x^2 + x - 2$.

MODEL		ALGEBRA
	Model $x^2 + x - 2$.	$x^2 + x - 2$
	Start by placing the x^2-tile in the upper left corner. *Arrange the unit tiles in a rectangle so that the top left corner of this rectangle touches the bottom right corner of the x^2-tile.* *To make a rectangle, you need to fill in the empty spaces, but there aren't enough x-tiles to fill in the empty spaces.*	
	Add a zero pair. Arrange the x-tiles to complete the rectangle. *The tiles in each row of the rectangle must be the same color.*	
x + 2; x − 1	*The total area represents the trinomial. The length and width represent the factors.*	$x^2 + x - 2 = (x - 1)(x + 2)$

The rectangle has width $x - 1$ and length $x + 2$. So, $x^2 + x - 2 = (x - 1)(x + 2)$.

Try This

9. Why can you add one red $-x$-tile and one yellow x-tile?

Use algebra tiles to factor each polynomial.

10. $x^2 - x - 2$
11. $x^2 - 2x - 3$
12. $x^2 - 5x + 4$
13. $x^2 - 7x + 10$
14. $x^2 - 2x + 1$
15. $x^2 - 6x + 5$
16. $x^2 + 5x - 6$
17. $x^2 + 3x - 4$
18. $x^2 - x - 6$
19. $x^2 + 3x - 10$
20. $x^2 - 2x - 8$
21. $x^2 + x - 12$

Close

Key Concept

You can factor trinomials by arranging the tiles into a rectangle such that the x^2-tile is in the upper left, the unit tiles are in the lower right, and the x-tiles fill in the remaining spaces. The dimensions of the rectangle are the factors.

Assessment

Journal Have students explain how to model and factor trinomial expressions. Explanations should include what to do when there are not enough x-tiles to fill the empty spaces.

Answers to *Try This*

9. Adding $-x$ and x gives you 0, so if you add both tiles, you don't change the value of the polynomial.
10. $(x - 2)(x + 1)$
11. $(x - 3)(x + 1)$
12. $(x - 1)(x - 4)$
13. $(x - 2)(x - 5)$
14. $(x - 1)(x - 1)$
15. $(x - 1)(x - 5)$
16. $(x - 1)(x + 6)$
17. $(x - 1)(x + 4)$
18. $(x - 3)(x + 2)$
19. $(x - 2)(x + 5)$
20. $(x - 4)(x + 2)$
21. $(x - 3)(x + 4)$

Teacher to Teacher

I have found that using algebra tiles really helps students achieve success with algebraic concepts. Since students are already familiar with the area of rectangles, connecting the factors of a trinomial with the dimensions of a rectangle provides a comfortable introduction to factoring trinomials.

Make sure that everyone knows what to call each tile so that students can discuss the ideas constructively in class and with each other outside of class.

Vicki Petty
Murfreesboro, TN

8-3 Organizer

Objective: Factor quadratic trinomials of the form $x^2 + bx + c$.

Online Edition
Tutorial Videos, Interactivity

Countdown to Mastery Week 18

Power Presentations with PowerPoint®

Warm Up

1. Which pair of factors of 8 has a sum of 9? 1 and 8
2. Which pair of factors of 30 has a sum of −17? −2 and −15

Multiply.

3. $(x + 2)(x + 3)$ $x^2 + 5x + 6$
4. $(r + 5)(r - 9)$ $r^2 - 4r - 45$

Also available on transparency

Math Humor

Q: What did the two binomials say when they were multiplied?

A: Curses! FOILed again!

California Standards

Algebra 1 11.0

8-3 Factoring $x^2 + bx + c$

California Standards

11.0 Students apply basic factoring techniques to second- and simple third-**degree polynomials.** These techniques include finding a common factor for all terms in a polynomial, recognizing the difference of two squares, and recognizing perfect squares of binomials.

Why learn this?

Factoring polynomials will help you find the dimensions of rectangular shapes, such as a fountain. (See Exercise 77.)

In Chapter 7, you learned how to multiply two binomials using the Distributive Property or the FOIL method. In this lesson, you will learn how to factor a trinomial into two binomials.

Notice that when you multiply $(x + 2)(x + 5)$, the constant term in the trinomial is the product of the constants in the binomials.

$$(x + 2)(x + 5) = x^2 + 7x + 10$$

Use this fact to factor some trinomials into binomial factors. Look for two integers (positive or negative) that are factors of the constant term in the trinomial. Write two binomials with those integers, and then multiply to check.

If no two factors of the constant term work, we say the trinomial is not factorable.

EXAMPLE 1 Factoring Trinomials

Factor $x^2 + 19x + 60$. Check your answer.

$(\square + \square)(\square + \square)$ *Write two sets of parentheses.*

$(x + \square)(x + \square)$ *The first term is x^2, so the variable terms have a coefficient of 1.*

The constant term in the trinomial is 60.

Try integer factors of 60 for the constant terms in the binomials.

$(x + 1)(x + 60) = x^2 + 61x + 60$ ✗

$(x + 2)(x + 30) = x^2 + 32x + 60$ ✗

$(x + 3)(x + 20) = x^2 + 23x + 60$ ✗

$(x + 4)(x + 15) = x^2 + 19x + 60$ ✓

The factors of $x^2 + 19x + 60$ are $(x + 4)$ and $(x + 15)$.

$x^2 + 19x + 60 = (x + 4)(x + 15)$

Check $(x + 4)(x + 15) = x^2 + 15x + 4x + 60$ *Use the FOIL method.*

$= x^2 + 19x + 60$ ✓ *The product is the original trinomial.*

Remember!

When you multiply two binomials, multiply:
First terms
Outer terms
Inner terms
Last terms

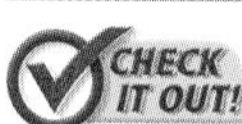

Factor each trinomial. Check your answer.

1a. $x^2 + 10x + 24$ **1b.** $x^2 + 7x + 12$ $(x + 4)(x + 3)$

1a. $(x + 4)(x + 6)$

1 Introduce

EXPLORATION

8-3 Factoring $x^2 + bx + c$

Look for patterns as you multiply binomials. The patterns that you discover will help you factor trinomials.

1. Complete the table by multiplying the binomial factors. Write the products as trinomials in the standard form $x^2 + bx + c$.

Factors	Product
$(x + 2)(x + 4)$	
$(x + 5)(x + 3)$	
$(x + 3)(x - 7)$	
$(x - 5)(x + 2)$	
$(x - 5)(x - 9)$	

2. Look at the constant terms of the trinomials. How are these related to the constant terms of the binomial factors?
3. Look at the coefficients of the middle terms of the trinomials. How are these related to the constant terms of the binomial factors?

THINK AND DISCUSS

4. **Discuss** what you know about the constant terms of the binomial factors of $x^2 + 10x + 24$.
5. **Explain** how you know that $(x + 12)(x + 2)$ is not a correct factorization of $x^2 + 10x + 24$.

Motivate

Ask students when they have seen inverse operations—for example, addition and subtraction, multiplication and division, squaring a number and finding its square root. Tell students that in this lesson, they will learn how to undo binomial multiplication by factoring.

Explorations and answers are provided in *Alternate Openers: Explorations Transparencies*.

The method of factoring used in Example 1 can be made more efficient. Look at the product of $(x + a)$ and $(x + b)$.

$$(x+a)(x+b) = x^2 + ax + bx + ab$$
$$= x^2 + (a+b)x + ab$$

The coefficient of the middle term is the sum of a and b. The third term is the product of a and b.

Factoring $x^2 + bx + c$

WORDS	EXAMPLE
To factor a quadratic trinomial of the form $x^2 + bx + c$, find two integer factors of c whose sum is b. If no such integers exist, we say the trinomial is not factorable.	To factor $x^2 + 9x + 18$, look for integer factors of 18 whose sum is 9. Factors of 18 | Sum 1 and 18 | 19 ✗ 2 and 9 | 11 ✗ 3 and 6 | 9 ✓ $x^2 + 9x + 18$ $(x+3)(x+6)$

When c is positive, its factors have the same sign. The sign of b tells you whether the factors are positive or negative. When b is positive, the factors are positive, and when b is negative, the factors are negative.

EXAMPLE 2 Factoring $x^2 + bx + c$ When c Is Positive

Factor each trinomial. Check your answer.

A $x^2 + 6x + 8$

$(x + \square)(x + \square)$ *$b = 6$ and $c = 8$; look for factors of 8 whose sum is 6.*

Factors of 8	Sum	
1 and 8	9	✗
2 and 4	6	✓

The factors needed are 2 and 4.

$(x+2)(x+4)$

Check $(x + 2)(x + 4) = x^2 + 4x + 2x + 8$ *Use the FOIL method.*

$= x^2 + 6x + 8$ ✓ *The product is the original trinomial.*

B $x^2 + 5x + 6$

$(x + \square)(x + \square)$ *$b = 5$ and $c = 6$; look for factors of 6 whose sum is 5.*

Factors of 6	Sum	
1 and 6	7	✗
2 and 3	5	✓

The factors needed are 2 and 3.

$(x+2)(x+3)$

Check $(x + 2)(x + 3) = x^2 + 3x + 2x + 6$ *Use the FOIL method.*

$= x^2 + 5x + 6$ ✓ *The product is the original trinomial.*

Power Presentations with PowerPoint®

Additional Examples

Example 1

Factor $x^2 + 15x + 36$. Check your answer.

$(x + 3)(x + 12)$

Example 2

Factor each trinomial. Check your answer.

A. $x^2 + 6x + 5$ $(x + 1)(x + 5)$

B. $x^2 + 6x + 9$ $(x + 3)(x + 3)$

C. $x^2 - 8x + 15$ $(x - 3)(x - 5)$

Also available on transparency

INTERVENTION

Questioning Strategies

EXAMPLE 1

- For which number do you try different pairs of factors?

EXAMPLE 2

- What does the sign of c tell you about the factors? Explain.
- What does the sign of b tell you about the factors? Explain.

Visual Suggest that students write down what the product of the two constants in the binomials should be and what their sum should be. They can write "P": and "S": next to the trinomial as a reminder to themselves.

$x^2 + 13x + 36$ P: 36

S: 13

2 Teach

Guided Instruction

Review the FOIL method before factoring any trinomials. Remind students that the FOIL method is an application of the Distributive Property. Have students examine the product of two binomials, such as $(x + 2)(x + 3) = x^2 + 5x + 6$, and discuss where each term in the trinomial came from. Lead them to see that $5x$ came from the sum of like terms $2x$ and $3x$ and that 6 came from the product of constants 2 and 3.

Universal Access

Through Graphic Organizers

Have students make a chart like the one below, filling in their own examples. Then have students factor each example.

b	c	Sign of Factors	Example
+	+	Both positive	$x^2 + 5x + 4$
−	+	Factor with greater abs. val. is negative.	$n^2 - 6n + 8$
−	−	Both negative	$t^2 - t - 6$
+	−	Factor with greater abs. val. is positive.	$q^2 + 3q - 18$

Power Presentations with PowerPoint®

Additional Examples

Example 3

Factor each trinomial.

A. $x^2 + x - 20$ $(x + 5)(x - 4)$

B. $x^2 - 3x - 18$ $(x - 6)(x + 3)$

Also available on transparency

INTERVENTION

Questioning Strategies

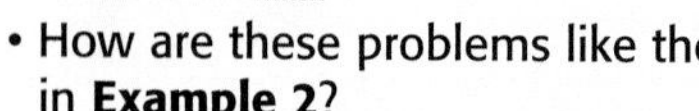

EXAMPLE 3

- How are these problems like those in **Example 2**?
- What does the sign of c tell you about the factors? Explain.
- How do you know which factor will be positive and which will be negative? Explain.

Inclusion As students begin to factor trinomials in which c is negative, remind them that absolute value is a number's distance from 0 on a number line.

Factor each trinomial. Check your answer.

C $x^2 - 10x + 16$

$(x + \square)(x + \square)$ *$b = -10$ and $c = 16$; look for factors of 16 whose sum is -10.*

Factors of 16	Sum	
−1 and −16	−17	✗
−2 and −8	−10	✓
−4 and −4	−8	✗

The factors needed are -2 and -8.

$(x - 2)(x - 8)$

Check $(x - 2)(x - 8) = x^2 - 8x - 2x + 16$ *Use the FOIL method.*

$= x^2 - 10x + 16$ ✓ *The product is the original trinomial.*

Factor each trinomial. Check your answer.

2a. $x^2 + 8x + 12$ $(x + 6)(x + 2)$ **2b.** $x^2 - 5x + 6$ $(x - 2)(x - 3)$

2c. $x^2 + 13x + 42$ $(x + 6)(x + 7)$ **2d.** $x^2 - 13x + 40$ $(x - 8)(x - 5)$

When c is negative, its factors have opposite signs. The sign of b tells you which factor is positive and which is negative. The factor with the greater absolute value has the same sign as b.

EXAMPLE 3 Factoring $x^2 + bx + c$ When c Is Negative

Factor each trinomial.

A $x^2 + 7x - 18$

$(x + \square)(x + \square)$ *$b = 7$ and $c = -18$; look for factors of -18 whose sum is 7. The factor with the greater absolute value is positive.*

Factors of −18	Sum	
−1 and 18	17	✗
−2 and 9	7	✓
−3 and 6	3	✗

The factors needed are -2 and 9.

$(x - 2)(x + 9)$

Helpful Hint

If you have trouble remembering the rules for which factor is positive and which is negative, you can try all the factor pairs and check their sums.

B $x^2 - 5x - 24$

$(x + \square)(x + \square)$ *$b = -5$ and $c = -24$; look for factors of -24 whose sum is -5. The factor with the greater absolute value is negative.*

Factors of −24	Sum	
1 and −24	−23	✗
2 and −12	−10	✗
3 and −8	−5	✓
4 and −6	−2	✗

The factors needed are 3 and -8.

$(x + 3)(x - 8)$

CHECK IT OUT! Factor each trinomial. Check your answer.

3a. $x^2 + 2x - 15$ **3b.** $x^2 - 6x + 8$ **3c.** $x^2 - 8x - 20$ $(x - 10)(x + 2)$

3a. $(x + 5)(x - 3)$

3b. $(x - 4)(x - 2)$

Answer to *Check It Out*

4.

n	$n^2 - 7n + 10$	$(n - 5)(n - 2)$
0	$0^2 - 7(0) + 10 = 10$	$(0 - 5)(0 - 2) = 10$
1	$1^2 - 7(1) + 10 = 4$	$(1 - 5)(1 - 2) = 4$
2	$2^2 - 7(2) + 10 = 0$	$(2 - 5)(2 - 2) = 0$
3	$3^2 - 7(3) + 10 = -2$	$(3 - 5)(3 - 2) = -2$
4	$4^2 - 7(4) + 10 = -2$	$(4 - 5)(4 - 2) = -2$

A polynomial and the factored form of the polynomial are equivalent expressions. When you evaluate these two expressions for the same value of the variable, the results are the same.

EXAMPLE 4 Evaluating Polynomials

Factor $n^2 + 11n + 24$. Show that the original polynomial and the factored form have the same value for $n = 0, 1, 2, 3,$ and 4.

$n^2 + 11n + 24$

$(n + \square)(n + \square)$ *$b = 11$ and $c = 24$; look for factors of 24 whose sum is 11.*

Factors of 24	Sum	
1 and 24	25	✗
2 and 12	14	✗
3 and 8	11	✓
4 and 6	10	✗

The factors needed are 3 and 8.

$(n + 3)(n + 8)$

Evaluate the original polynomial and the factored form for $n = 0, 1, 2, 3,$ and 4.

n	$n^2 + 11n + 24$
0	$0^2 + 11(0) + 24 = 24$
1	$1^2 + 11(1) + 24 = 36$
2	$2^2 + 11(2) + 24 = 50$
3	$3^2 + 11(3) + 24 = 66$
4	$4^2 + 11(4) + 24 = 84$

n	$(n + 3)(n + 8)$
0	$(0 + 3)(0 + 8) = 24$
1	$(1 + 3)(1 + 8) = 36$
2	$(2 + 3)(2 + 8) = 50$
3	$(3 + 3)(3 + 8) = 66$
4	$(4 + 3)(4 + 8) = 84$

The original polynomial and the factored form have the same value for the given values of n.

CHECK IT OUT!

4. Factor $n^2 - 7n + 10$. Show that the original polynomial and the factored form have the same value for $n = 0, 1, 2, 3,$ and 4.

$(n - 5)(n - 2)$

THINK AND DISCUSS

1. Explain in your own words how to factor $x^2 + 9x + 14$. Show how to check your answer.
2. Explain how you can determine the signs of the factors of c when factoring a trinomial of the form $x^2 + bx + c$.

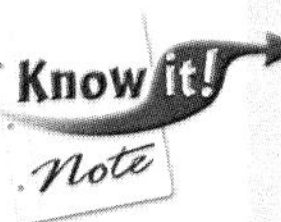
Know it!
Note

3. **GET ORGANIZED** Copy and complete the graphic organizer. In each box, write an example of a trinomial with the given properties and factor it.

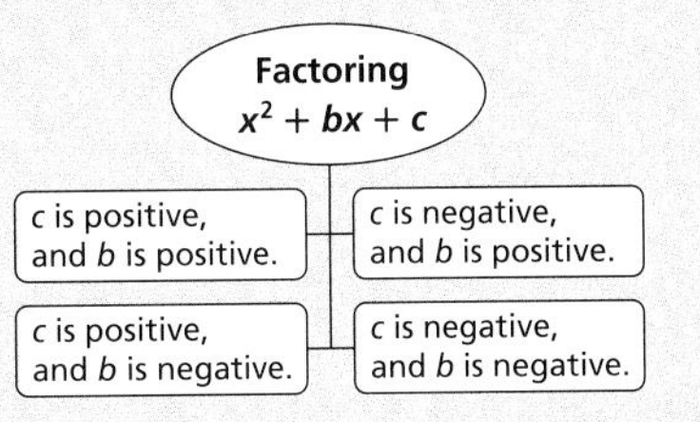
Factoring
$x^2 + bx + c$
c is positive, and b is positive.
c is negative, and b is positive.
c is positive, and b is negative.
c is negative, and b is negative.

COMMON ERROR ALERT

When factoring a trinomial with a negative c, students may write a minus sign in the binomial factor with the greater constant term. Remind students that the binomial factor with the greater constant term should have the same sign as b.

Power Presentations with PowerPoint®

Additional Examples

Example 4

Factor $y^2 + 10y + 21$. Show that the original polynomial and the factored form have the same value for $y = 0, 1, 2, 3,$ and 4.

$(y + 7)(y + 3)$

y	$y^2 + 10y + 21$
0	$0^2 + 10(0) + 21 = 21$
1	$1^2 + 10(1) + 21 = 32$
2	$2^2 + 10(2) + 21 = 45$
3	$3^2 + 10(3) + 21 = 60$
4	$4^2 + 10(4) + 21 = 77$

y	$(y + 7)(y + 3)$
0	$(0 + 7)(0 + 3) = 21$
1	$(1 + 7)(1 + 3) = 32$
2	$(2 + 7)(2 + 3) = 45$
3	$(3 + 7)(3 + 3) = 60$
4	$(4 + 7)(4 + 3) = 77$

Also available on transparency

INTERVENTION
Questioning Strategies

EXAMPLE 4

- How would you know if the trinomial was not factored correctly?

3 Close

Summarize

Review with students how to factor trinomials of all four types: two cases when c is positive and two cases when c is negative.

FORMATIVE ASSESSMENT and INTERVENTION

***Diagnose Before* the Lesson**
8-3 Warm Up, TE p. 496

***Monitor During* the Lesson**
Check It Out! Exercises, SE pp. 496–499
Questioning Strategies, TE pp. 497–499

***Assess After* the Lesson**
8-3 Lesson Quiz, TE p. 503
Alternative Assessment, TE p. 503

Answers to *Think and Discuss*

Possible answers:

1. Find the 2 factors of 14 that have a sum of 9: 2 and 7. Then use these numbers as the constants in the factors: $(x + 2)(x + 7)$.
2. For $x^2 + bx + c = (x + m)(x + n)$, if $c > 0$ and $b > 0$, $m > 0$ and $n > 0$. If $c > 0$ and $b < 0$, $m < 0$ and $n < 0$. If $c < 0$ and $b > 0$, the greater of m and n is positive and the lesser is negative. If $c < 0$ and $b < 0$, the greater of m and n is negative and the lesser is positive.
3. See p. A6.

8-3 Exercises

Assignment Guide

Assign *Guided Practice* exercises as necessary.

If you finished Examples **1–2**
Proficient 20–31, 66, 76, 77, 83
Advanced 20–31, 76, 77, 83, 89

If you finished Examples **1–4**
Proficient 20–56, 59, 67–82, 83–89 odd, 92–102
Advanced 20–38, 43, 57–65 odd, 67–102

Homework Quick Check
Quickly check key concepts.
Exercises: 20, 28, 36, 38, 59, 68

Answers

1. $(x+4)(x+9)$
2. $(x+3)(x+8)$
3. $(x+4)(x+10)$
4. $(x+4)(x+1)$
5. $(x+5)(x+1)$
6. $(x+3)(x+5)$
7. $(x+2)(x+8)$
8. $(x+1)(x+3)$
9. $(x-3)(x-8)$
10. $(x-2)(x-7)$
11. $(x-1)(x-6)$
12. $(x+4)(x+11)$
13. $(x+9)(x-3)$
14. $(x-7)(x+1)$
15. $(x-9)(x+5)$
16. $(x-6)(x+3)$
17. $(x-2)(x+1)$
18. $(x+6)(x-5)$
19. $(n+7)(n-1)$; for table see p. A23.

8-3 Exercises

California Standards Practice
10.0, 11.0, 15.0

go.hrw.com
Homework Help Online
KEYWORD: MA8CA 8-3
Parent Resources Online
KEYWORD: MA8CA Parent

GUIDED PRACTICE

SEE EXAMPLE 1 p. 496

Factor each trinomial. Check your answer.

1. $x^2 + 13x + 36$
2. $x^2 + 11x + 24$
3. $x^2 + 14x + 40$
4. $x^2 + 5x + 4$
5. $x^2 + 6x + 5$
6. $x^2 + 8x + 15$

SEE EXAMPLE 2 p. 497

7. $x^2 + 10x + 16$
8. $x^2 + 4x + 3$
9. $x^2 - 11x + 24$
10. $x^2 - 9x + 14$
11. $x^2 - 7x + 6$
12. $x^2 + 15x + 44$

SEE EXAMPLE 3 p. 498

13. $x^2 + 6x - 27$
14. $x^2 - 6x - 7$
15. $x^2 - 4x - 45$
16. $x^2 - 3x - 18$
17. $x^2 - x - 2$
18. $x^2 + x - 30$

SEE EXAMPLE 4 p. 499

19. Factor $n^2 + 6n - 7$. Show that the original polynomial and the factored form have the same value for $n = 0, 1, 2, 3,$ and 4.

PRACTICE AND PROBLEM SOLVING

Independent Practice For Exercises	See Example
20–25	1
26–31	2
32–37	3
38	4

Extra Practice
Skills Practice p. EP16
Application Practice p. EP31

Factor each trinomial. Check your answer.

20. $x^2 + 11x + 28$
21. $x^2 + 13x + 30$
22. $x^2 + 11x + 18$
23. $x^2 + 13x + 40$
24. $x^2 + 12x + 20$
25. $x^2 + 16x + 48$
26. $x^2 + 12x + 11$
27. $x^2 + 16x + 28$
28. $x^2 + 15x + 36$
29. $x^2 - 6x + 5$
30. $x^2 - 9x + 18$
31. $x^2 - 12x + 32$
32. $x^2 + x - 12$
33. $x^2 + 4x - 21$
34. $x^2 + 9x - 36$
35. $x^2 - 12x - 13$
36. $x^2 - 10x - 24$
37. $x^2 - 2x - 35$
38. Factor $n^2 - 12n - 45$. Show that the original polynomial and the factored form have the same value for $n = 0, 1, 2, 3,$ and 4.

Match each trinomial with its correct factorization.

39. $x^2 + 3x - 10$ **C**
40. $x^2 - 7x + 10$ **A**
41. $x^2 - 9x - 10$ **D**
42. $x^2 + 11x + 10$ **B**

A. $(x-2)(x-5)$
B. $(x+1)(x+10)$
C. $(x-2)(x+5)$
D. $(x+1)(x-10)$

43. **Write About It** Compare multiplying binomials with factoring polynomials into binomial factors. **They are inverse operations.**

Factor each trinomial, if possible. Check your answer.

44. $x^2 + x - 20$
45. $x^2 - 11x + 18$
46. $x^2 - 4x - 21$
47. $x^2 + 10x + 9$
48. $x^2 - 12x + 32$
49. $x^2 + 13x + 42$
50. $x^2 - 7x - 12$
51. $x^2 + 11x + 18$
52. $x^2 - 6x - 27$
53. $x^2 + 5x - 24$
54. $x^2 - 10x + 21$
55. $x^2 + 4x - 45$
56. Factor $n^2 + 11n + 28$. Show that the original polynomial and the factored form have the same value for $n = 0, 1, 2, 3,$ and 4.

20. $(x+4)(x+7)$
21. $(x+3)(x+10)$
22. $(x+9)(x+2)$
23. $(x+5)(x+8)$
24. $(x+10)(x+2)$
25. $(x+4)(x+12)$
26. $(x+11)(x+1)$
27. $(x+14)(x+2)$
28. $(x+12)(x+3)$
29. $(x-5)(x-1)$
30. $(x-3)(x-6)$
31. $(x-8)(x-4)$
32. $(x-3)(x+4)$

California Standards

Standard	Exercises
2.0	95–98
9.0	92–94
10.0	59c, 60–62, 77c, 91b
11.0	1–42, 44–59b, 60–66, 67c, 68, 73–77a, 79, 82–88, 91a, 99–102
15.0	67

8-3 PRACTICE A

LESSON 8-3 **Practice A**
Factoring $x^2 + bx + c$

Factor each trinomial.

1. $x^2 + 5x + 6$ — $(x+3)(x+2)$
2. $x^2 + 5x + 4$ — $(x+4)(x+1)$
3. $x^2 + 9x + 20$ — $(x+5)(x+4)$
4. $x^2 + 10x + 21$ — $(x+7)(x+3)$
5. $x^2 + 11x + 30$ — $(x+6)(x+5)$
6. $x^2 + 10x + 16$ — $(x+8)(x+2)$
7. $x^2 - 8x + 12$ — $(x-6)(x-2)$
8. $x^2 - 8x + 15$ — $(x-5)(x-3)$
9. $x^2 - 17x + 16$ — $(x-16)(x-1)$
10. $x^2 - 12x + 27$ — $(x-9)(x-3)$
11. $x^2 - 15x + 44$ — $(x-4)(x-11)$
12. $x^2 - 13x + 40$ — $(x-8)(x-5)$
13. $x^2 + 6x - 40$ — $(x+10)(x-4)$
14. $x^2 + 2x - 3$ — $(x+3)(x-1)$
15. $x^2 + 4x - 32$ — $(x+8)(x-4)$
16. $x^2 + 10x - 24$ — $(x+12)(x-2)$
17. $x^2 + 12x - 28$ — $(x+14)(x-2)$
18. $x^2 + 3x - 10$ — $(x+5)(x-2)$
19. $x^2 - 2x - 15$ — $(x+3)(x-5)$
20. $x^2 - 8x - 20$ — $(x+2)(x-10)$
21. $x^2 - 2x - 48$ — $(x+6)(x-8)$
22. $x^2 - x - 12$ — $(x+3)(x-4)$
23. $x^2 - 2x - 3$ — $(x+1)(x-3)$
24. $x^2 - x - 2$ — $(x+1)(x-2)$
25. Factor $n^2 + 6n + 5$. Complete the tables to show that the original polynomial and the factored form describe the same sequence of numbers for $n = 0, 1, 2, 3,$ and 4. $(n+1)(n+5)$

n	$n^2 + 6n + 5$
0	$0^2 + 6(0) + 5 = 5$
1	$1^2 + 6(1) + 5 = 12$
2	$2^2 + 6(2) + 5 = 21$
3	$3^2 + 6(3) + 5 = 32$
4	$4^2 + 6(4) + 5 = 45$

n	$(n+1)(n+5)$
0	$(0+1)(0+5) = 5$
1	$(1+1)(1+5) = 12$
2	$(2+1)(2+5) = 21$
3	$(3+1)(3+5) = 32$
4	$(4+1)(4+5) = 45$

8-3 PRACTICE B

LESSON 8-3 **Practice B**
Factoring $x^2 + bx + c$

Factor each trinomial.

1. $x^2 + 7x + 10$ — $(x+2)(x+5)$
2. $x^2 + 9x + 8$ — $(x+1)(x+8)$
3. $x^2 + 13x + 36$ — $(x+4)(x+9)$
4. $x^2 + 9x + 14$ — $(x+7)(x+2)$
5. $x^2 + 7x + 12$ — $(x+3)(x+4)$
6. $x^2 + 9x + 18$ — $(x+6)(x+3)$
7. $x^2 - 9x + 18$ — $(x-6)(x-3)$
8. $x^2 - 5x + 4$ — $(x-4)(x-1)$
9. $x^2 - 9x + 20$ — $(x-5)(x-4)$
10. $x^2 - 12x + 20$ — $(x-2)(x-10)$
11. $x^2 - 11x + 18$ — $(x-9)(x-2)$
12. $x^2 - 12x + 32$ — $(x-8)(x-4)$
13. $x^2 + 7x - 18$ — $(x+9)(x-2)$
14. $x^2 + 10x - 24$ — $(x+12)(x-2)$
15. $x^2 + 2x - 3$ — $(x+3)(x-1)$
16. $x^2 + 2x - 15$ — $(x+5)(x-3)$
17. $x^2 + 5x - 6$ — $(x+6)(x-1)$
18. $x^2 + 5x - 24$ — $(x+8)(x-3)$
19. $x^2 - 5x - 6$ — $(x+1)(x-6)$
20. $x^2 - 2x - 35$ — $(x+5)(x-7)$
21. $x^2 - 7x - 30$ — $(x+3)(x-10)$
22. $x^2 - x - 56$ — $(x+7)(x-8)$
23. $x^2 - 2x - 8$ — $(x+2)(x-4)$
24. $x^2 - x - 20$ — $(x+4)(x-5)$
25. Factor $n^2 + 5n - 24$. Show that the original polynomial and the factored form describe the same sequence of numbers for $n = 0, 1, 2, 3,$ and 4. $(n+8)(n-3)$

n	$n^2 + 5n - 24$
0	$0^2 + 5(0) - 24 = -24$
1	$1^2 + 5(1) - 24 = -18$
2	$2^2 + 5(2) - 24 = -10$
3	$3^2 + 5(3) - 24 = 0$
4	$4^2 + 5(4) - 24 = 12$

n	$(n+8)(n-3)$
0	$(0+8)(0-3) = -24$
1	$(1+8)(1-3) = -18$
2	$(2+8)(2-3) = -10$
3	$(3+8)(3-3) = 0$
4	$(4+8)(4-3) = 12$

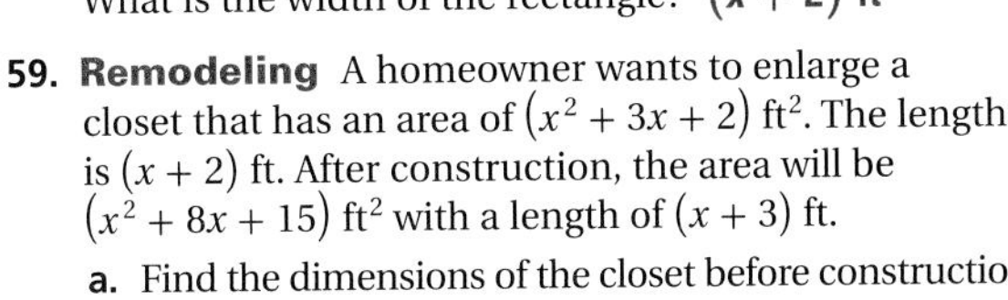

57. **Estimation** The graph shows the areas of rectangles with dimensions $(x + 1)$ yards and $(x + 2)$ yards. Estimate the value of x for a rectangle with area 9 square yards. **approximately 1.5**

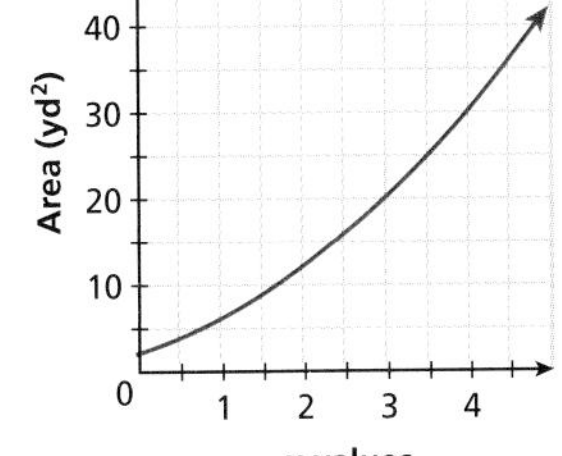

58. **Geometry** The area of a rectangle in square feet can be represented by $x^2 + 8x + 12$. The length is $(x + 6)$ ft. What is the width of the rectangle? $\mathbf{(x + 2)}$ **ft**

59. **Remodeling** A homeowner wants to enlarge a closet that has an area of $(x^2 + 3x + 2)$ ft^2. The length is $(x + 2)$ ft. After construction, the area will be $(x^2 + 8x + 15)$ ft^2 with a length of $(x + 3)$ ft.
   a. Find the dimensions of the closet before construction.
   b. Find the dimensions of the closet after construction.
   c. By how many feet will the length and width increase after construction? **The length will increase by 1 ft. The width will increase by 4 ft.**

LINK

Art

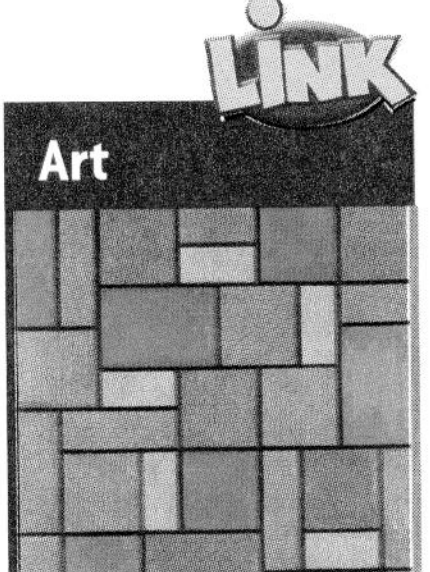

The Dutch painter Theo van Doesburg (1883–1931) is most famous for his paintings composed of lines and rectangles, such as the one shown above.

Art Write the polynomial modeled and then factor.

60.

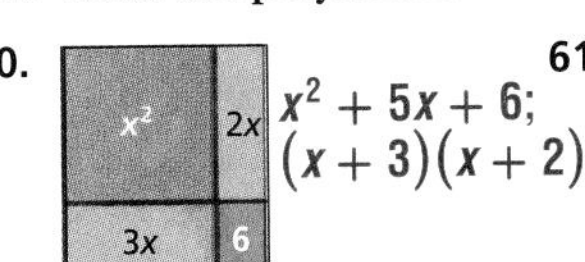

$x^2 + 5x + 6$; $(x + 3)(x + 2)$

61.

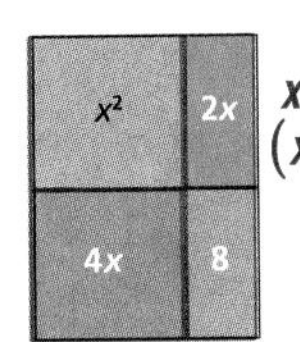

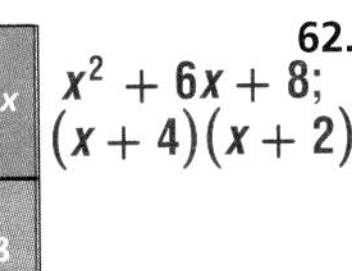

$x^2 + 6x + 8$; $(x + 4)(x + 2)$

62.

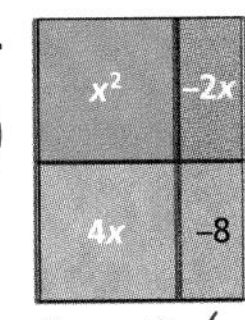

$x^2 + 2x - 8$; $(x + 4)(x - 2)$

Copy and complete the table.

	$x^2 + bx + c$	Sign of c	Binomial Factors	Signs of Numbers in Binomials
	$x^2 + 4x + 3$	Positive	$(x + 1)(x + 3)$	Both positive
63.	$x^2 - 4x + 3$	**Pos.**	$(x - 1)(x - 3)$	**Both neg.**
64.	$x^2 + 2x - 3$	**Neg.**	$(x - 1)(x + 3)$	**Neg.; pos.**
65.	$x^2 - 2x - 3$	**Neg.**	$(x + 1)(x - 3)$	**Pos.; neg.**

66. **Geometry** A rectangle has area $x^2 + 6x + 8$. The length is $x + 4$. Find the width of the rectangle. Could the rectangle be a square? Explain why or why not.
$x + 2$; no; Possible answer: $2 \neq 4$ so $(x + 2) \neq (x + 4)$

CONCEPT CONNECTION

67. This problem will prepare you for the Concept Connection on page 512.
The equation for the motion of an object with constant acceleration is $d = vt + \frac{1}{2}at^2$ where d is distance traveled in feet, v is starting velocity in feet per second, a is acceleration in feet per second squared, and t is time in seconds.
   a. Janna has two toy race cars on a track. One starts with a velocity of 0 ft/s and accelerates at 2 ft/s^2. Write an equation for the distance the car travels in time t. **a. $d = t^2$**
   b. The second car travels at a constant speed of 4 ft/s. Write an equation for the distance the second car travels in time t. (*Hint:* When speed is constant, the acceleration is 0 ft/s^2.) $\mathbf{d = 4t}$
   c. By setting the equations equal to each other you can determine when the cars have traveled the same distance: $t^2 = 4t$. This can be written as $t^2 - 4t = 0$. Factor the left side of the equation. $\mathbf{t(t - 4)}$

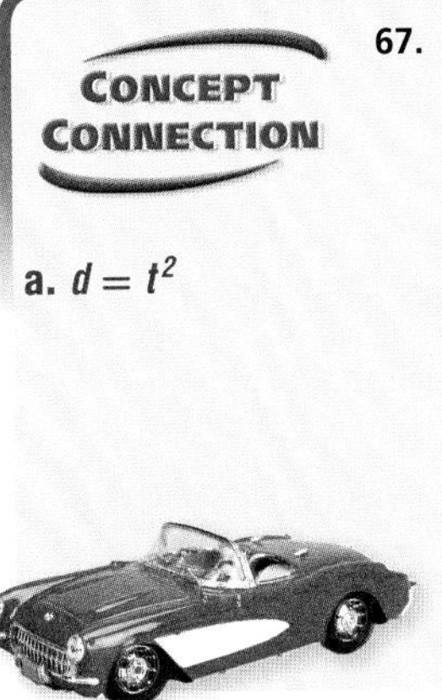

COMMON ERROR ALERT

Students might assign the larger value to length in part **b** of **Exercise 59.** This would yield a remodeled length of $x + 5$. Students may then carry the error over into part **c,** answering that length changed by 3 and width changed by 2. Tell students to read the problem carefully. Draw their attention to the last line. The problem clearly states that the new length is $x + 3$, so the new *width* is $x + 5$.

CONCEPT CONNECTION **Exercise 67** involves using the equation $d = vt + \frac{1}{2}at^2$ to calculate when two moving objects will be at the same location. This exercise prepares students for the Concept Connection on page 512.

Answers

33. $(x + 7)(x - 3)$
34. $(x + 12)(x - 3)$
35. $(x - 13)(x + 1)$
36. $(x - 12)(x + 2)$
37. $(x - 7)(x + 5)$
38. $(n - 15)(n + 3)$; for table see p. A23.
44. $(x + 5)(x - 4)$
45. $(x - 2)(x - 9)$
46. $(x + 3)(x - 7)$
47. $(x + 1)(x + 9)$
48. $(x - 4)(x - 8)$
49. $(x + 6)(x + 7)$
50. not factorable
51. $(x + 2)(x + 9)$
52. $(x + 3)(x - 9)$
53. $(x - 3)(x + 8)$
54. $(x - 3)(x - 7)$
55. $(x - 5)(x + 9)$
56. $(n + 4)(n + 7)$; for table see p. A23.

59a. length: $(x + 2)$ ft; width: $(x + 1)$ ft
b. length: $(x + 3)$ ft; width: $(x + 5)$ ft

8-3 PRACTICE C

LESSON 8-3 **Practice C**
Factoring $x^2 + bx + c$

Factor each trinomial.

1. $x^2 + 10x + 24$ — $(x + 6)(x + 4)$
2. $y^2 + 12y + 20$ — $(y + 2)(y + 10)$
3. $a^2 + 15a + 54$ — $(a + 9)(a + 6)$
4. $h^2 + 18h + 45$ — $(h + 15)(h + 3)$
5. $x^2 + 16x + 48$ — $(x + 12)(x + 4)$
6. $c^2 + 15c + 50$ — $(c + 5)(c + 10)$
7. $x^2 - 16x + 48$ — $(x - 12)(x - 4)$
8. $d^2 - 19d + 88$ — $(d - 11)(d - 8)$
9. $x^2 - 20x + 36$ — $(x - 2)(x - 18)$
10. $m^2 - 43m + 42$ — $(m - 1)(m - 42)$
11. $x^2 - 16x + 28$ — $(x - 2)(x - 14)$
12. $n^2 - 12n + 35$ — $(n - 7)(n - 5)$
13. $f^2 + 3f - 28$ — $(f + 7)(f - 4)$
14. $b^2 + 11b - 42$ — $(b + 14)(b - 3)$
15. $x^2 + 12x - 160$ — $(x + 20)(x - 8)$
16. $g^2 + 2g - 48$ — $(g + 8)(g - 6)$
17. $k^2 + 16k - 36$ — $(k + 18)(k - 2)$
18. $x^2 + 2x - 63$ — $(x + 9)(x - 7)$
19. $p^2 - 2p - 8$ — $(p + 2)(p - 4)$
20. $x^2 - x - 72$ — $(x + 8)(x - 9)$
21. $q^2 - 3q - 18$ — $(q + 3)(q - 6)$
22. $x^2 - 4x - 32$ — $(x + 4)(x - 8)$
23. $t^2 - 10t - 39$ — $(t + 3)(t - 13)$
24. $w^2 - 20w - 125$ — $(w + 5)(w - 25)$
25. Factor $n^2 + 8n - 48$. Show that the original polynomial and the factored form describe the same sequence of numbers for $n = 0, 1, 2, 3$, and 4. $(n + 12)(n - 4)$

n	$n^2 + 8n - 48$
0	$0^2 + 8(0) - 48 = -48$
1	$1^2 + 8(1) - 48 = -39$
2	$2^2 + 8(2) - 48 = -28$
3	$3^2 + 8(3) - 48 = -15$
4	$4^2 + 8(4) - 48 = 0$

n	$(n + 12)(n - 4)$
0	$(0 + 12)(0 - 4) = -48$
1	$(1 + 12)(1 - 4) = -39$
2	$(2 + 12)(2 - 4) = -28$
3	$(3 + 12)(3 - 4) = -15$
4	$(4 + 12)(4 - 4) = 0$

Multiple Choice Some students will be drawn to choice **A** for **Exercise 79** because $-4 + -6 = -10$. Remind them that the product of two negative numbers is positive.

Critical Thinking Have students substitute a single variable for the common binomial expression in **Exercises 86** and **88**. Then, when they have factored the trinomial, they can substitute the binomial expression back in for the single variable.

Answers

70. The correct factorization is $(x - 1)(x + 2)$.
71. The correct factorization is $(x - 4)(x + 1)$.
72. Many trinomials cannot be factored.
83. $(x^2 + 9)(x^2 + 9)$
84. $(y^2 - 8)(y^2 + 3)$
85. $(d^2 + 21)(d^2 + 1)$
86. $(u + v + 3)(u + v - 1)$
87. $(de - 5)(de + 4)$
88. $(m - n - 9)(m - n + 5)$

68. Construction The length of a platform is $(x + 7)$ ft. The area of the platform is $(x^2 + 9x + 14)$ ft^2. Find the width of the platform. Check your answer. **$(x + 2)$ ft**

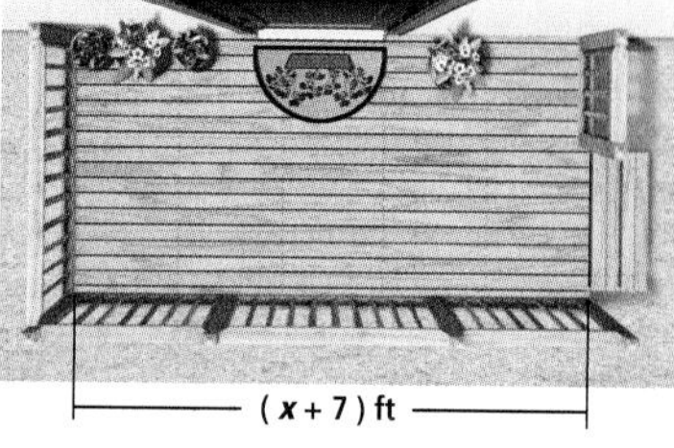

Reasoning **Tell whether each statement is true or false. If false, explain.**

69. The third term in a factorable trinomial is equal to the product of the constants in its binomial factors. **true**
70. The constants in the binomial factors of $x^2 + x - 2$ are both negative. **false**
71. The correct factorization of $x^2 - 3x - 4$ is $(x + 4)(x - 1)$. **false**
72. All trinomials of the form $x^2 + bx + c$ can be factored. **false**

Fill in the missing part of each factorization.

73. $x^2 - 6x + 8 = (x - 2)(x - \mathbf{4})$
74. $x^2 - 2x - 8 = (x + 2)(x - \mathbf{4})$
75. $x^2 + 2x - 8 = (x - 2)(x + \mathbf{4})$
76. $x^2 + 6x + 8 = (x + 2)(x + \mathbf{4})$

77. Construction The area of a rectangular fountain is $(x^2 + 12x + 20)$ ft^2. The width is $(x + 2)$ ft.

a. Find the length of the fountain. **$(x + 10)$ ft**

b. A 2-foot walkway is built around the fountain. Find the dimensions of the outside border of the walkway.

c. Find the total area covered by the fountain and walkway.

77b. $\ell = (x + 14)$ ft; $w = (x + 6)$ ft
c. $A = (x^2 + 20x + 84)$ ft^2

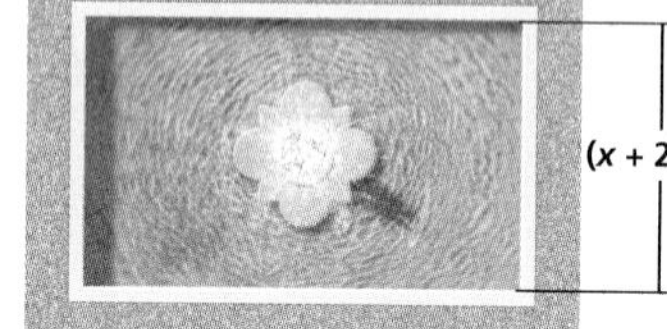

78. Critical Thinking Find all possible values of b so that $x^2 + bx + 6$ can be factored into binomial factors. **7, 5, −7, −5**

Multiple Choice **For Exercises 79–81, choose the best answer.**

79. Which is the correct factorization of $x^2 - 10x - 24$?

Ⓐ $(x - 4)(x - 6)$ Ⓒ $(x - 2)(x + 12)$
Ⓑ $(x + 4)(x - 6)$ **Ⓓ** $(x + 2)(x - 12)$

80. Which value of b would make $x^2 + bx - 20$ factorable?

Ⓐ 9 Ⓑ 12 **Ⓒ** 19 Ⓓ 21

81. Which value of b would NOT make $x^2 + bx - 36$ factorable?

Ⓐ 5 Ⓑ 9 **Ⓒ** 15 Ⓓ 16

82. Short Response What are the factors of $x^2 + 2x - 24$? Show and explain each step of factoring the polynomial. **$(x + 6)(x - 4)$**

CHALLENGE AND EXTEND

Factor each trinomial. Check your answer.

83. $x^4 + 18x^2 + 81$
84. $y^4 - 5y^2 - 24$
85. $d^4 + 22d^2 + 21$
86. $(u + v)^2 + 2(u + v) - 3$
87. $(de)^2 - (de) - 20$
88. $(m - n)^2 - 4(m - n) - 45$

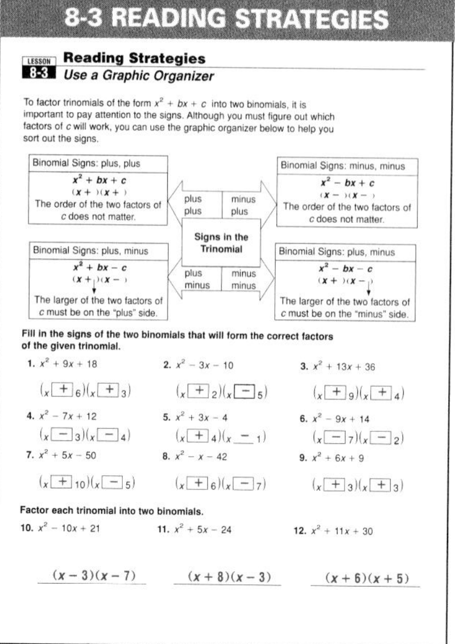

8-3 READING STRATEGIES

LESSON 8-3 **Reading Strategies**
Use a Graphic Organizer

To factor trinomials of the form $x^2 + bx + c$ into two binomials, it is important to pay attention to the signs. Although you must figure out which factors of c will work, you can use the graphic organizer below to help you sort out the signs.

Fill in the signs of the two binomials that will form the correct factors of the given trinomial.

1. $x^2 + 9x + 18$ $(x + 6)(x + 3)$
2. $x^2 - 3x - 10$ $(x + 2)(x - 5)$
3. $x^2 + 13x + 36$ $(x + 9)(x + 4)$
4. $x^2 - 7x + 12$ $(x - 3)(x - 4)$
5. $x^2 + 3x - 4$ $(x + 4)(x - 1)$
6. $x^2 - 9x + 14$ $(x - 7)(x - 2)$
7. $x^2 + 5x - 50$ $(x + 10)(x - 5)$
8. $x^2 - x - 42$ $(x + 6)(x - 7)$
9. $x^2 + 6x + 9$ $(x + 3)(x + 3)$

Factor each trinomial into two binomials.

10. $x^2 - 10x + 21$ $(x - 3)(x - 7)$
11. $x^2 + 5x - 24$ $(x + 8)(x - 3)$
12. $x^2 + 11x + 30$ $(x + 6)(x + 5)$

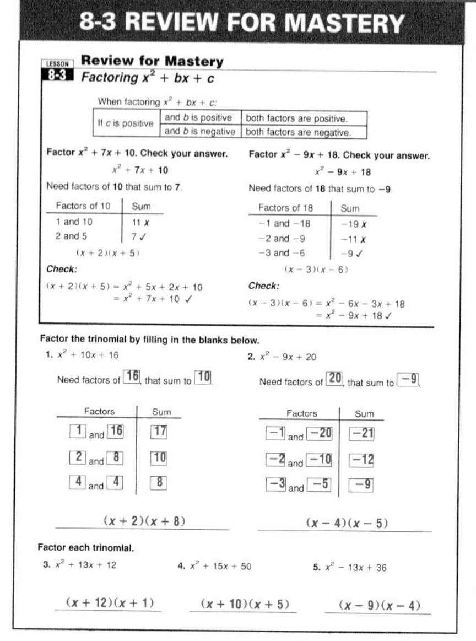

8-3 REVIEW FOR MASTERY

LESSON 8-3 **Review for Mastery**
Factoring $x^2 + bx + c$

When factoring $x^2 + bx + c$:

If c is positive	and b is positive	both factors are positive.
	and b is negative	both factors are negative.

Factor $x^2 + 7x + 10$. Check your answer.

$x^2 + 7x + 10$

Need factors of **10** that sum to **7**.

Factors of 10	Sum
1 and 10	11 ✗
2 and 5	7 ✓

$(x + 2)(x + 5)$

Check:

$(x + 2)(x + 5) = x^2 + 5x + 2x + 10$
$= x^2 + 7x + 10$ ✓

Factor $x^2 - 9x + 18$. Check your answer.

$x^2 - 9x + 18$

Need factors of **18** that sum to **−9**.

Factors of 18	Sum
−1 and −18	−19 ✗
−2 and −9	−11 ✗
−3 and −6	−9 ✓

$(x - 3)(x - 6)$

Check:

$(x - 3)(x - 6) = x^2 - 6x - 3x + 18$
$= x^2 - 9x + 18$ ✓

Factor the trinomial by filling in the blanks below.

1. $x^2 + 10x + 16$

Need factors of 16, that sum to 10.

Factors	Sum
1 and 16	17
2 and 8	10
4 and 4	8

$(x + 2)(x + 8)$

2. $x^2 - 9x + 20$

Need factors of 20, that sum to −9.

Factors	Sum
−1 and −20	−21
−2 and −10	−12
−3 and −5	−9

$(x - 4)(x - 5)$

Factor each trinomial.

3. $x^2 + 13x + 12$ $(x + 12)(x + 1)$
4. $x^2 + 15x + 50$ $(x + 10)(x + 5)$
5. $x^2 - 13x + 36$ $(x - 9)(x - 4)$

89. Find all possible values of b such that, when $x^2 + bx + 28$ is factored, both constants in the binomials are positive. **16; 11; 29**

90. Find all possible values of b such that, when $x^2 + bx + 32$ is factored, both constants in the binomials are negative. **−33; −18; −12**

91. **Landscaping** The area of Beth's rectangular garden is $(x^2 + 13x + 42)$ ft^2. The width is $(x + 6)$ ft.

Item	Cost
Fertilizer	$0.28/ft^2
Fencing	$2.00/ft

a. What is the length of the garden? $(x + 7)$ ft

b. Find the perimeter in terms of x. $(4x + 26)$ ft

c. Find the cost to fence the garden when x is 5. **$92.00**

d. Find the cost of fertilizer when x is 5. **$36.96**

e. Find the total cost to fence and fertilize Beth's garden when x is 5. **$128.96**

SPIRAL STANDARDS REVIEW

2.0, 9.0, 11.0

Solve each system by substitution. *(Lesson 6-4)*

92. $\begin{cases} 3x + y = 13 \\ x - 3y = 1 \end{cases}$ $(4, 1)$

93. $\begin{cases} 2x - y = 1 \\ x - y = -2 \end{cases}$ $(3, 5)$

94. $\begin{cases} -x - y = -2 \\ x - 2y = 20 \end{cases}$ $(8, -6)$

Simplify. *(Lesson 7-3)*

95. x^3x^2 x^5

96. $m^8n^3m^{-12}$ $\frac{n^3}{m^4}$

97. $(t^4)^3$ t^{12}

98. $(-2xy^3)^5$ $-32x^5y^{15}$

Factor each polynomial by grouping. *(Lesson 8-2)*

99. $x^3 + 2x^2 + 5x + 10$ $(x + 2)(x^2 + 5)$

100. $2n^3 - 8n^2 - 3n + 12$ $(n - 4)(2n^2 - 3)$

101. $2p^4 - 4p^3 + 7p - 14$ $(p - 2)(2p^3 + 7)$

102. $x^3 - 4x^2 + x - 4$ $(x - 4)(x^2 + 1)$

Career Path

go.hrw.com
Career Resources Online
KEYWORD: MA8CA Career

Q: What math classes did you take in high school?
A: Algebra 1, Algebra 2, and Geometry

Q: What college math classes have you taken?
A: I took several computer modeling and programming classes as well as Statistics and Probability.

Q: How is math used in some of your projects?
A: Computer applications help me analyze data collected from a local waste disposal site. I used my mathematical knowledge to make recommendations on how to preserve surrounding water supplies.

Q: What plans do you have for the future?
A: I enjoy my studies in the area of water pollution. I would also like to research more efficient uses of natural energy resources.

Jessica Rubino
Environmental Sciences major

Journal

Have students compare factoring a trinomial when c is negative and b is positive with factoring a trinomial when c is negative and b is negative. Students should explain what the signs of b and c tell you about the factors.

ALTERNATIVE ASSESSMENT

Have students write four trinomials by multiplying four pairs of binomials. In two of the trinomials, c should be positive. Have students trade papers and factor the trinomials they received.

Power Presentations with PowerPoint®

8-3 Lesson Quiz

Factor each trinomial.

1. $x^2 - 11x + 30$
$(x - 5)(x - 6)$

2. $x^2 + 10x + 9$
$(x + 1)(x + 9)$

3. $x^2 - 6x - 27$
$(x - 9)(x + 3)$

4. $x^2 + 14x - 32$
$(x + 16)(x - 2)$

5. Factor $n^2 + n - 6$. Show that the original polynomial and the factored form have the same value for $n = 0, 1, 2, 3,$ and 4. $(n + 3)(n - 2)$

n	$n^2 + n - 6$
0	$0^2 + 0 - 6 = -6$
1	$1^2 + 1 - 6 = -4$
2	$2^2 + 2 - 6 = 0$
3	$3^2 + 3 - 6 = 6$
4	$4^2 + 4 - 6 = 14$

n	$(n + 3)(n - 2)$
0	$(0 + 3)(0 - 2) = -6$
1	$(1 + 3)(1 - 2) = -4$
2	$(2 + 3)(2 - 2) = 0$
3	$(3 + 3)(3 - 2) = 6$
4	$(4 + 3)(4 - 2) = 14$

Also available on transparency

8-3 PROBLEM SOLVING

LESSON 8-3 **Problem Solving**
Factoring $x^2 + bx + c$

Write the correct answer.

1. A plot of land is rectangular and has an area of $x^2 - 5x - 24$ m^2. The length is $x + 3$ m. Find the width of the plot.
$x - 8$ m

2. An antique Persian carpet has an area of $(x^2 + x - 20)$ ft^2 and a length of $(x + 5)$ feet. The rug is displayed on a wall in a museum. The wall has a width of $(x + 2)$ feet and an area of $(x^2 + 17x + 30)$ ft^2. Write expressions for the length and width of both the rug and wall. Then find the dimensions of the rug and the wall if $x = 20$ feet.

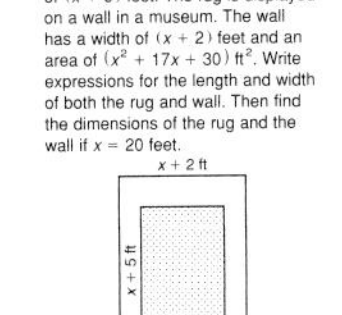

rug: $(x + 5)(x - 4)$, wall: $(x + 2)(x + 15)$;
rug: 16 ft by 25 ft, wall: 22 ft by 35 ft

3. The area of a poster board is $x^2 + 3x - 10$ inches. The width is $x - 2$ inches.

a. Write an expression for the length of the poster board.
$x + 5$

b. Find the dimensions of the poster board when $x = 14$.
12 in. by 19 in.

c. Write a polynomial for the area of the poster board if one inch is removed from each side.
$x^2 + x - 12$

The figure shows the plans for an addition on the back of a house. Use the figure to answer questions 4–6. Select the best answer.

Addition | $x - 10$
Original House | $x + 10$

4. The area of the addition is $(x^2 + 10x - 200)$ ft^2. What is its length?
A $(x - 20)$ feet
B $(x - 2)$ feet
Ⓒ $(x + 2)$ feet
D $(x + 20)$ feet

5. What is the area of the original house?
F $(x^2 - 10x - 200)$ ft^2
G $(x^2 + 8x - 20)$ ft^2
Ⓗ $(x^2 + 12x + 200)$ ft^2
J $(x^2 + 30x + 200)$ ft^2

6. The homeowners decide to extend the addition. The area with the addition is now $(x^2 + 12x - 160)$ ft^2. By how many feet was the addition extended?
A 1 foot
Ⓑ 2 feet
C 3 feet
D 4 feet

8-3 CHALLENGE

LESSON 8-3 **Challenge**
Pushing Back the Boundaries of Factoring

One day, Denise's mathematics teacher, Ms. Dolenze, asked her to factor $6x^2 + 5x + 1$. After puzzling over the problem for a while, Denise told Ms. Dolenze that the expression could not be factored. Amazed, Ms. Dolenze asked Denise why. "I could not find two binomials in x with integer coefficients whose product is $6x^2 + 5x + 1$," replied Denise. Then Ms. Dolenze quickly responded, "Why should that stop you?"

In the exercises that follow, you will see how to push back the boundaries of factoring.

In Exercise 1–4, answer each question in order to help Denise factor $6x^2 + 5x + 1$.

1. By what property of real numbers, can you justify $6x^2 + 5x + 1 = 6\left(x^2 + \frac{5}{6}x + \frac{1}{6}\right)$?
Distributive Property

2. Show that $\left(\frac{1}{2}\right)\left(\frac{1}{3}\right) = \frac{1}{6}$ and that $\frac{1}{2} + \frac{1}{3} = \frac{5}{6}$.
$\left(\frac{1}{2}\right)\left(\frac{1}{3}\right) = \frac{1 \times 1}{2 \times 3} = \frac{1}{6}$, $\frac{1}{2} + \frac{1}{3} = \frac{1}{2} \times \frac{3}{3} + \frac{1}{3} \times \frac{2}{2} = \frac{3 + 2}{2 \times 3} = \frac{5}{6}$

3. Show that $6\left(x + \frac{1}{2}\right)\left(x + \frac{1}{3}\right) = 6x^2 + 5x + 1$.
$6\left(x + \frac{1}{2}\right)\left(x + \frac{1}{3}\right) = 2\left(x + \frac{1}{2}\right) \times 3\left(x + \frac{1}{3}\right) = (2x + 1)(3x + 1)$
$= 6x^2 + 3x + 2x + 1 = 6x^2 + 5x + 1$

4. Is the product in Exercise 3 a factorization of $6x^2 + 5x + 1$? Is it necessary to find integers in order to factor a quadratic trinomial? Explain your response.
Yes; the given polynomial expression is written as a product of polynomials of lower degree. There is no requirement that the coefficients be integers.

Factor each quadratic trinomial as a number times a product of two linear binomials in x, each having rational numbers among the coefficients. Use Exercises 1–3 above as a model.

5. $15x^2 + 8x + 1$
$15\left(x + \frac{1}{5}\right)\left(x + \frac{1}{3}\right)$

6. $28x^2 + 11x + 1$
$28\left(x + \frac{1}{7}\right)\left(x + \frac{1}{4}\right)$

7. $6x^2 - 23x + 20$
$6\left(x - \frac{4}{3}\right)\left(x - \frac{5}{2}\right)$

8. $12x^2 + x - 35$
$12\left(x - \frac{5}{3}\right)\left(x + \frac{7}{4}\right)$

Organizer

Use with Lesson 8-4

Objective: Model and factor trinomials of the form $ax^2 + bx + c$.

Materials: algebra tiles

Teach

Discuss

This activity is similar to those on pages 494–495. Remind students that they may add additional tiles in zero pairs when necessary, and that they can check their answers by multiplying the factors.

Alternative Approach

Use the transparency mat and transparency algebra tiles.

Close

Key Concept

You can factor trinomials by arranging the tiles into a rectangle such that the x^2-tiles are in the upper left, the unit tiles are in the lower right, and the x-tiles fill in the remaining spaces. The dimensions of the rectangle are the factors.

Assessment

Journal Have students explain how algebra tiles model the factorization of trinomial expressions. Explanations should include what the final arrangement of tiles represents and how to find the factors from this arrangement.

California Standards

Algebra 1 11.0

8-4 Algebra LAB

Model Factorization of $ax^2 + bx + c$

Use with Lesson 8-4

You can use algebra tiles to factor a trinomial whose lead coefficient is not 1.

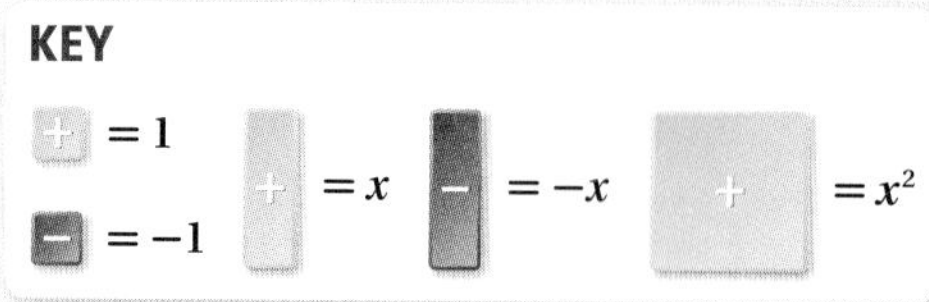

California Standards

11.0 Students apply basic factoring techniques to second- and simple third-**degree polynomials.** These techniques include finding a common factor for all terms in a polynomial, recognizing the difference of two squares, and recognizing perfect squares of binomials.

Activity 1

Use algebra tiles to factor $2x^2 + 5x + 2$.

MODEL		ALGEBRA
	Model $2x^2 + 5x + 2$.	$2x^2 + 5x + 2$
	Try to arrange all of the tiles in a rectangle. Place the x^2-tiles in the upper left corner. *Arrange the unit tiles in a rectangle so that the top left corner of this rectangle touches the bottom right corner of the second x^2-tile.* *Arrange the x-tiles so that all the tiles together make one large rectangle.* *This does not work. One x-tile is left over.*	$2x^2 + 5x + 2 \neq (x + 1)(2x + 2)$
	Rearrange the unit tiles to form another rectangle.	
$2x + 1$; $x + 2$	*Fill in the empty spaces with x-tiles. All 5 x-tiles fit. This is the correct arrangement.* *The total area represents the trinomial $2x^2 + 5x + 2$. The length $2x + 1$ and width $x + 2$ represent the factors.*	$2x^2 + 5x + 2 = (x + 2)(2x + 1)$

Try This

Use algebra tiles to factor each trinomial.

1. $3x^2 + 7x + 4$ **$(3x + 4)(x + 1)$**
2. $3x^2 + 4x - 4$ **$(3x - 2)(x + 2)$**
3. $2x^2 - x - 1$ **$(2x + 1)(x - 1)$**
4. $4x^2 - 8x + 3$ **$(2x - 3)(2x - 1)$**

8-4 Factoring $ax^2 + bx + c$

California Standards

11.0 Students apply basic factoring techniques to second- and simple third-degree **polynomials.** These techniques include finding a common factor for all terms in a polynomial, recognizing the difference of two squares, and recognizing perfect squares of binomials.

Why learn this?

The height of a football that has been kicked can be modeled by a factored polynomial. (See Exercise 75.)

In the previous lesson you factored trinomials of the form $x^2 + bx + c$. Now you will factor trinomials of the form $ax^2 + bx + c$, where $a \neq 0$ or 1.

When you multiply $(3x + 2)(2x + 5)$, the coefficient of the x^2-term is the product of the coefficients of the x-terms. Also, the constant term in the trinomial is the product of the constants in the binomials.

$$(3x+2)(2x+5) = 6x^2 + 19x + 10$$

To factor a trinomial like $ax^2 + bx + c$ into its binomial factors, first write two sets of parentheses: $(\square x + \square)(\square x + \square)$.

Write two integers that are factors of a next to the x's and two integers that are factors of c in the other blanks. Then multiply to see if the product is the original trinomial. If there are not two such integers, the trinomial is not factorable.

EXAMPLE 1 Factoring $ax^2 + bx + c$

Factor $4x^2 + 16x + 15$. Check your answer.

$(\square x + \square)(\square x + \square)$ *The first term is $4x^2$, so at least one variable term has a coefficient other than 1.*

The coefficient of the x^2-term is 4. The constant term in the trinomial is 15.

$(1x + 15)(4x + 1) = 4x^2 + 61x + 15$ ✗ *Try integer factors of 4 for the coefficients and integer factors of 15 for the constant terms.*

$(1x + 5)(4x + 3) = 4x^2 + 23x + 15$ ✗

$(1x + 3)(4x + 5) = 4x^2 + 17x + 15$ ✗

$(1x + 1)(4x + 15) = 4x^2 + 19x + 15$ ✗

$(2x + 15)(2x + 1) = 4x^2 + 32x + 15$ ✗

$(2x + 5)(2x + 3) = 4x^2 + 16x + 15$ ✓

Check $(2x + 5)(2x + 3) = 4x^2 + 10x + 6x + 15$ *Use the FOIL method.*

$= 4x^2 + 16x + 15$ ✓ *The product is the original trinomial.*

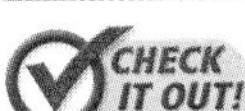

CHECK IT OUT! **Factor each trinomial. Check your answer.**

1a. $6x^2 + 11x + 3$ $(3x + 1)(2x + 3)$

1b. $3x^2 - 2x - 8$ $(3x + 4)(x - 2)$

8-4 Organizer

Objective: Factor quadratic trinomials of the form $ax^2 + bx + c$.

Online Edition
Tutorial Videos

Countdown to Mastery Week 18

Power Presentations with PowerPoint®

Warm Up

Find each product.

1. $(x - 2)(2x + 7)$ $2x^2 + 3x - 14$
2. $(3y + 4)(2y + 9)$ $6y^2 + 35y + 36$
3. $(3n - 5)(n - 7)$ $3n^2 - 26n + 35$

Factor each trinomial.

4. $x^2 + 4x - 32$ $(x - 4)(x + 8)$
5. $z^2 + 15z + 36$ $(z + 3)(z + 12)$
6. $h^2 - 17h + 72$ $(h - 8)(h - 9)$

Also available on transparency

Q: What is the hidden math term?

NOMIAL
NOMIAL

A: Binomial.

1 Introduce

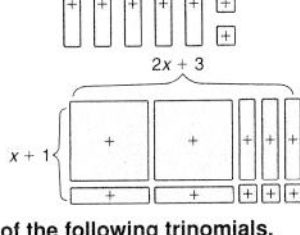

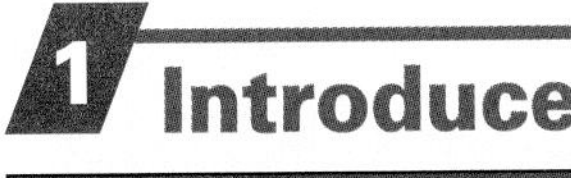

EXPLORATION

8-4 Factoring $ax^2 + bx + c$

You will need algebra tiles for this Exploration.

You can use algebra tiles to factor trinomials in the standard form $ax^2 + bx + c$.

For example, to factor $2x^2 + 5x + 3$, first use tiles to model the trinomial.

Then arrange the tiles to form a rectangle as shown.

The dimensions of the rectangle give the factorization: $2x^2 + 5x + 3 = (x + 1)(2x + 3)$.

Use algebra tiles to factor each of the following trinomials.

1. $2x^2 + 7x + 3$ 2. $2x^2 + 9x + 10$ 3. $4x^2 + 4x + 1$

THINK AND DISCUSS

4. **Explain** how the coefficients of the x-terms in the binomial factors are related to the coefficient of the x^2-term in the trinomial.
5. **Describe** one way in which factoring a trinomial in the form $ax^2 + bx + c$, where $a \neq 0$, is similar to factoring a trinomial in the form $x^2 + bx + c$.

Motivate

Write $6x^2 + 7x + 2$ on the board. Ask students how it is different from the trinomials they factored in Lesson 8-3. The x^2-term has a coefficient that is not one.

Tell students that because b depends on both a and c, this means that more factors, and their placements, will need to be tested.

Explorations and answers are provided in *Alternate Openers: Explorations Transparencies.*

California Standards

Algebra 1 11.0

Power Presentations with PowerPoint®

Additional Examples

Example 1

Factor $6x^2 + 11x + 4$. Check your answer.

$(3x + 4)(2x + 1)$

Example 2

Factor each trinomial. Check your answer.

A. $2x^2 + 17x + 21$

$(2x + 3)(x + 7)$

B. $3x^2 - 16x + 16$

$(x - 4)(3x - 4)$

Also available on transparency

INTERVENTION

Questioning Strategies

EXAMPLE 1

- How is factoring a trinomial in the form $ax^2 + bx + c$ similar to factoring a trinomial in the form $x^2 + bx + c$? How is it different?

EXAMPLE 2

- What is true about the signs of the factors of the last term if the middle term is positive? negative? Explain.
- What should the sum of the inner and outer products be?

Inclusion Confident students may have been able to factor the trinomials in the previous lesson in their heads. Remind students that careless errors are easy to make. To factor the trinomials in this lesson, these students may need to write out their work.

So, to factor $ax^2 + bx + c$, check the factors of a and the factors of c in the binomials. The sum of the products of the outer and inner terms should be b.

$$(\square x + \square)(\square x + \square) = ax^2 + bx + c$$

Product = a; Product = c; Sum of outer and inner products = b

Since you need to check all the factors of a and all the factors of c, it may be helpful to make a table. Then check the products of the outer and inner terms to see if the sum is b. You can multiply the binomials to check your answer.

EXAMPLE  **Factoring $ax^2 + bx + c$ When c Is Positive**

Factor each trinomial. Check your answer.

A $2x^2 + 11x + 12$

$(\square x + \square)(\square x + \square)$ *$a = 2$ and $c = 12$; Outer + Inner = 11*

Factors of 2	Factors of 12	Outer + Inner
1 and 2	1 and 12	$1(12) + 2(1) = 14$ ✗
1 and 2	12 and 1	$1(1) + 2(12) = 25$ ✗
1 and 2	2 and 6	$1(6) + 2(2) = 10$ ✗
1 and 2	6 and 2	$1(2) + 2(6) = 14$ ✗
1 and 2	3 and 4	$1(4) + 2(3) = 10$ ✗
1 and 2	4 and 3	$1(3) + 2(4) = 11$ ✓

$(x + 4)(2x + 3)$

Check $(x + 4)(2x + 3) = 2x^2 + 3x + 8x + 12$ *Use the FOIL method.*
$= 2x^2 + 11x + 12$ ✓

Remember!
When b is negative and c is positive, the factors of c are both negative.

B $5x^2 - 14x + 8$

$(\square x + \square)(\square x + \square)$ *$a = 5$ and $c = 8$; Outer + Inner = −14*

Factors of 5	Factors of 8	Outer + Inner
1 and 5	−1 and −8	$1(-8) + 5(-1) = -13$ ✗
1 and 5	−8 and −1	$1(-1) + 5(-8) = -41$ ✗
1 and 5	−2 and −4	$1(-4) + 5(-2) = -14$ ✓

$(x - 2)(5x - 4)$

Check $(x - 2)(5x - 4) = 5x^2 - 4x - 10x + 8$ *Use the FOIL method.*
$= 5x^2 - 14x + 8$ ✓

Factor each trinomial. Check your answer.

2a. $6x^2 + 17x + 5$ **$(2x + 5)(3x + 1)$**
2b. $9x^2 - 15x + 4$ **$(3x - 4)(3x - 1)$**
2c. $3x^2 + 13x + 12$ **$(3x + 4)(x + 3)$**

When c is negative, one factor of c will be positive and the other factor will be negative. Only some of the factors are shown in the examples, but you may need to check all of the possibilities.

2 Teach

Guided Instruction

Review factoring trinomials of the form $x^2 + bx + c$. Then have students factor trinomials of the form $ax^2 + bx + c$ by estimating and checking their answer. For **Examples 2, 3,** and **4,** use a table when teaching, and encourage students to use a table when working on their own. This will allow students to see what factors they already checked and prevent them from trying the same sets of factors more than once.

Universal Access

Advanced Learners/GATE

Present students with the following trinomials. Challenge students to find values of k for each trinomial that will make the trinomial factorable.

1. $x^2 + kx + 81$ ±82, ±30, ±18
2. $x^2 + 14x + k$ 13, 24, 33, ..., $n(14 - n)$
3. $kx^2 + 10x + 1$ 9, 16, 21, 24, 25

EXAMPLE 3 Factoring $ax^2 + bx + c$ When c Is Negative

Factor each trinomial. Check your answer.

A $4y^2 + 7y - 2$

$(\square y + \square)(\square y + \square)$ *a = 4 and c = −2; Outer + Inner = 7*

Factors of 4	Factors of −2	Outer + Inner
1 and 4	1 and −2	$1(-2) + (4)1 = 2$ ✗
1 and 4	−1 and 2	$(1)2 + 4(-1) = -2$ ✗
1 and 4	2 and −1	$1(-1) + (4)2 = 7$ ✓

$(y + 2)(4y - 1)$

Check $(y + 2)(4y - 1) = 4y^2 - y + 8y - 2$ *Use the FOIL method.*

$= 4y^2 + 7y - 2$ ✓

B $4x^2 + 19x - 5$

$(\square x + \square)(\square x + \square)$ *a = 4 and c = −5; Outer + Inner = 19*

Factors of 4	Factors of −5	Outer + Inner
1 and 4	1 and −5	$1(-5) + (4)1 = -1$ ✗
1 and 4	−1 and 5	$(1)5 + 4(-1) = 1$ ✗
1 and 4	5 and −1	$1(-1) + (4)5 = 19$ ✓

$(x + 5)(4x - 1)$

Check $(x + 5)(4x - 1) = 4x^2 - x + 20x - 5$ *Use the FOIL method.*

$= 4x^2 + 19x - 5$ ✓

C $2x^2 - 7x - 15$

$(\square x + \square)(\square x + \square)$ *a = 2 and c = −15; Outer + Inner = −7*

Factors of 2	Factors of −15	Outer + Inner
1 and 2	1 and −15	$1(-15) + (2)1 = -13$ ✗
1 and 2	−1 and 15	$(1)15 + 2(-1) = 13$ ✗
1 and 2	3 and −5	$1(-5) + (2)3 = 1$ ✗
1 and 2	−3 and 5	$(1)5 + 2(-3) = -1$ ✗
1 and 2	5 and −3	$1(-3) + (2)5 = 7$ ✗
1 and 2	−5 and 3	$(1)3 + 2(-5) = -7$ ✓

$(x - 5)(2x + 3)$

Check $(x - 5)(2x + 3) = 2x^2 + 3x - 10x - 15$ *Use the FOIL method.*

$= 2x^2 - 7x - 15$ ✓

Factor each trinomial. Check your answer.

3a. $6x^2 + 7x - 3$
$(3x - 1)(2x + 3)$

3b. $4n^2 - n - 3$
$(4n + 3)(n - 1)$

Students sometimes forget that every number has 1 and itself as two of its factors. Students may also forget negative factors. When students are making their lists of factors, remind them to try all possible factors.

Power Presentations with PowerPoint®

Additional Examples

Example 3

Factor each trinomial. Check your answer.

A. $3n^2 + 11n - 4$
$(n + 4)(3n - 1)$

B. $2x^2 + 9x - 18$
$(x + 6)(2x - 3)$

C. $4x^2 - 15x - 4$
$(x - 4)(4x + 1)$

Also available on transparency

INTERVENTION
Questioning Strategies

EXAMPLE 3

- What do you know about the binomials in the factored expression when the constant term in the trinomial is negative? Explain.

Teaching Tip **Multiple Representations** Show students that any trinomial can be written as a polynomial with four terms. It can then be factored by grouping. To factor $6x^2 + 19x + 15$, find ac and factors of ac that sum to b. Rewrite the trinomial using those factors: $6x^2 + 10x + 9x + 15$. Then factor by grouping.

$(6x^2 + 10x) + (9x + 15)$
$= 2x(3x + 5) + 3(3x + 5)$
$= (3x + 5)(2x + 3)$

Power Presentations with PowerPoint®

Additional Examples

Example 4

Factor $-2x^2 - 5x - 3$. Check your answer.

$-1(x + 1)(2x + 3)$

Also available on transparency

INTERVENTION
Questioning Strategies

EXAMPLE 4

- How do you know which term is the leading coefficient?
- What is the advantage to factoring out -1 in the first step?

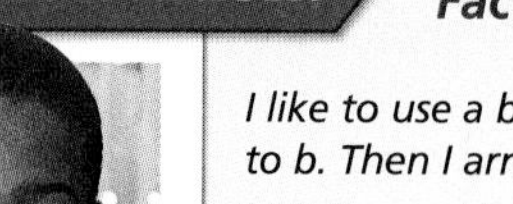

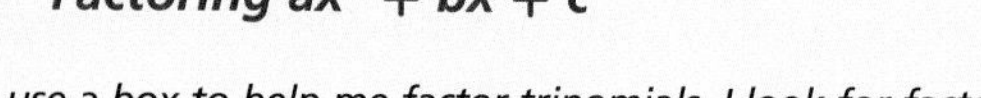

Student to Student — Factoring $ax^2 + bx + c$

I like to use a box to help me factor trinomials. I look for factors of ac that add to b. Then I arrange the terms in a box and factor.

To factor $6x^2 + 7x + 2$, first I find the factors I need.

$ac = 2(6) = 12 \quad b = 7$

Factors of 12	Sum
1 and 12	13
2 and 6	8
3 and 4	7

Then I rewrite the trinomial as $6x^2 + 3x + 4x + 2$.

Now I arrange $6x^2 + 3x + 4x + 2$ in a box and factor out the common factors from each row and column.

$6x^2$	$3x$	→ $3x$
$4x$	2	→ 2
↓ $2x$	↓ 1	

The factors are $(2x + 1)$ and $(3x + 2)$.

Reggie Wilson
Franklin High School

When the leading coefficient is negative, factor out -1 from each term before using other factoring methods.

EXAMPLE 4 Factoring $ax^2 + bx + c$ When a Is Negative

Factor $-2x^2 - 15x - 7$.

$-1(2x^2 + 15x + 7)$ — *Factor out -1.*

$-1(\square x + \square)(\square x + \square)$ — *$a = 2$ and $c = 7$; Outer + Inner = 15*

Factors of 2	Factors of 7	Outer + Inner	
1 and 2	1 and 7	$(1)7 + (2)1 = 9$	✗
1 and 2	7 and 1	$(1)1 + (2)7 = 15$	✓

$(x + 7)(2x + 1)$

$-1(x + 7)(2x + 1)$

Caution!

When you factor out -1 in an early step, you must carry it through the rest of the steps and into the answer.

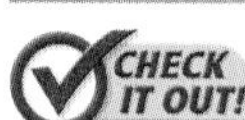

CHECK IT OUT! Factor each trinomial. Check your answer.

4a. $-6x^2 - 17x - 12$ $\quad -1(2x + 3)(3x + 4)$

4b. $-3x^2 - 17x - 10$ $\quad -1(3x + 2)(x + 5)$

THINK AND DISCUSS

1. Let a, b, and c be positive. If $ax^2 + bx + c$ is the product of two binomials, what do you know about the signs of the numbers in the binomials?

2. GET ORGANIZED Copy and complete the graphic organizer. Write each of the following trinomials in the appropriate box and factor each one.

$3x^2 + 10x - 8 \qquad 3x^2 + 10x + 8$
$3x^2 - 10x + 8 \qquad 3x^2 - 10x - 8$

Factoring $ax^2 + bx + c$	
$c > 0$	
$b > 0$	$b < 0$
$c < 0$	
$b < 0$	$b > 0$

3 Close

Summarize

Tell students that to factor a trinomial in the form $ax^2 + bx + c$, they should make a table, such that each row has two factors of a, two factors of c, and the sum of the inner and outer products. Remind them that if they factor out -1, they need to remember to put it in the factored form.

FORMATIVE ASSESSMENT and INTERVENTION

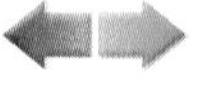

***Diagnose Before* the Lesson**
8-4 Warm Up, TE p. 505

***Monitor During* the Lesson**
Check It Out! Exercises, SE pp. 505–508
Questioning Strategies, TE p. 506–508

***Assess After* the Lesson**
8-4 Lesson Quiz, TE p. 511
Alternative Assessment, TE p. 511

Answers to *Think and Discuss*

1. They are both positive.
2. See p. A7.

8-4 Exercises

California Standards Practice
11.0, 15.0, 25.2

go.hrw.com
Homework Help Online
KEYWORD: MA8CA 8-4
Parent Resources Online
KEYWORD: MA8CA Parent

GUIDED PRACTICE

Factor each trinomial. Check your answer.

SEE EXAMPLE 1 p. 505

1. $2x^2 + 9x + 10$
2. $5x^2 + 31x + 6$
3. $5x^2 + 7x - 6$
4. $6x^2 + 37x + 6$
5. $3x^2 - 14x - 24$
6. $6x^2 + x - 2$

SEE EXAMPLE 2 p. 506

7. $5x^2 + 11x + 2$
8. $2x^2 + 11x + 5$
9. $4x^2 - 9x + 5$
10. $2y^2 - 11y + 14$
11. $5x^2 + 9x + 4$
12. $3x^2 + 7x + 2$

SEE EXAMPLE 3 p. 507

13. $4a^2 + 8a - 5$
14. $15x^2 + 4x - 3$
15. $2x^2 + x - 6$
16. $6n^2 - 11n - 10$
17. $10x^2 - 9x - 1$
18. $7x^2 - 3x - 10$

SEE EXAMPLE 4 p. 508

19. $-2x^2 + 5x + 12$
20. $-4n^2 - 16n + 9$
21. $-5x^2 + 7x + 6$
22. $-6x^2 + 13x - 2$
23. $-4x^2 - 8x + 5$
24. $-5x^2 + x + 18$

PRACTICE AND PROBLEM SOLVING

Independent Practice

For Exercises	See Example
25–33	1
34–42	2
43–48	3
49–51	4

Extra Practice
Skills Practice p. EP17
Application Practice p. EP31

Factor each trinomial. Check your answer.

25. $9x^2 + 9x + 2$
26. $2x^2 + 7x + 5$
27. $3n^2 + 8n + 4$
28. $10d^2 + 17d + 7$
29. $4c^2 - 17c + 15$
30. $6x^2 + 14x + 4$
31. $8x^2 + 22x + 5$
32. $6x^2 - 13x + 6$
33. $5x^2 + 9x - 18$
34. $6x^2 + 23x + 7$
35. $10n^2 - 17n + 7$
36. $3x^2 + 11x + 6$
37. $7x^2 + 15x + 2$
38. $3n^2 + 4n + 1$
39. $3x^2 - 19x + 20$
40. $6x^2 + 11x + 4$
41. $4x^2 - 31x + 21$
42. $10x^2 + 31x + 15$
43. $12y^2 + 17y - 5$
44. $3x^2 + 10x - 8$
45. $4x^2 + 4x - 3$
46. $2n^2 - 7n - 4$
47. $3x^2 - 4x - 15$
48. $3n^2 - n - 4$
49. $-4x^2 - 4x + 15$
50. $-3x^2 + 16x - 16$
51. $-3x^2 - x + 2$

Geometry For Exercises 52–54, write the polynomial modeled and then factor.

52.

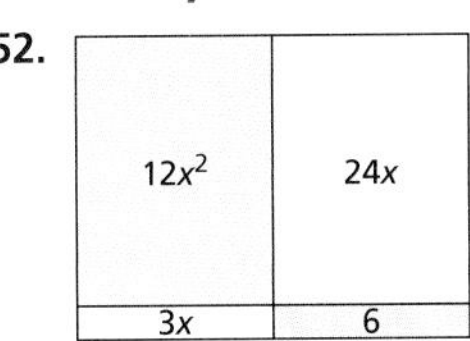

53.

$2x^2$	$-x$
$-4x$	2

54.

$5x^2$	$-4x$
$35x$	-28

Factor each trinomial, if possible. Check your answer.

55. $9n^2 + 17n + 8$
56. $2x^2 - 7x - 4$
57. $4x^2 - 12x + 5$
58. $5x^2 - 4x + 12$
59. $3x^2 + 14x + 16$
60. $-3x^2 - 11x + 4$
61. $6x^2 - x - 12$
62. $10a^2 + 11a + 3$
63. $4x^2 - 12x + 9$
64. $-6x^2 - 11x + 2$
65. $12x^2 - 8x + 1$
66. $-8x^2 - 7x + 1$
67. $15x^2 + 23x + 8$ **$(15x + 8)(x + 1)$**
68. $8x^2 - 4x - 4$ **$(8x + 4)(x - 1)$**
69. $9x^2 - x + 2$ **not factorable**

64. $(-6x + 1)(x + 2)$
65. $(6x - 1)(2x - 1)$
66. $(-8x + 1)(x + 1)$

8-4 Exercises

Assignment Guide

Assign *Guided Practice* exercises as necessary.

If you finished Examples **1–2**
Proficient 25–39, 58–70 even, 87, 89
Advanced 25–39, 58–70 even, 87, 89

If you finished Examples **1–4**
Proficient 25–76, 82–86, 89, 96–102
Advanced 25–51, 52–68 even, 70–75, 77–102

Homework Quick Check
Quickly check key concepts.
Exercises: 30, 35, 48, 50, 58, 70

Answers

1. $(2x + 5)(x + 2)$
2. $(x + 6)(5x + 1)$
3. $(5x - 3)(x + 2)$
4. $(x + 6)(6x + 1)$
5. $(3x + 4)(x - 6)$
6. $(2x - 1)(3x + 2)$
7. $(x + 2)(5x + 1)$
8. $(x + 5)(2x + 1)$
9. $(4x - 5)(x - 1)$
10. $(2y - 7)(y - 2)$
11. $(5x + 4)(x + 1)$
12. $(x + 2)(3x + 1)$
13. $(2a - 1)(2a + 5)$
14. $(3x - 1)(5x + 3)$
15. $(2x - 3)(x + 2)$
16. $(3n + 2)(2n - 5)$
17. $(10x + 1)(x - 1)$
18. $(x + 1)(7x - 10)$

19–63. See p. A23.

8-4 READING STRATEGIES

LESSON 8-4 Reading Strategies
Use a Model

Most people factor trinomials of the form $ax^2 + bx + c$ using a sort of organized guess-and-check method. Look at the model below.

Factor the trinomial $4x^2 - 17x - 15$ into two binomials.

- **Recall:** The acronym FOIL stands for First, Outer, Inner, Last.
- **Signs:** This trinomial requires a "plus" and a "minus" binomial.
- **Setup:** $(F + L)(F - L) \rightarrow (\ x + \ )(\ x - \ )$
- **"First":** The factorizations of 4 are: $1 \cdot 4$ and $2 \cdot 2$.
- **"Last":** The factorizations of 15 are: $1 \cdot 15$ and $3 \cdot 5$.
- **"Outer" and "Inner":** Guess-and-check these values in the binomials. The goal is to multiply the "Outer" terms and the "Inner" terms, and get a sum of −17.

(_x +_	)(	_x −_	)	Outer + Inner		
1	1	4	−15	$1 \cdot -15 + 1 \cdot 4$	= −11	No
1	15	4	−1	$1 \cdot -1 + 15 \cdot 4$	= 59	No
1	5	4	−3	$1 \cdot -3 + 5 \cdot 4$	= −7	No
1	3	4	−5	$1 \cdot -5 + 3 \cdot 4$	= 7	No
4	1	1	−15	$4 \cdot -15 + 1 \cdot 1$	= −59	No
4	15	1	−1	$4 \cdot -1 + 15 \cdot 1$	= 11	No
4	5	1	−3	$4 \cdot -3 + 5 \cdot 1$	= −7	No
4	**3**	**1**	**−5**	$4 \cdot -5 + 3 \cdot 1$	= −17	Yes

- **Answer:** $4x^2 - 17x - 15$ factors into $(4x + 3)(1x - 5)$, or just $(4x + 3)(x - 5)$.

Complete the following to guide you in factoring $3x^2 - 20x + 12$.

1. What are the factorizations of 3? **$1 \cdot 3$**
2. What are the factorizations of 12? **$1 \cdot 12$; $2 \cdot 6$; $3 \cdot 4$**
3. What signs are needed in each of the two binomials? **minus, minus**
4. Set up the binomials for factoring this polynomial. **$(\ x - \ )(\ x - \ )$**
5. Guess-and-check the factors that will result in the correct middle term coefficient of 20.

Possible answer:

(_x −_	)(	_x −_	)	Outer + Inner		
3	−1	1	−12	$3 \cdot -12 + -1 \cdot 1$	= −37	No
3	−12	1	−1	$3 \cdot -1 + -12 \cdot 1$	= −15	No
3	−4	1	−3	$3 \cdot -3 + -4 \cdot 1$	= −13	No
3	−3	1	−4	$3 \cdot -4 + -3 \cdot 1$	= −15	No
3	−6	1	−2	$3 \cdot -2 + -6 \cdot 1$	= −12	No
3	−2	1	−6	$3 \cdot -6 + -2 \cdot 1$	= −20	Yes

6. What is the final answer for factoring $3x^2 - 20x + 12$? **$(3x - 2)(x - 6)$**

8-4 REVIEW FOR MASTERY

LESSON 8-4 Review for Mastery
Factoring $ax^2 + bx + c$

When factoring $ax^2 + bx + c$, first find factors of a and c. Then check the products of the inner and outer terms to see if the sum is b.

Factor $2x^2 + 11x + 15$. Check your answer.

$2x^2 + 11x + 15 = (\ x + \ )(\ x + \ )$

Factors of 2	Factors of 15	Outer + Inner
1 and 2	1 and 15	$1 \cdot 15 + 2 \cdot 1 = 17$ ✗
1 and 2	15 and 1	$1 \cdot 1 + 2 \cdot 15 = 31$ ✗
1 and 2	5 and 3	$1 \cdot 3 + 2 \cdot 5 = 13$ ✗
1 and 2	3 and 5	$1 \cdot 5 + 2 \cdot 3 = 11$ ✓

$(x + 3)(2x + 5)$

Check:
$(x + 3)(2x + 5) = 2x^2 + 5x + 6x + 15$
$= 2x^2 + 11x + 15$ ✓

Factor $3x^2 - 23x + 14$. Check your answer.

$3x^2 - 23x + 14 = (\ x + \ )(\ x + \ )$

Factors of 3	Factors of 14	Outer + Inner
1 and 3	−1 and −14	$1 \cdot (-14) + 3 \cdot (-1) = -17$ ✗
1 and 3	−14 and −1	$1 \cdot (-1) + 3 \cdot (-14) = -42$ ✗
1 and 3	−2 and −7	$1 \cdot (-7) + 3 \cdot (-2) = -13$ ✗
1 and 3	−7 and −2	$1 \cdot (-2) + 3 \cdot (-7) = -23$ ✓

$(x - 7)(3x - 2)$

Check:
$(x - 7)(3x - 2) = 3x^2 - 2x - 21x + 14$
$= 3x^2 - 23x + 14$ ✓

1. Factor $5x^2 + 12x + 4$ by filling in the blanks below.

Factors	Factors	Outer + Inner
1 and 5	1 and 4	$1 \cdot 4 + 5 \cdot 1 = 9$
1 and 5	4 and 1	$1 \cdot 1 + 5 \cdot 4 = 21$
1 and 5	2 and 2	$1 \cdot 2 + 5 \cdot 2 = 12$

$(x + 2)(5x + 2)$

Factor each trinomial.

2. $3x^2 + 7x + 4$ **$(3x + 4)(x + 1)$**
3. $2x^2 - 13x + 21$ **$(2x - 7)(x - 3)$**
4. $4x^2 + 8x + 3$ **$(2x + 3)(2x + 1)$**

California Standards

Standard	Exercises
6.0	97–99
9.0	97–99
11.0	1–74, 75b, 77b, 78–81, 84–85, 87–92, 100–102
15.0	77
17.0	96
25.2	76

Teaching Tip **Geometry Link** In **Exercise 74,** have students draw a rectangle and label it with the original dimensions of the garden: w and $2w$. This will make it easier for them to see which factor of the factored expression is the length and which is the width.

CONCEPT CONNECTION **Exercise 77** involves solving a quadratic equation by factoring. This exercise prepares students for the Concept Connection on page 512.

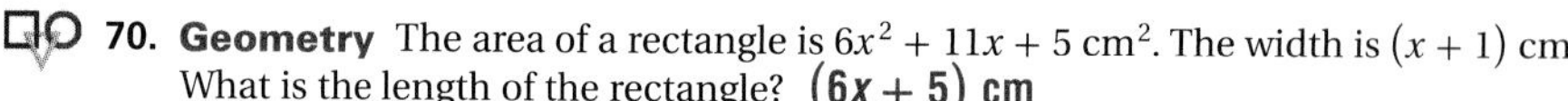

70. Geometry The area of a rectangle is $6x^2 + 11x + 5$ cm^2. The width is $(x + 1)$ cm. What is the length of the rectangle? **$(6x + 5)$ cm**

71. Write About It Write a paragraph describing how to factor $6x^2 + 13x + 6$. Show each step you would take and explain your steps. **$(2x + 3)(3x + 2)$; Check students' work.**

Complete each factorization.

72. $8x^2 + 18x - 5$

$8x^2 + 20x - 2x - 5$

$(8x^2 + 20x) - (2x + 5)$

$4x(2x + 5) - 1(2x + 5)$

$(4x - 1)(2x + 5)$

73. $4x^2 + 9x + 2$

$4x^2 + 8x + x + 2$

$(4x^2 + 8x) + (x + 2)$

$4x(x + 2) + 1(x + 2)$

$(4x + 1)(x + 2)$

74. Gardening The length of Rebecca's rectangular garden was two times the width w. Rebecca increased the length and width of the garden so that the area of the new garden is $(2w^2 + 7w + 6)$ square yards. By how much did Rebecca increase the length and the width of the garden?

74. width increased by 2 yd; length increased by 3 yd

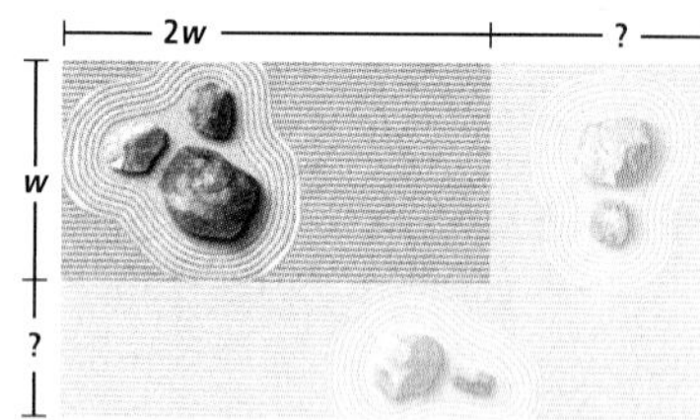

75. Physical Science The height of a football that has been thrown or kicked can be described by the expression $-16t^2 + vt + h$ where t is the time in seconds, v is the initial upward velocity, and h is the initial height in feet.

a. Write an expression for the height of a football at time t when the initial upward velocity is 20 feet per second and the initial height is 6 feet. **$-16t^2 + 20t + 6$**

b. Factor your expression from part **a.** Check your answer. **$-2(4t + 1)(2t - 3)$**

c. Find the height of the football after 1 second. **10 ft**

76. ///ERROR ANALYSIS/// A student attempted to factor $2x^2 + 11x + 12$ as shown. Find and explain the error. **The student tried factors of 12, but forgot to try factors of 2 also.**

$2x^2 + 11x + 12$

Factors of 12	Sum	
1 and 12	13	✓
2 and 6	8	x
3 and 4	7	x

$(2x + 1)(x + 12)$

77. This problem will prepare you for the Concept Connection on page 512.

The equation $d = 2t^2$ gives the distance from the start point of a toy boat that starts at rest and accelerates at 4 cm/s^2. The equation $d = 10t - 8$ gives the distance from the start point of a second boat that starts at rest 8 cm behind the first boat and travels at a constant rate of 10 cm/s.

a. By setting the equations equal to each other, you can determine when the cars are the same distance from the start point: $2t^2 = 10t - 8$. Use properties of algebra to collect all terms on the left side of the equation, leaving 0 on the right side. **$2t^2 - 10t + 8 = 0$**

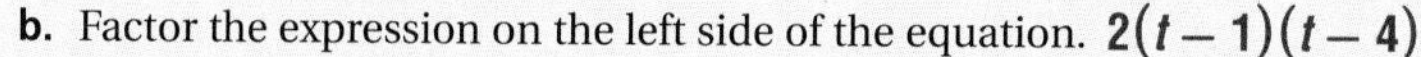

b. Factor the expression on the left side of the equation. **$2(t - 1)(t - 4)$**

c. The boats are the same distance from the start point at $t = 1$ and $t = 4$. Explain how the factors you found in part **b** are related to these two times. **When $t = 1$ or $t = 4$, one of the factors in part b is equal to 0, making the product equal to 0.**

8-4 PRACTICE A

8-4 PRACTICE C

8-4 PRACTICE B

LESSON 8-4 **Practice B**

Factoring $ax^2 + bx + c$

Factor each trinomial.

1. $2x^2 + 13x + 15$ **$(2x + 3)(x + 5)$**
2. $3x^2 + 10x + 8$ **$(3x + 4)(x + 2)$**
3. $4x^2 + 24x + 27$ **$(2x + 9)(2x + 3)$**
4. $5x^2 + 21x + 4$ **$(5x + 1)(x + 4)$**
5. $4x^2 + 11x + 7$ **$(4x + 7)(x + 1)$**
6. $6x^2 - 23x + 20$ **$(3x - 4)(2x - 5)$**
7. $7x^2 - 59x + 24$ **$(7x - 3)(x - 8)$**
8. $3x^2 - 14x + 15$ **$(3x - 5)(x - 3)$**
9. $8x^2 - 73x + 9$ **$(8x - 1)(x - 9)$**
10. $2x^2 + 11x - 13$ **$(2x + 13)(x - 1)$**
11. $3x^2 + 2x - 16$ **$(3x + 8)(x - 2)$**
12. $2x^2 + 17x - 30$ **$(x + 10)(2x - 3)$**
13. $8x^2 + 29x - 12$ **$(x + 4)(8x - 3)$**
14. $11x^2 + 25x - 24$ **$(x + 3)(11x - 8)$**
15. $9x^2 - 3x - 2$ **$(3x + 1)(3x - 2)$**
16. $12x^2 - 7x - 12$ **$(4x + 3)(3x - 4)$**
17. $9x^2 - 49x - 30$ **$(9x + 5)(x - 6)$**
18. $6x^2 + x - 40$ **$(3x + 8)(2x - 5)$**
19. $-12x^2 - 35x - 18$ **$-1(4x + 9)(3x + 2)$**
20. $-20x^2 + 29x - 6$ **$-1(5x - 6)(4x - 1)$**
21. $-2x^2 + 5x + 42$ **$-1(2x + 7)(x - 6)$**
22. The area of a rectangle is $20x^2 - 27x - 8$. The length is $4x + 1$. What is the width? **$5x - 8$**

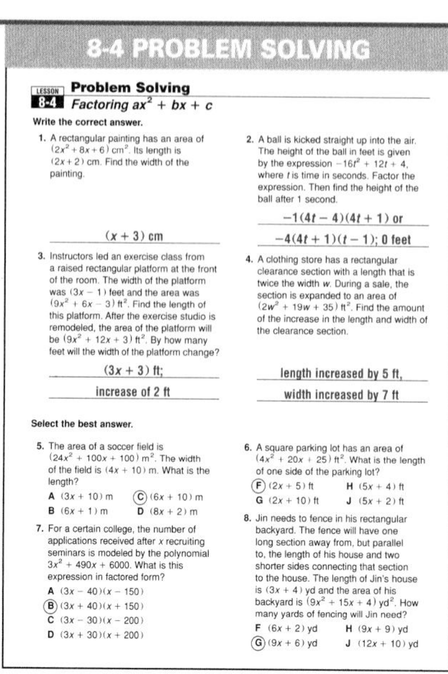

8-4 PROBLEM SOLVING

LESSON 8-4 **Problem Solving**

Factoring $ax^2 + bx + c$

Write the correct answer.

1. A rectangular painting has an area of $(2x^2 + 8x + 6)$ cm^2. Its length is $(2x + 2)$ cm. Find the width of the painting. **$(x + 3)$ cm**

2. A ball is kicked straight up into the air. The height of the ball in feet is given by the expression $-16t^2 + 12t + 4$, where t is time in seconds. Factor the expression. Then find the height of the ball after 1 second. **$-1(4t - 4)(4t + 1)$ or $-4(4t + 1)(t - 1)$; 0 feet**

3. Instructors led an exercise class from a raised rectangular platform at the front of the room. The width of the platform was $(3x - 1)$ feet and the area was $(9x^2 + 6x - 3)$ ft^2. Find the length of this platform. After the exercise studio is remodeled, the area of the platform will be $(9x^2 + 12x + 3)$ ft^2. By how many feet will the width of the platform change? **$(3x + 3)$ ft; increase of 2 ft**

4. A clothing store has a rectangular clearance section with a length that is twice the width w. During a sale, the section is expanded to an area of $(2w^2 + 19w + 35)$ ft^2. Find the amount of the increase in the length and width of the clearance section. **length increased by 5 ft, width increased by 7 ft**

Select the best answer.

5. The area of a soccer field is $(24x^2 + 100x + 100)$ m^2. The width of the field is $(4x + 10)$ m. What is the length?
   - A $(3x + 10)$ m
   - **(C)** $(6x + 10)$ m
   - B $(6x + 1)$ m
   - D $(8x + 2)$ m

6. A square parking lot has an area of $(4x^2 + 20x + 25)$ ft^2. What is the length of one side of the parking lot?
   - **(F)** $(2x + 5)$ ft
   - H $(5x + 4)$ ft
   - G $(2x + 10)$ ft
   - J $(5x + 2)$ ft

7. For a certain college, the number of applications received after x recruiting seminars is modeled by the polynomial $3x^2 + 490x + 6000$. What is this expression in factored form?
   - A $(3x - 40)(x - 150)$
   - **(B)** $(3x + 40)(x + 150)$
   - C $(3x - 30)(x - 200)$
   - D $(3x + 30)(x + 200)$

8. Jin needs to fence in his rectangular backyard. The fence will have one long section away from, but parallel to, the length of his house and two shorter sides connecting that section to the house. The length of Jin's house is $(3x + 4)$ yd and the area of his backyard is $(9x^2 + 15x + 4)$ yd^2. How many yards of fencing will Jin need?
   - F $(6x + 2)$ yd
   - H $(9x + 9)$ yd
   - **(G)** $(9x + 6)$ yd
   - J $(12x + 10)$ yd

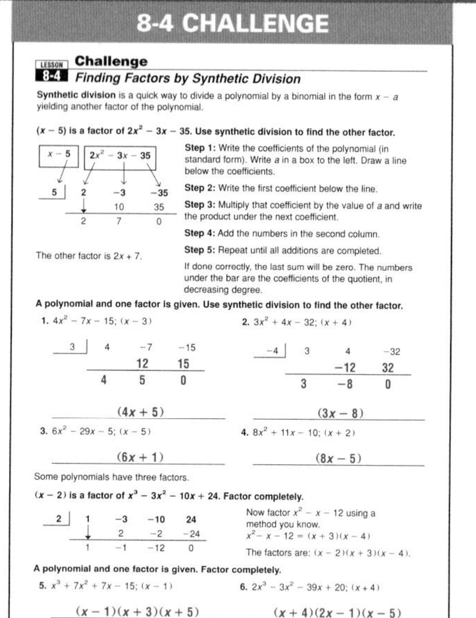

8-4 CHALLENGE

LESSON 8-4 **Challenge**

Finding Factors by Synthetic Division

Synthetic division is a quick way to divide a polynomial by a binomial in the form $x - a$ yielding another factor of the polynomial.

$(x - 5)$ is a factor of $2x^2 - 3x - 35$. Use synthetic division to find the other factor.

$x - 5$	$2x^2 - 3x - 35$		
5	2	−3	−35
	↓	10	35
	2	7	0

Step 1: Write the coefficients of the polynomial (in standard form). Write a in a box to the left. Draw a line below the coefficients.

Step 2: Write the first coefficient below the line.

Step 3: Multiply that coefficient by the value of a and write the product under the next coefficient.

Step 4: Add the numbers in the second column.

Step 5: Repeat until all additions are completed.

If done correctly, the last sum will be zero. The numbers under the bar are the coefficients of the quotient, in decreasing degree.

The other factor is $2x + 7$.

A polynomial and one factor is given. Use synthetic division to find the other factor.

1. $4x^2 - 7x - 15$; $(x - 3)$

3	4	−7	−15
		12	15
	4	5	0

$(4x + 5)$

2. $3x^2 + 4x - 32$; $(x + 4)$

−4	3	4	−32
		−12	32
	3	−8	0

$(3x - 8)$

3. $6x^2 - 29x - 5$; $(x - 5)$ **$(6x + 1)$**

4. $8x^2 + 11x - 10$; $(x + 2)$ **$(8x - 5)$**

Some polynomials have three factors.

$(x - 2)$ is a factor of $x^3 - 3x^2 - 10x + 24$. Factor completely.

2	1	−3	−10	24
	↓	2	−2	−24
	1	−1	−12	0

Now factor $x^2 - x - 12$ using a method you know.

$x^2 - x - 12 = (x + 3)(x - 4)$

The factors are: $(x - 2)(x + 3)(x - 4)$.

A polynomial and one factor is given. Factor completely.

5. $x^3 + 7x^2 + 7x - 15$; $(x - 1)$ **$(x - 1)(x + 3)(x + 5)$**

6. $2x^3 - 3x^2 - 39x + 20$; $(x + 4)$ **$(x + 4)(2x - 1)(x - 5)$**

Match each trinomial with its correct factorization.

78. $6x^2 - 29x - 5$ **D** A. $(x + 5)(6x + 1)$

79. $6x^2 - 31x + 5$ **B** B. $(x - 5)(6x - 1)$

80. $6x^2 + 31x + 5$ **A** C. $(x + 5)(6x - 1)$

81. $6x^2 + 29x - 5$ **C** D. $(x - 5)(6x + 1)$

82a. Both signs are pos., or both signs are neg.

b. One sign is pos., and the other is neg.

82. **Reasoning** A quadratic trinomial $ax^2 + bx + c$ has $a > 0$ and can be factored into the product of two binomials.

a. Explain what you know about the signs of the constants in the factors if $c > 0$.

b. Explain what you know about the signs of the constants in the factors if $c < 0$.

Multiple Choice For Exercises 83–86, choose the best answer.

83. What value of b would make $3x^2 + bx - 8$ factorable?

(A) 3 **(B) 10** (C) 11 (D) 25

84. Which product of binomials is represented by the model?

(A) $(x + 4)(3x + 5)$ **(C) $(x + 3)(5x + 4)$**

(B) $(x + 4)(5x + 3)$ (D) $(x + 5)(3x + 4)$

$5x^2$	$4x$
$15x$	12

85. Which binomial is a factor of $24x^2 - 49x + 2$?

(A) $x - 2$ (B) $x - 1$ (C) $x + 1$ (D) $x + 2$

86. Which value of c would make $2x^2 + x + c$ NOT factorable?

(A) −15 **(B) −9** (C) −6 (D) −1

CHALLENGE AND EXTEND

Factor each trinomial. Check your answer.

87. $1 + 4x + 4x^2$ 88. $1 - 14x + 49x^2$ 89. $1 + 18x + 81x^2$

90. $25 + 30x + 9x^2$ 91. $4 + 20x + 25x^2$ 92. $4 - 12x + 9x^2$

93. Find all possible values of b such that $3x^2 + bx + 2$ can be factored. **−7; −5; 5; 7**

94. Find all possible values of b such that $3x^2 + bx - 2$ can be factored. **−5; −1; 1; 5**

95. Find all possible values of b such that $5x^2 + bx + 1$ can be factored. **−6; 6**

SPIRAL STANDARDS REVIEW

6.0, 9.0, 11.0, 17.0

96. Archie makes $12 per hour and is paid for whole numbers of hours. The function $f(x) = 12x$ gives the amount of money that Archie makes in x hours. Graph this function and give its domain and range. *(Lesson 5-1)*
D: {0, 1, 2, 3, ...}; R: {0, 12, 24, 36, ...}

Graph each system of linear inequalities. Give two ordered pairs that are solutions and two that are not solutions. *(Lesson 6-6)*

97. $\begin{cases} y < -2x + 1 \\ y > 3x - 5 \end{cases}$ 98. $\begin{cases} y \geq -x + 2 \\ y \leq x - 3 \end{cases}$ 99. $\begin{cases} y \leq -4x \\ y > 2x - 6 \end{cases}$

Factor each trinomial. Check your answer. *(Lesson 8-3)*

100. $x^2 + 6x + 8$ **$(x + 2)(x + 4)$** 101. $x^2 - 8x - 9$ **$(x + 1)(x - 9)$** 102. $x^2 - 8x + 12$ **$(x - 2)(x - 6)$**

97. Possible answer: solutions: (−10, 0), (−20, 0); not solutions: (10, 0), (20, 0)

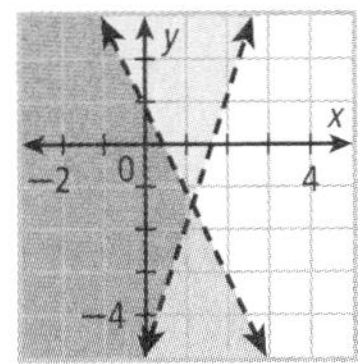

98. Possible answer: solutions: (4, 0), (5, 0); not solutions: (−4, 0), (−5, 0)

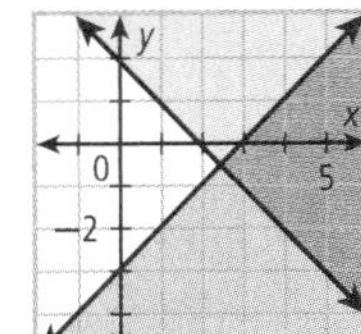

99. Possible answer: solutions: (−1, 0), (−2, 0); not solutions: (4, 0), (5, 0)

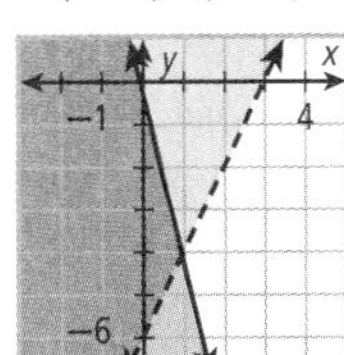

Teaching Tip **Multiple Choice** In **Exercise 84,** 1 and 5 are the only choices for the factors of a. Choices **A** and **D** can be eliminated.

Tell students that they can immediately eliminate **C** and **D** in **Exercise 85.** Because b is negative and c is positive, the constants will be subtracted in both binomials.

Answers

87. $(2x + 1)(2x + 1)$
88. $(7x - 1)(7x - 1)$
89. $(9x + 1)(9x + 1)$
90. $(3x + 5)(3x + 5)$
91. $(5x + 2)(5x + 2)$
92. $(3x - 2)(3x - 2)$
96.

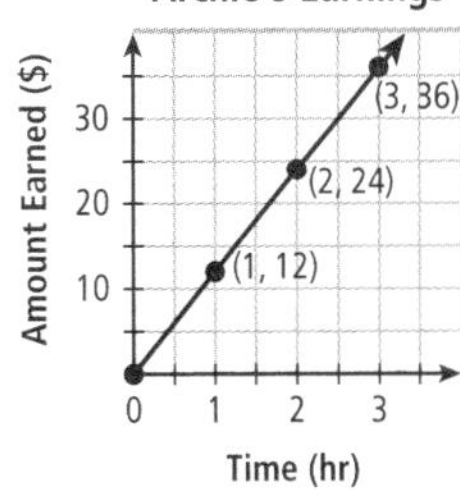

Journal

Have students explain how to factor a trinomial of the form $ax^2 + bx + c$ when a is negative.

ALTERNATIVE ASSESSMENT

Have students write binomials of the form $(x + a)$, $(x - a)$, $(ax + b)$, and $(ax - b)$. Then make six trinomials by multiplying each different pair. Have students give their trinomials to another student to factor.

Power Presentations with PowerPoint®

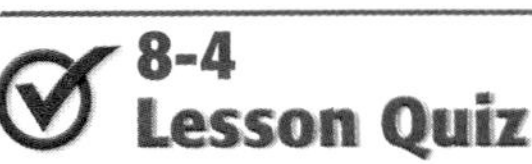

8-4 Lesson Quiz

Factor each trinomial. Check your answer.

1. $5x^2 + 17x + 6$
$(5x + 2)(x + 3)$
2. $2x^2 + 5x - 12$
$(2x - 3)(x + 4)$
3. $6x^2 - 23x + 7$
$(3x - 1)(2x - 7)$
4. $-4x^2 + 11x + 20$
$(-x + 4)(4x + 5)$
5. $-2x^2 + 7x - 3$
$(-2x + 1)(x - 3)$
6. $8x^2 + 27x + 9$
$(8x + 3)(x + 3)$

Also available on transparency

SECTION 8A

CONCEPT CONNECTION

Organizer

Objective: Assess students' ability to apply concepts and skills in Lessons 8-1 through 8-4 in a real-world format.

 Online Edition

 Countdown to Mastery Week 18

Problem	Text Reference
1	Lesson 8-1
2	Lesson 8-1
3	Lessons 8-2 and 8-3
4	Lessons 8-2 and 8-3
5	Lesson 8-1
6	Lesson 8-4

California Standards

11.0, 15.0

CHAPTER 8

CONCEPT CONNECTION

SECTION 8A

Factoring

Red Light, Green Light The equation for the motion of an object with constant acceleration is $d = vt + \frac{1}{2}at^2$ where d is distance traveled in meters, v is starting velocity in m/s, a is acceleration in m/s², and t is time in seconds.

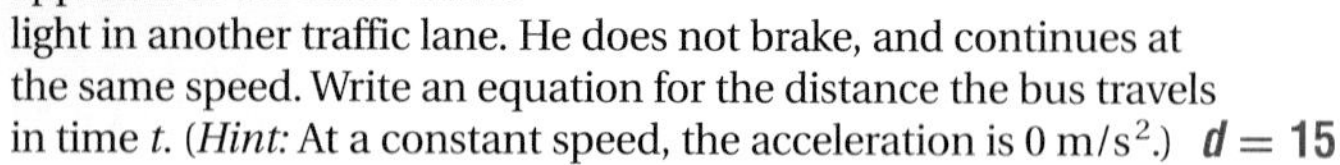

1. A car is stopped at a traffic light. The light changes to green and the driver starts to drive, accelerating at a rate of 4 m/s². Write an equation for the distance the car travels in time t. $d = 2t^2$
2. A bus is traveling at a speed of 15 m/s. The driver approaches the same traffic light in another traffic lane. He does not brake, and continues at the same speed. Write an equation for the distance the bus travels in time t. (*Hint:* At a constant speed, the acceleration is 0 m/s².) $d = 15t$
3. Set the equations equal to each other so you can determine when the car and bus are the same distance from the intersection. Collect all the terms on the left side of this new equation, leaving 0 on the right side. Factor the expression on the left side of the equation. Check your answer. $2t^2 - 15t = 0$; $t(2t - 15)$
4. Let $t = 0$ be the point at which the car is just starting to drive and the bus is even with the car. Find the other time when the vehicles will be the same distance from the intersection. $t = 7.5$ s
5. What distance will the two vehicles have traveled when they are again at the same distance from the intersection? $d = 112.5$ m
6. A truck traveling at 16 m/s is 24 meters behind the bus at $t = 0$. The equation $d = -24 + 16t$ gives the position of the truck. At what time will the truck be the same distance from the intersection as the bus? What will that distance be? $t = 24$ s; $d = 360$ m

INTERVENTION 

Scaffolding Questions

1. What is the initial velocity of an object that is stopped? zero m/s
2. What is the acceleration of an object that does not change velocity? zero m/s²
3. If the product of two numbers is zero, why is one of the numbers zero? Zero multiplied by any number is zero.
4. Explain why one solution to the equation for the car and bus is $t = 0$. The car and bus both start at the intersection with the traffic light.
5. How can you determine the distance traveled by the car? Substitute the time from Problem 4 in the equation from Problem 1.
6. Explain why $t = 0$ is not a solution for the car and truck. The car and truck are not at the same position when the light changes.

Extension

During what period of time is the truck ahead of the car? between $t = 2$ s and $t = 6$ s

Quiz for Lessons 8-1 Through 8-4

8-1 Factors and Greatest Common Factors

Write the prime factorization of each number.

1. 54 $2 \cdot 3^3$ 2. 42 $2 \cdot 3 \cdot 7$ 3. 50 $2 \cdot 5^2$ 4. 120 $2^3 \cdot 3 \cdot 5$ 5. 44 $2^2 \cdot 11$ 6. 78 $2 \cdot 3 \cdot 13$

Find the GCF of each pair of monomials.

7. $6p^3$ and $2p$ $2p$ 8. $12x^3$ and $18x^4$ $6x^3$ 9. -15 and $20s^4$ 5 10. $3a$ and $4b^2$ 1

11. Brent is making a wooden display case for his baseball collection. He has 24 balls from American League games and 30 balls from National League games. He wants to display the same number of baseballs in each row and does not want to put American League baseballs in the same row as National League baseballs. How many rows will Brent need in the display case to put the greatest number of baseballs possible in each row? 9

8-2 Factoring by GCF

Factor each polynomial. Check your answer.

12. $2d^3 + 4d$ $2d(d^2 + 2)$ 13. $m^2 - 8m^5$ $m^2(1 - 8m^3)$
14. $12x^4 - 8x^3 - 4x^2$ $4x^2(3x^2 - 2x - 1)$ 15. $3k^2 + 6k - 3$ $3(k^2 + 2k - 1)$
16. The surface area of a cone can be found using the expression $s\pi r + \pi r^2$, where s represents the slant height and r represents the radius of the base. Factor this expression. $\pi r(s + r)$

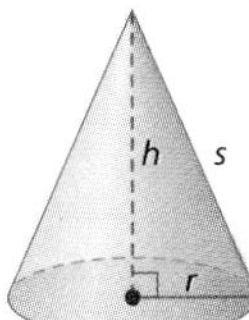

Factor each polynomial by grouping. Check your answer.

17. $w^3 - 4w^2 + w - 4$ $(w^2 + 1)(w - 4)$ 18. $3x^3 + 6x^2 - 4x - 8$ $(3x^2 - 4)(x + 2)$
19. $2p^3 - 6p^2 + 15 - 5p$ $(2p^2 - 5)(p - 3)$ 20. $n^3 - 6n^2 + 5n - 30$ $(n^2 + 5)(n - 6)$

8-3 Factoring $x^2 + bx + c$

Factor each trinomial. Check your answer.

21. $n^2 + 9n + 20$ 22. $d^2 - 6d - 7$ 23. $x^2 - 6x + 8$
24. $y^2 + 7y - 30$ 25. $k^2 - 6k + 5$ 26. $c^2 - 10c + 24$
27. Simplify and factor the polynomial $n(n + 3) - 4$. Show that the original polynomial and the factored form have the same value for $n = 0, 1, 2, 3,$ and 4.

8-4 Factoring $ax^2 + bx + c$

Factor each trinomial. Check your answer.

28. $2x^2 + 11x + 5$ 29. $3n^2 + 16n + 21$ 30. $5y^2 - 7y - 6$
31. $4g^2 - 10g + 6$ 32. $6p^2 - 18p - 24$ 33. $12d^2 + 7d - 12$
34. The area of a rectangle is $(8x^2 + 8x + 2)$ cm². The width is $(2x + 1)$ cm. What is the length of the rectangle? $(4x + 2)$ cm

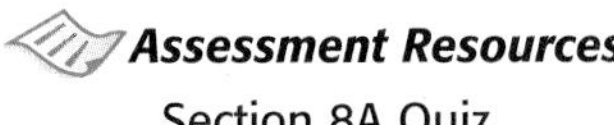

Organizer

Objective: Assess students' mastery of concepts and skills in Lessons 8-1 through 8-4.

Resources

Assessment Resources
Section 8A Quiz

Test & Practice Generator
One-Stop Planner®

INTERVENTION 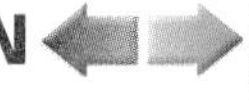

Resources

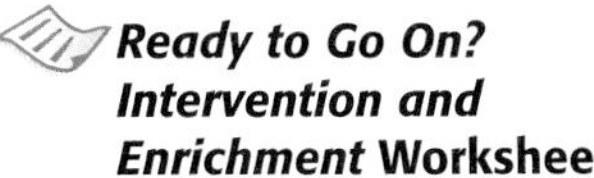

***Ready to Go On? Intervention and Enrichment* Worksheets**

***Ready to Go On?* CD-ROM**

***Ready to Go On?* Online**

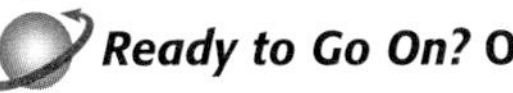

my.hrw.com

Answers

21. $(n + 4)(n + 5)$
22. $(d - 7)(d + 1)$
23. $(x - 4)(x - 2)$
24. $(y + 10)(y - 3)$
25. $(k - 5)(k - 1)$
26. $(c - 4)(c - 6)$
27–33. See p. A24.

READY TO GO ON? Diagnose and Prescribe

NO INTERVENE

Ready to Go On? Intervention	*Ready to Go On? Intervention,* Section 8A: Worksheets	CD-ROM	Online
Lesson 8-1 Prep for 11.0	8-1 Intervention	Activity 8-1	Diagnose and Prescribe Online
Lesson 8-2 11.0	8-2 Intervention	Activity 8-2	
Lesson 8-3 11.0	8-3 Intervention	Activity 8-3	
Lesson 8-4 11.0	8-4 Intervention	Activity 8-4	

YES ENRICH

Ready to Go On? Enrichment, Section 8A

Worksheets

CD-ROM

Online

Applying Factoring Methods

One-Minute Section Planner

Lesson	Lab Resources	Materials
Lesson 8-5 Factoring Special Products • Factor perfect-square trinomials. • Factor the difference of two squares. **11.0**	***Algebra Lab 8-5*** In *Chapter 8 Resource File*	**Optional** algebra tiles (MK)
Lesson 8-6 Choosing a Factoring Method • Choose an appropriate method for factoring a polynomial. • Combine methods for factoring a polynomial. **11.0**		

MK = *Manipulatives Kit*

Notes

Math Background: Teaching the Standards

Professional Development

FACTORING POLYNOMIALS 11.0

Lessons 8-5 and 8-6

Algebra is an extension of arithmetic. As such, there are many parallels between the two. For example, the arithmetic idea of factoring a number can be extended into the realm of algebra by considering factorizations of polynomials.

Factoring polynomials is an essential algebraic skill. As students will see in Chapter 9, it provides a powerful method for solving quadratic equations. However, students must first develop an arsenal of techniques for factoring.

FACTORING METHODS 11.0

Lesson 8-6

The simplest factoring methods are direct applications of the Distributive Property. In particular, the Distributive Property makes it possible to factor out the greatest common factor (GCF) of the terms of a polynomial.

For example, to factor the polynomial $3x^2 + 12x^3$, we may rewrite it as $3 \cdot x \cdot x + 2 \cdot 2 \cdot 3 \cdot x \cdot x \cdot x$, where the integer coefficients have been written in their prime factorizations. This form of the polynomial makes it easy to see that the GCF of the terms is $3x^2$, and by the Distributive Property, $3x^2 + 12x^3 = 3x^2(1 + 4x)$.

The Distributive Property is also at work when students use more general methods to factor binomials. To factor the polynomial $x^2 + 7x + 12$, students will look for two factors of 12 whose sum is 7. This leads to the factorization $(x + 4)(x + 3)$. However, it is instructive to look at the intermediate steps. Once the correct factors of 12 have been identified, we can write

1. $x^2 + 7x + 12 = x^2 + 3x + 4x + 12$

2. $= x(x + 3) + 4(x + 3)$

3. $= (x + 4)(x + 3)$

The Distributive Property has been used twice to go from Step 1 to Step 2 and has been applied again to go from Step 2 to Step 3. It is also useful to recognize that the polynomial on the right side of the equation in Step 1 consists of precisely the set of terms that result from multiplying $(x + 4)(x + 3)$ by using the FOIL method taught in Chapter 7. In other words, multiplying polynomials and factoring polynomials are inverse processes based on the Distributive Property.

UNFACTORABLE POLYNOMIALS  11.0

Lesson 8-6

Students should understand that some polynomials cannot be factored. For example, the binomials $x^2 + x + 1$ and $2x^2 + 5x + 4$ are unfactorable. Similar to arithmetic, we call these polynomials *prime polynomials*.

Note that when we say a polynomial is unfactorable in an Algebra 1 course, this generally means that it cannot be factored *over the integers*. In other words, the polynomial cannot be written as a product of polynomials of lesser degree whose terms have integer coefficients. However, it may be possible to factor the polynomial over other sets of numbers.

For example, consider the binomial $x^2 - 2$. This binomial is unfactorable over the integers, but it can be factored over the real numbers as $(x + \sqrt{2})(x - \sqrt{2})$. Furthermore, the binomial $x^2 + 4$ cannot be factored over the integers or over the real numbers, but it can be factored over the complex numbers as $(x + 2i)(x - 2i)$, where $i = \sqrt{-1}$. (Students will be introduced to the set of complex numbers in Algebra 2.)

To take this a step further, the Fundamental Theorem of Algebra asserts that every polynomial of degree $n \geq 1$ has n roots in the complex numbers. As a result, every polynomial can be completely factored (that is, written as a product of linear factors) in a unique way over the complex numbers, with the exception of different orderings of the factors. Thus, the Fundamental Theorem of Algebra is analogous to the Fundamental Theorem of Arithmetic, demonstrating once again that algebra is an extension of arithmetic.

8-5 Organizer

Objectives: Factor perfect-square trinomials.

Factor the difference of two squares.

Algebra Lab
In Chapter 8 Resource File

Online Edition
Tutorial Videos, Interactivity

Countdown to Mastery Week 19

Power Presentations with PowerPoint®

Warm Up

Determine whether the following are perfect squares. If so, find the square root.

1. 64 yes; 8 **2.** 36 yes; 6

3. 45 no **4.** x^2 yes; x

5. y^8 yes; y^4 **6.** $4x^6$ yes; $2x^3$

7. $9y^7$ no **8.** $49p^{10}$ yes; $7p^5$

Also available on transparency

Math Humor

Q: What did Polly Nomial call her spoiled triplets?

A: The perfect Tri Nomials.

California Standards

Algebra 1 11.0

8-5 Factoring Special Products

California Standards

11.0 Students apply basic factoring techniques to second- and simple third-**degree polynomials. These techniques include** finding a common factor for all terms in a polynomial, **recognizing the difference of two squares, and recognizing perfect squares of binomials.**

Who uses this?

Urban planners can use the area of a square park to find its length and width. (See Example 2.)

You studied the patterns of some special products of binomials in Chapter 7. You can use those patterns to factor certain polynomials.

A trinomial is a perfect square if:
- The first and last terms are perfect squares.
- The middle term is two times one factor from the first term and one factor from the last term.

$$9x^2 \quad + \quad 12x \quad + \quad 4$$
$$3x \cdot 3x \quad 2(3x \cdot 2) \quad 2 \cdot 2$$

Know it! Note

Factoring Perfect-Square Trinomials

PERFECT-SQUARE TRINOMIAL	EXAMPLES
$a^2 + 2ab + b^2 = (a + b)(a + b) = (a + b)^2$	$x^2 + 6x + 9 = (x + 3)(x + 3) = (x + 3)^2$
$a^2 - 2ab + b^2 = (a - b)(a - b) = (a - b)^2$	$x^2 - 2x + 1 = (x - 1)(x - 1) = (x - 1)^2$

EXAMPLE 1 Recognizing and Factoring Perfect-Square Trinomials

Determine whether each trinomial is a perfect square. If so, factor. If not, explain.

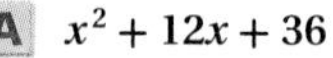

A $x^2 + 12x + 36$

$$x^2 + 12x + 36$$
$$x \cdot x \quad 2(x \cdot 6) \quad 6 \cdot 6$$

The trinomial is a perfect square. Factor.

Method 1 Factor.

$x^2 + 12x + 36$

Factors of 36	Sum	
1 and 36	37	✗
2 and 18	20	✗
3 and 12	15	✗
4 and 9	13	✗
6 and 6	12	✓

$(x + 6)(x + 6)$

Method 2 Use the rule.

$x^2 + 12x + 36$ — *$a = x$, $b = 6$*

$x^2 + 2(x)(6) + 6^2$ — *Write the trinomial as $a^2 + 2ab + b^2$.*

$(x + 6)^2$ — *Write the trinomial as $(a + b)^2$.*

1 Introduce

EXPLORATION

8-5 Factoring Special Products

In this Exploration, you will look for patterns as you find the squares of binomials.

1. Complete the table by writing each square as a product of two factors. Then find the product of the two factors and express the result as a trinomial.

Square	Factors	Product
$(x + 2)^2$	$(x + 2)(x + 2)$	$x^2 + 4x + 4$
$(x + 3)^3$		
$(x + 5)^2$		
$(x - 4)^2$		
$(2x + 5)^2$		
$(3x - 7)^2$		
$(5x + 1)^2$		

2. Look at the constant terms of the trinomials in your table. What do you notice?
3. Look at the x^2-terms of the trinomials in your table. What do you notice?

THINK AND DISCUSS

4. **Explain** whether it is possible for the constant term of a trinomial to be negative if the trinomial can be written as the square of a binomial.
5. **Discuss** whether you think $x^2 + 6x + 24$ can be written as the square of a binomial.

Motivate

Have students write all the steps for multiplying $(2x + 3)(2x - 3)$ using the FOIL method.

$(2x)(2x) + (2x)(-3) + (3)(2x) + (3)(-3)$

$= 4x^2 - 6x + 6x - 9$

$= 4x^2 - 9$

Ask students why there is no middle term in the final step. The sum of the inner product and the outer product is zero.

Explorations and answers are provided in *Alternate Openers: Explorations Transparencies.*

Determine whether each trinomial is a perfect square. If so, factor. If not, explain.

B $4x^2 - 12x + 9$

$$4x^2 - 12x + 9$$

$2x \cdot 2x \quad 2(2x \cdot 3) \quad 3 \cdot 3$ *The trinomial is a perfect square. Factor.*

$4x^2 - 12x + 9$	*$a = 2x, b = 3$*
$(2x)^2 - 2(2x)(3) + 3^2$	*$a^2 - 2ab + b^2$*
$(2x - 3)^2$	*$(a - b)^2$*

C $x^2 + 9x + 16$

$$x^2 + 9x + 16$$

$x \cdot x \quad 2(x \cdot 4) \quad 4 \cdot 4$ *$2(x \cdot 4) \neq 9x$*

$x^2 + 9x + 16$ is not a perfect-square trinomial because $9x \neq 2(x \cdot 4)$.

Remember!

You can check your answer by using the FOIL method.

For Example 1B,
$(2x - 3)^2 =$
$(2x - 3)(2x - 3) =$
$4x^2 - 6x - 6x + 9 =$
$4x^2 - 12x + 9$

CHECK IT OUT! Determine whether each trinomial is a perfect square. If so, factor. If not, explain.

1a. $x^2 + 4x + 4$ $(x + 2)^2$ **1b.** $x^2 - 14x + 49$ $(x - 7)^2$ **1c.** $9x^2 - 6x + 4$ no; $-6x \neq 2(3x)(2)$

EXAMPLE  ***Problem-Solving Application***

PROBLEM SOLVING

The park in the center of the Place des Vosges in Paris, France, is in the shape of a square. The area of the park is $(25x^2 + 70x + 49)$ ft². The side length of the park is in the form $cx + d$, where c and d are whole numbers. Find an expression in terms of x for the perimeter of the park. Find the perimeter when $x = 8$ ft.

1 Understand the Problem

The **answer** will be an expression for the perimeter of the park and the value of the expression when $x = 8$.

List the **important information:**

- The park is a square with area $(25x^2 + 70x + 49)$ft².
- The side length of the park is in the form $cx + d$, where c and d are whole numbers.

 **Make a Plan**

The formula for the area of a square is area = $(\text{side})^2$.

Factor $25x^2 + 70x + 49$ to find the side length of the park. Write a formula for the perimeter of the park, and evaluate the expression for $x = 8$.

2 Teach

Guided Instruction

Before beginning this lesson, review factoring trinomials and identifying perfect squares. Point out that perfect-square trinomials can be factored using the methods from the previous sections. Because these polynomials contain perfect-square numbers, easier methods are shown. Emphasize that factoring the difference of two squares is possible only for the difference. The sum of two squares cannot be factored.

Universal Access

Through Number Sense

Show students a quick way to rule out the possibility of a trinomial being a perfect-square trinomial. Remind them that if $ax^2 + bx + c$ is a perfect-square trinomial, then b must be an even number. This is because in a perfect-square trinomial, $b = 2 \cdot \sqrt{a} \cdot \sqrt{c}$. If b is even, then the trinomial *might* be a perfect square.

COMMON ERROR ALERT

When checking the answer for **Example 1A,** students might multiply $(x + 6)^2$ as $x^2 + 6^2 = x^2 + 36$. Encourage students to write $(x + 6)^2$ as $(x + 6)(x + 6)$ and then use the FOIL method.

Power Presentations with PowerPoint®

Additional Examples

Example 1

Determine whether each trinomial is a perfect square. If so, factor. If not, explain.

A. $9x^2 - 15x + 64$ not a perfect-square trinomial because $-15x \neq 2(3x \cdot 8)$

B. $81x^2 + 90x + 25$ $(9x + 5)^2$

C. $36x^2 - 10x + 14$ not a perfect-square trinomial because 14 is not a perfect square

Example 2

A rectangular piece of cloth must be cut to make a tablecloth. The area needed is $(16x^2 - 24x + 9)$ in². The dimensions of the cloth are of the form $cx - d$, where c and d are whole numbers. Find an expression for the perimeter of the cloth. Find the perimeter when $x = 11$ inches.

$16x - 12$; 164 in.

Also available on transparency 

INTERVENTION

Questioning Strategies

EXAMPLE **1**

- Identify the steps for determining whether a trinomial is a perfect-square trinomial.
- When factoring a perfect-square trinomial, do you think it is easier to list the factors or use the pattern? Explain your reasoning.

EXAMPLE **2**

- What must be true about the factors of a rectangular area for that area to be a square? Explain.

Teaching Tip **Inclusion** After completing Step 3 of **Example 2,** show that the numerical value of the perimeter could be found by first substituting $x = 8$ into $5x + 7$ to find the length of one side. Then the length of one side is 47 ft, and the perimeter is $47 \cdot 4$, or 188 ft.

3 Solve

$25x^2 + 70x + 49$	$a = 5x,\ b = 7$
$(5x)^2 + 2(5x)(7) + 7^2$	*Write the trinomial as* $a^2 + 2ab + b^2$.
$(5x + 7)^2$	*Write the trinomial as* $(a + b)^2$.

$$25x^2 + 70x + 49 = (5x + 7)(5x + 7)$$

Each side length of the park is $(5x + 7)$ ft.

Write a formula for the perimeter of the park.

$P = 4s$	*Write the formula for the perimeter of a square.*
$= 4(5x + 7)$	*Substitute the side length for s.*
$= 20x + 28$	*Distribute 4.*

An expression for the perimeter of the park in feet is $20x + 28$.

Evaluate the expression when $x = 8$.

$P = 20x + 28$	
$= 20(8) + 28$	*Substitute 8 for x.*
$= 188$	

When $x = 8$ ft, the perimeter of the park is 188 ft.

4 Look Back

For a square with a perimeter of 188 ft, the side length is $\frac{188}{4} = 47$ ft and the area is $47^2 = 2209\ \text{ft}^2$.

Evaluate $25x^2 + 70x + 49$ for $x = 8$:

$25(8)^2 + 70(8) + 49$

$1600 + 560 + 49$

2209 ✓

2. **What if...?** A company produces square sheets of aluminum, each of which has an area of $(9x^2 + 6x + 1)\ \text{m}^2$. The side length of each sheet is in the form $cx + d$, where c and d are whole numbers. Find an expression in terms of x for the perimeter of a sheet. Find the perimeter when $x = 3$ m. **$4(3x + 1)$ m; 40 m**

In Chapter 7 you learned that the difference of two squares has the form $a^2 - b^2$. The difference of two squares can be written as the product $(a + b)(a - b)$. You can use this pattern to factor some polynomials.

A polynomial is a difference of two squares if:

- There are two terms, one subtracted from the other.
- Both terms are perfect squares.

$$\underset{2x \cdot 2x}{4x^2} - \underset{3 \cdot 3}{9}$$

Factoring a Difference of Two Squares

DIFFERENCE OF TWO SQUARES	EXAMPLE
$a^2 - b^2 = (a + b)(a - b)$	$x^2 - 9 = (x + 3)(x - 3)$

Recall modeling the factors of trinomials with algebra tiles (MK). The tiles must be arranged in a rectangle. When the factors of a perfect-square trinomial are modeled with algebra tiles, the tiles will be arranged in a square.

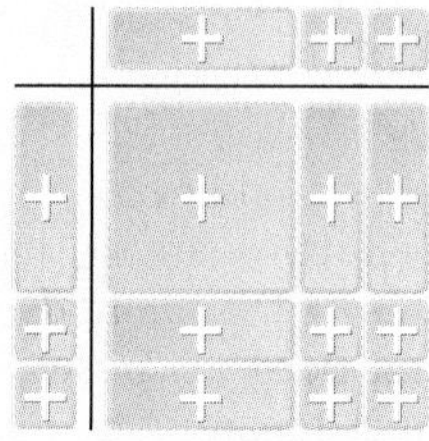

EXAMPLE 3 Recognizing and Factoring the Difference of Two Squares

Determine whether each binomial is a difference of two squares. If so, factor. If not, explain.

Reading Math

Recognize a difference of two squares: the coefficients of variable terms are perfect squares, powers on variable terms are even, and constants are perfect squares.

A $x^2 - 81$

$x^2 - 81$; $x \cdot x$ $\quad 9 \cdot 9$ — *The polynomial is a difference of two squares.*

$x^2 - 9^2$ — *$a = x$, $b = 9$*

$(x + 9)(x - 9)$ — *Write the polynomial as $(a + b)(a - b)$.*

$x^2 - 81 = (x + 9)(x - 9)$

B $9p^4 - 16q^2$

$9p^4 - 16q^2$; $3p^2 \cdot 3p^2$ $\quad 4q \cdot 4q$ — *The polynomial is a difference of two squares.*

$(3p^2)^2 - (4q)^2$ — *$a = 3p^2$, $b = 4q$*

$(3p^2 + 4q)(3p^2 - 4q)$ — *Write the polynomial as $(a + b)(a - b)$.*

$9p^4 - 16q^2 = (3p^2 + 4q)(3p^2 - 4q)$

C $x^6 - 7y^2$

$x^6 - 7y^2$; $x^3 \cdot x^3$ — *$7y^2$ is not a perfect square.*

$x^6 - 7y^2$ is not the difference of two squares because $7y^2$ is not a perfect square.

CHECK IT OUT! Determine whether the binomial is a difference of two squares. If so, factor. If not, explain.

3a. $1 - 4x^2$ $\quad$ $(1 - 2x)(1 + 2x)$

3b. $p^8 - 49q^6$ $\quad$ $(p^4 + 7q^3)(p^4 - 7q^3)$

3c. $16x^2 - 4y^5$ $\quad$ no; $4y^5$ is not a perfect square.

THINK AND DISCUSS

1. The binomial $1 - x^4$ is a difference of two squares. Use the rule to identify a and b in $1 - x^4$.
2. The polynomial $x^2 + 8x + 16$ is a perfect-square trinomial. Use the rule to identify a and b in $x^2 + 8x + 16$.

3. **GET ORGANIZED** Copy and complete the graphic organizer. Write an example of each type of special product and factor it.

Special Product	Factored Form
Perfect-square trinomial with positive coefficient of middle term	
Perfect-square trinomial with negative coefficient of middle term	
Difference of two squares	

Power Presentations with PowerPoint®

Additional Examples

Example 3

Determine whether each binomial is a difference of two squares. If so, factor. If not, explain.

A. $3p^2 - 9q^4$ $\quad$ no; $3p^2$ is not a perfect square.

B. $100x^2 - 4y^2$
$(10x + 2y)(10x - 2y)$

C. $x^4 - 25y^6$
$(x^2 + 5y^3)(x^2 - 5y^3)$

Also available on transparency

INTERVENTION

Questioning Strategies

EXAMPLE 3

- Explain why the product of binomials of the form $(a + b)(a - b)$ is not a trinomial.

Teaching Tip **Math Background** In **Example 3C,** students might think that x^6 is not a perfect square because the number 6 is not a perfect square. Remind them of the Product of Powers Property, which states that $a^m \cdot a^n = a^{m+n}$. Thus, x^6 is a perfect square because it can be written as $x^3 \cdot x^3$.

3 Close

Summarize

Have students name the characteristics of

- a perfect-square trinomial of the form $ax^2 + bx + c$. $\quad$ 1) a and c must be perfect squares. 2) $b = 2\sqrt{ac}$
- a difference of squares of the form $a^2 - b^2$. $\quad$ 1) Both terms must be perfect squares. 2) It must be a difference.

FORMATIVE ASSESSMENT

and INTERVENTION

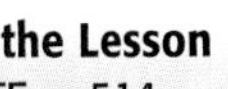

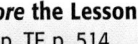

***Diagnose Before* the Lesson**
8-5 Warm Up, TE p. 514

***Monitor During* the Lesson**
Check It Out! Exercises, SE pp. 515–517
Questioning Strategies, TE pp. 515–517

***Assess After* the Lesson**
8-5 Lesson Quiz, TE p. 520
Alternative Assessment, TE p. 520

Answers to *Think and Discuss*

1. $a = 1$; $b = x^2$
2. $a = x$; $b = 4$
3. See p. A7.

8-5 Exercises

Assignment Guide

Assign *Guided Practice* exercises as necessary.

If you finished Examples **1–2**
Proficient 14–20, 27, 29, 38
Advanced 14–20, 27, 29, 38

If you finished Examples **1–3**
Proficient 14–40, 46–50, 55–64
Advanced 14–29, 30–34 even, 36–40, 47–64

Homework Quick Check
Quickly check key concepts.
Exercises: 14, 16, 20, 22, 26, 38

Answers

14. yes; $(2x - 1)^2$
15. No; the last term must be pos.
16. yes; $(6x - 1)^2$
17. no; $10x \neq 2(5x)(2)$
18. yes; $9(x + 1)^2$
19. yes; $(4x - 5)^2$
30. $(x - 4)^2$; perf.-square trinomial
31. $(10x + 9y)(10x - 9y)$; diff. of 2 squares
32. $(6x + 2)^2$; perf.-square trinomial
33. $(2r^3 + 5s^3)(2r^3 - 5s^3)$; diff. of 2 squares
34. $(7x - 5)^2$; perf.-square trinomial
35. $(x^7 + 12)(x^7 - 12)$; diff. of 2 squares

8-5 Exercises

California Standards Practice 10.0, 11.0, 25.2

go.hrw.com
Homework Help Online
KEYWORD: MA8CA 8-5
Parent Resources Online
KEYWORD: MA8CA Parent

GUIDED PRACTICE

SEE EXAMPLE 1 p. 514

Determine whether each trinomial is a perfect square. If so, factor. If not, explain.

1. $x^2 - 4x + 4$ yes; $(x - 2)^2$
2. $x^2 - 4x - 4$ No; the last term must be pos.
3. $9x^2 - 12x + 4$ yes; $(3x - 2)^2$
4. $x^2 + 2x + 1$ yes; $(x + 1)^2$
5. $x^2 - 6x + 9$ yes; $(x - 3)^2$
6. $x^2 - 6x - 9$ No; the last term must be pos.

SEE EXAMPLE 2 p. 515

7. **City Planning** A city purchases a rectangular plot of land with an area of $(x^2 + 24x + 144)$ yd^2 for a park. The dimensions of the plot are of the form $ax + b$, where a and b are whole numbers. Find an expression for the perimeter of the park. Find the perimeter when $x = 10$ yd. $4(x + 12)$; 88 yd

SEE EXAMPLE 3 p. 517

Determine whether each binomial is a difference of two squares. If so, factor. If not, explain.

8. $1 - 4x^2$
9. $s^2 - 4^2$ yes; $(s + 4)(s - 4)$
10. $81x^2 - 1$ yes; $(9x + 1)(9x - 1)$
11. $4x^4 - 9y^2$ yes; $(2x^2 + 3y)(2x^2 - 3y)$
12. $x^8 - 50$ No; 50 is not a perf. square.
13. $x^6 - 9$ yes; $(x^3 + 3)(x^3 - 3)$

8. yes; $(1 + 2x)(1 - 2x)$

PRACTICE AND PROBLEM SOLVING

Independent Practice	
For Exercises	See Example
14–19	1
20	2
21–26	3

Extra Practice
Skills Practice p. EP17
Application Practice p. EP31

Determine whether the trinomial is a perfect square. If so, factor. If not, explain.

14. $4x^2 - 4x + 1$
15. $4x^2 - 4x - 1$
16. $36x^2 - 12x + 1$
17. $25x^2 + 10x + 4$
18. $9x^2 + 18x + 9$
19. $16x^2 - 40x + 25$

20. **Measurement** You are given a sheet of paper and told to cut out a rectangular piece with an area of $(4x^2 - 44x + 121)$ mm^2. The dimensions of the rectangle have the form $ax - b$, where a and b are whole numbers. Find an expression for the perimeter of the rectangle you cut out. Find the perimeter when $x = 41$ mm. $4(2x - 11)$; 284 mm

Determine whether each binomial is a difference of two squares. If so, factor. If not, explain.

21. $1^2 - 4x^2$
22. $25m^2 - 16n^2$ yes; $(5m - 4)(5m + 4)$
23. $4x - 9y$ No; $4x$ and $9y$ are not perf. squares.
24. $49p^{12} - 9q^6$ yes; $(7p^6 - 3q^3)(7p^6 + 3q^3)$
25. $9^2 - 100x^4$ yes; $(9 - 10x^2)(9 + 10x^2)$
26. $x^3 - y^3$ No; x^3 and y^3 are not perf. squares.

21. yes; $(1 + 2x)(1 - 2x)$

Find the missing term in each perfect-square trinomial.

27. $x^2 + 14x +$ **49**
28. $9x^2 +$ **30x** $+ 25$
29. **$4y^2$** $- 36y + 81$

Factor each polynomial using the rule for perfect-square trinomials or the rule for a difference of two squares. Tell which rule you used and check your answer.

30. $x^2 - 8x + 16$
31. $100x^2 - 81y^2$
32. $36x^2 + 24x + 4$
33. $4r^6 - 25s^6$
34. $49x^2 - 70x + 25$
35. $x^{14} - 144$

36. **Write About It** What is similar about a perfect-square trinomial and a difference of two squares? What is different?
37. **Critical Thinking** Describe two ways to create a perfect-square trinomial.
38. For what value of b would $(x + b)(x + b)$ be the factored form of $x^2 - 22x + 121$? $b = -11$
39. For what value of c are the factors of $x^2 + cx + 256$ the same? $c = 32$

8-5 READING STRATEGIES

LESSON 8-5 Reading Strategies
Compare and Contrast

The chart below shows how to recognize and factor two special products.

Perfect Square Trinomial Ex: $x^2 + 6x + 9$	Contrast	Difference of Squares Ex: $4x^2 - 25$
3	Number of Terms	2
+ + or − +	Sign(s)	always −
$x^2 + 6x + 9$: $x \cdot x$, $2(x \cdot 3)$, $3 \cdot 3$	Pattern	$4x^2 - 25$: $2x \cdot 2x$, $5 \cdot 5$
binomial squared $(x + 3)(x + 3) = (x + 3)^2$	Factored Form	two binomials, opposite signs $(2x + 5)(2x - 5)$

Compare

The first term and last term of both special products are perfect squares.

Identify each of the following as a perfect square trinomial (P), a difference of squares (D), or neither (N).

1. $x^2 - 16$ D
2. $x^2 - 14x + 49$ P
3. $100x^2 - 36$ D
4. $4x^2 - 12x - 9$ N
5. $x^2 + 14x + 49$ P
6. $25x^2 + 64$ N

Factor each special product.

7. $16x^2 - 9$ $(4x + 3)(4x - 3)$
8. $121x^2 - 44x + 4$ $(11x - 2)^2$
9. $81x^2 - 1$ $(9x + 1)(9x - 1)$

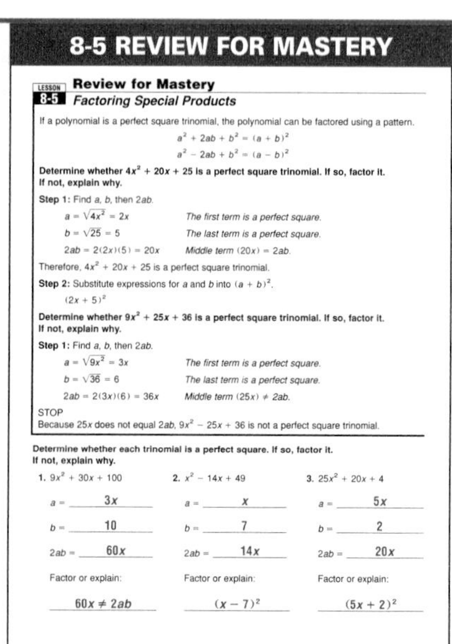

8-5 REVIEW FOR MASTERY

LESSON 8-5 Review for Mastery
Factoring Special Products

If a polynomial is a perfect square trinomial, the polynomial can be factored using a pattern.

$$a^2 + 2ab + b^2 = (a + b)^2$$
$$a^2 - 2ab + b^2 = (a - b)^2$$

Determine whether $4x^2 + 20x + 25$ is a perfect square trinomial. If so, factor it. If not, explain why.

Step 1: Find a, b, then $2ab$.

$a = \sqrt{4x^2} = 2x$ *The first term is a perfect square.*
$b = \sqrt{25} = 5$ *The last term is a perfect square.*
$2ab = 2(2x)(5) = 20x$ *Middle term $(20x) = 2ab$.*

Therefore, $4x^2 + 20x + 25$ is a perfect square trinomial.

Step 2: Substitute expressions for a and b into $(a + b)^2$.

$(2x + 5)^2$

Determine whether $9x^2 + 25x + 36$ is a perfect square trinomial. If so, factor it. If not, explain why.

Step 1: Find a, b, then $2ab$.

$a = \sqrt{9x^2} = 3x$ *The first term is a perfect square.*
$b = \sqrt{36} = 6$ *The last term is a perfect square.*
$2ab = 2(3x)(6) = 36x$ *Middle term $(25x) \neq 2ab$.*

STOP
Because $25x$ does not equal $2ab$, $9x^2 - 25x + 36$ is not a perfect square trinomial.

Determine whether each trinomial is a perfect square. If so, factor it. If not, explain why.

1. $9x^2 + 30x + 100$
$a =$ 3x
$b =$ 10
$2ab =$ 60x
Factor or explain: $60x \neq 2ab$

2. $x^2 - 14x + 49$
$a =$ x
$b =$ 7
$2ab =$ 14x
Factor or explain: $(x - 7)^2$

3. $25x^2 + 20x + 4$
$a =$ 5x
$b =$ 2
$2ab =$ 20x
Factor or explain: $(5x + 2)^2$

California Standards

Standard	Exercises
10.0	41b, 42b, 59–61
11.0	1–35, 40a, 41a, 42a, 42c, 45, 48, 50a, 50b, 51b–54, 62–64
16.0	55–58
17.0	55–58
18.0	55–58
25.2	46

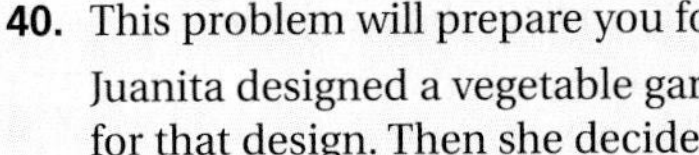

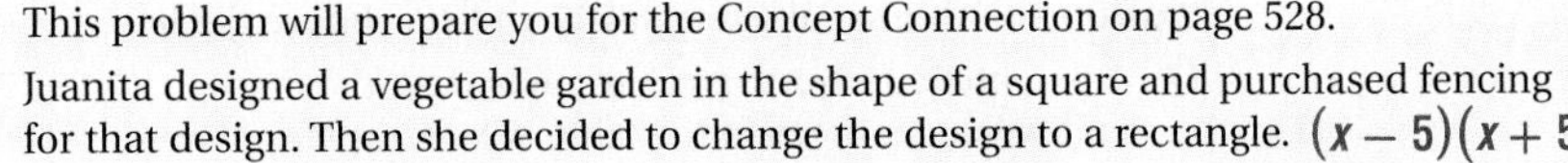

CONCEPT CONNECTION

40. This problem will prepare you for the Concept Connection on page 528.

Juanita designed a vegetable garden in the shape of a square and purchased fencing for that design. Then she decided to change the design to a rectangle. $(x-5)(x+5)$

a. The square garden had an area of x^2 ft². The area of the rectangular garden is (x^2-25) ft². Factor the expression for the area of the rectangular garden.

b. The rectangular garden must have the same perimeter as the square garden, so Juanita added a number of feet to the length and subtracted the same number of feet from the width. Use your factors from part **a** to determine how many feet were added to the length and subtracted from the width. **ℓ: added 5 ft; w: subtracted 5 ft**

c. If the original length of the square garden was 8 feet, what are the length and width of the new garden? **$\ell = 13$ ft; $w = 3$ ft**

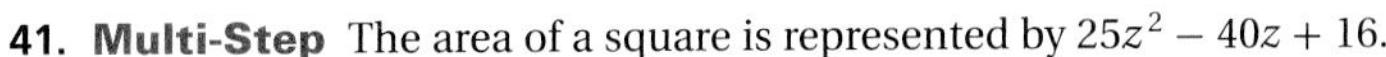

41. Multi-Step The area of a square is represented by $25z^2 - 40z + 16$.

a. What expression represents the length of a side of the square? **$5z - 4$**

b. What expression represents the perimeter of the square? **$20z - 16$**

c. What are the length of a side, the perimeter, and the area of the square when $z = 3$? **11; 44; 121**

42. Multi-Step A small rectangle is drawn inside a larger rectangle as shown.

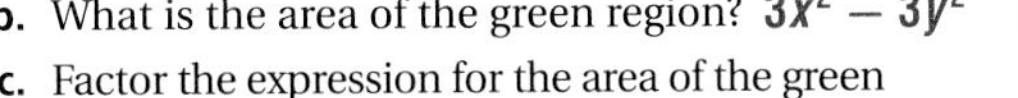

a. What is the area of each rectangle? **$3x^2$; $3y^2$**

b. What is the area of the green region? **$3x^2 - 3y^2$**

c. Factor the expression for the area of the green region. (*Hint:* First factor out the common factor of 3 and then factor the binomial.) **$3(x+y)(x-y)$**

43. Evaluate each expression for the values of x.

	x	$x^2 + 10x + 25$	$(x+5)^2$	$(x-5)^2$	$x^2 - 10x + 25$	$x^2 - 25$
a.	−5	**0**	**0**	**100**	**100**	**0**
b.	−1	**16**	**16**	**36**	**36**	**−24**
c.	0	**25**	**25**	**25**	**25**	**−25**
d.	1	**36**	**36**	**16**	**16**	**−24**
e.	5	**100**	**100**	**0**	**0**	**0**

44. In the table above, which columns have equivalent values? Explain why.

45. Geometry A model for the difference of two squares is shown below. Copy and complete the second figure by writing the missing labels.

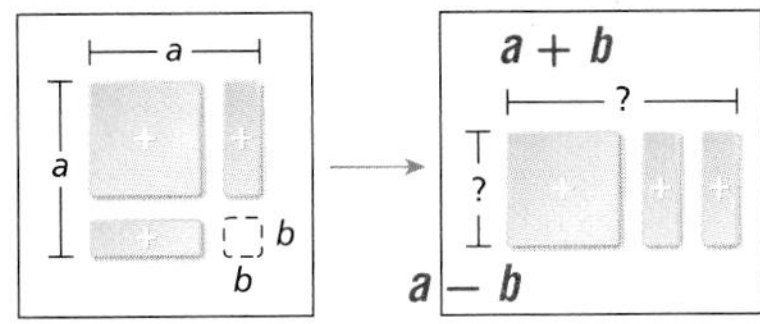

46. ERROR ANALYSIS Two students factored $25x^4 - 9y^2$. Which is incorrect? Explain the error.

Student A; $(5x)(5x) \neq 25x^4$ and $(-3)(3) \neq 9y^2$.

Ⓐ

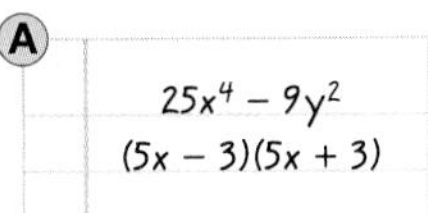

Ⓑ

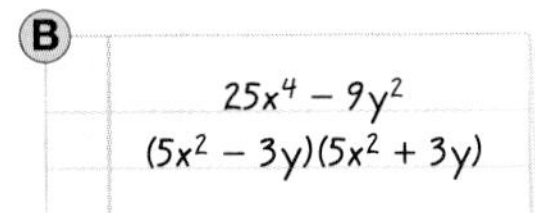

CONCEPT CONNECTION **Exercise 40** involves using factoring to find dimensions of squares and rectangles. This exercise prepares students for the Concept Connection on page 528.

Answers

36. They are similar in that the first and last terms of each are perfect squares. They are different in that a perfect-square trinomial has 3 terms and a difference of 2 squares has 2 terms.

37. Multiply a binomial by itself. Choose 2 perfect squares, find 2 times the product of their square roots, and then write these 3 expressions as a sum.

44. The first and second columns and the third and fourth columns have the same values. The second column is the factored form of the first column. The third column is the factored form of the fourth column.

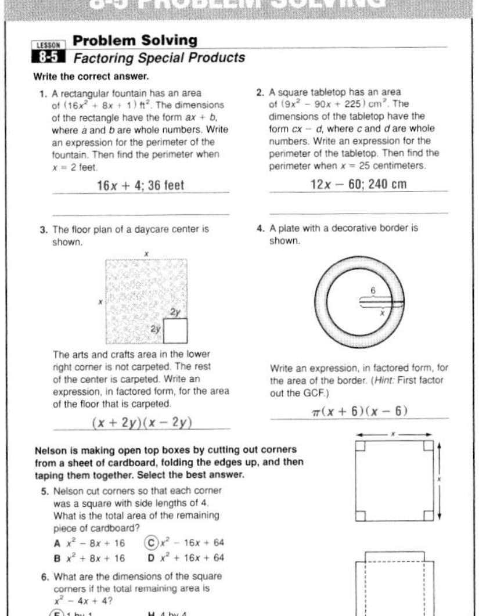

8-5 PROBLEM SOLVING

LESSON 8-5 **Problem Solving**
Factoring Special Products

Write the correct answer.

1. A rectangular fountain has an area of $(16x^2 + 8x + 1)$ ft². The dimensions of the rectangle have the form $ax + b$, where a and b are whole numbers. Write an expression for the perimeter of the fountain. Then find the perimeter when $x = 2$ feet.
$16x + 4$; 36 feet

2. A square tabletop has an area of $(9x^2 - 90x + 225)$ cm². The dimensions of the tabletop have the form $cx - d$, where c and d are whole numbers. Write an expression for the perimeter of the tabletop. Then find the perimeter when $x = 25$ centimeters.
$12x - 60$; 240 cm

3. The floor plan of a daycare center is shown.
The arts and crafts area in the lower right corner is not carpeted. The rest of the center is carpeted. Write an expression, in factored form, for the area of the floor that is carpeted.
$(x + 2y)(x - 2y)$

4. A plate with a decorative border is shown.
Write an expression, in factored form, for the area of the border. (*Hint:* First factor out the GCF.)
$\pi(x + 6)(x - 6)$

Nelson is making open top boxes by cutting out corners from a sheet of cardboard, folding the edges up, and then taping them together. Select the best answer.

5. Nelson cut corners so that each corner was a square with side lengths of 4. What is the total area of the remaining piece of cardboard?
A $x^2 - 8x + 16$ Ⓒ $x^2 - 16x + 64$
B $x^2 + 8x + 16$ D $x^2 + 16x + 64$

6. What are the dimensions of the square corners if the total remaining area is $x^2 - 4x + 4$?
Ⓕ 1 by 1 H 4 by 4
G 2 by 2 J 8 by 8

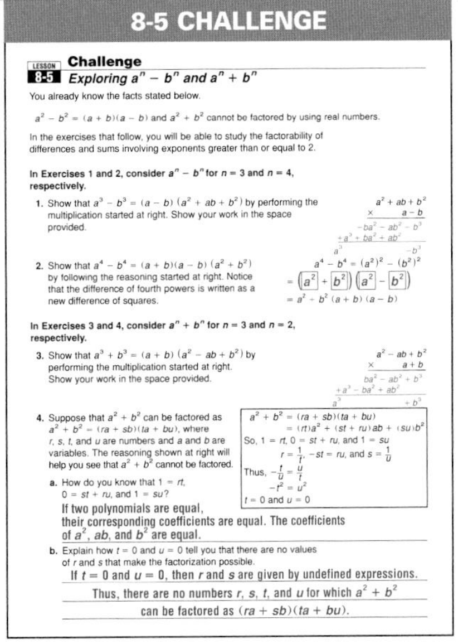

8-5 CHALLENGE

LESSON 8-5 **Challenge**
Exploring $a^n - b^n$ and $a^n + b^n$

You already know the facts stated below.

$a^2 - b^2 = (a + b)(a - b)$ and $a^2 + b^2$ cannot be factored by using real numbers.

In the exercises that follow, you will be able to study the factorability of differences and sums involving exponents greater than or equal to 2.

In Exercises 1 and 2, consider $a^n - b^n$ for $n = 3$ and $n = 4$, respectively.

1. Show that $a^3 - b^3 = (a - b)(a^2 + ab + b^2)$ by performing the multiplication started at right. Show your work in the space provided.
$a^2 + ab + b^2$
$\times \quad a - b$
$-ba^2 - ab^2 - b^3$
$+a^3 + ba^2 + ab^2$
$a^3 \qquad -b^3$

2. Show that $a^4 - b^4 = (a + b)(a - b)(a^2 + b^2)$ by following the reasoning started at right. Notice that the difference of fourth powers is written as a new difference of squares.
$a^4 - b^4 = (a^2)^2 - (b^2)^2$
$= (a^2 + b^2)(a^2 - b^2)$
$= a^2 + b^2 (a + b)(a - b)$

In Exercises 3 and 4, consider $a^n + b^n$ for $n = 3$ and $n = 2$, respectively.

3. Show that $a^3 + b^3 = (a + b)(a^2 - ab + b^2)$ by performing the multiplication started at right. Show your work in the space provided.
$a^2 - ab + b^2$
$\times \quad a + b$
$ba^2 - ab^2 + b^3$
$+a^3 - ba^2 + ab^2$
$a^3 \qquad + b^3$

4. Suppose that $a^2 + b^2$ can be factored as $a^2 + b^2 = (ra + sb)(ta + bu)$, where r, s, t, and u are numbers and a and b are variables. The reasoning shown at right will help you see that $a^2 + b^2$ cannot be factored.

$a^2 + b^2 = (ra + sb)(ta + bu)$
$= (rt)a^2 + (st + ru)ab + (su)b^2$
So, $1 = rt$, $0 = st + ru$, and $1 = su$
$r = \frac{1}{t}$, $-st = ru$, and $s = \frac{1}{u}$
Thus, $-\frac{t}{u} = \frac{u}{t}$
$-t^2 = u^2$
$t = 0$ and $u = 0$

a. How do you know that $1 = rt$, $0 = st + ru$, and $1 = su$?
If two polynomials are equal, their corresponding coefficients are equal. The coefficients of a^2, ab, and b^2 are equal.

b. Explain how $t = 0$ and $u = 0$ tell you that there are no values of r and s that make the factorization possible.
If $t = 0$ and $u = 0$, then r and s are given by undefined expressions. Thus, there are no numbers r, s, t, and u for which $a^2 + b^2$ can be factored as $(ra + sb)(ta + bu)$.

8-5 PRACTICE A

8-5 PRACTICE C

8-5 PRACTICE B

LESSON 8-5 **Practice B**
Factoring Special Products

Determine whether each trinomial is a perfect square. If so, factor it. If not, explain why.

1. $x^2 + 6x + 9$
yes; $(x + 3)^2$

2. $4x^2 + 20x + 25$
yes; $(2x + 5)^2$

3. $36x^2 - 24x + 16$
no; $24x \neq 2(6x \cdot 4)$

4. $9x^2 - 12x + 4$
yes; $(3x - 2)^2$

5. A rectangular fountain in the center of a shopping mall has an area of $(4x^2 + 12x + 9)$ ft². The dimensions of the fountain are of the form $cx + d$, where c and d are whole numbers. Find an expression for the perimeter of the fountain. Find the perimeter when $x = 2$ ft.
$4(2x + 3)$ ft; 28 ft

Determine whether each binomial is the difference of two squares. If so, factor it. If not, explain why.

6. $x^2 - 16$
yes; $(x + 4)(x - 4)$

7. $9b^4 - 200$
no; 200 is not a perfect square.

8. $1 - m^6$
yes; $(1 + m^3)(1 - m^3)$

9. $36s^2 - 4t^2$
yes; $(6s + 2t)(6s - 2t)$

10. $x^2y^2 + 196$
no; the operation between the two squares is addition.

Multiple Choice For **Exercise 47,** encourage students to write each expression in factored form before substituting values for x and y.

In **Exercise 48,** the trinomial contains only positive numbers. Therefore, the factored answer must contain only positive numbers, so **A, B,** and **C** can be eliminated.

Journal

Explain how you can find the missing term in the perfect-square trinomial $100x^2 + 120x + \square$.

Create one trinomial that is a perfect-square trinomial and one that is not. Factor the first trinomial. Explain why the second trinomial is not a perfect square. Repeat for the difference of two squares.

Power Presentations with PowerPoint®

8-5 Lesson Quiz

Determine whether each trinomial is a perfect square. If so, factor. If not, explain.

1. $64x^2 - 40x + 25$ not a perfect-square trinomial because $-40x \neq 2(8x \cdot 5)$
2. $121x^2 - 44x + 4$ $(11x - 2)^2$
3. $49x^2 + 140x + 100$ $(7x + 10)^2$
4. A fence will be built around a garden with an area of $(49x^2 + 56x + 16)$ ft². The dimensions of the garden are $cx + d$, where c and d are whole numbers. Find an expression for the perimeter of the garden. Find the perimeter when $x = 5$ feet. $P = 28x + 16$; 156 ft

Determine whether the binomial is a difference of two squares. If so, factor. If not, explain.

5. $9x^2 - 144y^4$ $(3x + 12y^2)(3x - 12y^2)$
6. $30x^2 - 64y^2$ Not a diff. of two squares; $30x^2$ is not a perfect square
7. $121x^2 - 4y^8$ $(11x + 2y^4)(11x - 2y^4)$

Also available on transparency

Multiple Choice For Exercises 47 and 48, choose the best answer.

47. A polynomial expression is evaluated for the x- and y-values shown in the table. Which expression was evaluated to give the values shown in the third column?

x	y	Value of Expression
0	0	0
−1	−1	0
1	1	0
1	−1	4

Ⓐ $x^2 - y^2$
Ⓑ $x^2 + 2xy + y^2$
Ⓒ $x^2 - 2xy + y^2$ (circled)
Ⓓ None of the above

48. The area of a square is $4x^2 + 20x + 25$. Which expression can also be used to model the area of the square?

Ⓐ $(2x - 5)(5 - 2x)$
Ⓑ $(2x + 5)(2x - 5)$
Ⓒ $(2x - 5)^2$
Ⓓ $(2x + 5)^2$ (circled)

49. **Gridded Response** Evaluate the polynomial expression $x^2 - 18x + 81$ for $x = 10$. **1**

CHALLENGE AND EXTEND

50. The binomial $81x^4 - 16$ can be factored using the rule for a difference of two squares.
   a. Fill in the factorization: $81x^4 - 16$
   $(9x^2 + \blacksquare)(\blacksquare - \blacksquare)$ **4; $9x^2$; 4**
   b. One binomial from part **a** can be further factored. Identify the binomial and factor it. What is the complete factorization of $81x^4 - 16$?
   c. Write your own binomial that can be factored twice as the difference of two squares. **Possible answer: $x^4 - 1 = (x^2 + 1)(x^2 - 1) = (x^2 + 1)(x + 1)(x - 1)$**
51. The expression $4 - (v + 2)^2$ is the difference of two squares, because it fits the rule $a^2 - b^2$.
   a. Identify a and b in the expression. **$a = 2$; $b = (v + 2)$**
   b. Factor and simplify $4 - (v + 2)^2$.
   $[2 + (v + 2)][2 - (v + 2)] = (v + 4)(-v) = -v^2 - 4v$

The *difference of cubes* is an expression of the form $a^3 - b^3$. It can be factored according to the rule $a^3 - b^3 = (a - b)(a^2 + ab + b^2)$. For each binomial, identify a and b, and factor using the rule. Check your answer.

52. $x^3 - 1$
53. $27y^3 - 64$
54. $n^6 - 8$

SPIRAL STANDARDS REVIEW

10.0, 11.0, 16.0, 17.0, 18.0

Find the domain and range for each relation and tell whether the relation is a function. *(Lesson 4-2)*

55. $\{(5, 2), (4, 1), (3, 0), (2, -1)\}$ **D: {5, 4, 3, 2}; R: {2, 1, 0, −1}; yes**
56. $\{(-3, 6), (-1, 6), (1, 6), (3, 6)\}$ **D: {−3, −1, 1, 3}; R: {6}; yes**
57. $\{(2, -8), (2, -2), (2, 4), (2, 10)\}$ **D: {2}; R: {−8, −2, 4, 10}; no**
58. $\{(-2, 4), (-1, 1), (0, 0), (1, 1)\}$ **D: {−2, −1, 0, 1}; R: {0, 1, 4}; yes**

Multiply. *(Lesson 7-7)*

59. $2a(3a^2 + 7a - 5)$ **$6a^3 + 14a^2 - 10a$**
60. $(x + 3)(x - 8)$ **$x^2 - 5x - 24$**
61. $(t - 4)^2$ **$t^2 - 8t + 16$**

Factor each trinomial. Check your answer. *(Lesson 8-3)*

62. $x^2 + 3x - 10$ **$(x + 5)(x - 2)$**
63. $x^2 - x - 12$ **$(x + 3)(x - 4)$**
64. $x^2 + 7x + 8$ **not factorable**

Answers

50b. $9x^2 - 4 = (3x + 2)(3x - 2)$; $(9x^2 + 4)(3x + 2)(3x - 2)$

52. $a = x$; $b = 1$; $(x - 1)(x^2 + x + 1)$

53. $a = 3y$; $b = 4$; $(3y - 4)(9y^2 + 12y + 16)$

54. $a = n^2$; $b = 2$; $(n^2 - 2)(n^4 + 2n + 4)$

Mental Math

Recognizing patterns of special products can help you perform calculations mentally.

Remember these special products that you studied in Chapter 7 and in Lesson 8-5.

Patterns of Special Products	
Difference of Two Squares	$(a+b)(a-b)=a^2-b^2$
Perfect-Square Trinomial	$(a+b)^2=a^2+2ab+b^2$ $(a-b)^2=a^2-2ab+b^2$

Example 1

Simplify 17^2-7^2.

This expression is a difference of two squares with $a=17$ and $b=7$.

$a^2-b^2=(a+b)(a-b)$ *Write the rule for a difference of two squares.*

$17^2-7^2=(17+7)(17-7)$ *Substitute 17 for a and 7 for b.*

$=(24)(10)$ *Simplify each group.*

$=240$

Example 2

Simplify $14^2+2(14)(6)+6^2$.

This expression is a perfect-square trinomial with $a=14$ and $b=6$.

$a^2+2ab+b^2=(a+b)^2$ *Write the rule for a perfect-square trinomial.*

$14^2+2(14)(6)+6^2=(14+6)^2$ *Substitute 14 for a and 6 for b.*

$=(20)^2$ *Simplify.*

$=400$

Try This

Simplify each expression using the rules for special products.

1. 18^2-12^2
2. $11^2+2(11)(14)+14^2$
3. 22^2-18^2
4. $38^2-2(38)(27)+27^2$
5. $29^2-2(29)(17)+17^2$
6. $55^2+2(55)(45)+45^2$
7. 14^2-9^2
8. 13^2-12^2
9. $14^2+2(14)(16)+16^2$

Organizer

See Skills Bank page SB3

Objective: Apply patterns of special products to performing multiplication mentally.

Teach

Remember

Students review and apply mental math techniques.

INTERVENTION For additional review and practice on mental math, see Skills Bank page SB3.

Close

Assess

Have students explain how to use patterns of special products and mental math to simplify **Try This Problems 4** and **8.**

Answers to *Try This*

1. $(18+12)(18-12)=30(6)=180$
2. $(11+14)^2=25^2=625$
3. $(22+18)(22-18)=40(4)=160$
4. $(38-27)^2=11^2=121$
5. $(29-17)^2=12^2=144$
6. $(55+45)^2=100^2=10{,}000$
7. $(14+9)(14-9)=23(5)=115$
8. $(13+12)(13-12)=25(1)=25$
9. $(14+16)^2=30^2=900$

8-6 Organizer

Objectives: Choose an appropriate method for factoring a polynomial.

Combine methods for factoring a polynomial.

Online Edition
Tutorial Videos

Countdown to Mastery Week 19

Power Presentations with PowerPoint®

Warm Up

Factor each trinomial.

1. $x^2 + 13x + 40$
   $(x + 5)(x + 8)$
2. $5x^2 - 18x - 8$
   $(5x + 2)(x - 4)$
3. Factor the perfect-square trinomial $16x^2 + 40x + 25$.
   $(4x + 5)(4x + 5)$
4. Factor $9x^2 - 25y^2$ using the difference of two squares.
   $(3x + 5y)(3x - 5y)$

Also available on transparency

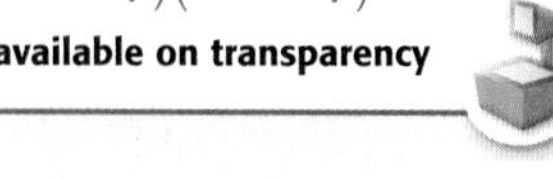

Math Humor

Q: Where do math teachers buy their products?

A: From the factor-*y*.

California Standards

Algebra 1 11.0

8-6 Choosing a Factoring Method

California Standards

11.0 Students apply basic factoring techniques to second- and simple third-degree polynomials. These techniques include finding a common factor for all terms in a polynomial, recognizing the difference of two squares, and recognizing perfect squares of binomials.

Why learn this?

You can factor polynomials to model the height of a leaping person or animal. (See Exercise 42.)

The height of a leaping frog can be modeled by a quadratic polynomial. Solving an equation that involves the polynomial may require factoring the polynomial.

Recall that a polynomial is fully or completely factored when it is written as a product of monomials and polynomials whose terms have no common factors other than 1.

EXAMPLE 1 Determining Whether an Expression Is Completely Factored

Tell whether each expression is completely factored. If not, factor it.

A $2x(x^2 + 4)$

$2x(x^2 + 4)$ *Neither 2x nor $x^2 + 4$ can be factored further.*

$2x(x^2 + 4)$ is completely factored.

Caution!

$x^2 + 4$ is a *sum* of squares, and cannot be factored.

B $(2x + 6)(x + 5)$

$(2x + 6)(x + 5)$ *2x + 6 can be factored further.*

$2(x + 3)(x + 5)$ *Factor out 2, the GCF of 2x and 6.*

$2(x + 3)(x + 5)$ is completely factored.

C $2n(n^2 + 4n - 21)$

$2n(n^2 + 4n - 21)$ *$n^2 + 4n - 21$ can be factored further.*

$2n(n + 7)(n - 3)$ *Factor $n^2 + 4n - 21$.*

$2n(n + 7)(n - 3)$ is completely factored.

CHECK IT OUT! **Tell whether each expression is completely factored. If not, factor it.**

1a. $5x^2(x - 1)$ **yes**

1b. $(4x + 4)(x + 1)$ **no; $4(x + 1)^2$**

To factor a polynomial completely, you may need to use more than one factoring method. Use the steps below to factor a polynomial completely.

Factoring Polynomials	
Step 1	Check for a greatest common factor.
Step 2	Check for a pattern that fits the difference of two squares or a perfect-square trinomial.
Step 3	To factor $x^2 + bx + c$, look for two integers whose sum is b and whose product is c. To factor $ax^2 + bx + c$, check integer factors of a and c in the binomial factors. The sum of the products of the outer and inner terms should be b.
Step 4	Check for common factors.

1 Introduce

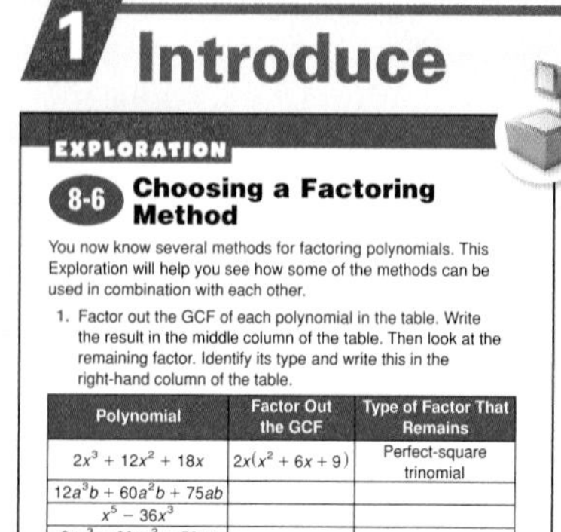

EXPLORATION

8-6 Choosing a Factoring Method

You now know several methods for factoring polynomials. This Exploration will help you see how some of the methods can be used in combination with each other.

1. Factor out the GCF of each polynomial in the table. Write the result in the middle column of the table. Then look at the remaining factor. Identify its type and write this in the right-hand column of the table.

Polynomial	Factor Out the GCF	Type of Factor That Remains
$2x^3 + 12x^2 + 18x$	$2x(x^2 + 6x + 9)$	Perfect-square trinomial
$12a^3b + 60a^2b + 75ab$		
$x^5 - 36x^3$		
$2xy^3 - 20xy^2 + 50xy$		
$3y^2 - 48y$		

2. Explain what you would do to continue factoring $2x^3 + 12x^2 + 18x$ after factoring out the GCF, $2x$.
3. Explain what you would do to continue factoring $x^5 - 36x^3$ after factoring out the GCF.

THINK AND DISCUSS

4. **Describe** the advantages of first factoring out the GCF when factoring a polynomial.
5. **Explain** how factoring out the GCF can be helpful even if the remaining factor is not one of the types that you

Motivate

Have students describe characteristics of the following polynomials. Possible answers:

$9x^2 - 25y^2$ first and last terms are perfect squares; difference of two terms

$3x + 6$ common factor in each term; binomial

$2x^3 + 6x^2 - 5x - 15$ four terms; common factor in first two terms; common factor in last two terms.

Explorations and answers are provided in *Alternate Openers: Explorations Transparencies.*

EXAMPLE 2 Factoring by GCF and Recognizing Patterns

Factor $-2xy^2 + 16xy - 32x$ completely. Check your answer.

$-2xy^2 + 16xy - 32x$

$-2x(y^2 - 8y + 16)$ *Factor out the GCF. $y^2 - 8y + 16$ is a perfect-square trinomial of the form $a^2 - 2ab + b^2$.*

$-2x(y-4)^2$ *$a = y$, $b = 4$*

Check $-2x(y-4)^2 = -2x(y^2 - 8y + 16)$
$= -2xy^2 + 16xy - 32x$ ✓

Factor each polynomial completely. Check your answer.

2a. $4x^3 + 16x^2 + 16x$
$4x(x+2)^2$

2b. $2x^2y - 2y^3$
$2y(x-y)(x+y)$

EXAMPLE 3 Factoring by Multiple Methods

Factor each polynomial completely.

A $2x^2 + 5x + 4$

$2x^2 + 5x + 4$ *The GCF is 1 and there is no pattern.*

$(\square x + \square)(\square x + \square)$ *$a = 2$ and $c = 4$; Outer + Inner = 5*

Factors of 2	Factors of 4	Outer + Inner	
1 and 2	1 and 4	$(1)4 + (2)1 = 6$	✗
1 and 2	4 and 1	$(1)1 + (2)4 = 9$	✗
1 and 2	2 and 2	$(1)2 + (2)2 = 6$	✗

$2x^2 + 5x + 4$ cannot be factored any further. It is factored completely.

Remember!

For a polynomial of the form $ax^2 + bx + c$, if there are no integers whose sum is b and whose product is ac, then the polynomial is said to be unfactorable.

B $3n^4 - 15n^3 + 12n^2$

$3n^2(n^2 - 5n + 4)$ *Factor out the GCF. There is no pattern.*

$(n + \square)(n + \square)$ *$b = -5$ and $c = 4$; look for integer factors of 4 whose sum is -5.*

Factors of 4	Sum	
-1 and -4	-5	✓
-2 and -2	-4	✗

The factors needed are -1 and -4.

$3n^2(n-1)(n-4)$

C $4x^3 + 18x^2 + 20x$

$2x(2x^2 + 9x + 10)$ *Factor out the GCF. There is no pattern.*

$(\square x + \square)(\square x + \square)$ *$a = 2$ and $c = 10$; Outer + Inner = 9*

Factors of 2	Factors of 10	Outer + Inner	
1 and 2	1 and 10	$(1)10 + (2)1 = 12$	✗
1 and 2	10 and 1	$(1)1 + (2)10 = 21$	✗
1 and 2	2 and 5	$(1)5 + (2)2 = 9$	✓

$(x+2)(2x+5)$

$2x(x+2)(2x+5)$

COMMON ERROR ALERT

Students often think the factoring is complete after using one factoring method. Remind students to continue to look for common factors and factoring patterns until the polynomial is completely factored.

Power Presentations with PowerPoint®

Additional Examples

Example 1

Tell whether each expression is completely factored. If not, factor it.

A. $3x^2(6x - 4)$ no; $6x^2(3x - 2)$

B. $(x^2 + 1)(x - 4)$ completely factored

C. $5x(x^2 - 2x - 3)$
no; $5x(x-3)(x+1)$

Example 2

Factor each polynomial completely. Check your answer.

A. $10x^2 + 48x + 32$
$2(5x+4)(x+4)$

B. $8x^6y^2 - 18x^2y^2$
$2x^2y^2(2x^2 - 3)(2x^2 + 3)$

Also available on transparency

INTERVENTION
Questioning Strategies

EXAMPLE 1

- How do you check that a polynomial has been completely factored?

EXAMPLE 2

- What are the benefits of looking for the GCF first when factoring a polynomial?

2 Teach

Guided Instruction

Be sure that students are comfortable with all methods of factoring before beginning this section. Encourage them to first look for the GCF, then look for a pattern (for difference of squares or perfect-square trinomial), and lastly begin checking factors for a and c. Remind students that some polynomials cannot be factored using integer coefficients. Have students check their answers to determine whether they have factored correctly.

Universal Access
Through Graphic Organizers

Have groups of students create flowcharts for factoring polynomials. Include:

- Look for GCF.
- If binomial, then difference of squares OR cannot factor.
- If trinomial, then perfect-square trinomial OR find factors of a and c OR cannot factor.
- If four or more terms, then factor by grouping OR cannot factor.
- Can it be factored more?

Power Presentations with PowerPoint®

Additional Examples

Example 3

Factor each polynomial completely. Check you answer.

A. $9x^2 + 3x - 2$
$(3x - 1)(3x + 2)$

B. $12b^3 + 48b^2 + 48b$
$12b(b + 2)^2$

C. $4y^2 + 12y - 72$
$4(y + 6)(y - 3)$

D. $(x^4 - x^2)$
$x^2(x + 1)(x - 1)$

Also available on transparency

INTERVENTION

Questioning Strategies

EXAMPLE 3

- For what type of polynomials do you consider factoring by grouping?
- What methods of factoring do you consider when factoring a trinomial?

Math Background Remind students that because of the Commutative Property of Multiplication, $(a + b)(a - b) = (a - b)(a + b)$. Thus the factors can be written in any order.

D $p^5 - p$

$p(p^4 - 1)$	*Factor out the GCF.*
$p(p^2 + 1)(p^2 - 1)$	*$p^4 - 1$ is a difference of two squares.*
$p(p^2 + 1)(p + 1)(p - 1)$	*$p^2 - 1$ is a difference of two squares.*

CHECK IT OUT! Factor each polynomial completely. Check your answer.

3a. $3x^2 + 7x + 4$ **3b.** $2p^5 + 10p^4 - 12p^3$
3c. $9q^6 + 30q^5 + 24q^4$ **3d.** $2x^4 + 18$

3a. $(3x + 4)(x + 1)$ **3b.** $2p^3(p + 6)(p - 1)$
3c. $3q^4(3q + 4)(q + 2)$ **3d.** $2(x^4 + 9)$

Know it! Note — Methods to Factor Polynomials

Any Polynomial—Look for the greatest common factor.

$ab - ac = a(b - c)$	$6x^2y + 10xy^2 = 2xy(3x + 5y)$

Binomials—Look for a difference of two squares.

$a^2 - b^2 = (a + b)(a - b)$	$x^2 - 9y^2 = (x + 3y)(x - 3y)$

Trinomials—Look for perfect-square trinomials and other factorable trinomials.

$a^2 + 2ab + b^2 = (a + b)^2$ $a^2 - 2ab + b^2 = (a - b)^2$	$x^2 + 4x + 4 = (x + 2)^2$ $x^2 - 2x + 1 = (x - 1)^2$
$x^2 + bx + c = (x + \square)(x + \square)$ $ax^2 + bx + c = (\square x + \square)(\square x + \square)$	$x^2 + 3x + 2 = (x + 1)(x + 2)$ $6x^2 + 7x + 2 = (2x + 1)(3x + 2)$

Polynomials of Four or More Terms—Factor by grouping.

$ax + bx + ay + by = x(a + b) + y(a + b)$ $= (x + y)(a + b)$	$2x^3 + 4x^2 + x + 2 = (2x^3 + 4x^2) + (x + 2)$ $= 2x^2(x + 2) + 1(x + 2)$ $= (x + 2)(2x^2 + 1)$

THINK AND DISCUSS

1. Give an expression that includes a polynomial that is not completely factored.

2. Give an example of an unfactorable binomial and an unfactorable trinomial.

3. GET ORGANIZED Copy the graphic organizer. Draw an arrow from each expression to the method you would use to factor it.

Factoring Methods	
Polynomial	**Method**
1. $16x^4 - 25y^8$	A. Factoring out the GCF
2. $x^2 + 10x + 25$	B. Factoring by grouping
3. $9t^2 + 27t + 18t^4$	C. Unfactorable
4. $a^2 + 3a - 7a - 21$	D. Difference of two squares
5. $100b^2 + 81$	E. Perfect-square trinomial

3 Close

Summarize

Ask students to state the method they would use **first** to factor the following polynomials.

$16x^2 - 25$ difference of squares

$3x^2 + 12x + 27$ GCF

$4x^3 + 20x^2 + x + 5$ factor by grouping

$8x^2 - 32$ GCF

$x^2 + x - 12$ find factors for -12

Point out that no matter what the first step is, the resulting factorization is the same.

FORMATIVE ASSESSMENT and INTERVENTION

***Diagnose Before* the Lesson**
8-6 Warm Up, TE p. 522

***Monitor During* the Lesson**
Check It Out! Exercises, SE pp. 522–524
Questioning Strategies, TE pp. 523–524

***Assess After* the Lesson**
8-6 Lesson Quiz, TE p. 527
Alternative Assessment, TE p. 527

Answers to *Think and Discuss*

1. Possible answer: $x^2 - 1$
2. Possible answers: $x^2 + 1$; $x^2 + x + 1$
3. See p. A7.

8-6 Exercises

California Standards Practice
11.0, 25.2

go.hrw.com
Homework Help Online
KEYWORD: MA8CA 8-6
Parent Resources Online
KEYWORD: MA8CA Parent

GUIDED PRACTICE

SEE EXAMPLE 1 p. 522

Tell whether each expression is completely factored. If not, factor it.

1. $3x(9x^2 + 1)$ yes
2. $2(4x^3 - 3x^2 - 8x)$
3. $2k^2(4 - k^3)$ yes
4. $(2x + 3)(3x - 5)$ yes
5. $4(4p^4 - 1)$
6. $a(a^3 + 2ab + b^2)$ yes

SEE EXAMPLE 2 p. 523

Factor each polynomial completely. Check your answer.

7. $3x^5 - 12x^3$
8. $4x^3 + 8x^2 + 4x$
9. $8pq^2 + 8pq + 2p$
10. $18rs^2 - 2r$
11. $mn^5 - m^3n$
12. $2x^2y - 20xy + 50y$

SEE EXAMPLE 3 p. 523

13. $6x^4 - 3x^3 - 9x^2$
14. $3y^2 + 14y + 4$
15. $p^5 + 3p^3 + p^2 + 3$
16. $7x^5 + 21x^4 - 28x^3$ $7x^3(x + 4)(x - 1)$
17. $2z^2 + 11z + 6$ unfactorable
18. $9p^2 - q^2 + 3p + q$ unfactorable

PRACTICE AND PROBLEM SOLVING

Independent Practice

For Exercises	See Example
19–24	1
25–30	2
31–36	3

Extra Practice
Skills Practice p. EP17
Application Practice p. EP31

Tell whether each expression is completely factored. If not, factor it.

19. $2x(y^3 - 4y^2 + 5y)$
20. $2r(25r^6 - 36)$
21. $3n^2(n^2 - 25)$
22. $2m(m + 1)(m + 4)$ yes
23. $2y^2(4x^2 + 9)$ yes
24. $4(7g + 9h^2)$ yes

Factor each polynomial completely. Check your answer.

25. $-4x^3 + 24x^2 - 36x$
26. $24r^2 - 6r^4$
27. $5d^2 - 60d + 135$
28. $4y^8 + 36y^7 + 81y^6$
29. $98x^3 - 50xy^2$
30. $4x^3y - 4x^2y - 8xy$
31. $5x^2 - 10x + 14$
32. $121x^2 + 36y^2$
33. $p^4 - 16$
34. $4m^6 - 30m^5 + 36m^4$ $2m^4(m - 6)(2m - 3)$
35. $2k^3 + 3k^2 + 6k + 9$ $(k^2 + 3)(2k + 3)$
36. $ab^4 - 16a$ $a(b^2 + 4)(b + 2)(b - 2)$

Write an expression for each situation. Factor your expression.

37. the square of Ella's age plus 12 times Ella's age plus 36 $x^2 + 12x + 36 = (x + 6)^2$
38. the square of the distance from point A to point B minus 81 $d^2 - 81 = (d - 9)(d + 9)$
39. the square of the number of seconds Bob can hold his breath minus 16 times the number of seconds plus 28 $s^2 - 16s + 28 = (s - 2)(s - 14)$
40. three times the square of apples on a tree minus 22 times the number of apples plus 35 $3a^2 - 22a + 35 = (a - 5)(3a - 7)$
41. the square of Beth's score minus 49 $b^2 - 49 = (b + 7)(b - 7)$
42. **Physical Science** The height in meters of a ballet dancer's center of mass when she leaps can be modeled by the polynomial $-5t^2 + 30t + 1$, where t is time in seconds after the jump. Tell whether the polynomial is fully factored when written as $-1(5t^2 - 30t - 1)$. Explain. yes; unfactorable
43. **Write About It** When asked to factor a polynomial completely, you first determine that the terms in the polynomial do not share any common factors. What would be your next step? Check for a pattern such as a perfect-square trinomial or a difference of 2 squares.

Factor and simplify each expression. Check your answer.

44. $12(x + 1)^2 + 60(x + 1) + 75$ $3(2x + 7)^2$
45. $(2x + 3)^2 - (x - 4)^2$ $(3x - 1)(x + 7)$
46. $45x(x - 2)^2 + 60x(x - 2) + 20x$ $5x(3x - 4)^2$
47. $(3x - 5)^2 - (y + 2)^2$ $(3x + y - 3)(3x - y - 7)$

8-6 Exercises

Assignment Guide

Assign *Guided Practice* exercises as necessary.

If you finished Examples **1–3**
Proficient 19–42, 44–58, 65–71
Advanced 19–36, 40, 42, 44–71

Homework Quick Check
Quickly check key concepts.
Exercises: 20, 22, 28, 32, 36, 42

Teaching Tip

Inclusion For **Exercises 25–36,** have students count the number of terms in the polynomial when deciding which factoring method to use. Four or more terms could indicate factoring by grouping, three terms could indicate the pattern for a perfect-square trinomial, and two terms could indicate the pattern for the difference of two squares.

Answers

2. no; $2x(4x^2 - 3x - 8)$
5. no; $4(2p^2 + 1)(2p^2 - 1)$
7. $3x^3(x + 2)(x - 2)$
8. $4x(x + 1)^2$
9. $2p(2q + 1)^2$
10. $2r(3s + 1)(3s - 1)$
11. $mn(n^2 + m)(n^2 - m)$
12. $2y(x - 5)^2$
13. $3x^2(2x - 3)(x + 1)$
14. unfactorable
15. $(p^3 + 1)(p^2 + 3)$
19. no; $2xy(y^2 - 4y + 5)$
20. no; $2r(5r^3 + 6)(5r^3 - 6)$
21. no; $3n^2(n + 5)(n - 5)$
25. $-4x(x - 3)^2$
26. $-1(6r^2)(r - 2)(r + 2)$
27. $5(d - 3)(d - 9)$
28. $y^6(2y + 9)^2$
29. $2x(7x + 5y)(7x - 5y)$
30. $4xy(x - 2)(x + 1)$
31. unfactorable
32. unfactorable
33. $(p^2 + 4)(p + 2)(p - 2)$

California Standards

Standard	Exercises
8.0	67, 68
11.0	1–41, 44–48a, 49, 55–58a, 59a, 60–63, 69–71
16.0	65, 66
17.0	65, 66
18.0	65, 66
25.2	51

CONCEPT CONNECTION Exercise **48** involves factoring a polynomial to find the dimensions of a rectangle. This exercise prepares students for the Concept Connection on page 528.

Teaching Tip **Multiple Choice** In **Exercise 56,** students who chose **A** may have factored out the GCF but forgotten to factor by using the difference of squares. Students who chose **B** may have factored by using the difference of squares but forgotten to factor out the GCF.

Students who chose **B** in **Exercise 57** may have forgotten to keep the subtraction sign with the 1 when using the Distributive Property.

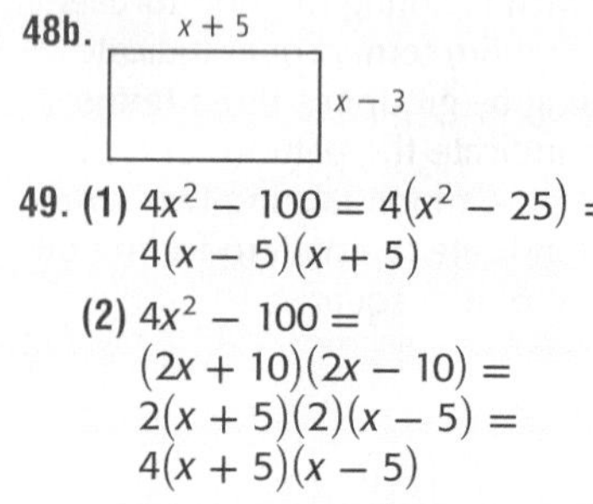

Answers

48b. (rectangle with length $x + 5$ and width $x - 3$)

49. (1) $4x^2 - 100 = 4(x^2 - 25) = 4(x - 5)(x + 5)$

(2) $4x^2 - 100 = (2x + 10)(2x - 10) = 2(x + 5)(2)(x - 5) = 4(x + 5)(x - 5)$

CONCEPT CONNECTION

48. This problem will prepare you for the Concept Connection on page 528.
  a. The area of a Marci's rectangular flower garden is $(x^2 + 2x - 15)$ ft². Factor this expression for area. Check your answer. $(x + 5)(x - 3)$
  b. Draw a diagram of the garden and label the length and width with your factors from part **a.**
  c. Find the length and width of the flower garden if $x = 7$ ft. $\ell = 12$ ft; $w = 4$ ft

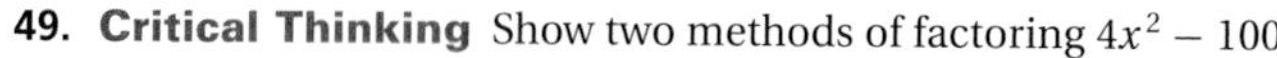

49. **Critical Thinking** Show two methods of factoring $4x^2 - 100$.

50. **Estimation** Estimate the value of $2x^2 + 5xy + 3y^2$ when $x = -10.1$ and $y = 10.05$. (*Hint:* Factor the expression first.) **approx. 0**

51. **///ERROR ANALYSIS///** Examine the factorization shown. Explain why the factorization is incorrect. **Possible answer:** $(2x - 1)^2 \neq 4x^2 - 4x - 1$

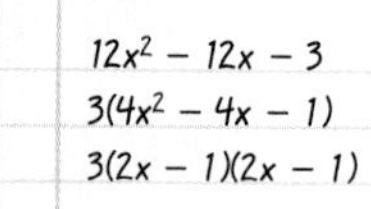

$12x^2 - 12x - 3$
$3(4x^2 - 4x - 1)$
$3(2x - 1)(2x - 1)$

LINK Math History

Blaise Pascal was a French mathematician who lived in the 1600s.

Math History Use the following information for Exercises 52–54.

The triangle at right is called *Pascal's Triangle.* The triangle starts with 1 and each of the other numbers in the triangle is the sum of the two numbers in the row above it.

Row	
0	1
1	1 1
2	1 2 1
3	1 3 3 1
4	1 4 6 4 1
5	1 5 10 10 5 1

Pascal's Triangle can be used to write the product of a binomial raised to an integer power. The numbers in each row give you the coefficients of each term in the product.

$$(a + b)^3 = a^3 + 3a^2b + 3ab^2 + b^3$$

The numbers in row 3 are 1, 3, 3, 1. These are the coefficients of the terms in the product $(a + b)^3$. The power of a decreases in each term and the power of b increases in each term.

Use the patterns you see in Pascal's Triangle to write the power of the binomial $a + b$ given by each product.

52. $a^6 + 6a^5b + 15a^4b^2 + 20a^3b^3 + 15a^2b^4 + 6ab^5 + b^6 = (a + b)^{\mathbf{6}}$

53. $a^8 + 8a^7b + 28a^6b^2 + 56a^5b^3 + 70a^4b^4 + 56a^3b^5 + 28a^2b^6 + 8ab^7 + b^8 = (a + b)^{\mathbf{8}}$

54. $a^7 + 7a^6b + 21a^5b^2 + 35a^4b^3 + 35a^3b^4 + 21a^2b^5 + 7ab^6 + b^7 = (a + b)^{\mathbf{7}}$

Multiple Choice For Exercises 55–57, choose the best answer.

55. Which expression equals $6x^2 + 7x - 10$?
  Ⓐ $(6x + 2)(x - 5)$
  Ⓑ $(2x + 5)(3x - 2)$
  Ⓒ $(x + 2)(6x - 5)$ (circled)
  Ⓓ $(3x + 2)(2x - 5)$

56. What is the complete factorization of $16x^{12} - 256$?
  Ⓐ $16(x^6 + 4)(x^6 - 4)$
  Ⓑ $(4x^6 + 16)(4x^6 - 16)$
  Ⓒ $16(x^6 + 4)(x^3 + 2)(x^3 - 2)$ (circled)
  Ⓓ $(4x^6 + 16)(2x^3 + 4)(2x^3 - 4)$

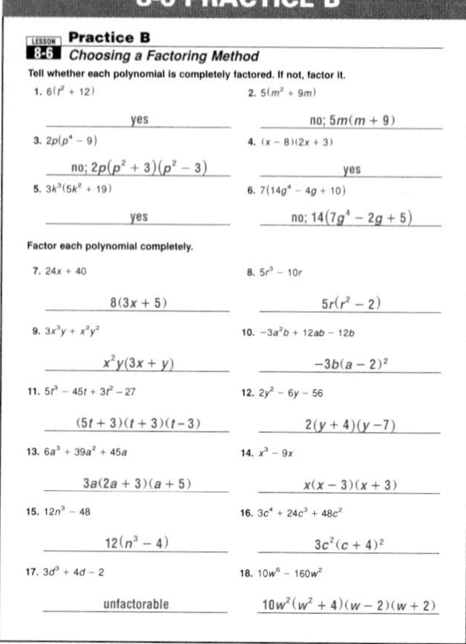

8-6 PRACTICE A

8-6 PRACTICE C

8-6 PRACTICE B

LESSON 8-6 **Practice B**
Choosing a Factoring Method

Tell whether each polynomial is completely factored. If not, factor it.

1. $6(t^2 + 12)$ yes
2. $5(m^2 + 9m)$ no; $5m(m + 9)$
3. $2p(p^4 - 9)$ no; $2p(p^2 + 3)(p^2 - 3)$
4. $(x - 8)(2x + 3)$ yes
5. $3k^3(5k^2 + 19)$ yes
6. $7(14g^4 - 4g + 10)$ no; $14(7g^4 - 2g + 5)$

Factor each polynomial completely.

7. $24x + 40$ $8(3x + 5)$
8. $5r^3 - 10r$ $5r(r^2 - 2)$
9. $3x^3y + x^2y^2$ $x^2y(3x + y)$
10. $-3a^2b + 12ab - 12b$ $-3b(a - 2)^2$
11. $5t^3 - 45t + 3t^2 - 27$ $(5t + 3)(t + 3)(t - 3)$
12. $2y^2 - 6y - 56$ $2(y + 4)(y - 7)$
13. $6a^3 + 39a^2 + 45a$ $3a(2a + 3)(a + 5)$
14. $x^3 - 9x$ $x(x - 3)(x + 3)$
15. $12n^3 - 48$ $12(n^3 - 4)$
16. $3c^4 + 24c^3 + 48c^2$ $3c^2(c + 4)^2$
17. $3d^3 + 4d - 2$ unfactorable
18. $10w^6 - 160w^2$ $10w^2(w^2 + 4)(w - 2)(w + 2)$

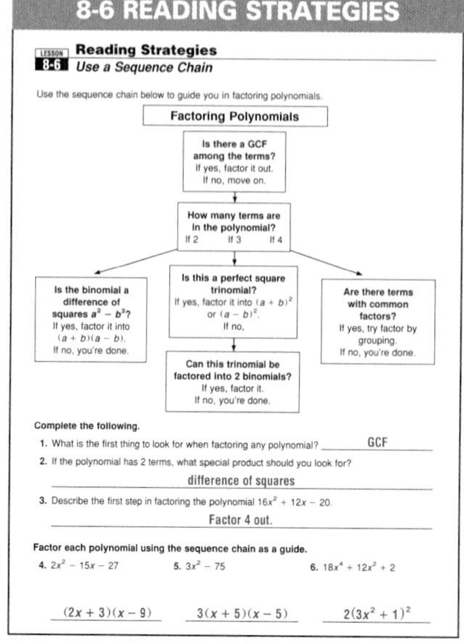

8-6 READING STRATEGIES

LESSON 8-6 **Reading Strategies**
Use a Sequence Chain

Use the sequence chain below to guide you in factoring polynomials.

Factoring Polynomials
Is there a GCF among the terms? If yes, factor it out. If no, move on.
How many terms are in the polynomial? If 2 If 3 If 4
Is the binomial a difference of squares $a^2 - b^2$? If yes, factor it into $(a + b)(a - b)$. If no, you're done.
Is this a perfect square trinomial? If yes, factor it into $(a + b)^2$ or $(a - b)^2$. If no,
Can this trinomial be factored into 2 binomials? If yes, factor it. If no, you're done.
Are there terms with common factors? If yes, try factor by grouping. If no, you're done.

Complete the following.

1. What is the first thing to look for when factoring any polynomial? GCF
2. If the polynomial has 2 terms, what special product should you look for? difference of squares
3. Describe the first step in factoring the polynomial $16x^2 + 12x - 20$. Factor 4 out.

Factor each polynomial using the sequence chain as a guide.

4. $2x^2 - 15x - 27$ $(2x + 3)(x - 9)$
5. $3x^2 - 75$ $3(x + 5)(x - 5)$
6. $18x^4 + 12x^2 + 2$ $2(3x^2 + 1)^2$

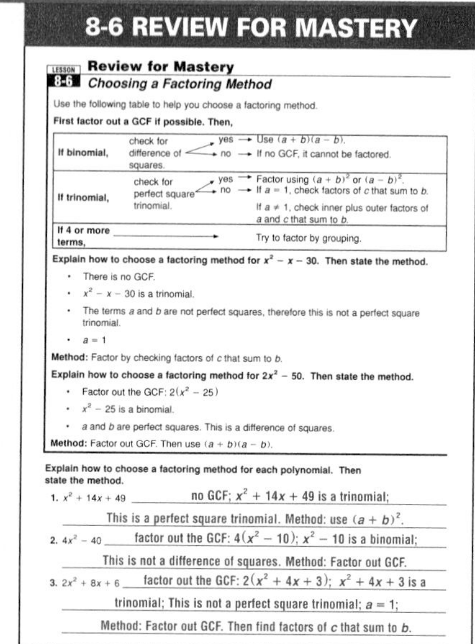

8-6 REVIEW FOR MASTERY

LESSON 8-6 **Review for Mastery**
Choosing a Factoring Method

Use the following table to help you choose a factoring method.

First factor out a GCF if possible. Then,

If binomial,	check for difference of squares.	yes → Use $(a + b)(a - b)$. no → If no GCF, it cannot be factored.
If trinomial,	check for perfect square trinomial.	yes → Factor using $(a + b)^2$ or $(a - b)^2$. no → If $a = 1$, check factors of c that sum to b. If $a \neq 1$, check inner plus outer factors of a and c that sum to b.
If 4 or more terms,	→	Try to factor by grouping.

Explain how to choose a factoring method for $x^2 - x - 30$. Then state the method.

- There is no GCF.
- $x^2 - x - 30$ is a trinomial.
- The terms a and b are not perfect squares, therefore this is not a perfect square trinomial.
- $a = 1$

Method: Factor by checking factors of c that sum to b.

Explain how to choose a factoring method for $2x^2 - 50$. Then state the method.

- Factor out the GCF: $2(x^2 - 25)$
- $x^2 - 25$ is a binomial.
- a and b are perfect squares. This is a difference of squares.

Method: Factor out GCF. Then use $(a + b)(a - b)$.

Explain how to choose a factoring method for each polynomial. Then state the method.

1. $x^2 + 14x + 49$ no GCF; $x^2 + 14x + 49$ is a trinomial; This is a perfect square trinomial. Method: use $(a + b)^2$.
2. $4x^2 - 40$ factor out the GCF: $4(x^2 - 10)$; $x^2 - 10$ is a binomial; This is not a difference of squares. Method: Factor out GCF.
3. $2x^2 + 8x + 6$ factor out the GCF: $2(x^2 + 4x + 3)$; $x^2 + 4x + 3$ is a trinomial; This is not a perfect square trinomial; $a = 1$; Method: Factor out GCF. Then find factors of c that sum to b.

57. Which of the expressions below represents the fifth step of the factorization?

Step 1: $40a^3 - 60a^2 - 10a + 15$

Step 2: $5(8a^3 - 12a^2 - 2a + 3)$

Step 3: $5[(8a^3 - 12a^2) - (2a - 3)]$

Step 4: $5[4a^2(2a - 3) - 1(2a - 3)]$

Step 5:

Step 6: $5(2a - 3)(2a + 1)(2a - 1)$

Ⓐ $5(2a - 3)(2a + 3)(4a^2 - 1)$ Ⓒ $5(2a - 3)(4a^2 - 1)$

Ⓑ $5(2a - 3)(4a^2 + 1)$ Ⓓ $5(2a - 3)(2a - 3)(4a^2 - 1)$

58. **Short Response** Use the polynomial $8x^3 + 24x^2 + 18x$ for the following.

a. Factor the polynomial. Explain each step and tell whether you used any rules for special products.

b. Explain another set of steps that could be used to factor the polynomial.
The polynomial could be factored by finding factors of 8 and factors of 18 that would result in 24 as the sum of the outer and inner products. Then one binomial would need to be factored again.

CHALLENGE AND EXTEND

59. **Geometry** The volume of the cylinder shown is represented by the expression $72\pi p^3 + 48\pi p^2 + 8\pi p$. The height of the cylinder is $8p$.

a. Factor the expression for volume. $V = 8p[\pi(3p + 1)^2]$

b. What expression represents the radius of the cylinder? $r = (3p + 1)$ cm

c. If the radius is 4 cm, what are the height and volume of the cylinder? $h = 8$ cm; $V = 128\pi$ cm^3

$V = \pi r^2 h$

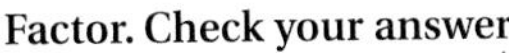

Factor. Check your answer.

60. $g^7 + g^3 + g^5 + g^4$ $g^3(g^4 + g^2 + g + 1)$

61. $h^2 + h^8 + h^6 + h^4$ $h^2(h^4 + 1)(h^2 + 1)$

62. $x^{n+2} + x^{n+1} + x^n$ $x^n(x^2 + x + 1)$

63. $x^{n+5} + x^{n+4} + x^{n+3}$ $x^{n+3}(x^2 + x + 1)$

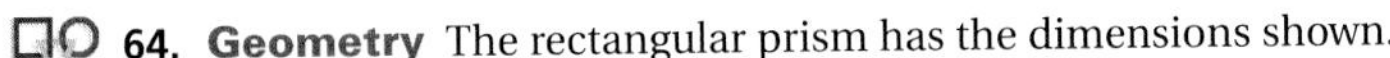

64. **Geometry** The rectangular prism has the dimensions shown.

a. Write expressions for the height and length of the prism using w. $h = w + 5$; $\ell = w + 9$

b. Write a polynomial that represents the volume of the prism using w. $V = w^3 + 14w^2 + 45w$

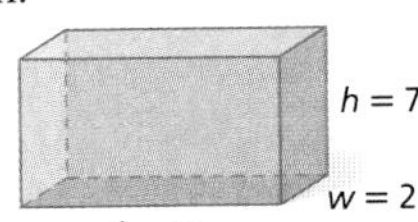

SPIRAL STANDARDS REVIEW 8.0, 11.0, 16.0, 17.0. 18.0

Give the domain and range of the relation. Tell whether the relation is a function. *(Lesson 4-2)*

65.

x	–1	0	1	2
y	–2	1	4	7

66.

x	1	2	3	1
y	–2	–1	0	–2

65. D: {–1, 0, 1, 2}; R: {–2, 1, 4, 7}; a function; each element in the domain is assigned to exactly 1 element in the range.

66. D {1, 2, 3}; R:{–2, 1, 0}; a function; each element in the domain is assigned to exactly 1 element in the range.

Identify which lines are perpendicular. *(Lesson 5-7)*

67. $y = -5x + 4$; $y = \frac{1}{5}x + 2$; $y = 5$; $y = 0$ **67.** $y = -5x + 4$ **and** $y = \frac{1}{5}x + 2$

68. $y = -x + 3$; $y = 8x$; $y = -\frac{1}{8}x + 5$; $y = x$ **68.** $y = -x + 3$ **and** $y = x$, $y = 8x$ **and** $y = -\frac{1}{8}x + 5$

Factor each trinomial. Check your answer. *(Lesson 8-4)*

69. $2x^2 + 13x + 15$ $(2x + 3)(x + 5)$

70. $4x^2 + 4x - 3$ $(2x - 1)(2x + 3)$

71. $6x^2 - 11x - 10$ $(3x + 2)(2x - 5)$

Teaching Tip **Geometry** In **Exercise 59,** students must factor an expression that represents the volume of a cylinder. Remind students that π is a number and can be factored out just like any other number.

Answer

58a. $8x^3 + 24x^2 + 18x = 2x(4x^2 + 12x + 9) = 2x(2x + 3)^2$; first I factored out the GCF, $2x$, and then I used the pattern for a perfect-square trinomial.

Journal

Explain what you think is the easiest type of polynomial to factor. Use an example to demonstrate.

ALTERNATIVE ASSESSMENT

Pair students. Have each student work backward to create three different polynomials that require at least two different factoring methods. Then have students switch papers and factor their partner's polynomials.

Power Presentations with PowerPoint®

8-6 Lesson Quiz

Tell whether the polynomial is completely factored. If not, factor it.

1. $(x + 3)(5x + 10)$
no; $5(x + 3)(x + 2)$

2. $3x^2(x^2 + 9)$
completely factored

Factor each polynomial completely. Check your answer.

3. $x^3 + 4x^2 + 3x + 12$
$(x + 4)(x^2 + 3)$

4. $4x^2 + 16x - 48$
$4(x + 6)(x - 2)$

5. $18x^2 - 3x - 3$
$3(3x + 1)(2x - 1)$

6. $18x^2 - 50y^2$
$2(3x + 5y)(3x - 5y)$

7. $5x - 20x^3 + 7 - 28x^2$
$(1 + 2x)(1 - 2x)(5x + 7)$

Also available on transparency

8-6 PROBLEM SOLVING

LESSON 8-6 Problem Solving
Choosing a Factoring Method

Write the correct answer.

1. A rectangular stage set up in a theater has an area of $(15x^2 + 3x - 12)$ square feet. Factor the polynomial completely.
$3(5x - 4)(x + 1)$

2. The area of a circular rug is $(16\pi k^2 - 16\pi k + 4\pi)$ m^2. Factor the expression completely. Then find the area of the rug if $k = 1$ meter.
$4\pi(2k - 1)^2$;
4π m^2

3. An artist framed a picture. The dimensions of the picture and frame are shown below.

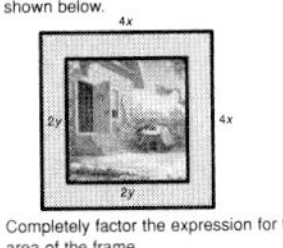

Completely factor the expression for the area of the frame.
$4(2x + y)(2x - y)$

4. The attendance for a team's basketball game can be approximated with the polynomial $-5x^2 + 80x + 285$, where x is the number of wins the team had in the previous month. Factor the polynomial completely. Then predict the attendance when the team won 4 games in the previous month.
$-5(x - 19)(x + 3)$;
525 attendees

Select the best answer.

5. The volume of a box can be modeled by the expression $7x^4 - 28$. Which shows this expression completely factored?
A $7(x^4 - 4)$
B $7(x^2 - 2)^2$
C $(7x^2 + 4)(x^2 - 7)$
Ⓓ $7(x^2 + 2)(x^2 - 2)$

6. The area of a Japanese rock garden is $(30x^2 + 3x - 6)$ square feet. Factor the polynomial completely.
F $3(10x^2 + x - 2)$
Ⓖ $3(2x + 1)(5x - 2)$
H $(6x + 3)(5x - 2)$
J $(15x - 6)(2x + 1)$

7. The money made from the sales of x mountain bikes is approximated by $20x^2 + 10x + 90$. Factor the expression completely.
A $2(10x + 9)(x + 5)$
B $5(4x^2 + 2x + 18)$
Ⓒ $10(2x^2 + x + 9)$
D The expression cannot be factored.

8. Kyle stood on a bridge and threw a rock up and over the side. The height of the rock, in meters, can be approximated by $-5t^2 + 5t + 24$, where t is the time in seconds after Kyle threw it. Completely factor the expression.
F $-5(t^2 + t + 24)$
G $(-5t + 3)(t + 8)$
H $-1(5t + 8)(t + 3)$
Ⓙ The expression cannot be factored.

8-6 CHALLENGE

LESSON 8-6 Challenge
Sum and Difference of Cubes

A sum of cubes can be factored using: $a^3 + b^3 = (a + b)(a^2 - ab + b^2)$.

Factor $x^3 + 125y^3$.

$(x)^3 + (5y)^3$ $a = x, b = 5y$

$(x + 5y)(x^2 - 5xy + 25y^2)$ *Substitute into $(a + b)(a^2 - ab + b^2)$.*

Factor each polynomial.

1. $x^3 + 8$ $(x + 2)(x^2 - 2x + 4)$
2. $64x^3 + y^3$ $(4x + y)(16x^2 - 4xy + y^2)$
3. $125x^3 + 216$ $(5x + 6)(25x^2 - 30x + 36)$

A difference of cubes can be factored using: $a^3 - b^3 = (a - b)(a^2 + ab + b^2)$.

Factor $8x^3 - 27$.

$(2x)^3 - (3)^3$ $a = 2x, b = 3$

$(2x - 3)(4x^2 + 6x + 9)$ *Substitute into $(a - b)(a^2 + ab + b^2)$.*

Factor each polynomial.

4. $x^3 - 64$ $(x - 4)(x^2 + 4x + 16)$
5. $343x^3 - y^3$ $(7x - y)(49x^2 + 7xy + y^2)$
6. $729x^3 - 1000$ $(9x - 10)(81x^2 + 90x + 100)$

You can use the sum and difference of cubes with other factoring methods to completely factor a polynomial.

Factor each polynomial completely.

7. $2x^3 - 54$ $2(x - 3)(x^2 + 3x + 9)$
8. $216x^3 + 8y^3$ $8(3x + y)(9x^2 - 3xy + y^2)$
9. $x^6 + 12x^3 + 32$ $(x + 2)(x^2 - 2x + 4)(x^3 + 4)$
10. $3x^6 + 18x^3 + 15$ $3(x^3 + 5)(x + 1)(x^2 - x + 1)$
11. $x^5 - 27x^2 - 9x^3 + 243$ $(x + 3)(x - 3)^2(x^2 + 3x + 9)$

Use difference of squares to factor each binomial. Then factor completely.

12. $729x^6 - 64$ $(3x + 2)(3x - 2)(9x^2 - 6x + 4)(9x^2 + 6x + 4)$
13. $64x^6 - y^6$ $(2x + y)(2x - y)(4x^2 - 2xy + y^2)(4x^2 + 2xy + y^2)$

CHAPTER 8

CONCEPT CONNECTION

SECTION 8B

SECTION 8B

CONCEPT CONNECTION

Organizer

Objective: Assess students' ability to apply concepts and skills in Lessons 8-5 through 8-6 in a real-world format.

Online Edition

Countdown to Mastery Week 19

Problem	Text Reference
1	Lesson 8-5
2	Lesson 2-1
3	Lesson 8-3
4	Lesson 8-6
5	Lesson 1-1
6	Skills Bank

Answers

1. $\ell = (x + 6)$ ft; $w = (x + 6)$ ft
2. $w = 12$ ft; $x = 6$; $A = 144$ ft^2
3. $\ell = (x + 12)$ ft; $w = (x + 2)$ ft

California Standards

Algebra 1 11.0

Factoring

Shaping the Environment The Environmental Awareness Club is going to plant a garden on the front lawn of the school. Henry suggests a garden in the shape of a square. Theona suggests a rectangular shape.

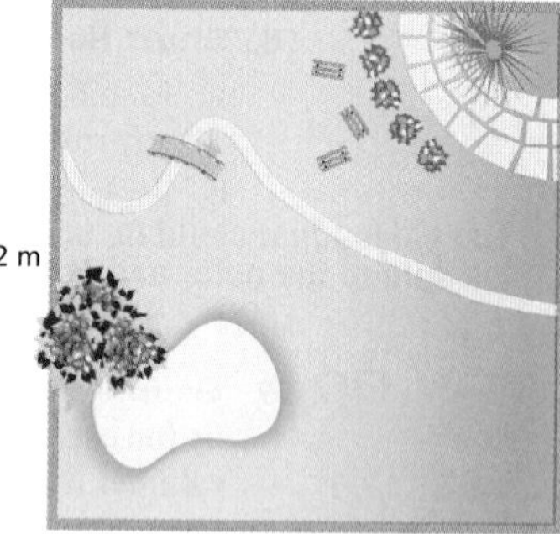

1. Henry's plans include a square garden with an area of $(x^2 + 12x + 36)$ m^2. Write expressions for the length and width of the square garden.
2. A drawing of the square garden shows a length of 12 m. What is the width of the square garden? What is the value of x? What is the total area of the square garden?
3. Theona's plans include a rectangular garden with an area of $(x^2 + 14x + 24)$ m^2. Write expressions for the length and width of the rectangular garden.

4. A drawing of the rectangular garden shows that the length is 6 m longer than the length of the square garden. What is the width of the rectangular garden? How much shorter is the width of the rectangular garden than the square garden? **$w = 8$ m; 4 m**
5. Find the perimeter of each garden in terms of x.
6. Which plan should the club choose if they want the garden that covers the most area? Which plan should the club choose if they want the garden that requires the least fencing around it? Explain your reasoning.

5. square garden: $4(x + 6)$ m; rectangular garden: $4(x + 7)$ m

6. Area of square garden: 144 m^2; area of rectangular garden: 144 m^2; the gardens have the same area; the perimeter of the square garden is less and requires less fencing.

INTERVENTION

Scaffolding Questions

1. When given the area, how can you find the length and width? Factor the area.
2. What values of x are reasonable? x must be positive.
3. Will the length and width be equal if the rectangle is not a square? no
4. Does it matter which side of the square garden you label as the width? No; the sides are all the same length.
5. What does perimeter describe? the distance around a figure
6. How do you know which garden requires the least fencing? The garden with the smaller perimeter requires less fencing.

Extension

Do you think the perimeter of two gardens with the same area will be larger for a square or rectangle? The perimeter will be larger for the rectangle.

Quiz for Lessons 8-5 Through 8-6

8-5 Factoring Special Products

Determine whether each trinomial is a perfect square. If so, factor. If not, explain.

1. $x^2 + 8x + 16$ yes; $(x + 4)^2$
2. $4x^2 - 20x + 25$ yes; $(2x - 5)^2$
3. $x^2 + 3x + 9$ no; $3x \neq 2(x)(3)$
4. $2x^2 - 4x + 4$
5. $9x^2 - 12x + 4$
6. $x^2 - 12x - 36$
7. An architect is designing rectangular windows with an area of $(x^2 + 20x + 100)$ ft^2. The dimensions of the windows are of the form $ax + b$, where a and b are whole numbers. Find an expression for the perimeter of the windows. Find the perimeter of a window when $x = 4$ ft. $4(x + 10)$ ft; 56 ft

Determine whether each binomial is a difference of two squares. If so, factor. If not, explain.

8. $x^2 - 121$
9. $4t^2 - 20$
10. $1 - 9y^4$
11. $25m^2 - 4m^6$
12. $16x^2 + 49$
13. $r^4 - t^2$
14. The area of a square is $(36d^2 - 36d + 9)$ in^2.
    a. What expression represents the length of a side of the square? $\ell = (6d - 3)$ in.
    b. What expression represents the perimeter of the square? $4(6d - 3)$ in.
    c. What are the length of a side, the perimeter, and the area of the square when $d = 2$ in.? 9 in; 36 in; 81 in^2

8-6 Choosing a Factoring Method

Tell whether each expression is completely factored. If not, factor it.

15. $5(x^2 + 3x + 1)$ yes
16. $6x(5x^2 - x)$ no; $6x^2(5x - 1)$
17. $3t(t^4 - 9)$ no; $3t(t^2 - 3)(t^2 + 3)$
18. $2(m^2 - 10m + 25)$ no; $2(m - 5)^2$
19. $3(2y^2 - 5)(y + 1)$ yes
20. $(2n + 6)(n - 4)$ no; $2(n + 3)(n - 4)$

Factor each polynomial completely. Check your answer.

21. $3x^3 - 12x^2 + 12x$
22. $16m^3 - 4m$
23. $5x^3y - 45xy$
24. $3t^2 + 5t - 1$
25. $3c^2 + 12c - 63$
26. $x^5 - 81x$

Write an expression for each situation. Then factor your expression.

27. the difference of the square of a board's length and 36
28. the square of Michael's age minus 8 times Michael's age plus 16
29. two times the square of a car's speed plus 2 times the car's speed minus 12
30. three times the cube of Jessie's height plus 3 times the square of Jessie's height minus 6 times Jessie's height
31. Write an expression for the area of the shaded region. Then factor the expression.

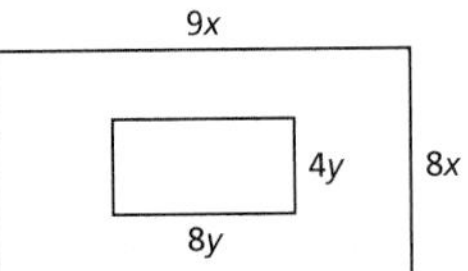

READY TO GO ON?

SECTION 8B

Organizer

Objective: Assess students' mastery of concepts and skills in Lessons 8-5 through 8-6.

Resources

Assessment Resources
Section 8B Quiz

INTERVENTION
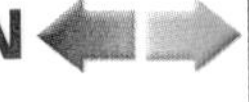

Resources

***Ready to Go On? Intervention and Enrichment* Worksheets**

Ready to Go On? CD-ROM

***Ready to Go On?* Online**

Answers

4. no; $-4x \neq 2(\sqrt{2}x)(2)$
5. yes; $(3x - 2)^2$
6. No; the last term must be positive.
8. yes; $(x - 11)(x + 11)$
9. no; 20 is not a perfect square.
10. yes; $(1 - 3y^2)(1 + 3y^2)$

11–13, 21–31. See p. A24.

READY TO GO ON? Diagnose and Prescribe

Ready to Go On? Intervention	*Ready to Go On? Intervention*, Section 8B: Worksheets	CD-ROM	Online
Lesson 8-5 11.0	8-5 Intervention	Activity 8-5	Diagnose and Prescribe Online
Lesson 8-6 11.0	8-6 Intervention	Activity 8-6	

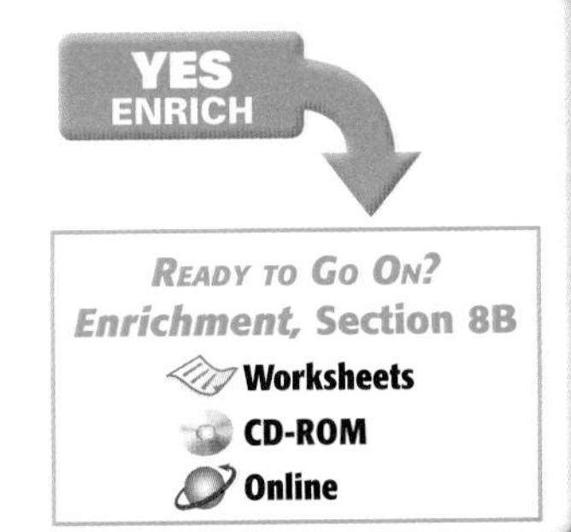

CHAPTER 8 **Study Guide: Review**

Organizer

Objective: Help students organize and review key concepts and skills presented in Chapter 8.

Online Edition
Multilingual Glossary

Resources

PuzzlePro
One-Stop Planner®

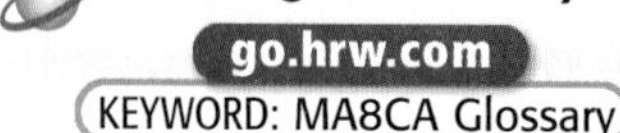

***Multilingual Glossary* Online**
go.hrw.com
KEYWORD: MA8CA Glossary

Lesson Tutorial Videos
CD-ROM

Test & Practice Generator
One-Stop Planner®

Answers

1. prime factorization
2. greatest common factor
3. $2^2 \cdot 3$
4. $2^2 \cdot 5$
5. 2^5
6. prime
7. $2^3 \cdot 5$
8. 2^6
9. $2 \cdot 3 \cdot 11$
10. $2 \cdot 3 \cdot 19$
11. 5
12. 12
13. 1
14. 27
15. 4
16. 3
17. $2x$
18. $9b^2$
19. $25r$
20. 6 boxes; 13 rows

CHAPTER 8

Study Guide: Review

Vocabulary

Complete the sentences below with vocabulary words from the list above.

1. A number written as a product so that each of its factors has no factors other than 1 and itself is the ___?___ .
2. The ___?___ of two monomials is the greatest of the factors that the monomials share.

8-1 Factors and Greatest Common Factors *(pp. 478–483)*

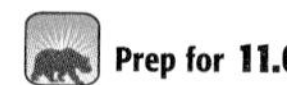

Prep for **11.0**

EXAMPLES

■ **Write the prime factorization of 84.**

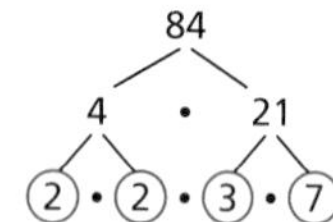

Write as a product.
Continue until all factors are prime.

■ **Write the prime factorization of 75.**

$$\begin{array}{r|l} 3 & 75 \\ 5 & 25 \\ 5 & 5 \\ & 1 \end{array}$$

Keep dividing by prime factors until the quotient is 1.

$75 = 3 \cdot 5 \cdot 5 = 3 \cdot 5^2$

■ **Find the GCF of 36 and 90.**

$36 = 2 \cdot \boxed{2} \cdot \boxed{3} \cdot \boxed{3}$
$90 = \boxed{2} \cdot \boxed{3} \cdot \boxed{3} \cdot 5$

Write the prime factorization of each number.

$2 \cdot 3 \cdot 3 = 18$

Find the product of the common factors.

The GCF of 36 and 90 is 18.

■ **Find the GCF of $10x^5$ and $4x^2$.**

$10x^5 = \boxed{2} \cdot 5 \cdot \boxed{x} \cdot \boxed{x} \cdot x \cdot x \cdot x$
$4x^2 = \boxed{2} \cdot 2 \cdot \boxed{x} \cdot \boxed{x}$

Write the prime factorization of each coefficient.
Write powers as products.

$2 \cdot \quad x \cdot x = 2x^2$

Find the product of the common factors.

The GCF of $10x^5$ and $4x^2$ is $2x^2$.

EXERCISES

Write the prime factorization of each number.

3. 12
4. 20
5. 32
6. 23
7. 40
8. 64
9. 66
10. 114

Find the GCF of each pair of numbers.

11. 15 and 50
12. 36 and 132
13. 29 and 30
14. 54 and 81
15. 20 and 48

Find the GCF of each pair of monomials.

16. $9m$ and 3
17. $4x$ and $2x^2$
18. $-18b^4$ and $27b^2$
19. $100r$ and $25r^5$
20. A hardware store carries 42 types of boxed nails and 36 types of boxed screws. The store manager wants to build a rack so that he can display the hardware in rows. He wants to put the same number of boxes in each row, but he wants no row to contain both nails and screws. What is the greatest number of boxes that he can display in one row? How many rows will there be if the manager puts the greatest number of boxes in each row?

8-2 Factoring by GCF *(pp. 487–493)*

11.0

EXAMPLES

■ **Factor $3t^3 - 9t^2$. Check your answer.**

$3t^3 = 3 \cdot t \cdot t \cdot t$
$9t^2 = 3 \cdot 3 \cdot t \cdot t$ — *Find the GCF.*

GCF: $3 \cdot t \cdot t = 3t^2$

$3t^3 - 9t^2 = 3t^2(t) - 3t^2(3)$
$= 3t^2(t - 3)$ — *Factor out the GCF.*

Check $3t^2(t - 3) = 3t^3 - 9t^2$ ✓

■ **Factor $-12s - 6s^3$. Check your answer.**

$-1(12s + 6s^3)$ — *Factor out −1.*

$12s = 2 \cdot 2 \cdot 3 \cdot s$
$6s^3 = 2 \cdot \quad 3 \cdot s \cdot s \cdot s$ — *Find the GCF.*

GCF: $2 \cdot 3 \cdot s = 6s$

$-1(12s + 6s^3)$

$1[(6s)(2) + (6s)(s^2)]$

$-1[(6s)(2 + s^2)]$

$-6s(2 + s^2)$ — *Factor out the GCF.*

Check $-6s(2 + s^2) = -12s - 6s^3$ ✓

■ **Factor $5(x - 7) + 3x(x - 7)$.**

$5(x - 7) + 3x(x - 7)$ — *The terms have a common factor of $(x - 7)$.*

$(x - 7)(5 + 3x)$ — *Factor out $(x - 7)$.*

■ **Factor $6b^3 + 8b + 15b^2 + 20$ by grouping.**

$(6b^3 + 8b) + (15b^2 + 20)$ — *Group terms that have a common factor.*

$2b(3b^2 + 4) + 5(3b^2 + 4)$ — *Factor each group.*

$(3b^2 + 4)(2b + 5)$ — *Factor out $(3b^2 + 4)$.*

■ **Factor $2m^3 - 6m^2 + 15 - 5m$. Check your answer.**

$(2m^3 - 6m^2) + (15 - 5m)$ — *Group terms.*

$2m^2(m - 3) + 5(3 - m)$ — *Factor each group.*

$2m^2(m - 3) + 5(-1)(m - 3)$ — *Rewrite $(3 - m)$ as $(-1)(m - 3)$.*

$2m^2(m - 3) - 5(m - 3)$ — *Simplify.*

$(m - 3)(2m^2 - 5)$ — *Factor out $(m - 3)$.*

Check $(m - 3)(2m^2 - 5)$

$2m^3 - 5m - 6m^2 + 15$
$2m^3 - 6m^2 + 15 - 5m$ ✓

EXERCISES

Factor each polynomial. Check your answer.

21. $5x - 15x^3$
22. $-16b + 32$
23. $-14v - 21$
24. $4a^2 - 12a - 8$
25. $5g^5 - 10g^3 - 15g$
26. $40p^2 - 10p + 30$
27. A civil engineer needs the area of a rectangular lot to be $(6x^2 + 5x)$ ft^2. Factor this polynomial to find expressions for the dimensions of the lot.

Factor each expression.

28. $2x(x - 4) + 9(x - 4)$
29. $t(3t + 5) - 6(3t + 5)$
30. $5(6 - n) - 3n(6 - n)$
31. $b(b + 4) + 2(b + 4)$
32. $x^2(x - 3) + 7(x - 3)$

Factor each polynomial by grouping. Check your answer.

33. $n^3 + n - 4n^2 - 4$
34. $6b^2 - 8b + 15b - 20$
35. $2h^3 - 7h + 14h^2 - 49$
36. $3t^2 + 18t + t + 6$
37. $10m^3 + 15m^2 - 2m - 3$
38. $8p^3 + 4p - 6p^2 - 3$
39. $5r - 10 + 2r - r^2$
40. $b^3 - 5b + 15 - 3b^2$
41. $6t - t^3 - 4t^2 + 24$
42. $12h - 3h^2 + h - 4$
43. $d - d^2 + d - 1$
44. $6b - 5b^2 + 10b - 12$
45. $5t - t^2 - t + 5$
46. $8b^2 - 2b^3 - 5b + 20$
47. $3r - 3r^2 - 1 + r$
48. Write an expression for the area of each of the two rectangles shown. Then write and factor an expression for the combined area.

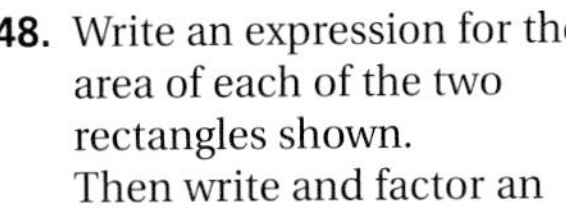

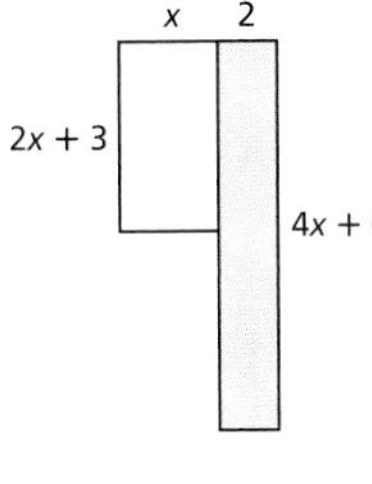

Answers

21. $5x(1 - 3x^2)$
22. $16(-b + 2)$
23. $-7(2v + 3)$
24. $4(a^2 - 3a - 2)$
25. $5g(g^2 - 3)(g^2 + 1)$
26. $10(4p^2 - p + 3)$
27. $(6x + 5)$ ft by x ft
28. $(2x + 9)(x - 4)$
29. $(t - 6)(3t + 5)$
30. $(5 - 3n)(6 - n)$
31. $(b + 2)(b + 4)$
32. $(x^2 + 7)(x - 3)$
33. $(n^2 + 1)(n - 4)$
34. $(2b + 5)(3b - 4)$
35. $(2h^2 - 7)(h + 7)$
36. $(3t + 1)(t + 6)$
37. $(5m^2 - 1)(2m + 3)$
38. $(4p - 3)(2p^2 + 1)$
39. $-1(r - 5)(r - 2)$
40. $(b^2 - 5)(b - 3)$
41. $(t + 4)(-t^2 + 6)$
42. $-1(3h - 1)(h - 4)$
43. $-1(d - 1)^2$
44. $(2 - b)(5b - 6)$
45. $(t + 1)(5 - t)$
46. $(2b^2 + 5)(4 - b)$
47. $-1(3r - 1)(r - 1)$
48. left rectangle: $2x^2 + 3x$; right rectangle: $8x + 12$; combined: $2x^2 + 8x + 3x + 12$; $(2x + 3)(x + 4)$

Answers

49. $(x+1)(x+5)$
50. $(x+2)(x+4)$
51. $(x+3)(x+5)$
52. $(x-6)(x-2)$
53. $(x+5)^2$
54. $(x-2)(x-11)$
55. $(x+4)(x+20)$
56. $(x-6)(x-20)$
57. $(x+12)(x-7)$
58. $(x+3)(x-8)$
59. $(x+4)(x-7)$
60. $(x-1)(x+5)$
61. $(x+3)(x-2)$
62. $(x+5)(x-4)$
63. $(x-8)(x+6)$
64. $(x-9)(x+4)$
65. $(x-12)(x+6)$
66. $(x-10)(x+7)$
67. $(x+20)(x-6)$
68. $(x+7)(x-1)$
69. $(y+3)$ m
70. $(2x+1)(x+5)$
71. $(3x+7)(x+1)$
72. $(2x-1)(x-1)$
73. $(3x+2)(x+2)$
74. $(5x+3)(x+5)$
75. $(2x-3)(3x-5)$
76. $(4x+5)(x+2)$
77. $(3x+4)(x+2)$
78. $(7x-2)(x-5)$
79. $(3x+2)(3x+4)$
80. $(2x+1)(x-1)$
81. $(3x+1)(x-4)$
82. $(2x-1)(x-5)$
83. $(7x+2)(x-3)$
84. $(5x+1)(x-2)$
85. $-1(2x-1)(3x+2)$
86. $(6x+5)(x-1)$
87. $(3x-2)(2x+7)$
88. $-1(2x+1)(2x-5)$
89. $-1(2x-3)(5x+2)$
90. $12x^2-11x-5$; $(4x-5)(3x+1)$

8-3 Factoring $x^2 + bx + c$ (pp. 496–503)

EXAMPLES

Factor each trinomial. Check your answer.

■ $x^2 + 14x + 45$

$(x + \square)(x + \square)$ *Look for factors of 45 whose sum is 14.*

$(x+9)(x+5)$

Check $(x+9)(x+5) = x^2 + 5x + 9x + 45$

$= x^2 + 14x + 45$ ✓

■ $x^2 + 6x - 27$

$(x + \square)(x - \square)$ *Look for factors of –27 whose sum is 6.*

$(x+9)(x-3)$

Check $(x+9)(x-3) = x^2 - 3x + 9x - 27$

$= x^2 + 6x - 27$ ✓

EXERCISES

Factor each trinomial. Check your answer.

49. $x^2 + 6x + 5$ **50.** $x^2 + 6x + 8$

51. $x^2 + 8x + 15$ **52.** $x^2 - 8x + 12$

53. $x^2 + 10x + 25$ **54.** $x^2 - 13x + 22$

55. $x^2 + 24x + 80$ **56.** $x^2 - 26x + 120$

57. $x^2 + 5x - 84$ **58.** $x^2 - 5x - 24$

59. $x^2 - 3x - 28$ **60.** $x^2 + 4x - 5$

61. $x^2 + x - 6$ **62.** $x^2 + x - 20$

63. $x^2 - 2x - 48$ **64.** $x^2 - 5x - 36$

65. $x^2 - 6x - 72$ **66.** $x^2 - 3x - 70$

67. $x^2 + 14x - 120$ **68.** $x^2 + 6x - 7$

69. The rectangle shown has an area of $(y^2 + 8y + 15)$ m². What is the width of the rectangle?

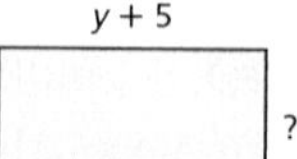

8-4 Factoring $ax^2 + bx + c$ (pp. 505–511)

EXAMPLES

Factor each trinomial.

■ $6x^2 + 17x + 5$

$(\square x + \square)(\square x + \square)$ *$a = 6$ and $c = 5$; Outer + Inner = 17*

Factors of 6	Factors of 5	Outer + Inner
1 and 6	5 and 1	$(1)1 + (6)5 = 31$
2 and 3	1 and 5	$(2)5 + (3)1 = 13$
2 and 3	5 and 1	$(2)1 + (3)5 = 17$

$(2x+5)(3x+1)$

■ $2n^2 - n - 10$

$(\square n + \square)(\square n + \square)$ *$a = 2$ and $c = -10$; Outer + Inner = –1*

Factors of 2	Factors of –10	Outer + Inner
1 and 2	1 and –10	$1(-10) + 2(1) = -8$
1 and 2	–1 and 10	$1(10) + 2(-1) = 8$
1 and 2	2 and –5	$1(-5) + 2(2) = -1$

$(1n+2)(2n-5) = (n+2)(2n-5)$

EXERCISES

Factor each trinomial. Check your answer.

70. $2x^2 + 11x + 5$ **71.** $3x^2 + 10x + 7$

72. $2x^2 - 3x + 1$ **73.** $3x^2 + 8x + 4$

74. $5x^2 + 28x + 15$ **75.** $6x^2 - 19x + 15$

76. $4x^2 + 13x + 10$ **77.** $3x^2 + 10x + 8$

78. $7x^2 - 37x + 10$ **79.** $9x^2 + 18x + 8$

80. $2x^2 - x - 1$ **81.** $3x^2 - 11x - 4$

82. $2x^2 - 11x + 5$ **83.** $7x^2 - 19x - 6$

84. $5x^2 - 9x - 2$ **85.** $-6x^2 - x + 2$

86. $6x^2 - x - 5$ **87.** $6x^2 + 17x - 14$

88. $-4x^2 + 8x + 5$ **89.** $-10x^2 + 11x + 6$

90. Write the polynomial modeled and then factor.

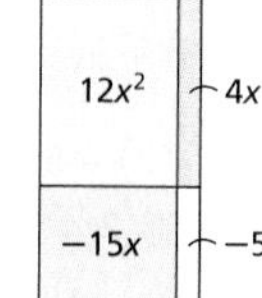

8-5 Factoring Special Products *(pp. 514–520)*

11.0

EXAMPLES

- Determine whether $x^2 + 18x + 81$ is a perfect square. If so, factor. If not, explain.

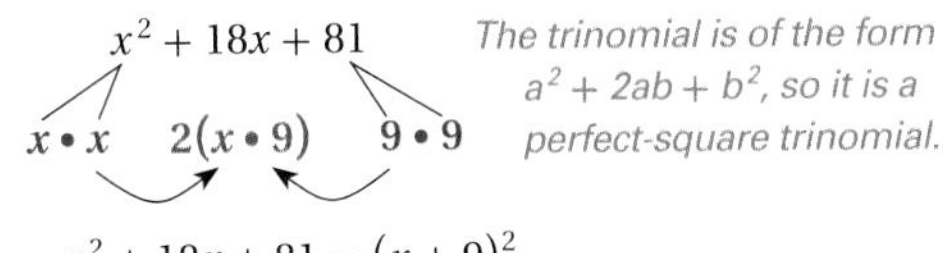

$x^2 + 18x + 81$
$x \cdot x$
$2(x \cdot 9)$
$9 \cdot 9$
The trinomial is of the form $a^2 + 2ab + b^2$, so it is a perfect-square trinomial.

$x^2 + 18x + 81 = (x + 9)^2$

- Determine whether $49x^4 - 25y^6$ is a difference of two squares. If so, factor. If not, explain.

$49x^4 - 25y^6$ — *The binomial is a difference of two squares.*

$7x^2 \cdot 7x^2 \quad 5y^3 \cdot 5y^3$

$(7x^2)^2 - (5y^3)^2$ — *$a = 7x^2$, $b = 5x^3$*

$(7x^2 + 5y^3)(7x^2 - 5y^3)$ — *Write the binomial as $(a + b)(a - b)$.*

$49x^4 - 25y^6 = (7x^2 + 5y^3)(7x^2 - 5y^3)$

EXERCISES

Determine whether each trinomial is a perfect square. If so, factor. If not, explain.

91. $x^2 + 12x + 36$ **92.** $x^2 + 5x + 25$
93. $4x^2 - 2x + 1$ **94.** $9x^2 + 12x + 4$
95. $16x^2 + 8x + 4$ **96.** $x^2 + 14x + 49$

Determine whether each binomial is a difference of two squares. If so, factor. If not, explain.

97. $100x^2 - 81$ **98.** $x^2 - 2$
99. $5x^4 - 10y^6$ **100.** $(-12)^2 - (x^3)^2$
101. $121b^2 + 9c^8$ **102.** $100p^2 - 25q^2$

Factor each polynomial using the pattern of perfect-square trinomials or the difference of two squares. Tell which pattern you used and check your answer.

103. $x^2 - 25$ **104.** $x^2 + 20x + 100$
105. $j^2 - k^4$ **106.** $9x^2 - 42x + 49$
107. $81x^2 + 144x + 64$ **108.** $16b^4 - 121c^6$

8-6 Choosing a Factoring Method *(pp. 522–527)*

11.0

EXAMPLES

- Tell whether $(3x - 9)(x + 4)$ is completely factored. If not, factor it.

$(3x - 9)(x + 4)$ — *$3x - 9$ can be factored.*
$3(x - 3)(x + 4)$ — *Factor out 3, the GCF of 3x and 9.*

- $3ab^2 - 48a$

$3a(b^2 - 16)$ — *Factor out the GCF.*
$3a(b + 4)(b - 4)$ — *Factor the difference of two squares.*

Check $3a(b + 4)(b - 4) = 3a(b^2 - 16)$
$= 3ab^2 - 48a$ ✓

- $2m^3 + 4m^2 - 48m$

$2m(m^2 + 2m - 24)$ — *Factor out the GCF.*
$2m(m - 4)(m + 6)$ — *Factor the trinomial.*

Check $2m(m - 4)(m + 6)$
$2m(m^2 + 2m - 24)$
$2m^3 + 4m^2 - 48m$ ✓

EXERCISES

Tell whether each polynomial is completely factored. If not, factor it.

109. $4x^2 + 10x + 6 = (4x + 6)(x + 1)$
110. $3y^2 + 75 = 3(y^2 + 25)$
111. $b^4 - 81 = (b^2 + 9)(b^2 - 9)$
112. $x^2 - 6x + 9 = (x - 3)^2$

Factor each polynomial completely. Check your answer.

113. $4x^2 - 64$ **114.** $3b^5 - 6b^4 - 24b^3$
115. $a^4b^3 - a^2b^5$ **116.** $t^{20} - t^4$
117. $5x^2 + 20x + 15$ **118.** $2x^4 - 50x^2$
119. $8t + 32 + 2st + 8s$
120. $25m^3 - 90m^2 - 40m$
121. $32x^4 - 48x^3 + 8x^2 - 12x$
122. $6s^4t + 12s^3t^2 + 6s^2t^3$
123. $10m^3 + 4m^2 - 90m - 36$

Answers

91. yes; $(x + 6)^2$
92. no; $5x \neq 2(x)(5)$
93. no; $-2x \neq 2(2x)(1)$
94. yes; $(3x + 2)^2$
95. no; $8x \neq 2(4x)(2)$
96. yes; $(x + 7)^2$
97. yes; $(10x - 9)(10x + 9)$
98. No; 2 is not a perfect square.
99. No; 5 and 10 are not perfect squares.
100. yes; $(-12 + x^3)(-12 - x^3)$
101. no; terms must be subtracted
102. yes; $25(2p + q)(2p - q)$
103. $(x - 5)(x + 5)$; difference of 2 squares
104. $(x + 10)^2$; perfect-square trinomial
105. $(j - k^2)(j + k^2)$; difference of 2 squares
106. $(3x - 7)^2$; perfect-square trinomial
107. $(9x + 8)^2$; perfect-square trinomial
108. $(4b^2 - 11c^3)(4b^2 + 11c^3)$; difference of 2 squares
109. no; $2(2x + 3)(x + 1)$
110. yes
111. no; $(b^2 + 9)(b - 3)(b + 3)$
112. yes
113. $4(x - 4)(x + 4)$
114. $3b^3(b - 4)(b + 2)$
115. $a^2b^3(a - b)(a + b)$
116. $t^4(t^8 + 1)(t^4 + 1)(t^2 + 1)(t + 1)(t - 1)$
117. $5(x + 3)(x + 1)$
118. $2x^2(x - 5)(x + 5)$
119. $2(s + 4)(t + 4)$
120. $5m(5m + 2)(m - 4)$
121. $4x(4x^2 + 1)(2x - 3)$
122. $6s^2t(s + t)^2$
123. $2(m + 3)(m - 3)(5m + 2)$

Organizer

Objective: Assess students' mastery of concepts and skills in Chapter 8.

Resources

Assessment Resources

Chapter 8 Tests

- Free Response (Levels A, B, C)
- Multiple Choice (Levels A, B, C)
- Performance Assessment

***IDEA Works!* CD-ROM**

Modified Chapter 8 Test

Answers

9. $(3 + 4c)(c - 5)$
10. $(5x^2 + 2)(2x - 5)$
11. $(y - 1)(4y^2 + 3)$
29. $8x(x + 4)(x + 5)$

California Standards

Standard	Exercises
11.0	6–34

Find the GCF of each pair of monomials.

1. $3t^4$ and $8t^2$ t^2
2. $2y^3$ and $-12y$ $2y$
3. $15n^5$ and $9n^4$ $3n^4$
4. Write the prime factorization of 360. $2^3 \cdot 3^2 \cdot 5$
5. A coin collector is arranging a display of three types of nickels. The types of nickels and number of each type are shown in the table. The collector wants to arrange them in rows with the same number in each row without having different types in the same row. How many rows will she need if she puts the greatest possible number of nickels in each row? **10 rows**

Type of Nickel	Number of Nickels
Liberty	16
Buffalo	24
Jefferson	40

Factor each expression.

6. $24m^2 + 4m^3$ $4m^2(6 + m)$
7. $9x^5 - 12x$ $3x(3x^4 - 4)$
8. $-2r^4 - 6$ $-2(r^4 + 3)$
9. $3(c - 5) + 4c(c - 5)$
10. $10x^3 + 4x - 25x^2 - 10$
11. $4y^3 - 4y^2 - 3 + 3y$
12. A model rocket is shot vertically from a deck into the air at a speed of 50 m/s. The expression $-5t^2 + 50t + 5$ gives the approximate height of the rocket after t seconds. Factor this expression. $-5(t^2 - 10t - 1)$

Factor each trinomial.

13. $x^2 + 6x + 5$ $(x + 5)(x + 1)$
14. $x^2 - 4x - 21$ $(x - 7)(x + 3)$
15. $x^2 - 8x + 15$ $(x - 5)(x - 3)$
16. $2x^2 + 9x + 7$ $(2x + 7)(x + 1)$
17. $2x^2 + 9x - 18$ $(2x - 3)(x + 6)$
18. $-3x^2 - 2x + 8$ $-1(3x - 4)(x + 2)$

Determine whether each trinomial is a perfect square. If so, factor. If not, explain.

19. $a^2 + 14a + 49$ yes; $(a + 7)^2$
20. $2x^2 + 10x + 25$ No; $2x^2$ is not a perf. square.
21. $9t^2 - 6t + 1$ yes; $(3t - 1)^2$

Determine whether each binomial is a difference of two squares. If so, factor. If not, explain.

22. $b^2 - 16$ yes; $(b - 4)(b + 4)$
23. $25y^2 - 10$ No; 10 is not a perf. square.
24. $9a^2 - b^{10}$ yes; $(3a - b^5)(3a + b^5)$
25. A company is producing rectangular sheets of plastic. Each has an area of $(9x^2 + 30x + 25)$ ft². The dimensions of each sheet are of the form $ax + b$, where a and b are whole numbers. Find an expression for the perimeter of a sheet. Find the perimeter when $x = 4$ ft. $P = 4(3x + 5)$ ft; 68 ft

Tell whether each expression is completely factored. If not, factor it.

26. $(6x - 3)(x + 5)$ no; $3(2x - 1)(x + 5)$
27. $(v^5 + 10)(v^5 - 10)$ yes
28. $(2b + 3)(3b - 2)$ yes

Factor each polynomial completely.

29. $8x^3 + 72x^2 + 160x$
30. $3x^5 - 27x^3$ $3x^3(x - 3)(x + 3)$
31. $8x^3 + 64x^2 - 20x - 160$ $4(2x^2 - 5)(x + 8)$
32. $cd^4 - c^7d^6$ $cd^4(1 - c^3d)(1 + c^3d)$
33. $100x^2 - 80x + 16$ $4(5x - 2)^2$
34. $7m^8 - 7$ $7(m^4 + 1)(m^2 + 1)(m + 1)(m - 1)$

FOCUS ON ACT

The ACT Mathematics test booklet usually has writing space for scratch work. If not, the administrator of the test should have blank paper for you to use. The scratch work is for your use only. Be sure to transfer your final answer to the answer sheet.

If you are unsure how to solve a problem, look through the answer choices. They may provide you with a clue to the solution method. It may take longer to work backward from the answer choices, so make sure you monitor your time.

You may want to time yourself as you take this practice test. It should take you about 6 minutes to complete.

1. What is the value of $c^2 - d^2$ if $c + d = 7$ and $c - d = -2$?
   - **(A)** -14
   - **(B)** -5
   - **(C)** 5
   - **(D)** 14
   - **(E)** 45

2. Which of the following is the complete factorization of $6a^3b + 3a^2b^3$?
   - **(F)** $6a^3b^3$
   - **(G)** $9a^5b^4$
   - **(H)** $3ab(2a^2 + ab^2)$
   - **(J)** $3a^2b(2a + b^2)$
   - **(K)** $(6a^3b)(3a^2b^3)$

3. Which of the following is a factor of $x^2 + 3x - 18$?
   - **(A)** $x + 2$
   - **(B)** $x + 3$
   - **(C)** $x + 6$
   - **(D)** $x + 9$
   - **(E)** $x + 18$

4. The binomial $x - 3$ is NOT a factor of which of the following trinomials?
   - **(F)** $2x^2 - x - 3$
   - **(G)** $2x^2 - 5x - 3$
   - **(H)** $2x^2 - 8x + 6$
   - **(J)** $3x^2 - 6x - 9$
   - **(K)** $3x^2 - 10x + 3$

5. For what value of n is $4x^2 + 20x + n^2 = (2x + n)^2$ true for any real number x?
   - **(A)** 4
   - **(B)** 5
   - **(C)** 8
   - **(D)** 10
   - **(E)** 25

6. What is the factored form of $x^2 + \frac{2x}{3} + \frac{x}{2} + \frac{2}{6}$?
   - **(F)** $\left(x + \frac{1}{3}\right)\left(x + \frac{1}{2}\right)$
   - **(G)** $\left(x + \frac{1}{2}\right)\left(x + \frac{2}{3}\right)$
   - **(H)** $\left(x + \frac{2}{3}\right)\left(x + \frac{1}{6}\right)$
   - **(J)** $(x + 2)\left(x + \frac{1}{3}\right)$
   - **(K)** $\left(x + \frac{1}{3}\right)\left(x + \frac{2}{3}\right)$

COLLEGE ENTRANCE EXAM PRACTICE CHAPTER 8

Organizer

Objective: Provide practice for college entrance exams such as the ACT.

Online Edition

Resources

College Entrance Exam Practice

Questions on the ACT represent the following content areas:

Pre-Algebra, 23%
Elementary Algebra, 17%
Intermediate Algebra, 15%
Coordinate Geometry, 15%
Plane Geometry, 23%
Trigonometry, 7%

Items on this page focus on:
- Elementary Algebra

Text References:

Item	1	2	3	4	5	6
Lesson	8-5	8-1	8-3	8-4	8-5	8-2

Teaching Tip

Multiple Choice

1. Students who chose **B** may have added the values of the factors instead of multiplying them. Students who chose **E** squared the value of each factor and subtracted the results.
2. Students who chose **H** found a factored form of the expression but did not find the greatest common factor to obtain the complete factorization. Remind students to check for any remaining common factors once they think they are done factoring.
3. Students who chose **B** may have factored the polynomial with the correct numerical values but the incorrect signs, i.e., as $(x + 3)(x - 6)$.
4. Students may spend too much time on this item if they try to factor each answer choice. Suggest that students start by considering the form of the unknown factor, given the coefficient of the x^2-term in each choice, and then use the constant term of the trinomial to find a possible constant term of the unknown factor.
5. Students who chose **E** found the value of n^2 instead of n. Students who chose **D** may have mistakenly thought that the middle term is twice the product of the terms of the squared binomial.
6. Students who did not choose **G** should check their work by multiplying the factors and seeing whether their answer matches the given expression.

Organizer

Objective: Provide opportunities to learn and practice common test-taking strategies.

Teaching Tip **Any Question Type** This Strategy for Success describes how to use key words and context clues to translate a word problem into a mathematical equation or expression. Encourage students to refer to the table as they answer the questions.

Any Question Type: Translate Words to Math

When reading a word problem, look for actions and context clues to help you translate the words into a mathematical equation or expression.

Some actions, such as those shown in this table, imply certain mathematical operations.

Action	Math Operation
Combining, increasing	Addition
Decreasing, reducing	Subtraction
Increasing or decreasing by a factor	Multiplication
Separating	Division

EXAMPLE 1

Short Response The polynomial $x^2 + 7x + 12$ represents the area of a rectangle in square meters. The width is $(x + 3)$ meters. Find the combined measure of the length and the width.

Use actions and context clues to translate the words into equations.

$x^2 + 7x + 12$ represents the **area of a rectangle** in square meters.
$x^2 + 7x + 12 \quad = \quad A$

The width is $(x + 3)$ meters.
$w = (x + 3)$

Find the **combined measure** of the **length** and the width.
$m = \ell + w$

Now use the equations to solve the problem.

$A = \ell w$	*Write the formula for area of a rectangle.*
$x^2 + 7x + 12 = \ell(x + 3)$	*Substitute $x^2 + 7x + 12$ for A and $(x + 3)$ for w.*
$(x + \boxed{?})(x + 3)$	*Factor $x^2 + 7x + 12$ to find an expression for the length.*
$(x + 4)(x + 3)$	*$3(4) = 12$; $3 + 4 = 7$*

The length is $(x + 4)$.

$m = \ell + w$	*Write the equation for the combined measure of the length and width.*
$m = (x + 4) + (x + 3)$	*Substitute $(x + 4)$ for ℓ and $(x + 3)$ for w.*
$m = 2x + 7$	*Combine like terms.*

The combined measure of the length and width is $(2x + 7)$ meters.

Sometimes you cannot write an expression or equation in the order that the actions appear. For example, the expression "4 years younger than Maria" is written mathematically as $m - 4$.

Read each test item and answer the questions that follow.

Item A
Short Response The width of Alvin's rectangular mural is 6 times the length x. Alvin plans to make a new mural with an area of $(6x^2 - 24x + 24)$ square meters. By how much did Alvin decrease the area of the mural? Show your work.

1. What important words or context clues are in the first sentence of the test item? Use these clues to write an expression that represents the width of the rectangle.
2. Write an equation to represent the area of Alvin's first mural.
3. What math operation does the action *decrease* represent?

Item B
Multiple Choice Which factored expression represents the phrase shown below?

the square of the number of hours it takes to empty a cistern minus 20 times the number of hours plus 64

Ⓐ $(h - 16)(h - 4)$
Ⓒ $(h - 8)(h - 8)$
Ⓑ $(h^2 - 20)(h - 64)$
Ⓓ $(h - 16)(h + 4)$

4. Which word in the phrase tells you to use an exponent in your expression?
5. What is the unknown value in the expression? Define a variable to represent this value.
6. Identify other action words and the mathematical operation phrase each one represents.

Item C
Multiple Choice A company owns two packaging plants. The polynomial $0.05x^2 + 16x - 9400$ models one plant's profit, where x is the number of units packaged. The polynomial $-0.01x^2 + 17x - 5400$ models the other plant's profit. If x is 25,000, what is the total profit of both plants?

Ⓐ –\$5,830,300
Ⓑ \$25,810,200
Ⓒ \$31,640,500
Ⓓ \$37,471,000

7. What mathematical symbol does the action *models* represent?
8. Write an equation for each plant that can be used to determine its profit P.
9. What mathematical operation does the term "total profit" represent?

Item D
Gridded Response One of the bases of a trapezoid is 12 meters greater than its height. The other base is 4 meters less than its height. Find the area of the trapezoid when the height is 6 meters.

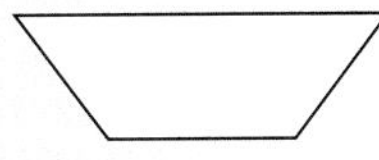

10. Identify the unknown dimension, and assign it a variable.
11. A student is unsure how many bases a trapezoid has. Identify the context clues that can help this student.
12. Make a list of the actions in the problem, and link each word to its mathematical meaning.
13. Write an expression for each base of the trapezoid.

Answers

1. *is, times*; $w = 6x$
2. $A = 6x^2$
3. subtraction
4. *square*
5. the number of hours; h
6. *minus* represents subtraction; *plus* represents addition
7. equal sign
8. $P_1 = 0.05x^2 + 16x - 9400$; $P_2 = -0.01x^2 + 17x - 5400$
9. addition
10. height; h
11. "One of the bases"; "the other base"; these clues show that there are 2 bases.
12. *Is* means "equals." *More than* represents addition. *Less than* represents subtraction.
13. $b_1 = h + 12$; $b_2 = h - 4$

Answers to Test Items

A. $(24x - 24)$ m^2
B. A
C. B
D. 60 m^2

California Standards
11.0

CHAPTER 8 MASTERING THE STANDARDS

Organizer

Objective: Provide review and practice for Chapters 1–8.

PREMIER Online Edition

Resources

Assessment Resources

Chapter 8 Cumulative Test

Focus on California Standards Benchmark Tests and Intervention

California Standards Practice CD-ROM

go.hrw.com
KEYWORD: MA8CA Practice

CHAPTER 8

MASTERING THE STANDARDS

go.hrw.com
Standards Practice Online
KEYWORD: MA8CA Practice

CUMULATIVE ASSESSMENT, CHAPTERS 1–8

Multiple Choice

1. A rectangle has an area of $(x^2 + 5x - 24)$ square units. Which of the following are possible expressions for the length and the width of the rectangle?

Ⓐ Length: $(x - 24)$ units; width: $(x + 1)$ units

Ⓑ Length: $(x - 4)$ units; width: $(x + 6)$ units

Ⓒ Length: $(x - 3)$ units; width: $(x + 8)$ units

Ⓓ Length: $(x + 12)$ units; width: $(x - 2)$ units

2. Which property of real numbers is used to transform the equation in Step 1 into the equation in Step 2?

Step 1: $4(x - 5) + 8 = 88$
Step 2: $4x - 20 + 8 = 88$
Step 3: $4x - 12 = 88$
Step 4: $4x = 100$
Step 5: $4x = 25$

Ⓐ Commutative Property of Multiplication

Ⓑ Associative Property of Multiplication

Ⓒ Multiplication Property

Ⓓ Distributive Property

3. If $\frac{2}{3}x - 9 = 3$, what is the value of the expression $8x - 3$?

Ⓐ -75 Ⓒ 61

Ⓑ -35 Ⓓ 141

4. Carlos and Bonita were just hired at a manufacturing plant. Carlos will earn $12.50 per hour. He will receive a hiring bonus of $300. Bonita will not get a hiring bonus, but she will earn $14.50 per hour. Which equation can you use to determine the number of hours *h* when both employees will have earned the same total amount?

Ⓐ $300 + 14.50h = 12.50h$

Ⓑ $14.50h + 300 = 12.50h$

Ⓒ $14.50h + 12.50h = 300$

Ⓓ $300 + 12.50h = 14.50h$

5. Which of the following expressions is equivalent to $x^2 - 8x + 16$?

Ⓐ $(x + 4)^2$ Ⓒ $(x + 8)(x + 2)$

Ⓑ $(x + 4)(x - 4)$ Ⓓ $(x - 4)^2$

6. Michael claims that the whole numbers are closed under subtraction. Stephanie disagrees. Which equation can Stephanie use as a counterexample to show that Michael's claim is false?

Ⓐ $6 - 4 = 2$

Ⓑ $-3 - 8 = -11$

Ⓒ $4 - 5 = -1$

Ⓓ $7 - (-2) = 9$

7. What is the value of *y* if the line through $(1, -1)$ and $(2, 2)$ is parallel to the line through $(-2, 1)$ and $(-1, y)$?

Ⓐ -8 Ⓒ 3

Ⓑ -2 Ⓓ 4

8. Which of the following shows the complete factorization of $2x^3 + 4x^2 - 6x$?

Ⓐ $(2x^2 - 2x)(x + 3)$

Ⓑ $2x(x^2 + 2x - 3)$

Ⓒ $2x(x - 1)(x + 3)$

Ⓓ $2(x^3 + 2x^2 - 3x)$

9. Which graph shows the solution set of the compound inequality $-9 \le 5 - 2x \le 13$?

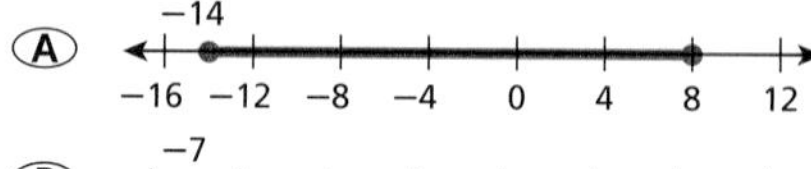

Teaching Tip **Multiple Choice** For **Item 7,** students may have trouble finding the equation of a line parallel to another line. If students chose **A,** they may have put a negative number in the x_1 position and forgotten to change subtracting a negative to adding the opposite. If students chose **B,** they may have incorrectly determined the slope of the first line to be −3. If students chose **C,** they chose the slope of the lines instead of the value for *y*.

For **Item 8,** students may not remember to factor all parts of the polynomial completely. If students chose **A,** they did not factor out the GCF from the first binomial. If students chose **B,** they did not factor the trinomial into two binomial factors. If students chose **D,** they did not factor out the GCF from the trinomial or factor the trinomial into two binomial factors.

California Standards

Standard	Items
2.0 🔑	13, 20
5.0 🔑	3, 4, 9
7.0 🔑	17
8.0	7, 16
9.0 🔑	10, 11
11.0	1, 5, 8, 12, 14, 15, 18, 19, 21, 22
24.3	6
25.1	2

Read problems, graphs, and diagrams carefully. If you are allowed to write in your test booklet, underline or circle important words, labels, or other information given in the problem.

10. Which point lies on the graph of both functions?

$f(x) = 2x - 10$
$g(x) = 10 - 2x$

(A) (5, 0)
(B) (1, −8)
(C) (0, 0)
(D) (2, 6)

11. Hayley plans to solve the system of equations below.

$$\begin{cases} x + 3y = 8 \\ 5x - y = 8 \end{cases}$$

Which of the following does NOT show an equation Hayley can use to solve the system of equations?

(A) $x + 3(5x - 8) = 8$
(B) $5(8 - 3y) - y = 8$
(C) $x = 8 - 3y$
(D) $5x - (-x + 8) = 8$

12. Which value of b would make $x^2 + bx - 2$ factorable?

(A) −2
(B) −1
(C) 0
(D) 3

13. Which expression is equivalent to $xy \cdot \left(x^3y^{\frac{1}{2}}\right)^4$?

(A) $x^4y^{\frac{3}{2}}$
(B) $x^{16}y^6$
(C) $x^{13}y^3$
(D) $x^8y^{\frac{11}{2}}$

Gridded Response

14. The complete factorization of $-12x^3 + 14x^2 + 6x$ is $-2x(ax + 1)(2x - 3)$. What is the value of a? **3**

15. The expression $x^2 + x + b$ is a perfect-square trinomial. What is the value of b? $\frac{1}{4}$

16. What is the slope of a line that is perpendicular to the line described by $2y + 5x = 6$? $\frac{2}{5}$

17. The point $(3, k)$ lies on the line $3x - 4y = 7$. What is the value of k? $\frac{1}{2}$

Short Response

18. The area of a certain circle is $\pi(9x^2 + 6x + 1)$ square centimeters. Find an expression for the length of the circle's radius. Explain how you found your answer.

19. A rectangle has an area of $(x^2 - 25)$ square feet.
   a. Use factoring to write possible expressions for the length and width of the rectangle.
   b. Use your expressions from part **a** to write an expression for the perimeter of the rectangle. Simplify the expression. $P = 4x$ **ft**
   c. Use your expressions from parts **a** and **b** to find the perimeter and the area of the rectangle when $x = 10$ feet. Show your work.
   $P = 40$ ft; $A = 75$ ft²

20. Write the numbers 57,000,000,000 and 19,000 in scientific notation. Then show how to divide 57,000,000,000 by 19,000 using properties of exponents.

21. Show that you can factor the expression $x^2y - 12 + 3y - 4x^2$ by grouping in two different ways.

Extended Response

22. The diagram below can be used to show that the expression $(a + b)^2$ is equivalent to the expression $a^2 + 2ab + b^2$.

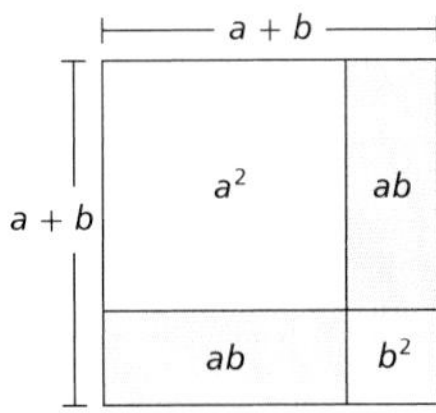

   a. Make a diagram similar to the one above to model the expression $(a + b + c)^2$. Label each distinct area.
   b. Use the labels from your diagram to write an expression equivalent to $(a + b + c)^2$.
   c. Show that your expression in part **b** is equivalent to $(a + b + c)^2$ by evaluating each expression for $a = 4$, $b = 2$, and $c = 1$.
   d. Factor $x^2 + y^2 + 9 + 2xy + 6x + 6y$. Show or explain how you found your answer.

22d. $(x + y + 3)^2$**; check students' work.**

Short-Response Rubric

Items 18–21

2 Points = The student's answer is an accurate and complete execution of the task or tasks.

1 Point = The student's answer contains attributes of an appropriate response but is flawed.

0 Points = The student's answer contains no attributes of an appropriate response.

Extended-Response Rubric

Item 22

4 Points = The student correctly draws and labels a diagram in part **a,** writes a correct expression in part **b,** correctly evaluates the expression in part **c,** and correctly factors in part **d** with an explanation.

3 Points = The student correctly draws and labels a diagram in part **a** and writes a correct expression in part **b** but does not show any work or give an explanation for part **c** or part **d.**

2 Points = The student answers all parts correctly but does not show any work or explanation, or the student correctly answers parts **a** and **b** but does not correctly answer parts **c** and **d.**

1 Point = The student draws and labels a diagram in part **a** but does not correctly answer other parts of the problem, or the student attempts to answer all parts of the problem but does not correctly answer any part.

0 Points = The student does not answer correctly or does not attempt all parts of the problem.

Answers

18. $A = \pi r^2 = (9x^2 + 6x + 1)\pi = (3x + 1)^2\pi$, so $r = (3x + 1)$ cm

19a. $\ell = (x + 5)$ ft; $w = (x - 5)$ ft

20. 5.7×10^{10}; 1.9×10^4; $\frac{5.7 \times 10^{10}}{1.9 \times 10^4} = \left(\frac{5.7}{1.9}\right) \times 10^{10-4} = 3 \times 10^6$

21. (1) $x^2y - 12 + 3y - 4x^2 =$
$(x^2y - 4x^2) + (3y - 12) =$
$x^2(y - 4) + 3(y - 4) =$
$(x^2 + 3)(y - 4)$

(2) $x^2y - 12 + 3y - 4x^2 =$
$(x^2y + 3y) + (-4x^2 - 12) =$
$y(x^2 + 3) - 4(x^2 + 3) =$
$(y - 4)(x^2 + 3)$

22a.

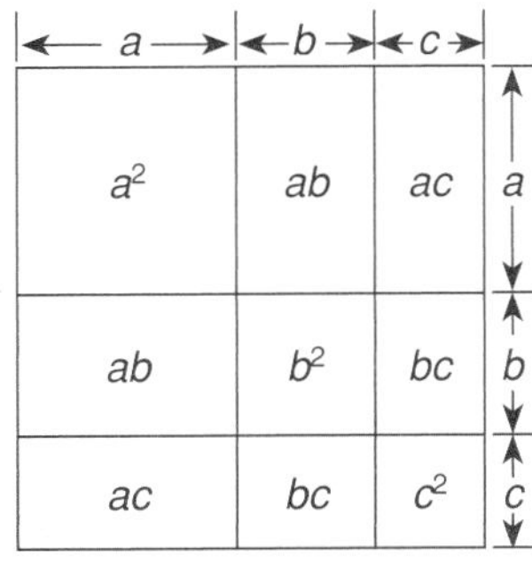

b. $a^2 + 2ab + b^2 + 2ac + 2bc + c^2$

c. Both expressions should equal 49.

Quadratic Functions and Equations

✔	Grade-level Standard
◄	Review
►	Beyond the Standards
A	Assessment
O	Optional

Pacing Guide

Calendar Planner
Teacher's **One-Stop** Planner®

Lesson/Lab		California Standards	Time	Advanced Students	Benchmark Students	Strategic Students
9-1	Quadratic Equations and Functions	7.0, 17.0, 21.0	50 min	✔	✔	✔
LAB	Explore the Axis of Symmetry	24.1	25 min	✔	✔	O
9-2	Factoring by GCF	21.0, 23.0	50 min	✔	✔	✔
9-3	Graphing Quadratic Funtions	21.0, 23.0	75 min	✔	✔	✔
Concept Connection		21.0, 23.0	25 min	A	A	O
Ready to Go On?			25 min	A	A	A
9-4	Solving Quadratic Equations by Graphing	21.0, 23.0	50 min	✔	✔	✔
LAB	Explore Roots, Zeros, and *x*-Intercepts	21.0	25 min	✔	✔	✔
9-5	Solving Quadratic Equations by Factoring	14.0, 23.0	50 min	✔	✔	✔
9-6	Solving Quadratic Equations by Using Square Roots	2.0, 23.0	50 min	✔	✔	✔
CN	The Distance Formula	Reinforcement of Grade 7 MG3.2	50 min	O	◄	◄
LAB	Model Completing the Square	Preparation for 14.0	25 min	O	✔	✔
9-7	Completing the Square	2.0, 14.0, 23.0	50 min	✔	✔	✔
9-8	The Quadratic Formula	19.0, 20.0	50 min	✔	✔	✔
9-8	The Discriminant	22.0, 23.0	50 min	✔	✔	✔
Concept Connection		11.0	25 min	A	A	O
Ready to Go On?			25 min	A	A	A
Study Guide: Review			50 min	✔	✔	✔
Chapter Test		11.0	50 min	A	A	A

* **Benchmark students** are achieving at or near grade level.

** **Strategic students** may be a year or more below grade level, and may require additional time for intervention.

Countdown to Mastery, Weeks 17, 18, 19

ONGOING ASSESSMENT and INTERVENTION

	DIAGNOSE	PRESCRIBE
Assess Prior Knowledge	**Before Chapter 9**	
	Diagnose readiness for the chapter.	Prescribe intervention.
	Are You Ready? SE p. 541	***Are You Ready? Intervention*** Skills 6, 64, 67, 69, 80
Formative Assessment	**Before Every Lesson**	
	Diagnose readiness for the lesson.	Prescribe intervention.
	Warm Up TE, every lesson	**Skills Bank** pp. SB1–SB32 **Review for Mastery** CRF Chapters 1–9
	During Every Lesson	
	Diagnose understanding of lesson concepts.	Prescribe intervention.
	Questioning Strategies TE, every example **Check It Out!** SE, every example **Think and Discuss** SE, every lesson **Write About It** SE, every lesson **Journal** TE, every lesson	**Reading Strategies** CRF, every lesson ***Success for ELL*** pp. 131–148 ***Lesson Tutorial Videos*** Chapter 9
	After Every Lesson	
	Diagnose mastery of lesson concepts.	Prescribe intervention.
	Lesson Quiz TE, every lesson **Alternative Assessment** TE, every lesson **Ready to Go On?** SE pp. 567, 611 ***Test and Practice Generator***	**Review for Mastery** CRF, every lesson **Problem Solving** CRF, every lesson ***Ready to Go On? Intervention*** Chapter 9 ***Homework Help Online***
	Before Chapter 9 Testing	
	Diagnose mastery of concepts in the chapter.	Prescribe intervention.
	Ready to Go On? SE pp. 567, 611 **Concept Connection** SE pp. 566, 610 **Section Quizzes** AR pp. 165–166 ***Test and Practice Generator***	***Ready to Go On? Intervention*** Chapter 9 **Scaffolding Questions** TE pp. 566, 610
	Before Assessment of California Standards	
	Diagnose mastery of California Standards.	Prescribe intervention.
	 ***Focus on California Standards: Benchmark Tests*** **Mastering the Standards** SE pp. 620–621 ***California Standards Practice* CD-ROM**	 ***Focus on California Standards: Intervention***
Summative Assessment	**After Chapter 9**	
	Check mastery of chapter concepts.	Prescribe intervention.
	Multiple-Choice Tests (Forms A, B, C) **Free-Response Tests (Forms A, B, C)** **Performance Assessment** AR pp. 179–180 ***Test and Practice Generator***	**Review for Mastery** CRF, every lesson ***Lesson Tutorial Videos*** Chapter 9

KEY: **SE** = *Student Edition* **TE** = *Teacher's Edition* **CRF** = *Chapter Resource File* **AR** = *Assessment Resources* Available online Available on CD-ROM

Supporting the Teacher

Chapter 9 Resource File

Family Involvement
pp. 1–4, 29–32

Practice A, B, C
pp. 5–7, 13–15, 21–23, 33–35, 41–43, 49–51, 57–59, 65–67, 73–75

Review for Mastery
pp. 8–9, 16–17, 24–25, 36–37, 44–45, 52–53, 60–61, 68–69, 76–77

Challenge
pp. 10, 18, 26, 38, 46, 54, 62, 70, 78

Problem Solving
pp. 11, 19, 27, 39, 47, 55, 63, 71, 79

Reading Strategies ELL
pp. 12, 20, 28, 40, 48, 56, 64, 72, 80

Algebra Lab
pp. 81–90

Workbooks

Homework and Practice Workbook 
Teacher's Edition .... pp. 56–64

Know-It Notebook SPANISH
Teacher's Guide .... Chapter 9

Review for Mastery Workbook SPANISH
Teacher's Guide .... pp. 111–128

Focus on California Standards: Intervention Workbook SPANISH
Teacher's Guide

Teacher Tools

Power Presentations
Complete PowerPoint® presentations for Chapter 9 lessons

Lesson Tutorial Videos 
Holt authors Ed Burger and Freddie Renfro present tutorials to support the Chapter 9 lessons.

Teacher's One-Stop Planner SPANISH
Easy access to all Chapter 9 resources and assessments, as well as software for lesson planning, test generation, and puzzle creation

IDEA Works!
Key Chapter 9 resources and assessments modified to address special learning needs

Solutions Key .... Chapter 9

Interactive Answers and Solutions

TechKeys

Lab Resources

Project Teacher Support 

Parent Resources

Transparencies

Lesson Transparencies, Volume 2 .... Chapter 9
- Teacher Tools
- Warm-ups
- Teaching Transparencies
- Lesson Quizzes

Alternate Openers: Explorations .... pp. 56–64

Countdown to Mastery .... pp. 38–43

Know-It Notebook .... Chapter 9
- Vocabulary
- Key Concepts
- Graphic Organizers
- Chapter Review
- Big Ideas

Technology Highlights for the Teacher

 **Power Presentations**

Dynamic presentations to engage students. Complete PowerPoint® presentations for every lesson in Chapter 9.

2-1 Solving One-Step Equations

Isolate a variable by using inverse operations which "undo" operations on the variable.

An equation is like a balanced scale. To keep the balance, perform the same operation on both sides.

Inverse Operations	
Operation	**Inverse Operation**
Addition	Subtraction
Subtraction	Addition

One-Stop Planner SPANISH

Easy access to Chapter 9 resources and assessments. Includes lesson planning, test generation, and puzzle creation software.

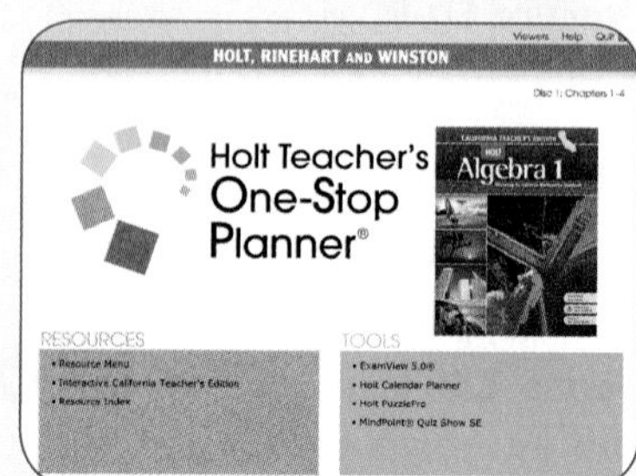

 **Premier Online Edition** 

Includes Tutorial Videos, Lesson Activities, Lesson Quizzes, Homework Help, Chapter Project and more.

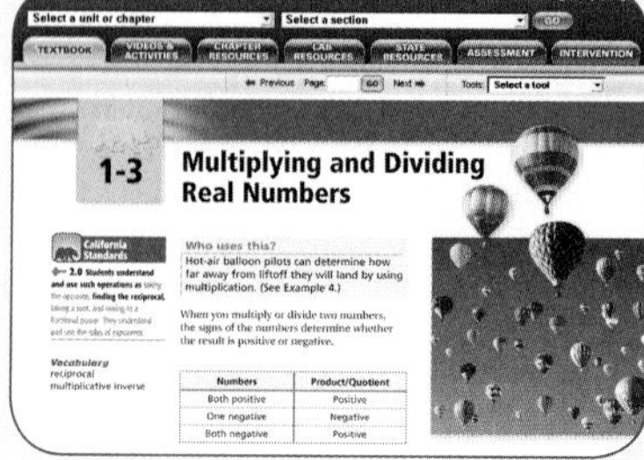

KEY: **SE** = *Student Edition* **TE** = *Teacher's Edition*  English Language Learners  Spanish available  Available online  Available on CD-ROM

Universal Access

Teaching Tips to help all students appear throughout the chapter. A few that target specific students are included in the lists below.

Strategic Students

Practice A	CRF, every lesson
Review for Mastery	CRF, every lesson
Reading Strategies	CRF, every lesson
Academic Vocabulary Connections	TE p. 542
Modeling	TE pp. 545, 554, 561
Questioning Strategies	TE, every example
Ready to Go On? Intervention	Chapter 9
Know-It Notebook SPANISH	Chapter 9
Homework Help Online	
Lesson Tutorial Videos SPANISH	
Online Interactivities SPANISH	

Special Needs Students

Practice A	CRF, every lesson
Review for Mastery	CRF, every lesson
Reading Strategies	CRF, every lesson
Academic Vocabulary Connections	TE p. 542
Inclusion	TE pp. 550, 556, 564, 593, 596, 600
IDEA Works! Modified Resources	Chapter 9
Ready to Go On? Intervention	Chapter 9
Know-It Notebook SPANISH	Chapter 9
Lesson Tutorial Videos SPANISH	
Online Interactivities SPANISH	

English Learners

ENGLISH LANGUAGE LEARNERS

Reading Strategies	CRF, every lesson
Vocabulary Exercises	SE, every exercise set
Academic Vocabulary Connections	TE p. 542
English Language Learners	TE p. 546
Language Support	TE pp. 546, 580
Success for English Language Learners	Chapter 9
Know-It Notebook SPANISH	Chapter 9
Multilingual Glossary	
Lesson Tutorial Videos SPANISH	

Benchmark Students

Practice B	CRF, every lesson
Problem Solving	CRF, every lesson
Academic Vocabulary Connections	TE p. 542
Questioning Strategies	TE, every example
Ready to Go On? Intervention	Chapter 9
Know-It Notebook SPANISH	Chapter 9
Homework Help Online	
Online Interactivities SPANISH	

Advanced Students

Practice C	CRF, every lesson
Challenge	CRF, every lesson
Reading and Writing Math EXTENSION	TE p. 543
Concept Connection EXTENSION	TE pp. 566, 610
Advanced Learners/GATE	TE pp. 570, 577
Ready to Go On? Enrichment	Chapter 9

Technology Highlights for Universal Access

Lesson Tutorial Videos SPANISH

Starring Holt authors Ed Burger and Freddie Renfro! Live tutorials to support every lesson in Chapter 9.

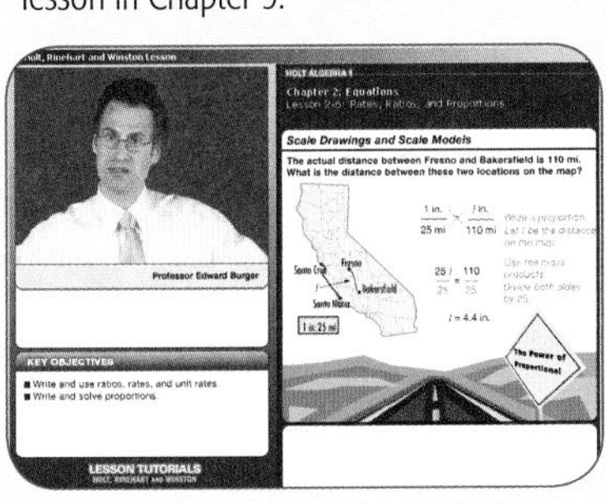

Multilingual Glossary

Searchable glossary includes definitions in English, Spanish, Vietnamese, Chinese, Hmong, Korean, and other languages.

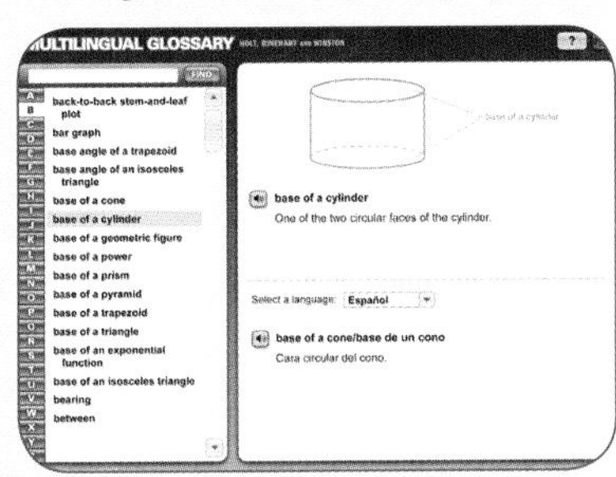

Online Interactivities SPANISH

Interactive tutorials provide visually engaging alternative opportunities to learn concepts and master skills.

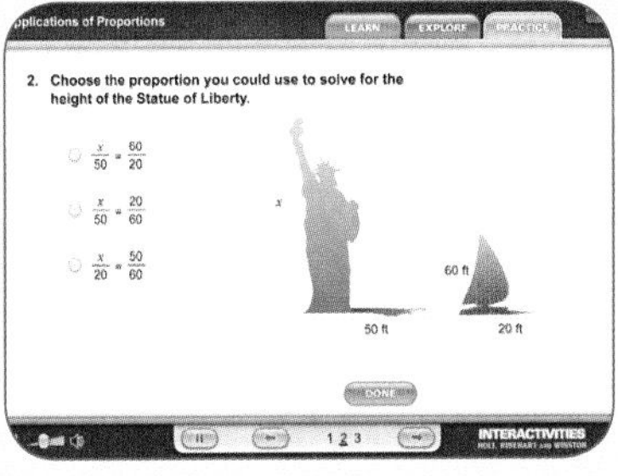

KEY: **SE** = *Student Edition* **TE** = *Teacher's Edition* **CRF** = *Chapter Resource File* SPANISH Spanish available 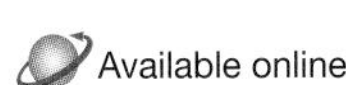 Available online  Available on CD-ROM

Ongoing Assessment

Assessing Prior Knowledge

Determine whether students have the prerequisite concepts and skills for success in Chapter 9.

Are You Ready? SPANISH .... SE p. 541
Warm Up .... TE, every lesson

Chapter and Standards Assessment

Provide review and practice for Chapter 9 and standards mastery.

Concept Connection .... SE pp. 566, 610
Study Guide: Review .... SE pp. 612–615
Strategies for Success .... SE pp. 618–619
Mastering the Standards .... SE pp. 620–621
College Entrance Exam Practice .... SE p. 617
***Countdown to Mastery* Transparencies** .... pp. 38–43
Focus on California Standards: Benchmark Tests
Focus on California Standards: Intervention Workbook
***California Standards Practice* CD-ROM** SPANISH
IDEA Works! Modified Worksheets and Tests

Alternative Assessment

Assess students' understanding of Chapter 9 concepts and combined problem-solving skills.

Alternative Assessment .... TE, every lesson
Performance Assessment .... AR pp. 179–180
Portfolio Assessment .... AR p. xxxiii
Chapter 9 Project

Daily Assessment

Provide formative assessment for each day of Chapter 9.

Questioning Strategies .... TE, every example
Think and Discuss .... SE, every lesson
Check It Out! Exercises .... SE, every example
Write About It .... SE, every lesson
Journal .... TE, every lesson
Lesson Quiz .... TE, every lesson
Alternative Assessment .... TE, every lesson
IDEA Works! Modified Lesson Quizzes .... Chapter 9

Weekly Assessment

Provide formative assessment for each week of Chapter 9.

Concept Connection .... SE pp. 566, 610
Ready to Go On? .... SE pp. 567, 611
Cumulative Assessment .... SE pp. 620–621
Test and Practice Generator SPANISH .... *One-Stop Planner*

Formal Assessment

Provide summative assessment of Chapter 9 mastery.

Section Quizzes .... AR pp. 165–166
Chapter 9 Test SPANISH .... SE p. 616
Chapter Test (Levels A, B, C) .... AR pp. 167–178
• Multiple Choice • Free Response
Cumulative Test .... AR pp. 181–184
Test and Practice Generator SPANISH .... *One-Stop Planner*

Technology Highlights for Ongoing Assessment

Are You Ready? SPANISH

Automatically assess readiness and prescribe intervention for Chapter 9 prerequisite skills.

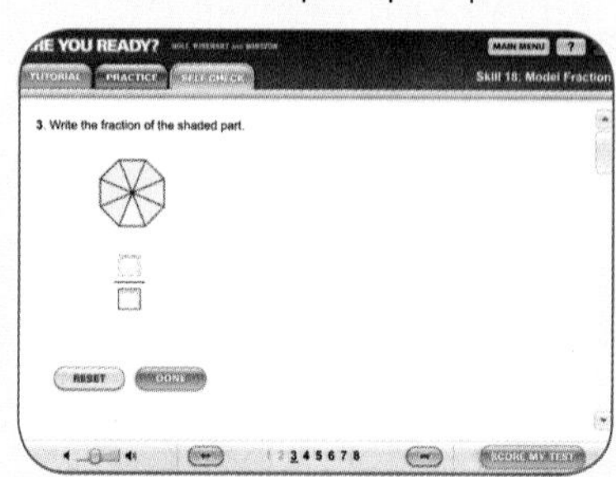

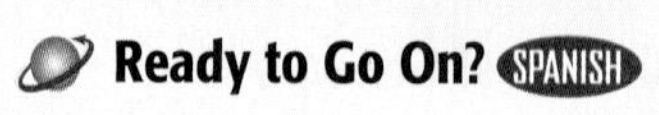

Ready to Go On? SPANISH

Automatically assess understanding of and prescribe intervention for Sections 9A and 9B.

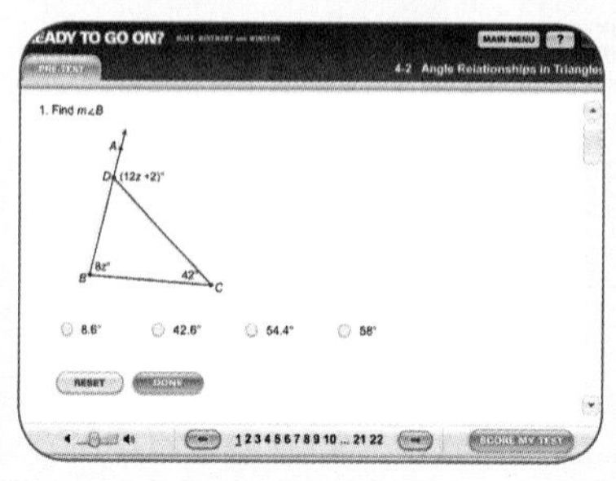

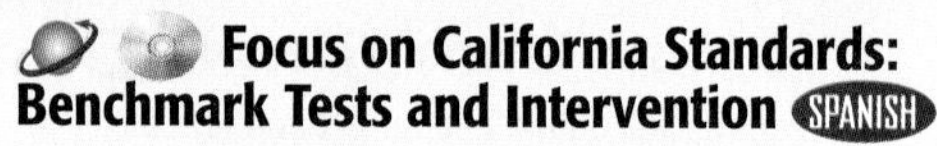

Focus on California Standards: Benchmark Tests and Intervention SPANISH

Automatically assess proficiency with California Algebra I Standards and provide intervention.

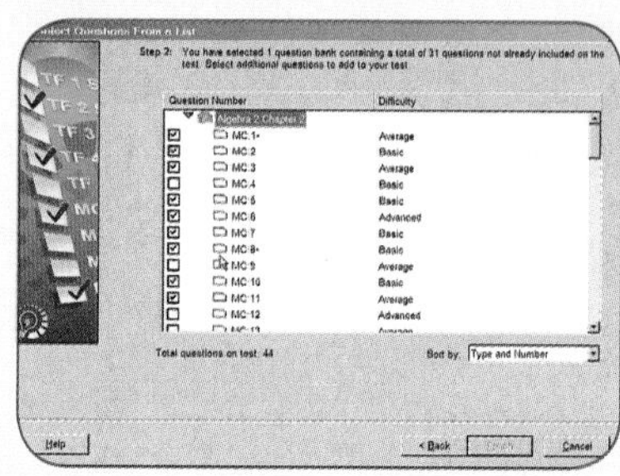

KEY: **SE** = *Student Edition* **TE** = *Teacher's Edition* **AR** = Assessment Resources  Spanish available  Available online  Available on CD-ROM

Three levels (A, B, C) of multiple-choice and free-response chapter tests are available in the *Assessment Resources.*

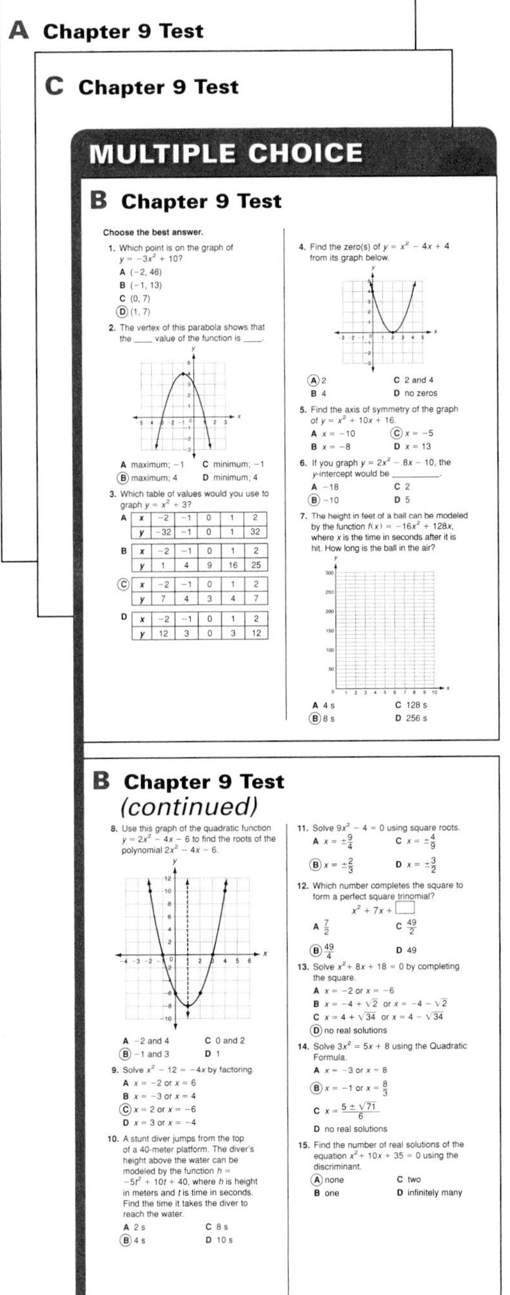

A Chapter 9 Test

C Chapter 9 Test

MULTIPLE CHOICE

B Chapter 9 Test

Choose the best answer.

1. Which point is on the graph of $y = -3x^2 + 10$?
A $(-2, 46)$
B $(-1, 13)$
C $(0, 7)$
Ⓓ $(1, 7)$

2. The vertex of this parabola shows that the ____ value of the function is ____.
A maximum; −1
C minimum; −1
Ⓑ maximum; 4
D minimum; 4

3. Which table of values would you use to graph $y = x^2 + 3$?

A

x	−2	−1	0	1	2
y	−32	−1	0	1	32

B

x	−2	−1	0	1	2
y	1	4	9	16	25

Ⓒ

x	−2	−1	0	1	2
y	7	4	3	4	7

D

x	−2	−1	0	1	2
y	12	3	0	3	12

4. Find the zero(s) of $y = x^2 - 4x + 4$ from its graph below.
Ⓐ 2
C 2 and 4
B 4
D no zeros

5. Find the axis of symmetry of the graph of $y = x^2 + 10x + 16$.
A $x = -10$
Ⓒ $x = -5$
B $x = -8$
D $x = 13$

6. If you graph $y = 2x^2 - 8x - 10$, the y-intercept would be ____.
A −18
C 2
Ⓑ −10
D 5

7. The height in feet of a ball can be modeled by the function $f(x) = -16x^2 + 128x$, where x is the time in seconds after it is hit. How long is the ball in the air?
A 4 s
C 128 s
Ⓑ 8 s
D 256 s

B Chapter 9 Test (continued)

8. Use this graph of the quadratic function $y = 2x^2 - 4x - 6$ to find the roots of the polynomial $2x^2 - 4x - 6$.
A −2 and 4
C 0 and 2
Ⓑ −1 and 3
D 1

9. Solve $x^2 - 12 = -4x$ by factoring.
A $x = -2$ or $x = 6$
B $x = -3$ or $x = 4$
Ⓒ $x = 2$ or $x = -6$
D $x = 3$ or $x = -4$

10. A stunt diver jumps from the top of a 40-meter platform. The diver's height above the water can be modeled by the function $h = -5t^2 + 10t + 40$, where h is height in meters and t is time in seconds. Find the time it takes the diver to reach the water.
A 2 s
C 8 s
Ⓑ 4 s
D 10 s

11. Solve $9x^2 - 4 = 0$ using square roots.
A $x = \pm\frac{9}{4}$
C $x = \pm\frac{4}{9}$
Ⓑ $x = \pm\frac{2}{3}$
D $x = \pm\frac{3}{2}$

12. Which number completes the square to form a perfect square trinomial? $x^2 + 7x + \square$
A $\frac{7}{2}$
C $\frac{49}{2}$
Ⓑ $\frac{49}{4}$
D 49

13. Solve $x^2 + 8x + 18 = 0$ by completing the square.
A $x = -2$ or $x = -6$
B $x = -4 + \sqrt{2}$ or $x = -4 - \sqrt{2}$
C $x = 4 + \sqrt{34}$ or $x = 4 - \sqrt{34}$
Ⓓ no real solutions

14. Solve $3x^2 = 5x + 8$ using the Quadratic Formula.
A $x = -3$ or $x = 8$
Ⓑ $x = -1$ or $x = \frac{8}{3}$
C $x = \frac{5 \pm \sqrt{71}}{6}$
D no real solutions

15. Find the number of real solutions of the equation $x^2 + 10x + 35 = 0$ using the discriminant.
Ⓐ none
C two
B one
D infinitely many

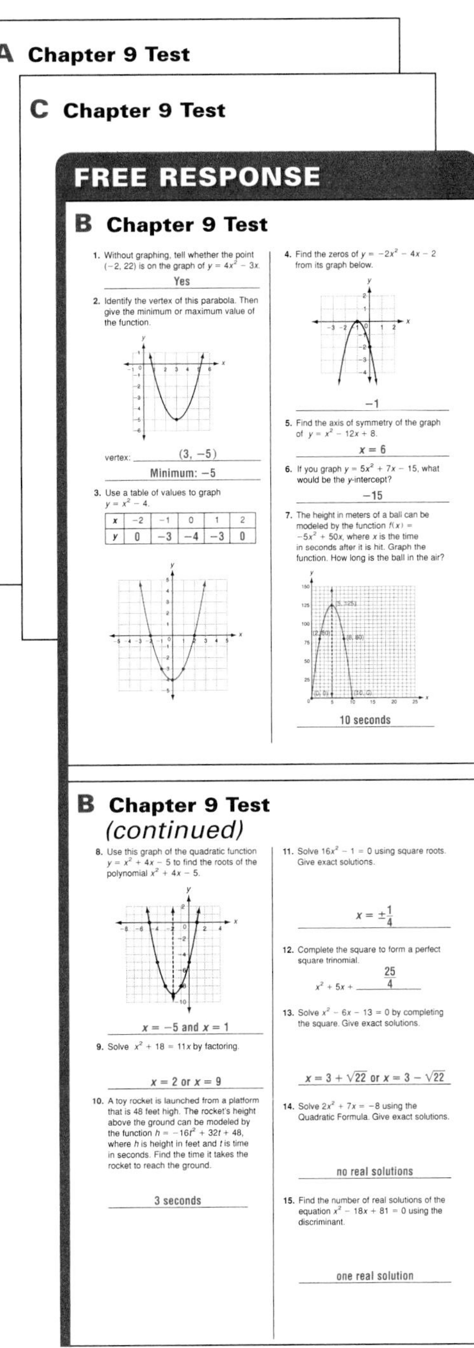

A Chapter 9 Test

C Chapter 9 Test

FREE RESPONSE

B Chapter 9 Test

1. Without graphing, tell whether the point $(-2, 22)$ is on the graph of $y = 4x^2 - 3x$.
Yes

2. Identify the vertex of this parabola. Then give the minimum or maximum value of the function.
vertex: $(3, -5)$
Minimum: −5

3. Use a table of values to graph $y = x^2 - 4$.

x	−2	−1	0	1	2
y	0	−3	−4	−3	0

4. Find the zeros of $y = -2x^2 - 4x - 2$ from its graph below.
−1

5. Find the axis of symmetry of the graph of $y = x^2 - 12x + 8$.
$x = 6$

6. If you graph $y = 5x^2 + 7x - 15$, what would be the y-intercept?
−15

7. The height in meters of a ball can be modeled by the function $f(x) = -5x^2 + 50x$, where x is the time in seconds after it is hit. Graph the function. How long is the ball in the air?
10 seconds

B Chapter 9 Test (continued)

8. Use this graph of the quadratic function $y = x^2 + 4x - 5$ to find the roots of the polynomial $x^2 + 4x - 5$.
$x = -5$ and $x = 1$

9. Solve $x^2 + 18 = 11x$ by factoring.
$x = 2$ or $x = 9$

10. A toy rocket is launched from a platform that is 48 feet high. The rocket's height above the ground can be modeled by the function $h = -16t^2 + 32t + 48$, where h is height in feet and t is time in seconds. Find the time it takes the rocket to reach the ground.
3 seconds

11. Solve $16x^2 - 1 = 0$ using square roots. Give exact solutions.
$x = \pm\frac{1}{4}$

12. Complete the square to form a perfect square trinomial.
$x^2 + 5x + \frac{25}{4}$

13. Solve $x^2 - 6x - 13 = 0$ by completing the square. Give exact solutions.
$x = 3 + \sqrt{22}$ or $x = 3 - \sqrt{22}$

14. Solve $2x^2 + 7x = -8$ using the Quadratic Formula. Give exact solutions.
no real solutions

15. Find the number of real solutions of the equation $x^2 - 18x + 81 = 0$ using the discriminant.
one real solution

Modified tests and worksheets found in *IDEA Works!*

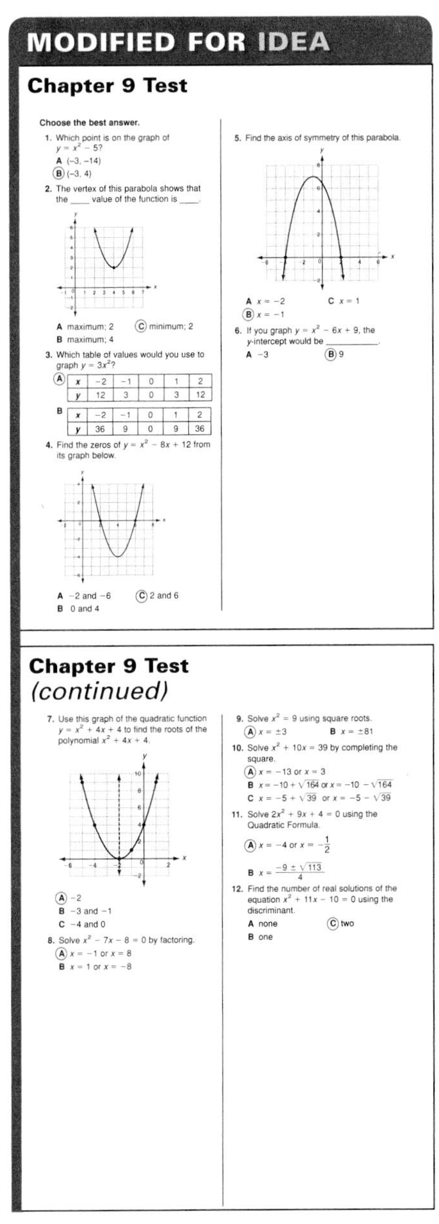

MODIFIED FOR IDEA

Chapter 9 Test

Choose the best answer.

1. Which point is on the graph of $y = x^2 - 5$?
A $(-3, -14)$
Ⓑ $(-3, 4)$

2. The vertex of this parabola shows that the ____ value of the function is ____.
A maximum; 2
Ⓒ minimum; 2
B maximum; 4

3. Which table of values would you use to graph $y = 3x^2$?

Ⓐ

x	−2	−1	0	1	2
y	12	3	0	3	12

B

x	−2	−1	0	1	2
y	36	9	0	9	36

4. Find the zeros of $y = x^2 - 8x + 12$ from its graph below.
A −2 and −6
Ⓒ 2 and 6
B 0 and 4

5. Find the axis of symmetry of this parabola.
A $x = -2$
C $x = 1$
Ⓑ $x = -1$

6. If you graph $y = x^2 - 6x + 9$, the y-intercept would be ____.
A −3
Ⓑ 9

Chapter 9 Test (continued)

7. Use this graph of the quadratic function $y = x^2 + 4x + 4$ to find the roots of the polynomial $x^2 + 4x + 4$.
Ⓐ −2
B −3 and −1
C −4 and 0

8. Solve $x^2 - 7x - 8 = 0$ by factoring.
Ⓐ $x = -1$ or $x = 8$
B $x = 1$ or $x = -8$

9. Solve $x^2 = 9$ using square roots.
Ⓐ $x = \pm 3$
B $x = \pm 81$

10. Solve $x^2 + 10x = 39$ by completing the square.
Ⓐ $x = -13$ or $x = 3$
B $x = -10 + \sqrt{164}$ or $x = -10 - \sqrt{164}$
C $x = -5 + \sqrt{39}$ or $x = -5 - \sqrt{39}$

11. Solve $2x^2 + 9x + 4 = 0$ using the Quadratic Formula.
Ⓐ $x = -4$ or $x = -\frac{1}{2}$
B $x = \frac{-9 \pm \sqrt{113}}{4}$

12. Find the number of real solutions of the equation $x^2 + 11x - 10 = 0$ using the discriminant.
A none
Ⓒ two
B one

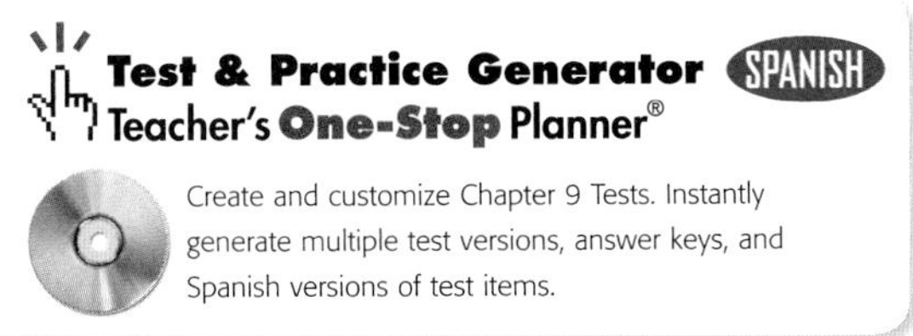

Test & Practice Generator
SPANISH
Teacher's One-Stop Planner®
Create and customize Chapter 9 Tests. Instantly generate multiple test versions, answer keys, and Spanish versions of test items.

CHAPTER 9

SECTION 9A
Quadratic Functions

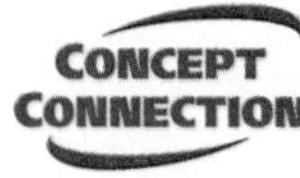

CONCEPT CONNECTION On page 566, students write, solve, and graph equations to model real-world rocket-flight situations.

Exercises designed to prepare students for success on the Concept Connection can be found on pages 550, 559, and 564.

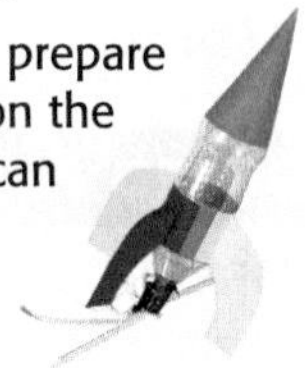

SECTION 9B
Solving Quadratic Equations

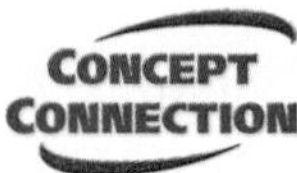

CONCEPT CONNECTION On page 610, students write, solve, and graph equations to model a real-world situation involving the flight of a golf ball.

Exercises designed to prepare students for success on the Concept Connection can be found on pages 572, 580, 586, 596, 603, and 608.

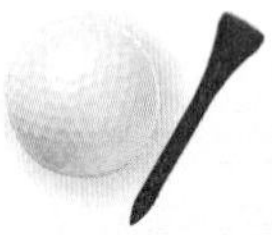

Algebra in *California*

One of the more common uses of quadratic functions and equations is the modeling of an object that is in "free fall," meaning that the only force acting on the object is gravity. Students will solve many problems involving objects in free fall throughout this chapter.

CHAPTER 9

Quadratic Functions and Equations

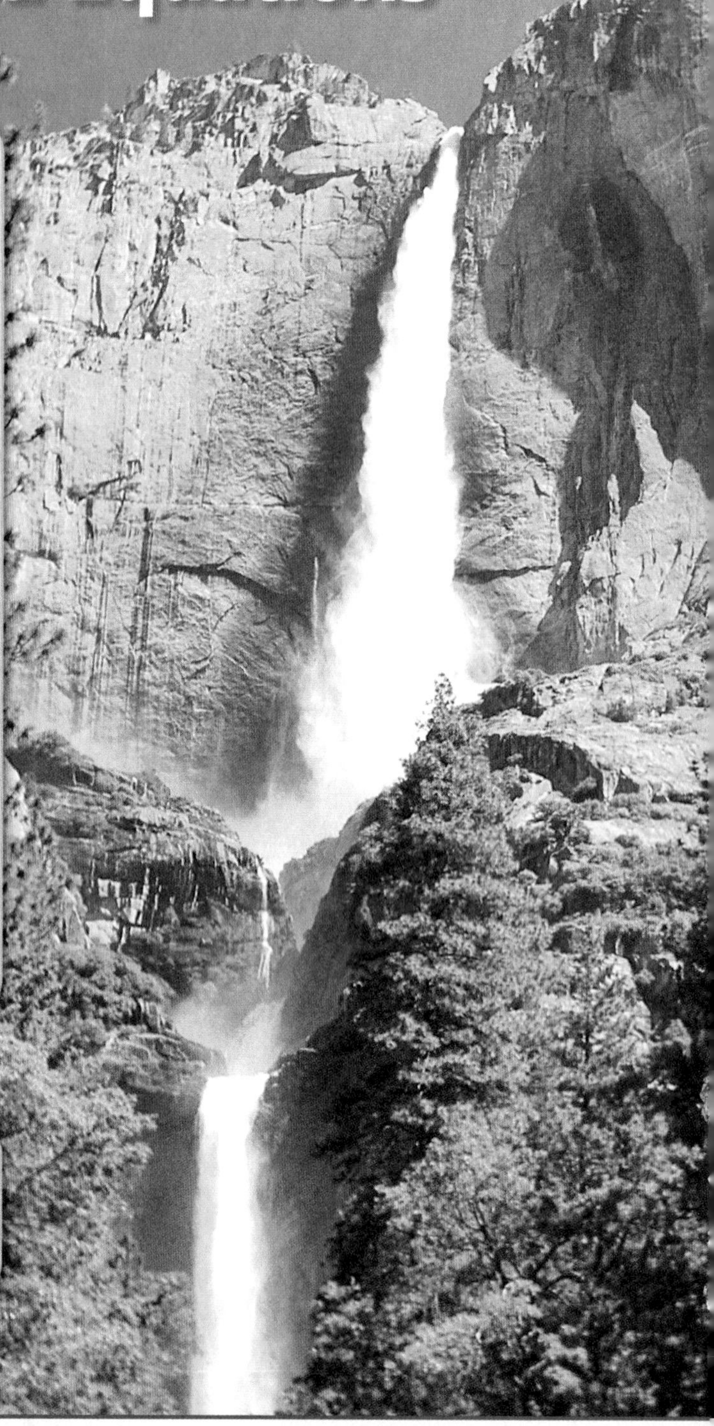

go.hrw.com
Chapter Project Online
KEYWORD: MA8CA ChProj

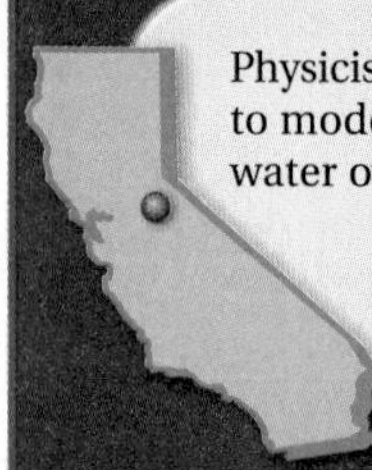

Physicists use quadratic equations to model falling objects such as water over a waterfall.

Yosemite Falls
Yosemite National Park, CA

About the Project

Free Falling

In the Chapter Project, students use a motion detector to collect data about falling objects. Students organize the height-time data, graph a function model, analyze the function, and then use the function model to make predictions.

Project Resources

All project resources for teachers and students are provided online.

Materials:

- an electronic data collection device, such as CBL or CBR, with a motion detector
- graphing calculator

go.hrw.com
Project Teacher Support
KEYWORD: MA8CA ProjectTS

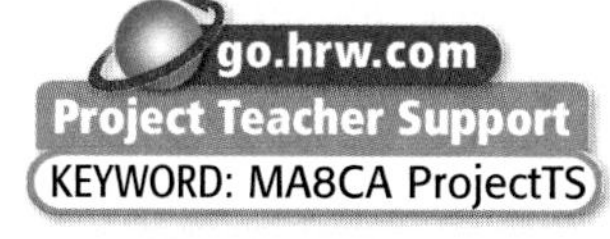

ARE YOU READY?

Vocabulary

Match each term on the left with a definition on the right.

1. factoring **A**
2. quadratic **D**
3. trinomial **C**
4. x-intercept **B**

A. the process of writing a number or an algebraic expression as a product

B. the x-coordinate of a point where a graph intersects the x-axis

C. a polynomial with three terms

D. a polynomial with degree 2

E. the first number of an ordered pair of numbers that describes the location of a point on the coordinate plane

Graph Functions

Graph each function.

5. $y = -2x + 8$
6. $y = (x + 1)^2$
7. $y = x^2 + 3$
8. $y = 2x^2$

Multiply Binomials

Find each product.

9. $(m + 2)(m + 5)$ **9.** $m^2 + 7m + 10$
10. $(y - 7)(y + 2)$ **10.** $y^2 - 5y - 14$
11. $(2a + 4)(5a + 6)$ $10a^2 + 32a + 24$
12. $(x + 1)(x + 1)$ $x^2 + 2x + 1$
13. $(t + 5)(t + 5)$ $t^2 + 10t + 25$
14. $(3n - 8)(3n - 8)$ $9n^2 - 48n + 64$

Factor Trinomials

Factor each polynomial completely.

15. $x^2 - 2x + 1$ $(x - 1)^2$
16. $x^2 + x - 2$ $(x + 2)(x - 1)$
17. $x^2 - 6x + 5$ $(x - 5)(x - 1)$
18. $x^2 - x - 12$ $(x - 4)(x + 3)$
19. $x^2 - 9x + 18$ $(x - 6)(x - 3)$
20. $x^2 - 7x - 18$ $(x - 9)(x + 2)$

Squares and Square Roots

Evaluate each expression.

21. $\sqrt{36}$ **6**
22. $\sqrt{121}$ **11**
23. $-\sqrt{64}$ **−8**
24. $\sqrt{16}\sqrt{81}$ **36**
25. $\sqrt{\frac{9}{25}}$ $\frac{3}{5}$
26. $-\sqrt{6(24)}$ **−12**

Solve Multi-Step Equations

Solve each equation. Check your answer.

27. $3m + 5 = 11$ **2**
28. $3t + 4 = 10$ **2**
29. $5n + 13 = 28$ **3**
30. $2(k - 4) + k = 7$ **5**
31. $10 = \frac{r}{3} + 8$ **6**
32. $2(y - 6) = 8.6$ **10.3**

ARE YOU READY?

CHAPTER 9

Organizer

Objective: Assess students' understanding of prerequisite skills.

Prerequisite Skills

Graph Functions
Multiply Binomials
Factor Trinomials
Squares and Square Roots
Solve Multi-Step Equations

Assessing Prior Knowledge

INTERVENTION 

Diagnose and Prescribe

Use this page to determine whether intervention is necessary or whether enrichment is appropriate.

Resources

 ***Are You Ready? Intervention and Enrichment*** **Worksheets**

 ***Are You Ready?*** **CD-ROM**

 ***Are You Ready?*** **Online**

my.hrw.com

Answers

5–8. See p. A24.

ARE YOU READY?
Diagnose and Prescribe

NO INTERVENE

Prerequisite Skill	*Are You Ready? Intervention,* Chapter 9 – Worksheets	CD-ROM	Online
Graph Functions	Skill 80	Activity 80	Diagnose and Prescribe Online
Multiply Binomials	Skill 64	Activity 64	
Factor Trinomials	Skill 67	Activity 67	
Squares and Square Roots	Skill 6	Activity 6	
Solve Multi-Step Equations	Skill 69	Activity 69	

***Are You Ready? Enrichment,* Chapter 9**
Worksheets
CD-ROM
Online

CHAPTER 9

Unpacking the Standards

Organizer

Objective: Help students understand the new concepts they will learn in Chapter 9.

Academic Vocabulary Connections

Becoming familiar with the academic vocabulary on this student page will be helpful to students. Discussing some of the vocabulary terms in the chapter also may be helpful.

1. The value of a function is determined by its rule. The rule is an algebraic expression. What is true about the algebraic expression that determines a **quadratic function**? Possible answer: it will be a polynomial of degree 2.
2. The shape of a **parabola** is similar to the shape of an open parachute. Predict the shape of a *parabola*. a curve
3. A **minimum** is a point on the graph of a curve with the least y-coordinate. How might a **maximum** be described? Possible answer: a point on a graph of a curve with the greatest y-coordinate
4. An axis is an imaginary line. Use this information and your understanding of symmetry to define the term **axis of symmetry**. Possible answer: an imaginary line that splits a figure such that one side matches the other

CHAPTER 9

Unpacking the Standards

The information below "unpacks" the standards. The Academic Vocabulary is highlighted and defined to help you understand the language of the standards. Refer to the lessons listed after each standard for help with the math terms and phrases. The Chapter Concept shows how the standard is applied in this chapter.

California Standard	Academic Vocabulary	Chapter Concept
14.0 Students solve a quadratic equation by factoring or completing the square. (Lessons **9-5, 9-7**)	**quadratic equation** an equation that has a variable term raised to the second power ***Example:*** $3x^2 - x + 5 = 0$	You use factoring to solve quadratic equations, and you learn a solution method called completing the square.
19.0 Students know the quadratic formula and are familiar with its proof by completing the square. (Lesson **9-8**)	**quadratic formula** a formula that can be used to solve any quadratic equation	You learn another solution method called the quadratic formula, and you understand why the formula works.
20.0 Students use the quadratic formula to find the roots of a second-degree polynomial and to solve quadratic equations. (Lesson **9-8**)	**roots of a polynomial** values of the variable for which the polynomial is equal to 0	You apply what you have learned about solving quadratic equations to quadratic polynomials.
21.0 Students graph quadratic functions and know that their roots are the x-intercepts. (Lessons **9-1, 9-2, 9-3, 9-4, Lab 9-4**)	**quadratic function** a function that is described by a quadratic equation ***Example:*** $y = 3x^2 - x + 5$	You extend your knowledge of functions to include quadratic functions and their properties.
22.0 Students use the quadratic formula or factoring techniques or both to determine whether the graph of a quadratic function will intersect the x-axis in zero, one, or two points. (Lesson **9-9**)	**technique** a way of doing something **determine** find out	You make connections between the solutions of a quadratic equation and the graph of a quadratic function.
23.0 Students apply quadratic equations to physical problems, such as the motion of an object under the force of gravity. (Lessons **9-2, 9-3, 9-4, 9-5, 9-6, 9-7**)	**apply** use **physical** having to do with scientific rules or ideas **motion** movement	You use quadratic equations to model situations involving gravity and other scientific theories.

Standards 2.0, 7.0, 17.0, 24.1, and 25.3 are also covered in this chapter. To see these standards unpacked, go to Chapter 1, p. 4; Chapter 2, p. 70; Chapter 4, p. 198; Chapter 5, p. 254.

Looking Back

Previously, students

- identified and graphed functions.
- solved for variables in formulas that stated rules for relationships among quantities.
- used factoring to solve equations.

In This Chapter

Students will study

- identifying and graphing quadratic functions.
- solving quadratic equations.
- using factoring to graph quadratic functions and solve quadratic equations.

Looking Forward

Students can use these skills

- to identify and graph rational functions.
- to solve radical equations.
- to simplify rational expressions using factoring.

Study Strategy: Learn Vocabulary

English-Language Arts Reading 8.1.3

Mathematics has a vocabulary all its own. Many new terms appear on the pages of your textbook. Learn these new terms as they are introduced. They will give you the necessary tools to understand new concepts.

Some tips to learning new vocabulary include:

- Look at the **context** in which a new word appears.
- Use **prefixes** or **suffixes** to figure out the word's meaning.
- Relate the new term to familiar **everyday words.** Keep in mind that a word's mathematical meaning may not exactly match its everyday meaning.

polynomial = many
intersection = overlap
conversion = change

Vocabulary Word	Study Tip	Definition
Polynomial	*The prefix "poly-" means many.*	*One monomial or the sum or the difference of monomials*
Intersection	*Relate it to the meaning of the "intersection of two roads".*	*The overlapping region that shows the solution to a system of equations*
Conversion Factor	*Relate it to the word "convert", which means change or alter.*	*Used to convert a measurement to different units*

Try This

Complete the chart.

	Vocabulary Word	Study Tips	Definition
1.	Trinomial		
2.	Independent system		
3.	Variable		

Use the context of each sentence to define the underlined word. Then relate the word to everyday words.

4. If two linear equations in a system have the same graph, the graphs are called <u>coincident</u> lines, or simply the same line.
5. In the formula $d = rt$, d is <u>isolated</u>.

Reading and Writing Math

Organizer

Objective: Help students apply strategies to understand and retain key concepts.

Resources

 ***Chapter 9 Resource File***
Reading Strategies

Study Strategy: Learn Vocabulary

ENGLISH LANGUAGE LEARNERS

Prefixes and suffixes are just a few letters long, but they can dramatically alter the meaning of a word. For instance, the prefix *a-* means "not," so *asymmetrical* means "not symmetrical."

When trying to determine the meaning of a new word based on the context in which it appears, don't just look at the sentence in which it appears. Consider the preceding and following sentences as well.

Extend As students work through Chapter 9, have them find the vocabulary words on the lesson pages. Have students figure out their meanings based on any of the strategies shown on this page, and use each vocabulary word appropriately in a sentence.

Answers to *Try This*

Possible answers:

1. The prefix *tri-* means "three"; a polynomial with only 3 terms.
2. Relate it to the word *independent*, which means "alone" or "by itself"; a system that has exactly one solution.
3. Relate it to the word *vary*, which means "differ" or "change"; a quantity that can change.
4. lines that are exactly the same
5. by itself

Reading 8.1.3 Use word meanings within the appropriate context and show ability to verify those meanings by definition, restatement, example, comparison, or contrast.

Quadratic Functions

One-Minute Section Planner

Lesson	Lab Resources	Materials
Lesson 9-1 Quadratic Equations and Functions • Identify quadratic functions and determine whether they have a minimum or maximum. • Graph a quadratic function and give its domain and range. **17.0, 21.0**	***Algebra Lab* 9-1** In *Chapter 9 Resource File*	**Optional** graphing calculator
9-2 Algebra Lab Explore the Axis of Symmetry • Find the equation of the axis of symmetry for a quadratic function. **24.1**		
Lesson 9-2 Characteristics of Quadratic Functions • Find the zeros of a quadratic function from its graph. • Find the axis of symmetry and the vertex of a parabola. **21.0, 23.0**	***Algebra Lab* 9-2** In *Chapter 9 Resource File*	**Optional** graphing calculator, jump rope
Lesson 9-3 Graphing Quadratic Functions • Graph a quadratic function in the form $y = ax^2 + bx + c$. **21.0, 23.0**	***Technology Lab* 9-3** In *Chapter 9 Resource File*	**Optional** graphing calculator

MK = *Manipulatives Kit*

Notes

Math Background: Teaching the Standards

QUADRATIC FUNCTIONS 21.0, 23.0

Lesson 9-1

A *quadratic function* is any function that can be written in the form $y = ax^2 + bx + c$, where a, b, and c are real numbers and $a \neq 0$. This is called the *standard form* of a quadratic function.

Lesson 9-1 shows several ways to identify a quadratic function. Another method, not mentioned in the text, is to use a table of values. Recall that linear functions have a constant rate of change. Therefore, in a table of values for a linear function, a constant change in the x-values corresponds to a constant change in the y-values. For quadratic functions, it is the rate of change itself that has a constant rate of change. In other words, when there is a constant change in x-values, a quadratic function has *constant second differences*. The table illustrates this for the quadratic function $y = x^2 + 3$.

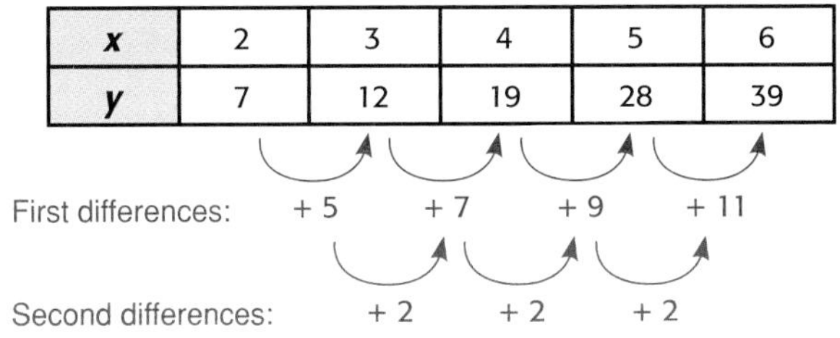

x	2	3	4	5	6
y	7	12	19	28	39

DEVELOPING QUADRATIC FUNCTIONS

Lessons 9-1 to 9-3

The simplest quadratic function is $y = x^2$. Its graph is a *parabola* that opens upward, has its vertex at the origin, and is symmetric about the y-axis. The graphs of all other quadratic functions may be built by performing a series of transformations on the graph of $y = x^2$.

For functions in the form $y = ax^2$ $(a \neq 0)$, the value of a determines the direction and shape of the parabola. If $a > 0$, the parabola opens upward; if $a < 0$, the parabola opens downward. If $|a| > 1$, the parabola is narrower than the graph of $y = x^2$; if $|a| < 1$, the parabola is wider than the graph of $y = x^2$.

The graph of a function in the form $y = a(x - h)^2$ is a horizontal translation of the graph of $y = ax^2$. For example, the graph of $y = 2(x - 3)^2$ is identical to the graph of $y = 2x^2$, but shifted 3 units to the right.

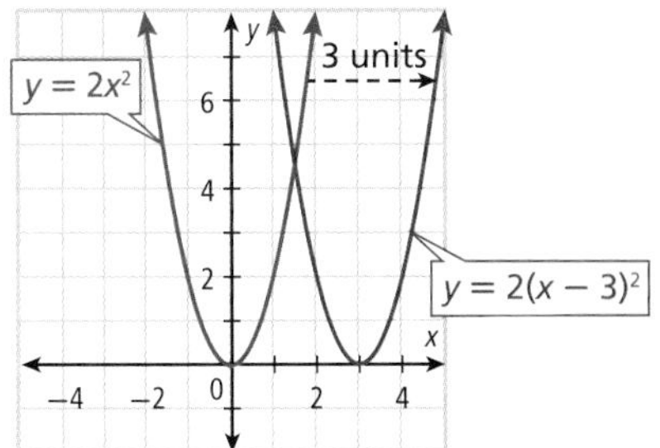

Finally, the constant k in $y = a(x - h)^2 + k$ represents a vertical translation of the graph of $y = a(x - h)^2$. The translation is k units upward if $k > 0$ and $|k|$ units downward if $k < 0$.

The equation $y = a(x - h)^2 + k$ is called the *vertex form* of a quadratic function. This form makes it easy to identify the vertex of the parabola, (h, k), and the axis of symmetry, $x = h$. (Students will study vertex form in Algebra 2.)

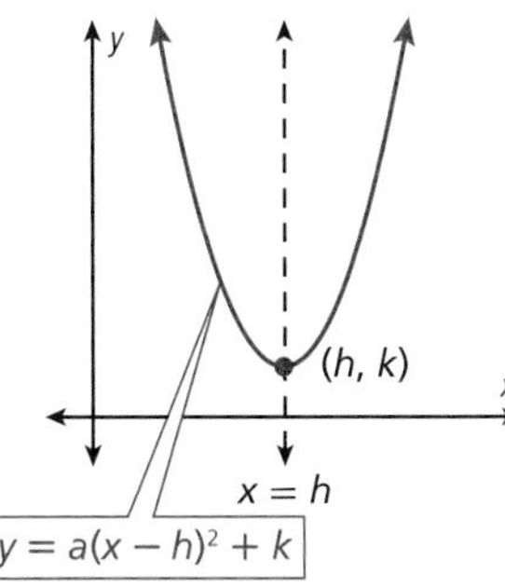

One way to find the formula for the axis of symmetry of a parabola $\left(x = -\frac{b}{2a}\right)$ is by using vertex form. As shown below, the basic idea is to transform vertex form into standard form and then write the equation of the axis of symmetry, $x = h$, in terms of a, b, and c.

$$y = a(x - h)^2 + k$$

$$y = a(x^2 - 2hx + h^2) + k$$

$$y = ax^2 - 2ahx + ah^2 + k$$

In standard form, the value of b is the coefficient of x, so $b = -2ah$. Solving for h gives $h = -\frac{b}{2a}$. Thus, the axis of symmetry is the vertical line $x = -\frac{b}{2a}$.

9-1 Organizer

Objectives: Identify quadratic functions and determine whether they have a minimum or maximum.

Graph a quadratic function and give its domain and range.

Algebra Lab
In *Chapter 9 Resource File*

Online Edition
Tutorial Videos

Countdown to Mastery Week 19

Power Presentations with PowerPoint®

Warm Up

1. Evaluate $x^2 + 5x$ for $x = 4$ and $x = -3$. 36; −6
2. Generate ordered pairs for the function $y = x^2 + 2$ for x-values −2, −1, 0, 1, and 2.

x	−2	−1	0	1	2
y	6	3	2	3	6

Also available on transparency

Q: Why can't quadratics ever be considered cool?

A: One of their terms is always a square.

California Standards

Algebra 1 21.0
Also covered:
17.0 Students determine the domain of independent variables and the range of dependent variables defined by a graph, a set of ordered pairs, or a symbolic expression.

9-1 Quadratic Equations and Functions

California Standards

21.0 Students graph quadratic functions and know that their roots are the x-intercepts.
Also covered: **17.0**

Vocabulary
quadratic equation
quadratic function
parabola
minimum value
maximum value
vertex

Why learn this?
The height of a soccer ball after it is kicked into the air can be described by a quadratic function. (See Exercise 60.)

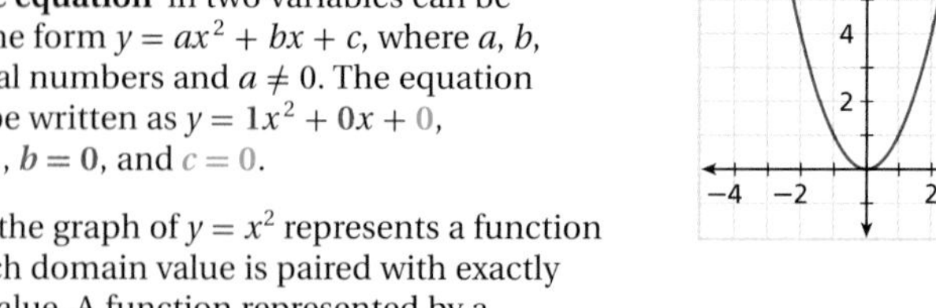

Solutions of the equation $y = x^2$ are shown in the graph. Notice that the graph is not linear. The equation $y = x^2$ is a *quadratic equation.* A **quadratic equation** in two variables can be written in the form $y = ax^2 + bx + c$, where a, b, and c are real numbers and $a \neq 0$. The equation $y = x^2$ can be written as $y = 1x^2 + 0x + 0$, where $a = 1$, $b = 0$, and $c = 0$.

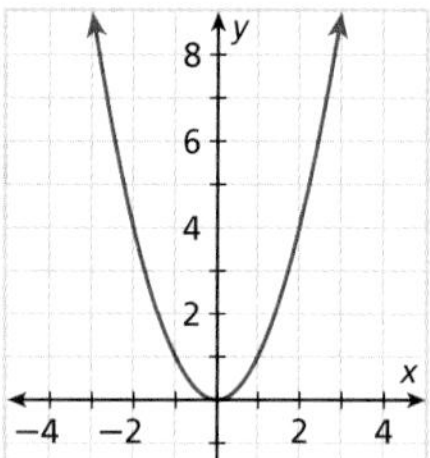

Notice that the graph of $y = x^2$ represents a function because each domain value is paired with exactly one range value. A function represented by a quadratic equation is a **quadratic function**.

Quadratic Equations and Their Graphs

For any quadratic equation in two variables
- all points on its graph are solutions to the equation.
- all solutions to the equation appear on its graph.

EXAMPLE 1 Determining Whether a Point Is on a Graph

Without graphing, tell whether each point is on the graph of $y = -3x^2 - 4$.

A $(2, 1)$

Substitute $(2, 1)$ into $y = -3x^2 - 4$.

$$y = -3x^2 - 4$$
$$1 \stackrel{?}{=} -3(2)^2 - 4$$
$$1 \stackrel{?}{=} -3 \cdot 4 - 4$$
$$1 \stackrel{?}{=} -12 - 4$$
$$1 \neq -16 \ ✗$$

Since $(2, 1)$ is not a solution of $y = -3x^2 - 4$, $(2, 1)$ is not on the graph.

B $(-1, -7)$

Substitute $(-1, -7)$ into $y = -3x^2 - 4$.

$$y = -3x^2 - 4$$
$$-7 \stackrel{?}{=} -3(-1)^2 - 4$$
$$-7 \stackrel{?}{=} -3 \cdot 1 - 4$$
$$-7 \stackrel{?}{=} -3 - 4$$
$$-7 = -7 \ ✓$$

Since $(-1, -7)$ is a solution of $y = -3x^2 - 4$, $(-1, -7)$ is on the graph.

Without graphing, tell whether each point is on the graph of $x^2 + y = 2$.

1a. $(1, 1)$ yes **1b.** $\left(\frac{1}{2}, \frac{3}{2}\right)$ no **1c.** $(-3.5, 10.5)$ no

1 Introduce

EXPLORATION

9-1 Identifying Quadratic Functions

In previous chapters, you learned about linear functions and their properties. In this lesson, you will begin to learn about quadratic functions and their properties.

1. Use the linear function $y = x - 1$ to complete the table.

x	y
−2	
−1	
0	
1	
2	

2. The function $y = x^2 - 1$ is quadratic. Use this quadratic function to complete the table.

x	y
−2	
−1	
0	
1	
2	

3. What happens to the graph of a function when $y = 0$?
4. How do the y-values for the quadratic function differ from the y-values for the linear function?

THINK AND DISCUSS

5. **Describe** what you notice about the number of zeros in the tables.
6. **Discuss** the effect that your answer to Problem 5 will have on the graph of the function.

Motivate

Have the class generate ordered-pair solutions of $y = x^2$. Plot the points where everyone can see. Ask students whether $y = x^2$ is a linear function. No Tell them that in this lesson they will learn about a type of nonlinear function called a quadratic function.

Explorations and answers are provided in *Alternate Openers: Explorations Transparencies*.

The graph of a quadratic function is a curve called a **parabola**. To graph a quadratic function, generate enough ordered pairs to see the shape of the parabola. Then connect the points with a smooth curve.

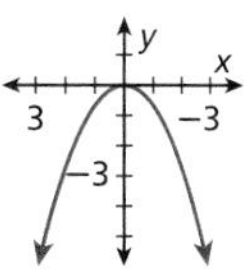

EXAMPLE 2 Graphing Quadratic Functions

Graph each quadratic function.

A $y = 2x^2$

x	$y = 2x^2$
−2	8
−1	2
0	0
1	2
2	8

Make a table of values. Choose values of x and use them to find values of y.

Graph the points. Then connect the points with a smooth curve.

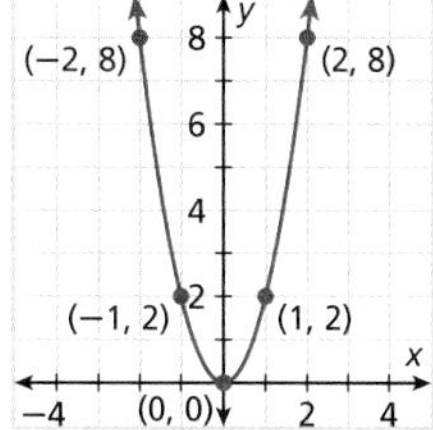

B $y = -2x^2$

x	$y = -2x^2$
−2	−8
−1	−2
0	0
1	−2
2	−8

Make a table of values. Choose values of x and use them to find values of y.

Graph the points. Then connect the points with a smooth curve.

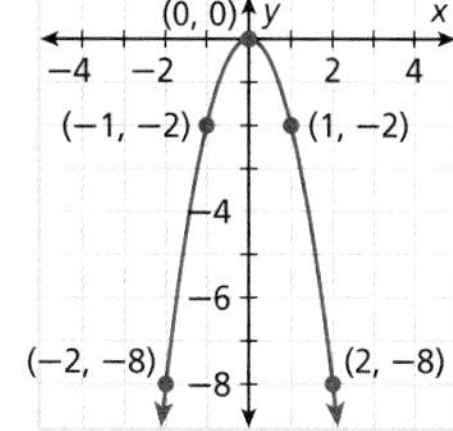

Helpful Hint

When choosing values of x, be sure to choose positive values, negative values, and 0.

2a.

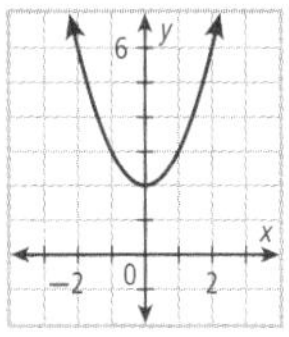

2b.

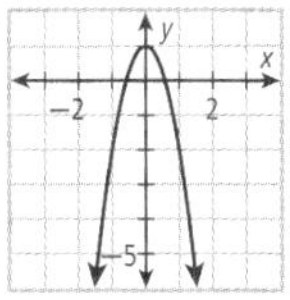

Graph each quadratic function.

2a. $y = x^2 + 2$ **2b.** $y = -3x^2 + 1$

As shown in the graphs in Examples 2A and 2B, some parabolas open upward and some open downward. Notice that the only difference between the two equations is the value of a. When a quadratic function is written in the form $y = ax^2 + bx + c$, the value of a determines the direction the parabola opens.

- A parabola opens upward when $a > 0$.
- A parabola opens downward when $a < 0$.

EXAMPLE 3 Identifying the Direction of a Parabola

Tell whether the graph of each quadratic function opens upward or downward. Explain.

A $y = 4x^2$

$y = 4x^2$

$a = 4$ *Identify the value of a.*

Since $a > 0$, the parabola opens upward.

COMMON ERROR ALERT

Students might think an equation needs three terms to be a quadratic equation. Remind them that the values of b and c can equal 0; only a cannot be 0.

Power Presentations with PowerPoint®

Additional Examples

Example 1

Without graphing, tell whether each point is on the graph of $y = \frac{1}{2}x^2 + 8$.

A. $(4, 16)$ yes

B. $(-2, 10)$ yes

C. $(-4, 0)$ no

Example 2

Graph each quadratic function.

A. $y = \frac{1}{3}x^2$

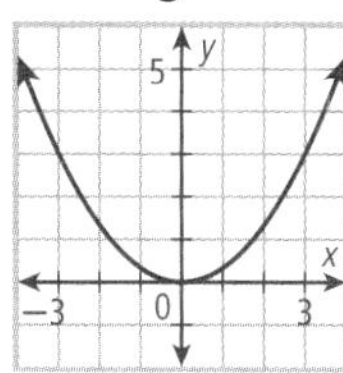

B. $y = -4x^2$

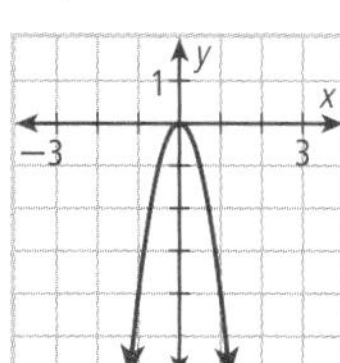

Also available on transparency

INTERVENTION

Questioning Strategies

EXAMPLE 1

- Why does substituting a point's coordinates into the equation tell you whether the point is on the graph?

EXAMPLE 2

- How do you know when you have enough values in the table to graph the parabola?

2 Teach

Guided Instruction

Show students how to identify quadratic functions given a function rule. Explain that the graph of a quadratic function is a parabola. Point out the parabolic shape, the symmetrical features, and the vertex of the graph.

Explain that the value of a in $y = ax^2 + bx + c$ determines whether the function has a minimum or a maximum value, which also determines the range.

Universal Access

Through Modeling

Display each function below one at a time. Have students discuss, in pairs, whether to lift their arms up in the shape of a U if the graph opens up or down in a shape of an upside-down U if the graph opens down and then demonstrate their decision.

$y = -3x^2 + 18$	down
$y = 5x + 8 - \frac{1}{5}x^2$	down
$-2x^2 + y = -5$	up
$y - \frac{1}{2}x^2 + 10 - x = 0$	up
$3x - y = -x^2$	up

Power Presentations with PowerPoint®

Additional Examples

Example 3

Tell whether the graph of each quadratic function opens upward or downward. Explain.

A. $y - \frac{1}{4}x^2 = x - 3$ upward; $a > 0$

B. $y = 5x - 3x^2$ downward; $a < 0$

Example 4

Identify the vertex of each parabola. Then give the minimum or maximum value of the function.

A.

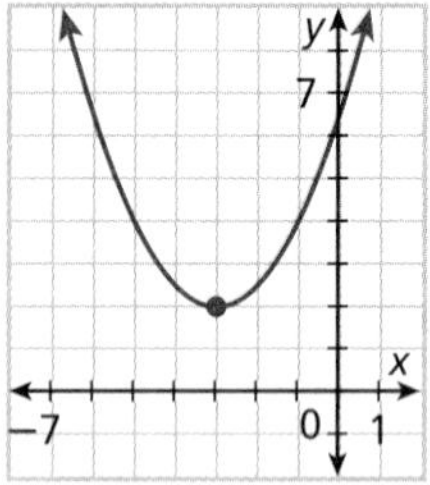

vertex: $(-3, 2)$; minimum: 2

B.

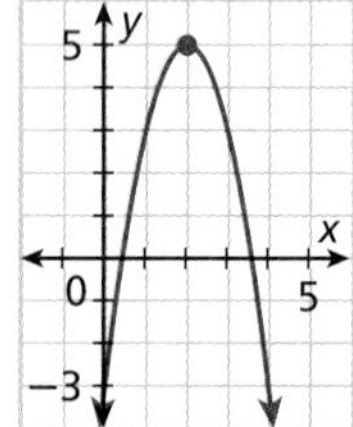

vertex: $(2, 5)$; maximum: 5

Also available on transparency

INTERVENTION
Questioning Strategies

EXAMPLE 3

- How do you determine from an equation of a function whether the graph will open upward or downward?
- Why is it necessary that the function be in the form $y = ax^2 + bx + c$ before determining whether the graph opens upward or downward?

EXAMPLE 4

- Are minimums and maximums x-values or y-values?

Tell whether the graph of each quadratic function opens upward or downward. Explain.

B $2x^2 + y = 5$

$$2x^2 + y = 5$$
$$\underline{-2x^2 \qquad -2x^2}$$
$$y = -2x^2 + 5$$
$$a = -2$$

Write the function in the form $y = ax^2 + bx + c$ by solving for y. Subtract $2x^2$ from both sides.

Identify the value of a.

Since $a < 0$, the parabola opens **downward**.

3a. Because $a < 0$, the parabola opens downward.

3b. Because $a > 0$, the parabola opens upward.

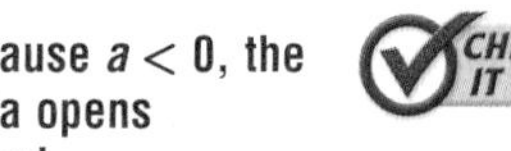

Tell whether the graph of each quadratic function opens upward or downward. Explain.

3a. $f(x) = -4x^2 - x + 1$ **3b.** $y - 5x^2 = 2x - 6$

The **minimum value** of a function is the least possible y-value for that function. The **maximum value** of a function is the greatest possible y-value for that function.

The highest or lowest point on a parabola is the **vertex**. Therefore, the minimum or maximum value of a quadratic function occurs at the vertex.

Know it! Note

Minimum and Maximum Values of Quadratic Functions

WORDS	If $a > 0$, the parabola opens upward, and the y-value of the vertex is the minimum value of the function.	If $a < 0$, the parabola opens downward, and the y-value of the vertex is the maximum value of the function.
GRAPHS	$y = x^2 + 6x + 9$ (Vertex: $(-3, 0)$; Minimum: 0)	$y = -x^2 + 6x - 4$ (Vertex: $(3, 5)$; Maximum: 5)

EXAMPLE 4 **Identifying the Vertex and the Minimum or Maximum**

Identify the vertex of each parabola. Then give the minimum or maximum value of the function.

A

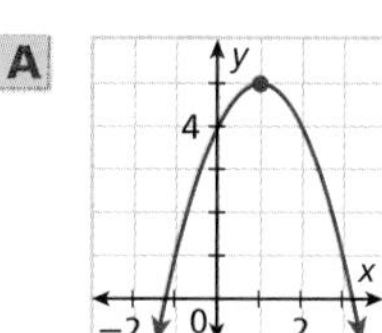

The vertex is $(1, 5)$, and the maximum is 5.

B

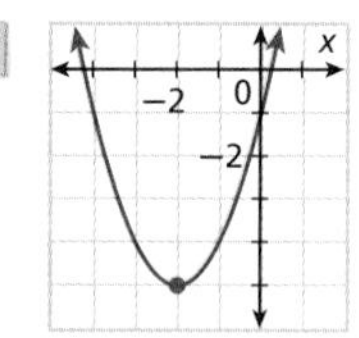

The vertex is $(-2, -5)$, and the minimum is -5.

Multiple Representations Have students graph several quadratic functions using a graphing calculator, and make a conjecture about whether each graph opens up or down prior to viewing the graph.

Language Support Discuss with students the meanings of *minimum* and *maximum* in common usage. Connect these everyday meanings with those that are used with parabolas by associating them with the maximum function value or minimum function value of a quadratic function.

ENGLISH LANGUAGE LEARNERS

Identify the vertex of each parabola. Then give the minimum or maximum value of the function.

4a.

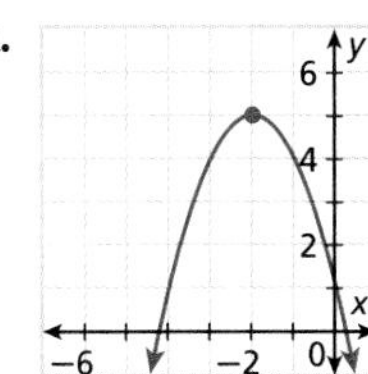

4b.

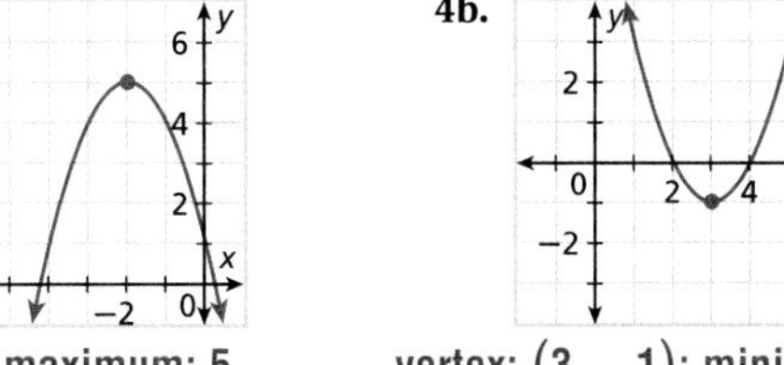

vertex: $(-2, 5)$; maximum: 5 vertex: $(3, -1)$; minimum: -1

Caution!

You may not be able to see the entire graph, but that does not mean the graph stops. Remember that the arrows indicate that the graph continues.

Unless a specific domain is given, the domain of a quadratic function is all real numbers. One way to find the range of a quadratic function is by looking at its graph.

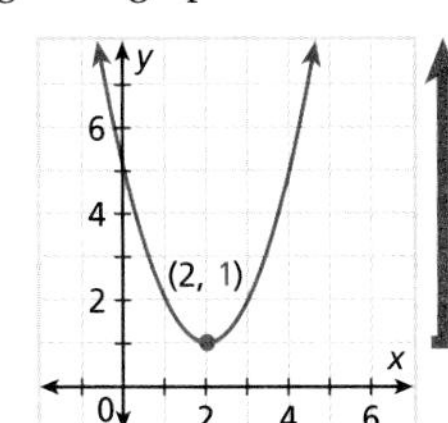

For the graph of $y = x^2 - 4x + 5$, the range begins at the minimum value of the function, where $y = 1$. All y-values greater than or equal to 1 appear somewhere on the graph. So the range is $y \geq 1$.

EXAMPLE 5 Finding Domain and Range

Find the domain and range.

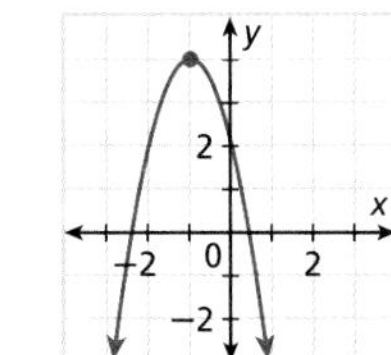

Step 1 The graph opens downward, so identify the maximum.
The vertex is $(-1, 4)$, so the maximum is 4.

Step 2 Find the domain and range.
D: all real numbers
R: $y \leq 4$

Find the domain and range.

5a.

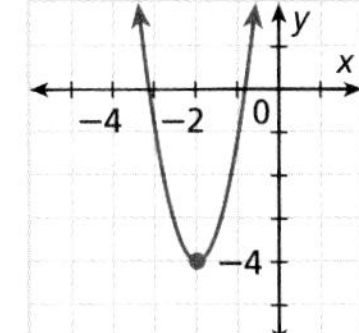

5b.

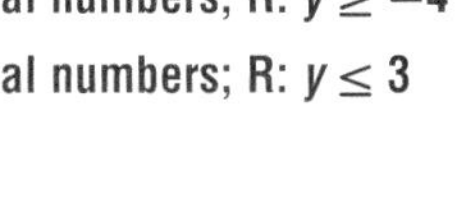

5a. D: all real numbers; R: $y \geq -4$

5b. D: all real numbers; R: $y \leq 3$

THINK AND DISCUSS

1. How can you identify a quadratic function?
2. **GET ORGANIZED** Copy and complete the graphic organizer. In each box, sketch and describe the graph and tell whether the function has a maximum value or a minimum value.

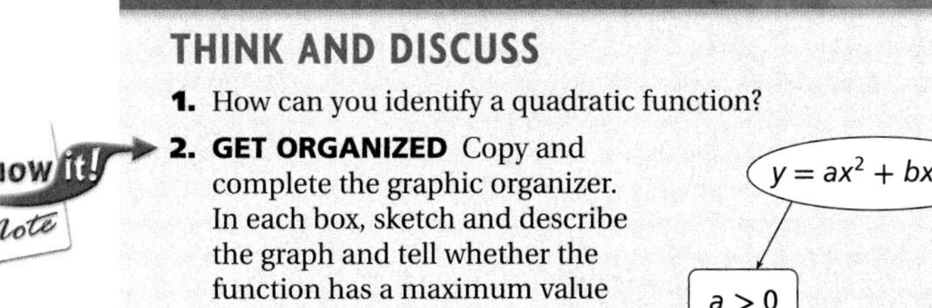

COMMON ERROR ALERT

Some students may automatically say that the function has a minimum when a parabola opens downward, and maximum when a parabola opens upward because of the word association. Tell students to visualize the graph before determining whether it has a minimum or maximum.

Power Presentations with PowerPoint®

Additional Examples

Example 5

Find the domain and range.

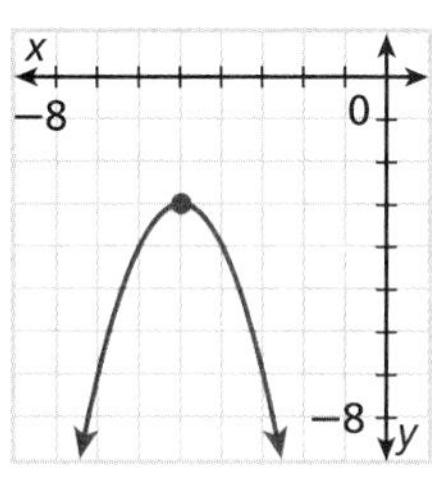

D: all real numbers
R: $y \leq -3$

Also available on transparency

INTERVENTION

Questioning Strategies

EXAMPLE 5

- Is the set of all real numbers the domain or the range? Is this true for all quadratic functions?

3 Close

Summarize

Write $y = 3x^2$ on the board. Ask students for the values of a, b, and c. Ask if the graph opens upward or downward and if the function has a minimum or maximum. Graph the function by generating and plotting ordered pairs. Continue with other quadratic functions as time allows.

FORMATIVE ASSESSMENT and INTERVENTION

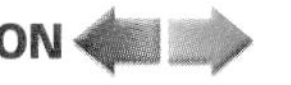

***Diagnose Before* the Lesson**
9-1 Warm Up, TE p. 544

***Monitor During* the Lesson**
Check It Out! Exercises, SE pp. 544–547
Questioning Strategies, TE pp. 545–547

***Assess After* the Lesson**
9-1 Lesson Quiz, TE p. 551
Alternative Assessment, TE p. 551

Answers to *Think and Discuss*

1. If the function can be written in the form $y = ax^2 + bx + c$, where $a \neq 0$, then it is quadratic.
2. See p. A7.

9-1 Exercises

Assignment Guide

Assign *Guided Practice* exercises as necessary.

If you finished Examples **1–3**
Proficient 28–40, 53–58, 61–68
Advanced 28–40, 53–58, 61–68, 76

If you finished Examples **1–5**
Proficient 28–83
Advanced 28–83

Homework Quick Check
Quickly check key concepts.
Exercises: 30, 34, 38, 42, 46

Answers

8. 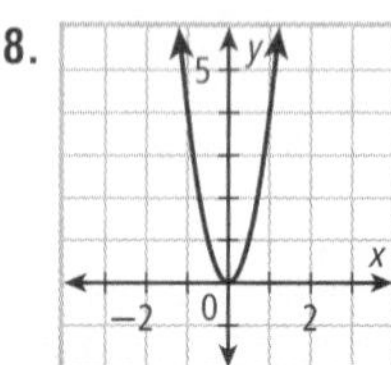

9. 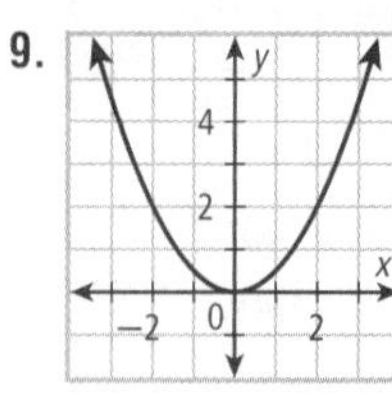

10. 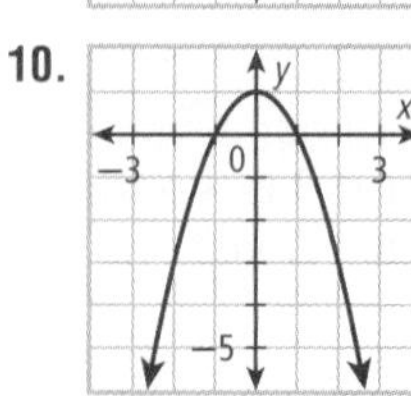

11. 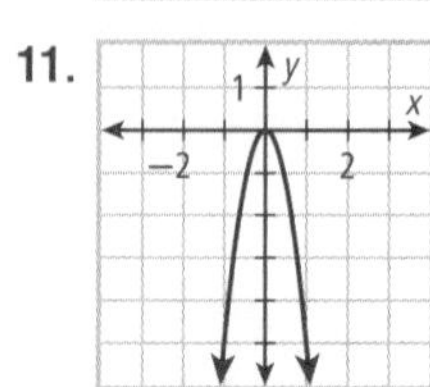

9-1 Exercises

California Standards Practice 15.0, 17.0, 21.0, 23.0

go.hrw.com
Homework Help Online
KEYWORD: MA8CA 9-1
Parent Resources Online
KEYWORD: MA8CA Parent

GUIDED PRACTICE

1. **Vocabulary** The y-value of the vertex of a parabola that opens upward is the ___?___ value of the function. (*maximum* or *minimum*) **minimum**

SEE EXAMPLE 1 p. 544

Without graphing, tell whether each point is on the graph of the given equation.

2. $y = x^2 + 9$; $(2, 11)$ **no**
3. $5x^2 + y = -40$; $(20, 20)$ **no**
4. $x^2 - 49 = y$; $(7, 0)$ **yes**
5. $y + 3 = 2x^2$; $(1.5, 1.5)$ **yes**
6. $y = x^2 - 10x + 25$; $(1, 15)$ **no**
7. $y = x^2 + 4x$; $(0, 0)$ **yes**

SEE EXAMPLE 2 p. 545

Graph each quadratic function.

8. $y = 4x^2$
9. $y = \frac{1}{2}x^2$
10. $y = -x^2 + 1$
11. $y = -5x^2$
12. $y = -x^2 - 3$
13. $y = 3 - 2x^2$
14. $y = x^2 + 4$
15. $y = -3x^2 - x$

SEE EXAMPLE 3 p. 545

Tell whether the graph of each quadratic function opens upward or downward. Explain.

16. $y = -3x^2 + 4x$ **downward; $a < 0$**
17. $y = 1 - 2x + 6x^2$ **$a > 0$; upward**
18. $y + x^2 = -x - 2$ **downward; $a < 0$**
19. $y + 2 = x^2$ **$a > 0$; upward**
20. $y - 2x^2 = -3$ **$a > 0$; upward**
21. $y + 2 + 3x^2 = 1$ **downward; $a < 0$**

SEE EXAMPLE 4 p. 546

Identify the vertex of each parabola. Then give the minimum or maximum value of the function.

22. 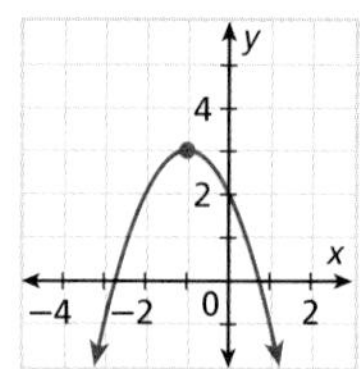

(−1, 3); maximum: 3

23. **(−3, −4); minimum: −4**

SEE EXAMPLE 5 p. 547

Find the domain and range.

24. 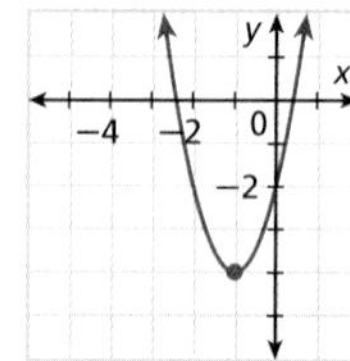

D: all real numbers; R: $y \geq -4$

25. 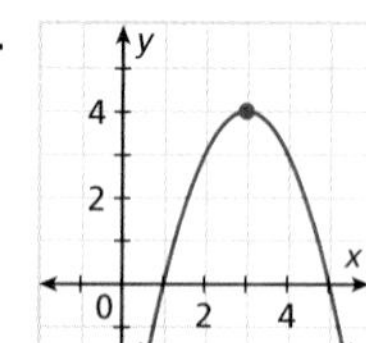

D: all real numbers; R: $y \leq 4$

26. 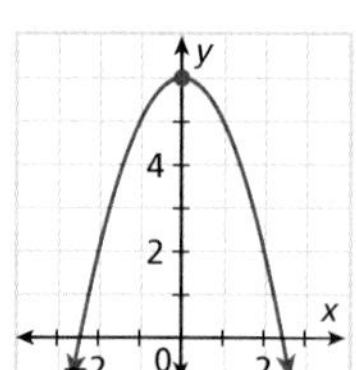

D: all real numbers; R: $y \leq 6$

27. 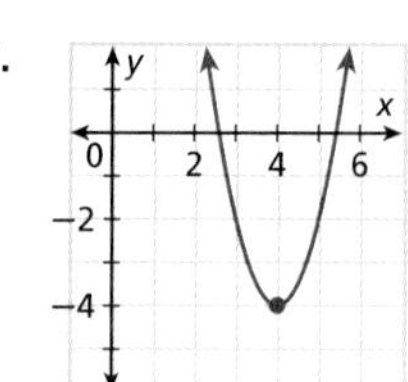

D: all real numbers; R: $y \geq -4$

California Standards

Standard	Exercises
2.0	78–80
16.0	82, 83
17.0	24–27, 43–46, 60b, 69b, 77
21.0	8–15, 34–37, 60a, 69a
23.0	59, 60c, 69c, 69d, 71, 76

9-1 READING STRATEGIES

LESSON 9-1 **Reading Strategies**
Understanding Concepts

Study the information about the example below to better understand quadratic functions.

Quadratic functions are written in the form $y = ax^2 + bx + c$, where $a \neq 0$.

The graph of a quadratic function is a *parabola*.

$y = -\frac{1}{2}x^2 + 3$

$a = -\frac{1}{2}$, $b = 0$ and $c = 3$

You can create a table of values to graph a quadratic function.

x	y
−4	−5
−2	1
0	3
2	1
4	−5

The graph of $y = -\frac{1}{2}x^2 + 3$ opens downward because $a < 0$.

vertex: (0, 3); *maximum*: 3

Recall that the domain is the set of x-values and the range is the set of y-values for a function.

D: all real numbers
R: $y \leq 3$

Complete the following.

1. Identify the values of a, b, and c in the quadratic function $y = 3x^2 - 5x + 2$.
$a = 3$, $b = -5$, $c = 2$
2. Does the graph of the function $y = 3x^2 - 5x + 2$ open upward or downward?
upward
3. Identify the domain and range for a function whose graph opens upward with vertex (0, −5).
D: all real numbers; R: $y \geq -5$

Answer the following about the function $y = 2x^2$.

4. Create a table of values for the function.
5. Graph the function.
6. What is the vertex of the graph?
(0, 0)
7. Does the graph open upward or or downward? Why?
upward; because $a > 0$.

x	y
−2	8
−1	2
0	0
1	2
2	8

9-1 REVIEW FOR MASTERY

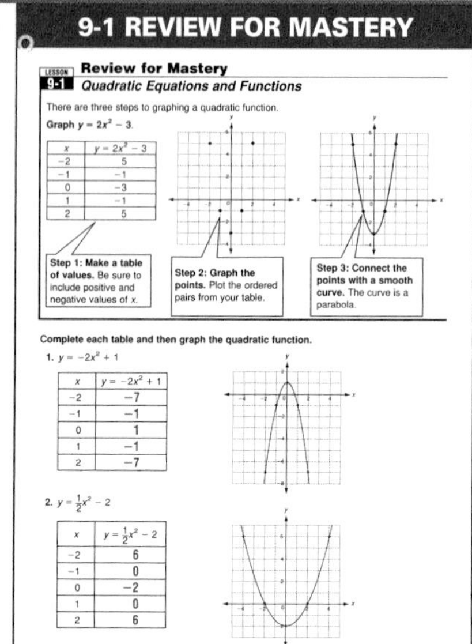

LESSON 9-1 **Review for Mastery**
Quadratic Equations and Functions

There are three steps to graphing a quadratic function.

Graph $y = 2x^2 - 3$.

x	$y = 2x^2 - 3$
−2	5
−1	−1
0	−3
1	−1
2	5

Step 1: Make a table of values. Be sure to include positive and negative values of x.

Step 2: Graph the points. Plot the ordered pairs from your table.

Step 3: Connect the points with a smooth curve. The curve is a parabola.

Complete each table and then graph the quadratic function.

1. $y = -2x^2 + 1$

x	$y = -2x^2 + 1$
−2	−7
−1	−1
0	1
1	−1
2	−7

2. $y = \frac{1}{2}x^2 - 2$

x	$y = \frac{1}{2}x^2 - 2$
−2	6
−1	0
0	−2
1	0
2	6

PRACTICE AND PROBLEM SOLVING

Independent Practice

For Exercises	See Example
28–33	1
34–37	2
38–40	3
41–42	4
43–46	5

Extra Practice
Skills Practice p. EP18
Application Practice p. EP32

Without graphing, tell whether each point is on the graph of the given equation.

28. $y = x^2 + 14$; $(-2, 10)$ **no**

29. $8x^2 - y = 8$; $(-1, 0)$ **yes**

30. $y = x^2 - 10x$; $(6, 8)$ **no**

31. $y = 2x^2 - 14$; $(5, 86)$ **no**

32. $y = 16x^2 + 1$; $\left(\frac{1}{2}, 5\right)$ **yes**

33. $y = -\frac{1}{3}x^2$; $(6, 12)$ **no**

Graph each quadratic function.

34. $y = x^2 - 5$ **35.** $y = -\frac{1}{2}x^2$ **36.** $y = -2x^2 + 2$ **37.** $y = 3x^2 - 2$

Tell whether the graph of each quadratic function opens upward or downward. Explain.

38. $y = 7x^2 - 4x$ **upward; $a > 0$**

39. $x - 3x^2 + y = 5$ **upward; $a > 0$**

40. $y = -\frac{2}{3}x^2$ **downward; $a < 0$**

Identify the vertex of each parabola. Then give the minimum or maximum value of the function.

41.

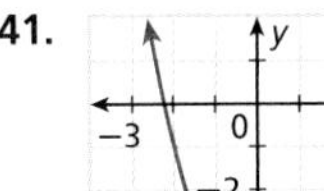

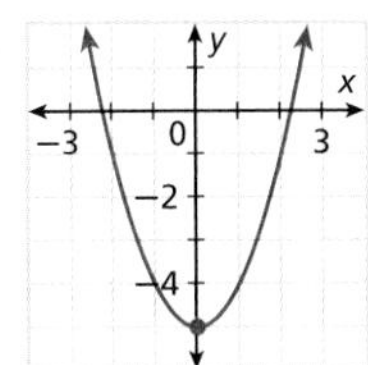

Vertex: $(0, -5)$; minimum: -5

42.

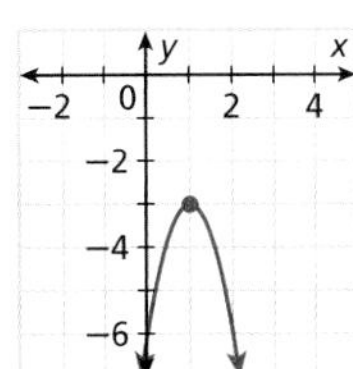

Vertex: $(1, -3)$; maximum: -3

Find the domain and range.

43.

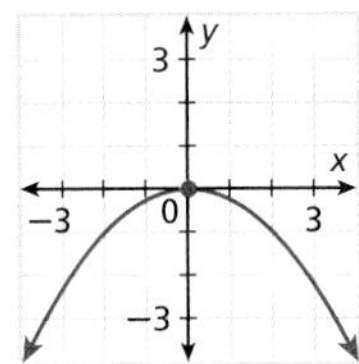

D: all real; numbers; R: $y \le 0$

44.

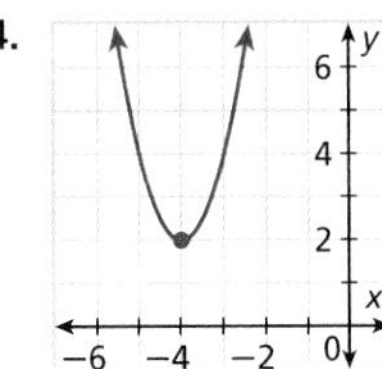

D: all real numbers; R: $y \ge 2$

45.

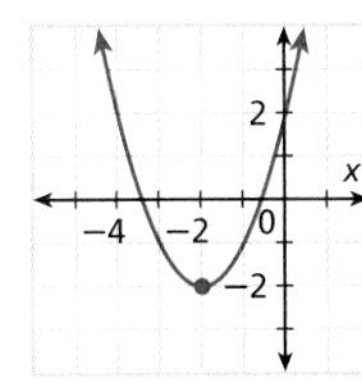

D: all real numbers; R: $y \ge -2$

46.

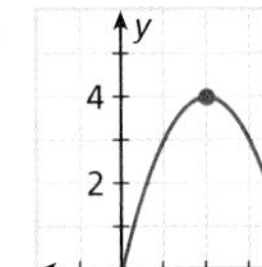

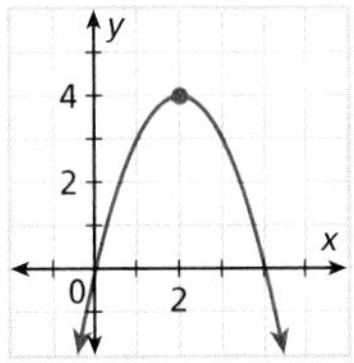

D: all real numbers; R: $y \le 4$

Reasoning Tell whether each statement is sometimes, always, or never true. Explain.

47. The graph of a quadratic function is a straight line. **never**

48. The range of a quadratic function is the set of all real numbers. **never**

49. The highest power of any variable term in a quadratic function is 2. **always**

50. The graph of a quadratic function contains the point $(0, 0)$. **sometimes**

51. The vertex of a parabola occurs at the minimum value of the function. **sometimes**

52. The graph of a quadratic function that has a minimum opens upward. **always**

Answers

12.

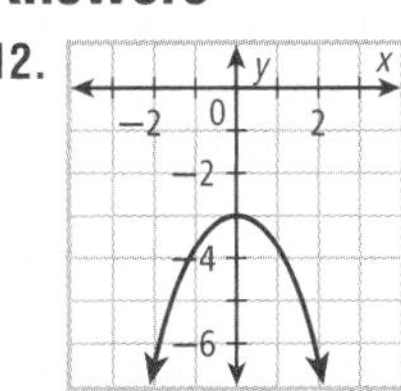

13.

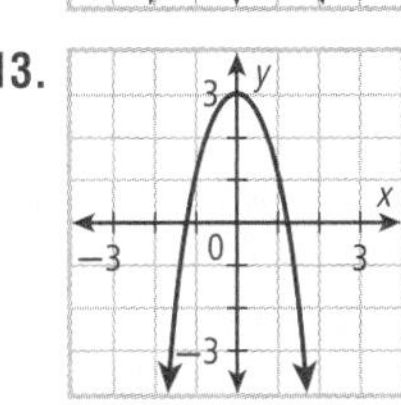

14, 15. See p. A24.

34.

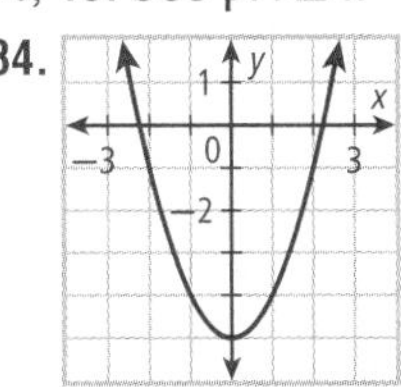

35.

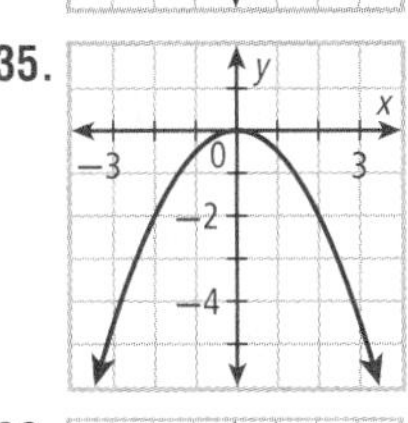

36.

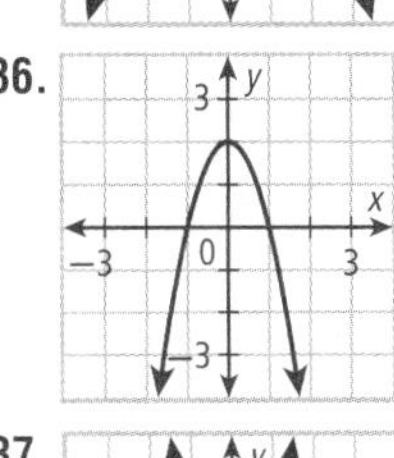

37.

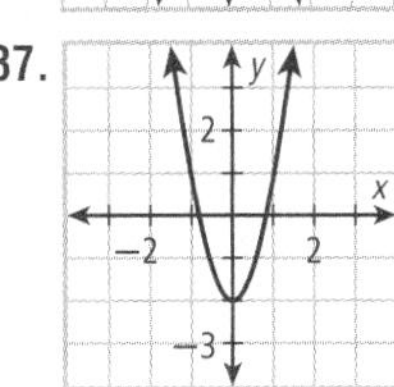

9-1 PROBLEM SOLVING

LESSON 9-1 Problem Solving
Quadratic Equations and Functions

Write the correct answer.

1. During a softball game, Kay hit a fly ball. The function $f(x) = -16t^2 + 64t + 4$ describes the height of the softball in feet. Make a table of values for the function and then graph it.

x	0	1	2	3	4
$f(x)$	4	52	68	52	4

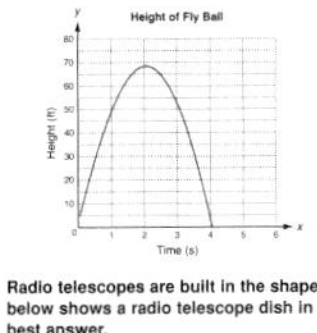

Height of Fly Ball

2. The graph shows the height y in feet of a golf ball after traveling x yards since being hit. Estimate the ball's maximum height. Estimate the distance the ball traveled when it reached its maximum height.

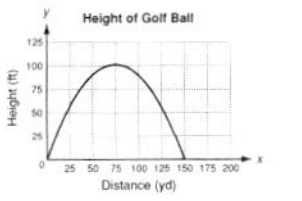

Height of Golf Ball

100 ft; 75 yd

Radio telescopes are built in the shape of a parabola. The graph below shows a radio telescope dish in cross-section. Select the best answer.

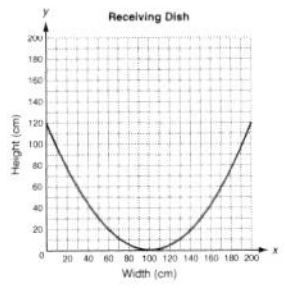

Receiving Dish

3. What is the vertex of this parabola?
A (0, 120)
(B) (100, 0)
C (200, 120)
D (100, 120)

4. What are the domain and range of this function?
F D: all real numbers R: all real numbers
G D: $x \ge 0$, R: $y \ge 0$
H D: $x \le 200$ R: $y \le 120$
(J) D: $0 \le x \le 200$ R: $0 \le y \le 120$

5. Which of the following could be the equation used by engineers to construct the radio telescope dish?
A $y = 1.2x + 120$
B $y = -1.2x + 120$
(C) $y = 0.012x^2 - 2.4x + 120$
D $y = -0.012x^2 - 2.4x + 120$

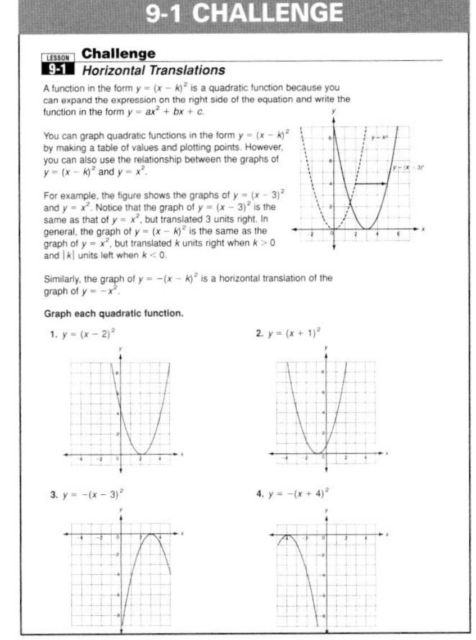

9-1 CHALLENGE

LESSON 9-1 Challenge
Horizontal Translations

A function in the form $y = (x - k)^2$ is a quadratic function because you can expand the expression on the right side of the equation and write the function in the form $y = ax^2 + bx + c$.

You can graph quadratic functions in the form $y = (x - k)^2$ by making a table of values and plotting points. However, you can also use the relationship between the graphs of $y = (x - k)^2$ and $y = x^2$.

For example, the figure shows the graphs of $y = (x - 3)^2$ and $y = x^2$. Notice that the graph of $y = (x - 3)^2$ is the same as that of $y = x^2$, but translated 3 units right. In general, the graph of $y = (x - k)^2$ is the same as the graph of $y = x^2$, but translated k units right when $k > 0$ and $|k|$ units left when $k < 0$.

Similarly, the graph of $y = -(x - k)^2$ is a horizontal translation of the graph of $y = -x^2$.

Graph each quadratic function.

1. $y = (x - 2)^2$
2. $y = (x + 1)^2$
3. $y = -(x - 3)^2$
4. $y = -(x + 4)^2$

9-1 PRACTICE A
9-1 PRACTICE C
9-1 PRACTICE B

LESSON 9-1 Practice B
Quadratic Equations and Functions

Tell whether each point is on the graph of $y = 3x^2 - 5$.

1. $(-3, -32)$ no
2. $(-2, 7)$ yes
3. $(1, -2)$ yes
4. $(5, 10)$ no

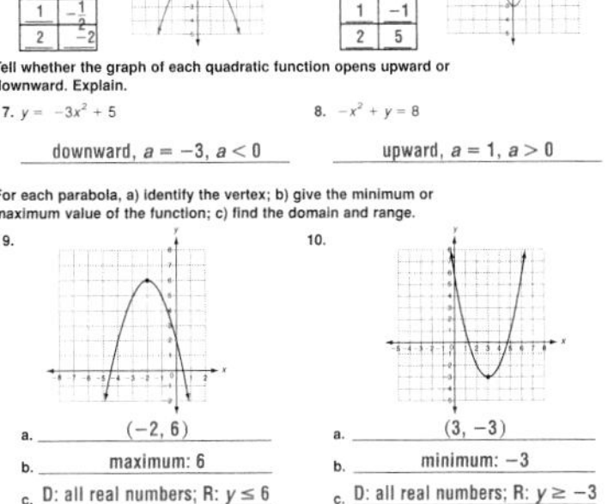

Graph each quadratic function.

5. $y = -\frac{1}{2}x^2$

x	y
−2	−2
−1	$-\frac{1}{2}$
0	0
1	$-\frac{1}{2}$
2	−2

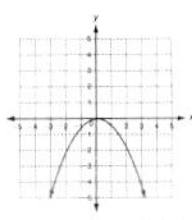

6. $y = 2x^2 - 3$

x	y
−2	5
−1	−1
0	−3
1	−1
2	5

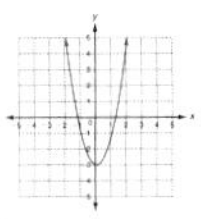

Tell whether the graph of each quadratic function opens upward or downward. Explain.

7. $y = -3x^2 + 5$ downward, $a = -3$, $a < 0$
8. $-x^2 + y = 8$ upward, $a = 1$, $a > 0$

For each parabola, a) identify the vertex; b) give the minimum or maximum value of the function; c) find the domain and range.

9.
a. $(-2, 6)$
b. maximum: 6
c. D: all real numbers; R: $y \le 6$

10.
a. $(3, -3)$
b. minimum: -3
c. D: all real numbers; R: $y \ge -3$

Inclusion In **Exercise 55,** remind students that the quantity $(x + 1)^2$ means $(x + 1)(x + 1)$, not $x^2 + 1$.

Technology In **Exercise 60,** students may want to use a graphing calculator to graph the function and then to explore that graph.

Exercise 71 involves showing that data of real-world height over time represent a quadratic function. This exercise prepares students for the Concept Connection on page 566.

Answers

59c. The independent variable x represents the time since the volleyball is served, so this makes sense only for nonnegative numbers.

60a. Soccer Ball Height

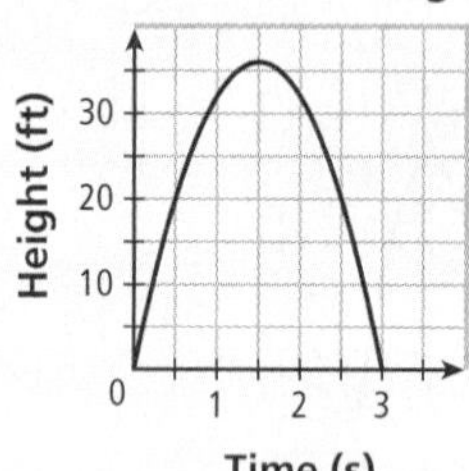

69a. Dolphin's Height

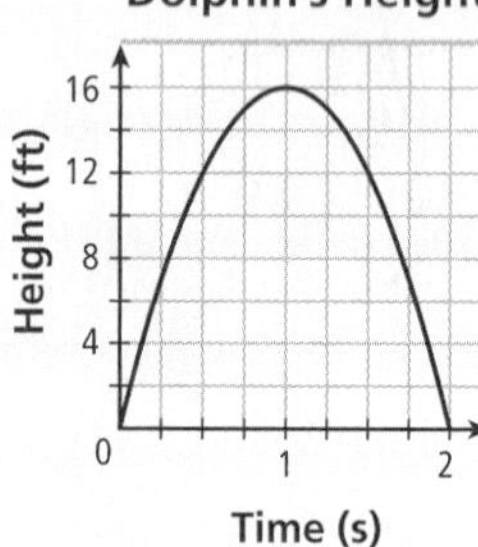

70a. A linear function can be written in the form $y = mx + b$. A quadratic function can be written in the form $y = ax^2 + bx + c$, where $a \neq 0$.

b. The graph of a linear function is a line. The graph of a quadratic function is a parabola.

71a. Bottle Rocket Launch

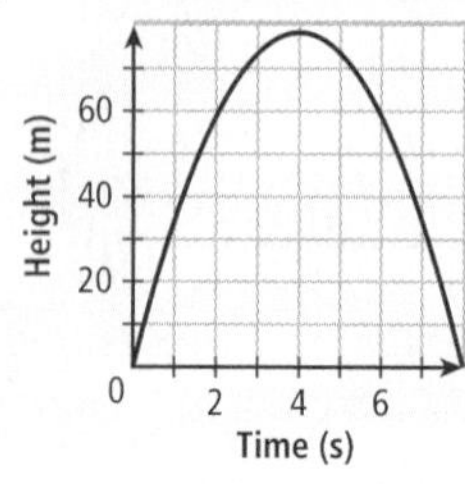

53. No; the value of a is 0.

54. yes; $y = 2x^2 + 3x - 5$

55. yes; $y = x^2 + 2x + 1$

56. yes; $y = -x^2 + 2x + 4$

57. yes; $y = 3x^2 + 0x - 9$

58. No; the function has a power greater than 2.

Tell whether each function is quadratic. If it is, write the function in the form $y = ax^2 + bx + c$. If not, explain why not.

53. $y = 3x - 1$
54. $y = 2x^2 - 5 + 3x$
55. $y = (x + 1)^2$
56. $y = 5 - (x - 1)^2$
57. $y = 3x^2 - 9$
58. $y = (x + 1)^3 - x^2$

59. **Estimation** The graph shows the approximate height y in meters of a volleyball x seconds after it is served.
    a. Estimate the time it takes for the volleyball to reach its greatest height. **about 0.375 s**
    b. Estimate the greatest height that the volleyball reaches. **about 2.25 m**
    c. **Critical Thinking** If the domain of a quadratic function is all real numbers, why is the domain of this function limited to nonnegative numbers?

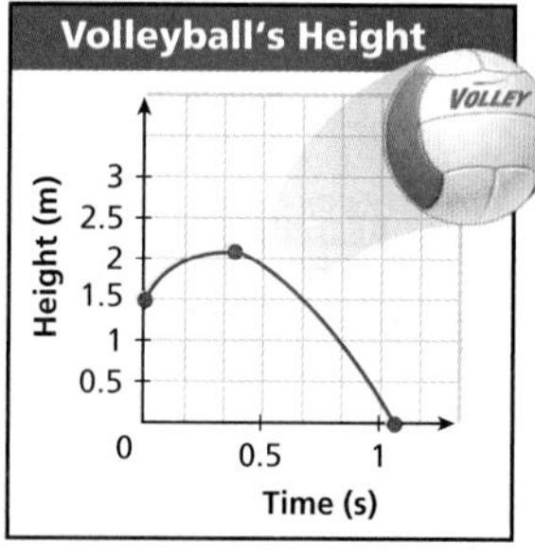

60. **Sports** The height in feet of a soccer ball x seconds after it is kicked into the air is modeled by the function $y = 48x - 16x^2$.
    a. Graph the function.
    b. In this situation, what values make sense for the domain? $x \geq 0$
    c. Does the soccer ball ever reach a height of 50 ft? How do you know? **No; the maximum y-value on the parabola is less than 50.**

Tell whether each function is linear, quadratic, or neither.

61. $y = \frac{1}{2}x - x^2$ **quadratic**
62. $y = \frac{1}{2}x - 3$ **linear**
63. $y + 3 = -x^2$ **quadratic**
64. $y = (x + 2)^2$ **quadratic**
65. $y = \frac{1}{2}x(x^2)$ **neither**
66. $y = \frac{3}{x^2}$ **neither**
67. $y = \frac{3}{2}x$ **linear**
68. $x^2 + 2x + 1 = y$ **quadratic**

69. **Marine Biology** A scientist records the motion of a dolphin as it jumps from the water. The function $h(t) = -16t^2 + 32t$ models the dolphin's height in feet above the water after t seconds.
    a. Graph the function.
    b. What domain makes sense for this situation? $t \geq 0$
    c. What is the dolphin's maximum height above the water? **16 ft**
    d. How long is the dolphin out of the water? **2 s**

70. **Write About It** Explain how to tell the difference between a linear function and a quadratic function when given each of the following:
    a. the equation
    b. the graph

CONCEPT CONNECTION

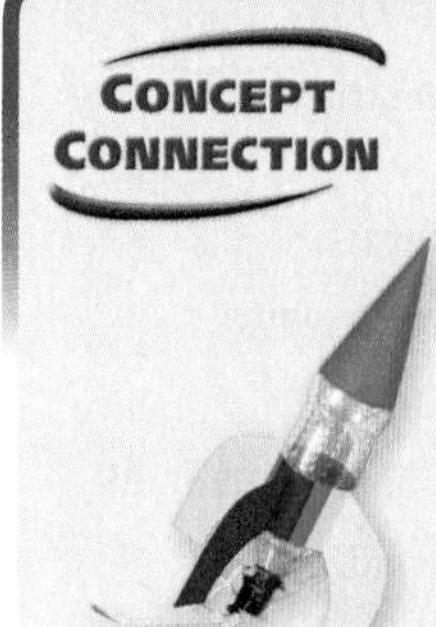

71. This problem will prepare you for the Concept Connection on page 566.
    A rocket team is using simulation software to create and study water bottle rockets. The team begins by simulating the launch of a rocket without a parachute. The table gives data for one rocket design.
    a. Graph the data and connect the points.
    b. Does this function have a maximum or a minimum? What does this value represent? **maximum; the greatest height reached by the rocket**

Time (s)	Height (m)
0	0
1	34.3
2	58.8
3	73.5
4	78.4
5	73.5
6	58.8
7	34.3
8	0

72. After the equation is solved for y, x^2 will be negative. This means the parabola opens downward and has a maximum.

72. **Critical Thinking** Given the function $-3 - y = x^2 + x$, why is it incorrect to state that the parabola opens upward and has a minimum?

Multiple Choice For Exercises 73 and 74, choose the best answer.

73. Which of the following could be the graph of a quadratic function?

(A)
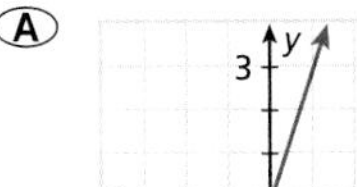

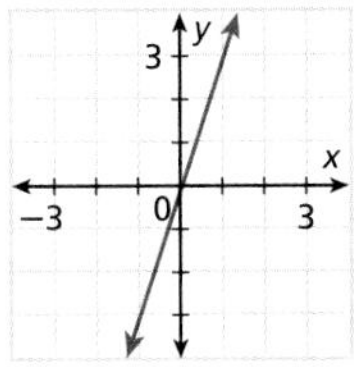

(C)
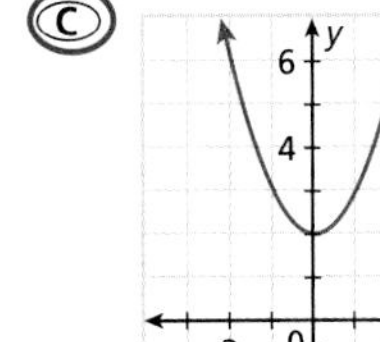

(B)
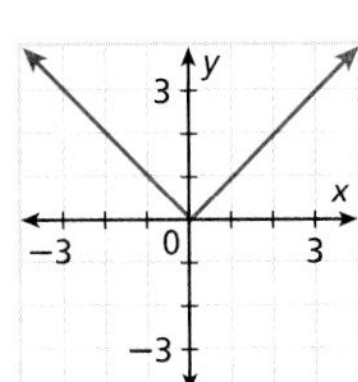

(D)
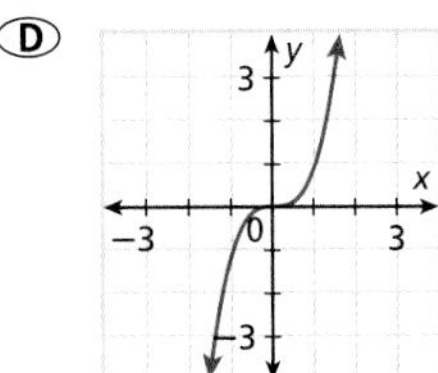

74. Which of the following quadratic functions has a maximum?

(A) $2x^2 - y = 3x - 2$

(B) $y = x^2 + 4x + 16$

(C) $y - x^2 + 6 = 9x$

(D) $y + 3x^2 = 9$

75.

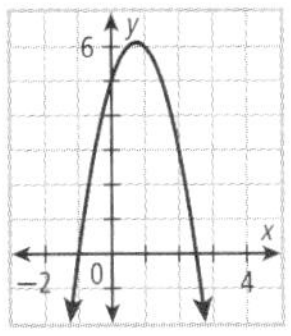

75. **Short Response** Is the function $f(x) = 5 - 2x^2 + 3x$ quadratic? Explain your answer by using two different methods of identification. Yes; the function can be written in the form $y = ax^2 + bx + c$, and the graph forms a parabola.

CHALLENGE AND EXTEND

76. **Multi-Step** A rectangular picture measuring 6 in. by 10 in. is surrounded by a frame with uniform width x. Write a quadratic function to show the combined area of the picture and frame. $y = 4x^2 + 32x + 60$

77. **Graphing Calculator** Use a graphing calculator to find the domain and range of the quadratic functions $y = x^2 - 4$ and $y = -(x+2)^2$. $y = x^2 - 4 \rightarrow$ D: all real numbers; R: $y \geq -4$; $y = -(x+2)^2 \rightarrow$ D: all real numbers; R: $y \leq 0$

SPIRAL STANDARDS REVIEW 2.0, 16.0

Write each number as a power of the given base. *(Lesson 1-4)*

78. 10,000; base 10 10^4

79. 16; base −2 $(-2)^4$

80. $\frac{8}{27}$; base $\frac{2}{3}$ $\left(\frac{2}{3}\right)^3$

81. A map shows a scale of 1 inch:3 miles. On the map, the distance from Lin's home to the park is $14\frac{1}{4}$ inches. What is the actual distance? *(Lesson 2-5)* $42\frac{3}{4}$ mi

Identify the independent and dependent variables. Write a rule in function notation for each situation. *(Lesson 4-3)*

82. Camp Wildwood has collected $400 in registration fees. It can enroll another 3 campers for $25 each. ind. var.: campers; dep. var.: fees; $f(x) = 25x + 400$

83. Sal works between 30 and 35 hours per week. He earns $9 per hour.

83. ind. var.: hours; dep. var.: pay; $f(x) = 9x$

Teaching Tip **Multiple Choice** If students chose **C** in **Exercise 74,** they may not have written the function in the form $y = ax^2 + bx + c$. Students who chose **A** may not have divided both sides by −1.

Journal

Have students describe relationships between a minimum or maximum, the vertex, and the range of a quadratic function.

ALTERNATIVE ASSESSMENT

Have students choose two of the quadratic functions from **Exercises 61–68,** write each in the form $y = ax^2 + bx + c$, and identify a, b, and c. Also have them identify the vertex, the minimum or maximum, the domain, and the range for each function.

Power Presentations with PowerPoint®

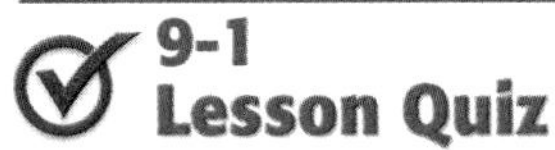

9-1 Lesson Quiz

1. Without graphing, tell whether (3, 12) is on the graph of $y = 2x^2 - 5$. no

2. Graph $y = 1.5x^2$.

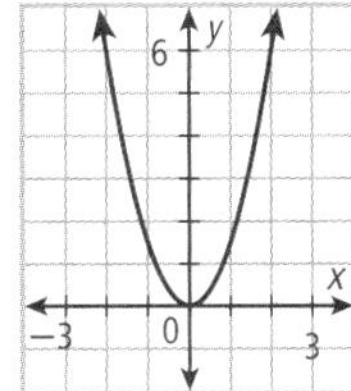

Use the graph for Problems 3–5.

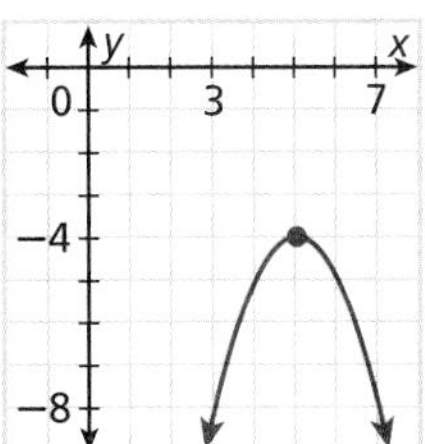

3. Identify the vertex. (5, −4)

4. Does the function have a minimum or maximum? What is it? max; −4

5. Find the domain and range. D: all real numbers; R: $y \leq -4$

Also available on transparency

Organizer

Use with Lesson 9-2

Objective: Find the equation of the axis of symmetry for a quadratic function.

Online Edition

Countdown to Mastery Week 20

Teach

Discuss

When there is no x-term in a quadratic function, then $b = 0$. Because 0 divided by any nonzero number is 0, the equation of the axis of symmetry in this type of function is always $x = 0$, which is the y-axis. When there is an x-term, the axis of symmetry is *not* $x = 0$.

Close

Key Concept

The equation of the axis of symmetry of a quadratic function of the form $y = ax^2 + bx + c$ is $x = -\frac{b}{2a}$.

Assessment

Journal Have students explain how to find the equation of the axis of symmetry for a quadratic function.

California Standards

Algebra 1 24.1

9-2 Algebra LAB

Use with Lesson 9-2

Explore the Axis of Symmetry

Every graph of a quadratic function is a parabola that is symmetric about a vertical line through its vertex called the *axis of symmetry.*

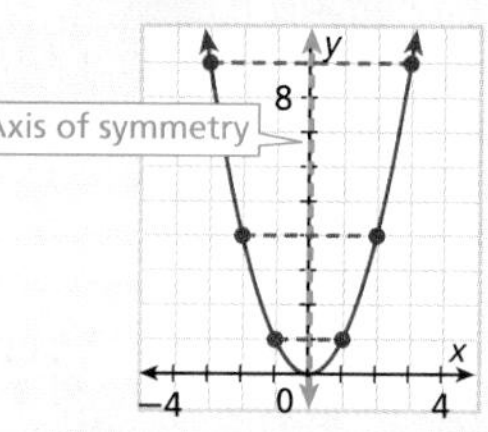

There is a relationship between a and b in the quadratic function and the equation of the axis of symmetry. In this activity, you will look at examples of quadratic functions and use inductive reasoning to make a conjecture about this relationship.

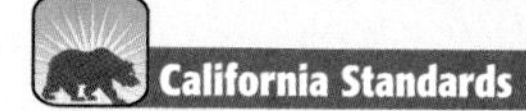

California Standards

24.1 Students explain the difference between inductive and deductive reasoning and identify and **provide examples** of each.

Activity

1 Complete the table.

Function	$y = 1x^2 - 2x - 3$	$y = -2x^2 - 8x - 6$	$y = -1x^2 + 4x$
Graph			
a	1	−2	−1
b	−2	−8	4
$\frac{b}{a}$	−2	4	−4
Axis of Symmetry (from graph)	$x = 1$	$x = -2$	$x = 2$

2 Compare the axis of symmetry with $\frac{b}{a}$ in your chart. What can you multiply $\frac{b}{a}$ by to get the number in the equation of the axis of symmetry? (*Hint:* Write and solve an equation to find the value.) Check your answer for each function. $-\frac{1}{2}$

3 Use your answer from Problem 2 to make a conjecture about the equation of the axis of symmetry of a quadratic function. $x =$ ___?___ $x = -\frac{1}{2}\left(\frac{b}{a}\right) = \frac{-b}{2a}$

Try This

For the graph of each quadratic function, find the equation of the axis of symmetry.

1. $y = 2x^2 + 12x - 7$ $x = -3$
2. $y = 4x^2 + 8x - 12$ $x = -1$
3. $y = 5x^2 - 20x + 10$ $x = 2$
4. $y = -3x^2 + 9x + 1$ $x = \frac{3}{2}$
5. $y = x^2 - 7$ $x = 0$
6. $y = 3x^2 + x + 4$ $x = -\frac{1}{6}$

9-2 Characteristics of Quadratic Functions

California Standards

21.0 Students graph quadratic functions and **know that their roots are the *x*-intercepts.**
Also covered: **23.0**

Vocabulary
zero of a function
axis of symmetry

Who uses this?
Engineers can use characteristics of quadratic functions to find the height of the arch supports of bridges. (See Example 5.)

Recall that an x-intercept of a function is a value of x when $y = 0$. A **zero of a function** is an x-value that makes the function equal to 0. So a zero of a function is the same as an x-intercept. Since a graph intersects the x-axis at the point or points containing an x-intercept, these intersections are also at the zeros of the function. A quadratic function may have one, two, or no zeros.

EXAMPLE 1 Finding Zeros of Quadratic Functions From Graphs

Find the zeros of each quadratic function from its graph. Check your answer.

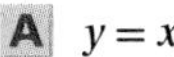

A $y = x^2 - x - 2$

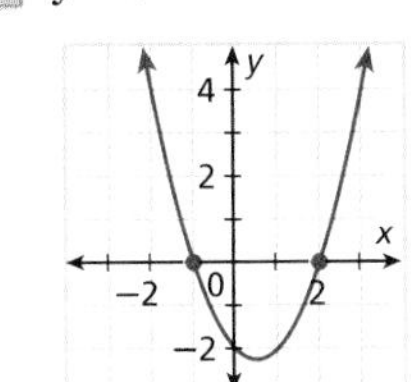

The zeros appear to be -1 and 2.

Check
$y = x^2 - x - 2$
$y = (-1)^2 - (-1) - 2$
$= 1 + 1 - 2 = 0$ ✓
$y = 2^2 - 2 - 2$
$= 4 - 2 - 2 = 0$ ✓

B $y = -2x^2 + 4x - 2$

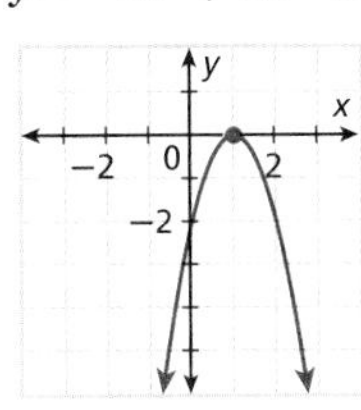

The only zero appears to be 1.

Check
$y = -2x^2 + 4x - 2$
$y = -2(1)^2 + 4(1) - 2$
$= -2(1) + 4 - 2$
$= -2 + 4 - 2$
$= 0$ ✓

C $y = \frac{1}{4}x^2 + 1$

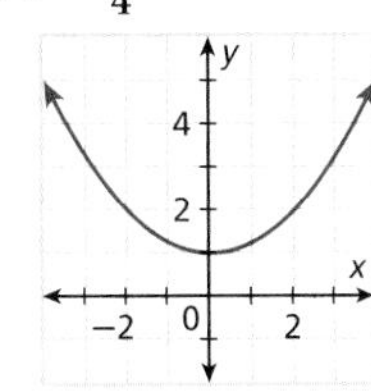

The graph does not cross the x-axis, so this function has no zeros.

Helpful Hint

Notice that if a function has only one zero, the zero is the x-coordinate of the vertex.

CHECK IT OUT! **Find the zeros of each quadratic function from its graph. Check your answer.**

1a. $y = -4x^2 - 2$ no zeros

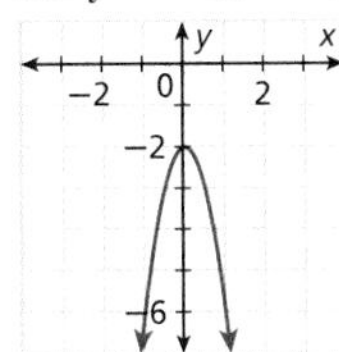

1b. $y = x^2 - 6x + 9$ 3

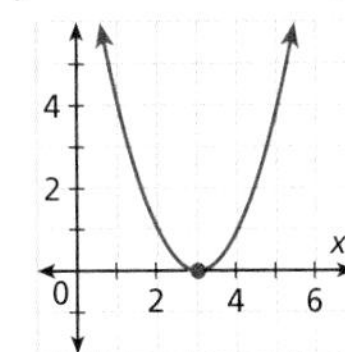

9-2 Organizer

Objectives: Find the zeros of a quadratic function from its graph.

Find the axis of symmetry and the vertex of a parabola.

Algebra Lab
In *Chapter 9 Resource File*

Online Edition
Tutorial Videos

Countdown to Mastery Week 20

Power Presentations with PowerPoint®

Warm Up

Find the *x*-intercept of each linear function.

1. $y = 2x - 3$ $\frac{3}{2}$

2. $y = -\frac{2}{3}x + \frac{7}{3}$ $\frac{7}{2}$

3. $y = 3x + 6$ -2

Evaluate each quadratic function for the given input values.

4. $y = -3x^2 + x - 2$, when $x = 2$
-12

5. $y = x^2 + 2x + 3$, when $x = -1$
2

Also available on transparency

Math Humor

Q: What do functions use to take their babies out for a walk?

A: A parabolator! (A *perambulator* is a baby carriage.)

1 Introduce

EXPLORATION

9-2 Characteristics of Quadratic Functions

In this Exploration, you will use your calculator to investigate quadratic functions.

1. Enter the function $y = x^2 - 2x - 8$ as **Y1**.
2. Press TBLSET GRAPH to view a table of values for the function. Use the arrow keys to scroll up and down the table. For which x-values does $y = 0$?

3. Press GRAPH to graph the function. At which points does the graph intersect the x-axis?
4. Now enter the function $y = x^2 - x + 3$ as **Y1**.

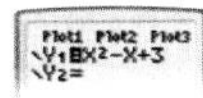

5. View a table for this function. For which x-values does $y = 0$?
6. View a graph of the function. At which points does the graph intersect the x-axis?

THINK AND DISCUSS

7. **Discuss** what you could conclude about the graph of a quadratic function that has only one value of x for which $y = 0$.

Motivate

Present students with some shapes, such as those below, and discuss lines of symmetry. Ask which shapes have a vertical line of symmetry and which have a horizontal line of symmetry.

Vertical: face, triangle, trapezoid, pentagon
Horizontal: arch

Explorations and answers are provided in *Alternate Openers: Explorations Transparencies.*

California Standards

Algebra 1 **21.0**
Also covered:
23.0 Students apply quadratic equations to physical problems, such as the motion of an object under the force of gravity.

Power Presentations with PowerPoint®

Additional Examples

Example 1

Find the zeros of each quadratic function from its graph. Check your answer.

A. $y = x^2 - 2x - 3$ $\quad -1, 3$

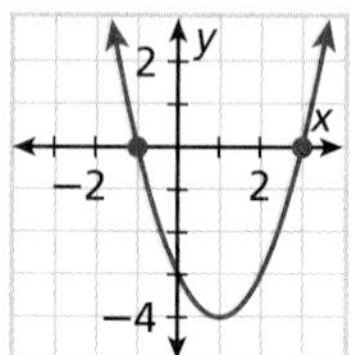

B. $y = x^2 + 8x + 16$ $\quad -4$

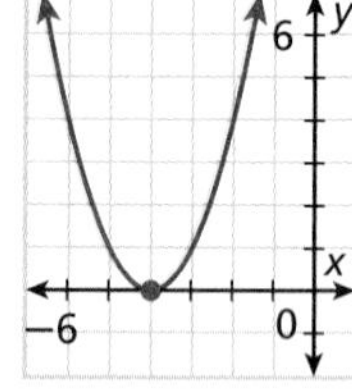

C. $y = -2x^2 - 2$ $\quad$ no zeros

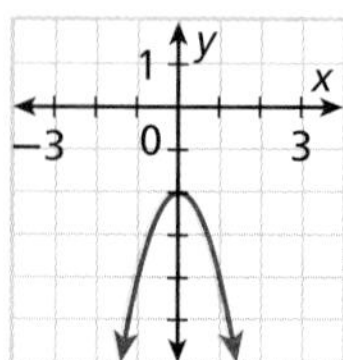

Also available on transparency

INTERVENTION
Questioning Strategies

EXAMPLE 1

- Which intercepts do you look for when looking for the zeros of a function?
- How are the zeros of a quadratic function related to the vertex of its graph?

The vertical line that divides a parabola into two symmetrical halves is the **axis of symmetry**. The axis of symmetry always passes through the vertex of the parabola. You can use the zeros to find the axis of symmetry.

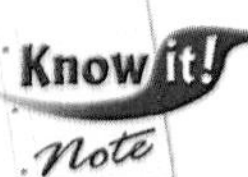

Finding the Axis of Symmetry by Using Zeros

WORDS	NUMBERS	GRAPH
One Zero If a function has one zero, use the *x*-coordinate of the vertex to find the axis of symmetry.	Vertex: (3, 0) Axis of symmetry: $x = 3$	$x = 3$; (3, 0)
Two Zeros If a function has two zeros, use the average of the two zeros to find the axis of symmetry.	Zeros: −4 and 0 $\frac{-4 + 0}{2} = \frac{-4}{2} = -2$ Axis of symmetry: $x = -2$	$x = -2$; (−4, 0), (0, 0)

EXAMPLE 2 Finding the Axis of Symmetry by Using Zeros

Find the axis of symmetry of each parabola.

A

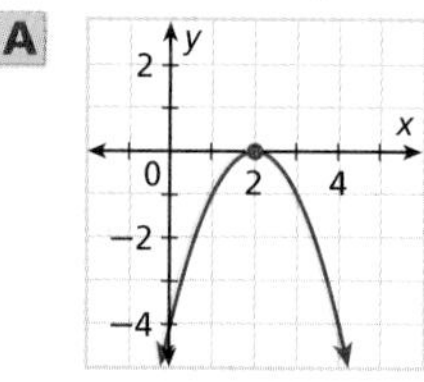

$(2, 0)$ *Identify the x-coordinate of the vertex.*

The axis of symmetry is $x = 2$.

B

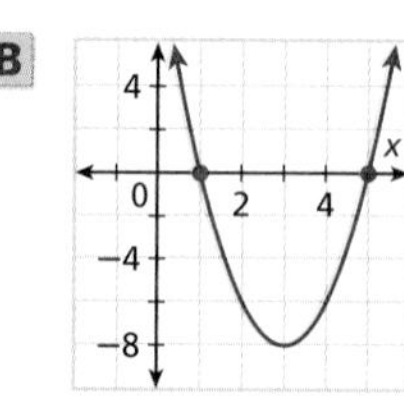

$\frac{1 + 5}{2} = \frac{6}{2} = 3$ *Find the average of the zeros.*

The axis of symmetry is $x = 3$.

CHECK IT OUT! Find the axis of symmetry of each parabola.

2a.

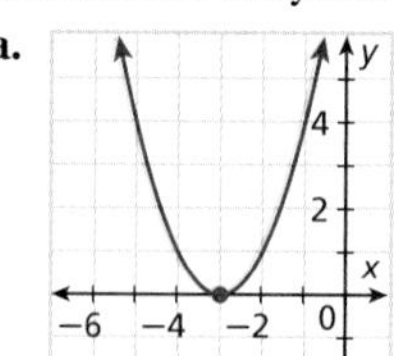

$x = -3$

2b.

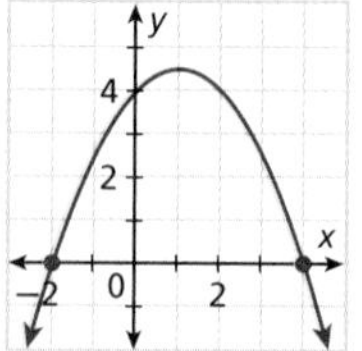

$x = 1$

2 Teach

Guided Instruction

Tell students that the zeros of a function can also be called the *x*-intercepts, or the *x*-values when $y = 0$. Explain that the *x*-value of the vertex is the mean (average) of the zeros.

Teaching Tip **Geometry** The axis of symmetry is a line of reflection because the figure on the left is a reflection of the figure on the right.

Universal Access
Through Modeling

Have two students hold the ends of a jump rope at the same height from the ground. Use a measuring tape to place the students 4 feet, 6 feet, and 8 feet apart. Point out that the lowest point of the jump rope is always halfway between the students. If there is space in the room, have the two students swing the rope. Show the class that when the rope is overhead, its highest point is also halfway between the two students.

If a function has no zeros or they are difficult to identify from a graph, you can use a formula to find the axis of symmetry. The formula works for all quadratic functions.

Finding the Axis of Symmetry by Using the Formula

FORMULA	EXAMPLE
For a quadratic function $y = ax^2 + bx + c$, the axis of symmetry is the vertical line $x = -\frac{b}{2a}$.	$y = 2x^2 + 4x + 5$ $x = -\frac{b}{2a}$ $= -\frac{4}{2(2)} = -1$ The axis of symmetry is $x = -1$.

EXAMPLE 3 Finding the Axis of Symmetry by Using the Formula

Find the axis of symmetry of the graph of $y = x^2 + 3x + 4$.

Step 1 Find the values of a and b.

$y = 1x^2 + 3x + 4$

$a = 1, b = 3$

Step 2 Use the formula $x = -\frac{b}{2a}$.

$x = -\frac{3}{2(1)} = -\frac{3}{2} = -1.5$

The axis of symmetry is $x = -1.5$.

3. Find the axis of symmetry of the graph of $y = 2x^2 + x + 3$. $x = -\frac{1}{4}$

Once you have found the axis of symmetry, you can use it to identify the vertex.

Finding the Vertex of a Parabola
Step 1 To find the x-coordinate of the vertex, find the axis of symmetry by using zeros or the formula.
Step 2 To find the corresponding y-coordinate, substitute the x-coordinate of the vertex into the function.
Step 3 Write the vertex as an ordered pair.

EXAMPLE 4 Finding the Vertex of a Parabola

Find the vertex.

A $y = -x^2 - 2x$

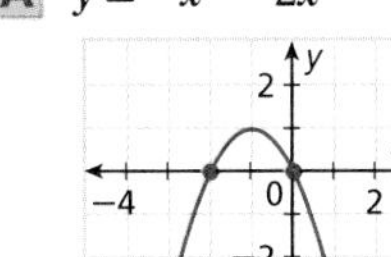

Step 1 Find the x-coordinate of the vertex.

The zeros are −2 and 0.

$x = \frac{-2 + 0}{2} = \frac{-2}{2} = -1$

Step 2 Find the y-coordinate of the vertex.

$y = -x^2 - 2x$ *Use the function rule.*

$= -(-1)^2 - 2(-1) = 1$ *Substitute −1 for x.*

Step 3 Write the ordered pair.

$(-1, 1)$

The vertex is $(-1, 1)$.

Helpful Hint

In Example 4A Step 2, use the order of operations to simplify the function.
$-(-1)^2 = -(1) = -1$

Power Presentations with PowerPoint®

Additional Examples

Example 2

Find the axis of symmetry of each parabola.

A.

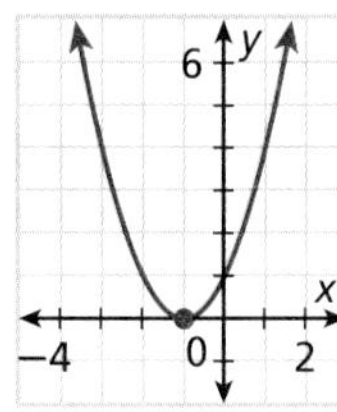

$x = -1$

B.

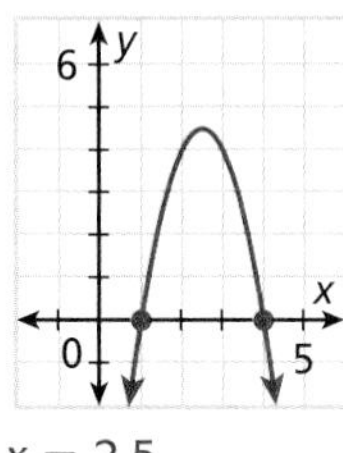

$x = 2.5$

Example 3

Find the axis of symmetry of the graph of $y = -3x^2 + 10x + 9$.
$x = \frac{5}{3}$

Also available on transparency

INTERVENTION

Questioning Strategies

EXAMPLE 2

- What does the axis of symmetry tell you about the graph?

EXAMPLE 3

- What values are used in the formula for the axis of symmetry?

Teaching Tip **Multiple Representations** Encourage students to use the formula to find the axis of symmetry when the zeros do not appear to be integers.

Teaching Tip **Inclusion** Remind students that when there appears to be no coefficient for a variable term, the coefficient is 1, and when there is a term missing, the coefficient of the term or the constant is 0.

Power Presentations with PowerPoint®

Additional Examples

Example 4

Find the vertex.

A. $y = 0.25x^2 + 2x + 3$ $(-4, -1)$

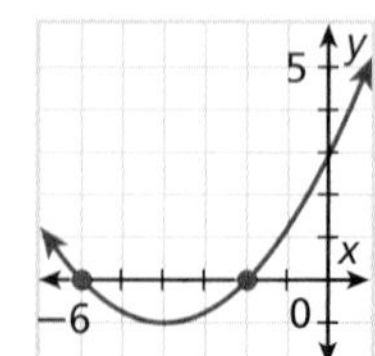

B. $y = -3x^2 + 6x - 7$ $(1, -4)$

Example 5

The graph of $f(x) = -0.06x^2 + 0.6x + 10.26$ can be used to model the height in meters of an arch support for a bridge, where the x-axis represents the water level and x represents the distance in meters from where the arch support enters the water. Can a sailboat that is 14 meters tall pass under the bridge? Explain. Since the height of the support is 11.76 m, the sailboat cannot pass under the bridge.

Also available on transparency

INTERVENTION
Questioning Strategies

EXAMPLE 4

- What is the relationship between the vertex and axis of symmetry?

EXAMPLE 5

- What do the zeros represent?
- What part of the graph do you need to find?

Reading Math Help students understand the meanings of the variables in **Example 5.** Explain that because the x-axis represents water level, the value of x represents the horizontal distance at water level from one side of the arch.

Find the vertex.

B $y = 5x^2 - 10x + 3$

Step 1 Find the x-coordinate of the vertex.

$a = 5, b = -10$ *Identify a and b.*

$x = -\frac{b}{2a}$

$= -\frac{-10}{2(5)} = -\frac{-10}{10} = 1$ *Substitute 5 for a and −10 for b.*

Step 2 Find the y-coordinate of the vertex.

$y = 5x^2 - 10x + 3$

$= 5(1)^2 - 10(1) + 3$ *Use the function rule.*

$= 5 - 10 + 3$ *Substitute 1 for x.*

$= -2$

Step 3 Write the ordered pair.

The vertex is $(1, -2)$.

4. Find the vertex of the graph of $y = x^2 - 4x - 10$. **(2, −14)**

EXAMPLE 5 *Architecture Application*

The height above water level of a curved arch support for a bridge can be modeled by $f(x) = -0.007x^2 + 0.84x + 0.8$, where x is the distance in feet from where the arch support enters the water. Can a sailboat that is 24 feet tall pass under the bridge? Explain.

The vertex represents the highest point of the arch support.

Step 1 Find the x-coordinate of the vertex.

$a = -0.007, b = 0.84$ *Identify a and b.*

$x = -\frac{b}{2a}$

$= -\frac{0.84}{2(-0.007)} = 60$ *Substitute −0.007 for a and 0.84 for b.*

Step 2 Find the y-coordinate of the vertex.

$f(x) = -0.007x^2 + 0.84x + 0.8$ *Use the function rule.*

$= -0.007(60)^2 + 0.84(60) + 0.8$ *Substitute 60 for x.*

$= 26$

Since the height of the arch support is 26 feet, the sailboat can pass under the bridge.

5. The height of a small rise in a roller coaster track is modeled by $f(x) = -0.07x^2 + 0.42x + 6.37$, where x is the distance in feet from a support pole at ground level. Find the height of the rise. **7 ft**

556 *Chapter 9 Quadratic Functions and Equations*

3 Close

Summarize

Review how to find the zeros of a function, the vertex, and the axis of symmetry from the graph. Remind students that there may not always be two zeros. Review how to find the axis of symmetry using the formula and how to determine the y-value of the vertex by substituting the value for x in the quadratic function.

FORMATIVE ASSESSMENT and INTERVENTION

***Diagnose Before* the Lesson**
9-2 Warm Up, TE p. 553

***Monitor During* the Lesson**
Check It Out! Exercises, SE pp. 553–556
Questioning Strategies, TE pp. 554–556

***Assess After* the Lesson**
9-2 Lesson Quiz, TE p. 559
Alternative Assessment, TE p. 559

THINK AND DISCUSS

1. How do you find the zeros of a function from its graph?
2. Describe how to find the axis of symmetry of a quadratic function if its graph does not cross the x-axis

3. **GET ORGANIZED** Copy and complete the graphic organizer. In each box, sketch a graph that fits the given description.

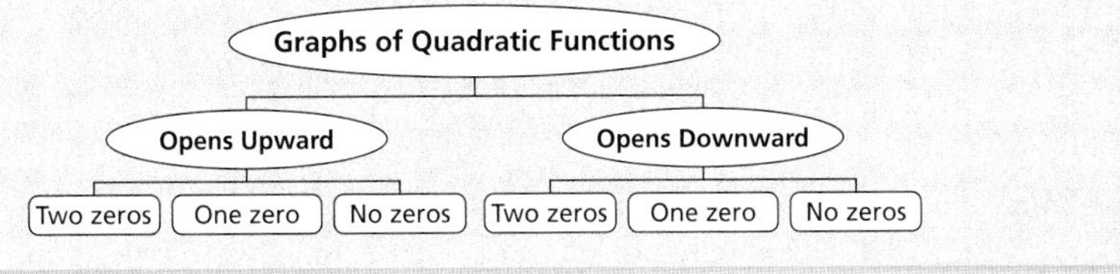

Answers to *Think and Discuss*

Possible answers:

1. Find the point(s) where the graph intersects the x-axis. The x-coordinates of these points are the zeros.
2. Using the quadratic function $y = ax^2 + bx + c$, find the values of a, b, and c. Then use the formula $x = -\frac{b}{2a}$ to find the equation of the axis of symmetry.
3. See p. A7.

9-2 Exercises

21.0, 23.0, 24.1

GUIDED PRACTICE

Vocabulary Apply the vocabulary from this lesson to answer each question.

1. Why is the *zero of a function* the same as an x-intercept of a function?
2. Where is the *axis of symmetry* of a parabola located?

SEE EXAMPLE 1 p. 553

Find the zeros of each quadratic function from its graph. Check your answer.

3. $y = x^2 + 2x + 1$

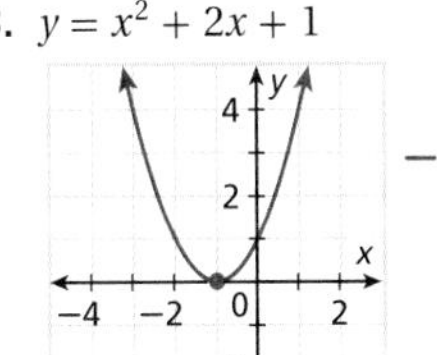

-1

4. $y = 9 - x^2$

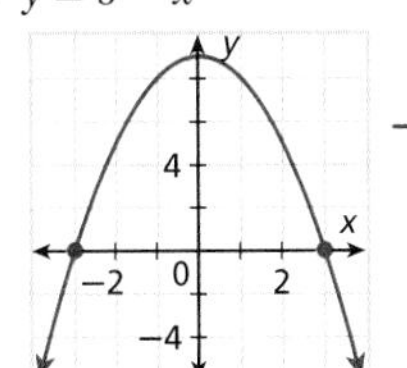

$-3, 3$

5. $y = -x^2 - x - 4$

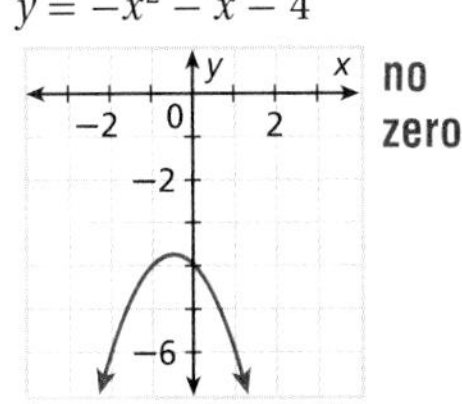

no zeros

SEE EXAMPLE 2 p. 554

Find the axis of symmetry of each parabola.

6.

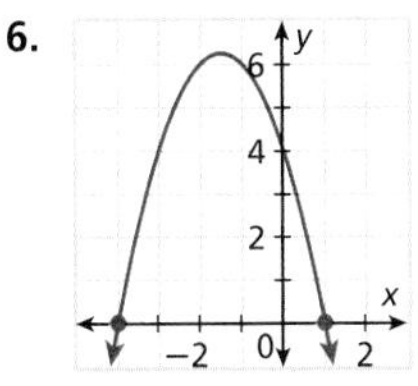

$x = -\frac{3}{2}$

7.

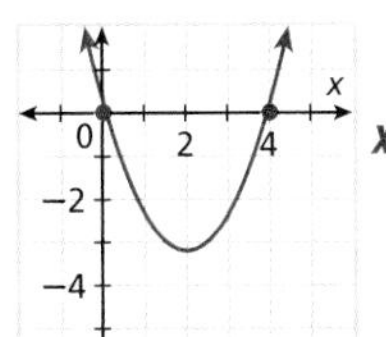

$x = 2$

8.

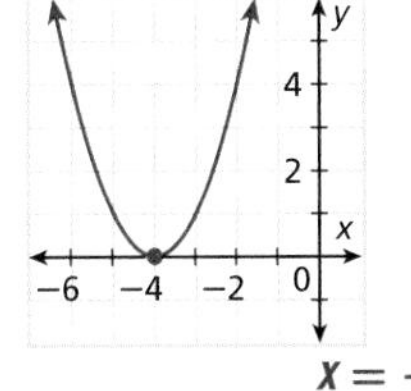

$x = -4$

SEE EXAMPLE 3 p. 555

For each quadratic function, find the axis of symmetry of its graph.

9. $y = x^2 + 4x - 7$ $x = -2$
10. $y = 3x^2 - 18x + 1$ $x = 3$
11. $y = 2x^2 + 3x - 4$ $x = -\frac{3}{4}$
12. $y = -3x^2 + x + 5$ $x = \frac{1}{6}$

9-2 Exercises

Assignment Guide

Assign *Guided Practice* exercises as necessary.

If you finished Examples **1–3**
Proficient 19–28, 37–39, 44
Advanced 19–28, 37–39, 44

If you finished Examples **1–5**
Proficient 19–44, 46–52
Advanced 19–52

Homework Quick Check
Quickly check key concepts.
Exercises: 20, 22, 26, 30, 34

Answers

1. An x-intercept is a value of x where $f(x) = 0$.
2. The axis of symmetry is the vertical line passing through the vertex that divides the parabola into 2 symmetric halves.

California Standards

Standard	Exercises
7.0	46–48
10.0	49
21.0	3–5, 19–21, 36c, 41
23.0	34, 36a, 36b, 36d, 45
24.1	35

Answers

35. The equation for the axis of symmetry is $x = -\frac{b}{2a}$. If $b = 0$, then the axis of symmetry is $x = 0$, or the y-axis.

36a. about (4, 77)

b. the time and height at the moment when the rocket was at its highest point

c. 0 and 8; the starting and ending times

d. $s = 4$; it is the midpoint between the two zeros and the x-coordinate of the vertex.

SEE EXAMPLE 4 p. 555

Find the vertex.

13. $y = -5x^2 + 10x + 3$ **(1, 8)**
14. 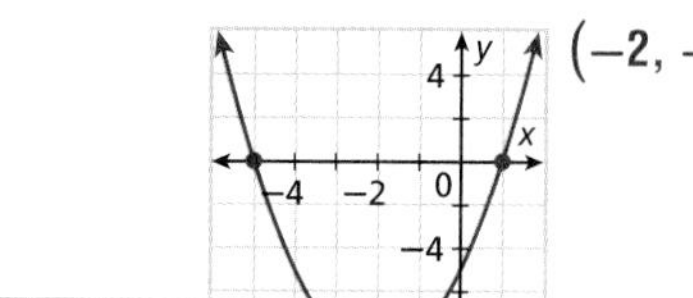

(−2, −9)
15. $y = x^2 + 4x - 7$ **(−2, −11)**
16. $y = \frac{1}{2}x^2 + 2x$ **(−2, −2)**
17. $y = -x^2 + 6x + 1$ **(3, 10)**

SEE EXAMPLE 5 p. 556

18. **Archery** The height in feet above the ground of an arrow t seconds after it is shot can be modeled by $y = -16t^2 + 63t + 4$. Can the arrow pass over a tree that is 68 feet tall? Explain. **No; the highest the arrow will go is about 66 feet.**

PRACTICE AND PROBLEM SOLVING

Independent Practice

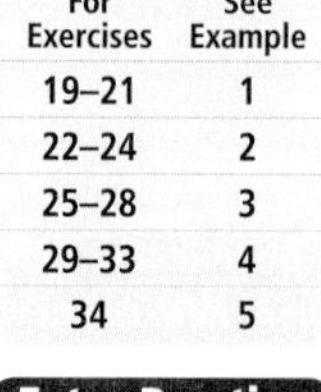

For Exercises	See Example
19–21	1
22–24	2
25–28	3
29–33	4
34	5

Extra Practice

Skills Practice p. EP18
Application Practice p. EP32

Find the zeros of each quadratic function from its graph. Check your answer.

19. $y = \frac{1}{4}x^2 - x + 3$

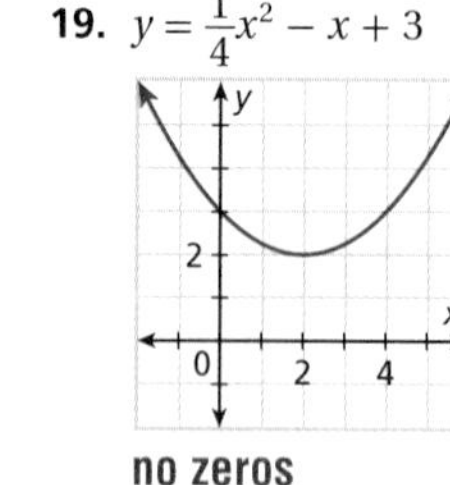

no zeros

20. $y = -\frac{1}{3}x^2$

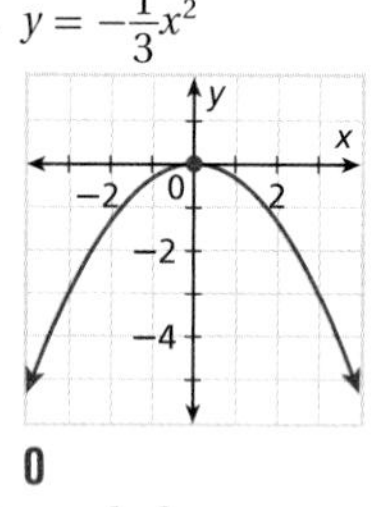

0

21. $y = x^2 + 10x + 16$

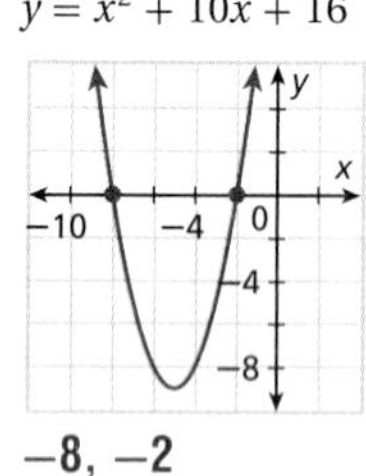

−8, −2

Find the axis of symmetry of each parabola.

22. 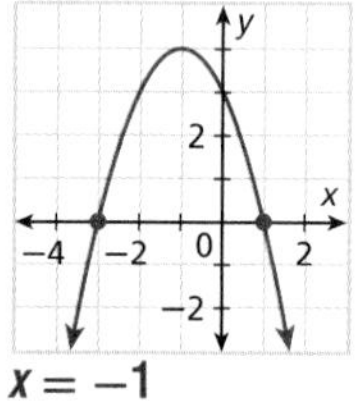

$x = -1$

23. 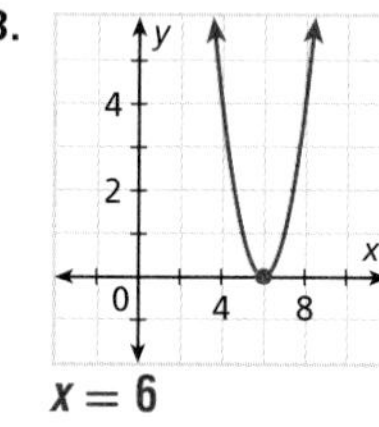

$x = 6$

24. 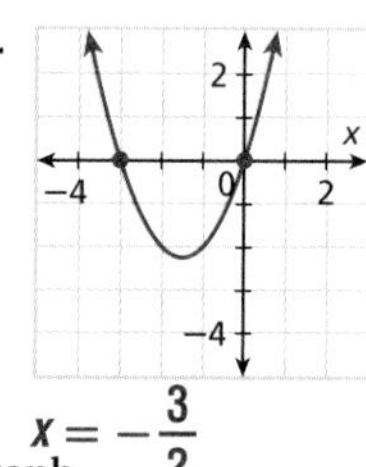

$x = -\frac{3}{2}$

For each quadratic function, find the axis of symmetry of its graph.

25. $y = x^2 + x + 2$ **$x = -\frac{1}{2}$**
26. $y = (3x + 3)(x - 6)$ **$x = \frac{5}{2}$**
27. $y = \frac{1}{2}x^2 - 5x + 4$ **$x = 5$**
28. $y + 2x^2 = \frac{1}{3}x - \frac{3}{4}$ **$x = \frac{1}{12}$**

Find the vertex.

29. $y = x(x + 7)$ **(−3.5, −12.25)**
30. 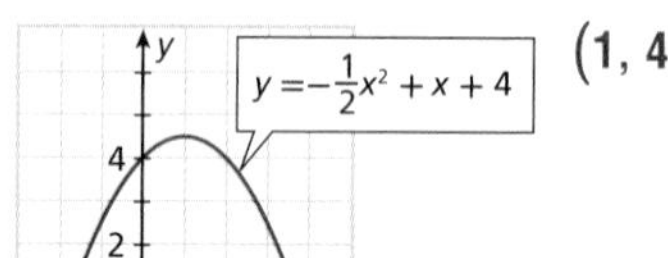

(1, 4.5)
31. $y - 8x = 16 - x^2$ **(4, 32)**
32. $y = -2x^2 - 8x - 3$ **(−2, 5)**
33. $y = -x^2 + \frac{1}{2}x + 2$ **$\left(\frac{1}{4}, 2\frac{1}{16}\right)$**

California LINK

Engineering

The Bixby Bridge in Big Sur, California, is a single span concrete arch bridge. It is over 700 feet long and over 260 feet high. Arch bridges are strong because the curve carries the weight of the bridge outward to the supports at the end.

34. **Engineering** The height in feet of the curved arch support for a pedestrian bridge over a creek can be modeled by $f(x) = -0.628x^2 + 4.5x$, where x is the distance in feet from where the arch support enters the water. If there is a flood that raises the level of the creek by 5.5 feet, will the top of the arch support be above the water? Explain. **Yes; the highest point of the arch support is about 8 feet above the creek.**

35. **Reasoning** For quadratic functions $y = ax^2 + bx + c$ in which $b = 0$, use deductive reasoning to show that the axis of symmetry is the y-axis.

9-2 PRACTICE A

9-2 PRACTICE C

9-2 PRACTICE B

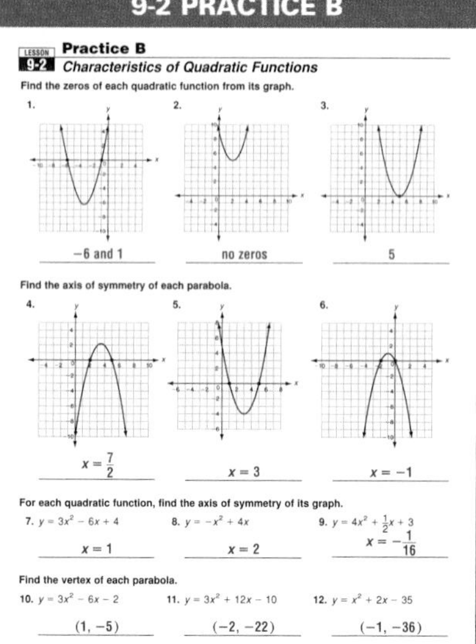

LESSON 9-2 **Practice B**
Characteristics of Quadratic Functions

Find the zeros of each quadratic function from its graph.

1. −6 and 1
2. no zeros
3. 5

Find the axis of symmetry of each parabola.

4. $x = \frac{7}{2}$
5. $x = 3$
6. $x = -1$

For each quadratic function, find the axis of symmetry of its graph.

7. $y = 3x^2 - 6x + 4$ $x = 1$
8. $y = -x^2 + 4x$ $x = 2$
9. $y = 4x^2 + \frac{1}{2}x + 3$ $x = -\frac{1}{16}$

Find the vertex of each parabola.

10. $y = 3x^2 - 6x - 2$ (1, −5)
11. $y = 3x^2 + 12x - 10$ (−2, −22)
12. $y = x^2 + 2x - 35$ (−1, −36)

9-2 READING STRATEGIES

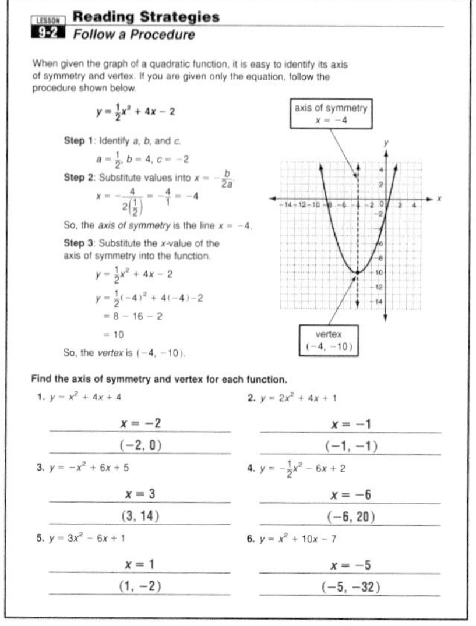

LESSON 9-2 **Reading Strategies**
Follow a Procedure

When given the graph of a quadratic function, it is easy to identify its axis of symmetry and vertex. If you are given only the equation, follow the procedure shown below.

$y = \frac{1}{2}x^2 + 4x - 2$

Step 1: Identify a, b, and c.
$a = \frac{1}{2}, b = 4, c = -2$

Step 2: Substitute values into $x = -\frac{b}{2a}$.
$x = -\frac{4}{2\left(\frac{1}{2}\right)} = -\frac{4}{1} = -4$

So, the *axis of symmetry* is the line $x = -4$.

Step 3: Substitute the x-value of the axis of symmetry into the function.
$y = \frac{1}{2}x^2 + 4x - 2$
$y = \frac{1}{2}(-4)^2 + 4(-4) - 2$
$= 8 - 16 - 2$
$= 10$

So, the *vertex* is (−4, −10).

axis of symmetry $x = -4$

vertex (−4, −10)

Find the axis of symmetry and vertex for each function.

1. $y = x^2 + 4x + 4$ $x = -2$; (−2, 0)
2. $y = 2x^2 + 4x + 1$ $x = -1$; (−1, −1)
3. $y = -x^2 + 6x + 5$ $x = 3$; (3, 14)
4. $y = -\frac{1}{2}x^2 - 6x + 2$ $x = -6$; (−6, 20)
5. $y = 3x^2 - 6x + 1$ $x = 1$; (1, −2)
6. $y = x^2 + 10x - 7$ $x = -5$; (−5, −32)

9-2 REVIEW FOR MASTERY

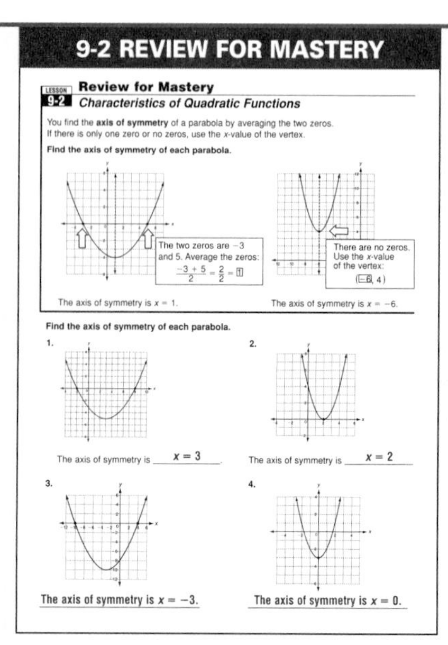

LESSON 9-2 **Review for Mastery**
Characteristics of Quadratic Functions

You find the **axis of symmetry** of a parabola by averaging the two zeros. If there is only one zero or no zeros, use the x-value of the vertex.

Find the axis of symmetry of each parabola.

The two zeros are −3 and 5. Average the zeros: $\frac{-3 + 5}{2} = \frac{2}{2} = 1$

The axis of symmetry is $x = 1$.

There are no zeros. Use the x-value of the vertex: (−6, 4)

The axis of symmetry is $x = -6$.

Find the axis of symmetry of each parabola.

1. The axis of symmetry is $x = 3$.
2. The axis of symmetry is $x = 2$
3. The axis of symmetry is $x = -3$.
4. The axis of symmetry is $x = 0$.

CONCEPT CONNECTION

36. This problem will prepare you for the Concept Connection on page 566.
    a. Use the graph of the height of a water bottle rocket to estimate the coordinates of the parabola's vertex.
    b. What does the vertex represent?
    c. Find the zeros of the function. What do they represent?
    d. Find the axis of symmetry. How is it related to the vertex and the zeros?

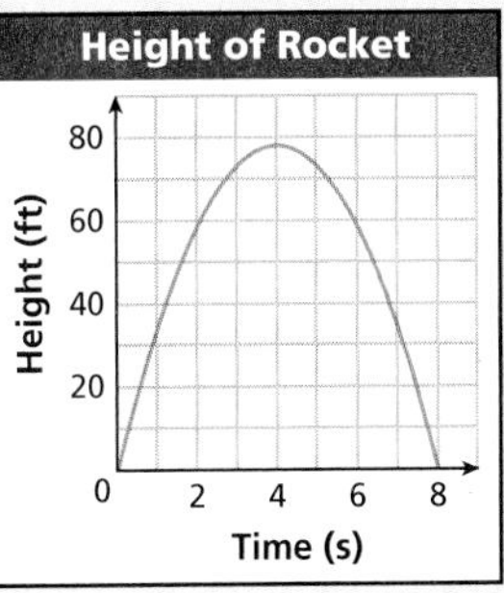

Graphing Calculator Tell how many zeros each quadratic function has.

37. $y = 8x^2 - 4x + 2$ **0**
38. $0 = y + 16x^2$ **1**
39. $\frac{1}{4}x^2 - 7x - 12 = y - 4$ **2**

40. **Write About It** If you are given the axis of symmetry of a parabola and know that the function has two zeros, how would you describe the location of the two zeros?
The two zeros are on either side of the axis of symmetry and are equidistant from it.

Multiple Choice For Exercises 41 and 42, choose the best answer.

41. Which function has the zeros shown in the graph?
    (A) $y = x^2 + 2x + 8$
    (C) $y = x^2 + 2x - 8$
    (B) $y = x^2 - 2x - 8$ (circled)
    (D) $y = 2x^2 - 2x + 8$

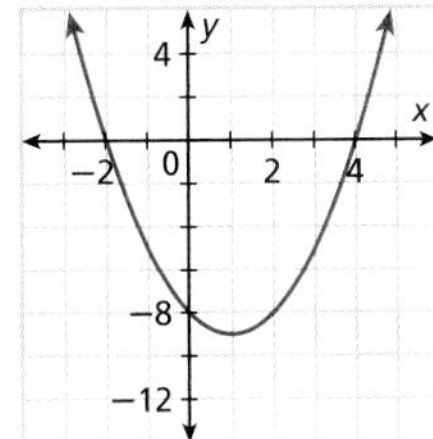

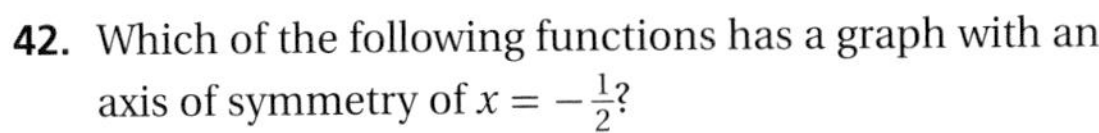

42. Which of the following functions has a graph with an axis of symmetry of $x = -\frac{1}{2}$?
    (A) $y = 2x^2 - 2x + 5$
    (C) $2x^2 + y = 2x + 5$
    (B) $2x + 5 = 2x^2 - y$
    (D) $2x - y = 5 - 2x^2$ (circled)

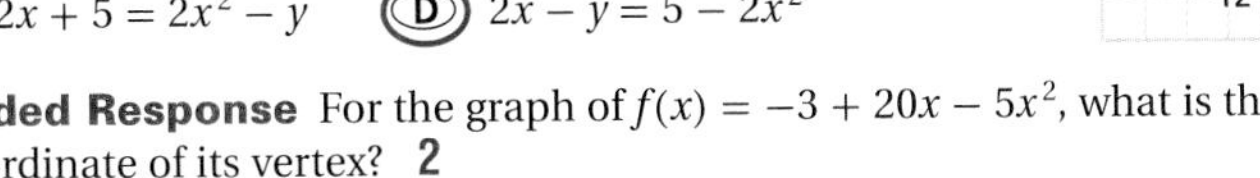

43. **Gridded Response** For the graph of $f(x) = -3 + 20x - 5x^2$, what is the x-coordinate of its vertex? **2**

CHALLENGE AND EXTEND

44. Describe the domain and range of a quadratic function that has exactly one zero and whose graph opens downward.

44. The domain is all real numbers, and the range is $y \leq 0$.

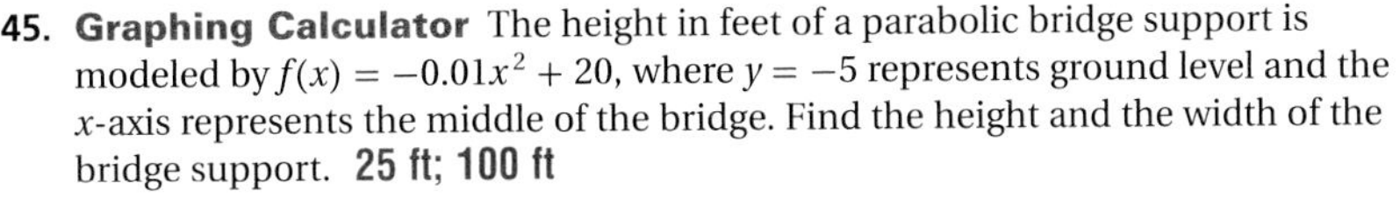

45. **Graphing Calculator** The height in feet of a parabolic bridge support is modeled by $f(x) = -0.01x^2 + 20$, where $y = -5$ represents ground level and the x-axis represents the middle of the bridge. Find the height and the width of the bridge support. **25 ft; 100 ft**

SPIRAL STANDARDS REVIEW

7.0, 10.0

Without graphing, tell whether each point lies on the graph of $2x + y = 8$. *(Lesson 5-1)*

46. $(1, 5)$ **no**
47. $(3, 2)$ **yes**
48. $(6, -4)$ **yes**

49. The length of a rug is 6 inches longer than its width. Write a polynomial that represents the area of the rug. *(Lesson 7-8)* $x^2 + 6x$

Without graphing, tell whether each point is on the graph of the given equation. *(Lesson 9-1)*

50. $y = 5x^2 - 7x$; $(2, 7)$ **no**
51. $x^2 - 5x = 2 + y$; $(1, -6)$ **yes**
52. $y = -x^2 - 6x + 1$; $(-5, 6)$ **yes**

CONCEPT CONNECTION **Exercise 36** involves finding the vertex of a parabola and telling what it represents. This exercise prepares students for the Concept Connection on page 566.

Teaching Tip **Multiple Choice** In **Exercise 41,** remind students that they can determine the *y*-intercept by substituting 0 for *x*. Students can immediately eliminate **A** and **D** because the graphs of those functions cross the *y*-axis at 8, not −8.

Journal

Have students explain how the vertex and the axis of symmetry are related graphically and algebraically.

ALTERNATIVE ASSESSMENT

Have students create two quadratic functions: one with one zero and the other with two zeros. Have them state the zeros, the axis of symmetry, and the vertex for each.

Power Presentations with PowerPoint®

9-2 Lesson Quiz

1. Find the zeros and the axis of symmetry.

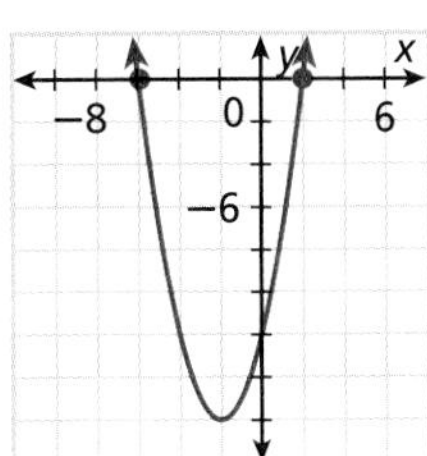

zeros: −6, 2; $x = -2$

2. Find the axis of symmetry and the vertex of the graph of $y = 3x^2 + 12x + 8$. $x = -2$; $(-2, -4)$
3. The graph of $f(x) = -0.01x^2 + x$ can be used to model the height in feet of a curved arch support for a bridge, where the x-axis represents the water level and x represents the distance in feet from where the arch support enters the water. Find the height of the highest point of the bridge. 25 ft

Also available on transparency

9-2 PROBLEM SOLVING

LESSON 9-2 Problem Solving
Characteristics of Quadratic Functions

Write the correct answer.

1. A superhero is trying to leap over a tall building. The function $f(x) = -16x^2 + 200x$ gives the superhero's height in feet as a function of time. The building is 612 feet high. Will the superhero make it over the building? Explain.
   Yes; the vertex is (6.25, 625) and 625 > 612

2. The graph shows the height of an arch support for a pedestrian bridge. 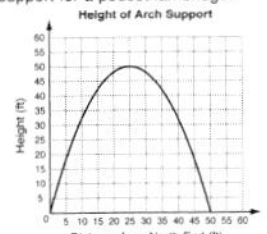
   Height of Arch Support
   Height (ft); Distance from North End (ft)
   Find the zeros (if any) and axis of symmetry of this parabola.
   0 and 50; $x = 25$

3. The distance between the cables suspending a bridge and the water below is given by the function $y = 0.02x^2 - 2x + 80$. Find the vertex of the graph.
   (50, 30)

After a heavy snowfall, Joe and Karin made an igloo. The dome of the igloo is in the shape of a parabola and the height of the igloo in inches is given by $f(x) = -0.03x^2 + 2.4x$. Select the best answer.

4. Joe wants to place a support in the middle of the igloo, along the axis of symmetry. How far from the edge of the igloo should he place the support?
   A 24 in. C 48 in.
   (B) 40 in. D 80 in.

5. Neither Joe nor Karin can stand up inside the igloo. How tall is the center of the igloo? (*Hint:* the top of the igloo is the vertex of the parabola.)
   F 24 in. **(H)** 48 in.
   G 40 in. J 80 in.

6. Karin graphs the parabola and looks at the zeros to see how wide the igloo is. What are the zeros of this parabola?
   A −80 and 80 **(C)** 0 and 80
   B −40 and 40 D 40 and 80

7. What is the vertex of the parabola that Karin graphed?
   F (20, 36) H (48, 40)
   (G) (40, 48) J (80, 0)

8. Which graph below is the graph that Karin made?
   A C
   B **(D)**

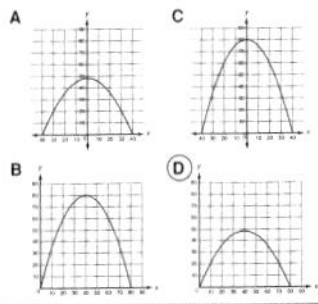

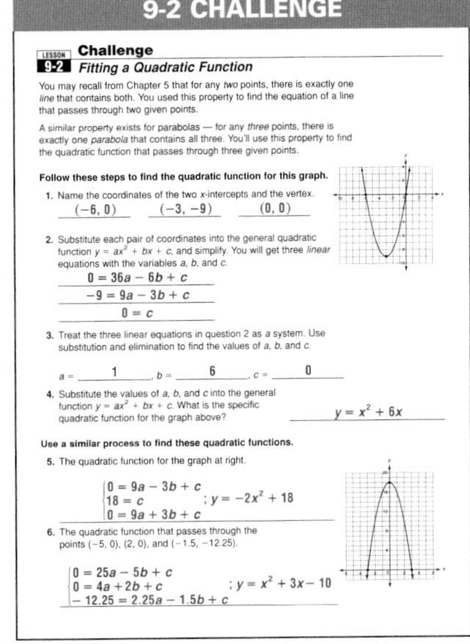

9-2 CHALLENGE

LESSON 9-2 Challenge
Fitting a Quadratic Function

You may recall from Chapter 5 that for any *two* points, there is exactly one *line* that contains both. You used this property to find the equation of a line that passes through two given points.

A similar property exists for parabolas — for any *three* points, there is exactly one *parabola* that contains all three. You'll use this property to find the quadratic function that passes through three given points.

Follow these steps to find the quadratic function for this graph.

1. Name the coordinates of the two x-intercepts and the vertex.
   (−6, 0) **(−3, −9)** **(0, 0)**

2. Substitute each pair of coordinates into the general quadratic function $y = ax^2 + bx + c$, and simplify. You will get three *linear* equations with the variables a, b, and c.
   $0 = 36a - 6b + c$
   $-9 = 9a - 3b + c$
   $0 = c$

3. Treat the three linear equations in question 2 as a system. Use substitution and elimination to find the values of a, b, and c.
   $a =$ **1**, $b =$ **6**, $c =$ **0**

4. Substitute the values of a, b, and c into the general function $y = ax^2 + bx + c$. What is the specific quadratic function for the graph above?
   $y = x^2 + 6x$

Use a similar process to find these quadratic functions.

5. The quadratic function for the graph at right.
   $\begin{cases} 0 = 9a - 3b + c \\ 18 = c \\ 0 = 9a + 3b + c \end{cases}$; $y = -2x^2 + 18$

6. The quadratic function that passes through the points (−5, 0), (2, 0), and (−1.5, −12.25).
   $\begin{cases} 0 = 25a - 5b + c \\ 0 = 4a + 2b + c \\ -12.25 = 2.25a - 1.5b + c \end{cases}$; $y = x^2 + 3x - 10$

9-3 Organizer

Objective: Graph a quadratic function in the form $y = ax^2 + bx + c$.

Technology Lab
In Chapter 9 Resource File

Online Edition
Tutorial Videos

Countdown to Mastery Week 20

Power Presentations with PowerPoint®

Warm Up

Find the axis of symmetry.

1. $y = 4x^2 - 7$ $\quad x = 0$
2. $y = x^2 - 3x + 1$ $\quad x = \frac{3}{2}$
3. $y = -2x^2 + 4x + 3$ $\quad x = 1$
4. $y = -2x^2 + 3x - 1$ $\quad x = \frac{3}{4}$

Find the vertex.

5. $y = x^2 + 4x + 5$ $\quad (-2, 1)$
6. $y = 3x^2 + 2$ $\quad (0, 2)$
7. $y = 2x^2 + 2x - 8$ $\quad \left(-\frac{1}{2}, -\frac{17}{2}\right)$

Also available on transparency

Math Humor

Q: What do you call a tough old math equation?

A: A battle-ax².

California Standards

Algebra 1 21.0, 23.0

9-3 Graphing Quadratic Functions

California Standards

21.0 Students graph quadratic functions and know that their roots are the *x*-intercepts.
23.0 Students apply quadratic equations to physical problems, such as the motion of an object under the force of gravity.

Why use this?

Graphs of quadratic functions can help you determine how high an object is tossed or kicked. (See Exercise 14.)

Recall that a *y*-intercept is the *y*-coordinate of the point where a graph intersects the *y*-axis. The *x*-coordinate of this point is always 0. For a quadratic function written in the form $y = ax^2 + bx + c$, when $x = 0$, $y = c$. So the *y*-intercept of a quadratic function is *c*.

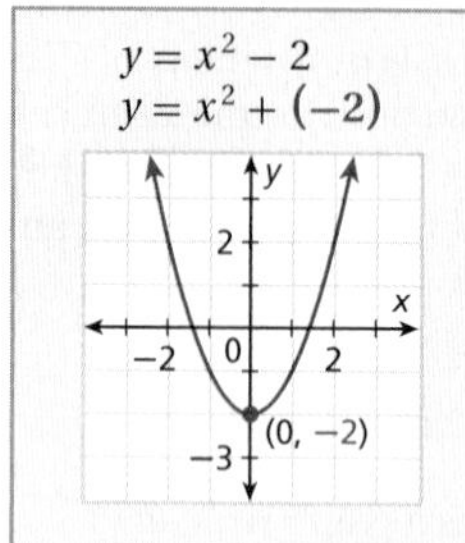

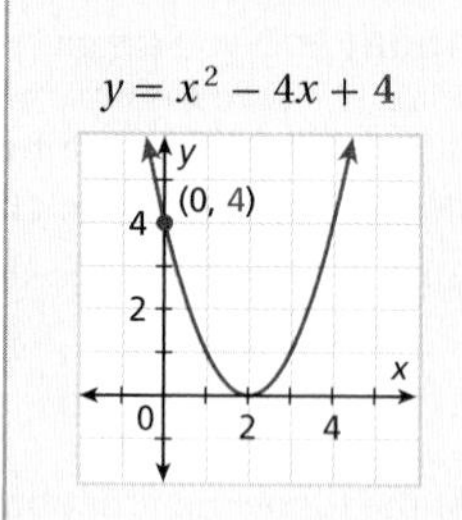

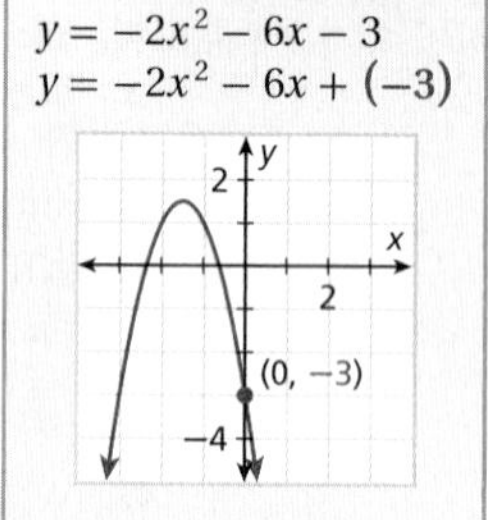

In the previous lesson, you found the axis of symmetry and vertex of a parabola. You can use these characteristics, the *y*-intercept, and symmetry to graph a quadratic function.

EXAMPLE 1 Graphing a Quadratic Function

Graph $y = x^2 - 4x - 5$.

Step 1 Find the axis of symmetry.

$x = -\frac{-4}{2(1)}$ — *Use $x = -\frac{b}{2a}$. Substitute 1 for a and −4 for b.*

$= 2$ — *Simplify.*

The axis of symmetry is $x = 2$.

Step 2 Find the vertex.

$y = x^2 - 4x - 5$

$= 2^2 - 4(2) - 5$ — *The x-coordinate of the vertex is 2. Substitute 2 for x.*

$= 4 - 8 - 5$ — *Simplify.*

$= -9$ — *The y-coordinate of the vertex is −9.*

The vertex is $(2, -9)$.

Step 3 Find the *y*-intercept.

$y = x^2 - 4x - 5$

$y = x^2 - 4x + (-5)$ — *Identify c.*

The *y*-intercept is −5; the graph passes through $(0, -5)$.

1 Introduce

EXPLORATION

9-3 Graphing Quadratic Functions

Recall that a *y*-intercept is the *y*-coordinate of a point where a graph intersects the *y*-axis. Use your calculator to explore the *y*-intercepts of some quadratic functions.

1. Use your calculator to graph each of the quadratic functions in the table. For each function, use the graph to identify the *y*-intercept.

Function	*y*-intercept
$y = x^2 - 2x + 3$	
$y = x^2 + x - 6$	
$y = -2x^2 + 3x + 4$	
$y = -\frac{1}{2}x^2 - x - 2$	
$y = 3x^2 - 5x$	

2. Look for a pattern in your table. In general, what can you say about the *y*-intercept of a quadratic function written in the form $y = ax^2 + bx + c$?
3. Without graphing the function, determine the *y*-intercept of $y = 4x^2 - 7x - 8$.

THINK AND DISCUSS

4. **Explain** how knowing the *y*-intercept of a quadratic function can help you sketch its graph.

Motivate

Discuss with students how the more they know about the properties of a geometric figure, the easier it is for them to sketch an accurate drawing of it. For example, if you know the length of a rectangle, you have only part of the information you need to draw it accurately. If you also know the width of the rectangle, then you can make an accurate drawing. Tell students that in this lesson they will learn to use the properties of parabolas to graph them.

Explorations and answers are provided in *Alternate Openers: Explorations Transparencies.*

Step 4 Find two more points on the same side of the axis of symmetry as the point containing the y-intercept.

Since the axis of symmetry is $x = 2$, choose x-values less than 2.

Let $x = 1$.		Let $x = -1$.
$y = 1^2 - 4(1) - 5$	*Substitute x-coordinates.*	$y = (-1)^2 - 4(-1) - 5$
$= 1 - 4 - 5$	*Simplify.*	$= 1 + 4 - 5$
$= -8$		$= 0$

Two other points are $(1, -8)$ and $(-1, 0)$.

Step 5 Graph the axis of symmetry, the vertex, the point containing the y-intercept, and two other points.

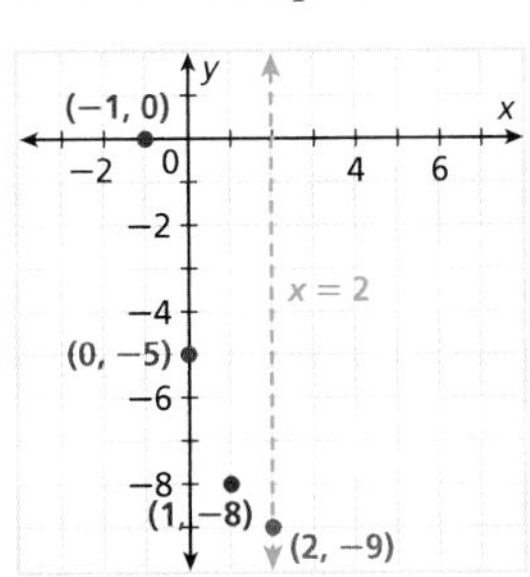

Step 6 Reflect the points across the axis of symmetry. Connect the points with a smooth curve.

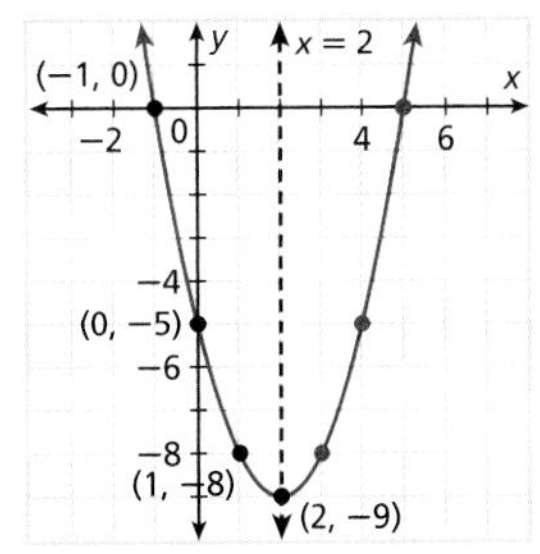

Helpful Hint

Because a parabola is symmetrical, each point is the same number of units away from the axis of symmetry as its reflected point.

1a.

1b.

Graph each quadratic function.

1a. $y = 2x^2 + 6x + 2$ **1b.** $y + 6x = x^2 + 9$

EXAMPLE 2 *Problem-Solving Application*

The height in feet of a football that is kicked can be modeled by the function $f(x) = -16x^2 + 64x$, where x is the time in seconds after it is kicked. Find the football's maximum height and the time it takes the football to reach this height. Then find how long the football is in the air.

Understand the Problem

The **answer** includes three parts: the maximum height, the time to reach the maximum height, and the time to reach the ground.

List the important information:

- The function $f(x) = -16x^2 + 64x$ models the height of the football after x seconds.

Make a Plan

Find the vertex of the graph because the maximum height of the football and the time it takes to reach it are the coordinates of the vertex. The football will hit the ground when its height is 0, so find the zeros of the function. You can do this by graphing.

Remember!

The vertex is the highest or lowest point on a parabola. Therefore, in the example, it gives the maximum height of the football.

COMMON ERROR ALERT

Some students get confused by multiple negative signs when using the formula to find the axis of symmetry. Encourage them to write the expression as $-\left(\frac{b}{2a}\right)$.

Power Presentations with PowerPoint®

Additional Examples

Example 1

Graph $y = 3x^2 - 6x + 1$.

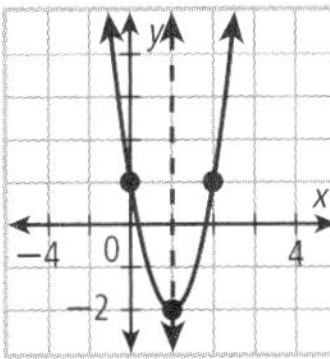

Example 2

The height in feet of a basketball that is thrown can be modeled by $f(x) = -16x^2 + 32x$, where x is the time in seconds after it is thrown. Find the basketball's maximum height and the time it takes the basketball to reach this height. Then find how long the basketball is in the air. 16 ft; 1 s; 2 s

Also available on transparency

INTERVENTION

Questioning Strategies

EXAMPLE **1**

- How do you know whether the parabola opens up or down?
- Can you have points both above and below the vertex?
- What does the axis of symmetry tell you about the graph?

EXAMPLE **2**

- What do the zeros represent in the problem?
- What is a reasonable domain and range in this situation?

2 Teach

Guided Instruction

Review the characteristics of a parabola with students. Show students how to use the information to graph the parabola. Then show how to interpret the graph of a quadratic function when it models a real-world relationship such as height over time.

Universal Access

Through Modeling

Have students in small groups create a scenario that could be represented by a quadratic function (see examples). Have them create a graph of their function using realistic labels and scales on the axes (they do not need to create a function rule) and present it to the class. They should tell the class what scenario is modeled by the graph, what the vertex and zeros represent, and what a reasonable domain and range are.

Reading Math Emphasize that the quadratic model in **Example 2** models height over time, whereas the quadratic models in Lesson 9-2 modeled height over distance. Point out that a height-over-time model does not represent the shape of the projectile's path and that the units on the axes are not both measures of length.

Critical Thinking Point out to students that, in **Example 2,** finding the y-intercept to be 0 means that 0 is a zero of the function. Reflect across the axis of symmetry to find the other zero at 4. You now have all the information needed to answer the question without graphing.

Solve

Step 1 Find the axis of symmetry.

$x = -\frac{64}{2(-16)}$ *Use $x = -\frac{b}{2a}$. Substitute −16 for a and 64 for b.*

$= -\frac{64}{-32} = 2$ *Simplify.*

The axis of symmetry is $x = 2$.

Step 2 Find the vertex.

$y = -16x^2 + 64x$

$= -16(2)^2 + 64(2)$ *The x-coordinate of the vertex is 2. Substitute 2 for x.*

$= -16(4) + 128$ *Simplify.*

$= -64 + 128$

$= 64$ *The y-coordinate of the vertex is 64.*

The vertex is $(2, 64)$.

Step 3 Find the y-intercept.

$y = -16x^2 + 64x + 0$ *Identify c.*

The y-intercept is 0; the graph passes through $(0, 0)$.

Step 4 Find another point on the same side of the axis of symmetry as the point containing the y-intercept.

Since the axis of symmetry is $x = 2$, choose an x-value that is less than 2. Let $x = 1$.

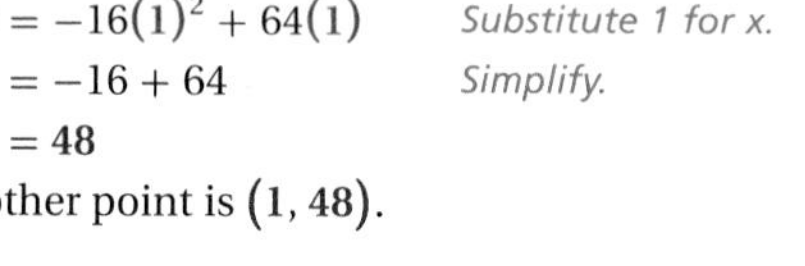

$y = -16(1)^2 + 64(1)$ *Substitute 1 for x.*

$= -16 + 64$ *Simplify.*

$= 48$

Another point is $(1, 48)$.

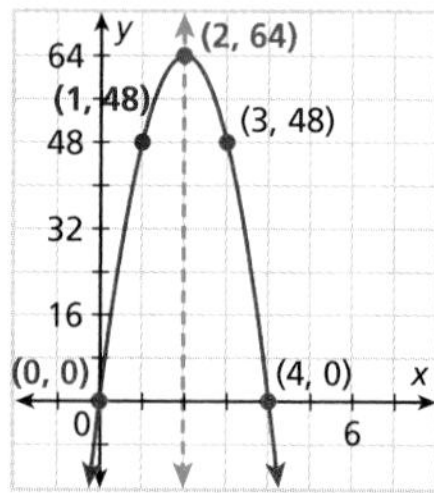

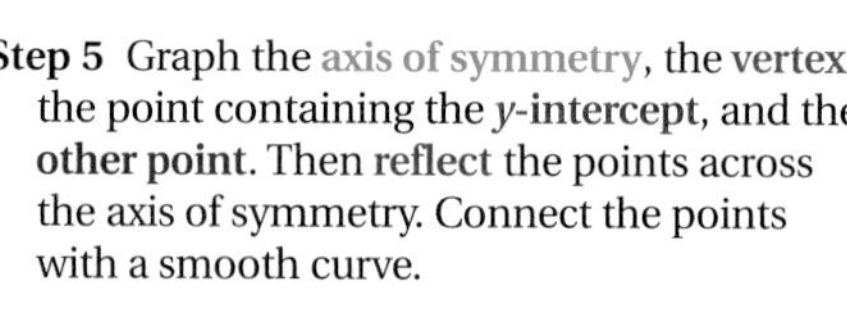

Step 5 Graph the axis of symmetry, the vertex, the point containing the y-intercept, and the other point. Then reflect the points across the axis of symmetry. Connect the points with a smooth curve.

The vertex is $(2, 64)$. So at 2 seconds, the football has reached its maximum height of 64 feet. The graph shows the zeros of the function are 0 and 4. At 0 seconds the football has not yet been kicked, and at 4 seconds it reaches the ground. The football is in the air for 4 seconds.

Look Back

Check by substituting $(2, 64)$ and $(4, 0)$ into the function.

$64 = -16(2)^2 + 64(2)$		$0 = -16(4)^2 + 64(4)$	
64	$-64 + 128$	0	$-256 + 256$
64	64 ✓	0	0 ✓

2. As Molly dives into her pool, her height in feet above the water can be modeled by the function $f(x) = -16x^2 + 24x$, where x is the time in seconds after she begins diving. Find the maximum height of her dive and the time it takes Molly to reach this height. Then find how long it takes her to reach the pool.

maximum height: 9 ft at 0.75 s; time it takes to reach the pool: 1.5 s

Teaching Tip

Multiple Representations Students can check the reasonableness of their graph by choosing a reflected point and substituting the ordered pair into the function. If it satisfies the function, the point was reflected correctly and the graph is reasonable.

3 Close

Summarize

Have students identify the vertex of each function. Then have them tell whether the parabola opens upward or downward.

$y = 4x^2 - 4$ $(0, -4)$; upward

$y = 2x^2 + 2x + 1$ $\left(-\frac{1}{2}, \frac{1}{2}\right)$; upward

$y = -x^2 + 6x - 7$ $(3, 2)$; downward

FORMATIVE ASSESSMENT and INTERVENTION

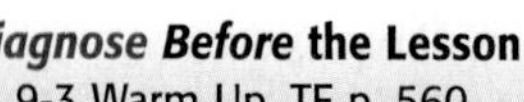

***Diagnose Before* the Lesson**
9-3 Warm Up, TE p. 560

***Monitor During* the Lesson**
Check It Out! Exercises, SE pp. 561–562
Questioning Strategies, TE p. 561

***Assess After* the Lesson**
9-3 Lesson Quiz, TE p. 565
Alternative Assessment, TE p. 565

THINK AND DISCUSS

1. Explain how to find the y-intercept of a quadratic function that is written in the form $ax^2 - y = bx + c$.
2. Explain how to graph a quadratic function.
3. What do you think the vertex and zeros of the function will tell you for the situation in the Check It Out for Example 2?
4. **GET ORGANIZED** Copy and complete the graphic organizer using your own quadratic function.

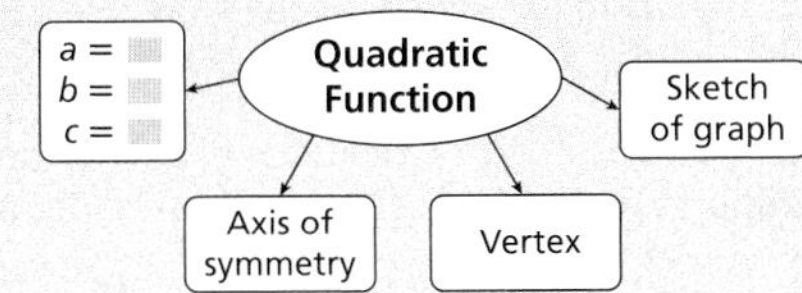

Answers to *Think and Discuss*

Possible answers:

1. First subtract ax^2 from both sides of the equation. Then divide both sides by −1. The resulting value of c is the y-intercept.
2. Find the axis of symmetry, the vertex, and any zeros. Draw a curve that passes through the points and is symmetrical about the axis.
3. The vertex is the maximum height of Molly's dive at the midpoint of the time she was in the air. The zeros are the start time of the dive and the time when she reaches the pool.
4. See p. A7.

9-3 Exercises

GUIDED PRACTICE

SEE EXAMPLE 1 p. 560

Graph each quadratic function.

1. $y = x^2 - 2x - 3$
2. $-y - 3x^2 = -3$
3. $y = 2x^2 + 2x - 4$
4. $y = x^2 + 4x - 8$
5. $y + x^2 + 5x + 2 = 0$
6. $y = 4x^2 + 2$

SEE EXAMPLE 2 p. 561

7. **Multi-Step** The height in feet of a golf ball that is hit from the ground can be modeled by the function $f(x) = -16x^2 + 96x$, where x is the time in seconds after the ball is hit. Find the ball's maximum height and the time it takes the ball to reach this height. Then find how long the ball is in the air.

maximum height: 144 ft at 3 s; time in the air: 6 s

PRACTICE AND PROBLEM SOLVING

For Exercises	See Example
8–13	1
14	2

Independent Practice

Extra Practice
Skills Practice p. EP18
Application Practice p. EP32

Graph each quadratic function.

8. $y = -4x^2 + 12x - 5$
9. $y = 3x^2 + 12x + 9$
10. $y - 7x^2 - 14x = 3$
11. $y = -x^2 + 2x$
12. $y - 1 = 4x^2 + 8x$
13. $y = -2x^2 - 3x + 4$

14. **Multi-Step** A juggler tosses a ring into the air. The height of the ring in feet above the juggler's hands can be modeled by the function $f(x) = -16x^2 + 16x$, where x is the time in seconds after the ring is tossed. Find the ring's maximum height above the juggler's hands and the time it takes the ring to reach this height. Then find how long the ring is in the air. **4 ft at 0.5 s; 1 s**

For each quadratic function, find the axis of symmetry and the vertex of its graph.

15. $y = x^2 - 8x$ **15. $x = 4$; $(4, -16)$**
16. $y = -x^2 + 6x - 4$ **16. $x = 3$; $(3, 5)$**
17. $y = 4 - 3x^2$ **$x = 0$; $(0, 4)$**
18. $y = -2x^2 - 4$ **$x = 0$; $(0, -4)$**
19. $y = -x^2 - x - 4$ **19. $x = -\frac{1}{2}$; $\left(-\frac{1}{2}, -\frac{15}{4}\right)$**
20. $y = x^2 + 8x + 16$ **$x = -4$; $(-4, 0)$**

Assignment Guide

Assign *Guided Practice* exercises as necessary.

If you finished Examples **1–2**
Proficient 8–41, 43–49
Advanced 8–49

Homework Quick Check
Quickly check key concepts.
Exercises: 8, 10, 14, 16, 24, 27

Answers

1.
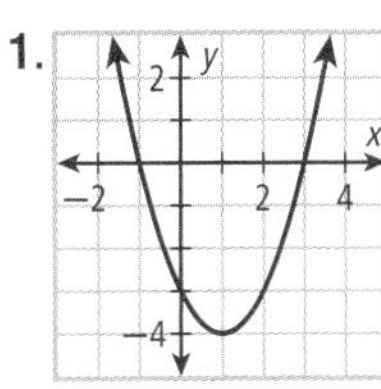

2.
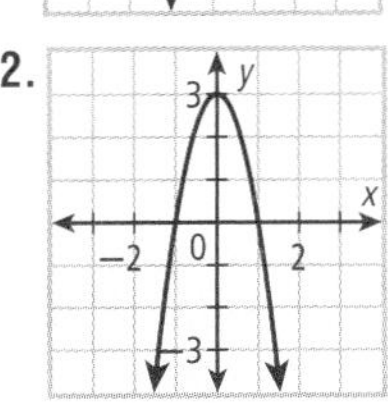

3.
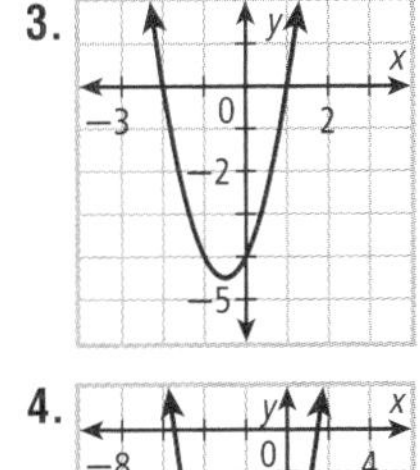

4.
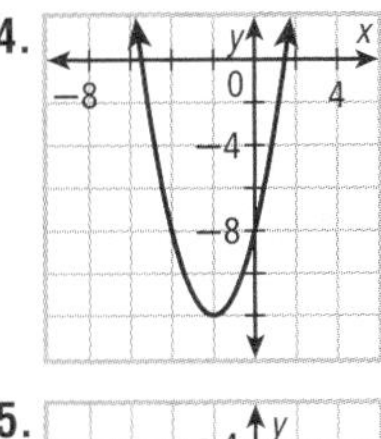

5.
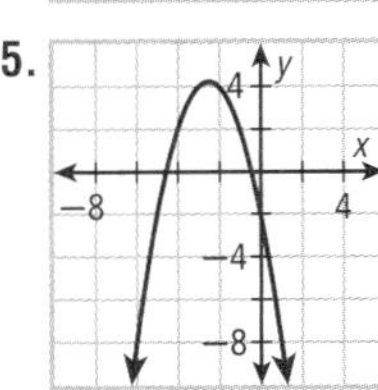

6.
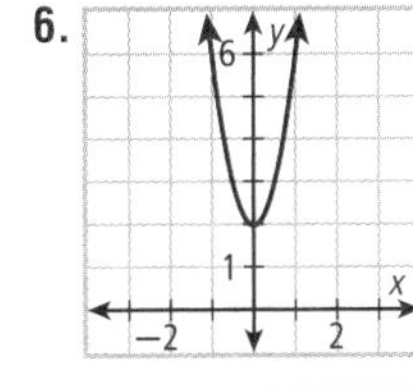

8.
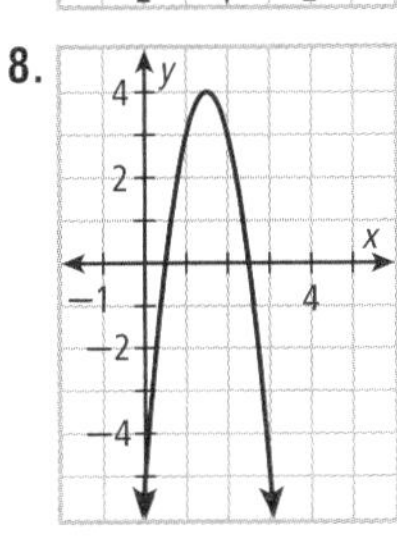

9.
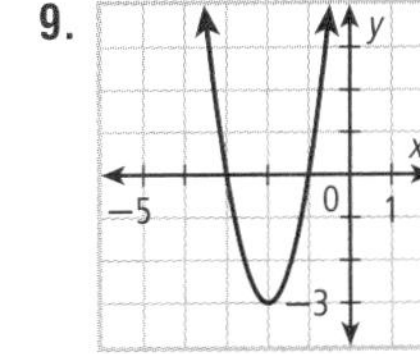

10.
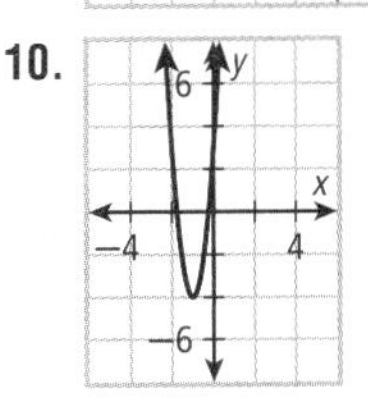

11.
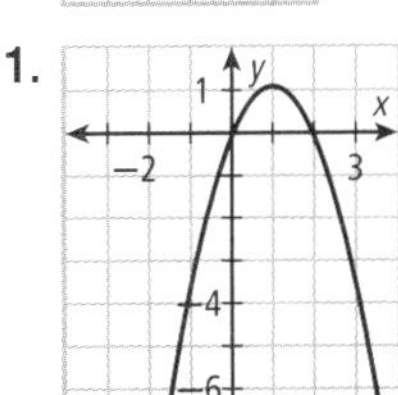

12.
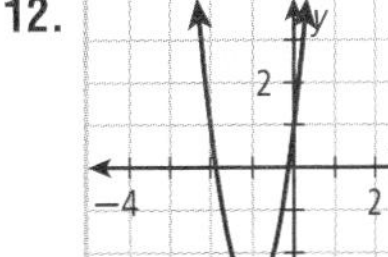

13.
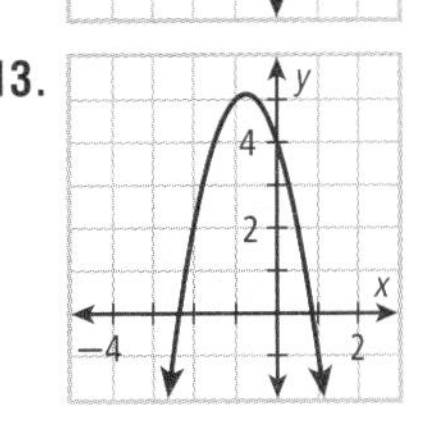

California Standards

Standard	Exercises
6.0	43–45
9.0	46–48
17.0	27b, 32, 36
21.0	1–6, 8–13, 21–26, 27a, 35c, 40, 41
23.0	7, 14, 27c, 30, 31, 35a, 35b, 35d, 49
25.2	28

Exercise 35 involves writing and using a quadratic model for projectile motion. This exercise prepares students for the Concept Connection on page 566.

Technology Students may want to use a graphing calculator to graph the function in **Exercise 27.**

Inclusion Students may be overwhelmed by all of the different variables used in **Exercise 35.** Help them understand what each variable represents: h is the dependent variable, and t is the independent variable. Then help students relate v_i to the coefficient b and h_i to the constant c. Show them that $-\frac{1}{2}a$ is the leading coefficient.

Answers

21–27a. See p. A24.

33. $(-1, 6)$; the axis of symmetry is a vertical line through the vertex. So its equation is $x = 0$. Reflect the point $(1, 6)$ across the axis of symmetry.

34. The x-coordinate of the vertex gives the axis of symmetry. If the range includes values greater than the y-coordinate of the vertex, then the parabola opens upward. If the range includes values less than the y-coordinate of the vertex, then the parabola opens downward.

35c–d. See p. A24.

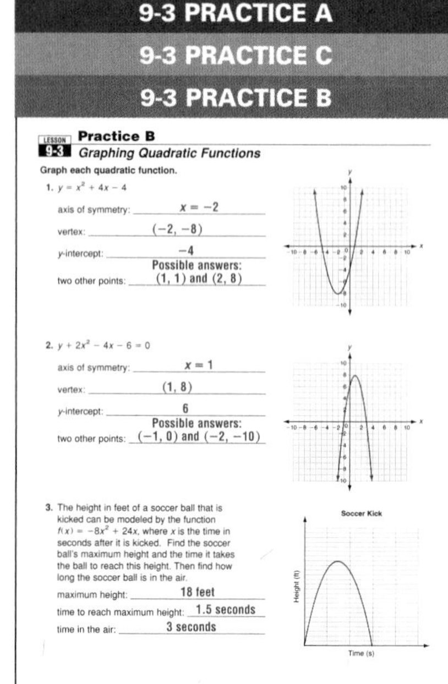
9-3 PRACTICE A

9-3 PRACTICE C

9-3 PRACTICE B

LESSON 9-3 **Practice B**
Graphing Quadratic Functions

Graph each quadratic function.

1. $y = x^2 + 4x - 4$

axis of symmetry: $x = -2$

vertex: $(-2, -8)$

y-intercept: -4

two other points: Possible answers: $(1, 1)$ and $(2, 8)$

2. $y + 2x^2 - 4x - 6 = 0$

axis of symmetry: $x = 1$

vertex: $(1, 8)$

y-intercept: 6

two other points: Possible answers: $(-1, 0)$ and $(-2, -10)$

3. The height in feet of a soccer ball that is kicked can be modeled by the function $f(x) = -8x^2 + 24x$, where x is the time in seconds after it is kicked. Find the soccer ball's maximum height and the time it takes the ball to reach this height. Then find how long the soccer ball is in the air.

maximum height: 18 feet

time to reach maximum height: 1.5 seconds

time in the air: 3 seconds

Soccer Kick

Height (ft)

Time (s)

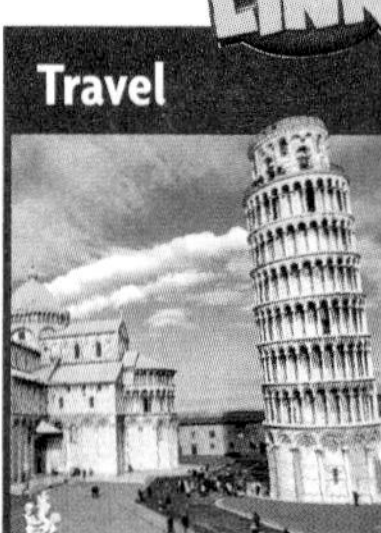

Building began on the Tower of Pisa, located in Pisa, Italy, in 1173. The tower started leaning after the third story was added. At the fifth story, attempts were made to correct the leaning. The tower was finally complete in 1350.

28. Student A is incorrect; the student incorrectly identified the values a and b.

29. $(-1, 4)$; reflect the given point across the axis of symmetry.

32. $0 \le x \le 4$; a negative radius does not make sense.

Graph each quadratic function. On your graph, label the coordinates of the vertex. Draw and label the axis of symmetry.

21. $y = -x^2$	**22.** $y = -x^2 + 4x$	**23.** $y = x^2 - 6x + 4$
24. $x + y = x^2$	**25.** $y + 4 = 3x^2$	**26.** $y + 2x^2 + 25 = -16x$

27. **Travel** While on a vacation in Italy, Rudy visited the Leaning Tower of Pisa. When he leaned over the railing to look down from the tower, his sunglasses fell off. The height in meters of the sunglasses as they fell can be approximated by the function $y = -5x^2 + 50$, where x is the time in seconds.

a. Graph the function.

b. What is a reasonable domain and range? **D: $0 \le x \le 3.16$; R: $0 \le y \le 50$**

c. How long did it take for the glasses to reach the ground? **3.16 s**

28. **///ERROR ANALYSIS///** Two students found the equation of the axis of symmetry for the graph of $f(x) = -x^2 - 2x + 1$. Who is incorrect? Explain the error.

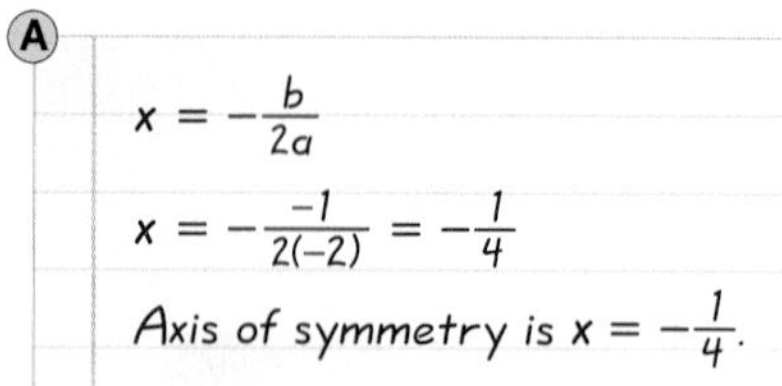

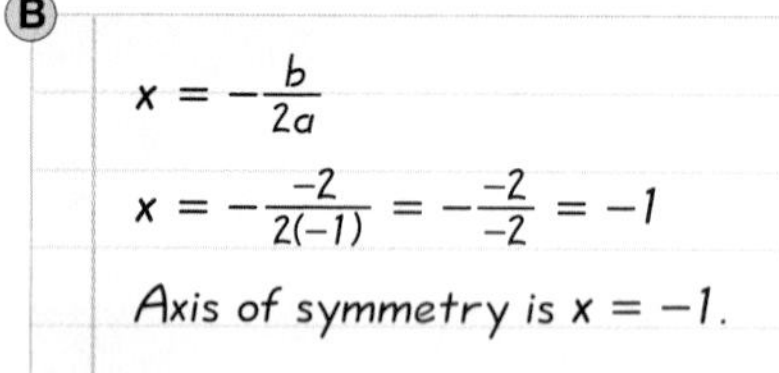

B
$x = -\frac{b}{2a}$
$x = -\frac{-2}{2(-1)} = -\frac{-2}{-2} = -1$
Axis of symmetry is $x = -1$.

29. **Critical Thinking** The point $(5, 4)$ lies on the graph of a quadratic function whose axis of symmetry is $x = 2$. Find another point on the graph. Explain how you found the point.

Engineering **Use the graph for Exercises 30–32. The velocity v in centimeters per second of a fluid flowing in a pipe varies according to the radius r of the pipe.**

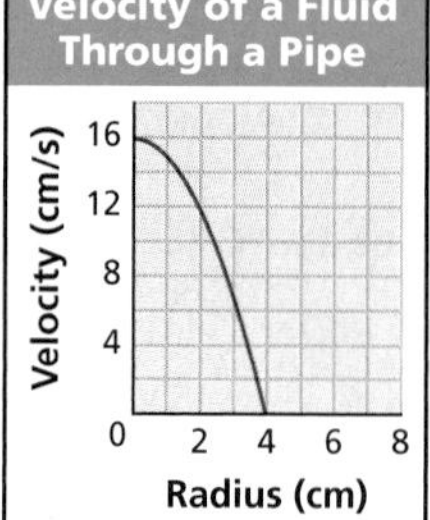

30. Find the radius of the pipe when the velocity is 7 cm/s. **3 cm**

31. Find the velocity of the fluid when the radius is 2 cm. **12 cm/s**

32. What is a reasonable domain for this function? Explain.

33. **Critical Thinking** The graph of a quadratic function has the vertex $(0, 5)$. One point on the graph is $(1, 6)$. Find another point on the graph. Explain how you found the point.

34. **Write About It** Explain how the vertex and the range can help you graph a quadratic function.

CONCEPT CONNECTION

35. This problem will prepare you for the Concept Connection on page 566.

A water bottle rocket is shot upward with an initial velocity of $v_i = 45$ ft/s from the roof of a school, which is at h_i, 50 ft above the ground. The equation $h = -\frac{1}{2}at^2 + v_i t + h_i$ models the rocket's height as a function of time. The acceleration due to gravity a is 32 ft/s². **$h(t) = -16t^2 + 45t + 50$**

a. Write the equation for height as a function of time for this situation.

b. Find the vertex of this parabola. **(1.4, 81.6)**

c. Sketch the graph of this parabola and label the vertex.

d. What do the coordinates of the vertex represent in terms of time and height?

9-3 READING STRATEGIES

LESSON 9-3 **Reading Strategies**
Use a Sequence Chain

Use this sequence chain to guide you in graphing quadratic functions of the form $y = ax^2 + bx + c$.

Sequence Chain: *Graphing Quadratic Functions*

1. **Find the axis of symmetry** by substituting values into $x = -\frac{b}{2a}$.
2. **Find the vertex** by substituting the value of x in the axis of symmetry into the equation to get y.
3. **Find the point that contains the y-intercept** by identifying c in the equation.
4. **Find two more points** on the same side of the axis of symmetry as the y-intercept.
5. **Graph the parts** of the parabola found in the first four steps.
6. **Reflect the points** across the axis of symmetry and connect with a smooth curve.

Graph each quadratic function. Show all the steps outlined above.

1. $y = x^2 + 6x + 5$

Step 1: $x = -3$

Step 2: $(-3, -4)$

Step 3: $(0, 5)$

Step 4: Possible answers: $(-2, -3)$ and $(-1, 0)$ Step 5 and Step 6

2. $y = -\frac{1}{2}x^2 + 6$

Step 1: $x = 0$

Step 2: $(0, 6)$

Step 3: $(0, 6)$

Step 4: Possible answers: $(-2, 4)$ and $(-4, -2)$ Step 5 and Step 6

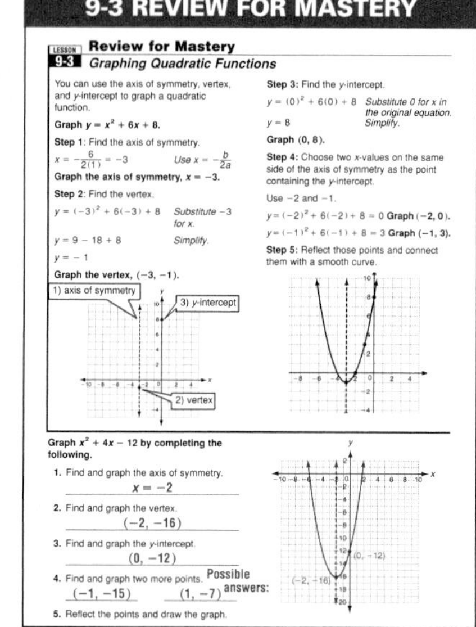
9-3 REVIEW FOR MASTERY

LESSON 9-3 **Review for Mastery**
Graphing Quadratic Functions

You can use the axis of symmetry, vertex, and y-intercept to graph a quadratic function.

Graph $y = x^2 + 6x + 8$.

Step 1: Find the axis of symmetry.

$x = -\frac{6}{2(1)} = -3$ *Use $x = -\frac{b}{2a}$*

Graph the axis of symmetry, $x = -3$.

Step 2: Find the vertex.

$y = (-3)^2 + 6(-3) + 8$ *Substitute −3 for x.*

$y = 9 - 18 + 8$ *Simplify.*

$y = -1$

Graph the vertex, $(-3, -1)$.

1) axis of symmetry

3) y-intercept

2) vertex

Step 3: Find the y-intercept.

$y = (0)^2 + 6(0) + 8$ *Substitute 0 for x in the original equation.*

$y = 8$ *Simplify.*

Graph $(0, 8)$.

Step 4: Choose two x-values on the same side of the axis of symmetry as the point containing the y-intercept.

Use −2 and −1.

$y = (-2)^2 + 6(-2) + 8 = 0$ **Graph $(-2, 0)$.**

$y = (-1)^2 + 6(-1) + 8 = 3$ **Graph $(-1, 3)$.**

Step 5: Reflect those points and connect them with a smooth curve.

Graph $x^2 + 4x - 12$ by completing the following.

1. Find and graph the axis of symmetry. $x = -2$

2. Find and graph the vertex. $(-2, -16)$

3. Find and graph the y-intercept. $(0, -12)$

4. Find and graph two more points. Possible answers: $(-1, -15)$ $(1, -7)$

5. Reflect the points and draw the graph.

36. Copy and complete the table for each function.

Function	Graph Opens	Axis of Symmetry	Vertex	Zeros	Domain and Range
$y = x^2 + 4$	Upward	$x =$ 0	(0, 4)	None	D: See R: left
$y = -x^2 + 4$	Downward	$x =$ 0	(0, 4)	−2, 2	D: margin. R:
$y + 8 - x^2 = -2x$	Upward	$x =$ 1	(1, −9)	−2, 4	D: R:

D: all real numbers
R: $y \geq 4$

D: all real numbers
R: $y \leq 4$

D: all real numbers
R: $y \geq -9$

Multiple Choice For Exercises 37–39, choose the best answer.

37. Which is the axis of symmetry for the graph of $f(x) = 6 - 5x + \frac{1}{2}x^2$?

(A) $x = 5$ (circled)   (B) $x = \frac{1}{20}$ (C) $x = -5$ (D) $x = -\frac{1}{20}$

38. What are the coordinates of the vertex for the graph of $f(x) = x^2 - 5x + 6$?

(A) $\left(-\frac{5}{2}, -\frac{1}{4}\right)$ (B) $\left(-\frac{5}{2}, \frac{1}{4}\right)$ (C) $\left(\frac{5}{2}, \frac{1}{4}\right)$ (D) $\left(\frac{5}{2}, -\frac{1}{4}\right)$ (circled)

39. Which function's graph has an axis of symmetry of $x = 1$ and a vertex of $(1, 8)$?

(A) $y = -x^2 + x + 8$ (C) $y = 2x^2 - 4x - 8$
(B) $y = x^2 + 8x + 1$ (D) $y = -3x^2 + 6x + 5$ (circled)

40. **Short Response** Graph $y = x^2 + 3x + 2$. What are the zeros, the axis of symmetry, and the coordinates of the vertex? Show your work.

CHALLENGE AND EXTEND

41. The graph of a quadratic function has its vertex at $(1, -4)$ and one zero of the function is 3. Find the other zero. Explain how you found the other zero.

42. The x-intercepts of a quadratic function are 3 and −3. The y-intercept is 6. What are the coordinates of the vertex? Does the function have a maximum or a minimum? Explain.

42. (0, 6); maximum; the parabola opens downward because the zeros are below the vertex, so the vertex is a maximum.

SPIRAL STANDARDS REVIEW

Find the x- and y-intercepts. *(Lesson 5-2)*

43. 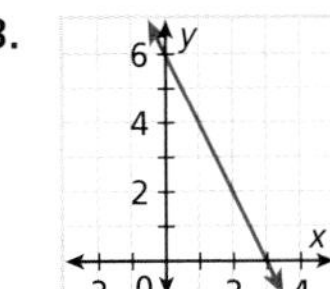 3; 6

44. 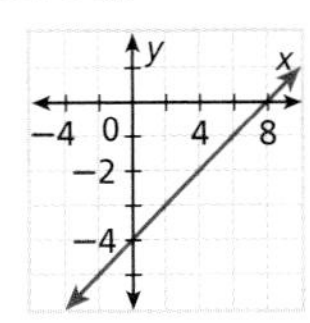 8; −4

45. 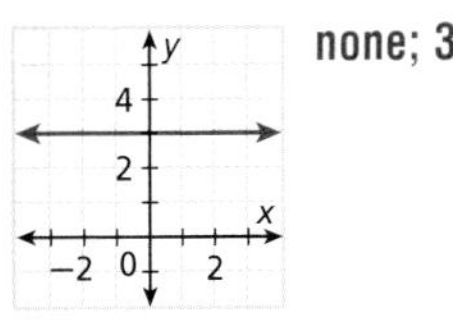 none; 3

Solve each system by using any method. Check your answer. *(Lessons 6-1, 6-2, and 6-3)*

46. $\begin{cases} 3x - y = 2 \\ x + 4y = 18 \end{cases}$ (2, 4)

47. $\begin{cases} 2x + 3y = 3 \\ 4x - y = 13 \end{cases}$ (3, −1)

48. $\begin{cases} -2x + 3y = 12 \\ 6x + y = 4 \end{cases}$ (0, 4)

49. Shelly kicks her ball into the air. The height in feet above the ground of the ball can be modeled by $y = -5x^2 + 10x$. Will Shelly's ball go over a fence that is 6 feet tall? Explain. *(Lesson 9-2)* No; the highest the ball will go is about 5 feet.

Teaching Tip

Multiple Choice Suggest that students rewrite the function in **Exercise 37** in the form $y = ax^2 + bx + c$ as a first step.

In **Exercise 38,** students can eliminate choices **A** and **B** before finding the axis of symmetry by counting the negative signs of $-\frac{b}{2a}$.

Answers

40. 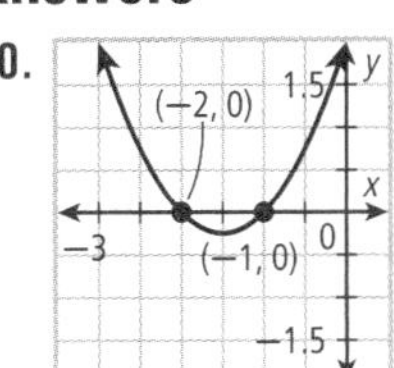

zeros: −2, −1

axis of symmetry: $x = -\frac{3}{2}$

vertex: $\left(-\frac{3}{2}, -\frac{1}{4}\right)$

41. −1; the axis of symmetry is $x = 1$. The given zero is 2 units right of the axis of symmetry. The other zero is 2 units left of the axis of symmetry.

Journal

Have students compare and contrast the process for graphing a linear function with the process for graphing a quadratic function.

ALTERNATIVE ASSESSMENT

Have students write and graph a quadratic function in the form $y = ax^2 + bx + c$, where a, b, and c are not zero. Have students give the domain and range of the function.

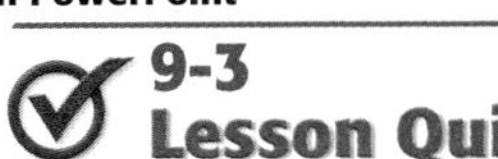

9-3 Lesson Quiz

1. Graph $y = -2x^2 - 8x + 4$.

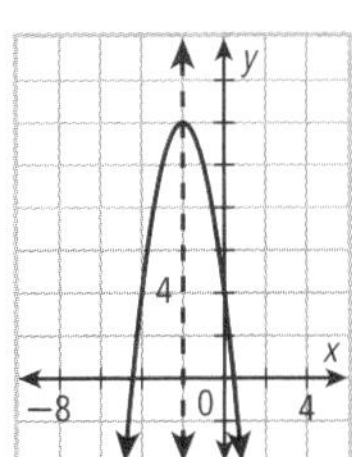

2. The height in feet of a fireworks shell can be modeled by $h(t) = -16t^2 + 224t$, where t is the time in seconds after it is fired. Find the maximum height of the shell, the time it takes to reach its maximum height, and the length of time the shell is in the air.

784 ft; 7 s; 14 s

Also available on transparency

9-3 PROBLEM SOLVING

LESSON 9-3 **Problem Solving**
Graphing Quadratic Functions

Write the correct answer.

1. An Olympic diver is competing for a medal. His height in feet above the water can be modeled by the function $f(x) = -3x^2 + 6x + 24$, where x is the time in seconds after he begins the dive. Graph the function. Then find how long it takes the diver to reach the water.

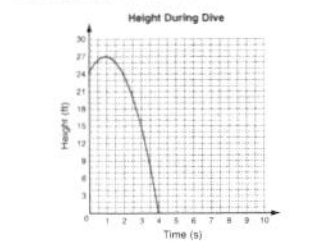

Height During Dive

4 seconds

2. Tanisha kicks a soccer ball during a game. The height of the ball, in feet, can be modeled by the function $f(x) = -16x^2 + 48x$, where x is the time in seconds after she kicks the ball. Graph the function. Find the maximum height of the ball and how long it takes the ball to reach that height.

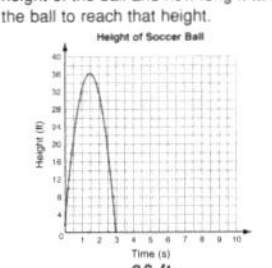

Height of Soccer Ball

36 ft; 1.5 seconds

A model rocket is launched from a platform into the air. Keona records its height at different times until it reaches its peak at 259 ft. Her graph of these points is shown below. Use this graph to answer questions 3–5.

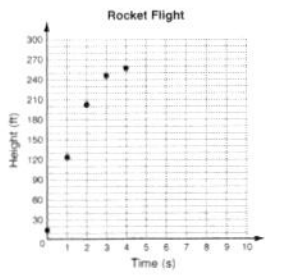

Rocket Flight

3. Keona wants to complete her graph by plotting the heights of the rocket as it descended. Which of the following points will she graph?

F (4, 180)   (H) (6, 200) (circled)
G (5, 150)   J (10, 0)

4. How long will the rocket be in the air?

A 4 seconds   (C) 8 seconds (circled)
B 6 seconds   D 10 seconds

5. Which of the following equations models the flight of the ball where x is the time in seconds and y is the height in feet?

A $16x^2 + 15x + 125$
B $16x^2 + 125x + 15$
(C) $-16x^2 + 125x + 15$ (circled)
D $-16x^2 + 15x + 125$

9-3 CHALLENGE

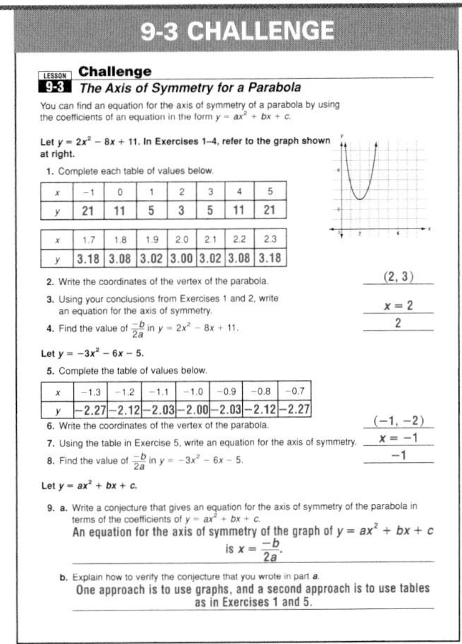

LESSON 9-3 **Challenge**
The Axis of Symmetry for a Parabola

You can find an equation for the axis of symmetry of a parabola by using the coefficients of an equation in the form $y = ax^2 + bx + c$.

Let $y = 2x^2 - 8x + 11$. In Exercises 1–4, refer to the graph shown at right.

1. Complete each table of values below.

x	−1	0	1	2	3	4	5
y	21	11	5	3	5	11	21

x	1.7	1.8	1.9	2.0	2.1	2.2	2.3
y	3.18	3.08	3.02	3.00	3.02	3.08	3.18

2. Write the coordinates of the vertex of the parabola. (2, 3)

3. Using your conclusions from Exercises 1 and 2, write an equation for the axis of symmetry. $x = 2$

4. Find the value of $\frac{-b}{2a}$ in $y = 2x^2 - 8x + 11$. 2

Let $y = -3x^2 - 6x - 5$.

5. Complete the table of values below.

x	−1.3	−1.2	−1.1	−1.0	−0.9	−0.8	−0.7
y	−2.27	−2.12	−2.03	−2.00	−2.03	−2.12	−2.27

6. Write the coordinates of the vertex of the parabola. (−1, −2)

7. Using the table in Exercise 5, write an equation for the axis of symmetry. $x = -1$

8. Find the value of $\frac{-b}{2a}$ in $y = -3x^2 - 6x - 5$. −1

Let $y = ax^2 + bx + c$.

9. a. Write a conjecture that gives an equation for the axis of symmetry of the parabola in terms of the coefficients of $y = ax^2 + bx + c$.

An equation for the axis of symmetry of the graph of $y = ax^2 + bx + c$ is $x = \frac{-b}{2a}$.

b. Explain how to verify the conjecture that you wrote in part *a*.

One approach is to use graphs, and a second approach is to use tables as in Exercises 1 and 5.

SECTION 9A CONCEPT CONNECTION

Organizer

Objective: Assess students' ability to apply concepts and skills in Lessons 9-1 through 9-3 in a real-world format.

Online Edition

Countdown to Mastery Week 20

Problem	Text Reference
1	Lesson 9-1
2	Lessons 9-1, 9-3
3	Lessons 9-2, 9-3
4	Lessons 9-2, 9-3
5	Lessons 9-2

Answers

1.

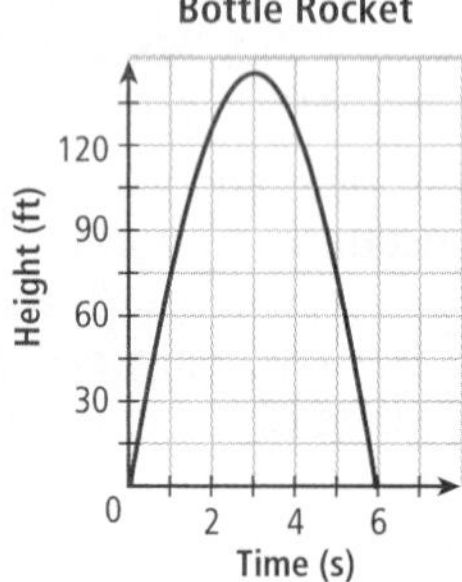

3. The x-coordinate represents the time when the water bottle rocket reaches its maximum height, which is represented by the y-coordinate.
4. 1.775 s; for $y = 110$ the corresponding x-coordinate is 1.775.

California Standards

Algebra 1 21.0, 23.0

CHAPTER 9

CONCEPT CONNECTION

SECTION 9A

Quadratic Functions

The Sky's the Limit The Physics Club is using computer simulation software to design a water bottle rocket that doesn't have a parachute. The data for their current design are shown in the table.

Time (s)	Height (ft)
0	0
1	80
2	128
3	144
4	128
5	80

1. Graph the data and connect the points.
2. Find and label the zeros, axis of symmetry, and vertex. 0 and 6; $x = 3$; $(3, 144)$
3. Explain what the x- and y-coordinates of the vertex represent in the context of the problem.
4. Estimate how many seconds it will take the rocket to reach 110 feet. Explain.

INTERVENTION

Scaffolding Questions

1. Do you need to graph negative x- or y-values? Explain. No; because neither time nor height can be negative.
2. Which points do you look for when finding the zeros of a function from its graph? points that contain the x-intercepts
3. Does this graph have a maximum or a minimum? maximum What are the labels on the axes of your graph? vertical axis: Height (ft), horizontal axis: Time (s)
4. Between what two heights given in the table would 110 ft belong? between 80 ft and 128 ft What are the times associated with those two heights? 1 s and 2 s

Extension

How could you find the time it takes the rocket to reach 130 ft? How many answers are there? Explain. Find the point(s) on the graph with y-coordinate 130. The corresponding x-coordinate(s) represent the time; 2; the parabola opens down, and 130 is less than the y-coordinate of the vertex, 144. So there will be 2 points with y-coordinate 130, one on either side of the vertex.

CHAPTER 9

SECTION 9A

Quiz for Lessons 9-1 Through 9-3

9-1 Quadratic Equations and Functions

Without graphing, tell whether each point is on the graph of the given equation.

1. $y + 2x^2 = 3x$; $(2, 2)$ **no**
2. $x^2 + y = 4$; $(3, -3)$ **no**
3. $y = -3x^2 - 12$; $(2.5, -6.75)$ **no**
4. $y - 3 = 3x^2$; $(2, 14)$ **no**
5. $y = x^2 - x + 5$; $(-3, 17)$ **yes**
6. $y + 5x^2 = 4 + x$; $(1, 1)$ **no**

Tell whether the graph of each quadratic function opens upward or downward and whether the parabola has a maximum or a minimum.

7. $y = -x^2 - 7x + 18$ **downward; maximum**
8. $y - 2x^2 = 4x + 3$ **upward; minimum**
9. $f(x) = 5x - 0.5x^2$ **downward; maximum**
10. Graph the function $y = \frac{1}{2}x^2 - 2$ and give the domain and range.

9-2 Characteristics of Quadratic Functions

Find the zeros of each function from its graph. Then find its the axis of symmetry.

11. 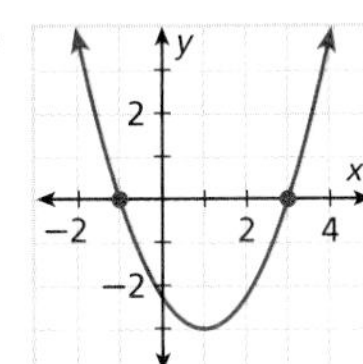
−1 and 3; $x = 1$

12. 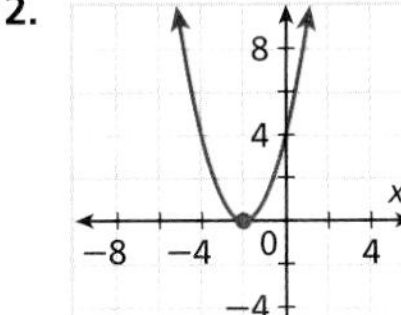
−2; $x = -2$

13. 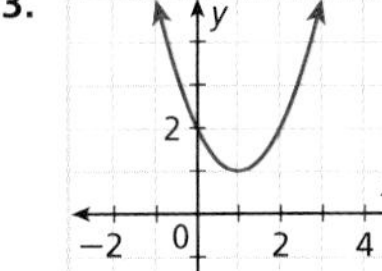
no zeros; $x = 1$

Find the vertex.

14. $y = x^2 + 6x + 2$ **(−3, −7)**
15. $y = 3 + 4x - 2x^2$ **(1, 5)**
16. $y = 3x^2 + 12x - 12$ **(−2, −24)**
17. $f(x) = x^2 + 2x - 8$ **(−1, −9)**
18. $y = x^2 + 8x - 20$ **(−4, −36)**
19. $f(x) = -x^2 - 12 + 8x$ **(4, 4)**

20. The height in feet of the curved roof of an aircraft hangar can be modeled by $y = -0.02x^2 + 1.6x$, where x is the distance in feet from one wall at ground level. How tall is the hangar? **32 ft**

9-3 Graphing Quadratic Functions

Graph each quadratic function.

21. $y = x^2 + 3x + 9$
22. $y = x^2 - 2x - 15$
23. $y = x^2 - 2x - 8$
24. $y = 2x^2 - 6$
25. $y = 4x^2 + 8x - 2$
26. $y = 2x^2 + 10x + 1$

27. The height in feet of a baseball after it is hit can be modeled by the function $f(x) = -16x^2 + 100x$, where x is the time in seconds after the ball is hit. Find the ball's maximum height and the time it takes the ball to reach this height. Then find how long the ball is in the air. **156.25 ft; 3.125 s; 6.25 s**

28. Trent is a kicker for his football team. The height in feet of a football after one of Trent's kicks can be modeled by the function $f(x) = -16x^2 + 55x$, where x is the time in seconds after the kick. Find the football's maximum height and the time it takes the ball to reach this height. Then find how long the ball is in the air. **47.27 ft; 1.72 s; 3.44 s**

READY TO GO ON? SECTION 9A

Organizer

Objective: Assess students' mastery of concepts and skills in Lessons 9-1 through 9-3.

Resources

 ***Assessment Resources***

Section 9A Quiz

Test & Practice Generator One-Stop Planner®

INTERVENTION 

Resources

 ***Ready to Go On? Intervention and Enrichment*** **Worksheets**

 ***Ready to Go On?*** **CD-ROM**

 ***Ready to Go On?*** **Online**

my.hrw.com

Answers

10, 21–26. See p. A24.

READY TO GO ON? Diagnose and Prescribe

Ready to Go On? Intervention	READY TO GO ON? *Intervention,* Section 9A Worksheets	CD-ROM	Online
Lesson 9-1 21.0	9-1 Intervention	Activity 9-1	Diagnose and Prescribe Online
Lesson 9-2 21.0	9-2 Intervention	Activity 9-2	
Lesson 9-3 21.0	9-3 Intervention	Activity 9-3	

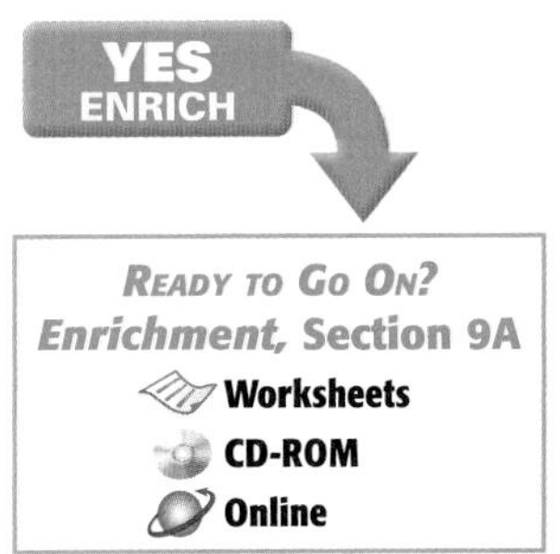

SECTION

Solving Quadratic Equations

One-Minute Section Planner

Lesson	Lab Resources	Materials
Lesson 9-4 Solving Quadratic Equations by Graphing • Solve quadratic equations by graphing. **21.0, 23.0**	***Algebra Lab*** In *Chapter 9 Resource File*	**Required** graphing calculator
9-4 Technology Lab Explore Roots, Zeros, and *x*-Intercepts • Use tables and graphs on a graphing calculator to explore the relationships between roots, zeros, and *x*-intercepts. **21.0**		**Required** graphing calculator
Lesson 9-5 Solving Quadratic Equations by Factoring • Solve quadratic equations by factoring. **14.0, 23.0**		**Optional** graphing calculator
Lesson 9-6 Solving Quadratic Equations by Using Square Roots • Solve quadratic equations by using square roots. **2.0, 23.0**		
9-7 Algebra Lab Model Completing the Square • Use algebra tiles to model completing the square. **14.0**		**Required** algebra tiles (MK)
Lesson 9-7 Completing the Square • Solve quadratic equations by completing the square. **14.0, 23.0**		**Required** graphing calculator **Optional** algebra tiles (MK)
Lesson 9-8 The Quadratic Formula • Solve quadratic equations by using the Quadratic Formula. **19.0, 20.0**		**Optional** graphing calculator
Lesson 9-9 The Discriminant • Determine the number of solutions of a quadratic equation by using the discriminant. **22.0, 23.0**		**Optional** graphing calculator

MK = *Manipulatives Kit*

Notes

Math Background: Teaching the Standards

Professional Development

QUADRATIC EQUATIONS

19.0, 20.0, 21.0, 22.0, 23.0

Lesson 9-4

A *quadratic equation* is an equation that can be written in the form $ax^2 + bx + c = 0$, where a, b, and c are real numbers and $a \neq 0$. This is the *standard form* of a quadratic equation. Every quadratic equation written in this form has a related quadratic function $y = ax^2 + bx + c$.

Just as with the solutions of all equations, a solution of a quadratic equation is a value of the variable that makes the equation true. One way to solve a quadratic equation in standard form is to graph the related quadratic function and find its x-intercepts.

For example, for the quadratic equation $x^2 + x - 6 = 0$, the graph of the related function $y = x^2 + x - 6$ is the set of all ordered pairs of the form $(x, x^2 + x - 6)$. It must be true that at any point where the graph intersects the x-axis, the y-coordinate is 0; that is, $x^2 + x - 6 = 0$. In other words, the x-intercepts of the graph are precisely the solutions of the quadratic equation.

Students should understand that this is a general method that works for any equation set equal to 0 whose related function can be graphed. For example, the linear equation $\frac{1}{2}x - 2 = 0$ may be solved by graphing the related linear function $y = \frac{1}{2}x - 2$ and noticing that the graph intersects the x-axis at $x = 4$.

SOLUTION METHODS

19.0, 20.0, 21.0, 22.0, 23.0

Lessons 9-4 to 9-8

Although graphing has the advantage of being a fairly intuitive solution method, it is often inefficient and imprecise. These drawbacks motivate the need for other solution techniques.

The method of solving a quadratic equation by factoring springs from the *Zero Product Property*: If the product of two real numbers is zero, then at least one of the numbers is zero. This property justifies solving quadratic equations by factoring. For example, to solve $x^2 + x - 6 = 0$, note that $x^2 + x - 6 = (x - 2)(x + 3)$. By the Zero Product Property, it must be true that $x - 2 = 0$ or $x + 3 = 0$, which gives the solutions 2 and -3.

Some quadratic equations do not lend themselves to factoring, so still more methods are needed. The techniques of completing the square and using the Quadratic Formula work for *any* quadratic equation.

It is essential for students to realize that all of the solution methods in Chapter 9 work only when the original quadratic equation is equal to zero (i.e., is written in standard form).

THE DISCRIMINANT

Lesson 9-9

Given a quadratic equation in standard form, the discriminant, $b^2 - 4ac$, offers an efficient means of determining the number of real solutions. If the discriminant is positive, there are two real solutions. If the discriminant is zero, there is one real solution. If the discriminant is negative, there are no real solutions.

According to the Fundamental Theorem of Algebra, every polynomial function of degree $n \geq 1$ has exactly n zeros. This means that all quadratic equations, whose related functions are polynomials of degree 2, have exactly two solutions. This may seem to contradict the previous discussion about the discriminant, but there are two important points.

If there is only one real solution, it has *multiplicity* 2. For example, the factored form of $x^2 - 2x + 1 = 0$ is $(x - 1)^2 = 0$, so $x = 1$ is the only solution. It is called a solution of multiplicity 2, meaning it is counted twice, since the factor $x - 1$ occurs twice. (An example of the analogous situation when dealing with numbers is $9 = 3^2$. Even though 3 is the only prime factor, we say that the prime factorization of 9 contains two factors.)

If there are no real solutions, the quadratic equation has two *complex* solutions. Complex numbers have the form $a + bi$, where a and b are real numbers and $i = \sqrt{-1}$. Students will study complex numbers in Algebra 2.

9-4 Organizer

Objective: Solve quadratic equations by graphing.

Algebra Lab
In *Chapter 9 Resource File*

Online Edition
Tutorial Videos, TechKeys

Countdown to Mastery Week 20

Power Presentations with PowerPoint®

Warm Up

1. Graph $y = x^2 + 4x + 3$.

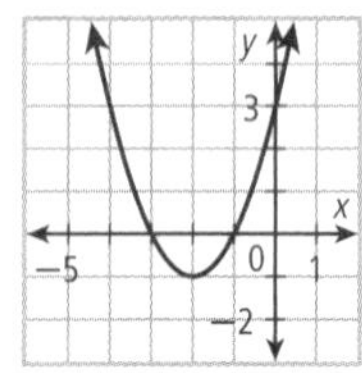

2. Identify the vertex and zeros of the function above. vertex: $(-2, -1)$; zeros: $-3, -1$

Also available on transparency

Math Humor

Q: What does a person have if they can easily find solutions to quadratic equations?

A: Zero visibility.

California Standards

Algebra 1 21.0
Also covered:
23.0 Students apply quadratic equations to physical problems, such as the motion of an object under the force of gravity.

9-4 Solving Quadratic Equations by Graphing

California Standards

21.0 Students graph quadratic functions and know that their roots are the *x*-intercepts.
Also covered: **23.0**

Who uses this?
Dolphin trainers can use solutions of quadratic equations to plan the choreography for their shows. (See Example 3.)

Every quadratic function has a related quadratic equation. The standard form of a quadratic equation is $ax^2 + bx + c = 0$, where a, b, and c are real numbers and $a \neq 0$.

When writing a quadratic function as its related quadratic equation, you replace y with 0.

$$y = ax^2 + bx + c$$
$$0 = ax^2 + bx + c$$

One way to solve a quadratic equation in standard form is to graph the related function and find the x-values where $y = 0$. In other words, find the zeros of the related function. Recall that a quadratic function may have two, one, or no zeros.

Solving Quadratic Equations by Graphing
Step 1 Write the related function.
Step 2 Graph the related function.
Step 3 Find the zeros of the related function.

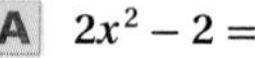

EXAMPLE 1 Solving Quadratic Equations by Graphing

Solve each equation by graphing the related function.

A $2x^2 - 2 = 0$

Step 1 Write the related function.
$2x^2 - 2 = y$, or $y = 2x^2 + 0x - 2$

Step 2 Graph the function.
- The axis of symmetry is $x = 0$.
- The vertex is $(0, -2)$.
- Two other points are $(1, 0)$ and $(2, 6)$.
- Graph the points and reflect them across the axis of symmetry.

Step 3 Find the zeros.
The zeros appear to be -1 and 1.
The solutions of $2x^2 - 2 = 0$ are -1 and 1.

Check

$2x^2 - 2$	$= 0$
$2(-1)^2 - 2$	0
$2(1) - 2$	0
$2 - 2$	0
0	0 ✓

Substitute −1 and 1 for x in the original equation.

$2x^2 - 2$	$= 0$
$2(1)^2 - 2$	0
$2(1) - 2$	0
$2 - 2$	0
0	0 ✓

1 Introduce

EXPLORATION
9-4 Solving Quadratic Equations by Graphing

Based on the appearance of each graph, determine the zeros of each quadratic function.

THINK AND DISCUSS

5. **Discuss** what must be true about the value of *y* when it corresponds to a zero of a function.
6. **Explain** the connection between the zeros of a function and the intersection of its graph with the line $y = 0$.

Motivate

Display the graph of a quadratic function with integer zeros, such as $y = 2x^2 + 14x + 24$. Discuss that the zeros of the function are the x-values that correspond to a y-value of 0. Remind students that a quadratic function can have two, one, or no real zeros. Have students find the zeros of the function displayed. -3 and -4 Tell students that in this lesson they will learn to solve quadratic equations by graphing.

Explorations and answers are provided in *Alternate Openers: Explorations Transparencies.*

Solve each equation by graphing the related function.

B $x^2 + 5 = 4x$

Step 1 Write the equation in standard form. Then write the related function.

$x^2 - 4x + 5 = 0$

$y = x^2 - 4x + 5$

Step 2 Graph the function.

Use a graphing calculator.

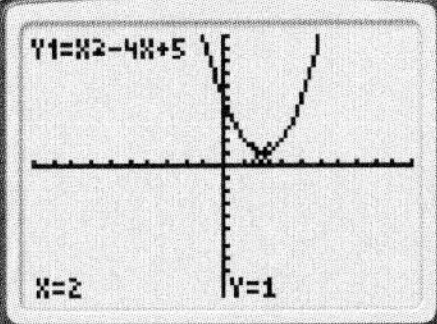

Step 3 Find the zeros.

The function appears to have no zeros.

The equation has no real-number solutions.

Solve each equation by graphing the related function.

1a. $x^2 - 8x - 16 = 2x^2$ **−4**

1b. $6x + 10 = -x^2$ **no zeros**

1c. $-x^2 + 4 = 0$ **−2, 2**

Recall from Chapter 7 that a root of a polynomial is a value of the variable that makes the polynomial equal to 0. So, finding the roots of a quadratic polynomial is the same as solving the related quadratic equation.

EXAMPLE 2 Finding Roots of Quadratic Polynomials

Find the roots of $-x^2 - 4x - 4$.

Step 1 Write the related equation.

$0 = -x^2 - 4x - 4$

Step 2 Write the related function.

$y = -x^2 - 4x - 4$

Step 3 Graph the function.

- The axis of symmetry is $x = -2$.
- The vertex is $(-2, 0)$.
- The y-intercept is -4.
- Another point is $(-1, -1)$.
- Graph the points and reflect them across the axis of symmetry.

Step 4 Find the zeros.

The only zero appears to be −2. This means −2 is the only root of $-x^2 - 4x - 4$.

Check $-x^2 - 4x - 4$

$-(-2)^2 - 4(-2) - 4$

$-(4) + 8 - 4$

$-4 + 4$

0 ✓

Find the roots of each quadratic polynomial.

2a. $x^2 + x - 2$ **1, −2**

2b. $9x^2 - 6x + 1$ $\frac{1}{3}$

2c. $3x^2 - 2x + 5$ **no real roots**

COMMON ERROR ALERT

Students may try to identify a, b, and c without first writing the equation in the form $ax^2 + bx + c = 0$. Remind students to rewrite the equation in the form $ax^2 + bx + c = 0$ so that the correct signs of each coefficient are identified.

Power Presentations with PowerPoint®

Additional Examples

Example 1

Solve each equation by graphing the related function.

A. $2x^2 - 18 = 0$ ± 3

B. $-12x + 18 = -2x^2$ 3

C. $2x^2 + 4x = -3$ ∅

Example 2

Find the roots of each quadratic polynomial.

A. $x^2 + 4x + 3$ −1, −3

B. $x^2 + x - 20$ −5, 4

C. $x^2 - 12x + 35$ 5, 7

Also available on transparency

INTERVENTION

Questioning Strategies

EXAMPLE 1

- If the vertex has a y-coordinate of 0, what does that tell you about the number of zeros of the function?
- Can a quadratic equation have more than two solutions?

EXAMPLE 2

- Why is finding the roots of a quadratic polynomial similar to solving a quadratic equation?

Teaching Tip **Critical Thinking** Explain to students how to solve the equation in **Example 1B** without a graphing calculator. First find the vertex. The vertex, $(2, 1)$, is above the x-axis, and because $a > 0$, the parabola opens upward. This means that the parabola never touches the x-axis and there are no real solutions.

Teaching Tip **Reading Math** Be sure that students understand that a quadratic equation in *standard form* means a quadratic equation in the form $ax^2 + bx + c = 0$.

2 Teach

Guided Instruction

Emphasize to students that graphing is imprecise and the graph may not always yield exact solutions. Although graphing calculators can do much of the graphing work, the student will need to be familiar with what the function should look like and how many zeros it will have before using a graphing calculator. Tell students that later in this chapter they will learn methods for finding precise solutions and that they may use graphing as a way to support their solutions found by those methods.

Universal Access

Through Multiple Representations

Show students how the equation $x^2 + x = 6$ can also be solved by graphing both sides of the equation, $y = x^2 + x$ and $y = 6$. By looking at where the two graphs intersect, you can find the x-values for which $y = 6$. 2, −3

Discuss with students that solving $x^2 + x = 6$ by finding the zeros of the related function $f(x) = x^2 + x - 6$ is the same as finding the x-values of the points where the graph intersects the x-axis.

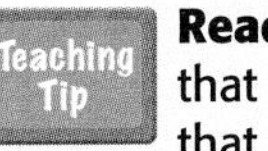

Power Presentations with PowerPoint®

Additional Examples

Example 3

A frog jumps straight up from the ground. The quadratic function $f(t) = -16t^2 + 12t$ models the frog's height above the ground after t seconds. About how long is the frog in the air? 0.75 s

Also available on transparency

INTERVENTION
Questioning Strategies

EXAMPLE 3

- What are the reasonable domain and range values for this function?
- How do you know which zero is the answer to the question?

Advanced Learners/GATE Have students solve $x^2 + x - 6 = 0$ by graphing the related function. 2, −3 Ask students to predict what the graph of $f(x) = -x^2 - x + 6$ will look like. reflection across the x-axis Then have students solve $-x^2 - x + 6 = 0$ by graphing. Are the solutions the same? yes What is the conclusion to be drawn? The opposite of a function will have the same zeros, and its graph will be a reflection across the x-axis.

Critical Thinking In **Example 3,** show students how they can examine the function to quickly see that 0 is a zero.

EXAMPLE 3 *Aquatics Application*

A dolphin jumps out of the water. The quadratic function $y = -16x^2 + 20x$ models the dolphin's height above the water after x seconds. About how long is the dolphin out of the water? Check your answer.

When the dolphin leaves the water, its height is 0, and when the dolphin reenters the water, its height is 0. So solve $0 = -16x^2 + 20x$ to find the times when the dolphin leaves and reenters the water.

Step 1 Write the related function.

$0 = -16x^2 + 20x$

$y = -16x^2 + 20x$

Step 2 Graph the function.

Use a graphing calculator.

Step 3 Use  to estimate the zeros.

The zeros appear to be 0 and 1.25.

The dolphin leaves the water at 0 seconds and reenters the water at 1.25 seconds.

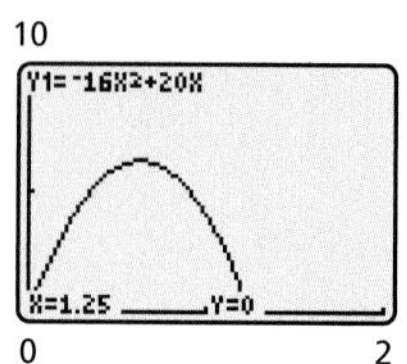

The dolphin is out of the water for about 1.25 seconds.

Check $0 = -16x^2 + 20x$

0	$-16(1.25)^2 + 20(1.25)$
0	$-16(1.5625) + 25$
0	$-25 + 25$
0	0 ✓

Substitute 1.25 for x in the original equation.

CHECK IT OUT! **3. What if...?** Another dolphin jumps out of the water. The quadratic function $y = -16x^2 + 32x$ models the dolphin's height above the water after x seconds. About how long is the dolphin out of the water? Check your answer. **2 s**

THINK AND DISCUSS

1. Describe the graph of a quadratic function whose related quadratic equation has only one solution.
2. Describe the graph of a quadratic function whose related quadratic equation has no real solutions.
3. Describe the graph of a quadratic function whose related quadratic equation has two solutions.

4. **GET ORGANIZED** Copy and complete the graphic organizer. In each of the boxes, write the steps for solving quadratic equations by graphing.

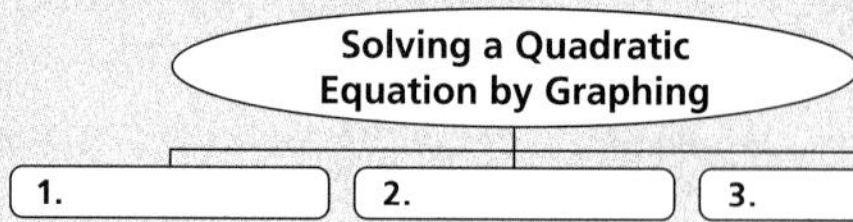

3 Close

Summarize

Review with students the steps for solving quadratic equations by graphing.

1. Write the equation in the form $ax^2 + bx + c = 0$.
2. Write the related function.
3. Graph the function.
4. Find the x-intercepts.

FORMATIVE ASSESSMENT and INTERVENTION

***Diagnose Before* the Lesson**
9-4 Warm Up, TE p. 568

***Monitor During* the Lesson**
Check It Out! Exercises, SE pp. 569–570
Questioning Strategies, TE pp. 569–570

***Assess After* the Lesson**
9-4 Lesson Quiz, TE p. 573
Alternative Assessment, TE p. 573

Answers to *Think and Discuss*

1. The vertex is on the x-axis.
2. Either the vertex is above the x-axis and the graph opens upward, or the vertex is below the x-axis and the graph opens downward.
3. Either the vertex is above the x-axis and the graph opens downward, or the vertex is below the x-axis and the graph opens upward.
4. See p. A7.

9-4 Exercises

California Standards Practice
21.0, 23.0, 25.3

go.hrw.com
Homework Help Online
KEYWORD: MA8CA 9-4
Parent Resources Online
KEYWORD: MA8CA Parent

GUIDED PRACTICE

SEE EXAMPLE 1 p. 568

Solve each equation by graphing the related function. Check your answer.

1. $x^2 - 4 = 0$ **−2, 2**
2. $x^2 = 16$ **−4, 4**
3. $-2x^2 - 6 = 0$ **∅**
4. $-x^2 + 12x - 36 = 0$ **6**
5. $-x^2 = -9$ **−3, 3**
6. $2x^2 = 3x^2 - 2x - 8$ **−2, 4**

SEE EXAMPLE 2 p. 569

Find the roots of each quadratic polynomial.

7. $x^2 - 6x + 9$ **3**
8. $-4x^2 - 8x - 4$ **−1**
9. $x^2 + 5x + 4$ **−4, −1**
10. $x^2 + 2$ **no real roots**
11. $x^2 - 6x - 7$ **−1, 7**
12. $x^2 + 5x + 8$ **no real roots**

SEE EXAMPLE 3 p. 570

13. **Sports** A baseball coach uses a pitching machine to simulate pop flies during practice. A baseball is shot out of the pitching machine with an initial velocity of 80 feet per second. The quadratic function $y = -16x^2 + 80x$ gives the height y of the baseball x seconds after being shot from the machine. How long is the baseball in the air? **5 s**

PRACTICE AND PROBLEM SOLVING

Independent Practice

For Exercises	See Example
14–19	1
20–22	2
23	3

Extra Practice
Skills Practice p. EP19
Application Practice p. EP32

Solve each equation by graphing the related function. Check your answer.

14. $-x^2 + 16 = 0$ **−4, 4**
15. $3x^2 = -7$ **∅**
16. $5x^2 - 12x + 10 = x^2 + 10x$ **$\frac{1}{2}$, 5**
17. $x^2 + 10x + 25 = 0$ **−5**
18. $-4x^2 - 24x = 36$ **−3**
19. $-9x^2 + 10x - 9 = -8x$ **1**

Find the roots of each quadratic polynomial.

20. $-x^2 - 1$ **no real roots**
21. $3x^2 - 27$ **−3, 3**
22. $2x^2 - 4x + 5$ **no real roots**

23. **Geography** Yosemite Falls in California is made of three smaller waterfalls. The upper fall drops 1450 feet. The height h in feet of a water droplet falling from the upper fall to the next fall is modeled by the quadratic function $h = -16t^2 + 1450$, where t is the time in seconds after the initial fall. Estimate the time it takes for the droplet to reach the next fall. **about 9.5 s**

Reasoning Tell whether each statement is always, sometimes, or never true. Explain.

24. If the graph of a quadratic function has its vertex at the origin, then the related quadratic equation has exactly one solution. **always**
25. If the graph of a quadratic function opens upward, then the related quadratic equation has two solutions. **sometimes**
26. If the graph of a quadratic function has its vertex on the x-axis, then the related quadratic equation has exactly one solution. **always**
27. If the graph of a quadratic function has its vertex in the first quadrant, then the related quadratic equation has two solutions. **sometimes**
28. A quadratic equation in the form $ax^2 - c = 0$, where $a < 0$ and $c > 0$, has two solutions. **never**

29. **Graphing Calculator** A fireworks shell is fired from a mortar. Its height is modeled by the quadratic function $h = -16(t - 7)^2 + 784$, where t is the time in seconds after the shell is fired and h is the height in feet. Graph the function. If the shell is supposed to explode at its maximum height, at what height should it explode? If the shell does not explode, how long will it take to return to the ground? **784 ft; 14 s**

9-4 Exercises

Assignment Guide

Assign *Guided Practice* exercises as necessary.

If you finished Examples **1–3**
Proficient 14–30, 36–42, 47–58
Advanced 14–30, 36–58

Homework Quick Check
Quickly check key concepts.
Exercises: 16, 18, 20, 22, 23, 29, 30

Answer

29.

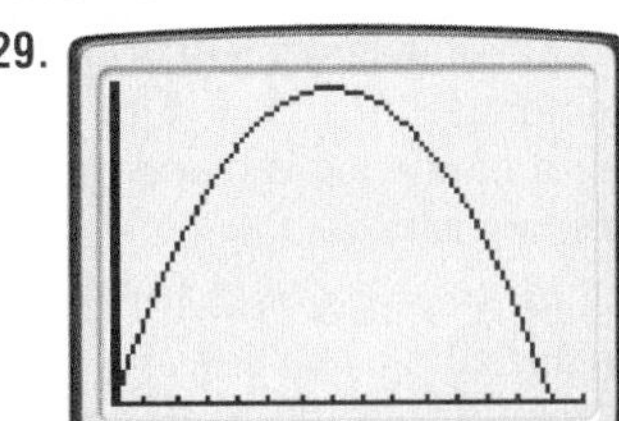

California Standards

Standard	Exercises
2.0	50–57
7.0	47–49
21.0	1–6, 14–19, 31, 42
23.0	13, 23, 29, 30, 32, 39, 58
25.3	28

Exercise 39 involves solving a quadratic equation by graphing to determine the amount of time an object is in the air and then analyzing the graph to find other information. This exercise prepares students for the Concept Connection on page 610.

Answers

30c. According to the graph, $x = 4$ is a sol. to the related equation, but $x = 4$ is not a sol. of $0 = -5x^2 + 10x$.

36a. $x - 4$, $x - 8$

b. $0 = x^2 - 24x + 80$

c. 4, 20

d. Two possible lengths for the hypotenuse; no; if $x = 4$, the length of one leg is 0 and the other leg is neg.

37. Look for y-values of 0. The corresponding x-values are the solutions. If there are no y-values equal to 0, look for sign changes in the y-values. Solutions are between the corresponding x-values.

38. $y = ax^2 - c$ $(a > 0, c > 0)$ will always have two zeros because its graph is a parabola that opens up with the vertex below the origin. By contrast, the graph of $y = ax^2 + c$ $(a > 0, c > 0)$ opens up with its vertex above the origin. It will never cross the x-axis.

39d. 84 ft; yes, at 1.5 s; 3.5 is 1 unit right of the axis of symm. $(x = 2.5)$. The ball will have the same ht. at the time represented by the pt. 1 unit left of the axis of symmetry.

30. Athletics The graph shows the height y in feet of a gymnast jumping off a vault after x seconds.

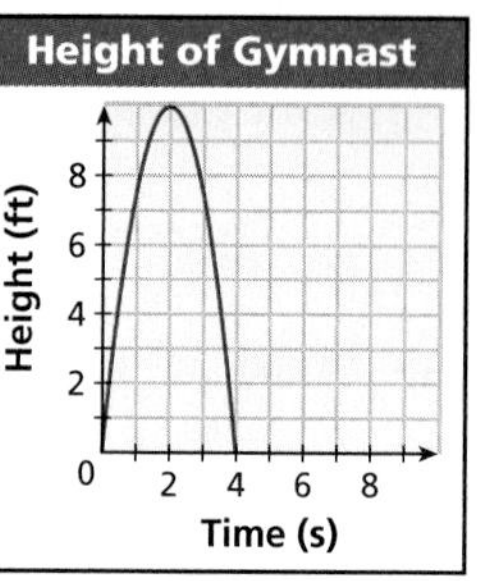

a. How long does the gymnast stay in the air? **4 s**

b. What is the maximum height that the gymnast reaches? **10 ft**

c. Explain why the function $y = -5x^2 + 10x$ cannot accurately model the gymnast's motion.

31. Solve the equation $x^2 = x + 12$ by graphing $y = x^2$ and $y = x + 12$ on the same coordinate plane and finding the x-coordinates of the points of intersection. Check your answer. **−3, 4**

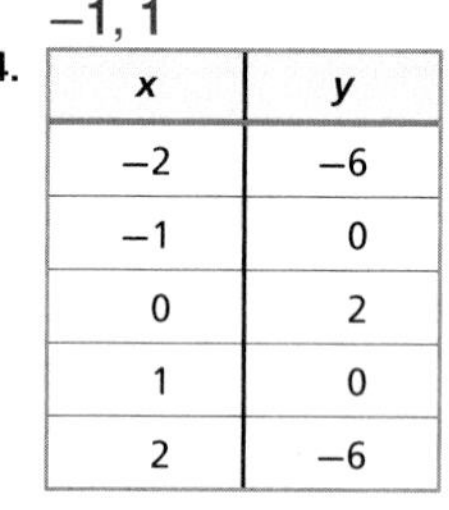

Biology

Some species of kangaroos are able to jump 30 feet in distance and 6 feet in height.

32. Biology The quadratic function $y = -5x^2 + 7x$ approximates the height y of a kangaroo x seconds after it has jumped. About how long does it take the kangaroo to return to the ground? **1.4 s**

For Exercises 33–35, use the table to determine the solutions of the related quadratic equation.

33. **−1**

x	y
−2	−1
−1	0
0	−1
1	−4
2	−9

34. **−1, 1**

x	y
−2	−6
−1	0
0	2
1	0
2	−6

35. **no real solutions**

x	y
−2	6
−1	3
0	2
1	3
2	6

36. Geometry The hypotenuse of a right triangle is 4 cm longer than one leg and 8 cm longer than the other leg. Let x represent the length of the hypotenuse.

a. Write an expression for the length of each leg in terms of x.

b. Use the Pythagorean Theorem to write an equation that can be solved for x.

c. Find the solutions of your equation from part **b**.

d. **Critical Thinking** What do the solutions of your equation represent? Are both solutions reasonable? Explain.

37. Write About It Explain how to find solutions of a quadratic equation by analyzing a table of values.

38. Critical Thinking Explain why a quadratic equation in the form $ax^2 - c = 0$, where $a > 0$ and $c > 0$, will always have two solutions. Then explain why a quadratic equation in the form $ax^2 + c = 0$, where $a > 0$ and $c > 0$, will never have any real-number solutions.

39. This problem will prepare you for the Concept Connection on page 610.

The quadratic equation $0 = -16t^2 + 80t$ gives the time t in seconds when a golf ball is at height 0 feet.

a. How long is the golf ball in the air? **5 s**

b. What is the maximum height of the golf ball? **100 ft**

c. After how many seconds is the ball at its maximum height? **2.5 s**

d. What is the height of the ball after 3.5 seconds? Is there another time when the ball reaches that height? Explain.

9-4 PRACTICE A

9-4 PRACTICE C

9-4 PRACTICE B

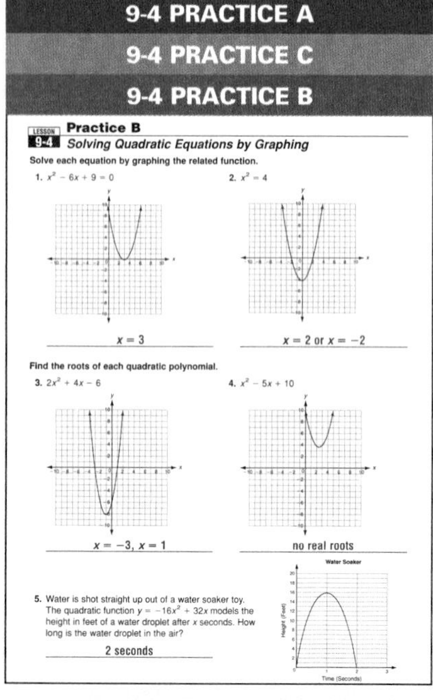

LESSON 9-4 **Practice B**

Solving Quadratic Equations by Graphing

Solve each equation by graphing the related function.

1. $x^2 - 6x + 9 = 0$ — $x = 3$
2. $x^2 - 4$ — $x = 2$ or $x = -2$

Find the roots of each quadratic polynomial.

3. $2x^2 + 4x - 6$ — $x = -3, x = 1$
4. $x^2 - 5x + 10$ — no real roots

5. Water is shot straight up out of a water soaker toy. The quadratic function $y = -16x^2 + 32x$ models the height in feet of a water droplet after x seconds. How long is the water droplet in the air? — 2 seconds

9-4 READING STRATEGIES

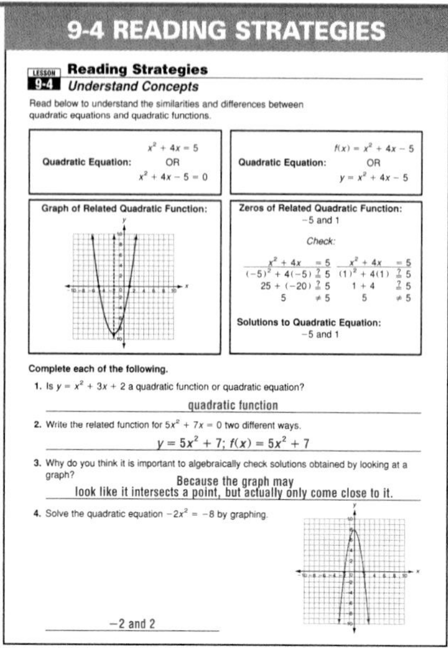

LESSON 9-4 **Reading Strategies**

Understand Concepts

Read below to understand the similarities and differences between quadratic equations and quadratic functions.

Quadratic Equation: $x^2 + 4x = 5$ OR $x^2 + 4x - 5 = 0$	Quadratic Equation: $f(x) = x^2 + 4x - 5$ OR $y = x^2 + 4x - 5$
Graph of Related Quadratic Function:	Zeros of Related Quadratic Function: −5 and 1
	Check: $x^2 + 4x = 5$; $(-5)^2 + 4(-5) \stackrel{?}{=} 5$; $25 + (-20) \stackrel{?}{=} 5$; $5 = 5$. $x^2 + 4x = 5$; $(1)^2 + 4(1) \stackrel{?}{=} 5$; $1 + 4 \stackrel{?}{=} 5$; $5 = 5$
	Solutions to Quadratic Equation: −5 and 1

Complete each of the following.

1. Is $y = x^2 + 3x + 2$ a quadratic function or quadratic equation? — quadratic function
2. Write the related function for $5x^2 + 7x = 0$ two different ways. — $y = 5x^2 + 7$; $f(x) = 5x^2 + 7$
3. Why do you think it is important to algebraically check solutions obtained by looking at a graph? — Because the graph may look like it intersects a point, but actually only come close to it.
4. Solve the quadratic equation $-2x^2 = -8$ by graphing. — −2 and 2

9-4 REVIEW FOR MASTERY

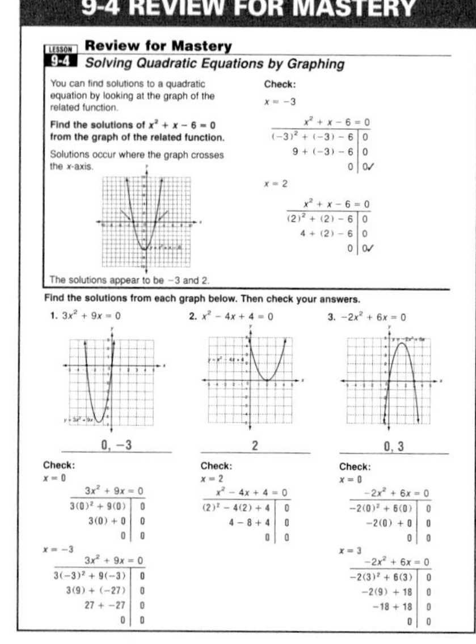

LESSON 9-4 **Review for Mastery**

Solving Quadratic Equations by Graphing

You can find solutions to a quadratic equation by looking at the graph of the related function.

Find the solutions of $x^2 + x - 6 = 0$ from the graph of the related function.

Solutions occur where the graph crosses the x-axis.

The solutions appear to be −3 and 2.

Check: $x = -3$: $x^2 + x - 6 = 0$; $(-3)^2 + (-3) - 6 = 0$; $9 + (-3) - 6 = 0$; $0 = 0$ ✓

$x = 2$: $x^2 + x - 6 = 0$; $(2)^2 + (2) - 6 = 0$; $4 + (2) - 6 = 0$; $0 = 0$ ✓

Find the solutions from each graph below. Then check your answers.

1. $3x^2 + 9x = 0$ — 0, −3. Check: $x = 0$: $3(0)^2 + 9(0) = 0$; $3(0) + 0 = 0$; $0 = 0$. $x = -3$: $3(-3)^2 + 9(-3) = 0$; $3(9) + (-27) = 0$; $27 + -27 = 0$; $0 = 0$
2. $x^2 - 4x + 4 = 0$ — 2. Check: $x = 2$: $(2)^2 - 4(2) + 4 = 0$; $4 - 8 + 4 = 0$; $0 = 0$
3. $-2x^2 + 6x = 0$ — 0, 3. Check: $x = 0$: $-2(0)^2 + 6(0) = 0$; $-2(0) + 0 = 0$; $0 = 0$. $x = 3$: $-2(3)^2 + 6(3) = 0$; $-2(9) + 18 = 0$; $-18 + 18 = 0$; $0 = 0$

Multiple Choice For Exercises 40 and 41, choose the best answer.

40. Use the graph to find the number of solutions of $-2x^2 + 2 = 0$.

(A) 0 (B) 1 **(C) 2** (D) 3

41. Which graph could be used to find the roots of $x^2 + 4x - 12$?

(A)

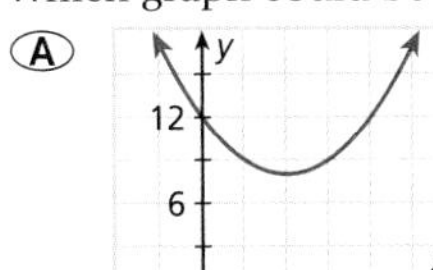

(C)

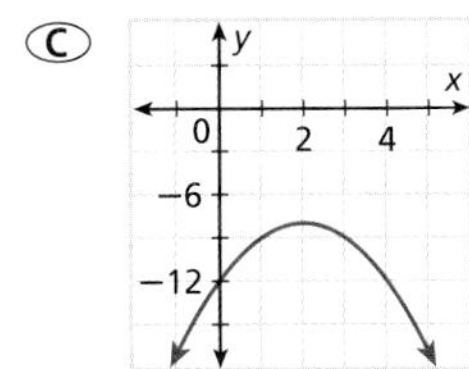

(B)

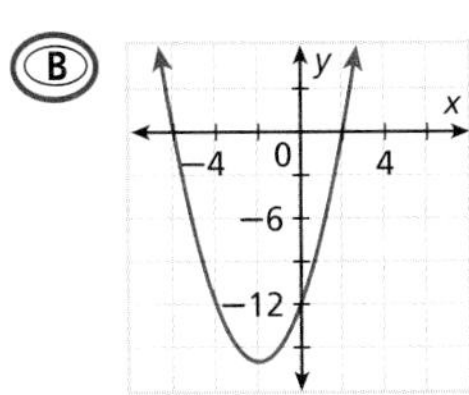

(D)

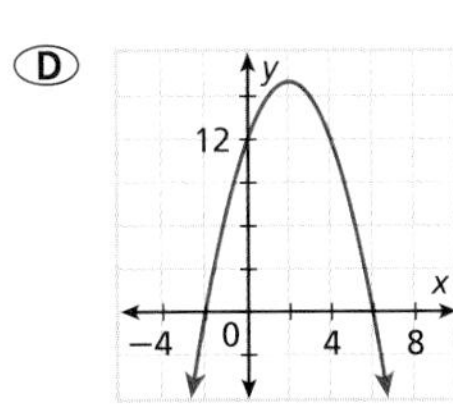

42. Short Response Find the solutions of $2x^2 + x - 1 = 0$ by graphing. Explain how the graph of the related function shows the solutions of the equation.

CHALLENGE AND EXTEND

Graphing Calculator Use a graphing calculator to estimate the solutions of each quadratic equation.

43. $\frac{5}{16}x + \frac{1}{4}x^2 = \frac{3}{5}$ **≈ −2.3, ≈ 1**

44. $1200x^2 - 650x - 100 = -200x - 175$ **∅**

45. $\frac{1}{5}x + \frac{3}{4}x^2 = \frac{7}{12}$ **≈ −1, ≈ 0.75**

46. $400x^2 - 100 = -300x + 456$ **≈ −1.6, ≈ 0.86**

SPIRAL STANDARDS REVIEW

2.0, 7.0, 23.0

Write an equation in point-slope form for the line with the given slope that contains the given point. *(Lesson 5-6)*

47. slope $= \frac{1}{2}$; $(2, 3)$ **47.** $y = \frac{1}{2}x + 2$

48. slope $= -3$; $(-2, 4)$ $y = -3x - 2$

49. slope $= 0$; $(2, 1)$ $y = 1$

Simplify. *(Lesson 7-4)*

50. $\frac{3^4}{3}$ **27**

51. $\frac{5^2 \cdot 2^4}{5 \cdot 2^2}$ **20**

52. $\frac{(x^4)^5}{(x^3)^3}$ x^{11}

53. $\left(\frac{x^3}{y^2}\right)^{-3}$ $\frac{y^6}{x^9}$

54. $\left(\frac{a^2b^3}{ab^2}\right)^3$ a^3b^3

55. $\left(\frac{4s}{3t}\right)^{-2}$ $\frac{9t^2}{16s^2}$

56. $\left(\frac{2}{3}\right)^{-3} \cdot \left(\frac{a^3}{b}\right)^{-2}$ **56.** $\frac{27b^2}{8a^6}$

57. $\left(\frac{-k^2}{5k^3}\right)^{-3}$ $-125k^3$

58. A baton is tossed into the air by a dancer. The height of the baton in feet above the dancer's hand can be modeled by $y = -10x^2 + 20x$ where x is the time in seconds after the toss. Find the baton's maximum height and the time it takes the baton to reach this height. Then find how long the baton is in the air. *(Lesson 9-3)* **10 ft at 1 s; 2 s**

Teaching Tip **Multiple Choice** In **Exercise 41,** remind students to consider the equation in the form $ax^2 + bx + c = 0$. Because $a > 0$, the graph opens upward, so **C** and **D** can be eliminated. By finding that the y-intercept of the related function is -12, **A** can also be eliminated.

Answer

42.

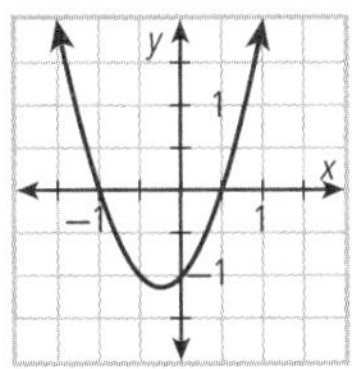

-1 and $\frac{1}{2}$; the x-intercepts are the solutions of the equation.

Journal

Have students explain how to find solutions to a quadratic equation by graphing the related function.

ALTERNATIVE ASSESSMENT

Have students write quadratic equation with two solutions. They should then solve by graphing. Then have them change either a, b, or c so that the equation has no solutions.

Power Presentations with PowerPoint®

9-4 Lesson Quiz

Solve each equation by graphing the related function.

1. $3x^2 - 12 = 0$ 2, −2

2. $x^2 + 2x = 8$ −4, 2

3. $3x - 5 = x^2$ ∅

4. $3x^2 + 3 = 6x$ 1

5. A rocket is shot straight up from the ground. The quadratic function $f(t) = -16t^2 + 96t$ models the rocket's height above the ground after t seconds. How long does it take for the rocket to return to the ground? 6 s

Also available on transparency

9-4 PROBLEM SOLVING

LESSON 9-4 **Problem Solving**
Solving Quadratic Equations by Graphing

The path of a certain firework in the air is modeled by the parabolic function $y = -16x^2 + 256x - 624$ where x is the number of seconds after the fuse is lit. Write the correct answer.

1. Graph the function on the grid below.

Flight of the Firework

2. The firework will explode when it reaches its highest point. How long after the fuse is lit will the firework explode and how high will the firework be? **8 seconds; 400 feet**

3. Based on the graph of the firework, what are the two zeros of this function? **$x = 3$; $x = 13$**

4. What is the meaning of each of the zeros you found in problem 3? **The firework launches at 3 s; The firework lands at 13 s**

Select the best answer.

5. The quadratic function $f(x) = -16x^2 + 90x$ models the height of a baseball in feet after x seconds. How long is the baseball in the air?

A 2.8125 s **(B) 5.625 s** C 11.25 s D 126.5625 s

6. The height of a football y in feet is given by the function $y = -16x^2 + 56x + 2$ where x is the time in seconds after the ball was kicked. This function is graphed below. How long was the football in the air?

Height of Football

A 0.5 seconds B 1.75 seconds C 2 seconds **(D) 3.5 seconds**

7. The function $y = -0.04x^2 + 2x$ models the height of an arch support for a bridge, where x is the distance in feet from where the arch supports enter the water. How many real solutions does this function have?

F 0 G 1 **(H) 2** J 3

9-4 CHALLENGE

LESSON 9-4 **Challenge**
Through the Tunnel

A parabolic tunnel is to be built for a two-lane road. The Department of Transportation (DOT) wants the tunnel to be wide enough for the two lanes and a walkway on either side.

An architect proposes a design that uses $y = -0.08x^2 + 2.88x$ to model the height of the ceiling in feet at a distance x feet from the bottom left. Your task is to determine whether the design will satisfy all of the DOT's requirements.

Use a graphing calculator as necessary.

1. What is the width of the tunnel from the bottom left to the bottom right? Explain how you solved this problem. **36 ft**
Solve $0 = -0.08x^2 + 2.88x$ by graphing on a graphing calculator. The zeros are 0 and 36.

2. According to state law, the maximum height of any vehicle is 13.5 ft. To the nearest foot, how close to the bottom left or bottom right could the tallest vehicle drive? Explain how you found your answer. **6 ft**
Solve $13.5 = -0.08x^2 + 2.88x$ by graphing $y = -0.08x^2 + 2.88x - 13.5$. The zeros are approximately 6 and 30.

3. According to state law, the standard width for one lane of road is 12 ft. Is the tunnel wide enough for two lanes? Is it wide enough for three lanes? Explain. **yes; no; Two lanes require 24 ft, which is exactly the width that is taller than 13.5 ft. Three lanes require 36 ft; the cars in the outside lanes would hit the tunnel walls.**

4. For the safety of pedestrians on the walkways, a 2-ft-wide wall will be built between the outside edges of the road and the walkways. If only two lanes are put in the middle of the tunnel, how much room is left on either side for the walkway? **4 ft**

5. Considering your answer to problem 4, will the ceiling of the walkways be tall enough for an "average" pedestrian to walk through? Explain. **Yes**
Evaluate $y = -0.08x^2 + 2.88x$ when $x = 4$ to find $y = 10.24$. Because an "average" pedestrian is shorter than 10 ft, the walkway will be tall enough.

6. Should the DOT accept or reject the architect's design? **accept**

Technology Lab Organizer

Use with Lesson 9-4

Objective: Use tables and graphs on a graphing calculator to explore the relationships between roots, zeros, and *x*-intercepts.

Materials: graphing calculator

Online Edition
Graphing Calculator, TechKeys

Countdown to Mastery Week 21

Teach

Discuss

Discuss how to use sign changes in *y*-values to approximate the zeros from a table when a *y*-value of 0 does not appear in the table.

Close

Key Concept

Finding the roots of a quadratic polynomial is the same as solving the related quadratic equation which is the same as finding the zeros of the related quadratic function.

Assessment

Journal Have students explain how to use a table to solve a quadratic equation with noninteger solutions.

California Standards

Algebra 1 21.0

9-4 Technology LAB

Use with Lesson 9-4

Explore Roots, Zeros, and *x*-Intercepts

The roots of a quadratic polynomial, the solutions of the related equation, and the *x*-intercepts, or zeros, of the related function are very closely connected. You can use tables or graphs to understand these connections.

California Standards

21.0 Students graph quadratic functions and know that their roots are the *x*-intercepts.

go.hrw.com
Lab Resources Online
KEYWORD: MA8CA Lab9

Activity 1

Find the roots of $5x^2 + 8x - 4$ by using a table. Check your answer.

1. To find the roots, solve $5x^2 + 8x - 4 = 0$
2. Enter the related function in $\mathbf{Y_1}$.
3. Press 2nd GRAPH (TABLE) to use the **TABLE** function.
4. Scroll through the values by using ▲ and ▼. Look for values of 0 in the $\mathbf{Y_1}$ column. The corresponding *x*-value is a zero of the function. There appears to be one zero at −2.

   Also look for places where the signs of nonzero *y*-values change. There is a zero between the corresponding *x*-values. So there is another zero somewhere between 0 and 1.
5. To get a better estimate of the zero, change the table settings. Press 2nd WINDOW (TBLSET) to view the **TABLE SETUP** screen. Set **TblStart = 0** and the step value **ΔTbl = .1**. Press 2nd GRAPH (TABLE) to see the table again.
6. Scroll through the values by using ▲ and ▼. The second zero appears to be at 0.4.

   The zeros of the function, −2 and 0.4, are the solutions of $5x^2 + 8x - 4 = 0$ and the roots of $5x^2 + 8x - 4$.

Plot1 Plot2 Plot3
\Y1 ■ 5X²+8X−4
\Y2=
\Y3=

X	Y1
-3	17
-2	0
-1	-7
0	-4
1	9
2	32
3	65

X=-2

The signs of the *y*-values change.

TABLE SETUP
TblStart=0
ΔTbl=.1
Indpnt: Auto Ask
Depend: Auto Ask

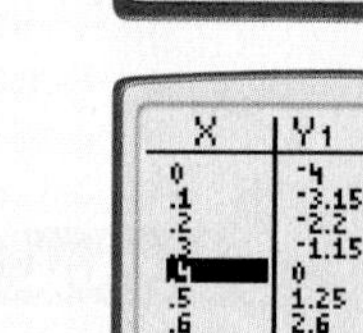

X	Y1
0	-4
.1	-3.15
.2	-2.2
.3	-1.15
.4	0
.5	1.25
.6	2.6

X=.4

Check

$5x^2 + 8x - 4 = 0$	
$5(-2)^2 + 8(-2) - 4$	0
$5(4) - 16 - 4$	0
$20 - 16 - 4$	0
0	0 ✓

$5x^2 + 8x - 4 = 0$	
$5(0.4)^2 + 8(0.4) - 4$	0
$5(0.16) + 3.2 - 4$	0
$0.8 + 3.2 - 4$	0
0	0 ✓

Try This

Find the roots of each polynomial by using a table. Check your answer.

1. $x^2 - 4x - 5$ **−1, 5**
2. $x^2 - x - 6$ **−2, 3**
3. $2x^2 + x - 1$ **−1, 0.5**
4. $5x^2 - 6x - 8$ **−0.8, 2**
5. **Critical Thinking** How would you find the zero of a function that showed a sign change in the *y*-values between the *x*-values 1.2 and 1.3?
6. **Make a Conjecture** If you scrolled up and down the list and found only positive values, what might you conclude?

Teaching Tip

Technology When changing the increments of *x* with the **TBLSET** function in **Activity 1,** consider also changing the *x*-value at which the table starts. This can reduce excess scrolling when locating sign changes in *y*. For instance, if you know there is a zero between 1 and 2, start the table at 1.

Answers to *Try This*

5. Possible answer: Change **Tblstart** to 1.2 and **ΔTbl** to 0.01 and scroll until I found zero.
6. Possible answer: The polynomial has no roots, the related equation has no solutions, and the related function has no zeros.

Activity 2

Solve $5x^2 + x - 8.4 = 0$ by using a table and a graph. Check your answer.

1. Enter the related function in $\mathbf{Y_1}$.

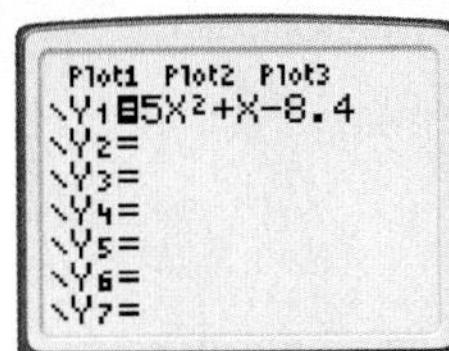

2. To view both the table and the graph at the same time, set your calculator to the Graph-Table mode. Press MODE and select **G-T**.

3. Press GRAPH. You should see the graph and the table. Notice that the function appears to have one negative zero and one positive zero near the y-axis.

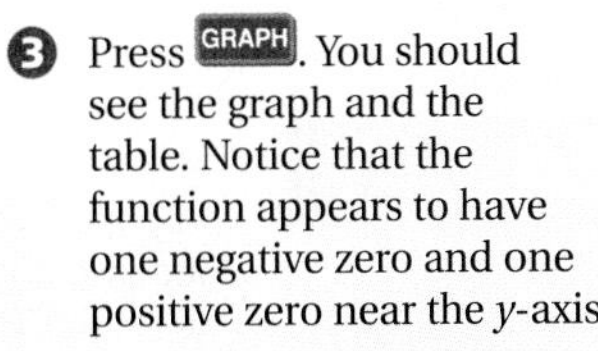

4. To get a closer view of the graph, press ZOOM and select **4:ZDecimal**.

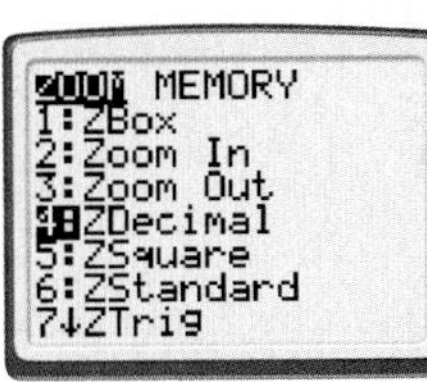

5. Press TRACE. Use ◀ to scroll to find the negative zero. The graph and the table show that the zero appears to be -1.4.

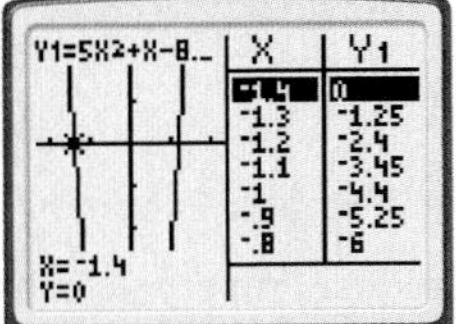

6. Use ▶ to scroll and find the positive zero. The graph and the table show that the zero appears to be 1.2.

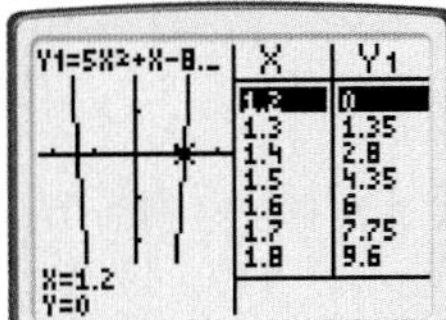

The solutions are -1.4 and 1.2.

Check

$5x^2 + x - 8.4$	$= 0$
$5(-1.4)^2 + (-1.4) - 8.4$	0
$5(1.96) - 1.4 - 8.4$	0
$9.8 - 1.4 - 8.4$	0
0	0 ✓

$5x^2 + x - 8.4$	$= 0$
$5(1.2)^2 + (1.2) - 8.4$	0
$5(1.44) + 1.2 - 8.4$	0
$7.2 + 1.2 - 8.4$	0
0	0 ✓

Try This

Solve each equation by using a table and a graph. Check your answer.

7. $2x^2 - x - 3 = 0$ **−1, 1.5**
8. $5x^2 + 13x + 6 = 0$ **−2, −0.6**
9. $10x^2 - 3x - 4$ **−0.5, 0.8**
10. $x^2 - 2x - 0.96 = 0$ **−0.4, 2.4**
11. **Critical Thinking** Suppose that when you graphed a quadratic function, you could see only one side of the graph and one zero. What methods would you use to try to find the other zero? **Possible answer: Set the window dimensions wider to see both zeros, and then trace to find the other zero.**

Teaching Tip

Technology When using a calculator, students should be aware of its limitations. For example, a calculator cannot store an infinite number of digits, so the values it uses for repeating decimals and irrational numbers are rounded. Graphs may be difficult to read on a pixellated screen. Discourage students from blindly accepting a calculator's answer. They should be able to verify that the answer is correct or at least reasonable.

9-5 Organizer

Objective: Solve quadratic equations by factoring.

Online Edition
Tutorial Videos

Countdown to Mastery Week 21

Power Presentations with PowerPoint®

Warm Up

Find each product.

1. $(x + 2)(x + 7)$ $\quad x^2 + 9x + 14$
2. $(x - 11)(x + 5)$ $\quad x^2 - 6x - 55$
3. $(x - 10)^2$ $\quad x^2 - 20x + 100$

Factor each polynomial.

4. $x^2 + 12x + 35$ $\quad (x + 5)(x + 7)$
5. $x^2 + 2x - 63$ $\quad (x - 7)(x + 9)$
6. $x^2 - 10x + 16$ $\quad (x - 2)(x - 8)$
7. $2x^2 - 16x + 32$ $\quad 2(x - 4)^2$

Also available on transparency

Math Humor

Citizen: Why is that quadratic equation lurking about our town?

Sheriff: He's searching for his roots.

California Standards

Algebra 1 14.0, 23.0

9-5 Solving Quadratic Equations by Factoring

California Standards

14.0 Students solve a quadratic equation by factoring or completing the square.
23.0 Students apply quadratic equations to physical problems, such as the motion of an object under the force of gravity.

Who uses this?
In order to determine how many seconds she will be in the air, a high diver can use a quadratic equation. (See Example 3.)

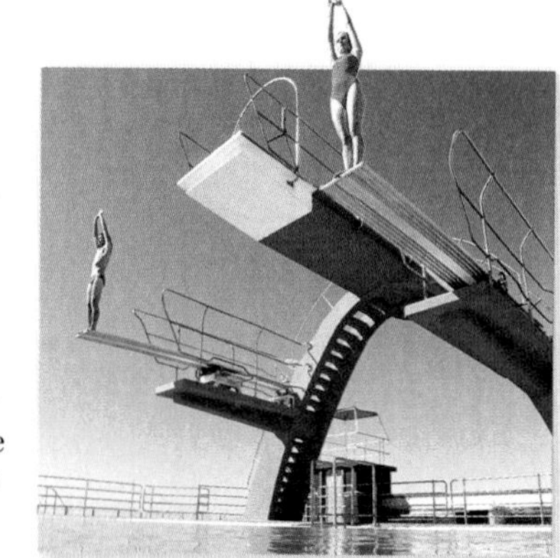

You have solved quadratic equations by graphing. Another method used to solve quadratic equations is to factor and use the Zero Product Property.

Know it! Note

Zero Product Property

WORDS	NUMBERS	ALGEBRA
If the product of two quantities equals zero, at least one of the quantities equals zero.	$3(0) = 0$ $0(4) = 0$	For all real numbers a and b, if $ab = 0$, then $a = 0$ or $b = 0$.

EXAMPLE 1 Using the Zero Product Property

Use the Zero Product Property to solve each equation. Check your answer.

A $(x - 3)(x + 7) = 0$

$x - 3 = 0$ or $x + 7 = 0$ *Use the Zero Product Property.*
$x = 3$ or $x = -7$ *Solve each equation.*

Check

$$\begin{array}{c|c} (x-3)(x+7) & 0 \\ \hline (3-3)(3+7) & 0 \\ (0)(10) & 0 \\ 0 & 0 \checkmark \end{array} \qquad \begin{array}{c|c} (x-3)(x+7) & 0 \\ \hline (-7-3)(-7+7) & 0 \\ (-10)(0) & 0 \\ 0 & 0 \checkmark \end{array}$$

Substitute each solution for x in the original equation.

B $(x)(x - 5) = 0$

$x = 0$ or $x - 5 = 0$ *Use the Zero Product Property.*
$x = 0$ or $x = 5$ *Solve the second equation.*

Check

$$\begin{array}{c|c} (x)(x-5) & 0 \\ \hline (0)(0-5) & 0 \\ (0)(-5) & 0 \\ 0 & 0 \checkmark \end{array} \qquad \begin{array}{c|c} (x)(x-5) & 0 \\ \hline (5)(5-5) & 0 \\ (5)(0) & 0 \\ 0 & 0 \checkmark \end{array}$$

Substitute each solution for x in the original equation.

CHECK IT OUT! Use the Zero Product Property to solve each equation. Check your answer.

1a. $(x)(x + 4) = 0$ **0, −4** **1b.** $(x + 4)(x - 3) = 0$ **−4, 3**

1 Introduce

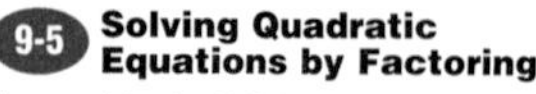

EXPLORATION

9-5 Solving Quadratic Equations by Factoring

Use your calculator for this Exploration.

1. Graph each function listed in the table, and use the graph to find the zeros of the function. Record the zeros and the number of zeros.

Function	Zeros	Number of Zeros
$y = (x - 2)(x + 1)$		
$y = (x + 3)(x + 7)$		
$y = (x + 6)(x - 1)$		
$y = (x - 2.5)(x - 5)$		
$y = (x - 4)^2$		
$y = (x + 3)^2$		

2. Predict the zeros of the function $y = (x - 7)(x + 10)$ without graphing.
3. Predict the zeros of the function $y = (x + 8)^2$ without graphing.

THINK AND DISCUSS

4. **Explain** how you predicted the zeros of the functions in Problems 2 and 3.
5. **Describe** any patterns you notice in your table.

Motivate

Display the linear equation $4x = x + 12$ and the quadratic equation $4x = x^2 + 12$. Ask students why they cannot solve for x in the quadratic equation as they would in the linear equation. Possible answer: The variable terms are not like terms and cannot be combined to isolate x.
Tell them that another method is needed to solve quadratic equations algebraically.

Explorations and answers are provided in *Alternate Openers: Explorations Transparencies.*

You may need to factor before using the Zero Product Property. You can check your answers by substituting into the original equation or by graphing. If the factored form of the equation has two different factors, the graph of the related function will cross the x-axis in two places. If the factored form has two identical factors, the graph will cross the x-axis in one place.

EXAMPLE 2 Solving Quadratic Equations by Factoring

Solve each quadratic equation by factoring. Check your answer.

Helpful Hint

To review factoring techniques, see Lessons 8-3 through 8-5.

A $x^2 + 7x + 10 = 0$

$(x+5)(x+2) = 0$	*Factor the trinomial.*
$x + 5 = 0$ or $x + 2 = 0$	*Use the Zero Product Property.*
$x = -5$ or $x = -2$	*Solve each equation.*

Check

$x^2 + 7x + 10 = 0$		$x^2 + 7x + 10 = 0$	
$(-5)^2 + 7(-5) + 10$	0	$(-2)^2 + 7(-2) + 10$	0
$25 - 35 + 10$	0	$4 - 14 + 10$	0
0	0 ✓	0	0 ✓

B $x^2 + 2x = 8$

$x^2 + 2x = 8$	*The equation must be written in standard form. Subtract 8 from both sides.*
$\underline{\quad -8 \quad -8}$	
$x^2 + 2x - 8 = 0$	
$(x+4)(x-2) = 0$	*Factor the trinomial.*
$x + 4 = 0$ or $x - 2 = 0$	*Use the Zero Product Property.*
$x = -4$ or $x = 2$	*Solve each equation.*

Check Graph the related quadratic function. Because there are two solutions found by factoring, the graph should cross the x-axis in two places.

Caution!

In some cases, it may be difficult to read the zeros from the graph. You can always check by substituting into the original equation.

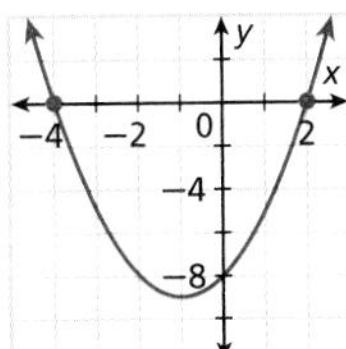

The graph of $y = x^2 + 2x - 8$ intersects the x-axis at $x = -4$ and $x = 2$, the same as the solutions found by factoring. ✓

C $x^2 + 2x + 1 = 0$

$(x+1)(x+1) = 0$	*Factor the trinomial.*
$x + 1 = 0$ or $x + 1 = 0$	*Use the Zero Product Property.*
$x = -1$ or $x = -1$	*Solve each equation.*

Both factors result in the same solution, so there is one solution, -1.

Check Graph the related quadratic function.

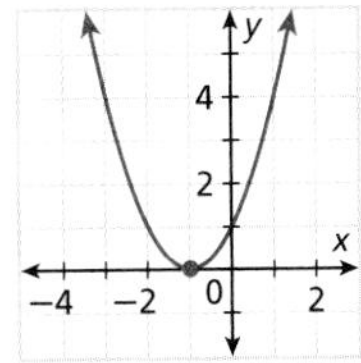

The graph of $y = x^2 + 2x + 1$ shows one zero at -1, the same as the solution found by factoring. ✓

COMMON ERROR ALERT

When solving quadratic equations by factoring, students sometimes choose the constants in the binomial factors as the solutions. For example, students might say that the solutions of $(x + 3)(x + 5) = 0$ are 3 and 5. Remind students to find the value of x that would make each factor equal 0.

$x + 3 = 0$ or $x + 5 = 0$

$x = -3$ $\qquad$ $x = -5$

Power Presentations with PowerPoint®

Additional Examples

Example 1

Use the Zero Product Property to solve each equation. Check your answer.

A. $(x - 7)(x + 2) = 0$ $\quad$ 7, −2

B. $(x - 2)(x) = 0$ $\quad$ 0, 2

Example 2

Solve each quadratic equation by factoring. Check your answer.

A. $x^2 - 6x + 8 = 0$ $\quad$ 4, 2

B. $x^2 + 4x = 21$ $\quad$ −7, 3

C. $x^2 - 12x + 36 = 0$ $\quad$ 6

D. $-2x^2 = 20x + 50$ $\quad$ −5

Also available on transparency

INTERVENTION Questioning Strategies

EXAMPLE 1

- Why do you set each factor equal to zero?
- How can you tell whether an expression is quadratic when it is written in factored form?

EXAMPLE 2

- Why must one side of the equation be equal to zero?
- What types of quadratic trinomials have only one solution?
- When the graph crosses the x-axis, what is the value of y?
- How can you use the factored form of an equation to predict the number of x-intercepts of the related function? What will those x-intercepts be?

2 Teach

Guided Instruction

Review multiplying binomials and factoring trinomials, including how to recognize perfect-square trinomials. Remind students that the first step in factoring is always to look for a GCF. Emphasize the importance of not using the Zero Product Property until one side of the equation is zero. Encourage students to substitute solutions into the original equations to check their answers.

Show students how to create quadratic equations with given solutions by working backward. For example, if the solutions are −2 and 5, then:

$$x = -2 \text{ or } x = 5$$
$$(x + 2)(x - 5) = 0$$
$$x^2 - 3x - 10 = 0$$

Explain that there are infinitely many equivalent equations that can be generated by performing the same operation on both sides.

Power Presentations with PowerPoint®

Additional Examples

Example 3

The height in feet above the water of a diver can be modeled by $h(t) = -16t^2 + 8t + 8$, where t is time in seconds after the diver jumps off a platform. Find the time it takes for the diver to reach the water. 1 s

Also available on transparency

INTERVENTION

Questioning Strategies

EXAMPLE 3

- What equation do you need to solve?
- What is a reasonable domain and range for this situation?

Helpful Hint

$(x - 3)(x - 3)$ is a perfect square. Since both factors are the same, you solve only one equation.

Solve each quadratic equation by factoring. Check your answer.

D $-2x^2 = 18 - 12x$

$-2x^2 + 12x - 18 = 0$	*Write the equation in standard form.*
$-2(x^2 - 6x + 9) = 0$	*Factor out the GCF, −2.*
$-2(x - 3)(x - 3) = 0$	*Factor the trinomial.*
$-2 \neq 0$ or $x - 3 = 0$	*Use the Zero Product Property. −2 cannot equal 0.*
$x = 3$	*Solve the remaining equation.*

The only solution is 3.

Check $-2x^2 = 18 - 12x$

$-2(3)^2$	$18 - 12(3)$	*Substitute 3 into the original equation.*
-18	$18 - 36$	
-18	-18 ✓	

CHECK IT OUT! Solve each quadratic equation by factoring. Check your answer.

2a. $x^2 - 6x + 9 = 0$ **3**

2b. $x^2 + 4x = 5$ **1, −5**

2c. $30x = -9x^2 - 25$ $-\frac{5}{3}$

2d. $3x^2 - 4x + 1 = 0$ $\frac{1}{3}$, **1**

EXAMPLE 3 ***Sports Application***

The height of a diver above the water during a dive can be modeled by $h = -16t^2 + 8t + 48$, where h is height in feet and t is time in seconds. Find the time it takes for the diver to reach the water.

$h = -16t^2 + 8t + 48$	
$0 = -16t^2 + 8t + 48$	*The diver reaches the water when h = 0.*
$0 = -8(2t^2 - t - 6)$	*Factor out the GCF, −8.*
$0 = -8(2t + 3)(t - 2)$	*Factor the trinomial.*
$-8 \neq 0,\ 2t + 3 = 0$ or $t - 2 = 0$	*Use the Zero Product Property.*
$2t = -3$ or $t = 2$	*Solve each equation.*
$t = -\frac{3}{2}$ ✗	*Since time cannot be negative, $-\frac{3}{2}$ does not make sense in this situation.*

It takes the diver 2 seconds to reach the water.

Check $0 = -16t^2 + 8t + 48$

0	$-16(2)^2 + 8(2) + 48$	*Substitute 2 into the original equation.*
0	$-64 + 16 + 48$	
0	0 ✓	

CHECK IT OUT! **3. What if...?** The equation for the height above the water for another diver can be modeled by $h = -16t^2 + 8t + 24$. Find the time it takes this diver to reach the water. **1.5 s**

3 Close

Summarize

Have students state the first step in solving each equation.

- $(x + 1)(x - 2) = 0$
  Set each factor equal to zero.
- $x^2 + 8x + 7 = 0$
  Factor the left side.
- $2x^2 - 16x + 30 = 0$
  Factor out 2 from each term in the trinomial.
- $x^2 - 9x - 10 = -18$
  Add 18 to each side.

FORMATIVE ASSESSMENT and INTERVENTION

***Diagnose Before* the Lesson**
9-5 Warm Up, TE p. 576

***Monitor During* the Lesson**
Check It Out! Exercises, SE pp. 576–578
Questioning Strategies, TE pp. 577–578

***Assess After* the Lesson**
9-5 Lesson Quiz, TE p. 581
Alternative Assessment, TE p. 581

THINK AND DISCUSS

1. Explain two ways to solve $x^2 + x - 6 = 0$. How are these two methods similar?
2. For the quadratic equation $0 = (x + 2)(x - 6)$, what are the x-intercepts of the related function?

3. **GET ORGANIZED** Copy and complete the graphic organizer. In each box, write a step used to solve a quadratic equation by factoring.

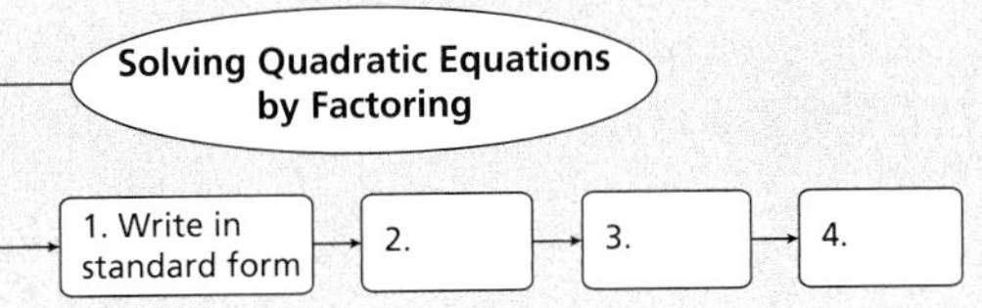

Answers to *Think and Discuss*

1. Possible answer: One method would be to factor and set each factor equal to 0. Another method would be to graph the related function, $y = x^2 + x - 6$, and find the x-intercepts. In both methods, 0 is important. In the factoring method, one side of the equation must be 0. In the graphing method, the solutions are where $y = 0$.
2. −2, 6
3. See p. A7.

9-5 Exercises

14.0, 23.0, 25.2

GUIDED PRACTICE

SEE EXAMPLE 1 p. 576

Use the Zero Product Property to solve each equation. Check your answer.

1. $(x + 2)(x - 8) = 0$ **−2, 8**
2. $(x - 6)(x - 5) = 0$ **6, 5**
3. $(x + 7)(x + 9) = 0$ **−7, −9**
4. $(x)(x - 1) = 0$ **0, 1**
5. $(x)(x + 11) = 0$ **−11, 0**
6. $(3x + 2)(4x - 1) = 0$ $-\frac{2}{3}, \frac{1}{4}$

SEE EXAMPLE 2 p. 577

Solve each quadratic equation by factoring. Check your answer.

7. $x^2 + 4x - 12 = 0$ **−6, 2**
8. $x^2 - 8x - 9 = 0$ **−1, 9**
9. $x^2 - 5x + 6 = 0$ **2, 3**
10. $x^2 - 3x = 10$ **−2, 5**
11. $x^2 + 10x = -16$ **−8, −2**
12. $x^2 + 2x = 15$ **−5, 3**
13. $x^2 - 8x + 16 = 0$ **4**
14. $-3x^2 = 18x + 27$ **−3**
15. $x^2 + 36 = 12x$ **6**
16. $x^2 + 14x + 49 = 0$ **−7**
17. $x^2 - 16x + 64 = 0$ **8**
18. $2x^2 + 6x = -18$ **∅**

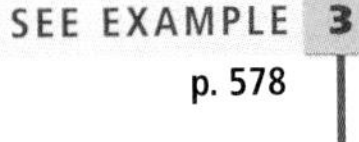

SEE EXAMPLE 3 p. 578

19. **Games** A group of friends tries to keep a beanbag from touching the ground without using their hands. Once the beanbag has been kicked, its height can be modeled by $h = -16t^2 + 14t + 2$, where h is the height in feet above the ground and t is the time in seconds. Find the time it takes the beanbag to reach the ground. **1 s**

PRACTICE AND PROBLEM SOLVING

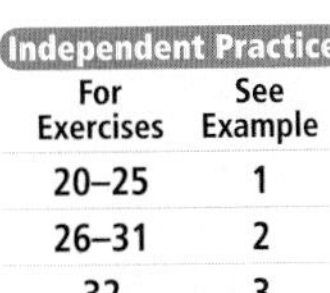

Independent Practice For Exercises	See Example
20–25	1
26–31	2
32	3

Extra Practice
Skills Practice p. EP19
Application Practice p. EP32

Use the Zero Product Property to solve each equation. Check your answer.

20. $(x - 8)(x + 6) = 0$ **−6, 8**
21. $(x + 4)(x + 7) = 0$ **−4, −7**
22. $(x - 2)(x - 5) = 0$ **2, 5**
23. $(x - 9)(x) = 0$ **9, 0**
24. $(x)(x + 25) = 0$ **0, −25**
25. $(2x + 1)(3x - 1) = 0$ $-\frac{1}{2}, \frac{1}{3}$

Solve each quadratic equation by factoring. Check your answer.

26. $x^2 + 8x + 15 = 0$ **−3, −5**
27. $x^2 - 2x - 8 = 0$ **−2, 4**
28. $x^2 - 4x + 3 = 0$ **1, 3**
29. $x^2 + 10x + 25 = 0$ **−5**
30. $x^2 - x = 12$ **−3, 4**
31. $-x^2 = 4x + 4$ **−2**

9-5 Exercises

Assignment Guide

Assign *Guided Practice* exercises as necessary.

If you finished Examples **1–2**
Proficient 20–31, 33–38, 45–46
Advanced 20–31, 33–39, 45–46

If you finished Examples **1–3**
Proficient 20–39, 40–44, 46–50, 54–62
Advanced 20–38, 40–45, 47–62

Homework Quick Check
Quickly check key concepts.
Exercises: 20, 24, 26, 30, 32, 44

California Standards

Standard	Exercises
2.0	54–57
14.0	7–18, 26–31
21.0	60–62
23.0	19, 32, 43, 47
25.2	39

Exercise 47 involves solving a quadratic equation by factoring to determine the amount of time an object is in the air and analyzing the graph to determine other information. This exercise prepares students for the Concept Connection on page 610.

Answers

40. $x(x+2)=24$; 4 and 6 or −6 and −4

45. No; the solutions of $x-2=5$ and $x+3=5$ are 7 and 2; 7 and 2 are not solutions of $(x-2)(x+3)=5$.

46. The Zero Product Property states that if the product of two numbers is 0, then at least one of the numbers must be 0. When you factor a quadratic equation in standard form, the product of the factors is 0, so one of the factors must be 0.

Language Support Students may not know what a tee box is in **Exercise 47.** In golf, a tee box is the designated area at each hole in which the initial shot is taken.

32. Multi-Step The height of a flare can be approximated by the function $h=-16t^2+95t+6$, where h is the height in feet and t is the time in seconds. Find the time it takes the flare to hit the ground. **6 s**

Determine the number of x-intercepts of each function.

33. $y=(x+8)(x+8)$ **1**
34. $(x-3)(x+3)=y$ **2**
35. $y=(x+7)^2$ **1**
36. $3x^2+12x+9=y$ **2**
37. $y=x^2+12x+36$ **1**
38. $(x-2)^2-9=y$ **2**

39. **ERROR ANALYSIS** Which solution is incorrect? Explain the error.

39. B; after factoring the polynomial, you should solve the equations $x-1=0$ and $x+2=0$. The correct solutions are 1 and −2.

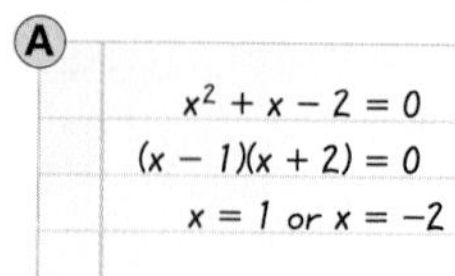

A

$x^2+x-2=0$
$(x-1)(x+2)=0$
$x=1$ or $x=-2$

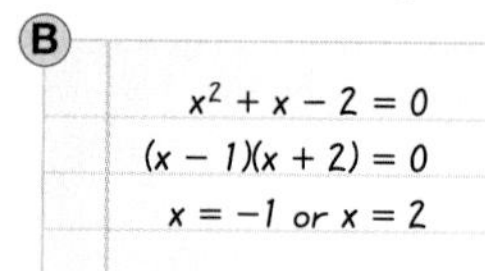

B

$x^2+x-2=0$
$(x-1)(x+2)=0$
$x=-1$ or $x=2$

40. Number Theory Write an equation that could be used to find two consecutive even integers whose product is 24. Let x represent the first integer. Solve the equation and give the two integers.

41. Geometry The photo shows a traditional thatched house as found in Santana, Madeira in Portugal. The front of the house is in the shape of a triangle. Suppose the base of the triangle is 1 m less than its height and the area of the triangle is 15 m². Find the height of the triangle. (*Hint:* Use $A=\frac{1}{2}bh$.) **6 m**

42. Multi-Step The length of a rectangle is 1 ft less than 3 times the width. The area is 310 ft². Find the dimensions of the rectangle. **$10\frac{1}{3}$ ft by 30 ft**

43. Physical Science The height of a fireworks rocket in meters can be approximated by $h=-5t^2+30t$, where h is the height in meters and t is time in seconds. Find the time it takes the rocket to reach the ground after it has been launched. **6 s**

44. Geometry One base of a trapezoid is the same length as the height of the trapezoid. The other base is 4 cm more than the height. The area of the trapezoid is 48 cm². Find the length of the shorter base. (*Hint:* Use $A=\frac{1}{2}h(b_1+b_2)$.) **6 cm**

x
x
x + 4

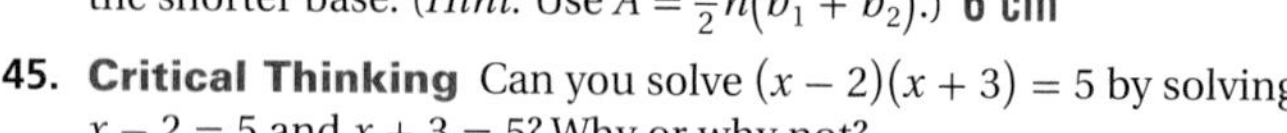

45. Critical Thinking Can you solve $(x-2)(x+3)=5$ by solving $x-2=5$ and $x+3=5$? Why or why not?

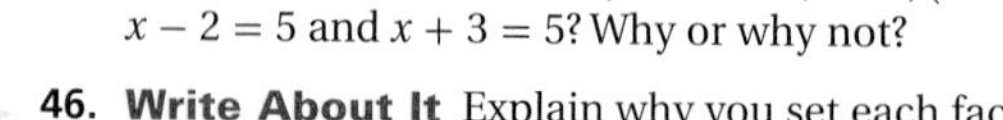

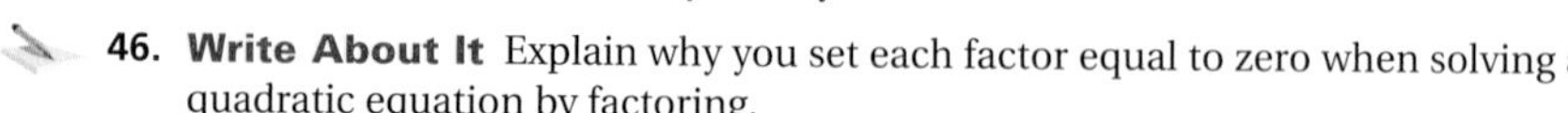

46. Write About It Explain why you set each factor equal to zero when solving a quadratic equation by factoring.

CONCEPT CONNECTION

47. This problem will prepare you for the Concept Connection on page 610.

A tee box is 48 feet above its fairway. Starting with an initial elevation of 48 ft at the tee box and an initial velocity of 32 ft/s, the quadratic equation $0=-16t^2+32t+48$ gives the time t in seconds when a golf ball is at height 0 feet on the fairway.

a. Solve the quadratic equation by factoring to see how long the ball is in the air. **3 s**

b. What is the height of the ball at 1 second? **64 ft**

c. Is the ball at its maximum height at 1 second? Explain. **Yes; the vertex is (1, 64), which represents the ball's maximum height of 64 ft after 1 s in the air.**

9-5 PRACTICE A

9-5 PRACTICE C

9-5 PRACTICE B

LESSON 9-5 **Practice B**
Solving Quadratic Equations by Factoring

Use the Zero Product Property to solve each equation. Check your answers.

1. $(x-1)(x-5)=0$
$x-1=0$ or $x-5=0$
$x=$ 1 or $x=$ 5

2. $(x-2)(x-9)=0$
$x-2=0$ or $x-9=0$
$x=$ 2 or $x=$ 9

3. $(x-2)(x+4)=0$ — 2; −4

4. $(2x+1)(x-6)=0$ — $-\frac{1}{2}$; −6

Solve each quadratic equation by factoring.

5. $x^2-3x=0$ — 0; 3
6. $x^2+4x+3=0$ — −3; −1
7. $x^2+5x-6=0$ — 1; −6
8. $x^2+11x+24=0$ — −3; −8
9. $x^2-12x+11=0$ — 1; 11
10. $x^2+18x-65=0$ — −13; −5
11. $x^2-4x-12=0$ — 6; −2
12. $x^2+11x+10=0$ — −1; −10
13. $x^2+12x+35=0$ — −5; −7
14. $2x^2-3x-5=0$ — $\frac{5}{2}$; −1
15. $3x^2-5x-2=0$ — $-\frac{1}{3}$; 2
16. $x^2=3x+40$ — 8; −5
17. $x^2-14=5x$ — 7; −2
18. $2x-1=-8x^2$ — $\frac{1}{4}$; $-\frac{1}{2}$
19. $x=10x^2-2$ — $-\frac{2}{5}$; $\frac{1}{2}$
20. $2x^2=13x+7$ — 7; $-\frac{1}{2}$
21. $6x^2+x=5$ — −1; $\frac{5}{6}$
22. $x^2=5x$ — 0; 5

23. The height of a flare fired from the deck of a ship in distress can be modeled by $h=-16t^2+104t+56$, where h is the height of the flare above water and t is the time in seconds. Find the time it takes the flare to hit the water. — 7 seconds

9-5 READING STRATEGIES

LESSON 9-5 **Reading Strategies**
Use a Concept Map

Use this concept map to understand the Zero Product Property.

Zero Product Property

Word Definition	Algebraic Definition
If you multiply two or more quantities, and the answer is 0, at least one of the quantities must be 0.	For all real numbers a and b, if $a\cdot b=0$, then $a=0$ or $b=0$.
Examples	**Application**
If $-4m=0$, then $m=0$. If $x(x+2)=0$, then $x=0$, or $x+2=0$. If $(t-5)(t+1)=0$, then $t-5=0$, or $t+1=0$.	Use the Zero Product Property to solve quadratic equations. $x^2-5x=6$ $x^2-5x-6=0$ $(x-6)(x+1)=0$ $x-6=0$ or $x+1=0$ $x=6, x=1$

Answer each of the following.

1. Look at the algebraic definition in the concept map. Do you think a and b can both be zero at the same time? Explain.
yes; because $0\times0=0$

2. Look at the application in the concept map. Why must the expression be factored before using the Zero Product Property?
Because you need two or more quantities being multiplied

3. Look at the second example in the concept map. If $x+2=0$, what must be the value of x? Why?
−2, because $-2+2=0$.

4. Give an algebraic example of the Zero Product Property with three factors.
If $abc=0$, then $a=0$, or $b=0$, or $c=0$.

Solve each quadratic equation by using the Zero Product Property.

5. $(x+5)(x-2)=0$ — $x=-5, x=2$
6. $x^2+x-12=0$ — $x=-4, x=3$
7. $2x^2=6x+20$ — $x=-2, x=5$

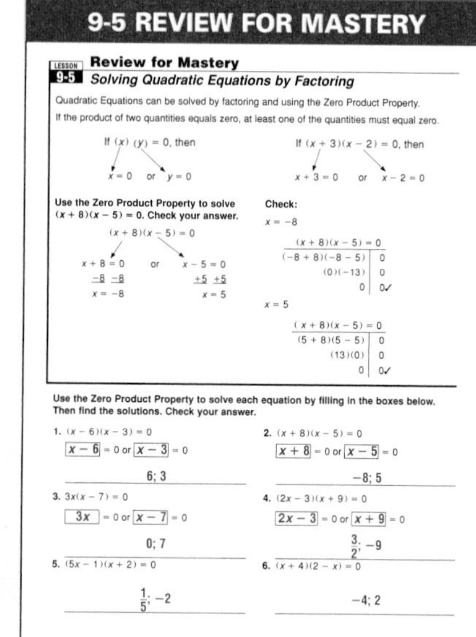

9-5 REVIEW FOR MASTERY

LESSON 9-5 **Review for Mastery**
Solving Quadratic Equations by Factoring

Quadratic Equations can be solved by factoring and using the Zero Product Property.

If the product of two quantities equals zero, at least one of the quantities must equal zero.

If $(x)(y)=0$, then $x=0$ or $y=0$

If $(x+3)(x-2)=0$, then $x+3=0$ or $x-2=0$

Use the Zero Product Property to solve $(x+8)(x-5)=0$. Check your answer.

$(x+8)(x-5)=0$
$x+8=0$ or $x-5=0$
$-8\ \ -8$ and $+5\ \ +5$
$x=-8$ or $x=5$

Check:

$x=-8$

$(x+8)(x-5)=0$	
$(-8+8)(-8-5)$	0
$(0)(-13)$	0
0	0✓

$x=5$

$(x+8)(x-5)=0$	
$(5+8)(5-5)$	0
$(13)(0)$	0
0	0✓

Use the Zero Product Property to solve each equation by filling in the boxes below. Then find the solutions. Check your answer.

1. $(x-6)(x-3)=0$
[x − 6] = 0 or [x − 3] = 0
6; 3

2. $(x+8)(x-5)=0$
[x + 8] = 0 or [x − 5] = 0
−8; 5

3. $3x(x-7)=0$
[3x] = 0 or [x − 7] = 0
0; 7

4. $(2x-3)(x+9)=0$
[2x − 3] = 0 or [x + 9] = 0
$\frac{3}{2}$; −9

5. $(5x-1)(x+2)=0$
$\frac{1}{5}$; −2

6. $(x+4)(2-x)=0$
−4; 2

Multiple Choice For Exercises 48 and 49, choose the best answer.

48. What are the solutions to $(x-1)(2x+5)=0$?

(A) -1 and $\frac{5}{2}$ (C) 1 and $-\frac{5}{2}$

(B) -1 and $\frac{2}{5}$ (D) 1 and $-\frac{2}{5}$

49. Which graph could be used to help solve the equation $x^2-5x+6=0$?

(A)
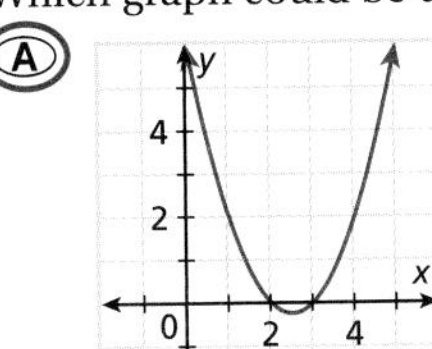

(C)
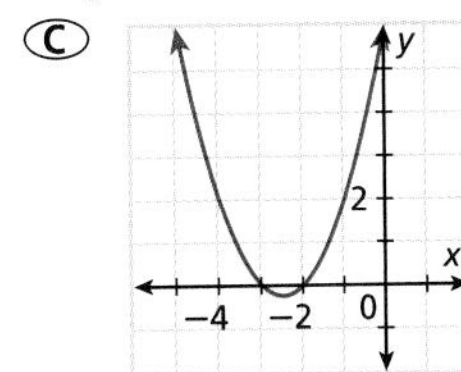

(B)
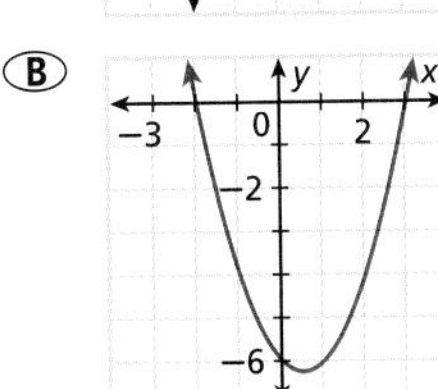

(D)
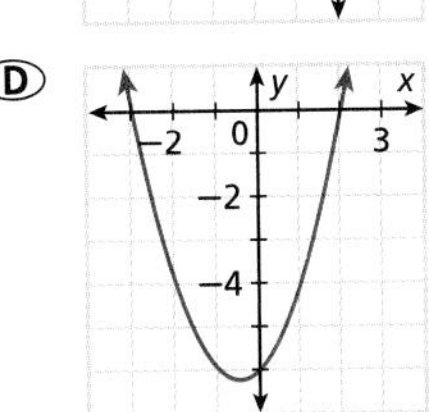

CHALLENGE AND EXTEND

Geometry Use the diagram for Exercises 50–52.

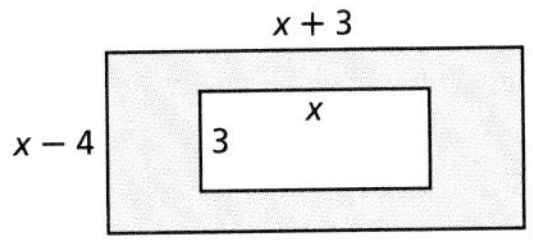

x + 3
x − 4
x
3

50. Write a polynomial to represent the area of the larger rectangle. x^2-x-12

51. Write a polynomial to represent the area of the smaller rectangle. $3x$

52. Write a polynomial to represent the area of the shaded region. Then solve for x given that the area of the shaded region is 48 square units. $x^2-4x-12=48$; $x=10$

53. **Reasoning** Suppose m and n are the roots of a quadratic polynomial. Name two points that must be on the graph of the related quadratic function. $(m, 0)$ and $(n, 0)$

SPIRAL STANDARDS REVIEW

Find each square root. (Lesson 1-5)

54. $\sqrt{121}$ 11

55. $-\sqrt{64}$ −8

56. $-\sqrt{100}$ −10

57. $\sqrt{225}$ 15

58. Veronica is 63 inches tall, and she is 4 inches shorter than her friend. Write and solve an equation to find the height of her friend. (Lesson 2-1) $f-4=63$; 67 in.

59. A tire manufacturer has 325 tires. Write and solve an equation to find the number of minivans m that can be built using this number of tires. Each minivan has 4 tires and 1 spare tire. (Lesson 2-1) $5m=325$; 65

Solve each equation by graphing the related function. Check your answer. (Lesson 9-4)

60. $x^2-49=0$ ± 7

61. $x^2=x+12$ 4, −3

62. $-x^2+8x=15$ 3, 5

Teaching Tip **Multiple Choice** In **Exercise 49,** students can examine the equation to see that the factors of 6 both have the same sign, so **B** and **D** can be eliminated. Because the x-term is negative, the factors of 6 are both negative, and the zeros are positive.

Journal

Explain why you must have 0 on one side of the equation in order to apply the Zero Product Property to solve an equation.

ALTERNATIVE ASSESSMENT

Have students use binomial factors to work backward to create two equivalent quadratic equations with given solutions.

Power Presentations with PowerPoint®

9-5 Lesson Quiz

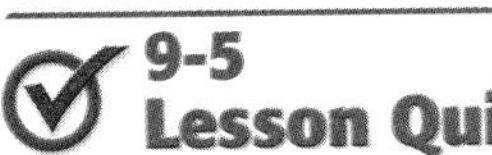

Use the Zero Product Property to solve each equation. Check your answer.

1. $(x-10)(x+5)=0$ 10, −5

2. $(x+5)(x)=0$ −5, 0

Solve each quadratic equation by factoring. Check your answer.

3. $x^2+16x+48=0$ −4, −12

4. $x^2-11x=-24$ 3, 8

5. $2x^2+12x-14=0$ 1, −7

6. $x^2+18x+81=0$ −9

7. $-4x^2=16x+16$ −2

8. The height of a rocket launched upward from a 160-foot cliff is modeled by the function $h(t)=-16t^2+48t+160$, where h is height in feet and t is time in seconds. Find the time it takes the rocket to reach the ground at the bottom of the cliff. 5 s

Also available on transparency

9-5 PROBLEM SOLVING

LESSON 9-5 Problem Solving
Solving Quadratic Equations by Factoring

Write the correct answer.

1. The height of an acorn falling out of a tree is $h=-16t^2+25$ where h is height in feet and t is time in seconds. Determine how long it takes the acorn to reach the ground. Check your answer by graphing the function.

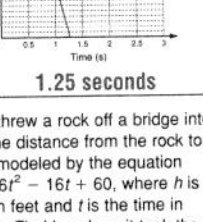

Height of Acorn
Height (ft)
Time (s)

1.25 seconds

2. An architect is designing a building with a right triangular footprint.

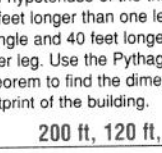

The hypotenuse of the triangle is 80 feet longer than one leg of the triangle and 40 feet longer than the other leg. Use the Pythagorean Theorem to find the dimensions of the footprint of the building.

200 ft, 120 ft, 160 ft

3. Robert threw a rock off a bridge into the river. The distance from the rock to the river is modeled by the equation $h=-16t^2-16t+60$, where h is the height in feet and t is the time in seconds. Find how long it took the rock to enter the water.

1.5 seconds

4. During a game of golf, Kayley hits her ball out of a sand trap. The equation $h=-16t^2+20t-4$ models the height of the golf ball in feet in relation to the number of t seconds since it was hit. Find how long it takes Kayley's golf ball to reach to green.

1 second

A new store is being built in the shape of a rectangle with a parking lot in the shape of an isosceles trapezoid. The parking lot and the store will share a side as shown. Select the best answer.

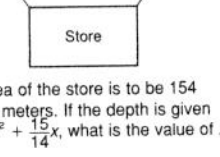

Parking lot
Store

5. The parking lot will have an area of 160 square meters. The shorter base is 4 m longer than the height of the trapezoid, and the longer base is 8 m longer than the height. What is the length of the shorter base?

F 10 meters H 18 meters
(G) 14 meters J 20 meters

6. The area of the store is to be 154 square meters. If the depth is given as $\frac{1}{14}x^2+\frac{15}{14}x$, what is the value of x?

(A) 7 C 14
B 11 D 28

7. What is the depth of the store in meters?

F 7 H 14
(G) 11 J 28

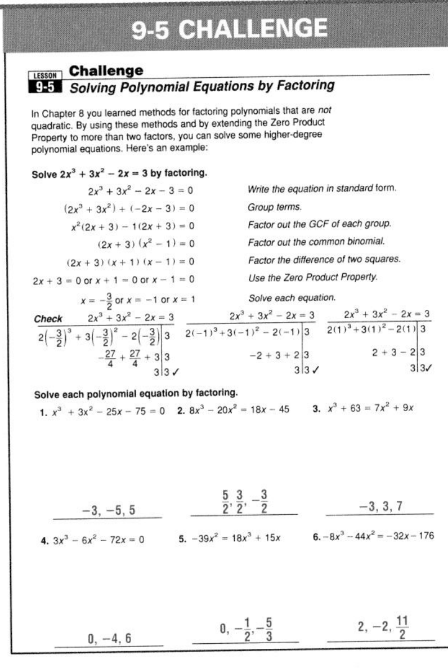

9-5 CHALLENGE

LESSON 9-5 Challenge
Solving Polynomial Equations by Factoring

In Chapter 8 you learned methods for factoring polynomials that are *not* quadratic. By using these methods and by extending the Zero Product Property to more than two factors, you can solve some higher-degree polynomial equations. Here's an example:

Solve $2x^3+3x^2-2x=3$ by factoring.

$2x^3+3x^2-2x-3=0$	*Write the equation in standard form.*
$(2x^3+3x^2)+(-2x-3)=0$	*Group terms.*
$x^2(2x+3)-1(2x+3)=0$	*Factor out the GCF of each group.*
$(2x+3)(x^2-1)=0$	*Factor out the common binomial.*
$(2x+3)(x+1)(x-1)=0$	*Factor the difference of two squares.*
$2x+3=0$ or $x+1=0$ or $x-1=0$	*Use the Zero Product Property.*
$x=-\frac{3}{2}$ or $x=-1$ or $x=1$	*Solve each equation.*

Check

$2x^3+3x^2-2x$	$=3$	$2x^3+3x^2-2x$	$=3$	$2x^3+3x^2-2x$	$=3$
$2\left(-\frac{3}{2}\right)^3+3\left(-\frac{3}{2}\right)^2-2\left(-\frac{3}{2}\right)$	3	$2(-1)^3+3(-1)^2-2(-1)$	3	$2(1)^3+3(1)^2-2(1)$	3
$-\frac{27}{4}+\frac{27}{4}+3$	3	$-2+3+2$	3	$2+3-2$	3
3	3 ✓	3	3 ✓	3	3 ✓

Solve each polynomial equation by factoring.

1. $x^3+3x^2-25x-75=0$ $-3, -5, 5$

2. $8x^3-20x^2=18x-45$ $\frac{5}{2}, \frac{3}{2}, -\frac{3}{2}$

3. $x^3+63=7x^2+9x$ $-3, 3, 7$

4. $3x^3-6x^2-72x=0$ $0, -4, 6$

5. $-39x^2=18x^3+15x$ $0, -\frac{1}{2}, -\frac{5}{3}$

6. $-8x^3-44x^2=-32x-176$ $2, -2, \frac{11}{2}$

9-6 Organizer

Objective: Solve quadratic equations by using square roots.

Online Edition
Tutorial Videos, TechKeys

Countdown to Mastery Week 21

Power Presentations with PowerPoint®

Warm Up

Find each square root.

1. $\sqrt{36}$ 6 **2.** $\sqrt{121}$ 11

3. $-\sqrt{625}$ -25 **4.** $\sqrt{\frac{4}{25}}$ $\frac{2}{5}$

Solve each equation.

5. $-6x = -60$ $x = 10$

6. $\frac{1}{5}x = 16$ $x = 80$

7. $2x - 40 = 0$ $x = 20$

8. $5x = 3$ $x = \frac{3}{5}$

Also available on transparency

Math Humor

Mother: Why did you rip up my garden?

Student: My math assignment is to find roots.

California Standards

Algebra 1 2.0, 23.0

9-6 Solving Quadratic Equations by Using Square Roots

California Standards

2.0 Students understand and use such operations as taking the opposite, finding the reciprocal, **taking a root,** and raising to a fractional power. They understand and use the rules of exponents.

23.0 Students apply quadratic equations to physical problems, such as the motion of an object under the force of gravity.

Why learn this?

Square roots can be used to find how much fencing is needed for a pen at a zoo. (See Example 4.)

Some quadratic equations cannot be easily solved by factoring. Square roots can be used to solve some of these quadratic equations. Recall from Lesson 1-5 that every positive real number has two square roots, one positive and one negative. (Remember also that the symbol $\sqrt{\ }$ indicates a nonnegative square root.)

$$3(3) = 3^2 = 9 \longrightarrow \sqrt{9} = 3 \quad \leftarrow \text{Positive square root of 9}$$

$$(-3)(-3) = (-3)^2 = 9 \longrightarrow -\sqrt{9} = -3 \quad \leftarrow \text{Negative square root of 9}$$

Reading Math

The expression ± 3 means "3 or -3" and is read "plus or minus three."

When you take a square root to solve an equation, you must find both the positive and negative square root. This is indicated by the symbol $\pm\sqrt{\ }$.

$$\pm\sqrt{9} = \pm 3 \quad \leftarrow \text{Positive and negative square roots of 9}$$

Know it! Note

Square-Root Property

WORDS	NUMBERS	ALGEBRA
To solve a quadratic equation in the form $x^2 = a$, take the square root of both sides.	$x^2 = 15$ $x = \pm\sqrt{15}$	If $x^2 = a$ and a is a positive real number, then $x = \pm\sqrt{a}$.

EXAMPLE 1 **Using Square Roots to Solve $x^2 = a$**

Solve using square roots. Check your answer.

A $x^2 = 16$

$x = \pm\sqrt{16}$ *Solve for x by taking the square root of both sides. Use ± to show both square roots.*

$x = \pm 4$

The solutions are 4 and -4.

Check

$x^2 = 16$	
$(4)^2$	16
16	16 ✓

Substitute 4 into the original equation.

$x^2 = 16$	
$(-4)^2$	16
16	16 ✓

Substitute −4 into the original equation.

1 Introduce

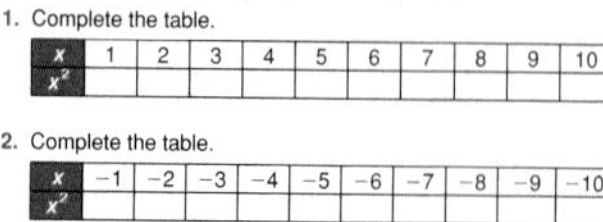

EXPLORATION

9-6 Solving Quadratic Equations by Using Square Roots

In this Exploration, you will use what you already know about squares to solve some simple quadratic equations.

1. Complete the table.

x	1	2	3	4	5	6	7	8	9	10
x^2										

2. Complete the table.

x	−1	−2	−3	−4	−5	−6	−7	−8	−9	−10
x^2										

3. Suppose $x^2 = 36$. What can you say about the value of x?

4. Suppose $x^2 = 100$. What can you say about the value of x?

5. In general, if a is a positive real number, how many solutions are there to the equation $x^2 = a$?

THINK AND DISCUSS

6. **Explain** how to find the solutions of $x^2 = 144$.

7. **Describe** how you can use your tables from Problems 1 and 2 to estimate the solutions of the equation $x^2 = 20$.

Motivate

Have students translate the following sentence into an algebraic equation: The sum of the square of a number and ten is forty-six. $x^2 + 10 = 46$

Have students find the values of x that make the sentence true. 6 and -6

Tell students that in this lesson they will learn algebraic methods for solving these types of equations.

Explorations and answers are provided in *Alternate Openers: Explorations Transparencies.*

Solve using square roots.

B $x^2 = -4$

$x = \pm\sqrt{-4}$ *There is no real number whose square is negative.*

There is no real solution. The solution set is the empty set, ∅.

Solve using square roots. Check your answer.

1a. $x^2 = 121$ **±11** **1b.** $x^2 = 0$ **0** **1c.** $x^2 = -16$ ∅

If a quadratic equation is not written in the form $x^2 = a$, use inverse operations to isolate x^2 before taking the square root of both sides.

Helpful Hint

The square root of 0 is neither positive nor negative. It is only 0.

EXAMPLE 2 Using Square Roots to Solve Quadratic Equations

Solve using square roots.

A $x^2 + 5 = 5$

$x^2 + 5 = 5$

$\underline{-5 \quad -5}$ *Subtract 5 from both sides.*

$x^2 = 0$

$x = \pm\sqrt{0} = 0$ *Take the square root of both sides.*

B $4x^2 - 25 = 0$

$4x^2 - 25 = 0$

$\underline{+25 \quad +25}$ *Add 25 to both sides.*

$\frac{4x^2}{4} = \frac{25}{4}$ *Divide by 4 on both sides.*

$x^2 = \frac{25}{4}$

$x = \pm\sqrt{\frac{25}{4}} = \pm\frac{5}{2}$ *Take the square root of both sides. Use ± to show both square roots.*

Check

$4x^2 - 25 = 0$	
$4\left(\frac{5}{2}\right)^2 - 25$	0
$\cancel{4}\left(\frac{25}{\cancel{4}}\right) - 25$	0
$25 - 25$	0 ✓

$4x^2 - 25 = 0$	
$4\left(-\frac{5}{2}\right)^2 - 25$	0
$\cancel{4}\left(\frac{25}{\cancel{4}}\right) - 25$	0
$25 - 25$	0 ✓

Solve by using square roots. Check your answer.

2a. $100x^2 + 49 = 0$ ∅ **2b.** $36x^2 = 1$ $\pm\frac{1}{6}$

When solving quadratic equations by using square roots, the solutions may be irrational. In this case, you can give the exact solutions by leaving the square root in your answer, or you can approximate the solutions.

EXAMPLE 3 Approximating Solutions

Solve. Round to the nearest hundredth.

A $x^2 = 10$

$x = \pm\sqrt{10}$ *Take the square root of both sides.*

$x \approx \pm 3.16$ *Estimate $\sqrt{10}$.*

The exact solutions are $\sqrt{10}$ and $-\sqrt{10}$.

The approximate solutions are 3.16 and −3.16.

COMMON ERROR ALERT

For equations like $4x^2 = 25$, students sometimes mentally stack the smaller number on top of the larger number and get $x^2 = \frac{4}{25}$. Remind students that the goal is to isolate x^2, so both sides will be divided by the coefficient of x^2.

Power Presentations with PowerPoint®

Additional Examples

Example 1

Solve using square roots. Check your answer.

A. $x^2 = 169$ ±13

B. $x^2 = -49$ ∅

Example 2

Solve using square roots. Check your answer.

A. $x^2 + 7 = 7$ 0

B. $16x^2 - 49 = 0$ $\pm\frac{7}{4}$

Also available on transparency

INTERVENTION

Questioning Strategies

EXAMPLES **1–2**

- Are there any real numbers whose square is negative?
- When does a quadratic equation have one solution?
- How do you take the square root of a fraction?

2 Teach

Guided Instruction

Discuss with students that squaring and finding square roots are inverse operations and can be used to isolate a variable in an equation. Remind students that if you take the square root of one side of the equation, you must also take the square root of the other side to maintain the balance. Emphasize the importance of finding both the positive and the negative square roots.

Universal Access

Through Visual Cues

On their own paper, encourage students to circle what is to be isolated in each step of solving equations in this lesson.

1. Circle the entire x^2-term and think of how it can be isolated.
2. Circle only x^2 and think of how it can be isolated.
3. Circle the x in x^2, showing that the last operation to be undone is the square.

Power Presentations with PowerPoint®

Additional Examples

Example 3

Solve. Round to the nearest hundredth.

A. $x^2 = 15$ ± 3.87

B. $-3x^2 + 90 = 0$ ± 5.48

Example 4

Ms. Pirzada is building a retaining wall along one of the long sides of her rectangular garden. The garden is twice as long as it is wide. It also has an area of 578 square feet. What will be the length of the retaining wall? 34 ft

Also available on transparency

INTERVENTION

Questioning Strategies

EXAMPLE 3

- Describe a method to approximate the solution without a calculator.

EXAMPLE 4

- Why is only one of the solutions to the equation used to answer the question?

Teaching Tip **Critical Thinking** Ask students what is wrong with solving the equation $x^2 = 3x$ by dividing both sides by x. Lead them to see that if they divide by x, the equation is $x = 3$, and they have lost the solution $x = 0$. Also, be sure they realize that if $x = 0$, division of both sides by x is undefined.

Solve. Round to the nearest hundredth.

B $0 = -2x^2 + 80$

$$0 = -2x^2 + 80$$
$$\underline{-80} \quad \underline{-80} \qquad \textit{Subtract 80 from both sides.}$$
$$-80 = -2x^2$$
$$\frac{-80}{-2} = \frac{-2x^2}{-2} \qquad \textit{Divide both sides by } -2.$$
$$40 = x^2$$
$$\pm\sqrt{40} = x \qquad \textit{Take the square root of both sides.}$$
$$x \approx \pm 6.32 \qquad \textit{Estimate } \sqrt{40}.$$

Remember!

To review estimating square roots, see Lesson 1-5.

The exact solutions are $\sqrt{40}$ and $-\sqrt{40}$.
The approximate solutions are 6.32 and −6.32.

Check Use a graphing calculator to support your answer.

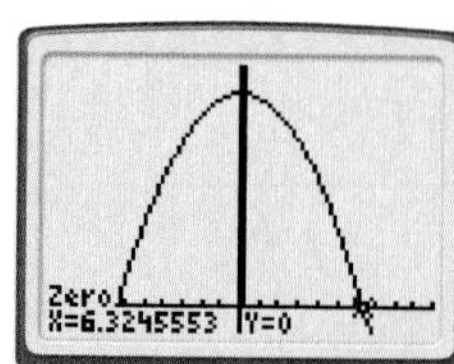

Use the zero function.
The approximate solutions are 6.32 and −6.32. ✓

CHECK IT OUT! Solve. Round to the nearest hundredth.

3a. $0 = 90 - x^2$ $\approx \pm 9.49$

3b. $2x^2 - 64 = 0$ $\approx \pm 5.66$

3c. $x^2 + 45 = 0$ $\varnothing$

EXAMPLE 4 *Consumer Application*

A zookeeper is buying fencing to enclose a pen at the zoo. The pen is an isosceles right triangle. There is already a fence on the side that borders a path. The area of the pen will be 4500 square feet. The zookeeper can buy the fencing in whole feet only. How many feet of fencing should he buy?

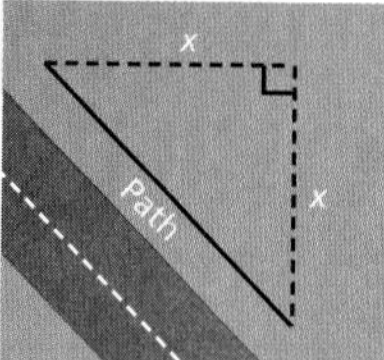

Remember!

An isosceles triangle has at least two sides of the same length.

See Skills Bank p. SB18.

Let x represent the length of one of the sides.

$$\frac{1}{2}bh = A \qquad \textit{Use the formula for area of a triangle.}$$
$$\frac{1}{2}x(x) = 4500 \qquad \textit{Substitute x for both b and h and 4500 for A.}$$
$$(2)\frac{1}{2}x^2 = 4500(2) \qquad \textit{Simplify. Multiply both sides by 2.}$$
$$x = \pm\sqrt{9000} \qquad \textit{Take the square root of both sides.}$$
$$x \approx \pm 94.9 \qquad \textit{Estimate } \sqrt{9000}.$$

Lengths are not negative, so $x \approx 94.9$ is the only solution that makes sense. The zookeeper needs 95 + 95, or 190, feet of fencing.

CHECK IT OUT! **4.** A lot is shaped like a trapezoid with bases x and $2x$. Its area is 6000 ft². Find x. Round to the nearest foot. (*Hint:* Use $A = \frac{1}{2}h(b_1 + b_2)$.) **45 ft**

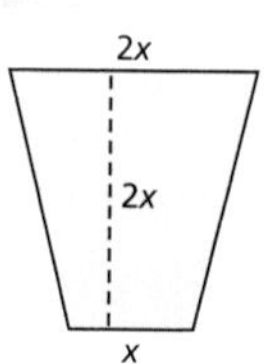

3 Close

Summarize

Review the steps for solving quadratic equations, comparing them to steps for solving linear equations: undo the operations performed on the variable. For quadratic equations, the last step is to take the square root of each side. Both the nonnegative and negative square roots are solutions.

Have students state the steps they would use to solve $5x^2 - 18 = 27$.

Add 18 to each side. Divide both sides by 5. Take the square root of both sides.

FORMATIVE ASSESSMENT and INTERVENTION

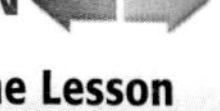

***Diagnose Before* the Lesson**
9-6 Warm Up, TE p. 582

***Monitor During* the Lesson**
Check It Out! Exercises, SE pp. 583–584
Questioning Strategies, TE pp. 583–584

***Assess After* the Lesson**
9-6 Lesson Quiz, TE p. 587
Alternative Assessment, TE p. 587

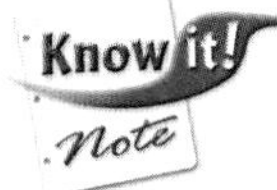

THINK AND DISCUSS

1. Explain why there are no solutions to the quadratic equation $x^2 = -9$.
2. Describe how to estimate the solutions of $4 = x^2 - 16$. What are the approximate solutions?
3. **GET ORGANIZED** Copy and complete the graphic organizer. In each box, write an example of a quadratic equation with the given number of solutions. Solve each equation.

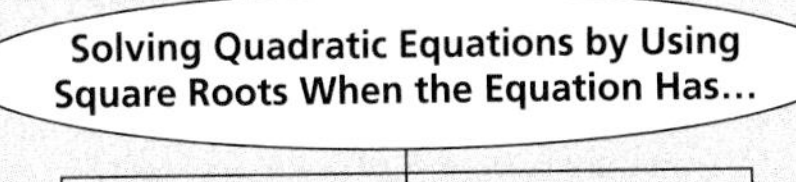

Answers to *Think and Discuss*

Possible answers:

1. There is no real number whose square is negative.
2. The equation is equivalent to $x^2 = 20$, so $x = \pm\sqrt{20}$. $\sqrt{20}$ is between 4 and 5, so x is approximately ± 4.5.
3. See p. A7.

9-6 Exercises

California Standards Practice
2.0, 23.0, 25.1, 25.2, 25.3

go.hrw.com
Homework Help Online
KEYWORD: MA8CA 9-6
Parent Resources Online
KEYWORD: MA8CA Parent

GUIDED PRACTICE

SEE EXAMPLE 1 p. 582

Solve using square roots. Check your answer.

1. $x^2 = 225$ ± 15
2. $x^2 = 49$ ± 7
3. $x^2 = -100$ $\varnothing$
4. $x^2 = 400$ ± 20
5. $-25 = x^2$ $\varnothing$
6. $36 = x^2$ ± 6

SEE EXAMPLE 2 p. 583

7. $3x^2 - 75 = 0$ ± 5
8. $0 = 81x^2 - 25$ $\pm\frac{5}{9}$
9. $49x^2 + 64 = 0$ $\varnothing$
10. $16x^2 + 10 = 131$ $\pm\frac{11}{4}$
11. $0 = 4x^2 - 16$ ± 2
12. $100x^2 + 26 = 10$ $\varnothing$

SEE EXAMPLE 3 p. 583

Solve. Round to the nearest hundredth.

13. $3x^2 = 81$ ± 5.20
14. $0 = x^2 - 60$ ± 7.75
15. $100 - 5x^2 = 0$ ± 4.47

SEE EXAMPLE 4 p. 584

16. **Geometry** The length of a rectangle is 3 times its width. The area of the rectangle is 170 square meters. Find the width. Round to the nearest tenth of a meter. (*Hint:* Use $A = bh$.) 7.5 m

PRACTICE AND PROBLEM SOLVING

Independent Practice

For Exercises	See Example
17–22	1
23–28	2
29–34	3
35	4

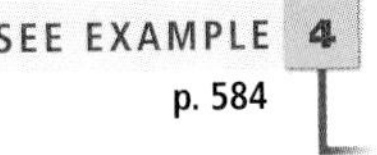

Extra Practice
Skills Practice p. EP19
Application Practice p. EP32

Solve using square roots. Check your answer.

17. $x^2 = 169$ ± 13
18. $x^2 = 25$ ± 5
19. $x^2 = -36$ $\varnothing$
20. $x^2 = 10{,}000$ ± 100
21. $-121 = x^2$ $\varnothing$
22. $625 = x^2$ ± 25
23. $4 - 81x^2 = 0$ $\pm\frac{2}{9}$
24. $-4x^2 - 49 = 0$ $\varnothing$
25. $64x^2 - 5 = 20$ $\pm\frac{5}{8}$
26. $9x^2 + 9 = 25$ $\pm\frac{4}{3}$
27. $49x^2 + 1 = 170$ $\pm\frac{13}{7}$
28. $81x^2 + 17 = 81$ $\pm\frac{8}{9}$

Solve. Round to the nearest hundredth.

29. $4x^2 = 88$ ± 4.69
30. $x^2 - 29 = 0$ ± 5.39
31. $x^2 + 40 = 144$ ± 10.20
32. $3x^2 - 84 = 0$ ± 5.29
33. $50 - x^2 = 0$ ± 7.07
34. $2x^2 - 10 = 64$ ± 6.08

9-6 Exercises

Assignment Guide

Assign *Guided Practice* Exercises as necessary.

If you finished Examples **1–2**
Proficient 17–28, 42, 43, 51
Advanced 17–28, 37, 42, 51

If you finished Examples **1–4**
Proficient 17–36, 38–50, 52–57, 59–67
Advanced 17–40, 42–50, 52–67

Homework Quick Check
Quickly check key concepts.
Exercises: 22, 24, 32, 35, 36, 44

Teacher to Teacher

Throughout the lesson and as students work through the exercises, it is important to remind them that the graph of the related function can be used to confirm each of their answers. This reminds students again of the relationship between the solutions of an algebraic equation, the zeros of the related function, and the points containing the x-intercepts of the function's graph.

Jill Springer
Henderson, KY

California Standards

Standard	Exercises
2.0	1–15, 17–34, 55–57
4.0	59
8.0	60, 61
14.0	62–67
23.0	35, 40, 46
25.1	47–50
25.2	41
25.3	42, 43

Teaching Tip **Geometry** In **Exercise 44,** students find a geometric mean. The geometric mean is used to find lengths in right triangles, and lengths cannot be negative.

CONCEPT CONNECTION **Exercise 46** involves graphing a quadratic function related to the height of a falling golf ball over time. This exercise prepares students for the Concept Connection on page 610.

Answer

46b.

t	$d = 16t^2$
0	0
1	16
2	64
3	144
4	256

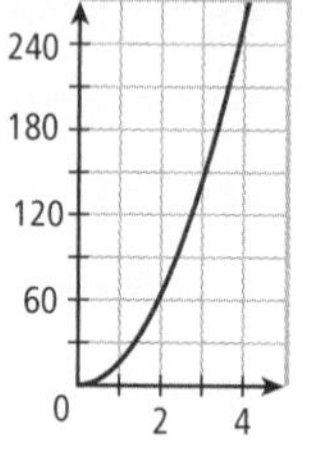

9-6 PRACTICE A

9-6 PRACTICE C

9-6 PRACTICE B

LESSON 9-6 **Practice B**
Solving Quadratic Equations by Using Square Roots

Solve using square roots. Check your answer.

1. $x^2 = 81$ — $x = \pm\sqrt{81}$; $x = \pm$ 9; The solutions are 9 and −9
2. $x^2 = 100$ — $x = \pm\sqrt{100}$; $x = \pm$ 10; The solutions are 10 and −10
3. $x^2 = 225$ — $x = \pm\sqrt{225}$; $x = \pm15$
4. $441 = x^2$ — $\pm\sqrt{441} = x$; $\pm21 = x$
5. $x^2 = -400$ — no real solutions
6. $3x^2 = 108$ — ±6
7. $100 = 4x^2$ — ±5
8. $x^2 + 7 = 71$ — ±8
9. $49x^2 - 64 = 0$ — $\pm\frac{8}{7}$
10. $-2x^2 = -162$ — ±9
11. $9x^2 + 100 = 0$ — no real solutions
12. $0 = 81x^2 - 121$ — $\pm\frac{11}{9}$
13. $100x^2 = 25$ — $\pm\frac{1}{2}$
14. $100x^2 = 121$ — $\pm\frac{11}{10}$

Solve. Round to the nearest hundredth.

15. $8x^2 = 56$ — ±2.65
16. $5 - x^2 = 20$ — no real solutions
17. $x^2 + 35 = 105$ — ±8.37
18. The height of a skydiver jumping out of an airplane is given by $h = -16t^2 + 3200$. How long will it take the skydiver to reach the ground? Round to the nearest tenth of a second. — 14.14 seconds
19. The height of a triangle is twice the length of its base. The area of the triangle is 50 m². Find the height and base to the nearest tenth of a meter. — height: 14.2 m, base: 7.1 m
20. The height of an acorn falling out of a tree is given by $h = -16t^2 + b$. If an acorn takes 1 second to fall to the ground. What is the value of b? — $b = 16$

35. **Entertainment** For a scene in a movie, a sack of money is dropped from the roof of a 600 ft skyscraper. The height of the sack above the ground is given by $h = -16t^2 + 600$, where t is the time in seconds. How long will it take the sack to reach the ground? Round to the nearest tenth of a second. **6.1 s**
36. **Geometry** The area of a square is 196 m². Find the dimensions of the square. **14 m × 14 m**
37. **Number Theory** If $a = 2b$ and $2ab = 36$, find all possible solutions for a and b. **$a = -6$ and $b = -3$ or $a = 6$ and $b = 3$**
38. **Estimation** The area y of any rectangle with side length x and one side twice as long as the other is represented by $y = 2x^2$. Use the graph to estimate the dimensions of such a rectangle whose area is 35 square feet. **about 4.2 ft by 8.4 ft**

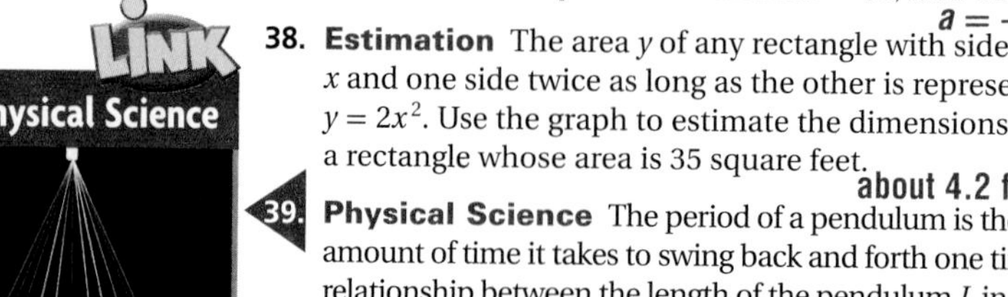

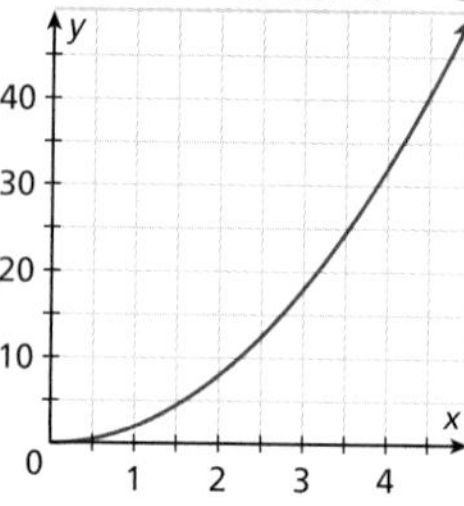

LINK Physical Science

The first pendulum clock was invented by Christian Huygens, a Dutch physicist and mathematician, around 1656. Early pendulum clocks swung about 50° to the left and right. Modern pendulum clocks swing only 10° to 15°.

39. **Physical Science** The period of a pendulum is the amount of time it takes to swing back and forth one time. The relationship between the length of the pendulum L in inches and the length of the period t in seconds can be approximated by $L = 9.78t^2$. Find the period of a pendulum whose length is 60 inches. Round to the nearest tenth of a second. **about 2.5 s**
40. **///ERROR ANALYSIS///** Which solution is incorrect? Explain the error.

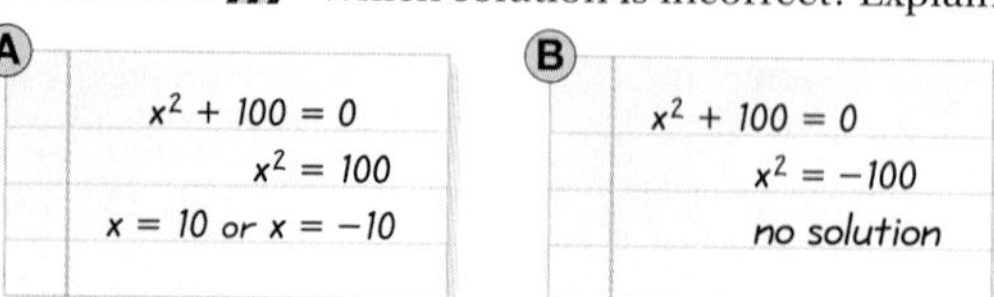

A	B
$x^2 + 100 = 0$	$x^2 + 100 = 0$
$x^2 = 100$	$x^2 = -100$
$x = 10$ or $x = -10$	no solution

A; 100 was added to the right side of the equation instead of subtracted.

Reasoning **Determine whether each statement is always, sometimes, or never true. Explain.**

41. There are two solutions to $x^2 = n$ when n is positive. **always**
42. If n is a rational number, then the solutions to $x^2 = n$ are rational numbers. **sometimes**
43. **Multi-Step** The height in feet of a soccer ball kicked upward from the ground with initial velocity 60 feet per second is modeled by $h = -16t^2 + 60t$, where t is the time in seconds. Find the time it takes for the ball to return to the ground. Round to the nearest hundredth of a second. **3.75 s**
44. **Geometry** The geometric mean of two positive numbers a and b is the positive number x such that $\frac{a}{x} = \frac{x}{b}$. Find the geometric mean of 2 and 18. **6**
45. **Critical Thinking** For the equation $x^2 = a$, describe the values of a that will result in each of the following.
    a. two solutions **a must be greater than 0.**
    b. one solution **a must be equal to 0.**
    c. no solution **a must be less than 0.**

CONCEPT CONNECTION

46. This problem will prepare you for the Concept Connection on page 610.
    The equation $d = 16t^2$ describes the distance d in feet that a golf ball falls in relation to the number of seconds t that it falls.
    a. How many seconds will it take a golf ball to drop to the ground from a height of 4 feet? **$\frac{1}{2}$ s**
    b. Make a table and graph the related function.
    c. How far will the golf ball drop in 1 second? **16 ft**
    d. How many seconds will it take the golf ball to drop 64 feet? **2 s**

9-6 READING STRATEGIES

LESSON 9-6 **Reading Strategies**
Making Connections

You've learned to solve quadratic equations by graphing. Equations that are in the form $ax^2 + c = 0$ (where $b = 0$) can also be solved by using square roots. Study the examples below to make the connection between solving quadratic equations by graphing and solving by using square roots.

Example 1: The equation $x^2 = 9$ has **2 solutions**.

Solve by using square roots:	Solve by graphing:
$x^2 = 9$; $x = \pm\sqrt{9}$; $x = \pm3$; $x = 3$ and $x = -3$; The solutions are 3 and −3.	$x^2 = 9$; $x^2 - 9 = 0$; $x^2 - 9 = y$; $y = x^2 - 9$; The graph has zeros at 3 and −3.

Example 2: The equation $x^2 = -9$ has **no real solutions**.

Solve by using square roots:	Solve by graphing:
$x^2 = -9$; $x = \pm\sqrt{-9}$; There is no real number whose square is negative. There are no solutions.	$x^2 = -9$; $x^2 + 9 = 0$; $x^2 + 9 = y$; $y = x^2 + 9$; The graph does not cross the x-axis.

Example 3: The equation $x^2 + 9 = 9$ has **1 solution**.

Solve by using square roots:	Solve by graphing:
$x^2 + 9 = 9$; $x^2 = 0$; $x = \pm\sqrt{0}$; $x = 0$; The solution is 0.	$x^2 + 9 = 9$; $x^2 + 0 = 0$; $x^2 = x$; $y = x^2$; The graph has a zero at 0.

Complete the following.

1. Solve $x^2 = 25$ by using square roots. $x = \pm5$
2. Sketch a graph of the related function $y = x^2 - 25$ to show that you get the same solution(s).
3. How many solutions does $x^2 = -36$ have? zero
   a. Explain, in terms of the graph: The parabola does not cross the x-axis.
   b. Explain, in terms of square roots: There is no real number whose square is negative.

9-6 REVIEW FOR MASTERY

LESSON 9-6 **Review for Mastery**
Solving Quadratic Equations by Using Square Roots

If a quadratic equation is in the form $x^2 = a$, you must take the square root of both sides to find the solutions. Remember to find both the positive and negative square roots.

Solve $x^2 = 36$ using square roots.

$x^2 = 36$; $\sqrt{x^2} = \pm\sqrt{36}$ Take the square root of both sides. $x = \pm6$. The solutions are 6 and −6.

Check: $x = 6$: $x^2 = 36$; $(6)^2 \stackrel{?}{=} 36$; $36 \stackrel{?}{=} 36$ ✓. $x = -6$: $x^2 = 36$; $(-6)^2 \stackrel{?}{=} 36$; $36 \stackrel{?}{=} 36$ ✓

Solve $2x^2 + 7 = 207$ using square roots.

$2x^2 + 7 = 207$; -7 -7 Add −7 to both sides. $2x^2 = 200$; $\frac{2x^2}{2} = \frac{200}{2}$ Divide both sides by 2. $\sqrt{x^2} = \pm\sqrt{100}$ Take the square root of both sides. $x = \pm10$. The solutions are 10 and −10.

Check: $x = 10$: $2x^2 + 7 \stackrel{?}{=} 207$; $2(10)^2 + 7 \stackrel{?}{=} 207$; $2(100) + 7 \stackrel{?}{=} 207$; $200 + 7 \stackrel{?}{=} 207$; $207 \stackrel{?}{=} 207$ ✓. $x = -10$: $2x^2 + 7 \stackrel{?}{=} 207$; $2(-10)^2 + 7 \stackrel{?}{=} 207$; $2(100) + 7 \stackrel{?}{=} 207$; $200 + 7 \stackrel{?}{=} 207$; $207 \stackrel{?}{=} 207$ ✓

Solve using square roots.

1. $x^2 = 81$ — ±9
2. $x^2 = 9$ — ±3
3. $x^2 = -64$ — no solution
4. $x^2 + 44 = 188$ — ±12
5. $x^2 - 12 = 37$ — ±7
6. $x^2 + 10 = 131$ — ±11
7. $3x^2 + 25 = 73$ — ±4
8. $5x^2 - 9 = 116$ — ±5
9. $-4x^2 + 42 = -102$ — ±6
10. $4x^2 - 11 = 25$ — ±3
11. $x^2 - 13 = 87$ — ±10
12. $-3x^2 + 200 = 8$ — ±8

For the quadratic equation $x^2 + a = 0$, determine whether each value of a will result in two rational solutions. Explain.

47. $-\frac{1}{2}$ no 48. $\frac{1}{2}$ no 49. $-\frac{1}{4}$ yes 50. $\frac{1}{4}$ no

51. $x^2 + 4 = 0$ is equivalent to $x^2 = -4$, which has no real solutions. $x^2 - 4 = 0$ is equivalent to $x^2 = 4$, which has two solutions (± 2).

51. **Write About It** Explain why the quadratic equation $x^2 + 4 = 0$ has no solutions but the quadratic equation $x^2 - 4 = 0$ has two solutions.

Multiple Choice For Exercises 52–54, choose the best answer.

52. The height of a cylinder is 100 cm, and the approximate volume is 1256 cm^3. Find the radius of the cylinder. Use 3.14 for π.

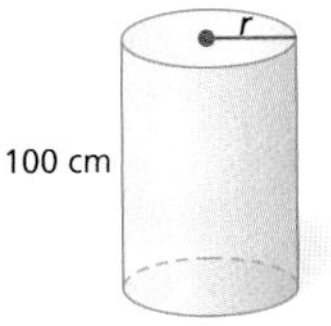

100 cm

r

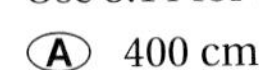
(A) 400 cm
(B) 20 cm
(C) 4 cm

(D) 2 cm

53. Which best describes the positive solution of $\frac{1}{2}x^2 = 20$?
(A) Between 4 and 5
(B) Between 5 and 6
(C) Between 6 and 7
(D) Between 7 and 8

54. Which best describes the solutions of $81x^2 - 169 = 0$?
(A) Two rational solutions
(B) Two irrational solutions
(C) No solution
(D) One solution

CHALLENGE AND EXTEND

Find the solutions of each equation. Check your answer.

55. $288x^2 - 19 = -1$ $\pm\frac{1}{4}$ 56. $-75x^2 = -48$ $\pm\frac{4}{5}$ 57. $x^2 = \frac{128}{242}$ $\pm\frac{8}{11}$

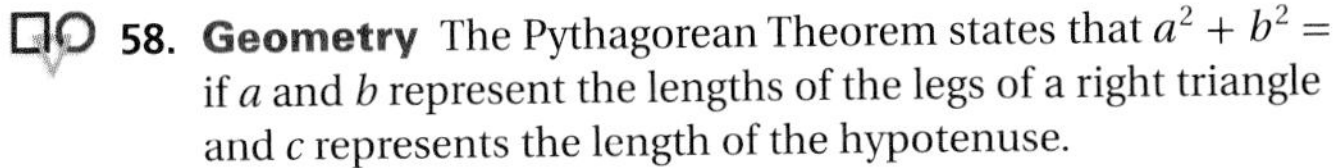

58. **Geometry** The Pythagorean Theorem states that $a^2 + b^2 = c^2$ if a and b represent the lengths of the legs of a right triangle and c represents the length of the hypotenuse.

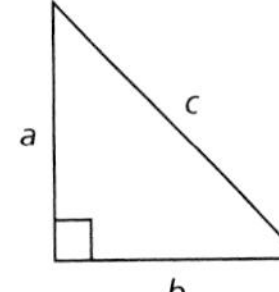

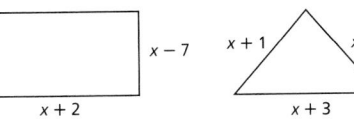

a. Find the length of the hypotenuse if the lengths of the legs are 9 cm and 12 cm. **15 cm**

b. Find the length of each leg of an isosceles right triangle whose hypotenuse is 10 cm. Round to the nearest tenth of a centimeter. **7.1 cm**

SPIRAL STANDARDS REVIEW

4.0, 8.0, 14.0

59. The figures shown have the same perimeter. What is the value of x? *(Lesson 2-4)* **13**

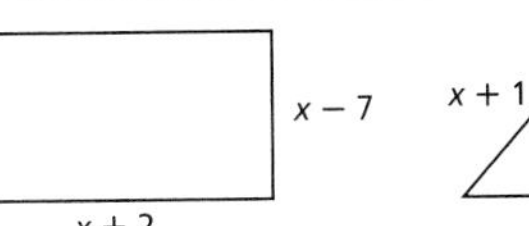

Identify which of the following lines are parallel. *(Lesson 5-7)*

60. $y = -2x + 3$, $2x - y = 8$, $6x - 2y = 10$, and $y + 4 = 2(3 - x)$ **$y = -2x + 3$ and $y + 4 = 2(3 - x)$**

61. $y = 4x - 7$; $-\frac{1}{4}x - y = -2$; $-y = 4(2 - x)$; and $x = 1 + 3y$ **$y = 4x - 7$ and $-y = 4(2 - x)$**

Solve each quadratic equation by factoring. Check your answer. *(Lesson 9-5)*

62. $x^2 - 6x + 8 = 0$ **2, 4** 63. $x^2 + 5x - 6 = 0$ **−6, 1** 64. $x^2 - 5x = 14$ **−2, 7**

65. $x^2 + x - 12 = 0$ **−4, 3** 66. $x^2 - 3x = 40$ **−5, 8** 67. $x^2 + 8x - 9 = 0$ **−9, 1**

Teaching Tip **Multiple Choice** For **Exercise 54,** remind students that rational numbers can be written in the form $\frac{a}{b}$, where a and b are integers and $b \neq 0$. For students who change the fraction to a decimal, remind them that repeating decimals are also rational.

Answers

47. $x = \pm\frac{\sqrt{2}}{2}$, which is irrational

48. $x = \pm\sqrt{-\frac{1}{2}}$; no real solutions

49. $x = \pm\frac{1}{2}$

50. $x = \pm\sqrt{-\frac{1}{4}}$; no real solutions

Journal

Have students explain how to solve an equation of the form $ax^2 + c = 0$ by using square roots.

ALTERNATIVE ASSESSMENT

Have students create and solve quadratic equations in standard form where 1) a and c are both positive, 2) a and c are both negative, and 3) a is positive and c is negative.

Power Presentations with PowerPoint®

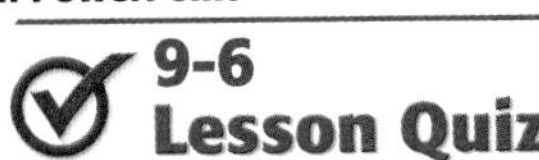

9-6 Lesson Quiz

Solve using square roots. Check your answer.

1. $x^2 - 195 = 1$ ± 14
2. $4x^2 - 18 = -9$ $\pm\frac{3}{2}$
3. $2x^2 - 10 = -12$ $\varnothing$
4. Solve $0 = -5x^2 + 225$. Round to the nearest hundredth. ± 6.71
5. A community swimming pool is in the shape of a trapezoid. The height of the trapezoid is twice as long as the shorter base and the longer base is twice as long as the height.

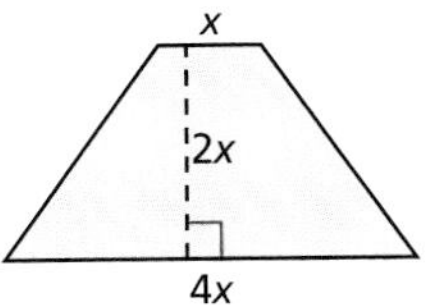

The area of the pool is 3675 square feet. What is the length of the longer base? Round to the nearest foot. (*Hint:* Use $A = \frac{1}{2}h(b_1 + b_2)$.) 108 feet

Also available on transparency

9-6 PROBLEM SOLVING

LESSON 9-6 **Problem Solving**
Solving Quadratic Equations by Using Square Roots

A furniture maker has designed a bookcase with the proportions shown in the diagram below. Write the correct answer.

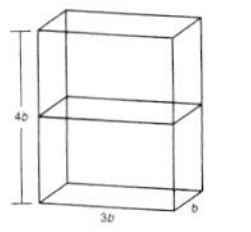

(Diagram: bookcase with height $4b$, width $3b$, depth b)

1. A customer has requested a bookcase with the two shelves having a total area of 864 square inches. What should b equal to meet the customer's specifications? **12 inches**

2. Barnard has a stain on his wall and would like to cover it up with a bookcase. What should b equal in order for the back of the bookcase to cover an area of 4800 square inches? **20 inches**

3. Bria would like to display her collection of soap carvings on top of her bookcase. The collection takes up an area of 400 square inches. What should b equal for the top of the bookcase to have the correct area? Round your answer to the nearest tenth of an inch. **11.5 inches**

4. Eliana would like to cover the side panels with silk. She has 1600 square inches of silk. What should b equal so that she can use all of her silk to completely cover the sides? Round your answer to the nearest tenth of an inch. **14.1 inches**

Select the best answer.

5. Carter plans to wallpaper the longest wall in his living room. The wall is twice as long as it is high and has an area of 162 square feet. What is the height of the wall?
A 8 feet C 12 feet
(B) 9 feet D 18 feet

6. An apple drops off the apple tree from a height of 8 feet. How long does it take the apple to reach the ground? Use the function $f(x) = -16x^2 + c$, where c is the initial height of a falling object, to find the answer.
F 0.5 seconds H 1 second
(G) 0.71 seconds J 2.23 seconds

7. Trinette cut a square tablecloth into 4 equal pieces that she used to make two pillow covers. The area of the tablecloth was 3600 square inches. What is the side length of each piece Trinette used to make the pillow covers?
A 20 inches C 60 inches
(B) 30 inches D 90 inches

8. Elton earns x dollars per hour at the bookstore. His mother, Evelyn, earns x^2 dollars per hour as a career counselor. Twice Evelyn's wage equals $84.50. What is Elton's hourly wage? Round your answer to the nearest cent.
F $4.60 H $9.19
(G) $6.50 J $13.00

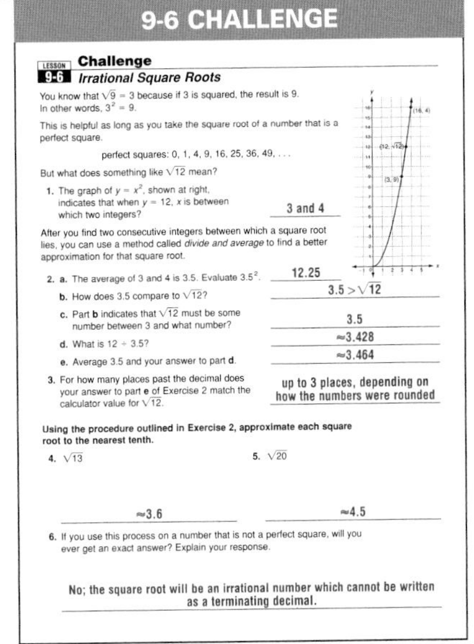

9-6 CHALLENGE

LESSON 9-6 **Challenge**
Irrational Square Roots

You know that $\sqrt{9} = 3$ because if 3 is squared, the result is 9. In other words, $3^2 = 9$.

This is helpful as long as you take the square root of a number that is a perfect square.

perfect squares: 0, 1, 4, 9, 16, 25, 36, 49, . . .

But what does something like $\sqrt{12}$ mean?

1. The graph of $y = x^2$, shown at right, indicates that when $y = 12$, x is between which two integers? **3 and 4**

After you find two consecutive integers between which a square root lies, you can use a method called *divide and average* to find a better approximation for that square root.

2. a. The average of 3 and 4 is 3.5. Evaluate 3.5^2. **12.25**
b. How does 3.5 compare to $\sqrt{12}$? **$3.5 > \sqrt{12}$**
c. Part **b** indicates that $\sqrt{12}$ must be some number between 3 and what number? **3.5**
d. What is $12 \div 3.5$? **≈3.428**
e. Average 3.5 and your answer to part **d**. **≈3.464**

3. For how many places past the decimal does your answer to part **e** of Exercise 2 match the calculator value for $\sqrt{12}$. **up to 3 places, depending on how the numbers were rounded**

Using the procedure outlined in Exercise 2, approximate each square root to the nearest tenth.

4. $\sqrt{13}$ **≈3.6** 5. $\sqrt{20}$ **≈4.5**

6. If you use this process on a number that is not a perfect square, will you ever get an exact answer? Explain your response. **No; the square root will be an irrational number which cannot be written as a terminating decimal.**

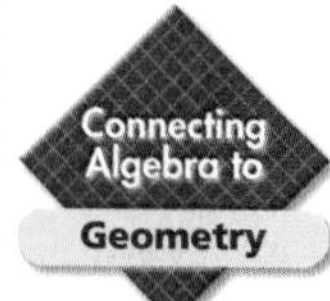

Organizer

See Skills Bank page SB19

Objective: Use the Distance Formula to find the distance between two points in the coordinate plane.

Teach

Remember

Students review and apply absolute value and the Pythagorean Theorem.

INTERVENTION For additional review and practice on finding the distance between two points in the coordinate plane, see Skills Bank page SB19.

Visual For **Example 1,** have students plot the points and count the units between them to see that the answer is correct. For **Example 2,** have students plot the points and estimate the distance between H and K before calculating it.

California Standards

Reinforcement of 7MG3.2

The Distance Formula

You can find the length of a vertical or horizontal line segment in the coordinate plane by subtracting coordinates.

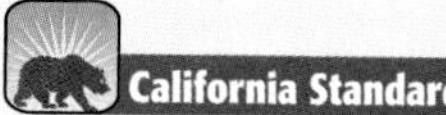

Reinforcement of 7MG3.2 Understand and use coordinate graphs to plot simple figures, **determine lengths** and areas related to them, and determine their image under translations and reflections.

WORDS	NUMBERS	ALGEBRA
The length of a vertical line segment is the absolute value of the difference between the y-coordinates of the endpoints.	$AB = \|2 - (-4)\| = \|6\| = 6$	The distance between $P(x_1, y_1)$ and $Q(x_1, y_2)$ is $\|y_2 - y_1\|$.
The length of a horizontal line segment is the absolute value of the difference between the x-coordinates of the endpoints.	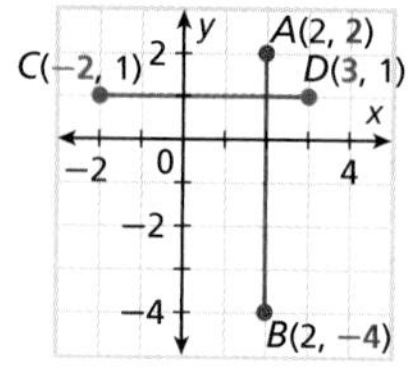 (graph: $C(-2, 1)$, $A(2, 2)$, $D(3, 1)$, $B(2, -4)$) $CD = \|-2 - 3\| = \|-5\| = 5$	The distance between $P(x_1, y_1)$ and $Q(x_2, y_1)$ is $\|x_2 - x_1\|$.

Example 1

Find the length of the line segment that connects $S(-4.5, 7.1)$ and $T(-4.5, 0.3)$.

The x-coordinates are the same, so this is a vertical line segment. Subtract the y-coordinates and find the absolute value of the difference.

$\|y_2 - y_1\|$	*Formula for the length of a vertical line segment*
$\|0.3 - 7.1\|$	*Substitute.*
$\|-6.8\| = 6.8$	*Subtract and find the absolute value.*

Try This

Find the length of the line segment that connects each pair of points.

1. $X(-1, 3)$ and $Y(4, 3)$ **5**
2. $M(5, -2)$ and $N(5, -8)$ **6**
3. $C(3, -1)$ and $D(3, 5)$ **6**
4. $P(14, -5)$ and $Q(25, -5)$ **11**
5. $A(-6, 0.5)$ and $B(-6, -4.3)$ **4.8**
6. $E(1.4, -0.7)$ and $F(3.8, -0.7)$ **2.4**

Find the length of each segment.

7. the altitude of $\triangle PQR$ **6**

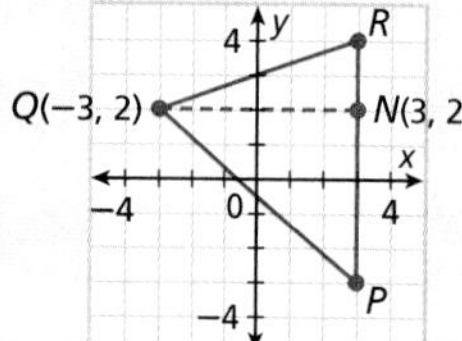

8. the height of parallelogram $EFGH$ **7**

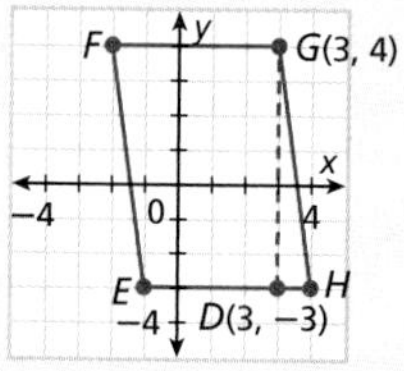

(graph: F, $G(3, 4)$, E, $D(3, -3)$, H)

9. the height of trapezoid $ACDF$ **5**

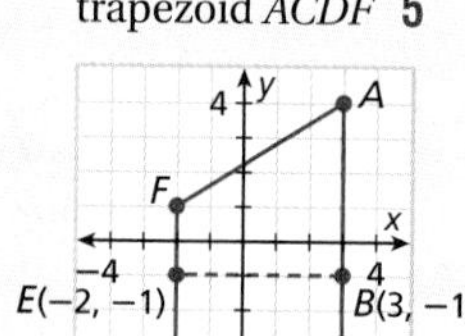

To find the length of a line segment that is not vertical or horizontal, such as PQ, think of it as the hypotenuse of a right triangle. Then you can use the Pythagorean Theorem.

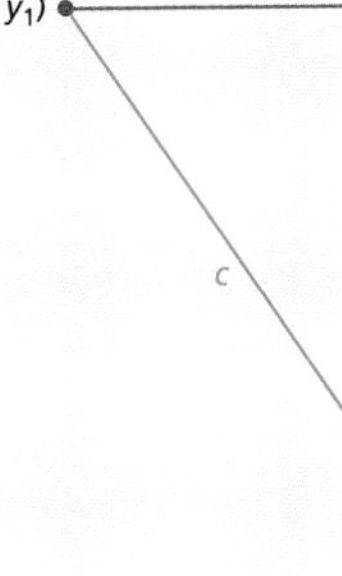

$c^2 = a^2 + b^2$	*Pythagorean Theorem*
$(PQ)^2 = (PR)^2 + (QR)^2$	*Substitute.*
$PQ = \sqrt{(PR)^2 + (QR)^2}$	*Solve for PQ. Use the positive square root to represent distance.*
$= \sqrt{\underbrace{(x_2 - x_1)^2}_{\text{Horizontal segment}} + \underbrace{(y_2 - y_1)^2}_{\text{Vertical segment}}}$	*Use the Formula to find the length of each segment.*

This is the Distance Formula.

The Distance Formula

The distance between points P and Q with coordinates $P(x_1, y_1)$ and $Q(x_2, y_2)$ is given by

$$D = \sqrt{(x_2 - x_1)^2 + (y_2 - y_1)^2}.$$

Example 2

Find the length of the line segment that connects $H(20, -11)$ and $K(-4, 18)$.

Use the Distance Formula. Let $(20, -11)$ be (x_1, y_1) and $(-4, 18)$ be (x_2, y_2).

$D = \sqrt{(x_2 - x_1)^2 + (y_2 - y_1)^2}$	*Write the formula.*
$= \sqrt{(-4 - 20)^2 + [18 - (-11)]^2}$	*Substitute.*
$= \sqrt{(-24)^2 + (29)^2}$	*Find the differences.*
$= \sqrt{576 + 841}$	*Square the differences.*
$= \sqrt{1417} \approx 37.64$	*Estimate the square root.*

Try This

Find the length of the line segment that connects each pair of points. Round to the nearest hundredth.

10. $F(-8, 3)$ and $G(-11, -4)$ **≈ 7.62**

11. $S(30, -15)$ and $T(-55, 40)$ **≈ 101.24**

12. $W(0.5, 1.2)$ and $X(0.6, 2.5)$ **≈ 1.30**

Find the length of each dashed line segment. Round to the nearest hundredth.

13. the altitude of $\triangle WYZ$ **≈ 5.38**

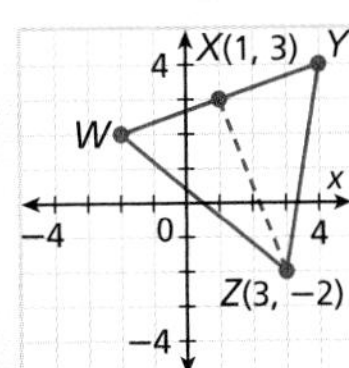

14. the height of parallelogram $ABCD$ **≈ 6.71**

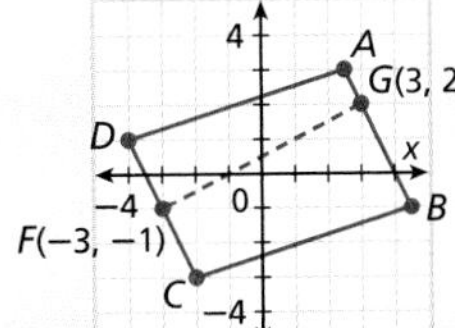

15. the height of trapezoid $LMNO$ **≈ 4.47**

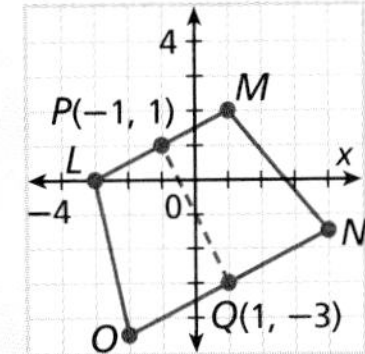

Close

Assess

Have students show that the Distance Formula works for horizontal and vertical line segments.

Organizer

Use with Lesson 9-7

Objective: Use algebra tiles to model completing the square.

Materials: algebra tiles

Online Edition

Teach

Discuss

In the second step of the activity, discuss why 9 unit tiles are added to the mat. Explain that the goal is to make a perfect square by adding unit tiles.

Close

Key Concept

You can use algebra tiles to model completing the square to form a perfect-square trinomial. Algebra tiles can be found in the Manipulatives Kit (MK). Note that completing the square results in a different expression that is not equivalent to the original expression.

Assessment

Journal Have students explain how to use algebra tiles to complete the square for $x^2 + 10x$. Have them write the new expression in factored form. $x^2 + 10x + 25$; $(x + 5)(x + 5)$, or $(x + 5)^2$

California Standards

Preparation for 14.0

9-7

Model Completing the Square

Use with Lesson 9-7

One way to solve a quadratic equation is by using a procedure called *completing the square.* In this procedure, you add something to a quadratic expression to make it a perfect-square trinomial. This procedure can be modeled with algebra tiles.

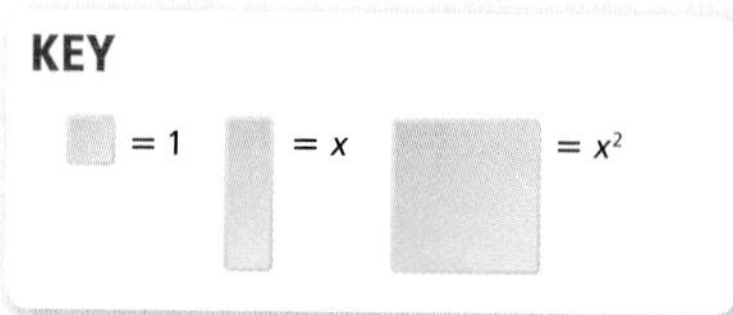

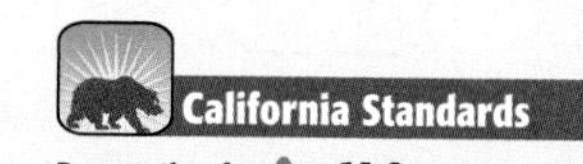

Preparation for 14.0 Students solve a quadratic equation by factoring or **completing the square.**

Activity

Use algebra tiles to model $x^2 + 6x$. Add unit tiles to complete a perfect-square trinomial. Then write the new expression in factored form.

MODEL		ALGEBRA
	Arrange the tiles to form part of a large square. *Part of the square is missing. How many unit tiles do you need to complete it?*	$x^2 + 6x$
	Complete the square by placing 9 unit tiles on the mat. *$x^2 + 6x + 9$ is a perfect-square trinomial.*	$x^2 + 6x + 9$
$x + 3$, $x + 3$	*Use the length and the width of the square to rewrite the area expression in factored form.*	$(x + 3)^2$

Try This

Use algebra tiles to model each expression. Add unit tiles to complete a perfect-square trinomial. Then write the new expression in factored form.

1. $x^2 + 4x$
2. $x^2 + 2x$
3. $x^2 + 10x$
4. $x^2 + 8x$
5. **Make a Conjecture** Examine the pattern in Problems 1–4. How many unit tiles would you have to add to make $x^2 + 12x$ a perfect-square trinomial? **36**

Answers to *Try This*

1. $x^2 + 4x + 4 = (x + 2)^2$
2. $x^2 + 2x + 1 = (x + 1)^2$
3. $x^2 + 10x + 25 = (x + 5)^2$
4. $x^2 + 8x + 16 = (x + 4)^2$

9-7 Completing the Square

California Standards

14.0 Students solve a quadratic equation by factoring or **completing the square.**
23.0 Students apply quadratic equations to physical problems, such as the motion of an object under the force of gravity.
Also covered: **2.0**

Vocabulary
completing the square

Who uses this?
Landscapers can solve quadratic equations to find dimensions of patios. (See Example 4.)

In the previous lesson, you solved quadratic equations by isolating x^2 and then using square roots. This method also works if the quadratic equation, when written in standard form, is a perfect square.

When a trinomial is a perfect square, there is a relationship between the coefficient of the x-term and the constant term.

$(x+n)^2$		$(x-n)^2$
$= x^2 + 2nx + n^2$	*Divide the coefficient of the x-term by 2. Then square the result to get the constant term.*	$= x^2 - 2nx + n^2$
$\left(\frac{2n}{2}\right)^2 = n^2$		$\left(\frac{-2n}{2}\right)^2 = n^2$

An expression in the form $x^2 + bx$ is not a perfect square. However, you can use the relationship shown above to add a term to $x^2 + bx$ to form a trinomial that is a perfect square. This is called **completing the square**.

Completing the Square

WORDS	NUMBERS	ALGEBRA
To complete the square of $x^2 + bx$, add $\left(\frac{b}{2}\right)^2$ to the expression. This will form a perfect-square trinomial.	$x^2 + 6x + \square$ $x^2 + 6x + \left(\frac{6}{2}\right)^2$ $x^2 + 6x + 9$ $(x+3)^2$	$x^2 + bx + \square$ $x^2 + bx + \left(\frac{b}{2}\right)^2$ $\left(x + \frac{b}{2}\right)^2$

EXAMPLE 1 Completing the Square

Complete the square to form a perfect-square trinomial.

A $x^2 + 10x + \square$		**B** $x^2 - 9x + \square$
$x^2 + 10x$	*Identify b.*	$x^2 + -9x$
$\left(\frac{10}{2}\right)^2 = 5^2 = 25$	*Find $\left(\frac{b}{2}\right)^2$.*	$\left(\frac{-9}{2}\right)^2 = \frac{81}{4}$
$x^2 + 10x + 25$	*Add $\left(\frac{b}{2}\right)^2$ to the expression.*	$x^2 - 9x + \frac{81}{4}$

CHECK IT OUT! **Complete the square to form a perfect-square trinomial.**
1a. $x^2 + 12x +$ **36** **1b.** $x^2 - 5x +$ $\frac{25}{4}$ **1c.** $8x + x^2 +$ **16**

To solve a quadratic equation in the form $x^2 + bx = c$, first complete the square of $x^2 + bx$. Then you can solve using square roots.

9-7 Organizer

Objective: Solve quadratic equations by completing the square.

Online Edition
Tutorial Videos

Countdown to Mastery Week 21

Power Presentations with PowerPoint®

Warm Up

Simplify.

1. $\left(\frac{7}{2}\right)^2$ $\frac{49}{4}$ **2.** $\left(\frac{10}{2}\right)^2 - 6$ 19

3. $\left(\frac{-9}{2}\right)^2$ $\frac{81}{4}$ **4.** $\left(\frac{3}{2}\right)^2 + 3$ $\frac{21}{4}$

Solve each quadratic equation by factoring.

5. $x^2 + 8x + 16 = 0$ −4

6. $x^2 - 22x + 121 = 0$ 11

7. $x^2 - 12x + 36 = 0$ 6

Also available on transparency

Math Humor

Q: What did the quadratic binomial say when he proposed to the constant?

A: You complete me.

1 Introduce

Recall that you can square a binomial by using the following rule:
$(a+b)^2 = (a+b)(a+b) = a^2 + 2ab + b^2$.

1. Complete the table by squaring the binomials.

Binomial Squared	Trinomial
$(x+2)^2$	$x^2 + 4x + 4$
$(x-5)^2$	
$(x+3)^2$	
$(x-4)^2$	
$(x-7)^2$	
$(x+9)^2$	

2. The trinomials in the table are perfect-square trinomials. In each of them, how is the constant term related to the coefficient of the x-term?

3. Suppose you know that $x^2 - 12x + \square$ is a perfect-square trinomial. What must be the value of the constant term?

4. What binomial was squared in order to get the perfect-square trinomial in Problem 3?

THINK AND DISCUSS

5. **Explain** how you found the constant term of the perfect-square trinomial in Problem 3.

Motivate

Display $x^2 + 8x + \square$. Have students find four numbers that make the trinomial factorable.
7, 12, 15, 16

Which makes it a perfect-square trinomial? 16

Explorations and answers are provided in *Alternate Openers: Explorations Transparencies.*

California Standards

Algebra 1 **14.0, 23.0**
Also covered:
2.0 Students understand and use such operations as taking the opposite, finding the reciprocal, **taking a root,** and raising to a fractional power. They understand and use the rules of exponents.

Power Presentations with PowerPoint®

Additional Examples

Example 1

Complete the square to form a perfect square trinomial.

A. $x^2 + 2x + \square$ 1

B. $x^2 - 6x + \square$ 9

Example 2

Solve by completing the square. Check your answer.

A. $x^2 + 16x = -15$ $-1, -15$

B. $x^2 - 4x - 6 = 0$ $2 \pm \sqrt{10}$

Also available on transparency

INTERVENTION

Questioning Strategies

EXAMPLE 1

- Can the number added ever be negative? Explain.

EXAMPLE 2

- In what form should the equation be before you find $\left(\frac{b}{2}\right)^2$?
- When will solutions be irrational? Give an example.

Math Background When the solution of a quadratic equation involves the square root of a negative number, we say it has no real solutions. In fact, these types of quadratic equations have nonreal solutions, called *complex numbers*. Students will study complex numbers in Algebra 2.

Solving a Quadratic Equation by Completing the Square
Step 1 Write the equation in the form $x^2 + bx = c$.
Step 2 Find $\left(\frac{b}{2}\right)^2$.
Step 3 Complete the square by adding $\left(\frac{b}{2}\right)^2$. Because this is an equation, you must add $\left(\frac{b}{2}\right)^2$ to both sides.
Step 4 Factor the perfect-square trinomial.
Step 5 Take the square root of both sides.
Step 6 Write two equations, using both the positive and negative square root, and solve each equation.

EXAMPLE 2 Solving $x^2 + bx = c$ by Completing the Square

Solve by completing the square. Check your answer.

A $x^2 + 14x = 15$

Step 1 $x^2 + 14x = 15$ — *The equation is in the form $x^2 + bx = c$.*

Step 2 $\left(\frac{14}{2}\right)^2 = 7^2 = 49$ — *Find $\left(\frac{b}{2}\right)^2$.*

Step 3 $x^2 + 14x + 49 = 15 + 49$ — *Complete the square.*

Step 4 $(x + 7)^2 = 64$ — *Factor and simplify.*

Step 5 $x + 7 = \pm 8$ — *Take the square root of both sides.*

Step 6 $x + 7 = 8$ or $x + 7 = -8$ — *Write and solve two equations.*

$x = 1$ or $x = -15$

Check

$x^2 + 14x$	$= 15$
$(1)^2 + 14(1)$	15
$1 + 14$	15
15	15 ✓

$x^2 + 14x$	$= 15$
$(-15)^2 + 14(-15)$	15
$225 - 210$	15
15	15 ✓

B $x^2 - 2x - 2 = 0$

Step 1 $x^2 + (-2x) = 2$ — *Write in the form $x^2 + bx = c$.*

Step 2 $\left(\frac{-2}{2}\right)^2 = (-1)^2 = 1$ — *Find $\left(\frac{b}{2}\right)^2$.*

Step 3 $x^2 - 2x + 1 = 2 + 1$ — *Complete the square.*

Step 4 $(x - 1)^2 = 3$ — *Factor and simplify.*

Step 5 $x - 1 = \pm\sqrt{3}$ — *Take the square root of both sides.*

Step 6 $x - 1 = \sqrt{3}$ or $x - 1 = -\sqrt{3}$ — *Write and solve two equations.*

$x = 1 + \sqrt{3}$ or $x = 1 - \sqrt{3}$

The exact solutions are $1 + \sqrt{3}$ and $1 - \sqrt{3}$.

Check Use a graphing calculator to check your answer.

```
(1+√(3))²-2(1+√(
3))-2
                0
(1-√(3))²-2(1-√(
3))-2
                0
```

Writing Math

The expressions $1 + \sqrt{3}$ and $1 - \sqrt{3}$ can be written as one expression: $1 \pm \sqrt{3}$, which is read as "1 plus or minus the square root of 3."

CHECK IT OUT! Solve by completing the square. Check your answer.

2a. $x^2 + 10x = -9$ **$-9, -1$** **2b.** $t^2 - 8t - 5 = 0$ **$4 \pm \sqrt{21}$**

2 Teach

Guided Instruction

Review how to factor perfect-square trinomials and how to solve quadratic equations by using square roots. Stress that the equation must be in the form $x^2 + bx = c$ before $\left(\frac{b}{2}\right)^2$ is added to both sides.

Visual Use algebra tiles (MK) as shown on page 590 to help students see how they are forming a perfect square.

Universal Access

Through Communication

Have students work in small groups to make a poster showing how to apply the six steps for solving quadratic equations by completing the square. Give each group a different equation to solve. Then have each group present their posters to the rest of the class, explaining each step.

EXAMPLE 3 Solving $ax^2 + bx = c$ by Completing the Square

Solve by completing the square.

A $3x^2 - 10x = -3$

Step 1 $\frac{3x^2}{3} - \frac{10x}{3} = \frac{-3}{3}$ *Divide both sides of the equation by 3 so that a = 1.*

$x^2 - \frac{10}{3}x = -1$

$x^2 + \left(-\frac{10}{3}x\right) = -1$ *Write in the form $x^2 + bx = c$.*

Step 2 $\left(-\frac{10}{3} \cdot \frac{1}{2}\right)^2 = \left(-\frac{10}{6}\right)^2 = \frac{100}{36} = \frac{25}{9}$ *Find $\left(\frac{b}{2}\right)^2$.*

Step 3 $x^2 - \frac{10}{3}x + \frac{25}{9} = -1 + \frac{25}{9}$ *Complete the square.*

$x^2 - \frac{10}{3}x + \frac{25}{9} = -\frac{9}{9} + \frac{25}{9}$ *Rewrite using like denominators.*

Step 4 $\left(x - \frac{5}{3}\right)^2 = \frac{16}{9}$ *Factor and simplify.*

Step 5 $x - \frac{5}{3} = \pm\frac{4}{3}$ *Take the square root of both sides.*

Step 6 $x - \frac{5}{3} = \frac{4}{3}$ or $x - \frac{5}{3} = -\frac{4}{3}$ *Write and solve two equations.*

$x = 3$ or $x = \frac{1}{3}$

B $-2x^2 + 12x - 20 = 0$

Step 1 $\frac{-2x^2}{-2} + \frac{12x}{-2} - \frac{20}{-2} = \frac{0}{-2}$ *Divide both sides of the equation by −2 so that a = 1.*

$x^2 - 6x + 10 = 0$

$x^2 - 6x = -10$ *Write in the form $x^2 + bx = c$.*

$x^2 + (-6x) = -10$

Step 2 $\left(\frac{-6}{2}\right)^2 = (-3)^2 = 9$ *Find $\left(\frac{b}{2}\right)^2$.*

Step 3 $x^2 - 6x + 9 = -10 + 9$ *Complete the square.*

Step 4 $(x - 3)^2 = -1$ *Factor and simplify.*

There is no real number whose square is negative, so there are no real solutions.

Remember!

Multiplying by $\frac{1}{2}$ is the same as dividing by 2.

CHECK IT OUT! Solve by completing the square. Check your answer.

3a. $3x^2 - 5x - 2 = 0$ $-\frac{1}{3}, 2$

3b. $4t^2 - 4t + 9 = 0$ ∅

EXAMPLE 4 *Problem-Solving Application*

A landscaper is designing a rectangular brick patio. She has enough bricks to cover 144 square feet. She wants the length of the patio to be 10 feet greater than the width. What dimensions should she use for the patio? Round to the nearest hundredth of a foot.

1 Understand the Problem

The **answer** will be the length and width of the patio.

COMMON ERROR ALERT

In **Example 3A,** students may have difficulty finding $\left(\frac{b}{2}\right)^2$ when b is a fraction. Remind them that dividing by 2 is the same as multiplying by $\frac{1}{2}$. For $b = \frac{10}{3}$, $\left(\frac{b}{2}\right)^2$ becomes $\left(\frac{1}{2} \cdot \frac{10}{3}\right)^2$, or $\left(\frac{10}{6}\right)^2$. Let students practice with a few examples and lead them to see that dividing a fraction in half is the same as doubling the denominator.

Power Presentations with PowerPoint®

Additional Examples

Example 3

Solve by completing the square.

A. $-3x^2 + 12x - 15 = 0$ ∅

B. $5x^2 + 19x = 4$ $-4, \frac{1}{5}$

Also available on transparency

INTERVENTION

Questioning Strategies

EXAMPLE 3

- When will there be no solutions?

Teaching Tip **Critical Thinking** Students can save time by checking that an equation has solutions by first finding the vertex of the related function's graph and using the value of a to see how the graph opens. In **Example 3B,** the graph of the related function has its vertex at (3, −2), below the x-axis, and opens down. Therefore, the graph does not intersect the x-axis and the equation has no solutions.

Teaching Tip **Inclusion** Remind students to always check their answers either by graphing the related function or by direct substitution into the original equation.

Teaching Tip **Math Background** In **Example 3,** tell students that to complete the square when $a \neq 1$, divide both sides of the equation by a. This results in an equation like those in **Example 2,** which can then be solved using the same methods. This strategy—transforming a new kind of problem into a problem whose solution method is known—is used often in mathematics.

Power Presentations with PowerPoint®

Additional Examples

Example 4

A rectangular room has an area of 195 square feet. Its width is 2 feet shorter than its length. Find the dimensions of the room. Round to the nearest hundredth of a foot, if necessary. 13 ft by 15 ft

Also available on transparency

INTERVENTION

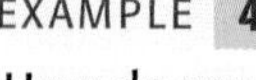

Questioning Strategies

EXAMPLE 4

- How do you know which of the two solutions to use?
- How would the equation be different if the area were triangular?

List the important information:

- There are enough bricks to cover 144 square feet.
- One edge of the patio is to be 10 feet longer than the other edge.

2 Make a Plan

Set the formula for the area of a rectangle equal to 144, the area of the patio. Solve the equation.

3 Solve

Let x be the width. Then $x + 10$ is the length. Use the formula for area of a rectangle.

ℓ	$\cdot$	w	=	A
length	**times**	**width**	=	**area of patio**
$x + 10$	$\cdot$	x	=	**144**

The equation is $(x + 10)x = 144$.

Step 1	$x^2 + 10x = 144$	*Simplify.*
Step 2	$\left(\frac{10}{2}\right)^2 = 5^2 = 25$	*Find* $\left(\frac{b}{2}\right)^2$.
Step 3	$x^2 + 10x + 25 = 144 + 25$	*Complete the square.*
Step 4	$(x + 5)^2 = 169$	*Factor the perfect-square trinomial.*
Step 5	$x + 5 = \pm 13$	*Take the square root of both sides.*
Step 6	$x + 5 = 13$ or $x + 5 = -13$	*Write and solve two equations.*
	$x = 8$ or $x = -18$	

Negative numbers are not reasonable for length, so $x = 8$ is the only solution that makes sense.

The width is 8 feet, and the length is $8 + 10$, or 18, feet.

Look Back

The length of the patio is 10 feet greater than the width. Also, $8(18) = 144$.

4. A rectangular room has an area of 400 ft^2. The length is 8 ft longer than the width. Find the dimensions of the room. Round to the nearest tenth of a foot. **16.4 ft by 24.4 ft**

THINK AND DISCUSS

1. Tell how to solve a quadratic equation in the form $x^2 + bx + c = 0$ by completing the square.

2. **GET ORGANIZED** Copy and complete the graphic organizer. In each box, write and solve an example of the given type of quadratic equation.

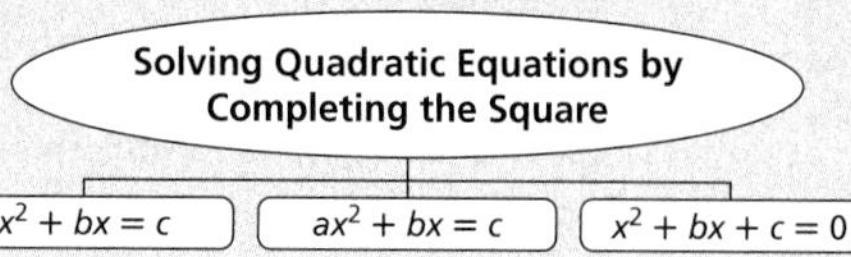

3 Close

Summarize

Review with students the steps to solve a quadratic equation by completing the square. Remind students that when they check their answers algebraically, they should substitute the values for x in the original equation, not in the equation with the value added for a perfect-square trinomial. For irrational solutions, students can check their answers on a graphing calculator.

FORMATIVE ASSESSMENT and INTERVENTION

***Diagnose Before* the Lesson**
9-7 Warm Up, TE p. 591

***Monitor During* the Lesson**
Check It Out! Exercises, SE pp. 591–594
Questioning Strategies, TE pp. 592–594

***Assess After* the Lesson**
9-7 Lesson Quiz, TE p. 597
Alternative Assessment, TE p. 597

Answers to *Think and Discuss*

1. Possible answer: Subtract c from both sides. Then add $\left(\frac{b}{2}\right)^2$ to both sides.
2. See p. A8.

California Standards Practice
2.0, 14.0, 21.0, 23.0, 25.2

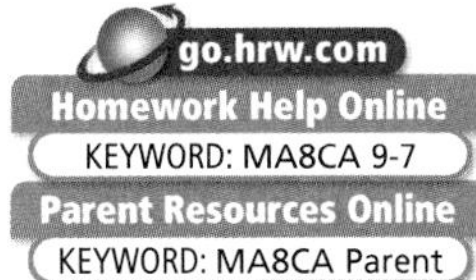

Homework Help Online
KEYWORD: MA8CA 9-7
Parent Resources Online
KEYWORD: MA8CA Parent

GUIDED PRACTICE

1. **Vocabulary** Describe in your own words how to *complete the square* for the equation $1 = x^2 + 4x$.

SEE EXAMPLE 1 p. 591

Complete the square to form a perfect-square trinomial.

2. $x^2 + 14x +$ **49**
3. $x^2 - 4x +$ **4**
4. $x^2 - 3x +$ **$\frac{9}{4}$**

SEE EXAMPLE 2 p. 592

Solve by completing the square. Check your answer.

5. $x^2 + 6x = -5$ **−5, −1**
6. $x^2 - 8x = 9$ **−1, 9**
7. $x^2 + x = 30$ **−6, 5**
8. $x^2 + 2x = 21$ **$-1 \pm \sqrt{22}$**
9. $x^2 - 10x = -9$ **1, 9**
10. $x^2 + 16x = 92$ **$-8 \pm \sqrt{156}$**

SEE EXAMPLE 3 p. 593

11. $-x^2 - 5x = -5$
12. $-x^2 - 3x + 2 = 0$
13. $-6x = 3x^2 + 9$ **∅**
14. $2x^2 - 6x = -10$ **∅**
15. $-x^2 + 8x - 6 = 0$ **$4 \pm \sqrt{10}$**
16. $4x^2 + 16 = -24x$ **$-3 \pm \sqrt{5}$**

SEE EXAMPLE 4 p. 593

17. **Multi-Step** The length of a rectangle is 4 meters longer than the width. The area of the rectangle is 80 square meters. Find the length and width. Round your answers to the nearest tenth of a meter. **7.2 m; 11.2 m**

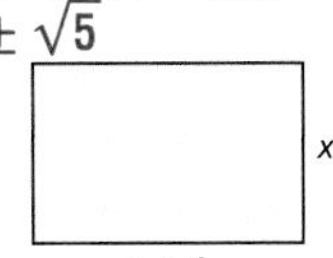

PRACTICE AND PROBLEM SOLVING

Independent Practice

For Exercises	See Example
18–20	1
21–26	2
27–32	3
33	4

Extra Practice
Skills Practice p. EP19
Application Practice p. EP32

Complete the square to form a perfect-square trinomial.

18. $x^2 - 16x +$ **64**
19. $x^2 - 2x +$ **1**
20. $x^2 + 11x +$ **$\frac{121}{4}$**

Solve by completing the square. Check your answer.

21. $x^2 - 10x = 24$ **−2, 12**
22. $x^2 - 6x = -9$ **3**
23. $x^2 + 15x = -26$ **−13, −2**
24. $x^2 + 6x = 16$ **−8, 2**
25. $x^2 - 2x = 48$ **−6, 8**
26. $x^2 + 12x = -36$ **−6**
27. $-x^2 + x + 6 = 0$ **−2, 3**
28. $2x^2 = -7x - 29$ **∅**
29. $-x^2 - x + 1 = 0$
30. $3x^2 - 6x - 9 = 0$ **3, −1**
31. $-x^2 = 15x + 30$
32. $2x^2 + 20x - 10 = 0$

33. **Geometry** The base of a parallelogram is 8 inches longer than twice the height. The area is 64 square inches. What is the height? **4 in.**

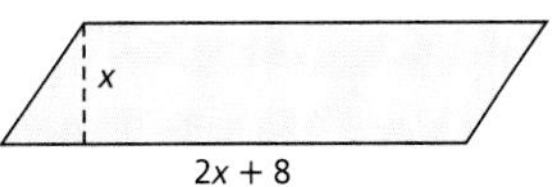

Solve each equation by completing the square. Check your answer.

34. $3x^2 + x = 10$ **$-2, \frac{5}{3}$**
35. $x^2 = 2x + 6$ **$1 \pm \sqrt{7}$**
36. $2a^2 = 5a + 12$ **$-\frac{3}{2}, 4$**
37. $2x^2 + 5x = 3$ **$-3, \frac{1}{2}$**
38. $4x = 7 - x^2$ **$-2 \pm \sqrt{11}$**
39. $8x = -x^2 + 20$ **−10, 2**

40. **Hobbies** The height in feet h of a water bottle rocket launched from a rooftop is given by the equation $h = -16t^2 + 320t + 32$, where t is the time in seconds. After the rocket is fired, how long will it take to return to the ground? Solve by completing the square. Round your answer to the nearest tenth of a second. **20.1 s**

Complete each trinomial so that it is a perfect square.

41. $x^2 + 18x +$ **81**
42. $x^2 - 100x +$ **2500**
43. $x^2 - 7x +$ **$\frac{49}{4}$**
44. $x^2 +$ **4** $x + 4$
45. $x^2 -$ **9** $x + \frac{81}{4}$
46. $x^2 +$ **$\frac{1}{3}$** $x + \frac{1}{36}$

9-7 Exercises

Assignment Guide

Assign *Guided Practice* exercises as necessary.

If you finished Examples **1–2**
Proficient 18–26, 35, 41–47
Advanced 18–26, 35, 41–47, 60

If you finished Examples **1–4**
Proficient 18–46, 48–67, 73–94
Advanced 18–46, 48–94

Homework Quick Check
Quickly check key concepts.
Exercises: 18, 24, 28, 33, 48

Teaching Tip

Concrete Manipulatives For **Exercise 1,** students can use a model such as algebra tiles in their descriptions.

Answers

1. Divide 4 by 2 and square the result: $\left(\frac{4}{2}\right)^2 = 4$. Add 4 to both sides of the equation: $5 = x^2 + 4x + 4$. Write the equation as $5 = (x + 2)^2$ Take the square root of both sides: $\pm\sqrt{5} = x + 2$. Solve for x: $x = -2 \pm \sqrt{5}$.

11. $\frac{-5 \pm 3\sqrt{5}}{2}$

12. $\frac{-3 \pm \sqrt{17}}{2}$

29. $\frac{-1 \pm \sqrt{5}}{2}$

31. $\frac{-15 \pm \sqrt{105}}{2}$

32. $-5 \pm \sqrt{30}$

California Standards

Standard	Exercises
2.0	49, 71, 83–94
6.0	73–76
10.0	77–82
14.0	5–16, 21–32, 48a, 67–69
21.0	48b
23.0	40, 61
25.2	49

Teaching Tip **Inclusion** To determine the width and length of the combined area in **Exercise 47,** suggest that students run their finger horizontally across the diagram from left to right. The distance is x, then 10, then x again, so the expression for width is $x + 10 + x$, or $2x + 10$. Then have students repeat for the length.

CONCEPT CONNECTION **Exercise 61** involves writing and solving a quadratic equation to solve a projectile problem. This exercise prepares students for the Concept Connection on page 610.

Answers

48b.

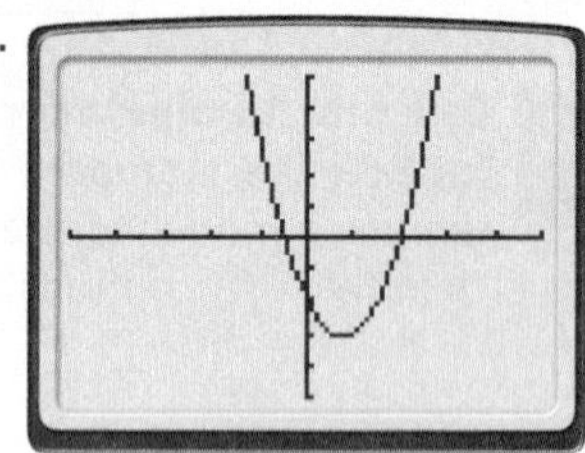

c. Use the Trace and Zoom functions to find where the graph crosses the x-axis, or use the Zero function to find where the graph intersects $y = 0$.

d. Possible answer: Completing the square takes several steps, but it produces the exact solutions. Graphing is fast, but you may get only approx. solutions.

59. Possible answer: Completing the square to solve $x^2 + 11x + 18 = 0$ involves fractions; completing the square to solve $x^2 + 20x - 21 = 0$ does not.

60. Add $2xy$. The perfect-square trinomial product of $(x + y)(x + y)$ simplifies to $x^2 + xy + xy + y^2$, or $x^2 + 2xy + y^2$. This is the equivalent of $x^2 + y^2 + 2xy$.

47. Multi-Step A roped-off area of width x is created around a 34-by-10-foot rectangular museum display of Egyptian artifacts, as shown. The combined area of the display and the roped-off area is 640 square feet. $(10 + 2x)(34 + 2x) = 640$

a. Write an equation for the combined area.

b. Find the width of the roped-off area. **3 ft**

10 ft
34 ft
x
x

48. Graphing Calculator Compare solving a quadratic equation by completing the square with finding the solutions on a graphing calculator.

a. Complete the square to solve $2x^2 - 3x - 2 = 0$. $-\frac{1}{2}, 2$

b. Use your graphing calculator to graph $y = 2x^2 - 3x - 2$.

c. Explain how to use this graph to find the solutions of $2x^2 - 3x - 2 = 0$.

d. Compare the two methods of solving the equation. What are the advantages and disadvantages of each?

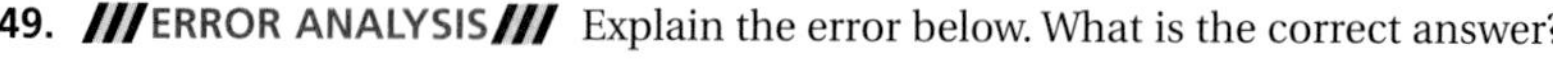

49. ///ERROR ANALYSIS/// Explain the error below. What is the correct answer?

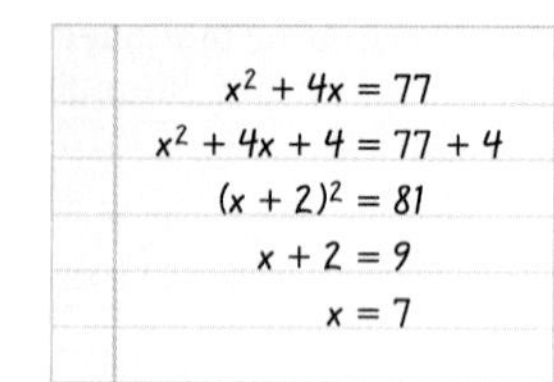

$x^2 + 4x = 77$
$x^2 + 4x + 4 = 77 + 4$
$(x + 2)^2 = 81$
$x + 2 = 9$
$x = 7$

If $(x + 2)^2 = 81$, then $x + 2 = 9$ or $x + 2 = -9$. The correct answer is $x = 7$ or $x = -11$.

Find the roots of each quadratic polynomial. Check your answer.

50. $5x^2 - 50x - 55$ **$-1, 11$**

51. $3x^2 + 36x + 27$ **$-6 \pm 3\sqrt{3}$**

52. $28x - 2x^2 - 26$ **1, 13**

53. $36x + 3x^2 + 108$ **-6**

54. $4x^2 + 32x + 44$ **$-4 \pm \sqrt{5}$**

55. $16x + 40 + 2x^2$ **no real roots**

56. $x^2 - 5x + 6$ **2, 3**

57. $x^2 + 6x + 18$ **no real roots**

58. $x^2 + x + 1$ **no real roots**

59. Write About It Jamal prefers to solve $x^2 + 20x - 21 = 0$ by completing the square. Heather prefers to solve $x^2 + 11x + 18 = 0$ by factoring. Explain their reasoning.

60. Critical Thinking What should be done to the binomial $x^2 + y^2$ to make it a perfect-square trinomial? Explain.

CONCEPT CONNECTION

61. This problem will prepare you for the Concept Connection on page 610.
The function $h(t) = -16t^2 + vt + c$ models the height in feet of a golf ball after t seconds when it is hit with initial velocity v from initial height c feet. A golfer stands on a tee box that is 32 feet above the fairway. He hits the golf ball from the tee at an initial velocity of 64 feet per second.

a. Write an equation that gives the time t when the golf ball lands on the fairway at height 0. $-16t^2 + 64t + 32 = 0$

b. What number would be added to both sides of the equation in part **a** to complete the square while solving for t? **4**

c. Solve the equation from part **a** by completing the square to find the time it takes the ball to reach the fairway. Round to the nearest tenth of a second. **≈ 4.4 s**

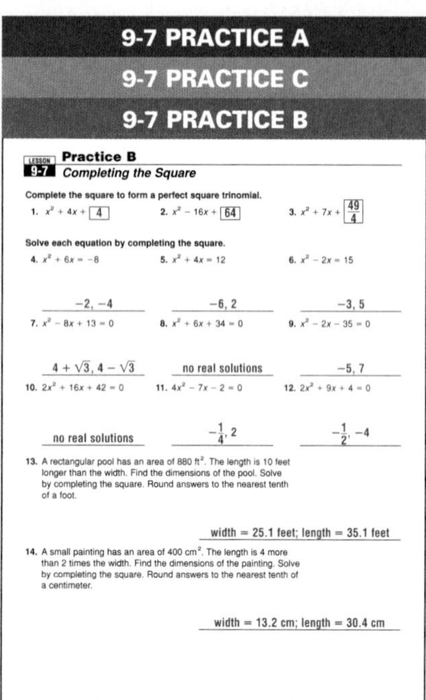

9-7 PRACTICE A
9-7 PRACTICE C
9-7 PRACTICE B

LESSON 9-7 **Practice B**
Completing the Square

Complete the square to form a perfect square trinomial.

1. $x^2 + 4x +$ [4] 2. $x^2 - 16x +$ [64] 3. $x^2 + 7x +$ [$\frac{49}{4}$]

Solve each equation by completing the square.

4. $x^2 + 6x = -8$ — $-2, -4$
5. $x^2 + 4x = 12$ — $-6, 2$
6. $x^2 - 2x = 15$ — $-3, 5$
7. $x^2 - 8x + 13 = 0$ — $4 + \sqrt{3}, 4 - \sqrt{3}$
8. $x^2 + 6x + 34 = 0$ — no real solutions
9. $x^2 - 2x - 35 = 0$ — $-5, 7$
10. $2x^2 + 16x + 42 = 0$ — no real solutions
11. $4x^2 - 7x - 2 = 0$ — $-\frac{1}{4}, 2$
12. $2x^2 + 9x + 4 = 0$ — $-\frac{1}{2}, -4$

13. A rectangular pool has an area of 880 ft². The length is 10 feet longer than the width. Find the dimensions of the pool. Solve by completing the square. Round answers to the nearest tenth of a foot.
width = 25.1 feet; length = 35.1 feet

14. A small painting has an area of 400 cm². The length is 4 more than 2 times the width. Find the dimensions of the painting. Solve by completing the square. Round answers to the nearest tenth of a centimeter.
width = 13.2 cm; length = 30.4 cm

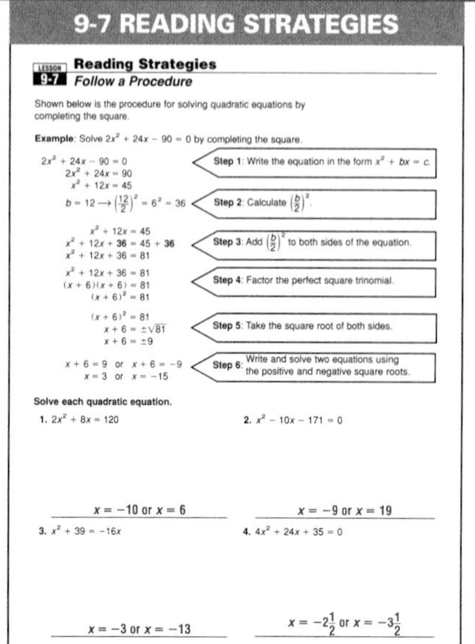

9-7 READING STRATEGIES

LESSON 9-7 **Reading Strategies**
Follow a Procedure

Shown below is the procedure for solving quadratic equations by completing the square.

Example: Solve $2x^2 + 24x - 90 = 0$ by completing the square.

$2x^2 + 24x - 90 = 0$
$2x^2 + 24x = 90$
$x^2 + 12x = 45$ — Step 1: Write the equation in the form $x^2 + bx = c$.

$b = 12 \rightarrow \left(\frac{12}{2}\right)^2 = 6^2 = 36$ — Step 2: Calculate $\left(\frac{b}{2}\right)^2$.

$x^2 + 12x = 45$
$x^2 + 12x + 36 = 45 + 36$
$x^2 + 12x + 36 = 81$ — Step 3: Add $\left(\frac{b}{2}\right)^2$ to both sides of the equation.

$x^2 + 12x + 36 = 81$
$(x + 6)(x + 6) = 81$
$(x + 6)^2 = 81$ — Step 4: Factor the perfect square trinomial.

$(x + 6)^2 = 81$
$x + 6 = \pm\sqrt{81}$
$x + 6 = \pm 9$ — Step 5: Take the square root of both sides.

$x + 6 = 9$ or $x + 6 = -9$
$x = 3$ or $x = -15$ — Step 6: Write and solve two equations using the positive and negative square roots.

Solve each quadratic equation.

1. $2x^2 + 8x = 120$ — $x = -10$ or $x = 6$
2. $x^2 - 10x - 171 = 0$ — $x = -9$ or $x = 19$
3. $x^2 + 39 = -16x$ — $x = -3$ or $x = -13$
4. $4x^2 + 24x + 35 = 0$ — $x = -2\frac{1}{2}$ or $x = -3\frac{1}{2}$

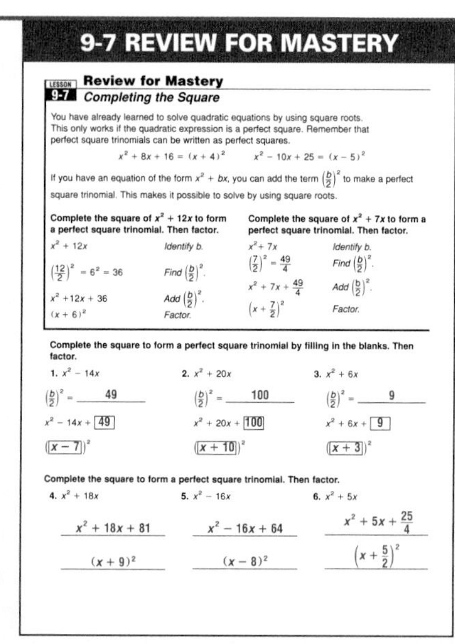

9-7 REVIEW FOR MASTERY

LESSON 9-7 **Review for Mastery**
Completing the Square

You have already learned to solve quadratic equations by using square roots. This only works if the quadratic expression is a perfect square. Remember that perfect square trinomials can be written as perfect squares.

$x^2 + 8x + 16 = (x + 4)^2$ $x^2 - 10x + 25 = (x - 5)^2$

If you have an equation of the form $x^2 + bx$, you can add the term $\left(\frac{b}{2}\right)^2$ to make a perfect square trinomial. This makes it possible to solve by using square roots.

Complete the square of $x^2 + 12x$ to form a perfect square trinomial. Then factor.		Complete the square of $x^2 + 7x$ to form a perfect square trinomial. Then factor.	
$x^2 + 12x$	Identify b.	$x^2 + 7x$	Identify b.
$\left(\frac{12}{2}\right)^2 = 6^2 = 36$	Find $\left(\frac{b}{2}\right)^2$.	$\left(\frac{7}{2}\right)^2 = \frac{49}{4}$	Find $\left(\frac{b}{2}\right)^2$.
$x^2 + 12x + 36$	Add $\left(\frac{b}{2}\right)^2$.	$x^2 + 7x + \frac{49}{4}$	Add $\left(\frac{b}{2}\right)^2$.
$(x + 6)^2$	Factor.	$\left(x + \frac{7}{2}\right)^2$	Factor.

Complete the square to form a perfect square trinomial by filling in the blanks. Then factor.

1. $x^2 - 14x$: $\left(\frac{b}{2}\right)^2 =$ 49; $x^2 - 14x +$ [49]; $(x - 7)^2$
2. $x^2 + 20x$: $\left(\frac{b}{2}\right)^2 =$ 100; $x^2 + 20x +$ [100]; $(x + 10)^2$
3. $x^2 + 6x$: $\left(\frac{b}{2}\right)^2 =$ 9; $x^2 + 6x +$ [9]; $(x + 3)^2$

Complete the square to form a perfect square trinomial. Then factor.

4. $x^2 + 18x$ — $x^2 + 18x + 81$; $(x + 9)^2$
5. $x^2 - 16x$ — $x^2 - 16x + 64$; $(x - 8)^2$
6. $x^2 + 5x$ — $x^2 + 5x + \frac{25}{4}$; $\left(x + \frac{5}{2}\right)^2$

62. **Write About It** Compare solving an equation of the form $x^2 + bx + c = 0$ by completing the square and solving an equation of the form $ax^2 + bx + c = 0$ by completing the square. **When solving an equation of the form $ax^2 + bx + c = 0$, you must first divide the equation by the coefficient a.**

Multiple Choice For Exercises 63–65, choose the best answer.

63. What value of c will make $x^2 + 16x + c$ a perfect-square trinomial?
(A) 32   **(B) 64**   (C) 128   (D) 256

64. What value of b will make $x^2 + b + 25$ a perfect-square trinomial?
(A) 5   (B) 5x   (C) 10   **(D) 10x**

65. Which of the following is closest to a solution of $3x^2 + 2x - 4 = 0$?
(A) 0   **(B) 1**   (C) 2   (D) 3

66. **Short Response** Solve $x^2 - 8x - 20 = 0$ by completing the square. Explain each step in your solution. **10, −2**

CHALLENGE AND EXTEND

Solve each equation by completing the square. Check your answer.

67. $6x^2 + 5x = 6$ $-\frac{3}{2}, \frac{2}{3}$
68. $7x + 3 = 6x^2$ $-\frac{1}{3}, \frac{3}{2}$
69. $4x = 1 - 3x^2$ $-\frac{2}{3} \pm \frac{\sqrt{7}}{3}$

70. What should be done to the binomial $ax^2 + bx$ to obtain a perfect-square trinomial?

71. Solve $ax^2 + bx = 0$ for x. $0, -\frac{b}{a}$

72. **Geometry** The hypotenuse of a right triangle is 20 cm. One of the legs is 4 cm longer than the other leg. Find the area of the triangle. (*Hint:* Use the Pythagorean Theorem.) **96 cm²**

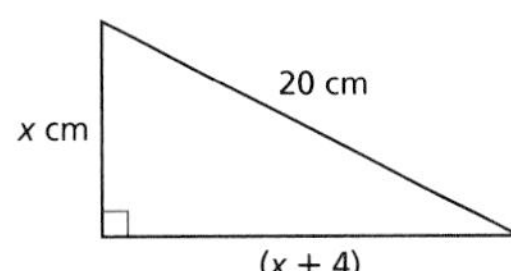

SPIRAL STANDARDS REVIEW

Graph the line with the given slope and y-intercept. *(Lesson 5-5)*

73. slope = 4, y-intercept = −3
74. slope = $-\frac{2}{3}$, y-intercept = 4
75. slope = −2, y-intercept = −2
76. slope = $-\frac{4}{3}$, y-intercept = 0

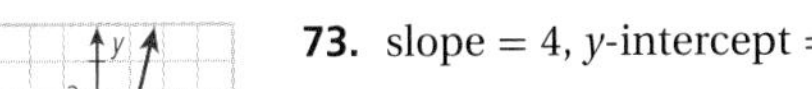

73. [graph]

74. [graph]

75. [graph]

Multiply. *(Lesson 7-8)*

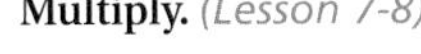

77. $(x - 4)^2$ $x^2 - 8x + 16$
78. $(x - 4)(x + 4)$ $x^2 - 16$
79. $(4 - t)^2$ $t^2 - 8t + 16$
80. $(2z + 3)^2$ $4z^2 + 12z + 9$
81. $(8b^2 - 2)(8b^2 + 2)$ $64b^4 - 4$
82. $(2x - 6)(2x + 6)$ $4x^2 - 36$

Solve using square roots. Check your answer. *(Lesson 9-6)*

83. $5x^2 = 5$ ± 1
84. $x^2 + 3 = 12$ ± 3
85. $5x^2 = 80$ ± 4
86. $9x^2 = 64$ $\pm\frac{8}{3}$
87. $25 + x^2 = 250$ ± 15
88. $64x^2 + 3 = 147$ $\pm\frac{3}{2}$

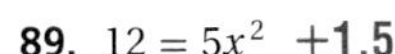

Solve. Round to the nearest hundredth. *(Lesson 9-6)*

89. $12 = 5x^2$ ± 1.55
90. $3x^2 - 4 = 15$ ± 2.52
91. $x^2 - 7 = 19$ ± 5.10
92. $6 + x^2 = 72$ ± 8.12
93. $10x^2 - 10 = 12$ ± 1.48
94. $2x^2 + 2 = 33$ ± 3.94

Teaching Tip

Multiple Choice In **Exercise 64,** explain to students that in this equation, *b* stands for *bx*, not the coefficient of *x*.

Explain that the best solution for the equation in **Exercise 65** is the value of *x* that makes the left side closest to zero.

Answers

70. Divide both terms by a:
$x^2 + \frac{b}{a}x$.
Then add half of $\frac{b}{a}$ squared:
$x^2 + \frac{b}{a}x + \left(\frac{b}{2a}\right)^2$.

76.

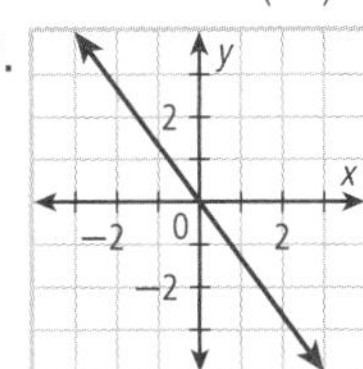

Journal

Have students explain what it means to complete the square.

ALTERNATIVE ASSESSMENT

Have students write an equation of the form $x^2 + bx = c$ that cannot be solved by factoring. Have them solve the equation by completing the square and justify each step.

Power Presentations with PowerPoint®

9-7 Lesson Quiz

Complete the square to form a perfect square trinomial.

1. $x^2 + 11x +$ ▢ $\frac{121}{4}$
2. $x^2 - 18x +$ ▢   81

Solve by completing the square.

3. $x^2 - 2x - 1 = 0$ $1 \pm \sqrt{2}$
4. $3x^2 + 6x = 144$ 6, −8
5. $4x^2 + 44x = 23$ $\frac{1}{2}, -\frac{23}{2}$
6. Dymond is painting a rectangular banner for a football game. She has enough paint to cover 120 ft². She wants the length of the banner to be 7 ft longer than the width. What dimensions should Dymond use for the banner? 8 ft by 15 ft

Also available on transparency

9-7 PROBLEM SOLVING

LESSON 9-7 Problem Solving
Completing the Square

The Ward family is redecorating several rooms of their house. Write the correct answer.

1. The Wards decided to use carpet tiles in the family room. The room has an area of 176 square feet and is 5 feet longer than it is wide. Find the dimensions of the family room.
11 ft by 16 ft

2. Angelique wants to have a rug that is 9 feet long and 7 feet wide in her bedroom. The rug will cover the whole floor except a border that is x feet wide. The area of her room is 167 square feet.
Find the width of the border, x. Round your answer to the nearest tenth of a foot.
2.5 ft

3. Giselle is going to frame a portrait of the family and place it on the mantle in the family room. The portrait is 10 inches longer than it is tall and will take up a total area of 1344 square inches once it is inside the 2 inch thick frame. Find the dimensions and area of the unframed portrait.
40 in. by 30 in.;
1200 square in.

Select the best answer.

4. The landing for the steps leading up to a county courthouse is shaped like a trapezoid. The area of the landing is 1500 square feet. The shorter base of the trapezoid is 15 feet longer than the height. The longer base is 5 feet longer than 3 times the height. What is the length of the longer base?
A 25 feet   **(C) 80 feet**
B 40 feet   D 95 feet

5. The height of a pumpkin launched from a cannon is given by the function $h = -16t^2 + 240t + 16$ where t is the time in seconds. How many seconds is the pumpkin in the air? Round your answer to the nearest tenth of a second.
F 7.5 seconds   H 16 seconds
(G) 15.1 seconds   J 32 seconds

6. Georgia works part-time at a daycare while she is going to college. She earned $160 last week. Georgia worked 12 more hours than the amount she is paid per hour. What is Georgia's hourly pay rate?
A $6.00   C $12.00
(B) $8.00   D $20.00

7. Part of the set for a play is a triangular piece of plywood. The area of the triangle is 20 square feet. The base is 3 feet longer than the height. What is the height of the triangle? Round your answer to the nearest tenth of a foot.
F 3 feet   H 3.9 feet
G 3.2 feet   **(J) 5 feet**

9-7 CHALLENGE

LESSON 9-7 Challenge
Using Coordinates of the Vertex to Explore X-intercepts

To write $y = x^2 - 7x + 3$ in the form $y = (x - h)^2 + k$, you could follow these steps.

$$y = x^2 - 7x + 3$$
$$y = x^2 - 7x + \left(\frac{-7}{2}\right)^2 + 3 - \left(\frac{-7}{2}\right)^2$$
$$y = \left(x - \frac{7}{2}\right)^2 + 3 - \frac{7^2}{4}$$

Notice that the number outside the parentheses has not been simplified; leaving it in this form will help you to see a pattern in the following exercises.

Use the method shown above to rewrite each function in the form $y = (x - h)^2 + k$.

1. $y = x^2 + 5x - 1$ $y = \left(x + \frac{5}{2}\right)^2 - 1 - \frac{5^2}{4}$
2. $y = x^2 - 11x + 6$ $y = \left(x - \frac{11}{2}\right)^2 + 6 - \frac{11^2}{4}$
3. $y = x^2 + bx + c$ $y = \left(x + \frac{b}{2}\right)^2 + c - \frac{b^2}{4}$

4. Recall that the vertex of the graph of $y = (x - h)^2 + k$ is at (h, k). Use your answer to Exercise 3 to give the coordinates of the vertex of the graph of $y = x^2 + bx + c$ in terms of b and c. $\left(\frac{-b}{2}, c - \frac{b^2}{4}\right)$

For Exercises 5–7, consider the parabola whose equation is $y = ax^2 + bx + c$.

5. How do you know that the graph of this parabola opens upward? $a > 0$

6. How does the y-coordinate of the vertex show whether the parabola crosses the x-axis? If the parabola opens upward and the y-coordinate of the vertex is greater than 0, then the parabola is completely above the x-axis. If it is less than 0, then the parabola crosses the x-axis at two points. If it is equal to 0, then the parabola touches the x-axis at one point.

7. How many x-intercepts does the graph of $y = x^2 + bx + c$ have if you know that
a. $c - \frac{b^2}{4} > 0$?   0
b. $c - \frac{b^2}{4} = 0$?   1
c. $c - \frac{b^2}{4} < 0$?   2

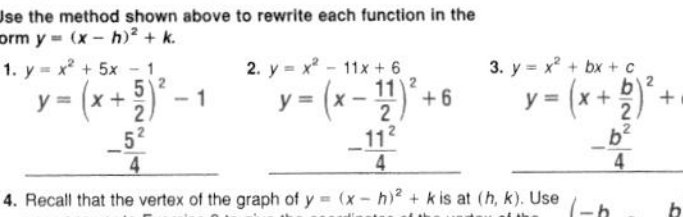

Use your answers to Exercises 4 and 7 to determine (a) the coordinates of the vertex and (b) the number of x-intercepts for each of the following functions.

8. $y = x^2 + 2x - 8$
a. (−1, −9)
b. 2

9. $y = x^2 - 9x + 18$
a. (4.5, −2.25)
b. 2

9-8 Organizer

Objective: Solve quadratic equations by using the Quadratic Formula.

Online Edition
Tutorial Videos

Countdown to Mastery Week 22

Power Presentations with PowerPoint®

Warm Up

Evaluate for $x = -2$, $y = 3$, and $z = -1$.

1. x^2 4 **2.** xyz 6

3. $x^2 - yz$ 7 **4.** $y - xz$ 1

5. $-x$ 2 **6.** $z^2 - xy$ 7

Also available on transparency

Math Humor

Q: What do you call a person who is crazy about solving quadratic equations?

A: A quadratic fanatic.

9-8 The Quadratic Formula

California Standards

19.0 Students know the quadratic formula and are familiar with its proof by completing the square.

20.0 Students use the quadratic formula to find the roots of a second-degree polynomial and **to solve quadratic equations.**

Why learn this?

You can use the Quadratic Formula to model the motion of objects, such as skipping stones. (See Exercise 62.)

In the previous lesson, you completed the square to solve quadratic equations. If you complete the square of $ax^2 + bx + c = 0$, you can derive the *Quadratic Formula.*

Numbers		Algebra
$2x^2 + 6x + 1 = 0$		$ax^2 + bx + c = 0, a \neq 0$
$\frac{2}{2}x^2 + \frac{6}{2}x + \frac{1}{2} = \frac{0}{2}$	*Divide both sides by a.*	$\frac{a}{a}x^2 + \frac{b}{a}x + \frac{c}{a} = \frac{0}{a}$
$x^2 + 3x + \frac{1}{2} = 0$		$x^2 + \frac{b}{a}x + \frac{c}{a} = 0$
$x^2 + 3x = -\frac{1}{2}$	*Subtract $\frac{c}{a}$ from both sides.*	$x^2 + \frac{b}{a}x = -\frac{c}{a}$
$x^2 + 3x + \left(\frac{3}{2}\right)^2 = -\frac{1}{2} + \left(\frac{3}{2}\right)^2$	*Complete the square.*	$x^2 + \frac{b}{a}x + \left(\frac{b}{2a}\right)^2 = -\frac{c}{a} + \left(\frac{b}{2a}\right)^2$
$\left(x + \frac{3}{2}\right)^2 = \frac{9}{4} - \frac{1}{2}$	*Factor and simplify.*	$\left(x + \frac{b}{2a}\right)^2 = \frac{b^2}{4a^2} - \frac{c}{a}$
$\left(x + \frac{3}{2}\right)^2 = \frac{9}{4} - \frac{2}{4}$	*Use common denominators.*	$\left(x + \frac{b}{2a}\right)^2 = \frac{b^2}{4a^2} - \frac{4ac}{4a^2}$
$\left(x + \frac{3}{2}\right)^2 = \frac{7}{4}$	*Simplify.*	$\left(x + \frac{b}{2a}\right)^2 = \frac{b^2 - 4ac}{4a^2}$
$x + \frac{3}{2} = \pm\frac{\sqrt{7}}{2}$	*Take square roots.*	$x + \frac{b}{2a} = \pm\frac{\sqrt{b^2 - 4ac}}{2a}$
$x = -\frac{3}{2} \pm \frac{\sqrt{7}}{2}$	*Subtract $\frac{b}{2a}$ from both sides.*	$x = -\frac{b}{2a} \pm \frac{\sqrt{b^2 - 4ac}}{2a}$
$x = \frac{-3 \pm \sqrt{7}}{2}$	*Simplify.*	$x = \frac{-b \pm \sqrt{b^2 - 4ac}}{2a}$

Remember!

To add or subtract fractions, you need a common denominator.

$$\frac{b^2}{4a^2} - \frac{c}{a} = \frac{b^2}{4a^2} - \frac{c}{a}\left(\frac{4a}{4a}\right) = \frac{b^2}{4a^2} - \frac{4ac}{4a^2} = \frac{b^2 - 4ac}{4a^2}$$

See Skills Bank p. SB8.

Know it! Note

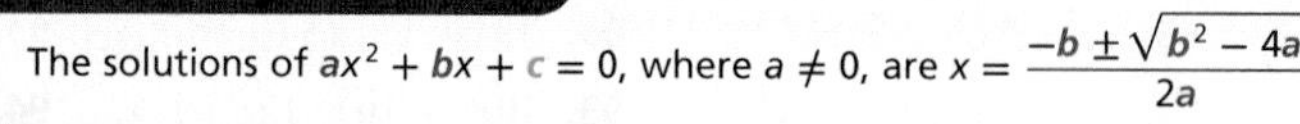

The Quadratic Formula

The solutions of $ax^2 + bx + c = 0$, where $a \neq 0$, are $x = \frac{-b \pm \sqrt{b^2 - 4ac}}{2a}$.

1 Introduce

EXPLORATION

9-8 The Quadratic Formula

You can use the standard form of a quadratic equation, $ax^2 + bx + c = 0$, to develop a formula for the solutions of any quadratic equation.

	$ax^2 + bx + c = 0$
1. Divide both sides by *a*.	$x^2 + \frac{b}{\square}x + \frac{c}{\square} = \square$
2. Subtract $\frac{c}{a}$ from both sides.	$x^2 + \frac{b}{\square}x = \square$
3. Complete the square.	$x^2 + \frac{b}{\square}x + \left(\square\right)^2 = \square + \left(\square\right)^2$
4. Factor the left side and simplify the right side.	$\left(x + \square\right)^2 = \frac{b^2}{4a^2} - \frac{c}{a}$
5. Use common denominators on the right side.	$\left(x + \square\right)^2 = \frac{b^2}{4a^2} - \frac{\square}{4a^2}$
6. Simplify the right side.	$\left(x + \square\right)^2 = \frac{b^2 - \square}{4a^2}$
7. Take the square root of both sides.	$x + \square = \pm\frac{\sqrt{\square - \square}}{2a}$
8. Subtract $\frac{b}{2a}$ from both sides.	$x = -\frac{b}{2a} \pm \frac{\sqrt{\square - \square}}{2a}$
9. Simplify.	$x = \frac{-b \pm \sqrt{b^2 - 4ac}}{2a}$

THINK AND DISCUSS

10. **Identify** the values of *a*, *b*, and *c* in $3x^2 - 4x - 12 = 0$.

11. Show how you can use the formula in Step 9, also known

Motivate

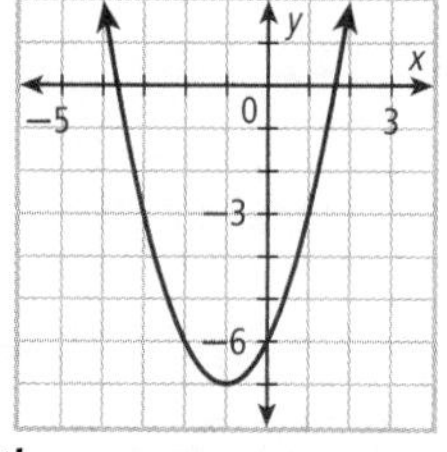

Have students graph $y = x^2 + 2x - 6$. Show students that the solutions of the related quadratic equation are not integers. Tell students they can find exact solutions to any quadratic equation by using the Quadratic Formula.

Explorations and answers are provided in *Alternate Openers: Explorations Transparencies.*

California Standards

Algebra 1 19.0, 20.0

EXAMPLE 1 **Using the Quadratic Formula**

Solve using the Quadratic Formula.

A $2x^2 + 3x - 5 = 0$

$2x^2 + 3x + (-5) = 0$ *Identify a, b, and c.*

$x = \dfrac{-b \pm \sqrt{b^2 - 4ac}}{2a}$ *Use the Quadratic Formula.*

$x = \dfrac{-3 \pm \sqrt{3^2 - 4(2)(-5)}}{2(2)}$ *Substitute 2 for a, 3 for b, and −5 for c.*

$x = \dfrac{-3 \pm \sqrt{9 - (-40)}}{4}$ *Simplify.*

$x = \dfrac{-3 \pm \sqrt{49}}{4} = \dfrac{-3 \pm 7}{4}$ *Simplify.*

$x = \dfrac{-3 + 7}{4}$ or $x = \dfrac{-3 - 7}{4}$ *Write as two equations.*

$x = 1$ or $x = -\dfrac{5}{2}$ *Solve each equation.*

Helpful Hint

You can graph the related quadratic function to see if your solutions are reasonable.

B $2x = x^2 - 3$

$1x^2 + (-2x) + (-3) = 0$ *Write in standard form.*

$x = \dfrac{-(-2) \pm \sqrt{(-2)^2 - 4(1)(-3)}}{2(1)}$ *Substitute 1 for a, −2 for b, and −3 for c.*

$x = \dfrac{2 \pm \sqrt{4 - (-12)}}{2}$ *Simplify.*

$x = \dfrac{2 \pm \sqrt{16}}{2} = \dfrac{2 \pm 4}{2}$ *Simplify.*

$x = \dfrac{2 + 4}{2}$ or $x = \dfrac{2 - 4}{2}$ *Write as two equations.*

$x = 3$ or $x = -1$ *Solve each equation.*

Solve using the Quadratic Formula. Check your answer.

1a. $-3x^2 + 5x + 2 = 0$ **$2, -\dfrac{1}{3}$** **1b.** $2 - 5x^2 = -9x$ **$2, -\dfrac{1}{5}$**

Because the Quadratic Formula contains a square root, the solutions may be irrational. You can give the exact solutions by leaving the square root in your answer, or you can approximate the solutions.

EXAMPLE 2 **Using the Quadratic Formula to Estimate Solutions**

Solve $x^2 - 2x - 4 = 0$ using the Quadratic Formula.

$x = \dfrac{-(-2) \pm \sqrt{(-2)^2 - 4(1)(-4)}}{2(1)}$

$x = \dfrac{2 \pm \sqrt{4 - (-16)}}{2} = \dfrac{2 \pm \sqrt{20}}{2}$

$x = \dfrac{2 + \sqrt{20}}{2}$ or $x = \dfrac{2 - \sqrt{20}}{2}$

Estimate $\sqrt{20}$: $x \approx 3.24$ or $x \approx -1.24$.

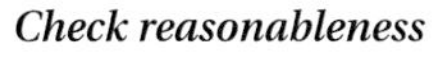

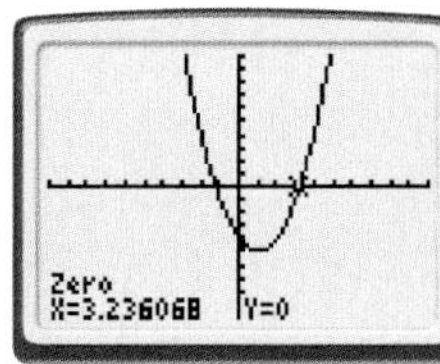

2. Solve $2x^2 - 8x + 1 = 0$ using the Quadratic Formula. **$\approx 0.13, \approx 3.87$**

COMMON ERROR ALERT

Students might make sign errors when using the Quadratic Formula. For example, they may make a mistake finding $-b$ when b is negative, or when subtracting $4ac$ when its value is negative. Encourage students to use parentheses when writing the formula:

$$x = \frac{-(b) \pm \sqrt{(b)^2 - 4(a)(c)}}{2(a)}$$

They can substitute the values of a, b, and c into the parentheses. If they are careful to then write down every step, this will reduce the likeliness of errors.

Power Presentations with PowerPoint®

Additional Examples

Example 1

Solve using the Quadratic Formula.

A. $6x^2 + 5x - 4 = 0$ $-\frac{4}{3}, \frac{1}{2}$

B. $x^2 = x + 20$ $-4, 5$

Example 2

Solve $x^2 + 3x - 7 = 0$ using the Quadratic Formula.

$\dfrac{-3 + \sqrt{37}}{2} \approx 1.54$,

$\dfrac{-3 - \sqrt{37}}{2} \approx -4.54$

Also available on transparency

2 Teach

Guided Instruction

Let students know that any quadratic equation can be solved by using the Quadratic Formula and it will always give exact solutions, but it may not always be the quickest method. Caution students to pay attention to signs when using the Quadratic Formula to avoid simple mistakes. It may be helpful for students to identify and write down the values of a, b, and c before substituting into the Quadratic Formula.

Universal Access

Through Auditory Cues

Help students remember the Quadratic Formula by singing it to the tune of "Row, Row, Row Your Boat" or "Pop Goes the Weasel."

x equals negative *b*
plus or minus square root
of *b* squared minus four *a c*
all over two *a*.

INTERVENTION

Questioning Strategies

EXAMPLES **1–2**

- How can you check your answer?
- Why is the symbol ± in the Quadratic Formula?
- Where does the Quadratic Formula come from?

Communicating Math Make sure students understand the difference between an exact solution and an approximation.

Power Presentations with PowerPoint®

Additional Examples

Example 3

Solve $x^2 - 9x + 20 = 0$. Use at least two different methods. Check your answer. 4, 5

Also available on transparency

INTERVENTION

Questioning Strategies

EXAMPLE 3

- Which of the methods for solving a quadratic equation give an exact answer every time? Explain.
- What are the advantages and disadvantages of each of the methods?

Inclusion To help prevent computational errors, some students find it helpful to circle everything after b^2 (including the subtraction sign), calculate that, and then add that answer to b^2.

For example,

$\sqrt{7^2 - 4(2)(-3)}$
$= \sqrt{49 + 24}$
$= \sqrt{73}$

Multiple Representations **Example 3** provides an opportunity to reinforce the connections between the solutions of a quadratic equation and the graph of its related function. Students should be able to explain that the number of solutions indicates the number of times the graph intersects the x-axis and that the x-value(s) of the intersection point(s) are equal to the solutions.

There is no one correct way to solve a quadratic equation. Many quadratic equations can be solved using several different methods: graphing, factoring, completing the square, using square roots, and using the Quadratic Formula.

EXAMPLE 3 Solving Using Different Methods

Solve $x^2 + 7x + 6 = 0$. Show your work.

Method 1 Solve by graphing.

$y = x^2 + 7x + 6$ — *Write the related quadratic function and graph it.*

The solutions are the x-intercepts, -6 and -1.

Method 2 Solve by factoring.

$x^2 + 7x + 6 = 0$

$(x + 6)(x + 1) = 0$ — *Factor.*

$x + 6 = 0$ or $x - 1 = 0$ — *Use the Zero Product Property.*

$x = -6$ or $x = -1$ — *Solve each equation.*

Method 3 Solve by completing the square.

$x^2 + 7x + 6 = 0$

$x^2 + 7x = -6$

$x^2 + 7x + \frac{49}{4} = -6 + \frac{49}{4}$ — *Add $\left(\frac{b}{2}\right)^2$ to both sides.*

$\left(x + \frac{7}{2}\right)^2 = \frac{25}{4}$ — *Factor and simplify.*

$x + \frac{7}{2} = \pm\frac{5}{2}$ — *Take the square root of both sides.*

$x + \frac{7}{2} = \frac{5}{2}$ or $x + \frac{7}{2} = -\frac{5}{2}$ — *Solve each equation.*

$x = -1$ or $x = -6$

Method 4 Solve using the Quadratic Formula.

$1x^2 + 7x + 6 = 0$ — *Identify a, b, and c.*

$x = \frac{-7 \pm \sqrt{7^2 - 4(1)(6)}}{2(1)}$ — *Substitute 1 for a, 7 for b, and 6 for c.*

$x = \frac{-7 \pm \sqrt{49 - 24}}{2}$ — *Simplify.*

$\frac{-7 \pm \sqrt{25}}{2}$

$\frac{-7 \pm 5}{2}$

$x = \frac{-7 + 5}{2}$ or $x = \frac{-7 - 5}{2}$ — *Write as two equations.*

$x = -1$ or $x = -6$ — *Solve each equation.*

Solve using at least two different methods. Check your answer.

3a. $x^2 + 7x + 10 = 0$ **−2, −5** **3b.** $-14 + x^2 = 5x$ **−2, 7** **3c.** $2x^2 + 4x - 21 = 0$ **≈ −4.39, ≈2.39**

Notice that all of the methods in Example 3 produce the same solutions, -1 and -6. The only method you cannot use to solve $x^2 + 7x + 6 = 0$ is using square roots. Sometimes one method is better for solving certain types of equations. The table below gives some advantages and disadvantages of the different methods.

Methods of Solving Quadratic Equations

METHOD	ADVANTAGES	DISADVANTAGES
Graphing	• Always works to give approximate solutions • Can quickly see the number of solutions	• Cannot always get an exact solution
Factoring	• Good method to try first • Straightforward if the equation is factorable	• Complicated if the equation is not easily factorable • Not all quadratic equations are factorable.
Using square roots	• Quick when the equation has no x-term	• Cannot easily use when there is an x-term
Completing the square	• Always works	• Sometimes involves difficult calculations
Using the Quadratic Formula	• Always works • Can always find exact solutions	• Other methods may be easier or less time consuming.

Student to Student

Solving Quadratic Equations

Binh Pham
Johnson High School

No matter what method I use, I like to check my answers for reasonableness by graphing.

I used the Quadratic Formula to solve $2x^2 - 7x - 10 = 0$. I found that $x \approx -1.09$ and $x \approx 4.59$. Then I graphed $y = 2x^2 - 7x - 10$. The x-intercepts appeared to be close to -1 and 4.5, so I knew my solutions were reasonable.

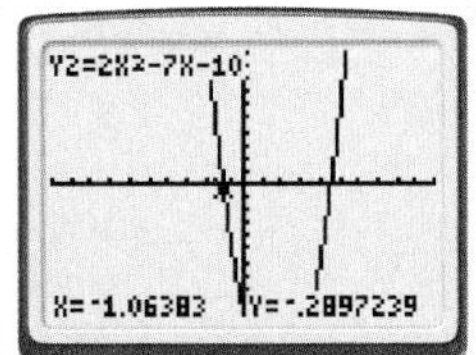

THINK AND DISCUSS

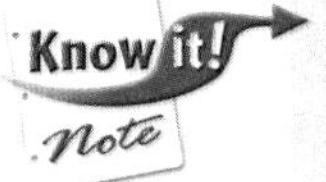

1. Choose a method to solve $x^2 + 5x + 4 = 0$ and explain why you chose that method.
2. **GET ORGANIZED** Copy and complete the graphic organizer. In each box, write the method you would use to solve each equation and explain why.

Equation	$x^2 + 5 = 20$	$x^2 + 6x + 9 = 0$	$3x^2 - 7 + 11 = 0$
Method			

3 Close

Summarize

Emphasize that all methods of solving a quadratic equation give the same answer. Tell students that the Quadratic Formula can be used to solve every equation, but other methods may be much simpler for given equations. They should learn to choose the most efficient method based on the equation.

FORMATIVE ASSESSMENT and INTERVENTION

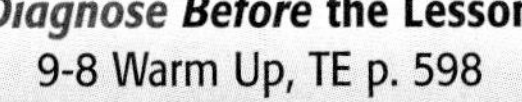

***Diagnose Before* the Lesson**
9-8 Warm Up, TE p. 598

***Monitor During* the Lesson**
Check It Out! Exercises, SE pp. 599–600
Questioning Strategies, TE pp. 599–600

***Assess After* the Lesson**
9-8 Lesson Quiz, TE p. 604
Alternative Assessment, TE p. 604

Answers to *Think and Discuss*

Possible answers:

1. $x = -1$ or $x = -4$, factoring method; least number of steps
2. See p. A8.

9-8 Exercises

Assignment Guide

Assign *Guided Practice* exercises as necessary.

If you finished Examples **1–3**

Proficient 19–48, 51, 53–62, 64–75, 78–89

Advanced 20–48 even, 49–52, 62, 63, 64–78 even, 79–89

Homework Quick Check
Quickly check key concepts.
Exercises: 20, 22, 26, 28, 32

Answers

34. $x^2 + 7 = 0; \varnothing$
35. $9x^2 - 12x + 4 = 0; x = \frac{2}{3}$
36. $x^2 - 16 = 0; x = \pm 4$
37. $2x^2 - 2x - 4 = 0; x = 2$ or $x = -1$
38. $x^2 - 2x - 8 = 0; x = 4$ or $x = -2$
39. $4x^2 + 7x - 2 = 0; x = \frac{1}{4}$ or $x = -2$
40. $4x^2 + 6x + 12 = 0; \varnothing$
41. $7.2x^2 + 3.6x = 0; x = 0$ or $x = -\frac{1}{2}$
42. $14x^2 - 6x + 6 = 0; \varnothing$

49. Possible answer: Check to see if the equation is a perfect square or if it can be quickly factored. If not, check if there is an x-term. If not, use square roots to solve. If there is an x-term, choose between completing the square or using the Quadratic Formula.

9-8 Exercises

California Standards Practice
19.0, 20.0, 23.0

go.hrw.com
Homework Help Online
KEYWORD: MA8CA 9-8
Parent Resources Online
KEYWORD: MA8CA Parent

GUIDED PRACTICE

SEE EXAMPLE 1 p. 599

Solve using the Quadratic Formula. Check your answer.

1. $x^2 - 5x + 4 = 0$ **1, 4**
2. $2x^2 = 7x - 3$ $\frac{1}{2}, 3$
3. $x^2 - 6x - 7 = 0$ **−1, 7**
4. $x^2 = -14x - 40$ **−4, −10**
5. $3x^2 - 2x = 8$ $-\frac{4}{3}, 2$
6. $4x^2 - 4x - 3 = 0$ $-\frac{1}{2}, \frac{3}{2}$

SEE EXAMPLE 2 p. 599

7. $2x^2 - 6 = 0$ $\approx \pm 1.73$
8. $x^2 + 6x + 3 = 0$ $\approx -5.45, \approx -0.55$
9. $x^2 - 7x + 2 = 0$ $\approx 0.30, \approx 6.70$
10. $3x^2 = -x + 5$ $\approx 1.14, \approx -1.47$
11. $x^2 - 4x - 7 = 0$ $\approx 5.32, \approx -1.32$
12. $2x^2 + x - 5 = 0$ $\approx -1.85, \approx 1.35$

SEE EXAMPLE 3 p. 600

Solve using at least two different methods. Check your answer.

13. $x^2 + x - 12 = 0$ **3, −4**
14. $x^2 + 6x + 9 = 0$ **−3**
15. $2x^2 - x - 1 = 0$ $-\frac{1}{2}, 1$
16. $4x^2 + 4x + 1 = 0$ $-\frac{1}{2}$
17. $2x^2 + 5x - 7 = 0$ $1, -\frac{7}{2}$
18. $9x = 2x^2 - 3x$ $\frac{3}{2}, -3$

PRACTICE AND PROBLEM SOLVING

Independent Practice	
For Exercises	See Example
19–21	1
22–24	2
25–33	3

Extra Practice
Skills Practice p. EP19
Application Practice p. EP32

Solve using the Quadratic Formula. Check your answer.

19. $3x^2 = 13x - 4$ $4, \frac{1}{3}$
20. $x^2 - 10x + 9 = 0$ **9, 1**
21. $1 = 3x^2 + 2x$ $\frac{1}{3}, -1$
22. $x^2 - 2x + 1 = 0$ **1**
23. $3x^2 - 5 = 0$ $\approx \pm 1.29$
24. $2x^2 + 6x = -4$ **−1, −2**

Solve using at least two different methods. Check your answer.

25. $x^2 + 4x + 3 = 0$ **−1, −3**
26. $x^2 + 2x = 15$ **3, −5**
27. $x^2 - 12 = -x$ **3, −4**
28. $x^2 - 6x = -9$ **3**
29. $x^2 + 12 = -7x$ **−3, −4**
30. $-x^2 + 81 = 0$ ± 9
31. $2x^2 + 7x + 6 = 0$ $-\frac{3}{2}, -2$
32. $3x^2 = 7 - 4x$ $1, -\frac{7}{3}$
33. $-7x = 12 + x^2$ **−3, −4**

Write each equation in standard form. Solve by using the Quadratic Formula. Check your answer.

34. $-7 = x^2$
35. $-12x = -9x^2 - 4$
36. $x^2 - 16 = 0$
37. $2x = -4 + 2x^2$
38. $x^2 = 2x + 8$
39. $2 = 7x + 4x^2$
40. $12 + 6x = -4x^2$
41. $7.2x^2 = -3.6x$
42. $6x = 14x^2 + 6$

Use the Quadratic Formula to find the x-intercepts. Check your answer.

43. $y + 21 = 2x^2 - x$ $\frac{7}{2}, -3$
44. $y = 5x^2 + 12x + 8$ **no x-intercepts**
45. $y = x^2 - 10x + 25$ **5**
46. $y = 3x^2 - 4x - 20$ $\frac{10}{3}, -2$
47. $y + 2x^2 = 9x + 18$ $-\frac{3}{2}, 6$
48. $y = 5x^2 - 8x - 4$ $2, -\frac{2}{5}$

49. **Write About It** Explain how you would decide which method to try first when solving a quadratic equation.

50. **Reasoning** Explain why the Quadratic Formula will not work for a function in the form $y = mx + b$. **Possible answer: If $a = 0$, then it is not a quadratic equation. Using the Quadratic Formula will result in zero in the denominator.**

9-8 READING STRATEGIES

LESSON 9-8 **Reading Strategies**
Follow a Procedure

The example shows the steps you should use to solve a quadratic equation with the Quadratic Formula.

Solve $x^2 - 4x = 21$ using the Quadratic Formula.

$x^2 - 4x = 21$
$x^2 - 4x - 21 = 0$ — **Step 1**: Write the equation in the form $ax^2 + bx + c = 0$.
$a = 1, b = -4, c = -21$ — **Step 2**: Identify a, b, and c.
$x = \frac{-b \pm \sqrt{b^2 - 4ac}}{2a}$
$x = \frac{-(-4) \pm \sqrt{(-4)^2 - 4(1)(-21)}}{2(1)}$ — **Step 3**: Substitute the values of a, b, and c in the Quadratic Formula.
$x = \frac{4 \pm \sqrt{16 + 84}}{2}$
$x = \frac{4 \pm \sqrt{100}}{2}$ — **Step 4**: Simplify.
$x = \frac{4 \pm 10}{2}$
$x = \frac{4 + 10}{2}$ or $x = \frac{4 - 10}{2}$ — **Step 5**: Write two equations.
$x = 7$ or $x = -3$ — **Step 6**: Solve each equation.

Solve each equation using the Quadratic Formula.

1. $x^2 + 8x - 9 = 0$ **1, −9**
2. $x^2 + 11x = -30$ **−5, −6**
3. $2x^2 + 7x - 4 = 0$ $\frac{1}{2}$ or -4
4. $3x^2 - 5x = 2$ $-\frac{1}{3}, 2$

9-8 REVIEW FOR MASTERY

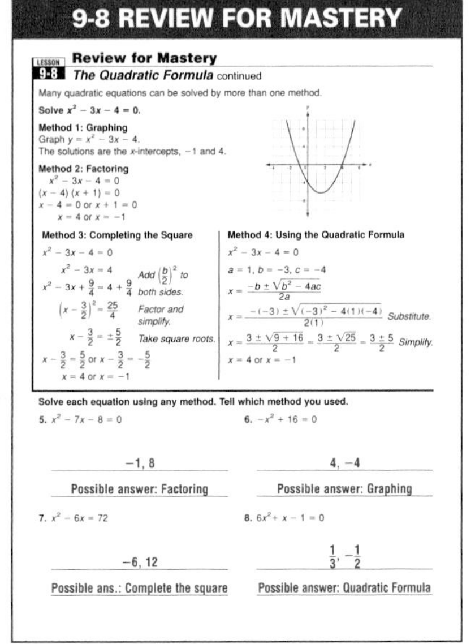

LESSON 9-8 **Review for Mastery**
The Quadratic Formula continued

Many quadratic equations can be solved by more than one method.

Solve $x^2 - 3x - 4 = 0$.

Method 1: Graphing
Graph $y = x^2 - 3x - 4$.
The solutions are the x-intercepts, −1 and 4.

Method 2: Factoring
$x^2 - 3x - 4 = 0$
$(x - 4)(x + 1) = 0$
$x - 4 = 0$ or $x + 1 = 0$
$x = 4$ or $x = -1$

Method 3: Completing the Square
$x^2 - 3x - 4 = 0$
$x^2 - 3x = 4$ — Add $\left(\frac{b}{2}\right)^2$ to both sides.
$x^2 - 3x + \frac{9}{4} = 4 + \frac{9}{4}$
$\left(x - \frac{3}{2}\right)^2 = \frac{25}{4}$ — Factor and simplify.
$x - \frac{3}{2} = \pm\frac{5}{2}$ — Take square roots.
$x - \frac{3}{2} = \frac{5}{2}$ or $x - \frac{3}{2} = -\frac{5}{2}$
$x = 4$ or $x = -1$

Method 4: Using the Quadratic Formula
$x^2 - 3x - 4 = 0$
$a = 1, b = -3, c = -4$
$x = \frac{-b \pm \sqrt{b^2 - 4ac}}{2a}$
$x = \frac{-(-3) \pm \sqrt{(-3)^2 - 4(1)(-4)}}{2(1)}$ Substitute.
$x = \frac{3 \pm \sqrt{9 + 16}}{2} = \frac{3 \pm \sqrt{25}}{2} = \frac{3 \pm 5}{2}$ Simplify.
$x = 4$ or $x = -1$

Solve each equation using any method. Tell which method you used.

5. $x^2 - 7x - 8 = 0$ **−1, 8** Possible answer: Factoring
6. $-x^2 + 16 = 0$ **4, −4** Possible answer: Graphing
7. $x^2 - 6x = 72$ **−6, 12** Possible ans.: Complete the square
8. $6x^2 + x - 1 = 0$ $\frac{1}{3}, -\frac{1}{2}$ Possible answer: Quadratic Formula

California Standards

Standard	Exercises
4.0	78–80
5.0	78–80
11.0	81–83
14.0	84–89
19.0	1–12, 19–24, 34–48, 51, 63–77
20.0	1–12, 19–24, 34–42, 51, 64–77
23.0	51, 52, 62, 70, 76, 77

CONCEPT CONNECTION

51. This problem will prepare you for the Concept Connection on page 610.
The equation $0 = -14t^2 + 65t + 25$ gives the time t when a golf ball is at height 0.
   a. Can you solve the equation by graphing?
   b. Can you solve the equation by using square roots? **b. No; the term $65t$ makes it difficult to use square roots.**
   c. Solve the quadratic equation using the Quadratic Formula. **$\approx -0.36, 5$**
   d. Explain why the Quadratic Formula is the best method to use for this equation.
d. Possible answer: the Quadratic Formula gave the most precise answer in the shortest amount of time.

52. **Physical Science** The distance in feet d traveled by an object with acceleration a in t seconds is given by the equation $d = \frac{1}{2}at^2$. If an object travels 64 ft with an acceleration of 32 ft/s^2, for how much time did it travel? **2 s**

For each quadratic equation, identify the values of *a*, *b*, and *c*.

53. $x^2 + x = -7$
54. $-5x^2 - 17 = 0$
55. $10x^2 + 2 - 17x = 0$
56. $16x^2 = 3x$
57. $1.5x + 3.7 = -0.5x^2$
58. $x^2 = 8 - 3x$
59. $\frac{1}{2}x^2 + 1 = -\frac{3}{4}x$
60. $-4x^2 = -9$
61. $-24x^2 + 13 = 29x$

62. **Multi-Step** Burke skips 3 stones over water. The height in centimeters h of each stone during its first skip can be modeled by a different quadratic function, as shown in the table, where s represents the number of milliseconds after the stone first hits the water. Use the table to find the length of time each stone was in the air during its first skip. Which stone was in the air the longest? **stone 1: 1.25 s; stone 2: 1 s; stone 3: 1.2 s; stone 1**

Stone	Quadratic Function
1	$-0.4s^2 + 0.5s = h$
2	$-0.3s^2 + 0.3s = h$
3	$-0.5s^2 + 0.6s = h$

63. **Critical Thinking** When using the Quadratic Formula to solve a quadratic equation in the form $ax^2 + bx + c$, explain what will happen when b^2 is less than $4ac$ and $4ac$ is positive.
Possible answer: the term under the square root sign will be negative.

Choose a method to solve each equation. Explain why you chose the method you did.

64. $-2 = x^2 + 3x$ **$-1, -2$**
65. $x^2 + 2x = 6 - 3x^2$ **$1, -\frac{3}{2}$**
66. $2x^2 - 3x = 8$ **$\approx 2.89, \approx -1.39$**
67. $-3x^2 - 8x + 1 = -10x$ **$-\frac{1}{3}, 1$**
68. $4x - 3x^2 + x = -8$ **$-1, \frac{8}{3}$**
69. $2x^2 + 9 = 15$ **$\pm\sqrt{3}$**

70. **Sports** A soccer player kicks a ball off the ground. The height of the ball can be modeled by the quadratic function $-0.5s^2 + 3s = h$, where s is the time in seconds after the kick and h is the height of the ball in feet.
   a. Find the maximum height of the ball. **4.5 ft**
   b. How long is the ball in the air? **6 s**
   c. Find the height of the ball after 2 seconds. **4 ft**
   d. How long would the ball be in the air if the ball was kicked from a platform 0.5 ft above the ground? Round your answer to the nearest tenth of a second. (*Hint:* In this situation, the function $-0.5s^2 + 3s + 0.5 = h$ models the height.) **6.2 s**

California LINK

Sports

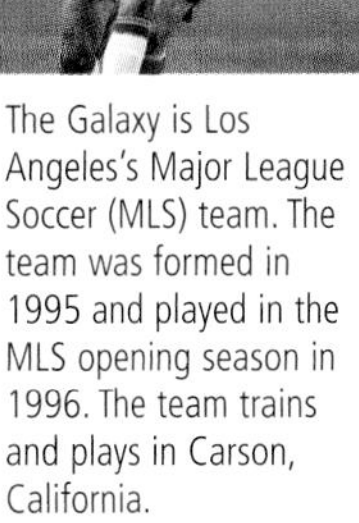

The Galaxy is Los Angeles's Major League Soccer (MLS) team. The team was formed in 1995 and played in the MLS opening season in 1996. The team trains and plays in Carson, California.

CONCEPT CONNECTION **Exercise 51** involves solving a quadratic equation to solve a projectile problem. This exercise prepares students for the Concept Connection on page 610.

Answers

51a. No; the solutions cannot be easily and precisely determined by graphing.

53–61. Possible answers given.

53. $a = 1, b = 1, c = 7$
54. $a = 5, b = 0, c = 17$
55. $a = 10, b = -17, c = 2$
56. $a = 16, b = -3, c = 0$
57. $a = 0.5, b = 1.5, c = 3.7$
58. $a = 1, b = 3, c = -8$
59. $a = \frac{1}{2}, b = \frac{3}{4}, c = 1$
60. $a = 4, b = 0, c = -9$
61. $a = 24, b = 29, c = -13$

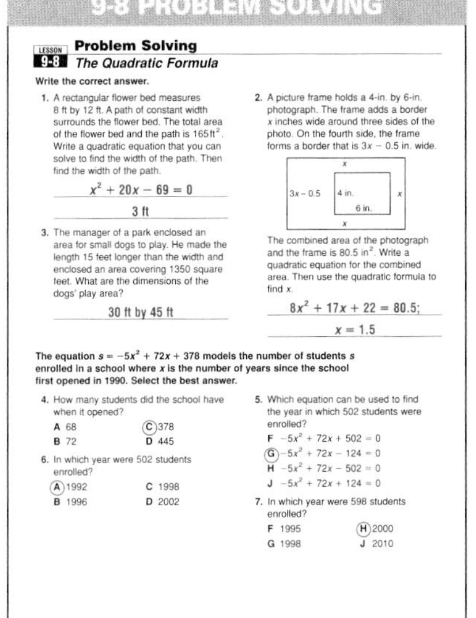

9-8 PROBLEM SOLVING

LESSON 9-8 **Problem Solving**
The Quadratic Formula

Write the correct answer.

1. A rectangular flower bed measures 8 ft by 12 ft. A path of constant width surrounds the flower bed. The total area of the flower bed and the path is 165 ft^2. Write a quadratic equation that you can solve to find the width of the path. Then find the width of the path.
$x^2 + 20x - 69 = 0$
3 ft

2. A picture frame holds a 4-in. by 6-in. photograph. The frame adds a border x inches wide around three sides of the photo. On the fourth side, the frame forms a border that is $3x - 0.5$ in. wide.

The combined area of the photograph and the frame is 80.5 in^2. Write a quadratic equation for the combined area. Then use the quadratic formula to find x.
$8x^2 + 17x + 22 = 80.5$;
$x = 1.5$

3. The manager of a park enclosed an area for small dogs to play. He made the length 15 feet longer than the width and enclosed an area covering 1350 square feet. What are the dimensions of the dogs' play area?
30 ft by 45 ft

The equation $s = -5x^2 + 72x + 378$ models the number of students s enrolled in a school where x is the number of years since the school first opened in 1990. Select the best answer.

4. How many students did the school have when it opened?
A 68 (C) 378
B 72 D 445

5. Which equation can be used to find the year in which 502 students were enrolled?
F $-5x^2 + 72x + 502 = 0$
(G) $-5x^2 + 72x - 124 = 0$
H $-5x^2 + 72x - 502 = 0$
J $-5x^2 + 72x + 124 = 0$

6. In which year were 502 students enrolled?
(A) 1992 C 1998
B 1996 D 2002

7. In which year were 598 students enrolled?
F 1995 (H) 2000
G 1998 J 2010

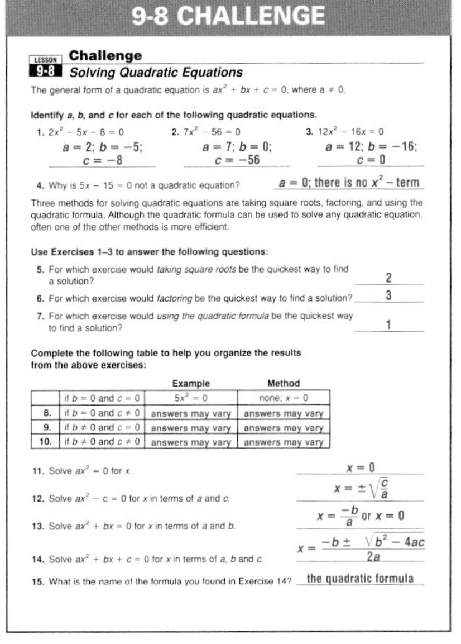

9-8 CHALLENGE

LESSON 9-8 **Challenge**
Solving Quadratic Equations

The general form of a quadratic equation is $ax^2 + bx + c = 0$, where $a \neq 0$.

Identify *a*, *b*, and *c* for each of the following quadratic equations.

1. $2x^2 - 5x - 8 = 0$ $a = 2; b = -5; c = -8$
2. $7x^2 - 56 = 0$ $a = 7; b = 0; c = -56$
3. $12x^2 - 16x = 0$ $a = 12; b = -16; c = 0$
4. Why is $5x - 15 = 0$ not a quadratic equation? $a = 0$; there is no x^2 – term

Three methods for solving quadratic equations are taking square roots, factoring, and using the quadratic formula. Although the quadratic formula can be used to solve any quadratic equation, often one of the other methods is more efficient.

Use Exercises 1–3 to answer the following questions:

5. For which exercise would *taking square roots* be the quickest way to find a solution? 2
6. For which exercise would *factoring* be the quickest way to find a solution? 3
7. For which exercise would *using the quadratic formula* be the quickest way to find a solution? 1

Complete the following table to help you organize the results from the above exercises:

		Example	Method
	if $b = 0$ and $c = 0$	$5x^2 = 0$	none; $x = 0$
8.	if $b = 0$ and $c \neq 0$	answers may vary	answers may vary
9.	if $b \neq 0$ and $c = 0$	answers may vary	answers may vary
10.	if $b \neq 0$ and $c \neq 0$	answers may vary	answers may vary

11. Solve $ax^2 = 0$ for x. $x = 0$
12. Solve $ax^2 - c = 0$ for x in terms of a and c. $x = \pm\sqrt{\frac{c}{a}}$
13. Solve $ax^2 + bx = 0$ for x in terms of a and b. $x = \frac{-b}{a}$ or $x = 0$
14. Solve $ax^2 + bx + c = 0$ for x in terms of a, b and c. $x = \frac{-b \pm \sqrt{b^2 - 4ac}}{2a}$
15. What is the name of the formula you found in Exercise 14? the quadratic formula

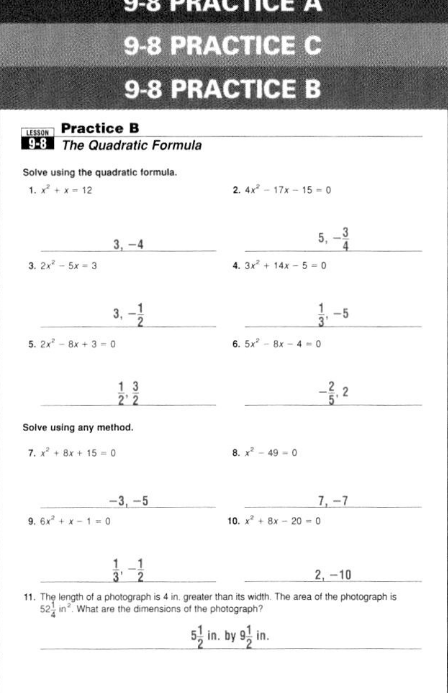

9-8 PRACTICE A
9-8 PRACTICE C
9-8 PRACTICE B

LESSON 9-8 **Practice B**
The Quadratic Formula

Solve using the quadratic formula.

1. $x^2 + x = 12$ $3, -4$
2. $4x^2 - 17x - 15 = 0$ $5, -\frac{3}{4}$
3. $2x^2 - 5x = 3$ $3, -\frac{1}{2}$
4. $3x^2 + 14x - 5 = 0$ $\frac{1}{3}, -5$
5. $2x^2 - 8x + 3 = 0$ $\frac{1}{2}, \frac{3}{2}$
6. $5x^2 - 8x - 4 = 0$ $-\frac{2}{5}, 2$

Solve using any method.

7. $x^2 + 8x + 15 = 0$ $-3, -5$
8. $x^2 - 49 = 0$ $7, -7$
9. $6x^2 + x - 1 = 0$ $\frac{1}{3}, -\frac{1}{2}$
10. $x^2 + 8x - 20 = 0$ $2, -10$
11. The length of a photograph is 4 in. greater than its width. The area of the photograph is $52\frac{1}{4}$ in^2. What are the dimensions of the photograph? $5\frac{1}{2}$ in. by $9\frac{1}{2}$ in.

Multiple Choice In **Exercise 74,** remind students that the first value in the Quadratic Formula is $-b$. We can see from the given solution that the value of b must be 5, so choices **B** and **C** can be eliminated.

Answers

76. Area of pen $= 40w - w^2$; the width and length are each 20 yd.
77. Yes; the three boundaries can be represented by x, $2x$, and $1000 - 3x$. The area is $\frac{1}{2}(2x)(x + 1000 - 3x)$, or $-2x^2 + 1000x$. So $-2x^2 + 1000x = 125{,}000$. Rewrite in standard form: $2x^2 - 1000x + 125{,}000 = 0$. The discriminant is 0, so there is exactly one solution.

Journal

Have students write about their preferred method of solving quadratic equations. Have them describe its advantages and disadvantages.

ALTERNATIVE ASSESSMENT

Have students write a quadratic equation. Have them use the Quadratic Formula to find the solution(s), if any exist. If there are no solutions, have them explain what this means.

Power Presentations with PowerPoint®

9-8 Lesson Quiz

1. Solve $x^2 + x = 12$ by using the Quadratic Formula. 3, −4
2. Solve $-3x^2 + 5x = 1$ by using the Quadratic Formula. $\approx 0.23, \approx 1.43$
3. Solve $8x^2 - 13x - 6 = 0$. Use at least two different methods. $2, -\frac{3}{8}$

Also available on transparency

71. **Business** The total profit p made by a manufacturing company is given by the equation $p = x^2 - x - 56$, where x is the number of items produced. Find the number of items the company needs to make to break even. **8**

72. On page 598, the equation $2x^2 + 6x + 1 = 0$ is solved by completing the square in order to show a specific example of the Quadratic Formula. Solve the equation $x^2 + 3x - 1 = 0$ in a similar manner. **Check students' work;** $\frac{-3 \pm \sqrt{13}}{2}$

Multiple Choice For Exercises 73–75, choose the best answer.

73. Which are the best approximations for the solutions of $x^2 + 6x - 14 = 0$?
    - (A) $\approx 7.1, \approx -1.4$
    - (B) $\approx 6.2, \approx 2.3$
    - (C) $\approx 1.8, \approx -7.8$
    - (D) $\approx 2.4, \approx -6.7$

74. Which quadratic equation has the solutions $x = \frac{-5 \pm \sqrt{25 - 56}}{4}$?
    - (A) $2x^2 + 5x + 6 = 0$
    - (B) $5x^2 + 2x + 7 = 0$
    - (C) $7x^2 + 2x + 5 = 0$
    - (D) $2x^2 + 5x + 7 = 0$

75. For which two consecutive integers is the following statement true?
    3 times the square of the first integer is equal to 7 more than 5 and the product of the second integer.
    - (A) 3, 4
    - (B) 5, 6
    - (C) 11, 12
    - (D) 8, 9

CHALLENGE AND EXTEND

76. **Agriculture** A rancher has 80 yards of fencing material to build a rectangular pen. Let w represent the width of the pen and write an equation giving the area of the pen. Find the dimensions of the pen when the area is 400 square yards.

77. **Agriculture** A farmer wants to make a four-sided grazing area using an existing fence for one side. His proposed grazing area is shown in the diagram. He has 1000 feet of fencing material available and he wants the western boundary of the grazing area to be twice as long as the northern boundary. Can he enclose a grazing area of 125,000 square feet? Explain why or why not. (*Hint:* Use the formula for the area of a trapezoid.)

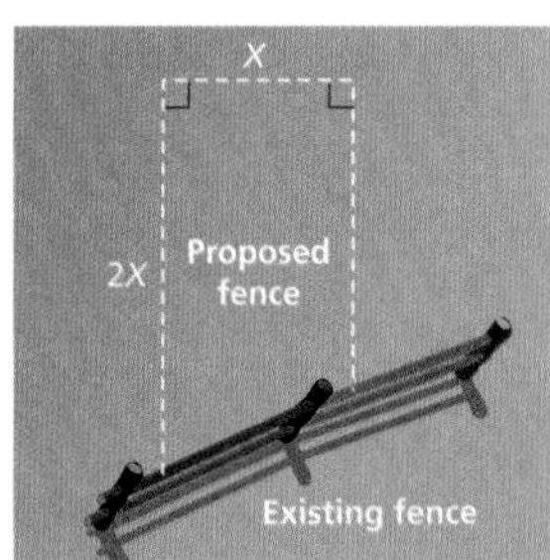

SPIRAL STANDARDS REVIEW

4.0, 5.0, 11.0, 14.0

Solve each inequality. Check your answer. (Lesson 3-5)

78. $3(3 - x) \geq 9$ $x \leq 0$
79. $2(x + 4) \geq 3x$ $x \leq 8$
80. $3(x + 5) > 4(x + 4)$ $x < -1$

Factor each polynomial by grouping. (Lesson 8-2)

81. $s^2r^3 + 5r^3 + 5t + s^2t$ $(r^3 + t)(s^2 + 5)$
82. $b^3 - 4b^2 + 2b - 8$ $(b^2 + 2)(b - 4)$
83. $n^5 - 6n^4 - 2n + 12$ $(n^4 - 2)(n - 6)$

Solve by completing the square. Check your answer. (Lesson 9-7)

84. $x^2 - 2x - 24 = 0$ **−4, 6**
85. $x^2 + 6x = 40$ **−10, 4**
86. $-3x^2 + 12x = 15$ ∅
87. $2x^2 + 10x = 12$ **−6, 1**
88. $3x^2 - 18x + 15 = 0$ **5, 1**
89. $4x^2 - 16x = 20$ **5, −1**

9-9 The Discriminant

California Standards

22.0 Students use the quadratic formula or factoring techniques or both **to determine whether the graph of a quadratic function will intersect the x-axis in zero, one, or two points.**

23.0 Students apply quadratic equations to physical problems, such as the motion of an object under the force of gravity.

Vocabulary
discriminant

Why learn this?

You can use the discriminant to determine whether the weight in a carnival strength test will reach a certain height. (See Example 3.)

Recall that quadratic equations can have two, one, or no real solutions. You can determine the number of solutions by evaluating the *discriminant.* If a quadratic equation is in standard form, its **discriminant** is $b^2 - 4ac$. Notice that this is the expression under the square root in the Quadratic Formula.

Equation	$x^2 - 4x + 3 = 0$	$x^2 + 2x + 1 = 0$	$x^2 - 2x + 2 = 0$
Graph of Related Function	The related function has two x-intercepts. 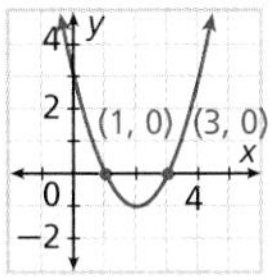 (graph: intercepts (1, 0), (3, 0))	The related function has one x-intercept. 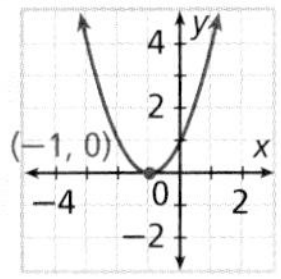 (graph: intercept (−1, 0))	The related function has no x-intercepts. 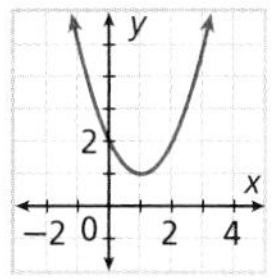
Discriminant	$a = 1, b = -4, c = 3$ $b^2 - 4ac =$ $(-4)^2 - 4(1)(3) = 4$ $b^2 - 4ac > 0$	$a = 1, b = 2, c = 1$ $b^2 - 4ac =$ $2^2 - 4(1)(1) = 0$ $b^2 - 4ac = 0$	$a = 1, b = -2, c = 2$ $b^2 - 4ac =$ $(-2)^2 - 4(1)(2) = -4$ $b^2 - 4ac < 0$
Number of Solutions	When $b^2 - 4ac$ is positive, it has two square roots. The Quadratic Formula gives two solutions.	When $b^2 - 4ac$ is 0, it has one square root. The Quadratic Formula gives one solution.	When $b^2 - 4ac$ is negative, it has no real square roots. The Quadratic Formula gives no real solutions.

Know it! Note

The Discriminant of $ax^2 + bx + c = 0$

If $b^2 - 4ac > 0$, the equation has **two** real solutions.
If $b^2 - 4ac = 0$, the equation has **one** real solution.
If $b^2 - 4ac < 0$, the equation has **no** real solutions.

EXAMPLE 1 Using the Discriminant

Find the number of solutions of $3x^2 + 10x + 2 = 0$.

$a = 3, b = 10, c = 2$ *Identify the values of a, b, and c.*

$b^2 - 4ac = 10^2 - 4(3)(2)$ *Substitute 3, 10, and 2 for a, b, and c.*

$= 100 - 24 = 76$ *Simplify.*

$b^2 - 4ac$ is positive. There are two solutions.

1 Introduce

EXPLORATION

9-9 The Discriminant

Use a calculator to explore quadratic equations of the form $ax^2 + bx + c = 0$.

1. Graph the related function for each of the quadratic equations in the table to determine how many real solutions each equation has. Then complete the table as shown.

Quadratic Equation	Number of Real Solutions	a	b	c	$b^2 - 4ac$	Is $b^2 - 4ac$ positive, negative, or zero?
$x^2 + 2x - 8 = 0$	2	1	2	−8	36	Positive
$x^2 - 8x + 16 = 0$						
$x^2 + 6x + 11 = 0$						
$2x^2 + 3x + 3 = 0$						
$4x^2 - 8x + 3 = 0$						
$4x^2 + 4x + 1 = 0$						

2. Look for a relationship between the number of real solutions and the value of $b^2 - 4ac$. What do you notice?

THINK AND DISCUSS

3. **Discuss** what you can conclude about a quadratic equation for which $b^2 - 4ac > 0$.
4. **Explain** what you know about the value of $b^2 - 4ac$ for a quadratic equation that has exactly one real solution.

Motivate

In this lesson, students will learn how to tell the number of solutions of a quadratic equation without graphing or solving. Point out to students that this information may make solving the equation simpler. For example, if there are no real solutions, you do not have to solve. If there is one solution, then the equation is factorable, and factoring can be used to solve.

Explorations and answers are provided in *Alternate Openers: Explorations Transparencies.*

9-9 Organizer

Objective: Determine the number of solutions of a quadratic equation by using the discriminant.

Online Edition
Tutorial Videos

Countdown to Mastery Week 22

Power Presentations with PowerPoint®

Warm Up

Use the Quadratic Formula to solve each equation.

1. $x^2 - 5x - 6 = 0$ −1, 6
2. $2x^2 + 2x - 24 = 0$ 3, −4
3. $x^2 - 10x + 25 = 0$ 5

Also available on transparency

Math Humor

Parent: What did you learn in school today?

Student: We learned about negative discriminants. It was unreal.

California Standards

Algebra 1 22.0, 23.0

Power Presentations with PowerPoint®

Additional Examples

Example 1

Find the number of solutions of each equation.

A. $3x^2 - 2x + 2 = 0$ no real solutions

B. $2x^2 + 11x + 12 = 0$ 2 solutions

C. $x^2 + 8x + 16 = 0$ 1 solution

Example 2

Find the number of x-intercepts of each function by using the discriminant.

A. $y = 2x^2 - 9x + 5$ 2

B. $y = 6x^2 - 4x + 5$ 0

Example 3

The ringer on a carnival strength test is 2 feet off the ground and is shot upward with an initial velocity of 30 feet per second. Will it reach a height of 20 feet? Use the discriminant to explain your answer. The discr. is neg., so there are no real solutions. The ringer will not reach 20 ft.

Also available on transparency

INTERVENTION

Questioning Strategies

EXAMPLE 1

- What part of the Quadratic Formula does the discriminant come from?
- Explain why the value of the discriminant indicates the number of solutions.

EXAMPLE 2

- Why does the discriminant tell you the number of x-intercepts?
- How can you use a graph to verify your answer?

EXAMPLE 3

- How do you use the given velocity in the Quadratic Formula?
- How do you use the given heights in the Quadratic Formula?

Find the number of solutions of each equation.

1a. $2x^2 - 2x + 3 = 0$ **0** **1b.** $x^2 + 4x + 4 = 0$ **1**

Recall that the solutions to a quadratic equation are the same as the x-intercepts of the related function. The discriminant can be used to find the number of x-intercepts.

EXAMPLE  **Using the Discriminant to Find the Number of x-Intercepts**

Find the number of x-intercepts of $y = 2x^2 + x + 1$ by using the discriminant.

$a = 2, b = 1, c = 1$ *Identify the values of a, b, and c.*

$b^2 - 4ac = 1^2 - 4(2)(1)$ *Substitute 2, 1, and 1 for a, b, and c.*

$= 1 - 8$ *Simplify.*

$= -7$

$b^2 - 4ac$ is negative.

There are no real solutions.

Therefore, the function $y = x^2 + x + 1$ has no x-intercepts. You can check by graphing. Notice that the graph does not intersect the x-axis.

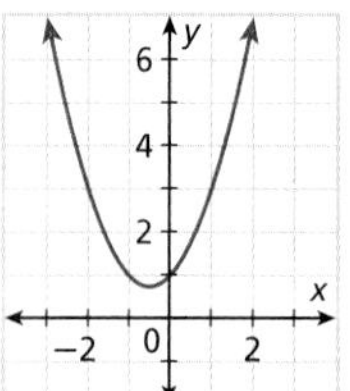

Find the number of x-intercepts of each function by using the discriminant.

2a. $y = 5x^2 + 3x + 1$ **0** **2b.** $y = x^2 - 9x + 4$ **2**

EXAMPLE  ***Physical Science Application***

The height h in feet of an object shot straight up with initial velocity v in feet per second is given by $h = -16t^2 + vt + c$, where c is the beginning height of the object above the ground.

A weight 1 foot above the ground on a carnival strength test is shot straight up with an initial velocity of 35 feet per second. Will it reach a height of 20 feet? Use the discriminant to explain your answer.

Helpful Hint

If the object is shot straight up from the ground, the initial height of the object above the ground equals 0.

$h = -16t^2 + vt + 1$

$20 = -16t^2 + 35t + 1$ *Substitute 20 for h, 35 for v, and 1 for c.*

$0 = -16t^2 + 35t + (-19)$ *Write the equation in standard form by subtracting 20 from both sides.*

$b^2 - 4ac$ *Evaluate the discriminant.*

$35^2 - 4(-16)(-19) = 9$ *Substitute −16 for a, 35 for b, and −19 for c.*

The discriminant is positive, so the equation has two solutions. In other words, there are two times t when the height h is 20. The weight will reach a height of 20 feet twice, once on the way up and once on the way down.

3. What if...? Suppose the weight is shot straight up from the ground with an initial velocity of 20 feet per second. Will it reach a height of 45 feet? Use the discriminant to explain your answer.

3. No; for the equation $45 = -16t^2 + 20t + 0$, the discriminant is negative, so the weight will not ring the bell.

2 Teach

Guided Instruction

Ensure that students understand how the discriminant determines the number of solutions of a quadratic equation. It may be helpful to have students identify the values of a, b, and c before evaluating the discriminant.

After **Example 2,** be sure students understand the connection between the x-intercepts (or zeros) of a quadratic function and the solutions of the related equation before moving on.

 Close

Summarize

Ask students to give a, b, and c for the following quadratic equations. Then use the discriminant to find the number of solutions.

- $x^2 + 3x = -7$ $a = 1, b = 3, c = 7$; no real solutions
- $3x^2 = 5x + 10$ $a = 3, b = -5, c = -10$; 2 solutions
- $12x + 2 = -18x^2$ $a = 18, b = 12, c = 2$; 1 solution

THINK AND DISCUSS

1. Describe how to use the discriminant to find the number of solutions to a quadratic equation.
2. Describe how the discriminant can be used to determine if an object will reach a given height.

3. **GET ORGANIZED** Copy and complete the graphic organizer. In each box, write the number of real solutions.

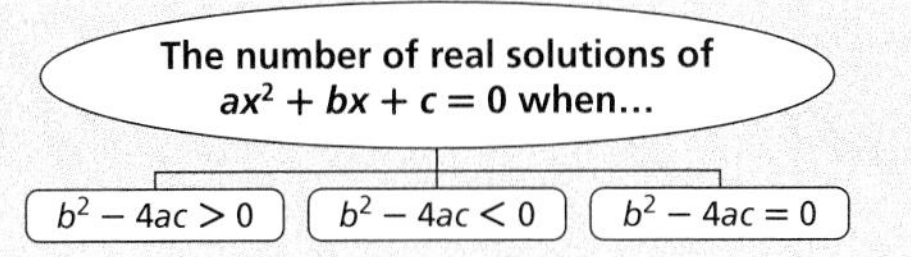

Answers to *Think and Discuss*

Possible answers:

1. If $b^2 - 4ac > 0$, there are 2 real solutions. If $b^2 - 4ac = 0$, there is 1 real solution. If $b^2 - 4ac < 0$, there are no real solutions.
2. If the discriminant is negative, there are no real solutions and the object will not reach the given height. If the discriminant is 0 or positive, there are 1 or 2 solutions, and the object will reach the given height.
3. See p. A8.

9-9 Exercises

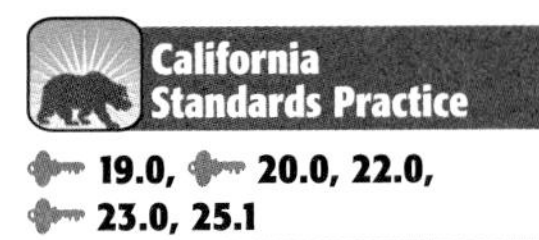

19.0, 20.0, 22.0, 23.0, 25.1

GUIDED PRACTICE

1. **Vocabulary** If the *discriminant* is negative, the quadratic equation has ___?___ solution(s). (*no*, *one*, or *two*) **no**

SEE EXAMPLE 1 p. 605

Find the number of solutions of each equation.

2. $2x^2 + 4x + 3 = 0$ **0**
3. $x^2 + 4x + 4 = 0$ **1**
4. $2x^2 - 11x + 6 = 0$ **2**
5. $x^2 + x + 1 = 0$ **0**
6. $3x^2 = 5x - 1$ **2**
7. $-2x + 3 = 2x^2$ **2**

SEE EXAMPLE 2 p. 606

Find the number of x-intercepts of each function by using the discriminant.

8. $y = 2x^2 + 12x + 18$ **1**
9. $y = 5x^2 + 3x + 4$ **0**
10. $y = -8x + 1 - x^2$ **2**
11. $y = x^2 + 2x + 3$ **0**
12. $y = -3x^2 + 5x - 1$ **2**
13. $y = 2x^2 - 2x + 3$ **0**

SEE EXAMPLE 3 p. 606

14. **Hobbies** The height above the ground in meters of a model rocket on a particular launch can be modeled by the equation $h = -4.9t^2 + 102t + 100$, where t is the time in seconds after its engine burns out 100 m above the ground. Will the rocket reach a height of 600 m? Use the discriminant to explain your answer. **Yes; the discriminant is positive.**

PRACTICE AND PROBLEM SOLVING

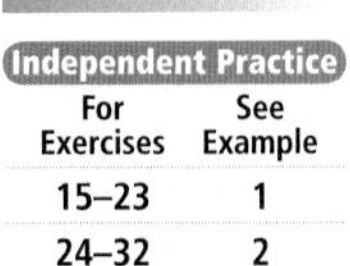

For Exercises	See Example
15–23	1
24–32	2
33	3

Extra Practice
Skills Practice p. EP19
Application Practice p. EP32

Find the number of solutions of each equation.

15. $2x = 3 + 2x^2$ **0**
16. $x^2 = 2x + 1$ **2**
17. $2 = 7x + 4x^2$ **2**
18. $-7 = x^2$ **0**
19. $-12x = -9x^2 - 4$ **1**
20. $x^2 - 14 = 0$ **2**
21. $y = 7.1x^2 - 1.8x + 4$ **0**
22. $y = -4x^2 - 6x + 2$ **2**
23. $y = 3x^2 + 6x + 3$ **1**

Find the number of x-intercepts of each function.

24. $y = x^2 + 4 + x$ **0**
25. $y = -17 + 2x^2$ **2**
26. $y = -6x - x^2 + 5$ **2**
27. $y = 5x^2 - 10x + 5$ **1**
28. $y = 14x^2 + 8x - 1$ **2**
29. $y = x^2 - 1.6x + 1.2$ **0**
30. $y = 4x^2 - 8x + 4$ **1**
31. $y = x^2 + 5x + 3$ **2**
32. $y = 3x^2 + 2x - 15$ **2**

9-9 Exercises

Assignment Guide

Assign *Guided Practice* exercises as necessary.

If you finished Examples **1–3**
Proficient 15–47, 49–52, 54–59, 61–73
Advanced 15–33, 47–73

Homework Quick Check
Quickly check key concepts.
Exercises: 16, 22, 24, 28, 33

FORMATIVE ASSESSMENT and INTERVENTION

***Diagnose Before* the Lesson**
9-9 Warm Up, TE p. 605

***Monitor During* the Lesson**
Check It Out! Exercises, SE p. 606
Questioning Strategies, TE p. 606

***Assess After* the Lesson**
9-9 Lesson Quiz, TE p. 609
Alternative Assessment, TE p. 609

California Standards

Standard	Exercises
2.0	61
7.0	62–67
11.0	68–70
19.0	34–45
20.0	34–45, 71–73
22.0	8–13, 24–32
23.0	14, 33, 47, 50
25.1	48, 53, 60

CONCEPT CONNECTION **Exercise 49** involves evaluating a discriminant to see whether a given height is possible. This exercise prepares students for the Concept Connection on page 610.

Answer

48. 2; 0; 1; $x^2 = k$ in standard form is $1x^2 + 0x - k = 0$ so $a = 1, b = 0, c = -k$, and $b^2 - 4ac = 4k$.
$k > 0$: positive discriminant,
$k < 0$: negative discriminant,
and $k = 0$: zero discriminant.

33. No; the discriminant is negative.

33. Multi-Step A gymnast who can stretch her arms up to reach 6 feet jumps straight up on a trampoline. The height of her feet above the trampoline can be modeled by the equation $h = -16x^2 + 12x$, where x is the time in seconds after her jump. Do the gymnast's hands reach a height of 10 feet above the trampoline? Use the discriminant to explain. (*Hint:* Let $h = 10 - 6$, or 4.)

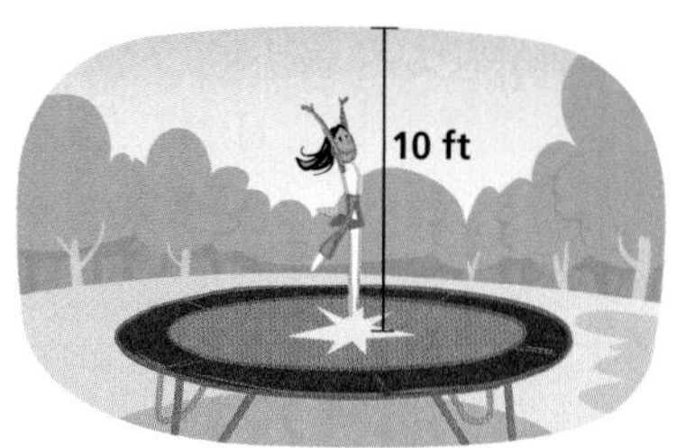

Solve.

34. $x^2 + 4x + 3 = 0$ **−3, −1**
35. $x^2 + 2x = 15$ **−5, 3**
36. $x^2 - 12 = -x$ **−4, 3**
37. $x^2 + 10x = 0$ **0, −10**
38. $x^2 - 144 = 0$ **−12, 12**
39. $x^2 - x - 30 = 0$ **6, −5**

Use the discriminant to determine the number of solutions of each equation. Then solve.

40. $3x^2 - 6x + 3 = 0$ **1 solution; 1**
41. $x^2 - 7x - 8 = 0$ **2 solutions; 8, −1**
42. $7x^2 + 6x + 2 = 0$ **no solutions**

Use the discriminant to determine the number of x-intercepts. Then find them.

43. $x^2 - 5x - 36 = y$ **2 x-intercepts; 9, −4**
44. $2x^2 - x + 6 = y$ **no x-intercepts**
45. $y = 9x^2 + 12x + 4$ **1 x-intercept; $-\frac{2}{3}$**

46. Copy and complete the table.

Quadratic Equation	Discriminant	Number of Solutions
$x^2 + 12x - 20 = 0$	224	**2**
$8x + x^2 = -16$	**0**	**1**
$0.5x^2 + x - 3 = 0$	**7**	**2**
$-3x^2 - 2x = 1$	**−8**	**0**

47. Sports A diver begins on a platform 10 meters above the surface of the water. The diver's height is given by the equation $h(t) = -4.9t^2 + 3.5t + 10$, where t is the time in seconds after the diver jumps.

a. How long does it take the diver to reach a point 1 meter above the water? **≈ 1.76 s**
b. How many solutions does your equation from part **a** have? **2**
c. Do all of the solutions to the equation make sense in the situation? Explain.

47c. No; negative solutions do not make sense because the variable represents time.

48. Reasoning How many solutions does the equation $x^2 = k$ have when $k > 0$, when $k < 0$, and when $k = 0$? Use the discriminant to explain.

CONCEPT CONNECTION

49. This problem will prepare you for the Concept Connection on page 610.
The equation $0 = -16t^2 + 80t + 20$ gives the time t when a golf ball is at height 0 after being hit.
a. Will the height of the golf ball reach 130 feet? Explain. **No; the discriminant is negative, so the equation has no real solutions.**
b. Will the golf ball reach a height of 116 feet? If so, when? **yes; 2 s and 3 s**
c. Solve the quadratic equation by using the Quadratic Formula. **5.24 s**

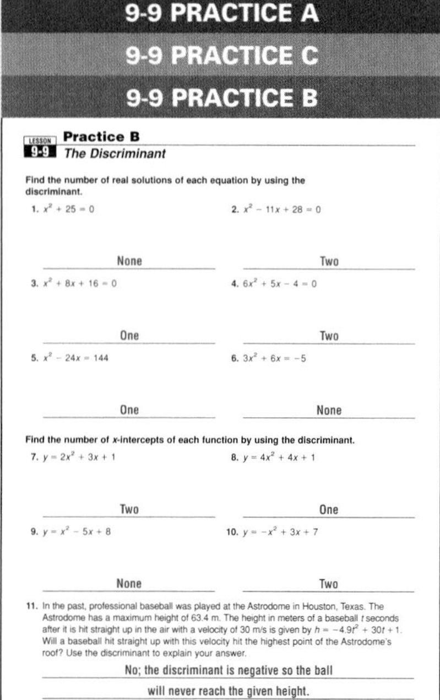

9-9 PRACTICE A
9-9 PRACTICE C
9-9 PRACTICE B

LESSON 9-9 **Practice B**
The Discriminant

Find the number of real solutions of each equation by using the discriminant.

1. $x^2 + 25 = 0$ — None
2. $x^2 - 11x + 28 = 0$ — Two
3. $x^2 + 8x + 16 = 0$ — One
4. $6x^2 + 5x - 4 = 0$ — Two
5. $x^2 - 24x = 144$ — One
6. $3x^2 + 6x = -5$ — None

Find the number of x-intercepts of each function by using the discriminant.

7. $y = 2x^2 + 3x + 1$ — Two
8. $y = 4x^2 + 4x + 1$ — One
9. $y = x^2 - 5x + 8$ — None
10. $y = -x^2 + 3x + 7$ — Two

11. In the past, professional baseball was played at the Astrodome in Houston, Texas. The Astrodome has a maximum height of 63.4 m. The height in meters of a baseball t seconds after it is hit straight up in the air with a velocity of 30 m/s is given by $h = -4.9t^2 + 30t + 1$. Will a baseball hit straight up with this velocity hit the highest point of the Astrodome's roof? Use the discriminant to explain your answer.
No; the discriminant is negative so the ball will never reach the given height.

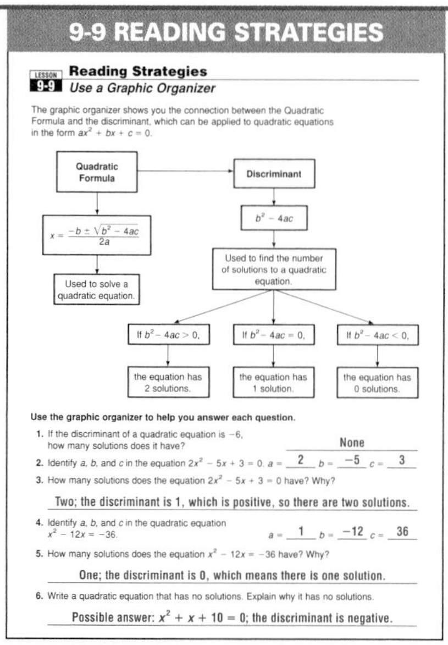

9-9 READING STRATEGIES

LESSON 9-9 **Reading Strategies**
Use a Graphic Organizer

The graphic organizer shows you the connection between the Quadratic Formula and the discriminant, which can be applied to quadratic equations in the form $ax^2 + bx + c = 0$.

Use the graphic organizer to help you answer each question.

1. If the discriminant of a quadratic equation is −6, how many solutions does it have? None
2. Identify a, b, and c in the equation $2x^2 - 5x + 3 = 0$. $a =$ 2 $b =$ −5 $c =$ 3
3. How many solutions does the equation $2x^2 - 5x + 3 = 0$ have? Why?
Two; the discriminant is 1, which is positive, so there are two solutions.
4. Identify a, b, and c in the quadratic equation $x^2 - 12x = -36$. $a =$ 1 $b =$ −12 $c =$ 36
5. How many solutions does the equation $x^2 - 12x = -36$ have? Why?
One; the discriminant is 0, which means there is one solution.
6. Write a quadratic equation that has no solutions. Explain why it has no solutions.
Possible answer: $x^2 + x + 10 = 0$; the discriminant is negative.

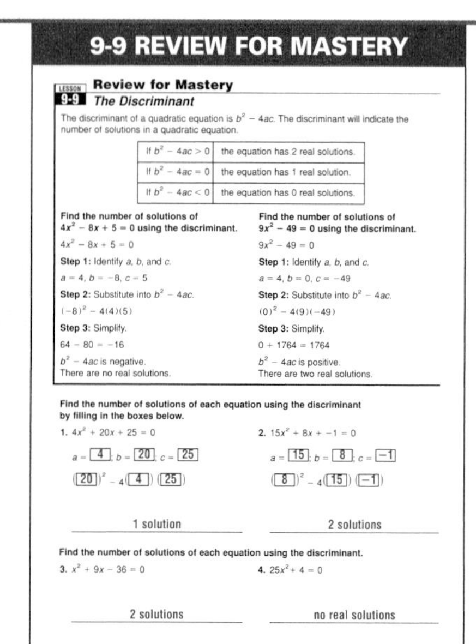

9-9 REVIEW FOR MASTERY

LESSON 9-9 **Review for Mastery**
The Discriminant

The discriminant of a quadratic equation is $b^2 - 4ac$. The discriminant will indicate the number of solutions in a quadratic equation.

If $b^2 - 4ac > 0$	the equation has 2 real solutions.
If $b^2 - 4ac = 0$	the equation has 1 real solution.
If $b^2 - 4ac < 0$	the equation has 0 real solutions.

Find the number of solutions of $4x^2 - 8x + 5 = 0$ using the discriminant.
$4x^2 - 8x + 5 = 0$
Step 1: Identify a, b, and c.
$a = 4, b = -8, c = 5$
Step 2: Substitute into $b^2 - 4ac$.
$(-8)^2 - 4(4)(5)$
Step 3: Simplify.
$64 - 80 = -16$
$b^2 - 4ac$ is negative.
There are no real solutions.

Find the number of solutions of $9x^2 - 49 = 0$ using the discriminant.
$9x^2 - 49 = 0$
Step 1: Identify a, b, and c.
$a = 4, b = 0, c = -49$
Step 2: Substitute into $b^2 - 4ac$.
$(0)^2 - 4(9)(-49)$
Step 3: Simplify.
$0 + 1764 = 1764$
$b^2 - 4ac$ is positive.
There are two real solutions.

Find the number of solutions of each equation using the discriminant by filling in the boxes below.

1. $4x^2 + 20x + 25 = 0$
$a =$ [4]; $b =$ [20]; $c =$ [25]
$([20])^2 - 4([4])([25])$
1 solution

2. $15x^2 + 8x + -1 = 0$
$a =$ [15]; $b =$ [8]; $c =$ [−1]
$([8])^2 - 4([15])([-1])$
2 solutions

Find the number of solutions of each equation using the discriminant.

3. $x^2 + 9x - 36 = 0$ — 2 solutions
4. $25x^2 + 4 = 0$ — no real solutions

50. **Write About It** How can you use the discriminant to save time when solving quadratic equations?

Multiple Choice **For Exercises 51 and 52, choose the best answer.**

51. How many solutions does $4x^2 - 3x + 1 = 0$ have?

(A) 0 (circled) (B) 1 (C) 2 (D) 4

52. For which of the following conditions does $ax^2 + bx + c = 0$ have two solutions?

I. $b^2 = 4ac$

II. $b^2 > 4ac$

III. $a = b, c = b$

(A) I only (B) II only (circled) (C) III only (D) II and III

CHALLENGE AND EXTEND

53. **Reasoning** Graph $y = x^2 + 6x + 1$ and use the discriminant to find the number of x-intercepts. Graph $y = x^2 + 6x + 1 + 20$ and use the discriminant to find the number of x-intercepts. Construct an argument about the change in c in the two equations and the effect on the discriminant and the number of solutions.

53. Possible answer: The change in c moves the graph of the equation above the x-axis. The move makes the discriminant less than zero, so there are no solutions.

Write each equation in standard form. Use the discriminant to determine the number of solutions. Then solve.

54. $2x^2 - 4x + 2x^2 - 13 = 3x - 11$

55. $41 - 5x^2 - 7 = -19x + 3x^2$

56. $8x^2 - 22 + 8x = 21x - 34$

57. $-5 + 32x^2 - 24x^2 + 44 = 6x$

58. $0.8x - 0.9 + 3.9x^2 = 1.9x^2 + 11.7x$

59. $7x - 3x + 2 = 2x^2 - 2 - 4x^2$

60. **Reasoning** The graph of $y = ax^2 - 6x + 1$ crosses the x-axis at two points. What are the possible values of a? $a < 9$

SPIRAL STANDARDS REVIEW

61. Thom recorded the ages of his neighbors for a school project. Write and solve an equation to find the average age of the families. *(Lesson 2-1)*

Family	Average Age
Davenports	31.5
Keenans	28.7
Simpsons	19.2
Nguyens	21.3
Williams	36.5

$a = \frac{31.5 + 28.7 + 19.2 + 21.3 + 36.5}{5}$; 27.44

Write an equation in point-slope form for the line with the given slope that contains the given point. *(Lesson 5-6)*

62. slope = 6; (2, 9) $y = 6x - 3$

63. slope = $\frac{1}{2}$; (6, 11) $y = \frac{1}{2}x + 8$

64. slope = −2; (3, −11) $y = -2x - 5$

65. slope = 3; (5, 12) $y = 3x - 3$

66. slope = 1; (4, 1) $y = x - 3$

67. slope = $\frac{3}{4}$; (12, 4) $y = \frac{3}{4}x - 5$

Factor each polynomial by grouping. *(Lesson 8-2)*

68. $3v + 3w^4 + vw^4 + v^2$ $(v + w^4)(v + 3)$

69. $-20 + 5y^2 + 4z - y^2z$ $(y + 2)(y - 2)(5 - z)$

70. $7k - 14 - 2k^2 + k^3$ $(k^2 + 7)(k - 2)$

Solve using the Quadratic Formula. Check your answer. *(Lesson 9-8)*

71. $2x^2 - 4x - 15 = 0$ $\approx -1.92, \approx 3.92$

72. $-x^2 = 10x + 21$ $-3, -7$

73. $4x^2 - 52x + 160 = 0$ $5, 8$

Multiple Choice In **Exercise 52,** students can write $b^2 - 4ac > 0$ and rearrange it, yielding $b^2 > 4ac$. Thus, **II** is true and choices **A** and **C** can be eliminated. To see whether III is true, substitute b for a and c^2 in $b^2 > 4ac$. This yields $b^2 > 4b^2$, which is false. So **III** is false, and **D** can be eliminated.

Answers

50. Possible answer: The discriminant tells how many solutions there are. If an equation looks difficult to solve, first use the discriminant to find out if it has any solutions. If it doesn't, you do not need to proceed any further.

54. $4x^2 - 7x - 2 = 0$; 2 solutions; $2, -\frac{1}{4}$

55. $8x^2 - 19x - 34 = 0$; 2 solutions; $\approx -1.19, \approx 3.57$

56. $8x^2 - 13x + 12 = 0$; ∅

57. $8x^2 - 6x + 39 = 0$; ∅

58. $2x^2 - 10.9x - 0.9 \neq 0$; 2 solutions; $\approx -0.08, \approx 5.53$

59. $2x^2 + 4x + 4 = 0$; ∅

Journal

Have students use examples to show the use of the discriminant to determine the number of solutions of a quadratic equation. Ask them to use a different equation as an example for each possibility.

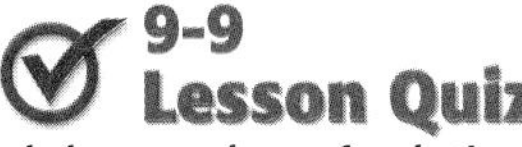

Have students explain how to find the value of the discriminant and how its value tells you the number of solutions of a quadratic equation.

Power Presentations with PowerPoint®

9-9 Lesson Quiz

1. Find the number of solutions of $5x^2 - 19x - 8 = 0$. 2

2. Find the number of x-intercepts of $y = 3x^2 + 2x - 4$ by using the discriminant. 2

3. An object is shot up from 4 ft off the ground with an initial velocity of 48 ft/s. Will it reach a height of 40 ft? Use the discriminant to explain your answer. The discr. is 0. The object will reach its max. height of 40 ft once.

Also available on transparency

9-9 PROBLEM SOLVING

LESSON 9-9 **Problem Solving**
The Discriminant

Write the correct answer.

1. Theo's flying disc got stuck in a tree 14 feet from the ground. Theo threw a shoe up at the disc to dislodge it. The height in feet of the shoe is given by the equation $h = -16t^2 + 25t + 6$, where t is the time in seconds. Determine whether the shoe hit the disc. Use the discriminant to explain your answer.

Yes; the discriminant (113) is positive.

2. Jaclyn shoots a basketball whose height in feet is modeled by the equation $y = -16t^2 + 24t + 5$, where t is the time in seconds after the ball is shot. Will the ball go high enough to reach the basket, which is located 10 feet above the ground? Explain.

Yes; the discriminant (256) is positive.

3. The population of cells in a Petri dish is modeled by $p = -4t^2 + 20t + 55$, where t is the number of hours since the start of the experiment. Does the population of cells ever reach 85? Why or why not?

No; the discriminant (−80) is negative.

4. Marisol launched a model rocket whose height in feet is given by $h = -16t^2 + 80t$, where t is the time in seconds. She claims that the rocket landed on the top of a 100-foot building. Is this possible? Why or why not?

Yes; the discriminant is 0 so $-16t^2 + 80t = 100$ has a solution.

The equation $h = -16t^2 + v_0t + 5$ gives the height of a ball in feet after t seconds when the ball is thrown upwards with an initial velocity of v_0 ft/s. The table shows the initial velocities at which three students threw a baseball. Use the table for Exercises 5 and 6. Select the best answer.

5. To determine if Samantha's baseball will reach a height of 10 ft, you can write a quadratic equation and find the discriminant. If you do this, what is the discriminant?

A −176
(B) 464 (circled)
C 704
D 1104

6. Which of the students' baseballs will reach a height of at least 12 ft?

A Samantha only
(B) Samantha and Ming only (circled)
C Samantha, Ming, and Bryan
D None of them

Student	Initial Velocity of Throw
Samantha	28 ft/s
Ming	24 ft/s
Bryan	20 ft/s

9-9 CHALLENGE

LESSON 9-9 **Challenge**
Writing Equations that Satisfy Given Conditions

You can use the discriminant to write equations that satisfy given conditions.

For example, consider an equation of the form $x^2 + 6x + c = 0$. The discriminant is $b^2 - 4ac$ or $36 - 4c$.

The equation has **no solutions** when the discriminant is negative.	The equation has **one solution** when the discriminant is zero.	The equation has **two solutions** when the discriminant is positive.
$36 - 4c < 0$ $36 < 4c$ $9 < c$	$36 - 4c = 0$ $36 = 4c$ $9 = c$	$36 - 4c > 0$ $36 > 4c$ $9 > c$
When $c > 9$, the equation has no solutions.	When $c = 9$, the equation has one solution.	When $c < 9$, the equation has two solutions.

Find values of a, b, or c that result in an equation that satisfies the given conditions.

1. $y = x^2 + 2x + c$ one solution $c = 1$

2. $y = x^2 + 4x + c$ two solutions $c < 4$

3. $y = 2x^2 + 6x + c$ no solutions $c > \frac{9}{2}$

4. $y = 3x^2 - 2x + c$ one solution $c = \frac{1}{3}$

5. $y = ax^2 + 2x + 4$ two solutions $a < \frac{1}{4}$

6. $y = ax^2 + 3x - 6$ one solution $a = -\frac{3}{8}$

7. $y = ax^2 - x + 2$ no solutions $a > \frac{1}{8}$

8. $y = x^2 + bx + 4$ one solution $b = 4$

9. $y = x^2 + bx + 4$ no solutions $-4 < b < 4$

10. $y = x^2 + bx + 4$ two solutions $b < -4$ or $b > 4$

SECTION 9B

Concept Connection

Organizer

Objective: Assess students' ability to apply concepts and skills in Lessons 9-4 through 9-9 in a real-world format.

Online Edition

Countdown to Mastery Week 22

Problem	Text Reference
1	Lesson 9-4
2	Lesson 9-4
3	Lesson 9-4
4	Lessons 9-4, 9-5
5	Lesson 9-8

CHAPTER 9

Concept Connection

SECTION 9B

Solving Quadratic Equations

Seeing Green A golf player hits a golf ball from a tee with an initial velocity of 80 feet per second. The height of the golf ball t seconds after it is hit is given by $h = -16t^2 + 80t$.

1. How long is the golf ball in the air? **5 s**
2. What is the maximum height of the golf ball? **100 ft**
3. How long after the golf ball is hit does it reach its maximum height? **2.5 s**
4. What is the height of the golf ball after 3.5 seconds? **84 ft**
5. At what times is the golf ball 64 feet in the air? Explain. **At 1 s and 4 s; Solve $64 = -16t^2 + 80t$. The solutions are 1 and 4.**

INTERVENTION

Scaffolding Questions

1. What is a reasonable domain for this situation? $0 \le t \le 5$
2. What is a reasonable range for this situation? $0 \le h \le 100$
3. What point represents the maximum height? the vertex
4. Does this problem ask for the value of an independent or dependent variable? dependent
5. What equation could you solve in order to answer this question? $64 = -16t^2 + 80t$

Extension

How would the function change if the golfer hit the ball with an initial velocity of 60 ft/s? How would the reasonable domain and range change? $h = -16t^2 + 60t$; reasonable domain: $0 \le t \le 3.75$; reasonable range: $0 \le h \le 56.25$.

California Standards

Algebra 1 23.0

CHAPTER 9

SECTION 9B

Quiz for Lessons 9-4 Through 9-9

9-4 Solving Quadratic Equations by Graphing

Solve each equation by graphing the related function.

1. $x^2 - 9 = 0$ ± 3
2. $x^2 + 3x - 4 = 0$ 1, −4
3. $4x^2 + 8x = 32$ 2, −4
4. The height of a fireworks rocket launched from a platform 35 feet above the ground can be approximated by $h = -5t^2 + 30t + 35$, where h is the height in meters and t is the time in seconds. Find the time it takes the rocket to reach the ground after it is launched. 7 s

9-5 Solving Quadratic Equations by Factoring

Use the Zero Product Property to solve each equation. Check your answer.

5. $(x + 1)(x + 3) = 0$ −1, −3
6. $(x - 6)(x - 3) = 0$ 6, 3
7. $x(x + 3) = 18$ −6, 3
8. $(x + 2)(x - 5) = 60$ −7, 10

Solve each quadratic equation by factoring. Check your answer.

9. $x^2 - 4x - 32 = 0$
10. $x^2 - 8x + 15 = 0$
11. $x^2 + x = 6$ 2, −3
12. $-8x - 33 = -x^2$ 11, −3
13. The height of a soccer ball kicked from the ground can be approximated by the function $h = -16t^2 + 64t$, where h is the height in feet and t is the time in seconds. Find the time it takes for the ball to return to the ground. 4 s

9-6 Solving Quadratic Equations by Using Square Roots

Solve using square roots. Check your answer.

14. $3x^2 = 48$ ± 4
15. $36x^2 - 49 = 0$ $\pm\frac{7}{6}$
16. $-12 = x^2 - 21$ ± 3
17. Solve $3x^2 + 5 = 21$. Round to the nearest hundredth. ± 2.31

9-7 Completing the Square

Complete the square to form a perfect-square trinomial.

18. $x^2 - 12x +$ 36
19. $x^2 + 4x +$ 4
20. $x^2 + 9x +$ $\frac{81}{4}$

Solve by completing the square. Check your answer.

21. $x^2 + 2x = 3$ 1, −3
22. $x^2 - 5 = 2x$ $1 \pm \sqrt{6}$
23. $x^2 + 7x = 8$ 1, −8

9-8 The Quadratic Formula

Solve using the Quadratic Formula. Round your answer to the nearest hundredth, if necessary.

24. $x^2 + 5x + 1 = 0$ −0.21, −4.79
25. $3x^2 + 1 = 2x$ $\varnothing$
26. $5x + 8 = 3x^2$ $-1, \frac{8}{3}$

9-9 The Discriminant

Find the number of solutions of each equation.

27. $2x^2 - 3x + 4 = 0$ 0
28. $x^2 + 1 + 2x = 0$ 1
29. $x^2 - 5 + 4x = 0$ 2

READY TO GO ON? SECTION 9B

Organizer

Objective: Assess students' mastery of concepts and skills in Lessons 9-4 through 9-9.

Resources

Assessment Resources
Section 9B Quiz

INTERVENTION

Resources

Ready to Go On? Intervention and Enrichment Worksheets

Ready to Go On? CD-ROM

Ready to Go On? Online

Answers

9. 8, −4
10. 3, 5

READY TO GO ON? Diagnose and Prescribe

Ready to Go On? Intervention	READY TO GO ON? Intervention, Section 9B: Worksheets	CD-ROM	Online
Lesson 9-4 21.0	9-4 Intervention	Activity 9-4	Diagnose and Prescribe Online
Lesson 9-5 14.0	9-5 Intervention	Activity 9-5	
Lesson 9-6 2.0	9-6 Intervention	Activity 9-6	
Lesson 9-7 14.0	9-7 Intervention	Activity 9-7	
Lesson 9-8 19.0	9-8 Intervention	Activity 9-8	
Lesson 9-9 22.0	9-9 Intervention	Activity 9-9	

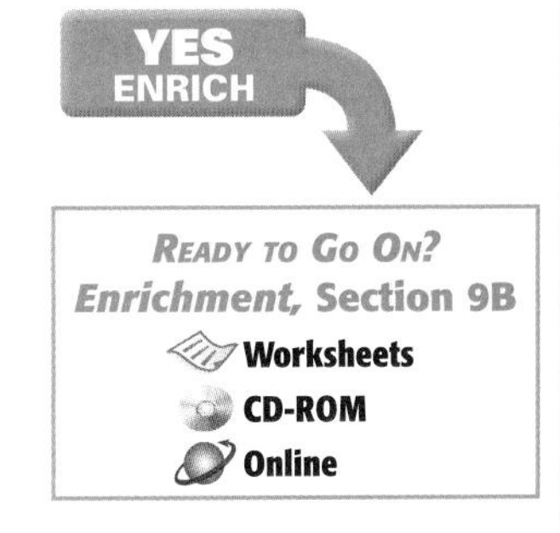

YES
ENRICH
READY TO GO ON? Enrichment, Section 9B
Worksheets
CD-ROM
Online

Study Guide: Review

Organizer

Objective: Help students organize and review key concepts and skills presented in Chapter 9.

Online Edition
Multilingual Glossary

Resources

PuzzlePro
One-Stop Planner®

Multilingual Glossary **Online**

go.hrw.com
KEYWORD: MA8CA Glossary

Lesson Tutorial Videos
CD-ROM

Test & Practice Generator
One-Stop Planner®

Answers

1. vertex
2. minimum; maximum
3. zero of a function
4. discriminant of a quadratic equation
5. Completing the square
6. yes
7. no
8. yes
9. no
10. 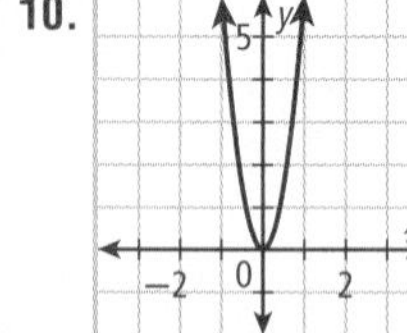
11. 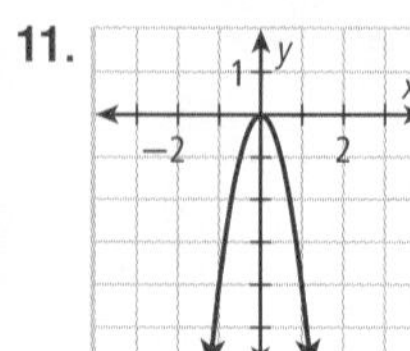
12. 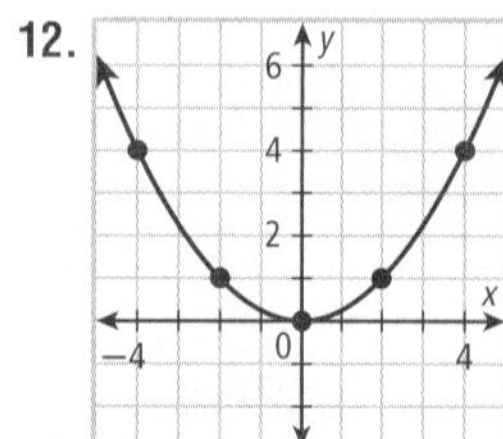
13. 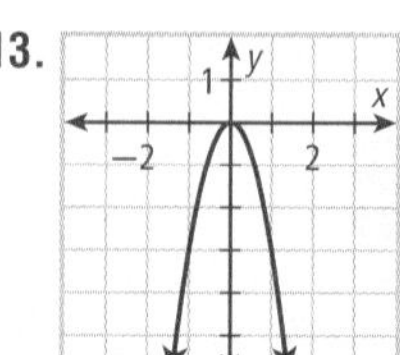
14. Upward; the value of a is positive.
15. Downward; the value of a is negative.
16. $(-2, -4)$; minimum: -4

CHAPTER 9

Study Guide: Review

Vocabulary

Complete the sentences below with vocabulary words from the list above.

1. The ___?___ is the highest or lowest point on a parabola.
2. A quadratic function has a ___?___ if its graph opens upward and a ___?___ if its graph opens downward.
3. A ___?___ can also be called an x-intercept of the function.
4. Finding the ___?___ can tell you how many real-number solutions a quadratic equation has.
5. ___?___ is a process that results in a perfect-square trinomial.

9-1 Quadratic Equations and Functions *(pp. 544–551)*

21.0

EXAMPLE

■ **Graph $y = -5x^2 + 40x$.**

Step 1 Make a table of values.

Choose values of x and use them to find values of y.

x	0	1	3	4	6	7	8
y	0	35	75	80	60	35	0

Step 2 Plot the points and connect them with a smooth curve.

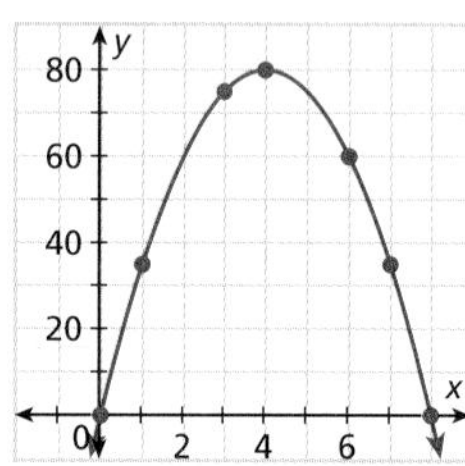

EXERCISES

Without graphing, tell whether each point is on the graph of the given equation.

6. $y = 2x^2 + 9x - 5$; $(1, 6)$
7. $y = -4x + 3 - 2x$; $(3, 15)$
8. $y - 2 = \frac{1}{2}x^2 + x$; $(4, 14)$
9. $y = 5x^2 + 8 + 7x$; $(-2, 16)$

Graph each quadratic function.

10. $y = 6x^2$
11. $y = -4x^2$
12. $y = \frac{1}{4}x^2$
13. $y = -3x^2$

Tell whether the graph of each function opens upward or downward. Explain.

14. $y = 5x^2 - 12$
15. $y = -x^2 + 3x - 7$
16. Identify the vertex of the parabola. Then give the minimum or maximum value of the function.

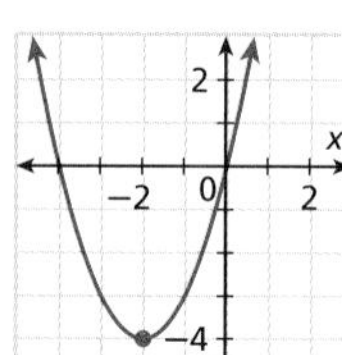

9-2 Characteristics of Quadratic Functions *(pp. 553–559)*

EXAMPLE

■ **Find the zeros of $y = 2x^2 - 4x - 6$ from its graph. Then find the axis of symmetry and the vertex.**

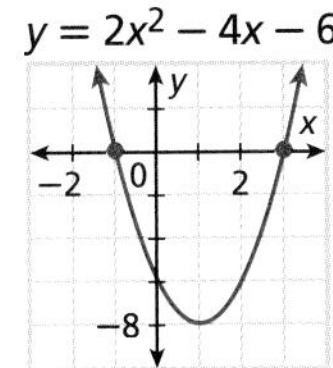

Step 1 Use the graph to find the zeros.
The zeros are -1 and 3.

Step 2 Find the axis of symmetry.

$$x = \frac{-1 + 3}{2} = \frac{2}{2} = 1$$ *Find the average of the zeros.*

The axis of symmetry is the vertical line $x = 1$.

Step 3 Find the vertex.

$y = 2x^2 - 4x - 6$
$y = 2(1)^2 - 4(1) - 6$
$y = -8$

Substitute 1 into the function to find the y-value of the vertex.

The vertex is $(1, -8)$.

EXERCISES

Find the zeros of each quadratic function from its graph. Check your answer.

17. $y = x^2 + 3x - 10$

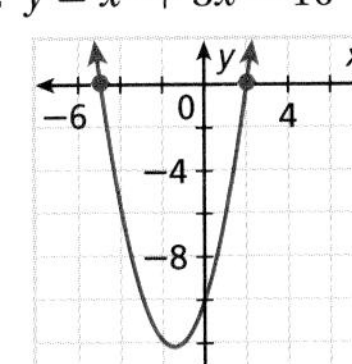

18. $y = x^2 - x - 2$

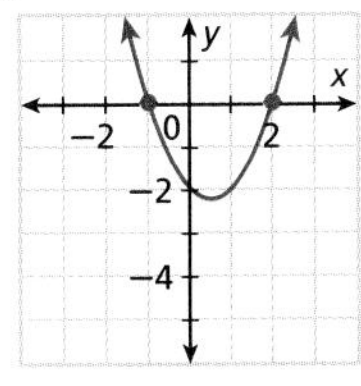

Find the axis of symmetry and vertex of each parabola.

19. $y = -x^2 + 12x - 32$

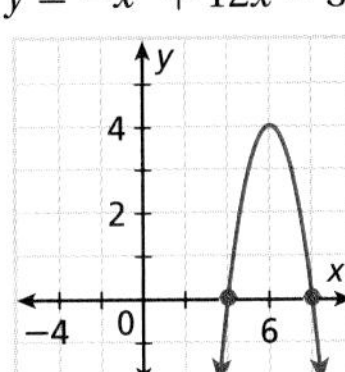

20. $y = 2x^2 + 4x - 16$

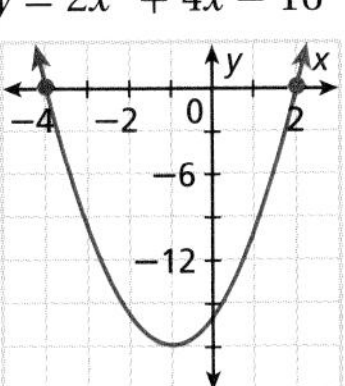

9-3 Graphing Quadratic Functions *(pp. 560–565)*

EXAMPLE

■ **Graph $y = 2x^2 - 8x - 10$.**

Step 1 Find the axis of symmetry.

$$x = \frac{-b}{2a} = \frac{-(-8)}{2(2)} = \frac{8}{4} = 2$$

The axis of symmetry is $x = 2$.

Step 2 Find the vertex.

$y = 2x^2 - 8x - 10$
$y = 2(2)^2 - 8(2) - 10$
$y = -18$

The vertex is $(2, -18)$.

Step 3 Find the y-intercept.
$c = -10$

Step 4 Find one more point on the graph.

$y = 2(-1)^2 - 8(-1) - 10 = 0$
Use $(-1, 0)$.

Step 5 Graph the axis of symmetry and the points. Reflect the points and connect with a smooth curve.

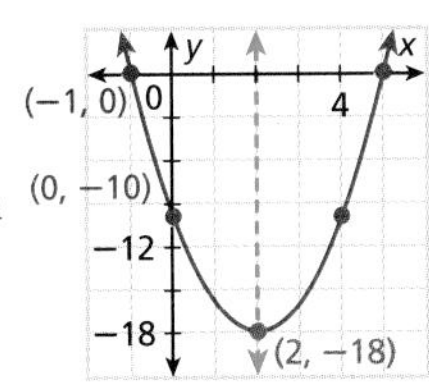

EXERCISES

Graph each quadratic function.

21. $y = x^2 + 6x + 6$

22. $y = x^2 - 4x - 12$

23. $y = x^2 - 8x + 7$

24. $y = 2x^2 - 6x - 8$

25. $3x^2 + 6x = y - 3$

26. $2 - 4x^2 + y = 8x - 10$

27. Water that is sprayed upward from a sprinkler with an initial velocity of 20 m/s can be approximated by the function $y = -5x^2 + 20x$, where y is the height of a drop of water x seconds after it is released. Graph this function. Find the time it takes a drop of water to reach its maximum height, the water's maximum height, and the time it takes the water to reach the ground.

Answers

17. $-5, 2$
18. $-1, 2$
19. $x = 6$; $(6, 4)$
20. $x = -1$; $(-1, -18)$
21.

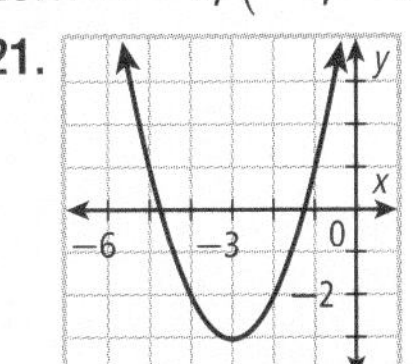

22.

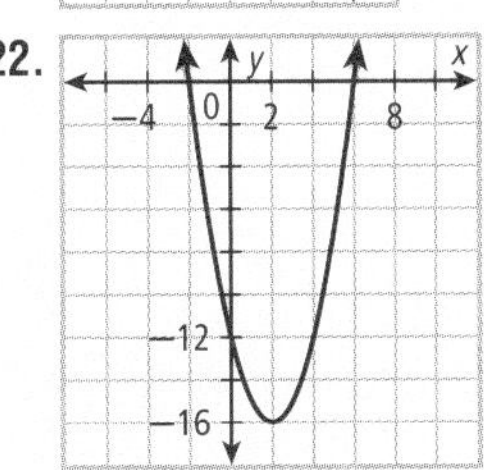

23.

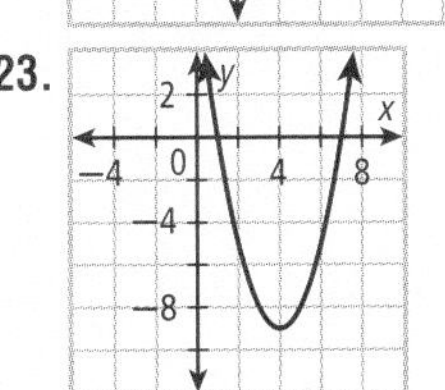

24.

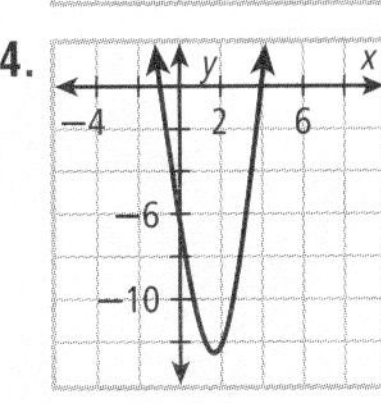

25.

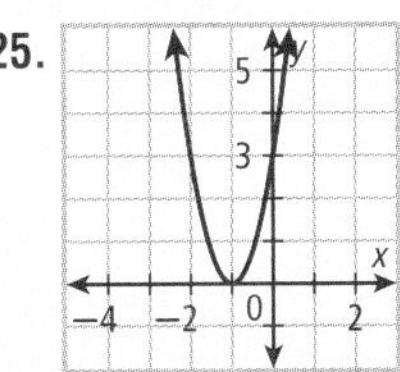

26.

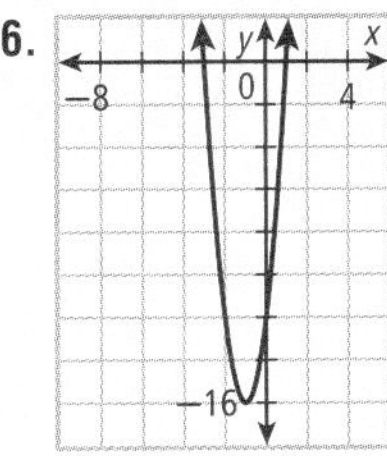

27.

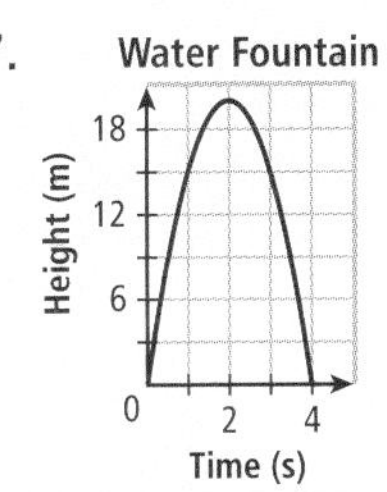

In 2 s, the water reaches its maximum height of 20 m. It takes a total of 4 s for the water to reach the ground.

Answers

28. $x = -3$ or $x = -1$

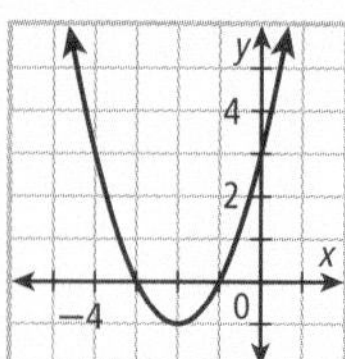

29. $x = -3$

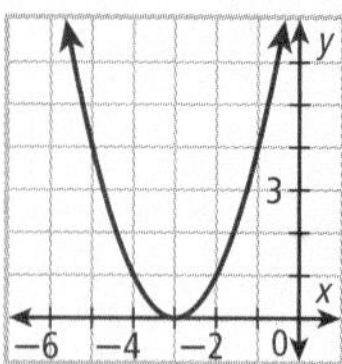

30. $\varnothing$

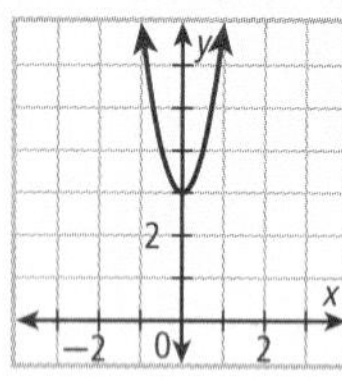

31. $x = 1$ or $x = 5$

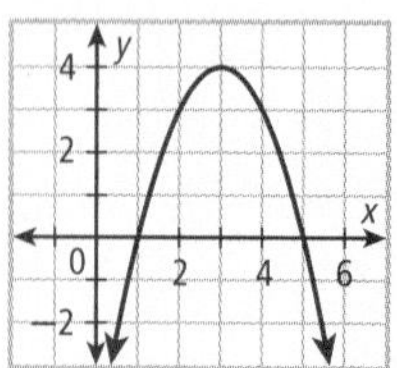

32. $x = 4$

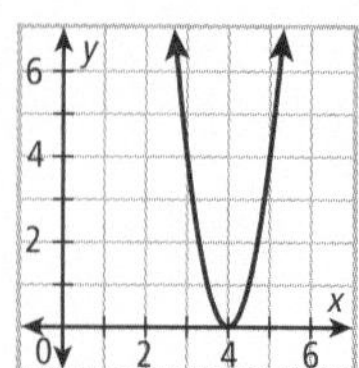

33. $x = \pm 1$

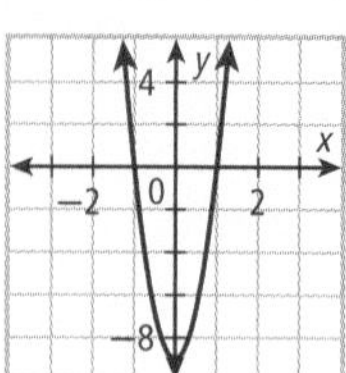

34. $\varnothing$

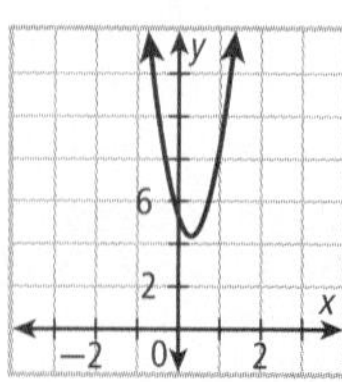

35. $x = -5$ or $x = -1$
36. $x = -7$ or $x = -2$
37. $x = -3$ or $x = 5$
38. $x = -1$ or $x = 2$
39. $x = -5$
40. $x = 4.5$
41. $x^2 + 2x = 48$; 6 ft

9-4 Solving Quadratic Equations by Graphing *(pp. 568–573)*

EXAMPLE

■ **Solve $-4 = 4x^2 - 8x$ by graphing the related function.**

Step 1 Write the equation in standard form.

$0 = 4x^2 - 8x + 4$

Step 2 Graph the related function, $y = 4x^2 - 8x + 4$.

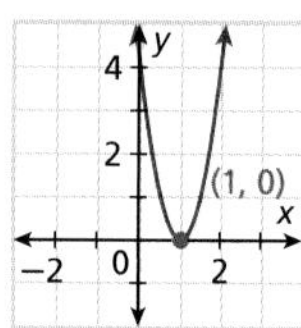

Step 3 Find the zeros. The only zero is 1. The solution is $x = 1$.

EXERCISES

Solve each equation by graphing the related function. Check your answer.

28. $0 = x^2 + 4x + 3$
29. $0 = x^2 + 6x + 9$
30. $-4x^2 = 3$
31. $x^2 + 5 = 6x$
32. $-4x^2 = 64 - 32x$
33. $9 = 9x^2$
34. $-3x^2 + 2x = 5$

9-5 Solving Quadratic Equations by Factoring *(pp. 576–581)*

EXAMPLE

■ **Solve $3x^2 - 6x = 24$ by factoring.**

$3x^2 - 6x = 24$	*Write the equation in standard form.*
$3x^2 - 6x - 24 = 0$	
$3(x^2 - 2x - 8) = 0$	*Factor out 3.*
$3(x + 2)(x - 4) = 0$	*Factor the trinomial.*
$3 \neq 0, x + 2 = 0$ or $x - 4 = 0$	*Zero Product Property*
$x = -2$ or $x = 4$	*Solve.*

EXERCISES

Solve each quadratic equation by factoring. Check your answer.

35. $x^2 + 6x + 5 = 0$
36. $x^2 + 9x + 14 = 0$
37. $x^2 - 2x - 15 = 0$
38. $2x^2 - 2x - 4 = 0$
39. $x^2 + 10x + 25 = 0$
40. $4x^2 - 36x = -81$
41. A rectangle is 2 feet longer than it is wide. The area of the rectangle is 48 square feet. Write and solve an equation to find the width.

9-6 Solving Quadratic Equations by Using Square Roots *(pp. 582–587)*

EXAMPLE

■ **Solve $2x^2 = 98$ using square roots.**

$\frac{2x^2}{2} = \frac{98}{2}$	*Divide both sides of the equation by 2 to isolate x^2.*
$x^2 = 49$	
$x = \pm\sqrt{49}$	*Take the square root of both sides.*
$x = \pm 7$	*Use ± to show both roots.*

EXERCISES

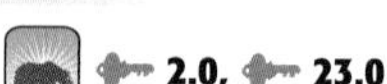

Solve using square roots. Check your answer.

42. $5x^2 = 320$
43. $-x^2 + 144 = 0$
44. $x^2 = -16$
45. $x^2 + 7 = 7$
46. $2x^2 = 50$
47. $4x^2 = 25$
48. A rectangle is twice as long as it is wide. The area of the rectangle is 32 square feet. Find the rectangle's width.

42. $x = \pm 8$
43. $x = \pm 12$
44. $\varnothing$
45. $x = 0$
46. $x = \pm 5$
47. $x = \pm\frac{5}{2}$
48. 4 ft

9-7 Completing the Square *(pp. 591–597)*

14.0, 23.0

EXAMPLE

■ **Solve $x^2 - 6x = -5$ by completing the square.**

$\left(\frac{-6}{2}\right)^2 = 9$ *Find $\left(\frac{b}{2}\right)^2$.*

$x^2 - 6x + 9 = -5 + 9$ *Complete the square.*

$x^2 - 6x + 9 = 4$

$(x - 3)^2 = 4$ *Factor the trinomial.*

$x - 3 = \pm\sqrt{4}$ *Take the square root of both sides.*

$x - 3 = 2$ or $x - 3 = -2$ *Solve each equation.*

$x = 5$ or $x = 1$

EXERCISES

Solve by completing the square. Check your answer.

49. $x^2 + 2x = 48$

50. $x^2 + 4x = 21$

51. $2x^2 - 12x + 10 = 0$

52. $x^2 - 10x = -20$

53. A homeowner is planning an addition to her house. The new family room will have an area of 192 square feet and its length will be 4 more feet than the width. What will the dimensions of the new room be? Round to the nearest hundredth.

9-8 The Quadratic Formula *(pp. 598–604)*

19.0, 20.0

EXAMPLE

■ **Solve $x^2 + 4x + 4 = 0$ using the Quadratic Formula.**

The equation $x^2 + 4x + 4 = 0$ is in standard form with $a = 1$, $b = 4$, and $c = 4$.

$x = \frac{-b \pm \sqrt{b^2 - 4ac}}{2a}$ *Write the Quadratic Formula.*

$= \frac{-4 \pm \sqrt{4^2 - 4(1)(4)}}{2(1)}$ *Substitute for a, b, and c.*

$= \frac{-4 \pm \sqrt{16 - 16}}{2}$ *Simplify.*

$= \frac{-4 \pm \sqrt{0}}{2} = \frac{-4}{2} = -2$

EXERCISES

Solve using the Quadratic Formula. Check your answer.

54. $x^2 - 5x - 6 = 0$

55. $2x^2 - 9x - 5 = 0$

56. $4x^2 - 8x + 4 = 0$

57. $x^2 - 6x = -7$

Solve using at least two different methods. Check your answer.

58. $0 = x^2 + 7.3x + 13.02$

59. $6 = 2x^2 + 4x$

60. $5x^2 + x + 3 = 0$

61. $-14x = 6x^2 + 4$

9-9 The Discriminant *(pp. 605–609)*

22.0, 23.0

EXAMPLE

■ **Find the number of solutions of $7x^2 + 8x + 1 = 0$.**

$a = 7, b = 8, c = 1$ *Identify the values of a, b, and c.*

$b^2 - 4ac = 8^2 - 4(7)(1)$ *Find the discriminant.*

$= 64 - 28$ *Simplify.*

$= 36$

$b^2 - 4ac$ is positive. There are two solutions.

EXERCISES

Find the number of solutions of each equation.

62. $x^2 - 12x + 36 = 0$

63. $3x^2 + 5 = 0$

64. $2x^2 - 13x = -20$

65. $6x^2 - 20 = 15x + 1$

Find the number of x-intercepts of each function by using the discriminant.

66. $6x + y = 7x^2 + 1$

67. $y = 3x^2 - x + 3$

68. $y = x^2 + 4x + 4$

69. $4x + y = x^2 + 5$

Answers

49. $x = -8$ or $x = 6$

50. $x = -7$ or $x = 3$

51. $x = 1$ or $x = 5$

52. $x = 5 \pm \sqrt{5}$, or ≈ 2.76, ≈ 7.24

53. 16 ft by 12 ft

54. $x = -1$ or $x = 6$

55. $x = -\frac{1}{2}$ or $x = 5$

56. $x = 1$

57. $x = \frac{6 \pm \sqrt{8}}{2}$, or ≈ 1.59, ≈ 4.41

58. $x = -3.1$ or $x = -4.2$

59. $x = 1$ or $x = -3$

60. $\varnothing$

61. $x = -\frac{1}{3}$ or $x = -2$

62. 1

63. 0

64. 2

65. 2

66. 2

67. 0

68. 1

69. 0

Organizer

Objective: Assess students' mastery of concepts and skills in Chapter 9.

Online Edition

Resources

Assessment Resources

Chapter 9 Tests
- Free Response (Levels A, B, C)
- Multiple Choice (Levels A, B, C)
- Performance Assessment

***IDEA Works!* CD-ROM**

Modified Chapter 9 Test

California Standards

Standard	Exercises
2.0	12–14
14.0	9–11, 15–17
19.0	19–21
21.0	7
22.0	22–24
23.0	8, 18

Without graphing, tell whether each point is on the graph of the given equation.

1. $6 - 16x^2 = 2y$; $(-1, -5)$ **yes**

2. $3x^2 + y = 4 + 3x$; $(2, 2)$ **no**

3. Tell whether the graph of $y = -2x^2 + 7x - 5$ opens upward or downward and whether the parabola has a maximum or a minimum. **downward; maximum**

4. Find the zeros of the quadratic function from its graph.

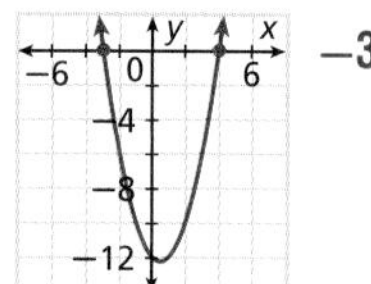

−3, 4

5. Find the axis of symmetry of the parabola.

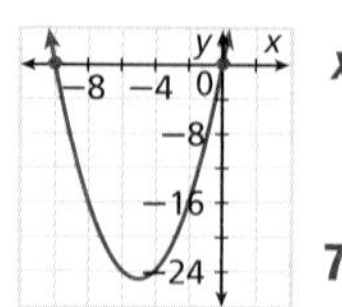

$x = -5$

6. Find the vertex of the graph of $y = x^2 + 6x + 8$. **(−3, −1)**

7. Graph $y = x^2 - 4x + 2$.

7. (graph)

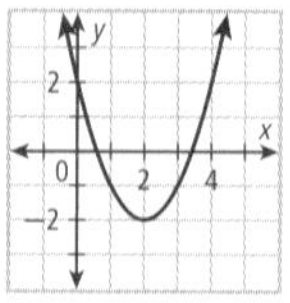

8. A rocket is launched with an initial velocity of 110 meters per second. The height h of the rocket in meters is approximated by the quadratic equation $h = -5t^2 + 110t$, where t is the time after launch in seconds. About how long after the launch does the rocket return to the ground? **about 22 s**

Solve each quadratic equation by factoring.

9. $x^2 + 6x + 5 = 0$ **−5, −1**

10. $x^2 - 12x = -36$ **6**

11. $x^2 - 81 = 0$ **±9**

Solve by using square roots.

12. $-2x^2 = -72$ **±6**

13. $9x^2 - 49 = 0$ $\pm\frac{7}{3}$

14. $3x^2 + 12 = 0$ **∅**

Solve by completing the square.

15. $x^2 + 10x = -21$ **−7, −3**

16. $x^2 - 6x + 4 = 0$ $3 \pm \sqrt{5}$

17. $2x^2 + 16x = 0$ **−8, 0**

18. A landscaper has enough cement to make a patio with an area of 150 square feet. The homeowner wants the length of the patio to be 6 feet longer than the width. What dimensions should be used for the patio? Round your answer to the nearest tenth of a foot. **9.6 ft by 15.6 ft**

Solve using the Quadratic Formula. Round to the nearest hundredth if necessary.

19. $x^2 + 3x - 40 = 0$ **−8, 5**

20. $2x^2 + 7x = -5$ $-\frac{5}{2}, -1$

21. $8x^2 + 3x - 1 = 0$ $\approx -0.59, \approx 0.21$

Find the number of x-intercepts of each function by using the discriminant.

22. $4x^2 - 4x + 1 = y$ **1**

23. $y = 2x^2 + 5x - 25$ **2**

24. $y = \frac{1}{2}x^2 + 8$ **no x-intercepts**

FOCUS ON SAT SUBJECT TESTS

In addition to the SAT, some colleges require the SAT Subject Tests for admission. Colleges that don't require the SAT Subject Tests may still use the scores to learn about your academic background and to place you in the appropriate college math class.

Take the SAT Subject Test in mathematics while the material is still fresh in your mind. You are not expected to be familiar with all of the test content, but you should have completed at least three years of college-prep math.

You may want to time yourself as you take this practice test. It should take you about 6 minutes to complete.

1. The graph below corresponds to which of the following quadratic functions?

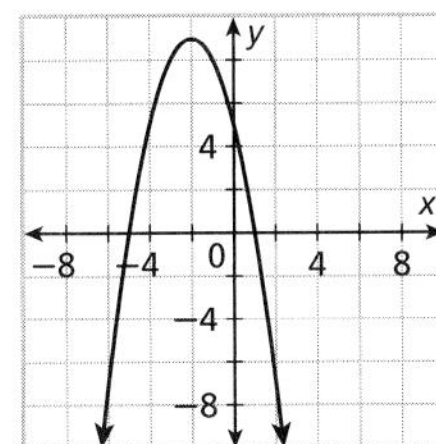

(A) $f(x) = x^2 + 4x - 5$

(B) $f(x) = -x^2 - 4x + 3$

(C) $f(x) = -x^2 + 5x - 4$

(D) $f(x) = -x^2 - 4x + 5$

(E) $f(x) = -x^2 - 3x + 5$

2. What is the sum of the solutions to the equation $9x^2 - 6x = 8$?

(A) $\frac{4}{3}$

(B) $\frac{2}{3}$

(C) $\frac{1}{3}$

(D) $-\frac{2}{3}$

(E) $-\frac{8}{3}$

3. If $h(x) = ax^2 + bx + c$, where $b^2 - 4ac < 0$ and $a < 0$, which of the following statements must be true?

I. The graph of $h(x)$ has no points in the first or second quadrants.
II. The graph of $h(x)$ has no points in the third or fourth quadrants.
III. The graph of $h(x)$ has points in all quadrants.

(A) I only

(B) II only

(C) III only

(D) I and II only

(E) None of the statements are true.

4. What is the axis of symmetry for the graph of a quadratic function whose zeros are −2 and 4?

(A) $x = -2$

(B) $x = 0$

(C) $x = 1$

(D) $x = 2$

(E) $x = 6$

5. How many real-number solutions does $0 = x^2 - 7x + 1$ have?

(A) None

(B) One

(C) Two

(D) All real numbers

(E) It is impossible to determine.

COLLEGE ENTRANCE EXAM PRACTICE

CHAPTER 9

Organizer

Objective: Provide practice for college entrance exams such as the SAT Mathematics Subject Tests.

Online Edition

Resources

College Entrance Exam Practice

Questions on the SAT Mathematics Subject Tests Levels 1 and 2 represent the following math content areas:

	Level	
	1	2
Algebra	30%	18%
Plane Euclidean Geometry	20%	0%
Coordinate Geometry	12%	12%
Three-dimensional Geometry	6%	8%
Trigonometry	8%	20%
Functions	12%	24%
Statistics/Probability	6%	6%
Miscellaneous	6%	12%

Items on this page focus on:
- Algebra
- Functions

Text References:

Item	1	2	3	4	5
Lesson	9-3	9-7	9-8	9-2	9-8

Multiple Choice

1. Students who chose **B** found the correct axis of symmetry but not the correct vertex or *y*-intercept. Students who chose **E** found the correct *y*-intercept but did not find the correct axis of symmetry.
2. Students who chose **A** or **D** found just one of the solutions of the equation. Students who chose **E** tried to find the product of the solutions of the equation.
3. Students who chose **B** did not use the fact that $a < 0$. Students who chose **D** may not realize that if statements I and II are both true, then the graph of $h(x)$ has no points.
4. Students who chose **E** found the distance between $x = -2$ and $x = 4$, not the point halfway between them. Students who chose **A** might not understand the meaning of the axis of symmetry.
5. Students who chose **A** or **B** may have made a computational error in using the discriminant or did not apply it correctly.

Organizer

Objective: Provide opportunities to learn and practice common test-taking strategies.

Online Edition

Extended Response This Strategy for Success explains how students should write an explanation to an extended-response test item. Students need to be aware that even if their calculations are correct, the item will not receive full credit if their explanation does not clearly support their work.

Give students a problem from the chapter. Once students work through the problem, have them explain out loud to a partner how they determined their answer. When students are comfortable doing this, have them write it down in paragraph form. Guide students to use complete sentences.

As students rewrite the response in **Problem 5,** encourage them to write neatly. If students are struggling with forming complete sentences, have them list their thought process in bulleted form.

CHAPTER 9

Extended Response: Explain Your Reasoning

Extended response test items often include multipart questions that evaluate your understanding of a math concept. To receive full credit, you must answer the problem correctly, show all of your work, and explain your reasoning. Use complete sentences and show your problem-solving method clearly.

EXAMPLE 1

Extended Response **Given $\frac{1}{2}x^2 + y = 4x - 3$ and $y = 2x - 12x$, identify which is a quadratic function. Provide an explanation for your decision. For the quadratic function, tell whether the graph of the function opens upward or downward and whether the parabola has a maximum or a minimum. Explain your reasoning.**

Read the solutions provided by two different students.

Student A

The quadratic function is $\frac{1}{2}x^2 + y = 4x - 3$ because it can be written in standard form, $y = -\frac{1}{2}x^2 + 4x - 3$, where a, b, and c are real numbers and $a \neq 0$. The other function, $y = 2x - 12x$, is not quadratic because there is no x^2- term.

The graph of this function will open downward because a, which is equal to $-\frac{1}{2}$, is less than 0. Because the parabola opens downward, the graph will have a maximum.

Excellent Explanation

The response includes the correct answers along with a detailed explanation for each part of the problem. The explanation is written using complete sentences and is presented in an order that is easy to follow and to understand. It is obvious that this student knows how to determine and interpret a quadratic function.

Student B

$\frac{1}{2}x^2 + y = 4x - 3$ There is an x^2.

When I graphed the function on my calculator, I saw a parabola that opened downward.

It had a maximum.

Poor Explanation

The response includes the correct answers, but the explanation does not include details. The student shows a lack of understanding of how to write and interpret a quadratic function in standard form.

Include as many details as possible to support your reasoning. This increases the chance of getting full credit for your response.

Read each test item and answer the questions that follow.

Item A

The height h in feet of a tennis ball x seconds after it is ejected from a serving machine is modeled by the function $h = -2t^2 - t + 10$, where t is the time in seconds after the ball is ejected. When does the ball first hit the ground? Explain your answers.

1. What should a student include in the explanation to receive full credit?
2. Read the two explanations below. Which explanation is better? Why?

Student A

$0 = -2t^2 - t + 10$

$t = 2$ or $t = -2.5$

2 seconds

Student B

When the ball hits the ground, the height will be 0.

$0 = -2t^2 - t + 10$

Solve by factoring: $0 = (-t + 2)(2t + 5)$

$-t + 2 = 0$ or $2t + 5 = 0$

$t = 2$ or $t = -\frac{5}{2}$

Time can't be negative, so the only solution is $t = 2$.

The ball hits the ground after 2 seconds.

Item B

The height of a golf ball can be modeled by the function $y = -5x^2 + 20x + 8$, where y is the height in meters above the ground and x is the time in seconds after the ball is hit. What is the ball's maximum height? How long does it take for the ball to reach this height? Explain.

3. A student correctly found the following answers. Use this information to write a clear and concise explanation.

Axis of symmetry is the vertical line at $x = 2$.
Vertex is at $(2, 28)$.
28 meters; 2 seconds
2 seconds versus 4 seconds

Item C

The function $h = -16t^2 + 96t$ represents the height in feet of a model rocket with an initial vertical velocity of 96 feet per second. Find the time that the rocket is in the air. Explain how you found your answer.

4. Read the two responses below.
   a. Which student provided the better explanation? Why?
   b. What advice would you give the other student to improve his or her explanation?

Student C

Graph the function $h = -16t^2 + 96t$, and then find the zeros. The first zero is when $t = 0$, when the rocket is launched. The second zero is when the rocket hits the ground: $t = 6$. The difference between 6 and 0 is the time that the rocket is in the air: 6 seconds.

Student D

6 seconds.

Graph the function to find how long the rocket is in the air, and find the values where it crosses the x-axis.

Item D

The base of a parallelogram is 12 centimeters more than its height. The area of the parallelogram is 13 square centimeters. Explain how to determine the height and base of the figure. What is the height? What is the base?

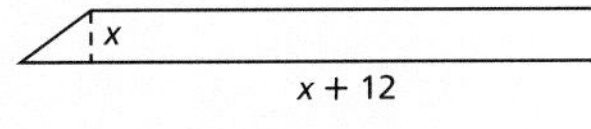

5. Read the following response. Identify any areas that need improvement. Rewrite the response so that it will receive full credit.

$x^2 + 12x + 36 = 49$ Complete the square.
$(x+6)^2 = 49$
$x + 6 = \sqrt{49}$
$x + 6 = \pm 7$; $x = 1$ or -13

base = 13, height = 1

Answers

Possible answers:

1. A student should include the method used to solve the equation, the work done to find the solutions, and an explanation of which solution to the quadratic equation is correct.
2. Student B gave the better explanation. It is written in complete sentences, and the thought process is clear. All parts of the question are explained thoroughly. Student A's explanation is not in complete sentences, and there is not enough support for the answers.
3. I used the function to calculate the axis of symmetry: $x = 2$. Then I used this value to determine the vertex of the function: $(2, 28)$. Therefore, the ball reaches its maximum height of 28 m in 2 s. When I graphed the function, I saw that the zeros of the function were at $t = 0$ and $t = 4$. The ball hits the ground in 4 s. It takes 2 s for the ball to reach its maximum height and 4 s for the ball to hit the ground.

4a. Student C provided the better explanation. This student used complete sentences and gave specific information about the solution of the problem.

b. I would advise student D to give more details to ensure that the answer could be found using his or her explanation. Also, I would advise student D to mention graphing the function and what the zeros of the function relate to.

5. The response should include an explanation of how to determine the height and base of the figure. Units should be included. Use the area formula to write an equation.

$A = bh = (x + 12)x = 13 \rightarrow x^2 + 12x = 13$. Solve for x, the height, by completing the square.
$x^2 + 12x + 36 = 49$
$(x + 6)^2 = 49$
$x + 6 = \sqrt{49}$
$x + 6 = \pm 7$; $x = 1$ or $x = -13$

The height is 1 cm and the base is $x + 12$, or 13 cm. The value of -13 for x can be eliminated because measurements cannot be negative values.

Answers to Test Items

A. yes; D: $0 \leq x \leq 2$; R: $0 \leq y \leq 10$
B. 28 m; 2 s
C. 6 s
D. $h = 1$ cm; $b = 13$ cm

California Standards

Algebra 1 23.0

MASTERING THE STANDARDS

Organizer

Objective: Provide review and practice for Chapters 1–9.

 Online Edition

Resources

 ***Assessment Resources***

Chapter 9 Cumulative Test

 **Focus on California Standards Benchmark Tests and Intervention**

 ***California Standards Practice* CD-ROM**

go.hrw.com
KEYWORD: MA8CA Practice

California Standards

Standard	Exercises
2.0	1
5.0	4, 5
7.0	9
8.0	14
9.0	16
10.0	12
11.0	2, 3
14.0	13, 20d
16.0	17a
17.0	17b
18.0	17a
20.0	15
21.0	6, 7, 11, 18, 20a, 20b
22.0	8, 19

go.hrw.com
Standards Practice Online
KEYWORD: MA8CA Practice

CUMULATIVE ASSESSMENT, CHAPTERS 1–9

Multiple Choice

1. Which expression is NOT equal to the other three?

Ⓐ 0^1 Ⓒ 1^0
Ⓑ 1^1 Ⓓ $(-1)^0$

2. Which of the following shows the complete factorization of $3x^3 - 3x^2 - 6x$?

Ⓐ $3(x^2 + x)(x - 2)$
Ⓑ $3(x^2 - x)(x + 2)$
Ⓒ $3x(x + 1)(x - 2)$
Ⓓ $3x(x - 1)(x + 2)$

3. The area of a circle is $\pi(9x^2 + 42x + 49)$. What is the circumference of the circle?

Ⓐ $\pi(3x + 7)$
Ⓑ $2\pi(3x + 7)$
Ⓒ $2\pi(3x + 7)^2$
Ⓓ $6x + 14$

4. Mike's Bikes charges $10.00 plus $3.50 per hour to rent a bike. The Pedal Palace charges $13.00 plus $2.50 per hour to rent a bike. Which inequality can you use to find the number of hours *h* for which renting a bike at the Pedal Palace is cheaper?

Ⓐ $10h + 3.5 > 13h + 2.5$
Ⓑ $10 + 3.5h > 13 + 2.5h$
Ⓒ $10h + 3.5 < 13h + 2.5$
Ⓓ $10 + 3.5h < 13 + 2.5h$

5. What is the numerical solution to the equation *five less than three times a number equals four more than eight times the number?*

Ⓐ $-\frac{9}{5}$ Ⓒ $-\frac{1}{5}$
Ⓑ $\frac{1}{11}$ Ⓓ $\frac{1}{5}$

6. Which function is graphed below?

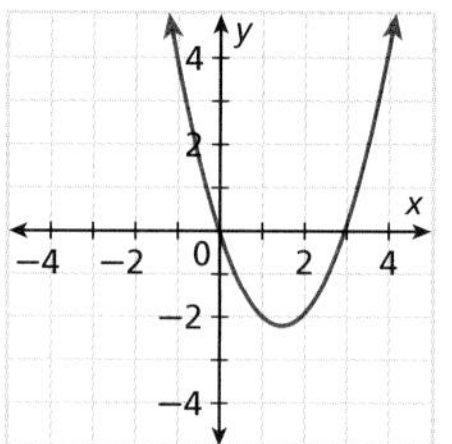

Ⓐ $y = -x^2 - 3x$
Ⓑ $y = -x^2 + 3x$
Ⓒ $y = x^2 + 3x$
Ⓓ $y = x^2 - 3x$

7. Which of the following is the graph of $f(x) = -x^2 + 2$?

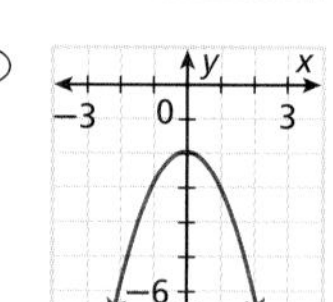

8. At how many points does the graph of $y = x^2 - 2x + 1$ intersect the *x*-axis?

Ⓐ none Ⓒ two
Ⓑ one Ⓓ three

9. What is the slope of the line that passes through the points (4, 7) and (5, 3)?

Ⓐ 4 Ⓒ −4
Ⓑ $\frac{1}{4}$ Ⓓ $-\frac{1}{4}$

 **Multiple Choice** When a quadratic function is written in the form $y = ax^2 + bx + c$, a negative coefficient of x^2 indicates that the graph opens downward. So choices **B** and **C** in **Item 7** can be eliminated.

When multiplying the factors in **Item 12,** students can multiply the first terms to get x^3 and the last terms to get −4. Doing so eliminates choices **A** and **D.**

The problems on many standardized tests are ordered from least to most difficult, but all items are usually worth the same amount of points. If you are stuck on a question near the end of the test, your time may be better spent rechecking your answers to earlier questions.

10. Putting Green Mini Golf charges a $4 golf club rental fee plus $1.25 per game. Good Times Golf charges a $1.25 golf club rental fee plus $3.75 per game. Which system of equations could be solved to determine for how many games the cost is the same at both places?

Ⓐ $\begin{cases} y = 4x + 1.25 \\ y = 3.75 + 1.25x \end{cases}$

Ⓑ $\begin{cases} y = 4 - 1.25x \\ y = -3.75 + 1.25x \end{cases}$

Ⓒ $\begin{cases} y = 1.25x + 4 \\ y = 3.75x + 1.25 \end{cases}$

Ⓓ $\begin{cases} y = 1.25x - 4 \\ y = 1.25x + 3.75 \end{cases}$

11. The graph of which function has an axis of symmetry of $x = -2$?

Ⓐ $y = 2x^2 - x + 3$

Ⓑ $y = 4x^2 + 2x + 3$

Ⓒ $y = x^2 - 2x + 3$

Ⓓ $y = x^2 + 4x + 3$

12. Which polynomial is the product of $x - 4$ and $x^2 - 4x + 1$?

Ⓐ $-4x^2 + 17x - 4$

Ⓑ $x^3 - 8x^2 + 17x - 4$

Ⓒ $x^3 + 17x - 4$

Ⓓ $x^3 - 15x + 4$

Gridded Response

13. The equation $2x^2 - 6x - 20 = 0$ has two solutions. One solution is -2. What is the other solution? **5**

14. What is the slope of a line that is parallel to the line described by $6x - 9y = 2$? $\frac{2}{3}$

15. Use the Quadratic Formula to find the positive solution of $4x^2 = 10x + 2$. Round your answer to the nearest hundredth. **2.69**

Short Response

16. Use the system $\begin{cases} y \le \frac{1}{3}x + 1 \\ y \le -2x + 2 \end{cases}$ for the following.

a. Sketch the region defined by the system.

b. Is $(1, -2)$ a solution of the system? Explain how you can use your graph to decide.
Yes; $(1, -2)$ is in the shaded region.

17. Consider the relation shown in the graph.

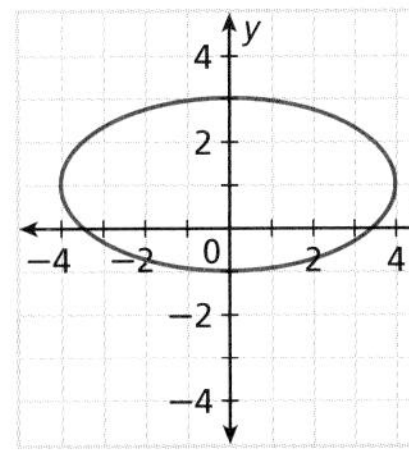

a. No; there are many domain values that have more than one range value.

a. Is the relation a function? Explain.

b. What are the domain and range of the relation? **D: $-4 \le x \le 4$; R: $-1 \le y \le 3$**

18. a. Show how to solve $x^2 - 2x - 8 = 0$ by graphing the related function. Show all your work. **-2, 4**

b. Show another way to solve the equation in part **a**. Show all your work.
Check students' work.

19. What can you say about the value of a if the equation $y = ax^2 - 8$ has no solutions? Explain. $a < 0$

Extended Response

20. The graph shows the quadratic function $f(x) = ax^2 + bx + c$.

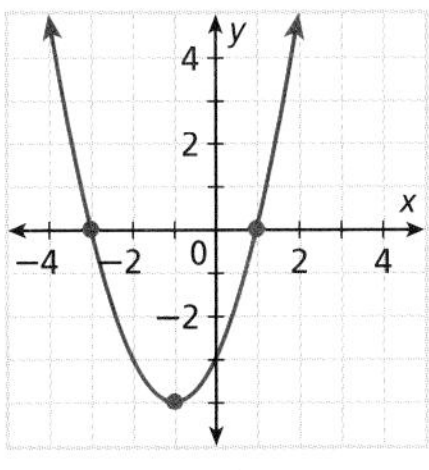

a. What are the solutions of the equation $0 = ax^2 + bx + c$? Explain how you know. **-3, 1**

b. If the point $(-5, 12)$ lies on the graph of $f(x)$, the point $(a, 12)$ also lies on the graph. Find the value of a. $a = 3$

c. What do you know about the relationship between the values of a and b? Use the coordinates of the vertex in your explanation. $b = 2a$

d. Use what you know about solving quadratic equations by factoring to make a conjecture about the values of a, b, and c in the function $f(x) = ax^2 + bx + c$.

Short-Response Rubric

Items 16–19

2 Points = The student's answer is an accurate and complete execution of the task or tasks.

1 Point = The student's answer contains attributes of an appropriate response but is flawed.

0 Points = The student's answer contains no attributes of an appropriate response.

Extended-Response Rubric

Item 20

4 Points = The student writes the correct solutions and an explanation in part **a,** gives a correct x-value and correct explanation in part **b,** explains the relationship between a and b and uses the vertex in the explanation in part **c,** and uses solutions to find factors and the values for a, b, and c in part **d.**

3 Points = The student writes the correct solutions and an explanation in part **a,** gives a correct x-value and some explanation in part **b,** explains the relationship between a and b with minor errors and uses the vertex in the explanation in part **c,** and uses solutions to find factors and the values for a, b, and c in part **d.**

2 Points = The student writes one correct solution with some explanation in part **a,** gives a correct x-value and some explanation in part **b,** explains the relationship between a and b with minor errors and does not use the vertex in the explanation in part **c,** and uses solutions to find only one factor and does not find the values for a, b, and c in part **d;** or the student attempts to answer all parts of the problem and answers two correctly.

1 Point = The student answers one part correctly but does not attempt all parts, or the student attempts to answer all parts of the problem but does not correctly answer any part.

0 Points = The student does not answer correctly and does not attempt all parts of the problem.

Answers

16a.

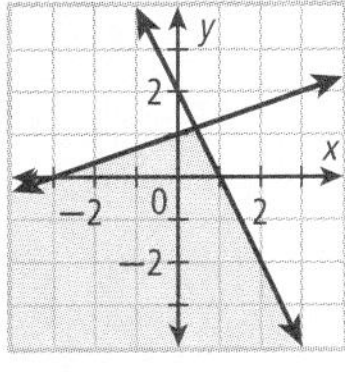

20d. If the solutions are -3 and 1, then $(x + 3)(x - 1) = 0$. So the equation is $x^2 + 2x - 3 = 0$, and $a = 1$, $b = 2$, and $c = -3$.

Rational Functions and Equations

✔	Grade-level Standard
◀	Review
▶	Beyond the Standards
A	Assessment
O	Optional

Pacing Guide

Calendar Planner
Teacher's One-Stop Planner®

Lesson/Lab	California Standards	Time	Advanced Students	Benchmark Students	Strategic Students
LAB Model Inverse Variation	Preparation for 13.0	25 min	O	✔	✔
10-1 Inverse Variation	Preparation for 13.0, 17.0	50 min	✔	✔	✔
10-2 Rational Functions	13.0, 17.0	50 min	✔	✔	✔
10-3 Simplifying Rational Expressions	12.0	50 min	✔	✔	✔
LAB Graph Rational Functions	13.0	25 min	✔	✔	✔
Concept Connection	15.0, 17.0	25 min	A	A	O
Ready to Go On?		25 min	A	A	A
10-4 Multiplying and Dividing Rational Expressions	13.0	75 min	✔	✔	✔
10-5 Adding and Subtracting Rational Expressions	13.0, 15.0	75 min	✔	✔	✔
LAB Model Polynomial Division	10.0	25 min	✔	✔	✔
10-6 Dividing Polynomials	10.0, 12.0	50 min	✔	✔	✔
10-7 Solving Rational Equations	Preparation for 15.0	50 min	✔	✔	✔
10-8 Applying Rational Equations	15.0	50 min	✔	✔	✔
Concept Connection	Preparation for 15.0	25 min	A	A	O
Ready to Go On?		25 min	A	A	A
Study Guide: Review		50 min	✔	✔	✔
Chapter Test	10.0, 12.0, 13.0, 15.0	50 min	A	A	A

* **Benchmark students** are achieving at or near grade level.

** **Strategic students** may be a year or more below grade level, and may require additional time for intervention.

Countdown to Mastery, Weeks 22, 23, 24

ONGOING ASSESSMENT and INTERVENTION

	DIAGNOSE	PRESCRIBE
Assess Prior Knowledge	**Before Chapter 10**	
	Diagnose readiness for the chapter. **Are You Ready?** SE p. 623	Prescribe intervention. ***Are You Ready? Intervention*** Skills 10, 48, 59, 63, 66
Formative Assessment	**Before Every Lesson**	
	Diagnose readiness for the lesson. **Warm Up** TE, every lesson	Prescribe intervention. **Skills Bank** pp. SB1–SB32 **Review for Mastery** CRF Chapters 1–10
	During Every Lesson	
	Diagnose understanding of lesson concepts. **Questioning Strategies** TE, every example **Check It Out!** SE, every example **Think and Discuss** SE, every lesson **Write About It** SE, every lesson **Journal** TE, every lesson	Prescribe intervention. **Reading Strategies** CRF, every lesson ***Success for ELL*** pp. 129–144 ***Lesson Tutorial Videos*** Chapter 10
	After Every Lesson	
	Diagnose mastery of lesson concepts. **Lesson Quiz** TE, every lesson **Alternative Assessment** TE, every lesson **Ready to Go On?** SE pp. 651, 685 ***Test and Practice Generator***	Prescribe intervention. **Review for Mastery** CRF, every lesson **Problem Solving** CRF, every lesson ***Ready to Go On? Intervention*** Chapter 10 ***Homework Help Online***
	Before Chapter 10 Testing	
	Diagnose mastery of concepts in the chapter. **Ready to Go On?** SE pp. 651, 685 **Concept Connection** SE pp. 650, 684 **Section Quizzes** AR pp. 185–186 ***Test and Practice Generator***	Prescribe intervention. ***Ready to Go On? Intervention*** Chapter 10 **Scaffolding Questions** TE pp. 650, 684
	Before Assessment of California Standards	
	Diagnose mastery of California Standards. ***Focus on California Standards: Benchmark Tests*** **Mastering the Standards** SE pp. 694–695 ***California Standards Practice* CD-ROM**	Prescribe intervention. ***Focus on California Standards: Intervention***
Summative Assessment	**After Chapter 10**	
	Check mastery of chapter concepts. **Multiple-Choice Tests (Forms A, B, C)** **Free-Response Tests (Forms A, B, C)** **Performance Assessment** AR pp. 199–200 ***Test and Practice Generator***	Prescribe intervention. **Review for Mastery** CRF, every lesson ***Lesson Tutorial Videos*** Chapter 10

KEY: **SE** = *Student Edition* **TE** = *Teacher's Edition* **CRF** = *Chapter Resource File* **AR** = *Assessment Resources*  Available online Available on CD-ROM

Supporting the Teacher

Chapter 10 Resource File

Family Involvement
pp. 1–4, 29–32

Practice A, B, C
pp. 5–7, 13–15, 21–23, 33–35, 41–43, 49–51, 57–59, 65–67

Review for Mastery
pp. 8–9, 16–17, 24–25, 36–37, 44–45, 52–53, 60–61, 68–69

Challenge
pp. 10, 18, 26, 38, 46, 54, 62, 70

Problem Solving
pp. 11, 19, 27, 39, 47, 55, 63, 71

Reading Strategies ELL
pp. 12, 20, 28, 40, 48, 56, 64, 72

Workbooks

Homework and Practice Workbook SPANISH
Teacher's Edition .... pp. 65–72

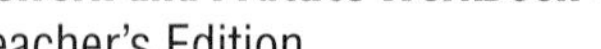

Know-It Notebook SPANISH
Teacher's Guide .... Chapter 10

Review for Mastery Workbook SPANISH
Teacher's Guide .... pp. 129–144

Focus on California Standards: Intervention Workbook SPANISH
Teacher's Guide

Teacher Tools

Power Presentations
Complete PowerPoint® presentations for Chapter 10 lessons

Lesson Tutorial Videos SPANISH
Holt authors Ed Burger and Freddie Renfro present tutorials to support the Chapter 10 lessons.

Teacher's One-Stop Planner SPANISH
Easy access to all Chapter 10 resources and assessments, as well as software for lesson planning, test generation, and puzzle creation

IDEA Works!
Key Chapter 10 resources and assessments modified to address special learning needs

Solutions Key .... Chapter 10

Interactive Answers and Solutions

TechKeys

Lab Resources

Project Teacher Support

Parent Resources 

Transparencies

Lesson Transparencies, Volume 2 .... Chapter 10
- Teacher Tools
- Warm-ups
- Teaching Transparencies
- Lesson Quizzes

Alternate Openers: Explorations .... pp. 65–72

Countdown to Mastery .... pp. 43–48

Know-It Notebook .... Chapter 10
- Vocabulary
- Key Concepts
- Graphic Organizers
- Chapter Review
- Big Ideas

Technology Highlights for the Teacher

Power Presentations
Dynamic presentations to engage students. Complete PowerPoint® presentations for every lesson in Chapter 10.

2-1 Solving One-Step Equations

Isolate a variable by using inverse operations which "undo" operations on the variable.

An equation is like a balanced scale. To keep the balance, perform the same operation on both sides.

Inverse Operations	
Operation	Inverse Operation
Addition	Subtraction
Subtraction	Addition

One-Stop Planner SPANISH
Easy access to Chapter 10 resources and assessments. Includes lesson planning, test generation, and puzzle creation software.

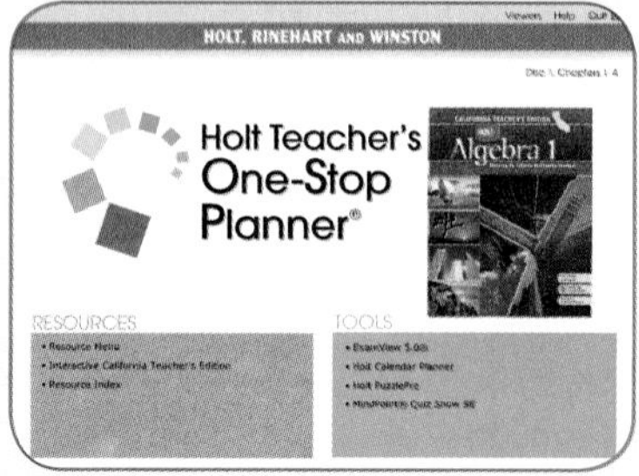

Premier Online Edition SPANISH
Includes Tutorial Videos, Lesson Activities, Lesson Quizzes, Homework Help, Chapter Project and more.

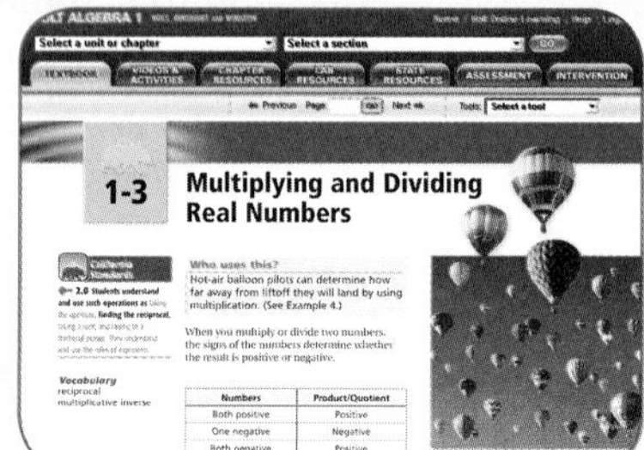

KEY: **SE** = *Student Edition* **TE** = *Teacher's Edition*  English Language Learners  Spanish available 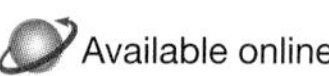 Available online Available on CD-ROM

Universal Access

Teaching Tips to help all students appear throughout the chapter. A few that target specific students are included in the lists below.

Strategic Students

Practice A .... CRF, every lesson
Review for Mastery .... CRF, every lesson
Reading Strategies .... CRF, every lesson
Academic Vocabulary Connections .... TE p. 624
Modeling .... TE pp. 636, 675
Questioning Strategies .... TE, every example
Ready to Go On? Intervention .... Chapter 10
Know-It Notebook SPANISH .... Chapter 10
Homework Help Online
Lesson Tutorial Videos SPANISH
Online Interactivities SPANISH

Special Needs Students

Practice A .... CRF, every lesson
Review for Mastery .... CRF, every lesson
Reading Strategies .... CRF, every lesson
Academic Vocabulary Connections .... TE p. 624
Inclusion .... TE pp. 643, 644, 654, 660, 669, 676, 677
IDEA Works! Modified Resources .... Chapter 10
Ready to Go On? Intervention .... Chapter 10
Know-It Notebook SPANISH .... Chapter 10
Lesson Tutorial Videos SPANISH
Online Interactivities SPANISH

English Learners

ENGLISH LANGUAGE LEARNERS

Reading Strategies .... CRF, every lesson
Vocabulary Exercises .... SE, every exercise set
Academic Vocabulary Connections .... TE p. 624
English Language Learners .... TE p. 635, 675
Language Support .... TE pp. 635, 675
Success for English Language Learners .... Chapter 10
Know-It Notebook SPANISH .... Chapter 10
Multilingual Glossary
Lesson Tutorial Videos SPANISH

Benchmark Students

Practice B .... CRF, every lesson
Problem Solving .... CRF, every lesson
Academic Vocabulary Connections .... TE p. 624
Questioning Strategies .... TE, every example
Ready to Go On? Intervention .... Chapter 10
Know-It Notebook SPANISH .... Chapter 10
Homework Help Online
Online Interactivities SPANISH

Advanced Students

Practice C .... CRF, every lesson
Challenge .... CRF, every lesson
Reading and Writing Math EXTENSION .... TE p. 625
Concept Connection EXTENSION .... TE pp. 650, 684
Advanced Learners/GATE .... TE p. 661
Ready to Go On? Enrichment .... Chapter 10

Technology Highlights for Universal Access

Lesson Tutorial Videos SPANISH

Starring Holt authors Ed Burger and Freddie Renfro! Live tutorials to support every lesson in Chapter 10.

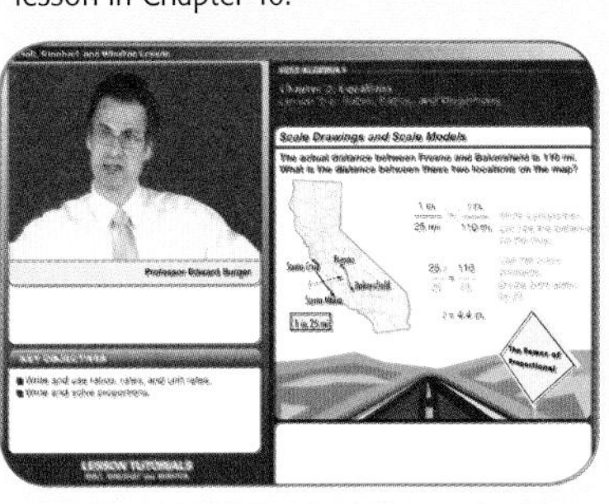

Multilingual Glossary

Searchable glossary includes definitions in English, Spanish, Vietnamese, Chinese, Hmong, Korean, and other languages.

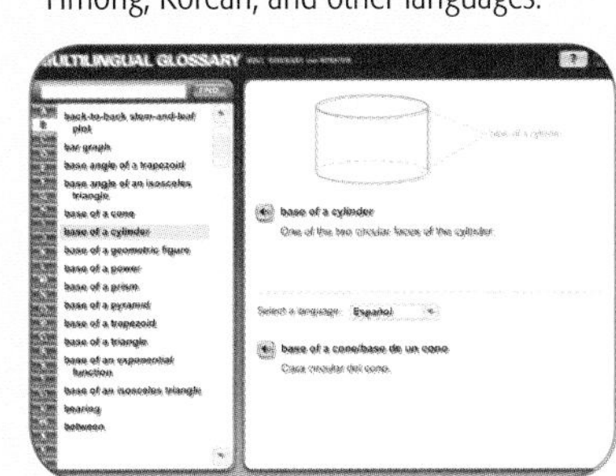

Online Interactivities SPANISH

Interactive tutorials provide visually engaging alternative opportunities to learn concepts and master skills.

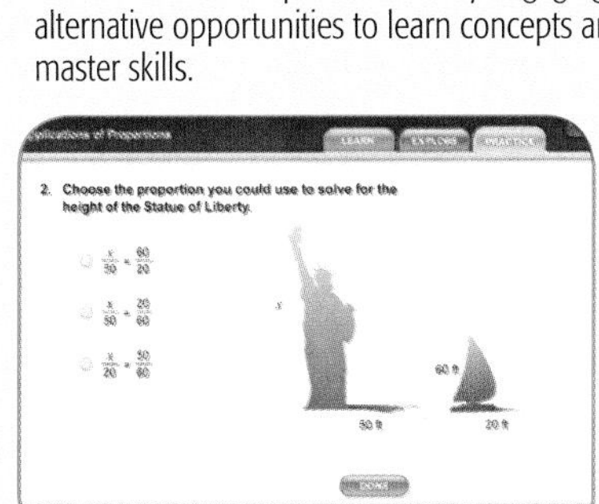

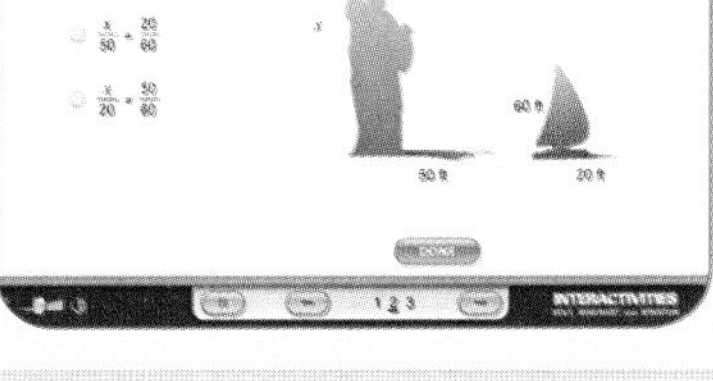

KEY: **SE** = *Student Edition* **TE** = *Teacher's Edition* **CRF** = *Chapter Resource File* SPANISH Spanish available  Available online  Available on CD-ROM

Ongoing Assessment

Assessing Prior Knowledge

Determine whether students have the prerequisite concepts and skills for success in Chapter 10.

Are You Ready? SPANISH .... SE p. 623
Warm Up .... TE, every lesson

Chapter and Standards Assessment

Provide review and practice for Chapter 10 and standards mastery.

Concept Connection .... SE pp. 650, 684
Study Guide: Review .... SE pp. 686–689
Strategies for Success .... SE pp. 692–693
Mastering the Standards .... SE pp. 694–695
College Entrance Exam Practice .... SE p. 691
***Countdown to Mastery* Transparencies** .... pp. 43–48
Focus on California Standards: Benchmark Tests
Focus on California Standards: Intervention Workbook
***California Standards Practice* CD-ROM** SPANISH
IDEA Works! Modified Worksheets and Tests

Alternative Assessment

Assess students' understanding of Chapter 10 concepts and combined problem-solving skills.

Alternative Assessment .... TE, every lesson
Performance Assessment .... AR pp. 199–200
Portfolio Assessment .... AR p. xxxiii
Chapter 10 Project

Daily Assessment

Provide formative assessment for each day of Chapter 10.

Questioning Strategies .... TE, every example
Think and Discuss .... SE, every lesson
Check It Out! Exercises .... SE, every example
Write About It .... SE, every lesson
Journal .... TE, every lesson
Lesson Quiz .... TE, every lesson
Alternative Assessment .... TE, every lesson
IDEA Works! Modified Lesson Quizzes .... Chapter 10

Weekly Assessment

Provide formative assessment for each week of Chapter 10.

Concept Connection .... SE pp. 650, 684
Ready to Go On? .... SE pp. 651, 685
Cumulative Assessment .... SE pp. 694–695
Test and Practice Generator SPANISH .... *One-Stop Planner*

Formal Assessment

Provide summative assessment of Chapter 10 mastery.

Section Quizzes .... AR pp. 185–186
Chapter 10 Test SPANISH .... SE p. 690
Chapter Test (Levels A, B, C) .... AR pp. 187–198
• Multiple Choice • Free Response
Cumulative Test .... AR pp. 201–204
Test and Practice Generator SPANISH .... *One-Stop Planner*

Technology Highlights for Ongoing Assessment

Automatically assess readiness and prescribe intervention for Chapter 10 prerequisite skills.

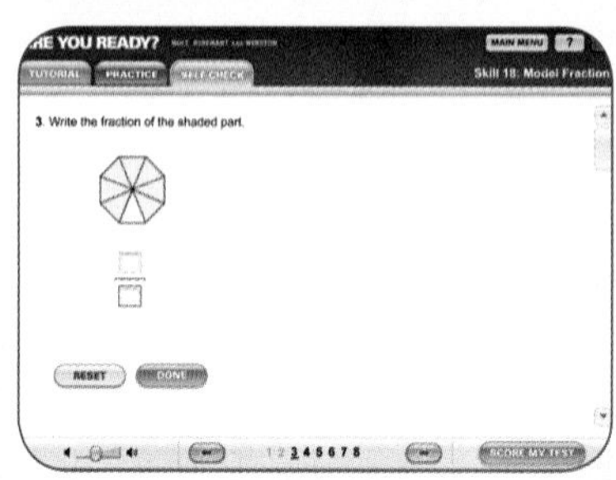

Automatically assess understanding of and prescribe intervention for Sections 10A and 10B.

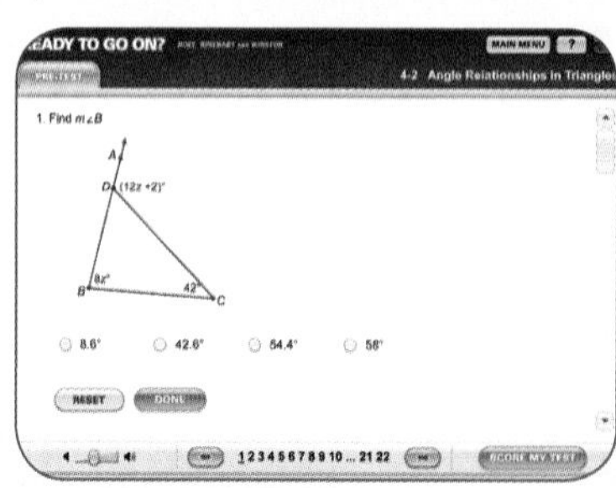

Automatically assess proficiency with California Algebra I Standards and provide intervention.

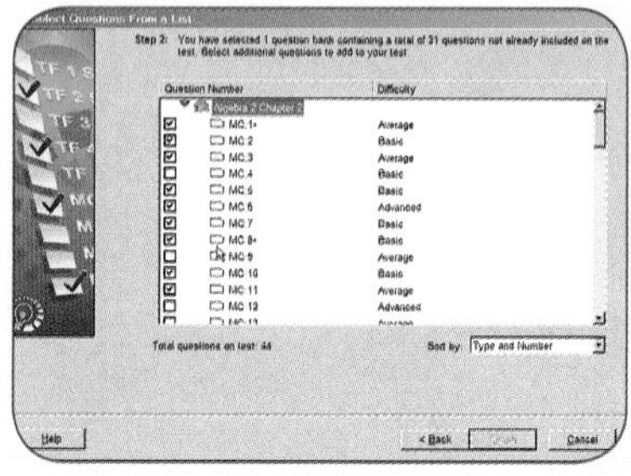

KEY: **SE** = *Student Edition* **TE** = *Teacher's Edition* **AR** = Assessment Resources  Spanish available  Available online Available on CD-ROM

Formal Assessment

Three levels (A, B, C) of multiple-choice and free-response chapter tests are available in the *Assessment Resources.*

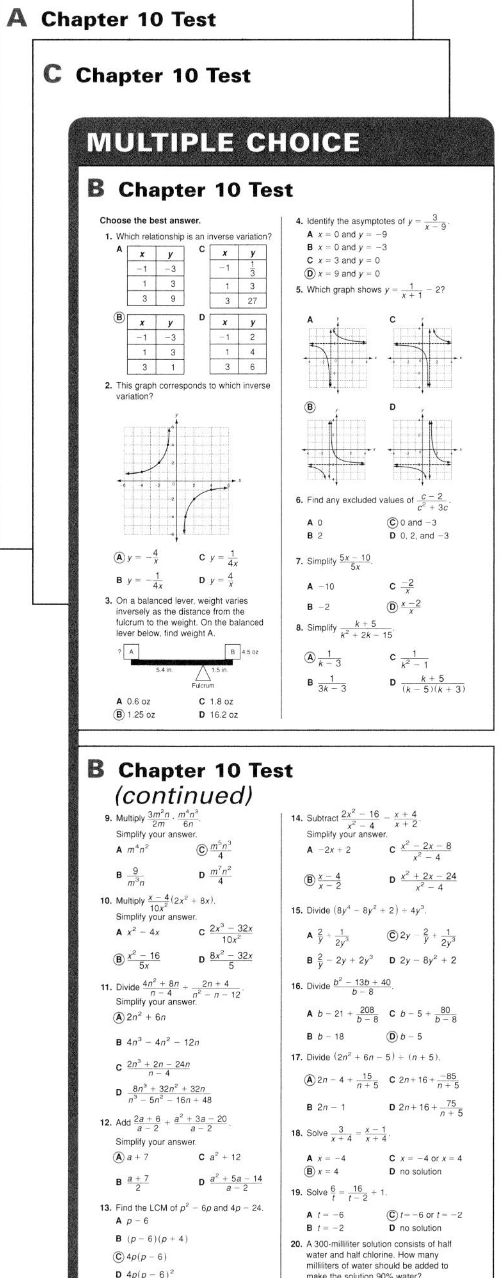

A Chapter 10 Test

C Chapter 10 Test

MULTIPLE CHOICE

B Chapter 10 Test

Choose the best answer.

1. Which relationship is an inverse variation?

A

x	y
−1	−3
1	3
3	9

C

x	y
−1	$\frac{1}{3}$
1	3
3	27

Ⓑ

x	y
−1	−3
1	3
3	1

D

x	y
−1	2
1	4
3	6

2. This graph corresponds to which inverse variation?

Ⓐ $y = -\frac{4}{x}$ C $y = \frac{1}{4x}$

B $y = -\frac{1}{4x}$ D $y = \frac{4}{x}$

3. On a balanced lever, weight varies inversely as the distance from the fulcrum to the weight. On the balanced lever below, find weight A.

A 0.6 oz C 1.8 oz

Ⓑ 1.25 oz D 16.2 oz

4. Identify the asymptotes of $y = \frac{3}{x-9}$.

A $x = 0$ and $y = -9$

B $x = 0$ and $y = -3$

C $x = 3$ and $y = 0$

Ⓓ $x = 9$ and $y = 0$

5. Which graph shows $y = \frac{1}{x+1} - 2$?

A C Ⓑ D

6. Find any excluded values of $\frac{c-2}{c^2+3c}$.

A 0 Ⓒ 0 and −3

B 2 D 0, 2, and −3

7. Simplify $\frac{5x-10}{5x}$.

A −10 C $\frac{-2}{x}$

B −2 Ⓓ $\frac{x-2}{x}$

8. Simplify $\frac{k+5}{k^2+2k-15}$.

Ⓐ $\frac{1}{k-3}$ C $\frac{1}{k^2-1}$

B $\frac{1}{3k-3}$ D $\frac{k+5}{(k-5)(k+3)}$

B Chapter 10 Test (continued)

9. Multiply $\frac{3m^2n}{2m} \cdot \frac{m^4n^3}{6n}$. Simplify your answer.

A m^4n^2 Ⓒ $\frac{m^5n^3}{4}$

B $\frac{9}{m^3n}$ D $\frac{m^7n^2}{4}$

10. Multiply $\frac{x-4}{10x^2}(2x^2+8x)$. Simplify your answer.

A $x^2 - 4x$ C $\frac{2x^3-32x}{10x^2}$

Ⓑ $\frac{x^2-16}{5x}$ D $\frac{8x^2-32x}{5}$

11. Divide $\frac{4n^2+8n}{n-4} \div \frac{2n+4}{n^2-n-12}$. Simplify your answer.

Ⓐ $2n^2 + 6n$

B $4n^3 - 4n^2 - 12n$

C $\frac{2n^3+2n-24n}{n-4}$

D $\frac{8n^3+32n^2+32n}{n^3-5n^2-16n+48}$

12. Add $\frac{2a+6}{a-2} + \frac{a^2+3a-20}{a-2}$. Simplify your answer.

Ⓐ $a + 7$ C $a^2 + 12$

B $\frac{a+7}{2}$ D $\frac{a^2+5a-14}{a-2}$

13. Find the LCM of $p^2 - 6p$ and $4p - 24$.

A $p - 6$

B $(p-6)(p+4)$

Ⓒ $4p(p-6)$

D $4p(p-6)^2$

14. Subtract $\frac{2x^2-16}{x^2-4} - \frac{x+4}{x+2}$. Simplify your answer.

A $-2x+2$ C $\frac{x^2-2x-8}{x^2-4}$

Ⓑ $\frac{x-4}{x-2}$ D $\frac{x^2+2x-24}{x^2-4}$

15. Divide $(8y^4 - 8y^2 + 2) \div 4y^3$.

A $\frac{2}{y} + \frac{1}{2y^3}$ Ⓒ $2y - \frac{2}{y} + \frac{1}{2y^3}$

B $\frac{2}{y} - 2y + 2y^3$ D $2y - 8y^2 + 2$

16. Divide $\frac{b^2-13b+40}{b-8}$.

A $b - 21 + \frac{208}{b-8}$ C $b - 5 + \frac{80}{b-8}$

B $b - 18$ Ⓓ $b - 5$

17. Divide $(2n^2 + 6n - 5) \div (n + 5)$.

Ⓐ $2n - 4 + \frac{15}{n+5}$ C $2n + 16 + \frac{-85}{n+5}$

B $2n - 1$ D $2n + 16 + \frac{75}{n+5}$

18. Solve $\frac{3}{x+4} = \frac{x-1}{x+4}$.

A $x = -4$ C $x = -4$ or $x = 4$

Ⓑ $x = 4$ D no solution

19. Solve $\frac{6}{t} = \frac{16}{t-2} + 1$.

A $t = -6$ Ⓒ $t = -6$ or $t = -2$

B $t = -2$ D no solution

20. A 300-milliliter solution consists of half water and half chlorine. How many milliliters of water should be added to make the solution 90% water?

A 33.3 ml C 150 ml

B 133.3 ml Ⓓ 1200 ml

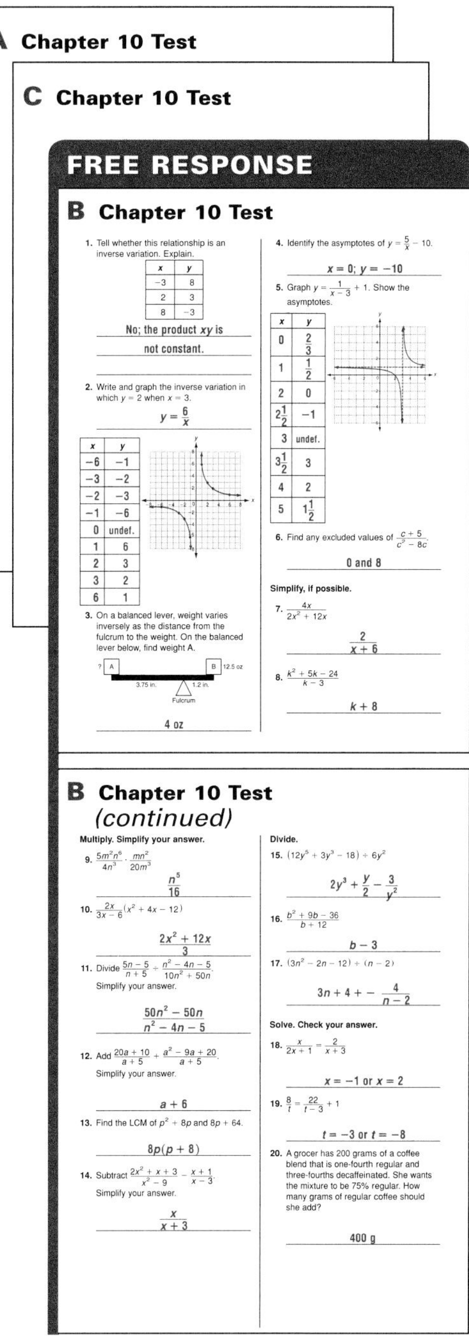

A Chapter 10 Test

C Chapter 10 Test

FREE RESPONSE

B Chapter 10 Test

1. Tell whether this relationship is an inverse variation. Explain.

x	y
−3	8
2	3
8	−3

No; the product *xy* is not constant.

2. Write and graph the inverse variation in which $y = 2$ when $x = 3$.

$y = \frac{6}{x}$

x	y
−6	−1
−3	−2
−2	−3
−1	−6
0	undef.
1	6
2	3
3	2
6	1

3. On a balanced lever, weight varies inversely as the distance from the fulcrum to the weight. On the balanced lever below, find weight A.

4 oz

4. Identify the asymptotes of $y = \frac{5}{x} - 10$.

$x = 0$; $y = -10$

5. Graph $y = \frac{1}{x-3} + 1$. Show the asymptotes.

x	y
0	$\frac{2}{3}$
1	$\frac{1}{2}$
2	0
$2\frac{1}{2}$	−1
3	undef.
$3\frac{1}{2}$	3
4	2
5	$1\frac{1}{2}$

6. Find any excluded values of $\frac{c+5}{c^2-8c}$.

0 and 8

Simplify, if possible.

7. $\frac{4x}{2x^2+12x}$

$\frac{2}{x+6}$

8. $\frac{k^2+5k-24}{k-3}$

$k + 8$

B Chapter 10 Test (continued)

Multiply. Simplify your answer.

9. $\frac{5m^2n^6}{4n^3} \cdot \frac{mn^2}{20m^3}$

$\frac{n^5}{16}$

10. $\frac{2x}{3x-6}(x^2+4x-12)$

$\frac{2x^2+12x}{3}$

11. Divide $\frac{5n-5}{n+5} \div \frac{n^2-4n-5}{10n^2+50n}$. Simplify your answer.

$\frac{50n^2-50n}{n^2-4n-5}$

12. Add $\frac{20a+10}{a+5} + \frac{a^2-9a+20}{a+5}$. Simplify your answer.

$a + 6$

13. Find the LCM of $p^2 + 8p$ and $8p + 64$.

$8p(p+8)$

14. Subtract $\frac{2x^2+x+3}{x^2-9} - \frac{x+1}{x-3}$. Simplify your answer.

$\frac{x}{x+3}$

Divide.

15. $(12y^5 + 3y^3 - 18) \div 6y^2$

$2y^3 + \frac{y}{2} - \frac{3}{y^2}$

16. $\frac{b^2+9b-36}{b+12}$

$b - 3$

17. $(3n^2 - 2n - 12) \div (n - 2)$

$3n + 4 + -\frac{4}{n-2}$

Solve. Check your answer.

18. $\frac{x}{2x+1} = \frac{2}{x+3}$

$x = -1$ or $x = 2$

19. $\frac{8}{t} = \frac{22}{t-3} + 1$

$t = -3$ or $t = -8$

20. A grocer has 200 grams of a coffee blend that is one-fourth regular and three-fourths decaffeinated. She wants the mixture to be 75% regular. How many grams of regular coffee should she add?

400 g

Modified tests and worksheets found in *IDEA Works!*

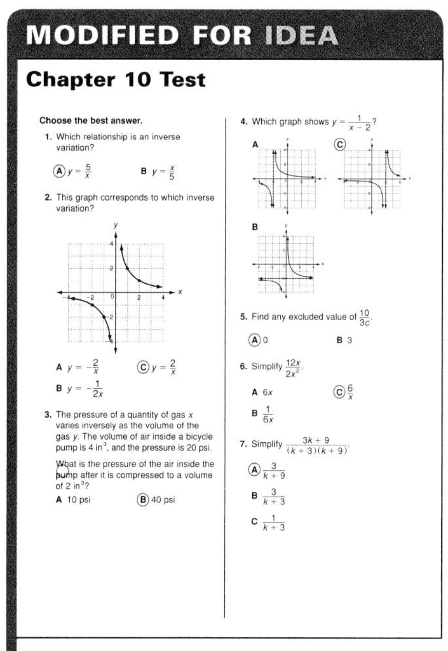

MODIFIED FOR IDEA

Chapter 10 Test

Choose the best answer.

1. Which relationship is an inverse variation?

Ⓐ $y = \frac{5}{x}$ B $y = \frac{x}{5}$

2. This graph corresponds to which inverse variation?

A $y = -\frac{2}{x}$ Ⓒ $y = \frac{2}{x}$

B $y = -\frac{1}{2x}$

3. The pressure of a quantity of gas *x* varies inversely as the volume of the gas *y*. The volume of air inside a bicycle pump is 4 in³, and the pressure is 20 psi. What is the pressure of the air inside the pump after it is compressed to a volume of 2 in³?

A 10 psi Ⓑ 40 psi

4. Which graph shows $y = \frac{1}{x-2}$?

A Ⓒ B

5. Find any excluded value of $\frac{10}{3c}$.

Ⓐ 0 B 3

6. Simplify $\frac{12x}{2x^2}$.

A $6x$ Ⓒ $\frac{6}{x}$

B $\frac{1}{6x}$

7. Simplify $\frac{3k+9}{(k+3)(k+9)}$.

Ⓐ $\frac{3}{k+9}$

B $\frac{3}{k+3}$

C $\frac{1}{k+3}$

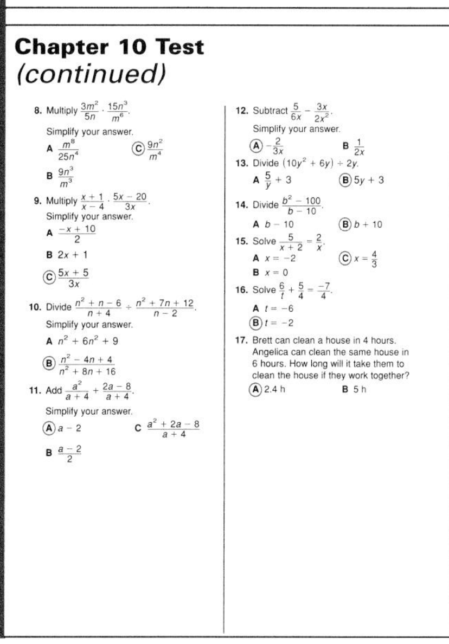

Chapter 10 Test (continued)

8. Multiply $\frac{3m^2}{5n} \cdot \frac{15n^3}{m^4}$. Simplify your answer.

A $\frac{m^6}{25n^4}$ Ⓒ $\frac{9n^2}{m^2}$

B $\frac{9n^3}{m^3}$

9. Multiply $\frac{x+1}{x-4} \cdot \frac{5x-20}{3x}$. Simplify your answer.

A $\frac{-x+10}{2}$

B $2x + 1$

Ⓒ $\frac{5x+5}{3x}$

10. Divide $\frac{n^2+n-6}{n+4} \div \frac{n^2+7n+12}{n-2}$. Simplify your answer.

A $n^2 + 6n^2 + 9$

Ⓑ $\frac{n^2-4n+4}{n^2+8n+16}$

11. Add $\frac{a^2}{a+4} + \frac{2a-8}{a+4}$. Simplify your answer.

Ⓐ $a - 2$ C $\frac{a^2+2a-8}{a+4}$

B $\frac{a-2}{2}$

12. Subtract $\frac{5}{6x} - \frac{3x}{2x^2}$. Simplify your answer.

Ⓐ $-\frac{2}{3x}$ B $\frac{1}{2x}$

13. Divide $(10y^2 + 6y) \div 2y$.

A $\frac{5}{y} + 3$ Ⓑ $5y + 3$

14. Divide $\frac{b^2-100}{b-10}$.

A $b - 10$ Ⓑ $b + 10$

15. Solve $\frac{5}{x+2} = \frac{2}{x}$.

A $x = -2$ Ⓒ $x = \frac{4}{3}$

B $x = 0$

16. Solve $\frac{6}{t} + \frac{5}{4} = \frac{-7}{4}$.

A $t = -6$

Ⓑ $t = -2$

17. Brett can clean a house in 4 hours. Angelica can clean the same house in 6 hours. How long will it take them to clean the house if they work together?

Ⓐ 2.4 h B 5 h

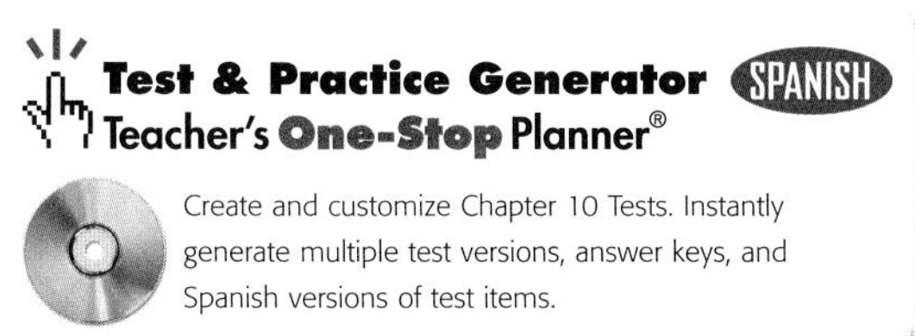

Create and customize Chapter 10 Tests. Instantly generate multiple test versions, answer keys, and Spanish versions of test items.

CHAPTER 10

SECTION **10A**

Rational Functions and Expressions

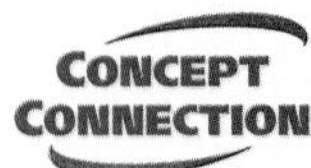

CONCEPT CONNECTION On page 650, students write, solve, and graph functions to model real-world construction situations.

Exercises designed to prepare students for success on the Concept Connection can be found on pages 632, 640, and 647.

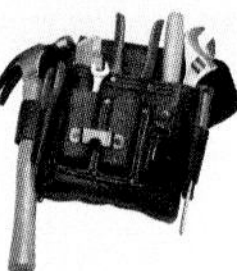

SECTION **10B**

Operations with Rational Expressions

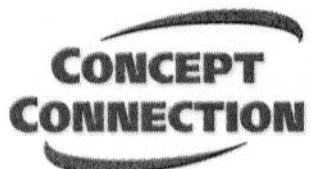

CONCEPT CONNECTION On page 684, students write, solve, and graph functions to model a real-world projection situation.

Exercises designed to prepare students for success on the Concept Connection can be found on pages 657, 664, 672, 677, and 682.

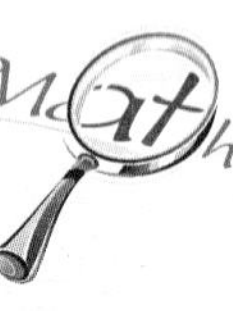

Algebra in *California*

This aerial view of the Golden Gate Bridge demonstrates perspective. Problems involving perspective can be solved by using ratios and rational expressions and equations. In this chapter, students will see how rational expressions, equations, and functions can be used in a variety of situations.

CHAPTER 10

Rational Functions and Equations

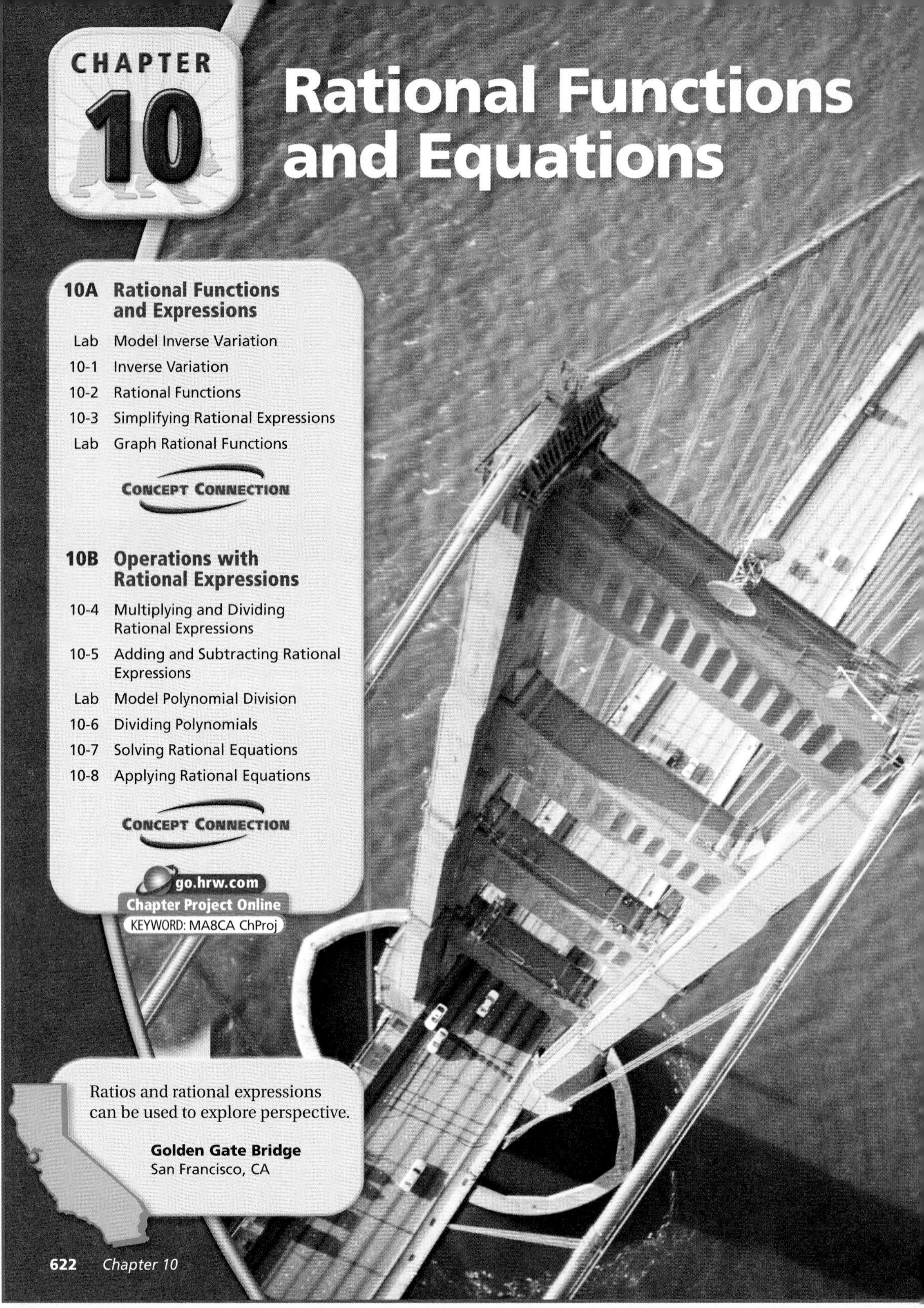

go.hrw.com
Chapter Project Online
KEYWORD: MA8CA ChProj

Ratios and rational expressions can be used to explore perspective.

Golden Gate Bridge
San Francisco, CA

622 *Chapter 10*

About the Project

By Design

In the first activity, students investigate linear perspective—how objects appear smaller when farther away. In the second activity, students design a new yogurt drink container that comfortably fits in an eight-year-old child's hand and that minimizes the cost of producing the container.

Project Resources

All project resources for teachers and students are provided online.

Materials:

- ruler
- customary tape measure
- metric tape measure
- cylindrical containers, such as water bottles, soda cans, juice cans, and soup cans

go.hrw.com
Project Teacher Support
KEYWORD: MA8CA ProjectTS

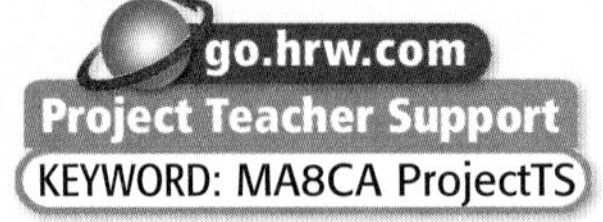

ARE YOU READY?

Vocabulary

Match each term on the left with a definition on the right.

1. perfect-square trinomial **F**
2. greatest common factor **A**
3. monomial **B**
4. polynomial **E**
5. reciprocals **C**

A. the greatest factor that is shared by two or more terms
B. a number, a variable, or a product of numbers and variables with whole-number exponents
C. two numbers whose product is 1
D. a polynomial with three terms
E. the sum or difference of monomials
F. a trinomial that is the result of squaring a binomial

Simplify Fractions

Simplify.

6. $\frac{12}{4}$ **3**
7. $\frac{100}{36}$ $\mathbf{2\frac{7}{9}}$
8. $\frac{240}{18}$ $\mathbf{13\frac{1}{3}}$
9. $\frac{121}{66}$ $\mathbf{1\frac{5}{6}}$

Add and Subtract Fractions

Add or subtract.

10. $\frac{1}{3}+\frac{1}{2}$ $\mathbf{\frac{5}{6}}$
11. $\frac{7}{8}-\frac{1}{6}$ $\mathbf{\frac{17}{24}}$
12. $\frac{3}{4}+\frac{2}{3}+\frac{1}{2}$ $\mathbf{1\frac{11}{12}}$
13. $\frac{5}{9}+\frac{1}{12}-\frac{1}{3}$ $\mathbf{\frac{11}{36}}$

Factor GCF from Polynomials

Factor each polynomial.

14. x^2+2x $\mathbf{x(x+2)}$
15. x^2+x $\mathbf{x(x+1)}$
16. $2x^2+x$ $\mathbf{x(2x+1)}$
17. x^2-x $\mathbf{x(x-1)}$
18. $3x^2+2x$ $\mathbf{x(3x+2)}$
19. $4x^2-4$ $\mathbf{4(x+1)(x-1)}$
20. $3x^2-6x$ $\mathbf{3x(x-2)}$
21. x^3-x^2 $\mathbf{x^2(x-1)}$

Properties of Exponents

Simplify each expression.

22. $4x \cdot 3x^2$ $\mathbf{12x^3}$
23. $-5 \cdot 2jk$ $\mathbf{-10jk}$
24. $-2a^3 \cdot 3a^4$ $\mathbf{-6a^7}$
25. $3ab \cdot 4a^2b$ $\mathbf{12a^3b^2}$
26. $2x \cdot 3y \cdot xy$ $\mathbf{6x^2y^2}$
27. $a^2b \cdot 3ab^3$ $\mathbf{3a^3b^4}$
28. $3rs \cdot 3rs^3$ $\mathbf{9r^2s^4}$
29. $5m^2n^2 \cdot 4mn^2$ $\mathbf{20m^3n^4}$

Simplify Polynomial Expressions

Simplify each expression.

30. $4x-2y-8y$ $\mathbf{4x-10y}$
31. $2r-4s+3s-8r$ $\mathbf{-6r-s}$
32. $ab^2-ab+4ab^2+2a^2b+a^2b^2$ $\mathbf{5ab^2-ab+2a^2b+a^2b^2}$
33. $3g(g-4)+g^2+g$ $\mathbf{4g^2-11g}$

ARE YOU READY? CHAPTER 10

Organizer

Objective: Assess students' understanding of prerequisite skills.

Prerequisite Skills

Simplify Fractions
Add and Subtract Fractions
Factor GCF from Polynomials
Properties of Exponents
Simplify Polynomial Expressions

Assessing Prior Knowledge

INTERVENTION

Diagnose and Prescribe

Use this page to determine whether intervention is necessary or whether enrichment is appropriate.

Resources

***Are You Ready? Intervention and Enrichment* Worksheets**

***Are You Ready?* CD-ROM**

***Are You Ready?* Online**

my.hrw.com

NO INTERVENE

ARE YOU READY?

Diagnose and Prescribe

YES ENRICH

Prerequisite Skill	*Are You Ready? Intervention,* Chapter 10 — Worksheets	CD-ROM	Online
Simplify Fractions	Skill 10	Activity 10	Diagnose and Prescribe Online
Add and Subtract Fractions	Skill 48	Activity 48	
Factor GCF from Polynomials	Skill 66	Activity 66	
Properties of Exponents	Skill 59	Activity 59	
Simplify Polynomial Expressions	Skill 63	Activity 63	

Are You Ready? Enrichment, **Chapter 10**

Worksheets

CD-ROM

Online

Organizer

Objective: Help students understand the new concepts they will learn in Chapter 10.

Academic Vocabulary Connections

Becoming familiar with the academic vocabulary on this student page will be helpful to students. Discussing some of the vocabulary terms in the chapter also may be helpful.

1. What are some other words that mean the same as *continuous*? The prefix *dis-* generally means "not." Describe what the graph of a **discontinuous function** might look like. Possible answer: Smooth, uninterrupted; the graph might have breaks in it.
2. A *direct variation* is a relationship between two variables, x and y, that can be written in the form $y = kx$ where $k \neq 0$. The inverse of a number x is $\frac{1}{x}$. Use this information to write the form of an **inverse variation**. $y = k \cdot \frac{1}{x}$ or $y = \frac{k}{x}$, where $k \neq 0$.
3. An *algebraic expression* contains one or more variables, numbers, or operations. A *rational number* can be written in the form of a fraction. Combine these terms to define **rational expression**. Possible answer: A rational expression contains variable(s), number(s), and operation(s) and can be written in the form of a fraction.

CHAPTER 10 Unpacking the Standards

The information below "unpacks" the standards. The Academic Vocabulary is highlighted and defined to help you understand the language of the standards. Refer to the lessons listed after each standard for help with the math terms and phrases. The Chapter Concept shows how the standard is applied in this chapter.

California Standard	Academic Vocabulary	Chapter Concept
10.0 Students add, subtract, multiply, and **divide monomials and polynomials. Students solve multistep problems, including word problems, by using these techniques.** (Lab **10-6**) (Lesson **10-6**)	**technique** a way of doing something	You use long division to divide a polynomial by a binomial.
12.0 Students simplify fractions with polynomials in the numerator and denominator by factoring both and reducing them to the lowest terms. (Lesson **10-3, 10-6**)	**factoring** expressing a quantity as a product of two or more quantities **reduce to lowest terms** simplify	You use division to write a rational expression in simpler form.
13.0 Students add, subtract, multiply, and divide rational expressions and functions. Students solve both computationally and conceptually challenging problems by using these techniques. (Lessons 10-1, 10-2, 10-3, **10-4, 10-5**)	**computational** having to do with numbers and operations **conceptual** having to do with general ideas	You add and subtract rational expressions with like and unlike denominators. You also use the rules you learned to multiply and divide fractions to multiply and divide rational expressions.
15.0 Students apply algebraic techniques to solve rate problems, work problems, and percent mixture problems. (Lesson **10-5, 10-7, 10-8**)	**percent mixture** a combination of parts that are expressed as percents of the whole	You learn how to solve rational equations so that you can solve real-world problems that involve rational expressions.

Standard 17.0 is also covered in this chapter. To see this standard unpacked, go to Chapter 4, p. 198.

Looking Back

Previously, students

- identified, wrote, and graphed equations of direct variation.
- simplified quadratic, exponential, and square-root expressions.
- solved linear and quadratic equations.

In This Chapter

Students will study

- how to identify, write, and graph equations of inverse variation.
- how to simplify rational expressions.
- how to solve rational equations.

Looking Forward

Students can use these skills

- to solve problems involving joint variation.
- to simplify complex rational expressions.
- to solve rational inequalities.

Study Strategy: Remember Formulas

In math, there are many formulas, properties, and rules that you should commit to memory.

To memorize a formula, create flash cards. Write the name of the formula on one side of a card. Write the formula on the other side of the card. You might also include a diagram or an example if helpful. Study your flash cards on a regular basis.

Sample Flash Card

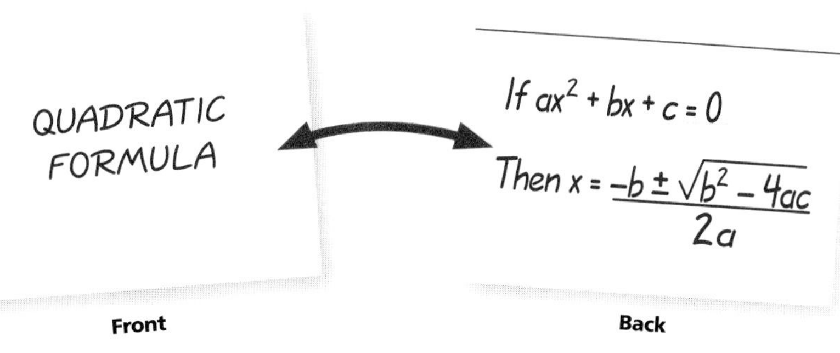

QUADRATIC FORMULA
If $ax^2 + bx + c = 0$
Then $x = \frac{-b \pm \sqrt{b^2 - 4ac}}{2a}$
Front
Back

Knowing when and how to apply a mathematical formula is as important as memorizing the formula itself.

To know what formula to apply, read the problem carefully.

> **Solve each quadratic equation.**
>
> **1.** $x^2 - 7x + 10 = 0$ **2.** $3x^2 - 4x - 1 = 0$ **3.** $x^2 - 10x + 25 = 0$

You can use the Quadratic Formula to solve all of these equations. But other solution methods may be simpler. The first problem can be easily solved by factoring. In the third problem, the left side of the equation is a perfect-square trinomial. This equation can be solved by factoring or by using square roots.

Read each problem. Then write the formula(s) needed to solve it. What helped you identify the formula?

1. Find the equation of the line with slope $\frac{2}{3}$ that passes through the point (1, 1).
2. The area of a rectangular pool is 120 square feet. The length is 1 foot less than twice the width. What is the perimeter of the pool?

Reading and Writing Math

Organizer

Objective: Help students apply strategies to understand and retain key concepts.

Resources

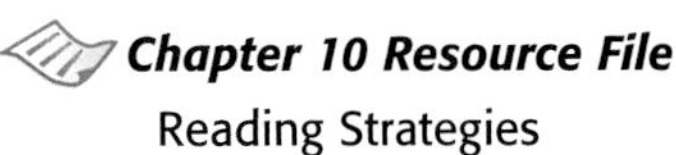

Reading Strategies

Study Strategy: Remember Formulas

Discuss A formula makes sense only when you know what each variable in the formula represents. For algebraic formulas, be careful with units. For instance, if t stands for time in years and the time is 6 months, the value of t is 0.5, not 6. Also consider the form of the number. If r stands for rate as a decimal and the rate is 25%, the value of r is 0.25, not 25.

When creating flash cards with geometric formulas, draw and label the figure with the same variables used in the formula.

Extend Students will need to know many of the formulas in this course for standardized tests. Have students use flashcards to quiz each other a few minutes each day.

Answers to *Try This*

Possible answers:

1. $y - y_1 = m(x - x_1)$; slope and a point are given.
2. $A = \ell w$; $P = 2\ell + 2w$; the words *area, rectangular, perimeter*

Rational Functions and Expressions

One-Minute Section Planner

Lesson	Lab Resources	Materials
10-1 Algebra Lab Model Inverse Variation • Use square tiles or grid paper to model the area of a rectangle as an inverse variation. **Prep for 13.0**		**Required** square tiles (MK) or grid paper
Lesson 10-1 Inverse Variation • Identify, write, and graph inverse variations. **Prep for 13.0, 17.0**		**Optional** cylindrical containers
Lesson 10-2 Rational Functions • Identify excluded values of rational functions. • Graph rational functions. **13.0, 17.0**		**Optional** graphing calculator
Lesson 10-3 Simplifying Rational Expressions • Simplify rational expressions. • Identify excluded values of rational expressions. **12.0**		**Optional** colored pencils (MK), graphing calculator
10-3 Technology Lab Graph Rational Functions • Use a graphing calculator to explore rational functions. **13.0**		**Required** graphing calculator

MK = *Manipulatives Kit*

Notes

Math Background: Teaching the Standards

Professional Development

RATIONAL FUNCTIONS 13.0

Lessons 10-1 and 10-2

The focus of this section is rational functions. In a general sense, many functions may be considered to be rational functions since a function may be written as a fraction with a denominator of 1. The linear and quadratic functions that students have already studied are rational functions. In this chapter, however, we limit rational functions to functions that are a quotient of polynomials in which the denominator has a degree of at least 1. In other words, these rational functions have a variable in the denominator.

INVERSE VARIATION 13.0

Lesson 10-1

The simplest rational functions are those given by inverse variations. These functions have the form $y = \frac{k}{x}$, where k is a nonzero constant and $x \neq 0$. In this case, the numerator is a polynomial of degree 0 (a constant) and the denominator is a polynomial of degree 1.

In an inverse variation with a positive value of k, the value of y increases as the value of x decreases. More generally, in any inverse variation, the absolute value of one variable increases while the absolute value of the other variable decreases.

The inverse relationship between the two variables can also be seen by rewriting the function in the form $xy = k$. This form shows that the product of x and y is a fixed, nonzero constant. Therefore, when one variable changes, the other variable must change accordingly to preserve the constant product. For example, when x is doubled, y must be halved. When x is halved, y is doubled.

The graph of an inverse variation is a *hyperbola*. Unlike other graphs students have seen up to this point, a hyperbola consists of two distinct "branches." When $k > 0$, the hyperbola lies in Quadrants I and III. When $k < 0$, the hyperbola lies in Quadrants II and IV. The x- and y-axes are *asymptotes*. That is, the curve approaches the axes arbitrarily closely, but never intersects the axes.

It is also worth noting that the graph of an inverse variation is a *discontinuous* graph. Informally speaking, this means that the complete graph cannot be drawn without lifting your pencil. The graphs of inverse variations are likely to be the first discontinuous graphs that students encounter.

Finally, the absolute value of k determines the shape of the hyperbola. The smaller the absolute value of k, the closer the curve is to the origin. This is illustrated in the graphs of $y = \frac{k}{x}$ for $k = 1, 6$, and 20.

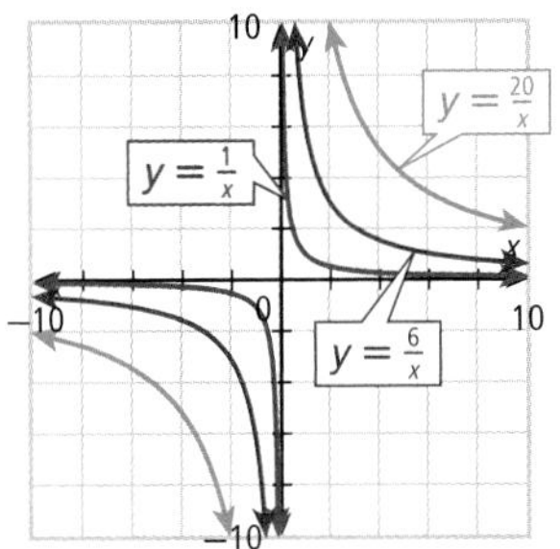

BASIC RATIONAL FUNCTIONS  13.0

Lesson 10-2

Although there are many different types of rational functions, in Lesson 10-2 the focus is on rational functions of the form $y = \frac{a}{x-b} + c$, where a, b, and c are real numbers and $a \neq 0$. These are indeed rational functions (that is, a quotient of polynomials) because they may be written equivalently as

$$\begin{aligned} y &= \frac{a}{x-b} + c \\ &= \frac{a}{x-b} + c \cdot \frac{x-b}{x-b} \\ &= \frac{a + c(x-b)}{x-b} \\ &= \frac{a + cx - cb}{x-b} \text{ for all } x \neq b. \end{aligned}$$

An inverse variation is a special case of this basic type of rational function. In an inverse variation, $b = c = 0$. Like graphs of inverse variations, the graph of any rational function that has the form $y = \frac{a}{x-b} + c$ is a hyperbola.

Organizer

Use with Lesson 10-1

Objective: Use square tiles or grid paper to model the area of a rectangle as an inverse variation.

Materials: square tiles or grid paper

 **Online Edition**

 **Countdown to Mastery Week 22**

Teach

Discuss

The area of a rectangle will never equal zero because each dimension must be greater than zero. Caution students against extending the graphs all the way to either axis.

Close

Key Concept

In an inverse-variation relationship, one value increases as the other decreases.

Assessment

Journal Have students list the characteristics they discovered about inverse-variation relationships.

Answer to *Activity*

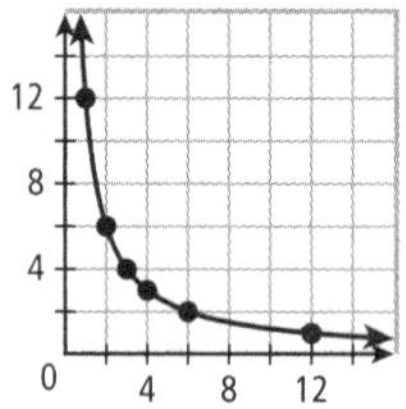

California Standards

Preparation for 13.0

10-1

Model Inverse Variation

Use with Lesson 10-1

The relationship between the width and the length of a rectangle with a constant area is an inverse variation. In this activity, you will study this relationship by modeling rectangles with square tiles or grid paper.

California Standards

Preparation for 13.0 Students add, subtract, multiply, and divide **rational** expressions and **functions.** Students solve both computationally and conceptually challenging problems by using these techniques.

Activity

Use 12 square tiles to form a rectangle with an area of 12 square units, or draw the rectangle on grid paper. Use a width of 1 unit and a length of 12 units.

Your rectangle should look like the one shown.

Using the same 12 square tiles, continue forming rectangles by changing the width and length until you have formed all the different rectangles you can that have an area of 12 square units. Copy and complete the table as you form each rectangle.

Width (x)	Length (y)	Area (xy)
1	12	12
2	**6**	12
3	**4**	12
4	**3**	12
6	**2**	12
12	**1**	12

Plot the ordered pairs from the table on a graph. Draw a smooth curve through the points.

Try This

1. Look at the table and graph above. What happens to the length as the width increases? Why? **Length decreases as width increases because the product of the length and width must always be 12.**
2. This relationship between length and width is an example of an *inverse variation.* Why do you think it is called that? **The value of one variable increases as the other decreases, so the variables move in opposite (inverse) directions.**
3. For each point, what does xy equal? Complete the equation $xy = \square$. Solve this equation for y. **At each point, xy equals 12; $xy = 12$; $y = \frac{12}{x}$.**
4. Form all the different rectangles that have an area of 24 square units. Record their widths and lengths in a table. Graph your results. Write an equation relating the width x and length y. $xy = 24$ **or** $y = \frac{24}{x}$
5. **Make a Conjecture** Using the equations you wrote in 3 and 4, what do you think the equation of any inverse variation might look like when solved for y? $y = \frac{k}{x}$

Answers to *Try This*

4.

Width (x)	Length (y)	Area (xy)
1	24	24
2	12	24
3	8	24
4	6	24
6	4	24
8	3	24
12	2	24
24	1	24

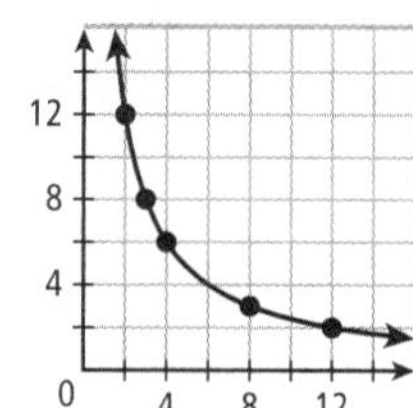

10-1 Inverse Variation

California Standards

Preparation for 🔑 13.0 Students add, subtract, multiply, and divide **rational** expressions and **functions.** Students solve both computationally and conceptually challenging problems by using these techniques.

Also covered: **17.0**

Vocabulary
inverse variation

Why learn this?
Inverse variation can be used to find the frequency at which a guitar string vibrates. (See Example 3.)

A relationship that can be written in the form $y = \frac{k}{x}$, where k is a nonzero constant and $x \neq 0$, is an **inverse variation**. The constant k is the constant of variation.

Multiplying both sides of $y = \frac{k}{x}$ by x gives $xy = k$. So, for any inverse variation, the product of x and y is a nonzero constant.

Inverse Variations

WORDS	NUMBERS	ALGEBRA
y varies inversely as x.	$y = \frac{3}{x}$	$y = \frac{k}{x}$
y is inversely proportional to x.	$xy = 3$	$xy = k\ (k \neq 0)$

There are two methods to determine whether a relationship between data is an inverse variation. You can write a function rule in $y = \frac{k}{x}$ form, or you can check whether xy is constant for each ordered pair.

EXAMPLE 1 **Identifying an Inverse Variation**

Tell whether each relationship is an inverse variation. Explain.

A

x	y
1	20
2	10
4	5

Method 1 Write a function rule.

$y = \frac{20}{x}$ *Can write in $y = \frac{k}{x}$ form.*

The relationship is an inverse variation.

Method 2 Find xy for each ordered pair.

$1(20) = 20, 2(10) = 20, 4(5) = 20$

The product xy is constant, so the relationship is an inverse variation.

B

x	y
2	6
3	9
6	18

Method 1 Write a function rule.

$y = 3x$ *Cannot write in $y = \frac{k}{x}$ form.*

The relationship is not an inverse variation.

Method 2 Find xy for each ordered pair.

$2(6) = 12, 3(9) = 27, 6(18) = 108$

The product xy is not constant, so the relationship is not an inverse variation.

10-1 Organizer

Objective: Identify, write, and graph inverse variations.

Online Edition
Tutorial Videos, Interactivity

Countdown to Mastery Week 22

Warm Up

Solve each proportion.

1. $\frac{2}{5} = \frac{4}{y}$ 10
2. $\frac{14}{9} = \frac{x}{2.7}$ 4.2
3. $\frac{3}{8} = \frac{x}{7}$ 2.625
4. $\frac{2y}{15} = \frac{1}{3}$ 2.5
5. The value of y varies directly with x, and $y = -6$ when $x = 3$. Find y when $x = -4$. 8
6. The value of y varies directly with x, and $y = 6$ when $x = 30$. Find y when $x = 45$. 9

Also available on transparency

Math Humor

Student: My love life is like inverse variation!

Friend: What do you mean?

Student: The more I'm interested in someone, the less they're interested in me!

1 Introduce

EXPLORATION

10-1 Inverse Variation

Jennifer's piano teacher tells her that she must practice for 12 hours in order to prepare for an upcoming recital.

1. Jennifer wants to practice for the same number of hours on each day that she practices. For example, if she practices on 6 days, she would have to practice 2 hours each day. Jennifer makes a table to consider her options. Complete the table.

Days	1	2			6	12
Hours per day		6	4	3		
Total Hours of Practice		12				

2. Make a graph of the number of hours per day as a function of the number of days.
3. Write an equation describing this relationship. Let x represent the number of days, and let y represent the number of hours per day.

Hours per day: 0, 2, 4, 6, 8, 10, 12
Number of Days: 0, 2, 4, 6, 8, 10, 12

THINK AND DISCUSS

4. **Explain** what happens to the number of hours per day as the number of days increases.

Motivate

Display three cylinders with the same height but increasing diameter. Tell students that the first cylinder is full of water. Have volunteers mark where they think the water height on the other cylinders will be if the water from the first cylinder is poured into them. Tell students that the amount of water remains constant, and as the diameter of the cylinders increase, the height of the water decreases.

Explorations and answers are provided in *Alternate Openers: Explorations Transparencies.*

California Standards

Preparation for 🔑 13.0

Also covered:

17.0 Students determine the domain of independent variables and the range of dependent variables defined by a graph, a set of ordered pairs, or **a symbolic expression.**

Power Presentations with PowerPoint®

Additional Examples

Example 1

Tell whether each relationship is an inverse variation. Explain.

A.

x	y
1	30
2	15
3	10

Yes; the product xy is constant.

B.

x	y
1	5
2	10
4	20

No; the product xy is not constant.

C. $2xy = 28$ Yes; the equation can be written in the form $y = \frac{k}{x}$.

Example 2

Write and graph the inverse variation in which $y = 0.5$ when $x = -12$. $y = \frac{-6}{x}$

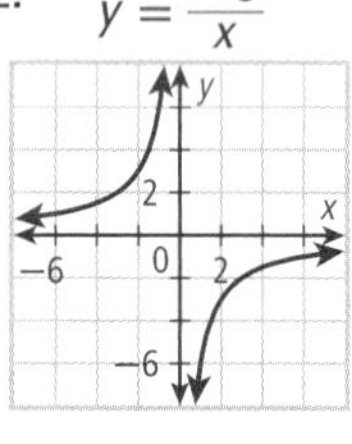

Also available on transparency

INTERVENTION
Questioning Strategies

EXAMPLE 1

- In an inverse variation, what does the product xy represent?

EXAMPLE 2

- How do you determine k?
- How do you use k to determine the rule for the inverse variation?
- Should you use zero as a value for x?

1a. No; the product xy is not constant.

1b. Yes; the product xy is constant.

1c. No; the equation cannot be written in the form $y = \frac{k}{x}$.

Tell whether each relationship is an inverse variation. Explain.

C $5xy = -21$

$\frac{5xy}{5} = \frac{-21}{5}$ *Find xy. Since xy is multiplied by 5, divide both sides by 5 to undo the multiplication.*

$xy = \frac{-21}{5}$ *Simplify.*

xy equals the constant $\frac{-21}{5}$, so the relationship is an inverse variation.

CHECK IT OUT! **Tell whether each relationship is an inverse variation. Explain.**

1a.

x	y
−12	24
1	−2
8	−16

1b.

x	y
3	3
9	1
18	0.5

1c. $2x + y = 10$

Helpful Hint

Since k is a nonzero constant, $xy \neq 0$. Therefore, neither x nor y can equal 0, and the graph will not intersect the x- or y-axes.

An inverse variation can also be identified by its graph. Some inverse variation graphs are shown. Notice that each graph has two parts that are not connected.

Also notice that none of the graphs contain $(0, 0)$. In other words, $(0, 0)$ can never be a solution of an inverse variation equation.

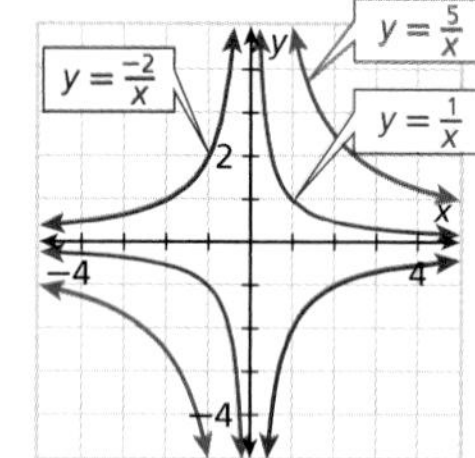

EXAMPLE 2 **Graphing an Inverse Variation**

Write and graph the inverse variation in which $y = 2$ when $x = 4$.

Step 1 Find k.

$k = xy$ *Write the rule for constant of variation.*

$= 4(2)$ *Substitute 4 for x and 2 for y.*

$= 8$

Step 2 Use the value of k to write an inverse variation equation.

$y = \frac{k}{x}$ *Write the rule for inverse variation.*

$y = \frac{8}{x}$ *Substitute 8 for k.*

Step 3 Use the equation to make a table of values.

x	−4	−2	−1	1	2	4
y	−2	−4	−8	8	4	2

Step 4 Plot the points and connect them with smooth curves.

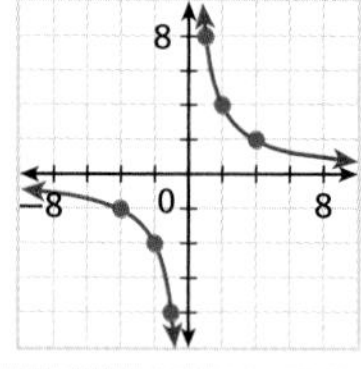

2.

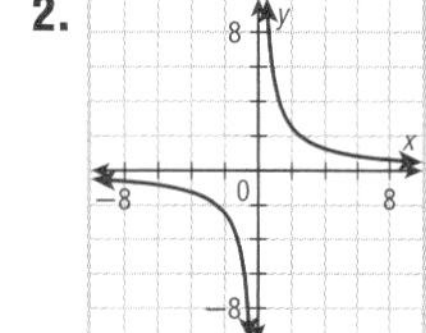

CHECK IT OUT! **2.** Write and graph the inverse variation in which $y = \frac{1}{2}$ when $x = 10$. $y = \frac{5}{x}$

2 Teach

Guided Instruction

Remind students that a direct variation is in the form $y = kx$ and means that as one variable increases, so does the other. Then show students that $y = \frac{k}{x}$ is the form of an inverse variation, which means that as one variable increases, the other decreases. When graphing inverse variations, show that the domain is all real numbers except zero and that the range is also all real numbers except zero.

Universal Access
Through Multiple Representations

Show students that the Product Rule for Inverse Variation can be seen from ordered pairs in a table. Display the following table and have students write a new table for values when $k = 12$.

$y = \frac{k}{x}$	
x_1	y_1
x_2	y_2

$y = \frac{12}{x}$	
2	6
4	3

Point out that the product of each row is 12, so the product of each xy pair is k.

EXAMPLE 3 *Music Application*

The inverse variation $xy = 2400$ relates the vibration frequency y in hertz (Hz) to the length x in centimeters of a guitar string. Determine a reasonable domain and range, and then graph this inverse variation.

Step 1 Solve the function for y.

$xy = 2400$

$y = \frac{2400}{x}$ *Divide both sides by x.*

Step 2 Decide on a reasonable domain and range.

$x > 0$ *Length is never negative and $x \neq 0$.*

$y > 0$ *Because x and xy are both positive, y is also positive.*

Step 3 Use values of the domain to generate reasonable ordered pairs.

x	20	40	60	120
y	120	60	40	20

Step 4 Plot the points. Connect them with a smooth curve.

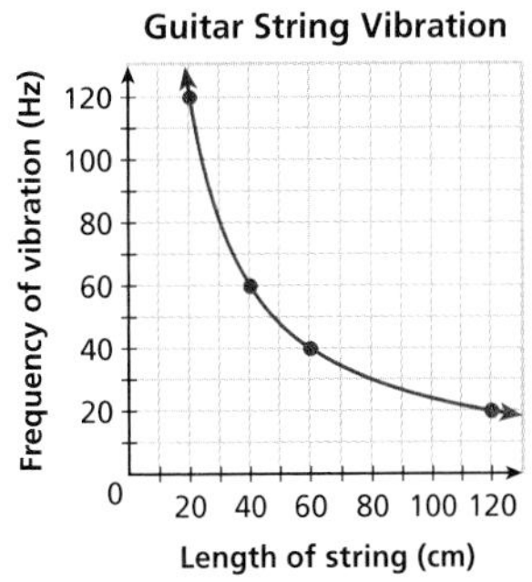

Remember!

Recall that sometimes domain and range are restricted in real-world situations.

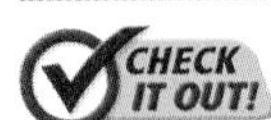

3. The inverse variation $xy = 100$ represents the relationship between the pressure x in atmospheres (atm) and the volume y in mm^3 of a certain gas. Determine a reasonable domain and range, and then graph this inverse variation. **D: $x > 0$; R: $y > 0$**

3.

The fact that $xy = k$ is the same for every ordered pair in any inverse variation can help you find missing values in the relationship.

Product Rule for Inverse Variation

If (x_1, y_1) and (x_2, y_2) are solutions of an inverse variation, then $x_1y_1 = x_2y_2$.

EXAMPLE 4 Using the Product Rule

Let $x_1 = 3$, $y_1 = 2$, and $y_2 = 6$. Let y vary inversely as x. Find x_2.

$x_1y_1 = x_2y_2$ *Write the Product Rule for Inverse Variation.*

$(3)(2) = x_2(6)$ *Substitute 3 for x_1, 2 for y_1, and 6 for y_2.*

$6 = 6x_2$ *Simplify.*

$\frac{6}{6} = \frac{6x_2}{6}$ *Solve for x_2 by dividing both sides by 6.*

$1 = x_2$ *Simplify.*

4. Let $x_1 = 2$, $y_1 = -6$, and $x_2 = -4$. Let y vary inversely as x. Find y_2. **3**

Reading Math Remind students that *reciprocal* is another word for multiplicative inverse. Thus, for inverse variation, y equals k times the reciprocal of x. ENGLISH LANGUAGE LEARNERS

COMMON ERROR ALERT

Because the form of an inverse variation contains a fraction, students might divide x by y, or y by x, to find k. Encourage students to start each problem by writing one of the given formulas.

Power Presentations with PowerPoint®

Additional Examples

Example 3

The inverse variation $xy = 350$ relates the constant speed x in mi/h to the time y in hours that it takes to travel 350 miles. Determine a reasonable domain and range and then graph this inverse variation. $x > 0, y > 0$

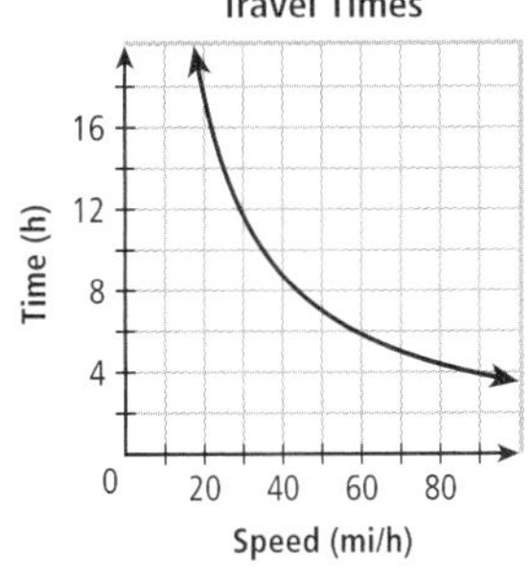

Example 4

Let $x_1 = 5$, $x_2 = 3$, and $y_2 = 10$. Let y vary inversely as x. Find y_1. 6

Also available on transparency

INTERVENTION

Questioning Strategies

EXAMPLE 3

- How can you use the equation to check your estimate?
- Why is this graph only in Quadrant I?

EXAMPLE 4

- How does the Product Rule for Inverse Variation relate to the methods used to determine whether a relationship between data is an inverse variation?

Power Presentations with PowerPoint®

Additional Examples

Example 5

Boyle's law states that the pressure of a quantity of gas x varies inversely as the volume of the gas y. The volume of a gas inside a container is 400 in^3 and the pressure is 25 psi. What is the pressure when the volume is compressed to 125 in^3? 80 psi

Also available on transparency

INTERVENTION
Questioning Strategies

EXAMPLE 5

- How do you determine x_1y_1 and x_2y_2?
- How can you tell whether your answer is reasonable?

EXAMPLE 5 *Physical Science Application*

Boyle's law states that the pressure of a quantity of gas x varies inversely as the volume of the gas y. The volume of air inside a bicycle pump is 5.2 in^3, and the pressure is 15.5 pounds per square inch (psi). Assuming no air escapes, what is the pressure of the air inside the pump after the handle is pushed in and the air is compressed to a volume of 2.6 in^3?

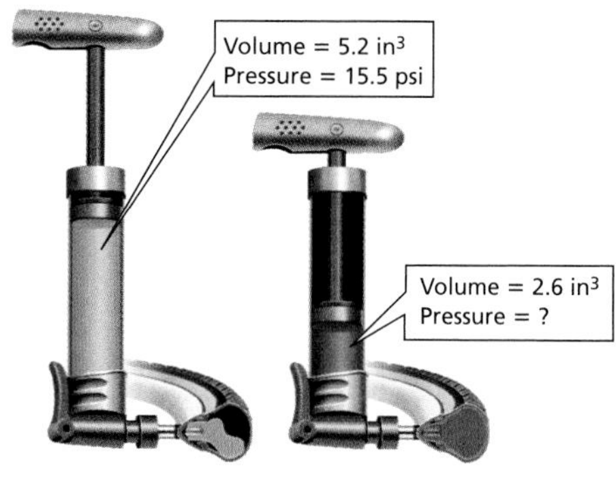

Reading Math 

In Example 5, x_1 and y_1 represent volume and pressure **before** the handle is pushed in, and x_2 and y_2 represent volume and pressure **after** the handle is pushed in.

$x_1y_1 = x_2y_2$ — *Use the Product Rule for Inverse Variation.*

$(5.2)(15.5) = (2.6)y_2$ — *Substitute 5.2 for x_1, 15.5 for y_1, and 2.6 for x_2.*

$80.6 = 2.6y_2$ — *Simplify.*

$\frac{80.6}{2.6} = \frac{2.6y_2}{2.6}$ — *Solve for y_2 by dividing both sides by 2.6.*

$31 = y_2$ — *Simplify.*

The pressure after the handle is pushed in is 31 psi.

CHECK IT OUT! 5. On a balanced lever, weight varies inversely as the distance from the fulcrum to the weight. The diagram shows a balanced lever. How much does the child weigh? **80.625 lb**

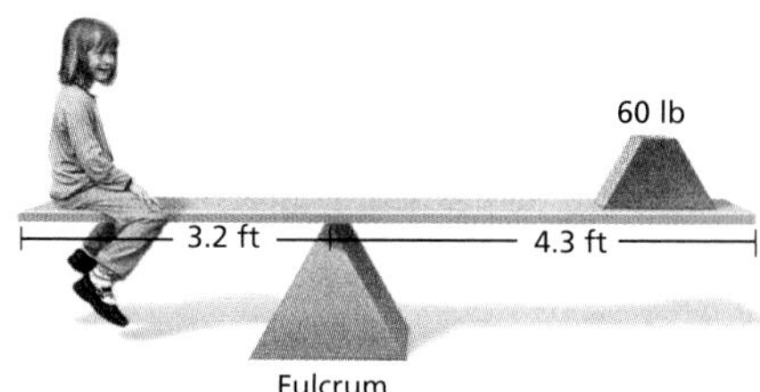

THINK AND DISCUSS

1. Name two ways you can identify an inverse variation.
2. **GET ORGANIZED** Copy and complete the graphic organizer. In each box, write an example of the parts of the given inverse variation.

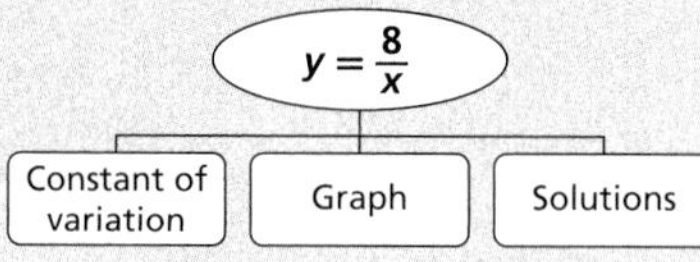

3 Close

Summarize

Remind students that in an inverse variation, $xy = k$ is the same for every ordered pair. An inverse variation can also be written in the form $y = \frac{k}{x}$. The variation can be graphed by generating ordered pairs. Have students describe the characteristics of inverse-variation graphs.

FORMATIVE ASSESSMENT and INTERVENTION

***Diagnose Before* the Lesson**
10-1 Warm Up, TE p. 627

***Monitor During* the Lesson**
Check It Out! Exercises, SE pp. 628–630
Questioning Strategies, TE pp. 628–630

***Assess After* the Lesson**
10-1 Lesson Quiz, TE p. 633
Alternative Assessment, TE p. 633

Answers to *Think and Discuss*

Possible answers:

1. The function rule will have the form $y = \frac{k}{x}$, and xy will be the same nonzero constant for each ordered pair.
2. See p. A8.

California Standards Practice
Preparation for 13.0; 17.0

go.hrw.com
Homework Help Online
KEYWORD: MA8CA 10-1
Parent Resources Online
KEYWORD: MA8CA Parent

GUIDED PRACTICE

1. **Vocabulary** Describe the graph of an *inverse variation*. The graph of an inverse variation consists of 2 disconnected branches.

SEE EXAMPLE 1 p. 627

Tell whether each relationship is an inverse variation. Explain.

2.

x	y
1	8
4	2
2	4

Yes; the product xy is constant.

3.

x	y
$\frac{1}{6}$	1
$\frac{1}{3}$	2
2	12

No; the product xy is not constant.

4. $x + y = 8$ No; the equation cannot be written in the form $y = \frac{k}{x}$.

5. $4xy = 3$ Yes; xy equals the constant $\frac{3}{4}$.

SEE EXAMPLE 2 p. 628

6. Write and graph the inverse variation in which $y = 2$ when $x = 2$. $y = \frac{4}{x}$

7. Write and graph the inverse variation in which $y = 6$ when $x = -1$. $y = \frac{-6}{x}$

SEE EXAMPLE 3 p. 629

8. **Travel** The inverse variation $xy = 30$ relates the constant speed x in mi/h to the time y in hours that it takes to travel 30 miles. Determine a reasonable domain and range, and then graph this inverse variation.

SEE EXAMPLE 4 p. 629

9. Let $x_1 = 3$, $y_1 = 12$, and $x_2 = 9$. Let y vary inversely as x. Find y_2. 4

10. Let $x_1 = 1$, $y_1 = 4$, and $y_2 = 16$. Let y vary inversely as x. Find x_2. $\frac{1}{4}$

SEE EXAMPLE 5 p. 630

11. **Mechanics** The rotational speed of a gear varies inversely as the number of teeth on the gear. A gear with 12 teeth has a rotational speed of 60 rpm. How many teeth are on a gear that has a rotational speed of 45 rpm? 16 teeth

PRACTICE AND PROBLEM SOLVING

Independent Practice

For Exercises	See Example
12–15	1
16–17	2
18	3
19–20	4
21	5

Extra Practice
Skills Practice p. EP20
Application Practice p. EP33

16. $y = \frac{-10}{x}$
17. $y = \frac{2}{x}$

Tell whether each relationship is an inverse variation. Explain.

12.

x	y
3	−3
−5	5
7	−7

No; the product xy is not constant.

13.

x	y
2	5
0.5	20
8	1.25

Yes; the product xy is constant.

14. $x = \frac{13}{y}$ yes; can be written in the form $y = \frac{k}{x}$

15. $y = 5x$ no; cannot be written in the form $y = \frac{k}{x}$

16. Write and graph the inverse variation in which $y = -2$ when $x = 5$.

17. Write and graph the inverse variation in which $y = -6$ when $x = -\frac{1}{3}$.

18. **Engineering** The inverse variation $xy = 12$ relates the current x in amps to the resistance y in ohms of a circuit attached to a 12-volt battery. Determine a reasonable domain and range, and then graph this inverse variation.

19. Let $x_1 = -3$, $y_1 = -4$, and $y_2 = 6$. Let y vary inversely as x. Find x_2. 2

20. Let $x_1 = 7$, $y_1 = 9$, and $x_2 = 6$. Let y vary inversely as x. Find y_2. 10.5

Assignment Guide

Assign *Guided Practice* exercises as necessary.

If you finished Examples **1–3**
Proficient 12–18, 22–27, 35
Advanced 12–18, 22–27, 35

If you finished Examples **1–5**
Proficient 12–31, 38–46, 48–53
Advanced 12–22, 31–53

Homework Quick Check
Quickly check key concepts.
Exercises: 12, 14, 16, 18, 20, 22

Answers

6.

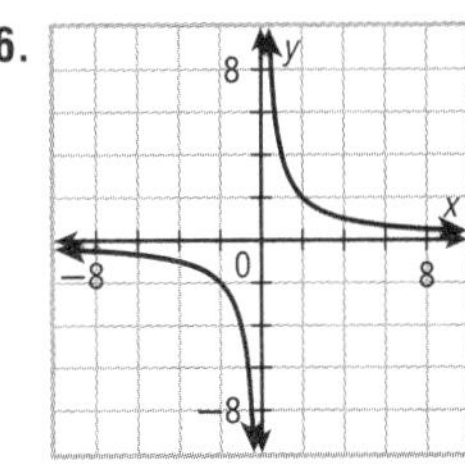

7.

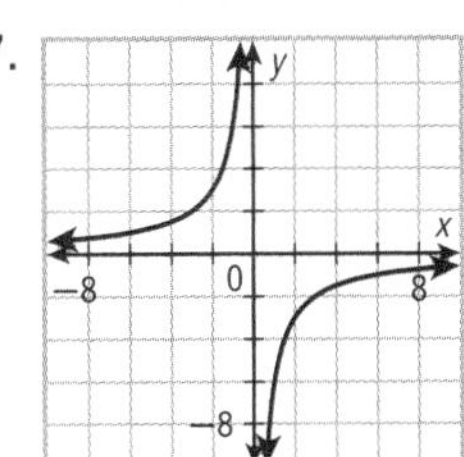

8. D: $x > 0$; R: $y > 0$;

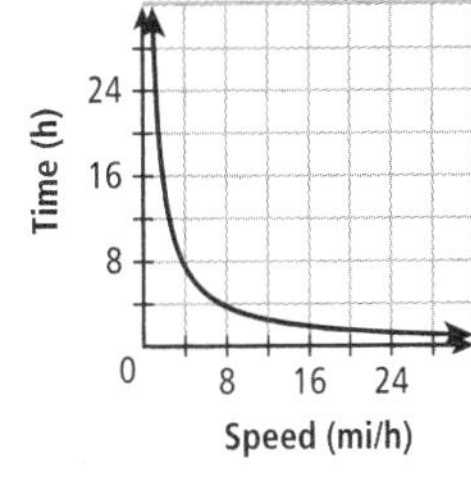

16.

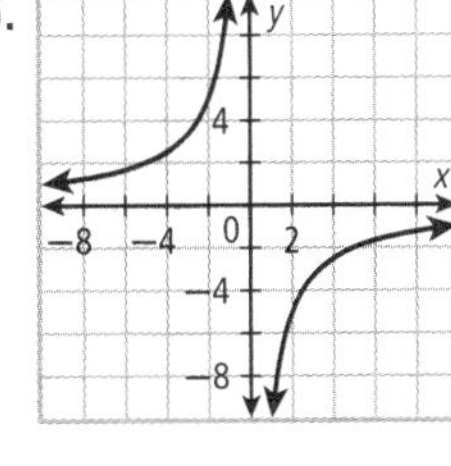

17.

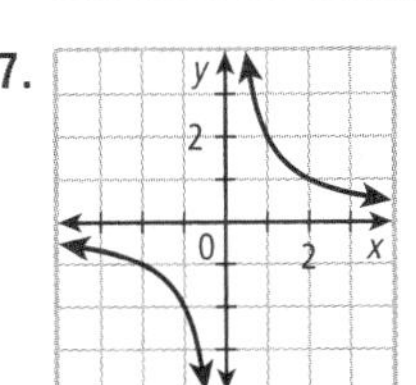

18. D: $x > 0$; R: $y > 0$;

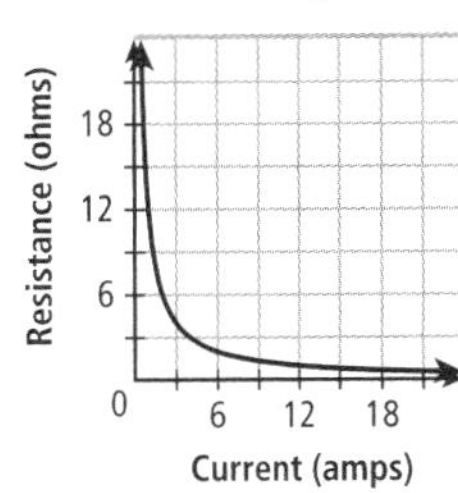

California Standards

Standard	Exercises
Prep for 13.0	6, 7, 9–11, 16, 17, 19–22, 44, 46, 47
14.0	50–52
16.0	48, 49
17.0	8, 18, 35, 48, 49
18.0	48, 49

Exercise 40 involves writing an inverse-variation function. This exercise prepares students for the Concept Connection on page 650.

Answers

35. $y = \frac{2000}{x}$; D: natural numbers; R: $y > 0$

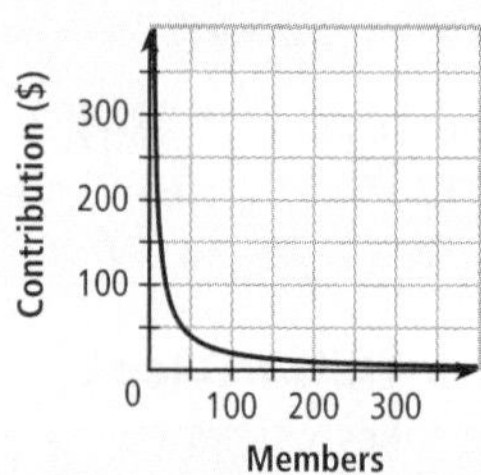

38. Substitute the known values of x and y into $y = \frac{k}{x}$ and solve for k. Use this value of k in the equation $y = \frac{k}{x}$.

39. Inverse function, inverse operations, additive inverse, etc.; all of the terms involve moving in opposite directions; inverse variation describes a relationship in which the variables move in opposite directions (one increases while the other decreases).

40c.

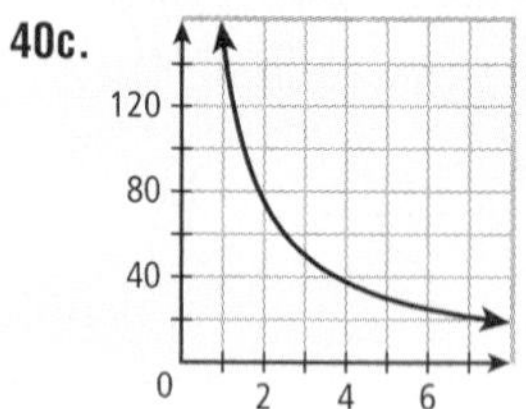

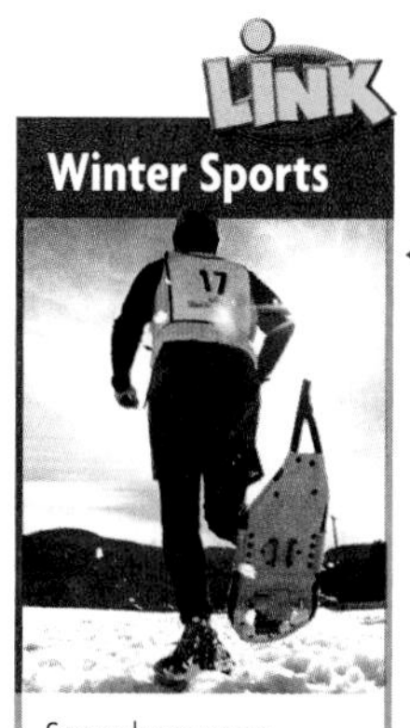

LINK Winter Sports

Snowshoes were originally made of wooden frames strung with animal intestines. Modern snowshoes are made with steel frames and may have cleats for gripping the snow.

21. **Home Economics** The length of fabric that June can afford varies inversely as the price per yard of the fabric. June can afford exactly 5 yards of fabric that costs \$10.50 per yard. How many yards of fabric that costs \$4.25 per yard can June buy? (Assume that she can only buy whole yards.) **12 yd**

22. **Winter Sports** When a person is snowshoeing, the pressure on the top of the snow in psi varies inversely as the area of the bottom of the snowshoe in square inches. The constant of variation is the weight of the person wearing the snowshoes in pounds.
    a. Helen weighs 120 pounds. About how much pressure does she put on top of the snow if she wears snowshoes that cover 360 in^2? **$\frac{1}{3}$ psi**
    b. Max weighs 207 pounds. If he exerts 0.4 psi of pressure on top of the snow, what is the area of the bottom of his snowshoes in square inches? **517.5 in^2**

Determine if each equation represents a direct variation, an inverse variation, or neither. Find the constant of variation when one exists.

23. $y = 8x$ **direct; 8**
24. $y = \frac{14}{x}$ **inverse; 14**
25. $y = \frac{1}{3}x - 2$ **neither**
26. $y = \frac{1}{5}x$ **direct; $\frac{1}{5}$**
27. $y = 4\frac{3}{x}$ **inverse; 12**
28. $y = \frac{x}{2} + 7$ **neither**
29. $y = \frac{15}{x}$ **inverse; 15**
30. $y = 5x$ **direct; 5**

31. **Multi-Step** A track team is competing in a 10 km race. The distance will be evenly divided among the team members. Write an equation that represents the distance d each runner will run if there are n runners. Does this represent a direct variation, inverse variation, or neither? **$d = \frac{10}{n}$; inverse**

Determine whether each data set represents a direct variation, an inverse variation, or neither.

32.

x	2	4	8
y	5	10	20

direct

33.

x	6	12	15
y	6	8	9

neither

34.

x	1	2	3
y	12	6	4

inverse

35. **Multi-Step** Your club awards one student a \$2000 scholarship each year, and each member contributes an equal amount. Your contribution y depends on the number of members x. Write and graph an inverse variation equation that represents this situation. What are a reasonable domain and range?

36. **Estimation** Estimate the value of y if y is inversely proportional to x, $x = 4$, and the constant of variation is 6π. **4.5**

37. Why will the point $(0, 0)$ never be a solution to an inverse variation?

37. In an inverse variation function, $xy = k$, and $k \neq 0$. So neither x nor y can be 0.

38. **Write About It** Explain how to write an inverse variation equation of the form $y = \frac{k}{x}$ when values of x and y are known.

39. **Write About It** List all the mathematical terms you know that contain the word *inverse*. How are these terms all similar? How is *inverse variation* similar to these terms?

40. This problem will prepare you for the Concept Connection on page 650. The total number of workdays it takes to build the frame of a house varies inversely as the number of people working in a crew. Let x be the number of people in the crew, and let y be the number of workdays.
    a. Find the constant of variation when $y = 75$ and $x = 2$. **$k = 150$**
    b. Write the rule for the inverse of variation equation. **$y = \frac{150}{x}$**
    c. Graph the equation of this inverse variation.

632 *Chapter 10 Rational Functions and Equations*

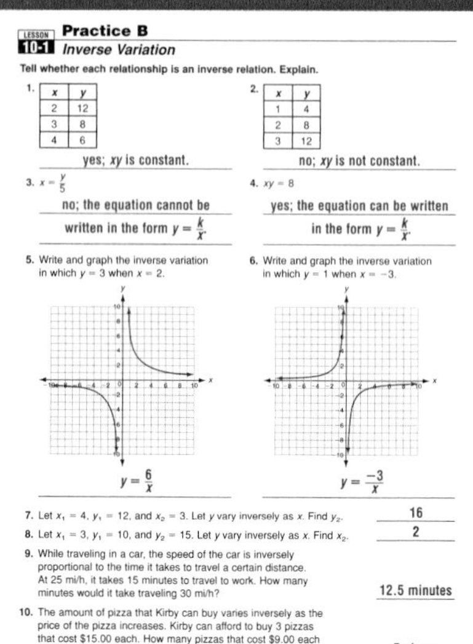

10-1 PRACTICE A
10-1 PRACTICE C
10-1 PRACTICE B

LESSON 10-1 Practice B
Inverse Variation

Tell whether each relationship is an inverse relation. Explain.

1. | x | y |
|---|---|
| 2 | 12 |
| 3 | 8 |
| 4 | 6 |

yes; xy is constant.

2. | x | y |
|---|---|
| 1 | 4 |
| 2 | 8 |
| 3 | 12 |

no; xy is not constant.

3. $x = \frac{y}{5}$ no; the equation cannot be written in the form $y = \frac{k}{x}$.

4. $xy = 8$ yes; the equation can be written in the form $y = \frac{k}{x}$.

5. Write and graph the inverse variation in which $y = 3$ when $x = 2$. $y = \frac{6}{x}$

6. Write and graph the inverse variation in which $y = 1$ when $x = -3$. $y = \frac{-3}{x}$

7. Let $x_1 = 4$, $y_1 = 12$, and $x_2 = 3$. Let y vary inversely as x. Find y_2. 16

8. Let $x_1 = 3$, $y_1 = 10$, and $y_2 = 15$. Let y vary inversely as x. Find x_2. 2

9. While traveling in a car, the speed of the car is inversely proportional to the time it takes to travel a certain distance. At 25 mi/h, it takes 15 minutes to travel to work. How many minutes would it take traveling 30 mi/h? 12.5 minutes

10. The amount of pizza that Kirby can buy varies inversely as the price of the pizza increases. Kirby can afford to buy 3 pizzas that cost \$15.00 each. How many pizzas that cost \$9.00 each can Kirby buy? 5 pizzas

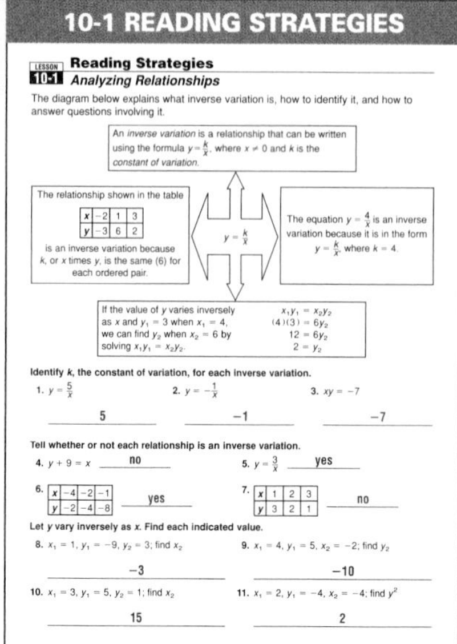

10-1 READING STRATEGIES

LESSON 10-1 Reading Strategies
Analyzing Relationships

The diagram below explains what inverse variation is, how to identify it, and how to answer questions involving it.

An inverse variation is a relationship that can be written using the formula $y = \frac{k}{x}$, where $x \neq 0$ and k is the constant of variation.

The relationship shown in the table

x	-2	1	3
y	-3	6	2

is an inverse variation because k, or x times y, is the same (6) for each ordered pair.

$y = \frac{k}{x}$

The equation $y = \frac{4}{x}$ is an inverse variation because it is in the form $y = \frac{k}{x}$, where $k = 4$.

If the value of y varies inversely as x and $y_1 = 3$ when $x_1 = 4$, we can find y_2 when $x_2 = 6$ by solving $x_1y_1 = x_2y_2$.
$x_1y_1 = x_2y_2$
$(4)(3) = 6y_2$
$12 = 6y_2$
$2 = y_2$

Identify k, the constant of variation, for each inverse variation.

1. $y = \frac{5}{x}$ 5
2. $y = -\frac{1}{x}$ −1
3. $xy = -7$ −7

Tell whether or not each relationship is an inverse variation.

4. $y + 9 = x$ no
5. $y = \frac{3}{x}$ yes
6. | x | -4 | -2 | -1 |
|---|---|---|---|
| y | -2 | -4 | -8 |

yes

7. | x | 1 | 2 | 3 |
|---|---|---|---|
| y | 3 | 2 | 1 |

no

Let y vary inversely as x. Find each indicated value.

8. $x_1 = 1$, $y_1 = -9$, $y_2 = 3$; find x_2 −3
9. $x_1 = 4$, $y_1 = 5$, $x_2 = -2$; find y_2 −10
10. $x_1 = 3$, $y_1 = 5$, $y_2 = 1$; find x_2 15
11. $x_1 = 2$, $y_1 = -4$, $x_2 = -4$; find y^2 2

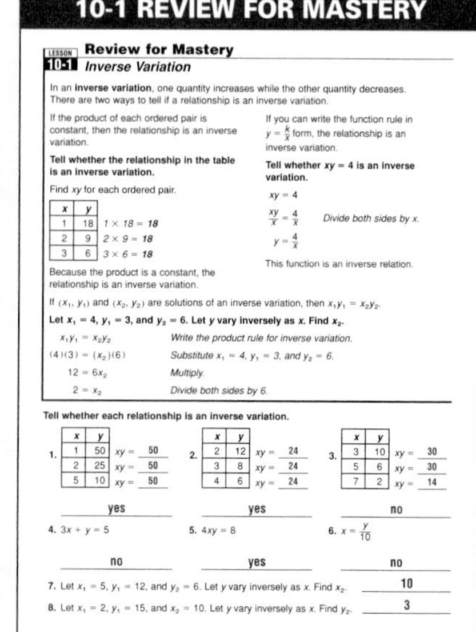

10-1 REVIEW FOR MASTERY

LESSON 10-1 Review for Mastery
Inverse Variation

In an **inverse variation**, one quantity increases while the other quantity decreases. There are two ways to tell if a relationship is an inverse variation.

If the product of each ordered pair is constant, then the relationship is an inverse variation.

If you can write the function rule in $y = \frac{k}{x}$ form, the relationship is an inverse variation.

Tell whether the relationship in the table is an inverse variation.

Find xy for each ordered pair.

x	y	
1	18	$1 \times 18 = 18$
2	9	$2 \times 9 = 18$
3	6	$3 \times 6 = 18$

Because the product is a constant, the relationship is an inverse variation.

Tell whether $xy = 4$ is an inverse variation.

$xy = 4$
$\frac{xy}{x} = \frac{4}{x}$ Divide both sides by x.
$y = \frac{4}{x}$

This function is an inverse relation.

If (x_1, y_1) and (x_2, y_2) are solutions of an inverse variation, then $x_1y_1 = x_2y_2$.

Let $x_1 = 4$, $y_1 = 3$, and $y_2 = 6$. Let y_2 vary inversely as x. Find x_2.

$x_1y_1 = x_2y_2$ Write the product rule for inverse variation.
$(4)(3) = (x_2)(6)$ Substitute $x_1 = 4$, $y_1 = 3$, and $y_2 = 6$.
$12 = 6x_2$ Multiply.
$2 = x_2$ Divide both sides by 6.

Tell whether each relationship is an inverse variation.

1. | x | y | |
|---|---|---|
| 1 | 50 | xy = 50 |
| 2 | 25 | xy = 50 |
| 5 | 10 | xy = 50 |

yes

2. | x | y | |
|---|---|---|
| 2 | 12 | xy = 24 |
| 3 | 8 | xy = 24 |
| 4 | 6 | xy = 24 |

yes

3. | x | y | |
|---|---|---|
| 3 | 10 | xy = 30 |
| 5 | 6 | xy = 30 |
| 7 | 2 | xy = 14 |

no

4. $3x + y = 5$ no
5. $4xy = 8$ yes
6. $x = \frac{y}{10}$ no

7. Let $x_1 = 5$, $y_1 = 12$, and $y_2 = 6$. Let y vary inversely as x. Find x_2. 10
8. Let $x_1 = 2$, $y_1 = 15$, and $x_2 = 10$. Let y vary inversely as x. Find y_2. 3

Multiple Choice For Exercises 41–43, choose the best answer.

41. Which equation best represents the graph?

Ⓐ $y = -\frac{1}{4}x$ ⒸⒸ $y = -\frac{4}{x}$ (circled)

Ⓑ $y = \frac{1}{4}x$ Ⓓ $y = \frac{4}{x}$

42. Determine the constant of variation if y varies inversely as x and $y = 2$ when $x = 7$.

Ⓐ $\frac{2}{7}$ Ⓑ $\frac{7}{2}$ Ⓒ 3.5 Ⓓ 14 (circled)

43. Which of the following relationships does NOT represent an inverse variation?

Ⓐ

x	2	4	5
y	10	5	4

Ⓒ (circled)

x	2	4	5
y	8	16	20

Ⓑ $y = \frac{17.5}{x}$ Ⓓ $\frac{11}{2} = xy$

44. Gridded Response At a carnival, the number of tickets Brad can buy is inversely proportional to the price of the tickets. He can afford 12 tickets that cost $2.50 each. How many tickets can Brad buy if each costs $3.00? **10**

CHALLENGE AND EXTEND

45. The definition of inverse variation says that k is a nonzero constant. What function would $y = \frac{k}{x}$ represent if $k = 0$? **the linear function $y = 0$**

46. Mechanics A part of a car's braking system uses a lever to multiply the force applied to the brake pedal. The force at the end of a lever varies inversely with the distance from the fulcrum. Point P is the end of the lever. A force of 2 lb is applied to the brake pedal. What is the force created at the point P? **12 lb**

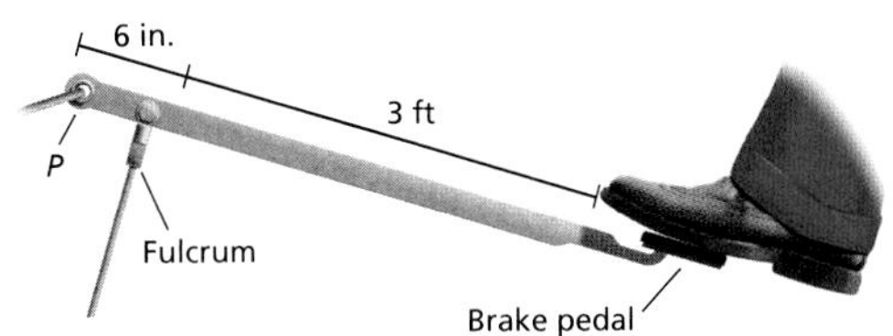

47. Communication The strength of a radio signal varies inversely with the square of the distance from the transmitter. A signal has a strength of 2000 watts when it is 4 kilometers from the transmitter. What is the strength of the signal 6 kilometers from the transmitter? **approx. 888.9 watts**

SPIRAL STANDARDS REVIEW

14.0, 16.0, 17.0, 18.0

Find the domain and range for each relation. Tell whether the relation is a function. *(Lesson 4-2)*

48. $\{(-2, -4), (-2, -2), (-2, 0), (-2, 2)\}$ **D: {−2}; R: {−4, −2, 0, 2}; no**

49. $\{(-4, 5), (-2, 3), (0, 1), (2, 3), (4, 5)\}$ **D: {−4, −2, 0, 2, 4}; R: {1, 3, 5}; yes**

Solve by completing the square. *(Lesson 9-7)*

50. $x^2 + 12x = 45$ **3, −15** **51.** $d^2 - 6d - 7 = 0$ **−1, 7** **52.** $2y^2 + 6y = -\frac{5}{2}$ **$-\frac{5}{2}, -\frac{1}{2}$**

53. Find the number of solutions of $4x^2 + 3x - 6 = 0$ using the discriminant. *(Lesson 9-9)* **2**

Multiple Choice Choices **A** and **B** in **Exercise 41** are functions whose graphs are lines because they can be written in the form $y = mx + b$.

For **Exercise 42,** remind students that $xy = k$, so the answer is found by multiplying 2 and 7.

Journal

Have students explain the difference between the graphs of $y = \frac{x}{2}$ and $y = \frac{2}{x}$.

ALTERNATIVE ASSESSMENT

Have students find x_1 when $y_1 = 4$, $x_2 = 2$, $y_2 = 8$, and y varies inversely as x. Then have students write and graph the inverse variation.

Power Presentations with PowerPoint®

10-1 Lesson Quiz

1. Write and graph the inverse variation in which $y = 0.25$ when $x = 12$. $y = \frac{3}{x}$

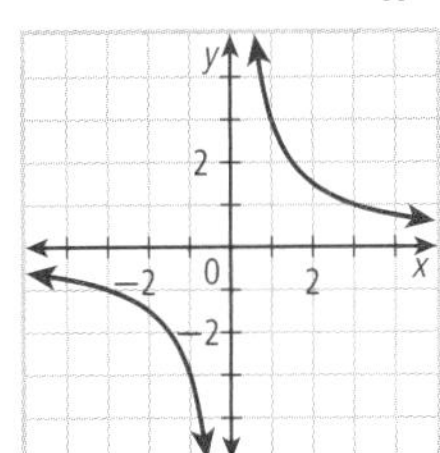

2. The inverse variation $xy = 210$ relates the length y in cm to the width x in cm of a rectangle with an area of 210 cm². Determine a reasonable domain and range, and then graph this inverse variation.

$x > 0, y > 0$

Rectangle Dimensions

Length (cm)

Width (cm)

3. Let $x_1 = 12$, $y_1 = -4$, and $y_2 = 6$, and let y vary inversely as x. Find x_2. −8

Also available on transparency

10-1 PROBLEM SOLVING

LESSON 10-1 Problem Solving
Inverse Variation

The number of gallons of gasoline that Isaac can afford y varies inversely as the price per gallon x. Isaac can afford 12 gal when the price is $2.50 per gallon.

1. Write an inverse variation for this situation.
   $xy = 30$ or $y = \frac{30}{x}$
2. Determine a reasonable domain and range.
   $x > 0$ and $y > 0$
3. Complete this table of ordered pairs and graph the inverse variation.

x	1.50	2.50	3.00	5.00	10.00
y	20	12	10	6	3

Number of Gallons

Price per Gallon ($)

4. Find the number of gallons Isaac can afford when the price is $3.75 per gallon.
   8 gal

Select the best answer.

5. The inverse variation $xy = 9$ relates the current x in amps to the resistance y in ohms of a circuit attached to a 9-volt battery. What is the resistance of the circuit when the current is 1.8 amps?
   A 0.2 ohms C 10.8 ohms
   Ⓑ 5 ohms D 16.2 ohms
6. Boyle's law states that the pressure of a quantity of gas x varies inversely as the volume of the gas y. The volume of air inside a bicycle pump is 6.1 in³, and the pressure is 18.3 psi. Which equation represents this situation?
   F $y = 3x$ H $y = 111.63x$
   G $y = \frac{3}{x}$ Ⓙ $y = \frac{111.63}{x}$
7. The time it takes to drive between two cities varies inversely as speed. Dolores can drive between Houston, Texas, and San Antonio, Texas, in 3.5 h at 60 mi/h. How long will the trip take if she drives 70 mi/h? (Round your answer to the nearest tenth.)
   A 2.3 h Ⓒ 3 h
   B 2.6 h D 4.1 h
8. On a balanced lever, weight varies inversely as the distance from the fulcrum. Angie weighs 120 lb. When she sits $2\frac{1}{2}$ ft from the fulcrum of a seesaw, she balances with her brother, who weighs 80 lb. How far is her brother from the fulcrum of the seesaw?
   F $\frac{4}{15}$ ft H $1\frac{2}{3}$ ft
   G $\frac{3}{5}$ ft Ⓙ $3\frac{3}{4}$ ft

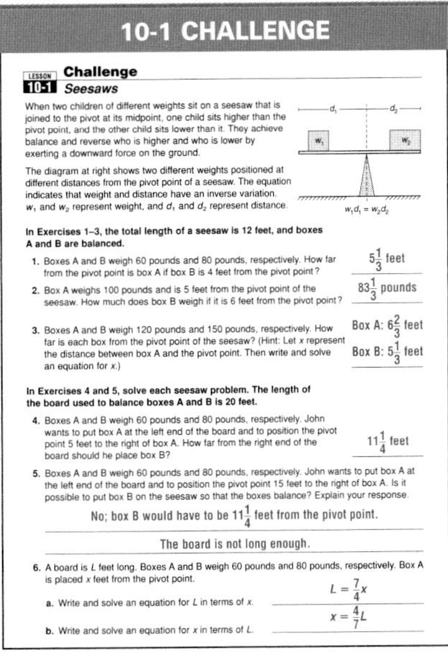

10-1 CHALLENGE

LESSON 10-1 Challenge
Seesaws

When two children of different weights sit on a seesaw that is joined to the pivot at its midpoint, one child sits higher than the pivot point, and the other child sits lower than it. They achieve balance and reverse who is higher and who is lower by exerting a downward force on the ground.

The diagram at right shows two different weights positioned at different distances from the pivot point of a seesaw. The equation indicates that weight and distance have an inverse variation. w_1 and w_2 represent weight, and d_1 and d_2 represent distance.

$w_1d_1 = w_2d_2$

In Exercises 1–3, the total length of a seesaw is 12 feet, and boxes A and B are balanced.

1. Boxes A and B weigh 60 pounds and 80 pounds, respectively. How far from the pivot point is box A if box B is 4 feet from the pivot point? $5\frac{1}{3}$ feet
2. Box A weighs 100 pounds and is 5 feet from the pivot point of the seesaw. How much does box B weigh if it is 6 feet from the pivot point? $83\frac{1}{3}$ pounds
3. Boxes A and B weigh 120 pounds and 150 pounds, respectively. How far is each box from the pivot point of the seesaw? (Hint: Let x represent the distance between box A and the pivot point. Then write and solve an equation for x.) Box A: $6\frac{2}{3}$ feet; Box B: $5\frac{1}{3}$ feet

In Exercises 4 and 5, solve each seesaw problem. The length of the board used to balance boxes A and B is 20 feet.

4. Boxes A and B weigh 60 pounds and 80 pounds, respectively. John wants to put box A at the left end of the board and to position the pivot point 5 feet to the right of box A. How far from the right end of the board should he place box B? $11\frac{1}{4}$ feet
5. Boxes A and B weigh 60 pounds and 80 pounds, respectively. John wants to put box A at the left end of the board and to position the pivot point 15 feet to the right of box A. Is it possible to put box B on the seesaw so that the boxes balance? Explain your response.
   No; box B would have to be $11\frac{1}{4}$ feet from the pivot point.
   The board is not long enough.
6. A board is L feet long. Boxes A and B weigh 60 pounds and 80 pounds, respectively. Box A is placed x feet from the pivot point.
   a. Write and solve an equation for L in terms of x. $L = \frac{7}{4}x$
   b. Write and solve an equation for x in terms of L. $x = \frac{4}{7}L$

10-2 Organizer

Objectives: Identify excluded values of rational functions.

Graph rational functions.

Online Edition
Tutorial Videos

Countdown to Mastery Week 23

Power Presentations with PowerPoint®

Warm Up

The inverse variation $xy = 8$ relates the constant speed x in mi/h to the time y in hours that it takes to travel 8 miles. Graph this inverse variation.

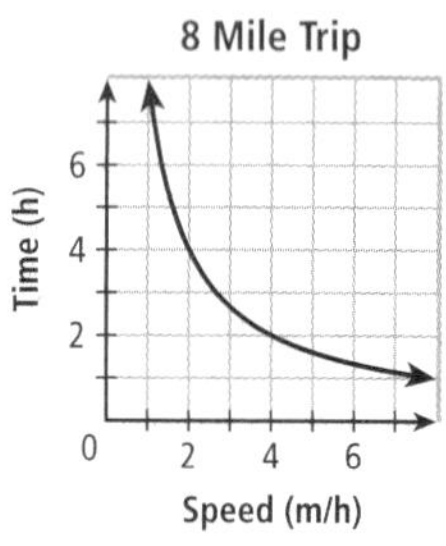

Also available on transparency

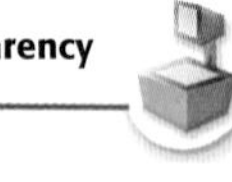

Math Humor

Q: What do math teachers carry their math books in?

A: Asymp-tote bags

California Standards

Algebra 1 13.0

Also covered:

17.0 Students determine the domain of independent variables and the range of dependent variables defined by a graph, a set of ordered pairs, or a **symbolic expression.**

10-2 Rational Functions

13.0 Students add, subtract, multiply, and divide **rational** expressions and **functions.** Students solve both computationally and conceptually challenging problems by using these techniques.

Also covered: **17.0**

Who uses this?

Gemologists can use rational functions to maximize reflected light. (See Example 4.)

A **rational function** is a function whose rule is a quotient of polynomials. The inverse variations you studied in the previous lesson are a special type of rational function.

$$\text{Rational functions: } y = \frac{2}{x},\ y = \frac{3}{4 - 2x},\ y = \frac{1}{x^2}$$

For any function involving x and y, an **excluded value** is any x-value that makes the function value y undefined. For a rational function, an excluded value is any value that makes the denominator equal 0.

Vocabulary
rational function
excluded value
discontinuous function
asymptote

EXAMPLE 1 Identifying Excluded Values

Identify any excluded values for each rational function.

A $y = \frac{8}{x}$

$x = 0$ *Set the denominator equal to 0.*

The excluded value is 0.

B $y = \frac{3}{x + 3}$

$x + 3 = 0$ *Set the denominator equal to 0.*

$x = -3$ *Solve for x.*

The excluded value is -3.

C $y = \frac{4}{x^2 + 1}$

$x^2 + 1 = 0$ *Set the denominator equal to 0.*

$x^2 = -1$

This equation has no real solutions, so the function has no excluded values.

Identify any excluded values for each rational function.

1a. $y = \frac{10}{x}$ **0** **1b.** $y = \frac{4}{x - 1}$ **1** **1c.** $y = -\frac{5}{x + 4}$ **−4**

Many rational functions are **discontinuous functions**, meaning their graphs contain one or more jumps, breaks, or holes. This occurs at an excluded value.

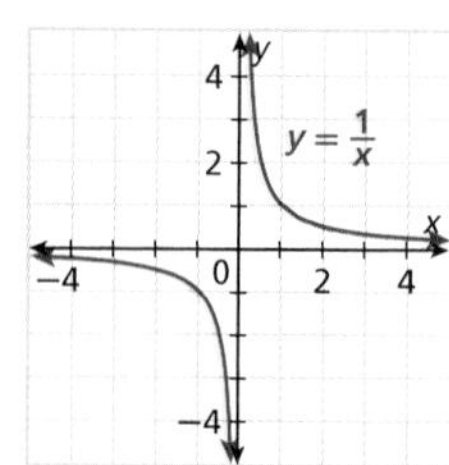

One place that a graph of a rational function may be discontinuous is at an *asymptote*. An **asymptote** is a line that a graph gets closer to as the absolute value of a variable increases. In the graph shown, both the x- and y-axes are asymptotes. A graph will get closer and closer to but never touch its asymptotes.

1 Introduce

EXPLORATION

10-2 Rational Functions

You can use a graphing calculator to explore rational functions.

Enter the function $y = \frac{1}{x}$ into your graphing calculator. Graph the function in the standard decimal window by pressing ZOOM, selecting **6:ZStandard**, pressing ZOOM again, and selecting **4:ZDecimal**. Press TRACE. Use the left and right arrow keys to move the cursor along the graph.

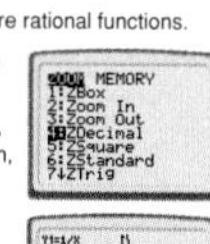

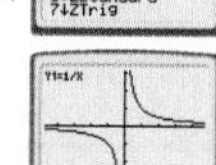

1. What happens to the y-values as the x-values increase from 0?
2. What happens when $x = 0$? Why?
3. Press 2nd GRAPH to view a table of values for the function. What y-value does the table show at $x = 0$?
4. Now graph $y = \frac{1}{x - 1}$. For what value of x is there no y-value?

THINK AND DISCUSS

5. **Discuss** how the graph of $y = \frac{1}{x - 1}$ is related to the graph of $y = \frac{1}{x}$.
6. **Explain** what you think would happen if you graphed $y = \frac{1}{\ldots}$. For what x-value would there be no y-value?

Motivate

Ask students what values are in the domain of $y = \frac{1}{x}$. All real numbers except 0

Ask why x may not equal 0. The expression $\frac{1}{0}$ is undefined.

Tell students that the functions they will be graphing in this lesson are similar to $y = \frac{1}{x}$ and will also be undefined for certain values of x.

Explorations and answers are provided in *Alternate Openers: Explorations Transparencies.*

Look at the graph of $y = \frac{1}{x}$. The denominator is 0 when $x = 0$, so 0 is an excluded value. This means there is a vertical asymptote at $x = 0$. Notice the horizontal asymptote at $y = 0$. This is because there is no value of x for which $y = 0$.

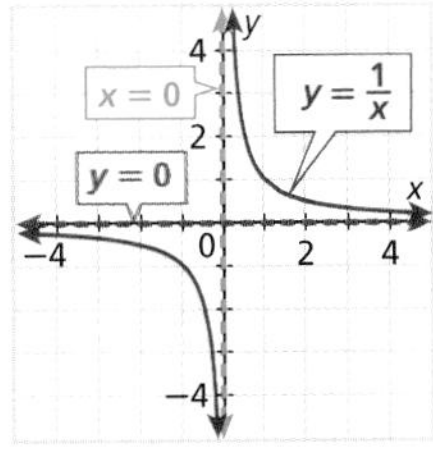

Writing Math

Vertical lines are written in the form $x = b$, and horizontal lines are written in the form $y = c$.

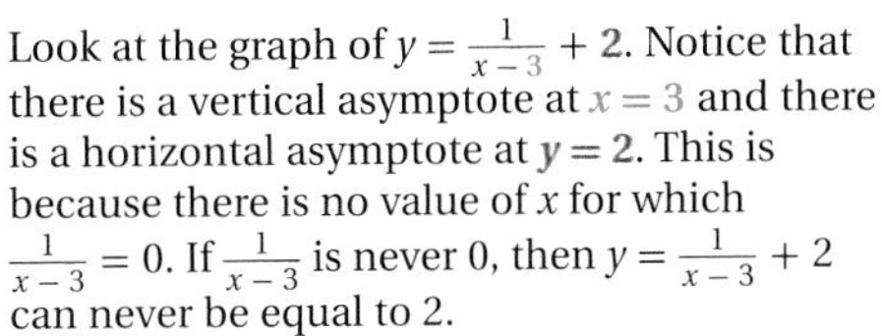

Look at the graph of $y = \frac{1}{x-3} + 2$. Notice that there is a vertical asymptote at $x = 3$ and there is a horizontal asymptote at $y = 2$. This is because there is no value of x for which $\frac{1}{x-3} = 0$. If $\frac{1}{x-3}$ is never 0, then $y = \frac{1}{x-3} + 2$ can never be equal to 2.

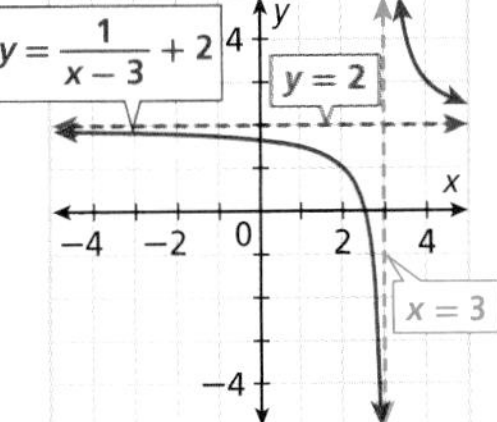

Know it! Note

Identifying Asymptotes

WORDS	EXAMPLES	
A rational function in the form $y = \frac{a}{x-b} + c$ has a vertical asymptote at the excluded value $(x = b)$ and a horizontal asymptote at $y = c$.	$y = \frac{2}{x}$ $= \frac{2}{x-0} + 0$ Vertical asymptote: $x = 0$ Horizontal asymptote: $y = 0$	$y = \frac{1}{x+2} + 4$ $= \frac{1}{x-(-2)} + 4$ Vertical asymptote: $x = -2$ Horizontal asymptote: $y = 4$

EXAMPLE 2 Identifying Asymptotes

Identify the asymptotes.

A $y = \frac{1}{x-6}$

Step 1 Write in $y = \frac{1}{x-b} + c$ form.

$$y = \frac{1}{x-6} + 0$$

Step 2 Identify the asymptotes.

vertical: $x = 6$

horizontal: $y = 0$

B $y = \frac{2}{3x-10} - 7$

Step 1 Identify the vertical asymptote.

$3x - 10 = 0$ *Find the excluded value. Set the denominator equal to 0.*

$\underline{+10 \quad +10}$ *Add 10 to both sides.*

$3x = 10$

$x = \frac{10}{3}$ *Solve for x. $\frac{10}{3}$ is an excluded value.*

COMMON ERROR ALERT

Students might use the value of b, rather than $-b$, in the vertical asymptote. Remind students that the vertical asymptote is at the excluded value, which is found by setting the denominator equal to 0 and solving.

Power Presentations with PowerPoint®

Additional Examples

Example 1

Identify any excluded values for each rational function.

A. $y = \frac{2}{x}$ 0

B. $y = \frac{6}{x-2}$ 2

Example 2

Identify the asymptotes.

A. $y = \frac{3}{x+7}$ $x = -7; y = 0$

B. $y = \frac{1}{2x-3} + 8$ $x = \frac{3}{2}; y = 8$

Also available on transparency

INTERVENTION

Questioning Strategies

EXAMPLE 1

- How do you determine the excluded value?

EXAMPLE 2

- What is the difference between the vertical and horizontal asymptotes?

Language Support Ask students what it means if they are *included* in a group. Tell them that *excluded* is the opposite of included. Students can also think of an *excluded* value as an *exception*.

ENGLISH LANGUAGE LEARNERS

2 Teach

Guided Instruction

Introduce examples of rational functions. (Rational functions with variables in both the numerator and denominator will be studied in Algebra 2.) Remind students that a number cannot be divided by zero, so a fraction with a zero in the denominator is undefined. After identifying excluded values, identify vertical asymptotes, show how they are related to the excluded value, and then identify horizontal asymptotes. Then show how to graph by generating ordered pairs.

Universal Access

Through Multiple Representations

Help students understand why a horizontal asymptote occurs at c in $y = \frac{a}{x+b} + c$ by having them fill in a table with ordered pairs for the function $y = \frac{2}{x+1} + 4$. Have students choose larger and larger values for x. Ask what happens to the fraction as x gets larger. gets closer to 0 Ask what happens to the value of y as the fraction gets closer to zero. gets closer to 4 Do the same for smaller and smaller values for x.

Power Presentations with PowerPoint®

Additional Examples

Example 3

Graph each function.

A. $y = \frac{2}{x - 3}$

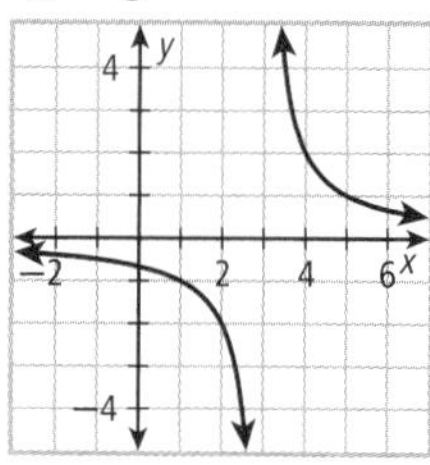

B. $y = \frac{1}{x + 4} - 2$

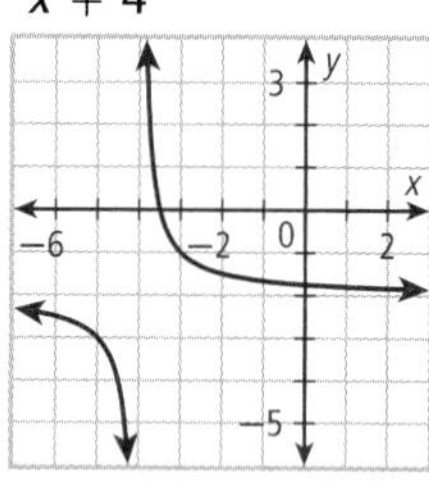

Also available on transparency

INTERVENTION

Questioning Strategies

EXAMPLE 3

- Could you plot and connect the points in the table before graphing the asymptotes?

Answers to *Check It Out*

3a.

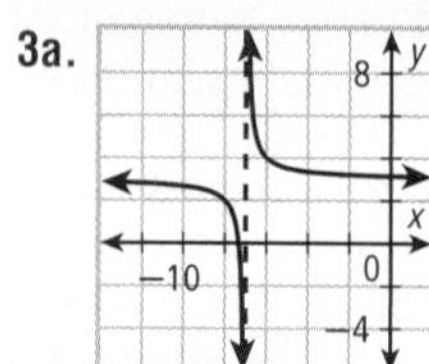

b.

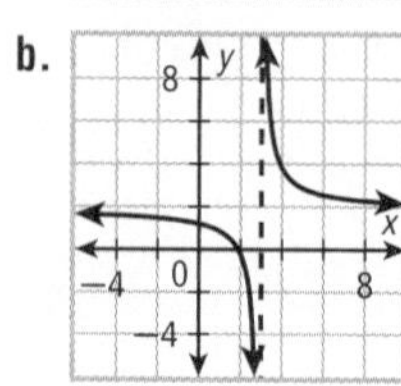

Step 2 Identify the horizontal asymptote.

$c = -7$ *−7 can be written as + (−7)*

$y = -7$ *y = c*

vertical asymptote: $x = \frac{10}{3}$; horizontal asymptote: $y = -7$

Identify the asymptotes.

2a. $y = \frac{2}{x-5}$ **$x = 5$; $y = 0$**

2b. $y = \frac{1}{4x+16} + 5$ **$x = -4$; $y = 5$**

2c. $y = \frac{3}{x+77} - 15$ **$x = -77$; $y = -15$**

To graph a rational function in the form $y = \frac{a}{x-b} + c$, you can use the asymptotes and a table of values.

EXAMPLE 3 Graphing Rational Functions Using Asymptotes

Graph each function.

A $y = \frac{2}{x+1}$

Step 1 Identify the asymptotes.

vertical: $x = -1$ *Use x = b. x + 1 = x − (−1), so b = −1.*

horizontal : $y = 0$ *Use y = c. c = 0*

Step 2 Graph the asymptotes using dashed lines.

Step 3 Make a table of values. Choose x-values on both sides of the vertical asymptote.

x	−3	−2	$-\frac{3}{2}$	$-\frac{1}{2}$	0	1
y	−1	−2	−4	4	2	1

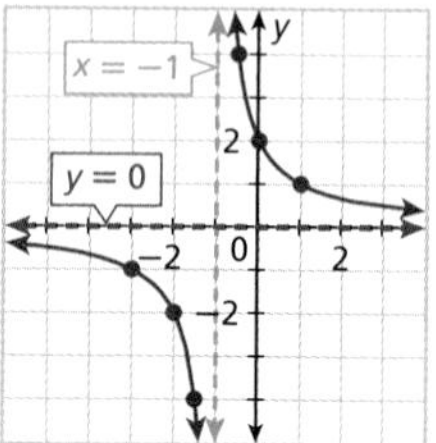

Step 4 Plot the points and connect them with smooth curves. The curves should not touch the asymptotes.

B $y = \frac{1}{x-2} - 4$

Step 1 Identify the asymptotes.

vertical: $x = 2$ *Use x = b. b = 2*

horizontal: $y = -4$ *Use y = c. c = −4*

Step 2 Graph the asymptotes using dashed lines.

Step 3 Make a table of values. Choose x-values on both sides of the vertical asymptote.

x	−2	0	1	3	4
y	−4.25	−4.5	−5	−3	−3.5

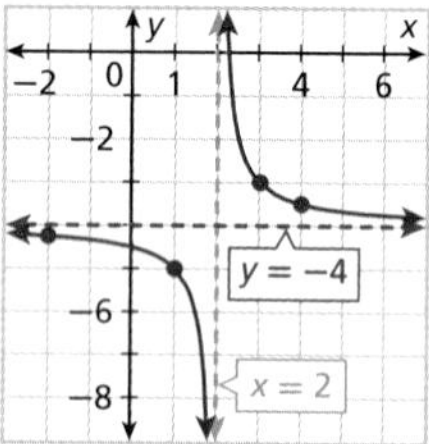

Step 4 Plot the points and connect them with smooth curves. The curves should not touch the asymptotes.

Graph each function.

3a. $y = \frac{1}{x+7} + 3$ **3b.** $y = \frac{2}{x-3} + 2$

Universal Access

Through Modeling

Help students understand how a change in the numerator affects the graph of a rational function by having them graph the following on their graphing calculators:

$y = \frac{1}{x}$; $y = \frac{5}{x}$; $y = \frac{10}{x}$

Then have students make predictions about the shapes of $y = \frac{25}{x}$ and $y = \frac{50}{x}$.

EXAMPLE 4 *Gemology Application*

Some diamonds are cut using ratios calculated by the mathematician Marcel Tolkowsky in 1919. The amount of light reflected up through the top of a diamond (brilliancy) can be maximized using the ratio between the width of the diamond and the depth of the diamond. A gemologist has a diamond with a width of 9 millimeters. If x represents the depth of the diamond, then $y = \frac{9}{x}$ represents the brilliancy ratio y.

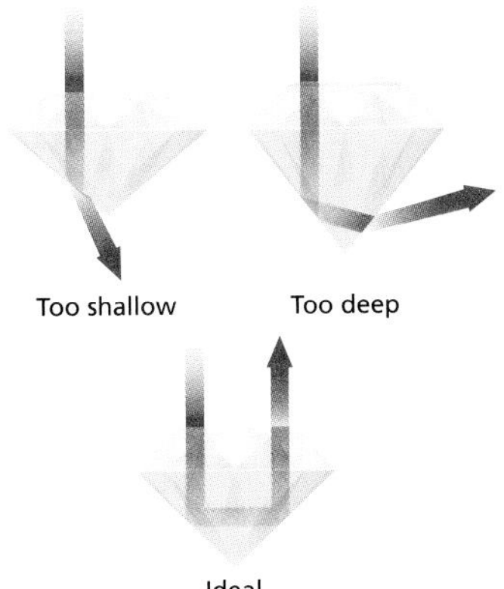

a. Describe a reasonable domain and range.

Both the depth of the diamond and the brilliancy ratio will be nonnegative, so nonnegative values are reasonable for the domain and range.

b. Graph the function.

Step 1 Identify the vertical and horizontal asymptotes.

vertical: $x = 0$ *Use $x = b$. $b = 0$*

horizontal: $y = 0$ *Use $y = c$. $c = 0$*

Step 2 Graph the asymptotes using dashed lines. The asymptotes will be the x- and y-axes.

Step 3 Since the domain is restricted to nonnegative values, only choose x-values on the right side of the vertical asymptote.

Depth of Diamond (mm)	2	3	4.5	9
Brilliancy Ratio	4.5	3	2	1

Step 4 Plot the points and connect them with smooth curves.

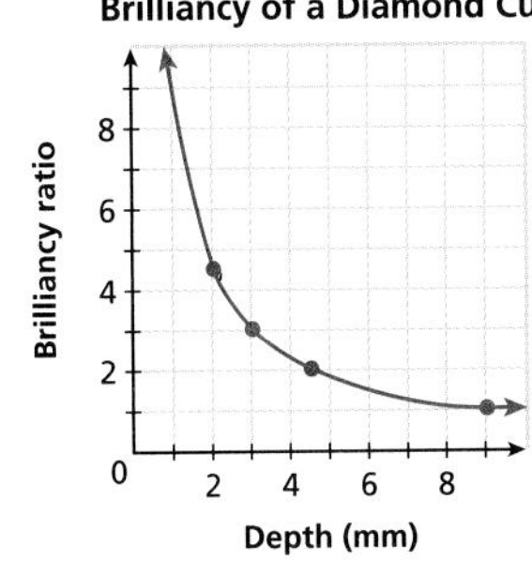

4. A librarian has a budget of \$500 to buy copies of a software program. She will receive 10 free copies when she sets up an account with the supplier. The number of copies y of the program that she can buy is given by $y = \frac{500}{x} + 10$, where x is the price per copy. **D: $x > 0$; R: natural numbers > 10**

   a. Describe a reasonable domain and range.

   b. Graph the function.

Power Presentations with PowerPoint®

Additional Examples

Example 4

Your club has \$75 with which to purchase snacks to sell at an afterschool game. The number of snacks y that you can buy, if the average price of the snacks is x dollars, is given by $y = \frac{75}{x}$.

a. Describe the reasonable domain and range values. Domain is positive values; range is positive values.

b. Graph the function.

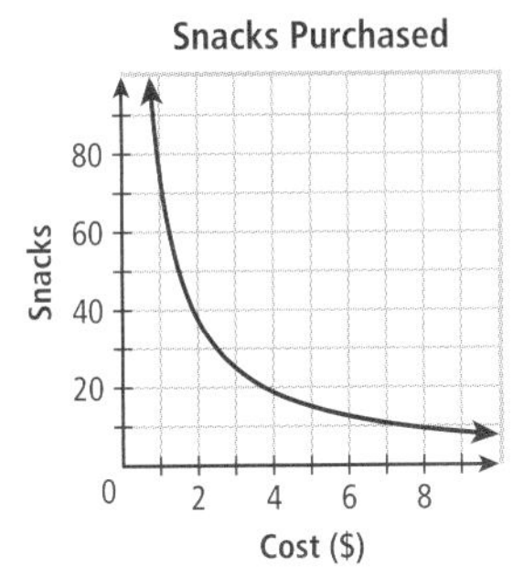

Also available on transparency

INTERVENTION

Questioning Strategies

EXAMPLE 4

- How can the asymptotes help you determine a reasonable domain and range?

Answer to *Check It Out*

4b.

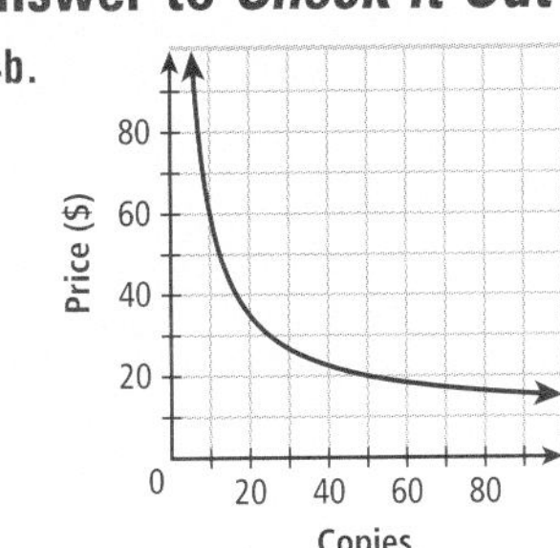

The table shows some of the properties of the three types of functions you have studied and their graphs.

Know it! Note

Types of Functions

LINEAR FUNCTIONS

$y = mx + b$

- Graph is a straight line.
- m is the slope. When $m = 0$, the graph is a horizontal line.
- When $m < 0$, the graph slopes down from left to right.
- When $m > 0$, the graph slopes up from left to right.
- b is the y-intercept.

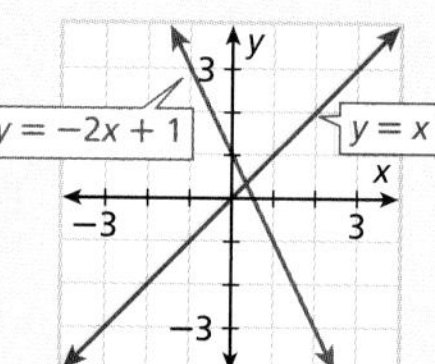

QUADRATIC FUNCTIONS

$y = ax^2 + bx + c,\ a \neq 0$

- Graph is a parabola.
- When $a > 0$, the parabola opens up.
- When $a < 0$, the parabola opens down.
- The axis of symmetry is the vertical line $x = -\frac{b}{2a}$.
- The function has a maximum or minimum value at the vertex.

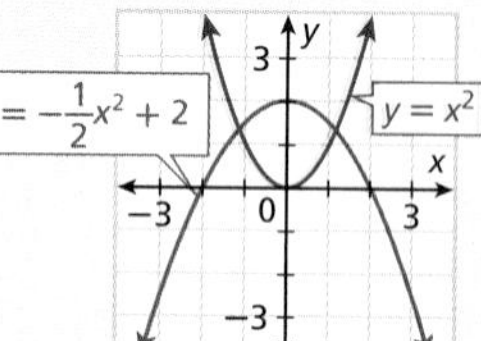

RATIONAL FUNCTIONS OF THE FORM $y = \frac{a}{x - b} + c$

$y = \frac{1}{x - b} + c$

- Graph is discontinuous.
- b is an excluded value; $x = b$ is the vertical asymptote.
- $y = c$ is the horizontal asymptote.

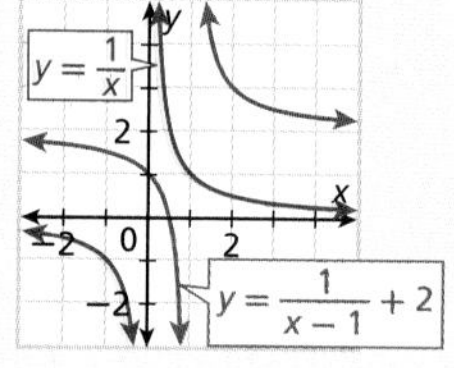

THINK AND DISCUSS

1. Does $y = \frac{1}{x - 5}$ have any excluded values? Explain.
2. Tell how to find the vertical and horizontal asymptotes of $y = \frac{1}{x + 9} - 5$.
3. **GET ORGANIZED** Copy and complete the graphic organizer. In each box, find the asymptotes for the given rational function.

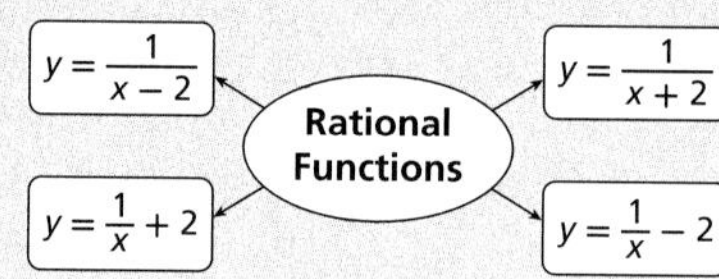

3 Close

Summarize

Tell students that the first step to graphing a rational function is graphing the asymptotes. Then the function can be sketched from a table of values. Have students name the asymptotes for $y = \frac{2}{x + 7} + 8$. $x = -7$; $y = 8$

FORMATIVE ASSESSMENT and INTERVENTION

***Diagnose Before* the Lesson**
10-2 Warm Up, TE p. 634

***Monitor During* the Lesson**
Check It Out! Exercises, SE pp. 634–637
Questioning Strategies, TE pp. 635–637

***Assess After* the Lesson**
10-2 Lesson Quiz, TE p. 641
Alternative Assessment, TE p. 641

Answers to *Think and Discuss*

1. Yes; the function is undefined at $x = 5$.
2. To find the vertical asymptote, set $x + 9$ equal to 0 and solve for x. The vertical asymptote is $x = -9$. To find the horizontal asymptote, look at the constant term. The horizontal asymptote is $y = -5$.
3. See p. A8.

10-2 Exercises

California Standards Practice
13.0, 15.0, 17.0, 24.1, 25.2

go.hrw.com
Homework Help Online
KEYWORD: MA8CA 10-2
Parent Resources Online
KEYWORD: MA8CA Parent

GUIDED PRACTICE

1. **Vocabulary** An x-value that makes a function undefined is a(n) ___?___. (*asymptote* or *excluded value*) **excluded value**

SEE EXAMPLE 1 p. 634

Identify any excluded values for each rational function.

2. $y = \frac{4}{x}$ **0**
3. $y = \frac{2}{x^2 + 3}$ **none**
4. $y = -\frac{2}{x}$ **0**
5. $y = \frac{16}{x - 4}$ **4**

SEE EXAMPLE 2 p. 635

Identify the asymptotes.

6. $y = \frac{1}{x - 3}$ **$x = 3$; $y = 0$**
7. $y = \frac{4}{3x + 15}$ **$x = -5$; $y = 0$**
8. $y = \frac{2}{3x - 5} + 2$ **$x = \frac{5}{3}$; $y = 2$**
9. $y = \frac{1}{x + 9} - 10$ **$x = -9$; $y = -10$**

SEE EXAMPLE 3 p. 636

Graph each function.

10. $y = \frac{2}{x + 6}$
11. $y = \frac{1}{x - 2} - 6$
12. $y = \frac{1}{x} + 2$
13. $y = \frac{1}{x - 3} - 2$

SEE EXAMPLE 4 p. 637

14. **Catering** A caterer has \$100 in her budget for fruit. Slicing and delivery of each pound of fruit costs \$5. If x represents the cost per pound of the fruit itself, then $y = \frac{100}{x + 5}$ represents the number of pounds y she can buy.
    a. Describe a reasonable domain and range. **D: $x > 0$; R: $0 < y < 20$**
    b. Graph the function.

PRACTICE AND PROBLEM SOLVING

Independent Practice

For Exercises	See Example
15–18	1
19–22	2
23–26	3
27	4

Extra Practice
Skills Practice p. EP20
Application Practice p. EP33

Identify any excluded values for each rational function.

15. $y = \frac{7}{x}$ **0**
16. $y = \frac{1}{x - 4}$ **4**
17. $y = -\frac{15}{x}$ **0**
18. $y = \frac{12}{x - 5}$ **5**

Identify the asymptotes.

19. $y = \frac{9}{x - 4}$ **$x = 4$; $y = 0$**
20. $y = \frac{2}{x + 4}$ **$x = -4$; $y = 0$**
21. $y = \frac{7}{4x - 12} + 4$ **$x = 3$; $y = 4$**
22. $y = \frac{7}{3x + 5} - 9$ **$x = -\frac{5}{3}$; $y = -9$**

Graph each function.

23. $y = \frac{5}{x - 5}$
24. $y = \frac{1}{x + 5} - 6$
25. $y = \frac{1}{x + 4}$
26. $y = \frac{1}{x - 4} + 2$

27. **Business** A wholesaler is buying auto parts. He has \$200 to spend. He receives 5 parts free with the order. The number of parts y he can buy, if the average price of the parts is x dollars, is $y = \frac{200}{x} + 5$.
    a. Describe a reasonable domain and range. **D: $x > 0$; R: natural numbers > 5**
    b. Graph the function.

Find the excluded value for each rational function.

28. $y = \frac{4}{x}$ **0**
29. $y = \frac{1}{x - 7}$ **7**
30. $y = \frac{2}{x + 4}$ **−4**
31. $y = \frac{3}{2x + 1}$ **$-\frac{1}{2}$**

Graph each rational function. Show the asymptotes.

32. $y = \frac{1}{x - 2}$
33. $y = \frac{2}{x} + 3$
34. $y = \frac{3}{x + 1} + 2$
35. $y = \frac{1}{x - 4} - 1$

36. The function $y = \frac{60}{x^2}$ relates the luminescence in lumens y of a 60-watt lightbulb viewed from a distance of x ft. Graph this function.

Teacher to Teacher

At the end of this lesson, there is a summary chart of functions. At this point, I like to include a real-world application for each type of function.

I give a worksheet with four columns: Name of Function, Equation, Graph, and Real-World Connection. I fill in one blank, and students fill in the other three.

Connie Johnsen
Harker Heights, TX

10-2 Exercises

Assignment Guide

Assign *Guided Practice* exercises as necessary.

If you finished Examples **1–2**
Proficient 15–22, 28–31
Advanced 15–22, 28–31, 59

If you finished Examples **1–4**
Proficient 15–50, 55–61, 64–73
Advanced 15–36, 44–73

Homework Quick Check
Quickly check key concepts.
Exercises: 18, 20, 22, 24, 27, 36

Number Sense When the denominator of a rational expression is x as in **Exercises 2, 4, 15,** and **17,** the excluded value is 0 regardless of whether the expression is positive or negative.

Answers

10–13. See p. A25.

14b.

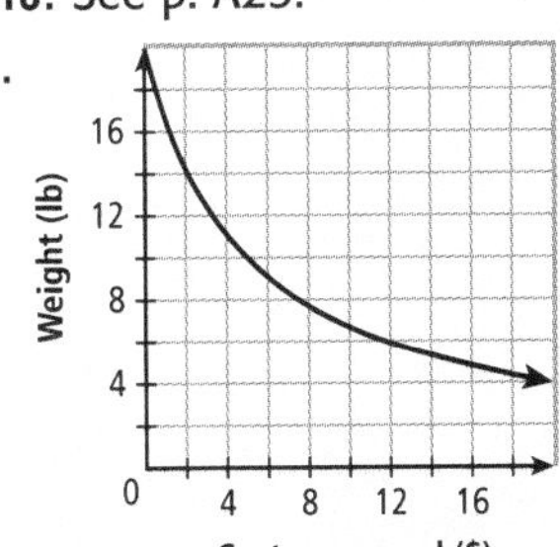

23–26, 27b, 32–36. See p. A25.

California Standards

Standard	Exercises
2.0	73
4.0	64–69
13.0	2–9, 15–22, 28–31, 36–40
14.0	70–72
15.0	46, 56a
17.0	14a, 27a, 45, 51–54, 56b, 61b, 61c
24.1	57
25.2	44

CONCEPT CONNECTION **Exercise 56** involves writing a rational function and finding the asymptotes. This exercise prepares students for the Concept Connection on page 650.

Answers

44. Student B is incorrect. The student identified the value at which there is a vertical asymptote ($x = -2$).

45, 46a. See p. A25.

47. translated 6 units right

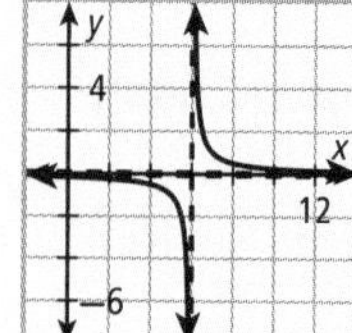

48. translated 7 units left

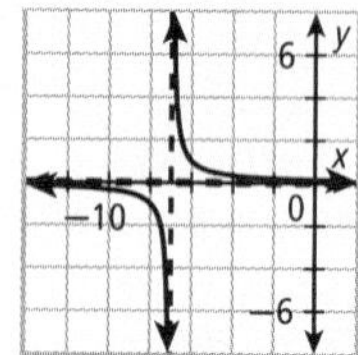

49. translated 4 units up

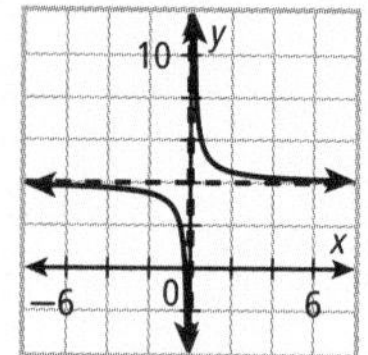

50. translated 2 units right and 9 units down

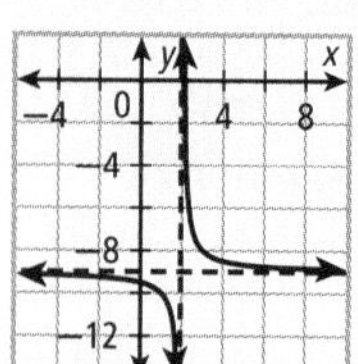

56c. See p. A25.

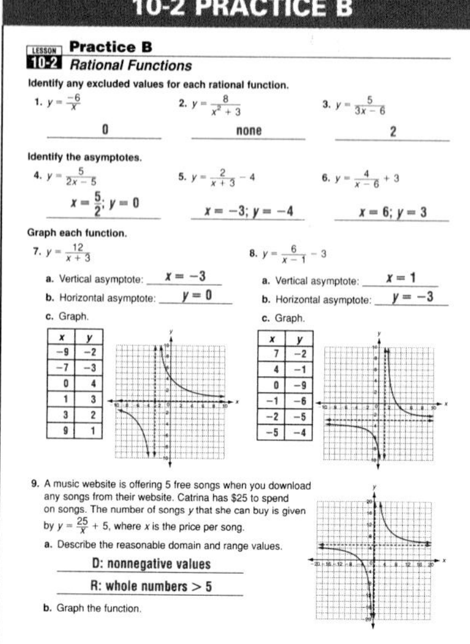

10-2 PRACTICE A

10-2 PRACTICE C

10-2 PRACTICE B

LESSON 10-2 **Practice B**
Rational Functions

Identify any excluded values for each rational function.

1. $y = \frac{-6}{x}$ 0
2. $y = \frac{8}{x^2 + 3}$ none
3. $y = \frac{5}{3x - 6}$ 2

Identify the asymptotes.

4. $y = \frac{5}{2x - 5}$ $x = \frac{5}{2}$; $y = 0$
5. $y = \frac{2}{x + 3} - 4$ $x = -3$; $y = -4$
6. $y = \frac{4}{x - 6} + 3$ $x = 6$; $y = 3$

Graph each function.

7. $y = \frac{12}{x + 3}$
   a. Vertical asymptote: $x = -3$
   b. Horizontal asymptote: $y = 0$
   c. Graph.

x	y
−9	−2
−7	−3
0	4
1	3
3	2
9	1

8. $y = \frac{6}{x - 1} - 3$
   a. Vertical asymptote: $x = 1$
   b. Horizontal asymptote: $y = -3$
   c. Graph.

x	y
7	−2
4	−1
0	−9
−1	−6
−2	−5
−5	−4

9. A music website is offering 5 free songs when you download any songs from their website. Catrina has $25 to spend on songs. The number of songs y that she can buy is given by $y = \frac{25}{x} + 5$, where x is the price per song.
   a. Describe the reasonable domain and range values.
   D: nonnegative values
   R: whole numbers > 5
   b. Graph the function.

Identify the asymptotes of each rational function.

37. $y = \frac{7}{x + 1}$ $x = -1$; $y = 0$

38. $y = \frac{1}{x} - 5$ $x = 0$; $y = -5$

39. $y = \frac{12}{x - 2} + 5$ $x = 2$; $y = 5$

40. $y = \frac{18}{x + 3} - 9$ $x = -3$; $y = -9$

Match each graph with one of the following functions.

A. $y = \frac{1}{x + 1} + 2$

B. $y = \frac{1}{x + 2} - 1$

C. $y = \frac{1}{x - 2} + 1$

41. B

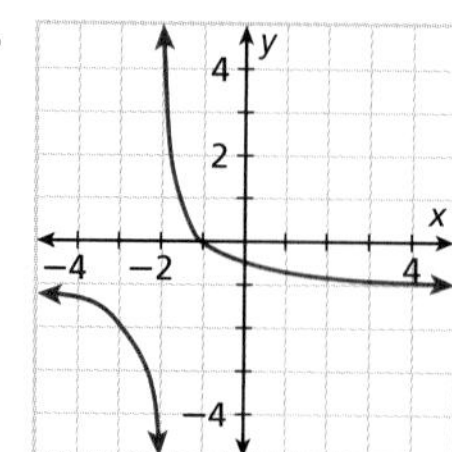

42. A

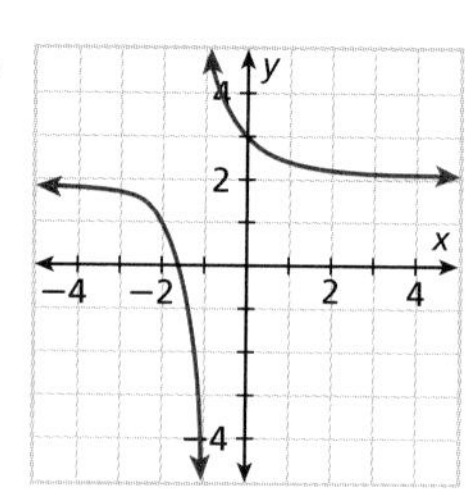

43. C

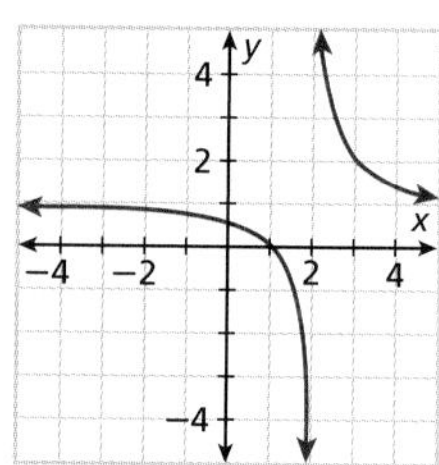

44. **///ERROR ANALYSIS///** In finding the horizontal asymptote of $y = \frac{1}{x + 2} - 3$, student A said the asymptote is at $y = -3$, and student B said it is at $y = -2$. Who is incorrect? Explain the error.

45. **Finance** The time in months y that it will take to pay off a bill of $1200, when x dollars are paid each month and the finance charge is $15 per month, is $y = \frac{1200}{x - 15}$. Describe a reasonable domain and range, and graph the function.

46. The table shows how long it takes different size landscaping teams to complete a project.
   a. Graph the data.
   b. Write a rational function to represent the data. $y = \frac{60}{x}$
   c. How many hours would it take 12 landscapers to complete the project? 5 h

Landscapers	Time (h)
2	30
4	15
5	12
10	6

Graph each function. Compare its graph to the graph of $y = \frac{1}{x}$.

47. $y = \frac{1}{x - 6}$

48. $y = \frac{1}{x + 7}$

49. $y = \frac{1}{x} + 4$

50. $y = \frac{1}{x - 2} - 9$

Find the domain that makes the range positive.

51. $y = \frac{10}{x - 2}$ $x > 2$

52. $y = \frac{10}{x + 2}$ $x > -2$

53. $y = \frac{5}{5x + 1}$ $x > -\frac{1}{5}$

54. $y = \frac{4}{3x - 7}$ $x > \frac{7}{3}$

55. **Critical Thinking** In which quadrants would you find the graph of $y = \frac{a}{x}$ when a is positive? when a is negative? I and III; II and IV

CONCEPT CONNECTION

56. This problem will prepare you for the Concept Connection on page 650.
It takes a total of 250 workdays to build a house for charity. For example, if 2 workers build the house, it takes them 125 actual construction days. If 10 workers are present, it takes 25 construction days to build the house.
   a. Write a function that represents the number of construction days to build as a function of the number of workers. $y = \frac{250}{x}$
   b. What is the domain of this function? D: natural numbers
   c. Sketch a graph of the function.

10-2 READING STRATEGIES

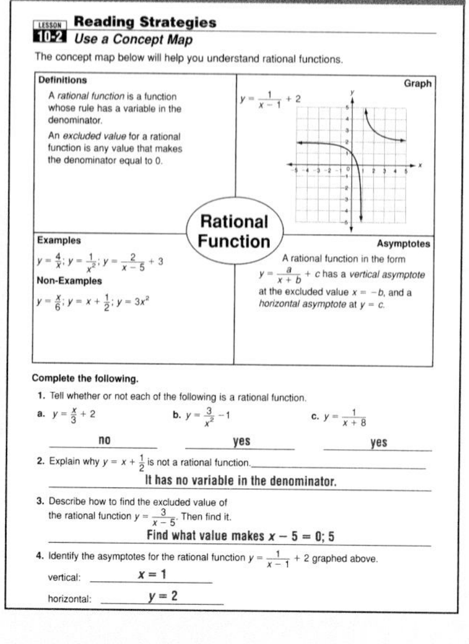

LESSON 10-2 **Reading Strategies**
Use a Concept Map

The concept map below will help you understand rational functions.

Rational Function

Definitions
A *rational function* is a function whose rule has a variable in the denominator.
An *excluded value* for a rational function is any value that makes the denominator equal to 0.

Graph
$y = \frac{1}{x - 1} + 2$

Examples
$y = \frac{4}{x}$; $y = \frac{1}{x^2}$; $y = \frac{2}{x - 5} + 3$

Non-Examples
$y = \frac{x}{6}$; $y = x + \frac{1}{2}$; $y = 3x^2$

Asymptotes
A rational function in the form $y = \frac{a}{x + b} + c$ has a *vertical asymptote* at the excluded value $x = -b$, and a *horizontal asymptote* at $y = c$.

Complete the following.

1. Tell whether or not each of the following is a rational function.
   a. $y = \frac{x}{3} + 2$ no
   b. $y = \frac{3}{x^2} - 1$ yes
   c. $y = \frac{1}{x + 8}$ yes
2. Explain why $y = x + \frac{1}{2}$ is not a rational function. It has no variable in the denominator.
3. Describe how to find the excluded value of the rational function $y = \frac{3}{x - 5}$. Then find it. Find what value makes $x - 5 = 0$; 5
4. Identify the asymptotes for the rational function $y = \frac{1}{x - 1} + 2$ graphed above.
   vertical: $x = 1$
   horizontal: $y = 2$

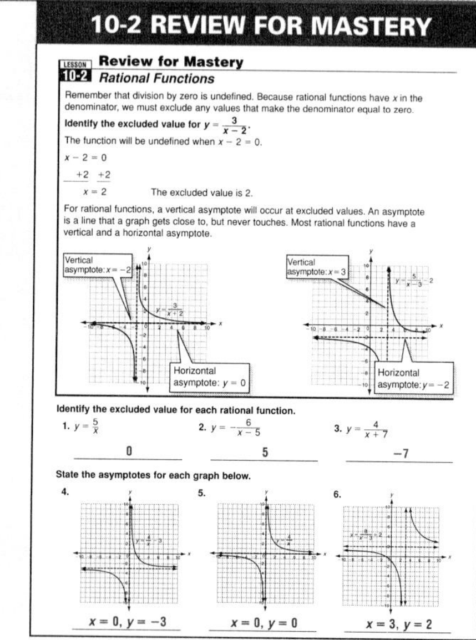

10-2 REVIEW FOR MASTERY

LESSON 10-2 **Review for Mastery**
Rational Functions

Remember that division by zero is undefined. Because rational functions have x in the denominator, we must exclude any values that make the denominator equal to zero.

Identify the excluded value for $y = \frac{3}{x - 2}$.

The function will be undefined when $x - 2 = 0$.

$x - 2 = 0$
$\underline{\quad +2 \quad +2}$
$x = 2$ The excluded value is 2.

For rational functions, a vertical asymptote will occur at excluded values. An asymptote is a line that a graph gets close to, but never touches. Most rational functions have a vertical and a horizontal asymptote.

Identify the excluded value for each rational function.

1. $y = \frac{5}{x}$ 0
2. $y = -\frac{6}{x - 5}$ 5
3. $y = \frac{4}{x + 7}$ −7

State the asymptotes for each graph below.

4. $x = 0$, $y = -3$
5. $x = 0$, $y = 0$
6. $x = 3$, $y = 2$

57. Reasoning Graph each pair of functions. Then use inductive reasoning to make a conjecture about the relationship between the graphs of the rational functions $y = \frac{k}{x}$ and $y = \frac{-k}{x}$.

For help with inductive reasoning, see p. 233 and pp. 280–281.

a. $y = \frac{1}{x}; y = \frac{-1}{x}$ b. $y = \frac{3}{x}; y = \frac{-3}{x}$ c. $y = \frac{5}{x}; y = \frac{-5}{x}$

Multiple Choice For Exercises 58 and 59, choose the best answer.

58. Which function is graphed?

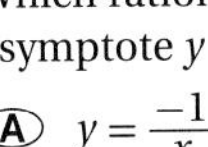

(A) $y = \frac{2}{x+3} - 4$ (C) $y = \frac{2}{x-3} + 4$

(B) $y = \frac{2}{x+4} - 3$ (D) $y = \frac{2}{x-4} + 3$

59. Which rational function has a graph with the horizontal asymptote $y = -1$?

(A) $y = \frac{-1}{x}$ (C) $y = \frac{1}{x+1}$

(B) $y = \frac{1}{x-1}$ (D) $y = \frac{1}{x} - 1$

60. **Short Response** Write a rational function whose graph is the same shape as the graph of $f(x) = \frac{1}{x}$, but has a vertical asymptote at $x = -2$ and a horizontal asymptote at $y = -3$. Graph the function. $f(x) = \frac{1}{x+2} - 3$

CHALLENGE AND EXTEND

61. Graph the equation $y = \frac{1}{x^2+1}$.
    a. Does this equation represent a rational function? Explain. **Yes; the function is a quotient of polynomials.**
    b. What is the domain of the function? **D: all real numbers**
    c. What is the range of the function? **R: $0 < y \leq 1$**
    d. Is the graph discontinuous? **no**

62. **Graphing Calculator** Are the graphs of $f(x) = \frac{(x-3)(x-1)}{(x-3)}$ and $g(x) = x - 1$ identical? Explain. (*Hint:* Are there any excluded values?)

63. **Critical Thinking** Write the equation of a rational function that has a horizontal asymptote at $y = 3$ and a vertical asymptote at $x = -2$ and contains the point $(1, 4)$. **Possible answer: $y = \frac{3}{x+2} + 3$**

SPIRAL STANDARDS REVIEW

Solve each inequality. *(Lesson 3-5)*

64. $4t + 5 < 3(t + 3)$ **$t < 4$**
65. $2(r + 1) \geq r - 6$ **$r \geq -8$**
66. $j + 10 < 4j - 29$ **$j > 13$**
67. $5(g + 2) \leq 2g - 5$ **$g \leq -5$**
68. $c - 5 > 2c + 7$ **$c < -12$**
69. $6(m - 2) < 2(6 - m)$ **$m < 3$**

Solve each quadratic equation by factoring. *(Lesson 9-5)*

70. $4 - x^2 = 0$ **± 2**
71. $3x^2 = x^2 + 2x + 12$ **$-2, 3$**
72. $-x^2 = -6x + 9$ **3**

73. Marie has a square piece of cloth. She needs another piece with a length 2 inches shorter than the side of the square piece and a width 2 inches longer. The area for the new piece of cloth is 780 in^2. What will be the dimensions of the new piece of cloth? *(Lesson 9-6)* **26 in. by 30 in.**

Teaching Tip **Multiple Choice** Students who chose **C** in **Exercise 59** chose a function with a vertical asymptote at $x = -1$.

Answers

57. See p. A25.

60–61. For graphs, see p. A25.

62. No; the graph of $f(x)$ has an excluded value at $x = 3$. The graph of $g(x)$ has no excluded values.

Journal

Have students explain the steps for graphing a rational function.

Create a rational function with a vertical asymptote at 4 and horizontal asymptote at −3. Then graph the function.

Power Presentations with PowerPoint®

10-2 Lesson Quiz

Identify any excluded values for each rational function.

1. $y = \frac{12}{x}$ 0
2. $y = \frac{7}{x-5}$ 5
3. Identify the asymptotes of $y = \frac{6}{x+4}$ and then graph the function. $x = -4; y = 0$

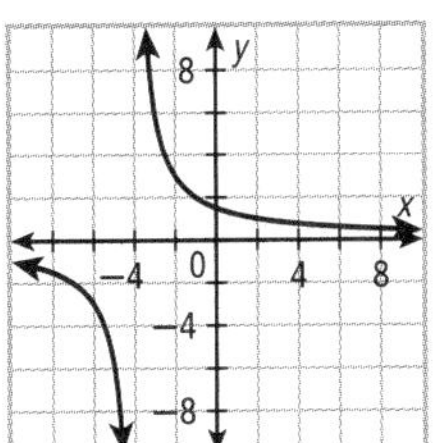

4. You have $100 to spend on CDs. A CD club advertises 6 free CDs for anyone who becomes a member. The number of CDs y that you can receive is given by $y = \frac{100}{x} + 6$, where x is the average price per CD.
    a. Describe the reasonable domain and range values.
       D: $x > 0$
       R: natural numbers > 6
    b. Graph the function.

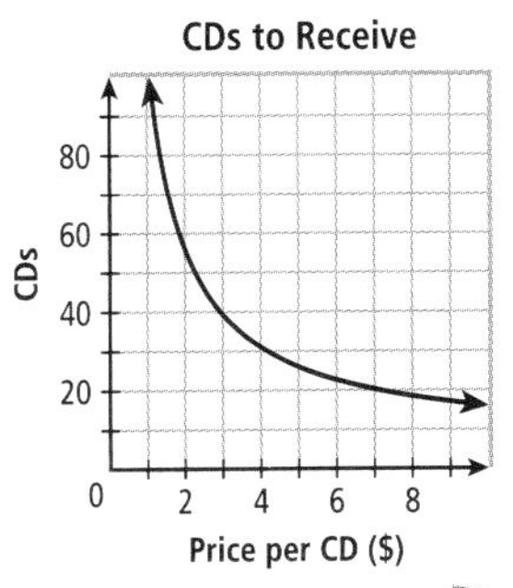

Also available on transparency

10-2 PROBLEM SOLVING

LESSON 10-2 **Problem Solving**
Rational Functions

Gabrielle saves $100 and decides to join a CD Club. As a member, she gets 12 CDs free and then must buy the rest at the regular price of x dollars. The number of CDs y she can buy is $y = \frac{100}{x} + 12$.

1. Determine a reasonable domain and range. **D: $x > 0$; R: natural numbers greater than 12**
2. Identify the vertical and horizontal asymptotes. **$x = 0$ and $y = 12$**
3. Complete this table of ordered pairs and graph the rational function.

x	5	10	20	25
y	32	22	17	16

Number of CDs; Regular Price of Each CD ($); 0, 4, 8, 12, 16, 20, 24, 28, 32, 36

4. Gabrielle learns that the regular price of a CD is $17.90. How many CDs can she buy through the Club with $100? **17**

Select the best answer. For 5–6, refer to the situation above.

5. Before joining the CD Club, Gabrielle learns about the Student Savings Card. If she buys a card for $20, she gets $5 off every CD she buys at the local record store. If each CD costs x dollars at the local record store, then the number of CDs y she can buy is $y = \frac{100 - 20}{x - 5}$. The average price of each CD at the local record store is $14.95. How many CDs can she buy with the Card and $100?
   A 4 C 10
   (B) 8 D 12
6. Gabrielle realizes she must pay $2.95 for shipping and handling on every CD from the club, including the 12 free CDs. That changes the function for the club to $y = \frac{100 - 2.95(12)}{x + 2.95} + 12$. If the regular price is still $17.90, how many CDs can she buy through the Club?
   F 3 H 16
   (G) 15 J 18
7. At x meters away from a very loud stereo speaker, the intensity of the sound y in watts per square meter is given by $y = \frac{0.0016}{x^2}$. What is the intensity when you stand 4 meters away?
   (A) 0.0001 W/m^2 C 0.0004 W/m^2
   B 0.0002 W/m^2 D 0.0008 W/m^2

10-2 CHALLENGE

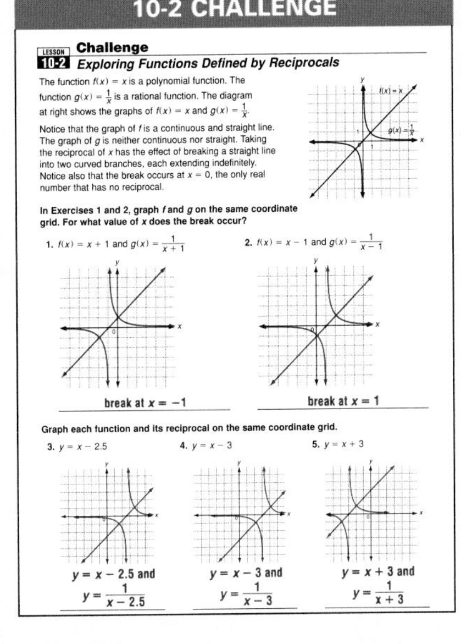

LESSON 10-2 **Challenge**
Exploring Functions Defined by Reciprocals

The function $f(x) = x$ is a polynomial function. The function $g(x) = \frac{1}{x}$ is a rational function. The diagram at right shows the graphs of $f(x) = x$ and $g(x) = \frac{1}{x}$.

Notice that the graph of f is a continuous and straight line. The graph of g is neither continuous nor straight. Taking the reciprocal of x has the effect of breaking a straight line into two curved branches, each extending indefinitely. Notice also that the break occurs at $x = 0$, the only real number that has no reciprocal.

In Exercises 1 and 2, graph f and g on the same coordinate grid. For what value of x does the break occur?

1. $f(x) = x + 1$ and $g(x) = \frac{1}{x+1}$ **break at $x = -1$**
2. $f(x) = x - 1$ and $g(x) = \frac{1}{x-1}$ **break at $x = 1$**

Graph each function and its reciprocal on the same coordinate grid.

3. $y = x - 2.5$ **$y = x - 2.5$ and $y = \frac{1}{x - 2.5}$**
4. $y = x - 3$ **$y = x - 3$ and $y = \frac{1}{x - 3}$**
5. $y = x + 3$ **$y = x + 3$ and $y = \frac{1}{x + 3}$**

10-3 Organizer

Objectives: Simplify rational expressions.

Identify excluded values of rational expressions.

Online Edition
Tutorial Videos

Countdown to Mastery Week 23

Power Presentations with PowerPoint®

Warm Up

Simplify each expression.

1. $\frac{12}{40}$ $\frac{3}{10}$ **2.** $\frac{24}{60}$ $\frac{2}{5}$

Factor each expression.

3. $x^2 + 5x + 6$ $(x + 2)(x + 3)$

4. $4x^2 - 64$ $4(x + 4)(x - 4)$

5. $2x^2 + 3x + 1$ $(2x + 1)(x + 1)$

6. $9x^2 + 60x + 100$ $(3x + 10)^2$

Also available on transparency

Math Humor

Q: Why was the number so happy to get accepted into the Rational Expression Club?

A: It didn't want to be excluded.

California Standards

Algebra 1 🔑 **12.0**

10-3 Simplifying Rational Expressions

California Standards

🔑 **12.0 Students simplify fractions with polynomials in the numerator and denominator by factoring both and reducing them to the lowest terms.**

Vocabulary
rational expression

Why learn this?
The shapes and sizes of plants and animals are partly determined by the ratio of surface area to volume.

If an animal's body is small and its surface area is large, the rate of heat loss will be high. Hummingbirds must maintain a high metabolism to compensate for the loss of body heat due to having a high surface-area-to-volume ratio. Formulas for surface-area-to-volume ratios are *rational expressions.*

A **rational expression** is an algebraic expression whose numerator and denominator are polynomials. The value of the polynomial expression in the denominator cannot be zero since division by zero is undefined. This means that rational expressions, like rational functions, may have excluded values.

EXAMPLE 1 Identifying Excluded Values

Find any excluded values of each rational expression.

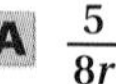

A $\frac{5}{8r}$

$8r = 0$ *Set the denominator equal to 0.*

$r = \frac{0}{8} = 0$ *Solve for r by dividing both sides by 8.*

The excluded value is 0.

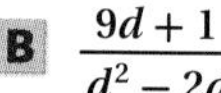

B $\frac{9d + 1}{d^2 - 2d}$

$d^2 - 2d = 0$ *Set the denominator equal to 0.*

$d(d - 2) = 0$ *Factor.*

$d = 0$ or $d - 2 = 0$ *Use the Zero Product Property.*

$d = 0$ or $d = 2$ *Solve for d.*

The excluded values are 0 and 2.

C $\frac{x + 4}{x^2 + 5x + 6}$

$x^2 + 5x + 6 = 0$ *Set the denominator equal to 0.*

$(x + 3)(x + 2) = 0$ *Factor.*

$x + 3 = 0$ or $x + 2 = 0$ *Use the Zero Product Property.*

$x = -3$ or $x = -2$ *Solve each equation for x.*

The excluded values are -3 and -2.

Remember!
To review the Zero Product Property, see Lesson 9-5.
To review factoring trinomials, see Chapter 8.

CHECK IT OUT! **Find any excluded values of each rational expression.**

1a. $\frac{12}{t^2 + 5}$ **none** **1b.** $\frac{3b}{b^2 + 5b}$ **0, −5** **1c.** $\frac{3k^2}{k^2 + 7k + 12}$ **−3, −4**

1 Introduce

EXPLORATION

10-3 Simplifying Rational Expressions

You can use your calculator to help you compare expressions.

1. Consider the functions $y = \frac{2x^2 + 6x}{2x^2}$ and $y = \frac{x + 3}{x}$. What are the excluded values for these functions?

2. Evaluate each function for the x-values in the table.

x	$y = \frac{2x^2 + 6x}{2x^2}$	$y = \frac{x + 3}{x}$
1		
3		
6		

3. Enter the functions into your calculator as shown. Press GRAPH. What do you notice?

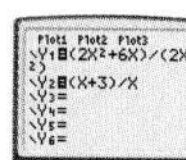

4. Press 2nd GRAPH to view a table of values for the functions. What do you notice?

THINK AND DISCUSS

5. **Explain** what you can conclude about the expressions $\frac{2x^2 + 6x}{2x^2}$ and $\frac{x + 3}{x}$.

6. **Describe** how the numerator and denominator of $\frac{2x^2 + 6x}{2x^2}$

Motivate

Review with students that $\frac{24}{50}$ can be written as $\frac{2 \cdot 2 \cdot 2 \cdot 3}{2 \cdot 5 \cdot 5}$ and that when the common factor of 2 is divided out, the expression equals $\frac{2 \cdot 2 \cdot 3}{5 \cdot 5} = \frac{12}{25}$. Ask students to conjecture about how to simplify rational expressions.

Explorations and answers are provided in *Alternate Openers: Explorations Transparencies.*

A rational expression is in its simplest form when the numerator and denominator have no common factors except 1. Remember that to simplify fractions you can divide out common factors that appear in both the numerator and the denominator. You can do the same to simplify rational expressions.

EXAMPLE 2 **Simplifying Rational Expressions**

Simplify each rational expression, if possible. Identify any excluded values.

A $\frac{3t^3}{12t}$

$\frac{3t^3}{3 \cdot 4t}$ — *Factor 12.*

$\frac{\cancel{3}\cancel{t^3}^{t^2}}{\cancel{3} \cdot 4\cancel{t}}$ — *Divide out common factors. Note that if t = 0, the expression is undefined.*

$\frac{t^2}{4}; t \neq 0$ — *Simplify. The excluded value is 0.*

B $\frac{3x^2 - 9x}{x - 3}$

$\frac{3x(x-3)}{x-3}$ — *Factor the numerator.*

$\frac{3x\cancel{(x-3)}}{\cancel{x-3}}$ — *Divide out common factors. Note that if x = 3, the expression is undefined.*

$3x; x \neq 3$ — *Simplify. The excluded value is 3.*

C $\frac{c}{c+5}$

$\frac{c}{c+5}; c \neq -5$ — *The numerator and denominator have no common factors. The excluded value is −5.*

Caution!

Be sure to use the original denominator when finding excluded values. The excluded values may not be "seen" in the simplified denominator.

CHECK IT OUT! **Simplify each rational expression, if possible. Identify any excluded values.**

2a. $\frac{5m^2}{15m}$ $\frac{m}{3}; m \neq 0$ **2b.** $\frac{6p^3 + 12p}{p^2 + 2}$ $6p$ **2c.** $\frac{3n}{n-2}$ $\frac{3n}{n-2}; n \neq 2$

From this point forward, you do not need to include excluded values in your answers unless they are asked for.

EXAMPLE 3 **Simplifying Rational Expressions with Trinomials**

Simplify each rational expression, if possible.

A $\frac{k+1}{k^2 - 4k - 5}$

$\frac{k+1}{(k+1)(k-5)}$ — *Factor the numerator and the denominator when possible.*

$\frac{\cancel{k+1}^1}{\cancel{(k+1)}(k-5)}$ — *Divide out common factors.*

$\frac{1}{k-5}$ — *Simplify.*

B $\frac{y^2 - 16}{y^2 - 8y + 16}$

$\frac{(y+4)(y-4)}{(y-4)(y-4)}$

$\frac{(y+4)\cancel{(y-4)}}{(y-4)\cancel{(y-4)}}$

$\frac{y+4}{y-4}$

2 Teach

Guided Instruction

Review factoring using the GCF, factorable trinomials, perfect-square trinomials, difference of squares, and grouping. Tell students that finding the excluded values for rational expressions is the same as for rational functions: find values that make the denominator equal to zero. As you work through each example, stress that *factors* are divided out. Terms that are added or subtracted are not.

Universal Access

Through Number Sense

Ask students whether $\frac{x+5}{x+7}$ can be simplified to $\frac{5}{7}$. No Tell students that whenever they are not sure if a step in simplifying an expression is correct, they can substitute real numbers. For example, since $\frac{4+5}{4+7} \neq \frac{5}{7}$, then $\frac{x+5}{x+7}$ cannot be simplified to $\frac{5}{7}$.

COMMON ERROR ALERT

When identifying excluded values, students might forget to include zero for the monomial variable factor in expressions like $d(d - 2)$. Remind them of the Zero Product Property: If $ab = 0$, then $a = 0$ or $b = 0$.

Power Presentations with PowerPoint®

Additional Examples

Example 1

Find any excluded values of each rational expression.

A. $\frac{6}{g+4}$ -4

B. $\frac{2x+1}{x^2 - 15x}$ $0, 15$

C. $\frac{y-2}{y^2 + 5y + 4}$ $-1, -4$

Example 2

Simplify each rational expression, if possible. Identify any excluded values.

A. $\frac{2r^4}{14r}$ $\frac{r^3}{7}; r \neq 0$

B. $\frac{6n^2 + 3n}{2n + 1}$ $3n; n \neq -\frac{1}{2}$

C. $\frac{12p}{3p - 2}$ $\frac{12p}{3p-2}; p \neq \frac{2}{3}$

Also available on transparency

INTERVENTION

Questioning Strategies

EXAMPLE 1

- Why are some values excluded?

EXAMPLE 2

- How can a simplified rational expression have an excluded value when its denominator has no variables?

Inclusion Some students may benefit from fully factoring the numerator and denominator before simplifying. For instance, in **Example 2A,** begin by writing $\frac{3t^3}{12t} = \frac{3 \cdot t \cdot t \cdot t}{3 \cdot 2 \cdot 2 \cdot t}$. This makes it easier to see and divide out common factors: $\frac{\cancel{3} \cdot t \cdot t \cdot \cancel{t}}{\cancel{3} \cdot 2 \cdot 2 \cdot \cancel{t}} = \frac{t \cdot t}{2 \cdot 2} = \frac{t^2}{4}$

Inclusion Before introducing **Example 4,** help students understand that when the numerator and denominator are opposites, the expression is equal to −1. For example, $\frac{5-3}{3-5} = \frac{2}{-2} = -1$.

Power Presentations with PowerPoint®

Additional Examples

Example 3

Simplify each rational expression, if possible.

A. $\frac{x+2}{x^2+5x+6}$ $\frac{1}{x+3}$

B. $\frac{w^2-4}{w^2-8w+12}$ $\frac{w+2}{w-6}$

Example 4

Simplify each rational expression, if possible.

A. $\frac{5x-10}{4-x^2}$ $-\frac{5}{2+x}$

B. $\frac{18-6r}{2r^2+8r-42}$ $-\frac{3}{r+7}$

Also available on transparency

INTERVENTION

Questioning Strategies

EXAMPLE **3**

- How is simplifying a rational expression similar to simplifying a fraction? How is it different?

EXAMPLE **4**

- How is −1 used to simplify opposite binomials?

Simplify each rational expression, if possible.

3a. $\frac{r+2}{r^2+7r+10}$ $\frac{1}{r+5}$ **3b.** $\frac{b^2-25}{b^2+10b+25}$ $\frac{b-5}{b+5}$

Recall from Chapter 8 that opposite binomials can help you factor polynomials. Recognizing opposite binomials can also help you simplify rational expressions.

Consider $\frac{x-3}{3-x}$. The numerator and denominator are opposite binomials. Therefore,

$$\frac{x-3}{3-x} = \frac{x-3}{-x+3} = \frac{\cancel{x-3}^1}{-1\cancel{(x-3)}} = \frac{1}{-1} = -1.$$

EXAMPLE 4 Simplifying Rational Expressions Using Opposite Binomials

Simplify each rational expression, if possible.

A $\frac{2x-10}{25-x^2}$

A		B
$\frac{2(x-5)}{(5-x)(5+x)}$	*Factor.*	$\frac{2(1-m)}{2(m+2)(m-1)}$
$\frac{2(x-5)}{(5-x)(5+x)}$	*Identify opposite binomials.*	$\frac{2(1-m)}{2(m+2)(m-1)}$
$\frac{2(x-5)}{-1(x-5)(5+x)}$	*Rewrite one opposite binomial.*	$\frac{2(1-m)}{2(m+2)(-1)(1-m)}$
$\frac{2\cancel{(x-5)}}{-1\cancel{(x-5)}(5+x)}$	*Divide out common factors.*	$\frac{\cancel{2}\cancel{(1-m)}^1}{\cancel{2}(m+2)(-1)\cancel{(1-m)}}$
$-\frac{2}{5+x}$	*Simplify.*	$-\frac{1}{m+2}$

B $\frac{2-2m}{2m^2+2m-4}$

Simplify each rational expression, if possible.

4a. $\frac{3x-12}{16-x^2}$ $-\frac{3}{4+x}$ **4b.** $\frac{6-2x}{2x^2-4x-6}$ $-\frac{1}{x+1}$ **4c.** $\frac{3x-33}{x^2-121}$ $\frac{3}{x+11}$

Student to Student

Opposite Binomials

Tanika Brown, Washington High School

I didn't understand why the quotient of opposite binomials simplified to −1. My teacher showed me an example on a number line:

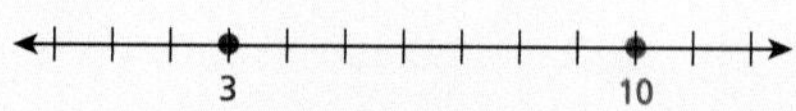

The distance between 3 and 10 is always the same (7 units). But depending on the order of the subtraction, the difference could be positive or negative.

10 − 3 = 7 3 − 10 = −7

So whenever you divide something in the form $\frac{a-b}{b-a}$, you get a number divided by its opposite, which is always −1.

Visual When dividing out common factors, encourage students to use a different colored pencil (MK) to strike out each matching pair of factors. Some students will find it helpful to circle the remaining factors before writing the simplified answer.

EXAMPLE 5 Biology Application

Water evaporates from a plant's surface. In two plants with different surface areas, the same volume of water will evaporate at a faster rate from the plant with the greater surface area. In the desert, plants must conserve water in order to survive. This means that the greater a plant's surface-area-to-volume ratio, the less likely the plant is to survive in the desert.

a. What is the surface-area-to-volume ratio of a spherical barrel cactus? (*Hint:* For a sphere, $S = 4\pi r^2$ and $V = \frac{4}{3}\pi r^3$.)

$\frac{4\pi r^2}{\frac{4}{3}\pi r^3}$ *Write the ratio of surface area to volume.*

$\frac{4\cancel{\pi} r^2}{\frac{4}{3}\cancel{\pi} r^3}$ *Divide out common factors.*

$\frac{4\cancel{r^2}}{\frac{4}{3}\cancel{r^3}r}$ *Use properties of exponents.*

$\frac{4}{r} \cdot \frac{3}{4}$ *To divide by $\frac{4}{3}$, multiply by its reciprocal, $\frac{3}{4}$.*

$\frac{\cancel{4}}{r} \cdot \frac{3}{\cancel{4}}$ *Divide out common factors.*

$\frac{3}{r}$ *Simplify.*

b. Which barrel cactus has a greater chance of survival in the desert, one with a radius of 4 inches or one with a radius of 7 inches? Explain.

$\frac{3}{r} = \frac{3}{4}$ $\frac{3}{r} = \frac{3}{7}$ *Write the ratio of surface area to volume twice. Substitute 4 and 7 for r.*

$\frac{3}{4} > \frac{3}{7}$ *Compare the ratios.*

The cactus with a radius of 7 inches has a greater chance of survival because its surface-area-to-volume ratio is lesser.

Remember!

For two fractions with the same numerator, the value of the fraction with a greater denominator is less than the value of the other fraction.

$9 > 3$

$\frac{2}{9} < \frac{2}{3}$

CHECK IT OUT! 5. Which barrel cactus has less of a chance to survive in the desert, one with a radius of 6 inches or one with a radius of 3 inches? Explain. **The barrel cactus with a radius of 3 inches has less chance of survival because its surface-area-to-volume ratio is greater.**

THINK AND DISCUSS

1. Write a rational expression that has an excluded value that cannot be identified when the expression is in its simplified form.

Know it! Note

2. **GET ORGANIZED** Copy and complete the graphic organizer. In each box, write and simplify one of the given rational expressions using the most appropriate method. $\frac{x-3}{x^2-6x+9}$, $\frac{5x^4}{x^2}$, $\frac{4-x}{x-4}$, $\frac{4x^2-4x}{8x}$

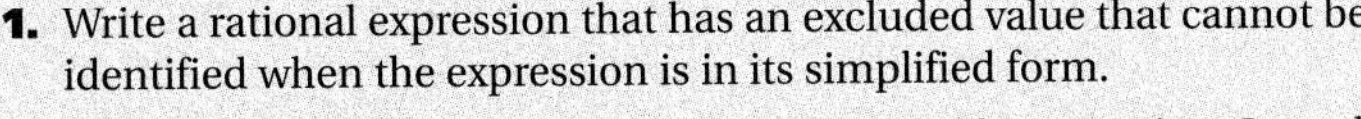

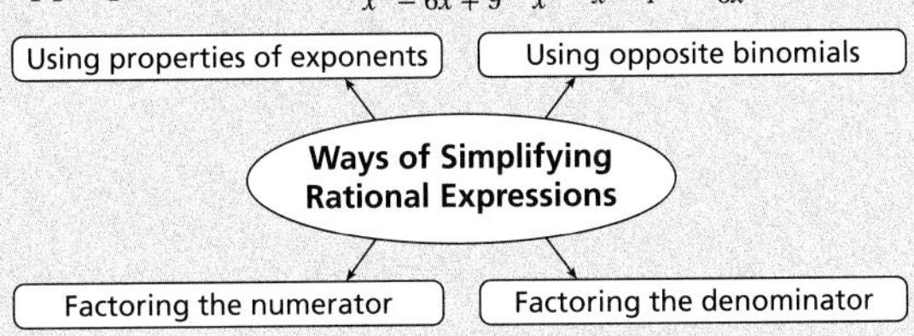

Power Presentations with PowerPoint®

Additional Examples

Example 5

A theater at an amusement park is shaped like a sphere. The sphere is held up with support rods.

a. What is the ratio of the theater's volume to its surface area? (*Hint:* For a sphere, $V = \frac{4}{3}\pi r^3$ and $S = 4\pi r^2$.) $\frac{r}{3}$

b. Use this ratio to find the ratio of the theater's volume to its surface area when the radius is 45 feet. 15

Also available on transparency

INTERVENTION

Questioning Strategies

EXAMPLE 5

- How do you know which expression is written in the numerator and which is written in the denominator?

3 Close

Summarize

Remind students that they must use the original, not simplified, denominator of a rational expression when finding excluded values.

Ask students why x and 2 in $\frac{x^2+2}{x+4}$ cannot be divided out. They are not factors.

FORMATIVE ASSESSMENT and INTERVENTION

Diagnose Before **the Lesson**
10-3 Warm Up, TE p. 642

Monitor During **the Lesson**
Check It Out! Exercises, SE pp. 642–645
Questioning Strategies, TE pp. 643–645

Assess After **the Lesson**
10-3 Lesson Quiz, TE p. 648
Alternative Assessment, TE p. 648

Answers to *Think and Discuss*

Possible answers:

1. The expression $\frac{x+2}{x^2+5x+6}$ has the excluded values −2 and −3, but −2 cannot be identified as an excluded value in the simplified form, $\frac{1}{x+3}$.
2. See p. A8.

10-3 Exercises

Assignment Guide

Assign *Guided Practice* exercises as necessary.

If you finished Examples **1–3**
Proficient 24–37, 43–45
Advanced 24–37, 43–45, 59–61

If you finished Examples **1–5**
Proficient 24–61, 68–76
Advanced 24–42, 49–76

Homework Quick Check
Quickly check key concepts.
Exercises: 26, 28, 34, 38, 41

Multiple Representations For the formula of the area of a trapezoid in **Exercise 23**, the 2 in the denominator can be written as a coefficient of $\frac{1}{2}$, so the area of a trapezoid can be expressed as $\frac{1}{2}(b_1 + b_2)h$ or $\frac{1}{2}h(b_1 + b_2)$.

10-3 Exercises

California Standards Practice
Preparation for 13.0; 12.0, 15.0

go.hrw.com
Homework Help Online
KEYWORD: MA8CA 10-3
Parent Resources Online
KEYWORD: MA8CA Parent

GUIDED PRACTICE

1. **Vocabulary** What is true about both the numerator and denominator of rational expressions? **Both the numerator and denominator are polynomials.**

SEE EXAMPLE 1 p. 642

Find any excluded values of each rational expression.

2. $\frac{5}{m}$ **0**
3. $\frac{x+2}{x^2-8x}$ **0, 8**
4. $\frac{p^2}{p^2-2p-15}$ **−3, 5**

SEE EXAMPLE 2 p. 643

Simplify each rational expression, if possible. Identify any excluded values.

5. $\frac{4a^2}{8a}$ $\frac{a}{2}$**; $a \neq 0$**
6. $\frac{2d^2+12d}{d+6}$ **$2d$; $d \neq -6$**
7. $\frac{2}{y+3}$ $\frac{2}{y+3}$**; $y \neq -3$**
8. $\frac{10}{5-y}$ $\frac{10}{5-y}$**; $y \neq 5$**
9. $\frac{2h}{2h+4}$ $\frac{h}{h+2}$**; $h \neq -2$**
10. $\frac{3(x+4)}{6x}$ $\frac{x+4}{2x}$**; $x \neq 0$**

SEE EXAMPLE 3 p. 643

Simplify each rational expression, if possible.

11. $\frac{b+4}{b^2+5b+4}$ $\frac{1}{b+1}$
12. $\frac{s^2-4}{s^2+4s+4}$ $\frac{s-2}{s+2}$
13. $\frac{c^2+5c+6}{(c+3)(c-4)}$ $\frac{c+2}{c-4}$
14. $\frac{(x-2)(x+1)}{x^2+4x+3}$ $\frac{x-2}{x+3}$
15. $\frac{j^2-25}{j^2+2j-15}$ $\frac{j-5}{j-3}$
16. $\frac{p+1}{p^2-4p-5}$ $\frac{1}{p-5}$

SEE EXAMPLE 4 p. 644

17. $\frac{2n-16}{64-n^2}$ $-\frac{2}{8+n}$
18. $\frac{8-4x}{2x^2-12x+16}$ $-\frac{2}{x-4}$
19. $\frac{10-5r}{r^2+4r-12}$ $\frac{-5}{r+6}$
20. $\frac{2x-14}{49-x^2}$ $-\frac{2}{7+x}$
21. $\frac{5q-50}{100-q^2}$ $-\frac{5}{10+q}$
22. $\frac{36-12a}{a^2+2a-15}$ $-\frac{12}{a+5}$

SEE EXAMPLE 5 p. 645

23. **Construction** The side of a triangular roof is to have the same height h and base b_2 as the side of a trapezoidal roof.

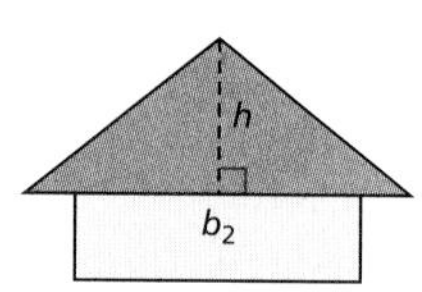

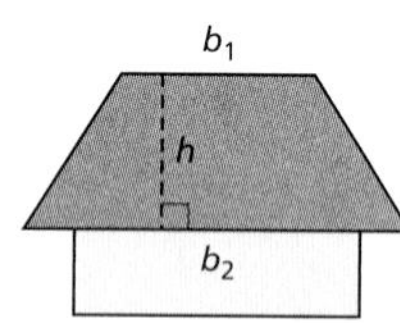

a. What is the ratio of the area of the triangular roof to the area of the trapezoidal roof? $\frac{b_2}{b_1+b_2}$
(*Hint:* For a triangle, $A = \frac{1}{2}b_2h$. For a trapezoid, $A = \frac{b_1+b_2}{2}h$.)

b. Compare the ratio from part **a** to what the ratio will be if b_1 is doubled for the trapezoidal roof and b_2 is doubled for both roofs. **They will be the same:** $\frac{b_2}{b_1+b_2}$.

PRACTICE AND PROBLEM SOLVING

Find any excluded values of each rational expression.

24. $\frac{c}{c^2+c}$ **−1, 0**
25. $\frac{2}{-3x}$ **0**
26. $\frac{4}{x^2-3x-10}$ **−2, 5**
27. $\frac{n^2-1}{2n^2-7n-4}$ $-\frac{1}{2}$**, 4**

Simplify each rational expression, if possible. Identify any excluded values.

28. $\frac{4d^3+4d^2}{d+1}$ **$4d^2$; $d \neq -1$**
29. $\frac{3m^2}{m-4}$ **already simplified; $m \neq 4$**
30. $\frac{10y^4}{2y}$ **$5y^3$; $y \neq 0$**
31. $\frac{2t^2}{16t}$ $\frac{t}{8}$**; $t \neq 0$**

California Standards

Standard	Exercises
2.0	73–76
6.0	70–72
12.0	5–22, 28–40, 43–51, 62–64
Prep for 13.0	2–4, 24–27, 56–58, 65–67
15.0	52
17.0	68, 69

10-3 READING STRATEGIES

LESSON 10-3 **Reading Strategies**
Use a Table

The table below shows examples of the many ways that rational expressions can be simplified.

Use Properties of Exponents	Factor out Common Monomials	Factor Trinomials & Special Products	Use Opposite Binomials
$\frac{4m^5}{24m^2}$	$\frac{2b^2-18b}{b-9}$	$\frac{x^2-9}{x^2+2x-15}$	$\frac{6t-t^2}{t^2-4t-12}$
$\frac{m^3}{6}$	$\frac{2b(b-9)}{b-9}$	$\frac{(x+3)(x-3)}{(x+5)(x-3)}$	$\frac{t(6-t)}{(t+2)(t-6)}$
	$2b$	$\frac{x+3}{x+5}$	$\frac{t(-1)(t-6)}{(t+2)(t-6)}$
			$-\frac{t}{(t+2)}$

Use the table to answer the following.

1. Look at the first column. Explain how $\frac{4m^5}{24m^2}$ was simplified to $\frac{m^3}{6}$. **$\frac{4}{24}$ simplified to $\frac{1}{6}$ and the exponents were subtracted, making $\frac{m^5}{m^2} = m^3$.**
2. Look at the second column. What expression was divided out of the numerator and denominator? **$b-9$**
3. Look at the third column. What type of special product was in the numerator? **difference of squares**
4. Look at the fourth column. What happened in the numerator? **$(6-t)$ became $(-1)(t-6)$**

Simplify each rational expression.

5. $\frac{3t^4}{9t^6}$ **$\frac{1}{3t^2}$**
6. $\frac{n^4-3n^3}{2n^2-6n}$ **$\frac{n^2}{2}$**
7. $\frac{4c+4}{2c^2-5c-7}$ **$\frac{4}{2c-7}$**
8. $\frac{18-2x}{x^2-81}$ **$-\frac{2}{x+9}$**

10-3 REVIEW FOR MASTERY

LESSON 10-3 **Review for Mastery**
Simplifying Rational Expressions

A **rational expression** is an algebraic expression whose numerator and denominator are polynomials.

Exclude any values from a rational expression that make the denominator equal zero.

Find any excluded value of $\frac{6x}{x^2-5x}$.

$\frac{6x}{x^2-5x}$
$x^2-5x=0$ *Set denominator = 0.*
$x(x-5)=0$ *Factor.*
$x=0$ or $x-5=0$ *Zero Product*
$+5 \quad +5$ *Property*
$x=5$

The excluded values are 0 and 5.

Simplify $\frac{x+4}{2x^2+8x}$, if possible. Identify any excluded values.

$\frac{x+4}{2x^2+8x}$
$\frac{x+4}{2x(x+4)}$ Factor the denominator.
Find excluded values here.
$\frac{(x+4)^1}{2x(x+4)^1}$ Divide out common factors.
$\frac{1}{2x}$ Simplify.

Remember to find the excluded value from the original equation (not the simplified one).
The excluded values are 0 and −4.

Identify any excluded values.

1. $\frac{3}{4x}$ **0**
2. $\frac{5x}{3x^2+15x}$ **0; −5**
3. $\frac{6}{x^2-5x-14}$ **−2, 7**

Simplify each rational expression, if possible. Identify any excluded values.

4. $\frac{4x}{20x^3}$ **$\frac{1}{5x^2}$; $x \neq 0$**
5. $\frac{x+3}{x-4}$ **$\frac{x+3}{x-4}$; $x \neq 4$**
6. $\frac{27x}{3x^2}$ **$\frac{9}{x}$; $x \neq 0$**
7. $\frac{6}{3x+9}$ **$\frac{2}{x+3}$; $x \neq -3$**
8. $\frac{x+4}{2x^2+8x}$ **$\frac{1}{2x}$; $x \neq 0$, $x \neq -4$**
9. $\frac{5x^2-20x}{x-4}$ **$5x$; $x \neq 4$**

Independent Practice

For Exercises	See Example
24–27	1
28–31	2
32–37	3
38–40	4
41	5

Extra Practice

Skills Practice p. EP20

Application Practice p. EP33

Simplify each rational expression, if possible.

32. $\frac{q-6}{q^2-9q+18}$ **$\frac{1}{q-3}$**
33. $\frac{z^2-2z+1}{z^2-1}$ **$\frac{z-1}{z+1}$**
34. $\frac{t-3}{t^2-5t+6}$ **$\frac{1}{t-2}$**
35. $\frac{p^2-6p-7}{p^2-4p-5}$ **$\frac{p-7}{p-5}$**
36. $\frac{x^2-1}{x^2+4x+3}$ **$\frac{x-1}{x+3}$**
37. $\frac{2x-4}{x^2-6x+8}$ **$\frac{2}{x-4}$**
38. $\frac{20-4x}{x^2-25}$ **$-\frac{4}{x+5}$**
39. $\frac{3-3b}{3b^2+18b-21}$ **$-\frac{1}{b+7}$**
40. $\frac{3v-36}{144-v^2}$ **$-\frac{3}{12+v}$**

41. **Geometry** When choosing package sizes, a company wants a package that uses the least amount of material to hold the greatest volume of product.
    a. What is the surface-area-to-volume ratio for a rectangular prism? (*Hint:* For a rectangular prism, $S = 2\ell w + 2\ell h + 2wh$ and $V = \ell wh$.)
    b. Which box should the company choose? Explain.

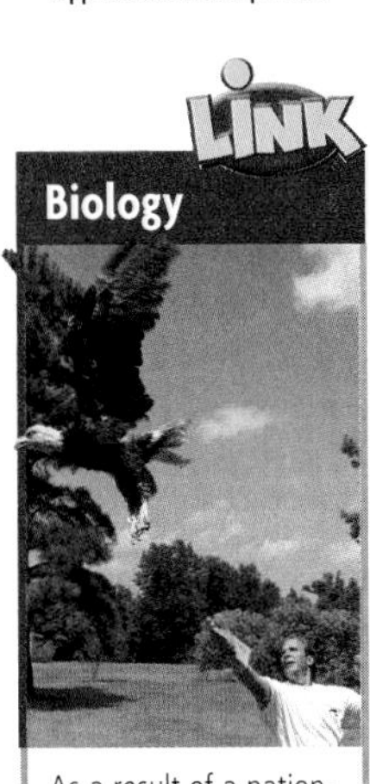

As a result of a nation-wide policy of protection and reintroduction, the population of bald eagles in the lower 48 states grew from 417 nesting pairs in 1963 to more than 6400 nesting pairs in 2000.

Source: U.S. Fish and Wildlife Service

42. **Biology** The table gives information on two populations of animals that were released into the wild. Suppose 16 more predators and 20 more prey are released into the area. Write and simplify a rational expression to show the ratio of predator to prey. **$\frac{4x+16}{5x+20}$; $\frac{4}{5}$**

	Predator	Prey
Original Population	x	x
Population 5 Years Later	$4x$	$5x$

Simplify each rational expression, if possible.

43. $\frac{p^2+12p+36}{12p+72}$ **$\frac{p+6}{12}$**
44. $\frac{3n^3+33n^2+15n}{3n^3+15n}$ **$\frac{n^2+11n+5}{n^2+5}$**
45. $\frac{a}{2a+a}$ **$\frac{1}{3}$**
46. $\frac{j-5}{j^2-25}$ **$\frac{1}{j+5}$**
47. $\frac{6w^2+11w-7}{6w-3}$ **$\frac{3w+7}{3}$**
48. $\frac{n^2-n-56}{n^2-16n+64}$ **$\frac{n+7}{n-8}$**
49. $\frac{(x+1)^2}{x^2+2x+1}$ **1**
50. $\frac{5}{(x+5)^2}$ **already simplified**
51. $\frac{25-x^2}{x^2-3x-10}$ **$-\frac{5+x}{x+2}$**

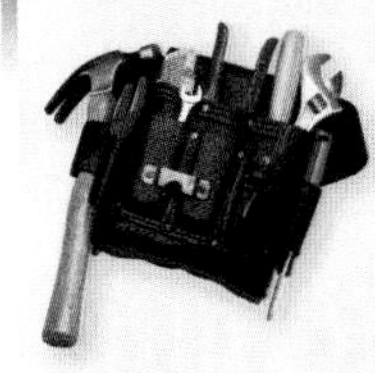

52. This problem will prepare you for the Concept Connection on page 650.

    It takes 250 workdays to build a house. The number of construction days is determined by the size of the crew. The crew includes one manager who supervises workers and checks for problems, but does not do any building.
    a. The table shows the number of construction days as a function of the number of workers. Copy and complete the table.
    b. Use the table to write a function that represents the number of construction days. **$y = \frac{250}{x-1}$**
    c. Identify the excluded values of the function. **$x = 1$**

Crew Size (x)	Workdays / Workers	Construction Days (y)
2	$\frac{250}{2-1}$	250
3	$\frac{250}{3-1}$	**125**
6	**$\frac{250}{6-1}$**	**50**
11	**$\frac{250}{11-1}$**	25

CONCEPT CONNECTION **Exercise 52** involves writing a rational function. This exercise prepares students for the Concept Connection on page 650.

Answers

41a. $\frac{2(\ell w + \ell h + wh)}{\ell wh}$

b. Box A; the surface area of box A is 184 in^2 and the surface area of box B is 232 in^2. The volumes are the same, so the company should use the box with less surface area, box A.

10-3 PROBLEM SOLVING

Problem Solving
LESSON 10-3 *Simplifying Rational Expressions*

A food company is considering two types of cylindrical cans for a new trail mix. The company wants a can that uses the least material for the greatest volume. For a cylinder, $S = 2\pi r^2 + 2\pi rh$ and $V = \pi r^2 h$.

1. What is the surface-area-to-volume ratio for any cylinder? **$\frac{2(r+h)}{rh}$**
2. Can A has radius 2 in. and height 3 in. What is the surface-area-to-volume ratio for Can A? **$\frac{10}{6} = 1.\overline{6}$**
3. Can B has radius 1.5 in. and height 4 in. What is the surface-area-to-volume ratio for Can B? **$\frac{11}{6} = 1.8\overline{3}$**
4. Which can should the company choose? Explain. **Can A; the ratio is lesser, Can A uses less material for each unit of volume.**

Select the best answer.

5. For any circle with radius r, $P = 2\pi r$ and $A = \pi r^2$. Which expression represents the perimeter-to-area ratio?
   A $2r$ C $\frac{r}{2}$
   (B) $\frac{2}{r}$ D $\frac{1}{2r}$
6. Tyrone takes an 8-by-8 square piece of cardboard and cuts x-by-x squares out of each corner. (All units are inches.) He then folds up the sides to form a box with no top. Which expression represents the surface-area-to-volume ratio? (*Hint:* For the surface area, find the area of the entire piece of cardboard and subtract the squares that were removed.)
   (8; x; 8 − 2x; There is no top.)
   F $\frac{1}{x}$ H $\frac{8}{x(4-x)}$
   G $\frac{1}{2x(1-16x)}$ **(J)** $\frac{4+x}{x(4-x)}$
7. In 2000, there are x mountain lions (predators) and x deer (prey) in a wildlife preserve. In 2005, the populations level off at $3x$ mountain lions and $4x$ deer, for a predator-to-prey ratio of $\frac{3}{4}$. If the wildlife preserve adds 12 more deer in 2007, how many mountain lions should also be added to keep the predator-to-prey ratio equivalent to $\frac{3}{4}$?
   (A) 9 C 16
   B 12 D 20

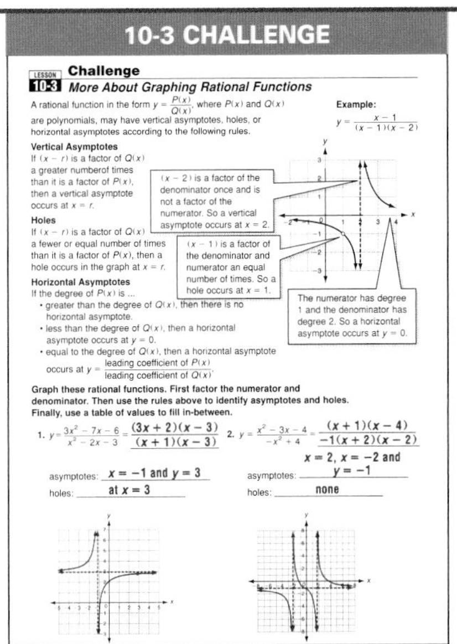

10-3 CHALLENGE

Challenge
LESSON 10-3 *More About Graphing Rational Functions*

A rational function in the form $y = \frac{P(x)}{Q(x)}$, where $P(x)$ and $Q(x)$ are polynomials, may have vertical asymptotes, holes, or horizontal asymptotes according to the following rules.

Vertical Asymptotes
If $(x - r)$ is a factor of $Q(x)$ a greater numberof times than it is a factor of $P(x)$, then a vertical asymptote occurs at $x = r$.

Holes
If $(x - r)$ is a factor of $Q(x)$ a fewer or equal number of times than it is a factor of $P(x)$, then a hole occurs in the graph at $x = r$.

Horizontal Asymptotes
If the degree of $P(x)$ is ...
- greater than the degree of $Q(x)$, then there is no horizontal asymptote.
- less than the degree of $Q(x)$, then a horizontal asymptote occurs at $y = 0$.
- equal to the degree of $Q(x)$, then a horizontal asymptote occurs at $y = \frac{\text{leading coefficient of } P(x)}{\text{leading coefficient of } Q(x)}$.

Example: $y = \frac{x-1}{(x-1)(x-2)}$

$(x - 2)$ is a factor of the denominator once and is not a factor of the numerator. So a vertical asymptote occurs at $x = 2$.

$(x - 1)$ is a factor of the denominator and numerator an equal number of times. So a hole occurs at $x = 1$.

The numerator has degree 1 and the denominator has degree 2. So a horizontal asymptote occurs at $y = 0$.

Graph these rational functions. First factor the numerator and denominator. Then use the rules above to identify asymptotes and holes. Finally, use a table of values to fill in-between.

1. $y = \frac{3x^2-7x-6}{x^2-2x-3} = \frac{(3x+2)(x-3)}{(x+1)(x-3)}$
   asymptotes: **$x = -1$ and $y = 3$**
   holes: **at $x = 3$**
2. $y = \frac{x^2-3x-4}{-x^2+4} = \frac{(x+1)(x-4)}{-1(x+2)(x-2)}$
   asymptotes: **$x = 2$, $x = -2$ and $y = -1$**
   holes: **none**

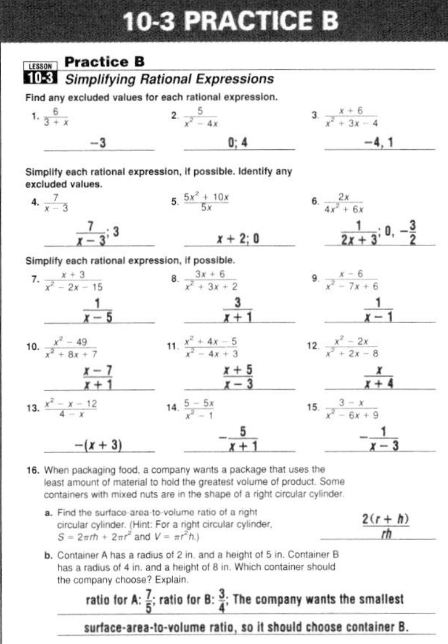

10-3 PRACTICE A
10-3 PRACTICE C
10-3 PRACTICE B

Practice B
LESSON 10-3 *Simplifying Rational Expressions*

Find any excluded values for each rational expression.

1. $\frac{6}{3+x}$ **−3**
2. $\frac{5}{x^2-4x}$ **0; 4**
3. $\frac{x+6}{x^2+3x-4}$ **−4, 1**

Simplify each rational expression, if possible. Identify any excluded values.

4. $\frac{7}{x-3}$ **$\frac{7}{x-3}$; 3**
5. $\frac{5x^2+10x}{5x}$ **$x + 2$; 0**
6. $\frac{2x}{4x^2+6x}$ **$\frac{1}{2x+3}$; 0, $-\frac{3}{2}$**

Simplify each rational expression, if possible.

7. $\frac{x+3}{x^2-2x-15}$ **$\frac{1}{x-5}$**
8. $\frac{3x+6}{x^2+3x+2}$ **$\frac{3}{x+1}$**
9. $\frac{x-6}{x^2-7x+6}$ **$\frac{1}{x-1}$**
10. $\frac{x^2-49}{x^2+8x+7}$ **$\frac{x-7}{x+1}$**
11. $\frac{x^2+4x-5}{x^2-4x+3}$ **$\frac{x+5}{x-3}$**
12. $\frac{x^2-2x}{x^2+2x-8}$ **$\frac{x}{x+4}$**
13. $\frac{x^2-x-12}{4-x}$ **$-(x+3)$**
14. $\frac{5-5x}{x^2-1}$ **$-\frac{5}{x+1}$**
15. $\frac{3-x}{x^2-6x+9}$ **$-\frac{1}{x-3}$**

16. When packaging food, a company wants a package that uses the least amount of material to hold the greatest volume of product. Some containers with mixed nuts are in the shape of a right circular cylinder.
    a. Find the surface-area-to-volume ratio of a right circular cylinder. (Hint: For a right circular cylinder, $S = 2\pi rh + 2\pi r^2$ and $V = \pi r^2 h$.) **$\frac{2(r+h)}{rh}$**
    b. Container A has a radius of 2 in. and a height of 5 in. Container B has a radius of 4 in. and a height of 8 in. Which container should the company choose? Explain.
    ratio for A: $\frac{7}{5}$; ratio for B: $\frac{3}{4}$; The company wants the smallest surface-area-to-volume ratio, so it should choose container B.

Geometry In **Exercise 53,** the area of a square is s^2, where s is the length of one side. Because a cube has 6 square faces, the surface area is $6s^2$.

Multiple Choice In **Exercise 56,** students who chose **C** may have factored incorrectly. Students who chose **A** may have simply matched the numbers given in the problem.

Journal

Have students compare and contrast simplifying fractions and simplifying rational expressions.

ALTERNATIVE ASSESSMENT

Write $\frac{(x+a)(x+a)}{(x+a)(x+b)}$ and $\frac{c(x-d)}{(x+c)(d-x)}$ on the board. Have students replace a, b, c, and d with positive integers and then multiply the factors. Have students then exchange those two expressions with a partner. Tell students to simplify their partner's expressions and identify the excluded values.

Power Presentations with PowerPoint®

10-3 Lesson Quiz

Find any excluded values of each rational expression.

1. $\frac{3}{4x}$ 0
2. $\frac{4h^2}{3h^2 - 6h}$ 0, 2

Simplify each rational expression, if possible.

3. $\frac{5t^3}{10t^2 + 15t}$ $\frac{t^2}{2t + 3}$
4. $\frac{m + 2}{m^2 - 3m - 10}$ $\frac{1}{m - 5}$
5. $\frac{n^2 - 1}{1 - n}$ $-n - 1$
6. Calvino is building a rectangular tree house. The length is 10 feet longer than the width. His friend Fabio is also building a tree house, but his is square. The sides of Fabio's tree house are equal to the width of Calvino's tree house.
   a. What is the ratio of the area of Calvino's tree house to the area of Fabio's tree house? $\frac{x + 10}{x}$
   b. Use this ratio to find the ratio of the areas if the width of Calvino's tree house is 14 feet. $\frac{12}{7}$

Also available on transparency

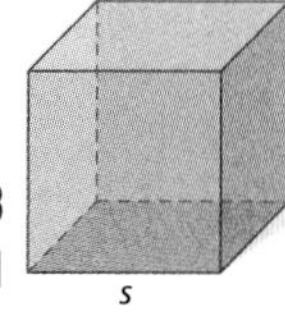

53. **Geometry** Let s represent the length of an edge of a cube.
    a. Write the ratio of a cube's surface area to volume in simplified form. (*Hint:* For a cube, $S = 6s^2$.) $\frac{6}{s}$
    b. What is the ratio of the cube's surface area to volume when $s = 2$? **3**
    c. What is the ratio of the cube's surface area to volume when $s = 6$? **1**

54. **Write About It** Explain how to find excluded values for a rational expression. **Set the denominator equal to 0 and solve for the variable.**

55. **Critical Thinking** Give an example of a rational expression that has x in both the numerator and denominator, but cannot be simplified. **Possible answer:** $\frac{x}{x+1}$

Multiple Choice For Exercises 56 and 57, choose the best answer.

56. Which expression is undefined for $x = 4$ and $x = -1$?
    Ⓐ $\frac{x-1}{x+4}$ Ⓑ $\frac{x-4}{x+4}$ Ⓒ $\frac{x}{x^2+3x-4}$ Ⓓ $\frac{x}{x^2-3x-4}$

57. Which expression is the ratio of the area of a triangle to the area of a rectangle that has the same base and height?
    Ⓐ $\frac{1}{2}$ Ⓑ $\frac{bh}{2}$ Ⓒ $\frac{(bh)^2}{2}$ Ⓓ 2

58. **Gridded Response** What is the excluded value for $\frac{x-4}{x^2-8x+16}$? **4**

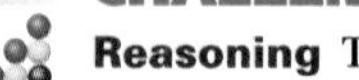

CHALLENGE AND EXTEND

Reasoning Tell whether each statement is sometimes, always, or never true. Explain.

59. A rational expression has an excluded value.
60. A rational expression has a variable inside a square root in the numerator. **Never; the numerator must be a polynomial.**
61. The graph of a rational function has at least one asymptote.

Simplify each rational expression.

62. $\frac{9v - 6v^2}{4v^2 - 4v - 3}$ $-\frac{3v}{2v+1}$
63. $\frac{2a^2 - 7a + 3}{2a^2 + 9a - 5}$ $\frac{a-3}{a+5}$
64. $\frac{0.25y - 0.10}{0.25y^2 - 0.04}$ $\frac{5}{5y+2}$

Identify any excluded values of each rational expression.

65. $\frac{\frac{1}{4}x^2 - 7x + 49}{\frac{1}{4}x^2 - 49}$ ± 14
66. $\frac{-80x + 40x^2 + 40}{-30 - 30x^2 + 60x}$ 1
67. $\frac{6x + 12}{12x + 6x^2}$ $-2, 0$

SPIRAL STANDARDS REVIEW 2.0, 6.0, 17.0

Give the domain and range of each relation. *(Lesson 4-2)*

68.

x	3	1	2	9
y	4	2	6	5

D: {1, 2, 3, 9}; R: {2, 4, 5, 6}

69.

x	4	29	5	25
y	2	2	−7	22

D: {4, 5, 25, 29}; R: {−7, 2, 22}

Use intercepts to graph the line described by each equation. *(Lesson 5-2)*

70. $5x - 3y = -15$
71. $y = 8x - 8$
72. $\frac{1}{2}x + y = 2$

Simplify. *(Lesson 7-1)*

73. $5h^{-3}$ $\frac{5}{h^3}$
74. $s^{-2}t^6$ $\frac{t^6}{s^2}$
75. $\frac{12}{b^4}$ already simplified
76. $\frac{v^{-3}}{w^{-4}}$ $\frac{w^4}{v^3}$

Answers

59. Sometimes; the rational expression $\frac{1}{x+1}$ has -1 as an excluded value, but the rational expression $\frac{1}{x^2+1}$ has no excluded values.

61. Sometimes; the rational function $y = \frac{1}{x+1}$ has $x = -1$ as an asymptote, but the rational function $y = \frac{x^2+1}{x+1}$ has no asymptotes.

70.

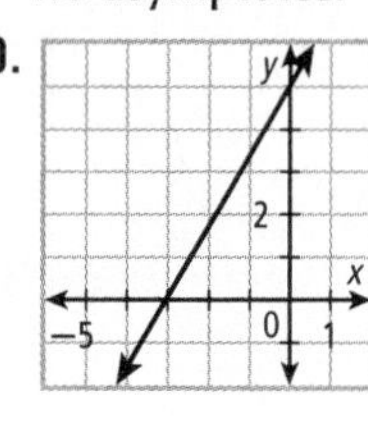

71.

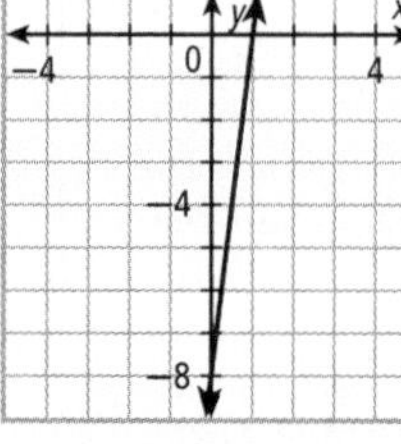

72.

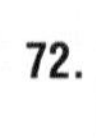

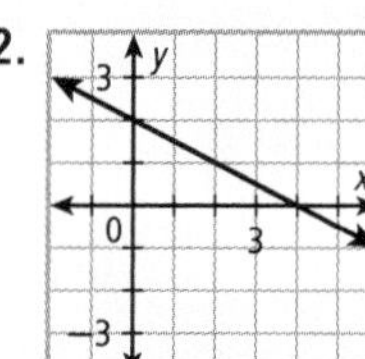

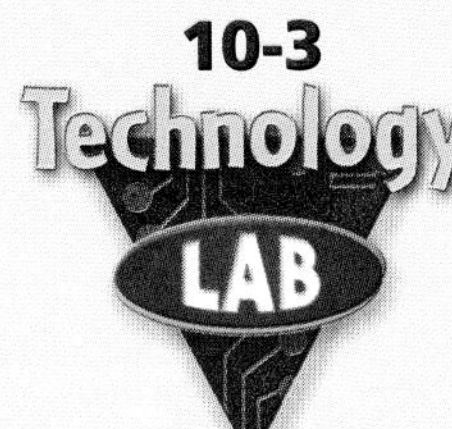

Graph Rational Functions

You can use a graphing calculator to graph rational functions and to compare graphs of rational functions before and after they are simplified.

Use with Lesson 10-3

California Standards

13.0 Students add, subtract, multiply, and divide **rational** expressions and **functions.** Students solve both computationally and conceptually challenging problems by using these techniques.

Activity

Simplify $y = \frac{x-1}{x^2-5x+4}$ and give any excluded values. Then graph both the original function and the simplified function, and compare the graphs.

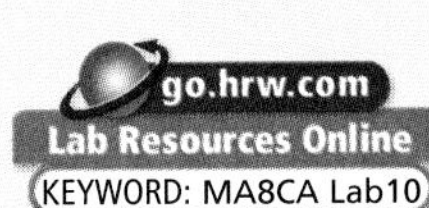

1. Simplify the function and find the excluded values.
   $\frac{x-1}{x^2-5x+4} = \frac{x-1}{(x-1)(x-4)} = \frac{1}{x-4}$; excluded values: 4, 1

2. Enter $y = \frac{x-1}{x^2-5x+4}$ and $y = \frac{1}{x-4}$ into your calculator as shown and press GRAPH.

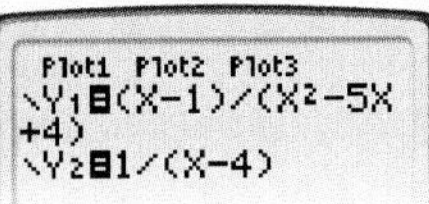

3. To compare the graphs, press TRACE. At the top of the screen, you can see which graph the cursor is on. To change between graphs, press ▲ and ▼.

4. The graphs appear to be the same, but check the excluded values, 4 and 1. While on **Y1,** press 4 ENTER. Notice that there is no y-value at $x = 4$. The function is undefined.

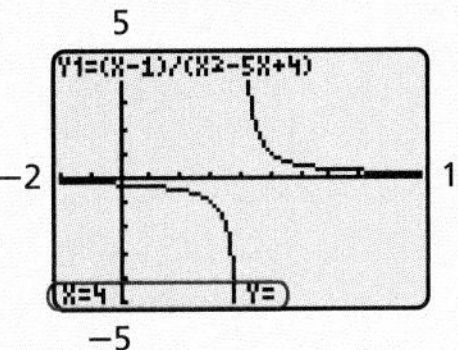

5. Press ▼ to switch to **Y2** and press 4 ENTER. This function is also undefined at $x = 4$. The graphs are the same at this excluded value.

6. Return to **Y1** and press 1 ENTER. This function is undefined at $x = 1$. However, this is not a vertical asymptote. Instead, this graph has a "hole" at $x = 1$.

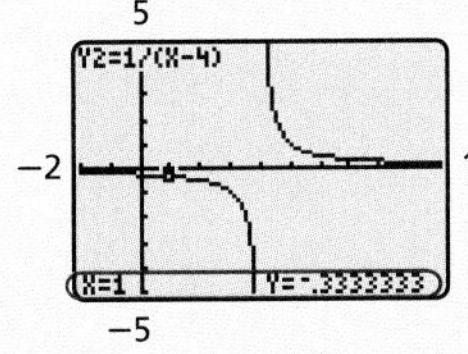

7. Switch to **Y2** and press 1 ENTER. This function is defined at $x = 1$. So the two graphs are the same except at $x = 1$.

Try This

1. Why is $x = 1$ an excluded value for one function but not for the other?
2. Are the functions $y = \frac{x-1}{x^2-5x+4}$ and $y = \frac{1}{x-4}$ truly equivalent for all values of x? Explain.
3. **Make a Conjecture** Complete each statement.
   a. If a value of x is excluded from a function and its simplified form, it appears on the graph as a(n) ___?___. **asymptote**
   b. If a value of x is excluded from a function but not its simplified form, it appears on the graph as a(n) ___?___. **hole**

Answers to *Try This*

1. When the denominator of $y = \frac{x-1}{(x-1)(x-4)}$ is set equal to 0 and solved for x, then x equals 1 or 4. However, when the denominator of $y = \frac{1}{x-4}$ is set equal to 0, the excluded value seems to be only 4.
2. No; for the value of $x = 1$, $y = \frac{x-1}{x^2-5x+4}$ is undefined, while $y = \frac{1}{x-4}$ is defined as $-\frac{1}{3}$.

Organizer

Use with Lesson 10-3

Objective: Use a graphing calculator to explore rational functions.

Materials: graphing calculator

Online Edition
Graphing Calculator, TechKeys

Countdown to Mastery Week 23

Teach

Discuss

Tell students they can use the TABLE feature to compare the excluded values for each expression.

Close

Key Concept

Graphing calculators offer support for problems involving rational functions and expressions.

Assessment

Journal Have students explain how to show support for an algebraic simplification of a rational expression with a graphing calculator.

California Standards

Algebra 1 13.0

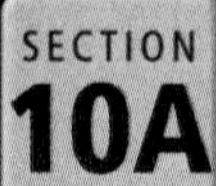

CONCEPT CONNECTION

Organizer

Objective: Assess students' ability to apply concepts and skills from Lessons 10-1 through 10-3 in a real-world format.

Problem	Text Reference
1	Lesson 10-2
2	Lessons 10-1, 10-2, 10-3
3	Lesson 10-1
4–6	Lesson 10-2
7	Lessons 10-1, 10-2, 10-3

Answer

2. $y = \frac{200}{x}$; x = the number of people in the crew; y = the number of construction days; inverse variation

California Standards

15.0, 17.0

CONCEPT CONNECTION

SECTION 10A

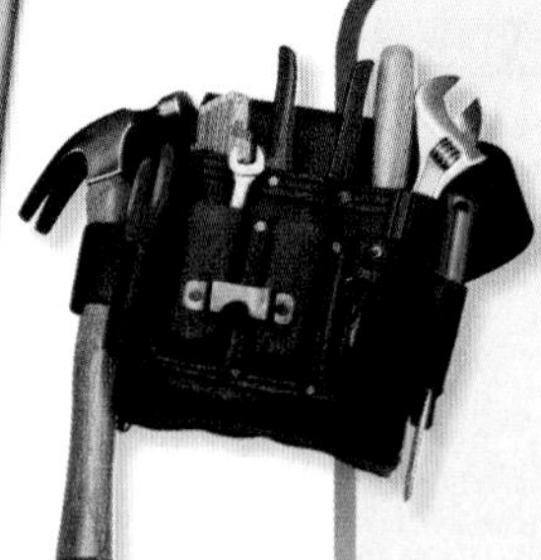

Rational Functions and Expressions

Construction Daze

Robert is part of a volunteer crew constructing houses for low-income families. The table shows how many construction days it takes to complete a house for work crews of various sizes.

Crew Size	Construction Days	Workdays
2	100	200
4	50	200
8	25	200
10	20	200
20	10	200

1. Working at the same rate, how many construction days should it take a crew of 40 people to build the house? **5**
2. Express the number of construction days as a function of the crew size. Define the variables. What type of relationship is formed in the situation?
3. Explain how the crew size affects the number of construction days. **As the crew size increases, the number of construction days decreases.**
4. About how many construction days would it take a crew of 32 to complete a house? **6.25**
5. If a crew can complete a house in 12.5 days, how many people are in the crew? **16**
6. What are a reasonable domain and range of the function? **D: natural numbers; R: $y > 0$**
7. Suppose there are two managers that do not contribute to the work of building the house, yet are counted as part of the crew. Express the number of construction days as a function of the crew size. What are the asymptotes of this function? Graph the function. $y = \frac{200}{x-2}$; $x = 2$ and $y = 0$

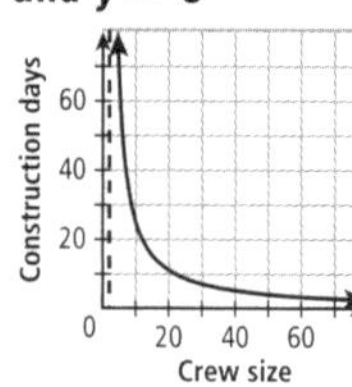

INTERVENTION

Scaffolding Questions

1. What is the pattern in the table? As the crew doubles, workdays halve.

2–3. What is the constant? construction units

4–5. What do the variables represent in the function you wrote for **Problem 2**? crew size and workdays

6. Does it make sense to have a negative number of people or days? no

7. What is the new variable expression for crew size? $x - 2$

Extension

Assuming that crew size varies inversely as workdays, how long would it take 12 workers to complete a house that requires 250 construction tasks?

$y = \frac{250}{12} = 20\frac{5}{6}$, or almost 21 days

READY TO GO ON?

Quiz for Lessons 10-1 Through 10-3

10-1 Inverse Variation

Tell whether each relationship represents an inverse variation. Explain.

1.

x	−5	−4	−3
y	10	−8	6

No; the product xy is not constant.

2.

x	18	9	6
y	2	4	6

Yes; the product xy is constant.

3. $y = \frac{3}{x}$ **yes**
4. $y + x = \frac{3}{4}$ **no**
5. $xy = -2$ **yes**
6. $y = \frac{x}{5}$ **no**
7. Write and graph the inverse variation in which $y = 3$ when $x = 2$. $y = \frac{6}{x}$
8. Write and graph the inverse variation in which $y = 4$ when $x = -1$. $y = \frac{-4}{x}$
9. The number of calculators Mrs. Hopkins can buy for the classroom varies inversely as the cost of each calculator. She can buy 24 calculators that cost \$60 each. How many calculators can she buy if they cost \$80 each? **18 calculators**

10-2 Rational Functions

Identify any excluded values and the asymptotes for each rational function. Then graph each function.

10. $y = \frac{12}{x}$
11. $y = \frac{6}{x + 2}$
12. $y = \frac{4}{x - 1}$
13. $y = \frac{2}{x + 1} - 3$
14. Jeff builds model train layouts. He has \$75 to spend on packages of miniature landscape items. He receives 6 free packages with each order. The number of packages y that Jeff can buy is given by $y = \frac{75}{x} + 6$, where x represents the cost of each package in dollars. Describe the reasonable domain and range values and graph the function. **D: $x > 0$; R: natural numbers > 6**

10-3 Simplifying Rational Expressions

Find any excluded values of each rational expression.

15. $\frac{15}{n}$ **0**
16. $\frac{p}{p - 8}$ **8**
17. $\frac{x + 2}{x^2 + 6x + 8}$ **−4, −2**
18. $\frac{t - 1}{t^2 + t}$ **−1, 0**

Simplify each rational expression, if possible. Identify any excluded values.

19. $\frac{3x^2}{6x^3}$ $\frac{1}{2x}$; $x \neq 0$
20. $\frac{2n}{n^2 - 3n}$
21. $\frac{s + 1}{s^2 - 4s - 5}$
22. $\frac{12 - 3x}{x^2 - 8x + 16}$
23. Suppose a cone and a cylinder have the same radius and that the slant height ℓ of the cone is the same as the height h of the cylinder. Find the ratio of the cone's surface area to the cylinder's surface area. $\frac{1}{2}$

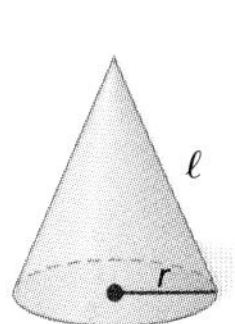

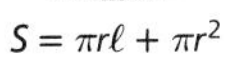
$S = \pi r\ell + \pi r^2$

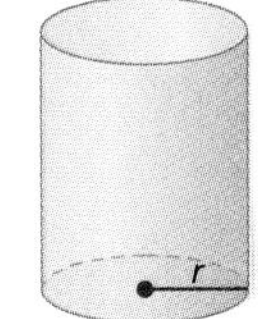

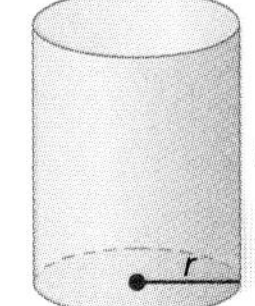
$S = 2\pi rh + 2\pi r^2$

20. $\frac{2}{n - 3}$; $n \neq 0, 3$
21. $\frac{1}{s - 5}$; $s \neq -1, 5$
22. $-\frac{3}{x - 4}$; $x \neq 4$

READY TO GO ON?

SECTION 10A

Organizer

Objective: Assess students' mastery of concepts and skills in Lessons 10-1 through 10-3.

Countdown to Mastery Week 23

Resources

Assessment Resources

Section 10A Quiz

Test & Practice Generator
One-Stop Planner®

INTERVENTION

Resources

***Ready to Go On? Intervention and Enrichment* Worksheets**

***Ready to Go On?* CD-ROM**

***Ready to Go On?* Online**

my.hrw.com

Answers

3. $xy = 3$
4. cannot be written in the form $y = \frac{k}{x}$

5–6. See p. A25.

7–8, 10–14. For graphs, see p. A25.

READY TO GO ON?
Diagnose and Prescribe

NO INTERVENE

Ready to Go On? Intervention	*Ready to Go On? Intervention,* Section 10A: Worksheets	CD-ROM	Online
Lesson 10-1 Prep for 13.0	10-1 Intervention	Activity 10-1	Diagnose and Prescribe Online
Lesson 10-2 Prep for 13.0	10-2 Intervention	Activity 10-2	
Lesson 10-3 12.0	10-3 Intervention	Activity 10-3	

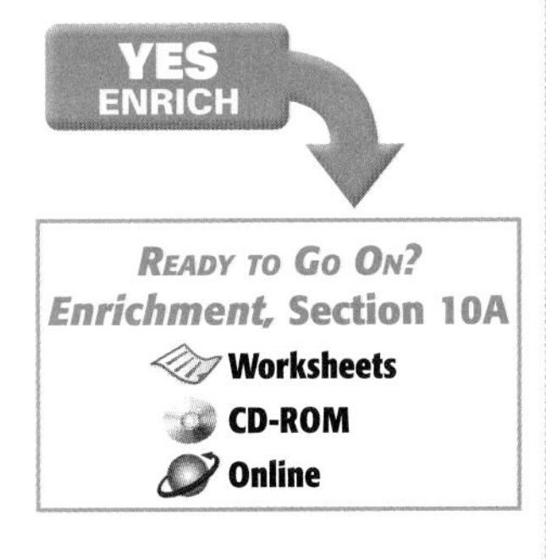
YES ENRICH

***Ready to Go On? Enrichment,* Section 10A**
- Worksheets
- CD-ROM
- Online

Operations with Rational Expressions

One-Minute Section Planner

Lesson	Lab Resources	Materials
Lesson 10-4 Multiplying and Dividing Rational Expressions • Multiply and divide rational expressions. **13.0**		
Lesson 10-5 Adding and Subtracting Rational Expressions • Add and subtract rational expressions with like denominators. • Add and subtract rational expressions with unlike denominators. **13.0, 15.0**		
10-6 Algebra Lab Model Polynomial Division • Use algebra tiles to model polynomial division. **10.0**		**Required** algebra tiles (MK)
Lesson 10-6 Dividing Polynomials • Divide a polynomial by a monomial or binomial. **10.0, 12.0**		**Optional** grid paper
Lesson 10-7 Solving Rational Equations • Solve rational equations. • Identify extraneous solutions. **15.0**		**Optional** 2 containers with different size pouring spouts, 1 bowl, graphing calculator
Lesson 10-8 Applying Rational Equations • Use rational equations to solve application problems. **15.0**		

MK = *Manipulatives Kit*

Notes

Math Background: Teaching the Standards

RATIONAL EXPRESSIONS

 10.0, 12.0, 13.0

Lessons 10-3 to 10-5

A *rational expression* is an expression whose numerator and denominator are polynomials. In the same way that a fraction cannot have a denominator of zero, a rational expression is not defined for values of the variable that make the polynomial in the denominator equal to zero. These values of the variable are called *excluded values*.

Students should understand that not all rational expressions have excluded values. For example, the rational expression $\frac{1}{x^2+1}$ has the polynomial $x^2 + 1$ as its denominator. This polynomial is not equal to zero for any real value of x. Thus, the rational expression has no excluded values; it is defined for all values of x. Equivalently, one can say that the domain of the rational function $y = \frac{1}{x^2+1}$ is all real numbers.

SIMPLIFYING RATIONAL EXPRESSIONS

 12.0

Lesson 10-3

Simplifying a rational expression is analogous to simplifying a fraction. Common factors that appear in both the numerator and the denominator may be divided out. However, it is important to be careful when there are excluded values. Once a rational expression has been simplified, it may no longer be possible to identify the excluded values; however, the expression remains undefined for these values.

For example, students may be quick to state that the expression $\frac{x^2}{x}$ "is the same as x." To decide whether this is true, it is instructive to consider the related functions. The function $y = x$ is defined for all real values of x, and its graph is a straight line through the origin. On the other hand, the rational expression $\frac{x^2}{x}$ has an excluded value at $x = 0$. Therefore, the rational function $y = \frac{x^2}{x}$ is not defined at $x = 0$, and its graph is a straight line with a "hole" at the origin.

Comparing the two graphs shows that $\frac{x^2}{x} = x$ for all values of x except $x = 0$. In other words, the expressions are equal except at the excluded value.

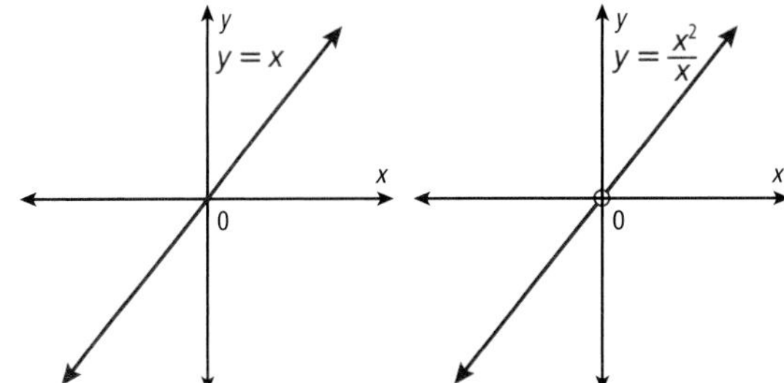

OPERATIONS ON RATIONAL EXPRESSIONS

 10.0, 13.0

Lessons 10-4 and 10-5

In general, operations on rational expressions are similar to operations on fractions, as long as excluded values are identified. The table below summarizes these similarities. In the table, $a(x)$, $b(x)$, $c(x)$, and $d(x)$ are polynomials.

Fractions	Rational Expressions
Addition and Subtraction	
$\frac{a}{b} \pm \frac{c}{d} = \frac{ad \pm bc}{bd}$ $(b, d \neq 0)$	$\frac{a(x)}{b(x)} \pm \frac{c(x)}{d(x)} = \frac{a(x)d(x) \pm b(x)c(x)}{b(x)d(x)}$ (except where $b(x), d(x) = 0$)
Multiplication	
$\frac{a}{b} \cdot \frac{c}{d} = \frac{ac}{bd}$ $(b, d \neq 0)$	$\frac{a(x)}{b(x)} \cdot \frac{c(x)}{d(x)} = \frac{a(x)c(x)}{b(x)d(x)}$ (except where $b(x), d(x) = 0$)
Division	
$\frac{a}{b} \div \frac{c}{d} = \frac{a}{b} \cdot \frac{d}{c} = \frac{ad}{bc}$ $(b, c, d \neq 0)$	$\frac{a(x)}{b(x)} \div \frac{c(x)}{d(x)} = \frac{a(x)}{b(x)} \cdot \frac{d(x)}{c(x)}$ $= \frac{a(x)d(x)}{b(x)c(x)}$ (except where $b(x), c(x), d(x) = 0$)

Note also that the Cross Product Property holds for rational expressions. That is, if $\frac{a(x)}{b(x)} = \frac{c(x)}{d(x)}$, then $a(x)d(x) = b(x)c(x)$, except where $b(x), d(x) = 0$.

10-4 Organizer

Objective: Multiply and divide rational expressions.

Online Edition
Tutorial Videos

Countdown to Mastery Week 23

Power Presentations with PowerPoint®

Warm Up

Multiply.

1. $2x^2(x+3)$ $\quad 2x^3 + 6x^2$
2. $(x-5)(3x+7)$ $\quad 3x^2 - 8x - 35$
3. $3x(x^2+2x+2)$ $\quad 3x^3 + 6x^2 + 6x$
4. Simplify $\frac{12x^{12}y^{10}}{40x^5y^{15}}$. $\quad \frac{3x^7}{10y^5}$

Divide. Simplify your answer.

5. $\frac{2}{3} \div \frac{1}{2}$ $\quad \frac{4}{3}$ 6. $\frac{3}{5} \div \frac{11}{3}$ $\quad \frac{9}{55}$
7. $\frac{2}{5} \div \frac{7}{15}$ $\quad \frac{6}{7}$ 8. $\frac{3}{4} \div \frac{9}{16}$ $\quad \frac{4}{3}$

Also available on transparency

Q: What do you call a rational expression when it enlists in the military?

A: A national rational.

California Standards

Algebra 1 13.0

10-4 Multiplying and Dividing Rational Expressions

California Standards

13.0 Students add, subtract, **multiply, and divide rational expressions** and functions. **Students solve both computationally and conceptually challenging problems by using these techniques.**

Why learn this?

You can multiply rational expressions to determine the probabilities of winning prizes at carnivals. (See Example 5.)

The rules for multiplying rational expressions are the same as the rules for multiplying fractions. You multiply the numerators, and you multiply the denominators.

Know it! Note

Multiplying Rational Expressions

If a, b, c, and d are nonzero polynomials, then $\frac{a}{b} \cdot \frac{c}{d} = \frac{ac}{bd}$.

EXAMPLE 1 Multiplying Rational Expressions

Multiply. Simplify your answer.

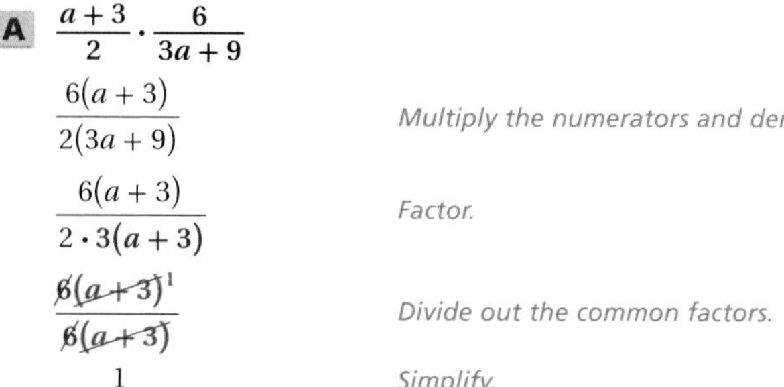

A $\frac{a+3}{2} \cdot \frac{6}{3a+9}$

$\frac{6(a+3)}{2(3a+9)}$ *Multiply the numerators and denominators.*

$\frac{6(a+3)}{2 \cdot 3(a+3)}$ *Factor.*

$\frac{\cancel{6}\cancel{(a+3)}^1}{\cancel{6}\cancel{(a+3)}}$ *Divide out the common factors.*

1 *Simplify.*

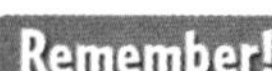

Remember!

Review the Quotient of Powers Property in Lesson 7-4.

$\frac{a^m}{a^n} = a^{m-n}$

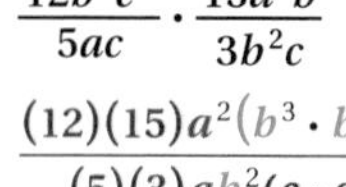

B $\frac{12b^3c^2}{5ac} \cdot \frac{15a^2b}{3b^2c}$

$\frac{(12)(15)a^2(b^3 \cdot b)c^2}{(5)(3)ab^2(c \cdot c)}$ *Multiply the numerators and the denominators. Arrange the expression so like variables are together.*

$\frac{180a^2b^4c^2}{15ab^2c^2}$ *Simplify.*

$12a^1b^2c^0$ *Divide out common factors. Use properties of exponents.*

$12ab^2$ *Simplify. Remember that $c^0 = 1$.*

C $\frac{5x^2}{2y^3} \cdot \frac{3x}{2y^2}$

$\frac{15x^3}{4y^5}$ *Multiply. There are no common factors, so the product cannot be simplified.*

1 Introduce

EXPLORATION

10-4 Multiplying and Dividing Rational Expressions

You can compare expressions by evaluating them for different values of the variables.

1. Complete the table. Evaluate each expression for the given values of the variables.

x	y	$\frac{x}{2y} \cdot \frac{3x}{y}$	$\frac{3x^2}{2y^2}$
1	1		
1	3		
2	4		

2. What do you notice in the table?
3. Complete the table. Evaluate each expression for the given values of the variables.

m	n	$\frac{3}{m^2} \cdot \frac{2n}{m}$	$\frac{6n}{m^3}$
1	2		
2	2		
3	1		

4. What do you notice in the table?

THINK AND DISCUSS

5. **Explain** how you can multiply $\frac{a}{b} \cdot \frac{c}{d}$, where a, b, c, and d are nonzero polynomials.

Motivate

Write $\frac{4}{5} \cdot \frac{3}{10}$ on the board. Review with students two different ways to find the simplified product. (1) Multiply the numerators and then denominators, and then divide out a factor of 2. (2) Divide out 2 from 4 and 10, and then multiply the remaining numerators and denominators. Explain that the same procedures apply to multiplying rational expressions.

Explorations and answers are provided in *Alternate Openers: Explorations Transparencies*.

Multiply. Simplify your answer.

1a. $\frac{(c-4)}{5} \cdot \frac{45}{(-4c+16)}$ $-\frac{9}{4}$ 1b. $\frac{5y^5z}{3xy^2z} \cdot \frac{2x^4y^2}{4xy}$ $\frac{5x^2y^4}{6}$

EXAMPLE 2 Multiplying a Rational Expression by a Polynomial

Remember!

Just as you can write an integer as a fraction, you can write any expression as a rational expression by writing it with a denominator of 1.

Multiply $(x^2+8x+15)\frac{4}{2x+6}$. Simplify your answer.

$\frac{x^2+8x+15}{1} \cdot \frac{4}{2x+6}$ *Write the polynomial over 1.*

$\frac{(x+3)(x+5)}{1} \cdot \frac{4}{2(x+3)}$ *Factor the numerator and denominator.*

$\frac{\cancel{(x+3)}(x+5)\cancel{4}^2}{\cancel{2}\cancel{(x+3)}}$ *Divide out common factors.*

$2x+10$ *Multiply remaining factors.*

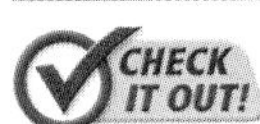

2. Multiply $\frac{m-5}{m^2-4m-12} \cdot 3m+6$. Simplify your answer. $\frac{3m-15}{m-6}$

There are two methods for simplifying rational expressions. You can **simplify first** by dividing out common factors and **then multiply** the remaining factors. You can also **multiply first** and **then simplify**. Using either method will result in the same answer.

EXAMPLE 3 Multiplying Rational Expressions Containing Polynomials

Multiply $\frac{4d^3+4d}{16f} \cdot \frac{2f}{7d^2f+7f}$. Simplify your answer.

Method 1 Simplify first.

$\frac{4d^3+4d}{16f} \cdot \frac{2f}{7d^2f+7f}$

$\frac{4d(d^2+1)}{16f} \cdot \frac{2f}{7f(d^2+1)}$ *Factor.*

$\frac{\cancel{4}d\cancel{(d^2+1)}}{\cancel{16}^2\cancel{f}} \cdot \frac{\cancel{2f}}{7f\cancel{(d^2+1)}}$ *Divide out common factors.*

Then multiply.

$\frac{d}{14f}$ *Simplify.*

Method 2 Multiply first.

$\frac{4d^3+4d}{16f} \cdot \frac{2f}{7d^2f+7f}$

$\frac{(4d^3+4d)2f}{16f(7d^2f+7f)}$ *Multiply.*

$\frac{8d^3f+8df}{112d^2f^2+112f^2}$ *Distribute.*

Then simplify.

$\frac{8df(d^2+1)}{112f^2(d^2+1)}$ *Factor.*

$\frac{\cancel{8}d\cancel{f}\cancel{(d^2+1)}}{\cancel{112}^{14}\cancel{f^2}^f\cancel{(d^2+1)}}$ *Divide out common factors.*

$\frac{d}{14f}$ *Simplify.*

3a. $\frac{n+4}{n^2+2n}$
3b. $\frac{p^2-p-20}{p^3+16p}$

Multiply. Simplify your answer.

3a. $\frac{n-5}{n^2+4n} \cdot \frac{n^2+8n+16}{n^2-3n-10}$ 3b. $\frac{p+4}{p^2+2p} \cdot \frac{p^2-3p-10}{p^2+16}$

COMMON ERROR ALERT

Students might divide out common factors in a division problem before rewriting the division as multiplication by the reciprocal. For example, $\frac{1}{2} \div \frac{2}{3}$: $\frac{1}{\cancel{2}_1} \div \frac{\cancel{2}^1}{3} = \frac{1}{1} \cdot \frac{3}{1} = 3$. The correct solution is $\frac{1}{2} \div \frac{2}{3} = \frac{1}{2} \cdot \frac{3}{2} = \frac{3}{4}$. Remind students that the first step in a division problem is to rewrite it as a multiplication problem.

Power Presentations with PowerPoint®

Additional Examples

Example 1

Multiply. Simplify your answer.

A. $\frac{c-1}{2} \cdot \frac{4}{3c-3}$ $\frac{2}{3}$

B. $\frac{8x^2y^3}{5yz^2} \cdot \frac{10y^2z^2}{16y^3}$ x^2y

C. $\frac{6r^2}{5s^3} \cdot \frac{3r^2}{7s}$ $\frac{18r^4}{35s^4}$

Example 2

Multiply $(x^2-6x+9) \cdot \frac{2x}{6x-18}$.

Simplify your answer. $\frac{x^2-3x}{3}$

Example 3

Multiply $\frac{3a^2+6a}{12b^2} \cdot \frac{2b^3}{3ab+6b}$.

Simplify your answer. $\frac{a}{6}$

Also available on transparency

INTERVENTION

Questioning Strategies

EXAMPLE 1

- How do you find common factors?

EXAMPLE 2

- What does it mean to divide out common factors?

EXAMPLE 3

- Which method do you prefer? Why?

2 Teach

Guided Instruction

Review multiplying and dividing fractions. Then show how to multiply and divide rational expressions.

Before **Example 5,** review independent and dependent events. In **Example 5,** the events are dependent because there is no replacement between the two picks.

Communicating Math Have students go to the board to demonstrate different methods of multiplying and simplifying.

Universal Access

Through Visual Cues

Encourage students to align like factors in the numerator and denominator. Students can even draw lines to separate the factors. When a factor isn't in the numerator or denominator, use 1. For **Example 3 Method 2,** the second step can be written as:

8	d	f	d^2+1
112	1	f^2	d^2+1

Then simplify:

1	d	1	1
14	1	f	1

$= \frac{d}{14f}$

Power Presentations with PowerPoint®

Additional Examples

Example 4

Divide. Simplify your answer.

A. $\frac{2}{g} \div \frac{g+4}{g^2}$ $\frac{2g}{g+4}$

B. $\frac{1-n^2}{n} \div \frac{n-1}{n^2-4n}$ $-n^2+3n+4$

C. $\frac{4xy^2}{y} \div (2x^2+6x)$ $\frac{2y}{x+3}$

Also available on transparency

INTERVENTION

Questioning Strategies

EXAMPLE 4

- Why do you multiply by the reciprocal?

Inclusion Remind students that they can check their answers by substituting a user-friendly number into both the original and simplified expressions. The answers should be the same.

The rules for dividing rational expressions are the same as the rules for dividing fractions. To divide by a rational expression, multiply by its reciprocal.

Dividing Rational Expressions

If a, b, c, and d are nonzero polynomials, then $\frac{a}{b} \div \frac{c}{d} = \frac{a}{b} \cdot \frac{d}{c} = \frac{ad}{bc}$.

EXAMPLE 4 Dividing by Rational Expressions and Polynomials

Divide. Simplify your answer.

A $\frac{1}{x} \div \frac{x-2}{2x}$

$\frac{1}{x} \cdot \frac{2x}{x-2}$ — *Write as multiplication by the reciprocal.*

$\frac{1(2x)}{x(x-2)}$ — *Multiply the numerators and the denominators.*

$\frac{2\cancel{x}}{\cancel{x}(x-2)}$ — *Divide out common factors.*

$\frac{2}{x-2}$ — *Simplify.*

B $\frac{x^2-2x}{x} \div \frac{2-x}{x^2+2x+1}$

$\frac{x^2-2x}{x} \cdot \frac{x^2+2x+1}{2-x}$ — *Write as multiplication by the reciprocal.*

$\frac{x(x-2)}{x} \cdot \frac{(x+1)(x+1)}{2-x}$ — *Factor.*

$\frac{x(x-2)}{x} \cdot \frac{(x+1)(x+1)}{-1(x-2)}$ — *Rewrite one opposite binomial.*

$\frac{\cancel{x}\cancel{(x-2)}^1}{\cancel{x}} \cdot \frac{(x+1)(x+1)}{-1\cancel{(x-2)}}$ — *Divide out common factors.*

$-(x+1)^2$ — *Multiply.*

C $\frac{3a^2b}{b} \div (3a^2+6a)$

$\frac{3a^2b}{b} \div \frac{3a^2+6a}{1}$ — *Write the binomial over 1.*

$\frac{3a^2b}{b} \cdot \frac{1}{3a^2+6a}$ — *Write as multiplication by the reciprocal.*

$\frac{3a^2b}{b(3a^2+6a)}$ — *Multiply the numerators and the denominators.*

$\frac{\cancel{3}\cancel{a^2}^a\cancel{b}}{\cancel{b}[\cancel{3a}(a+2)]}$ — *Factor. Divide out common factors.*

$\frac{a}{(a+2)}$ — *Simplify.*

Divide. Simplify your answer.

4a. $\frac{3}{x^2} \div \frac{x^3}{(x-5)}$ $\frac{3x-15}{x^5}$

4b. $\frac{18vw^2}{6v} \div \frac{3v^2x^4}{2w^4x}$ $\frac{2w^6}{v^2x^3}$

4c. $\frac{x^2-x}{x+2} \div (x^2+2x-3)$ $\frac{x}{x^2+5x+6}$

EXAMPLE 5 ***Probability Application***

Marty is playing a carnival game. He needs to pick two items out of a bag without looking. The bag has red and blue items. There are three more red items than blue items.

a. Write and simplify an expression that represents the probability that Marty will pick two blue items without replacing the first item.

Let x = the number of blue items.

Blue + **Red** = **Total**	*Write expressions for the number of each color item and for the total number of items.*
$x + x + 3 = 2x + 3$	

The probability of picking a blue item and then another blue item is the product of the probabilities of the individual events.

$$P(\text{blue, blue}) = \frac{x}{2x+3} \cdot \frac{x-1}{2x+2}$$

$$= \frac{x}{(2x+3)} \cdot \frac{x-1}{2(x+1)}$$

$$= \frac{x(x-1)}{2(2x+3)(x+1)}$$

b. What is the probability that Marty picks two blue items if there are 10 blue items in the bag before his first pick? Round your answer to the nearest hundredth.

Since x represents the number of blue items, substitute 10 for x.

$$P(\text{blue, blue}) = \frac{10(10-1)}{2(2 \cdot 10 + 3)(10 + 1)}$$ *Substitute.*

$$= \frac{10(9)}{2(23)(11)} = \frac{90}{506} \approx 0.18$$ *Use the order of operations to simplify.*

The probability is approximately 0.18.

Remember!

For a review of probability topics, see Skills Bank pp. SB29–SB32.

CHECK IT OUT! 5. **What if...?** There are 50 blue items in the bag before Marty's first pick. What is the probability that Marty picks two blue items? Round your answer to the nearest hundredth. $\approx$ **0.23**

THINK AND DISCUSS

1. Explain how to divide by a polynomial.

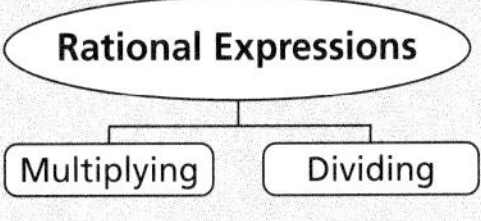

2. GET ORGANIZED Copy and complete the graphic organizer. In each box, describe how to perform the operation with rational expressions.

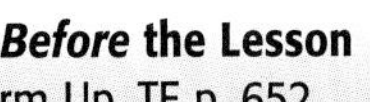

Power Presentations with PowerPoint®

Additional Examples

Example 5

Tanya is playing a carnival game. She needs to pick 2 cards out of a deck without looking. The deck has cards with numbers and cards with letters. There are 6 more letter cards than number cards.

a. Write and simplify an expression that represents the probability that Tanya will pick 2 number cards. $\frac{x(x-1)}{2(x+3)(2x+5)}$

b. What is the probability that Tanya picks 2 number cards if there are 25 number cards in the deck before her first pick? Round your answer to the nearest hundredth. 0.19

Also available on transparency

INTERVENTION

Questioning Strategies

EXAMPLE 5

- How do you find the total number of items?
- Why are the numerator and the denominator of the second expression different from the first expression?
- For what type of situation would the first and second fractions be the same?

3 Close

Summarize

Remind students that the methods for multiplying and dividing rational expressions are similar to those for multiplying and dividing fractions. They need to look for common factors that divide out to simplify the product or quotient. Tell students to write their work carefully, using the lines in their notebooks and completely crossing out simplified terms, to avoid careless errors.

FORMATIVE ASSESSMENT and INTERVENTION

***Diagnose Before* the Lesson**
10-4 Warm Up, TE p. 652

***Monitor During* the Lesson**
Check It Out! Exercises, SE pp. 653–655
Questioning Strategies, TE pp. 653–655

***Assess After* the Lesson**
10-4 Lesson Quiz, TE p. 658
Alternative Assessment, TE p. 658

Answers to *Think and Discuss*

Possible answers:

1. Dividing by a polynomial is the same as multiplying by the reciprocal of the polynomial.
2. See p. A8.

10-4 Exercises

Assignment Guide

Assign *Guided Practice* exercises as necessary.

If you finished Examples **1–3**
Proficient 23–31, 38, 40
Advanced 23–31, 38, 40

If you finished Examples **1–5**
Proficient 23–51, 56–63
Advanced 23–35, 37–63

Homework Quick Check
Quickly check key concepts.
Exercises: 24, 28, 30, 32, 35

Number Sense Exercise 33 contains opposite binomials $(a - 4)$ and $(4 - a)$. Remind students that the quotient of opposite binomials is -1. For example, $\frac{6-3}{3-6} = \frac{3}{-3} = -1$.

Answers

8. $\frac{5x^2 + 20x + 20}{6x^2}$
9. $\frac{m^2 - 10m}{2}$
10. $\frac{p^2 - 7p}{2}$
11. $a^3 + 10a^2 + 25a$
12. $\frac{-c^2 + 2c}{4}$
16. $\frac{3p^2q^3 + 12q^4 - 4p^2 - 16q}{q}$
20. $\frac{m - 1}{2m - 4}$
21. $\frac{1}{3x - 15}$
22a. $\frac{x(x + 10)}{(2x + 10)(2x + 9)}$

California Standards

Standard	Exercises
4.0 🔑	56, 57
8.0	58–60
12.0 🔑	63
13.0 🔑	1–21, 35, 37–44, 46–55
25.2	36

10-4 Exercises

California Standards Practice
🔑 13.0, 25.2

go.hrw.com
Homework Help Online
KEYWORD: MA8CA 10-4
Parent Resources Online
KEYWORD: MA8CA Parent

GUIDED PRACTICE

SEE EXAMPLE 1 p. 652

Multiply. Simplify your answer.

1. $\frac{4hj^2}{10j^3} \cdot \frac{3h^3k}{h^3k^3}$ $\mathbf{\frac{6h}{5jk^2}}$
2. $\frac{4y}{x^5} \cdot \frac{2yz^2}{9x^2}$ $\mathbf{\frac{8y^2z^2}{9x^7}}$
3. $\frac{x-2}{x+3} \cdot \frac{4x+12}{6}$ $\mathbf{\frac{2x-4}{3}}$
4. $\frac{ab}{c} \cdot \frac{2a^2}{3c}$ $\mathbf{\frac{2a^3b}{3c^2}}$
5. $\frac{7c^4d}{10c} \cdot \frac{5a}{21c^3d}$ $\mathbf{\frac{a}{6}}$
6. $\frac{12p^2q}{5p} \cdot \frac{15p^4q^3}{12q}$ $\mathbf{3p^5q^3}$

SEE EXAMPLE 2 p. 653

7. $\frac{12}{4y+8}(y^2 - 4)$ $\mathbf{3y - 6}$
8. $\frac{x+2}{6x^2}(5x + 10)$
9. $\frac{3m}{6m+18}(m^2 - 7m - 30)$
10. $\frac{4p}{8p+16}(p^2 - 5p - 14)$
11. $\frac{a^2}{a}(a^2 + 10a + 25)$
12. $\frac{-c}{4c+4}(c^2 - c - 2)$

SEE EXAMPLE 3 p. 653

13. $\frac{a^2 + 6ab}{b} \cdot \frac{5 + 3a}{3a^2b + 5ab}$ $\mathbf{\frac{a + 6b}{b^2}}$
14. $\frac{x^2 + 5x + 4}{x - 4} \cdot \frac{x^2 - 2x - 8}{x^2 + 6x + 8}$ $\mathbf{x + 1}$
15. $\frac{j - 1}{j^2 - 4j + 3} \cdot \frac{j^2 - 5j + 6}{2j - 4}$ $\mathbf{\frac{1}{2}}$
16. $\frac{p^3 + 4pq}{p} \cdot \frac{6q^3 - 8}{2q}$
17. $\frac{r^2 + 15r + 14}{r^2 - 16} \cdot \frac{2r + 8}{r + 1}$ $\mathbf{\frac{2r + 28}{r - 4}}$
18. $\frac{y - 8}{y^2 - 1} \cdot \frac{y + 2}{y^2 - 49}$ $\mathbf{\frac{y^2 - 6y - 16}{y^4 - 50y^2 + 49}}$

SEE EXAMPLE 4 p. 654

Divide. Simplify your answer.

19. $\frac{3a^4b}{2a^2c^3} \div \frac{12a^2c}{8c^4}$ $\mathbf{b}$
20. $\frac{2m^3 + 2m}{m^2 - 2m} \div \frac{4m^2 + 4}{m - 1}$
21. $\frac{x^2 + 4x - 5}{3x - 3} \div (x^2 - 25)$

SEE EXAMPLE 5 p. 655

22. **Probability** While playing a game, Rachel pulls two tiles out of a bag without looking and without replacing the first tile. The bag has two colors of tiles—black and white. There are 10 more white tiles than black tiles.
    a. Write and simplify an expression that represents the probability that Rachel will pick a black tile, then a white tile.
    b. What is the probability that Rachel pulls a black tile and then a white tile if there are 5 black tiles in the bag before her first pick? Round your answer to the nearest hundredth. $\mathbf{\approx 0.20}$

PRACTICE AND PROBLEM SOLVING

Independent Practice	
For Exercises	See Example
23–25	1
26–28	2
29–31	3
32–34	4
35	5

Extra Practice
Skills Practice p. EP21
Application Practice p. EP33

Multiply. Simplify your answer.

23. $\frac{p^6q^2}{7r^3} \cdot \frac{-3p^2}{r}$ $\mathbf{-\frac{3p^8q^2}{7r^4}}$
24. $\frac{3r^2t}{6st^3} \cdot \frac{2r^2s^3t^2}{8r^4s^2}$ $\mathbf{\frac{1}{8}}$
25. $\frac{10}{y + 5} \cdot \frac{y + 2}{3}$ $\mathbf{\frac{10y + 20}{3y + 15}}$
26. $\frac{3}{2a + 6}(a^2 + 4a + 3)$ $\mathbf{\frac{3a + 3}{2}}$
27. $\frac{4m^2 - 8m}{m^2 + 6m - 16}(m^2 + 7m - 8)$ $\mathbf{4m^2 - 4m}$
28. $\frac{x}{2x^2 - 12x + 18}(2x^2 - 4x - 6)$ $\mathbf{\frac{x^2 + x}{x - 3}}$
29. $\frac{6n^2 + 18n}{n^2 + 9n + 8} \cdot \frac{n^2 - 1}{2n + 6}$ $\mathbf{\frac{3n^2 - 3n}{n + 8}}$
30. $\frac{3a^2b}{5a^3 + 10a^2b} \cdot \frac{2a + 4b}{6a^3b + 6a^2b^2}$ $\mathbf{\frac{1}{5a^3 + 5a^2b}}$
31. $\frac{t^2 - 100}{5t + 50} \cdot \frac{5}{t - 10}$ $\mathbf{1}$

Divide. Simplify your answer.

32. $\frac{6j^2k^5}{5j} \div \frac{4j^3k^3}{3j}$ $\mathbf{\frac{9k^2}{10j}}$
33. $\frac{a - 4}{a^2} \div (8a - 2a^2)$ $\mathbf{-\frac{1}{2a^3}}$
34. $\frac{x^2 - 9}{x^2 + 6x + 9} \div \frac{4x^2 - 12x}{16x}$ $\mathbf{\frac{4}{x + 3}}$

10-4 READING STRATEGIES

LESSON 10-4 **Reading Strategies**
Connecting Concepts

The rules for multiplying and dividing rational expressions are the same as the rules for multiplying and dividing fractions. Look at the connections below.

FRACTIONS | RATIONAL EXPRESSIONS

Rule 1: $\frac{a}{b} \cdot \frac{c}{d} = \frac{ac}{bd}$
$\frac{8}{9} \cdot \frac{3}{5} = \frac{8 \cdot 3}{9 \cdot 5} = \cdots$ | $\frac{m+2}{4} \cdot \frac{8}{3m+6} = \frac{8(m+2)}{4(3m+6)} = \cdots$

Rule 2: $\frac{a}{b} \cdot c = \frac{a}{b} \cdot \frac{c}{1}$ and $\frac{a}{b} \div c = \frac{a}{b} \div \frac{c}{1}$
$\frac{3}{4} \cdot 16 = \frac{3}{4} \cdot \frac{16}{1} = \cdots$ | $\frac{6}{2x+10} \cdot (x^2 + 3x - 10) = \frac{6}{2x+10} \cdot \frac{x^2+3x-10}{1} = \cdots$

Rule 3: $\frac{a}{b} \div \frac{c}{d} = \frac{a}{b} \cdot \frac{d}{c}$
$\frac{1}{12} \div \frac{2}{3} = \frac{1}{12} \cdot \frac{3}{2} = \cdots$ | $\frac{3ab^4}{a^3} \div \frac{3ab}{ab^2} = \frac{3ab^4}{a^3} \cdot \frac{ab^2}{3ab} = \cdots$

Finish multiplying and dividing the rational expressions given above so that each is simplified completely.

1. Rule 1 $\frac{2}{3}$
2. Rule 2 $3(x - 2)$
3. Rule 3 $\frac{b^5}{a^2}$

Multiply or divide. Simplify your answer.

4. $\frac{3}{t+2} \cdot (t^2 - 4)$ $3t - 6$
5. $\frac{m+5}{4} \div (3m + 15)$ $\frac{1}{12}$
6. $\frac{x^2y^3}{8y} \cdot \frac{10x^4}{xy^2}$ $\frac{5x^5}{4}$

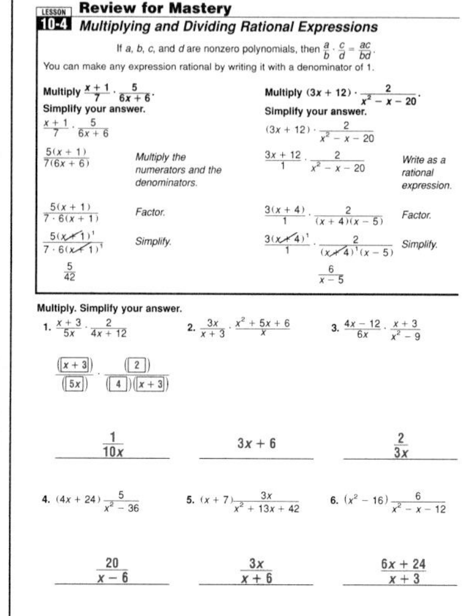

10-4 REVIEW FOR MASTERY

LESSON 10-4 **Review for Mastery**
Multiplying and Dividing Rational Expressions

If a, b, c, and d are nonzero polynomials, then $\frac{a}{b} \cdot \frac{c}{d} = \frac{ac}{bd}$.
You can make any expression rational by writing it with a denominator of 1.

Multiply $\frac{x+1}{7} \cdot \frac{5}{6x+6}$. Simplify your answer.

$\frac{x+1}{7} \cdot \frac{5}{6x+6}$
$\frac{5(x+1)}{7(6x+6)}$ — *Multiply the numerators and the denominators.*
$\frac{5(x+1)}{7 \cdot 6(x+1)}$ — *Factor.*
$\frac{5(x+1)^1}{7 \cdot 6(x+1)^1}$ — *Simplify.*
$\frac{5}{42}$

Multiply $(3x + 12) \cdot \frac{2}{x^2 - x - 20}$. Simplify your answer.

$(3x + 12) \cdot \frac{2}{x^2 - x - 20}$
$\frac{3x+12}{1} \cdot \frac{2}{x^2 - x - 20}$ — *Write as a rational expression.*
$\frac{3(x+4)}{1} \cdot \frac{2}{(x+4)(x-5)}$ — *Factor.*
$\frac{3(x+4)^1}{1} \cdot \frac{2}{(x+4)^1(x-5)}$ — *Simplify.*
$\frac{6}{x-5}$

Multiply. Simplify your answer.

1. $\frac{x+3}{5x} \cdot \frac{2}{4x+12}$ — $\frac{(x+3)}{(5x)} \cdot \frac{(2)}{(4)(x+3)}$ — $\frac{1}{10x}$
2. $\frac{3x}{x+3} \cdot \frac{x^2+5x+6}{x}$ — $3x + 6$
3. $\frac{4x-12}{6x} \cdot \frac{x+3}{x^2-9}$ — $\frac{2}{3x}$
4. $(4x + 24)\frac{5}{x^2 - 36}$ — $\frac{20}{x-6}$
5. $(x + 7)\frac{3x}{x^2 + 13x + 42}$ — $\frac{3x}{x+6}$
6. $(x^2 - 16)\frac{6}{x^2 - x - 12}$ — $\frac{6x+24}{x+3}$

35. Entertainment A carnival game board is covered completely in small balloons. You throw darts at the board and try to pop the balloons.

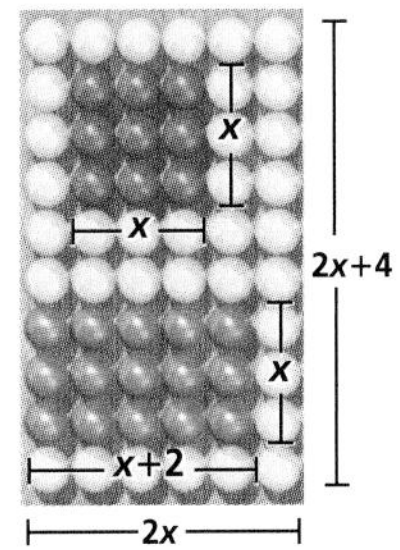

a. Write and simplify an expression describing the probability that the next two balloons popped are red and then blue. (*Hint:* Write the probabilities as ratios of the areas of rectangles.)

$\dfrac{x^2}{4(4x^2 + 8x - 1)}$

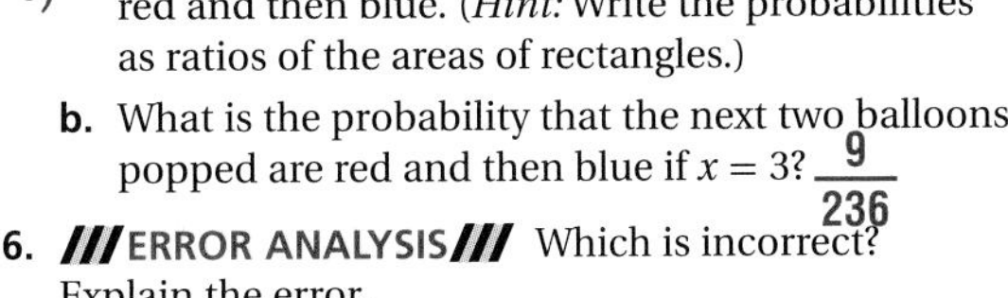
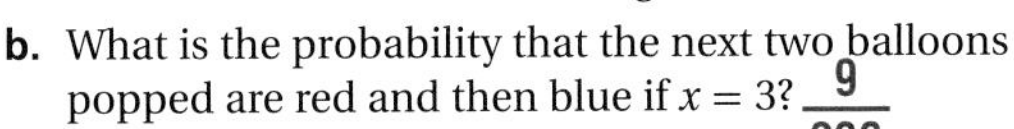

b. What is the probability that the next two balloons popped are red and then blue if $x = 3$? $\dfrac{9}{236}$

36. ///ERROR ANALYSIS/// Which is incorrect? Explain the error.

Student A is incorrect because individual terms (rather than factors) were divided out.

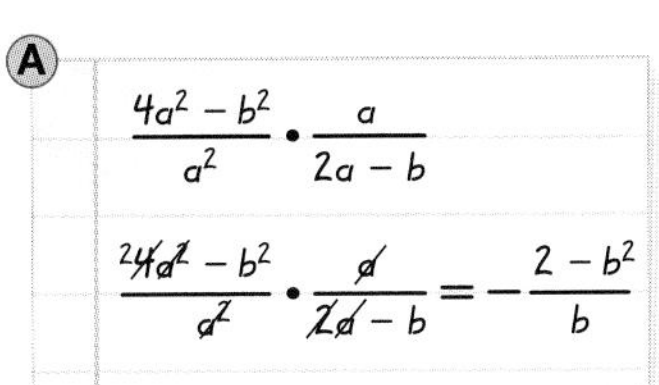

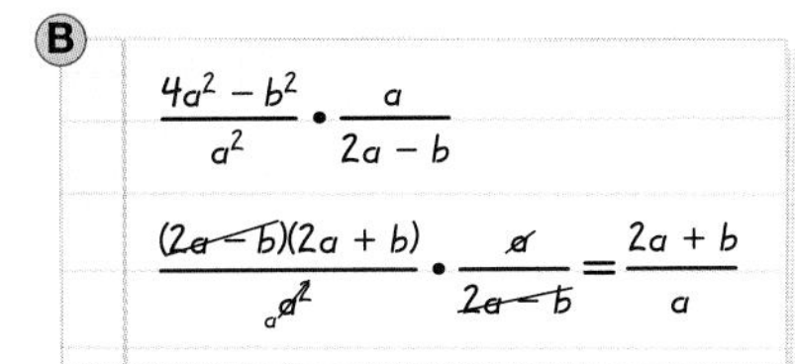

B
$\frac{4a^2 - b^2}{a^2} \cdot \frac{a}{2a - b}$
$\frac{(2a - b)(2a + b)}{a^2} \cdot \frac{a}{2a - b} = \frac{2a + b}{a}$

37. Critical Thinking Which of the following expressions is NOT equivalent to the other three? Explain why.

b; the other 3 expressions are all equivalent to $\frac{x}{y^2}$, but b simplifies to $\frac{4x}{y^2}$.

a. $\dfrac{4x^2}{x^2 - 3x} \cdot \dfrac{2x - 6}{8y^2}$

b. $\dfrac{6xy^2}{x^2} \div \dfrac{3y^4}{2x^2}$

c. $\dfrac{10x^4y}{5xy^2} \div 2x^2y$

d. $\dfrac{4x}{xy^2 + 2y^2} \cdot \dfrac{x^2 - 4}{4x - 8}$

Multiply or divide. Simplify your answer.

38. $\dfrac{5p^3}{p^2q} \cdot \dfrac{2q^3}{p^2}$ $\quad \dfrac{10q^2}{p}$

39. $\dfrac{6m^2 - 18m}{12m^3 + 12m^2} \div \dfrac{m^2 - 9}{m^2 + 4m + 3}$ $\quad \dfrac{1}{2m}$

40. $\dfrac{2x^2}{4x - 8} \cdot \dfrac{x^2 - 5x + 6}{x^5}$ $\quad \dfrac{x - 3}{2x^3}$

41. $\dfrac{x^2 - 9}{4x} \div (4x^2 - 36)$ $\quad \dfrac{1}{16x}$

42. $\dfrac{33m - 3m^2}{-2m - 4} \div \dfrac{6m - 66}{m^2 - 4m}$ $\quad \dfrac{m^3 - 4m^2}{4m + 8}$

43. $\dfrac{12w^4x^7}{3w^3} \cdot \dfrac{w^{-1}x^{-7}}{4}$ $\quad 1$

44. Write About It Explain how to divide $\frac{1}{m} \div \frac{3}{4m}$.

Multiply $\frac{1}{m}$ by $\frac{4m}{3}$. Then divide out the common factor m to get a final answer of $\frac{4}{3}$.

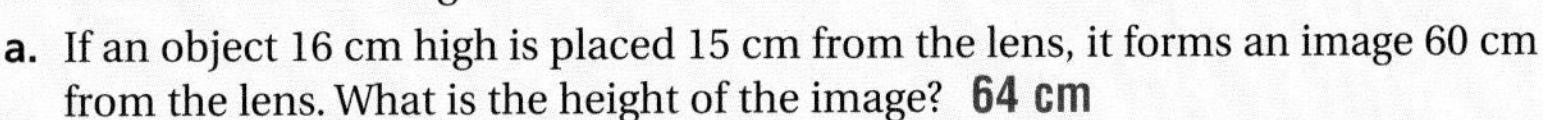
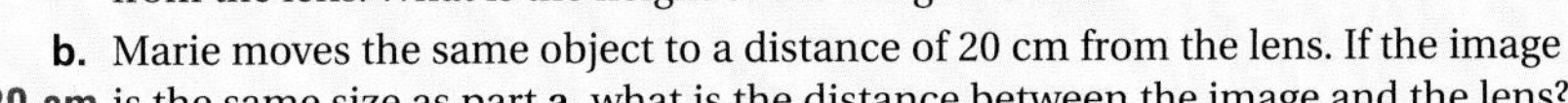

45. This problem will prepare you for the Concept Connection on page 684.

The size of an image projected on a screen depends on how far the object is from the lens, the magnification of the lens, and the distance between the image and the lens. Magnification of a lens is $M = \frac{I}{O} = \frac{y}{x}$ where I is the height of the image, O is the height of the object, x is the distance of the object from the lens, and y is the distance of the image from the lens.

a. If an object 16 cm high is placed 15 cm from the lens, it forms an image 60 cm from the lens. What is the height of the image? **64 cm**

b. Marie moves the same object to a distance of 20 cm from the lens. If the image is the same size as part **a**, what is the distance between the image and the lens? **80 cm**

c. What is the magnification of the lens? **4**

CONCEPT CONNECTION **Exercise 45** involves a variation function that describes magnification. This exercise prepares students for the Concept Connection on page 684.

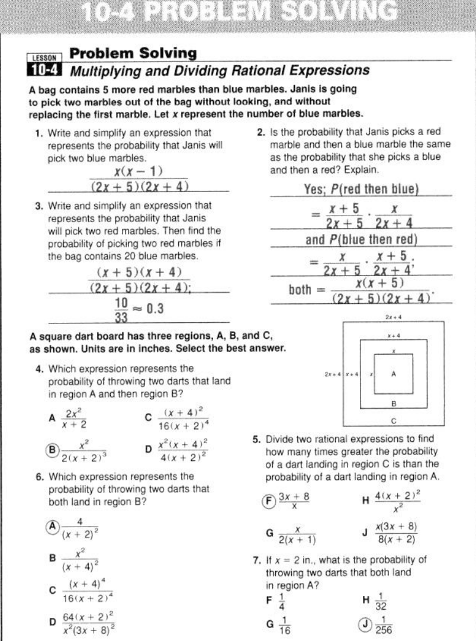

10-4 PROBLEM SOLVING

LESSON 10-4 **Problem Solving**
Multiplying and Dividing Rational Expressions

A bag contains 5 more red marbles than blue marbles. Janis is going to pick two marbles out of the bag without looking, and without replacing the first marble. Let x represent the number of blue marbles.

1. Write and simplify an expression that represents the probability that Janis will pick two blue marbles.
$\dfrac{x(x - 1)}{(2x + 5)(2x + 4)}$

2. Is the probability that Janis picks a red marble and then a blue marble the same as the probability that she picks a blue and then a red? Explain.
Yes; P(red then blue) $= \dfrac{x + 5}{2x + 5} \cdot \dfrac{x}{2x + 4}$ and P(blue then red) $= \dfrac{x}{2x + 5} \cdot \dfrac{x + 5}{2x + 4}$; both $= \dfrac{x(x + 5)}{(2x + 5)(2x + 4)}$.

3. Write and simplify an expression that represents the probability that Janis will pick two red marbles. Then find the probability of picking two red marbles if the bag contains 20 blue marbles.
$\dfrac{(x + 5)(x + 4)}{(2x + 5)(2x + 4)}$; $\dfrac{10}{33} \approx 0.3$

A square dart board has three regions, A, B, and C, as shown. Units are in inches. Select the best answer.

2x + 4, x + 4, x, A, B, C

4. Which expression represents the probability of throwing two darts that land in region A and then region B?
A $\dfrac{2x^2}{x + 2}$
(B) $\dfrac{x^2}{2(x + 2)^3}$
C $\dfrac{(x + 4)^2}{16(x + 2)^4}$
D $\dfrac{x^2(x + 4)^2}{4(x + 2)^2}$

5. Divide two rational expressions to find how many times greater the probability of a dart landing in region C is than the probability of a dart landing in region A.
(F) $\dfrac{3x + 8}{x}$
G $\dfrac{x}{2(x + 1)}$
H $\dfrac{4(x + 2)^2}{x^2}$
J $\dfrac{x(3x + 8)}{8(x + 2)}$

6. Which expression represents the probability of throwing two darts that both land in region B?
(A) $\dfrac{4}{(x + 2)^2}$
B $\dfrac{x^2}{(x + 4)^2}$
C $\dfrac{(x + 4)^4}{16(x + 2)^4}$
D $\dfrac{64(x + 2)^2}{x^2(3x + 8)^2}$

7. If $x = 2$ in., what is the probability of throwing two darts that both land in region A?
F $\frac{1}{4}$
G $\frac{1}{16}$
H $\frac{1}{32}$
(J) $\frac{1}{256}$

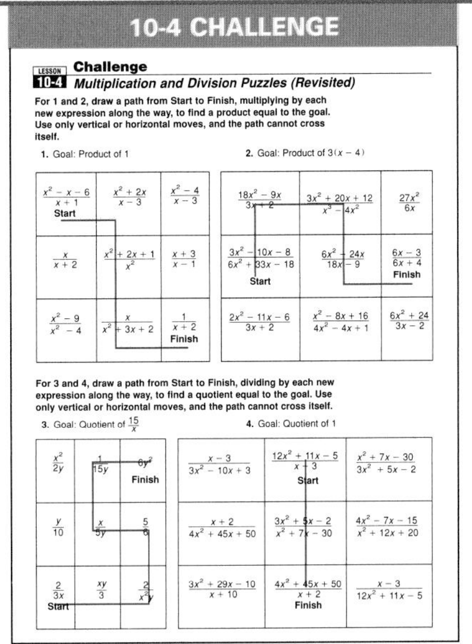

10-4 CHALLENGE

LESSON 10-4 **Challenge**
Multiplication and Division Puzzles (Revisited)

For 1 and 2, draw a path from Start to Finish, multiplying by each new expression along the way, to find a product equal to the goal. Use only vertical or horizontal moves, and the path cannot cross itself.

1. Goal: Product of 1

$\frac{x^2 - x - 6}{x + 1}$ Start	$\frac{x^2 + 2x}{x - 3}$	$\frac{x^2 - 4}{x - 3}$
$\frac{x}{x + 2}$	$\frac{x^2 + 2x + 1}{x^2}$	$\frac{x + 3}{x - 1}$
$\frac{x^2 - 9}{x^2 - 4}$	$\frac{x}{x^2 + 3x + 2}$	$\frac{1}{x + 2}$ Finish

2. Goal: Product of $3(x - 4)$

$\frac{18x^2 - 9x}{3x + 2}$	$\frac{3x^2 + 20x + 12}{x^3 - 4x^2}$	$\frac{27x^2}{6x}$
$\frac{3x^2 - 10x - 8}{6x^2 + 33x - 18}$ Start	$\frac{6x^2 + 24x}{18x - 9}$	$\frac{6x - 3}{6x + 4}$ Finish
$\frac{2x^2 - 11x - 6}{3x + 2}$	$\frac{x^2 - 8x + 16}{4x^2 - 4x + 1}$	$\frac{6x^2 + 24}{3x - 2}$

For 3 and 4, draw a path from Start to Finish, dividing by each new expression along the way, to find a quotient equal to the goal. Use only vertical or horizontal moves, and the path cannot cross itself.

3. Goal: Quotient of $\frac{15}{x}$

$\frac{x^2}{2y}$	$\frac{1}{15y}$	$6y^2$ Finish
$\frac{y}{10}$	$\frac{x}{5y}$	$\frac{5}{6}$
$\frac{2}{3x}$ Start	$\frac{xy}{3}$	$\frac{2}{x^2y}$

4. Goal: Quotient of 1

$\frac{x - 3}{3x^2 - 10x + 3}$	$\frac{12x^2 + 11x - 5}{x + 3}$ Start	$\frac{x^2 + 7x - 30}{3x^2 + 5x - 2}$
$\frac{x + 2}{4x^2 + 45x + 50}$	$\frac{3x^2 + 5x - 2}{x^2 + 7x - 30}$	$\frac{4x^2 - 7x - 15}{x^2 + 12x + 20}$
$\frac{3x^2 + 29x - 10}{x + 10}$	$\frac{4x^2 + 45x + 50}{x + 2}$ Finish	$\frac{x - 3}{12x^2 + 11x - 5}$

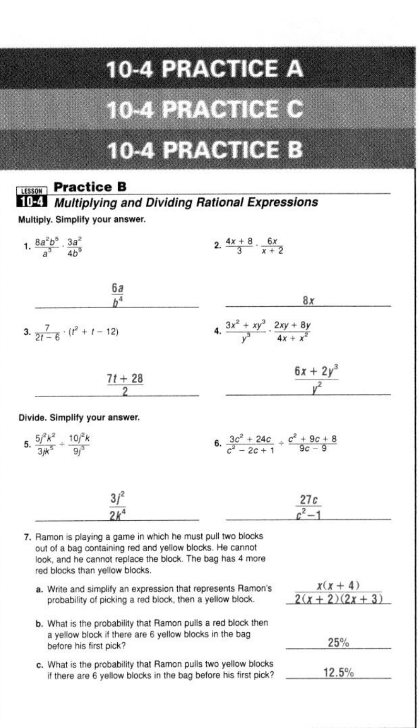

10-4 PRACTICE A

10-4 PRACTICE C

10-4 PRACTICE B

LESSON 10-4 **Practice B**
Multiplying and Dividing Rational Expressions

Multiply. Simplify your answer.

1. $\dfrac{8a^2b^5}{a^3} \cdot \dfrac{3a^2}{4b^9}$ $\quad \dfrac{6a}{b^4}$

2. $\dfrac{4x + 8}{3} \cdot \dfrac{6x}{x + 2}$ $\quad 8x$

3. $\dfrac{7}{2t - 6} \cdot (t^2 + t - 12)$ $\quad \dfrac{7t + 28}{2}$

4. $\dfrac{3x^2 + xy^3}{y^3} \cdot \dfrac{2xy + 8y}{4x + x^2}$ $\quad \dfrac{6x + 2y^3}{y^2}$

Divide. Simplify your answer.

5. $\dfrac{5j^2k^2}{3jk^5} \div \dfrac{10j^2k}{9j^3}$ $\quad \dfrac{3j^2}{2k^4}$

6. $\dfrac{3c^2 + 24c}{c^2 - 2c + 1} \div \dfrac{c^2 + 9c + 8}{9c - 9}$ $\quad \dfrac{27c}{c^2 - 1}$

7. Ramon is playing a game in which he must pull two blocks out of a bag containing red and yellow blocks. He cannot look, and he cannot replace the block. The bag has 4 more red blocks than yellow blocks.

a. Write and simplify an expression that represents Ramon's probability of picking a red block, then a yellow block. $\quad \dfrac{x(x + 4)}{2(x + 2)(2x + 3)}$

b. What is the probability that Ramon pulls a red block then a yellow block if there are 6 yellow blocks in the bag before his first pick? $\quad$ 25%

c. What is the probability that Ramon pulls two yellow blocks if there are 6 yellow blocks in the bag before his first pick? $\quad$ 12.5%

Multiple Choice Students who chose **B** for **Exercise 46** may not have found the middle term of the trinomial in the numerator. Remind them to use FOIL to multiply two binomials. Students who chose **C** may have written the reciprocal of the second expression and then multiplied.

Journal

Explain how to multiply a rational expression by a polynomial.

ALTERNATIVE ASSESSMENT

Have students write a multiplication problem and a division problem that have the same rational expression as a solution.

Power Presentations with PowerPoint®

10-4 Lesson Quiz

Multiply. Simplify your answer.

1. $\frac{b-2}{3} \cdot \frac{12}{2b-4}$ 2
2. $\frac{3m^2}{n} \cdot \frac{m^3}{2n^2}$ $\frac{3m^5}{2n^3}$
3. $\frac{3x^2+3x}{6y} \cdot \frac{12y^2}{7x^2y+7xy}$ $\frac{6}{7}$

Divide. Simplify your answer.

4. $\frac{3}{b} \div \frac{b+1}{2b}$ $\frac{6}{b+1}$
5. $\frac{4gh^3}{h} \div (2g^2 - 8g)$ $\frac{2h^2}{g-4}$
6. A bag contains purple and green toy cars. There are 9 more purple cars than green cars.
   a. Write and simplify an expression to represent the probability that someone will pick a purple car and a green car. $\frac{x(x+9)}{2(x+4)(2x+9)}$
   b. What is the probability of someone picking a purple car and a green car if there are 12 green cars before the first pick? Round to the nearest hundredth. 0.24

Also available on transparency

Multiple Choice For Exercises 46–48, choose the best answer.

46. Which expression is equivalent to $\frac{t+4}{9} \cdot \frac{t+4}{3}$?
    (A) $\frac{(t+4)^2}{27}$ (B) $\frac{t^2+16}{27}$ (C) $\frac{1}{3}$ (D) $\frac{1}{27}$

47. Identify the product $-\frac{20b^2}{a^2} \cdot \frac{3ab}{15b}$.
    (A) $-\frac{a}{4b^2}$ (B) $-4b^2$ (C) $-\frac{4b^2}{a}$ (D) $-\frac{b^2}{4a}$

48. Which of the following is equivalent to $\frac{2x}{x+5}$?
    (A) $\frac{x-2}{8x} \cdot \frac{4}{x^2+3x-10}$ (C) $\frac{x-2}{4} \div \frac{x^2+3x-10}{8x}$
    (B) $\frac{x^2-3x-10}{8x} \cdot \frac{4}{x-2}$ (D) $\frac{x^2-3x-10}{4} \div \frac{x-2}{8x}$

49. **Short Response** Simplify $\frac{x^2-10x+24}{3x^2-12x} \div (x^2-3x-18)$. Show your work. $\frac{1}{3x^2+9x}$

CHALLENGE AND EXTEND

Simplify.

50. $\frac{x-3}{3x-6} \cdot \frac{3x+12}{x+1} \cdot \frac{2x-4}{x^2+x-12}$ $\frac{2}{x+1}$
51. $\frac{x^2-1}{x+2} \div \frac{3x+3}{x+2} \div (x-1)$ $\frac{1}{3}$

A *complex fraction* is a fraction that contains one or more fractions in the numerator or the denominator. Simplify each complex fraction.
$\left(\textit{Hint: } \text{Use the rule } \frac{\frac{a}{b}}{\frac{c}{d}} = \frac{a}{b} \div \frac{c}{d}.\right)$

52. $\frac{\frac{c+5}{c^2-4}}{\frac{c^2+6c+5}{c+2}}$ $\frac{1}{c^2-c-2}$
53. $\frac{\frac{x^2y}{xz^3}}{\frac{x^2y}{x^2z}}$ $\frac{x}{z^2}$
54. $\frac{\frac{x^2}{2} \cdot \frac{x}{3}}{\frac{x}{6}}$ x^2
55. $\frac{\frac{a+1}{a^2+6a+5}}{\frac{2a+2}{a+5}}$ $\frac{1}{2a+2}$

SPIRAL STANDARDS REVIEW

4.0, 8.0, 12.0

56. Danny runs laps around the track each week. This week, he wants to run at least 12 laps. He ran 3 laps earlier in the week, and today he ran 2 laps. Write and solve an inequality to determine how many more laps Danny has to run to meet his goal. *(Lesson 3-4)* $3 + 2 + x \geq 12; x \geq 7$

57. Pierce has \$30 to spend on a night out. He already spent \$12 on dinner and \$9 on a movie ticket. He will spend some money m on movie-theatre snacks. Write and solve an inequality that will show all the values of m that Pierce can spend on snacks. *(Lesson 3-4)* $12 + 9 + m \leq 30; 0 \leq m \leq 9$

Identify which lines are parallel. *(Lesson 5-7)*

58. $y = 3x + 4$; $y = 7$; $y = -3x + 4$, $y = 2$ $y = 7$ and $y = 2$
59. $y = 5x - 7$; $y = -x + 5$; $y = -x - 7$, $y = 5x + 5$ $y = 5x - 7$ and $y = 5x + 5$; $y = -x + 5$ and $y = -x - 7$
60. $y = -7x$; $y = 12$; $y = -x + 4$, $y = -7x + 5$ $y = -7x$ and $y = -7x + 5$

Simplify each rational expression, if possible. Identify any excluded values. *(Lesson 10-3)*

61. $\frac{x+2}{x^2-4}$ $\frac{1}{x-2}$; $x \neq 2, -2$
62. $\frac{2(x-3)}{3(x+4)}$
63. $\frac{4x-10}{2x^2-8}$

62. $\frac{2(x-3)}{3(x+4)}$; $x \neq -4$

63. $\frac{2x-5}{x^2-4}$; $x \neq 2, -2$

10-5 Adding and Subtracting Rational Expressions

California Standards

🔑 **13.0 Students add, subtract,** multiply, and divide **rational expressions** and functions. **Students solve both computationally and conceptually challenging problems by using these techniques.**

Also covered: 🔑 **15.0**

Who uses this?

Kayakers can use rational expressions to figure out travel time for different river trips. (See Example 5.)

The rules for adding rational expressions are the same as the rules for adding fractions. If the denominators are the same, you add the numerators and keep the common denominator.

$$\frac{3}{8}+\frac{2}{8}=\frac{3+2}{8}=\frac{5}{8}$$

Know it! Note

Adding Rational Expressions with Like Denominators

If a, b, and c represent polynomials and $c \neq 0$, then $\frac{a}{c}+\frac{b}{c}=\frac{a+b}{c}$.

EXAMPLE 1 Adding Rational Expressions with Like Denominators

Add. Simplify your answer.

A $\frac{3b}{b^2}+\frac{5b}{b^2}$

$\frac{3b+5b}{b^2}=\frac{8\cancel{b}}{\cancel{b^2}^{\,b}}$ *Combine like terms in the numerator. Divide out common factors.*

$=\frac{8}{b}$ *Simplify.*

B $\frac{x^2-8x}{x-4}+\frac{2x+8}{x-4}$

$\frac{x^2-8x+2x+8}{x-4}=\frac{x^2-6x+8}{x-4}$ *Combine like terms in the numerator.*

$=\frac{(x-2)\cancel{(x-4)}}{\cancel{x-4}}$ *Factor. Divide out common factors.*

$=x-2$ *Simplify.*

C $\frac{2m+4}{m^2-9}+\frac{2}{m^2-9}$

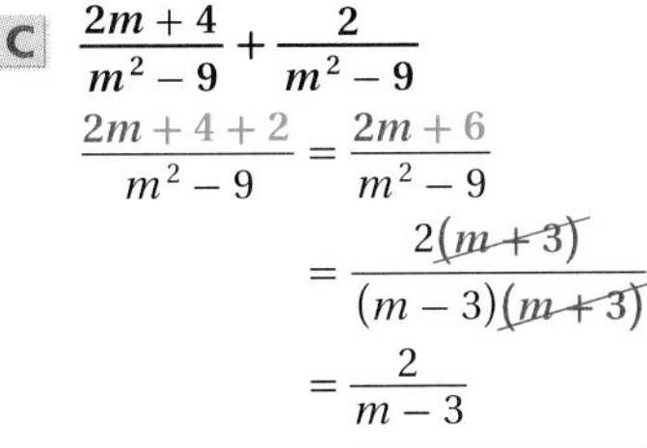

$\frac{2m+4+2}{m^2-9}=\frac{2m+6}{m^2-9}$ *Combine like terms in the numerator.*

$=\frac{2\cancel{(m+3)}}{(m-3)\cancel{(m+3)}}$ *Factor. Divide out common factors.*

$=\frac{2}{m-3}$ *Simplify.*

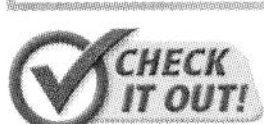

CHECK IT OUT! Add. Simplify your answer.

1a. $\frac{n}{2n}+\frac{3n}{2n}$ **2**

1b. $\frac{3y^2}{y+1}+\frac{3y}{y+1}$ **3y**

10-5 Organizer

Objectives: Add and subtract rational expressions with like denominators.

Add and subtract rational expressions with unlike denominators.

Online Edition
Tutorial Videos, Interactivity

Countdown to Mastery Week 24

Power Presentations with PowerPoint®

Warm Up

Add. Simplify your answer.

1. $\frac{3}{4}+\frac{3}{4}$ $\frac{3}{2}$ **2.** $\frac{5}{6}+\frac{1}{6}$ 1

3. $\frac{1}{4}+\frac{2}{3}$ $\frac{11}{12}$ **4.** $\frac{1}{2}+\frac{2}{5}$ $\frac{9}{10}$

Subtract. Simplify your answer.

5. $\frac{5}{8}-\frac{1}{8}$ $\frac{1}{2}$ **6.** $\frac{4}{3}-\left(-\frac{1}{3}\right)$ $\frac{5}{3}$

7. $\frac{7}{9}-\frac{1}{5}$ $\frac{26}{45}$ **8.** $\frac{2}{5}-1$ $-\frac{3}{5}$

Also available on transparency

Math Humor

Q: Why is the common denominator absent?

A: He's home with a common cold.

1 Introduce

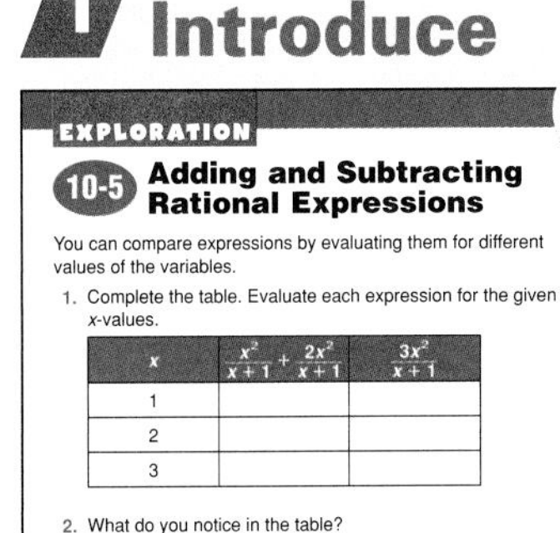

EXPLORATION

10-5 Adding and Subtracting Rational Expressions

You can compare expressions by evaluating them for different values of the variables.

1. Complete the table. Evaluate each expression for the given x-values.

x	$\frac{x^2}{x+1}+\frac{2x^2}{x+1}$	$\frac{3x^2}{x+1}$
1		
2		
3		

2. What do you notice in the table?

3. Complete the table. Evaluate each expression for the given p-values.

p	$\frac{p+2}{p^2}+\frac{p+1}{p^2}$	$\frac{2p+3}{p^2}$
1		
3		
5		

4. What do you notice in the table?

THINK AND DISCUSS

Motivate

Review with students how to add fractions with like and unlike denominators. Explain that adding rational expressions requires the same steps—add numerators when denominators are common.

Explorations and answers are provided in *Alternate Openers: Explorations Transparencies.*

California Standards

Algebra 1 🔑 **13.0**

Also covered:

🔑 **15.0 Students apply algebraic techniques to solve rate problems,** work problems, and percent mixture problems.

Power Presentations with PowerPoint®

Additional Examples

Example 1

Add. Simplify your answer.

A. $\frac{2x}{x^4} + \frac{4x}{x^4}$ $\frac{6}{x^3}$

B. $\frac{m^2 + 2m}{m + 4} + \frac{3m + 4}{m + 4}$ $m + 1$

C. $\frac{3k - 18}{k^2 - 16} + \frac{6}{k^2 - 16}$ $\frac{3}{k + 4}$

Example 2

Subtract. Simplify your answer.

$\frac{6y - 6}{y^2 + 4y - 12} - \frac{y + 4}{y^2 + 4y - 12}$

$\frac{5}{y + 6}$

Example 3

Find the LCM of the given expressions.

A. $12x^2y$, $9xy^3$ $36x^2y^3$

B. $c^2 + 8c + 15$, $3c^2 + 18c + 27$
$3(c + 3)^2(c + 5)$

Also available on transparency

INTERVENTION

Questioning Strategies

EXAMPLE 1

- How are these examples similar to adding fractions?
- Why should the numerator be factored when possible?

EXAMPLE 2

- How do you combine numerators?
- How does subtracting expressions affect the numerator of the second fraction?

EXAMPLE 3

- What does LCM mean?
- How is finding the LCM of two whole numbers similar to or different from finding the LCM of two expressions?

Inclusion When identifying the LCM of two expressions, tell students that each expression must divide into the LCM. Therefore, the degree of the LCM must be greater than or equal to the degree of each individual expression.

EXAMPLE **2** **Subtracting Rational Expressions with Like Denominators**

Subtract. Simplify your answer.

$$\frac{3m - 6}{m^2 + m - 6} - \frac{-m + 2}{m^2 + m - 6}$$

$$\frac{3m - 6 - (-m + 2)}{m^2 + m - 6} = \frac{3m - 6 + m - 2}{m^2 + m - 6}$$ *Subtract numerators.*

$$= \frac{4m - 8}{m^2 + m - 6}$$ *Combine like terms.*

$$= \frac{4(m - 2)}{(m + 3)(m - 2)}$$ *Factor. Divide out common factors.*

$$= \frac{4}{m + 3}$$ *Simplify.*

Caution!

Make sure you add the opposite of each term in the numerator of the second expression when subtracting rational expressions.

Subtract. Simplify your answer.

2a. $\frac{5a + 2}{a^2 - 4} - \frac{2a - 4}{a^2 - 4}$ $\frac{3}{a - 2}$ **2b.** $\frac{2b + 14}{b^2 + 3b - 4} - \frac{-2b + 2}{b^2 + 3b - 4}$ $\frac{4b + 12}{b^2 + 3b - 4}$

As with fractions, rational expressions must have a common denominator before they can be added or subtracted. If they do not have a common denominator, you can use any common multiple of the denominators to find one. You can also use the least common multiple (LCM) of the denominators.

To find the LCM of two expressions, write the prime factorization of both expressions. Line up the factors as shown. To find the LCM, multiply one number from each column.

$6x^2 = 2 \cdot 3 \cdot x \cdot x$
$8x = 2 \cdot 2 \cdot 2 \cdot x$
$\text{LCM} = 2 \cdot 2 \cdot 2 \cdot 3 \cdot x \cdot x = 24x^2$

$5x + 15 = 5(x + 3)$
$x^2 - 9 = (x + 3)(x - 3)$
$\text{LCM} = 5(x + 3)(x - 3)$

EXAMPLE **3** **Identifying the Least Common Multiple**

Find the LCM of the given expressions.

A $24a^3, 4a$

$24a^3 = 2 \cdot 2 \cdot 2 \cdot 3 \cdot a \cdot a \cdot a$
$4a = 2 \cdot 2 \cdot a$
$\text{LCM} = 2 \cdot 2 \cdot 2 \cdot 3 \cdot a \cdot a \cdot a = 24a^3$

Write the prime factorization of each expression. Align common factors.

B $2d^2 + 10d + 12, d^2 + 7d + 12$

$2d^2 + 10d + 12 = 2(d^2 + 5d + 6)$ *Factor each expression.*
$= 2(d + 3)(d + 2)$ *Align common factors.*
$d^2 + 7d + 12 = (d + 3)(d + 4)$
$\text{LCM} = 2(d + 3)(d + 2)(d + 4)$

Find the LCM of the given expressions. $(x - 6)(x + 2)(x + 5)$

3a. $5f^2h, 15fh^2$ **3b.** $x^2 - 4x - 12, (x - 6)(x + 5)$

3a. $15f^2h^2$

2 Teach

Guided Instruction

After adding and subtracting with like denominators, review how to find the LCM of two numbers, such as 12 and 20. Then find the LCM of expressions with just one variable, such as $12x^2$ and $20x^5$, and then more than one variable, such as $12x^2y^3$ and $20x^6y$. Finally, include expressions with binomial factors. Show how the LCD is used to add and subtract rational expressions with unlike denominators.

Universal Access

Through Number Sense

Sometimes students get confused about how to find the LCM because the word *least* causes them to choose the least number of different common factors. Emphasize that *least* in LCM describes the common multiples, not the common factors. Remind students to check that the LCM they find is really a multiple, not just a factor, of both expressions.

The LCM of the denominators of rational expressions is also called the least common denominator, or LCD, of the rational expressions. You can use the LCD to add or subtract rational expressions.

Adding or Subtracting Rational Expressions
Step 1 Identify a common denominator.
Step 2 Multiply each expression by an appropriate form of 1 so that each term has the common denominator as its denominator.
Step 3 Write each expression using the common denominator.
Step 4 Add or subtract the numerators, combining like terms as needed.
Step 5 Factor as needed.
Step 6 Simplify as needed.

EXAMPLE 4 **Adding and Subtracting with Unlike Denominators**

Add or subtract. Simplify your answer.

A $\frac{3x}{6x^2} + \frac{2x}{4x}$

$6x^2 = 2 \cdot 3 \cdot x \cdot x$

Step 1 $4x = 2 \cdot 2 \cdot x$ *Identify the LCD.*

$\text{LCD} = 2 \cdot 2 \cdot 3 \cdot x \cdot x = 12x^2$

Step 2 $\frac{3x}{6x^2}\left(\frac{2}{2}\right) + \frac{2x}{4x}\left(\frac{3x}{3x}\right)$ *Multiply each expression by an appropriate form of 1.*

Step 3 $\frac{6x}{12x^2} + \frac{6x^2}{12x^2}$ *Write each expression using the LCD.*

Step 4 $\frac{6x + 6x^2}{12x^2}$ *Add the numerators.*

Step 5 $\frac{\cancel{6}\cancel{x}(1 + x)}{\cancel{6} \cdot 2\cancel{x^2}^{x}}$ *Factor and divide out common factors.*

Step 6 $\frac{1 + x}{2x}$ *Simplify.*

B $\frac{1}{m - 3} - \frac{5}{3 - m}$

Step 1 The denominators are opposite binomials.
The LCD can be either $m - 3$ or $3 - m$. *Identify the LCD.*

Step 2 $\frac{1}{m - 3} - \frac{5}{3 - m}\left(\frac{-1}{-1}\right)$ *Multiply the second expression by $\frac{-1}{-1}$ to get an LCD of $m - 3$.*

Step 3 $\frac{1}{m - 3} - \frac{-5}{m - 3}$ *Write each expression using the LCD.*

Step 4 $\frac{1 - (-5)}{m - 3}$ *Subtract the numerators.*

Steps 5, 6 $\frac{6}{m - 3}$ *No factoring is needed, so just simplify.*

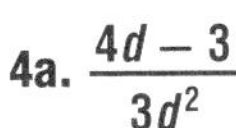

Remember!

Expressions like $m - 3$ and $3 - m$ are opposite binominals.
$3 - m = -1(m - 3)$
and
$m - 3 = -1(3 - m)$

CHECK IT OUT! **Add or subtract. Simplify your answer.**

4a. $\frac{4}{3d} - \frac{2d}{2d^3}$ **4b.** $\frac{a^2 + 4a}{a^2 + 2a - 8} + \frac{8}{a - 2}$ $\frac{a + 8}{a - 2}$

4a. $\frac{4d - 3}{3d^2}$

COMMON ERROR ALERT

When finding a common denominator using opposite binomials, students might multiply only the denominator by -1. Remind students that the only way the expression remains equivalent is to multiply both the numerator and denominator by -1, which is equivalent to multiplying the expression by 1.

Power Presentations with PowerPoint®

Additional Examples

Example 4

Add or subtract. Simplify your answer.

A. $\frac{2n}{5n^3} + \frac{4n}{2n^2}$ $\frac{10n + 2}{5n^2}$

B. $\frac{2}{5 - w} - \frac{5}{w - 5}$ $-\frac{7}{w - 5}$

Also available on transparency

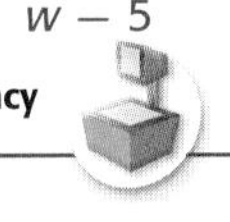

INTERVENTION

Questioning Strategies

EXAMPLE 4

- How do you determine the common denominator for two expressions?
- Would simplifying the expressions before finding the LCD change the LCD? Would it change the final answer?

Universal Access

Advanced Learners/GATE

Show students that a negative sign can be distributed to the numerator or denominator. The resulting equivalent expressions can look very different.

$$-\frac{x + 3}{x - 7} = \frac{-(x + 3)}{x - 7} = \frac{-x - 3}{x - 7}$$

$$-\frac{x + 3}{x - 7} = \frac{x + 3}{-(x - 7)} = \frac{x + 3}{-x + 7}$$

Have students practice writing expressions in various equivalent ways.

Power Presentations with PowerPoint®

Additional Examples

Example 5

Roland needs to take supplies by canoe to some friends camping 2 miles upriver and then return to his own campsite. Roland's average paddling rate is about twice the speed of the river's current.

a. Write and simplify an expression for how long it will take Roland to canoe round trip. $\frac{8}{3x}$

b. The speed of the river's current is 2.5 miles per hour. About how long will it take Roland to make the round trip? 64 minutes

Also available on transparency

INTERVENTION
Questioning Strategies

EXAMPLE 5

- Why are the numerators in the two expressions the same?
- Why are the denominators in the two expressions different?
- How do you change the fractional answer to minutes?

Diversity Canoes are open boats with paddles that are single-ended. Most kayaks have a closed top, and their paddles are usually double-ended.

EXAMPLE 5 *Recreation Application*

Katy wants to find out how long it will take to kayak 1 mile up a river and return to her starting point. Katy's average paddling rate is 4 times the speed of the river's current.

a. Write and simplify an expression for the time it will take Katy to kayak the round-trip in terms of the rate of the river's current.

Step 1 Write expressions for the distances and rates in the problem.

The distance in both directions is 1 mile.

Let x represent the rate of the current, and let $4x$ represent Katy's paddling rate.

Katy's rate against the current is $4x - x$, or $3x$.

Katy's rate with the current is $4x + x$, or $5x$.

Step 2 Use a table to write expressions for time.

Helpful Hint

To write expressions for time in terms of distance and rate, solve $d = rt$ for t.

$t = \frac{d}{r}$

Direction	Distance (mi)	Rate (mi/h)	Time (h) = $\frac{\text{distance}}{\text{rate}}$
Upstream (against current)	1	$3x$	$\frac{1}{3x}$
Downstream (with current)	1	$5x$	$\frac{1}{5x}$

Step 3 Write and simplify an expression for the total time.

total time = time upstream + time downstream

$$\text{total time} = \frac{1}{3x} + \frac{1}{5x} \quad \textit{Substitute known values.}$$

$$= \frac{1}{3x}\left(\frac{5}{5}\right) + \frac{1}{5x}\left(\frac{3}{3}\right) \quad \textit{Multiply each fraction by an appropriate form of 1.}$$

$$= \frac{5}{15x} + \frac{3}{15x} \quad \textit{Write each expression using the LCD, 15x.}$$

$$= \frac{8}{15x} \quad \textit{Add the numerators.}$$

b. The rate of the river is 2 miles per hour. How long will it take Katy to kayak round trip?

$$\frac{8}{15(2)} = \frac{4}{15} \quad \textit{Substitute 2 for x. Simplify.}$$

It will take Katy $\frac{4}{15}$ of an hour, or 16 minutes, to kayak the round-trip.

5. What if?... Katy's average paddling rate increases to 5 times the speed of the current. Now how long will it take Katy to kayak the round trip? $\frac{5}{24}$ h, or 12.5 min

THINK AND DISCUSS

1. Explain how to find the least common denominator of rational expressions.
2. **GET ORGANIZED** Copy and complete the graphic organizer. In each box, compare and contrast operations with fractions and rational expressions.

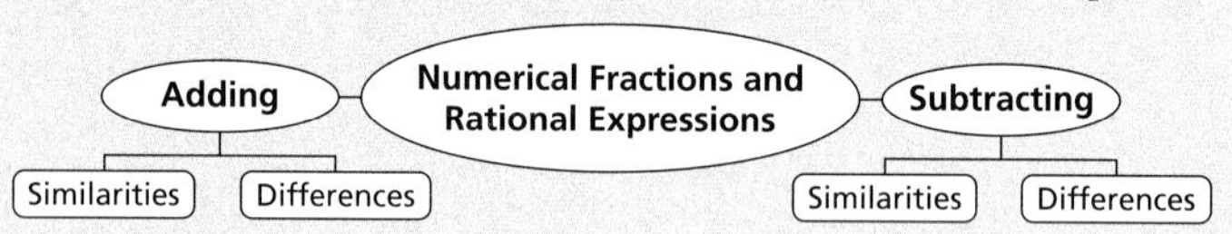

3 Close

Summarize

Tell students that rational expressions, like fractions, can be added or subtracted only if they have a common denominator. One way to get a common denominator is to use the LCD, which is the LCM of the denominators, although any common multiple will work (it just means more simplifying later in the problem). For example, $\frac{1}{x^2} + \frac{1}{x^3}$ can be written as $\frac{x}{x^3} + \frac{1}{x^3}$ or $\frac{x^3}{x^5} + \frac{x^2}{x^5}$. Both expressions simplify to $\frac{x+1}{x^3}$.

FORMATIVE ASSESSMENT and INTERVENTION

***Diagnose Before* the Lesson**
10-5 Warm Up, TE p. 659

***Monitor During* the Lesson**
Check It Out! Exercises, SE pp. 659–662
Questioning Strategies, TE pp. 660–662

***Assess After* the Lesson**
10-5 Lesson Quiz, TE p. 665
Alternative Assessment, TE p. 665

Answers to *Think and Discuss*

Possible answers:

1. Factor the denominators. Then write each factor the greatest number of times it appears in the denominators.
2. See p. A8.

10-5 Exercises

California Standards Practice
13.0, 15.0, 25.2

go.hrw.com
Homework Help Online
KEYWORD: MA8CA 10-5
Parent Resources Online
KEYWORD: MA8CA Parent

GUIDED PRACTICE

SEE EXAMPLE 1 p. 659

Add. Simplify your answer.

1. $\frac{y}{3y^2}+\frac{5y}{3y^2}$ $\frac{2}{y}$
2. $\frac{4m+30}{m+5}+\frac{m^2+8m+5}{m+5}$ $m+7$
3. $\frac{x}{x^2-16}+\frac{4}{x^2-16}$ $\frac{1}{x-4}$

SEE EXAMPLE 2 p. 660

Subtract. Simplify your answer.

4. $\frac{7}{2x^3}-\frac{3}{2x^3}$ $\frac{2}{x^3}$
5. $\frac{7a-2}{a^2+3a+2}-\frac{5a-6}{a^2+3a+2}$ $\frac{2}{a+1}$
6. $\frac{3x^2+1}{2x+2}-\frac{2x^2-2x}{2x+2}$ $\frac{x+1}{2}$

SEE EXAMPLE 3 p. 660

Find the LCM of the given expressions.

7. $3xy^2, 6x^3yz$ $6x^3y^2z$
8. $x^2+9x+20, (x+5)(x-4)$ $(x+5)(x+4)(x-4)$
9. $y^2-16, (y+9)(y-4)$ $(y+4)(y-4)(y+9)$

SEE EXAMPLE 4 p. 661

Add or subtract. Simplify your answer.

10. $\frac{3}{c}-\frac{4}{3c}$ $\frac{5}{3c}$
11. $\frac{x^2+x}{x^2+3x+2}+\frac{3}{x+2}$ $\frac{x+3}{x+2}$
12. $\frac{2x}{x-5}+\frac{x}{5-x}$ $\frac{x}{x-5}$

SEE EXAMPLE 5 p. 662

13. **Travel** The Escobar family went on a car trip. They drove 100 miles on country roads and 240 miles on the highway. They drove 50% faster on the highway than on the country roads. Let r represent their rate on country roads in miles per hour.
    a. Write and simplify an expression that represents the number of hours it took the Escobar family to complete their trip in terms of r. (*Hint:* 50% faster means 150% of the original rate.) $\frac{260}{r}$
    b. Find their total travel time if they drove the posted speed limit. $6\frac{1}{2}$ h

PRACTICE AND PROBLEM SOLVING

Independent Practice

For Exercises	See Example
14–16	1
17–19	2
20–25	3
26–31	4
32	5

Extra Practice
Skills Practice p. EP21
Application Practice p. EP33

Add. Simplify your answer.

14. $\frac{4y}{y^3}+\frac{4y}{y^3}$ $\frac{8}{y^2}$
15. $\frac{a^2-3}{a+3}+\frac{2a}{a+3}$ $a-1$
16. $\frac{4x-13}{x^2-5x+6}+\frac{1}{x^2-5x+6}$ $\frac{4}{x-2}$

Subtract. Simplify your answer.

17. $\frac{m^2}{m-6}-\frac{6m}{m-6}$ m
18. $\frac{c+3}{4c^2-25}-\frac{-c+8}{4c^2-25}$ $\frac{1}{2c+5}$
19. $\frac{-2a^2-9a}{a-2}-\frac{-5a^2-4a+2}{a-2}$ $3a+1$

Find the LCM of the given expressions.

20. $4jk^4m, 25jm$ $100jk^4m$
21. $12a^2+4a, 27a+9$ $36a(3a+1)$
22. p^2-3p, pqr^2 $pqr^2(p-3)$
23. $5xy^2z, 10y^3$ $10xy^3z$
24. $5x^2, 7x-14$ $35x^2(x-2)$
25. $y^2+7y+10, y^2+9y+20$ $(y+5)(y+4)(y+2)$

Add or subtract. Simplify your answer.

26. $\frac{2x}{5x}+\frac{10x}{3x^2}$ $\frac{6x+50}{15x}$
27. $\frac{y^2-y}{y^2-4y+3}-\frac{2y-2}{3y-9}$
28. $\frac{-3t}{t-4}-\frac{2t+4}{4-t}$ -1
29. $\frac{z}{3z^2}+\frac{4}{7z}$ $\frac{19}{21z}$
30. $\frac{5x}{2x-6}+\frac{x+2}{3-x}$
31. $\frac{3m}{4m-8}-\frac{m^2}{m^2-4m+4}$

27. $\frac{y+2}{3(y-3)}$

10-5 Exercises

Assignment Guide

Assign *Guided Practice* exercises as necessary.

If you finished Examples **1–2**
Proficient 14–19, 34–35
Advanced 14–19, 34–35

If you finished Examples **1–5**
Proficient 14–43, 46–52, 57–68
Advanced 14–33, 43–68

Homework Quick Check
Quickly check key concepts.
Exercises: 16, 18, 22, 27, 28, 32

Number Sense In **Exercise 13,** students may write $0.50r$ for the rate of highway driving. Remind students to add 50% to 100% of the rate of the country-road driving:
$(100\%)r+(50\%)r=(150\%)r=1.5r$

Answers

30. $\frac{3x-4}{2(x-3)}$

31. $\frac{-m^2-6m}{4(m-2)^2}$

California Standards

Standard	Exercises
11.0	57–62
12.0	66–68
13.0	1–6, 10–12, 14–19, 26–31, 34–42, 45, 50, 51, 53–56
14.0	63–65
15.0	13, 32, 33, 52
25.2	43

CONCEPT CONNECTION **Exercise 46** involves subtracting rational expressions. This exercise prepares students for the Concept Connection on page 684.

Answers

40. $\dfrac{y^2+9}{4y^3}$

41. $\dfrac{8x+20}{(x+4)(x+2)}$

42. $\dfrac{2y^2+3y-3}{3(y+3)(y-3)}$

45. Possible answer: $\dfrac{3x}{x+1}+\dfrac{-2x}{x+1}$

46a. He subtracted $\frac{1}{x}$ from both sides of the equation.

b. He subtracted $\frac{1}{x}$ from $\frac{1}{12}$ by finding a common denominator $(12x)$.

53. $\dfrac{x-4y}{(x+y)(x-y)}$; $x \neq y$ and $x \neq -y$

54. $\dfrac{19m+40}{10m^2}$; $m \neq 0$

55. $\dfrac{az+by+cx}{xyz}$; $x \neq 0$, $y \neq 0$, and $z \neq 0$

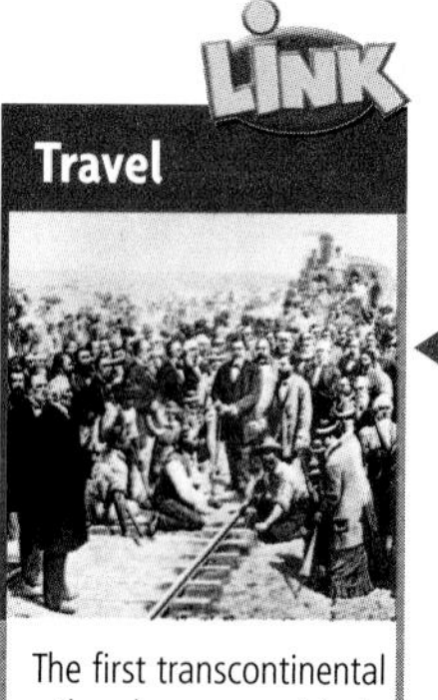

Travel

The first transcontinental railroad was completed in Utah on May 10, 1869. The occasion was commemorated with a golden spike that connected the eastern and western tracks.

32. **Fitness** Ira walks one mile from his house to the recreation center. After playing basketball, he walks home at only 85% of his normal walking speed. Let w be Ira's normal rate of walking.
 a. Write an expression to represent Ira's round-trip walking time. $\dfrac{37}{17w}$
 b. If Ira's normal rate of walking is 3 miles per hour, how long did it take for him to complete his walking? $\dfrac{37}{51}$ h, or $\approx$ 44 min

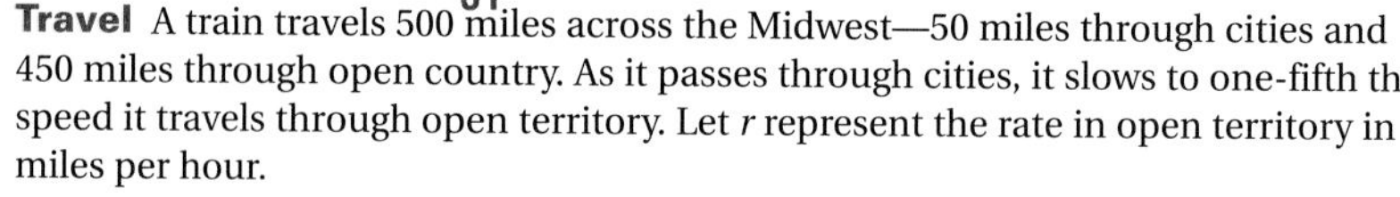

33. **Travel** A train travels 500 miles across the Midwest—50 miles through cities and 450 miles through open country. As it passes through cities, it slows to one-fifth the speed it travels through open territory. Let r represent the rate in open territory in miles per hour.
 a. Write and simplify an expression that represents the number of hours it takes the train to travel 500 miles in terms of r. $\dfrac{700}{r}$
 b. Find the total travel time if the train's rate through open territory is 50 miles per hour. **14 h**
 c. **Critical Thinking** If you knew the time it took the train to make the round-trip, how could you find its average rate? **Divide the total distance (500 mi) by the total time.**

Add or subtract. Simplify your answer.

34. $\dfrac{10}{5+y}+\dfrac{2y}{5+y}$ **2**

35. $\dfrac{7}{49-c^2}-\dfrac{c}{49-c^2}$ $\dfrac{1}{7+c}$

36. $\dfrac{6a}{a-12}+\dfrac{4}{12-a}$ $\dfrac{6a-4}{a-12}$

37. $\dfrac{b}{2b^3}+\dfrac{3}{3b^2}$ $\dfrac{3}{2b^2}$

38. $\dfrac{r^2+2r}{r+3}-\dfrac{2r+9}{r+3}$ $r-3$

39. $\dfrac{x^2-2x}{3x-15}-\dfrac{8x-25}{3x-15}$ $\dfrac{x-5}{3}$

40. $\dfrac{2y}{8y^2}+\dfrac{9}{4y^3}$

41. $\dfrac{2}{x+2}+\dfrac{6}{x+4}$

42. $\dfrac{2y}{3y-9}-\dfrac{y+1}{y^2-9}$

43. **ERROR ANALYSIS** Two students were asked to find the excluded values of the expression $\dfrac{p}{p^2-p-12}-\dfrac{4}{p^2-p-12}$. Student A identified the excluded value as $p=-3$. Student B identified the excluded values as $p=-3$ and $p=4$. Who is incorrect? What is the error?

43. Student A is incorrect. The student may have subtracted and then simplified before setting the denominator equal to 0. 4 is also an excluded value.

44. **Multi-Step** At the spring fair there is a square Velcro target as shown. A player tosses a ball, which will stick to the target in some random spot. If the ball sticks to a spot in either the small square or the circle, the player wins a prize. What is the probability that a player will win a prize, assuming the ball sticks somewhere on the target? Round your answer to the nearest hundredth. **0.46**

x 3x x 3x x

45. **Critical Thinking** Write two expressions whose sum is $\dfrac{x}{x+1}$.

46. This problem will prepare you for the Concept Connection on page 684.
Jonathan is studying light in his science class. He finds that a magnifying glass can be used to project upside-down images on a piece of paper. The equation $\frac{1}{f}=\frac{1}{x}+\frac{1}{y}$ relates the focal length of the lens f, the distance of the object from the lens x, and the distance of the image from the lens y. The focal length of Jonathan's lens is 12 cm.
 a. Jonathan wants to write y, the distance of the image from the lens, as a function of x, the distance of the object from the lens. To begin, he rewrote the equation as $\frac{1}{y}=\frac{1}{12}-\frac{1}{x}$. Explain how he did this.
 b. Explain how Jonathan simplified the equation in part **a** to $\frac{1}{y}=\frac{x-12}{12x}$.

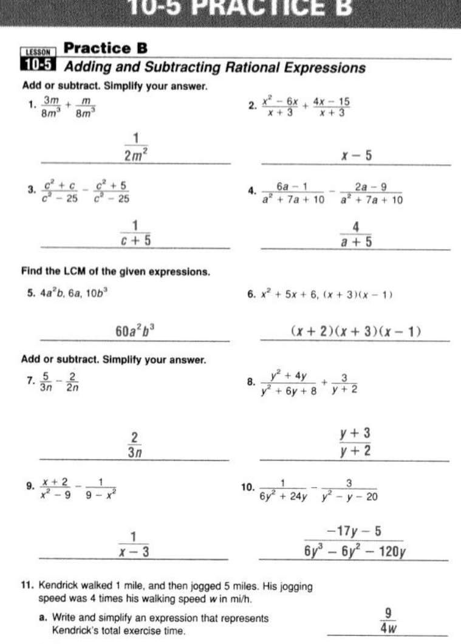

10-5 PRACTICE A

10-5 PRACTICE C

10-5 PRACTICE B

LESSON 10-5 **Practice B**
Adding and Subtracting Rational Expressions

Add or subtract. Simplify your answer.

1. $\frac{3m}{8m^3}+\frac{m}{8m^3}$ — $\frac{1}{2m^2}$
2. $\frac{x^2-6x}{x+3}+\frac{4x-15}{x+3}$ — $x-5$
3. $\frac{c^2+c}{c^2-25}-\frac{c^2+5}{c^2-25}$ — $\frac{1}{c+5}$
4. $\frac{6a-1}{a^2+7a+10}-\frac{2a-9}{a^2+7a+10}$ — $\frac{4}{a+5}$

Find the LCM of the given expressions.

5. $4a^2b$, $6a$, $10b^3$ — $60a^2b^3$
6. x^2+5x+6, $(x+3)(x-1)$ — $(x+2)(x+3)(x-1)$

Add or subtract. Simplify your answer.

7. $\frac{5}{3n}-\frac{2}{2n}$ — $\frac{2}{3n}$
8. $\frac{y^2+4y}{y^2+6y+8}+\frac{3}{y+2}$ — $\frac{y+3}{y+2}$
9. $\frac{x+2}{x^2-9}-\frac{1}{9-x^2}$ — $\frac{1}{x-3}$
10. $\frac{1}{6y^2+24y}-\frac{3}{y^2-y-20}$ — $\frac{-17y-5}{6y^3-6y^2-120y}$

11. Kendrick walked 1 mile, and then jogged 5 miles. His jogging speed was 4 times his walking speed w in mi/h.
 a. Write and simplify an expression that represents Kendrick's total exercise time. — $\frac{9}{4w}$
 b. How many minutes did Kendrick exercise if his walking speed was 3 mi/h? — 45 min

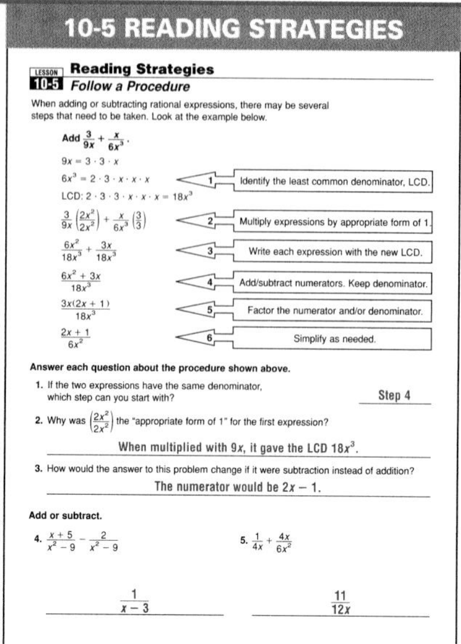

10-5 READING STRATEGIES

LESSON 10-5 **Reading Strategies**
Follow a Procedure

When adding or subtracting rational expressions, there may be several steps that need to be taken. Look at the example below.

Add $\frac{3}{9x}+\frac{x}{6x^3}$.

$9x = 3\cdot 3\cdot x$
$6x^3 = 2\cdot 3\cdot x\cdot x\cdot x$
LCD: $2\cdot 3\cdot 3\cdot x\cdot x\cdot x = 18x^3$ — 1. Identify the least common denominator, LCD.

$\frac{3}{9x}\left(\frac{2x^2}{2x^2}\right)+\frac{x}{6x^3}\left(\frac{3}{3}\right)$ — 2. Multiply expressions by appropriate form of 1.

$\frac{6x^2}{18x^3}+\frac{3x}{18x^3}$ — 3. Write each expression with the new LCD.

$\frac{6x^2+3x}{18x^3}$ — 4. Add/subtract numerators. Keep denominator.

$\frac{3x(2x+1)}{18x^3}$ — 5. Factor the numerator and/or denominator.

$\frac{2x+1}{6x^2}$ — 6. Simplify as needed.

Answer each question about the procedure shown above.

1. If the two expressions have the same denominator, which step can you start with? — Step 4
2. Why was $\left(\frac{2x^2}{2x^2}\right)$ the "appropriate form of 1" for the first expression? — When multiplied with $9x$, it gave the LCD $18x^3$.
3. How would the answer to this problem change if it were subtraction instead of addition? — The numerator would be $2x-1$.

Add or subtract.

4. $\frac{x+5}{x^2-9}-\frac{2}{x^2-9}$ — $\frac{1}{x-3}$
5. $\frac{1}{4x}+\frac{4x}{6x^2}$ — $\frac{11}{12x}$

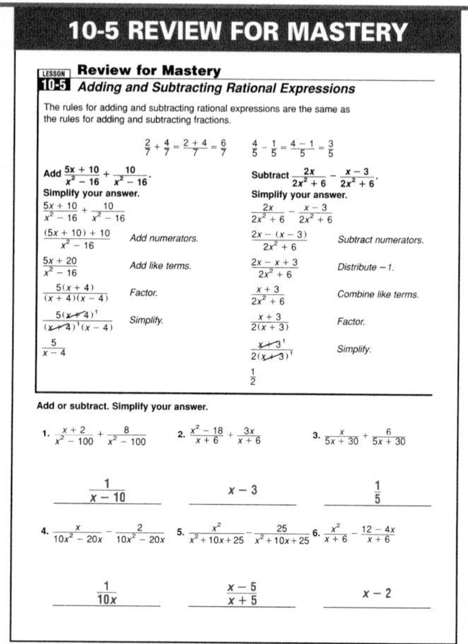

10-5 REVIEW FOR MASTERY

LESSON 10-5 **Review for Mastery**
Adding and Subtracting Rational Expressions

The rules for adding and subtracting rational expressions are the same as the rules for adding and subtracting fractions.

$\frac{2}{7}+\frac{4}{7}=\frac{2+4}{7}=\frac{6}{7}$ $\quad$ $\frac{4}{5}-\frac{1}{5}=\frac{4-1}{5}=\frac{3}{5}$

Add $\frac{5x+10}{x^2-16}+\frac{10}{x^2-16}$.
Simplify your answer.

$\frac{5x+10}{x^2-16}+\frac{10}{x^2-16}$
$\frac{(5x+10)+10}{x^2-16}$ *Add numerators.*
$\frac{5x+20}{x^2-16}$ *Add like terms.*
$\frac{5(x+4)}{(x+4)(x-4)}$ *Factor.*
$\frac{5(x+4)^1}{(x+4)^1(x-4)}$ *Simplify.*
$\frac{5}{x-4}$

Subtract $\frac{2x}{2x^2+6}-\frac{x-3}{2x^2+6}$.
Simplify your answer.

$\frac{2x}{2x^2+6}-\frac{x-3}{2x^2+6}$
$\frac{2x-(x-3)}{2x^2+6}$ *Subtract numerators.*
$\frac{2x-x+3}{2x^2+6}$ *Distribute −1.*
$\frac{x+3}{2x^2+6}$ *Combine like terms.*
$\frac{x+3}{2(x+3)}$ *Factor.*
$\frac{x+3^1}{2(x+3)^1}$ *Simplify.*
$\frac{1}{2}$

Add or subtract. Simplify your answer.

1. $\frac{x+2}{x^2-100}+\frac{8}{x^2-100}$ — $\frac{1}{x-10}$
2. $\frac{x^2-18}{x+6}+\frac{3x}{x+6}$ — $x-3$
3. $\frac{x}{5x+30}+\frac{6}{5x+30}$ — $\frac{1}{5}$
4. $\frac{x}{10x^2-20x}-\frac{2}{10x^2-20x}$ — $\frac{1}{10x}$
5. $\frac{x^2}{x^2+10x+25}-\frac{25}{x^2+10x+25}$ — $\frac{x-5}{x+5}$
6. $\frac{x^2}{x+6}-\frac{12-4x}{x+6}$ — $x-2$

47. **Critical Thinking** Identify three common denominators that could be used to add $\frac{3}{2x^2}$ to $\frac{3}{4x}$. **$4x^2$; $8x^2$; $8x^3$**

48. **Write About It** Explain how to find the least common denominator of two rational expressions when the denominators are opposite binomials.

48. In this case, either binomial can be used as the least common denominator. After selecting the binomial for the denominator, change the other binomial to match by multiplying it by −1.

Multiple Choice For Exercises 49–51, choose the best answer.

49. What is the LCD of $\frac{6}{3p+3}$ and $\frac{4}{p+1}$?

Ⓐ $p + 1$ Ⓑ 12 Ⓒ $3p + 1$ **Ⓓ** $3p + 3$

50. Simplify $\frac{4}{2x} - \frac{1}{x}$.

Ⓐ $\frac{1}{x}$ Ⓑ $\frac{3}{x}$ Ⓒ $\frac{5}{x}$ Ⓓ $\frac{3}{2x}$

51. Which of the following is equivalent to $\frac{2x}{x-2}$?

Ⓐ $\frac{x}{x+2} + \frac{x}{x-2}$ Ⓒ $\frac{x^2+4x}{x^2-4} + \frac{x}{x+2}$

Ⓑ $\frac{2x}{x^2-4} + \frac{4}{x-2}$ **Ⓓ** $\frac{x}{x+2} + \frac{x^2+6x}{x^2-4}$

52. **Extended Response** Andrea biked 3 miles to the post office and 5 miles to the library. The rate at which she biked to the library was three times faster than her rate to the post office r.

a. Write an expression that represents Andrea's total biking time in hours. Explain what each part of your expression means in the situation.

52a. $\frac{3}{r} + \frac{5}{3r}$; time to post office: $\frac{3}{r}$; time to library: $\frac{5}{3r}$

b. Simplify the expression. **$\frac{14}{3r}$**

c. How long did it take Andrea to bike the 8 miles if her biking rate to the post office was 3 miles per hour? **$\frac{14}{9}$ h or, ≈ 1 h 33 min**

CHALLENGE AND EXTEND

Add or subtract and simplify. Find the excluded values.

53. $\frac{3}{x+y} - \frac{2x+y}{x^2-y^2}$ 54. $\frac{3}{2m} + \frac{4}{m^2} + \frac{2}{5m}$ 55. $\frac{a}{xy} + \frac{b}{xz} + \frac{c}{yz}$

56. Simplify the complex fraction $\dfrac{\frac{1}{x} - \frac{1}{y}}{\frac{x}{xy} - \frac{1}{x}}$. (*Hint:* Simplify the numerator and denominator of the complex fraction first.) **−1**

SPIRAL STANDARDS REVIEW

11.0, 12.0, 14.0

Factor each polynomial. Check your answer. (Lesson 8-2)

57. $2x^2 - 5 - 13x + 4x^2$ 58. $6a + 2a^3 - 2 - 10a^2$ 59. $15h + 5h^2 - 20h - 60$ **$5(h+3)(h-4)$**

60. $12s^3 + 8s^2$ **$4s^2(3s+2)$** 61. $56t^3 - 14t^2 - 42t$ **$14t(4t+3)(t-1)$** 62. $-10 + 2m^2 + m^3 - 5m$ **$(m^2-5)(m+2)$**

Solve each quadratic equation by factoring. Check your answer. (Lesson 9-5)

63. $d^2 - 4d - 12 = 0$ **−2, 6** 64. $2g^2 - 9g = -4$ **$\frac{1}{2}$, 4** 65. $9x^2 + 6x + 1 = 0$ **$-\frac{1}{3}$**

Simplify each rational expression, if possible. Identify any excluded values. (Lesson 10-3)

66. $\frac{2t^2-8}{t^2-4}$ **2; $t \neq \pm 2$** 67. $\frac{n^2+5n}{n^2+3n-10}$ 68. $\frac{4-x}{x^2-16}$ **$-\frac{1}{x+4}$; $x \neq \pm 4$**

67. $\frac{n}{n-2}$; −5, 2

Teaching Tip **Multiple Choice** Students who chose **C** for **Exercise 49** may have identified 3 and $p + 1$ as factors but forgot to distribute when multiplying.

Students who chose **B** for **Exercise 50** may have either added the expressions or subtracted both the numerator and the denominator.

Answers

57. $(2x - 5)(3x + 1)$

58. $2(a^3 - 5a^2 + 3a - 1)$

Journal

Have students explain how to find the LCM of $6x^2y$ and $9x$.

ALTERNATIVE ASSESSMENT

Have students select and answer one addition or subtraction problem with unlike denominators from the exercises. Tell them to show and explain each step as if teaching it to someone for the first time.

Power Presentations with PowerPoint®

10-5 Lesson Quiz

Add or subtract. Simplify your answer.

1. $\frac{3h}{h^2} + \frac{2h}{h^2}$ $\frac{5}{h}$

2. $\frac{x+4}{x^2} - \frac{2x+4}{x^2}$ $-\frac{1}{x}$

3. $\frac{5}{2fh^3} + \frac{g}{f^2h}$ $\frac{5f+2gh^2}{2f^2h^3}$

4. $\frac{7}{h-5} - \frac{4}{5-h}$ $\frac{11}{h-5}$

5. $\frac{5x-30}{x^2-13x+42} + \frac{11}{x^2-6x-7}$ $\frac{5x+16}{x^2-6x-7}$

6. Vong drove 98 miles on interstate highways and 80 miles on state roads. He drove 25% faster on the interstate highways than on the state roads. Let r represent his rate on the state roads in miles per hour.

a. Write and simplify an expression that represents the number of hours Vong drove in terms of r. $\frac{198}{1.25r}$

b. Find Vong's driving time if he averaged 55 miles per hour on the state roads. about 2 h 53 min

Also available on transparency

10-5 PROBLEM SOLVING

LESSON 10-5 Problem Solving
Adding and Subtracting Rational Expressions

Adib is kayaking on the Peconic River in Long Island, New York. He paddles his kayak at an average rate of 3 mi/h, but does not know the rate of the river's current. Adib plans to kayak upstream 2 mi and then back downstream to his starting point.

1. Let x represent the rate of the current in the Peconic River in miles per hour. Write and simplify an expression for the total time of Adib's round trip. **$\frac{12}{(3-x)(3+x)}$**

2. If the rate of the river's current is 2 mi/h, how long will it take Adib to kayak round trip? **$\frac{12}{5}$ h, or 2.4 h, or 2 h 24 min**

3. If the rate of the river's current is 3 mi/h, how long will it take Adib to kayak round trip? Explain what your answer could mean in this context. **$\frac{12}{0}$ = undefined; because the rate of the current is equal to Adib's rate of paddling, he remains stationary and is never able to kayak upstream.**

Select the best answer.

4. Terry drives 2 mi on city streets, and 20 mi on the highway. Her speed on the highway is three times her speed on the city streets r, in miles per hour. Write and simplify and expression that represents the length of Terry's trip in hours.

A $\frac{13}{3r}$ **Ⓒ** $\frac{26}{3r}$
B $\frac{22}{4r}$ D $\frac{62}{3r}$

5. Nahuel walks 1 km to school at a rate of w km/h. When he gets to school, he realizes that he forgot his math book, so he jogs back home and back to school at a rate 4 km/h faster than his walking rate. Write and simplify an expression that represents the length of Nahuel's entire trip to school in hours.

F $\frac{3}{2w}$ H $\frac{2(w+1)}{w(w+2)}$
G $\frac{3}{2(w+2)}$ **Ⓙ** $\frac{3w+4}{w(w+4)}$

6. A test consists of 4 free response questions and 50 multiple choice questions. The test's writers assume an average student can do x free response questions per hour, and four times as many multiple choice questions per hour. If an average student can do 6 free response questions per hour, how long is the test?

A $1\frac{4}{5}$ h C $3\frac{3}{8}$ h
Ⓑ $2\frac{3}{4}$ h D $5\frac{2}{3}$ h

7. In a carnival game, Beth runs 100 m to a table, picks up water balloons, and runs back to the starting line. Beth originally runs to the table at a rate of y m/s, but runs 1 m/s slower when she carries the balloons. If Beth originally runs 5 m/s, how long, to the nearest second, does it take her to finish?

F 10 s H 37 s
G 22 s **Ⓙ** 45 s

10-5 CHALLENGE

LESSON 10-5 Challenge
Average Speed

At 8 A.M., Mr. Varhalla drives from home to work. Because of rush-hour traffic, he is only able to drive 40 mi/h.

At 3 P.M. he leaves work early to drive back home. Because he avoids rush-hour traffic, he is able to drive the same distance at 65 mi/h.

1. Let d represent the distance in miles between home and work. What is the total distance of Mr. Varhalla's round trip? **$2d$**

2. Write an expression for the time in hours that it takes Mr. Varhalla to drive from home to work. **$\frac{d}{40}$**

3. Write an expression for the time in hours that it takes him to drive from work back home. **$\frac{d}{65}$**

4. Write (but don't simplify) an addition expression for the total time in hours of Mr. Varhalla's round trip. **$\frac{d}{40} + \frac{d}{65}$**

5. Because $d = rt$, you can find average speed for the entire round trip by dividing the total distance by the total time, or $r = \frac{d}{t}$. Write a complex fraction that represents Mr. Varhalla's average speed in miles per hour. **$\dfrac{2d}{\frac{d}{40} + \frac{d}{65}}$**

6. Simplify the complex fraction to find Mr. Varhalla's average speed in miles per hour. Round to the nearest tenth. **≈49.5 mi/h**

7. Is the average speed for the round trip the same as the average of the speeds 40 mi/h and 65 mi/h? **No; the average of 40 mi/h and 65 mi/h is $\frac{40+65}{2}$ = 52.5 mi/h.**

Use what you have learned in questions 1–7 to solve these problems. For each, first write a complex fraction that represents average speed and then simplify it to find the average speed. Round your answers to the nearest tenth.

8. Teri drives 30 mi/h from home to the hardware store. After loading her truck with lumber, she drives 15 mi/h back home. What is Teri's average speed in miles per hour for the entire round trip? **20 mi/h**

9. Kevin runs four laps around Piedmont Park at 10 mi/h. Then, to cool down, he walks one more lap at 3 mi/h. What is Kevin's average speed for the entire workout? (*Hint:* Let d represent the distance of one lap.) **6.8 mi/h**

Organizer

Use with Lesson 10-6

Objective: Use algebra tiles to model polynomial division.

Materials: algebra tiles

Online Edition

Teach

Discuss

Students need to add zero pairs to their polynomial model when the required tiles for filling the rectangle are not available.

Close

Key Concept

After modeling the polynomial and placing tiles for the length, the width can be found by completing the rectangle and reading the width.

Assessment

Journal Have students choose one expression from the Try This exercises and explain in detail how to find the quotient by using algebra tiles.

Algebra 1 10.0

10-6

Use with Lesson 10-6

Model Polynomial Division

Some polynomial divisions can be modeled by algebra tiles. If a polynomial can be modeled by a rectangle, then its factors are represented by the length and width of the rectangle. If one factor is a divisor, then the other factor is a quotient.

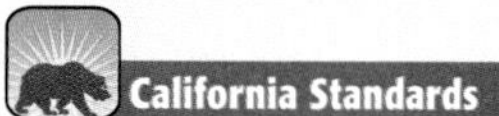

10.0 Students add, subtract, multiply, and **divide** monomials and **polynomials.** Students solve multistep problems, including word problems, by using these techniques.

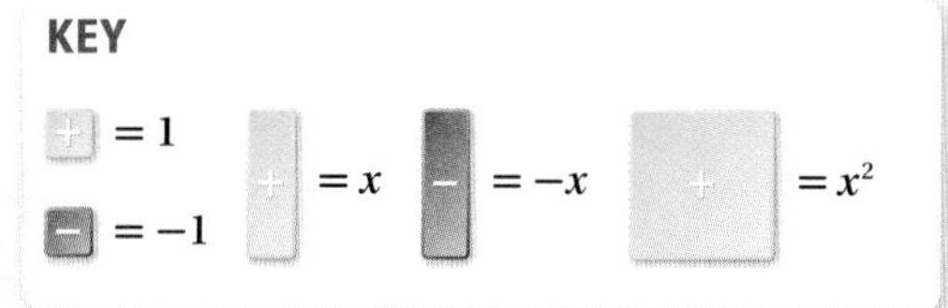

Activity 1

Use algebra tiles to find the quotient $(x^2 + 5x + 6) \div (x + 2)$.

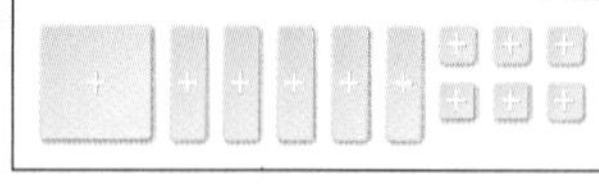

Model $x^2 + 5x + 6$.

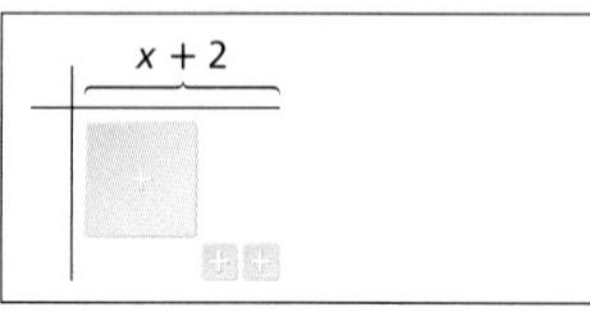

Try to form a rectangle with a length of $x + 2$.

Place the x^2-tile in the upper-left corner. Then place two unit tiles in a row at the lower-right corner.

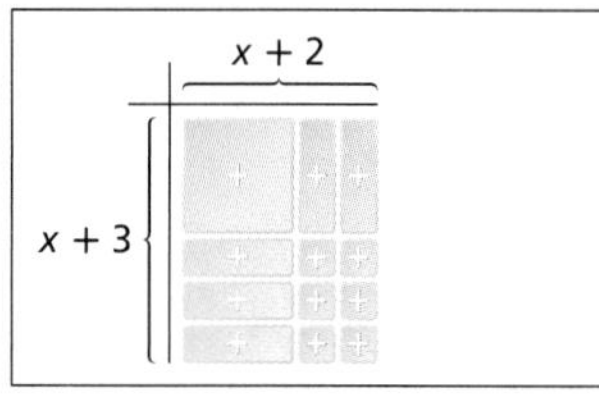

Try to use all the remaining tiles to complete a rectangle.

If you can complete a rectangle, then the width of the rectangle is the quotient.

The rectangle has length $x + 2$ and width $x + 3$. So, $(x^2 + 5x + 6) \div (x + 2) = x + 3$.

You can check your answer by multiplying.	$(x + 3)(x + 2)$ $x^2 + 2x + 3x + 6$ $x^2 + 5x + 6$ ✓	*Use the FOIL method.*

Try This

Use algebra tiles to find each quotient.

1. $(x^2 + 5x + 4) \div (x + 1)$ **$x + 4$**
2. $(x^2 + 7x + 10) \div (x + 5)$ **$x + 2$**
3. $(x^2 + 4x - 5) \div (x - 1)$ **$x + 5$**
4. $(2x^2 + 5x + 2) \div (x + 2)$ **$2x + 1$**
5. $(x^2 - 6x + 8) \div (x - 2)$ **$x - 4$**
6. $(2x^2 - x - 3) \div (x + 1)$ **$2x - 3$**
7. Describe what happens when you try to model $(x^2 - 4x + 3) \div (x + 1)$.

Answer to *Try This*

7. There is no arrangement of tiles that will form a rectangle with a side length of $x + 1$ because $x + 1$ is not a factor of $x^2 - 4x + 3$.

10-6 Dividing Polynomials

California Standards

10.0 Students add, subtract, multiply, and **divide** monomials and **polynomials.** Students solve multistep problems, including word problems, by using these techniques.
12.0 Students simplify fractions with polynomials in the numerator and denominator by factoring both and reducing them to the lowest terms.

Why learn this?
Division of polynomials can be used to compare the energy produced by solar panels.

The electrical power (in watts) produced by a solar panel is directly proportional to the surface area of the solar panel. Division of polynomials can be used to compare energy production by solar panels of different sizes.

To divide a polynomial by a monomial, you can first write the division as a rational expression. Then divide each term in the polynomial by the monomial.

EXAMPLE 1 Dividing a Polynomial by a Monomial

Divide $(6x^3 + 8x^2 - 4x) \div 2x$.

$\frac{6x^3 + 8x^2 - 4x}{2x}$ *Write as a rational expression.*

$\frac{6x^3}{2x} + \frac{8x^2}{2x} - \frac{4x}{2x}$ *Divide each term in the polynomial by the monomial 2x.*

$\frac{\cancel{6}^3 \cancel{x^3}^{x^2}}{\cancel{2x}} + \frac{\cancel{8}^4 \cancel{x^2}^{x}}{\cancel{2x}} - \frac{\cancel{4}^2 \cancel{x}}{\cancel{2x}}$ *Divide out common factors in each term.*

$3x^2 + 4x - 2$ *Simplify.*

CHECK IT OUT! Divide. Check your answer.

1a. $(8p^3 - 4p^2 + 12p) \div (-4p^2)$ $\quad -2p + 1 - \frac{3}{p}$

1b. $(6x^3 + 2x - 15) \div 6x$ $\quad x^2 + \frac{1}{3} - \frac{5}{2x}$

Division of a polynomial by a binomial is similar to division of whole numbers.

Know it! Note — Dividing Polynomials

	WORDS	NUMBERS	POLYNOMIALS
Step 1	Factor the numerator and/or denominator if possible.	$\frac{168}{3} = \frac{56 \cdot 3}{3}$	$\frac{r^2 + 3r + 2}{r + 2} = \frac{(r + 2)(r + 1)}{(r + 2)}$
Step 2	Divide out any common factors.	$\frac{56 \cdot \cancel{3}}{\cancel{3}}$	$\frac{\cancel{(r + 2)}(r + 1)}{\cancel{(r + 2)}}$
Step 3	Simplify.	56	$r + 1$

10-6 Organizer

Objective: Divide a polynomial by a monomial or binomial.

Online Edition Tutorial Videos

Countdown to Mastery Week 24

Power Presentations with PowerPoint®

Warm Up

Divide.

1. $m^2n \div mn^4$ $\quad \frac{m}{n^3}$

2. $2x^3y^2 \div 6xy$ $\quad \frac{x^2y}{3}$

3. $(3a + 6a^2) \div 3a^2b$ $\quad \frac{1 + 2a}{ab}$

Factor each expression.

4. $5x^2 + 16x + 12$ $\quad (5x + 6)(x + 2)$

5. $16p^2 - 72p + 81$ $\quad (4p - 9)^2$

Also available on transparency

Math Humor

Q: What do math teachers train their parrots to say?

A: Polly want to factor?

1 Introduce

EXPLORATION

10-6 Dividing Polynomials

Recall that multiplication and division are inverse operations. If you know that $ab = c$, you can also write $\frac{c}{a} = b$, where $a \neq 0$.

1. Multiply to show that $4x(3x^2 - 2x + 5) = 12x^3 - 8x^2 + 20x$.
2. Based on the equation in Problem 1, complete the following: $\frac{12x^3 - 8x^2 + 20x}{4x} =$ ___?___
3. Use this idea to help you complete the table. In each row, first multiply to find the product of the polynomials. Then write a related quotient.

Product	Related Quotient
$2y(y^2 + 3y - 1) =$ ___?___	$\frac{?}{2y} =$ ___?___
$4m^2(m^2 + 2m + 9) =$ ___?___	$\frac{?}{4m^2} =$ ___?___
$3c(c^3 - c^2 - 2) =$ ___?___	$\frac{?}{3c} =$ ___?___

THINK AND DISCUSS

4. **Describe** a rule for dividing a polynomial by a monomial.
5. **Show** how you can use your rule to find the quotient $\frac{x^3 + x^2 + x}{x}$.

Motivate

Have students solve $14\overline{)186{,}509}$ using long division. 13,322 R 1, or $13{,}322\frac{1}{14}$

Ask how they can check their answer. Multiply 13,322 by 14 and add 1.

Tell students they will learn to use long division to divide polynomials.

Explorations and answers are provided in *Alternate Openers: Explorations Transparencies.*

California Standards

10.0, 12.0

Power Presentations with PowerPoint®

Additional Examples

Example 1

Divide $(5x^3 - 20x^2 + 30x) \div 5x$.
$x^2 - 4x + 6$

Example 2

Divide. Check your answer.

A. $\dfrac{x^2 + 2x - 15}{x - 3}$ $x + 5$

B. $\dfrac{2x^2 - 7x - 4}{x^2 - x - 12}$ $\dfrac{2x + 1}{x + 3}$

Also available on transparency

INTERVENTION
Questioning Strategies

EXAMPLE 1

- How are common factors divided out?

EXAMPLE 2

- Why would writing each term of the numerator over the denominator not be a good first step in this type of problem?
- Why should you factor the numerator?

EXAMPLE 2 Dividing a Polynomial by a Binomial

Helpful Hint

Put each term of the numerator over the denominator only when the denominator is a monomial. If the denominator is a polynomial, try to factor first.

Divide.

A $\dfrac{c^2 + 4c - 5}{c - 1}$

$\dfrac{(c + 5)(c - 1)}{c - 1}$ *Factor the numerator.*

$\dfrac{(c + 5)\cancel{(c - 1)}}{\cancel{(c - 1)}}$ *Divide out common factors.*

$c + 5$ *Simplify.*

B $\dfrac{3x^2 - 10x - 8}{4 - x}$

$\dfrac{(3x + 2)(x - 4)}{4 - x}$ *Factor the numerator.*

$\dfrac{(3x + 2)(x - 4)}{-1(x - 4)}$ *Factor one opposite binomial.*

$\dfrac{(3x + 2)\cancel{(x - 4)}}{-1\cancel{(x - 4)}}$ *Divide out common factors.*

$-3x - 2$ *Simplify.*

CHECK IT OUT! Divide. Check your answer.

2a. $\dfrac{10 + 7k + k^2}{k + 2}$ $k + 5$ **2b.** $\dfrac{b^2 - 49}{b + 7}$ $b - 7$ **2c.** $\dfrac{s^2 + 12s + 36}{s + 6}$ $s + 6$

Recall how you used long division to divide whole numbers as shown at right. You can also use long division to divide polynomials. An example is shown below.

$$\begin{array}{r} 15 \\ 23\overline{)345} \\ \underline{-23} \\ 115 \\ \underline{-115} \\ 0 \end{array}$$

$$(x^2 + 3x + 2) \div (x + 2)$$

Divisor — Quotient — Dividend

$$\begin{array}{r} x + 1 \\ x + 2\overline{)x^2 + 3x + 2} \\ \underline{x^2 + 2x} \\ x + 2 \\ \underline{x + 2} \\ 0 \end{array}$$

Using Long Division to Divide a Polynomial by a Binomial	
Step 1	Write the binomial and polynomial in standard form.
Step 2	Divide the first term of the dividend by the first term of the divisor. This is the first term of the quotient.
Step 3	Multiply this first term of the quotient by the binomial divisor and place the product under the dividend, aligning like terms.
Step 4	Subtract the product from the dividend.
Step 5	Bring down the next term in the dividend.
Step 6	Repeat Steps 2–5 as necessary until you get 0 or until the degree of the remainder is less than the degree of the binomial.

2 Teach

Guided Instruction

Review the process of long division with numbers. Also review the standard form of a polynomial: terms are written in order from highest to lowest degree. Stress the importance of writing polynomials in standard form and using a zero as a placeholder for a missing term, when necessary.

Universal Access

Through Visual Cues

Some students may have more success with their long division by using centimeter grid paper to help align like terms. Show students how to put each term and operation symbol of the long division problem into a separate box of the grid paper. For example:

x	+	3	$2x^2$	+	$9x$	+	14

EXAMPLE 3 Polynomial Long Division

Divide using long division. Check your answer.

A $(x^2 + 2 + 3x) \div (x + 2)$

Step 1 $x + 2\overline{)x^2 + 3x + 2}$ — *Write in long division form with expressions in standard form.*

Step 2
$$\begin{array}{r} x \\ x + 2\overline{)x^2 + 3x + 2} \end{array}$$
Divide the first term of the dividend by the first term of the divisor to get the first term of the quotient.

Step 3
$$\begin{array}{r} x \\ x + 2\overline{)x^2 + 3x + 2} \\ x^2 + 2x \end{array}$$
Multiply the first term of the quotient by the binomial divisor. Place the product under the dividend, aligning like terms.

Step 4
$$\begin{array}{r} x \\ x + 2\overline{)x^2 + 3x + 2} \\ -(x^2 + 2x) \\ 0 + x \end{array}$$
Subtract the product from the dividend.

Step 5
$$\begin{array}{r} x \\ x + 2\overline{)x^2 + 3x + 2} \\ -(x^2 + 2x)\downarrow \\ x + 2 \end{array}$$
Bring down the next term in the dividend.

Step 6
$$\begin{array}{r} x + 1 \\ x + 2\overline{)x^2 + 3x + 2} \\ -(x^2 + 2x) \\ x + 2 \\ -(x + 2) \\ 0 \end{array}$$
Repeat Steps 2–5 as necessary.
The remainder is 0.

Check Multiply the answer and the divisor.
$(x + 2)(x + 1)$
$x^2 + x + 2x + 2$
$x^2 + 3x + 2$ ✓

B $\dfrac{x^2 + 4x + 3}{x + 1}$

$x + 1\overline{)x^2 + 4x + 3}$ — *Write in long division form.*

$$\begin{array}{r} x + 3 \\ x + 1\overline{)x^2 + 4x + 3} \\ -(x^2 + x)\downarrow \\ 3x + 3 \\ -(3x + 3) \\ 0 \end{array}$$

$x^2 \div x = x$
Multiply $x \cdot (x + 1)$. Subtract.
Bring down the 3. $3x \div x = 3$
Multiply $3(x + 1)$. Subtract.
The remainder is 0.

Check Multiply the answer and the divisor.
$(x + 1)(x + 3)$
$x^2 + 3x + 1x + 3$
$x^2 + 4x + 3$ ✓

Helpful Hint

When the remainder is 0, you can check your simplified answer by multiplying it by the divisor. You should get the numerator.

Divide using long division. Check your answer.

3a. $(2y^2 - 5y - 3) \div (y - 3)$ **$2y + 1$**

3b. $(a^2 - 8a + 12) \div (a - 6)$ **$a - 2$**

COMMON ERROR ALERT

In Step 3 of **Example 3A,** students might multiply the first term of the quotient only by the first term of the divisor. Remind students to use the Distributive Property in this step.

Inclusion In Step 4 of **Example 3A,** subtracting the product can be thought of as adding the opposite of the product. Tell students to change the sign of each term and then add.

Power Presentations with PowerPoint®

Additional Examples

Example 3

Divide using long division. Check your answer.

A. $(x^2 + 10x + 21) \div (x + 3)$
$(x + 7)$

B. $\dfrac{x^2 - 2x - 8}{x - 4}$ $x + 2$

Also available on transparency

INTERVENTION

Questioning Strategies

EXAMPLE 3

- What does it mean to divide by a binomial?
- When would you choose long division instead of factoring and dividing out? Why?

Math Connections Introduce long division of polynomials by having students work some numerical problems that require long division. Then show how polynomial long division parallels this process.

Critical Thinking Show students how to check their answers for long division with remainders by multiplying the divisor by each term of the quotient. For example:

$(3x^2 + 11x + 16) \div (x + 2) = 3x + 5 + \dfrac{6}{x + 2}$

Check: $(x + 2)\left(3x + 5 + \dfrac{6}{x + 2}\right)$

$= 3x(x + 2) + 5(x + 2) + \left(\dfrac{6}{x + 2}\right)(x + 2)$

$= 3x^2 + 6x + 5x + 10 + 6 = 3x^2 + 11x + 16$

Power Presentations with PowerPoint®

Additional Examples

Example 4

Divide $(3x^2 + 19x + 26) \div (x + 5)$.

$3x + 4 + \frac{6}{x + 5}$

Example 5

Divide $(x^3 - 7 - 4x) \div (x - 3)$.

$x^2 + 3x + 5 + \frac{8}{x - 5}$

Also available on transparency

INTERVENTION

Questioning Strategies

EXAMPLE 4

- What does having a remainder mean?
- Is it possible to check the answer when the answer contains a remainder? Explain.

EXAMPLE 5

- When dividing polynomials, in what form should the dividend be written?
- How is a placeholder created when dividing polynomials?

Sometimes the divisor is not a factor of the dividend, so the remainder is not 0. Then the remainder can be written as a rational expression.

EXAMPLE 4 Long Division with a Remainder

Divide $(2x^2 + 3x - 6) \div (x - 2)$.

$x - 2\overline{)2x^2 + 3x - 6}$	*Write in long division form.*
$2x + 7$ over $x - 2\overline{)2x^2 + 3x - 6}$	*$2x^2 \div x = 2x$*
$-(2x^2 - 4x)$	*Multiply $2x(x - 2)$. Subtract.*
$7x - 6$	*Bring down the -6. $7x \div x = 7$*
$-(7x - 14)$	*Multiply $7(x - 2)$. Subtract.*
8	*The remainder is 8.*
$\frac{8}{x - 2}$	*Write the remainder as a rational expression using the divisor as the denominator.*
$2x + 7 + \frac{8}{x - 2}$	*Write the quotient with the remainder.*

Divide.

4a. $(3m^2 + 4m - 2) \div (m + 3)$ $3m - 5 + \frac{13}{m + 3}$

4b. $(y^2 + 3y + 2) \div (y - 3)$ $y + 6 + \frac{20}{y - 3}$

Sometimes you need to write a placeholder for a term using a zero coefficient. This is best seen if you write the polynomials in standard form.

EXAMPLE 5 Dividing Polynomials That Have a Zero Coefficient

Divide $(3x - 4x^3 - 15) \div (2x + 3)$.

$(-4x^3 + 3x - 15) \div (2x + 3)$	*Write the polynomials in standard form.*
$2x + 3\overline{)-4x^3 + 0x^2 + 3x - 15}$	*Write in long division form. Use $0x^2$ as a placeholder for the x^2 term.*
$-2x^2 + 3x - 3$ over $2x + 3\overline{)-4x^3 + 0x^2 + 3x - 15}$	*$-4x^3 \div 2x = -2x^2$*
$-(-4x^3 - 6x^2)$	*Multiply $-2x^2(2x + 3)$. Subtract.*
$6x^2 + 3x$	*Bring down $3x$. $6x^2 \div 2x = 3x$*
$-(6x^2 + 9x)$	*Multiply $3x(2x + 3)$. Subtract.*
$-6x - 15$	*Bring down -15. $-6x \div 2x = -3$*
$-(-6x - 9)$	*Multiply $-3(2x + 3)$. Subtract.*
-6	*The remainder is -6.*

$$(3x - 4x^3 - 15) \div (2x + 3) = -2x^2 + 3x - 3 + \frac{-6}{2x + 3}.$$

Remember!

Recall from Chapter 7 that a polynomial in one variable is written in standard form when the degrees of the terms go from greatest to least.

Divide.

5a. $(1 - 4x^2 + x^3) \div (x - 2)$ $x^2 - 2x - 4 + \frac{-7}{x - 2}$

5b. $(4p - 1 + 2p^3) \div (p + 1)$ $2p^2 - 2p + 6 + \frac{-7}{p + 1}$

3 Close

Summarize

Tell students that long division always results in the correct answer, but for sake of time, they should try to factor the polynomials first and see whether any factors divide out. When using long division, remind students to write the dividend in standard form, using a placeholder with a coefficient of zero for any missing terms. Also remind students that in Step 4 *(subtract the product from the dividend)* they must change the sign of each term in the product.

FORMATIVE ASSESSMENT and INTERVENTION

***Diagnose Before* the Lesson**
10-6 Warm Up, TE p. 667

***Monitor During* the Lesson**
Check It Out! Exercises, SE pp. 667–670
Questioning Strategies, TE pp. 668–670

***Assess After* the Lesson**
10-6 Lesson Quiz, TE p. 673
Alternative Assessment, TE p. 673

THINK AND DISCUSS

1. When dividing a polynomial by a binomial, what does it mean when the remainder is 0?
2. Suppose that the final answer to a polynomial division problem is $x - 5 + \frac{3}{x+2}$. Find an excluded value. Justify your answer.

3. **GET ORGANIZED** Copy and complete the graphic organizer. In each box, show an example.

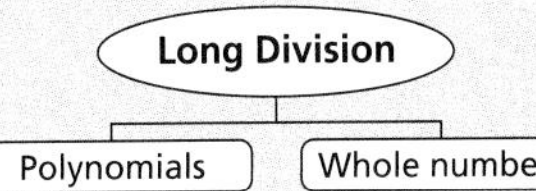

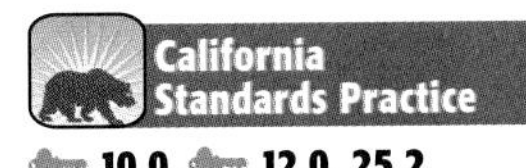

Answers to *Think and Discuss*

Possible answers:

1. It means the binomial is a factor of the polynomial.
2. $x \neq -2$; the denominator of the remainder cannot equal zero.
3. See p. A8.

10-6 Exercises

California Standards Practice
10.0, 12.0, 25.2

go.hrw.com
Homework Help Online
KEYWORD: MA8CA 10-6
Parent Resources Online
KEYWORD: MA8CA Parent

GUIDED PRACTICE

SEE EXAMPLE 1 p. 667

Divide. Check your answer.

1. $(4x^2 - x) \div 2x$
2. $(16a^4 - 4a^3) \div 4a$
3. $(21b^2 - 14b + 24) \div 3b$
4. $(18r^2 - 12r + 6) \div -6r$
5. $(6x^3 + 12x^2 + 9x) \div 3x^2$
6. $(5m^4 + 15m^2 - 10) \div 5m^3$

SEE EXAMPLE 2 p. 668

7. $\frac{2x^2 - x - 3}{x + 1}$ **$2x - 3$**
8. $\frac{a^2 - a - 12}{a - 4}$ **$a + 3$**
9. $\frac{6y^2 + 11y - 10}{3y - 2}$ **$2y + 5$**
10. $\frac{t^2 - 6t + 8}{t - 4}$ **$t - 2$**
11. $\frac{x^2 + 16x + 15}{x + 15}$ **$x + 1$**
12. $\frac{p^2 - p - 20}{p + 4}$ **$p - 5$**

SEE EXAMPLE 3 p. 669

Divide using long division. Check your answer.

13. $(c^2 + 7c + 12) \div (c + 4)$ **$c + 3$**
14. $(3s^2 - 12s - 15) \div (s - 5)$ **$3s + 3$**
15. $\frac{x^2 + 5x - 14}{x + 7}$ **$x - 2$**
16. $\frac{x^2 + 4x - 12}{x - 2}$ **$x + 6$**

SEE EXAMPLE 4 p. 670

17. $(a^2 + 4a + 3) \div (a + 2)$
18. $(2r^2 + 11r + 5) \div (r - 3)$
19. $(n^2 + 8n + 15) \div (n + 4)$
20. $(2t^2 - t + 4) \div (t - 1)$
21. $(8n^2 - 6n - 7) \div (2n + 1)$
22. $(b^2 - b + 1) \div (b + 2)$

SEE EXAMPLE 5 p. 670

23. $(3x - 2x^3 - 10) \div (3 + x)$
24. $(3p^3 - 2p^2 - 4) \div (p - 2)$
25. $(m^2 + 2) \div (m - 1)$
26. $(3x^2 + 4x^3 - 5) \div (5 + x)$
27. $(4k^3 - 2k - 8) \div (k + 1)$
28. $(j^3 + 6j + 2) \div (j + 4)$

PRACTICE AND PROBLEM SOLVING

Divide. Check your answer.

29. $(9t^3 + 12t^2 - 6t) \div 3t^2$
30. $(5n^3 - 10n + 15) \div (-5n)$
31. $(-16p^4 + 4p^3 + 8) \div 4p^3$
32. $\frac{4r^2 - 9r + 2}{r - 2}$ **$4r - 1$**
33. $\frac{8t^2 + 2t - 3}{2t - 1}$ **$4t + 3$**
34. $\frac{3g^2 + 7g - 6}{g + 3}$ **$3g - 2$**

10-6 Exercises

Assignment Guide

Assign *Guided Practice* exercises as necessary.

If you finished Examples **1–2**
Proficient 29–34, 46, 48
Advanced 29–34, 46, 48

If you finished Examples **1–5**
Proficient 29–62, 67–71
Advanced 29–45, 49–71

Homework Quick Check
Quickly check key concepts.
Exercises: 30, 32, 38, 40, 44

Answers

1. $2x - \frac{1}{2}$
2. $4a^3 - a^2$
3. $7b - \frac{14}{3} + \frac{8}{b}$
4. $-3r + 2 - \frac{1}{r}$
5. $2x + 4 + \frac{3}{x}$
6. $m + \frac{3}{m} - \frac{2}{m^3}$

Answers

17. $a + 2 + \frac{-1}{a + 2}$
18. $2r + 17 + \frac{56}{r - 3}$
19. $n + 4 + \frac{-1}{n + 4}$
20. $2t + 1 + \frac{5}{t - 1}$
21. $4n - 5 + \frac{-2}{2n + 1}$
22. $b - 3 + \frac{7}{b + 2}$
23. $-2x^2 + 6x - 15 + \frac{35}{x + 3}$
24. $3p^2 + 4p + 8 + \frac{12}{p - 2}$
25. $m + 1 + \frac{3}{m - 1}$
26. $4x^2 - 17x + 85 + \frac{-430}{x + 5}$
27. $4k^2 - 4k + 2 + \frac{-10}{k + 1}$
28. $j^2 - 4j + 22 + \frac{-86}{j + 4}$
29. $3t + 4 - \frac{2}{t}$
30. $-n^2 + 2 - \frac{3}{n}$
31. $-4p + 1 + \frac{2}{p^3}$

California Standards

Standard	Exercises
3.0	68
5.0	67
10.0	1–6, 13–31, 35–44, 51, 55, 58–66
12.0	7–12, 32–34, 50, 56, 57
13.0	69–71
25.2	52

CONCEPT CONNECTION Exercise 53 involves writing and graphing a rational function. This exercise prepares students for the Concept Connection on page 684.

Answers

39. $3x + 4 + \frac{14}{x - 2}$

40. $2m + 3 + \frac{5}{m + 1}$

41. $3x + 1 + \frac{-2}{2x - 1}$

42. $m^2 + 5m + 23 + \frac{200}{2m - 10}$

43. $2t^2 - 6t + 25 + \frac{-216}{3t + 9}$

44. $p^3 + 3p^2 + 2p + 7 + \frac{22}{p - 3}$

49a. The values of y are negative and decreasing.

b. The values of y are positive and decreasing.

53b.

X	Y1
11	-132
12	ERROR
13	156
14	84
15	60
16	48
17	40.8

Y1=12X/(X−12)

Independent Practice	
For Exercises	See Example
29–31	1
32–34	2
35–38	3
39–41	4
42–44	5

Extra Practice
Skills Practice p. EP21
Application Practice p. EP33

Divide using long division. Check your answer.

35. $(x^2 - 5x + 6) \div (x - 2)$ **$x - 3$**
36. $(2m^2 + 8m + 8) \div (m + 2)$ **$2m + 4$**
37. $(6a^2 + 7a - 3) \div (2a + 3)$ **$3a - 1$**
38. $(3x^2 - 10x - 8) \div (x - 4)$ **$3x + 2$**
39. $(3x^2 - 2x + 6) \div (x - 2)$
40. $(2m^2 + 5m + 8) \div (m + 1)$
41. $(6x^2 - x - 3) \div (2x - 1)$
42. $(2m^3 - 4m - 30) \div (2m - 10)$
43. $(6t^3 + 21t + 9) \div (3t + 9)$
44. $(p^4 - 7p^2 + p + 1) \div (p - 3)$

45. **Multi-Step** Find the value of n so that $x - 4$ is a factor of $x^2 + x + n$. **-20**

Geometry The area of each of three rectangles is $(2x^2 - 3x - 2)$ cm². Below are the different widths of the rectangles. Find each corresponding length.

46. $x - 2$ **$2x + 1$**
47. $x + 1$ **$2x - 5 + \frac{3}{x + 1}$**
48. $2x + 1$ **$x - 2$**

49. **Graphing Calculator** Use the table of values for $f(x) = \frac{(x^2 + 3x + 4)}{x - 5}$ to answer the following.

a. Describe what is happening to the values of y as x increases from 2 to 4.

b. Describe what is happening to the values of y as x increases from 6 to 8.

c. Explain why there is no value in the y column when x is 5. **The function is not defined at $x = 5$.**

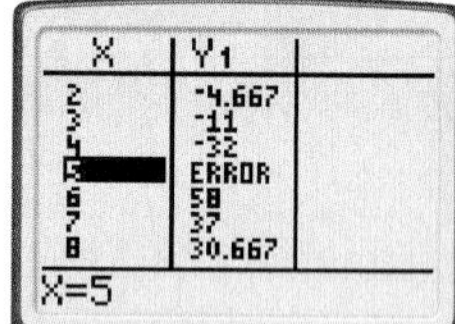

X	Y1
2	-4.667
3	-11
4	-32
5	ERROR
6	58
7	37
8	30.667

X=5

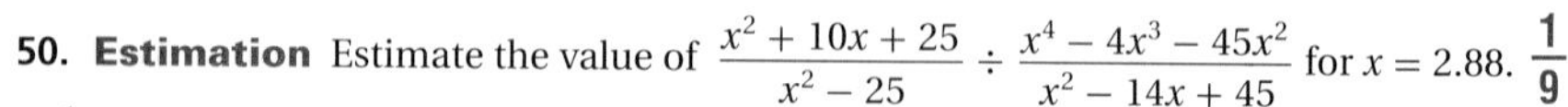

50. **Estimation** Estimate the value of $\frac{x^2 + 10x + 25}{x^2 - 25} \div \frac{x^4 - 4x^3 - 45x^2}{x^2 - 14x + 45}$ for $x = 2.88$. **$\frac{1}{9}$**

51. **Solar Energy** The greater the area of a solar panel, the greater the number of watts of energy produced. The area of two solar panels A and B, in square meters, can be represented by $A = m^2 + 3m + 2$ and $B = 2m + 2$. Divide the polynomials to find an expression that represents the ratio of the area of A to the area of B. **$0.5m + 1$**

California LINK

Solar Energy

High school students can compete in the Dell-Winston School Solar Car Challenge, in which teams of participants design, build, and race cars powered by solar energy. The team above is from Walnut High School in Walnut, CA. The name of their car is "QuikSolar."

52. **///ERROR ANALYSIS///** Two students attempted to divide $\frac{4x^2 - 6x + 12}{-2x}$. Which is incorrect? Explain the error.

Student B is incorrect. The second term should be positive.

A

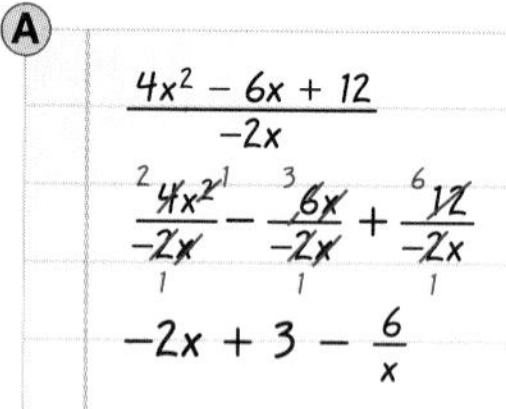

$\frac{4x^2 - 6x + 12}{-2x}$

$-2x + 3 - \frac{6}{x}$

B

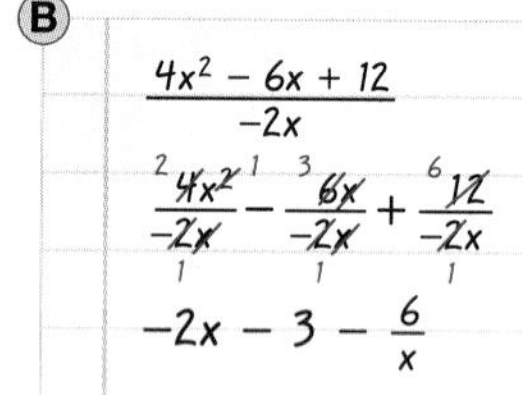

$\frac{4x^2 - 6x + 12}{-2x}$

$-2x - 3 - \frac{6}{x}$

CONCEPT CONNECTION

53. This problem will prepare you for the Concept Connection on page 684. Jonathan continues to study lenses and uses the equation $\frac{1}{y} = \frac{x - 12}{12x}$.

a. Jonathan wants to write y, the distance of the image from the lens, as a function of x, the distance of the object from the lens. What is the equation solved for y? **$y = \frac{12x}{x - 12}$**

b. Use a graphing calculator to create a table of values for the function $y(x)$. For which value of x is the function undefined? **The function is undefined at $x = 12$.**

10-6 PRACTICE A

10-6 PRACTICE C

10-6 PRACTICE B

LESSON 10-6 **Practice B**
Dividing Polynomials

Divide.

1. $(15c^3 + 3c^2) \div 3c$ **$5c^2 + c$**
2. $(20b^4 - 12b + 4) \div 4b$ **$5b^3 - 3 + \frac{1}{b}$**
3. $(27q^6 - 3q^3 + 18) \div 9q^5$ **$3q - \frac{1}{3q^2} + \frac{2}{q^5}$**
4. $(15t^4 - 30t^2 + 6) \div 15t^3$ **$t - \frac{2}{t} + \frac{2}{5t^3}$**
5. $(d^2 - 4d - 77) \div (d - 11)$ **$d + 7$**
6. $(x^2 - 12x + 27) \div (x - 3)$ **$x - 9$**
7 $(9p^2 + 6p + 1) \div (3p + 1)$ **$3p + 1$**
8. $(4b^2 + b - 3) \div (b + 1)$ **$4b - 3$**

Divide using long division.

9. $\frac{m^2 + 4m - 12}{m + 6}$ **$m - 2$**
10. $(12y^2 + 31y + 14) \div (y + 2)$ **$12y + 7$**
11. $(t^2 + t - 6) \div (t - 1)$ **$t + 2 + \frac{-4}{t - 1}$**
12. $(3p^3 + 4p - 6) \div (p + 2)$ **$3p^2 - 6p + 16 + \frac{-38}{p + 2}$**

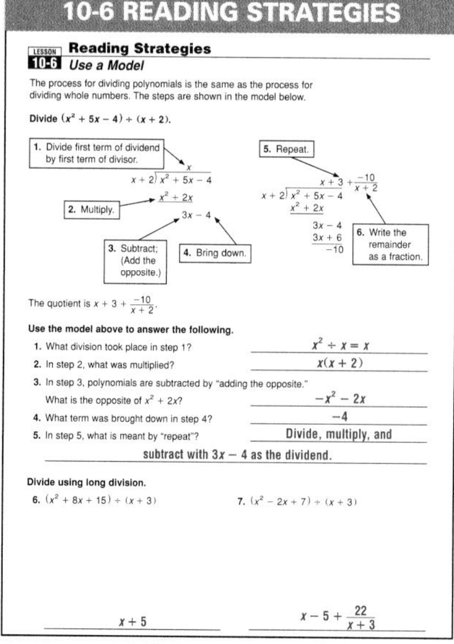

10-6 READING STRATEGIES

LESSON 10-6 **Reading Strategies**
Use a Model

The process for dividing polynomials is the same as the process for dividing whole numbers. The steps are shown in the model below.

Divide $(x^2 + 5x - 4) \div (x + 2)$.

1. Divide first term of dividend by first term of divisor.
2. Multiply.
3. Subtract; (Add the opposite.)
4. Bring down.
5. Repeat.
6. Write the remainder as a fraction.

The quotient is $x + 3 + \frac{-10}{x + 2}$.

Use the model above to answer the following.

1. What division took place in step 1? **$x^2 \div x = x$**
2. In step 2, what was multiplied? **$x(x + 2)$**
3. In step 3, polynomials are subtracted by "adding the opposite." What is the opposite of $x^2 + 2x$? **$-x^2 - 2x$**
4. What term was brought down in step 4? **-4**
5. In step 5, what is meant by "repeat"? **Divide, multiply, and subtract with $3x - 4$ as the dividend.**

Divide using long division.

6. $(x^2 + 8x + 15) \div (x + 3)$ **$x + 5$**
7. $(x^2 - 2x + 7) \div (x + 3)$ **$x - 5 + \frac{22}{x + 3}$**

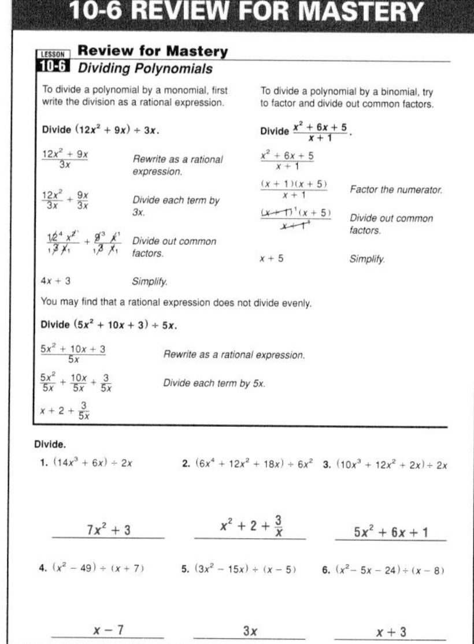

10-6 REVIEW FOR MASTERY

LESSON 10-6 **Review for Mastery**
Dividing Polynomials

To divide a polynomial by a monomial, first write the division as a rational expression.

Divide $(12x^2 + 9x) \div 3x$.

$\frac{12x^2 + 9x}{3x}$ *Rewrite as a rational expression.*

$\frac{12x^2}{3x} + \frac{9x}{3x}$ *Divide each term by 3x.*

Divide out common factors.

$4x + 3$ *Simplify.*

To divide a polynomial by a binomial, try to factor and divide out common factors.

Divide $\frac{x^2 + 6x + 5}{x + 1}$.

$\frac{x^2 + 6x + 5}{x + 1}$

$\frac{(x + 1)(x + 5)}{x + 1}$ *Factor the numerator.*

Divide out common factors.

$x + 5$ *Simplify.*

You may find that a rational expression does not divide evenly.

Divide $(5x^2 + 10x + 3) \div 5x$.

$\frac{5x^2 + 10x + 3}{5x}$ *Rewrite as a rational expression.*

$\frac{5x^2}{5x} + \frac{10x}{5x} + \frac{3}{5x}$ *Divide each term by 5x.*

$x + 2 + \frac{3}{5x}$

Divide.

1. $(14x^3 + 6x) \div 2x$ **$7x^2 + 3$**
2. $(6x^4 + 12x^2 + 18x) \div 6x^2$ **$x^2 + 2 + \frac{3}{x}$**
3. $(10x^3 + 12x^2 + 2x) \div 2x$ **$5x^2 + 6x + 1$**
4. $(x^2 - 49) \div (x + 7)$ **$x - 7$**
5. $(3x^2 - 15x) \div (x - 5)$ **$3x$**
6. $(x^2 - 5x - 24) \div (x - 8)$ **$x + 3$**

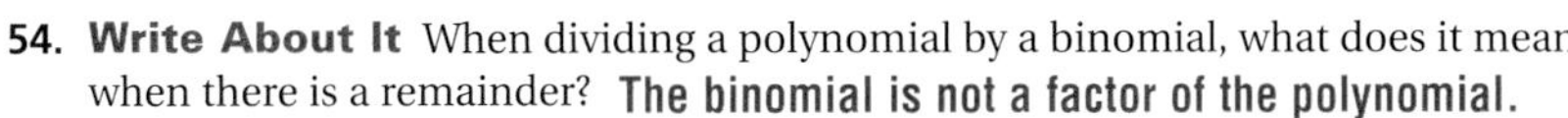

54. **Write About It** When dividing a polynomial by a binomial, what does it mean when there is a remainder? **The binomial is not a factor of the polynomial.**

55. **Critical Thinking** Divide $2x + 3\overline{)2x^2 + 7x + 6}$. Find a value for each expression by substituting 10 for x in the original problem. Repeat the division. Compare the results of each division. **Possible answer: $x + 2$; $276 \div 23 = 12$; when $x = 10$, $x + 2 = 12$, so the results are equal.**

56. **Write About It** Is $3x + 2$ a factor of $3x^2 + 14x + 8$? Explain.

56. Yes; there is no remainder when you divide $3x^2 + 14x + 8$ by $3x + 2$, so $3x + 2$ must be a factor of $3x^2 + 14x + 8$.

Multiple Choice For Exercises 57–60, choose the best answer.

57. Which expression has an excluded value of $-\frac{1}{2}$?

Ⓐ $\frac{4x^2 - 2x - 2}{4x - 2}$ Ⓑ $\frac{4x^2 - 2x - 2}{2x - 4}$ **Ⓒ** $\frac{4x^2 - 2x - 2}{4x + 2}$ Ⓓ $\frac{4x^2 - 2x - 2}{2x + 4}$

58. Find $(x^2 - 1) \div (x + 2)$.

Ⓐ $x - 2 + \frac{-5}{x + 2}$ **Ⓑ** $x - 2 + \frac{3}{x + 2}$ Ⓒ $x + 2 + \frac{-5}{x - 2}$ Ⓓ $x + 2 + \frac{3}{x - 2}$

59. Which expression is a factor of $x^2 - 4x - 5$?

Ⓐ $x - 1$ **Ⓑ** $x + 1$ Ⓒ $x - 4$ Ⓓ $x + 5$

60. Which of the following expressions is equivalent to $(x^3 + 2x^2 + 3x + 1) \div (x - 1)$?

Ⓐ $x^2 + 3x + 6 + \frac{7}{x - 1}$ Ⓒ $x^2 + 3x + 6 + \frac{-5}{x - 1}$

Ⓑ $x^2 + x + 2 + \frac{-1}{x - 1}$ Ⓓ $x^2 + x + 2 + \frac{3}{x - 1}$

CHALLENGE AND EXTEND

Divide. Simplify your answer.

61. $(6x^3y - x^2 + 4xy^2) \div (2x^2y)$ **$3x - \frac{1}{2y} + \frac{2y}{x}$**

62. $(x^3 - 1) \div (x - 1)$ **$x^2 + x + 1$**

63. $(x^3 + 2x^2 - x - 2) \div (x^2 - 1)$ **$x + 2$**

64. $(x^3 + 8) \div (x + 2)$ **$x^2 - 2x + 4$**

65. **Geometry** The base of a triangle is $(2x + 4)$ m and the area is $(2x^2 + 5x + 2)$ m². How much longer is the base than the height? **3 m**

66. **Geometry** The formula for finding the volume of a cylinder is $V = BH$, where B is the area of the base of the cylinder and H is the height.

a. Find the height of the cylinder given that $V = \pi(x^3 + 4x^2 + 5x + 2)$ and $B = \pi(x^2 + 2x + 1)$. **$x + 2$**

b. Find an expression for the radius of the base. **$x + 1$**

SPIRAL STANDARDS REVIEW

67. Billy and James are collecting guitar picks. James has 38 picks and adds 2 to his collection every week. Billy starts with 2 picks and collects 14 picks a week. Write and solve an equation to find the number of weeks it will take Billy to accumulate the same number of picks as James. *(Lesson 2-4)* **$38 + 2w = 2 + 14w$; 3 weeks**

68. Jane is shopping for a new phone. She wants to spend $130 on the phone, but she is willing to pay within $25 of her ideal price. Write and solve an absolute-value equation to find the maximum and minimum prices Jane is willing to pay. *(Lesson 2-7)* **$|x - 130| = 25$; $105; $155**

Multiply. Simplify your answer. *(Lesson 10-4)*

69. $(x^2 + 4x + 3) \cdot \frac{8}{2(x + 3)}$ **$4(x + 1)$**

70. $\frac{9xy^2}{2x^3} \cdot \frac{8y}{3x^4}$ **$\frac{12y^3}{x^6}$**

71. $\frac{2k^2 + 4k^3}{k + 1} \cdot \frac{k^2 + 3k + 2}{2k^2}$ **$2k^2 + 5k + 2$**

Teaching Tip

Multiple Choice Remind students that in **Exercise 57,** an excluded value occurs when the denominator equals zero. Because the excluded value is negative, the possible choices are **C** and **D;** the denominators involve addition, and subtraction is the inverse operation.

In long division, a remainder is written over the divisor. Therefore, choices **C** and **D** in **Exercise 58** can be eliminated.

Journal

Have students explain the difference between dividing by a monomial and dividing by a binomial. Have them give an example of each.

ALTERNATIVE ASSESSMENT

Have students divide $(2x^2 + 5x + 3) \div (x + 1)$ by factoring and then by long division.

Power Presentations with PowerPoint®

10-6 Lesson Quiz

Divide.

1. $(12x^2 - 4x^2 + 20x) \div 4x$ $3x^2 - x + 5$

2. $\frac{2x^2 - 7x - 15}{x - 5}$ $2x + 3$

3. $\frac{x^2 + 3x - 10}{x + 5}$ $x - 2$

4. $\frac{x^2 - 6x - 27}{x - 9}$ $x + 3$

Divide using long division.

5. $(x^2 + 4x + 7) \div (x + 1)$ $x + 3 + \frac{4}{x + 1}$

6. $(8x^2 + 2x^3 + 7) \div (x + 3)$ $2x^2 + 2x - 6 + \frac{25}{x + 3}$

Also available on transparency

10-6 PROBLEM SOLVING

LESSON 10-6 **Problem Solving**
Dividing Polynomials

Write the correct answer.

1. The area of a rectangle is $x^2 + 2x - 8$ m², and the width is $x - 2$ m. Find the length. **$x + 4$ m**

2. On the dartboard below, the area of the outside ring is the difference between the area of the two largest circles, or $\pi(x + 4)^2 - \pi(x + 2)^2$ in². The area of the bull's-eye is πx^2 in². Expand and divide $[\pi(x + 4)^2 - \pi(x + 2)^2] \div \pi x^2$ to find the ratio of the area of the outside ring to the bull's-eye.

x in. 2 in. 2 in.

$\frac{4}{x} + \frac{12}{x^2}$

3. The area of a rectangular piece of paper is $4n^2 - 4n - 9$ cm². Then a triangle with area $2n + 6$ cm² is cut from one corner of the paper. What is the ratio of the area of the paper that remains to the area of the triangle that was removed? (*Hint:* First subtract to find the area of the paper that remains.) **$2n - 9 + \frac{39}{2n + 6}$**

Select the best answer.

4. The area of a triangle is $8a^2 - 10a$ ft², and the height is $4a$ ft. Find the base. (*Hint:* Solve $A = \frac{1}{2}bh$ for b.)

A $a - \frac{5a}{4}$ ft C $4a - \frac{5a}{2}$ ft

B $2a - \frac{5a}{2}$ ft **Ⓓ** $4a - 5$ ft

5. The volume of a rectangular prism is $2x^3 + 9x^2 - 11x - 30$ cm³, and the height is $x + 5$ cm. Find the area of the base. ($V = BH$, where B is the area of the base and H is the height.)

Ⓕ $2x^2 - x - 6$ cm²

G $2x^2 - x - 16 + \frac{-110}{x + 5}$ cm²

H $2x^2 + 4x - 16 + \frac{-35}{x + 5}$ cm²

J $2x^2 + 19x + 84 + \frac{390}{x + 5}$ cm²

6. The volume of a cylinder is $V = \pi r^2 h$, where r is the radius and h is the height. The volume of a certain cylinder is $\pi(n^3 - 6n^2 - 36n + 216)$ in³, and the radius is $n - 6$ in. Find the height. (*Hint:* To divide by r^2, divide by r twice.)

A n in. **Ⓒ** $n + 6$ in.

B $n - 6$ in. D $n^2 - 36$ in.

10-6 CHALLENGE

LESSON 10-6 **Challenge**
The Remainder Theorem

For 1–5, use the polynomial $P(x) = 2x^2 + 3x - 5$.

1. Use long division to divide $P(x) \div (x - 2)$.
   a. What value do you get for the remainder? **9**
   b. Now evaluate $P(2)$. What value do you get? **9**
2. Use long division to divide $P(x) \div (x - 1)$.
   a. What value do you get for the remainder? **0**
   b. Now evaluate $P(1)$. What value do you get? **0**
3. Use long division to divide $P(x) \div x$.
   a. What value do you get for the remainder? **−5**
   b. Now evaluate $P(0)$. What value do you get? **−5**
4. Use long division to divide $P(x) \div (x + 1)$.
   a. What value do you get for the remainder? **−6**
   b. Now evaluate $P(-1)$. What value do you get? **−6**
5. Use long division to divide $P(x) \div (x + 2)$.
   a. What value do you get for the remainder? **−3**
   b. Now evaluate $P(-2)$. What value do you get? **−3**
6. Look for a pattern in your results and complete this theorem.

   Polynomial Remainder Theorem: If a polynomial $P(x)$ is divided by $(x - r)$, then the remainder is a constant given by **$P(r)$**.
7. Your results in question 2 are unique. What do they tell you about the binomial $(x - 1)$?
   Because the remainder is zero, $(x - 1)$ is a factor of $2x^2 + 3x - 5$: $(x - 1)(2x + 5)$.
8. Given $Q(x) = 6x^4 - 31x^3 - 49x^2 + 104x + 60$, explain how you could determine whether a binomial of the form $(x - r)$ is a factor of $Q(x)$ without doing long division.
   Evaluate $Q(r)$; if $Q(r) = 0$, then the binomial $(x - r)$ is a factor.
9. a. Is $(x - 1)$ a factor of $Q(x)$? Justify.
   No; $Q(1) = 6(1)^4 - 31(1)^3 - 49(1)^2 + 104(1) + 60 = 90 \neq 0$

   b. Is $(x + 2)$ a factor of $Q(x)$? Justify.
   Yes; $Q(-2) = 6(-2)^4 - 31(-2)^3 - 49(-2)^2 + 104(-2) + 60 = 0$

10-7 Organizer

Objectives: Solve rational equations.

Identify extraneous solutions.

Online Edition
Tutorial Videos

Countdown to Mastery Week 24

Power Presentations with PowerPoint®

Warm Up

1. Find the LCM of x, $2x^2$, and 6. $6x^2$
2. Find the LCM of $p^2 - 4p$ and $p^2 - 16$. $p(p-4)(p+4)$

Multiply. Simplify your answer.

3. $\frac{5x}{3y} \cdot \frac{2x^2}{7}$ $\frac{10x^3}{21y}$
4. $(x^2 - 9) \cdot \frac{4}{x+3}$ $4x - 12$
5. $\frac{x^2 - x - 30}{x - 1} \cdot \frac{x^2 - 1}{4x^2 - 20x - 24}$ $\frac{x+5}{4}$

Also available on transparency

Math Humor

Q: How do you know when a math teacher is insane?

A: The teacher can no longer solve rational equations.

California Standards

Preparation for 15.0

10-7 Solving Rational Equations

California Standards

Preparation for 15.0 Students apply algebraic techniques to solve rate problems, work problems, and percent mixture problems.

Vocabulary
rational equation
extraneous solution

Who uses this?
Athletes can use rational equations to determine how to improve their statistics. (See Exercise 44.)

A **rational equation** is an equation that contains one or more rational expressions. If a rational equation is a proportion, it can be solved using the Cross Product Property.

EXAMPLE 1 Solving Rational Equations by Using Cross Products

Solve $\frac{3}{t-3} = \frac{2}{t}$. Check your answer.

$\frac{3}{t-3} = \frac{2}{t}$ *Use cross products.*

$3t = (t-3)(2)$

$3t = 2t - 6$ *Distribute 2 on the right side.*

$t = -6$ *Subtract 2t from both sides.*

Check $\frac{3}{t-3} = \frac{2}{t}$ *Substitute −6 for t in the original equation.*

$\frac{3}{-6-3}$	$\frac{2}{-6}$
$\frac{3}{-9}$	$\frac{2}{-6}$
$-\frac{1}{3}$	$-\frac{1}{3}$ ✓

CHECK IT OUT! Solve. Check your answer.

1a. $\frac{1}{n} = \frac{3}{n+4}$ 2 **1b.** $\frac{4}{h+1} = \frac{2}{h}$ 1 **1c.** $\frac{21}{x-7} = \frac{3}{x}$ $-\frac{7}{6}$

Some rational equations contain sums or differences of rational expressions. To solve these, you must find a common denominator for all the rational expressions in the equation.

EXAMPLE 2 Solving Rational Equations by Using the LCD

Solve $\frac{1}{c} + \frac{3}{2c} = \frac{2}{c+1}$. Check your answer.

Step 1 Find the LCD.

$2c(c+1)$ *Include every factor of the denominators.*

Step 2 Multiply both sides by the LCD.

$$2c(c+1)\left(\frac{1}{c} + \frac{3}{2c}\right) = 2c(c+1)\left(\frac{2}{c+1}\right)$$

$$2c(c+1)\left(\frac{1}{c}\right) + 2c(c+1)\left(\frac{3}{2c}\right) = 2c(c+1)\left(\frac{2}{c+1}\right)$$ *Distribute on the left side.*

1 Introduce

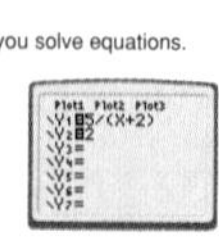

EXPLORATION

10-7 Solving Rational Equations

You can use a graphing calculator to help you solve equations.

To solve the equation $\frac{5}{x+2} = 2$, enter each side of the equation into your calculator as a separate function.

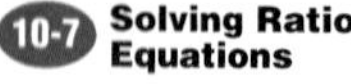

Graph the functions in the standard decimal window by pressing ZOOM, selecting **6:ZStandard**, pressing ZOOM again, and selecting **4:ZDecimal**.

1. Find the intersection of the graphs by pressing TRACE and using the arrow keys to move to the point of intersection. What is the x-value of the point of intersection?
2. Use substitution to verify that this value of x is a solution.
3. Use the same method to solve the equation $\frac{2}{x-1} = x$.

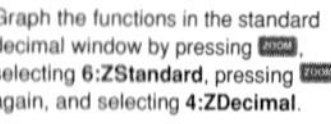

THINK AND DISCUSS

4. **Describe** how the solution of $\frac{2}{x-1} = x$ differs from the solution of $\frac{5}{x+2} = 2$.
5. **Explain** how you could solve $\frac{2}{x-1} = x$ using a table of values.

Motivate

Have students use cross products to solve the following proportion:

$\frac{x}{4} = \frac{12}{8}$ 6

Tell students that in this lesson they will learn to use cross products to solve rational equations that are proportions.

Explorations and answers are provided in *Alternate Openers: Explorations Transparencies.*

Step 3 Simplify and solve.

$$2\cancel{c}(c+1)\left(\frac{1}{\cancel{c}}\right) + \cancel{2c}(c+1)\left(\frac{3}{\cancel{2c}}\right) = 2c\cancel{(c+1)}\left(\frac{2}{\cancel{c+1}}\right)$$ *Divide out common factors in each term.*

$2(c+1) + (c+1)3 = (2c)2$ *Simplify.*

$2c + 2 + 3c + 3 = 4c$ *Distribute and multiply.*

$5c + 5 = 4c$ *Combine like terms.*

$c + 5 = 0$ *Subtract 4c from both sides.*

$c = -5$ *Subtract 5 from both sides.*

Check

$\frac{1}{c} + \frac{3}{2c}$	$= \frac{2}{c+1}$
$\frac{1}{-5} + \frac{3}{2(-5)}$	$\frac{2}{-5+1}$
$\frac{2}{-10} + \frac{3}{-10}$	$\frac{2}{-4}$
$-\frac{5}{10}$ or $-\frac{1}{2}$	$-\frac{1}{2}$ ✓

Solve each equation. Check your answer.

2a. $\frac{2}{a+1} + \frac{1}{a+1} = \frac{4}{a}$ **−4** **2b.** $\frac{6}{j+2} - \frac{10}{j} = \frac{4}{2j}$ **−4**

When you multiply each side of an equation by the LCD, you may get an *extraneous solution*. An **extraneous solution** is a solution to a resulting equation that is not a solution to the original equation. Because of extraneous solutions, it is especially important to check your answers.

EXAMPLE 3 Extraneous Solutions

Solve $\frac{x-9}{x^2-9} = \frac{-3}{x-3}$. Check your answer.

$(x-9)(x-3) = -3(x^2-9)$ *Use cross products.*

$x^2 - 12x + 27 = -3x^2 + 27$ *Multiply the left side. Distribute −3 on the right side.*

$4x^2 - 12x + 27 = 27$ *Add $3x^2$ to both sides.*

$4x^2 - 12x = 0$ *Subtract 27 from both sides.*

$4x(x-3) = 0$ *Factor the quadratic expression.*

$4x = 0$ or $x - 3 = 0$ *Use the Zero Product Property.*

$x = 0$ or $x = 3$ *Solve for x.*

Check

$\frac{x-9}{x^2-9}$	$= \frac{-3}{x-3}$
$\frac{0-9}{0^2-9}$	$\frac{-3}{0-3}$
$\frac{-9}{-9}$	$\frac{-3}{-3}$
1	1 ✓

$\frac{x-9}{x^2-9}$	$= \frac{-3}{x-3}$
$\frac{3-9}{3^2-9}$	$\frac{-3}{3-3}$
$\frac{-6}{0}$	$\frac{-3}{0}$

Because both $\frac{-6}{0}$ and $\frac{-3}{0}$ are undefined, 3 is not a solution.

3 is an extraneous solution. The only solution is 0.

Solve. Check your answer.

3a. $\frac{3}{x-7} = \frac{x-2}{x-7}$ **5** **3b.** $\frac{x+1}{x-2} = \frac{4}{x-3}$ **1, 5** **3c.** $\frac{9}{x^2+2x} = \frac{6}{x^2}$ **4**

COMMON ERROR ALERT

After multiplying both sides of an equation by the LCD, students might think they should still have something in the denominator. Remind students that correctly multiplying by the LCD eliminates the denominators.

Power Presentations with PowerPoint®

Additional Examples

Example 1

Solve $\frac{5}{x-2} = \frac{3}{x}$. Check your answer. −3

Example 2

Solve each equation. Check your answer.

A. $\frac{2}{x+1} + \frac{3}{x} = \frac{5}{2x}$. $-\frac{1}{5}$

B. $\frac{4}{x} - \frac{3}{x^2} = 1$. 3; 1

Example 3

Solve $\frac{2}{x+1} = \frac{x-6}{x^2-1}$. Check your answer. −4; −1 is extraneous.

Also available on transparency

INTERVENTION

Questioning Strategies

EXAMPLES **1–2**

- When can you use cross products to solve a rational equation?
- What is the purpose of multiplying both sides by the LCD?

EXAMPLE **3**

- How are the extraneous solutions related to the denominators in the equation?
- Are excluded values always extraneous solutions?

Language Support Explain that sometimes *extra* is good, like extra credit, but in math, the *extra* in *extraneous* refers to something that is not valid or that is irrelevant and not wanted. English Language Learners

2 Teach

Guided Instruction

Review finding the LCM of rational expressions. Although **Example 1** can be solved by multiplying both sides of the equation by the LCD, as in **Example 2,** it is easier to solve most proportions by using cross products. Point out that the "working together" problems can apply to either people or machines that are working together to complete a task. They can also be stated with any unit of time (seconds, minutes, hours, etc.). Emphasize the importance of checking solutions to rule out extraneous solutions.

Universal Access

Through Modeling

Obtain two containers with different-sized pouring spouts and one bowl so that students can create their own "working together" experiment. Fill each container with water (or sand) and have students write and solve the equation for the amount of time it takes to fill the bowl using both containers simultaneously. Have students "check" their answer by filling the bowl using both containers simultaneously.

Answers to *Think and Discuss*

Possible answers:

1. Some solutions may be extraneous and make the expressions undefined.
2. 3 and −3
3. Because the denominators are the same, the expressions would be equal only when $x = 4$. Since 4 is an excluded value, there is no solution.
4. See p. A9.

THINK AND DISCUSS

1. Why is it important to check your answers to rational equations?
2. For what values of x are the rational expressions in the equation $\frac{x}{x-3} = \frac{2}{x+3}$ undefined?
3. Explain why some rational equations, such as $\frac{x}{x-4} = \frac{4}{x-4}$, have no solutions.

4. **GET ORGANIZED** Copy and complete the graphic organizer. In each box, write the solution and check.

Solving Rational Equations

Solve by using cross products.	Solve by using the LCD.
$\frac{3}{x} = \frac{2}{x+1}$	$\frac{7}{x-1} - \frac{4}{x-1} = \frac{6}{x}$

10-7 Exercises

Assignment Guide

Assign *Guided Practice* exercises as necessary.

If you finished Examples **1–2**
Proficient 24–35, 44
Advanced 24–35, 44

If you finished Examples **1–4**
Proficient 24–43, 45–51, 55–62
Advanced 24–43, 45–62

Homework Quick Check
Quickly check key concepts.
Exercises: 26, 30, 34, 40

Inclusion Remind students that the right side of the equation in **Exercise 8** can be written as $\frac{3}{1}$. The equation can then be solved using cross products.

10-7 Exercises

Preparation for 15.0; 25.1

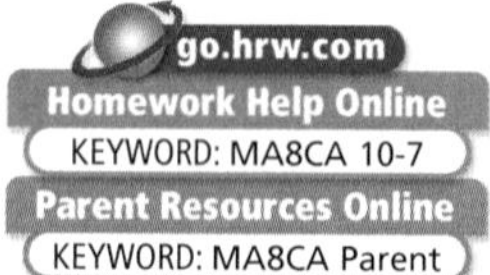

GUIDED PRACTICE

Vocabulary Apply the vocabulary from this lesson to answer each question.

1. A(n) ___?___ contains one or more rational expressions. (*extraneous solution* or *rational equation*) **rational equation**
2. A(n) ___?___ is a solution to a resulting equation that is not a solution to the original equation. (*extraneous solution* or *rational equation*) **extraneous solution**

Solve. Check your answer.

SEE EXAMPLE 1 p. 674

3. $\frac{3}{x+4} = \frac{2}{x}$ **8**
4. $\frac{5}{s-6} = \frac{4}{s}$ **−24**
5. $\frac{20}{p+100} = \frac{-10}{2p}$ **−20**
6. $\frac{4}{j} = \frac{1}{j+2}$ $-\frac{8}{3}$
7. $\frac{3}{x-4} = \frac{9}{x-2}$ **5**
8. $\frac{6}{2x-1} = 3$ $\frac{3}{2}$

SEE EXAMPLE 2 p. 674

9. $\frac{6}{x} - \frac{5}{x} = \frac{1}{3}$ **3**
10. $\frac{a}{9} + \frac{1}{3} = \frac{2}{5}$ $\frac{3}{5}$
11. $\frac{3}{x+1} = \frac{2}{x} + \frac{3}{x}$ $-\frac{5}{2}$
12. $\frac{8}{d} = \frac{1}{d+2} - \frac{3}{d}$ $-\frac{11}{5}$
13. $\frac{3}{s-6} = \frac{4}{s} + \frac{1}{2s}$ **18**
14. $\frac{7}{r} + \frac{2}{r-1} = \frac{-1}{2r}$ $\frac{15}{19}$
15. $\frac{3}{a-4} = \frac{a}{a-2}$ **1, 6**
16. $\frac{r}{2} - \frac{2}{r} = \frac{5}{6}$ **3,** $-\frac{4}{3}$
17. $\frac{6}{n} = \frac{7}{n^2} - 1$ **−7, 1**
18. $\frac{4}{x+1} = x - 2$ **−2, 3**
19. $\frac{5}{a^2} = \frac{-4}{a} + 1$ **−1, 5**
20. $\frac{1}{p} = \frac{-3}{p^2} + 2$ **−1,** $\frac{3}{2}$

SEE EXAMPLE 3 p. 675

Solve. Check your answer.

21. $\frac{3}{c-4} = \frac{c-1}{c-4}$ ∅
22. $\frac{w+3}{w^2-1} - \frac{2w}{w-1} = 1$
23. $\frac{3x-7}{x-5} + \frac{x}{2} = \frac{8}{x-5}$

22. $-\frac{4}{3}$; 1 is extraneous.
23. −6; 5 is extraneous.

3 Close

Summarize

Tell students that if a rational equation is a proportion, they can solve the equation by using cross products. Otherwise, they need to multiply every term on both sides by a common denominator to eliminate the denominators. Remind students that they need to check their answers because some may be extraneous. Have students solve the following equations and check their answers:

$\frac{5}{x} = \frac{6}{x+2}$ 10 $\quad \frac{7}{x} + \frac{4}{x^2} = 2 - \frac{1}{2}$; 4

FORMATIVE ASSESSMENT and INTERVENTION

Diagnose Before **the Lesson**
10-7 Warm Up, TE p. 674

Monitor During **the Lesson**
Check It Out! Exercises, SE pp. 674–675
Questioning Strategies, TE p. 675

Assess After **the Lesson**
10-7 Lesson Quiz, TE p. 678
Alternative Assessment, TE p. 678

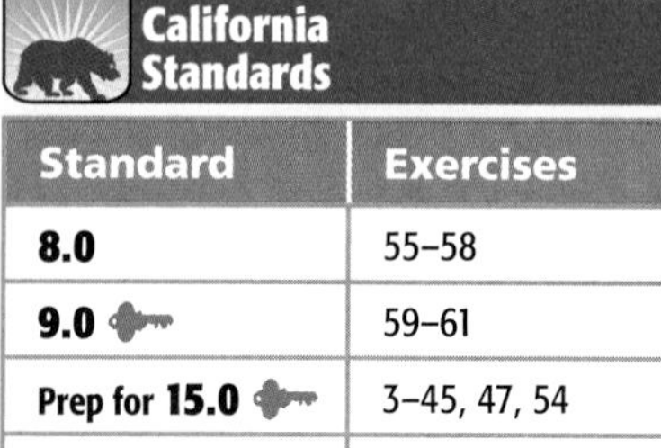

Standard	Exercises
8.0	55–58
9.0	59–61
Prep for 15.0	3–45, 47, 54
25.1	52

PRACTICE AND PROBLEM SOLVING

Independent Practice	
For Exercises	See Example
24–27	1
28–35	2
36–43	3

Extra Practice
Skills Practice p. EP21
Application Practice p. EP33

Solve. Check your answer.

24. $\frac{8}{x-2} = \frac{2}{x+1}$ −2
25. $\frac{12}{3n-1} = \frac{3}{n}$ −1
26. $\frac{x}{x+4} = \frac{x}{x-1}$ 0
27. $\frac{9}{x+5} = \frac{4}{x}$ 4
28. $\frac{6}{s} - \frac{2}{s} = 5$ $\frac{4}{5}$
29. $\frac{1}{2x} + \frac{1}{4x} = \frac{7}{8x}$ ∅
30. $\frac{7}{c} - \frac{2}{c} = \frac{4}{c-1}$ 5
31. $\frac{9}{m} - \frac{3}{2m} = \frac{15}{m}$ ∅
32. $\frac{3}{x^2} = \frac{2}{x}$ $\frac{3}{2}$
33. $\frac{r}{3} - 3 = -\frac{6}{r}$ 3, 6
34. $\frac{6}{x^2} = \frac{1}{2} + \frac{1}{2x}$ −4, 3
35. $\frac{8}{3x^2} = \frac{2}{x} - \frac{1}{3}$ 2, 4

Solve. Check your answer.

36. $\frac{x+4}{x+1} = \frac{3}{x-3}$ −3, 5
37. $\frac{x+1}{x-4} = \frac{3(x+1)}{x-4}$ −1
38. $\frac{5x}{x-3} = 8 + \frac{15}{x-3}$ ∅
39. $\frac{3t}{t-3} = \frac{t+4}{t-3}$ 2
40. $\frac{2}{x} = \frac{x+1}{x^2-1}$ 2
41. $\frac{1}{x} = \frac{x-4}{x^2-16}$ ∅
42. $\frac{x+2}{3} = \frac{x+7}{x+3}$ −5, 3
43. $\frac{x+4}{2x-2} = \frac{x+3}{x-1}$ −2

44a. $86\frac{2}{3}\%$
b. $\frac{39+f}{45+f} = 0.9$; 15 free throws

44. **Multi-Step** Clancy has been keeping his free throw statistics. Use his data to write the ratio of the number of free throws Clancy has made to the number of attempts.

Clancy's Free Throws	
Attempts	Made
45	39

a. What percentage has he made?
b. Write and solve an equation to find how many free throws *f* Clancy would have to make in a row to improve his free-throw percentage to 90%. (*Hint:* Clancy needs to make *f* more free throws in *f* more attempts.)

45. Karla and Andrew are sorting their book collections. Karla has 12 books and divides them evenly into stacks. Andrew has 18 books and evenly divides his books into 2 fewer stacks than Karla. He also has 6 more books in each stack than Karla. Copy and complete the table. Then find the number of stacks of books Karla has. 4

	Karla	Andrew
Books	12	18
Stacks	x	$x-2$
Books per Stack	$\frac{12}{x}$	$\frac{18}{x-2}$

CONCEPT CONNECTION

46. This problem will prepare you for the Concept Connection on page 684.
Blanca sets up a lens with a focal length *f* of 15 cm and places a candle 24 cm from the lens. She knows that $\frac{1}{f} = \frac{1}{x} + \frac{1}{y}$ where *x* is the distance of the object from the lens and *y* is the distance of the image from the lens.
a. Write the equation using the given values. $\frac{1}{15} = \frac{1}{24} + \frac{1}{y}$
b. For the values of *f* and *x* given above, how far will the image appear from the lens? 40 cm
c. How will distance between the image and the lens be affected if Blanca uses a lens with a focal length of 18 cm? It will increase to 72 cm.

Teaching Tip **Inclusion** The rational expressions on the left side of the equations in **Exercises 28** and **30** have common denominators. Students can subtract the expressions and then solve the resulting proportion with cross products.

CONCEPT CONNECTION **Exercise 46** involves solving a problem about focal length by writing and solving a rational equation. This exercise prepares students for the Concept Connection on page 684.

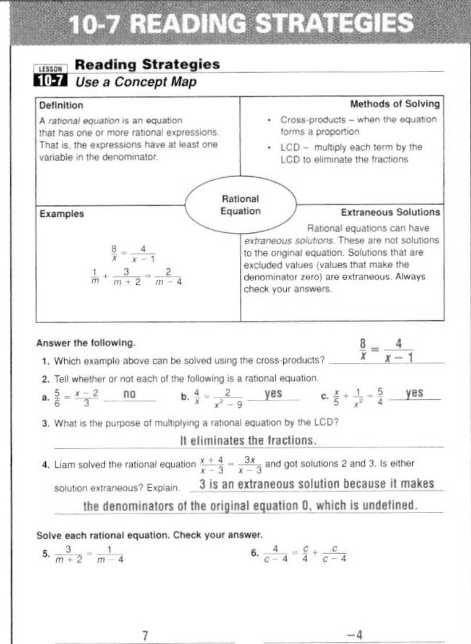

10-7 READING STRATEGIES

LESSON 10-7 **Reading Strategies**
Use a Concept Map

Rational Equation

Definition	Methods of Solving
A *rational equation* is an equation that has one or more rational expressions. That is, the expressions have at least one variable in the denominator.	• Cross-products – when the equation forms a proportion • LCD – multiply each term by the LCD to eliminate the fractions
Examples	**Extraneous Solutions**
$\frac{8}{x} = \frac{4}{x-1}$ $\frac{1}{m} + \frac{3}{m+2} = \frac{2}{m-4}$	Rational equations can have *extraneous solutions*. These are not solutions to the original equation. Solutions that are excluded values (values that make the denominator zero) are extraneous. Always check your answers.

Answer the following.
1. Which example above can be solved using the cross-products? $\frac{8}{x} = \frac{4}{x-1}$
2. Tell whether or not each of the following is a rational equation.
a. $\frac{5}{6} = \frac{x-2}{3}$ no   b. $\frac{4}{x} = \frac{2}{x^2-9}$ yes   c. $\frac{x}{5} + \frac{1}{x^2} = \frac{5}{4}$ yes
3. What is the purpose of multiplying a rational equation by the LCD?
It eliminates the fractions.
4. Liam solved the rational equation $\frac{x+4}{x-3} = \frac{3x}{x-3}$ and got solutions 2 and 3. Is either solution extraneous? Explain. 3 is an extraneous solution because it makes the denominators of the original equation 0, which is undefined.

Solve each rational equation. Check your answer.
5. $\frac{3}{m+2} = \frac{1}{m-4}$ 7
6. $\frac{4}{c-4} = \frac{c}{4} + \frac{c}{c-4}$ −4

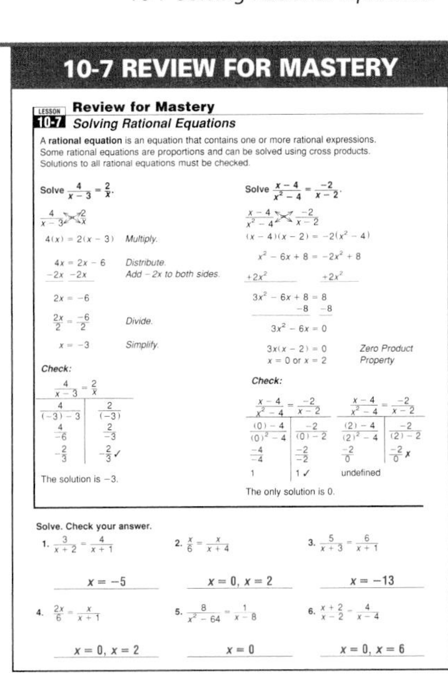

10-7 REVIEW FOR MASTERY

LESSON 10-7 **Review for Mastery**
Solving Rational Equations

A **rational equation** is an equation that contains one or more rational expressions. Some rational equations are proportions and can be solved using cross products. Solutions to all rational equations must be checked.

Solve $\frac{4}{x-3} = \frac{2}{x}$.

$\frac{4}{x-3} \times \frac{2}{x}$
$4(x) = 2(x-3)$ *Multiply.*
$4x = 2x - 6$ *Distribute.*
$-2x \quad -2x$ *Add −2x to both sides.*
$2x = -6$
$\frac{2x}{2} = \frac{-6}{2}$ *Divide.*
$x = -3$ *Simplify.*

Check:
$\frac{4}{x-3} = \frac{2}{x}$

$\frac{4}{(-3)-3}$	$\frac{2}{(-3)}$
$\frac{4}{-6}$	$\frac{2}{-3}$
$-\frac{2}{3}$	$-\frac{2}{3}$ ✓

The solution is −3.

Solve $\frac{x-4}{x^2-4} = \frac{-2}{x-2}$.

$\frac{x-4}{x^2-4} \times \frac{-2}{x-2}$
$(x-4)(x-2) = -2(x^2-4)$
$x^2 - 6x + 8 = -2x^2 + 8$
$+2x^2 \quad +2x^2$
$3x^2 - 6x + 8 = 8$
$-8 \quad -8$
$3x^2 - 6x = 0$
$3x(x-2) = 0$ *Zero Product Property*
$x = 0$ or $x = 2$

Check:

$\frac{x-4}{x^2-4}$	$\frac{-2}{x-2}$	$\frac{x-4}{x^2-4}$	$\frac{-2}{x-2}$
$\frac{(0)-4}{(0)^2-4}$	$\frac{-2}{(0)-2}$	$\frac{(2)-4}{(2)^2-4}$	$\frac{-2}{(2)-2}$
$\frac{-4}{-4}$	$\frac{-2}{-2}$	$\frac{-2}{0}$	$\frac{-2}{0}$ ✗
1	1 ✓	undefined	

The only solution is 0.

Solve. Check your answer.
1. $\frac{3}{x+2} = \frac{4}{x+1}$ $x = -5$
2. $\frac{x}{6} = \frac{x}{x+4}$ $x = 0, x = 2$
3. $\frac{5}{x+3} = \frac{6}{x+1}$ $x = -13$
4. $\frac{2x}{6} = \frac{x}{x+1}$ $x = 0, x = 2$
5. $\frac{8}{x^2-64} = \frac{1}{x-8}$ $x = 0$
6. $\frac{x+2}{x-2} = \frac{4}{x-4}$ $x = 0, x = 6$

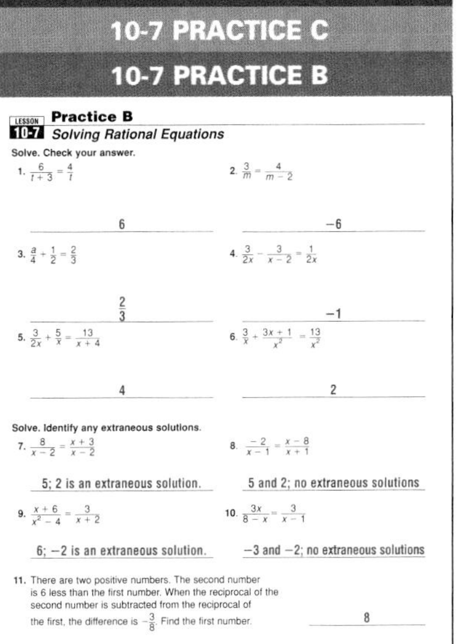

10-7 PRACTICE A
10-7 PRACTICE C
10-7 PRACTICE B

LESSON 10-7 **Practice B**
Solving Rational Equations

Solve. Check your answer.
1. $\frac{6}{t+3} = \frac{4}{t}$ 6
2. $\frac{3}{m} = \frac{4}{m-2}$ −6
3. $\frac{a}{4} + \frac{1}{2} = \frac{2}{3}$ $\frac{2}{3}$
4. $\frac{3}{2x} - \frac{3}{x-2} = \frac{1}{2x}$ −1
5. $\frac{3}{2x} + \frac{5}{x} = \frac{13}{x+4}$ 4
6. $\frac{3}{x} + \frac{3x+1}{x^2} = \frac{13}{x^2}$ 2

Solve. Identify any extraneous solutions.
7. $\frac{8}{x-2} = \frac{x+3}{x-2}$ 5; 2 is an extraneous solution.
8. $\frac{-2}{x-1} = \frac{x-8}{x+1}$ 5 and 2; no extraneous solutions
9. $\frac{x+6}{x^2-4} = \frac{3}{x+2}$ 6; −2 is an extraneous solution.
10. $\frac{3x}{8-x} = \frac{3}{x-1}$ −3 and −2; no extraneous solutions
11. There are two positive numbers. The second number is 6 less than the first number. When the reciprocal of the second number is subtracted from the reciprocal of the first, the difference is $-\frac{3}{8}$. Find the first number.   8

Teaching Tip **Multiple Choice** In **Exercise 50,** choices **B** and **D** are excluded values and cannot be solutions. These can be eliminated. Students could then substitute either 1 or −1 for x in the equation. If it makes a true statement, it's the answer. If it makes a false statement, the other choice is the answer.

Answers

48. 4; possible answer: first add the fractions on the left to get $\frac{4}{x} = \frac{3}{x-1}$. Then cross multiply and solve to find $x = 4$. This method may be easier than finding the LCD.
55. $y = 3x + 1$ and $y = 3x - 1$ are parallel.
56. $y = -2x$ and $y = \frac{1}{2}x + 4$ are perpendicular.
57. $y = x - 2$ and $y = x + 3$ are parallel; $y = -x - 3$ is perpendicular to both $y = x - 2$ and $y = x + 3$.
58. $x = -\frac{2}{3}x + 2$ and $y = \frac{3}{2}x + 3$ are perpendicular.

Journal

Have students describe the advantages of solving using cross products and of solving using the LCD. Then have students compare the methods.

ALTERNATIVE ASSESSMENT

Have students solve the following equations:

$$\frac{4}{x+2} = \frac{3}{x}$$

$$\frac{4}{x+2} + \frac{3}{x} = 1$$

Students should then explain their methods for solving each equation.

Power Presentations with PowerPoint®

10-7 Lesson Quiz

Solve each equation. Check your answer.

1. $\frac{x-4}{5} = \frac{x}{6}$ 24
2. $\frac{12}{x^2} = \frac{1}{x} + 1$ −4, 3
3. $\frac{3}{4x} + \frac{2}{x+6} = \frac{5}{8}$ $-3\frac{3}{5}, 2$
4. Solve $\frac{1}{x+1} + \frac{x}{x-3} = \frac{12}{x^2 - 2x - 3}$. Check your answer. −5

Also available on transparency

47. No; you can only use cross multiplication if the equation is in the form of a proportion.

47. **Critical Thinking** Can you cross multiply to solve all rational equations? If so, explain. If not, how do you identify which ones can be solved using cross products?

48. **Write About It** Solve $\frac{1}{x} + \frac{3}{x} = \frac{3}{x-1}$. Explain each step and why you chose the method you used.

Multiple Choice For Exercises 49–51, choose the best answer.

49. Which value is an extraneous solution to $\frac{x}{x+4} - \frac{4}{x-4} = \frac{x^2+16}{x^2-16}$?

Ⓐ −16 **Ⓑ −4** Ⓒ 4 Ⓓ 16

50. Which is a solution to $\frac{x+2}{x-3} - \frac{1}{x} = \frac{3}{x^2-3x}$?

Ⓐ −1 Ⓑ 0 Ⓒ 1 Ⓓ 3

51. What are the solutions of $\frac{5}{x^2} = \frac{1}{3} + \frac{2}{3x}$?

Ⓐ −3 and 5 Ⓑ −3 and 2 Ⓒ 2 and 3 **Ⓓ 3 and −5**

CHALLENGE AND EXTEND

52. **Reasoning** Below is a solution to the rational equation $\frac{3}{x} = \frac{6}{x+4}$. Use an algebraic property to justify each step.

Statements	Reasons
a. $3(x + 4) = 6x$	Cross Product Property
b. $3x + 12 = 6x$	Distributive Property
c. $12 = 3x$	Subtraction Property of Equality
d. $4 = x$	Division Property of Equality

53. For what value of a will the equation $\frac{x+4}{x-a} = \frac{7}{x-a}$ have no solution? **3**

54. Jill has a 10-year-old sister and a sister who will be 12 next year. The equation $\frac{10}{j} + \frac{12}{j+1} = 4$, where j is Jill's age, describes the relationship between the ages of Jill and her sisters. Angela has one sister who is 16 this year and a sister who will be 18 next year. The equation $\frac{16}{a} + \frac{18}{a+1} = 4$, where a is Angela's age, describes the relationship between the ages of Angela and her sisters. What is the difference between Jill's and Angela's ages? **3 yr**

SPIRAL STANDARDS REVIEW 8.0, 9.0

Identify which lines are parallel and which lines are perpendicular. *(Lesson 5-8)*

55. $y = \frac{1}{3}x$; $y = 3x + 1$; $y = 3x - 1$

56. $y = -2x$; $y = 2x - 2$; $y = \frac{1}{2}x + 4$

57. $y = -x - 3$; $y = x - 2$; $y = x + 3$

58. $y = -\frac{2}{3}x + 2$; $y = \frac{3}{2}x + 3$; $y = -\frac{3}{2}x - 1$

Solve each system by elimination. *(Lesson 6-3)*

59. $\begin{cases} x - y = -3 \\ 2x + 2y = 22 \end{cases}$ **(4, 7)**

60. $\begin{cases} x - 2y = 18 \\ 2x + 3y = 15 \end{cases}$ **(12, −3)**

61. $\begin{cases} -3x - 2y = 27 \\ 4x - 3y = -2 \end{cases}$ **(−5, −6)**

62. Find the number of solutions of $7x^2 + 5x - 13 = 0$ using the discriminant. **2** *(Lesson 9-9)*

10-7 PROBLEM SOLVING

LESSON 10-7 **Problem Solving**
Solving Rational Equations

Write the correct answer.

1. A library has a collection of 400 DVDs of which 160 are comedies. A librarian wants to add comedy DVDs to the collection so that 50% of the DVDs are comedies. How many comedy DVDs should be added? **80**

2. There are 80 cartons of milk at a school cafeteria and 22 of them contain nonfat milk. The rest contain low-fat milk. A cafeteria employee wants 60% of the cartons to contain nonfat milk. How many cartons of nonfat milk should she add? **65**

3. When Carolyn walks 1 mi/h faster than her usual rate, she can cover 12 miles in the same amount of time she normally covers 9 miles. What is her usual rate? (*Hint:* time = $\frac{\text{distance}}{\text{rate}}$) **3 mi/h**

4. Lena and Kendall drive at the same rate. It takes Kendall 2 hours longer to drive 275 miles than it takes Lena to drive 165 miles. How long does it take Lena to drive 165 miles? What is Lena's rate? (*Hint:* rate = $\frac{\text{distance}}{\text{time}}$) **3 h; 55 mi/h**

Select the best answer.

5. With a 50 mi/h tailwind, a plane flies 1200 miles in the same amount of time it can travel 1000 miles with a 50 mi/h headwind. What is the plane's speed in still air?

A 500 mi/h **Ⓒ 550 mi/h**
B 525 mi/h D 600 mi/h

6. Ms. Myers is ordering copies of a novel for her English class. At Books Galore, the novels cost a total of \$160. At Book Basement, each book is \$2 more expensive and the total cost for the same number of books is \$200. Which rational equation can be used to find the price p of each book at Books Galore?

F $\frac{160}{p} = \frac{200}{p} - 2$ H $\frac{160}{p} = \frac{200}{p-2}$
G $\frac{160}{p} = \frac{200}{p} + 2$ **Ⓙ $\frac{160}{p} = \frac{200}{p+2}$**

7. Kevin keeps track of his results when he plays his favorite video game. The table at right shows his data. He wants to know how many games he must win in a row so that his winning percentage will be 75%. Which rational equation should he solve?

Ⓐ $\frac{12+x}{20+x} = 0.75$ C $\frac{12+x}{20} = 0.75$
B $\frac{20+x}{12+x} = 0.75$ D $\frac{12}{20+x} = 0.75$

Video Game Results

Number of Wins	Number of Games Played	Winning Percentage
12	20	$\frac{12}{20} = 0.6 = 60\%$

10-7 CHALLENGE

LESSON 10-7 **Challenge**
Exploring Reciprocals, Rational Equations, and Integer Solutions

In this lesson, you learned how to solve rational equations in one variable. Each equation below is a rational equation in two variables, x and y.

$\frac{1}{x} + \frac{1}{y} = 1$ $\frac{1}{x} + \frac{1}{y} = 2$ $\frac{1}{x} + \frac{1}{y} = \frac{1}{2}$

In the exercises on this page, assume that x and y are positive integers.

Find one solution to each equation of the form $\frac{1}{x} + \frac{1}{y} = \frac{1}{n}$, where n is a positive integer.

1. $\frac{1}{x} + \frac{1}{y} = 1$ **$x = 2, y = 2$**
2. $\frac{1}{x} + \frac{1}{y} = \frac{1}{2}$ **Possible answer: $x = 4, y = 4$**
3. $\frac{1}{x} + \frac{1}{y} = \frac{1}{4}$ **Possible answer: $x = 8, y = 8$**
4. $\frac{1}{x} + \frac{1}{y} = \frac{1}{6}$ **Possible answer: $x = 12, y = 12$**
5. $\frac{1}{x} + \frac{1}{y} = \frac{1}{8}$ **Possible answer: $x = 16, y = 16$**
6. $\frac{1}{x} + \frac{1}{y} = \frac{1}{100}$ **Possible answer: $x = 200, y = 200$**

7. Suppose that you are given $\frac{1}{x} + \frac{1}{y} = \frac{1}{n}$, where n is an even positive integer. Based on your work in Exercises 1–6, write formulas in terms of n for x and for y. **$x = 2n, y = 2n$**

8. a. Let $\frac{1}{x} + \frac{1}{y} = 2$. Show that $x = 1$ and $y = 1$ are solutions to the equation by using substitution. **$\frac{1}{1} + \frac{1}{1} = 2$**

b. If x and y are positive integers other than 1, then $0 < \frac{1}{x} < 1$ and $0 < \frac{1}{y} < 1$. Explain how this fact helps you show that there are no positive integer solutions to $\frac{1}{x} + \frac{1}{y} = 2$ other than $x = 1$ and $y = 1$.

If x and y are integers with $0 < \frac{1}{x} < 1$ and $0 < \frac{1}{y} < 1$, then $0 < \frac{1}{x} + \frac{1}{y} < 2$. Therefore, $\frac{1}{x} + \frac{1}{y} = 2$ is only true when $x = 1$ and $y = 1$.

c. How does the reasoning in Part b help you show that, when n is an integer greater than 2 and x and y are positive integers, the equation $\frac{1}{x} + \frac{1}{y} = n$ has no integer solutions?

Since $0 < \frac{1}{x} + \frac{1}{y} < 2$, there are no positive integers x and y for $n > 2$.

Use trial and error to help you decide whether the given equation has any integer solutions. If so, state one solution.

9. $\frac{1}{x} + \frac{1}{y} = \frac{1}{3}$ **Possible answer: $x = 6, y = 6$**
10. $\frac{1}{x} + \frac{1}{y} = \frac{1}{5}$ **Possible answer: $x = 10, y = 10$**

10-8 Applying Rational Equations

California Standards

15.0 Students apply algebraic techniques to solve rate problems, work problems, and percent mixture problems.

Why learn this?

You can use rational equations to find out how long it takes two people working together to complete a job.

When two people team up to complete a job, each person completes a fraction of the whole job. You can use this idea to write and solve a rational equation to find how long it will take to complete a job.

EXAMPLE 1 ***Gardening Application***

Danielle can weed a garden in 2 hours. It takes Omar 3 hours to weed the same garden. How long will it take them to weed the garden if they work together?

Let h be the number of hours Danielle and Omar need to weed the garden. Danielle weeds the garden in 2 hours, so she weeds $\frac{1}{2}$ of the garden per hour. Omar weeds the garden in 3 hours, so he weeds $\frac{1}{3}$ of the garden per hour. The table shows the part of the garden that each person weeds in h hours.

Danielle's Part	+	Omar's Part	=	Whole Garden
$\frac{1}{2}h$	+	$\frac{1}{3}h$	=	1

$\frac{1}{2}h + \frac{1}{3}h = 1$ *Solve this equation for h.*

$6\left(\frac{1}{2}h + \frac{1}{3}h\right) = 6(1)$ *Multiply both sides by the LCD, 6.*

$3h + 2h = 6$ *Distribute 6 on the left side.*

$5h = 6$ *Combine like terms.*

$h = \frac{6}{5} = 1\frac{1}{5}$ *Divide by 5 on both sides.*

Working together, Danielle and Omar can weed the garden in $1\frac{1}{5}$ hours, or 1 hour 12 minutes.

Check Danielle weeds $\frac{1}{2}$ of the garden per hour, so in $1\frac{1}{5}$ hours, she weeds $\frac{1}{2} \cdot \frac{6}{5} = \frac{3}{5}$ of the garden. Omar weeds $\frac{1}{3}$ of the garden per hour, so in $1\frac{1}{5}$ hours, he weeds $\frac{1}{3} \cdot \frac{6}{5} = \frac{2}{5}$ of the garden. Together, they weed $\frac{3}{5} + \frac{2}{5} = 1$ garden.

CHECK IT OUT!

1. Cindy mows a lawn in 50 minutes. It takes Sara 40 minutes to mow the same lawn. How long will it take them to mow the lawn if they work together? **$22\frac{2}{9}$ min, or about 22 min 13 s**

10-8 Organizer

Objective: Use rational equations to solve application problems.

Online Edition
Tutorial Videos, Interactivities

Countdown to Mastery Week 24

Power Presentations with PowerPoint®

Warm Up

Multiply. Simplify your answer.

1. $\frac{6x^2}{y} \cdot \frac{y^3}{2x^2}$ $3y^2$

2. $\frac{m^2 + m}{3m} \cdot \frac{3}{m + 1}$ 1

3. $\frac{a^3 - a}{a + 1} \cdot \frac{a^2}{a - 1}$ a^3

Solve.

4. $\frac{1}{t} + \frac{1}{2t} = 4$ $\frac{3}{8}$

5. $\frac{4}{m - 1} = 1 + \frac{6}{m}$ $-3, 2$

Also available on transparency

Math Humor

Q: What do you get when you solve a rational equation correctly?

A: A reasonable answer

1 Introduce

EXPLORATION

10-8 Applying Rational Equations

Jared wants to fill a small pool with water. He can use a black hose or a green hose.

1. The black hose can fill the pool in 20 minutes. Complete the table.

Black Hose						
Time (min)	1	2	4	5	10	20
Fraction of Pool Filled	$\frac{1}{20}$					

2. Look for a pattern in the table. What fraction of the pool is filled in *m* minutes?
3. The green hose can fill the pool in 40 min. Complete the table.

Green Hose						
Time (min)	1	2	4	5	10	20
Fraction of Pool Filled	$\frac{1}{40}$					

4. Look for a pattern in the table. What fraction of the pool is filled in *m* minutes?
5. Jared decides to use both hoses at the same time. Write an expression for the fraction of the pool that is filled in *m* minutes. (*Hint:* Add the expressions from Steps 2 and 4.)

THINK AND DISCUSS

6. **Explain** how to use the expression you wrote in Step 5 to find the fraction of the pool that can be filled in 10 minutes

Motivate

Present the following situation to the class. Mike can wallpaper a room in 6 hours. Trisha can wallpaper the same room in 4 hours.

Ask students to "guestimate" how long it will take Mike and Trisha to do the job together. Record students' predictions on the board. Then tell them they will learn how to use rational equations to solve this type of problem.

Explorations and answers are provided in *Alternate Openers: Explorations Transparencies.*

California Standards

Algebra 1 **15.0**

Power Presentations with PowerPoint®

Additional Examples

Example 1

Jessica can clean her apartment in 5 hours. Her roommate can clean the apartment in 4 hours. How long will it take them to clean the apartment if they work together? $2\frac{2}{9}$ h, or about 2 h 13 min

Example 2

Omar has 20 oz of a snack mix that is half peanuts and half raisins. How many ounces of peanuts should he add to make a mix that is 70% peanuts? $13\frac{1}{3}$ oz

Example 3

Amber runs along a 16-mile trail while Dave walks. Amber runs 4 mi/h faster than Dave walks. It takes Dave 2 hours longer than Amber to cover the 16 miles. How long does it take Amber to complete the trip? 2 h

Also available on transparency

INTERVENTION

Questioning Strategies

EXAMPLE 1

- How can you determine the fraction of the job that each person does in h hours?

EXAMPLE 2

- How do you find the percent of alcohol in the solution?

EXAMPLE 3

- What are the relationships between distance, rate, and time?
- How can you write an equation using the information in the Rate column? What is the rate?

EXAMPLE 2 *Chemistry Application*

A chemist has 500 milliliters of a solution that is half alcohol. He needs a solution that is 60% alcohol. How many milliliters of alcohol should he add?

Let a be the number of milliliters of alcohol that the chemist should add.

The table shows the amount of alcohol and the total amount of the solution.

	Alcohol (mL)	Total (mL)
Original	250	500
New	$250 + a$	$500 + a$

The new solution is 60% alcohol, so $\frac{250 + a}{500 + a} = 0.6$. Solve for a.

$250 + a = 0.6(500 + a)$ *Multiply both sides by 500 + a.*

$250 + a = 300 + 0.6a$ *Distribute 0.6 on the right side.*

$0.4a = 50$ *Subtract 250 from both sides and 0.6a from both sides.*

$a = 125$ *Divide both sides by 0.4.*

The chemist should add 125 mL of alcohol to the solution.

CHECK IT OUT! **2.** Suppose the chemist wants a solution that is 80% alcohol. How many milliliters of alcohol should he add? **750 mL**

EXAMPLE 3 *Transportation Application*

A passenger train travels 20 mi/h faster than a freight train, and it takes the passenger train 2 hours less time to travel 240 miles. How long does the freight train take to make the trip?

Remember!
distance = rate • time, so rate = $\frac{\text{distance}}{\text{time}}$.

Let t be the time it takes the freight train to travel 240 miles.

	Distance (mi)	Time (h)	Rate (mi/h)
Freight Train	240	t	$\frac{240}{t}$
Passenger Train	240	$t - 2$	$\frac{240}{t - 2}$

The passenger train is 20 mi/h faster, so $\frac{240}{t-2} = \frac{240}{t} + 20$.

$t(t-2)\frac{240}{t-2} = t(t-2)\left(\frac{240}{t} + 20\right)$ *Multiply both sides by the LCD.*

$240t = (t-2)240 + (t^2 - 2t)(20)$ *Distribute t(t − 2) on the right side. Simplify.*

$240t = 240t - 480 + 20t^2 - 40t$ *Distribute and multiply.*

$0 = 20t^2 - 40t - 480$ *Subtract 240t from both sides.*

$0 = t^2 - 2t - 24$ *Divide both sides by 20.*

$0 = (t-6)(t+4)$, so $t = -4, 6$ *Factor and solve. Time is nonnegative, so −4 is extraneous.*

The freight train makes the trip in 6 hours.

CHECK IT OUT! **3.** Ryan drives 10 mi/h slower than Maya, and it takes Ryan 1 hour longer to travel 300 miles. How long does it take Maya to make the trip? **5 h**

2 Teach

Guided Instruction

Tell students they will learn how to use rational equations to solve several types of real-world problems. Point out that "working together" problems can apply to either people or machines working together to complete a task. They can also be stated with any unit of time (seconds, minutes, hours, etc.). Emphasize the importance of checking solutions to rule out extraneous solutions.

3 Close

Summarize

Revisit the problem that was presented in the Motivate section of the lesson. Ask students to write a rational equation for the problem, and then have them solve it to find the solution. $\frac{h}{6} + \frac{h}{4} = 1$; 2.4 h, or 2 h 24 min

Conclude by having students compare the actual answer with their earlier predictions. Ask students if the answer seems reasonable.

THINK AND DISCUSS

1. Explain why it makes sense that the answer to Example 1 is less than the time it takes Danielle or Omar to weed the garden when working alone.
2. **GET ORGANIZED** Copy and complete the graphic organizer. In each box, write an example of each type of application and its solution.

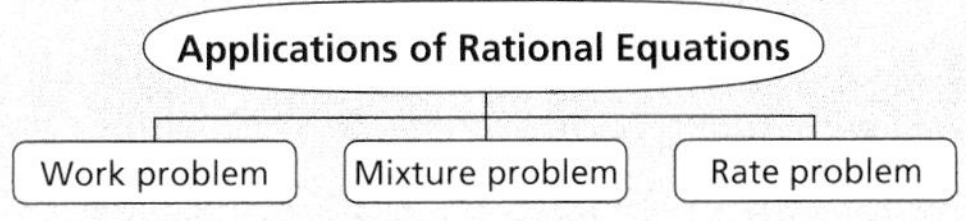

10-8 Exercises

GUIDED PRACTICE

SEE EXAMPLE 1 p. 679

1. Summer can paint a room in 3 hours. Louise can paint the room in 5 hours. How many hours will it take them to paint the room if they work together? $1\frac{7}{8}$ h

SEE EXAMPLE 2 p. 680

2. **Cooking** A chef has 4 quarts of a soup that consists of equal parts chicken stock and vegetable stock. She wants to make a soup that is 75% chicken stock. How many quarts of chicken stock should she add to the mixture? 4 qt

SEE EXAMPLE 3 p. 680

3. **Fitness** Connor and Matt walk a 12-mile course as part of a fitness program. Matt walks 1 mi/h faster than Connor, and it takes him 1 hour less than Connor to complete the course. How long does it take Connor to complete the course? 4 h

PRACTICE AND PROBLEM SOLVING

Independent Practice

For Exercises	See Example
4–5	1
6	2
7	3

Extra Practice
Skills Practice p. EP21
Application Practice p. EP33

4. **Technology** Lawrence's old robotic vacuum can clean his apartment in $1\frac{1}{2}$ hours. His new robotic vacuum can clean his apartment in 45 minutes. How long will it take both vacuums working together to clean his apartment? 30 min

5. The table shows the time it takes for pipes of different sizes to fill a reservoir with water. How long would it take for both pipes working at the same time to fill the reservoir? 4 h

Pipe Output	
Diameter (ft)	Time to Fill Reservoir (h)
2	12
3	6

6. Maria has 8 cups of a fruit punch that consists of 25% orange juice and 75% apple juice. She wants to make a drink that is 40% orange juice. How many cups of orange juice should Maria add to the mixture? 2 c

7. **Transportation** The average speed of an express train is 15 mi/h faster than the average speed of a local train. It takes the local train 2 hours longer than the express train to cover 360 miles. What is the average speed of the express train? 60 mi/h

Answers to *Think and Discuss*

Possible answers:

1. Danielle can weed the garden by herself in 2 hours, so with Armin's help it makes sense that they finish in less than 2 hours.
2. See p. A9.

10-8 Exercises

Assignment Guide

Assign *Guided Practice* Exercises as necessary.

If you finished Examples **1–3**
Proficient 4–11, 13–18, 21–38
Advanced 4–7, 10, 11, 13–38

Homework Quick Check
Quickly check key concepts.
Exercises: 4, 5, 6, 10, 11

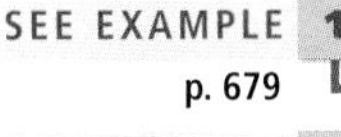

FORMATIVE ASSESSMENT and INTERVENTION

***Diagnose Before* the Lesson**
10-8 Warm Up, TE p. 679

***Monitor During* the Lesson**
Check It Out! Exercises, SE pp. 679–680
Questioning Strategies, TE pp. 680

***Assess After* the Lesson**
10-8 Lesson Quiz, TE p. 683
Alternative Assessment, TE p. 683

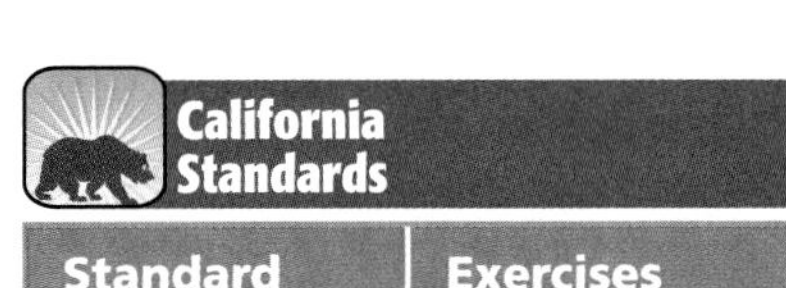

Standard	Exercises
7.0	21–26
11.0	27–32
12.0	33–38
15.0	1–8, 10, 14–20
25.2	12

Exercise 13 involves writing and solving a rational equation to determine how far an object should be placed from a lens. This exercise prepares students for the Concept Connection on page 684.

Answers

15. Possible answer: A cook has 6 cups of a soup that consists of equal amounts of chicken stock and beef stock. How many cups of chicken stock should be added so that the soup is 60% chicken stock? Answer: 1.5 cups
27. $(2x + 3)^2$
28. $(3x - 1)^2$
29. The last term must be pos.
30. The middle term must be −28.
31. The last term must be pos.
32. The middle term must be 48.

8. **Sports** A race consists of a 20-mile bike ride and a 12-mile run. Jen's rate while biking is 4 mi/h faster than while running. She completes the race in 4 hours.
   a. Let r be Jen's rate while biking. Copy and complete the table.
   b. Use the information in the Time column to write a rational equation.
   c. Solve the equation to find Jen's rate while biking. **10 mi/h**

	Distance (mi)	Rate (mi/h)	Time (h)
Biking	**20**	r	$\frac{20}{r}$
Running	12	$r - 4$	$\frac{12}{r-4}$

8b. $\frac{20}{r} + \frac{12}{r-4} = 4$

9. **Geometry** Both rectangle A and rectangle B have areas of 96 m². The length of B is twice the length of A. The width of A is 4 m greater than the width of B.
   a. Let ℓ be the length of rectangle A. Copy and complete the table.

	Area (m²)	Length (m)	Width (m)
Rectangle A	96	ℓ	$\frac{96}{\ell}$
Rectangle B	**96**	2ℓ	$\frac{96}{2\ell}$

   b. Use the information in the Width column to write a rational equation.
   c. Solve the equation to find the length and width of rectangle A.

9b. $\frac{96}{\ell} = \frac{96}{2\ell} + 4$

9c. Length : 12 m; width: 8 m

10. **Multi-Step** The manager of a copy center can use two of the machines in the graph to make 1000 photocopies of a leaflet. Will the job be completed more quickly with machines A and D or with machines B and C? Explain.

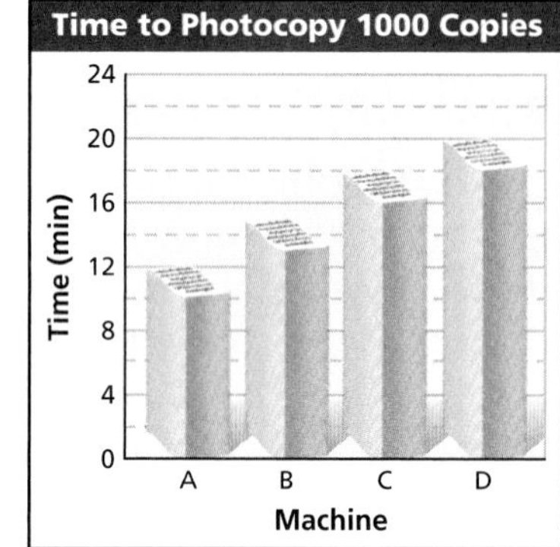

10. Machines A and D; these machines take 7.5 min, while machines B and C take about 8.2 min.

11. A number plus the reciprocal of the number is $\frac{5}{4}$ of the number. What is the number? **−2 or 2**

12. **ERROR ANALYSIS** Jordan can wash the windows in his house in 4 hours. His brother can do the job in 6 hours. They want to know how long it will take if they work together. Which solution to the problem is incorrect? Explain the error.

12. B is incorrect. The correct rational equation is $\frac{h}{4} + \frac{h}{6} = 1$.

A

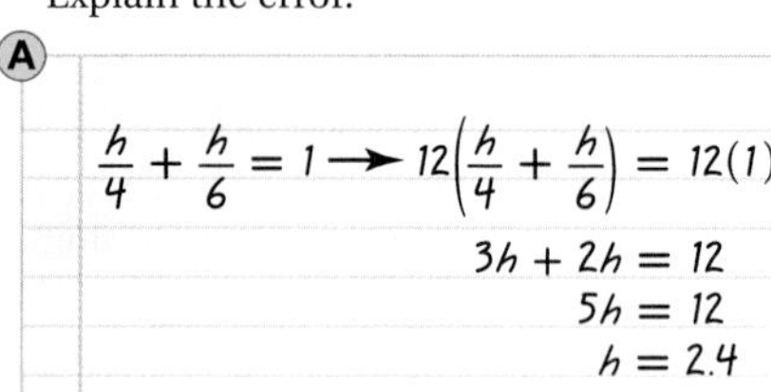

$\frac{h}{4} + \frac{h}{6} = 1 \rightarrow 12\left(\frac{h}{4} + \frac{h}{6}\right) = 12(1)$
$3h + 2h = 12$
$5h = 12$
$h = 2.4$

B

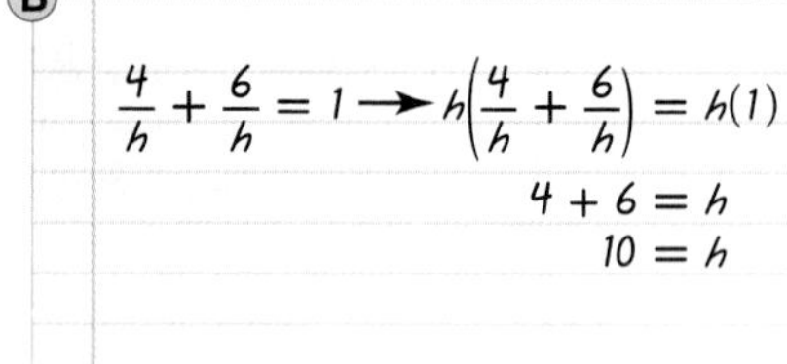

13. This problem will prepare you for the Concept Connection on page 684.
    Melinda has a lens with a focal length f of 12 cm. She wants to place a candle so that the distance from the candle to the lens is 10 cm more than the distance from the candle's image to the lens. She knows that $\frac{1}{f} = \frac{1}{x} + \frac{1}{y}$, where x is the distance from the object to the lens and y is the distance from the image to the lens.
    a. Write and solve a rational equation to find the distance from the candle to the lens.
    b. How far will the candle's image be from the lens? **20 cm**

a. $\frac{1}{12} = \frac{1}{x} + \frac{1}{x - 10}$; 30 cm

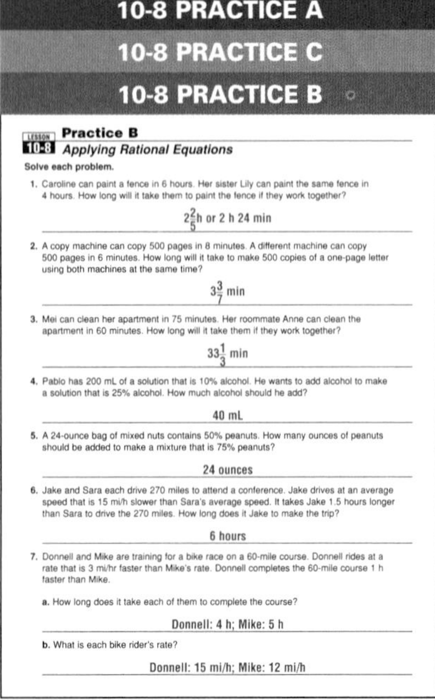

10-8 PRACTICE A

10-8 PRACTICE C

10-8 PRACTICE B

LESSON 10-8 **Practice B**
Applying Rational Equations

Solve each problem.

1. Caroline can paint a fence in 6 hours. Her sister Lily can paint the same fence in 4 hours. How long will it take them to paint the fence if they work together?
   $2\frac{2}{5}$h or 2 h 24 min
2. A copy machine can copy 500 pages in 8 minutes. A different machine can copy 500 pages in 6 minutes. How long will it take to make 500 copies of a one-page letter using both machines at the same time?
   $3\frac{3}{7}$ min
3. Mei can clean her apartment in 75 minutes. Her roommate Anne can clean the apartment in 60 minutes. How long will it take them if they work together?
   $33\frac{1}{3}$ min
4. Pablo has 200 mL of a solution that is 10% alcohol. He wants to add alcohol to make a solution that is 25% alcohol. How much alcohol should he add?
   40 mL
5. A 24-ounce bag of mixed nuts contains 50% peanuts. How many ounces of peanuts should be added to make a mixture that is 75% peanuts?
   24 ounces
6. Jake and Sara each drive 270 miles to attend a conference. Jake drives at an average speed that is 15 mi/h slower than Sara's average speed. It takes Jake 1.5 hours longer than Sara to drive the 270 miles. How long does it Jake to make the trip?
   6 hours
7. Donnell and Mike are training for a bike race on a 60-mile course. Donnell rides at a rate that is 3 mi/hr faster than Mike's rate. Donnell completes the 60-mile course 1 h faster than Mike.
   a. How long does it take each of them to complete the course?
   Donnell: 4 h; Mike: 5 h
   b. What is each bike rider's rate?
   Donnell: 15 mi/h; Mike: 12 mi/h

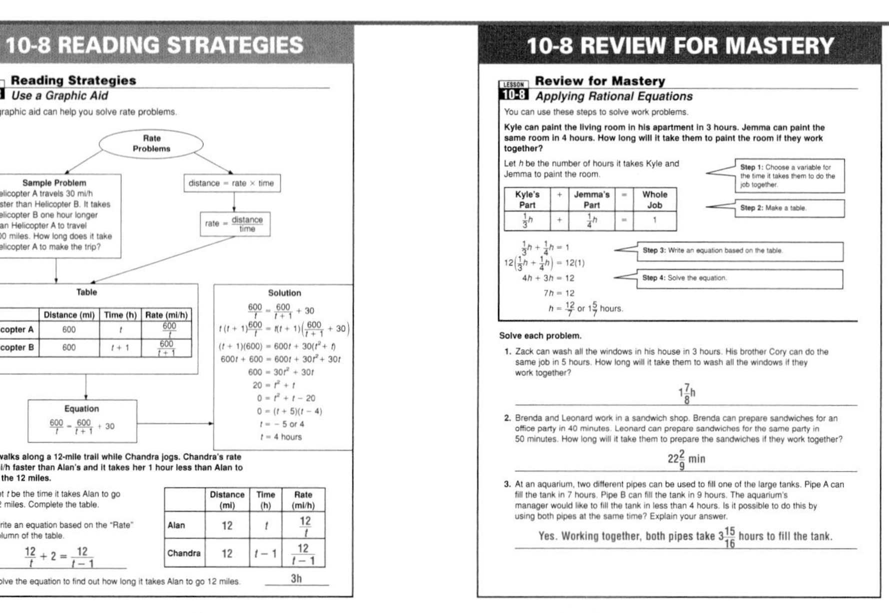

10-8 READING STRATEGIES

LESSON 10-8 **Reading Strategies**
Use a Graphic Aid

This graphic aid can help you solve rate problems.

Rate Problems

Sample Problem
Helicopter A travels 30 mi/h faster than Helicopter B. It takes Helicopter B one hour longer than Helicopter A to travel 600 miles. How long does it take Helicopter A to make the trip?

distance = rate × time

rate = $\frac{\text{distance}}{\text{time}}$

Table

	Distance (mi)	Time (h)	Rate (mi/h)
Helicopter A	600	t	$\frac{600}{t}$
Helicopter B	600	$t + 1$	$\frac{600}{t+1}$

Equation
$\frac{600}{t} = \frac{600}{t+1} + 30$

Solution
$\frac{600}{t} = \frac{600}{t+1} + 30$
$t(t+1)\frac{600}{t} = t(t+1)\left(\frac{600}{t+1} + 30\right)$
$(t+1)(600) = 600t + 30(t^2 + t)$
$600t + 600 = 600t + 30t^2 + 30t$
$600 = 30t^2 + 30t$
$20 = t^2 + t$
$0 = t^2 + t - 20$
$0 = (t+5)(t-4)$
$t = -5$ or 4
$t = 4$ hours

Alan walks along a 12-mile trail while Chandra jogs. Chandra's rate is 2 mi/h faster than Alan's and it takes her 1 hour less than Alan to cover the 12 miles.

1. Let t be the time it takes Alan to go 12 miles. Complete the table.
2. Write an equation based on the "Rate" column of the table.
   $\frac{12}{t} + 2 = \frac{12}{t-1}$

	Distance (mi)	Time (h)	Rate (mi/h)
Alan	12	t	$\frac{12}{t}$
Chandra	12	$t - 1$	$\frac{12}{t-1}$

3. Solve the equation to find out how long it takes Alan to go 12 miles. 3h

10-8 REVIEW FOR MASTERY

LESSON 10-8 **Review for Mastery**
Applying Rational Equations

You can use these steps to solve work problems.

Kyle can paint the living room in his apartment in 3 hours. Jemma can paint the same room in 4 hours. How long will it take them to paint the room if they work together?

Let h be the number of hours it takes Kyle and Jemma to paint the room.

Step 1: Choose a variable for the time it takes them to do the job together.

Kyle's Part	+	Jemma's Part	=	Whole Job
$\frac{1}{3}h$	+	$\frac{1}{4}h$	=	1

Step 2: Make a table.

$\frac{1}{3}h + \frac{1}{4}h = 1$

Step 3: Write an equation based on the table.

$12\left(\frac{1}{3}h + \frac{1}{4}h\right) = 12(1)$
$4h + 3h = 12$

Step 4: Solve the equation.

$7h = 12$
$h = \frac{12}{7}$ or $1\frac{5}{7}$ hours.

Solve each problem.

1. Zack can wash all the windows in his house in 3 hours. His brother Cory can do the same job in 5 hours. How long will it take them to wash all the windows if they work together?
   $1\frac{7}{8}$h
2. Brenda and Leonard work in a sandwich shop. Brenda can prepare sandwiches for an office party in 40 minutes. Leonard can prepare sandwiches for the same party in 50 minutes. How long will it take them to prepare the sandwiches if they work together?
   $22\frac{2}{9}$ min
3. At an aquarium, two different pipes can be used to fill one of the large tanks. Pipe A can fill the tank in 7 hours. Pipe B can fill the tank in 9 hours. The aquarium's manager would like to fill the tank in less than 4 hours. Is it possible to do this by using both pipes at the same time? Explain your answer.
   Yes. Working together, both pipes take $3\frac{15}{16}$ hours to fill the tank.

14. It will take 24 min, which is half the time it takes them to mow the lawn individually. This makes sense since they split the work evenly.

14. **Critical Thinking** Working individually, Tyrone and Cheryl can each mow the lawn in 48 minutes. How long will it take them to mow the lawn if they work together? What do you notice about your answer? Explain why this makes sense.

15. **Write About It** Write an original problem that can be solved using a rational equation. Include the solution to the problem.

Multiple Choice For Exercises 16 and 17, choose the best answer.

16. A chemist has 80 milliliters of a solution that consists of equal amounts of water and ethanol. The chemist wants to make a solution that is 70% water. Which equation can be used to find the additional amount of water w that should be added to the solution?

    (A) (circled) $\frac{40+w}{80+w}=0.7$ (B) $\frac{w}{80}+\frac{w}{40}=0.7$ (C) $\frac{80+w}{40+w}=0.7$ (D) $\frac{80}{w}+\frac{40}{w}=0.7$

17. Ms. Yamashiro can grade her students' homework in 30 minutes. Her teaching assistant can grade the same papers in 45 minutes. If they work together, how long will it take them to grade the papers?

    (A) 9 minutes (B) (circled) 18 minutes (C) 37.5 minutes (D) 75 minutes

CHALLENGE AND EXTEND

Time Needed to Empty Tank	
Drain A	3 hours
Drain B	6 hours
Drain C	4 hours

18. A water tank contains three drains. The table shows the time it takes for each drain to empty the tank. How long does it take to empty the tank when all three drains are used? $1\frac{1}{3}$ h, or 1 h 20 min

19. Luke, Eddie, and Ryan can complete a job in 1 hour and 20 minutes if they work together. Working alone, it takes Ryan 1 hour more to complete the job than it takes Luke, and Luke works twice as fast as Eddie. How much time would it take each to complete the job working alone? Eddie: 6 h; Luke: 3 h; Ryan: 4 h

20. A bowl contains fruit punch that is $\frac{1}{2}$ cranberry juice. When 6 cups of cranberry juice are added to the bowl, the resulting punch is $\frac{2}{3}$ cranberry juice. How many cups of punch were in the bowl to start with? 12 c

SPIRAL STANDARDS REVIEW

7.0, 11.0, 12.0

Without graphing, tell whether each point is on the graph of $4x+2y=14$. *(Lesson 5-1)*

21. $(1, 5)$ yes
22. $(0, 8)$ no
23. $(-2, 11)$ yes
24. $(5, -2)$ no
25. $(9, -11)$ yes
26. $(4, -2)$ no

Determine whether each trinomial is a perfect square. If so, factor. If not, explain. *(Lesson 8-5)*

27. $4x^2+12x+9$ yes
28. $9x^2-6x+1$ yes
29. $16x^2-24x-9$ no
30. $49x^2-4x+4$ no
31. $25x^2+8x-16$ no
32. $36x^2+8x+16$ no

Divide. Check your answer. *(Lesson 10-6)*

33. $\frac{x^2+3x+2}{x+2}$ $x+1$
34. $\frac{x^2-6x-16}{x-8}$ $x+2$
35. $\frac{x^2+7x+12}{x+3}$ $x+4$
36. $\frac{x^2-4x+21}{x-7}$ $x+3$
37. $\frac{x^2-9x+18}{x-3}$ $x-6$
38. $\frac{x^2-3x-40}{x+5}$ $x-8$

COMMON ERROR ALERT

In **Exercise 11,** students may have difficulty writing the reciprocal of a general number. Although students may understand that the reciprocal of 7 is $\frac{1}{7}$, they may not realize that the reciprocal of the variable x is $\frac{1}{x}$. Remind students that the product of a number and its reciprocal is 1 and that $x \cdot \frac{1}{x} = 1$.

Teaching Tip

Multiple Choice In **Exercise 17,** when the teacher and the assistant work together, their total time to grade the papers must be less than the time it would take either of them to complete the task individually. Students can eliminate **C** and **D**.

Journal

Suppose it takes Mark 20 minutes to wash a car and it takes Amanda 30 minutes to wash the same car. Have students explain how to set up an equation to find how long it would take them working together.

ALTERNATIVE ASSESSMENT

Have students choose one of the three types of problems presented in this lesson. Then have them write an original problem of that type, provide a complete solution, and show how to check the answer.

Power Presentations with PowerPoint®

10-8 Lesson Quiz

1. Pipe A can fill a storage tank in 40 minutes. Pipe B can fill the tank in 80 minutes. How long does it take to fill the tank using both pipes at the same time? $26\frac{2}{3}$ min, or 26 min 40 s
2. An 8 oz smoothie is made up of 50% strawberries and 50% yogurt. How many ounces of strawberries should be added to make a smoothie that is 60% strawberries? 2 oz
3. Carlos bikes 3 mi/h faster than Tim. It takes Tim 1 hour longer than Carlos to bike 36 miles. How long does it take Carlos to bike 36 miles? 3 h

Also available on transparency

10-8 PROBLEM SOLVING

LESSON 10-8 Problem Solving
Applying Rational Equations

Write the correct answer.

1. Alex can remodel a bathroom in 2 days. Abraham can remodel the same bathroom in 4 days. How long will it take them to remodel the bathroom if they work together?
   $1\frac{1}{3}$ days
2. A 100-mL solution contains 30 mL of acid. How many milliliters of acid would need to be added to the solution to turn it into a 50% acid solution?
   40 mL
3. When only the cold faucet is fully turned on, a bathtub fills in 8 minutes. When only the hot faucet is fully turned on, the same bathtub fills in 12 minutes. If both the cold and hot faucets are turned on, how long will it take to fill the bathtub?
   $4\frac{4}{5}$ min
4. Marcus jogs 4 mi around a track at an average rate of r mi/h. Then he cools down by walking 1 mi at a rate 3 mi/h slower. His whole workout lasts 1 h. At what rates did Marcus jog and walk?
   jog: 6 mi/h; walk: 3 mi/h

Select the best answer.

5. Ms. Spinoni can prepare a mass-mailing of 500 letters in 10 hours. Mr. Harris can prepare a mass-mailing of 500 letters in 15 hours. How long will it take them to prepare a mass-mailing of 1000 letters if they work together? (*Hint:* The complete job is twice as big.)
   A 6 h C $12\frac{1}{2}$ h
   (B) (circled) 12 h D 25 h
6. At a cafeteria, the automatic ice machine can completely fill itself in 20 minutes. During lunch time, customers can completely empty the ice machine in 30 minutes. At the start of lunch time, the ice machine is completely empty and it starts making ice at the same time that customers start taking ice. How long will it take for the machine to be completely full? (*Hint:* The customers *take away* ice.)
   F 12 min H 30 min
   G 20 min (J) (circled) 60 min

10-8 CHALLENGE

LESSON 10-8 Challenge
Formulating a Formula

Most work problems can be solved using the same method. In fact, you can replace the numbers in the problem with variables to develop a formula that you can use to solve any work problem.

1. Suppose Adam can do a job in a hours and Bianca can do the same job in b hours. Let h be the number of hours it takes them to do the job when they work together. Complete the table.

Adam's Part	+	Bianca's Part	=	Whole Job
$\frac{1}{a}h$	+	$\frac{1}{b}h$	=	1

2. Write an equation based on the table.
   $\frac{1}{a}h+\frac{1}{b}h=1$
3. Solve the equation for h. (*Hint:* When you are done, one side of the equation will contain only h. The other side will contain a fraction expressed in terms of a and b.)
   $h=\frac{ab}{a+b}$

Use your equation from Step 3 as a formula to help you solve each problem.

4. Javier can deliver the newspapers on his route in 1 hour. Rick can deliver the newspapers on the same route in 2 hours. How long will it take them to deliver the newspapers if they work together?
   $\frac{2}{3}$ h or 40 min
5. Cheryl can set up chairs for a school play in 40 minutes. Wei can set up the chairs in 60 minutes. How long will it take them to set up the chairs if they work together?
   24 min
6. Working together, Latrell and Paul can weed a yard in 12 minutes. Working alone, it takes Latrell 20 minutes to do the job. How long does it take Paul to do the job working alone?
   30 min
7. It takes $27\frac{3}{11}$ minutes to print a batch of posters using two printers. One of the printers can do the job by itself in 50 minutes. How long would it take the other printer to do the job by itself?
   60 min

SECTION 10B

CONCEPT CONNECTION

Organizer

Objective: Assess students' ability to apply concepts and skills from Lessons 10-4 through 10-8 in a real-world format.

Online Edition

Problem	Text Reference
1	Lesson 10-5
2	Lesson 10-2
3	Lesson 10-2
4	Lesson 10-1
5	Lesson 10-1

Answers

2.

x	y
0	0
2	−2.5
4	−6.667
6	−15
8	−40
10	Undefined
12	60
14	35
16	26.667

3.

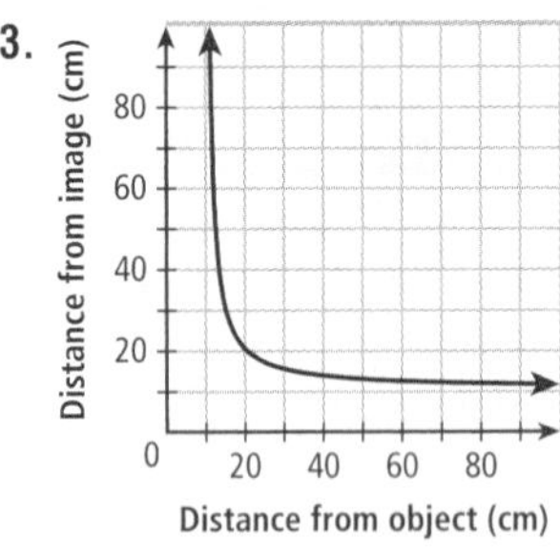

5. Magnification remains the same.

California Standards

Preparation for 15.0

CHAPTER 10

CONCEPT CONNECTION

SECTION 10B

Operations with Rational Expressions and Equations

An Upside-Down World Jamal is studying lenses and their images for a science project. He finds in a science book that a magnifying glass can be used to project upside-down images on a screen. The equation $\frac{1}{f} = \frac{1}{x} + \frac{1}{y}$ relates the focal length of the lens f, the distance of the object from the lens x, and the distance of the image from the lens y. The focal length of Jamal's lens is 10 cm.

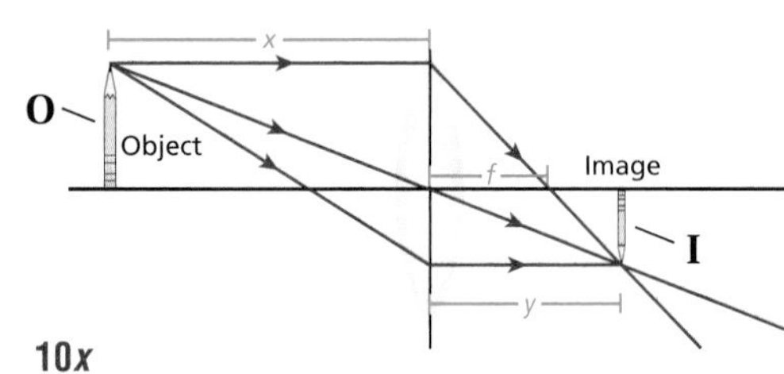

1. Solve the given equation for y using the given value of f. $y = \frac{10x}{x - 10}$
2. Jamal experiments with a candle, the lens, and a screen. Given that the focal length remains constant, use a table for the x-values 0, 2, 4, 6, 8, 10, 12, 14, and 16 cm. For which x-values are the y-values positive? **The y-values are positive for $x > 10$.**
3. Graph the function $y(x)$. Label the axes.

Magnification for images is the ratio of the height of the image to the height of the object. This is also equal to the ratio of the distance between the image and the lens and the distance between the object and the lens: $M = \frac{I}{O} = \frac{y}{x}$. I is the height of the image, O is the height of the object, y is the distance of the image from the lens, and x is the distance of the object from the lens.

4. If the height of a candle is 15 cm and the projected image of that candle is 37.5 cm, what is the magnification of the lens? **2.5**
5. As Jamal moves the candle further from the lens (increases x), and the distance between the lens and the screen decreases (y decreases), does the magnification M stay the same, increase, or decrease?

INTERVENTION

Scaffolding Questions

1. What is the first step in solving for y? Subtract $\frac{1}{x}$ from both sides.

2–3. What values are excluded? 10 What are the asymptotes? $y = 0$, $x = 10$

4. What variable represents the height of the candle? O

5. Which is greater, $\frac{1}{5}$ or $\frac{1}{6}$? $\frac{1}{5}$

Extension

Use the magnification equation to find the image height I as a function of the object distance x for an object 5 cm tall and a focal length of 10 cm.

$I = \frac{50x}{x(x - 10)}$

CHAPTER 10

SECTION 10B

Quiz for Lessons 10-4 Through 10-8

10-4 Multiplying and Dividing Rational Expressions

Multiply. Simplify your answer.

1. $\frac{n+3}{n-5} \cdot (n^2 - 5n)$ $n^2 + 3n$
2. $\frac{6xy^2}{2x^2y^6} \cdot \frac{6x^4y^4}{9x^3}$ 2
3. $\frac{3h^3 - 6h}{10g^2} \cdot \frac{4g}{gh^2 - 2g}$ $\frac{6h}{5g^2}$
4. $\frac{m^2 + m - 2}{m^2 - 2m - 8} \cdot \frac{m^2 - 8m + 16}{3m - 3}$ $\frac{m-4}{3}$

Divide. Simplify your answer.

5. $\frac{2}{n^3} \div \frac{n-6}{n^5}$ $\frac{2n^2}{n-6}$
6. $\frac{2x^2 + 8x + 6}{x} \div \frac{2x^2 + 2x}{x^3 - x^2}$ $x^2 + 2x - 3$
7. $\frac{8b^3c}{b^2c} \div (4b^2 + 4b)$ $\frac{2}{b+1}$

10-5 Adding and Subtracting Rational Expressions

Add or subtract. Simplify your answer.

8. $\frac{15}{2p} - \frac{13}{2p}$ $\frac{1}{p}$
9. $\frac{3m^2}{4m^5} + \frac{5m^2}{4m^5}$ $\frac{2}{m^3}$
10. $\frac{x^2 + 8x}{x-2} - \frac{3x + 14}{x-2}$ $x + 7$
11. $\frac{2t}{4t^2} + \frac{2}{t}$ $\frac{5}{2t}$
12. $\frac{m^2 - m - 2}{m^2 + 6m + 5} - \frac{2}{m+5}$ $\frac{m-4}{m+5}$
13. $\frac{4x}{x-2} + \frac{3x}{2-x}$ $\frac{x}{x-2}$

10-6 Dividing Polynomials

Divide. Check your answer.

14. $(6d^2 + 4d) \div 2d$ $3d + 2$
15. $(15x^4 + 3x^3 - x) \div (-3x^2)$ $-5x^2 - x + \frac{1}{3x}$
16. $(2x^2 - 7x - 4) \div (2x + 1)$ $x - 4$

Divide using long division. Check your answer.

17. $(a^2 + 3a - 10) \div (a - 2)$ $a + 5$
18. $(4y^2 - 9) \div (2y - 3)$ $2y + 3$
19. $(2x^2 + 5x - 8) \div (x + 2)$ $2x + 1 + \frac{-10}{x+2}$

10-7 Solving Rational Equations

Solve. Check your answer.

20. $\frac{3}{x} = \frac{4}{x-1}$ -3
21. $\frac{1}{x} = \frac{2}{x^2}$ 2
22. $\frac{2}{t} + \frac{4}{3t} = \frac{4}{t+2}$ 10
23. $\frac{4}{n^2} = \frac{7}{n} + 2$ $-4; \frac{1}{2}$
24. $\frac{d+2}{d+8} = \frac{-6}{d+8}$ ∅
25. $\frac{x-6}{x^2-6} = \frac{-4}{x-4}$ 2; 0

10-8 Applying Rational Equations

26. It takes Dustin 2 hours to shovel the snow from his driveway and sidewalk. It takes his sister 3 hours to shovel the same area. How long will it take them to shovel the walk if they work together? $1\frac{1}{5}$ h
27. A chemistry student needs to make a solution that is 70% water and 30% hydrochloric acid. The student's current mixture of 300 mL is 60% water and 40% hydrochloric acid. How much water must the student add to achieve his desired solution? 100 mL

READY TO GO ON? SECTION 10B

Organizer

Objective: Assess students' mastery of concepts and skills in Lessons 10-4 through 10-8.

Resources

Assessment Resources

Section 10B Quiz

INTERVENTION

Resources

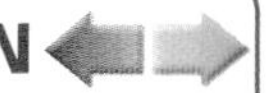

Ready to Go On? Intervention and Enrichment **Worksheets**

Ready to Go On? **CD-ROM**

Ready to Go On? **Online**

my.hrw.com

READY TO GO ON? Diagnose and Prescribe

Ready to Go On? Intervention	Ready to Go On? Intervention, Section 10B: Worksheets	CD-ROM	Online
Lesson 10-4 13.0	10-4 Intervention	Activity 10-4	Diagnose and Prescribe Online
Lesson 10-5 13.0	10-5 Intervention	Activity 10-5	
Lesson 10-6 10.0	10-6 Intervention	Activity 10-6	
Lesson 10-7 Prep for 15.0	10-7 Intervention	Activity 10-7	
Lesson 10-8 15.0	10-8 Intervention	Activity 10-8	

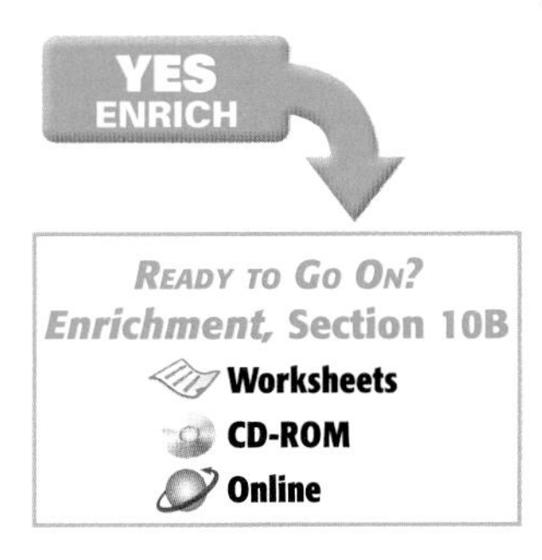

YES
ENRICH
Ready to Go On? Enrichment, Section 10B
Worksheets
CD-ROM
Online

Study Guide: Review

Organizer

Objective: Help students organize and review key concepts and skills presented in Chapter 10.

Online Edition
Multilingual Glossary

Resources

PuzzlePro
One-Stop Planner®

***Multilingual Glossary* Online**

go.hrw.com
KEYWORD: MA8CA Glossary

Lesson Tutorial Videos
CD-ROM

Test & Practice Generator
One-Stop Planner®

Answers

1. rational expression
2. rational function
3. rational equation
4. inverse variation
5. discontinuous function
6. Yes; the product xy is constant.
7. No; the product xy is not constant.
8. $y = -\frac{4}{x}$

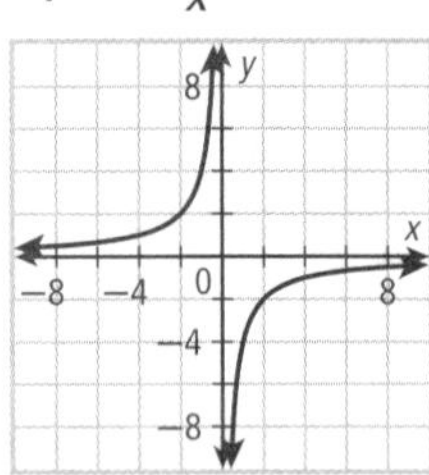

9. $y = \frac{1}{x}$

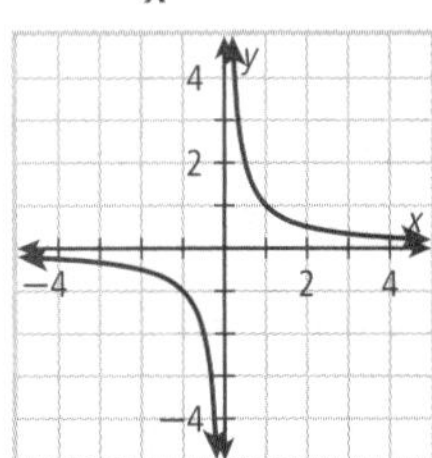

10. −15
11. $13,200

Study Guide: Review

Vocabulary

asymptote	634	**inverse variation**	627
discontinuous function	634	**rational equation**	674
excluded value	634	**rational expression**	642
extraneous solution	675	**rational function**	634

Complete the sentences below with vocabulary words from the list above.

1. A(n) ___?___ is an algebraic expression whose numerator and denominator are polynomials.
2. A function whose rule is a quotient of polynomials in which the denominator has a degree of at least 1 is a(n) ___?___ .
3. A(n) ___?___ is an equation that contains one or more rational expressions.
4. A(n) ___?___ is a relationship that can be written in the form $y = \frac{k}{x}$, where k is a nonzero constant.
5. A function is a(n) ___?___ if its graph contains one or more jumps, breaks, or holes.

10-1 Inverse Variation *(pp. 627–633)*

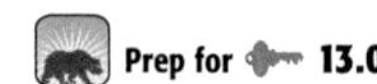

Prep for 13.0

EXAMPLE

- **Write and graph the inverse variation in which $y = 2$ when $x = 3$.**

$y = \frac{k}{x}$ *Use the form $y = \frac{k}{x}$.*

$2 = \frac{k}{3}$ *Substitute known values.*

$6 = k$ *Multiply by 3 to find the value of k.*

$y = \frac{6}{x}$ *Substitute 6 for k in $y = \frac{k}{x}$.*

x	−6	−3	−2	−1	0	1	2	3	6
y	−1	−2	−3	−6	und.	6	3	2	1

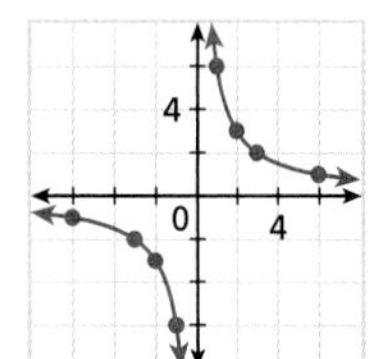

Make a table of values and plot the points.

EXERCISES

Tell whether each relationship represents an inverse variation. Explain.

6.

x	y
4	−3
−12	1
6	−2

7.

x	y
2	4
6	8
10	12

8. Write and graph the inverse variation in which $y = 4$ when $x = -1$.
9. Write and graph the inverse variation in which $y = \frac{1}{2}$ when $x = 2$.
10. Let $x_1 = 5$, $y_1 = -6$, and $x_2 = 2$. Let y vary inversely as x. Find y_2.
11. The number of fleet vehicles a town can afford to buy varies inversely as the price of each car. If the town can afford 3 cars priced at $22,000 each, what must the price of a car be in order for the town to purchase 5 of them?

10-2 Rational Functions *(pp. 634–641)*

Prep for 13.0

EXAMPLE

- Graph the function $y = \frac{1}{x+1} + 3$.

Find the asymptotes.

$x = -1$ *$b = -1$*

$y = 3$ *$c = 3$*

Graph the asymptotes using dashed lines.

Make a table of values. Choose x-values on both sides of the vertical asymptote.

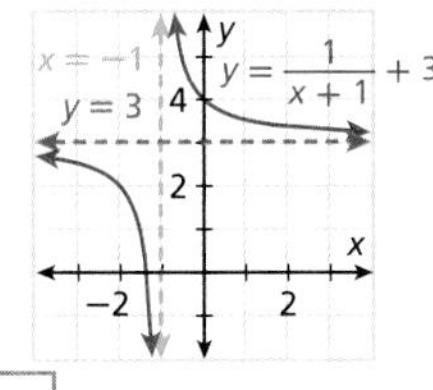

x	−3	−2	0	1
y	$\frac{5}{2}$	2	4	$\frac{7}{2}$

Plot the points and connect them with smooth curves.

EXERCISES

Identify any excluded values and the asymptotes for each rational function.

12. $y = \frac{1}{x+4}$

13. $y = \frac{1}{x+1} + 3$

14. $y = \frac{-5}{2x+6} - 4$

15. $y = \frac{2}{4x-7} + 5$

Graph each function.

16. $y = \frac{3}{x}$

17. $y = \frac{4}{x+5}$

18. $y = \frac{1}{x+4} - 2$

19. $y = \frac{1}{x-6} + 2$

20. A rectangle has an area of 24 cm^2. If x represents the width, then $y = \frac{24}{x}$ represents the length y. Describe the reasonable domain and range values and graph the function.

10-3 Simplifying Rational Expressions *(pp. 642–648)*

12.0

EXAMPLE

Simplify the rational expression, if possible. Identify any excluded values.

- $\frac{x-1}{x^2+2x-3}$

$\frac{x-1}{(x+3)(x-1)}$ *Factor the denominator.*

$\frac{\cancel{x-1}^{1}}{(x+3)\cancel{(x-1)}}$ *Divide out common factors.*

$\frac{1}{x+3}$ *Simplify.*

Identify the excluded values.

$x^2 + 2x - 3 = 0$ *Set the denominator equal to 0.*

$(x+3)(x-1) = 0$ *Factor.*

$x + 3 = 0$ or $x - 1 = 0$ *Use the Zero Product Property.*

$x = -3$ or $x = 1$ *Solve each equation.*

The excluded values are −3 and 1.

EXERCISES

Identify any excluded values of each rational expression.

21. $\frac{3}{5p}$

22. $\frac{-2}{r-7}$

23. $\frac{t}{t^2-t}$

24. $\frac{-4}{x^2-4x-5}$

25. $\frac{x-1}{x^2-25}$

26. $\frac{x+4}{x^2-11x+28}$

Simplify each rational expression, if possible. Identify any excluded values.

27. $\frac{7r^2}{21r^3}$

28. $\frac{3k^2}{6k^3-9k^2}$

29. $\frac{x+6}{x^2+4x-12}$

30. $\frac{2x-6}{9-x^2}$

31. $\frac{3x+15}{x^2+4x-5}$

32. $\frac{x^2+9x+18}{x^2+x-30}$

33. What is the ratio of the area of the square to the area of the circle?

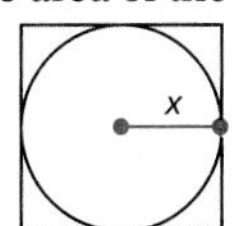

Answers

12. −4; $x = -4$; $y = 0$
13. −1; $x = -1$; $y = 3$
14. −3; $x = -3$; $y = -4$
15. $\frac{7}{4}$; $x = \frac{7}{4}$; $y = 5$
16.

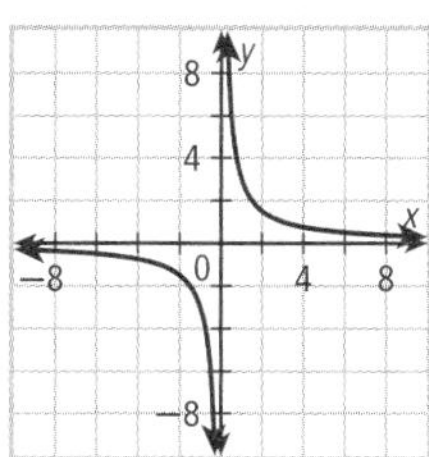

17.

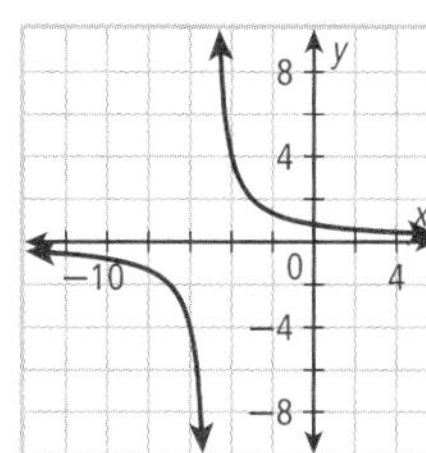

18.

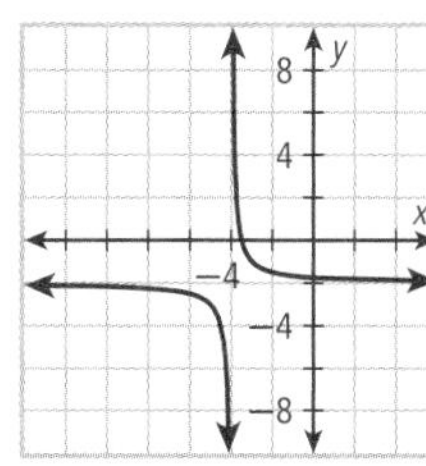

19.

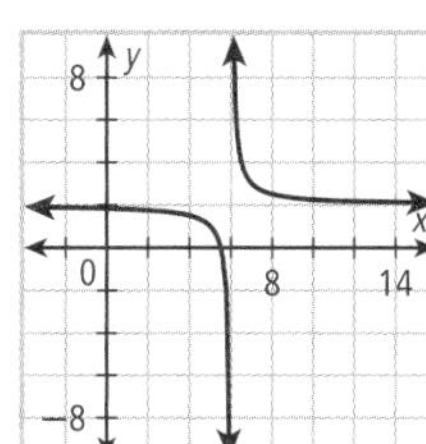

20. D: $x > 0$; R: $y > 0$

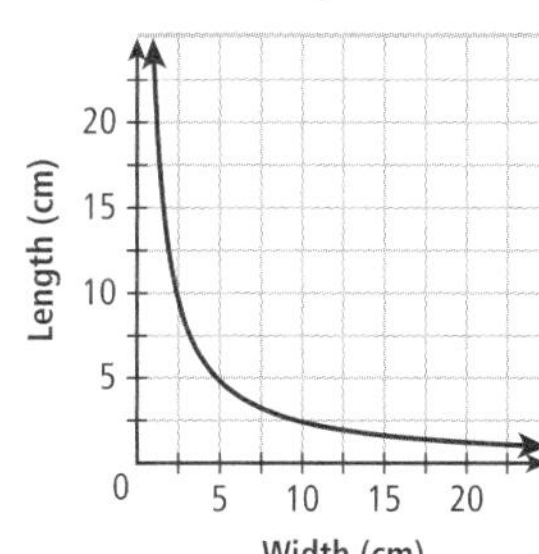

21. 0
22. 7
23. 0, 1
24. −1, 5
25. 5, −5
26. 4, 7
27. $\frac{1}{3r}$; $r \neq 0$
28. $\frac{1}{2k-3}$; $k \neq 0, \frac{3}{2}$
29. $\frac{1}{x-2}$; $x \neq -6, 2$
30. $\frac{-2}{x+3}$; $x \neq \pm 3$
31. $\frac{3}{x-1}$; $x \neq -5, 1$
32. $\frac{x+3}{x-5}$; $x \neq -6, 5$
33. $\frac{4}{\pi}$

Answers

34. $\frac{2b^2 + 2b}{3}$
35. $\frac{4x^2 - 12x}{3}$
36. $\frac{15b^2}{2}$
37. $\frac{12n^3}{m}$
38. $\frac{b + 2}{2b^2 + 8b}$
39. $\frac{x^2 + 2x - 3}{4x^2 - 16}$
40. $10a^2b^2$
41. $10x(x - 3)$
42. $\frac{b^2 + 8}{2b}$
43. $\frac{3x^2 + 2x - 4}{x^2 - 2}$
44. $\frac{8p - 2}{p^2 - 4p + 2}$
45. $\frac{5b - 1}{7 - b}$
46. $\frac{-10}{n^2 - 1}$
47. $\frac{7m + 2}{10m^2}$
48. $\frac{h^2 + 5h - 1}{h - 5}$
49. $\frac{40}{3r}$

10-4 Multiplying and Dividing Rational Expressions *(pp. 652–658)*

 13.0

EXAMPLE

■ Divide. Simplify your answer.

$$\frac{32x^2y^2}{7z} \div \frac{2xy^2}{28xz^3}$$

$$\frac{32x^2y^2}{7z} \cdot \frac{28xz^3}{2xy^2}$$ *Multiply by the reciprocal.*

$$\frac{\cancel{32}^{16} x^2 \cancel{y^2}}{\cancel{7z}} \cdot \frac{\cancel{28}^4 \cancel{x} \cancel{z^3}^{z^2}}{\cancel{2} \cancel{x} \cancel{y^2}}$$ *Divide out common factors.*

$$64x^2z^2$$ *Simplify.*

EXERCISES

Multiply or divide. Simplify your answer.

34. $\frac{2b}{3b - 6} \cdot (b^2 - b - 2)$

35. $\frac{4x}{3x + 9} \cdot (x^2 - 9)$

36. $\frac{5ab^2}{2ab} \cdot \frac{3a^2b^2}{a^2b}$

37. $16n^3 \div \frac{4m^2n}{3mn}$

38. $\frac{b + 2}{2b^2 + 12b} \cdot \frac{b^2 + 2b - 24}{b^2 - 16}$

39. $\frac{x^2 + 2x - 3}{4x} \div \frac{x^2 - 4}{x}$

10-5 Adding and Subtracting Rational Expressions *(pp. 659–665)*

 13.0

EXAMPLES

Add or subtract. Simplify your answer.

■ $$\frac{7x}{3xy} - \frac{x^2 - 3x}{3xy}$$

$$\frac{7x - (x^2 - 3x)}{3xy}$$ *Subtract numerators.*

$$\frac{7x - x^2 + 3x}{3xy}$$ *Distribute.*

$$\frac{10x - x^2}{3xy}$$ *Simplify.*

■ $$\frac{3w}{w - 5} + \frac{4}{w^2 - 2w - 15}$$

$$\frac{3w}{w - 5} + \frac{4}{(w - 5)(w + 3)}$$ *Factor to find the LCD.*

$$\frac{3w(w + 3)}{(w - 5)(w + 3)} + \frac{4}{(w - 5)(w + 3)}$$ *Write each expression using the LCD.*

$$\frac{3w^2 + 9w}{(w - 5)(w + 3)} + \frac{4}{(w - 5)(w + 3)}$$

$$\frac{3w^2 + 9w + 4}{(w - 5)(w + 3)}$$ *Add and simplify.*

EXERCISES

Find the LCM of the given expressions.

40. $5a^2b$, $10ab^2$

41. $2x^2 - 6x$, $5x - 15$

Add or subtract. Simplify your answer.

42. $\frac{b^2}{2b} + \frac{8}{2b}$

43. $\frac{3x^2 - 4}{x^2 - 2} + \frac{2x}{x^2 - 2}$

44. $\frac{8p}{p^2 - 4p + 2} - \frac{2}{p^2 - 4p + 2}$

45. $\frac{3b + 4}{7 - b} - \frac{5 - 2b}{7 - b}$

46. $\frac{n - 5}{n^2 - 1} - \frac{n + 5}{n^2 - 1}$

47. $\frac{3}{5m} + \frac{m + 2}{10m^2}$

48. $\frac{h^2 + 2h}{h - 5} - \frac{3h - 1}{5 - h}$

49. A scout troop hikes 10 miles to the top of a mountain. Because the return trip is downhill, the scouts are able to hike 3 times faster on their way down. Let r represent the troop's rate to the mountaintop. Write and simplify an expression for the round-trip hiking time in terms of r.

10-6 Dividing Polynomials *(pp. 667–673)*

10.0, 12.0

EXAMPLE

■ Divide $(4x^3 - 2x^2 + 5x - 1) \div (x - 2)$.

$$\begin{array}{r} 4x^2 + 6x + 17 \\ x-2\,\overline{)\,4x^3 - 2x^2 + 5x - 1} \\ -(4x^3 - 8x^2) \\ \hline 6x^2 + 5x \\ -(6x^2 - 12x) \\ \hline 17x - 1 \\ -(17x - 34) \\ \hline 33 \end{array}$$

$$4x^2 + 6x + 17 + \frac{33}{x-2}$$

EXERCISES

Divide. Check your answer.

50. $(-5x^3 + 10x - 25) \div (-5x^2)$

51. $\dfrac{x^2 - 8x - 20}{x - 10}$

52. $\dfrac{6n^2 - 13n - 5}{2n - 5}$

Divide using long division. Check your answer.

53. $(x^2 + 5x + 6) \div (x + 3)$

54. $(x^2 + x - 30) \div (x - 5)$

55. $(3b^3 - 4b + 2) \div (b - 2)$

10-7 Solving Rational Equations *(pp. 674–678)*

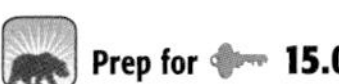

Prep for 15.0

EXAMPLE

■ Solve $\dfrac{3}{x+3} = \dfrac{2}{x}$. Check your answer.

$3x = 2(x+3)$ *Use cross products.*

$3x = 2x + 6$ *Distribute.*

$\underline{-2x \quad -2x}$ *Subtract 2x from both sides.*

$x = 6$

Check

$\dfrac{3}{x+3}$	$= \dfrac{2}{x}$
$\dfrac{3}{6+3}$	$\dfrac{2}{6}$
$\dfrac{3}{9}$	$\dfrac{1}{3}$
$\dfrac{1}{3}$	$\dfrac{1}{3}$ ✓

EXERCISES

Solve. Check your answer.

56. $-4 = \dfrac{3}{r}$

57. $\dfrac{6}{7} = \dfrac{x}{2}$

58. $\dfrac{6}{b} = \dfrac{-5}{3+b}$

59. $\dfrac{7}{3y^2} = \dfrac{-2}{y}$

60. $\dfrac{2}{x-1} = \dfrac{3x}{1-x}$

61. $\dfrac{2x}{x^2} + \dfrac{1}{x^2} = 3$

62. $\dfrac{2}{3} + \dfrac{4}{x} = \dfrac{6}{3x}$

63. $-\dfrac{1}{3x} + \dfrac{x}{4} = -\dfrac{1}{12x}$

64. $\dfrac{2}{3b} + 4 = \dfrac{1}{3b}$

65. $\dfrac{4}{x-4} = \dfrac{8}{x^2 - 16}$

66. $\dfrac{5x - 10}{x+1} = \dfrac{x}{2}$

67. $\dfrac{2x}{x+3} + \dfrac{x}{4} = \dfrac{3}{x+3}$

68. $\dfrac{9m}{m-5} = 7 - \dfrac{3}{m-5}$

69. $\dfrac{x-4}{x^2-4} = \dfrac{-2}{x-2}$

10-8 Applying Rational Equations *(pp. 679–683)*

15.0

EXAMPLE

■ **Armin can clean a house in 5 hours. It takes Greg 7 hours to clean the same house. How long will it take them if they work together?**

$35\left(\frac{1}{5}h + \frac{1}{7}h\right) = 35(1)$ *Multiply both sides by the LCD, 35*

$7h + 5h = 35$ *Distribute 35 on the left side.*

$12h = 35$ *Combine like terms.*

$h = \frac{35}{12} = 2\frac{11}{12}$ *Divide both sides by 12.*

Together they can clean the house in $2\frac{11}{12}$ h, or 2 h 55 min.

EXERCISES

70. A liquid poured into pipe A fills a storage tank in 12 hours. The same liquid poured into pipe B fills the tank in 18 hours. How long would it take to fill the tank if the liquid is poured into both pipes at the same time?

71. A chemist has 400 milliliters of a solution that is 40% water and 60% chlorine. She wants a solution that is 50% water and 50% chlorine. How many milliliters of water should she add to the solution?

Answers

50. $x - \frac{2}{x} + \frac{5}{x^2}$
51. $x + 2$
52. $3n + 1$
53. $x + 2$
54. $x + 6$
55. $3b^2 + 6b + 8 + \frac{18}{b-2}$
56. $-\frac{3}{4}$
57. $\frac{12}{7}$
58. $-\frac{18}{11}$
59. $-\frac{7}{6}$
60. $-\frac{2}{3}$
61. $-\frac{1}{3}$, 1
62. -3
63. ± 1
64. $-\frac{1}{12}$
65. -2
66. 4, 5
67. -12, 1
68. -19
69. 0
70. $7\frac{1}{5}$ h, or 7 h 12 min
71. 80 mL

Organizer

Objective: Assess students' mastery of concepts and skills presented in Chapter 10.

Online Edition

Resources

 ***Assessment Resources***

Chapter 10 Tests

- Free Response (Levels A, B, C)
- Multiple Choice (Levels A, B, C)
- Performance Assessment

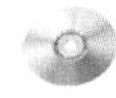 ***IDEA Works!* CD-ROM**

Modified Chapter 10 Test

Test & Practice Generator One-Stop Planner®

Standard	Exercises
10.0	25–27a
12.0	6–9
13.0	10–24
15.0	31

CHAPTER TEST

1. Write and graph the inverse variation in which $y = -4$ when $x = 2$. $y = -\frac{8}{x}$
2. The number of posters the Spanish Club can buy varies inversely as the cost of each poster. The club can buy 15 posters that cost \$2.60 each. How many posters can the club buy if they cost \$3.25 each? 12

Identify any excluded values and the asymptotes for each rational function.

3. $y = \frac{3}{x+1}$ $x \neq -1$; $x = -1$, $y = 0$
4. $y = \frac{1}{2x-1} + 5$ $x \neq \frac{1}{2}$; $x = \frac{1}{2}$, $y = 5$
5. $y = \frac{1}{x+3} - 3$ $x \neq -3$; $x = -3$, $y = -3$

Simplify each rational expression, if possible. Identify any excluded values.

6. $\frac{2b}{4b^2}$ $\frac{1}{2b}$; $b \neq 0$
7. $\frac{x^2-16}{x^2+3x-4}$ $\frac{x-4}{x-1}$; $x \neq -4, 1$
8. $\frac{b^2-2b-15}{5-b}$ $-b-3$; $b \neq 5$
9. $\frac{x^2+4x-5}{x^2-25}$ $\frac{x-1}{x-5}$; $x \neq \pm 5$

Multiply. Simplify your answer.

10. $\frac{-4}{x^2-9} \cdot (x-3)$ $\frac{-4}{x+3}$
11. $\frac{2a^2b^2}{5b^3} \cdot \frac{15a^2b}{8a^4}$ $\frac{3}{4}$
12. $\frac{x^2-x-12}{x^2-16} \cdot \frac{x^2+x-12}{x^2+3x+2}$ $\frac{x^2-9}{x^2+3x+2}$

Divide. Simplify your answer.

13. $\frac{4x^2y^4}{3xy^2} \div \frac{12xy}{15x^3y^2}$ $\frac{5x^3y^3}{3}$
14. $\frac{3b^2-6b}{2b^3+3b^2} \div \frac{2b-4}{8b+12}$ $\frac{6}{b}$
15. $\frac{x^2+2x-15}{x^2-9} \div \frac{x^2-25}{x^2+3x+2}$ $\frac{x^2+3x+2}{x^2-2x-15}$

Add or subtract. Simplify your answer.

16. $\frac{b^2+3}{5b} + \frac{4}{5b}$ $\frac{b^2+7}{5b}$
17. $\frac{5x-2}{x^2+2} - \frac{2x}{x^2+2}$ $\frac{3x-2}{x^2+2}$
18. $\frac{2}{3x^2} - \frac{5-2x}{3x^2}$ $\frac{-3+2x}{3x^2}$
19. $\frac{3m}{2m^2} + \frac{1}{2m}$ $\frac{2}{m}$
20. $\frac{3x}{2x+4} - \frac{1}{x+2}$ $\frac{3x-2}{2x+4}$
21. $\frac{y^2+4}{y-3} + \frac{y^2}{3-y}$ $\frac{4}{y-3}$

Divide.

22. $(8t^2 - 2t) \div 2t$ $4t - 1$
23. $\frac{3x^2+2x-8}{x+2}$ $3x - 4$
24. $\frac{k^2-2k-35}{k+5}$ $k - 7$

Divide using long division.

25. $(2w^2 + 5w - 12) \div (w + 4)$ $2w - 3$
26. $(x^2 - 4x + 9) \div (x + 2)$ $x - 6 + \frac{21}{x+2}$
27. The area of a rectangle can be modeled by $A(x) = x^3 - 1$. The length is $x - 1$.
    a. Find a polynomial to represent the width of the rectangle. $x^2 + x + 1$
    b. Find the width when x is 6 cm. 43 cm

Solve. Check your answer.

28. $\frac{2}{x-1} = \frac{9}{2x-3}$ $\frac{3}{5}$
29. $\frac{3}{n-1} = \frac{n}{n+4}$ $-2, 6$
30. $\frac{2}{n+2} = \frac{n-4}{n^2-4}$ 0
31. Julio can wash and wax the family car in 2 hours. It takes Leo 3 hours to wash and wax the same car. How long will it take them to wash and wax the car if they work together? $1\frac{1}{5}$ h, or 1 h 12 min

Answer

1. 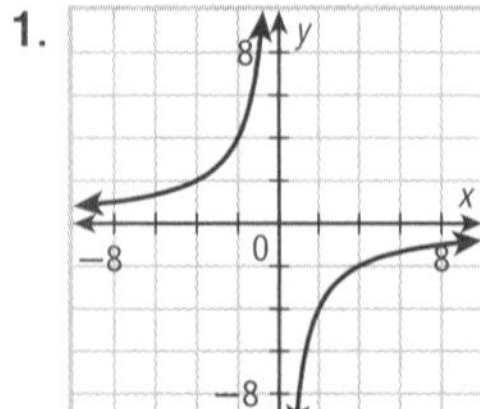

College Entrance Exam Practice

FOCUS ON SAT MATHEMATICS SUBJECT TESTS

The topics covered on each SAT Mathematics Subject Test vary only slightly each time the test is given. Find out the general distribution of test items across topics, and then identify the areas you need to concentrate on while studying.

To prepare for the SAT Math Subject Tests, start reviewing material several months before your test date. Take sample tests to find the areas you need to focus on. You are not expected to have studied all topics on the test.

You may want to time yourself as you take this practice test. It should take you about 6 minutes to complete.

1. Which set of ordered pairs satisfies an inverse variation?
   (A) $(6, 3)$ and $(8, 4)$
   (B) $(2, -3)$ and $(4, 5)$
   (C) $(4, -2)$ and $(-5, 10)$
   (D) $(2, 6)$ and $(-3, -4)$
   (E) $\left(4, \frac{1}{4}\right)$ and $\left(-4, \frac{1}{4}\right)$

2. If $\frac{3}{x+3} = \frac{7x}{x^2-9}$, what is x?
   (A) -12
   (B) -3
   (C) $-\frac{9}{4}$
   (D) $\frac{9}{4}$
   (E) 3

3. What is h if $(x^3 + 2x^2 - 4x + h) \div (x + 1)$ has a remainder of 15?
   (A) -10
   (B) -5
   (C) 5
   (D) 10
   (E) 20

4. The graph of which function is shown?

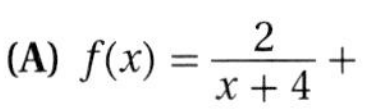
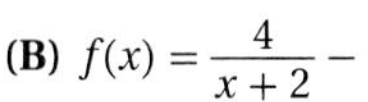
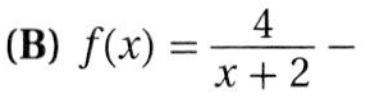

   (A) $f(x) = \frac{2}{x+4} + 1$
   (B) $f(x) = \frac{4}{x+2} - 1$
   (C) $f(x) = \frac{4}{x-2} + 1$
   (D) $f(x) = \frac{4}{x-2} - 1$
   (E) $f(x) = \frac{2}{x-4} + 1$

5. Which function has the same graph as $f(x) = \frac{x^2 - 4x - 5}{x^2 - 3x - 10}$ except at $x = 5$?
   (A) $g(x) = \frac{x-1}{x-2}$
   (B) $g(x) = \frac{x+1}{x+2}$
   (C) $g(x) = \frac{x+1}{(x-5)(x+2)}$
   (D) $g(x) = \frac{(x+5)(x-1)}{x+2}$
   (E) $g(x) = \frac{(x-5)(x+1)}{x-2}$

Organizer

Objective: Provide practice for college entrance exams such as the SAT Mathematics Subject Tests.

Premier **Online Edition**

Resources

College Entrance Exam Practice

Questions on the SAT Mathematics Subject Tests Levels I and II represent the following math content areas:

	Level	
	I	II
Algebra	30%	18%
Plane Euclidean Geometry	20%	0%
Coordinate Geometry	12%	12%
Three-dimensional Geometry	6%	8%
Trigonometry	8%	20%
Functions	12%	24%
Statistics/Probability	6%	6%
Miscellaneous	6%	12%

Items on this page focus on:
- Algebra
- Functions

Text References:

Item	1	2	3	4	5
Lesson	10-1	10-7	10-6	10-2	10-3

Multiple Choice

1. Students who chose **A** might think that if (x_1, y_1) and (x_2, y_2) are solutions of an inverse variation, then $x_1y_2 = x_2y_1$. Students who chose **C** might think that if (x_1, y_1) and (x_2, y_2) are solutions of an inverse variation, then $x_1x_2 = y_1y_2$.
2. Students who chose **B** did not check their answer. This choice is an extraneous solution and an excluded value.
3. Students who chose **E** may not have distributed signs correctly in the process of long division. Remind students to check their work if they have time.
4. Students who chose **B** may have thought that the numerator should be $x + 2$ because the graph is shifted 2 units to the right. Students who chose **C** did not recognize that the graph has a horizontal asymptote of $y = -1$.
5. Students who chose **A** may have factored $f(x)$ incorrectly as $\frac{(x+5)(x-1)}{(x+5)(x-2)}$ and then cancelled the common factor. Students who chose **C** may have factored $f(x)$ correctly but did not cancel the common factor from both the numerator and denominator.

Organizer

Objective: Provide opportunities to learn and practice common test-taking strategies.

 Online Edition

Teaching Tip **Multiple Choice** This Strategy for Success focuses on choosing the best option when there are multiple correct answers or combinations of answers. Remind students to read the problem statement and options thoroughly. Tell students to investigate each possible combination of answers before moving to the next test item.

As students practice this strategy, tell them to eliminate options as they progress through a problem. If they can eliminate one statement, the correct response is sometimes obvious.

CHAPTER 10 STRATEGIES FOR SUCCESS

Multiple Choice: Choose Combinations of Answers

Some multiple-choice test items require selecting a combination of correct answers. The correct response is the most complete option available. To solve this type of test item, determine if each statement is true or false. Then choose the option that includes each correct statement.

EXAMPLE 1

Which of the following has an excluded value of −5?

I. $\frac{5}{x-5}$

II. $\frac{8x^2+36x-20}{2(x+5)}$

III. $\frac{x^2-10}{5x+25} \cdot \frac{5}{x+10}$

IV. $\frac{2(x+2)}{2x^2+12x+10}$

Ⓐ I only

Ⓑ II and III

Ⓒ II, III, and IV

Ⓓ III and IV

Look at each statement separately and determine whether it is true. You can keep track of which statements are true in a table.

Statement	True/False
I	False
II	True
III	True
IV	True

Statement I
The denominator, $x - 5$, equals 0 when $x = 5$.

Statement I does not answer the question, so it is false.

Statement II
The denominator, $2(x + 5)$, equals 0 when $x = -5$.

Statement II does answer the question, so it is true.

Statement III
The denominator, $(5x + 25)(x + 10)$, equals 0 when $x = -5$ or $x = -10$.

Statement III does answer the question, so it is true.

Statement IV
The denominator, $2x^2 + 12x + 10$, can be factored as $2(x + 5)(x + 1)$. This expression equals 0 when $x = -5$ or $x = -1$.

Statement IV does answer the question, so it is true.

Statements II, III, and IV are all true. Option C is the correct response because it includes all the true statements.

Options B and D contain some of the true statements, but option C is the **most complete** answer.

Evaluate all of the statements before deciding on an answer choice. Make a table to keep track of whether each statement is true or false.

Read each test item and answer the questions that follow.

Item A

Which dimensions represent a rectangle that has an area equivalent to the expression $2x^2 + 18x + 16$?

I. $\ell = x + 8$

$w = 2(x + 1)$

II. $\ell = 2x + 2$

$w = \frac{x^2 + 3x - 40}{x - 5}$

III. $\ell = x + 2$

$w = \frac{(2x + 2)(x + 4)}{1} \cdot \frac{(3x - 1)}{(3x^2 - 11x - 4)}$

(A) I only (C) I and II

(B) III only (D) I, II, and III

1. How do you determine the area of a rectangle?
2. Daisy realized that the area of the rectangle described in I was equivalent to the given area and selected option A as her response. Do you agree? Explain your reasoning.
3. Write a simplified expression for the width of the rectangle described in II.
4. Explain each step for determining the area of the rectangle described in III.
5. If the rectangle described in II has an area equivalent to the given expression, then which options can you eliminate?

Item B

Which expression is undefined for $x = 3$ or $x = -2$?

I. $2x + 12 \cdot \frac{4}{2(x - 3)(x + 6)}$

III. $\frac{(x - 2)}{(x + 2)(x - 1)}$

II. $\frac{9x - 1}{x^2 + 3}$

IV. $\frac{14}{x^2 - x - 6}$

(A) I, III, and IV (C) III and IV

(B) I and II (D) I and IV

6. When is an expression undefined?
7. Henry determined that expression I is undefined when $x = 3$. He decides it is an incorrect answer because the expression is defined when $x = -2$. Should he select option C by process of elimination? Explain your reasoning.
8. Make a table to determine the correct response.

Item C

Which rational function has a graph with a horizontal asymptote of $y = 4$?

I. $y = \frac{-4}{x}$

III. $y = \frac{1}{x - 4}$

II. $y = \frac{1}{x} + 4$

IV. $y = -\frac{1}{x} + 4$

(A) I and III (C) I and II

(B) II only (D) II and IV

9. Where does the horizontal asymptote of the function in statement I occur?
10. Using your answer from Problem 9, which option(s) can you eliminate? Explain your reasoning.
11. Look at the options remaining. Which statement would be best to check next? Explain your reasoning.

Answers

Possible answers:

1. $A = \ell w$
2. No; she should have checked to see if the other rectangles also have an area that is equivalent to the given expression.
3. $x + 8$
4. Simplify the width by factoring the denominator of the second expression. Then divide out common factors and multiply. Then multiply the length and the width and simplify the result.
5. **A** and **B**
6. when the value of the denominator is zero
7. No; the problem asks for expressions that are undefined for $x = 3$ or $x = -2$, not necessarily both.
8. **A** is the correct response.

Statement	True/False
I	True
II	False
III	True
IV	True

9. $y = 0$
10. **A** and **C** can be eliminated because the function in statement I does not have a horizontal asymptote of $y = 4$.
11. Statement **IV** should be checked next. If it is false, then by elimination, the correct response is **B.**

Answers to Test Items

A. C

B. A

C. D

California Standards

10.0

MASTERING THE STANDARDS

Organizer

Objective: Provide review and practice for Chapters 1–10.

Online Edition

Resources

Assessment Resources
Chapter 10 Cumulative Test

Focus on California Standards Benchmark Tests and Intervention

***California Standards Practice* CD-ROM**

go.hrw.com
KEYWORD: MA8CA Practice

California Standards

Standard	Exercises
2.0	18
6.0	6
7.0	2
8.0	4
9.0	23
10.0	10, 13
11.0	11, 16, 22
12.0	5, 15, 20
13.0	7, 8
15.0	21
17.0	14, 24a
20.0	17
21.0	3, 9
22.0	1

CUMULATIVE ASSESSMENT, CHAPTERS 1–10

Multiple Choice

1. At how many points does the graph of $y = (x - 6)^2$ intersect the x-axis?

(A) none
(B) one (circled)
(C) two
(D) three

2. Which point lies on the line described by $2x - 3y - 9 = 0$?

(A) $(-2, 2)$
(B) $(4, -5)$
(C) $(0, 3)$
(D) $(3, -1)$ (circled)

3. Which function is shown in the graph?

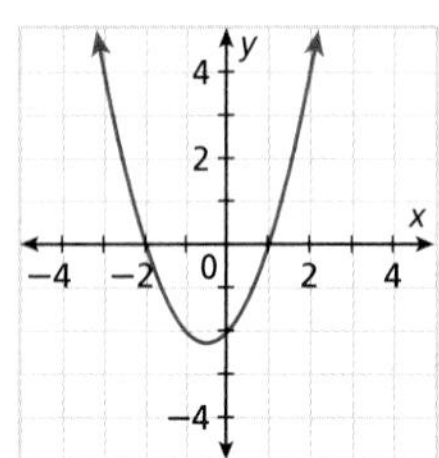

(A) $y = x^2 + x - 2$ (circled)
(B) $y = x^2 - x - 2$
(C) $y = -x^2 - x + 2$
(D) $y = x^2 - 2$

4. A city map is laid out on a coordinate plane. Elm Street is described by the line $x + 2y = -6$. Oak Street intersects Elm Street at a right angle. Which of the following could be the equation for Oak Street?

(A) $2x + y = 5$
(B) $-2x + y = 3$ (circled)
(C) $x + 2y = 4$
(D) $-x - 2y = 8$

5. Which expression is NOT equivalent to $\frac{3}{x-1}$?

(A) $\frac{3x+6}{x^2+x-2}$
(B) $\frac{3x-3}{x^2-2x+1}$
(C) $\frac{3x+3}{x^2-1}$
(D) $\frac{3x-3}{x-1}$ (circled)

6. What are the x- and y-intercepts of the line described by $6x - 2y = 4$?

(A) x-intercept: $\frac{2}{3}$; y-intercept: 2
(B) x-intercept: $-\frac{2}{3}$; y-intercept: 2
(C) x-intercept: $\frac{2}{3}$; y-intercept: -2 (circled)
(D) x-intercept: -2; y-intercept: $\frac{2}{3}$

7. Which expression is equivalent to $\frac{3m^2n}{5m} \cdot \frac{20mn}{n^6}$?

(A) $\frac{12m^2}{n^4}$ (circled)
(B) $\frac{12m^3}{n^3}$
(C) $12m^2n^3$
(D) $\frac{12m}{n}$

8. Simplify $\frac{3}{x} + \frac{3}{5x}$.

(A) $\frac{1}{x}$
(B) $\frac{18}{10x}$
(C) $\frac{18}{5x}$ (circled)
(D) $\frac{1}{2x}$

9. Which of these is the graph of $y = x^2 - 4x + 4$?

(A)
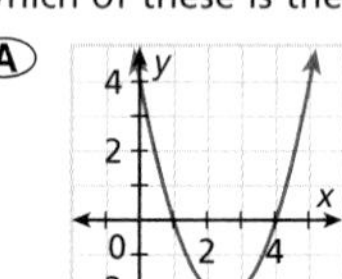

(C) (circled)
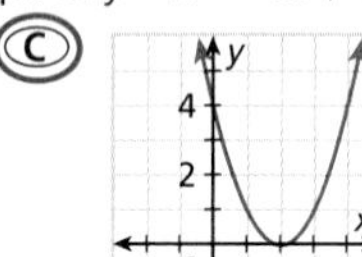

(B)
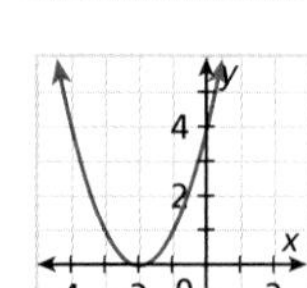

(D)
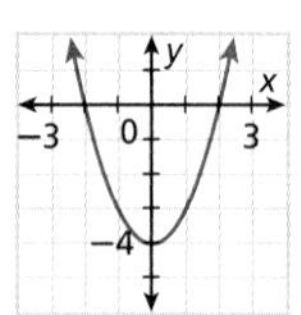

Teaching Tip

Multiple Choice Students who chose **C** in **Item 2** may have made a sign error when calculating.

Students who chose **B** in **Item 8** correctly rewrote $\frac{3}{x}$ as $\frac{15}{5x}$ but then added the denominators as well as the numerators.

In **Item 11**, the given polynomial has a constant term. Only **A** allows for this.

10. What is $(-12x^6 + x) \div (-4x^2)$?

Ⓐ $3x^3 - \frac{1}{4x}$ Ⓒ $3x^5$

Ⓑ $3x^4 - \frac{1}{4x}$ Ⓓ $3x^4 + x$

11. What is the greatest common factor of the terms of the polynomial $6x^3 - 18x^2 + 12x + 3$?

Ⓐ 3 Ⓒ $6x$

Ⓑ $3x$ Ⓓ $6x^2$

12. Which is a solution to $\frac{n}{n+2} = \frac{-8}{n}$?

Ⓐ -4 Ⓒ 2

Ⓑ -2 Ⓓ 4

13. Which of the following is equivalent to $\left(\frac{2x^5y^2}{8x}\right)^{-2}$?

Ⓐ $\frac{16}{x^8y^4}$ Ⓒ $\frac{4}{x^4y^2}$

Ⓑ $\frac{x^8}{16y^4}$ Ⓓ $\frac{x^5}{16}$

14. Which of the following is a true statement about the function $y = \frac{1}{x}$?

Ⓐ The domain is all real numbers.

Ⓑ The range is all real numbers.

Ⓒ The domain is all real numbers except 0.

Ⓓ The range is all real numbers except 1.

If you are allowed to write in your test booklet, you may want to add additional information to a given diagram. Be sure to mark your answer on the answer sheet because you will not receive any credit for marks in the test booklet.

Gridded Response

15. What is the excluded value for the rational expression $\frac{x^2 - 4}{3x - 6}$? **2**

16. The trinomial $x^2 - 6x + c$ is a perfect square trinomial. What is the value of c? **9**

17. Find the positive solution of the equation $x^2 + 5x - 4 = 0$. Round your answer to the nearest tenth. **0.7**

18. What is the value of $4^0 - (2^{-3})$? **7/8**

19. Identify the excluded value for $y = \frac{x-4}{x-2}$. **2**

Short Response

20. Mr. Lui wrote $\frac{15 - 5x}{x^2 - 9x + 18}$ on the board.

 a. Explain what kind of expression it is.

 b. Simplify the expression. Show your work.

 c. Identify any excluded values.

21. Lynne can paint a wall in 40 minutes. Jeff can paint the same wall in 60 minutes. How long will it take Lynne and Jeff to paint the wall if they work together? Show your work. **24 min**

22. What are 2 values of b that will make $2x^2 - bx - 20$ factorable? Explain your answer.
Possible answers: ± 3, ± 6, ± 18

23. The sum of the digits of a two-digit number is 11. If 45 is added to the number, the digits will be reversed.

 a. Write a system of equations that you can use to find the digits of the number. Tell what each variable represents.

 b. Solve the system of equations to find the two-digit number. Show your work. **38**

Extended Response

24. Principal Farley has $200 to pay for some teachers to attend a technology conference. The company hosting the conference is allowing 2 teachers to attend for free. The number of teachers y that can be sent to the conference is given by the function $y = \frac{200}{x} + 2$, where x is the cost per teacher.

 a. Describe the reasonable domain and range values for this function.

 b. Identify the vertical and horizontal asymptotes.

 c. Graph the function.

 d. Give two points on the graph whose coordinates are whole numbers and describe what they mean in the context of this situation.

24a. D: $x > 0$; R: natural numbers > 2

b. $x = 0$, $y = 2$

d. (50, 6) and (100, 4); at a cost of $50 per teacher, 6 teachers attend; at a cost of $100 per teacher, 4 teachers attend.

Short-Response Rubric

Items 20–23

2 Points = The student's answer is an accurate and complete execution of the task or tasks.

1 Point = The student's answer contains attributes of an appropriate response but is flawed.

0 Points = The student's answer contains no attributes of an appropriate response.

Extended-Response Rubric

Item 24

4 Points = The student gives a reasonable domain and range in part **a,** identifies the vertical and horizontal asymptotes correctly in part **b,** graphs the function correctly in part **c,** and gives the two whole-number solutions and describes what they mean in part **d.**

3 Points = The student gives a reasonable domain and range in part **a,** identifies the vertical and horizontal asymptotes correctly in part **b,** graphs the function in part **c,** and gives two whole-number solutions but only partially describes what they mean in part **d.**

2 Points = The student gives a reasonable domain and range with a minor error in part **a,** identifies the vertical and horizontal asymptotes in part **b,** graphs the function in part **c,** and gives one whole-number solution and describes what it means in part **d** or gives two whole-number solutions but does not explain what they mean.

1 Point = The student answers one part correctly but does not attempt all parts, or the student attempts to answer all parts of the problem but does not correctly answer any part.

0 Points = The student does not answer correctly and does not attempt all parts of the problem.

Answers

20a. rational expression

 b. $-\frac{5}{x-6}$

 c. 3, 6

23a. Let a be the tens digit and b be the ones digit.

 $a + b = 11$

 $10b + a = 10a + b + 45$

24c.

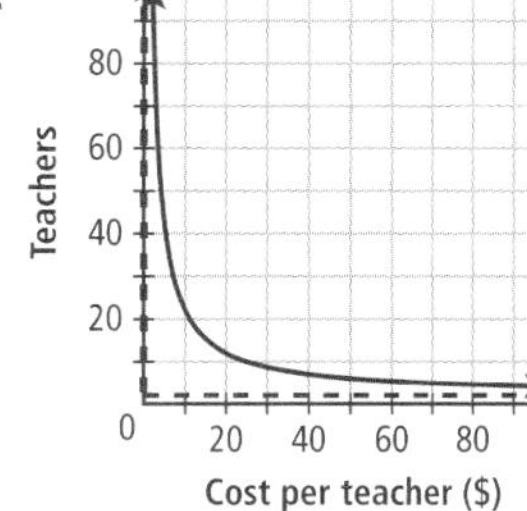

Preview of Algebra II

Radical and Exponential Functions

✔	Grade-level Standard
◄	Review
►	Beyond the Standards
A	Assessment
○	Optional

Pacing Guide

Calendar Planner
Teacher's **One-Stop** Planner®

Lesson/Lab	California Standards	Time	Advanced Students	Benchmark Students	Strategic Students
11-1 Square-Root Functions	Extension of 2.0, 17.0	50 min	►	○	○
11-2 Radical Expressions	Extension of 2.0	50 min	►	○	○
11-3 Adding and Subtracting Radical Expressions	Extension of 2.0	100 min	►	○	○
11-4 Multiplying and Dividing Radical Expressions	Extension of 2.0	100 min	►	○	○
11-5 Solving Radical Equations	Extension of 2.0	100 min	►	○	○
Concept Connection	Extension of 2.0	25 min	A	A	○
Ready to Go On?		25 min	A	A	A
11-6 Geometric Sequences	Preparation for Algebra II 22.0	100 min	►	○	○
11-7 Exponential Functions	Preview of Algebra II 12.0	50 min	►	○	○
CN Changing Dimensions	Reinforcement of Grade 7 MG2.3	25 min	○	◄	◄
LAB Model Growth and Decay	2.0	25 min	►	○	○
11-8 Exponential Growth and Decay	Preview of Algebra II 12.0	50 min	►	○	○
11-9 Linear, Quadratic, and Exponential Models	Extension of 7.0, Preview of Algebra II 12.0	100 min	►	○	○
Concept Connection	Preview of Algebra II 12.0	25 min	A	A	○
Ready to Go On?		25 min	A	A	A
Study Guide: Review		50 min	✔	✔	✔
Chapter Test	Extension of 2.0, Extension of 7.0, Preview of Algebra II 12.0, Preparation for Algebra II 22.0	50 min	A	A	A

* **Benchmark students** are achieving at or near grade level.

** **Strategic students** may be a year or more below grade level, and may require additional time for intervention.

ONGOING ASSESSMENT and INTERVENTION

	DIAGNOSE	PRESCRIBE
Assess Prior Knowledge	**Before Chapter 11**	
	Diagnose readiness for the chapter.	Prescribe intervention.
	Are You Ready? SE p. 697	***Are You Ready? Intervention*** Skills 6, 8, 14, 31, 62, 80
Formative Assessment	**Before Every Lesson**	
	Diagnose readiness for the lesson.	Prescribe intervention.
	Warm Up TE, every lesson	**Skills Bank** pp. SB1–SB32 **Review for Mastery** CRF Chapters 1–11
	During Every Lesson	
	Diagnose understanding of lesson concepts.	Prescribe intervention.
	Questioning Strategies TE, every example **Check It Out!** SE, every example **Think and Discuss** SE, every lesson **Write About It** SE, every lesson **Journal** TE, every lesson	**Reading Strategies** CRF, every lesson ***Success for ELL*** pp. 145–162 ***Lesson Tutorial Videos*** Chapter 11
	After Every Lesson	
	Diagnose mastery of lesson concepts.	Prescribe intervention.
	Lesson Quiz TE, every lesson **Alternative Assessment** TE, every lesson **Ready to Go On?** SE pp. 731, 763 ***Test and Practice Generator***	**Review for Mastery** CRF, every lesson **Problem Solving** CRF, every lesson ***Ready to Go On? Intervention*** Chapter 11 ***Homework Help Online***
	Before Chapter 11 Testing	
	Diagnose mastery of concepts in the chapter.	Prescribe intervention.
	Ready to Go On? SE pp. 731, 763 **Concept Connection** SE pp. 730, 762 **Section Quizzes** AR pp. 205–206 ***Test and Practice Generator***	***Ready to Go On? Intervention*** Chapter 11 **Scaffolding Questions** TE pp. 730, 762
	Before Assessment of California Standards	
	Diagnose mastery of California Standards.	Prescribe intervention.
	Focus on California Standards: Benchmark Tests **Mastering the Standards** SE pp. 772–773 ***California Standards Practice* CD-ROM**	***Focus on California Standards: Intervention***
Summative Assessment	**After Chapter 11**	
	Check mastery of chapter concepts.	Prescribe intervention.
	Multiple-Choice Tests (Forms A, B, C) **Free-Response Tests (Forms A, B, C)** **Performance Assessment** AR pp. 219–220 ***Test and Practice Generator***	**Review for Mastery** CRF, every lesson ***Lesson Tutorial Videos*** Chapter 11

KEY: **SE** = *Student Edition* **TE** = *Teacher's Edition* **CRF** = *Chapter Resource File* **AR** = *Assessment Resources*  Available online Available on CD-ROM

Supporting the Teacher

Chapter 11 Resource File

Family Involvement
pp. 1–4, 45–48

Practice A, B, C
pp. 5–7, 13–15, 21–23, 29–31, 37–39, 49–51, 57–59, 65–67, 73–75

Review for Mastery
pp. 8–9, 16–17, 24–25, 32–33, 40–41, 52–53, 60–61, 68–69, 76–77

Challenge
pp. 10, 18, 26, 34, 42, 54, 62, 70, 78

Problem Solving
pp. 11, 19, 27, 35, 43, 55, 63, 71, 79

Reading Strategies ELL
pp. 12, 20, 28, 36, 44, 56, 64, 72, 80

Algebra Lab
pp. 81–83

Workbooks

Homework and Practice Workbook SPANISH
Teacher's Edition .... pp. 73–81

Know-It Notebook SPANISH
Teacher's Guide .... Chapter 11

Review for Mastery Workbook SPANISH
Teacher's Guide .... pp. 145–162

Focus on California Standards: Intervention Workbook SPANISH
Teacher's Guide

Teacher Tools

Power Presentations
Complete PowerPoint® presentations for Chapter 11 lessons

Lesson Tutorial Videos SPANISH
Holt authors Ed Burger and Freddie Renfro present tutorials to support the Chapter 11 lessons.

Teacher's One-Stop Planner SPANISH
Easy access to all Chapter 11 resources and assessments, as well as software for lesson planning, test generation, and puzzle creation

IDEA Works!
Key Chapter 11 resources and assessments modified to address special learning needs

Solutions Key .... Chapter 11

Interactive Answers and Solutions

TechKeys

Lab Resources

Project Teacher Support 

Parent Resources 

Transparencies

Lesson Transparencies, Volume 2 .... Chapter 11
- Teacher Tools
- Warm-ups
- Teaching Transparencies
- Lesson Quizzes

Alternate Openers: Explorations .... pp. 73–81

Know-It Notebook .... Chapter 11
- Vocabulary
- Key Concepts
- Graphic Organizers
- Chapter Review
- Big Ideas

Technology Highlights for the Teacher

 Power Presentations

Dynamic presentations to engage students. Complete PowerPoint® presentations for every lesson in Chapter 11.

2-1 Solving One-Step Equations

Isolate a variable by using inverse operations which "undo" operations on the variable.

An equation is like a balanced scale. To keep the balance, perform the same operation on both sides.

Inverse Operations	
Operation	Inverse Operation
Addition	Subtraction
Subtraction	Addition

 One-Stop Planner SPANISH

Easy access to Chapter 11 resources and assessments. Includes lesson planning, test generation, and puzzle creation software.

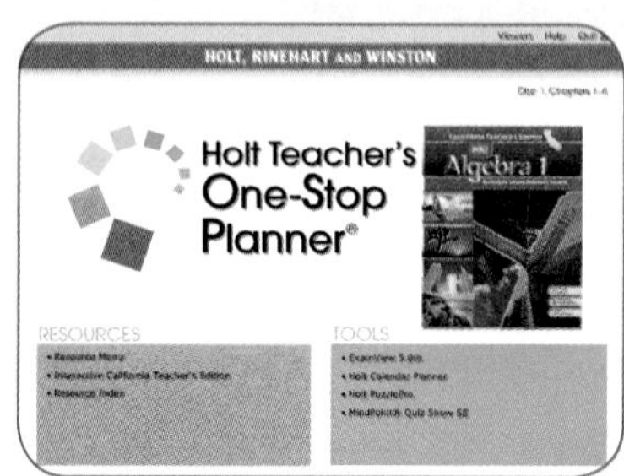

 Premier Online Edition SPANISH

Includes Tutorial Videos, Lesson Activities, Lesson Quizzes, Homework Help, Chapter Project and more.

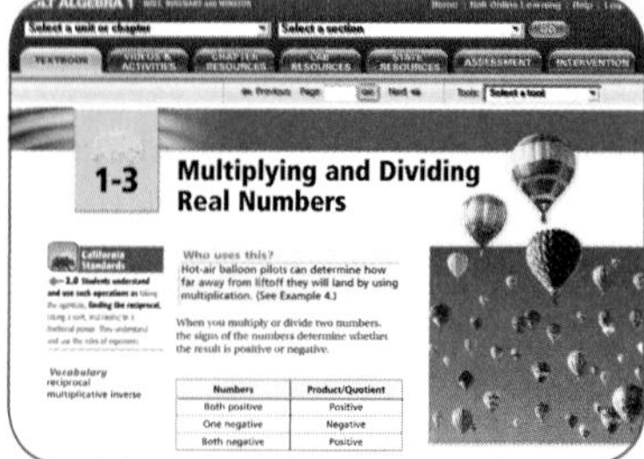

KEY: **SE** = *Student Edition* **TE** = *Teacher's Edition* ELL English Language Learners SPANISH Spanish available Available online  Available on CD-ROM

Universal Access

Teaching Tips to help all students appear throughout the chapter. A few that target specific students are included in the lists below.

Strategic Students

Practice A ...... CRF, every lesson
Review for Mastery ...... CRF, every lesson
Reading Strategies ...... CRF, every lesson
Academic Vocabulary Connections ...... TE p. 698
Modeling ...... TE p. 749
Questioning Strategies ...... TE, every example
Ready to Go On? Intervention ...... Chapter 11
Know-It Notebook SPANISH ...... Chapter 11
Homework Help Online
Lesson Tutorial Videos SPANISH
Online Interactivities SPANISH

Special Needs Students

Practice A ...... CRF, every lesson
Review for Mastery ...... CRF, every lesson
Reading Strategies ...... CRF, every lesson
Academic Vocabulary Connections ...... TE p. 698
Inclusion ...... TE pp. 702, 707, 740, 749, 756, 759
IDEA Works! Modified Resources ...... Chapter 11
Ready to Go On? Intervention ...... Chapter 11
Know-It Notebook SPANISH ...... Chapter 11
Lesson Tutorial Videos SPANISH
Online Interactivities SPANISH

English Learners

ENGLISH LANGUAGE LEARNERS

Reading Strategies ...... CRF, every lesson
Vocabulary Exercises ...... SE, every exercise set
Academic Vocabulary Connections ...... TE p. 698
English Language Learners ...... TE pp. 718, 748
Language Support ...... TE pp. 718, 748
Success for English Language Learners ...... Chapter 11
Know-It Notebook SPANISH ...... Chapter 11
Multilingual Glossary
Lesson Tutorial Videos SPANISH

Benchmark Students

Practice B ...... CRF, every lesson
Problem Solving ...... CRF, every lesson
Academic Vocabulary Connections ...... TE p. 698
Questioning Strategies ...... TE, every example
Ready to Go On? Intervention ...... Chapter 11
Know-It Notebook SPANISH ...... Chapter 11
Homework Help Online
Online Interactivities SPANISH

Advanced Students

Practice C ...... CRF, every lesson
Challenge ...... CRF, every lesson
Reading and Writing Math EXTENSION ...... TE p. 699
Concept Connection EXTENSION ...... TE pp. 730, 762
Advanced Learners/GATE ...... TE pp. 733, 734, 750
Ready to Go On? Enrichment ...... Chapter 11

Technology Highlights for Universal Access

Lesson Tutorial Videos 

Starring Holt authors Ed Burger and Freddie Renfro! Live tutorials to support every lesson in Chapter 11.

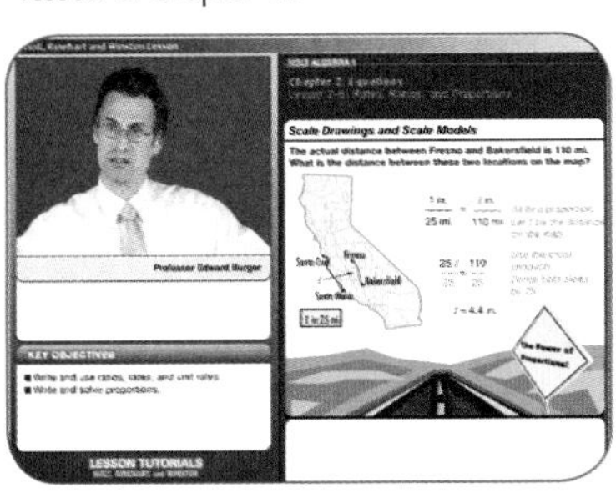

Multilingual Glossary

Searchable glossary includes definitions in English, Spanish, Vietnamese, Chinese, Hmong, Korean, and other languages.

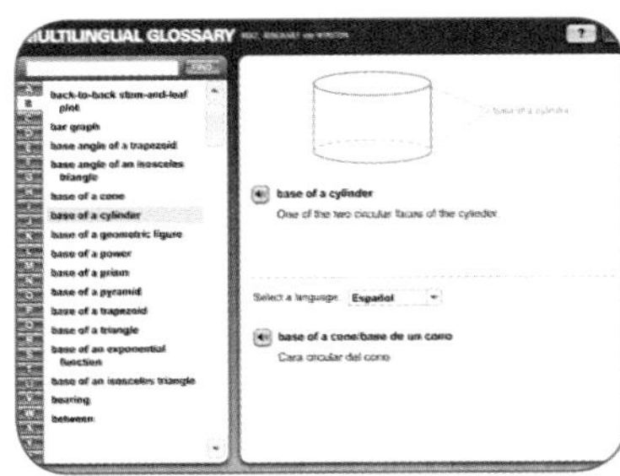

Online Interactivities 

Interactive tutorials provide visually engaging alternative opportunities to learn concepts and master skills.

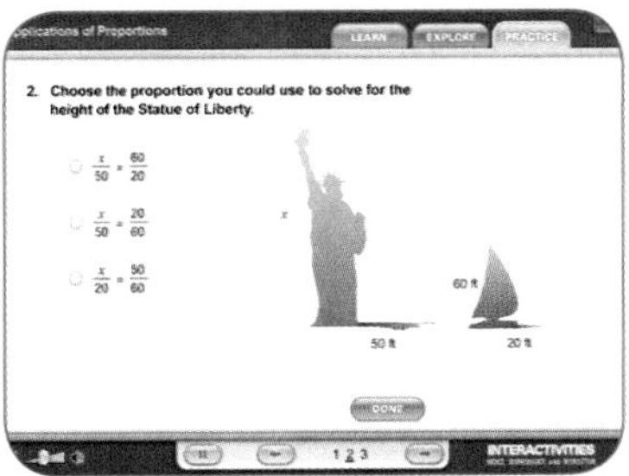

KEY: **SE** = *Student Edition* **TE** = *Teacher's Edition* **CRF** = *Chapter Resource File*  Spanish available 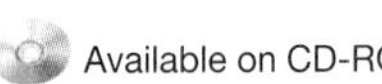 Available online Available on CD-ROM

Ongoing Assessment

Assessing Prior Knowledge

Determine whether students have the prerequisite concepts and skills for success in Chapter 11.

Are You Ready? SPANISH .... SE p. 697
Warm Up .... TE, every lesson

Chapter and Standards Assessment

Provide review and practice for Chapter 11 and standards mastery.

Concept Connection .... SE pp. 730, 762
Study Guide: Review .... SE pp. 764–767
Strategies for Success .... SE pp. 770–771
Mastering the Standards .... SE pp. 772–773
College Entrance Exam Practice .... SE p. 769
Focus on California Standards: Benchmark Tests
Focus on California Standards: Intervention Workbook
California Standards Practice CD-ROM SPANISH
IDEA Works! Modified Worksheets and Tests

Alternative Assessment

Assess students' understanding of Chapter 11 concepts and combined problem-solving skills.

Alternative Assessment .... TE, every lesson
Performance Assessment .... AR pp. 219–220
Portfolio Assessment .... AR p. xxiii
Chapter 11 Project

Daily Assessment

Provide formative assessment for each day of Chapter 11.

Questioning Strategies .... TE, every example
Think and Discuss .... SE, every lesson
Check It Out! Exercises .... SE, every example
Write About It .... SE, every lesson
Journal .... TE, every lesson
Lesson Quiz .... TE, every lesson
Alternative Assessment .... TE, every lesson
IDEA Works! Modified Lesson Quizzes .... Chapter 11

Weekly Assessment

Provide formative assessment for each week of Chapter 11.

Concept Connection .... SE pp. 730, 762
Ready to Go On? .... SE pp. 731, 763
Cumulative Assessment .... SE pp. 764–767
Test and Practice Generator SPANISH .. *One-Stop Planner*

Formal Assessment

Provide summative assessment of Chapter 11 mastery.

Section Quizzes .... AR pp. 205–206
Chapter 11 Test SPANISH .... SE p. 768
Chapter Test (Levels A, B, C) .... AR pp. 207–218
• Multiple Choice • Free Response
Cumulative Test .... AR pp. 221–224
Test and Practice Generator SPANISH .. *One-Stop Planner*

Technology Highlights for Ongoing Assessment

Are You Ready? SPANISH

Automatically assess readiness and prescribe intervention for Chapter 11 prerequisite skills.

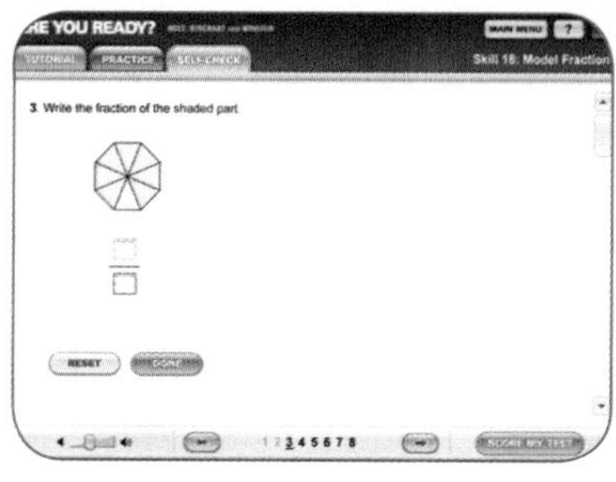

Ready to Go On? SPANISH

Automatically assess understanding of and prescribe intervention for Sections 11A and 11B.

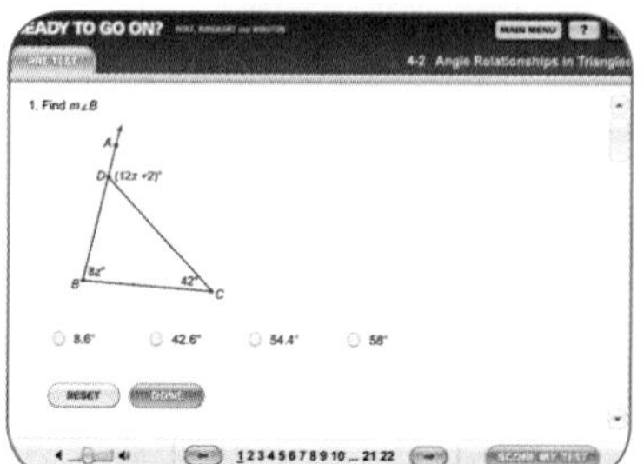

Focus on California Standards: Benchmark Tests and Intervention SPANISH

Automatically assess proficiency with California Algebra I Standards and provide intervention.

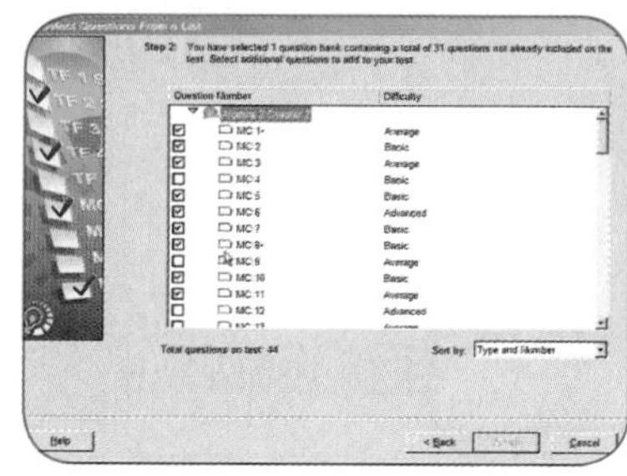

KEY: **SE** = *Student Edition* **TE** = *Teacher's Edition* **AR** = Assessment Resources  Spanish available  Available online  Available on CD-ROM

Formal Assessment

Three levels (A, B, C) of multiple-choice and free-response chapter tests are available in the *Assessment Resources.*

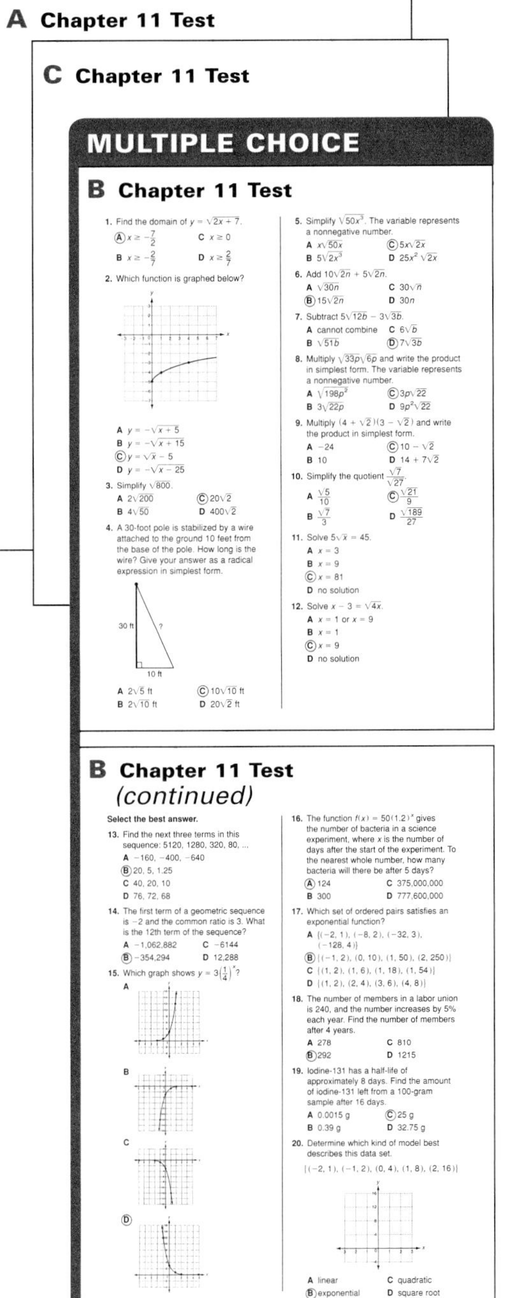

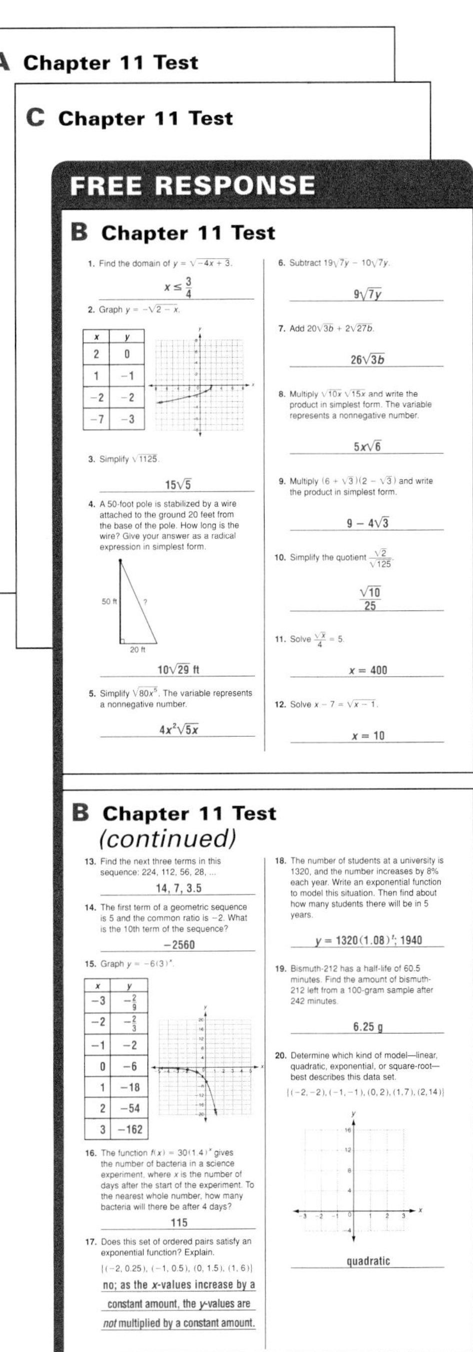

Modified tests and worksheets found in *IDEA Works!*

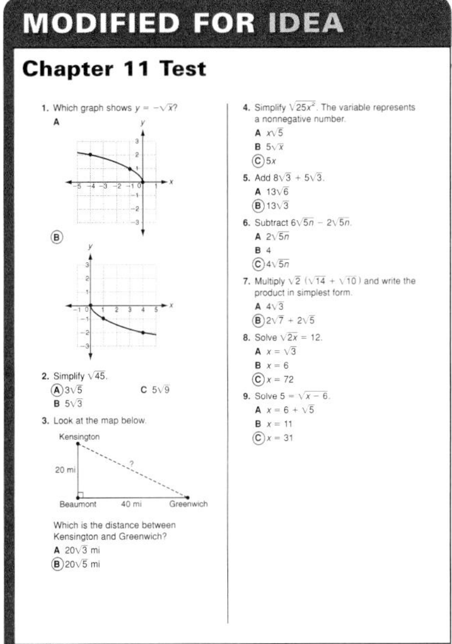

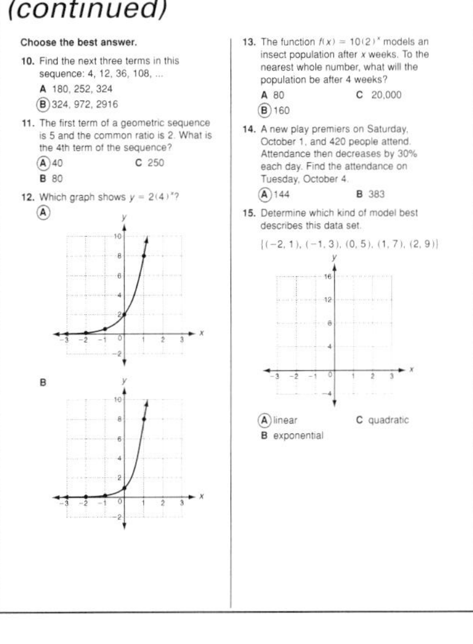

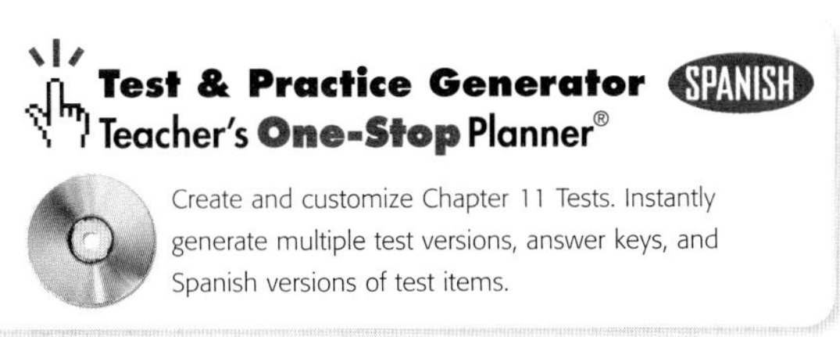

Create and customize Chapter 11 Tests. Instantly generate multiple test versions, answer keys, and Spanish versions of test items.

SECTION 11A
Radical Functions and Equations

On page 730, students solve radical equations to model real-world velocity and distance situations.

Exercises designed to prepare students for success on the Concept Connection can be found on pages 703, 709, 714, 720, and 728.

SECTION 11B
Exponential Functions

On page 762, students write and graph functions to model real-world college tuition situations.

Exercises designed to prepare students for success on the Concept Connection can be found on pages 736, 743, 753, and 760.

Algebra in *California*

Exponential growth and decay functions have many varied real-world applications, such as populations, interest payments, and radioactive decay. Students will learn about exponential growth and decay in Lesson 11-8 of this chapter.

CHAPTER 11

Preview of Algebra II

Radical and Exponential Functions

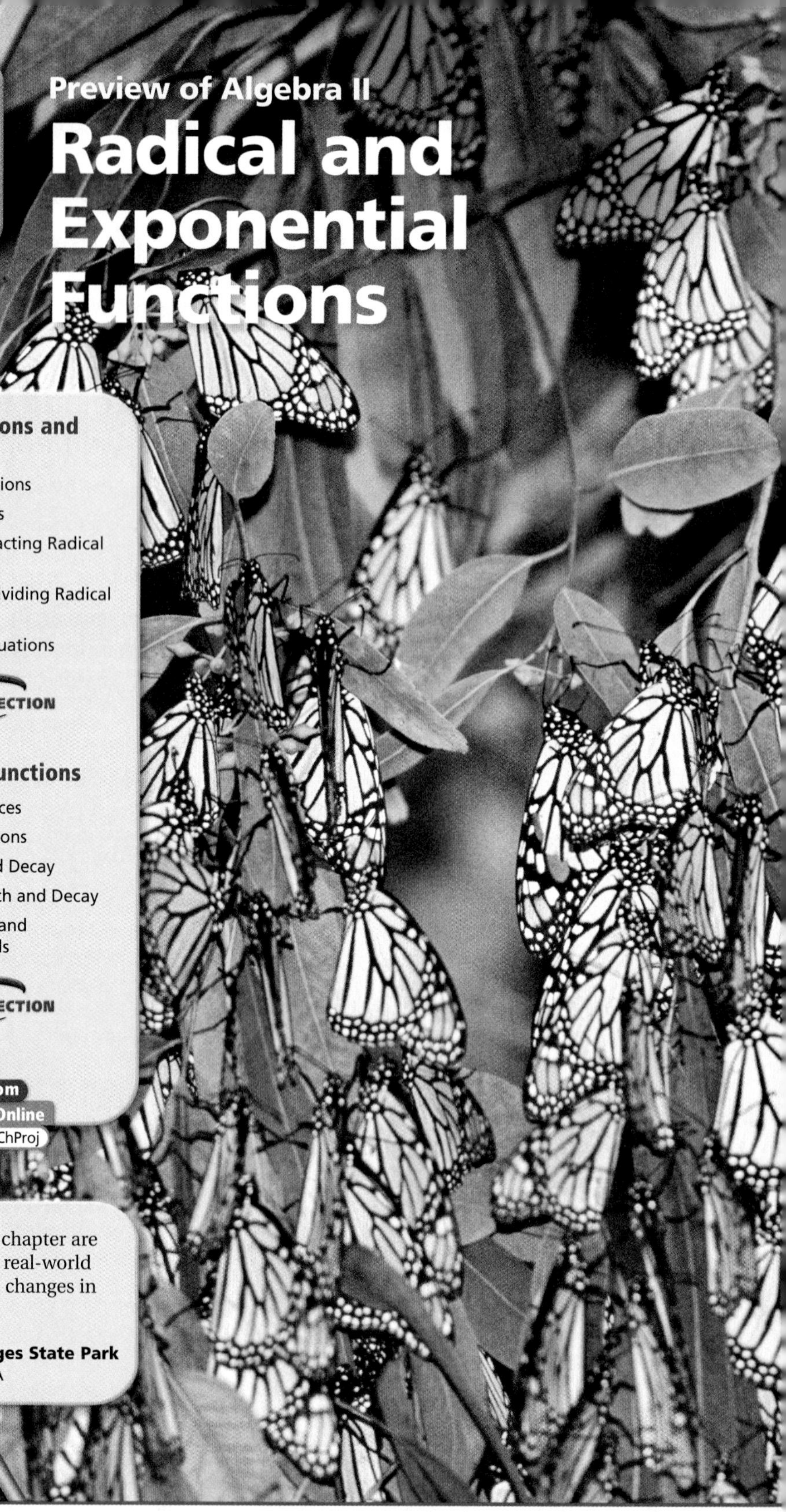

go.hrw.com
Chapter Project Online
KEYWORD: MA8CA ChProj

The concepts in this chapter are used to model many real-world phenomena, such as changes in wildlife populations.

Natural Bridges State Park
Santa Cruz, CA

696 Chapter 11

About the Project

Population Explosion

Students research population data, model the growth or decay two ways, and predict the population for the next 10 years using both models. Students decide which model is the more reasonable model and justify their reasoning.

Students also conduct a pendulum experiment to determine how the length of the string impacts the time it takes for one complete swing.

Project Resources

All project resources for teachers and students are provided online.

Materials:
- graphing calculator
- washer, string, centimeter tape measure, stopwatch

ARE YOU READY?

Vocabulary

Match each term on the left with a definition on the right.

1. like terms **B**
2. square root **F**
3. domain **C**
4. perfect square **E**
5. exponent **D**

A. the set of second elements of a relation
B. terms that contain the same variable raised to the same power
C. the set of first elements of a relation
D. a number that tells how many times a base is used as a factor
E. a number whose positive square root is a whole number
F. one of two equal factors of a number

Squares and Square Roots

Find each square root.

6. $\sqrt{36}$ **6**
7. $\sqrt{81}$ **9**
8. $\sqrt{25}$ **5**
9. $\sqrt{64}$ **8**

Pythagorean Theorem

Find the length of the hypotenuse in each right triangle.

10. 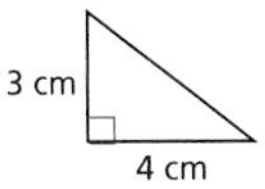 **5 cm**

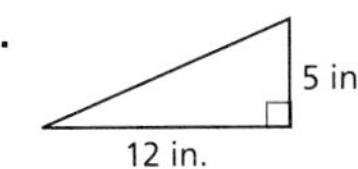

11. **13 in.**

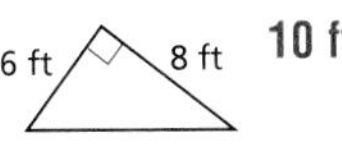

12. 6 ft, 8 ft **10 ft**

Multiply Monomials and Polynomials

Multiply.

13. $5(2m - 3)$ **$10m - 15$**
14. $3x(8x + 9)$ **$24x^2 + 27x$**
15. $2t(3t - 1)$ **$6t^2 - 2t$**
16. $4r(4r - 5)$ **$16r^2 - 20r$**

Evaluate Powers

Find the value of each expression.

17. 2^4 **16**
18. 5^0 **1**
19. $7 \cdot 3^2$ **63**
20. $3 \cdot 5^3$ **375**
21. 3^5 **243**
22. $-6^2 + 8^1$ **−28**
23. $40 \cdot 2^3$ **320**
24. $7^2 \cdot 3^1$ **147**

Graph Functions

Graph each function.

25. $y = 8$
26. $y = x + 3$
27. $y = x^2 - 4$
28. $y = x^2 + 2$

Fractions, Decimals, and Percents

Write each percent as a decimal.

29. 50% **0.5**
30. 25% **0.25**
31. 15.2% **0.152**
32. 200% **2.0**
33. 1.9% **0.019**
34. 0.3% **0.003**
35. 0.1% **0.001**
36. 1.04% **0.0104**

ARE YOU READY? CHAPTER 11

Organizer

Objective: Assess students' understanding of prerequisite skills.

Prerequisite Skills

- Squares and Square Roots
- Pythagorean Theorem
- Multiply Monomials and Polynomials
- Evaluate Powers
- Graph Functions
- Fractions, Decimals, and Percents

Assessing Prior Knowledge

INTERVENTION

Diagnose and Prescribe

Use this page to determine whether intervention is necessary or whether enrichment is appropriate.

Resources

***Are You Ready? Intervention and Enrichment* Worksheets**

***Are You Ready?* CD-ROM**

***Are You Ready?* Online**

my.hrw.com

Answers

25–28. See p. A26.

ARE YOU READY? Diagnose and Prescribe

NO INTERVENE

Prerequisite Skill	*Are You Ready? Intervention*, Chapter 11 Worksheets	CD-ROM	Online
Squares and Square Roots	Skill 6	Activity 6	Diagnose and Prescribe Online
Pythagorean Theorem	Skill 31	Activity 31	
Multiply Monomials and Polynomials	Skill 62	Activity 62	
Evaluate Powers	Skill 8	Activity 8	
Graph Functions	Skill 80	Activity 80	
Fractions, Decimals, and Percents	Skill 14	Activity 14	

YES ENRICH

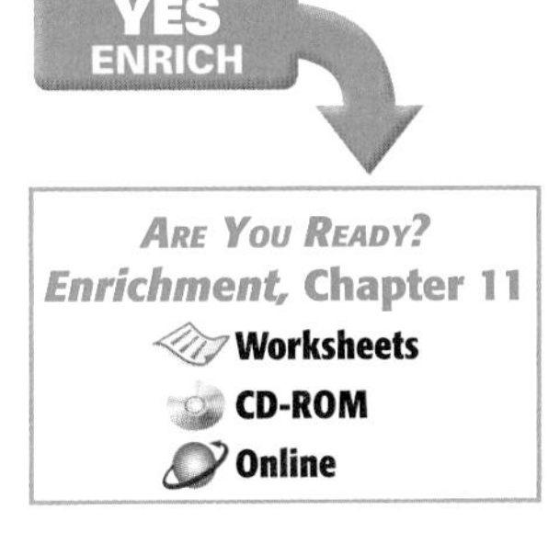

Are You Ready? Enrichment, Chapter 11
Worksheets
CD-ROM
Online

CHAPTER 11 Unpacking the Standards

Organizer

Objective: Help students understand the new concepts they will learn in Chapter 11.

Academic Vocabulary Connections

Becoming familiar with the academic vocabulary on this student page will be helpful to students. Discussing some of the vocabulary terms in the chapter also may be helpful.

1. What does it mean when several items have something "in common"? What is a ratio? What do you think **common ratio** means? There is something about them that is the same; a comparison of two numbers; when you divide the terms, the resulting values will be the same.
2. In the division problem $2\overline{)50}$ (quotient 25), the *dividend* is 50. If a *radicand* is similar to a dividend, then what is the **radicand** in $\sqrt{16} = 4$? 16
3. The symbol that indicates a root, $\sqrt{}$, is called a *radical*. Use this knowledge to define ***radical expression*** and ***radical equation.*** an expression with a root; an equation with a root

CHAPTER 11

Unpacking the Standards

The information below "unpacks" the standards. The Academic Vocabulary is highlighted and defined to help you understand the language of the standards. Refer to the lessons listed after each standard for help with the math terms and phrases. The Chapter Concept shows how the standard is applied in this chapter.

California Standard	Academic Vocabulary	Chapter Concept
Extension of 1A2.0 Students understand and use such operations as taking the opposite, finding the reciprocal, **taking a root,** and raising to a fractional power. **They understand and use the rules of exponents.** (Lessons **11-1, 11-2, 11-3, 11-4, 11-5**)	**operations** calculations you use when you work out a problem	You learn to calculate and graph square-root functions. ***Example:*** $y = \sqrt{2x + 1}$ You also learn how to add, subtract, multiply, and divide expressions that have radicals.
1A17.0 Students determine the domain of independent variables and the range of dependent variables defined **by** a graph, a set of ordered pairs, or **a symbolic expression.** (Lesson **11-1**)	**independent** not determined by anything else	You find the x-values that make the value under the radical sign greater than or equal to zero.
Preview of Algebra II 12.0 Students know the laws of fractional exponents, **understand exponential functions, and use these functions in problems involving exponential growth and decay.** (Lessons **11-7, 11-8**)	**growth** an increase **decay** a decrease	You find the value of exponential functions by substituting numbers for the variable that appears as the exponent. You also learn to identify, write, and graph functions that contain exponents.
Preview of Algebra II Preparation for 2A22.0 Students find the general term and the sums of arithmetic series and **of both finite and infinite geometric series.** (Lesson **11-6**)	**general** applying to every member of a group	You find an expression that describes every term in a geometric sequence.

Looking Back

Previously, students

- solved linear and quadratic equations.
- identified and extended arithmetic sequences.
- identified and graphed linear functions and quadratic functions.

In This Chapter

Students will study

- solving radical equations.
- identifying geometric sequences.
- identifying exponential and square-root functions.

Looking Forward

Students can use these skills

- to solve complicated formulas in courses such as Geometry.
- to explore exponential growth and decay models which are used in science.
- to analyze more-complicated functions in later math courses, such as Calculus.

Study Strategy: Prepare for Your Final Exam

Math is a cumulative subject, so your final exam will probably cover all of the material you have learned since the beginning of the course. Preparation is essential for you to be successful on your final exam. It may help you to make a study timeline like the one below.

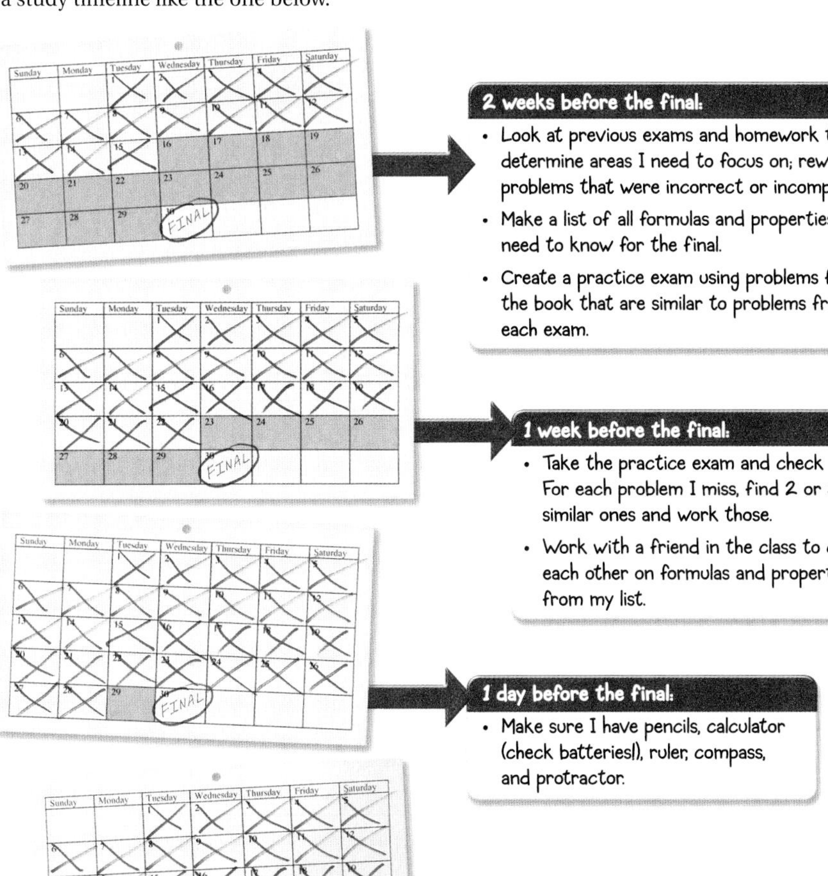

2 weeks before the final:
• Look at previous exams and homework to determine areas I need to focus on; rework problems that were incorrect or incomplete.
• Make a list of all formulas and properties I need to know for the final.
• Create a practice exam using problems from the book that are similar to problems from each exam.
1 week before the final:
• Take the practice exam and check it. For each problem I miss, find 2 or 3 similar ones and work those.
• Work with a friend in the class to quiz each other on formulas and properties from my list.
1 day before the final:
• Make sure I have pencils, calculator (check batteries!), ruler, compass, and protractor.
FINAL

Try This

1. Create a timeline that you will use to study for your final exam.

Reading and Writing Math

Organizer

Objective: Help students apply strategies to understand and retain key concepts.

Resources

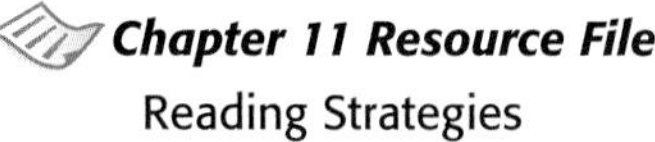
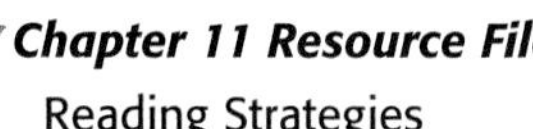

Reading Strategies

Study Strategy: Prepare for Your Final Exam

Discuss For the two weeks before the final exam, students can place each of the 11 chapters into a block on a calendar, using those days to review previous exams, homework, formulas, properties, and vocabulary from that chapter.

Extend As students work through the exercises in Chapter 11, have them identify which skills are new to the chapter and which are from previous chapters. For example, graphing square-root functions in Lesson 11-1 requires that students be able to evaluate square roots—a skill taught in Chapter 1. Describing a data set with a linear equation in Lesson 11-9 requires finding the slope and y-intercept; these skills were taught in Chapter 5.

Answer to *Try This*

1. Check students' work.

Radical Functions and Equations

One-Minute Section Planner

Lesson	Lab Resources	Materials
Lesson 11-1 Square-Root Functions • Identify square-root functions and their domains. • Graph square-root functions. **Extension of 2.0**		**Optional** graphing calculator, index cards
Lesson 11-2 Radical Expressions • Simplify radical expressions. **Extension of 2.0**		**Optional** calculator
Lesson 11-3 Adding and Subtracting Radical Expressions • Add and subtract radical expressions. **Extension of 2.0**	***Algebra Lab* 11-3** In *Chapter 11 Resource File*	**Optional** graphing calculator
Lesson 11-4 Multiplying and Dividing Radical Expressions • Multiply and divide radical expressions. • Rationalize denominators. **Extension of 2.0**		**Optional** graphing calculator
Lesson 11-5 Solving Radical Equations • Solve radical equations. **Extension of 2.0**		**Optional** graphing calculator

MK = *Manipulatives Kit*

Notes

Math Background: Teaching the Standards

RADICAL FUNCTIONS

Lessons 11-1 to 11-5

A *radical function* is a function whose rule contains a variable within a radical. For example, $y = \sqrt[3]{x^5}$ is a radical function. In this course, the emphasis is on square-root functions, which are a particular kind of radical functions. A *square-root function* is a function whose rule contains a variable under a square-root sign, such as $y = \sqrt{3x + 5}$. The simplest square-root function is $y = \sqrt{x}$. (Students may need to be reminded that the symbol $\sqrt{\ }$ indicates a principal, or nonnegative, square root.)

Because the square root of a negative number is undefined in the real numbers, the domains of square-root functions are restricted to those values of the variable for which the expression under the radical sign is nonnegative. The domain of $y = \sqrt{x}$ is $x \geq 0$; the domain of $y = \sqrt{3x + 5}$ of is $x \geq -\frac{5}{3}$.

THE FUNCTION $y = \sqrt{x}$

Lesson 11-1

When dealing with square roots and square-root functions, it is useful to understand the inverse relationship between $y = x^2$ and $y = \sqrt{x}$. In general, given a relation defined by a set of ordered pairs (x, y), the *inverse relation* is the set of all ordered pairs (y, x). The graph of an inverse relation is the reflection of the original relation over the line $y = x$. The following graph shows that $y = \pm\sqrt{x}$ is the inverse relation of $y = x^2$ because its graph is the reflection of the graph of $y = x^2$ over the line $y = x$.

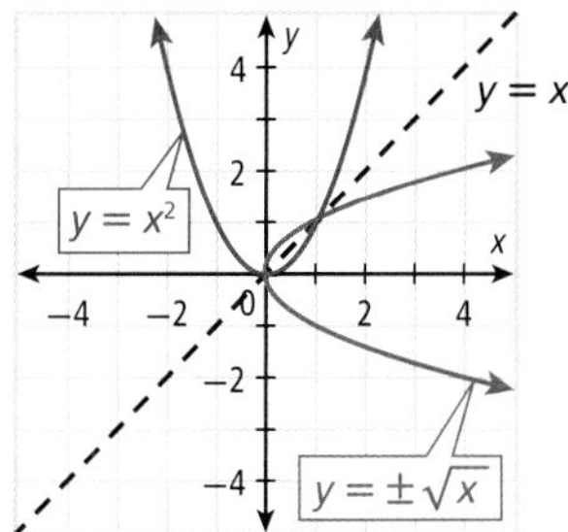

Given a rule for a relation, you can find the rule for the inverse relation by exchanging x and y in the original rule and then solving for y. For the function $y = x^2$, exchanging x and y gives $x = y^2$. To solve for y, take the square root of both sides. This shows that the inverse relation of $y = x^2$ is described by $y = \pm\sqrt{x}$.

The inverse of a function may or may not be a function. For example, $y = \pm\sqrt{x}$, which is the inverse of the function $y = x^2$, is not itself a function; we can see from the graph that every domain value is paired with two range values. However, the relation becomes a function when the range is restricted to the principal square root of x; that is, $y = \sqrt{x}$. Note that this corresponds to the portion of the graph of $y = \pm\sqrt{x}$ that lies above the x-axis.

GRAPHING SQUARE-ROOT FUNCTIONS

Lesson 11-1

Most of the square-root functions that students graph in this chapter are transformations of the graph of $y = \sqrt{x}$. For example, the graph of $y = \sqrt{x} + c$ is a vertical translation of the graph of $y = \sqrt{x}$. The graph is translated c units up if $c > 0$ and $|c|$ units down if $c < 0$. Similarly, the graph of $y = \sqrt{x - a}$ is a horizontal translation of the graph of $y = \sqrt{x}$. The graph is translated a units to the right if $a > 0$ and $|a|$ units to the left if $a < 0$.

This approach offers a convenient way to graph a square-root function, different from the method shown in the text. To graph $y = \sqrt{x + 4} - 3$, begin with the graph of $y = \sqrt{x}$, translate it 4 units to the left (since, in this case, $a = -4$) and then 3 units down.

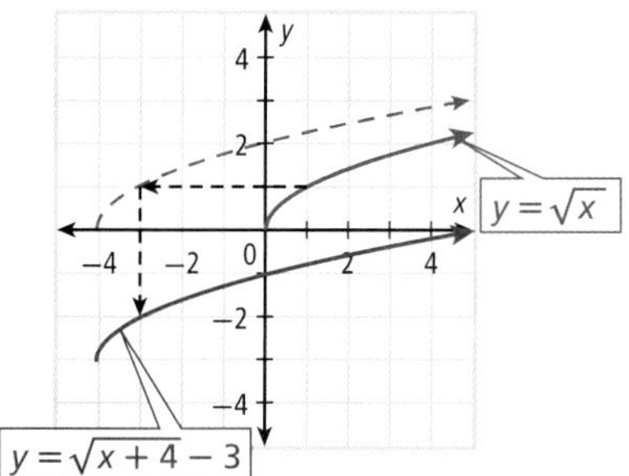

Notice how the transformations affect the domain and range.

This concept can in fact be extended to all functions. In general, the graph of $y = f(x - a) + c$ is the graph of $y = f(x)$ translated $|a|$ units horizontally (left or right, depending on the sign of a) and $|c|$ units vertically (up or down, depending on the sign of c).

11-1 Organizer

Objectives: Identify square-root functions and their domains.

Graph square-root functions.

Online Edition
Tutorial Videos, Interactivity

Power Presentations with PowerPoint®

Warm Up

Find each square root.

1. $\sqrt{36}$ 6 **2.** $\sqrt{144}$ 12

3. $-\sqrt{400}$ −20 **4.** $\sqrt{-196}$ undef.

Solve each inequality.

5. $x + 5 \geq 0$ $x \geq -5$

6. $0 \leq 4x - 8$ $x \geq 2$

7. $0 \leq 3x$ $x \geq 0$

8. $10 - 3x \geq 0$ $x \leq \frac{10}{3}$

Compare. Write <, >, or =.

9. $\sqrt{45}$ ■ 7 <

10. $\sqrt{12}$ ■ 3 >

Also available on transparency

Math Humor

Q: Why did the square-root function lose the singing competition?

A: He didn't have a full range.

11-1 Square-Root Functions

California Standards

Extension of 🔑 2.0 Students understand and use such operations as taking the opposite, finding the reciprocal, **taking a root**, and raising to a fractional power. They understand and use the rules of exponents.

Also covered: **17.0**

Vocabulary
square-root function

Who uses this?
Astronauts can use square-root functions to calculate their speed in free fall.

Astronauts at NASA practice living in the weightlessness of space by training in the KC-135, also known as the "Vomit Comet." This aircraft flies to a certain altitude and then free falls for a period of time, simulating a zero-gravity environment.

The function $y = 8\sqrt{x}$ gives the speed in feet per second of an object in free fall after falling x feet. This function is different from others you have seen so far. It contains a variable under the square-root sign, $\sqrt{\ }$.

Know it! Note

Square-Root Function

WORDS	EXAMPLES	NONEXAMPLES
A **square-root function** is a function whose rule contains a variable under a square-root sign.	$y = \sqrt{x}$ $y = \sqrt{2x + 1}$ $y = 3\sqrt{\frac{x}{2}} - 6$	$y = x^2$ $y = \frac{2}{x + 1}$ $y = \sqrt{3}x$

EXAMPLE 1 Evaluating Square-Root Functions

A **Find the speed of an object in free fall after it has fallen 4 feet.**

$y = 8\sqrt{x}$ *Write the speed function.*
$= 8\sqrt{4}$ *Substitute 4 for x.*
$= 8(2)$ *Simplify.*
$= 16$

After an object has fallen 4 feet, its speed is 16 ft/s.

B **Find the speed of an object in free fall after it has fallen 50 feet. Round your answer to the nearest tenth.**

$y = 8\sqrt{x}$ *Write the speed function.*
$= 8\sqrt{50}$ *Substitute 50 for x.*
≈ 56.6 *Use a calculator.*

After an object has fallen 50 feet, its speed is about 56.6 ft/s.

Helpful Hint

Check that your answer is reasonable. In Example 1B, $8\sqrt{49} = 8(7) = 56$, so $8\sqrt{50} \approx 56.6$ is reasonable.

CHECK IT OUT!

1a. Find the speed of an object in free fall after it has fallen 25 feet.

1b. Find the speed of an object in free fall after it has fallen 15 feet. Round your answer to the nearest hundredth.

1a. 40 ft/s
1b. 30.98 ft/s

1 Introduce

EXPLORATION

11-1 Square-Root Functions

The figure shows a square with side length *s*.

1. Write an equation that expresses the area *A* of the square as a function of *s*.
2. Solve the equation for *s*.
3. Use the equation to help you complete the table.

A	1	4	16	36	64	81	100
s							

4. Plot the points in your table on the coordinate plane.

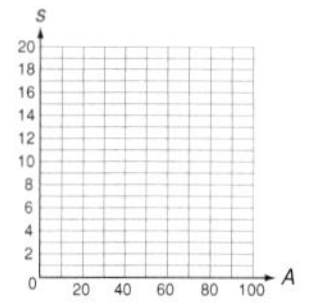

THINK AND DISCUSS

5. **Explain** how you could add additional points to your graph.
6. **Describe** the domain of the function you graphed.

Motivate

Have students find ordered-pair solutions of $y = \sqrt{x}$ using x-values of −9, −4, −1, 0, 1, 4, and 9. $\{(0, 0), (1, 1), (4, 2), (9, 3)\}$ Ask students what happened when they used a negative number for x. Possible answer: There is no y-value because the square root of a negative number is undefined.

Explorations and answers are provided in *Alternate Openers: Explorations Transparencies*.

California Standards

Extension of 🔑 2.0

Also covered:

17.0 Students determine the domain of independent variables and the range of dependent variables **defined by** a graph, a set of ordered pairs, or **a symbolic expression.**

Recall that the square root of a negative number is not a real number. The domain (x-values) of a square-root function is restricted to numbers that make the value under the radical sign greater than or equal to 0.

EXAMPLE 2 Finding the Domain of Square-Root Functions

Find the domain of each square-root function.

A $y = \sqrt{x+4} - 3$

$x + 4 \geq 0$ — *The expression under the radical sign must be greater than or equal to 0.*

$x \geq -4$ — *Solve the inequality. Subtract 4 from both sides.*

B $y = \sqrt{3(x-2)}$

$3(x-2) \geq 0$ — *The expression under the radical sign must be greater than or equal to 0.*

$3x - 6 \geq 0$ — *Solve the inequality. Distribute 3 on the left side.*

$3x \geq 6$ — *Add 6 to both sides.*

$x \geq 2$ — *Divide both sides by 3.*

Helpful Hint

Another way to solve the inequality in Example 2B is to first divide both sides by 3 and then add 2 to both sides.

CHECK IT OUT! 2. Find the domain of $y = \sqrt{2x-1}$ $x \geq \frac{1}{2}$

The function $y = \sqrt{x}$ is graphed at right. Notice there are no x-values to the left of 0 because the domain is $x \geq 0$.

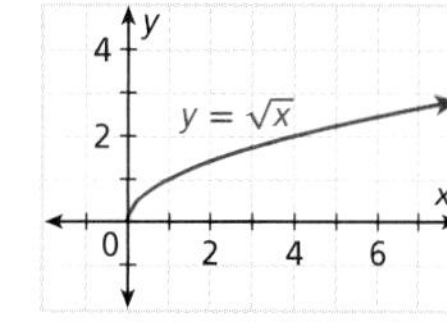

Remember that the symbol $\sqrt{\ }$ indicates the positive square root only. For this reason, the range of $y = \sqrt{x}$ is $y \geq 0$.

EXAMPLE 3 Graphing Square-Root Functions

Graph $y = \sqrt{2x} + 3$.

Step 1 Find the domain of the function.

$2x \geq 0$ — *The expression under the radical sign must be greater than or equal to 0.*

$x \geq 0$ — *Solve the inequality by dividing both sides by 2.*

Step 2 Choose x-values greater than or equal to 0 and generate ordered pairs.

x	$y = \sqrt{2x} + 3$
0	3
2	5
8	7
18	9
32	11

Step 3 Plot the points. Then connect them with a smooth curve.

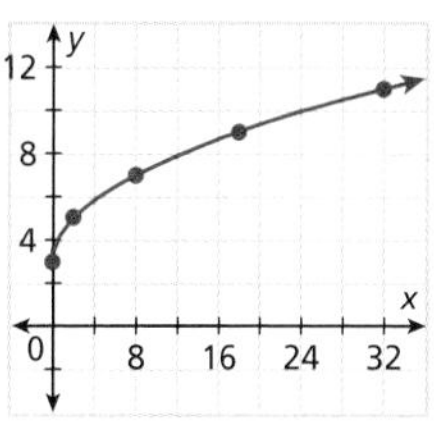

Helpful Hint

In Example 3, when generating ordered pairs, choose x-values that make the expression under the radical sign a perfect square.

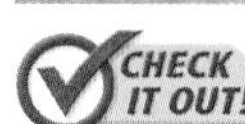

CHECK IT OUT! 3. Graph $y = \sqrt{x-4}$

Power Presentations with PowerPoint®

Additional Examples

Example 1

The function $y = 8\sqrt{x}$ gives the speed in feet per second of an object in free fall after falling x feet.

A. Find the speed of an object in free fall after it has fallen 16 feet. 32 ft/s

B. Find the speed of an object in free fall after it has fallen 20 feet. Round your answer to the nearest tenth. 35.8 ft/s

Example 2

Find the domain of each square-root function.

A. $y = 1 + \sqrt{x-4}$ $x \geq 4$

B. $y = \sqrt{4(x+3)}$ $x \geq -3$

Example 3

Graph $y = \sqrt{x-3}$.

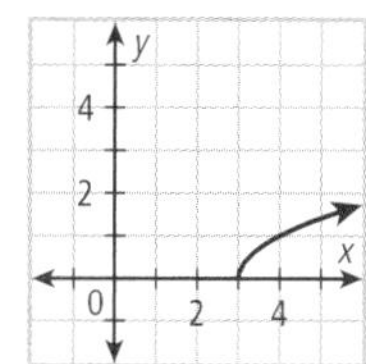

Also available on transparency

INTERVENTION

Questioning Strategies

EXAMPLE 1

- Why is $y = \sqrt{2}x$ not a square-root function?

EXAMPLE 2

- How do you choose which expression should be set greater than or equal to zero?

EXAMPLE 3

- How is the graph of a square-root function similar to the graph of an exponential function? How is it different?

2 Teach

Guided Instruction

First review square roots, perfect squares, and estimating square roots that are not perfect squares. In **Example 2,** remind students that radical signs are used as grouping symbols in the order of operations. Tell students that it is necessary to know the domain of a square-root function so that appropriate x-values are chosen when graphing such functions.

Answer to *Check it Out!*

3.

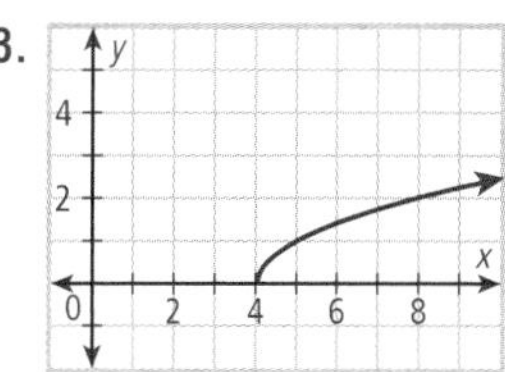

THINK AND DISCUSS

1. How do you find the domain of a square-root function?
2. **GET ORGANIZED** Copy and complete the graphic organizer. In each box, graph the function and give its domain.

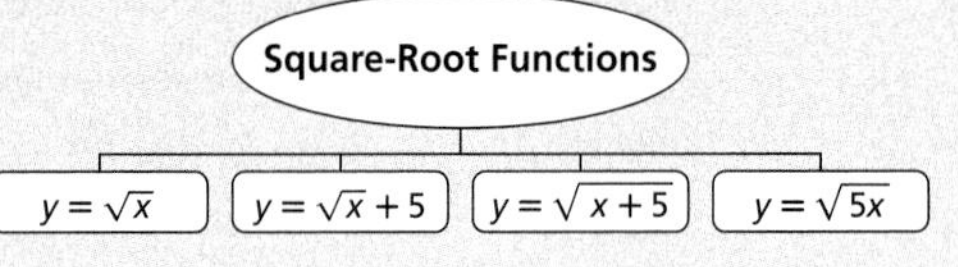

Answers to *Think and Discuss*

Possible answers:

1. Set the expression under the square-root sign greater than or equal to zero and solve.
2. See p. A9.

11-1 Exercises

Extension of 2.0; 17.0, 24.1

GUIDED PRACTICE

1. There is no variable under the square-root sign.

1. **Vocabulary** Explain why $y = x + \sqrt{3}$ is not a *square-root function.*

SEE EXAMPLE 1 p. 700

2. **Geometry** In a right triangle, $c = \sqrt{a^2 + b^2}$, where c is the length of the hypotenuse (the longest side) and a and b are the lengths of the legs (the other two sides). What is the length of the hypotenuse of a right triangle if its legs measure 14 cm and 8 cm? Round your answer to the nearest hundredth. **16.12 cm**

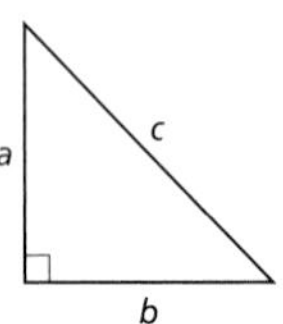

SEE EXAMPLE 2 p. 701

Find the domain of each square-root function.

3. $y = \sqrt{x + 6}$ **$x \geq -6$**
4. $y = 4 - \sqrt{3 - x}$ **$x \leq 3$**
5. $y = \sqrt{2x} - 5$ **$x \geq 0$**
6. $y = \sqrt{x + 2}$ **$x \geq -2$**
7. $y = \sqrt{3x + 9}$ **$x \geq -3$**
8. $y = x + \sqrt{x - 5}$ **$x \geq 5$**

SEE EXAMPLE 3 p. 701

Graph each square-root function.

9. $y = \sqrt{x - 1}$
10. $y = -\sqrt{2x}$
11. $y = \sqrt{x} + 1$
12. $y = \sqrt{x} - 12$
13. $y = \sqrt{4 - x}$
14. $y = \sqrt{x + 4}$

PRACTICE AND PROBLEM SOLVING

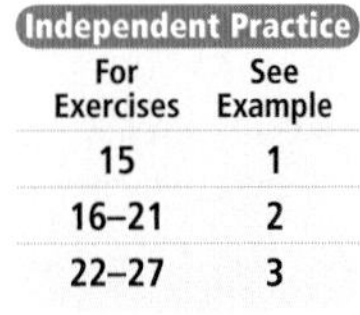

Independent Practice

For Exercises	See Example
15	1
16–21	2
22–27	3

Extra Practice
Skills Practice p. EP22
Application Practice p. EP34

15. **Law Enforcement** At the scene of a car accident, police measure the length of the skid marks to estimate the speed that the car was traveling. On dry concrete, $f(x) = \sqrt{24x}$ gives the speed in mi/h when the length of the skid mark is x feet. Find the speed that a car was traveling if it left a skid mark that was 104 ft long. Round your answer to the nearest hundredth. **49.96 mi/h**

Find the domain of each square-root function.

16. $y = \sqrt{-2x + 3}$ **$x \leq \frac{3}{2}$**
17. $y = 2\sqrt{x + 1} - 2$ **$x \geq -1$**
18. $y = \sqrt{3(x + 2)} - 1$ **$x \geq -\frac{5}{3}$**
19. $y = \sqrt{2(x + 4)} - 3$ **$x \geq -4$**
20. $y = 7\sqrt{\frac{x}{5} - 8}$ **$x \geq 40$**
21. $y = \sqrt{2(3x - 6)}$ **$x \geq 2$**

Graph each square-root function.

22. $y = \sqrt{x - 5}$
23. $y = \sqrt{2x} - 4$
24. $y = -1 - \sqrt{x}$
25. $y = \sqrt{x} - 4$
26. $y = 3\sqrt{x - 6}$
27. $y = \frac{1}{2}\sqrt{x + 4}$

11-1 Exercises

Assignment Guide

Assign *Guided Practice* exercises as necessary.

If you finished Examples **1–2**
Proficient 15–21, 28
Advanced 15–21, 28, 41–43

If you finished Examples **1–3**
Proficient 15–32, 36–40, 49–64
Advanced 15, 16–32 even, 33–64

Homework Quick Check
Quickly check key concepts.
Exercises: 15, 16, 20, 22, 24, 28

Teaching Tip

Inclusion For **Exercises 4** and **16** remind students that the direction of an inequality symbol is switched when both sides of the inequality are multiplied or divided by a negative number.

Answers

9–14, 22–27. See p. A26.

Universal Access

Through Cooperative Learning

Have students work in pairs. Each pair should make two sets of index cards: one set with square-root functions and another with the corresponding domains. Have each pair trade cards with another pair. The students can then work together to match each function to its domain.

3 Close

Summarize

Tell students that to find the domain of a square-root function, they need to set the expression under the radical sign greater than or equal to 0 and solve for x.

To graph the square-root function, students should use x-values from the domain to generate ordered pairs. Remind students to choose x-values that make the expression under the radical sign a perfect square. This will simplify calculations as well as graphing.

FORMATIVE ASSESSMENT

and INTERVENTION

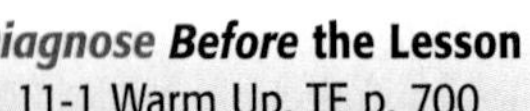

***Diagnose Before* the Lesson**
11-1 Warm Up, TE p. 700

***Monitor During* the Lesson**
Check It Out! Exercises, SE pp. 700–701
Questioning Strategies, TE pp. 701–701

***Assess After* the Lesson**
11-1 Lesson Quiz, TE p. 704
Alternative Assessment, TE p. 704

28. **Geometry** If you know a circle's area, you can use the formula $r = \sqrt{\frac{A}{\pi}}$ to find the radius. What is the radius of a circle whose area is 60 cm²? Use 3.14 for π. Round your answer to the nearest hundredth of a centimeter. **4.37 cm**

29. **Graphing Calculator** Use a graphing calculator for the following.
    a. Graph $y = \sqrt{x}$, $y = \frac{1}{2}\sqrt{x}$, $y = 2\sqrt{x}$, $y = 3\sqrt{x}$, and $y = 4\sqrt{x}$ on the same screen.
    b. What is the domain of each function? $x \geq 0$
    c. What is the range of each function? $y \geq 0$
    d. **Reasoning** Use inductive reasoning to make a conjecture about the characteristics of the graph of $y = a\sqrt{x}$ for $a > 0$.

30. **Graphing Calculator** Use a graphing calculator for the following.
    a. Graph $y = -\sqrt{x}$, $y = -\frac{1}{2}\sqrt{x}$, $y = -2\sqrt{x}$, $y = -3\sqrt{x}$, and $y = -4\sqrt{x}$ on the same screen.
    b. What is the domain of each function? $x \geq 0$
    c. What is the range of each function? $y \leq 0$
    d. **Reasoning** Use inductive reasoning to make a conjecture about the characteristics of $y = a\sqrt{x}$ for $a < 0$.

30d. Possible answer: It has a max. value of 0 and curves to the right. As a decreases, the curve becomes steeper.

Geology

In December 2004, devastating tsunamis struck south and southeast Asia and eastern Africa. A worldwide relief effort ensued. Aid from the United States, both public and private, totaled over $2 billion in the year following the disaster.

31. **Geology** Tsunamis are large waves that move across deep oceans at high speeds. When tsunamis hit shallow water, their energy moves them upward into a destructive force. The speed of a tsunami in meters per second can be found using the function $y = \sqrt{9.8x}$, where x is the depth of the water in meters. Graph this function. Then find the speed of a tsunami when the water depth is 500 meters. **70 m/s**

32. **Astronomy** A planet's *escape velocity* is the initial velocity that an object must have to escape the planet's gravity. Escape velocity v in meters per second can be found by using the formula $v = \sqrt{2gr}$, where g is the planet's surface gravity and r is the planet's radius. Find the escape velocity for each planet in the table to the nearest whole number. **Mercury: 4214 m/s; Venus: 10,361 m/s; Earth: 11,200 m/s; Mars: 5016 m/s**

Planet	g (m/s²)	r (m)
Mercury	3.7	2.4×10^6
Venus	8.8	6.1×10^6
Earth	9.8	6.4×10^6
Mars	3.7	3.4×10^6

33. **Critical Thinking** Can the range of a square-root function be all real numbers? Explain.

34. **Multi-Step** For the function $y = \sqrt{3(x - 5)}$, find the value of y that corresponds to the least possible value for x. **0**

35. **Write About It** Explain how to find the domain of a square-root function. Why is the domain not all real numbers?

CONCEPT CONNECTION

36. This problem will prepare you for the Concept Connection on page 730.
    a. The Ocean Motion ride at Ohio's Cedar Point amusement park is a giant ship that swings like a pendulum. If a pendulum is under the influence of gravity only, then the time in seconds that it takes for one complete swing back and forth (called the pendulum's period) is $T = 2\pi\sqrt{\frac{\ell}{32}}$, where ℓ is the length of the pendulum in feet. What is the domain of this function? $\ell \geq 0$
    b. What is the period of a pendulum whose length is 80 feet? Use 3.14 for π and round your answer to the nearest hundredth. **9.93 s**
    c. The length of the Ocean Motion pendulum is about 80 feet. Do you think your answer to part **b** is its period? Explain why or why not.

Teaching Tip

Science Link Escape velocity is discussed in **Exercise 32.** Explain that if you throw an object up, it falls back down because of gravity. But if you could throw it up fast enough, gravity would not be able to pull it back down. From the surface of Earth, the escape velocity is about 25,000 miles per hour.

CONCEPT CONNECTION **Exercise 36** involves evaluating square-root functions. This exercise prepares students for the Concept Connection on page 730.

Answers

29a. 20

0 20

29d. Possible answer: It has a min. value of 0 and curves to the right. As a increases, the curve becomes steeper.

30a.

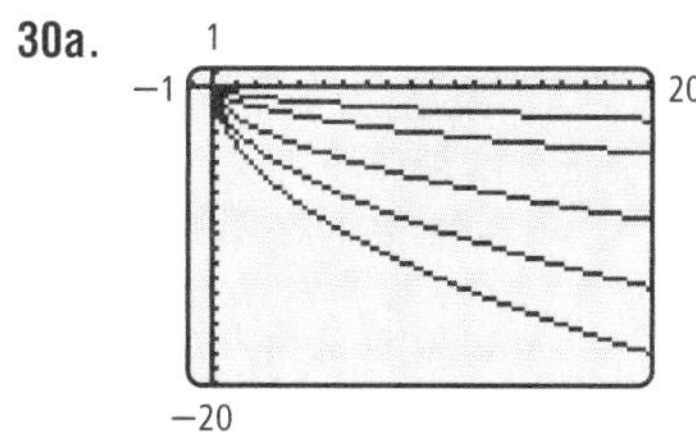

31. For graph, see p. A26.

33. See p. A26.

35. Set the expression under the square root sign ≥ 0; because the square root of a neg. number is not a real number.

36c. See p. A26.

11-1 READING STRATEGIES

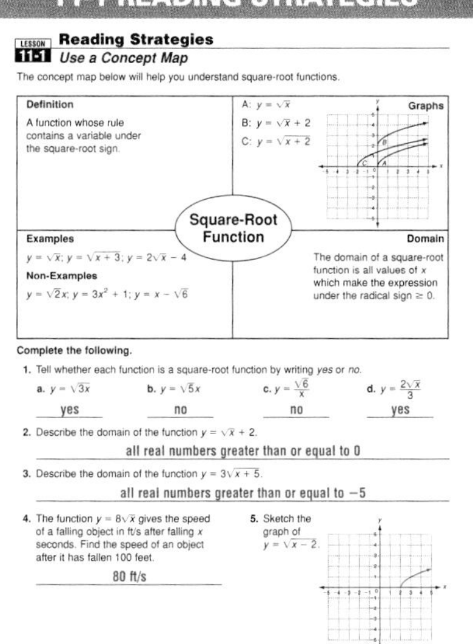

LESSON 11-1 Reading Strategies
Use a Concept Map

The concept map below will help you understand square-root functions.

Definition: A function whose rule contains a variable under the square-root sign.

Graphs: A: $y = \sqrt{x}$; B: $y = \sqrt{x} + 2$; C: $y = \sqrt{x + 2}$

Square-Root Function

Examples: $y = \sqrt{x}$; $y = \sqrt{x + 3}$; $y = 2\sqrt{x} - 4$
Non-Examples: $y = \sqrt{2}x$; $y = 3x^2 + 1$; $y = x - \sqrt{6}$

Domain: The domain of a square-root function is all values of x which make the expression under the radical sign ≥ 0.

Complete the following.

1. Tell whether each function is a square-root function by writing *yes* or *no*.
a. $y = \sqrt{3x}$ yes b. $y = \sqrt{5}x$ no c. $y = \frac{\sqrt{6}}{x}$ no d. $y = \frac{2\sqrt{x}}{3}$ yes

2. Describe the domain of the function $y = \sqrt{x} + 2$. all real numbers greater than or equal to 0

3. Describe the domain of the function $y = 3\sqrt{x + 5}$. all real numbers greater than or equal to −5

4. The function $y = 8\sqrt{x}$ gives the speed of a falling object in ft/s after falling x seconds. Find the speed of an object after it has fallen 100 feet. 80 ft/s

5. Sketch the graph of $y = \sqrt{x - 2}$.

11-1 REVIEW FOR MASTERY

LESSON 11-1 Review for Mastery
Square-Root Functions

A square-root function is a function in which the independent variable is under the square-root sign.

Square-root functions	Not square-root functions
$y = \sqrt{2x + 3}$	$y = 2x + \sqrt{3}$
$y = 4 + \sqrt{x}$	$y = \sqrt{4}x$

Determine whether $y = 5 + \frac{\sqrt{x}}{2}$ is a square-root function. Explain.
Because x is under the square-root sign, this is a square-root function.

The square root of a negative number is not a real number. Therefore, the x-values must be restricted to numbers that make the value under the radical sign greater than or equal to 0.

Find the domain of $y = \sqrt{x + 5}$.
$x + 5$ is under the radical sign.
$x + 5$ must be greater than or equal to zero.
$x + 5 \geq 0$
$-5 \quad -5$ *Add −5 to both sides.*
$x \geq -5$
The domain is the set of all real numbers greater than or equal to −5.

Find the domain of $y = 3 - \sqrt{4x - 12}$.
$4x - 12$ is under the radical sign.
$4x - 12$ must be greater than or equal to zero.
$4x - 12 \geq 0$
$+12 \quad +12$ *Add 12 to both sides.*
$4x \geq 12$
$\frac{4x}{4} \geq \frac{12}{4}$ *Divide each side by 4.*
$x \geq 3$
The domain is the set of all real numbers greater than or equal to 3.

Determine whether the following are square-root functions. Explain.
1. $y = \sqrt{8} + x$ no, x is not under the square-root sign.
2. $y = \sqrt{8 + x}$ yes, x is under the square-root sign.

Find the domain of each square-root function.
3. $y = \sqrt{5x - 8}$ $x \geq \frac{8}{5}$
4. $y = 6 + \sqrt{x}$ $x \geq 0$
5. $y = \sqrt{3x} - 5$ $x \geq 0$
6. $y = \sqrt{2(x - 5)}$ $x \geq 5$
7. $y = \sqrt{\frac{x}{5}} - 8$ $x \geq 0$
8. $y = \sqrt{\frac{x}{3} + 2}$ $x \geq -6$

11-1 PRACTICE A

11-1 PRACTICE C

11-1 PRACTICE B

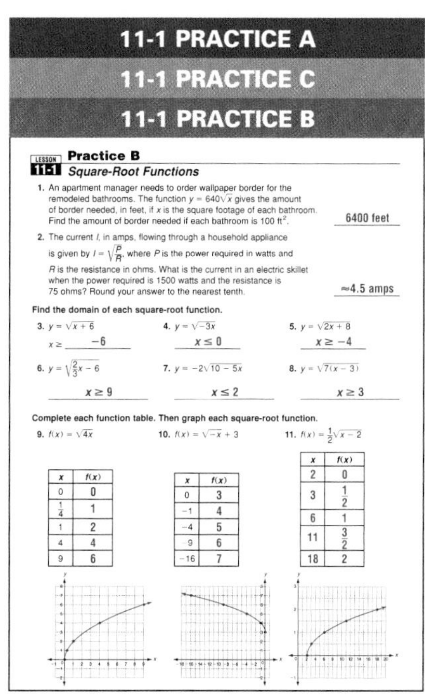

LESSON 11-1 Practice B
Square-Root Functions

1. An apartment manager needs to order wallpaper border for the remodeled bathrooms. The function $y = 640\sqrt{x}$ gives the amount of border needed, in feet, if x is the square footage of each bathroom. Find the amount of border needed if each bathroom is 100 ft². 6400 feet

2. The current I, in amps, flowing through a household appliance is given by $I = \sqrt{\frac{P}{R}}$, where P is the power required in watts and R is the resistance in ohms. What is the current in an electric skillet when the power required is 1500 watts and the resistance is 75 ohms? Round your answer to the nearest tenth. ≈4.5 amps

Find the domain of each square-root function.
3. $y = \sqrt{x + 6}$ $x \geq -6$
4. $y = \sqrt{-3x}$ $x \leq 0$
5. $y = \sqrt{2x + 8}$ $x \geq -4$
6. $y = \sqrt{\frac{2}{3}x - 6}$ $x \geq 9$
7. $y = -2\sqrt{10 - 5x}$ $x \leq 2$
8. $y = \sqrt{7(x - 3)}$ $x \geq 3$

Complete each function table. Then graph each square-root function.
9. $f(x) = \sqrt{4x}$ 10. $f(x) = \sqrt{-x} + 3$ 11. $f(x) = \frac{1}{2}\sqrt{x - 2}$

x	$f(x)$
0	0
$\frac{1}{4}$	1
1	2
4	4
9	6

x	$f(x)$
0	3
−1	4
−4	5
−9	6
−16	7

x	$f(x)$
2	0
3	$\frac{1}{2}$
6	1
11	$\frac{3}{2}$
18	2

Multiple Choice Students who chose **B** in **Exercise 39** may have forgotten to take the square root after taking one-fifth of x.

Answers

50–52. For graphs, see p. A26.

Journal

Have students describe the graph of $y = \sqrt{x}$ and compare it to the graph of $y = -\sqrt{x}$.

Alternative Assessment

Have students graph $y = \sqrt{2(x + 1)} - 6$ by generating at least five ordered pairs. Then have them state the domain and range of the function.

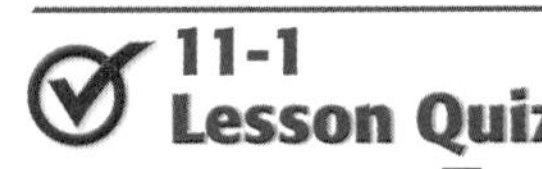

Power Presentations with PowerPoint®

11-1 Lesson Quiz

1. Use the formula $r = \sqrt{\frac{A}{\pi}}$ to find the radius of a circle whose area is 28 in^2. Use 3.14 for π. Round your answer to the nearest tenth of an inch. 3.0 in.

Find the domain of each square-root function.

2. $y = \sqrt{3x} - 1$ $x \geq 0$
3. $y = -\sqrt{2x + 1}$ $x \geq -\frac{1}{2}$
4. $y = \sqrt{2(x - 5)}$ $x \geq 5$

Graph each square-root function.

5. $y = 2 + \sqrt{3x}$

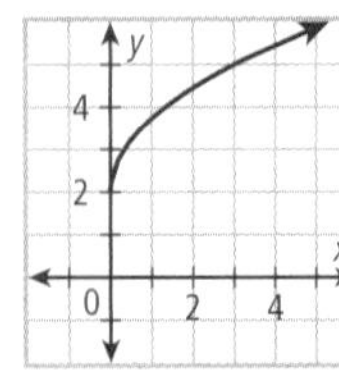

6. $y = \sqrt{x + 1}$

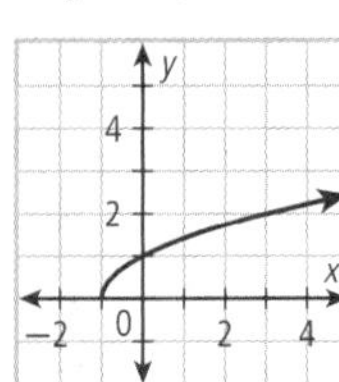

Also available on transparency

Multiple Choice For Exercises 37–39, choose the best answer.

37. Which function is graphed at right?
    (A) $y = \sqrt{x + 3}$ (circled)   (C) $y = \sqrt{x - 3}$
    (B) $y = \sqrt{x} + 3$ (D) $y = \sqrt{x} - 3$

38. Which function has domain $x \geq 2$?
    (A) $y = \sqrt{2x}$ (C) $y = \sqrt{\frac{x}{2}}$
    (B) $y = \sqrt{x + 2}$ (D) $y = \sqrt{x - 2}$ (circled)

39. The function $y = \sqrt{\frac{1}{5}x}$ gives the approximate time y in seconds that it takes an object to fall to the ground from a height of x meters. About how long will it take an object 25 meters above the ground to fall to the ground?
    (A) 11.2 seconds   (C) 2.2 seconds (circled)
    (B) 5 seconds   (D) 0.4 seconds

40. **Gridded Response** If $g(x) = \sqrt{4x} - 1$, what is $g(9)$? **5**

CHALLENGE AND EXTEND

Find the domain of each function.

41. $y = \sqrt{x^2 - 25}$ **$x \leq -5$ OR $x \geq 5$**
42. $y = \sqrt{x^2 + 5x + 6}$ **$x \leq -3$ OR $x \geq -2$**
43. $y = \sqrt{2x^2 + 5x - 12}$ **$x \leq -4$ OR $x \geq \frac{3}{2}$**

Find the domain and range of each function.

44. $y = 2 - \sqrt{x + 3}$ **D: $x \geq -3$; R: $y \leq 2$**
45. $y = 4 - \sqrt{3 - x}$ **D: $x \leq 3$; R: $y \leq 4$**
46. $y = 6 - \sqrt{\frac{x}{2}}$ **D: $x \geq 0$; R: $y \leq 6$**

47. Give an example of a square-root function whose graph is above the x-axis.
    47. Possible answer: $y = \sqrt{x} + 6$
48. Give an example of a square-root function whose graph is in Quadrant IV.
    48. Possible answer: $y = -\sqrt{x - 1} - 1$
49. **Multi-Step** Justin is given the function $y = 3 - \sqrt{2(x - 5)}$ and $x = 2, 4, 5$, and 7. He notices that two of these values are not in the function's domain.
    a. Which two values are not in the domain? How do you know?
    49a. 2, 4; when $x = 2$ or $x = 4$, the expression under the square root sign is neg.
    b. What are the values of y for the two given x-values that are in the domain? **3, 1**

SPIRAL STANDARDS REVIEW

6.0, 10.0

Write each equation in slope-intercept form, and then graph. (Lesson 5-5)

50. $2y = 4x - 8$ **50. $y = 2x - 4$**
51. $3x + 6y = 12$ **51. $y = -\frac{1}{2}x + 2$**
52. $2x = -y - 9$ **52. $y = -2x - 9$**

Find each product. (Lesson 7-9)

53. $(3x - 1)^2$ **$9x^2 - 6x + 1$**
54. $(2x - 5)(2x + 5)$ **$4x^2 - 25$**
55. $(a - b^2c)^2$ **$a^2 - 2ab^2c + b^4c^2$**
56. $(x^2 + 2y)^2$ **56. $x^4 + 4x^2y + 4y^2$**
57. $(3r - 2s)(3r + 2s)$ **57. $9r^2 - 4s^2$**
58. $(a^3b^2 - c^4)(a^3b^2 + c^4)$ **58. $a^6b^4 - c^8$**

Divide by using long division. Check your answer. (Lesson 10-6)

59. $(x^2 - 12x - 28) \div (x + 2)$ **$x - 14$**
60. $(y^2 - 2y - 15) \div (y + 3)$ **$y - 5$**
61. $(2r^2 - 9r - 5) \div (r - 5)$ **$2r + 1$**
62. $(t^2 + 4t - 21) \div (t + 7)$ **$t - 3$**
63. $\frac{(3s^2 - 14s - 24)}{s - 6}$ **$3s + 4$**
64. $\frac{(h^2 + 11h + 24)}{(h + 3)}$ **$h + 8$**

704 Chapter 11 Radical and Exponential Functions

11-1 PROBLEM SOLVING

LESSON 11-1 Problem Solving
Square-Root Functions

Write the correct answer.

1. Use the formula $r = \sqrt{\frac{A}{\pi}}$ to find the radius of a circular fountain with an area of 200 square feet. Use 3.14 for π. Round your answer to the nearest foot.
   8 ft
2. The manager of a magazine gives a rating to each article written using $y = \sqrt{10x}$ where x is the number of positive responses received about that article. What rating would the manager give an article if it received 21 positive responses? (Round to the nearest tenth.)
   14.5
3. The distance to the horizon (in km) from an aircraft can be roughly approximated using $y = 4\sqrt{x}$ where x is the aircraft's altitude in meters. Graph this function.

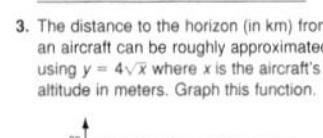

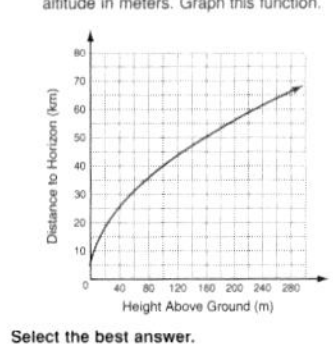

4. The amount of water flowing through a hose in gallons per minute is given by $y = 35\sqrt{x}$ where x is the nozzle pressure in pounds per square inch. What is the water flow in the hose if the pressure is 25 pounds per square inch?
   175 gal/min

Select the best answer.

5. The diameter of a can of tuna is found by $d = 2\sqrt{\frac{V}{\pi h}}$ where V is volume and h is height. To the nearest cm, what is the radius of a tuna can with a volume of 150 cm^3 and a height of 3 cm?
   A 2 cm   C 8 cm
   (B) 4 cm   D 16 cm
6. The side length of the base of a square pyramid can be found by $s = \sqrt{\frac{3V}{h}}$ where V is volume and h is height. To the nearest meter, what is the side length of the base of a square pyramid if its volume is 13,653 m^3 and its height is 40 m?
   F 3 m   (H) 32 m
   G 18 m   J 55 m
7. The radius of a ball is found by $r = \sqrt{\frac{S}{4\pi}}$ where S is surface area. To the nearest tenth of an inch, what is the radius of a ball with a surface area of 154 in^2?
   (A) 3.5 in.   C 7.0 in.
   B 6.2 in.   D 12.3 in.

11-1 CHALLENGE

LESSON 11-1 Challenge
Inverses of Relations

If you start with 5 and add 2, you get 7. Then if you take 7 and subtract 2, you get 5 again. That's because addition and subtraction are *inverse operations* that "undo" each other. Notice that what you start with and what you end with flip-flop.

Start with 5. $5 + 2 = 7$ End with 7.
Start with 7. $7 - 2 = 5$ End with 5.

Relations also have inverses that undo each other. Two **inverse relations** will flip-flop inputs and outputs.

$y = 2x + 3 \longrightarrow y = 2(5) + 3 = 10 + 3 = 13$ (Input 5, Output 13)

So, one way to find the inverse of a relation is to flip-flop the input (x) and the output (y).

$y = \frac{x - 3}{2} \longrightarrow y = \frac{13 - 3}{2} = \frac{10}{2} = 5$ (Input 13, Output 5)

Find the inverse of $y = x - 6$.

$x = y - 6$ *Flip-flop x and y.*
$+6 \quad +6$ *Use inverse operations.*
$x + 6 = y$ *Solve for y.*

The inverse relation is $y = x + 6$.

Flip-flop x and y to find the inverse of each relation.

1. $y = x + 10$ **$y = x - 10$**
2. $y = \frac{x}{5}$ **$y = 5x$**
3. $y = -3x + 6$ **$y = -\frac{1}{3}x + 2$**
4. $y = x^2$ (*Hint:* Review Lesson 9-7.) **$y = \pm\sqrt{x}$**
5. $y = (x + 2)^2$ **$y = \pm\sqrt{x} - 2$**
6. $y = \frac{1}{4}x^2 - 2$ **$y = \pm\sqrt{4x + 8}$**
7. On a graphing calculator, enter each relation into **Y1** and its inverse into **Y2**, and graph in a square window (ZOOM **Zsquare**). (For 4–6, enter each inverse as two halves in **Y2** and **Y3**.) Describe any patterns.
   The line or curve of each original relation is reflected across the line $y = x$ to create the line or curve of the inverse relation.
8. Notice that all of the original relations in 1–6 are functions. For which are the inverses also functions? **1, 2, and 3**
9. In Lesson 11–5, you may have noticed that the graph of the function $f(x) = \sqrt{x}$ looks like half of a sideways parabola. Explain why this is.
   The graph of $y = x^2$ is a parabola, and the inverse relation $y = \pm\sqrt{x}$ is the same parabola reflected across the line $y = x$. The graph of $f(x) = \sqrt{x}$ is the top (positive) half of $y = \pm\sqrt{x}$.

11-2 Radical Expressions

California Standards

Extension of 2.0 Students understand and use such operations as taking the opposite, finding the reciprocal, **taking a root,** and raising to a fractional power. **They understand and use the rules of exponents.**

Vocabulary
radical expression
radicand

Why learn this?

You can use a radical expression to find the length of a throw in baseball. (See Example 5.)

An expression that contains a radical sign ($\sqrt{\ }$) is a **radical expression**. There are many types of radical expressions (such as square roots, cube roots, fourth roots, and so on), but in this chapter, you will study radical expressions that contain only square roots.

Examples of radical expressions: $\sqrt{14}$ $\quad\sqrt{\ell^2 + w^2}$ $\quad\sqrt{2gd}$ $\quad\frac{\sqrt{d}}{4}$ $\quad 5\sqrt{2}$

The expression under a radical sign is the **radicand**. A radicand may contain numbers, variables, or both. It may contain one term or more than one term.

Know it! Note

Simplest Form of a Square-Root Expression

An expression containing square roots is in simplest form when

- the radicand has no perfect square factors other than 1.
- the radicand has no fractions.
- there are no square roots in any denominator.

Helpful Hint

- $\sqrt{x^2} = |x|$
- $\sqrt{x^4} = x^2$
- $\sqrt{x^6} = |x^3|$

Remember that $\sqrt{\ }$ indicates a nonnegative square root. When you simplify a square-root expression containing variables, you must be sure that your answer is not negative. For example, you might think that $\sqrt{x^2} = x$. But this is incorrect because you do not know if x is positive or negative.

If $x = 3$, then $\sqrt{x^2} = \sqrt{3^2} = \sqrt{9} = 3$. In this case, $\sqrt{x^2} = x$.

If $x = -3$, then $\sqrt{x^2} = \sqrt{(-3)^2} = \sqrt{9} = 3$. In this case, $\sqrt{x^2} \neq x$.

In both cases $\sqrt{x^2} = |x|$. This is the correct simplification of $\sqrt{x^2}$.

EXAMPLE 1 Simplifying Square-Root Expressions

Simplify each expression.

A $\sqrt{\frac{2}{72}}$

$\sqrt{\frac{2}{72}} = \sqrt{\frac{1}{36}}$

$= \frac{1}{6}$

B $\sqrt{3^2 + 4^2}$

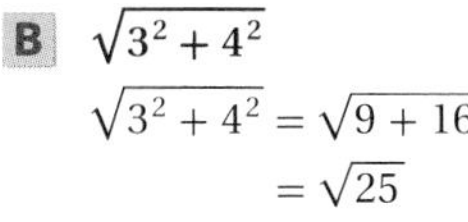

$\sqrt{3^2 + 4^2} = \sqrt{9 + 16}$

$= \sqrt{25}$

$= 5$

C $\sqrt{x^2 + 8x + 16}$

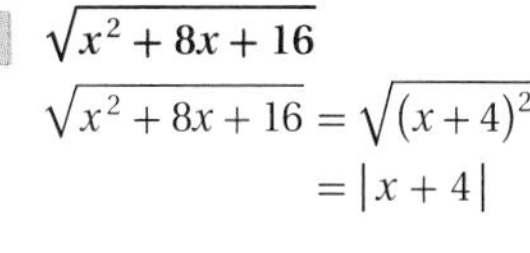

$\sqrt{x^2 + 8x + 16} = \sqrt{(x+4)^2}$

$= |x + 4|$

CHECK IT OUT! Simplify each expression.

1a. $\sqrt{\frac{256}{4}}$ **8** **1b.** $\sqrt{40 + 9}$ **7** **1c.** $\sqrt{5^2 + 12^2}$ **13** **1d.** $\sqrt{(3 - x)^2}$ $|3 - x|$

11-2 Organizer

Objective: Simplify radical expressions.

PREMIER Online Edition
Tutorial Videos

Power Presentations with PowerPoint®

Warm Up

Identify the perfect square in each set.

1. 45 81 27 111 81

2. 156 99 8 25 25

3. 256 84 12 1000 256

4. 35 216 196 72 196

Write each number as a product of prime numbers.

5. 36 2 • 2 • 3 • 3

6. 64 2 • 2 • 2 • 2 • 2 • 2

7. 196 2 • 2 • 7 • 7

8. 24 2 • 2 • 2 • 3

Also available on transparency

Math Fact !!!

The symbol ℞ was used as a square-root symbol in the thirteenth century. The symbol used today was not introduced until the seventeenth century and is thought to have evolved from a single dot and a diagonal pen stroke.

1 Introduce

EXPLORATION

11-2 Radical Expressions

You will need a calculator for this Exploration.

1. Use your calculator to find a decimal approximation for each expression in the table. Round to the nearest thousandth.

Expression	Decimal Approximation	Expression	Decimal Approximation
$\sqrt{3}\sqrt{6}$		$\sqrt{18}$	
$\sqrt{2}\sqrt{17}$		$\sqrt{34}$	
$\sqrt{50}\sqrt{3}$		$\sqrt{150}$	
$\sqrt{5}\sqrt{2}\sqrt{3}$		$\sqrt{30}$	

2. What do you notice in the table?
3. Use your calculator to find a decimal approximation for each expression in the table. Round to the nearest thousandth.

Expression	Decimal Approximation	Expression	Decimal Approximation
$\frac{\sqrt{10}}{\sqrt{2}}$		$\sqrt{5}$	
$\frac{\sqrt{38}}{\sqrt{19}}$		$\sqrt{2}$	
$\frac{\sqrt{30}}{\sqrt{5}}$		$\sqrt{6}$	

4. What do you notice in the table?

THINK AND DISCUSS

5. **Describe** any conjectures that you can make based on your findings.

Motivate

Have students list pairs of numbers whose product is 48. 1 • 48, 2 • 24, 3 • 16, 4 • 12, 6 • 8

Which pairs include a number that is a perfect square? 3 • 16, 4 • 12

Tell students that factoring numbers so that one number is a perfect square is an essential skill in this lesson.

Explorations and answers are provided in *Alternate Openers: Explorations Transparencies.*

California Standards

Extension of 2.0

Power Presentations with PowerPoint®

Additional Examples

Example 1

Simplify each expression.

A. $\sqrt{\frac{2}{50}}$ $\frac{1}{5}$ **B.** $\sqrt{8^2 + 15^2}$ 17

C. $\sqrt{x^2 - 6x + 9}$ $|x - 3|$

Example 2

Simplify. All variables represent nonnegative numbers.

A. $\sqrt{24}$ $2\sqrt{6}$ **B.** $\sqrt{x^3y^4}$ $xy^2\sqrt{x}$

Example 3

Simplify. All variables represent nonnegative numbers.

A. $\sqrt{\frac{5}{4}}$ $\frac{\sqrt{5}}{2}$ **B.** $\sqrt{\frac{m^3}{9m}}$ $\frac{m}{3}$

Example 4

Simplify. All variables represent nonnegative numbers.

A. $\sqrt{\frac{108}{25}}$ $\frac{6\sqrt{3}}{5}$ **B.** $\sqrt{\frac{9x^3}{16}}$ $\frac{3x\sqrt{x}}{4}$

Also available on transparency

INTERVENTION

Questioning Strategies

EXAMPLE 1

- How do you know when a radical expression is simplified?
- When do radical expressions require absolute-value signs in the simplified answer? Why?

EXAMPLE 2

- How do you choose the factors when using the Product Property of Square Roots?

EXAMPLES 3–4

- When would you simplify a fraction before using the Quotient Property of Square Roots?
- How is the Quotient Property of Square Roots similar to the Product Property of Square Roots?

Product Property of Square Roots

WORDS	NUMBERS	ALGEBRA
For any nonnegative real numbers *a* and *b*, the square root of *ab* is equal to the square root of *a* times the square root of *b*.	$\sqrt{4(25)} = \sqrt{100} = 10$ $\sqrt{4(25)} = \sqrt{4}\sqrt{25} = 2(5) = 10$	$\sqrt{ab} = \sqrt{a}\sqrt{b}$, where $a \geq 0$ and $b \geq 0$

EXAMPLE **2** **Using the Product Property of Square Roots**

Simplify. All variables represent nonnegative numbers.

Helpful Hint

When factoring the radicand, use factors that are perfect squares. In Example 2A, you could have factored 18 as 6 · 3, but this contains no perfect squares.

A $\sqrt{18}$

$\sqrt{18} = \sqrt{9(2)}$ *Factor the radicand using perfect squares.*

$= \sqrt{9}\sqrt{2}$ *Product Property of Square Roots*

$= 3\sqrt{2}$ *Simplify.*

B $\sqrt{x^4y^3}$

$\sqrt{x^4y^3} = \sqrt{x^4}\sqrt{y^3}$ *Product Property of Square Roots*

$= \sqrt{x^4}\sqrt{y^2}\sqrt{y}$ *Product Property of Square Roots*

$= x^2y\sqrt{y}$ *Since y is nonnegative, $\sqrt{y^2} = y$.*

Simplify. All variables represent nonnegative numbers.

2a. $\sqrt{128}$ $8\sqrt{2}$ **2b.** $\sqrt{x^3y^2}$ $xy\sqrt{x}$ **2c.** $\sqrt{48a^2b}$ $4a\sqrt{3b}$

Quotient Property of Square Roots

WORDS	NUMBERS	ALGEBRA
For any real numbers *a* and *b* ($a \geq 0$ and $b > 0$), the square root of $\frac{a}{b}$ is equal to the square root of *a* divided by the square root of *b*.	$\sqrt{\frac{36}{4}} = \sqrt{9} = 3$ $\sqrt{\frac{36}{4}} = \frac{\sqrt{36}}{\sqrt{4}} = \frac{6}{2} = 3$	$\sqrt{\frac{a}{b}} = \frac{\sqrt{a}}{\sqrt{b}}$, where $a \geq 0$ and $b > 0$

EXAMPLE **3** **Using the Quotient Property of Square Roots**

Simplify. All variables represent nonnegative numbers.

A $\sqrt{\frac{5}{9}}$

$\sqrt{\frac{5}{9}} = \frac{\sqrt{5}}{\sqrt{9}}$ *Quotient Property of Square Roots*

$= \frac{\sqrt{5}}{3}$ *Simplify.*

B $\sqrt{\frac{a^5}{81a}}$

$\sqrt{\frac{a^5}{81a}} = \sqrt{\frac{a^4}{81}}$ *Simplify.*

$= \frac{\sqrt{a^4}}{\sqrt{81}}$ *Quotient Property of Square Roots*

$= \frac{a^2}{9}$ *Simplify.*

2 Teach

Guided Instruction

Introduce radical expressions and give some examples that are simplified and some that are not simplified, stating why they aren't simplified. Show students how to simplify radical expressions, stressing that they must read the direction lines. If it is not stated that all variables represent nonnegative numbers, as in **Example 1,** students may have to use absolute-value symbols for expressions containing variables to show that the answer is not negative.

Universal Access

Through Cognitive Strategies

Show students how to simplify a radical expression by completely factoring the radicand. Every pair can be "pulled out" and written outside the radical one time.

$\sqrt{108}$	$\sqrt{x^3y^4}$
$\sqrt{(2 \cdot 2) \cdot (3 \cdot 3) \cdot 3}$	$\sqrt{(x \cdot x) \cdot x \cdot (y \cdot y) \cdot (y \cdot y)}$
$2 \cdot 3\sqrt{3}$	$x \cdot y \cdot y\sqrt{x}$
$6\sqrt{3}$	$xy^2\sqrt{x}$

Simplify. All variables represent nonnegative numbers.

3a. $\sqrt{\frac{12}{27}}$ $\frac{2}{3}$ 3b. $\sqrt{\frac{36}{x^4}}$ $\frac{6}{x^2}$ 3c. $\sqrt{\frac{y^6}{4}}$ $\frac{y^3}{2}$

EXAMPLE 4 **Using the Product and Quotient Properties Together**

Simplify. All variables represent nonnegative numbers.

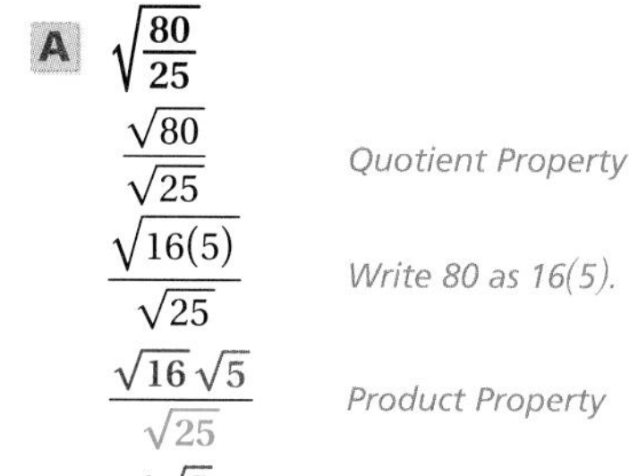

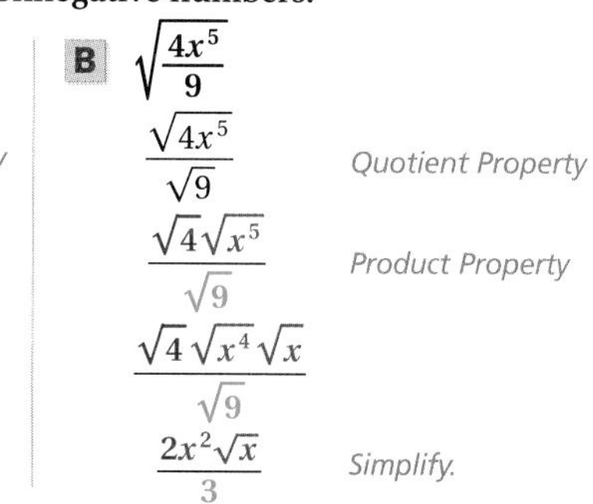

A $\sqrt{\frac{80}{25}}$

$\frac{\sqrt{80}}{\sqrt{25}}$ *Quotient Property*

$\frac{\sqrt{16(5)}}{\sqrt{25}}$ *Write 80 as 16(5).*

$\frac{\sqrt{16}\sqrt{5}}{\sqrt{25}}$ *Product Property*

$\frac{4\sqrt{5}}{5}$ *Simplify.*

B $\sqrt{\frac{4x^5}{9}}$

$\frac{\sqrt{4x^5}}{\sqrt{9}}$ *Quotient Property*

$\frac{\sqrt{4}\sqrt{x^5}}{\sqrt{9}}$ *Product Property*

$\frac{\sqrt{4}\sqrt{x^4}\sqrt{x}}{\sqrt{9}}$

$\frac{2x^2\sqrt{x}}{3}$ *Simplify.*

Caution!

In the expression $\frac{4\sqrt{5}}{5}$, $\sqrt{5}$ and 5 are not common factors. $\frac{4\sqrt{5}}{5}$ is completely simplified.

Simplify. All variables represent nonnegative numbers.

4a. $\sqrt{\frac{20}{49}}$ $\frac{2\sqrt{5}}{7}$ 4b. $\sqrt{\frac{z^5}{25y^2}}$ $\frac{z^2\sqrt{z}}{5y}$ 4c. $\sqrt{\frac{p^6}{q^{10}}}$ $\frac{p^3}{q^5}$

EXAMPLE 5 ***Sports Application***

A baseball diamond is a square with sides of 90 feet. How far is a throw from third base to first base? Give the answer as a radical expression in simplest form. Then estimate the length to the nearest tenth of a foot.

The distance from third base to first base is the hypotenuse of a right triangle. Use the Pythagorean Theorem: $c^2 = a^2 + b^2$.

$c = \sqrt{a^2 + b^2}$ *Solve for c.*

$= \sqrt{(90)^2 + (90)^2}$ *Substitute 90 for a and b.*

$= \sqrt{8100 + 8100}$ *Simplify.*

$= \sqrt{16{,}200}$

$= \sqrt{100(81)(2)}$ *Factor 16,200 using perfect squares.*

$= \sqrt{100}\sqrt{81}\sqrt{2}$ *Use the Product Property of Square Roots.*

$= 10(9)\sqrt{2}$

$= 90\sqrt{2}$ *Simplify.*

≈ 127.3 *Use a calculator and round to the nearest tenth.*

The distance is $90\sqrt{2}$, or about 127.3, feet.

5. A softball diamond is a square with sides of 60 feet. How long is a throw from third base to first base in softball? Give the answer as a radical expression in simplest form. Then estimate the length to the nearest tenth of a foot. **$60\sqrt{2}$ ft; 84.9 ft**

COMMON ERROR ALERT

Students might write the square root of a sum as the sum of the square roots. For example, they may write $\sqrt{3^2 + 4^2} = 3 + 4 = 7$ instead of $\sqrt{3^2 + 4^2} = \sqrt{9 + 16} = \sqrt{25} = 5$. Remind students that the radical sign acts as a grouping symbol in determining the order of operations.

Teaching Tip **Inclusion** While $\sqrt{72} = \sqrt{9 \cdot 8}$ is a true statement, $\sqrt{72} = \sqrt{36 \cdot 2}$ is easier to simplify. Students should quickly learn that using the largest perfect-square factor is "easier" and leads to the simplified form more quickly. A chart of perfect squares may help them identify this factor.

Teaching Tip **Geometry** The diagonal of a square divides the square into two isosceles right triangles. The diagonal is the hypotenuse of each. It is always equal to $\sqrt{2}$ times the length of a leg.

Power Presentations with PowerPoint®

Additional Examples

Example 5

A quadrangle on a college campus is a square with sides of 250 feet. If a student takes a shortcut by walking diagonally across the quadrangle, how far does he walk? Give the answer as a radical expression in simplest form. Then estimate the length to the nearest tenth of a foot. $250\sqrt{2}$ ft; about 353.6 ft

Also available on transparency

INTERVENTION

Questioning Strategies

EXAMPLE 5

- Why is the Pythagorean Theorem used?

3 Close

Summarize

Have students list the three criteria that must be satisfied in order for a radical expression to be simplified.
no perfect square factors other than 1, no fractions in radicand, no square roots in any denominator
Tell students that when the radicand is a constant, they should write factors that are perfect squares.

FORMATIVE ASSESSMENT and INTERVENTION

***Diagnose Before* the Lesson**
11-2 Warm Up, TE p. 705

***Monitor During* the Lesson**
Check It Out! Exercises, SE pp. 705–707
Questioning Strategies, TE pp. 706–707

***Assess After* the Lesson**
11-2 Lesson Quiz, TE p. 710
Alternative Assessment, TE p. 710

Answers to *Think and Discuss*

1. $\sqrt{144} = 12$;
   $(\sqrt{16})(\sqrt{9}) = 4(3) = 12$;
   $\sqrt{25} = 5$; $\sqrt{\frac{100}{4}} = \frac{10}{2} = 5$
2. Both properties contain the expressions $\sqrt{a}$ and $\sqrt{b}$, which are undefined if a and b are negative.
3. See p. A9.

11-2 Exercises

Assignment Guide

Assign *Guided Practice* exercises as necessary.

If you finished Examples **1–3**
Proficient 24–39
Advanced 24–39, 70

If you finished Examples **1–5**
Proficient 24–83
Advanced 24–83

Homework Quick Check
Quickly check key concepts.
Exercises: 26, 30, 34, 38, 40, 44

Teaching Tip

Number Sense Remind students of divisibility rules. If the number formed by the last two digits of a number is divisible by 4, as in **Exercises 17–19, 34,** and **35,** then the number is divisible by 4. If the sum of the digits of a number is divisible by 9, as in **Exercises 7, 17, 22,** and **34,** the number is divisible by 9.

THINK AND DISCUSS

1. Show two ways to evaluate each of the following expressions: $\sqrt{16(9)}$, $\sqrt{\frac{100}{4}}$
2. In the Product and Quotient Properties of Square Roots, why can't a or b be negative?

3. **GET ORGANIZED** Copy and complete the graphic organizer. In each box, write the property and give an example.

	Product Property of Square Roots	Quotient Property of Square Roots
Words		
Example		

11-2 Exercises

Extension of 2.0; 24.1

GUIDED PRACTICE

1. **Vocabulary** In the expression $\sqrt{3x-6}+7$, what is the *radicand*? $3x - 6$

SEE EXAMPLE 1 p. 705

Simplify each expression.

2. $\sqrt{81}$ 9
3. $\sqrt{\frac{98}{2}}$ 7
4. $\sqrt{(a+7)^2}$ $|a+7|$

SEE EXAMPLE 2 p. 706

Simplify. All variables represent nonnegative numbers.

5. $\sqrt{180}$ $6\sqrt{5}$
6. $\sqrt{40}$ $2\sqrt{10}$
7. $\sqrt{648}$ $18\sqrt{2}$
8. $\sqrt{m^5n^3}$ $m^2n\sqrt{mn}$
9. $\sqrt{32x^4y^3}$ $4x^2y\sqrt{2y}$
10. $\sqrt{200a^2b}$ $10a\sqrt{2b}$

SEE EXAMPLE 3 p. 706

11. $\sqrt{\frac{17}{25}}$ $\frac{\sqrt{17}}{5}$
12. $\sqrt{\frac{7}{16}}$ $\frac{\sqrt{7}}{4}$
13. $\sqrt{\frac{6}{49}}$ $\frac{\sqrt{6}}{7}$
14. $\sqrt{\frac{b}{c^2}}$ $\frac{\sqrt{b}}{c}$
15. $\sqrt{\frac{4x^2}{36x}}$ $\frac{\sqrt{x}}{3}$
16. $\sqrt{\frac{7a^4}{9a^3}}$ $\frac{\sqrt{7a}}{3}$

SEE EXAMPLE 4 p. 707

17. $\sqrt{\frac{108}{49}}$ $\frac{6\sqrt{3}}{7}$
18. $\sqrt{\frac{204}{25}}$ $\frac{2\sqrt{51}}{5}$
19. $\sqrt{\frac{512}{81}}$ $\frac{16\sqrt{2}}{9}$
20. $\sqrt{\frac{1}{36x^2}}$ $\frac{1}{6x}$
21. $\sqrt{\frac{50x^2}{169}}$ $\frac{5x\sqrt{2}}{13}$
22. $\sqrt{\frac{72x^7}{4x^4}}$ $3x\sqrt{2x}$

SEE EXAMPLE 5 p. 707

23. **Recreation** Your boat is traveling due north from a dock. Your friend's boat left at the same time from the same dock and is headed due east. After an hour, your friend calls and tells you that he has just stopped because of engine trouble. How far must you travel to meet your friend? Give your answer as a radical expression in simplest form. Then estimate the distance to the nearest mile. $5\sqrt{41}$ mi; 32 mi

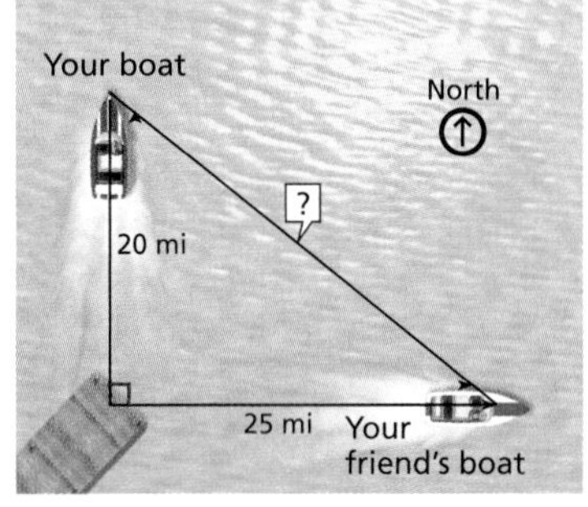

11-2 READING STRATEGIES

LESSON 11-2 Reading Strategies
Follow a Procedure

When simplifying radical expressions, there may be several steps that need to be taken. Look at the example below.

Simplify $\sqrt{\frac{12x^6}{25y^2}}$. All variables represent nonnegative numbers.

$\sqrt{\frac{12x^6}{25y^2}} = \frac{\sqrt{12x^6}}{\sqrt{25y^2}}$ — 1 Use the Quotient Property of Square Roots.

$= \frac{\sqrt{12}\sqrt{x^6}}{\sqrt{25}\sqrt{y^2}}$ — 2 Use the Product Property of Square Roots.

$= \frac{\sqrt{4}\sqrt{3}\sqrt{x^6}}{\sqrt{25}\sqrt{y^2}}$ — 3 Write radicands as products with perfect squares.

$= \frac{2\sqrt{3}x^3}{5y}$ — 4 Simplify.

Answer each question about the procedure shown above.

1. Which property is used to "separate" the fraction under a radical into two radicals?
   Quotient Property of Square Roots
2. In step 3, which property is used to write $\sqrt{12}$ as $\sqrt{4}\sqrt{3}$?
   Product Property of Square Roots
3. Describe the rule of exponents from Chapter 7 that is used to simplify $\sqrt{x^6}$ to x^3.
   When multiplying powers with the same base, add the exponents.
   So $x^3 \cdot x^3 = x^6$.

Simplify each radical expression. All variables represent nonnegative numbers.

4. $\sqrt{36x^2y^5}$ $6xy^2\sqrt{y}$
5. $\sqrt{\frac{8x^{10}}{36x^4}}$ $\frac{x^3\sqrt{2}}{3}$
6. $\sqrt{\frac{18x}{49y^8}}$ $\frac{3\sqrt{2x}}{7y^4}$
7. $\sqrt{44x^4y^4}$ $2\sqrt{11}x^2y^2$
8. $\sqrt{\frac{32x^5}{9y^8}}$ $\frac{4x^2\sqrt{2x}}{3y^4}$
9. $\sqrt{\frac{200x^{10}}{100}}$ $\sqrt{2}x^5$

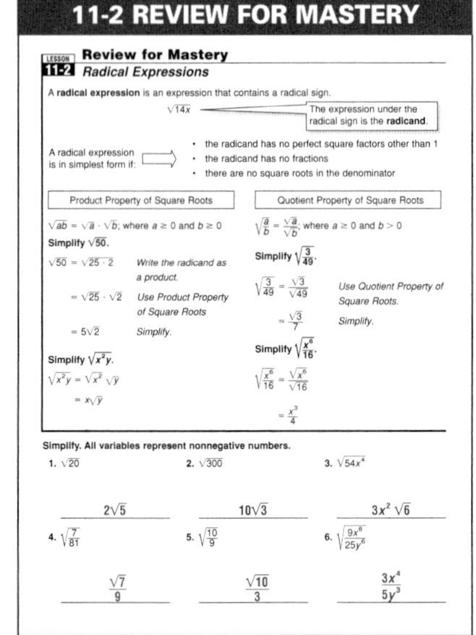

11-2 REVIEW FOR MASTERY

LESSON 11-2 Review for Mastery
Radical Expressions

A **radical expression** is an expression that contains a radical sign.

$\sqrt{14x}$ — The expression under the radical sign is the **radicand**.

A radical expression is in simplest form if:
- the radicand has no perfect square factors other than 1
- the radicand has no fractions
- there are no square roots in the denominator

Product Property of Square Roots	Quotient Property of Square Roots
$\sqrt{ab} = \sqrt{a} \cdot \sqrt{b}$; where $a \geq 0$ and $b \geq 0$	$\sqrt{\frac{a}{b}} = \frac{\sqrt{a}}{\sqrt{b}}$; where $a \geq 0$ and $b > 0$

Simplify $\sqrt{50}$.

$\sqrt{50} = \sqrt{25 \cdot 2}$ *Write the radicand as a product.*
$= \sqrt{25} \cdot \sqrt{2}$ *Use Product Property of Square Roots*
$= 5\sqrt{2}$ *Simplify.*

Simplify $\sqrt{x^2y}$.

$\sqrt{x^2y} = \sqrt{x^2}\sqrt{y}$
$= x\sqrt{y}$

Simplify $\sqrt{\frac{3}{49}}$.

$\sqrt{\frac{3}{49}} = \frac{\sqrt{3}}{\sqrt{49}}$ *Use Quotient Property of Square Roots.*
$= \frac{\sqrt{3}}{7}$ *Simplify.*

Simplify $\sqrt{\frac{x^6}{16}}$.

$\sqrt{\frac{x^6}{16}} = \frac{\sqrt{x^6}}{\sqrt{16}}$
$= \frac{x^3}{4}$

Simplify. All variables represent nonnegative numbers.

1. $\sqrt{20}$ $2\sqrt{5}$
2. $\sqrt{300}$ $10\sqrt{3}$
3. $\sqrt{54x^4}$ $3x^2\sqrt{6}$
4. $\sqrt{\frac{7}{81}}$ $\frac{\sqrt{7}}{9}$
5. $\sqrt{\frac{10}{9}}$ $\frac{\sqrt{10}}{3}$
6. $\sqrt{\frac{9x^8}{25y^6}}$ $\frac{3x^4}{5y^3}$

PRACTICE AND PROBLEM SOLVING

Independent Practice	
For Exercises	See Example
24–31	1
32–35	2
36–39	3
40–43	4
44	5

Extra Practice
Skills Practice p. EP22
Application Practice p. EP34

Simplify.

24. $\sqrt{100}$ **10**
25. $\sqrt{\frac{800}{2}}$ **20**
26. $\sqrt{3^2 + 4^2}$ **5**
27. $\sqrt{3 \cdot 27}$ **9**
28. $\sqrt{a^4}$ **a^2**
29. $\sqrt{(x+1)^2}$ **$|x+1|$**
30. $\sqrt{(5-x)^2}$ **$|5-x|$**
31. $\sqrt{(x-3)^2}$ **$|x-3|$**

Simplify. All variables represent nonnegative numbers.

32. $\sqrt{125}$ **$5\sqrt{5}$**
33. $\sqrt{4000}$ **$20\sqrt{10}$**
34. $\sqrt{216a^2b^2}$ **$6ab\sqrt{6}$**
35. $\sqrt{320r^2s^2}$ **$8rs\sqrt{5}$**
36. $\sqrt{\frac{15}{64}}$ **$\frac{\sqrt{15}}{8}$**
37. $\sqrt{\frac{45}{4}}$ **$\frac{3\sqrt{5}}{2}$**
38. $\sqrt{\frac{64a^4}{4a^6}}$ **$\frac{4}{a}$**
39. $\sqrt{\frac{14z^3}{9z^3}}$ **$\frac{\sqrt{14}}{3}$**
40. $\sqrt{\frac{128}{81}}$ **$\frac{8\sqrt{2}}{9}$**
41. $\sqrt{\frac{x^3}{y^6}}$ **$\frac{x\sqrt{x}}{y^3}$**
42. $\sqrt{\frac{150}{196x^2}}$ **$\frac{5\sqrt{6}}{14x}$**
43. $\sqrt{\frac{192s^3}{49s}}$ **$\frac{8s\sqrt{3}}{7}$**

44. **Amusement Parks** A thrill ride at an amusement park carries riders 160 feet straight up and then releases them for a free fall. The time t in seconds that it takes an object in free fall to reach the ground is $t = \sqrt{\frac{d}{16}}$, where d is the distance in feet that it falls. How long does it take the riders to reach the ground? Give your answer as a radical expression in simplest form. Then estimate the answer to the nearest tenth of a second. **$\sqrt{10}$ s; 3.2 s**

Simplify. All variables represent nonnegative numbers.

45. $-4\sqrt{75}$ **$-20\sqrt{3}$**
46. $-\sqrt{80}$ **$-4\sqrt{5}$**
47. $5x\sqrt{63}$ **$15x\sqrt{7}$**
48. $3\sqrt{48x}$ **$12\sqrt{3x}$**
49. $2\sqrt{\frac{x^2}{4}}$ **x**
50. $\frac{1}{2}\sqrt{\frac{1}{25}}$ **$\frac{1}{10}$**
51. $3x\sqrt{\frac{x^5}{81}}$ **$\frac{x^3\sqrt{x}}{3}$**
52. $\frac{12}{x}\sqrt{\frac{x^2y}{36}}$ **$2\sqrt{y}$**

Use the Product Property or the Quotient Property of Square Roots to write each expression as a single square root. Then simplify if possible.

53. $\sqrt{12}\sqrt{3}$ **$\sqrt{36}$; 6**
54. $\sqrt{18}\sqrt{8}$ **$\sqrt{144}$; 12**
55. $\sqrt{10}\sqrt{5}$
56. $\sqrt{8}\sqrt{14}$
57. $\frac{\sqrt{33}}{\sqrt{11}}$ **$\sqrt{3}$**
58. $\frac{\sqrt{24}}{\sqrt{2}}$ **$\sqrt{12}$; $2\sqrt{3}$**
59. $\frac{\sqrt{60}}{\sqrt{3}}$ **$\sqrt{20}$; $2\sqrt{5}$**
60. $\frac{\sqrt{72}}{\sqrt{9}}$ **$\sqrt{8}$; $2\sqrt{2}$**

55. $\sqrt{50}$; $5\sqrt{2}$

56. $\sqrt{112}$; $4\sqrt{7}$

61. **Multi-Step** How many whole feet of fencing would be needed to enclose the triangular garden that is sketched at right? Explain your answer.

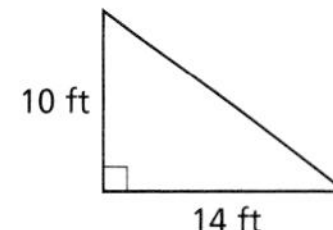

61. 42 ft; length of missing side ≈ 17.2 ft, which will need to be rounded up to 18.
$10 + 14 + 18 = 42$ ft

62. **Write About It** Write a series of steps that you could use to simplify $\sqrt{\frac{28}{49}}$.

CONCEPT CONNECTION

63. This problem will prepare you for the Concept Connection on page 730.

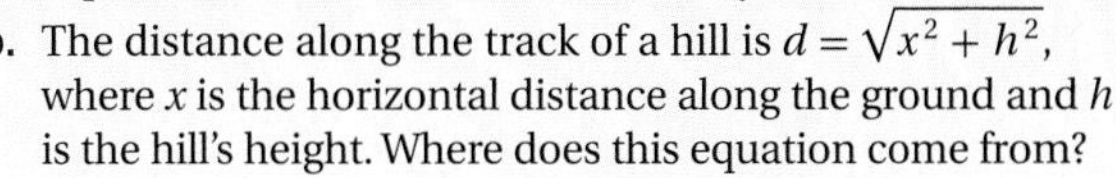

a. The vertical component of a roller coaster's speed in feet per second at the bottom of a hill is $v = \sqrt{64h}$, where h is the hill's height in feet. Simplify this expression. Then estimate the velocity at the bottom of a 137-foot hill.

b. The distance along the track of a hill is $d = \sqrt{x^2 + h^2}$, where x is the horizontal distance along the ground and h is the hill's height. Where does this equation come from?

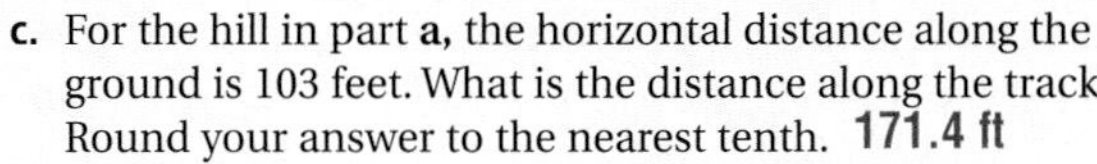

c. For the hill in part **a**, the horizontal distance along the ground is 103 feet. What is the distance along the track? Round your answer to the nearest tenth. **171.4 ft**

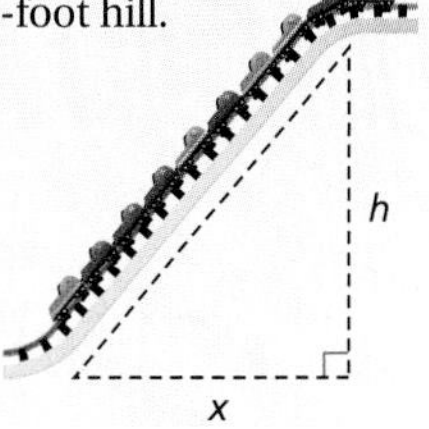

a. $v = 8\sqrt{h}$; 93.6 ft/s
b. Pythagorean Theorem

Teaching Tip

Communicating Math Not all denominators are perfect squares as in **Exercises 36–43.** Lesson 11-4 addresses denominators that are not perfect squares.

CONCEPT CONNECTION **Exercise 63** involves using formulas with radical expressions. This exercise prepares students for the Concept Connection on page 730.

Answer

62. Possible answer: Use the Quotient Property of Square Roots:

$$\sqrt{\frac{28}{49}} = \frac{\sqrt{28}}{\sqrt{49}}.$$

Then use the Product Property of Square Roots in the numerator:

$$\frac{\sqrt{28}}{\sqrt{49}} = \frac{\sqrt{4 \cdot 7}}{\sqrt{49}} = \frac{\sqrt{4}\sqrt{7}}{\sqrt{49}}.$$

Then simplify by taking the square roots of the perfect squares:

$$\frac{\sqrt{4}\sqrt{7}}{\sqrt{49}} = \frac{2\sqrt{7}}{7}.$$

11-2 PROBLEM SOLVING

LESSON 11-2 Problem Solving
Radical Expressions

Write the correct answer.

1. Annalise walks 200 meters from her house, turns a corner, and then walks another 100 meters to the bus stop. She wants to know how much shorter her walk would be if she cut across the field. Find the distance across the field from Annalise's house to the bus stop. Give your answer as a radical expression in simplest form. Then find the difference in the two routes to the nearest meter.

100 m
200 m

224 m; 76 m

2. A construction worker drops a nail from some scaffolding 192 feet from the ground. The nail is in freefall. The time t in seconds for an object in freefall to reach the ground is $t = \sqrt{\frac{d}{16}}$, where d is the distance in feet that it falls. The speed v in feet per second of an object in freefall is modeled by $v = 8\sqrt{d}$. Determine how long it takes the nail to reach the ground. Also find the speed the nail is traveling at 192 feet. Give your answers as radical expressions in simplest form. Then estimate the time to the nearest second and the speed to the nearest foot per second.

time: $2\sqrt{3}$ s, 3 s

speed: $64\sqrt{3}$ ft/s, 111 ft/s

Police officers determine the speed a car was traveling when the driver slammed on the brakes by measuring the length of skid marks left by the tires. On dry concrete, $f(x) = \sqrt{24x}$ gives the speed in mi/h when the length of the skid marks is x feet. The graph shows lengths of skid marks from several cars. Select the best answer.

Length of Skid Marks
Length (feet)
Car A 140, Car B 52, Car C 90, Car D 110
Car

3. Which shows the speed of car A in simplest radical form?
A $\sqrt{3360}$ mi/h
B $2\sqrt{840}$ mi/h
(C) $4\sqrt{210}$ mi/h
D $16\sqrt{210}$ mi/h

4. Which shows the speed of car B in simplest radical form?
F $2\sqrt{78}$ mi/h
(G) $4\sqrt{78}$ mi/h
H $8\sqrt{78}$ mi/h
J $16\sqrt{78}$ mi/h

5. Which shows the speed of car C in simplest radical form?
A $2\sqrt{540}$ mi/h
B $4\sqrt{135}$ mi/h
(C) $12\sqrt{15}$ mi/h
D $16\sqrt{135}$ mi/h

6. The driver of car D claims his skids marks were really only 60% as long as officers claim they were. If the driver is telling the truth, what was his speed in simplest radical form?
F $\sqrt{66}$ mi/h
G $\sqrt{1584}$ mi/h
H $2\sqrt{396}$ mi/h
(J) $12\sqrt{11}$ mi/h

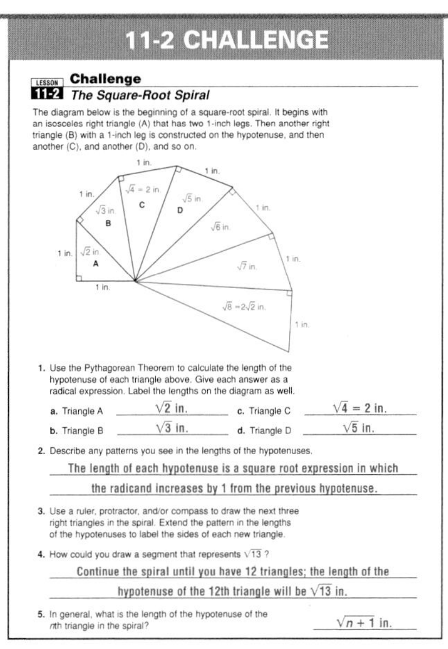

11-2 CHALLENGE

LESSON 11-2 Challenge
The Square-Root Spiral

The diagram below is the beginning of a square-root spiral. It begins with an isosceles right triangle (A) that has two 1-inch legs. Then another right triangle (B) with a 1-inch leg is constructed on the hypotenuse, and then another (C), and another (D), and so on.

1. Use the Pythagorean Theorem to calculate the length of the hypotenuse of each triangle above. Give each answer as a radical expression. Label the lengths on the diagram as well.

a. Triangle A $\sqrt{2}$ in.
b. Triangle B $\sqrt{3}$ in.
c. Triangle C $\sqrt{4} = 2$ in.
d. Triangle D $\sqrt{5}$ in.

2. Describe any patterns you see in the lengths of the hypotenuses.
The length of each hypotenuse is a square root expression in which the radicand increases by 1 from the previous hypotenuse.

3. Use a ruler, protractor, and/or compass to draw the next three right triangles in the spiral. Extend the pattern in the lengths of the hypotenuses to label the sides of each new triangle.

4. How could you draw a segment that represents $\sqrt{13}$?
Continue the spiral until you have 12 triangles; the length of the hypotenuse of the 12th triangle will be $\sqrt{13}$ in.

5. In general, what is the length of the hypotenuse of the nth triangle in the spiral? $\sqrt{n+1}$ in.

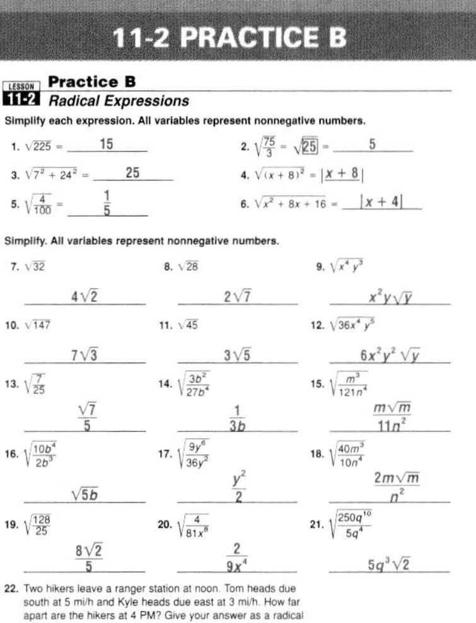

11-2 PRACTICE A
11-2 PRACTICE C
11-2 PRACTICE B

LESSON 11-2 Practice B
Radical Expressions

Simplify each expression. All variables represent nonnegative numbers.

1. $\sqrt{225}$ = 15
2. $\sqrt{\frac{75}{3}} = \sqrt{25}$ = 5
3. $\sqrt{7^2 + 24^2}$ = 25
4. $\sqrt{(x+8)^2}$ = $|x+8|$
5. $\sqrt{\frac{4}{100}}$ = $\frac{1}{5}$
6. $\sqrt{x^2 + 8x + 16}$ = $|x+4|$

Simplify. All variables represent nonnegative numbers.

7. $\sqrt{32}$ — $4\sqrt{2}$
8. $\sqrt{28}$ — $2\sqrt{7}$
9. $\sqrt{x^4y^3}$ — $x^2y\sqrt{y}$
10. $\sqrt{147}$ — $7\sqrt{3}$
11. $\sqrt{45}$ — $3\sqrt{5}$
12. $\sqrt{36x^4y^5}$ — $6x^2y^2\sqrt{y}$
13. $\sqrt{\frac{7}{25}}$ — $\frac{\sqrt{7}}{5}$
14. $\sqrt{\frac{3b^2}{27b^4}}$ — $\frac{1}{3b}$
15. $\sqrt{\frac{m^3}{121n^4}}$ — $\frac{m\sqrt{m}}{11n^2}$
16. $\sqrt{\frac{10b^4}{2b^3}}$ — $\sqrt{5b}$
17. $\sqrt{\frac{9y^6}{36y^2}}$ — $\frac{y^2}{2}$
18. $\sqrt{\frac{40m^3}{10n^4}}$ — $\frac{2m\sqrt{m}}{n^2}$
19. $\sqrt{\frac{128}{25}}$ — $\frac{8\sqrt{2}}{5}$
20. $\sqrt{\frac{4}{81x^8}}$ — $\frac{2}{9x^4}$
21. $\sqrt{\frac{250q^{10}}{5q^4}}$ — $5q^3\sqrt{2}$

22. Two hikers leave a ranger station at noon. Tom heads due south at 5 mi/h and Kyle heads due east at 3 mi/h. How far apart are the hikers at 4 PM? Give your answer as a radical expression in simplest form. Then estimate the distance to the nearest tenth of a mile.

$4\sqrt{34}$ mi; 23.3 mi

Multiple Choice
In **Exercise 67,** choices **A** and **D** are easily eliminated because the radicands are perfect squares. Students who chose **B** probably did not see that 16 is a factor of 48.
In **Exercise 69,** students need to first take the square root of 100 to get the side length of the square. Then they can use the Pythagorean Theorem to determine the length of the diagonal.

Journal

Have students explain the Product and Quotient Properties of Square Roots, using examples as needed.

ALTERNATIVE ASSESSMENT

Write $\sqrt{\frac{800x^5}{25x}}$ on the board. Have students simplify the expression and explain when the variable needs an absolute-value symbol.

Power Presentations with PowerPoint®

11-2 Lesson Quiz

Simplify each expression.

1. $\sqrt{31 + 5}$ 6
2. $\sqrt{x^2 + 10x + 25}$ $|x + 5|$

Simplify. All variables represent nonnegative numbers.

3. $\sqrt{50}$ $5\sqrt{2}$
4. $\sqrt{\frac{28}{81}}$ $\frac{2\sqrt{7}}{9}$
5. $\sqrt{a^3b^5}$ $ab^2\sqrt{ab}$
6. $\sqrt{\frac{27x^3}{48}}$ $\frac{3x\sqrt{x}}{4}$
7. Two archaeologists leave from the same campsite. One travels 10 miles due north and the other travels 6 miles due west. How far apart are the archaeologists? Give the answer as a radical expression in simplest form. Then estimate the distance to the nearest tenth of a mile. $2\sqrt{34}$ mi; 11.7 mi

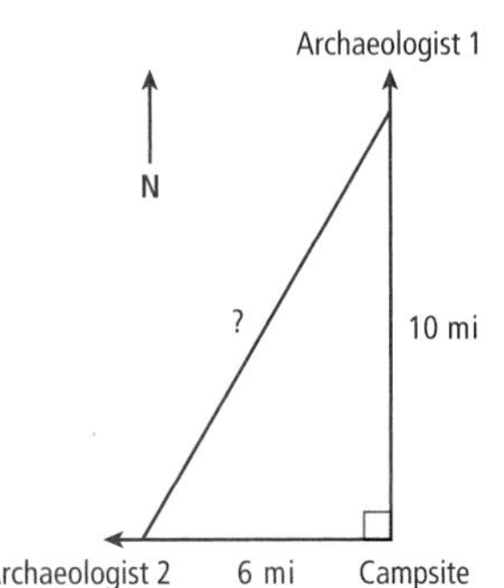

Also available on transparency

64. Critical Thinking The Product Property of Square Roots states that $\sqrt{ab} = \sqrt{a}\sqrt{b}$, where $a \geq 0$ and $b \geq 0$. Why must a and b be greater than or equal to zero?
Possible answer: The square root of a neg. number is not a real number.

65. Architecture The formula $d = \frac{\sqrt{6h}}{3}$ estimates the distance d in miles that a person can see to the horizon from h feet above the ground. Find the distance you could see to the horizon from the top of each building in the graph. Give your answers as radical expressions in simplest form and as estimates to the nearest tenth of a mile.

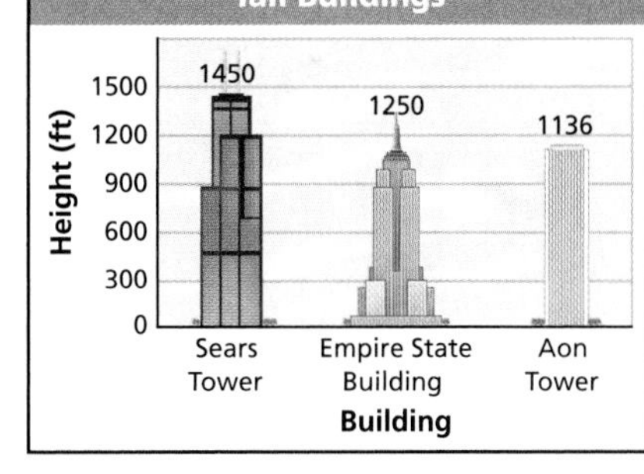

LINK Math History

Heron of Alexandria, Egypt, also called Hero, lived around 60 C.E. Heron's formula for the area of a triangle can be found in Book I of his *Metrica.*

66. Math History Heron's formula for the area A of a triangle is $A = \sqrt{s(s - a)(s - b)(s - c)}$, where a, b, and c are the side lengths and $s = \frac{1}{2}(a + b + c)$. Find the area of a triangle with side lengths of 7 m, 9 m, and 12 m. Give your answer as a radical expression in simplest form and as an estimate to the nearest tenth. **$14\sqrt{5}$ m²; 31.3 m²**

Multiple Choice For Exercises 67–69, choose the best answer.

67. Which expression is in simplest form?
Ⓐ $\sqrt{49}$ Ⓑ $\sqrt{48}$ **Ⓒ $\sqrt{35}$**   Ⓓ $\sqrt{36}$

68. Which expression is equal to $\sqrt{60}$?
Ⓐ $2\sqrt{15}$ Ⓑ $6\sqrt{10}$ Ⓒ $15\sqrt{2}$ Ⓓ $10\sqrt{60}$

69. How long is the diagonal of a square whose area is 100 square feet?
Ⓐ $2\sqrt{10}$ feet   Ⓑ 10 feet   **Ⓒ $10\sqrt{2}$ feet**   Ⓓ 20 feet

CHALLENGE AND EXTEND

73f. Possible answer: If n is even, then x^n is always nonnegative, so abs. value is not necessary. If n is odd, then x^n may be neg., so abs. value is necessary to ensure the square root is nonnegative.

Simplify. All radicands represent nonnegative numbers.

70. $\sqrt{4x + 16}$ **$2\sqrt{x + 4}$**   **71.** $\sqrt{x^3 + x^2}$ **$x\sqrt{x + 1}$**   **72.** $\sqrt{9x^3 - 18x^2}$ **$3x\sqrt{x - 2}$**

73. Let x represent any real number (including negative numbers). Simplify each of the following expressions, using absolute-value symbols when necessary.
a. $\sqrt{x^2}$ **$|x|$**   **b.** $\sqrt{x^4}$ **x^2**   **c.** $\sqrt{x^6}$ **$|x^3|$**   **d.** $\sqrt{x^8}$ **x^4**   **e.** $\sqrt{x^{10}}$ **$|x^5|$**
f. Reasoning Use your results in parts **a–e** and inductive reasoning to make a conjecture about the following statement: For any nonnegative integer n, $\sqrt{x^{2n}} =$ **x^n** if n is even, and $\sqrt{x^{2n}} =$ **$|x^n|$** if n is odd. Explain why you think your conjecture is true.

SPIRAL STANDARDS REVIEW
7.0, 17.0

Without graphing, tell whether each point is on the graph of the given line. *(Lesson 5-1)*

74. $-5x + 4y = 12$; $(1, 2)$ **no**   **75.** $6x + 3y = 9$; $(2, -1)$ **yes**
76. $12x - 2y = 18$; $(2, 3)$ **yes**   **77.** $-4x - 4y = 14$; $(-5, 1)$ **no**

Find the domain of each square-root function. *(Lesson 11-1)*

78. $y = \sqrt{x + 5}$ **$x \geq -5$**   **79.** $y = \sqrt{2x - 4}$ **$x \geq 2$**   **80.** $y = 3\sqrt{-x - 3} + 5$ **$x \leq -3$**
81. $y = 7 - \sqrt{x - 1}$ **$x \geq 1$**   **82.** $y = 9\sqrt{x} + 3$ **$x \geq 0$**   **83.** $y = \sqrt{-x + 6}$ **$x \leq 6$**

Answer

65. Sears: $\frac{10\sqrt{87}}{3}$ mi; 31.1 mi
Empire: $\frac{50\sqrt{3}}{3}$ mi; 28.9 mi
Aon: $\frac{4\sqrt{426}}{3}$ mi; 27.5 mi

11-3 Adding and Subtracting Radical Expressions

California Standards

Extension of 2.0
Students understand and use such operations as taking the opposite, finding the reciprocal, **taking a root,** and raising to a fractional power. They understand and use the rules of exponents.

Vocabulary
like radicals

Why learn this?
You can add or subtract radical expressions to find perimeter. (See Example 3.)

Square-root expressions with the same radicand are examples of **like radicals**.

Like Radicals	$2\sqrt{5}$ and $4\sqrt{5}$	$6\sqrt{x}$ and $-2\sqrt{x}$	$3\sqrt{4t}$ and $\sqrt{4t}$
Unlike Radicals	2 and $\sqrt{15}$	$6\sqrt{x}$ and $\sqrt{6x}$	$3\sqrt{2}$ and $2\sqrt{3}$

Like radicals can be combined by adding or subtracting. You can use the Distributive Property to show how this is done:

$$2\sqrt{5} + 4\sqrt{5} = (2 + 4)\sqrt{5} = 6\sqrt{5}$$

$$6\sqrt{x} - 2\sqrt{x} = (6 - 2)\sqrt{x} = 4\sqrt{x}$$

Notice that you can combine like radicals by adding or subtracting the numbers multiplied by the radical and keeping the radical the same.

EXAMPLE 1 Adding and Subtracting Square-Root Expressions

Add or subtract.

A $3\sqrt{7} + 8\sqrt{7}$
$3\sqrt{7} + 8\sqrt{7}$ — *The terms are like radicals.*
$11\sqrt{7}$

B $9\sqrt{y} - \sqrt{y}$
$9\sqrt{y} - 1\sqrt{y}$ — *$\sqrt{y} = 1\sqrt{y}$; the terms are like radicals.*
$8\sqrt{y}$

C $12\sqrt{2} - 4\sqrt{11}$
$12\sqrt{2} - 4\sqrt{11}$ — *The terms are unlike radicals. Do not combine.*

D $-8\sqrt{3d} + 6\sqrt{2d} + 10\sqrt{3d}$
$-8\sqrt{3d} + 6\sqrt{2d} + 10\sqrt{3d}$ — *Identify like radicals.*
$2\sqrt{3d} + 6\sqrt{2d}$ — *Combine like radicals.*

Helpful Hint

Combining like radicals is similar to combining like terms.
$2\sqrt{5} + 4\sqrt{5} = 6\sqrt{5}$
$2x + 4x = 6x$

CHECK IT OUT! Add or subtract.

1a. $5\sqrt{7} - 6\sqrt{7}$ $-\sqrt{7}$
1b. $8\sqrt{3} - 5\sqrt{3}$ $3\sqrt{3}$
1c. $4\sqrt{n} + 4\sqrt{n}$ $8\sqrt{n}$
1d. $\sqrt{2s} - \sqrt{5s} + 9\sqrt{5s}$ $\sqrt{2s} + 8\sqrt{5s}$

Sometimes radicals do not appear to be like until they are simplified. Simplify all radicals in an expression before trying to identify like radicals.

11-3 Organizer

Objective: Add and subtract radical expressions.

Algebra Lab
In *Chapter 11 Resource File*

Online Edition
Tutorial Videos

Power Presentations with PowerPoint®

Warm Up

Simplify each expression.

1. $14x + 15y - 12y + x$ $15x + 3y$

2. $9xy + 2xy - 8xy$ $3xy$

3. $-3(a + b) + 5\left(2 + \frac{2}{5}b\right)$ $-3a - b + 10$

Simplify. All variables represent nonnegative numbers.

4. $\sqrt{96}$ $4\sqrt{6}$

5. $\sqrt{x^9y^{10}}$ $x^4y^5\sqrt{x}$

6. $\sqrt{\frac{72a^5}{81}}$ $\frac{2a^2\sqrt{2a}}{3}$

Also available on transparency

Math Humor

Q: What did the surfer say when he saw the square root of two?
A: Radical, dude!

1 Introduce

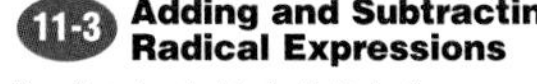

EXPLORATION

11-3 Adding and Subtracting Radical Expressions

You will need a calculator for this Exploration.

1. Find a decimal approximation for each expression in the table. Round to the nearest thousandth.

Expression	Decimal Approximation	Expression	Decimal Approximation
$2\sqrt{3} + 3\sqrt{3}$		$5\sqrt{3}$	
$8\sqrt{2} - 5\sqrt{2}$		$3\sqrt{2}$	
$4\sqrt{7} + 11\sqrt{7}$		$15\sqrt{7}$	

2. What do you notice in the table?
3. Find a decimal approximation for each expression in the table. Round to the nearest thousandth.

Expression	Decimal Approximation	Expression	Decimal Approximation
$\sqrt{7} + \sqrt{3}$		$\sqrt{10}$	
$\sqrt{25} + \sqrt{9}$		$\sqrt{34}$	
$\sqrt{17} - \sqrt{5}$		$\sqrt{12}$	

THINK AND DISCUSS

4. **Describe** a conjecture you can make based on your findings in the first table.
5. **Discuss** whether $\sqrt{a} + \sqrt{b} = \sqrt{a + b}$ and whether $\sqrt{a} - \sqrt{b} = \sqrt{a - b}$.

Motivate

Write the following on the board. $3a + 8a =$ ___

Ask students to simplify this expression by filling in the blank. After they have written $3a + 8a = \underline{11a}$, substitute $\sqrt{7}$ for a and have them simplify $3\sqrt{7} + 8\sqrt{7} =$ ___ by filling in the blank.
$3\sqrt{7} + 8\sqrt{7} = \underline{11\sqrt{7}}$

Ask students how many terms are in the simplified expression. 1

Explorations and answers are provided in *Alternate Openers: Explorations Transparencies.*

California Standards

Extension of 2.0

Power Presentations with PowerPoint®

Additional Examples

Example 1

Add or subtract.

A. $9\sqrt{3} - 4\sqrt{3}$ $\quad 5\sqrt{3}$

B. $6\sqrt{x} + 8\sqrt{y}$ $\quad 6\sqrt{x} + 8\sqrt{y}$

C. $\sqrt{m} - 7\sqrt{m}$ $\quad -6\sqrt{m}$

D. $2\sqrt{xy} + 2\sqrt{y} + 9\sqrt{xy}$ $\quad 11\sqrt{xy} + 2\sqrt{y}$

Example 2

Simplify each expression. All variables represent nonnegative numbers.

A. $\sqrt{45} - \sqrt{20}$ $\quad \sqrt{5}$

B. $9\sqrt{75} + 2\sqrt{50}$ $\quad 45\sqrt{3} + 10\sqrt{2}$

C. $\sqrt{75y} - 2\sqrt{27y} + \sqrt{48y}$ $\quad 3\sqrt{3y}$

Example 3

Find the perimeter of the triangle. Give the answer as a radical expression in simplest form.

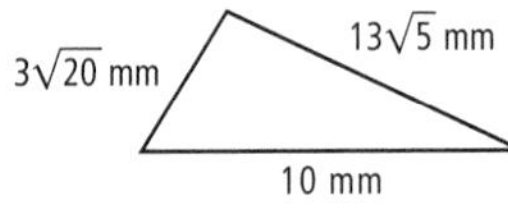

$(19\sqrt{5} + 10)$ mm

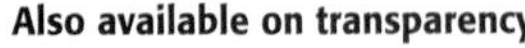

Also available on transparency

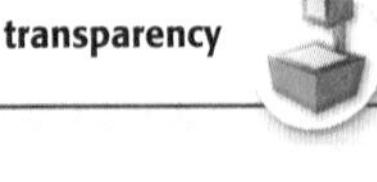

INTERVENTION

Questioning Strategies

EXAMPLES **1–3**

- How do you know which terms can be combined?
- How do you decide which numbers to use when you write a radicand as a product?

EXAMPLE 2 **Simplifying Before Adding or Subtracting**

Simplify each expression. All variables represent nonnegative numbers.

A $\sqrt{12} + \sqrt{27}$

$\sqrt{4(3)} + \sqrt{9(3)}$	*Factor the radicands using perfect squares.*
$\sqrt{4}\sqrt{3} + \sqrt{9}\sqrt{3}$	*Product Property of Square Roots*
$2\sqrt{3} + 3\sqrt{3}$	*Simplify.*
$5\sqrt{3}$	*Combine like radicals.*

B $3\sqrt{8} + \sqrt{45}$

$3\sqrt{4(2)} + \sqrt{9(5)}$	*Factor the radicands using perfect squares.*
$3\sqrt{4}\sqrt{2} + \sqrt{9}\sqrt{5}$	*Product Property of Square Roots*
$3(2)\sqrt{2} + 3\sqrt{5}$	*Simplify.*
$6\sqrt{2} + 3\sqrt{5}$	*The terms are unlike radicals. Do not combine.*

Remember!

When you write a radicand as a product, make at least one factor a perfect square.

C $5\sqrt{28x} - 8\sqrt{7x}$

$5\sqrt{4(7x)} - 8\sqrt{7x}$	*Factor 28x using a perfect square.*
$5\sqrt{4}\sqrt{7x} - 8\sqrt{7x}$	*Product Property of Square Roots*
$5(2)\sqrt{7x} - 8\sqrt{7x}$	*Simplify.*
$10\sqrt{7x} - 8\sqrt{7x}$	
$2\sqrt{7x}$	*Combine like radicals.*

D $\sqrt{125b} + 3\sqrt{20b} - \sqrt{45b}$

$\sqrt{25(5b)} + 3\sqrt{4(5b)} - \sqrt{9(5b)}$	*Factor the radicands using perfect squares.*
$\sqrt{25}\sqrt{5b} + 3\sqrt{4}\sqrt{5b} - \sqrt{9}\sqrt{5b}$	*Product Property of Square Roots*
$5\sqrt{5b} + 3(2)\sqrt{5b} - 3\sqrt{5b}$	*Simplify.*
$5\sqrt{5b} + 6\sqrt{5b} - 3\sqrt{5b}$	
$8\sqrt{5b}$	*Combine like radicals.*

CHECK IT OUT! Simplify each expression. All variables represent nonnegative numbers.

2a. $\sqrt{54} + \sqrt{24}$ $\quad$ **$5\sqrt{6}$** $\quad$ **2b.** $4\sqrt{27} - \sqrt{18}$ $\quad$ **$12\sqrt{3} - 3\sqrt{2}$** $\quad$ **2c.** $\sqrt{12y} + \sqrt{27y}$ $\quad$ **$5\sqrt{3y}$**

EXAMPLE 3 ***Geometry Application***

Find the perimeter of the triangle. Give your answer as a radical expression in simplest form.

$5\sqrt{7}$ cm $\quad \sqrt{28}$ cm $\quad$ 12 cm

$12 + 5\sqrt{7} + \sqrt{28}$	*Write an expression for perimeter.*
$12 + 5\sqrt{7} + \sqrt{4(7)}$	*Factor 28 using a perfect square.*
$12 + 5\sqrt{7} + \sqrt{4}\sqrt{7}$	*Product Property of Square Roots*
$12 + 5\sqrt{7} + 2\sqrt{7}$	*Simplify.*
$12 + 7\sqrt{7}$	*Combine like radicals.*

The perimeter is $(12 + 7\sqrt{7})$ cm.

CHECK IT OUT! **3.** Find the perimeter of a rectangle whose length is $2\sqrt{b}$ inches and whose width is $3\sqrt{b}$ inches. Give your answer as a radical expression in simplest form. **$10\sqrt{b}$ in.**

2 Teach

Guided Instruction

Students can use their calculators to check numerical problems by comparing the values of the original and simplified expressions. Students can check algebraic problems by substituting a number for the variable in the original and simplified expressions and then comparing their values. Calculator displays show only the first part of an irrational number. Show students how to type in expressions involving radicals all at once, avoiding the need to write down partial calculations.

3 Close

Summarize

Tell students that terms with like radicals can be combined by adding or subtracting the coefficients and keeping the radical the same. As a first step, all radicals should be simplified until the expressions under the radical signs have no perfect square factors.

FORMATIVE ASSESSMENT and INTERVENTION

***Diagnose Before* the Lesson**
11-3 Warm Up, TE p. 711

***Monitor During* the Lesson**
Check It Out! Exercises, SE pp. 711–712
Questioning Strategies, TE p. 712

***Assess After* the Lesson**
11-3 Lesson Quiz, TE p. 715
Alternative Assessment, TE p. 715

THINK AND DISCUSS

1. Rearrange the following into two groups of like radicals: $2\sqrt{6}$, $6\sqrt{5}$, $\sqrt{600}$, $\sqrt{150}$, $-\sqrt{20}$, $\sqrt{5}$.
2. Tell why you should simplify radicals before adding and subtracting expressions with radicals.

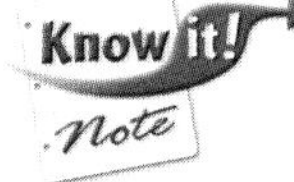

3. **GET ORGANIZED** Copy and complete the graphic organizer.

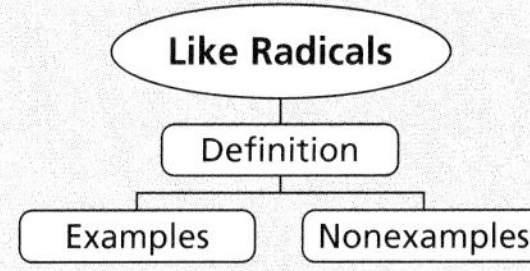

11-3 Exercises

Extension of 2.0; 25.2

GUIDED PRACTICE

1. **Vocabulary** Give an example of *like radicals*. **Possible answer: $4\sqrt{6}$ and $-2\sqrt{6}$**

SEE EXAMPLE 1 p. 711

Add or subtract.

2. $14\sqrt{3} - 6\sqrt{3}$ **$8\sqrt{3}$**
3. $9\sqrt{5} + \sqrt{5}$ **$10\sqrt{5}$**
4. $6\sqrt{2} + 5\sqrt{2} - 15\sqrt{2}$ **$-4\sqrt{2}$**
5. $3\sqrt{7} + 5\sqrt{2}$ **$3\sqrt{7} + 5\sqrt{2}$**
6. $5\sqrt{a} - 9\sqrt{a}$ **$-4\sqrt{a}$**
7. $9\sqrt{6a} + 6\sqrt{5a} - 4\sqrt{6a}$ **$5\sqrt{6a} + 6\sqrt{5a}$**

SEE EXAMPLE 2 p. 712

Simplify each expression. All variables represent nonnegative numbers.

8. $\sqrt{32} - \sqrt{8}$ **$2\sqrt{2}$**
9. $4\sqrt{12} + \sqrt{75}$ **$13\sqrt{3}$**
10. $2\sqrt{3} + 5\sqrt{12} - \sqrt{27}$ **$9\sqrt{3}$**
11. $\sqrt{20x} - \sqrt{45x}$ **$-\sqrt{5x}$**
12. $\sqrt{28c} + 9\sqrt{24c}$ **$2\sqrt{7c} + 18\sqrt{6c}$**
13. $\sqrt{50t} - 2\sqrt{12t} + 3\sqrt{2t}$ **$8\sqrt{2t} - 4\sqrt{3t}$**

SEE EXAMPLE 3 p. 712

14. **Geometry** Find the perimeter of the trapezoid shown. Give your answer as a radical expression in simplest form. **$12\sqrt{2}$ in.**

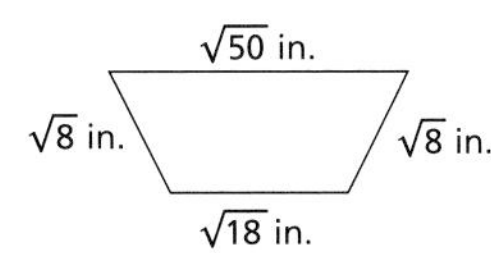

PRACTICE AND PROBLEM SOLVING

Independent Practice

For Exercises	See Example
15–20	1
21–29	2
30	3

Extra Practice
Skills Practice p. EP22
Application Practice p. EP34

Add or subtract.

15. $4\sqrt{3} + 2\sqrt{3}$ **$6\sqrt{3}$**
16. $\frac{1}{2}\sqrt{72} - 12$ **$3\sqrt{2} - 12$**
17. $2\sqrt{11} + \sqrt{11} - 6\sqrt{11}$ **$-3\sqrt{11}$**
18. $6\sqrt{7} + 7\sqrt{6}$ **$6\sqrt{7} + 7\sqrt{6}$**
19. $-3\sqrt{n} - \sqrt{n}$ **$-4\sqrt{n}$**
20. $2\sqrt{2y} + 3\sqrt{2y} - 2\sqrt{3y}$ **$5\sqrt{2y} - 2\sqrt{3y}$**

Simplify each expression. All variables represent nonnegative numbers.

21. $\sqrt{175} + \sqrt{28}$ **$7\sqrt{7}$**
22. $2\sqrt{80} - \sqrt{20}$ **$6\sqrt{5}$**
23. $5\sqrt{8} - \sqrt{32} + 2\sqrt{18}$ **$12\sqrt{2}$**
24. $\sqrt{150r} + \sqrt{54r}$ **$8\sqrt{6r}$**
25. $\sqrt{63x} - 4\sqrt{27x}$
26. $\sqrt{48p} + 3\sqrt{18p} - 2\sqrt{27p}$
27. $\sqrt{180j} - \sqrt{45j}$ **$3\sqrt{5j}$**
28. $3\sqrt{90c} - \sqrt{40c}$ **$7\sqrt{10c}$**
29. $2\sqrt{75m} - \sqrt{12m} - \sqrt{108m}$

Answers to *Think and Discuss*

1. $2\sqrt{6}$, $\sqrt{600} = 10\sqrt{6}$, $\sqrt{150} = 5\sqrt{6}$;
$6\sqrt{5}$, $-\sqrt{20} = -2\sqrt{5}$, $\sqrt{5}$
2. Possible answer: Without simplifying, you cannot tell which terms are like radicals.
3. See p. A9.

11-3 Exercises

Assignment Guide

Assign *Guided Practice* exercises as necessary.

If you finished Examples **1–3**
Proficient 15–30, 32–38 even, 39, 40–48 even, 49–63, 71–78
Advanced 16–30 even, 31–47, 49–78

Homework Quick Check
Quickly check key concepts.
Exercises: 16, 20, 22, 26, 30, 40

Answers

25. $3\sqrt{7x} - 12\sqrt{3x}$
26. $9\sqrt{2p} - 2\sqrt{3p}$
29. $2\sqrt{3m}$

Teaching Tip **Math Background** Remind students that radical expressions can be written as exponential expressions. For instance, $\sqrt{x} = x^{\frac{1}{2}}$. Therefore, the like radicals $18\sqrt{ab}$ and $10\sqrt{ab}$ in **Exercise 32** are like terms because they are terms that contain the same variable to the same power, $18a^{\frac{1}{2}}b^{\frac{1}{2}}$ and $10a^{\frac{1}{2}}b^{\frac{1}{2}}$.

Exercise 56 involves using the radius and diameter of a circle. This exercise prepares students for the Concept Connection on page 730.

Answers

39c. Because the areas found in parts **a** and **b** must be equal, the model shows that $3\sqrt{11} + 2\sqrt{11} + 5\sqrt{11} = (3 + 2 + 5)\sqrt{11} = 10\sqrt{11}$.

49. Possible answer: Like radicals have the same number, variable, or numbers and variables under the radical sign; examples: $\sqrt{2}$ and $3\sqrt{2}$; nonexamples: $\sqrt{5}$ and $\sqrt{3}$.

30. Fitness What is the total length of the jogging path? Give your answer as a radical expression in simplest form. **$2 + 4\sqrt{2}$ mi**

Simplify each expression. All variables represent nonnegative numbers.

31. $5\sqrt{7} + 7\sqrt{7}$ **$12\sqrt{7}$**
32. $18\sqrt{ab} - 10\sqrt{ab}$ **$8\sqrt{ab}$**
33. $-3\sqrt{3} + 3\sqrt{3}$ **0**
34. $\sqrt{98} + \sqrt{128}$ **$15\sqrt{2}$**
35. $\sqrt{300} - \sqrt{27}$ **$7\sqrt{3}$**
36. $\sqrt{45x} + \sqrt{500x}$ **$13\sqrt{5x}$**
37. $\frac{5}{2}\sqrt{8} + \frac{\sqrt{32}}{2}$ **$7\sqrt{2}$**
38. $\frac{1}{6}\sqrt{18} - \frac{\sqrt{2}}{2}$ **0**

39. Geometry Use the diagram to answer the following:

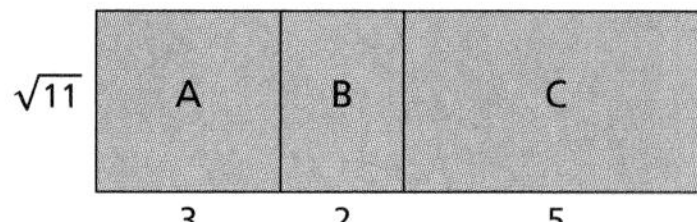

a. What is the area of section A? section B? section C? **$3\sqrt{11}$; $2\sqrt{11}$; $5\sqrt{11}$**
b. What is the combined area of the three sections?
c. Explain how this model relates to adding like radicals.

39b. $10\sqrt{11}$

Simplify each expression. All variables represent nonnegative numbers.

40. $\sqrt{450ab} - \sqrt{50ab}$ **$10\sqrt{2ab}$**
41. $\sqrt{12} + \sqrt{125} + \sqrt{25}$ **$2\sqrt{3} + 5\sqrt{5} + 5$**
42. $\sqrt{338} - \sqrt{18}$ **$10\sqrt{2}$**
43. $\sqrt{700x} - \sqrt{28x} - \sqrt{70x}$ **$8\sqrt{7x} - \sqrt{70x}$**
44. $-3\sqrt{90} - 3\sqrt{160}$ **$-21\sqrt{10}$**
45. $7\sqrt{80k} + 2\sqrt{20k} + \sqrt{45k}$ **$35\sqrt{5k}$**
46. $\sqrt{24abc} + \sqrt{600abc}$ **$12\sqrt{6abc}$**
47. $\sqrt{12} + \sqrt{20} + \sqrt{27} + \sqrt{45}$ **$5\sqrt{3} + 5\sqrt{5}$**

48. ///ERROR ANALYSIS/// Which expressions are simplified incorrectly? Explain the error in each incorrect simplification.

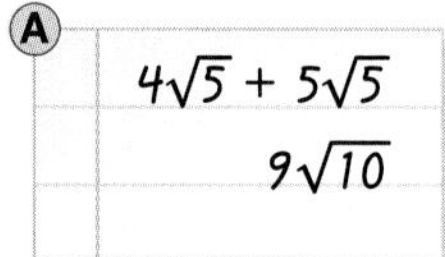

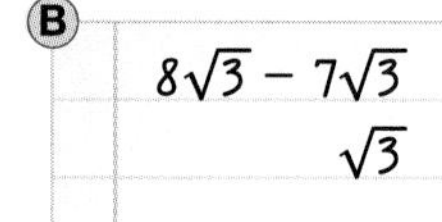

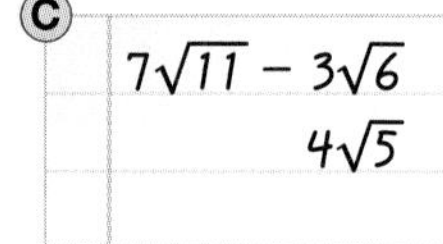

48. A and C are incorrect. In A, the radicands were added. In C, the radicals were not like radicals but they were incorrectly combined by subtracting the radicands.

49. Write About It Tell how to identify like radicals. Give examples and nonexamples of like radicals in your answer.

Complete each box to make a true statement.

50. $5\sqrt{ab} + 2\sqrt{\boxed{ab}} - 3\sqrt{a} = 7\sqrt{ab} - 3\sqrt{a}$
51. $4\sqrt{x} - \sqrt{\boxed{9}\,x} = \sqrt{x}$
52. $5\sqrt{2} - \sqrt{\boxed{8}} + \sqrt{2} = 4\sqrt{2}$
53. $\sqrt{\boxed{18}} + 8\sqrt{2} = 11\sqrt{2}$
54. $3\sqrt{3} + 2\sqrt{3} + \sqrt{\boxed{48}} = 9\sqrt{3}$
55. $2x - \sqrt{\boxed{}} = -4x$ **$36x^2$**

56. This problem will prepare you for the Concept Connection on page 730.
a. The first Ferris wheel was designed by George W. Ferris and introduced at the 1893 Chicago World's Fair. Its diameter was 250 feet. What was its radius? **125 ft**
b. For a rider halfway up on the ride, the distance from the boarding point can be found by using the equation $d = \sqrt{2r^2}$, where r is the radius of the wheel. Explain where this equation comes from. (*Hint:* Draw a picture.) **Pythagorean Theorem**

11-3 PRACTICE A

11-3 PRACTICE C

11-3 PRACTICE B

LESSON 11-3 Practice B
Adding and Subtracting Radical Expressions

Add or subtract. All variables represent nonnegative numbers.

1. $9\sqrt{7} + 4\sqrt{7} =$ **13** $\sqrt{7}$
2. $-10\sqrt{5} + 2\sqrt{5} =$ **−8** $\sqrt{5}$
3. $4\sqrt{y} + 6\sqrt{y} =$ **$10\sqrt{y}$**
4. $-2\sqrt{3b} + 10\sqrt{3b} =$ **$8\sqrt{3b}$**
5. $6\sqrt{15} - \sqrt{15} + \sqrt{15} =$ **$6\sqrt{15}$**
6. $5\sqrt{2} - 3\sqrt{2x} - 4\sqrt{2} =$ **$\sqrt{2} - 3\sqrt{2x}$**

Simplify each expression. All variables represent nonnegative numbers.

7. $\sqrt{108} + \sqrt{75}$ **$11\sqrt{3}$**
8. $\sqrt{63} + \sqrt{175} + \sqrt{112}$ **$12\sqrt{7}$**
9. $\sqrt{28x} + \sqrt{63x}$ **$5\sqrt{7x}$**
10. $\sqrt{45} + \sqrt{180}$ **$9\sqrt{5}$**
11. $\sqrt{52} - \sqrt{1300}$ **$-8\sqrt{13}$**
12. $5\sqrt{98} - 3\sqrt{32}$ **$23\sqrt{2}$**
13. $\sqrt{32} + \sqrt{128}$ **$12\sqrt{2}$**
14. $\sqrt{147} + 6\sqrt{3}$ **$13\sqrt{3}$**
15. $\sqrt{168} + \sqrt{42}$ **$3\sqrt{42}$**
16. $5\sqrt{17} + 17\sqrt{5}$ **$5\sqrt{17} + 17\sqrt{5}$**
17. $6\sqrt{3} + \sqrt{300}$ **$16\sqrt{3}$**
18. $-2\sqrt{3b} + \sqrt{27b}$ **$\sqrt{3b}$**
19. $4\sqrt{2m} + 6\sqrt{3m} - 4\sqrt{2m}$ **$6\sqrt{3m}$**
20. $\sqrt{50m} + \sqrt{72m}$ **$11\sqrt{2m}$**
21. $\sqrt{16z} + 2\sqrt{8z} - 3\sqrt{z}$ **$\sqrt{z} + 4\sqrt{2z}$**
22. $\sqrt{216t} + \sqrt{96t}$ **$10\sqrt{6t}$**
23. $4\sqrt{52x} + \sqrt{117x} - 2\sqrt{13}$ **$11\sqrt{13x} - 2\sqrt{13}$**
24. $3\sqrt{96k} + 2\sqrt{180}$ **$12\sqrt{6k} + 12\sqrt{5}$**
25. Write the numbers $3\sqrt{8}$, $4\sqrt{2}$ and $\sqrt{50}$ in order from least to greatest. **$4\sqrt{2}$, $\sqrt{50}$, $3\sqrt{8}$**
26. The map at right shows the path traveled by a delivery person on his afternoon route. Write the total distance traveled as a simplified radical expression. **$5 + 8\sqrt{7}$ miles**

√28 mi
3 mi
2√7 mi
2 mi
√112 mi

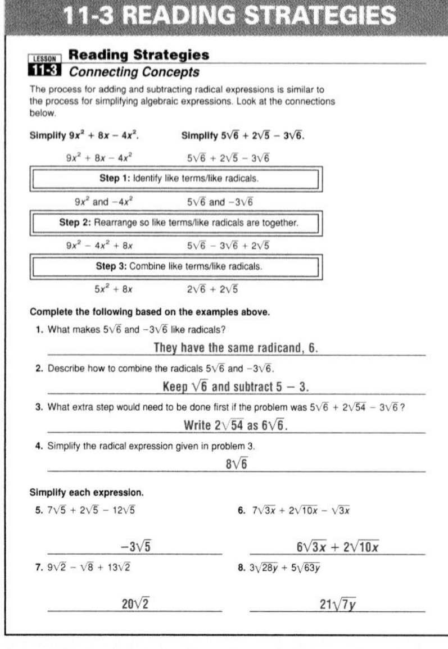

11-3 READING STRATEGIES

LESSON 11-3 Reading Strategies
Connecting Concepts

The process for adding and subtracting radical expressions is similar to the process for simplifying algebraic expressions. Look at the connections below.

Simplify $9x^2 + 8x - 4x^2$.	**Simplify $5\sqrt{6} + 2\sqrt{5} - 3\sqrt{6}$.**
$9x^2 + 8x - 4x^2$	$5\sqrt{6} + 2\sqrt{5} - 3\sqrt{6}$
Step 1: Identify like terms/like radicals.	
$9x^2$ and $-4x^2$	$5\sqrt{6}$ and $-3\sqrt{6}$
Step 2: Rearrange so like terms/like radicals are together.	
$9x^2 - 4x^2 + 8x$	$5\sqrt{6} - 3\sqrt{6} + 2\sqrt{5}$
Step 3: Combine like terms/like radicals.	
$5x^2 + 8x$	$2\sqrt{6} + 2\sqrt{5}$

Complete the following based on the examples above.

1. What makes $5\sqrt{6}$ and $-3\sqrt{6}$ like radicals? **They have the same radicand, 6.**
2. Describe how to combine the radicals $5\sqrt{6}$ and $-3\sqrt{6}$. **Keep $\sqrt{6}$ and subtract 5 − 3.**
3. What extra step would need to be done first if the problem was $5\sqrt{6} + 2\sqrt{54} - 3\sqrt{6}$? **Write $2\sqrt{54}$ as $6\sqrt{6}$.**
4. Simplify the radical expression given in problem 3. **$8\sqrt{6}$**

Simplify each expression.

5. $7\sqrt{5} + 2\sqrt{5} - 12\sqrt{5}$ **$-3\sqrt{5}$**
6. $7\sqrt{3x} + 2\sqrt{10x} - \sqrt{3x}$ **$6\sqrt{3x} + 2\sqrt{10x}$**
7. $9\sqrt{2} - \sqrt{8} + 13\sqrt{2}$ **$20\sqrt{2}$**
8. $3\sqrt{28y} + 5\sqrt{63y}$ **$21\sqrt{7y}$**

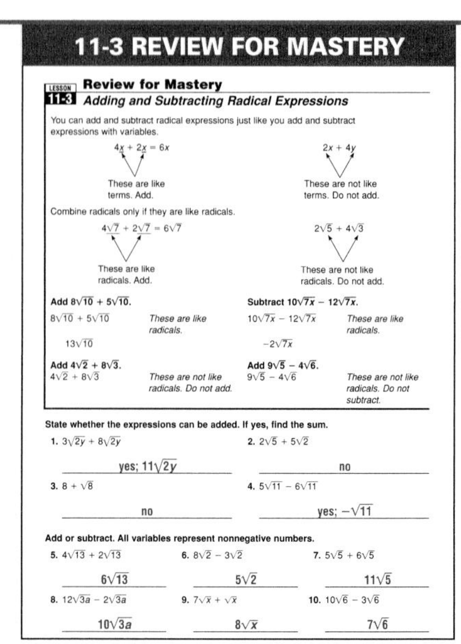

11-3 REVIEW FOR MASTERY

LESSON 11-3 Review for Mastery
Adding and Subtracting Radical Expressions

You can add and subtract radical expressions just like you add and subtract expressions with variables.

$4x + 2x = 6x$ — These are like terms. Add.
$2x + 4y$ — These are not like terms. Do not add.

Combine radicals only if they are like radicals.

$4\sqrt{7} + 2\sqrt{7} = 6\sqrt{7}$ — These are like radicals. Add.
$2\sqrt{5} + 4\sqrt{3}$ — These are not like radicals. Do not add.

Add $8\sqrt{10} + 5\sqrt{10}$.
$8\sqrt{10} + 5\sqrt{10}$ *These are like radicals.*
$13\sqrt{10}$

Subtract $10\sqrt{7x} - 12\sqrt{7x}$.
$10\sqrt{7x} - 12\sqrt{7x}$ *These are like radicals.*
$-2\sqrt{7x}$

Add $4\sqrt{2} + 8\sqrt{3}$.
$4\sqrt{2} + 8\sqrt{3}$ *These are not like radicals. Do not add.*

Add $9\sqrt{5} - 4\sqrt{6}$.
$9\sqrt{5} - 4\sqrt{6}$ *These are not like radicals. Do not subtract.*

State whether the expressions can be added. If yes, find the sum.

1. $3\sqrt{2y} + 8\sqrt{2y}$ **yes; $11\sqrt{2y}$**
2. $2\sqrt{5} + 5\sqrt{2}$ **no**
3. $8 + \sqrt{8}$ **no**
4. $5\sqrt{11} - 6\sqrt{11}$ **yes; $-\sqrt{11}$**

Add or subtract. All variables represent nonnegative numbers.

5. $4\sqrt{13} + 2\sqrt{13}$ **$6\sqrt{13}$**
6. $8\sqrt{2} - 3\sqrt{2}$ **$5\sqrt{2}$**
7. $5\sqrt{5} + 6\sqrt{5}$ **$11\sqrt{5}$**
8. $12\sqrt{3a} - 2\sqrt{3a}$ **$10\sqrt{3a}$**
9. $7\sqrt{x} + \sqrt{x}$ **$8\sqrt{x}$**
10. $10\sqrt{6} - 3\sqrt{6}$ **$7\sqrt{6}$**

57. **Multi-Step** A square has an area of 48 in^2. Another square has an area of 12 in^2. Write a simplified radical expression for the perimeter of each square. Then write a simplified radical expression for the combined perimeters of the two squares. **$16\sqrt{3}$ in.; $8\sqrt{3}$ in.; $24\sqrt{3}$ in.**

58. **Critical Thinking** How are like radicals similar to like terms?
The radical is similar to a variable. To add or subtract, combine coefficients.

Multiple Choice For Exercises 59–61, choose the best answer.

59. Which of the following expressions CANNOT be simplified?
   - Ⓐ $3\sqrt{5} + 4\sqrt{5}$
   - Ⓒ $2\sqrt{8} + 3\sqrt{2}$
   - **(Ⓑ)** $5\sqrt{6} + 6\sqrt{5}$
   - Ⓓ $3\sqrt{12} + \sqrt{27}$

60. What is $-5\sqrt{7x} + 6\sqrt{7x}$?
   - **(Ⓐ)** $\sqrt{7x}$
   - Ⓑ $\sqrt{14x^2}$
   - Ⓒ $\sqrt{14x}$
   - Ⓓ $7x$

61. What is $\sqrt{18} - \sqrt{2}$?
   - **(Ⓐ)** $2\sqrt{2}$
   - Ⓑ 4
   - Ⓒ $4\sqrt{2}$
   - Ⓓ $8\sqrt{2}$

CHALLENGE AND EXTEND

Simplify. All radicands represent nonnegative numbers.

62. $5\sqrt{x-5} + 2\sqrt{x-5}$ **$7\sqrt{x-5}$**
63. $x\sqrt{x} + 2\sqrt{x}$ **$\sqrt{x}(x+2)$**
64. $4\sqrt{x-3} + \sqrt{25x-75}$ **$9\sqrt{x-3}$**
65. $2\sqrt{x+7} - \sqrt{4x+28}$ **0**
66. $\sqrt{4x^3+24x^2} + \sqrt{x^3+6x^2}$ **$3x\sqrt{x+6}$**
67. $\sqrt{x^3-x^2} + \sqrt{4x-4}$ **$(x+2)\sqrt{x-1}$**
68. $\sqrt{x^3+2x^2} - \sqrt{x+2}$ **$(x-1)\sqrt{x+2}$**
69. $\sqrt{9x+9} - \sqrt{x^3+2x^2}$

69. $3\sqrt{x+1} - x\sqrt{x+2}$

70. **Geometry** Find the area of the trapezoid. Use the formula $A = \frac{1}{2}h(b_1 + b_2)$. **50 cm^2**

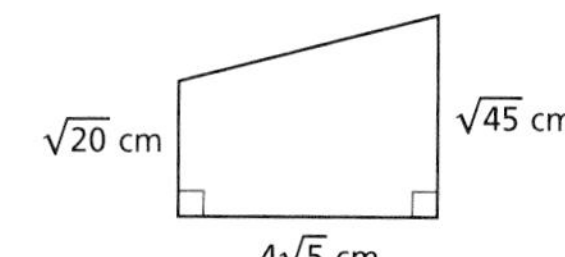

SPIRAL STANDARDS REVIEW

8.0, 14.0, 17.0, 25.1

71. Use slope to show that $ABCD$ is a parallelogram. *(Lesson 5-7)*

72. Use slope to show that XYZ is a right triangle. *(Lesson 5-7)*

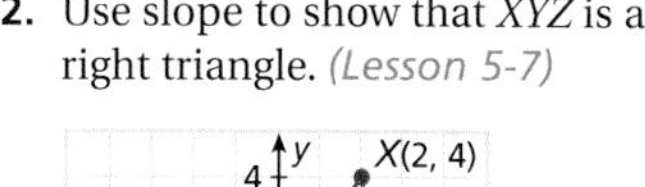

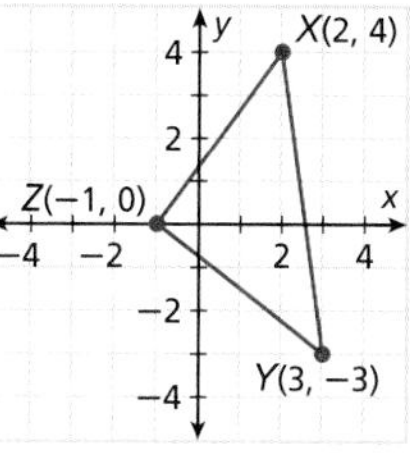

71. $m_{AB} = 1$, $m_{BC} = \frac{1}{6}$, $m_{CD} = 1$, $m_{AD} = \frac{1}{6}$. Since $m_{AB} = m_{CD}$, $\overline{AB} \parallel \overline{CD}$. Since $m_{BC} = m_{AD}$, $\overline{BC} \parallel \overline{AD}$. Since both pairs of opp. sides are par., $ABCD$ is a parallelogram.

72. $m_{XZ} = \frac{4}{3}$; $m_{YZ} = -\frac{3}{4}$; since the prod. of the slopes is −1, $\overline{XZ} \perp \overline{YZ}$, making XYZ a rt. triangle.

Solve each quadratic equation by factoring. Check your answer. *(Lesson 9-5)*

73. $x^2 + 2x - 3 = 0$ **−3, 1**
74. $x^2 + 5x + 4 = 0$ **−1, −4**
75. $x^2 - 7x - 18 = 0$ **9, −2**

Find the domain of each square-root function. *(Lesson 11-1)*

76. $y = \sqrt{4x-2}$ **$x \geq \frac{1}{2}$**
77. $y = -2\sqrt{x+3}$ **$x \geq -3$**
78. $y = 1 + \sqrt{x+6}$ **$x \geq -6$**

11-3 PROBLEM SOLVING

LESSON 11-3 Problem Solving
Adding and Subtracting Radical Expressions

Write the correct answer as a radical expression in simplest form.

1. The parks department is installing a fence along a scenic overlook. The area to be fenced has 3 sides measuring $4\sqrt{5}$ feet, $3\sqrt{5}$ feet, and $5\sqrt{5}$ feet. Find the total amount of fencing that needs to be installed.
$12\sqrt{5}$ ft

2. A rectangular laundry room has a length of $\sqrt{54}$ feet and a width of $\sqrt{48}$ feet. Find the perimeter of the laundry room.
$6\sqrt{6} + 8\sqrt{3}$ ft

3. Mr. Lansberry bought four watermelons for a family reunion. The watermelons weighed $\sqrt{75}$ pounds, $\sqrt{108}$ pounds, $\sqrt{125}$ pounds, and $\sqrt{80}$ pounds. How many pounds of watermelon did Mr. Lansberry bring to the reunion?
$11\sqrt{3} + 9\sqrt{5}$ lbs

4. Travon is hanging the same wallpaper border in two rooms. One room is a perfect square with an area of 120 square feet. The other room, a rectangle, has a width of $\sqrt{30}$ feet and a length of 8 feet. How much wallpaper border does Travon need to go around the perimeter of the two rooms?
$10\sqrt{30} + 16$ ft

Select the best answer.

5. A cafeteria tray is shaped like an isosceles trapezoid. The bases measure $\sqrt{180}$ in. and $\sqrt{320}$ in. The legs measure $\sqrt{80}$ in. Find the perimeter of the tray.
   - A $2\sqrt{145}$ in.
   - C $18\sqrt{5}$ in.
   - B $2\sqrt{165}$ in.
   - **(D)** $22\sqrt{5}$ in.

6. Jack, Aislinn, Mercedes, and Dae are a team participating in a relay at a fall festival. Jack's time was $7\sqrt{2}$ seconds, Aislinn's was $12\sqrt{2}$ seconds, Mercedes's was $6\sqrt{2}$ seconds, and Dae's was $9\sqrt{2}$ seconds. What was the team's total time?
   - F 24 s
   - **(H)** $34\sqrt{2}$ s
   - G $24\sqrt{2}$ s
   - J 68 s

7. Lily has two picture frames she is replacing. The first frame is shaped like a regular octagon, and all sides measure $\sqrt{12}$ in. The second frame is shaped like a rectangle; the length and width are $\sqrt{60}$ in. and $\sqrt{12}$ in. respectively. How much total framing will she need?
   - A $2\sqrt{6} + 2\sqrt{15}$ in.
   - B $4\sqrt{3} + 2\sqrt{15}$ in.
   - C $16\sqrt{3} + 4\sqrt{15}$ in.
   - **(D)** $20\sqrt{3} + 4\sqrt{15}$ in.

8. A triangular pennant has two sides that measure $28\sqrt{3}$ centimeters and a third side that measures $7\sqrt{3}$ centimeters. Mrs. Kwan is sewing 2 rows of gold ribbon around the perimeter of the pennant. How much ribbon does she need?
   - F $63\sqrt{3}$ cm
   - **(H)** $126\sqrt{3}$ cm
   - G $70\sqrt{3}$ cm
   - J 189 cm

11-3 CHALLENGE

LESSON 11-3 Challenge
Radical Concentration

This game is for 2 players. Each should have paper and a pencil.

Preparation:

- Cut out the 16 game cards below. You can make the cards sturdier and not see-through by mounting them on cardboard with glue or tape.
- Put all of the game cards upside-down on a table and mix them up. Keeping the cards upside-down, arrange them into a 4-by-4 grid.

Game Play:

- Player 1 picks any two cards and turns them right-side up. The player identifies whether the two expressions can simplify to be like radicals.
  - If the expressions *can* be like radicals, then Player 1 adds them. Player 2 checks the opponent's addition. If the sum is correct, Player 1 removes and keeps the two cards.
  - If the expressions are *not* like radicals, or Player 1 adds incorrectly, the cards remain and are turned upside-down again.
- Players alternate, repeating the process described above. To improve their chances of winning, both players should remember what expressions have been revealed and where they are located.
- After all cards are removed, the winner is the player with the most cards.

$9\sqrt{2}$	$6\sqrt{3}$	$12\sqrt{5}$	$10\sqrt{7}$
$3\sqrt{8}$	$7\sqrt{10}$	$\sqrt{18}$	$3\sqrt{20}$
$\sqrt{25}$	$\sqrt{27}$	$2\sqrt{36}$	$\sqrt{50}$
$\sqrt{80}$	$2\sqrt{125}$	$\sqrt{343}$	$\sqrt{1000}$

COMMON ERROR ALERT

With so much focus on looking for perfect squares, students might accidentally take the square root of a number that is not under a radical sign. For example, in **Exercise 30,** they might write $4\sqrt{2}$ as $2\sqrt{2}$. Remind them to take square roots only of numbers under the radical sign.

Multiple Choice In **Exercise 61,** students who chose **B** probably subtracted the numbers under each radical sign and then took the square root. Students who chose **C** may have added the simplified terms. Students who chose **D** likely did not take the square root of 9 after writing 18 as a product.

Journal

Have students explain how to combine $3\sqrt{f} + 10\sqrt{f} + 5\sqrt{f}$ by using the Distributive Property.

Have students simplify $\sqrt{1200x} + \sqrt{300x} + \sqrt{9x}$ step by step, writing the justification for each step as they go.

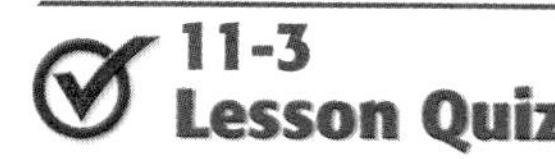

11-3 Lesson Quiz

Add or subtract.

1. $18\sqrt{6} + 22\sqrt{6}$ **$40\sqrt{6}$**
2. $3\sqrt{x} + 3\sqrt{3x}$ **$3\sqrt{x} + 3\sqrt{3x}$**
3. $-4\sqrt{11y} - 14\sqrt{10y} + 2\sqrt{10y} + \sqrt{11y}$ **$-3\sqrt{11y} - 12\sqrt{10y}$**

Simplify each expression.

4. $\sqrt{242} - \sqrt{128}$ **$3\sqrt{2}$**
5. $\sqrt{108yz} + 3\sqrt{98yz} + 2\sqrt{75yz}$ **$16\sqrt{3yz} + 21\sqrt{2yz}$**
6. Find the perimeter of the trapezoid. Give the answer as a radical expression in simplest form. **$(10\sqrt{6} + 2)$ ft**

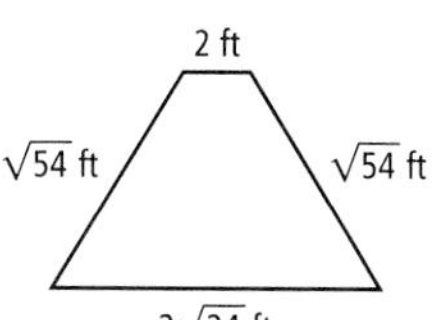

Also available on transparency

11-4 Organizer

Objectives: Multiply and divide radical expressions.

Rationalize denominators.

 **Online Edition**
Tutorial Videos

Power Presentations with PowerPoint®

Warm Up

Simplify each expression.

1. $\sqrt{72}$ $6\sqrt{2}$
2. $\sqrt{x^5}$ $x^2\sqrt{x}$
3. $\sqrt{\dfrac{24}{9}}$ $\dfrac{2\sqrt{6}}{3}$
4. $\sqrt{\dfrac{18}{x^2}}$ $\dfrac{3\sqrt{2}}{|x|}$

Also available on transparency

Math Humor

Q: Why did the troublemaker keep failing his test on radical expressions?

A: He kept trying to rationalize his behavior instead of the denominators.

California Standards

Extension of 2.0

11-4 Multiplying and Dividing Radical Expressions

California Standards

Extension of 2.0 **Students understand and use such operations as** taking the opposite, finding the reciprocal, **taking a root,** and raising to a fractional power. **They understand and use the rules of exponents.**

Who uses this?

Electricians can divide radical expressions to find how much current runs through an appliance. (See Exercise 68.)

Off the Mark. Cartoon copyrighted by Mark Parisi, printed with permission.

You can use the Product and Quotient Properties of square roots you have already learned to multiply and divide expressions containing square roots.

EXAMPLE 1 Multiplying Square Roots

Multiply. Write each product in simplest form. All variables represent nonnegative numbers.

A $\sqrt{3}\sqrt{6}$

$\sqrt{3(6)}$	*Product Property of Square Roots*
$\sqrt{18}$	*Multiply the factors in the radicand.*
$\sqrt{9(2)}$	*Factor 18 using a perfect-square factor.*
$\sqrt{9}\sqrt{2}$	*Product Property of Square Roots*
$3\sqrt{2}$	*Simplify.*

B $(5\sqrt{3})^2$

$5\sqrt{3}\cdot 5\sqrt{3}$	*Expand the expression.*
$5(5)\sqrt{3}\sqrt{3}$	*Commutative Property of Multiplication*
$25\sqrt{3(3)}$	*Product Property of Square Roots*
$25\sqrt{9}$	*Simplify the radicand.*
$25(3)$	*Simplify the square root.*
75	*Multiply.*

Helpful Hint

For all nonnegative real numbers a, $\sqrt{a}\sqrt{a} = a$. So, in Example 1B, you can reduce the number of steps by immediately writing $\sqrt{3}\sqrt{3}$ as 3.

C $2\sqrt{8x}\sqrt{4x}$

$2\sqrt{8x(4x)}$	*Product Property of Square Roots*
$2\sqrt{32x^2}$	*Multiply the factors in the radicand.*
$2\sqrt{16(2)x^2}$	*Factor 32 using a perfect-square factor.*
$2\sqrt{16}\sqrt{2}\sqrt{x^2}$	*Product Property of Square Roots*
$2(4)\sqrt{2}(x)$	*Simplify.*
$8x\sqrt{2}$	

1 Introduce

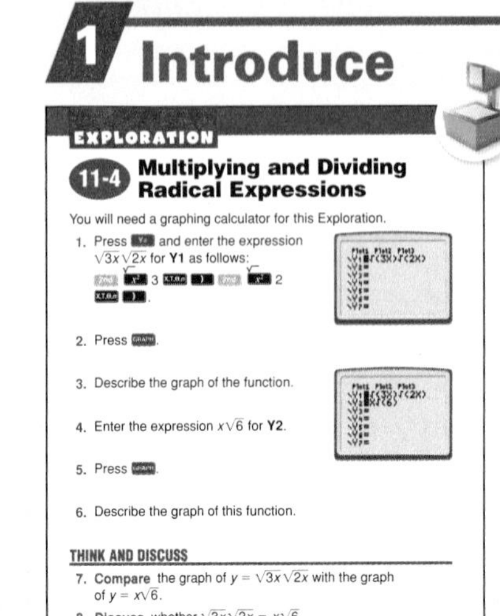

EXPLORATION

11-4 Multiplying and Dividing Radical Expressions

You will need a graphing calculator for this Exploration.

1. Press Y= and enter the expression $\sqrt{3x}\sqrt{2x}$ for **Y1** as follows:
2. Press GRAPH.
3. Describe the graph of the function.
4. Enter the expression $x\sqrt{6}$ for **Y2**.
5. Press GRAPH.
6. Describe the graph of this function.

THINK AND DISCUSS

7. **Compare** the graph of $y = \sqrt{3x}\sqrt{2x}$ with the graph of $y = x\sqrt{6}$.
8. **Discuss** whether $\sqrt{3x}\sqrt{2x} = x\sqrt{6}$.

Motivate

Display the two expressions $8(\sqrt{2})$ and $\sqrt{8(2)}$. Ask students if the two expressions are equivalent. No, $8(\sqrt{2}) \approx 11.31$ and $\sqrt{8(2)} = 4$. Tell students that when multiplying radical expressions, they must pay attention to whether the numbers are outside or inside the radical sign.

Explorations and answers are provided in *Alternate Openers: Explorations Transparencies.*

Multiply. Write each product in simplest form. All variables represent nonnegative numbers.

1a. $\sqrt{5}\sqrt{10}$ $5\sqrt{2}$ 1b. $(3\sqrt{7})^2$ 63 1c. $\sqrt{2m}\sqrt{14m}$ $2m\sqrt{7}$

EXAMPLE **2** **Using the Distributive Property**

Multiply. Write each product in simplest form.

A $\sqrt{2}(5+\sqrt{12})$

$\sqrt{2}(5+\sqrt{12})$	
$\sqrt{2}(5)+\sqrt{2}\sqrt{12}$	*Distribute $\sqrt{2}$.*
$5\sqrt{2}+\sqrt{2(12)}$	*Product Property of Square Roots*
$5\sqrt{2}+\sqrt{24}$	*Multiply the factors in the second radicand.*
$5\sqrt{2}+\sqrt{4(6)}$	*Factor 24 using a perfect-square factor.*
$5\sqrt{2}+\sqrt{4}\sqrt{6}$	*Product Property of Square Roots*
$5\sqrt{2}+2\sqrt{6}$	*Simplify.*

B $\sqrt{3}(\sqrt{3}-\sqrt{5})$

$\sqrt{3}(\sqrt{3}-\sqrt{5})$	
$\sqrt{3}\sqrt{3}-\sqrt{3}\sqrt{5}$	*Distribute $\sqrt{3}$.*
$3-\sqrt{3(5)}$	*Product Property of Square Roots*
$3-\sqrt{15}$	*Multiply the factors in the second radicand.*

Multiply. Write each product in simplest form.

2a. $\sqrt{6}(\sqrt{8}-3)$ $4\sqrt{3}-3\sqrt{6}$ 2b. $\sqrt{5}(\sqrt{10}+4\sqrt{3})$ $5\sqrt{2}+4\sqrt{15}$

Remember!

First terms
Outer terms
Inner terms
Last terms
See Lesson 7-8.

In Chapter 7, you multiplied binomials by using the FOIL method. The same method can be used to multiply square-root expressions that contain two terms.

$$(4+\sqrt{3})(5+\sqrt{3}) = 4(5) + 4\sqrt{3}+5\sqrt{3} + \sqrt{3}\sqrt{3}$$
$$= 20 \quad + 9\sqrt{3} \quad + 3 \quad = \quad 23+9\sqrt{3}$$

EXAMPLE **3** **Multiplying Sums and Differences of Radicals**

Multiply. Write each product in simplest form.

A $(4+\sqrt{5})(3-\sqrt{5})$

$12-4\sqrt{5}+3\sqrt{5}-5$	*Use the FOIL method.*
$7-\sqrt{5}$	*Simplify by combining like terms.*

B $(\sqrt{7}-5)^2$

$(\sqrt{7}-5)(\sqrt{7}-5)$	*Expand the expression.*
$7-5\sqrt{7}-5\sqrt{7}+25$	*Use the FOIL method.*
$32-10\sqrt{7}$	*Simplify by combining like terms.*

Multiply. Write each product in simplest form.

3a. $(9+\sqrt{2})^2$ $83+18\sqrt{2}$ 3b. $(4-\sqrt{3})(\sqrt{3}+5)$ $17-\sqrt{3}$

2 Teach

Guided Instruction

Review the Product Property of Square Roots as it was used in Lessons 11-2 and 11-3: $\sqrt{ab}=\sqrt{a}\sqrt{b}$. In **Example 4,** point out that rationalizing the denominator does not change the value of the quotient. For all examples, show that the simplified answers are equivalent to the original expressions by finding each value on a calculator.

Universal Access

Through Communication

Show students 2 different ways to begin simplifying $\frac{5}{\sqrt{8}}$ (shown below). Discuss the pros and cons of each method.

1. Multiply by $\frac{\sqrt{8}}{\sqrt{8}}$.
2. Simplify $\sqrt{8}$ to $2\sqrt{2}$. Then multiply by $\frac{\sqrt{2}}{\sqrt{2}}$.

COMMON ERROR ALERT

When distributing in **Example 2A,** students may mistakenly think that $\sqrt{2}(5)=\sqrt{10}$. Suggest to students that they estimate each square root separately to see that $\sqrt{2}(5) \approx 7.07$, while $\sqrt{10}\approx 3.16$. Also emphasize that $\sqrt{2}(5)=5\sqrt{2}$ by the Commutative Property of Multiplication.

Power Presentations with PowerPoint®

Additional Examples

Example 1

Multiply. Write each product in simplest form. All variables represent nonnegative numbers.

A. $\sqrt{8}\sqrt{6}$ $4\sqrt{3}$

B. $(2\sqrt{5})^2$ 20

C. $\sqrt{3y}\sqrt{12y}$ $6y$

Example 2

Multiply. Write each product in simplest form.

A. $\sqrt{3}(7-\sqrt{8})$ $7\sqrt{3}-2\sqrt{6}$

B. $\sqrt{2}(\sqrt{8}+\sqrt{18})$ 10

Example 3

Multiply. Write each product in simplest form.

A. $(3-\sqrt{8})(2+\sqrt{8})$ $-2+2\sqrt{2}$

B. $(4+\sqrt{3})^2$ $19+8\sqrt{3}$

Also available on transparency

INTERVENTION

Questioning Strategies

EXAMPLES **1–2**

- When is a product of radicals in simplest form?

EXAMPLE **3**

- How is **Example 3B** similar to squaring a binomial?
- Why are there only two terms in the product instead of three?

Power Presentations with PowerPoint®

Additional Examples

Example 4

Simplify each quotient. All variables represent nonnegative numbers.

A. $\frac{\sqrt{11}}{\sqrt{3}}$ $\frac{\sqrt{33}}{3}$

B. $\frac{\sqrt{13m}}{\sqrt{20}}$ $\frac{\sqrt{65m}}{10}$

Also available on transparency

INTERVENTION

Questioning Strategies

EXAMPLE 4

- When is it necessary to rationalize the denominator?
- Why does the process of rationalizing the denominator not change the value of the expression?

Language Support Dissect the phrase *rationalizing the denominator*. The square root of a nonperfect square is an irrational number. The number below the fraction bar is the denominator. So rationalizing the denominator means making the number below the fraction bar a rational number.

ENGLISH LANGUAGE LEARNERS

A quotient with a square root in the denominator is **not** simplified. To simplify these expressions, multiply by a form of 1 to get a perfect-square radicand in the denominator. This is called *rationalizing the denominator.*

EXAMPLE 4 Rationalizing the Denominator

Simplify each quotient. All variables represent nonnegative numbers.

A 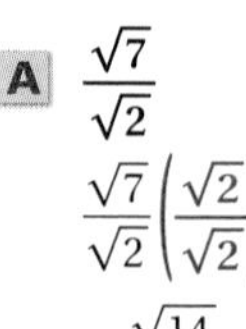

$\frac{\sqrt{7}}{\sqrt{2}}$

$\frac{\sqrt{7}}{\sqrt{2}}\left(\frac{\sqrt{2}}{\sqrt{2}}\right)$ *Multiply by a form of 1 to get a perfect-square radicand in the denominator.*

$\frac{\sqrt{14}}{2}$ *Product Property of Square Roots*

B 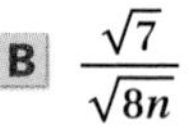

$\frac{\sqrt{7}}{\sqrt{8n}}$

$\frac{\sqrt{7}}{\sqrt{4(2n)}}$ *Write 8n using a perfect-square factor.*

$\frac{\sqrt{7}}{2\sqrt{2n}}$ *Simplify the denominator.*

$\frac{\sqrt{7}}{2\sqrt{2n}}\left(\frac{\sqrt{2n}}{\sqrt{2n}}\right)$ *Multiply by a form of 1 to get a perfect-square radicand in the denominator.*

$\frac{\sqrt{14n}}{2\sqrt{4n^2}}$ *Product Property of Square Roots*

$\frac{\sqrt{14n}}{2(2n)}$ *Simplify the square root in the denominator.*

$\frac{\sqrt{14n}}{4n}$ *Simplify the denominator.*

Helpful Hint

Use the square root in the denominator to find the appropriate form of 1 for multiplication.

Simplify each quotient. All variables represent nonnegative numbers.

4a. $\frac{\sqrt{13}}{\sqrt{5}}$ $\frac{\sqrt{65}}{5}$ **4b.** $\frac{\sqrt{7a}}{\sqrt{12}}$ $\frac{\sqrt{21a}}{6}$ **4c.** $\frac{2\sqrt{80}}{\sqrt{7}}$ $\frac{8\sqrt{35}}{7}$

THINK AND DISCUSS

1. Explain why multiplying $\frac{\sqrt{6}}{\sqrt{5}}$ by $\frac{\sqrt{5}}{\sqrt{5}}$ does not change the value of $\frac{\sqrt{6}}{\sqrt{5}}$.

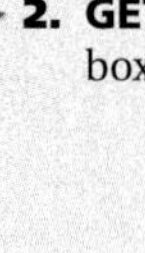

2. **GET ORGANIZED** Copy and complete the graphic organizer. In each box, give an example and show how to simplify it.

Multiplying Radical Expressions
- Multiplying two square roots
- Using the Distributive Property
- Using FOIL

3 Close

Summarize

Have students multiply and write each product in simplest form.

$\sqrt{6}\sqrt{10}$ $2\sqrt{15}$

$(2+\sqrt{7})(3+\sqrt{5})$ $6+2\sqrt{5}+3\sqrt{7}+\sqrt{35}$

Have students simplify the quotient below.

$\frac{2\sqrt{3}}{\sqrt{18}}$ $\frac{\sqrt{6}}{3}$

FORMATIVE ASSESSMENT and INTERVENTION

***Diagnose Before* the Lesson**
11-4 Warm Up, TE p. 716

***Monitor During* the Lesson**
Check It Out! Exercises, SE pp. 716–718
Questioning Strategies, TE p. 717–718

***Assess After* the Lesson**
11-4 Lesson Quiz, TE p. 721
Alternative Assessment, TE p. 721

Answers to *Think and Discuss*

1. $\frac{\sqrt{5}}{\sqrt{5}}$ is equal to 1, so multiplying by $\frac{\sqrt{5}}{\sqrt{5}}$ does not change the value of the original expression.
2. See p. A9.

Exercises

GUIDED PRACTICE

SEE EXAMPLE 1 p. 716

Multiply. Write each product in simplest form. All variables represent nonnegative numbers.

1. $\sqrt{2}\sqrt{3}$ **$\sqrt{6}$**
2. $\sqrt{3}\sqrt{8}$ **$2\sqrt{6}$**
3. $(5\sqrt{5})^2$ **125**
4. $(4\sqrt{2})^2$ **32**
5. $3\sqrt{3a}\sqrt{10}$ **$3\sqrt{30a}$**
6. $2\sqrt{15p}\sqrt{3p}$ **$6p\sqrt{5}$**

SEE EXAMPLE 2 p. 717

7. $\sqrt{6}(2+\sqrt{7})$ **$2\sqrt{6}+\sqrt{42}$**
8. $\sqrt{3}(5-\sqrt{3})$ **$5\sqrt{3}-3$**
9. $\sqrt{7}(\sqrt{5}-\sqrt{3})$
10. $\sqrt{2}(\sqrt{10}+8\sqrt{2})$
11. $\sqrt{5}(\sqrt{15}+4)$
12. $\sqrt{2}(\sqrt{6}-\sqrt{2})$

SEE EXAMPLE 3 p. 717

13. $(2+\sqrt{2})(5+\sqrt{2})$
14. $(4+\sqrt{6})(3-\sqrt{6})$
15. $(\sqrt{3}-4)(\sqrt{3}+2)$
16. $(5+\sqrt{3})^2$ **$28+10\sqrt{3}$**
17. $(\sqrt{6}-5\sqrt{3})^2$ **$81-30\sqrt{2}$**
18. $(6+3\sqrt{2})^2$ **$54+36\sqrt{2}$**

SEE EXAMPLE 4 p. 718

Simplify each quotient. All variables represent nonnegative numbers.

19. $\frac{\sqrt{13}}{\sqrt{2}}$ **$\frac{\sqrt{26}}{2}$**
20. $\frac{\sqrt{20}}{\sqrt{8}}$ **$\frac{\sqrt{10}}{2}$**
21. $\frac{\sqrt{11}}{6\sqrt{3}}$ **$\frac{\sqrt{33}}{18}$**
22. $\frac{\sqrt{28}}{\sqrt{3s}}$ **$\frac{2\sqrt{21s}}{3s}$**
23. $\frac{2}{\sqrt{7}}$ **$\frac{2\sqrt{7}}{7}$**
24. $\frac{3}{\sqrt{6}}$ **$\frac{\sqrt{6}}{2}$**
25. $\frac{1}{\sqrt{5x}}$ **$\frac{\sqrt{5x}}{5x}$**
26. $\frac{\sqrt{3}}{\sqrt{x}}$ **$\frac{\sqrt{3x}}{x}$**

PRACTICE AND PROBLEM SOLVING

Independent Practice	
For Exercises	See Example
27–32	1
33–38	2
39–44	3
45–52	4

Extra Practice
Skills Practice p. EP22
Application Practice p. EP34

Multiply. Write each product in simplest form. All variables represent nonnegative numbers.

27. $\sqrt{3}\sqrt{5}\sqrt{6}$ **$3\sqrt{10}$**
28. $3\sqrt{6}(5\sqrt{6})$ **90**
29. $(2\sqrt{2})^2$ **8**
30. $(3\sqrt{6})^2$ **54**
31. $\sqrt{21d}(2\sqrt{3d})$ **$6d\sqrt{7}$**
32. $4\sqrt{5n}(2\sqrt{5n})(3\sqrt{3n})$
33. $\sqrt{5}(4-\sqrt{10})$
34. $\sqrt{2}(\sqrt{6}+2)$
35. $\sqrt{2}(\sqrt{6}-\sqrt{10})$
36. $3\sqrt{3}(\sqrt{8}-2\sqrt{6})$
37. $\sqrt{3}(\sqrt{3}+12)$
38. $\sqrt{8}(\sqrt{10}+\sqrt{2})$
39. $(15+\sqrt{15})(4+\sqrt{15})$
40. $(\sqrt{6}+4)(\sqrt{2}-7)$
41. $(3-\sqrt{2})(4+\sqrt{2})$
42. $(\sqrt{5}-5)^2$ **$30-10\sqrt{5}$**
43. $(\sqrt{3}+8)^2$ **$67+16\sqrt{3}$**
44. $(2\sqrt{3}+4\sqrt{5})^2$ **$92+16\sqrt{15}$**

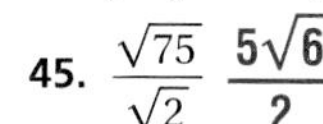

Simplify each quotient. All variables represent nonnegative numbers.

45. $\frac{\sqrt{75}}{\sqrt{2}}$ **$\frac{5\sqrt{6}}{2}$**
46. $\frac{\sqrt{5}}{4\sqrt{8}}$ **$\frac{\sqrt{10}}{16}$**
47. $\frac{\sqrt{27}}{3\sqrt{x}}$ **$\frac{\sqrt{3x}}{x}$**
48. $\frac{\sqrt{48k}}{\sqrt{5}}$ **$\frac{4\sqrt{15k}}{5}$**
49. $\frac{\sqrt{49x}}{\sqrt{2}}$ **$\frac{7\sqrt{2x}}{2}$**
50. $\frac{3\sqrt{27}}{\sqrt{b}}$ **$\frac{9\sqrt{3b}}{b}$**
51. $\frac{\sqrt{12y}}{\sqrt{3}}$ **$2\sqrt{y}$**
52. $\frac{\sqrt{12t}}{\sqrt{6}}$ **$\sqrt{2t}$**

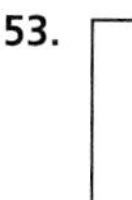

Geometry Find the area of each figure. Give your answer as a radical expression in simplest form.

53.

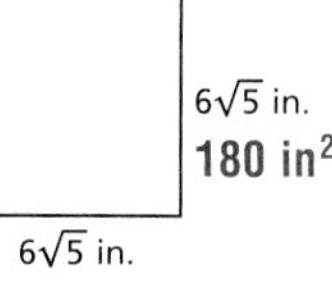

180 in²

54.

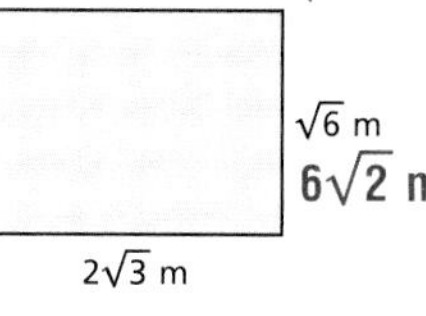

$6\sqrt{2}$ m²

55.

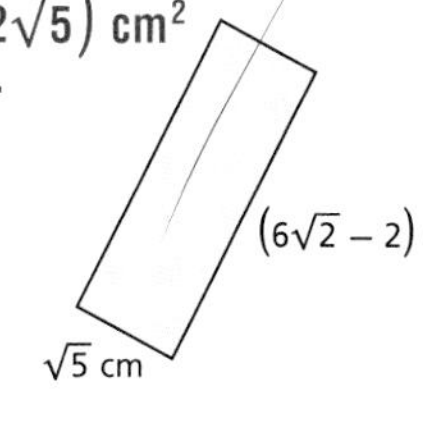

55. $(6\sqrt{10}-2\sqrt{5})$ cm²

11-4 Exercises

Assignment Guide

Assign *Guided Practice* exercises as necessary.

If you finished Examples **1–2**
Proficient 27–38, 53–55
Advanced 27–38, 53–55

If you finished Examples **1–4**
Proficient 27–77, 78–84 even, 87–99
Advanced 27–69, 74–99

Homework Quick Check
Quickly check key concepts.
Exercises: 28, 32, 36, 38, 42, 46

Answers

9. $\sqrt{35}-\sqrt{21}$
10. $2\sqrt{5}+16$
11. $5\sqrt{3}+4\sqrt{5}$
12. $2\sqrt{3}-2$
13. $12+7\sqrt{2}$
14. $6-\sqrt{6}$
15. $-5-2\sqrt{3}$
32. $120n\sqrt{3n}$
33. $4\sqrt{5}-5\sqrt{2}$
34. $2\sqrt{3}+2\sqrt{2}$
35. $2\sqrt{3}-2\sqrt{5}$
36. $6\sqrt{6}-18\sqrt{2}$
37. $3+12\sqrt{3}$
38. $4\sqrt{5}+4$
39. $75+19\sqrt{15}$
40. $2\sqrt{3}-7\sqrt{6}+4\sqrt{2}-28$
41. $10-\sqrt{2}$

Multiple Representations In **Exercise 69,** students could rewrite the expression as $\frac{\pi\sqrt{2\ell}}{4}$ before substituting 3 for ℓ.

CONCEPT CONNECTION **Exercise 74** involves evaluating radical expressions. This exercise prepares students for the Concept Connection on page 730.

Answers

73. Possible answer: $\frac{1}{\sqrt{3}}$; multiply the fraction by $\frac{\sqrt{3}}{\sqrt{3}}$. This will rationalize the denominator, since $\sqrt{3}\sqrt{3} = 3$.

74b. 5.6 s; it takes more than twice as long to go up the tower as it does to come down.

LINK **Electricity**

People began using wind to generate electricity in the early twentieth century. A modern wind turbine is 120–180 feet tall and, depending on its construction, can generate up to 1 megawatt of power.

Simplify. All variables represent nonnegative numbers.

56. $\sqrt{3}\left(\frac{\sqrt{2}}{\sqrt{7}}\right)$ **$\frac{\sqrt{42}}{7}$**

57. $\frac{15\sqrt{10}}{5\sqrt{3}}$ **$\sqrt{30}$**

58. $\frac{6+\sqrt{18}}{3}$ **$2+\sqrt{2}$**

59. $(\sqrt{3}-4)(\sqrt{3}+2)$ **$-5-2\sqrt{3}$**

60. $\sqrt{2}(6+\sqrt{12})$ **$6\sqrt{2}+2\sqrt{6}$**

61. $\frac{\sqrt{1}+\sqrt{25}}{\sqrt{2}}$ **$3\sqrt{2}$**

62. $\frac{\sqrt{15}+\sqrt{10}}{\sqrt{5}}$ **$\sqrt{3}+\sqrt{2}$**

63. $\sqrt{12}(\sqrt{3}+8)^2$ **$134\sqrt{3}+96$**

64. $\sqrt{3}(4-2\sqrt{5})$ **$4\sqrt{3}-2\sqrt{15}$**

65. $(\sqrt{x}-\sqrt{y})^2$ **$x-2\sqrt{xy}+y$**

66. $(\sqrt{x}-5)(3\sqrt{x}+7)$ **$3x-8\sqrt{x}-35$**

67. $(\sqrt{3}+\sqrt{x})^2$ **$3+2\sqrt{3x}+x$**

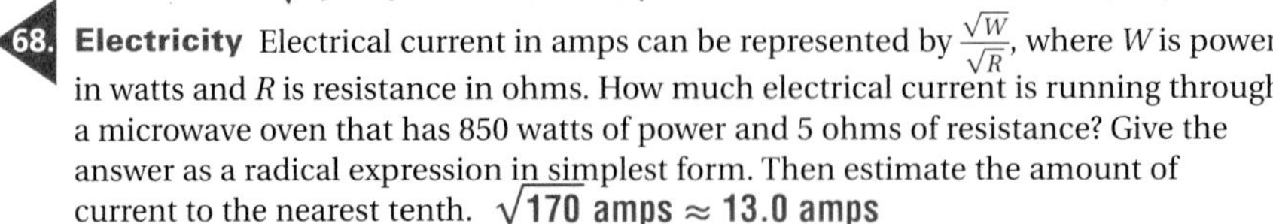

68. **Electricity** Electrical current in amps can be represented by $\frac{\sqrt{W}}{\sqrt{R}}$, where W is power in watts and R is resistance in ohms. How much electrical current is running through a microwave oven that has 850 watts of power and 5 ohms of resistance? Give the answer as a radical expression in simplest form. Then estimate the amount of current to the nearest tenth. **$\sqrt{170}$ amps ≈ 13.0 amps**

69. **Physical Science** The *period* of a pendulum is the amount of time it takes the pendulum to make one complete swing and return to its starting point. The period of a pendulum in seconds can be represented by $2\pi\sqrt{\frac{\ell}{32}}$, where ℓ is the length of the pendulum in feet. What is the period of a pendulum whose length is 3 feet? Give the answer as a radical expression in simplest form. Then estimate the period to the nearest tenth. **$\frac{\pi\sqrt{6}}{4}$ s ≈ 1.9 s**

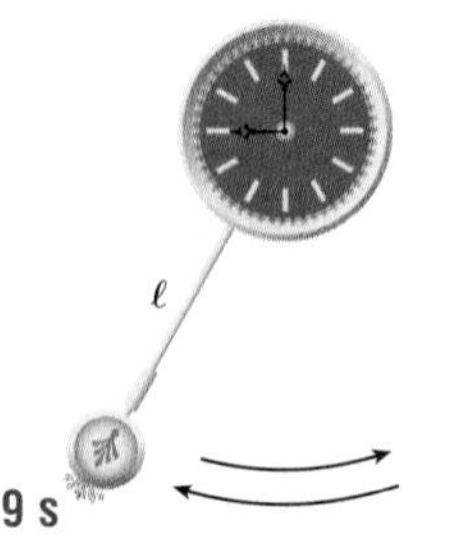

Geometry Find the area of each triangle. Give the exact answer in simplest form. (*Hint:* The formula for the area of a triangle is $A = \frac{1}{2}bh$.)

70. 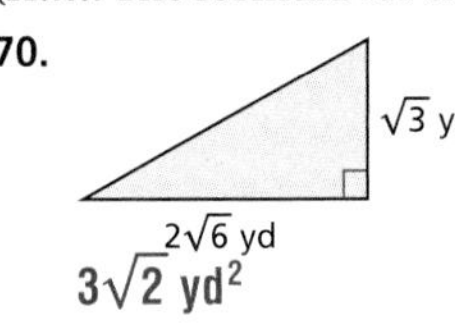

$3\sqrt{2}$ yd²

71. 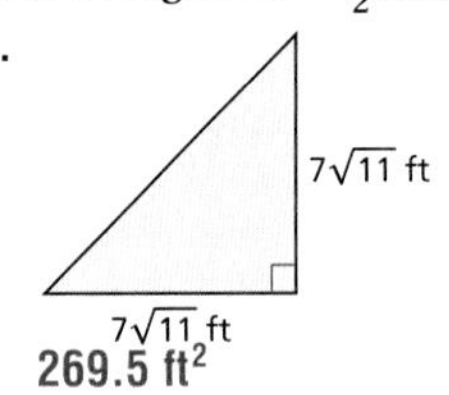

269.5 ft²

72. 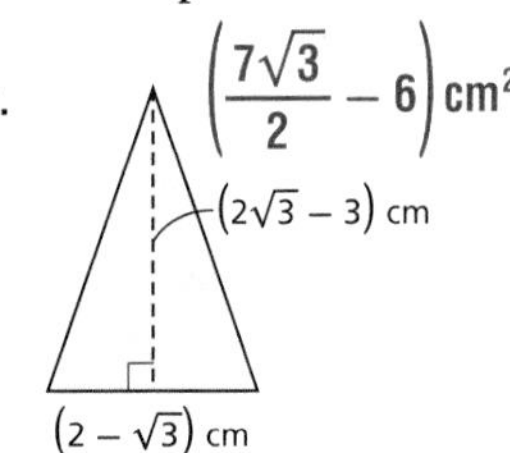

$\left(\frac{7\sqrt{3}}{2}-6\right)$ cm²

73. **Write About It** Describe an expression for which you would have to rationalize the denominator. How would you do it? Include an explanation of how you would choose what to multiply the original expression by.

CONCEPT CONNECTION

74. This problem will prepare you for the Concept Connection on page 730.

a. Many amusement parks have free-fall rides in which cars travel straight up a tower and then are allowed to fall back to the ground. The time in seconds for any object in free fall is $t = \sqrt{\frac{d}{16}}$, where d is the distance that the object falls in feet. On a particular free-fall ride, the cars are in free fall for 100 feet. How long does free fall last on this ride? **2.5 s**

b. The cars in the ride from part **a** travel up the tower at a speed of 18 feet per second. How long does this trip take? Round your answer to the nearest tenth. How does this time compare with the time spent in free fall?

11-4 PRACTICE A

11-4 PRACTICE C

11-4 PRACTICE B

LESSON 11-4 **Practice B**
Multiplying and Dividing Radical Expressions

Multiply. Write each product in simplest form. All variables represent nonnegative numbers.

1. $\sqrt{15}\cdot\sqrt{6}$ — $\sqrt{15\cdot 6}$ — **$3\sqrt{10}$**
2. $(3\sqrt{6})^2$ — $3\sqrt{6}\cdot 3\sqrt{6}$ — **54**
3. $4\sqrt{7x}\cdot\sqrt{20x}$ — $4\cdot\sqrt{(7x)(20x)}$ — **$8x\sqrt{35}$**
4. $\sqrt{12}\cdot\sqrt{5}$ **$2\sqrt{15}$**
5. $(2\sqrt{7})^2$ **28**
6. $-2\sqrt{5b}\cdot\sqrt{10b}$ **$-10b\sqrt{2}$**
7. $3\sqrt{10y}\sqrt{6y}$ **$6y\sqrt{15}$**
8. $\sqrt{8}(\sqrt{12}-\sqrt{2})$ **$4\sqrt{6}-4$**
9. $\sqrt{2x}(\sqrt{5}+\sqrt{2x})$ **$\sqrt{10x}+2x$**
10. $\sqrt{2}(\sqrt{7}-5)$ **$\sqrt{14}-5\sqrt{2}$**
11. $\sqrt{10}(\sqrt{5m}-\sqrt{4})$ **$5\sqrt{2m}-2\sqrt{10}$**
12. $(4+\sqrt{3})(2-\sqrt{3})$ **$5-2\sqrt{3}$**
13. $\sqrt{3}(\sqrt{8}-6)$ **$2\sqrt{6}-6\sqrt{3}$**
14. $\sqrt{5}(\sqrt{2}+\sqrt{8})$ **$3\sqrt{10}$**
15. $(5+\sqrt{2})(6-\sqrt{2})$ **$28+\sqrt{2}$**
16. $\sqrt{5}(\sqrt{2}-\sqrt{6})$ **$\sqrt{10}-\sqrt{30}$**
17. $(3-\sqrt{2})(5+\sqrt{2})$ **$13-2\sqrt{2}$**
18. $(7+\sqrt{3})(7-\sqrt{3})$ **46**

Simplify each quotient. All variables represent nonnegative numbers.

19. $\frac{\sqrt{2}}{\sqrt{6}}$ **$\frac{\sqrt{3}}{3}$**
20. $\frac{\sqrt{10}}{\sqrt{11}}$ **$\frac{\sqrt{110}}{11}$**
21. $\frac{\sqrt{13}}{\sqrt{50t}}$ **$\frac{\sqrt{26t}}{10t}$**
22. $\frac{\sqrt{7}}{\sqrt{15}}$ **$\frac{\sqrt{105}}{15}$**
23. $\frac{\sqrt{2}}{\sqrt{17}}$ **$\frac{\sqrt{34}}{17}$**
24. $\frac{\sqrt{32}}{\sqrt{48z}}$ **$\frac{\sqrt{6z}}{3z}$**
25. $\frac{\sqrt{3}}{\sqrt{3a}}$ **$\frac{\sqrt{a}}{a}$**
26. $\frac{\sqrt{8x}}{\sqrt{5}}$ **$\frac{2\sqrt{10x}}{5}$**
27. $-\frac{\sqrt{75k}}{10\sqrt{2k}}$ **$-\frac{\sqrt{6}}{4}$**

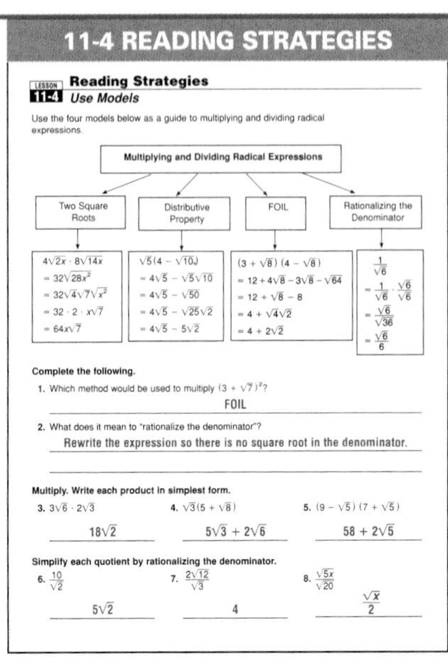

11-4 READING STRATEGIES

LESSON 11-4 **Reading Strategies**
Use Models

Use the four models below as a guide to multiplying and dividing radical expressions.

Complete the following.

1. Which method would be used to multiply $(3+\sqrt{7})^2$? **FOIL**
2. What does it mean to "rationalize the denominator"? **Rewrite the expression so there is no square root in the denominator.**

Multiply. Write each product in simplest form.

3. $3\sqrt{6}\cdot 2\sqrt{3}$ **$18\sqrt{2}$**
4. $\sqrt{3}(5+\sqrt{8})$ **$5\sqrt{3}+2\sqrt{6}$**
5. $(9-\sqrt{5})(7+\sqrt{5})$ **$58+2\sqrt{5}$**

Simplify each quotient by rationalizing the denominator.

6. $\frac{10}{\sqrt{2}}$ **$5\sqrt{2}$**
7. $\frac{2\sqrt{12}}{\sqrt{3}}$ **4**
8. $\frac{\sqrt{5x}}{\sqrt{20}}$ **$\frac{\sqrt{x}}{2}$**

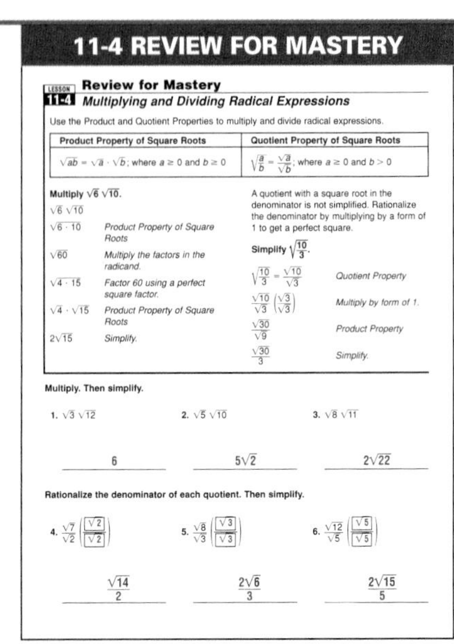

11-4 REVIEW FOR MASTERY

LESSON 11-4 **Review for Mastery**
Multiplying and Dividing Radical Expressions

Use the Product and Quotient Properties to multiply and divide radical expressions.

Product Property of Square Roots	Quotient Property of Square Roots
$\sqrt{ab} = \sqrt{a}\cdot\sqrt{b}$; where $a \ge 0$ and $b \ge 0$	$\sqrt{\frac{a}{b}} = \frac{\sqrt{a}}{\sqrt{b}}$; where $a \ge 0$ and $b > 0$

Multiply $\sqrt{6}\sqrt{10}$.

$\sqrt{6}\sqrt{10}$	
$\sqrt{6\cdot 10}$	*Product Property of Square Roots*
$\sqrt{60}$	*Multiply the factors in the radicand.*
$\sqrt{4\cdot 15}$	*Factor 60 using a perfect square factor.*
$\sqrt{4}\cdot\sqrt{15}$	*Product Property of Square Roots*
$2\sqrt{15}$	*Simplify.*

A quotient with a square root in the denominator is not simplified. Rationalize the denominator by multiplying by a form of 1 to get a perfect square.

Simplify $\sqrt{\frac{10}{3}}$.

$\sqrt{\frac{10}{3}} = \frac{\sqrt{10}}{\sqrt{3}}$	*Quotient Property*
$\frac{\sqrt{10}}{\sqrt{3}}\left(\frac{\sqrt{3}}{\sqrt{3}}\right)$	*Multiply by form of 1.*
$\frac{\sqrt{30}}{\sqrt{9}}$	*Product Property*
$\frac{\sqrt{30}}{3}$	*Simplify.*

Multiply. Then simplify.

1. $\sqrt{3}\sqrt{12}$ **6**
2. $\sqrt{5}\sqrt{10}$ **$5\sqrt{2}$**
3. $\sqrt{8}\sqrt{11}$ **$2\sqrt{22}$**

Rationalize the denominator of each quotient. Then simplify.

4. $\frac{\sqrt{7}}{\sqrt{2}}\left(\frac{\sqrt{2}}{\sqrt{2}}\right)$ **$\frac{\sqrt{14}}{2}$**
5. $\frac{\sqrt{8}}{\sqrt{3}}\left(\frac{\sqrt{3}}{\sqrt{3}}\right)$ **$\frac{2\sqrt{6}}{3}$**
6. $\frac{\sqrt{12}}{\sqrt{5}}\left(\frac{\sqrt{5}}{\sqrt{5}}\right)$ **$\frac{2\sqrt{15}}{5}$**

Multiple Choice For Exercises 75–77, choose the best answer.

75. What is the product of $3\sqrt{5}$ and $\sqrt{15}$?

Ⓐ $5\sqrt{3}$ (B) $15\sqrt{3}$ Ⓒ $15\sqrt{15}$ Ⓓ $45\sqrt{5}$

76. Which of the following is the result of rationalizing the denominator in the expression $\frac{4}{3\sqrt{2}}$?

Ⓐ $\frac{\sqrt{2}}{3}$ Ⓑ $2\sqrt{2}$ (C) $\frac{2\sqrt{2}}{3}$ Ⓓ $\frac{3\sqrt{2}}{2}$

77. Which of the following is equivalent to $\left(5\sqrt{10}\right)^2$?

Ⓐ 50 Ⓑ 100 Ⓒ 125 (D) 250

CHALLENGE AND EXTEND

The expressions $\sqrt{a} + \sqrt{b}$ and $\sqrt{a} - \sqrt{b}$ are called *conjugates*. When a and b are nonnegative, you can use the FOIL to multiply conjugates as follows:

$$\left(\sqrt{a} - \sqrt{b}\right)\left(\sqrt{a} + \sqrt{b}\right) = a + \sqrt{ab} - \sqrt{ab} - b = a - b$$

$$\left(\sqrt{3} - \sqrt{5}\right)\left(\sqrt{3} + \sqrt{5}\right) = 3 + \sqrt{15} - \sqrt{15} - 5 = 3 - 5 = -2$$

Notice that the product does not contain any square roots. This means that you can use conjugates to rationalize denominators that contain sums or differences of square roots:

$$\frac{\sqrt{2}}{\sqrt{7} + \sqrt{2}}\left(\frac{\sqrt{7} - \sqrt{2}}{\sqrt{7} - \sqrt{2}}\right) = \frac{\sqrt{2}\left(\sqrt{7} - \sqrt{2}\right)}{\left(\sqrt{7} + \sqrt{2}\right)\left(\sqrt{7} - \sqrt{2}\right)} = \frac{\sqrt{14} - \sqrt{4}}{7 - 2} = \frac{\sqrt{14} - 2}{5}$$

Simplify.

78. $\frac{4}{\sqrt{3} - \sqrt{2}}$ $4\sqrt{3} + 4\sqrt{2}$

79. $\frac{8}{\sqrt{3} + \sqrt{5}}$ $-4\sqrt{3} + 4\sqrt{5}$

80. $\frac{\sqrt{5}}{\sqrt{10} + \sqrt{3}}$ $\frac{5\sqrt{2} - \sqrt{15}}{7}$

81. $\frac{\sqrt{2} + \sqrt{3}}{\sqrt{2} - \sqrt{3}}$ $-5 - 2\sqrt{6}$

82. $\frac{\sqrt{3}}{\sqrt{2} + \sqrt{3}}$ $3 - \sqrt{6}$

83. $\frac{\sqrt{2}}{\sqrt{8} + \sqrt{6}}$ $2 - \sqrt{3}$

84. $\frac{6}{\sqrt{2} + \sqrt{3}}$ $6\sqrt{3} - 6\sqrt{2}$

85. $\frac{2}{\sqrt{6} - \sqrt{5}}$ $2\sqrt{6} + 2\sqrt{5}$

86. **Geometry** One rectangle is $4\sqrt{6}$ feet long and $\sqrt{2}$ feet wide. Another rectangle is $8\sqrt{2}$ feet long and $2\sqrt{6}$ feet wide. How much more area does the larger rectangle cover than the smaller rectangle? (*Hint:* The formula for the area of a rectangle is $A = \ell w$.) $24\sqrt{3}$ ft²

SPIRAL STANDARDS REVIEW

2.0, 4.0, 11.0

Solve each inequality. (Lesson 3-5)

87. $2(x + 5) > 3x + 2$ $x < 8$

88. $x + 1 \geq 5(x - 3)$ $x \leq 4$

89. $x(3 + 2) \geq 14 - 2x$ $x \geq 2$

Factor each polynomial completely. Check your answer. (Lesson 8-6)

90. $x^2 + 7x - 30$

91. $6x^2 + 11x + 3$

92. $x^2 - 16$

93. $3x^2 + 30x + 75$ $3(x + 5)^2$

94. $2x^4 - 18$ $2(x^2 + 3)(x^2 - 3)$

95. $8x^3 - 20x^2 - 12x$ $4x(2x + 1)(x - 3)$

90. $(x - 3)(x + 10)$

91. $(3x + 1)(2x + 3)$

92. $(x + 4)(x - 4)$

Simplify. All variables represent nonnegative numbers. (Lesson 11-2)

96. $\sqrt{360}$ $6\sqrt{10}$

97. $\sqrt{\frac{72}{16}}$ $\frac{3\sqrt{2}}{2}$

98. $\sqrt{\frac{49x^2}{64y^4}}$ $\frac{7x}{8y^2}$

99. $\sqrt{\frac{50a^7}{9a^3}}$ $\frac{5a^2\sqrt{2}}{3}$

Teaching Tip **Multiple Choice** Students choosing **A** in **Exercise 75** chose the simplified form of $\sqrt{75}$ instead of $3\sqrt{75}$.

Students who chose **A** in **Exercise 77** most likely forgot to square the 5 outside the radical sign. Remind them to square every factor inside the parentheses:

$\left(5\sqrt{10}\right)^2 = 5^2\left(\sqrt{10}\right)^2 = 25 \cdot 10 = 250$

Journal

Have students explain how to multiply and simplify the product of $3\sqrt{5}$ and $2\sqrt{10}$.

ALTERNATIVE ASSESSMENT

Have students write a square-root expression that contains two terms. Then have them write the simplified form of the square of their expression. Next, have students write a fraction so that the denominator is a square root that is not a perfect square. Have them simplify their fraction.

Power Presentations with PowerPoint®

11-4 Lesson Quiz

Multiply. Write each product in simplest form. All variables represent nonnegative numbers.

1. $\sqrt{5}\sqrt{10}$ $5\sqrt{2}$
2. $3\sqrt{6x}\sqrt{8x}$ $12x\sqrt{3}$
3. $\sqrt{2}\left(\sqrt{7} + \sqrt{2}\right)$ $\sqrt{14} + 2$
4. $\left(2 + \sqrt{5}\right)^2$ $9 + 4\sqrt{5}$
5. $\left(3\sqrt{6}\right)^2$ 54
6. $\sqrt{3}\left(5 - \sqrt{18}\right)$ $5\sqrt{3} - 3\sqrt{6}$
7. $\left(6 + \sqrt{3}\right)\left(2 - \sqrt{3}\right)$ $9 - 4\sqrt{3}$

Simplify each quotient. All variables represent nonnegative numbers.

8. $\frac{\sqrt{5}}{\sqrt{6}}$ $\frac{\sqrt{30}}{6}$

9. $\frac{\sqrt{3x}}{\sqrt{18}}$ $\frac{\sqrt{6x}}{6}$

Also available on transparency

11-4 PROBLEM SOLVING

LESSON 11-4 **Problem Solving**
Multiplying and Dividing Radical Expressions

Write each correct answer as a radical expression in simplest form.

1. The expression $\sqrt{\frac{W}{R}}$ models the electrical current in amperes, where W is power in watts and R is resistance in ohms. How much electrical current is running through an appliance with 500 watts of power and 16 ohms of resistance?

$\frac{5\sqrt{5}}{2}$ amps

2. The diagram shows the dimensions of a dining table. With a leaf in place, the table expands to seat eight people.

$28\sqrt{10}$ in.

$8\sqrt{6}$ in.

Find the area of the table.

$448\sqrt{15}$ in²

Find the area of the table with the addition of a leaf that measures $8\sqrt{6}$ inches by $18\sqrt{3}$ inches.

$448\sqrt{15} + 432\sqrt{2}$ in²

3. Riley's new bedroom is a perfect square. Each side measures $2\sqrt{3}$ meters. Find the area and perimeter of Riley's bedroom.

area: 12 m²

perimeter: $8\sqrt{3}$ m

Select the best answer.

4. R.J. lives in a studio apartment. The apartment is rectangular with a width of $10 + 4\sqrt{2}$ feet and a length of $20 + 11\sqrt{2}$ feet. What is the area of R.J.'s apartment?

A 60 ft²
B 288 ft²
C $200 + 190\sqrt{2}$ ft²
(D) $288 + 190\sqrt{2}$ ft²

5. The volume of water in a lake, in gallons, can be represented by $x\sqrt{2}$. Heavy rains are forecast. The volume of water is expected to increase $\sqrt{2}$ times. How many gallons of water are expected in the lake after the rain?

F $\frac{x}{2}$ gallons
G x gallons
H $x\sqrt{2}$ gallons
(J) $2x$ gallons

6. The area of a rectangular window is 40 square feet. The length is $\sqrt{20}$ feet. What is the width of the window?

A $\sqrt{2}$ feet
(C) $4\sqrt{5}$ feet
B 2 feet
D $4\sqrt{10}$ feet

7. The height of a triangle can be found using $h = \frac{2A}{b}$ where A is the area and b is the base of the triangle. Which shows the height of a triangle with an area of $\sqrt{90}$ cm² and a base of $\sqrt{5}$ cm written in simplest form?

F $2\sqrt{18}$ cm
(H) $6\sqrt{2}$ cm
G $3\sqrt{18}$ cm
J $18\sqrt{2}$ cm

11-4 CHALLENGE

LESSON 11-4 **Challenge**
Irrational Roots of Quadratic Equations

The solutions of a quadratic equation are sometimes called *roots*, but that has nothing to do with whether or not the solution contains a square root. If a solution does contain a square root, it is called an *irrational root*.

1. Is $x = -5 + \sqrt{3}$ an irrational root of $0 = x^2 + 10x + 22$? Substitute and simplify to find out.

Yes; $\left(-5 + \sqrt{3}\right)^2 + 10\left(-5 + \sqrt{3}\right) + 22 = \left(28 - 10\sqrt{3}\right) + \left(-50 + 10\sqrt{3}\right) + 22 = 0$

2. Use the Quadratic Formula to find all roots of $0 = x^2 + 10x + 22$. Does this support your answer to question 1?

$x = -5 \pm \sqrt{3}$; yes, $x = -5 + \sqrt{3}$ is one of the two roots.

3. Is $x = 1 - 3\sqrt{2}$ an irrational root of $0 = 4x^2 - 4x - 17$? Substitute and simplify to find out.

No; $4\left(1 - 3\sqrt{2}\right)^2 - 4\left(1 - 3\sqrt{2}\right) - 17 = \left(76 - 24\sqrt{2}\right) - \left(4 - 12\sqrt{2}\right) - 17 = 55 - 12\sqrt{2} \neq 0$

4. Use the Quadratic Formula to find all roots of $0 = 4x^2 - 4x - 17$. Does this support your answer to question 3?

$x = \frac{1 \pm 3\sqrt{2}}{2} = \frac{1}{2} \pm \frac{3}{2}\sqrt{2}$; yes, $x = 1 - 3\sqrt{2}$ is *not* one of the two roots.

5. Look at the roots that you found in questions 2 and 4. Based on these few examples, complete these conjectures about the irrational roots of quadratic equations that have rational coefficients:

a. In general, the irrational roots are conjugates of each other.

b. If one root is $m + n\sqrt{p}$, then the other root is $m - n\sqrt{p}$.

6. Explain how the Quadratic Formula guarantees that your conjectures in question 5 will hold true any time a quadratic equation has irrational roots?

The quadratic formula includes ± square root; irrational roots will always be conjugates.

7. Recall that when the discriminant $(b^2 - 4ac)$ is greater than zero, there are two real solutions. What must be true about the discriminant for there to be two irrational solutions?

$b^2 - 4ac$ would have to be greater than zero and *not* a perfect square.

11-5 Organizer

Objective: Solve radical equations.

Online Edition
Tutorial Videos

Power Presentations with PowerPoint®

Warm Up

Solve each equation.

1. $3x + 5 = 17$ 4
2. $4x + 1 = 2x - 3$ -2
3. $\frac{x}{7} = 5$ 35
4. $(x + 7)(x - 4) = 0$ $-7, 4$
5. $x^2 - 11x + 30 = 0$ 6, 5
6. $x^2 = 2x + 15$ 5, -3

Also available on transparency

Math Humor

Q: What did Mr. and Mrs. Square find when they were researching their family history?

A. Square roots.

California Standards

Extension of 2.0

11-5 Solving Radical Equations

California Standards

Extension of 2.0 **Students understand and use such operations as** taking the opposite, finding the reciprocal, **taking a root,** and raising to a fractional power. **They understand and use the rules of exponents.**

Vocabulary
radical equation

Who uses this?
Meteorologists can use radical equations to estimate the size of a storm. (See Exercise 76.)

A **radical equation** is an equation that contains a variable within a radical. In this chapter, you will study radical equations that contain only square roots.

Recall that you use inverse operations to solve equations. For nonnegative numbers, squaring and taking the square root are inverse operations. When an equation contains a variable within a square root, you can solve by squaring both sides of the equation.

Power Property of Equality

WORDS	NUMBERS	ALGEBRA
You can square both sides of an equation, and the resulting equation is still true.	$3 = 1 + 2$ $(3)^2 = (1 + 2)^2$ $9 = 9$	If a and b are real numbers and $a = b$, then $a^2 = b^2$.

EXAMPLE 1 Solving Simple Radical Equations

Solve each equation. Check your answer.

A $\sqrt{x} = 8$

$(\sqrt{x})^2 = (8)^2$ *Square both sides.*

$x = 64$

Check

$\sqrt{x} = 8$	
$\sqrt{64}$	8
8	8 ✓

Substitute 64 for x in the original equation.
Simplify.

B $6 = \sqrt{4x}$

$(6)^2 = (\sqrt{4x})^2$ *Square both sides.*

$36 = 4x$

$9 = x$ *Divide both sides by 4.*

Check

$6 = \sqrt{4x}$	
6	$\sqrt{4(9)}$
6	$\sqrt{36}$
6	6 ✓

Substitute 9 for x in the original equation.
Simplify.

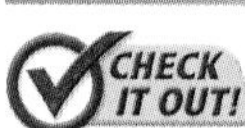

Solve each equation. Check your answer.

1a. $\sqrt{x} = 6$ **36** **1b.** $9 = \sqrt{27x}$ **3** **1c.** $\sqrt{3x} = 1$ $\frac{1}{3}$ **1d.** $\sqrt{\frac{x}{3}} = 2$ **12**

1 Introduce

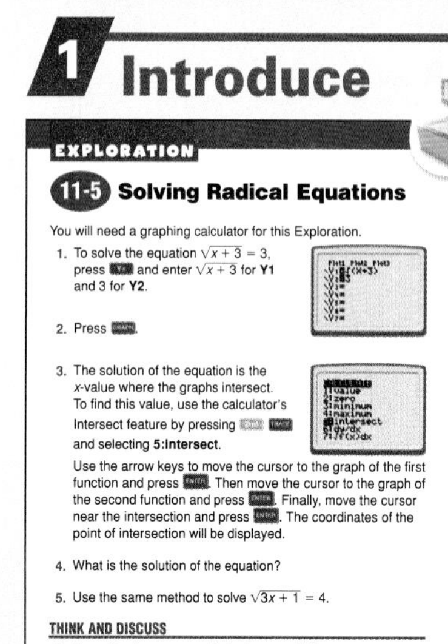
EXPLORATION

11-5 Solving Radical Equations

You will need a graphing calculator for this Exploration.

1. To solve the equation $\sqrt{x + 3} = 3$, press Y= and enter $\sqrt{x + 3}$ for **Y1** and 3 for **Y2**.
2. Press GRAPH.
3. The solution of the equation is the x-value where the graphs intersect. To find this value, use the calculator's Intersect feature by pressing 2nd TRACE and selecting **5:Intersect**.
   Use the arrow keys to move the cursor to the graph of the first function and press ENTER. Then move the cursor to the graph of the second function and press ENTER. Finally, move the cursor near the intersection and press ENTER. The coordinates of the point of intersection will be displayed.
4. What is the solution of the equation?
5. Use the same method to solve $\sqrt{3x + 1} = 4$.

THINK AND DISCUSS

6. **Describe** how you could check your solutions.
7. **Discuss** what you think would happen if you tried to use this

Motivate

Have students use guess and check to find the correct value of x in $8 = \sqrt{2x}$. $x = 32$

Have students use guess and check to solve $\sqrt{7x + 4} - 9 = 0$. $x = 11$

Tell students that in this lesson they will learn methods to help them solve more complicated radical equations such as the second type.

Explorations and answers are provided in *Alternate Openers: Explorations Transparencies.*

Some square-root equations do not have the square root isolated. To solve these equations, you may have to isolate the square root before squaring both sides. You can do this by using one or more inverse operations.

EXAMPLE 2 Solving Radical Equations by Adding or Subtracting

Solve each equation. Check your answer.

A $\sqrt{x}+3=10$

$\sqrt{x}=7$ *Subtract 3 from both sides.*

$(\sqrt{x})^2=(7)^2$ *Square both sides.*

$x=49$

Check

$\sqrt{x}+3$	10
$\sqrt{49}+3$	10
$7+3$	10
10	10 ✓

B $\sqrt{x-5}=4$

$(\sqrt{x-5})^2=(4)^2$ *Square both sides.*

$x-5=16$

$x=21$ *Add 5 to both sides.*

Check

$\sqrt{x-5}$	4
$\sqrt{21-5}$	4
$\sqrt{16}$	4
4	4 ✓

C $\sqrt{2x-1}+4=7$

$\sqrt{2x-1}=3$ *Subtract 4 from both sides.*

$(\sqrt{2x-1})^2=(3)^2$ *Square both sides.*

$2x-1=9$

$2x=10$ *Add 1 to both sides.*

$x=5$ *Divide both sides by 2.*

Check

$\sqrt{2x-1}+4$	7
$\sqrt{2(5)-1}+4$	7
$\sqrt{10-1}+4$	7
$\sqrt{9}+4$	7
$3+4$	7
7	7 ✓

Solve each equation. Check your answer.

2a. $\sqrt{x}-2=1$ **9** **2b.** $\sqrt{x+7}=5$ **18** **2c.** $\sqrt{3x+7}-1=3$ **3**

EXAMPLE 3 Solving Radical Equations by Multiplying or Dividing

Solve each equation. Check your answer.

A $3\sqrt{x}=21$

Method 1

$3\sqrt{x}=21$

$\sqrt{x}=7$ *Divide both sides by 3.*

$(\sqrt{x})^2=(7)^2$ *Square both sides.*

$x=49$

Method 2

$3\sqrt{x}=21$

$(3\sqrt{x})^2=21^2$ *Square both sides.*

$9x=441$

$x=49$ *Divide both sides by 9.*

Check

$3\sqrt{x}$	21	
$3\sqrt{49}$	21	*Substitute 49 for x in the original equation.*
$3(7)$	21	*Simplify.*
21	21 ✓	

2 Teach

Guided Instruction

Tell students that the goal in solving a radical equation is the same as it was for linear equations: to isolate the variable by using inverse operations. In **Example 4B,** students might try to square both sides of an equation as a first step. Explain that, while this is not incorrect, if they make that choice, they must square the entire left side, which would require using FOIL and many algebraic steps. Encourage students to move one term to the other side to reduce the number of steps and the possibility of error.

Math Background Show students how the Power Property of Equality is derived from the Multiplication Property of Equality. If $a=b$, then $a^2=ab$. (Multiply both sides by a.) Also, if $a=b$, then $ab=b^2$. (Multiply both sides by b.) Since both a^2 and b^2 are equal to ab, $a^2=b^2$.

COMMON ERROR ALERT

When squaring the product of a constant and a radical, students might forget to square the constant. For example, they might write $(3\sqrt{x})^2$ as $3x$. Show students that $(3\sqrt{x})^2=(3\sqrt{x})(3\sqrt{x})=9x$.

Power Presentations with PowerPoint®

Additional Examples

Example 1

Solve each equation. Check your answer.

A. $\sqrt{x}=5$ 25

B. $10=\sqrt{2x}$ 50

Example 2

Solve each equation. Check your answer.

A. $\sqrt{x}-4=5$ 81

B. $\sqrt{x+3}=7$ 46

C. $\sqrt{5x+1}+6=10$ 3

Example 3

Solve each equation. Check your answer.

A. $4\sqrt{x}=32$ 64

B. $6=\dfrac{\sqrt{x}}{2}$ 144

Also available on transparency

INTERVENTION

Questioning Strategies

EXAMPLE 1

- What inverse operation isolates the variable in a radical equation?

EXAMPLE 2

- How do you choose whether to square both sides or to add or subtract for your first step?

EXAMPLE 3

- How are the two methods similar? How are they different?

Power Presentations with PowerPoint®

Additional Examples

Example 4

Solve each equation. Check your answer.

A. $\sqrt{2x-1} = \sqrt{x+7}$ 8

B. $\sqrt{5x-4} - \sqrt{6} = 0$ 2

Also available on transparency

INTERVENTION

Questioning Strategies

EXAMPLE 4

- Why is it more efficient to have only one radical term on each side when solving a radical equation?

Multiple Representations Solutions to equations like those in **Example 4B** can be checked by graphing the related function and finding the zero. When checking answers by substitution, remind students of the importance of using the original equation and not any of the equations in the solution process.

Solve each equation. Check your answer.

B $\dfrac{\sqrt{x}}{3} = 5$

Method 1		Method 2	
$\sqrt{x} = 15$	*Multiply both sides by 3.*	$\left(\dfrac{\sqrt{x}}{3}\right)^2 = (5)^2$	*Square both sides.*
$(\sqrt{x})^2 = (15)^2$	*Square both sides.*	$\dfrac{x}{9} = 25$	
$x = 225$		$x = 225$	*Multiply both sides by 9.*

Check $\dfrac{\sqrt{x}}{3} = 5$

$\dfrac{\sqrt{225}}{3}$	5	*Substitute 225 for x in the original equation.*
$\dfrac{15}{3}$	5	*Simplify.*
5	5 ✓	

Solve each equation. Check your answer.

3a. $2\sqrt{x} = 22$ **121**   **3b.** $2 = \dfrac{\sqrt{x}}{4}$ **64**   **3c.** $\dfrac{2\sqrt{x}}{5} = 4$ **100**

EXAMPLE **4** **Solving Radical Equations with Square Roots on Both Sides**

Solve each equation. Check your answer.

A $\sqrt{x+1} = \sqrt{3}$

$\left(\sqrt{x+1}\right)^2 = \left(\sqrt{3}\right)^2$ *Square both sides.*

$x + 1 = 3$

$x = 2$ *Subtract 1 from both sides.*

Check $\sqrt{x+1} = \sqrt{3}$

$\sqrt{2+1}$	$\sqrt{3}$
$\sqrt{3}$	$\sqrt{3}$ ✓

B $\sqrt{x+8} - \sqrt{3x} = 0$

$\sqrt{x+8} = \sqrt{3x}$ *Add $\sqrt{3x}$ to both sides.*

$\left(\sqrt{x+8}\right)^2 = \left(\sqrt{3x}\right)^2$ *Square both sides.*

$x + 8 = 3x$

$8 = 2x$ *Subtract x from both sides.*

$4 = x$ *Divide both sides by 2.*

Check $\sqrt{x+8} - \sqrt{3x} = 0$

$\sqrt{4+8} - \sqrt{3(4)}$	0
$\sqrt{12} - \sqrt{12}$	0
0	0 ✓

Solve each equation. Check your answer.

4a. $\sqrt{3x+2} = \sqrt{x+6}$ **2**   **4b.** $\sqrt{2x-5} - \sqrt{6} = 0$ $\mathbf{\dfrac{11}{2}}$

Remember!

Recall from Chapter 10 that an extraneous solution is a number that is not a solution of the original equation. See Lesson 10-7.

Squaring both sides of an equation may result in an extraneous solution.

Suppose your original equation is $x = 3$. $x = 3$

Square both sides. Now you have a new equation. $x^2 = 9$

Solve this new equation for x by taking the square root of both sides. $\sqrt{x^2} = \sqrt{9}$; $x = 3$ or $x = -3$

Now there are two solutions of the new equation. One $(x = 3)$ is a solution of the original equation. The other $(x = -3)$ is extraneous—it is not a solution of the original equation. Because of extraneous solutions, it is especially important to check your answers to radical equations.

Universal Access

Through Multiple Representations

Show students how to use a graphing calculator to determine how many solutions a radical equation has. First rewrite the equation so that one side is 0. Then substitute y for 0 and check the graph for x-intercepts. For $11 + \sqrt{5x} = 6$ in **Check It Out 5,** graph $y = 5 + \sqrt{5x}$. It does not cross the x-axis; it has no solution. You can also graph $y = 11 + \sqrt{5x}$ and $y = 6$ and see that they do not intersect.

EXAMPLE 5 Extraneous Solutions

Solve $\sqrt{6-x} = x$. Check your answer.

$\left(\sqrt{6-x}\right)^2 = (x)^2$	*Square both sides.*
$6 - x = x^2$	
$x^2 + x - 6 = 0$	*Write in standard form.*
$(x-2)(x+3) = 0$	*Factor.*
$x - 2 = 0$ or $x + 3 = 0$	*Zero-Product Property*
$x = 2$ or $x = -3$	*Solve for x.*

Helpful Hint

The equation in Example 5 has one solution. If all of the solutions of an equation are extraneous, then the original equation has no solutions.

Check

$\sqrt{6-x}$	x	
$\sqrt{6-2}$	2	*Substitute 2 for x in the equation.*
$\sqrt{4}$	2	
2	2 ✓	

$\sqrt{6-x}$	x	
$\sqrt{6-(-3)}$	−3	*Substitute −3 for x in the equation.*
$\sqrt{9}$	−3	
3	−3 ✗	

−3 does not check; it is extraneous. The only solution is 2.

CHECK IT OUT! Solve each equation. Check your answer.

5a. $11 + \sqrt{5x} = 6$ ∅ **5b.** $x = \sqrt{-3x - 2}$ ∅ **5c.** $x - 2 = \sqrt{x}$ **4**

EXAMPLE 6 *Geometry Application*

Geometry

A rectangle has an area of 52 square feet. Its length is 13 feet, and its width is $\sqrt{x}$ feet. What is the value of x? What is the width of the rectangle?

$A = 52 \text{ ft}^2$ $\sqrt{x}$ ft

13 ft

$A = \ell w$	*Use the formula for area of a rectangle.*
$52 = 13\sqrt{x}$	*Substitute 52 for A, 13 for ℓ, and $\sqrt{x}$ for w.*
$\frac{52}{13} = \frac{13\sqrt{x}}{13}$	*Divide both sides by 13.*
$4 = \sqrt{x}$	
$4^2 = \left(\sqrt{x}\right)^2$	*Square both sides.*
$16 = x$	

Check $A = \ell w$

52	$13\sqrt{x}$	
52	$13\sqrt{16}$	*Substitute 16 for x in the equation.*
52	13(4)	
52	52 ✓	

The value of x is 16. The width of the rectangle is $\sqrt{16} = 4$ feet.

CHECK IT OUT! **6.** A rectangle has an area of 15 cm². Its width is 5 cm, and its length is $\left(\sqrt{x+1}\right)$ cm. What is the value of x? What is the length of the rectangle? **8; 3 cm**

Power Presentations with PowerPoint®

Additional Examples

Example 5

Solve each equation. Check your answer.

A. $12 + \sqrt{6x} = 6$ ∅

B. $x = \sqrt{2x + 3}$ 3

Example 6

A triangle has an area of 36 square feet. Its base is 8 feet, and its height is $\sqrt{x - 1}$ feet. What is the value of x? What is the height of the triangle? 82; 9 ft

Also available on transparency

INTERVENTION

Questioning Strategies

EXAMPLE 5

- Why is it necessary to check your answers when solving radical equations?

EXAMPLE 6

- Is it necessary to find the value of x in order to determine the width of the rectangle? Explain.

3 Close

Summarize

Have students state the first step they would take to solve each equation.

$15 = \sqrt{x}$ Square both sides.

$\sqrt{3x} + 1 = 6$ Subtract 1 from both sides.

$\sqrt{3x + 1} = 6$ Square both sides.

$\frac{\sqrt{x}}{5} = 8$ Multiply both sides by 5, or square both sides.

$\sqrt{x + 2} - \sqrt{2x} = 0$ Add $\sqrt{2x}$ to both sides.

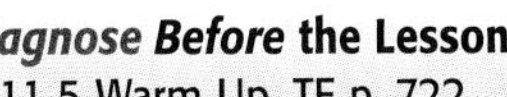

FORMATIVE ASSESSMENT and INTERVENTION

***Diagnose Before* the Lesson**
11-5 Warm Up, TE p. 722

***Monitor During* the Lesson**
Check It Out! Exercises, SE pp. 722–725
Questioning Strategies, TE pp. 723–725

***Assess After* the Lesson**
11-5 Lesson Quiz, TE p. 729
Alternative Assessment, TE p. 729

Answers to *Think and Discuss*

Possible answers:

1. Possible answer: Method 1 is preferable because 21 is easily divided by 3 and dividing by 3 first keeps the numbers small.
2. Subtract 3 from both sides. After doing this, you can square both sides to eliminate the radical.
3. See p. A9.

THINK AND DISCUSS

1. Compare the two methods used in Example 3A. Which method do you prefer? Why?
2. What is the first step to solve $\sqrt{x-2}+3=8$? Why?

3. **GET ORGANIZED** Copy and complete the graphic organizer. Write and solve a radical equation, using the boxes to show each step.

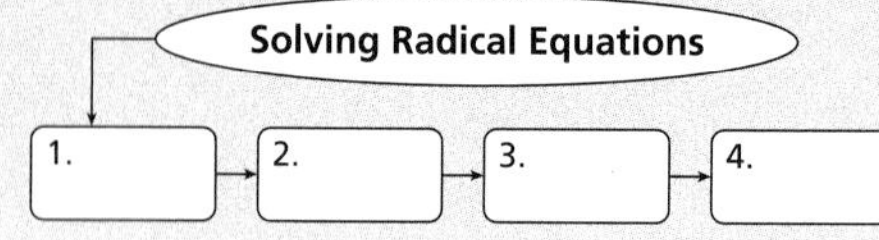

11-5 Exercises

Assignment Guide

Assign *Guided Practice* exercises as necessary.

If you finished Examples **1–3**
Proficient 41–52, 69, 70, 74, 80
Advanced 41–52, 69, 70, 74, 80

If you finished Examples **1–6**
Proficient 42–76 even, 78–82, 84–91, 98, 99, 101–110
Advanced 42–66 even, 67–82, 84–110

Homework Quick Check
Quickly check key concepts.
Exercises: 42, 48, 50, 56, 64, 67

Answers

32. ∅
33. ∅
34. $\frac{1}{4}$
35. 4
36. ∅
37. 2
38. 2
39. ∅

11-5 Exercises

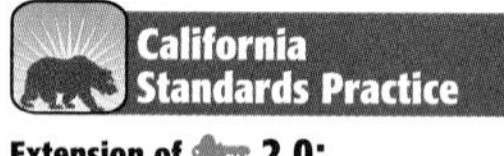

Extension of 2.0; 25.2

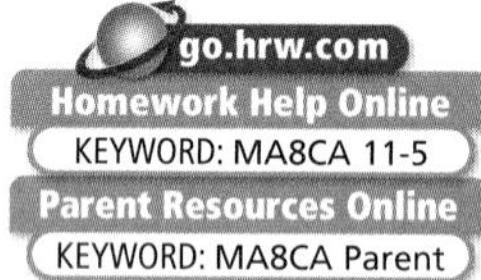

GUIDED PRACTICE

1. **Vocabulary** Is $x=\sqrt{3}$ a *radical equation*? Why or why not?
No; it does not contain a variable under the radical sign.

SEE EXAMPLE 1 p. 722

Solve each equation. Check your answer.

2. $\sqrt{x}=7$ **49**
3. $4=\sqrt{-2y}$ **−8**
4. $\sqrt{20a}=10$ **5**
5. $12=\sqrt{-x}$ **−144**

SEE EXAMPLE 2 p. 723

6. $\sqrt{x}+6=11$ **25**
7. $\sqrt{2x-5}=7$ **27**
8. $\sqrt{2-a}=3$ **−7**
9. $\sqrt{2x}-3=7$ **50**
10. $\sqrt{x-2}=3$ **11**
11. $\sqrt{x+3}=1$ **−2**
12. $\sqrt{x-1}=2$ **5**
13. $\sqrt{4y+13}-1=6$ **9**

SEE EXAMPLE 3 p. 723

14. $-2\sqrt{x}=-10$ **25**
15. $\frac{\sqrt{a}}{2}=4$ **64**
16. $5\sqrt{-x}=20$ **−16**
17. $\frac{3\sqrt{x}}{4}=3$ **16**
18. $\frac{5\sqrt{x}}{6}=10$ **144**
19. $2\sqrt{x}=8$ **16**
20. $\frac{\sqrt{x}}{3}=3$ **81**
21. $\frac{3\sqrt{x}}{2}=1$ $\mathbf{\frac{4}{9}}$
22. $13\sqrt{2x}=26$ **2**
23. $\frac{\sqrt{x}}{5}=2$ **100**
24. $\frac{\sqrt{x-7}}{3}=1$ **16**
25. $4\sqrt{2x-1}=12$ **5**

SEE EXAMPLE 4 p. 724

Solve each equation. Check your answer.

26. $\sqrt{5-x}=\sqrt{6x-2}$ **1**
27. $\sqrt{x+7}=\sqrt{3x-19}$ **13**
28. $0=\sqrt{2x}-\sqrt{x+3}$ **3**
29. $\sqrt{x-5}=\sqrt{7-x}$ **6**
30. $\sqrt{-x}=\sqrt{2x+1}$ $\mathbf{-\frac{1}{3}}$
31. $\sqrt{3x+1}-\sqrt{2x+3}=0$ **2**

SEE EXAMPLE 5 p. 725

Solve each equation. Check your answer.

32. $\sqrt{x-5}+5=0$
33. $\sqrt{3x}+5=3$
34. $\sqrt{2-7x}=2x$
35. $x=\sqrt{12+x}$
36. $6+\sqrt{x-1}=4$
37. $\sqrt{6-3x}+2=x$
38. $\sqrt{x-2}=2-x$
39. $10+\sqrt{x}=5$

SEE EXAMPLE 6 p. 725

40. **Geometry** A trapezoid has an area of 14 cm². The length of one base is 4 cm and the length of the other base is 10 cm. The height is $\left(\sqrt{2x+3}\right)$ cm. What is the value of *x*? What is the height of the trapezoid? (*Hint:* The formula for the area of a trapezoid is $A=\frac{1}{2}(b_1+b_2)h$.) $\mathbf{x=\frac{1}{2}}$**; 2 cm**

11-5 PRACTICE A

LESSON 11-5 Practice A
Solving Radical Equations

Solve each equation. Check your answer. All variables represent nonnegative numbers.

1. $\sqrt{x}=9$
$(\sqrt{x})^2=(9)^2$
$x=$ 81
2. $\sqrt{2x}=6$
$(\sqrt{2x})^2=(6)^2$
$2x=$ 36
$x=$ 18
3. $\sqrt{2x}-3=5$
$\sqrt{2x}=$ 8
$(\sqrt{2x})^2=($ 8 $)^2$
$2x=$ 64
$x=$ 32
4. $4\sqrt{x}=100$
$\sqrt{x}=$ 25
625
5. $\frac{\sqrt{x-2}}{4}=2$
$\sqrt{x-2}=$ 8
66
6. $\frac{3\sqrt{2x+1}}{5}=3$
$3\sqrt{2x+1}=$ 15
12
7. $5\sqrt{x}=50$ 100
8. $\frac{\sqrt{x+3}}{2}=5$ 97
9. $\frac{2\sqrt{2x+1}}{3}=6$ 40
10. $\sqrt{2x+3}=\sqrt{3x}$ 3
11. $\sqrt{4x+1}=\sqrt{5x-5}$ 6
12. $\sqrt{4x+4}-\sqrt{20}=0$ 4

Solve each equation. Check your answer to determine whether any solution is extraneous. All variables represent nonnegative numbers.

13. $x-4=\sqrt{x-2}$
$(x-4)^2=(\sqrt{x-2})^2$
$x^2-8x+16=x-2$
$x^2-9x+18=0$
$x=$ 6 or $x=$ 3

Check:

$x-4$	$\sqrt{x-2}$
$6-4$	$\sqrt{6-2}$
2	$\sqrt{4}$
2	2

$x-4$	$\sqrt{x-2}$
$3-4$	$\sqrt{3-2}$
−1	$\sqrt{1}$
−1	1

The only solution is 6.

14. $x-12=\sqrt{16x}$ 36
15. $\sqrt{4x}+12=8$ no solution
16. The area of a triangle is 15 m². The height is 6 m, and the length of the base is $\sqrt{3x-5}$ m. What is the value of *x*? 10

11-5 PRACTICE B

LESSON 11-5 Practice B
Solving Radical Equations

Solve each equation. Check your answer. All variables represent nonnegative numbers.

1. $\sqrt{x}=11$
$(\sqrt{x})^2=(11)^2$
$x=$ 121
2. $\frac{\sqrt{x}}{3}=5$
$\sqrt{x}=15$
$x=$ 225
3. $\sqrt{3x}+5=11$
$\sqrt{3x}=$ 6
$3x=$ 36
$x=$ 12
4. $2\sqrt{x}=16$ 64
5. $\frac{\sqrt{4x}}{2}=4$ 16
6. $\frac{3\sqrt{20x+4}}{4}=6$ 3
7. $\sqrt{x+5}=9$ 76
8. $\frac{\sqrt{x}}{4}=1$ 16
9. $\frac{3\sqrt{2x}}{4}=12$ 128
10. $\frac{\sqrt{2x}}{4}=2$ 32
11. $\frac{\sqrt{x+5}}{3}=4$ 139
12. $3\sqrt{6-x}=6$ 2
13. $\sqrt{10-x}=\sqrt{x-2}$ 6
14. $\sqrt{x+2}=\sqrt{2x-1}$ 3
15. $\sqrt{2x+10}-\sqrt{x+13}=0$ 3
16. $\sqrt{-x}=\sqrt{x+128}$ −64
17. $\sqrt{4+x}=5\sqrt{x-20}$ 21
18. $4+x=\sqrt{x+4}$ −4; −3
19. $-3\sqrt{x}=8$ no solution
20. $x=\sqrt{2x+15}$ 5
21. According to Heron's formula, the area of a triangle is given by $A=\sqrt{s(s-a)(s-b)(s-c)}$, where *s* is equal to one half its perimeter, and *a*, *b*, and *c* are the lengths of its sides. If a triangle has area 20 m², $s=10$ m, $a=5$ m and $b=2$ m, what is *c*? 9 m

PRACTICE AND PROBLEM SOLVING

Independent Practice	
For Exercises	See Example
41–44	1
45–48	2
49–52	3
53–58	4
59–66	5
67	6

Extra Practice
Skills Practice p. EP22
Application Practice p. EP34

Solve each equation. Check your answer.

41. $\sqrt{3x} = 12$ **48** 42. $2 = \sqrt{-2x}$ **−2** 43. $\sqrt{-a} = 5$ **−25** 44. $11 = \sqrt{c}$ **121**

45. $\sqrt{x-7} = 8$ **71** 46. $\sqrt{x} - 4 = 0$ **16** 47. $\sqrt{1-3x} = 5$ **−8** 48. $\sqrt{5x+1} + 2 = 6$ **3**

49. $5\sqrt{x} = 30$ **36** 50. $\frac{\sqrt{2x}}{2} = 4$ **32** 51. $5\sqrt{-x} = 20$ **−16** 52. $3\sqrt{3p} = 9$ **3**

Solve each equation. Check your answer.

53. $\sqrt{3x-13} = \sqrt{x+3}$ **8** 54. $\sqrt{x} - \sqrt{6-x} = 0$ **3** 55. $\sqrt{x+5} = \sqrt{2x-4}$ **9**

56. $\sqrt{4x-2} = \sqrt{3x+4}$ **6** 57. $\sqrt{5x-6} = \sqrt{16-6x}$ **2** 58. $\sqrt{12x-3} = \sqrt{4x+93}$ **12**

Solve each equation. Check your answer.

59. $\sqrt{x+6} = 1$ **−5** 60. $-2\sqrt{x} = 6$ **∅** 61. $x = \sqrt{2x+15}$ **5** 62. $\sqrt{6x} + 9 = 2$ **∅**

64. 12 **66. ∅**

63. $\sqrt{4-3x} = x$ **1** 64. $\sqrt{5x+4} = x - 4$ 65. $\sqrt{2x+2} = 2x$ **1** 66. $\sqrt{x+3} + 10 = 7$

67. **Geometry** A triangle has an area of 60 in^2. Its base is 10 inches and its height is $\sqrt{x}$ inches. What is the value of x? What is the height of the triangle? (*Hint:* The formula for the area of a triangle is $A = \frac{1}{2}bh$.) **$x = 144$; 12 in.**

Translate each sentence into an equation. Then solve the equation and check your answer.

68. The square root of three times a number is nine. **$\sqrt{3x} = 9$; 27**

69. The difference of the square root of a number and three is four. **$\sqrt{x} - 3 = 4$; 49**

70. The square root of the difference of a number and three is four. **$\sqrt{x-3} = 4$; 19**

71. A number is equal to the square root of the sum of that number and six. **$x = \sqrt{x+6}$; 3**

Geometry Find the dimensions of each rectangle given its perimeter.

72. 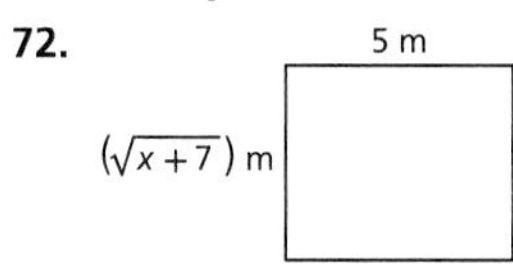

5 m by 4 m

73.

3 in. by 1 in.

74. 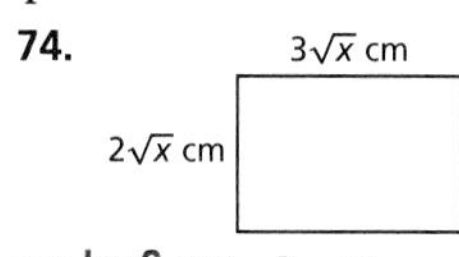

9 cm by 6 cm

California LINK — Transportation

State Highway 1 (sometimes called the Pacific Coast Highway) closely follows the terrain and contours of the California coastline. It was the first designated scenic highway in the state.

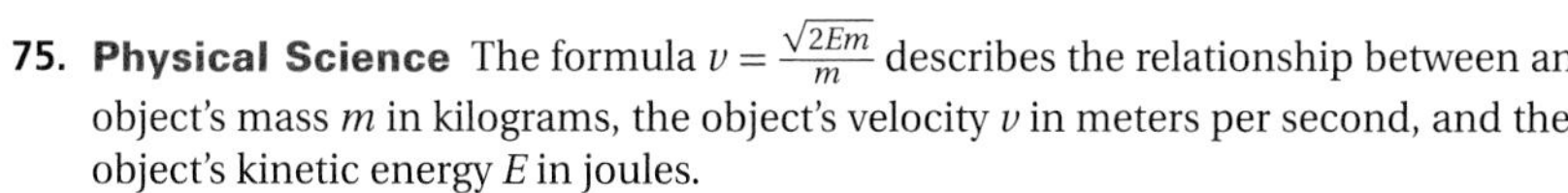

75. **Physical Science** The formula $v = \frac{\sqrt{2Em}}{m}$ describes the relationship between an object's mass m in kilograms, the object's velocity v in meters per second, and the object's kinetic energy E in joules.
   a. A baseball with a mass of 0.14 kg is thrown with a velocity of 28 m/s. How much kinetic energy does the baseball have? **54.88 joules**
   b. What is the kinetic energy of an object at rest ($v = 0$)? **0 joules**

76. **Meteorology** The formula $t = \sqrt{\frac{d^2}{216}}$ gives the time t in hours that a storm with diameter d miles will last. What is the diameter of a storm that lasts 1 hour? Round your answer to the nearest hundredth. **14.70 mi**

77. **Transportation** A sharp curve may require a driver to slow down to avoid going off the road. The equation $v = \sqrt{2.5r}$ describes the relationship between the radius r in feet of an unbanked curve and the maximum velocity v in miles per hour that a car can safely go around the curve. An engineer is designing a highway with a maximum speed limit of 65 mi/h. What is the radius of an unbanked curve for which this is the maximum safe speed? **1690 ft**

COMMON ERROR ALERT

In **Exercise 16,** students may think there is no solution because there is a negative in the radicand. Remind students that there is no real solution if the radical expression, in this case $-x$, is equal to a negative number. However, if x is negative, then $-x$ is positive and can therefore appear in a radicand and there will be a real solution.

11-5 PRACTICE C

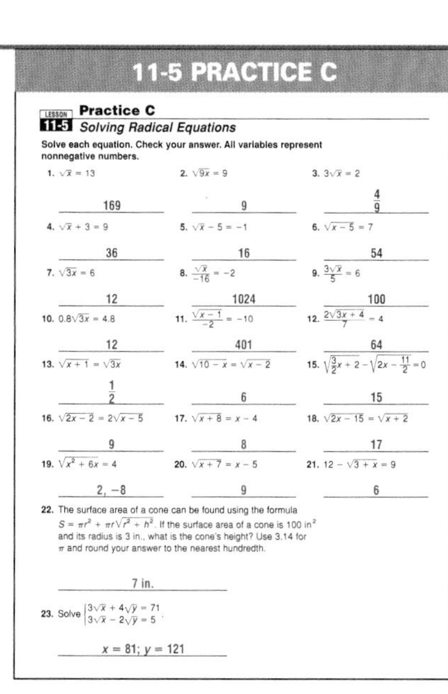

LESSON 11-5 **Practice C**
Solving Radical Equations

Solve each equation. Check your answer. All variables represent nonnegative numbers.

1. $\sqrt{x} = 13$ **169**
2. $\sqrt{9x} = 9$ **9**
3. $3\sqrt{x} = 2$ **$\frac{4}{9}$**
4. $\sqrt{x} + 3 = 9$ **36**
5. $\sqrt{x} - 5 = -1$ **16**
6. $\sqrt{x-5} = 7$ **54**
7. $\sqrt{3x} = 6$ **12**
8. $\frac{\sqrt{x}}{-16} = -2$ **1024**
9. $\frac{3\sqrt{x}}{5} = 6$ **100**
10. $0.8\sqrt{3x} = 4.8$ **12**
11. $\frac{\sqrt{x-1}}{-2} = -10$ **401**
12. $\frac{2\sqrt{3x+4}}{7} = 4$ **64**
13. $\sqrt{x+1} = \sqrt{3x}$ **$\frac{1}{2}$**
14. $\sqrt{10-x} = \sqrt{x-2}$ **6**
15. $\sqrt{\frac{3}{2}x+2} - \sqrt{2x-\frac{11}{2}} = 0$ **15**
16. $\sqrt{2x-2} = 2\sqrt{x-5}$ **9**
17. $\sqrt{x+8} = x - 4$ **8**
18. $\sqrt{2x-15} = \sqrt{x+2}$ **17**
19. $\sqrt{x^2+6x} = 4$ **2, −8**
20. $\sqrt{x+7} = x - 5$ **9**
21. $12 - \sqrt{3+x} = 9$ **6**

22. The surface area of a cone can be found using the formula $S = \pi r^2 + \pi r\sqrt{r^2+h^2}$. If the surface area of a cone is 100 in^2 and its radius is 3 in., what is the cone's height? Use 3.14 for π and round your answer to the nearest hundredth. **7 in.**

23. Solve $\begin{cases} 3\sqrt{x} + 4\sqrt{y} = 71 \\ 3\sqrt{x} - 2\sqrt{y} = 5 \end{cases}$ **$x = 81$; $y = 121$**

Exercise 86 involves solving radical equations. This exercise prepares students for the Concept Connection on page 730.

Answers

82. Sometimes; for the equation $\sqrt{2x} = \sqrt{x^2 - 3}$, the value of x must be nonnegative in order for the left side to be defined, so the statement is true. For the equation $\sqrt{7 - x} = 3$, the solution is -2 and the statement is false.

98a.

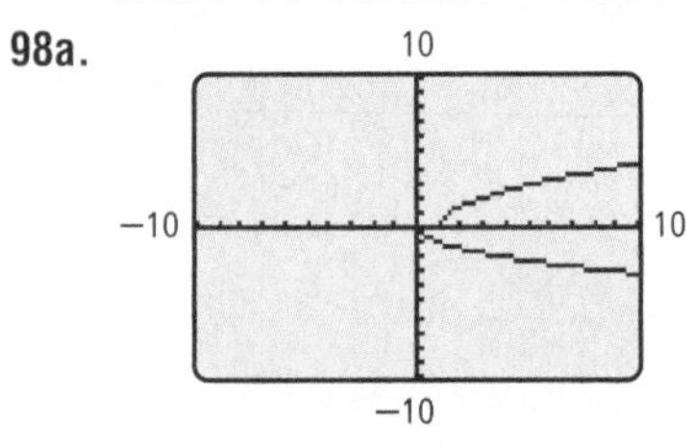

99a.

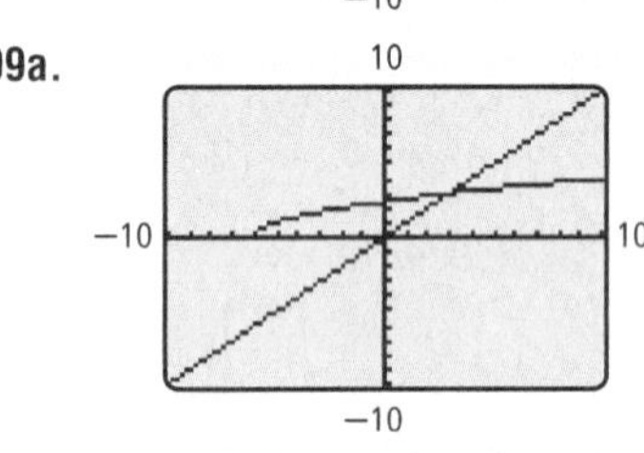

101. D: {−6, 1, 3, 5}; R: {2, 3, 4}
102. D: {−2, 4, 12}; R: {1, 3, 8}
103. D: {3, 4, 6, 7, 9}; R: {−8, −5, 0, 1, 2}
104. D: {−3, 2, 4, 5}; R: {2, 5, 6, 7}

108.

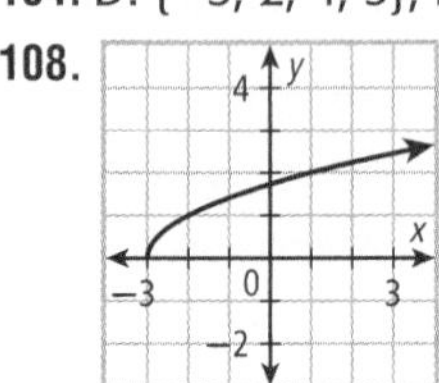

109.

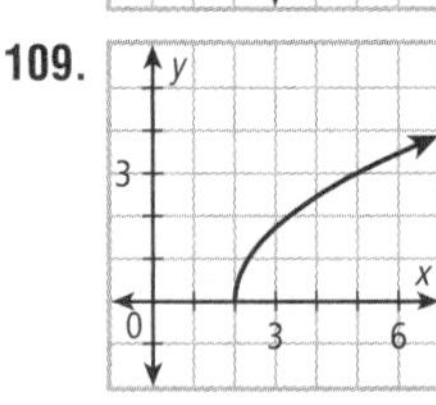

110.

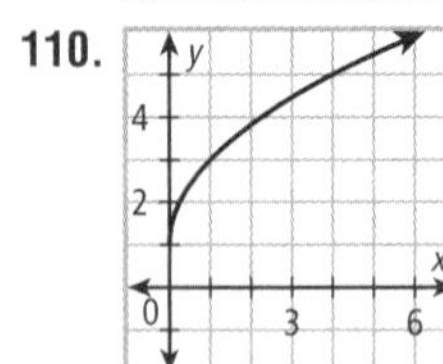

78. **Write About It** Explain why it is important to check solutions when solving radical equations. **Radical equations may have extraneous solutions.**

79. **Multi-Step** Solve for x and y in the equations $\sqrt{x} + \sqrt{y} = \sqrt{81}$ and $6\sqrt{y} = 24$. (*Hint:* Solve for y first, and then use substitution to solve for x.) $\boldsymbol{x = 25;\ y = 16}$

Reasoning **Tell whether the following statements are *always, sometimes,* or *never* true. If the answer is *sometimes,* give one example that is true and one that is false.**

80. If $a = b$, then $a^2 = b^2$. **always**

81. If $a^2 = b^2$, then $a = b$. **Sometimes; for $a = b = 2$, the statement is true. For $a = 2$ and $b = -2$, the statement is false.**

82. When solving radical equations, the value of the variable is nonnegative.

83. **/// ERROR ANALYSIS ///** Two students solved $\sqrt{5 - x} = \sqrt{x + 9}$. Which is incorrect? Explain the error.

83. Student B made an error in going from $5 - x = x + 9$ to $4 = 2x$. The student should have added x to both sides and subtracted 9 from both sides to get $-4 = 2x$.

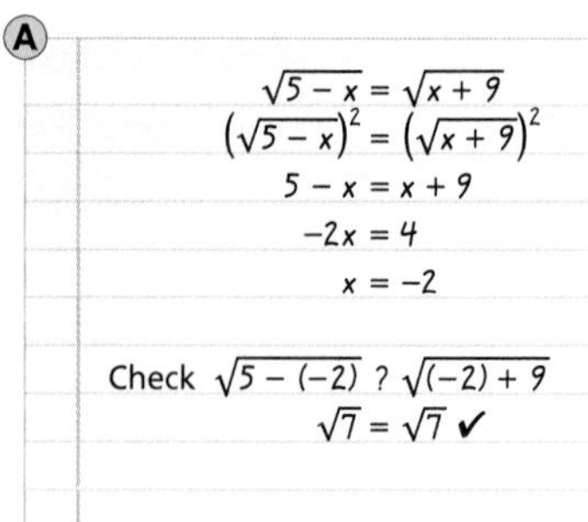

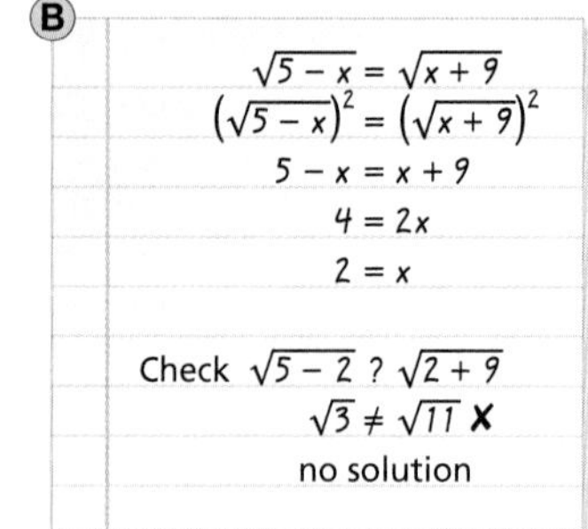

84. **Estimation** The relationship between a circle's radius and its area can be modeled by $r = \sqrt{\frac{A}{\pi}}$, where r is the radius and A is the area. Solutions to this equation are graphed at right. Use the graph to estimate the radius of a circle with an area of 29 m². **3 m**

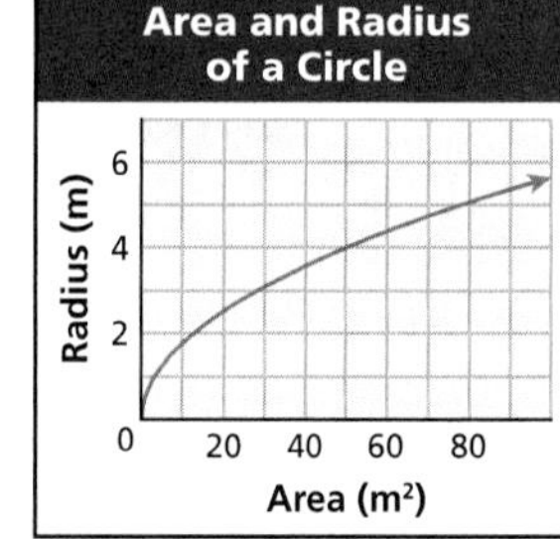

85. **Critical Thinking** Suppose that the equation $\sqrt{-x} = k$ has a solution. What does that tell you about the value of x? the value of k? Explain.

85. $x \le 0$ since the square root is only defined for nonneg. values. $k \ge 0$ since the value of the square root must be nonneg.

CONCEPT CONNECTION

86. This problem will prepare you for the Concept Connection on page 730.

a. The Demon Drop is a free-fall ride at Ohio's Cedar Point amusement park. The maximum speed on the Demon Drop is 42 miles per hour. Convert this speed to feet per second. (*Hint:* There are 5280 feet in a mile.) **61.6 ft/s**

b. The Demon Drop is 131 feet tall. Most of the drop is a vertical free fall, but near the bottom, the track curves so that the cars slow down gradually. The velocity of any object in free fall is $v = 8\sqrt{d}$, where v is the velocity in feet per second and d is the distance the object has fallen in feet. Use this equation and your answer to part **a** to estimate the free-fall distance. **≈59.29 ft**

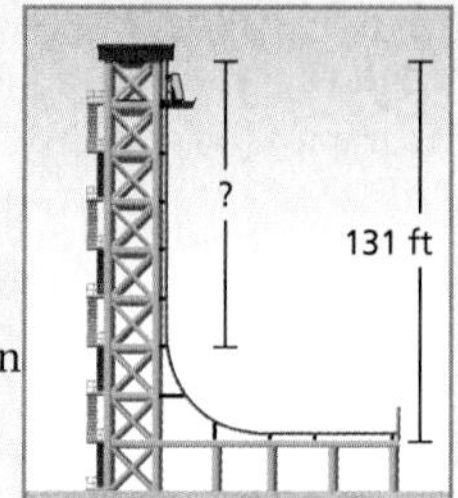

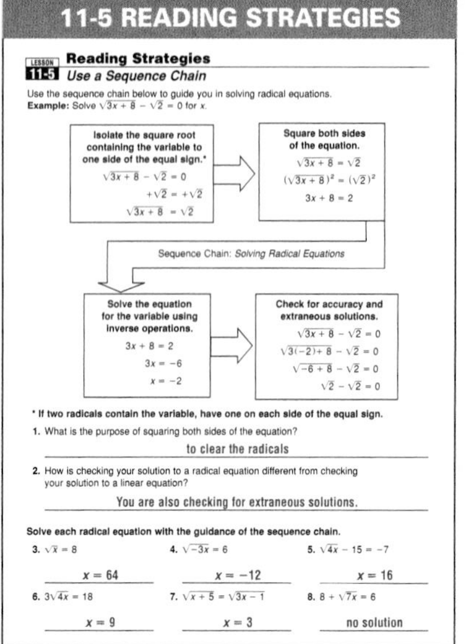

11-5 READING STRATEGIES

LESSON 11-5 **Reading Strategies**
Use a Sequence Chain

Use the sequence chain below to guide you in solving radical equations.
Example: Solve $\sqrt{3x + 8} - \sqrt{2} = 0$ for x.

Isolate the square root containing the variable to one side of the equal sign.* $\sqrt{3x+8} - \sqrt{2} = 0$; $+\sqrt{2} = +\sqrt{2}$; $\sqrt{3x+8} = \sqrt{2}$

Square both sides of the equation. $\sqrt{3x+8} = \sqrt{2}$; $(\sqrt{3x+8})^2 = (\sqrt{2})^2$; $3x + 8 = 2$

Sequence Chain: *Solving Radical Equations*

Solve the equation for the variable using inverse operations. $3x + 8 = 2$; $3x = -6$; $x = -2$

Check for accuracy and extraneous solutions. $\sqrt{3x+8} - \sqrt{2} = 0$; $\sqrt{3(-2)+8} - \sqrt{2} = 0$; $\sqrt{-6+8} - \sqrt{2} = 0$; $\sqrt{2} - \sqrt{2} = 0$

*** If two radicals contain the variable, have one on each side of the equal sign.**

1. What is the purpose of squaring both sides of the equation?
to clear the radicals

2. How is checking your solution to a radical equation different from checking your solution to a linear equation?
You are also checking for extraneous solutions.

Solve each radical equation with the guidance of the sequence chain.

3. $\sqrt{x} = 8$ — $x = 64$
4. $\sqrt{-3x} = 6$ — $x = -12$
5. $\sqrt{4x} - 15 = -7$ — $x = 16$
6. $3\sqrt{4x} = 18$ — $x = 9$
7. $\sqrt{x+5} = \sqrt{3x-1}$ — $x = 3$
8. $8 + \sqrt{7x} = 6$ — no solution

11-5 REVIEW FOR MASTERY

LESSON 11-5 **Review for Mastery**
Solving Radical Equations

A **radical equation** is an equation that contains a variable within a radical.
You can square both sides of an equation, and the resulting equation is still true.

Solve $\sqrt{x} = 7$.
$\sqrt{x} = 7$
$(\sqrt{x})^2 = (7)^2$ *Square both sides.*
$x = 49$

Check:
$\sqrt{x} = 7$
$\sqrt{49} \stackrel{?}{=} 7$ *Substitute 49 for x in the original equation.*
$7 = 7$ ✓

Sometimes you first need to isolate the variable.

Solve $4\sqrt{x} = 20$.
$4\sqrt{x} = 20$
$\frac{4\sqrt{x}}{4} = \frac{20}{4}$ *Divide both sides by 4.*
$\sqrt{x} = 5$
$(\sqrt{x})^2 = (5)^2$ *Square both sides.*
$x = 25$

Check:
$4\sqrt{x} = 20$
$4\sqrt{25} \stackrel{?}{=} 20$ *Substitute 25 for x in the original equation.*
$4(5) \stackrel{?}{=} 20$
$20 = 20$ ✓

Sometimes a solution will not check in the original equation. This is an **extraneous solution**.

Solve $\sqrt{x} + 3 = 1$.
$\sqrt{x} + 3 = 1$
$-3 \quad -3$ *Add −3 to both sides.*
$\sqrt{x} = -2$
$(\sqrt{x})^2 = (-2)^2$ *Square both sides.*
$x = 4$

Check:
$\sqrt{x} + 3 = 1$
$\sqrt{4} + 3 \stackrel{?}{=} 1$ *Substitute 4 for x in the original equation.*
$2 + 3 \stackrel{?}{=} 1$
$5 \stackrel{?}{=} 1$ ✘ *The solution is extraneous.*

The equation has no solution.

Solve each equation. Check your answer. All variables represent nonnegative numbers.

1. $\sqrt{x} = 12$ — 144
2. $\sqrt{x} - 6 = -1$ — 25
3. $\sqrt{x} + 8 = 2$ — no solution
4. $8\sqrt{x} = 80$ — 100
5. $\frac{\sqrt{x}}{4} = 2$ — 64
6. $\sqrt{4x - 7} = 9$ — 22

Multiple Choice For Exercises 87–91, choose the best answer.

87. Which of the following is the solution of $\sqrt{8-2x}-2=2$?

Ⓐ −4   Ⓑ −2   Ⓒ 2   Ⓓ 4

88. For which of the following values of k does the equation $\sqrt{x+1}+k=0$ have no real solution?

Ⓐ −2   Ⓑ −1   Ⓒ 0   Ⓓ 1

89. Which of the following is the solution of $x=\sqrt{12-x}$?

Ⓐ −4   Ⓑ −3   Ⓒ 3   Ⓓ 4

90. Which of the following is the solution of $\sqrt{x+13}=5\sqrt{x-11}$?

Ⓐ 9   Ⓑ 12   Ⓒ 16   Ⓓ 17

91. Which of the following is an extraneous solution of $\sqrt{3x-2}=x-2$?

Ⓐ 1   Ⓑ 2   Ⓒ 3   Ⓓ 6

CHALLENGE AND EXTEND

Solve each equation. Check your answer.

92. $\sqrt{x+3}=x+1$ **1**   93. $\sqrt{x-1}=x-1$ **1, 2**   94. $x-1=\sqrt{2x+6}$ **5**

95. $\sqrt{x^2+5x+11}=x+3$ **2**   96. $\sqrt{x^2+9x+14}=x+4$ **2**   97. $x+2=\sqrt{x^2+5x+4}$ **0**

98b. The equation has no solution. This is clear from the graphs since they do not intersect.

98. **Graphing Calculator** Solve $\sqrt{2x-2}=-\sqrt{x}$ and check your answer. Then use your graphing calculator for the following:
   a. Graph $y=\sqrt{2x-2}$ and $y=-\sqrt{x}$ on the same screen. Make a sketch of the graphs.
   b. Use the graphs in part **a** to explain your solution to $\sqrt{2x-2}=-\sqrt{x}$.

99. **Graphing Calculator** Solve $x=\sqrt{x+6}$ and check your answer. Then use your graphing calculator for the following:
   a. Graph $y=x$ and $y=\sqrt{x+6}$ on the same screen. Make a sketch of the graphs.
   b. Use the graphs in part **a** to explain your solution to $x=\sqrt{x+6}$.

99b. The solution is $x=3$, which is the x-value of the point where the graphs intersect.

100. Find the domain for the function $y=\frac{4}{\sqrt{x-2}}$. Is the domain for this function different from the domain for the function $y=\sqrt{x-2}$? Why or why not?

100. $x>2$; no; in the first function $x\neq 2$ because the denom. cannot equal 0, but the domain of the second function is $x\geq 2$.

SPIRAL STANDARDS REVIEW
9.0, 17.0

Give the domain and range of each relation. *(Lesson 4-2)*

101. $\{(1,3),(-6,2),(3,2),(5,4)\}$ 102. $\{(-2,1),(12,3),(-2,3),(4,8)\}$

103.

x	3	4	6	7	9
y	2	1	0	−5	−8

104.

x	5	2	−3	4	5
y	7	2	6	2	5

Solve each system by substitution. *(Lesson 6-2)*

105. $\begin{cases} y=2x+5 \\ y=5x-4 \end{cases}$ **(3, 11)**   106. $\begin{cases} y=6x-17 \\ y=-x+11 \end{cases}$ **(4, 7)**   107. $\begin{cases} y=-3x+12 \\ y=x-8 \end{cases}$ **(5, −3)**

Graph each square-root function. *(Lesson 11-1)*

108. $f(x)=\sqrt{x+3}$ 109. $f(x)=\sqrt{3x-6}$ 110. $f(x)=2\sqrt{x}+1$

Teaching Tip

Multiple Choice A radical equation has no real solution if the radical expression is equal to a negative number. In **Exercise 88,** moving k to the other side yields $-k$ on the right side. The only way to obtain a negative number on the right side is to substitute a number greater than zero for k.

Journal

Explain how the process of solving radical equations sometimes generates extraneous solutions.

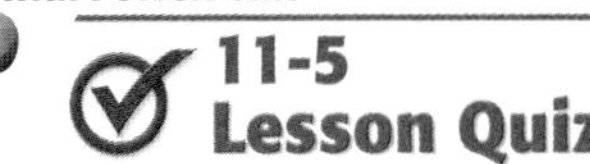

ALTERNATIVE ASSESSMENT

Have students solve the following equations, justifying each step along the way. Solutions must include answer checking.

1. $\sqrt{-2x+3}=\sqrt{x}$
2. $\sqrt{-2x+3}=x$

Power Presentations with PowerPoint®

11-5 Lesson Quiz

Solve each equation. Check your answer.

1. $\frac{2\sqrt{x}}{3}=4$ 36
2. $\sqrt{5x}=15$ 45
3. $\sqrt{5x}+8=3$ ∅
4. $\sqrt{4x+5}-2=5$ 11
5. $\sqrt{3x+1}-\sqrt{2x+5}=0$ 4
6. $x=\sqrt{2x+8}$ 4
7. A triangle has an area of 48 square feet. Its base is 6 feet, and its height is $\sqrt{x+3}$ feet. What is the value of x? What is the height of the triangle? 253; 16 ft

Also available on transparency

11-5 PROBLEM SOLVING

LESSON 11-5 **Problem Solving**
Solving Radical Equations

Write the correct answer.

1. The perimeter of the marching band's practice field is 360 yards. Its length and width are shown in the diagram.

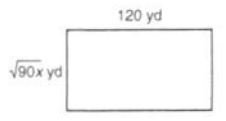

120 yd; $\sqrt{90x}$ yd

Find the value of x and the width of the field. Then calculate the area of the field.

$x=40$
width = 60 yd
Area = 7200 yd^2

2. The formula $v=\frac{\sqrt{2Em}}{m}$ describes the relationship between an object's mass m in kilograms, its velocity v in meters per second, and its kinetic energy E in joules. A bowling ball with a mass of 5 kg is thrown with a velocity of 8 meters per second. Determine the kinetic energy of the bowling ball.

160 joules

3. An office has storage closet with an area of 48 square feet. The length of the closet is 8 feet. The width is $2\sqrt{11-x}$ feet. Find the value of x and the width of the closet.

$x=2$
6 feet

Select the best answer.

4. The equation $v=\sqrt{2.5r}$ describes the relationship between the radius r in feet of an unbanked curve and the maximum velocity v in miles per hour that a car can safely go around the curve. A primary road with a speed limit of 35 miles per hour curves through a residential area. What is the radius of the unbanked curve?

A 14 feet   C 450 feet
B 49 feet   Ⓓ 490 feet

5. The remains of a structure on an archeological site are laid out in the shape of a rectangle. The area of the rectangle is 12 square meters. The width is 3 meters and the length is $\sqrt{x+6}$ meters. What is the value of x?

F 4   H 12
Ⓖ 10   J 16

6. A building sits on a lot that is shaped like a triangle with a base of 120 feet and a height of $\sqrt{5000x}$ feet. The area of the lot is 12,000 square feet. Which length represents the height of the triangle?

A 8 feet   Ⓒ 200 feet
B 100 feet   D 400 feet

7. Gretchen mixes her own bubble bath using essential oils. She uses a jar that holds $\sqrt{33}$ ounces. Gretchen fills the jar with $\sqrt{x-4}$ ounces of bubble solution and oils. What is the value of x?

Ⓕ 37   H 1089
G 39   J 1093

11-5 CHALLENGE

LESSON 11-5 **Challenge**
Solving Radical Equations

The function $y=\sqrt{x}$ is the parent function from which you can write each of the functions below.

$y=\sqrt{x}+2$ $y=\sqrt{x}+4$ $y=\sqrt{x}+6$
$y=\sqrt{x-2}$ $y=\sqrt{x-4}$ $y=\sqrt{x-6}$

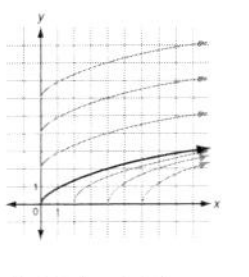

All six functions are graphed at right along with the parent function, which is darker than the other graphs.

The graphs of $y=\sqrt{x}+2$, $y=\sqrt{x}+4$, and $y=\sqrt{x}+6$ are the three curves directly above the graph of $y=\sqrt{x}$. Use the graphs to explain why the equations below have no solution.

1. $\sqrt{x}+2=\sqrt{x}+4$ **Their graphs do not intersect.**
2. $\sqrt{x}+2=\sqrt{x}+6$ **Their graphs do not intersect.**
3. $\sqrt{x}+4=\sqrt{x}+6$ **Their graphs do not intersect.**

The graphs of $y=\sqrt{x-2}$, $y=\sqrt{x-4}$, and $y=\sqrt{x-6}$ are the three curves below the graph of $y=\sqrt{x}$. Show algebraically that each equation below has no solution.

4. $\sqrt{x-2}=\sqrt{x-4}$ **$x-2\neq x-4$ for all values of x**
5. $\sqrt{x-2}=\sqrt{x-6}$ **$x-2\neq x-6$ for all values of x**
6. $\sqrt{x-4}=\sqrt{x-6}$ **$x-4\neq x-6$ for all values of x**

The diagram above suggests that the graphs of $y=\sqrt{x-2}$, $y=\sqrt{x-4}$, and $y=\sqrt{x-6}$ get closer to the graph of $y=\sqrt{x}$ as x gets larger.

7. Complete the table below. Round values to the nearest thousandth.

x	10	20	50	100	200	500	1000	5000
$\sqrt{x}$	3.162	4.472	7.071	10	14.142	22.361	31.623	70.711
$\sqrt{x-2}$	2.828	4.243	6.928	9.899	14.071	22.316	31.591	70.697
$\sqrt{x}-\sqrt{x-2}$	0.334	0.229	0.143	0.101	0.071	0.045	0.032	0.014

8. Let n be a positive integer. Write and justify a conjecture about $\sqrt{x}=\sqrt{x-n}$.

In the expression $\sqrt{x}-\sqrt{x-n}$, as n remains constant and x becomes larger, the expression gets closer to 0 in value.

SECTION 11A

CONCEPT CONNECTION

Organizer

Objective: Assess students' ability to apply concepts and skills in Lessons 11-1 through 11-5 in a real-world format.

Problem	Text Reference
1	Skills Bank p. SB20
2	Lesson 11-2
3	Skills Bank p. SB12
4	Lesson 11-3
5	Lesson 11-3

CHAPTER 11

SECTION 11A

CONCEPT CONNECTION

Radical Functions and Equations

Eye in the Sky The London Eye is a giant observation wheel in London, England. It carries people in enclosed capsules around its circumference. Opened on December 31, 1999, to welcome the new millennium, its diameter is 135 meters. On the London Eye, riders can see a distance of 40 kilometers.

1. What is the circumference of the London Eye? Use 3.14 for π. **423.9 m**
2. The London Eye's velocity in meters per second can be found using the equation $v = \sqrt{0.001r}$, where r is the radius of the wheel in meters. Find the velocity in meters per second. Round to the nearest hundredth. **0.26 m/s**
3. Another way to find the velocity is to divide the distance around the wheel by the time for the ride. A ride on the London Eye lasts 30 minutes.
   a. Use this method to find the velocity of the wheel in meters per second to the nearest hundredth. **0.24 m/s**
   b. Is your answer to part **a** the same as your answer to problem 2? If not, explain any differences. **Differences are due to rounding.**
4. When a rider is at the highest point on the London Eye, how far is he from the bottom of the ride? Explain. **135 m; the required dist. is the diam. of the wheel.**
5. When a rider is at half the maximum height, her distance from the bottom of the ride can be found using the equation $d = \sqrt{2r^2}$. Explain where this equation comes from. Then find this distance. Round to the nearest hundredth. **Pythagorean Theorem; $d \approx 95.46$ m**

INTERVENTION

Scaffolding Questions

1. What is the circumference of a circle? distance around the outside of the circle
2. What formula is used to calculate the circumference of a circle? $C = \pi d$ or $C = 2\pi r$
3. How do we calculate the speed of an object moving at a constant speed? Speed is distance divided by time.
4. How would this apply to an object moving around the edge of a circle? Speed is circumference divided by time.
5. How do you find the distance between two points? Use the distance formula, which is the Pythagorean Theorem.

Extension

If the diameter increases and the time for the ride remains the same, what happens to the velocity? increases **Explain.** If the diameter increases, the distance traveled increases. To travel a greater distance in the same time, velocity must increase.

California Standards

Extension of 2.0

CHAPTER 11

SECTION 11A

Quiz for Lessons 11-1 Through 11-5

11-1 Square-Root Functions

1. The distance in kilometers that a person can see to the horizon can be approximated by the formula $D = 113\sqrt{h}$, where h is the person's height in kilometers above sea level. What is the distance to the horizon observed by a mountain climber who is 0.3 km above sea level? Round your answer to the nearest tenth. **61.9 km**

Find the domain of each square-root function.

2. $y = \sqrt{3x} - 7$ $x \geq 0$
3. $y = \sqrt{x - 5}$ $x \geq 5$
4. $y = \sqrt{2x - 6}$ $x \geq 3$

Graph each square-root function.

5. $y = \sqrt{x - 6}$
6. $y = \sqrt{x} + 5$
7. $y = \sqrt{8 - 4x}$

11-2 Radical Expressions

Simplify. All variables represent nonnegative numbers.

8. $\sqrt{75}$ $5\sqrt{3}$
9. $\sqrt{\frac{300}{3}}$ 10
10. $\sqrt{a^2b^3}$ $ab\sqrt{b}$
11. $\sqrt{98xy^2}$ $7y\sqrt{2x}$
12. $\sqrt{\frac{32}{25}}$ $\frac{4\sqrt{2}}{5}$
13. $\sqrt{\frac{128}{121}}$ $\frac{8\sqrt{2}}{11}$
14. $\sqrt{\frac{4b^2}{81}}$ $\frac{2b}{9}$
15. $\sqrt{\frac{75a^9}{49a^3}}$ $\frac{5a^3\sqrt{3}}{7}$
16. How long is the diagonal of a rectangular television screen that is 19.2 inches long and 14.4 inches high? **24 in.**

11-3 Adding and Subtracting Radical Expressions

Simplify each expression. All variables represent nonnegative numbers.

17. $12\sqrt{7} - 5\sqrt{7}$ $7\sqrt{7}$
18. $3\sqrt{x} + 3\sqrt{x}$ $6\sqrt{x}$
19. $\sqrt{12} + \sqrt{75}$ $7\sqrt{3}$
20. $5\sqrt{50} + \sqrt{98}$ $32\sqrt{2}$
21. $4\sqrt{3} - 3\sqrt{4}$ $4\sqrt{3} - 6$
22. $\sqrt{98x} + \sqrt{18x} - \sqrt{200x}$ 0

11-4 Multiplying and Dividing Radical Expressions

Multiply. Write each product in simplest form. All variables represent nonnegative numbers.

23. $\sqrt{6}\sqrt{11}$ $\sqrt{66}$
24. $\sqrt{3}\sqrt{8}$ $2\sqrt{6}$
25. $4\sqrt{12x}\sqrt{3x}$ $24x$
26. $(3 - \sqrt{3})(5 + \sqrt{3})$ $12 - 2\sqrt{3}$

Simplify each quotient. All variables represent nonnegative numbers.

27. $\frac{\sqrt{19}}{\sqrt{3}}$ $\frac{\sqrt{57}}{3}$
28. $\frac{\sqrt{14}}{\sqrt{8}}$ $\frac{\sqrt{7}}{2}$
29. $\frac{\sqrt{6b}}{\sqrt{8}}$ $\frac{\sqrt{3b}}{2}$
30. $\frac{\sqrt{27}}{\sqrt{3t}}$ $\frac{3\sqrt{t}}{t}$

11-5 Solving Radical Equations

Solve each equation. Check your answer.

31. $\sqrt{x} - 4 = 21$ 625
32. $-3\sqrt{x} = -12$ 16
33. $\frac{5\sqrt{x}}{2} = 40$ 256
34. $\sqrt{4x - 2} - \sqrt{43 - x} = 0$ 9
35. $\sqrt{20 + x} = x$ 5
36. $\sqrt{4x} + 12 = 10$ $\varnothing$

READY TO GO ON? SECTION 11A

Organizer

Objective: Assess students' mastery of concepts and skills in Lessons 11-1 through 11-5.

Resources

Assessment Resources

Section 11A Quiz

INTERVENTION

Resources

Ready to Go On? Intervention and Enrichment **Worksheets**

Ready to Go On? **CD-ROM**

Ready to Go On? **Online**

Answers

5–7. See p. A26.

READY TO GO ON? Diagnose and Prescribe

Ready to Go On? Intervention	*Ready to Go On? Intervention,* Section 11A		
	Worksheets	CD-ROM	Online
Lesson 11-1 Ext. of 2.0	11-1 Intervention	Activity 11-1	Diagnose and Prescribe Online
Lesson 11-2 Ext. of 2.0	11-2 Intervention	Activity 11-2	
Lesson 11-3 Ext. of 2.0	11-3 Intervention	Activity 11-3	
Lesson 11-4 Ext. of 2.0	11-4 Intervention	Activity 11-4	
Lesson 11-5 Ext. of 2.0	11-5 Intervention	Activity 11-5	

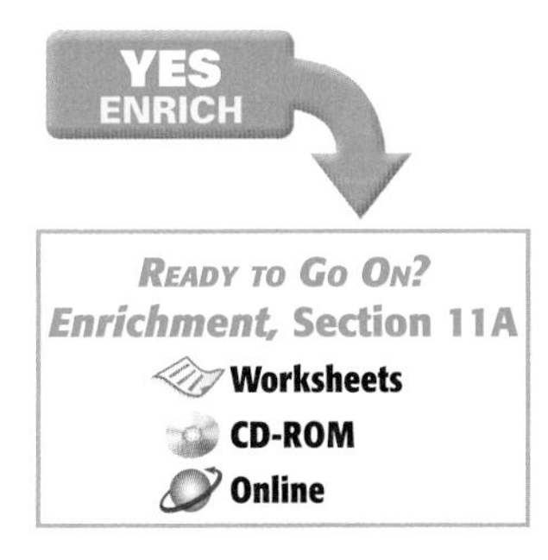

YES
ENRICH
Ready to Go On? Enrichment, Section 11A
Worksheets
CD-ROM
Online

SECTION 11B

Exponential Functions

One-Minute Section Planner

Lesson	Lab Resources	Materials
Lesson 11-6 Geometric Sequences • Recognize and extend geometric sequences. • Find the *n*th term of a geometric sequence. **Preview of Algebra II** **Preparation for 22.0**		**Required** calculator
Lesson 11-7 Exponential Functions • Evaluate exponential functions. • Identify and graph exponential functions. **Preview of Algebra II 12.0**		**Required** graphing calculator
11-8 Algebra Lab Model Growth and Decay • Fold and cut paper to model exponential growth and decay. **1A2.0**		**Required** notebook paper, scissors
Lesson 11-8 Exponential Growth and Decay • Solve problems involving exponential growth and decay. **Preview of Algebra II 12.0**	***Algebra Lab* 11–8** In *Chapter 11 Resource File*	**Required** graphing calculator
Lesson 11-9 Linear, Quadratic, and Exponential Models • Compare linear, quadratic, and exponential models. • Given a set of data, decide which type of function models the data and write an equation to describe the function. **Preview of Algebra II 12.0;** **Extension of 1A7.0**		**Optional** graphing calculator

MK = *Manipulatives Kit*

Notes

Math Background: Teaching the Standards

GEOMETRIC SEQUENCES AND EXPONENTIAL FUNCTIONS

Lessons 11-6 and 11-7

To understand the connection between geometric sequences and exponential functions, we begin with the definition of *exponential function*: a function of the form $y = ab^x$, where $a \neq 0$, $b > 0$, and $b \neq 1$. At this point, students have seen b^x defined for limited x-values only (namely, rational numbers), but the domain of an exponential function is all real numbers. Students will fill in this gap in future courses and can be assured in the meantime that they may draw a smooth, continuous curve when graphing an exponential function.

For $a > 0$, the range of an exponential function is all positive real numbers, as illustrated in the graph of $y = 3(2)^x$.

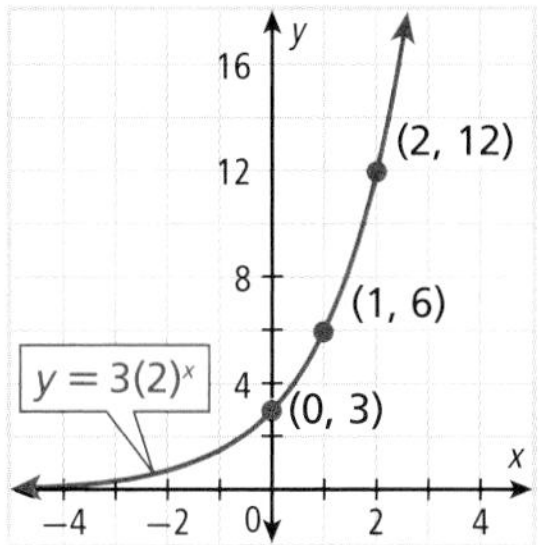

When the domain is restricted to the whole numbers, the graph becomes a set of discrete points, the first few of which are shown above. The points' y-values are 3, 6, 12, ... ; this is precisely the *geometric sequence* $a_n = 3(2)^{n-1}$. In other words, a geometric sequence is simply an exponential function with a restricted domain. (Note that the domain is usually restricted to the natural numbers, so that the first term of the sequence corresponds to the input value 1 rather than 0.)

EXPONENTIAL GROWTH AND DECAY

Lesson 11-8

Exponential growth and decay are important applications of exponential functions.

Exponential growth occurs when a quantity increases by the same rate in each time period. Thus, exponential growth can be understood as an extension of percent change in which a percent increase is repeatedly applied. *Exponential decay* occurs when a quantity decreases by the same rate in each time period, and, similar to exponential growth, can be understood as an extension of percent change in which a percent decrease is repeatedly applied.

In an exponential growth situation with initial amount a ($a > 0$) and rate of growth r expressed as a decimal, after one time period, the new amount is $a + ar$, or $a(1 + r)$. After the second time period, the new amount is $a(1 + r)(1 + r)$, or $a(1 + r)^2$. Continuing in this way shows that after t time periods, the final amount y is given by $y = a(1 + r)^t$. For exponential decay, a similar argument shows that the final amount y after t time periods is given by $y = a(1 - r)^t$.

An important attribute of exponential growth and decay is the fact that the amount added or subtracted in each time period is proportional to the amount already present. For exponential growth, this means that as the amount becomes greater, the amount of increase in each time period also becomes greater. Contrast this to linear growth, in which the amount of increase remains constant.

COMPOUND INTEREST

Lesson 11-8

Compound interest is closely related to exponential growth. In fact, for interest compounded once per year, the formula is analogous to that for exponential growth: $A = P(1 + r)^t$, where P represents the principal and A represents the total balance after t years. If interest is compounded n times per year, then the rate must be divided by n, and because there are nt periods in t years, the formula becomes $A = P(1 + \frac{r}{n})^{nt}$.

As n increases, we approach a situation in which interest is compounded continuously. In future courses, students will study continuously compounded interest, which is given by $A = Pe^{rt}$ where $e \approx 2.71828$.

11-6 Organizer

Objectives: Recognize and extend geometric sequences.

Find the *n*th term of a geometric sequence.

Power Presentations with PowerPoint®

Warm Up

Find the value of each expression.

1. 2^5 32 **2.** 2^{-5} $\frac{1}{32}$

3. -3^4 -81 **4.** $(-3)^4$ 81

5. $(0.2)^3$ 0.008 **6.** $7(-4)^2$ 112

7. $15\left(\frac{1}{3}\right)^3$ $\frac{5}{9}$

8. $12(-0.4)^3$ -0.768

Also available on transparency

Math Humor

Q: What type of dress did the rectangle wear to the prom?

A: A dress with geometric sequins.

California Standards

Preview of Algebra II
Preparation for 22.0

11-6 Geometric Sequences

California Standards

Preview of Algebra II
Preparation for 22.0 Students find the general term and the sums of arithmetic series and **of both finite and infinite geometric series.**

Vocabulary
geometric sequence
common ratio

Who uses this?
Bungee jumpers can use geometric sequences to calculate how high they will bounce.

The table shows the heights of a bungee jumper's bounces.

Bounce	1	2	3
Height (ft)	200	80	32

The height of the bounces shown in the table above form a *geometric sequence.* In a **geometric sequence**, the ratio of successive terms is the same number *r*, called the **common ratio**.

EXAMPLE 1 Extending Geometric Sequences

Find the next three terms in each geometric sequence.

A 1, 3, 9, 27, ...

Step 1 Find the value of *r* by dividing each term by the one before it.

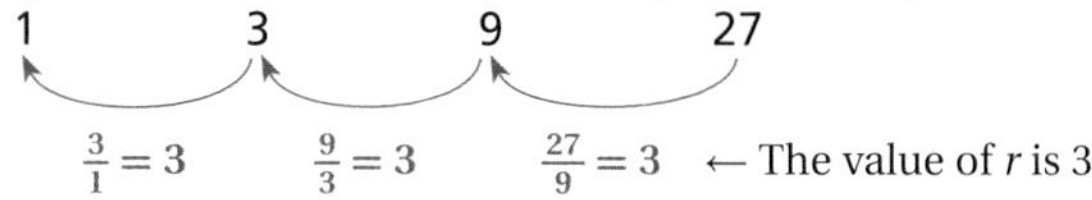

1 3 9 27

$\frac{3}{1}=3$ $\frac{9}{3}=3$ $\frac{27}{9}=3$ ← The value of *r* is 3.

Step 2 Multiply each term by 3 to find the next three terms.

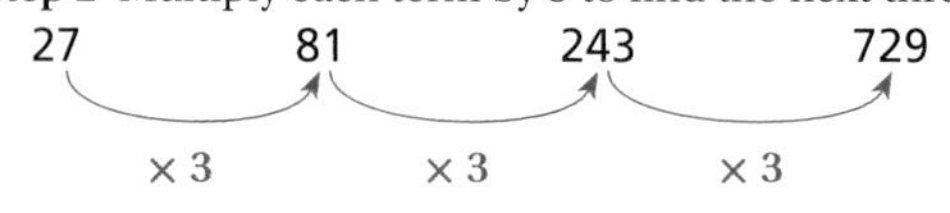

27 81 243 729

×3 ×3 ×3

The next three terms are 81, 243, and 729.

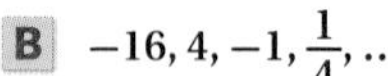

Helpful Hint

When the terms in a geometric sequence alternate between positive and negative, the value of *r* is negative.

B $-16, 4, -1, \frac{1}{4}, \ldots$

Step 1 Find the value of *r* by dividing each term by the one before it.

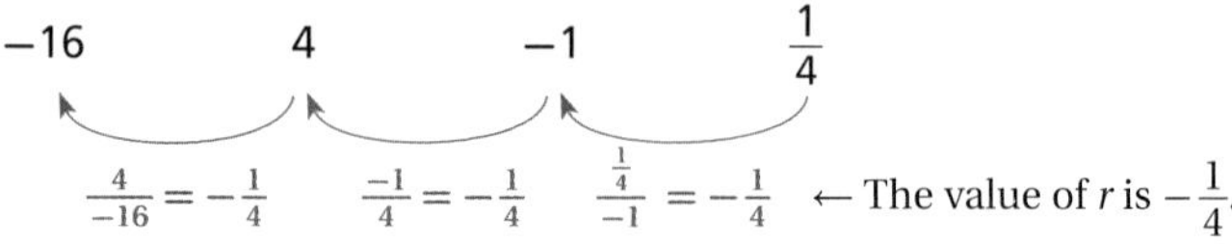

-16 4 -1 $\frac{1}{4}$

$\frac{4}{-16}=-\frac{1}{4}$ $\frac{-1}{4}=-\frac{1}{4}$ $\frac{\frac{1}{4}}{-1}=-\frac{1}{4}$ ← The value of *r* is $-\frac{1}{4}$.

Step 2 Multiply each term by $-\frac{1}{4}$ to find the next three terms.

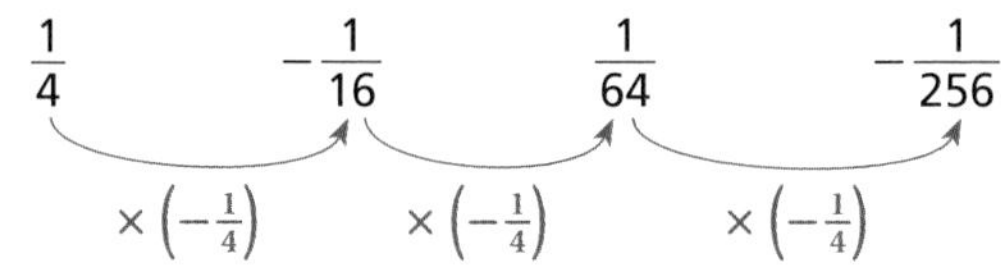

$\frac{1}{4}$ $-\frac{1}{16}$ $\frac{1}{64}$ $-\frac{1}{256}$

$\times\left(-\frac{1}{4}\right)$ $\times\left(-\frac{1}{4}\right)$ $\times\left(-\frac{1}{4}\right)$

The next three terms are $-\frac{1}{16}, \frac{1}{64}$, and $-\frac{1}{256}$.

1 Introduce

EXPLORATION

11-6 Geometric Sequences

Marcella's grandmother wants to begin saving for Marcella's college education. She decides that the first year she will save $1 and that each year thereafter she will save twice as much as the previous year.

1. Complete the table.

Year	1	2	3	4	5	6	7
Amount ($)	1	2	4				

2. Look at the amounts in the table above. What is the ratio of any amount to the one before it?
3. Rewrite the amounts as powers of 2.

Year	1	2	3	4	5	6	7
Amount ($)	2^0	2^1					

4. How is the exponent in each rewritten amount related to the year?

THINK AND DISCUSS

5. **Show** how to write a rule that you can use to predict the amount of money saved in year *n*.
6. **Explain** how you can use your rule to find the amount of money saved in year 10.

Motivate

Have students solve the following problem:

You are given 1 cent on the first of 20 days. Each day you will receive twice the amount as the previous day. How much will you receive on the 20th day? $5242.88

Ask students how they figured out the answer. Possible answer: I wrote the amount received for the first day and then doubled the amount for the next 19 days.

Explorations and answers are provided in *Alternate Openers: Explorations Transparencies*

Math Background: Teaching the Standards

GEOMETRIC SEQUENCES AND EXPONENTIAL FUNCTIONS

Lessons 11-6 and 11-7

To understand the connection between geometric sequences and exponential functions, we begin with the definition of *exponential function*: a function of the form $y = ab^x$, where $a \neq 0$, $b > 0$, and $b \neq 1$. At this point, students have seen b^x defined for limited x-values only (namely, rational numbers), but the domain of an exponential function is all real numbers. Students will fill in this gap in future courses and can be assured in the meantime that they may draw a smooth, continuous curve when graphing an exponential function.

For $a > 0$, the range of an exponential function is all positive real numbers, as illustrated in the graph of $y = 3(2)^x$.

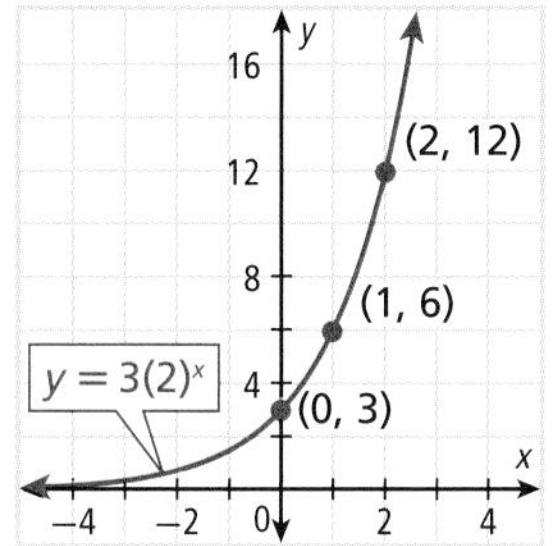

When the domain is restricted to the whole numbers, the graph becomes a set of discrete points, the first few of which are shown above. The points' y-values are 3, 6, 12, ... ; this is precisely the *geometric sequence* $a_n = 3(2)^{n-1}$. In other words, a geometric sequence is simply an exponential function with a restricted domain. (Note that the domain is usually restricted to the natural numbers, so that the first term of the sequence corresponds to the input value 1 rather than 0.)

EXPONENTIAL GROWTH AND DECAY

Lesson 11-8

Exponential growth and decay are important applications of exponential functions.

Exponential growth occurs when a quantity increases by the same rate in each time period. Thus, exponential growth can be understood as an extension of percent change in which a percent increase is repeatedly applied. *Exponential decay* occurs when a quantity decreases by the same rate in each time period, and, similar to exponential growth, can be understood as an extension of percent change in which a percent decrease is repeatedly applied.

In an exponential growth situation with initial amount a ($a > 0$) and rate of growth r expressed as a decimal, after one time period, the new amount is $a + ar$, or $a(1 + r)$. After the second time period, the new amount is $a(1 + r)(1 + r)$, or $a(1 + r)^2$. Continuing in this way shows that after t time periods, the final amount y is given by $y = a(1 + r)^t$. For exponential decay, a similar argument shows that the final amount y after t time periods is given by $y = a(1 - r)^t$.

An important attribute of exponential growth and decay is the fact that the amount added or subtracted in each time period is proportional to the amount already present. For exponential growth, this means that as the amount becomes greater, the amount of increase in each time period also becomes greater. Contrast this to linear growth, in which the amount of increase remains constant.

COMPOUND INTEREST

Lesson 11-8

Compound interest is closely related to exponential growth. In fact, for interest compounded once per year, the formula is analogous to that for exponential growth: $A = P(1 + r)^t$, where P represents the principal and A represents the total balance after t years. If interest is compounded n times per year, then the rate must be divided by n, and because there are nt periods in t years, the formula becomes $A = P(1 + \frac{r}{n})^{nt}$.

As n increases, we approach a situation in which interest is compounded continuously. In future courses, students will study continuously compounded interest, which is given by $A = Pe^{rt}$ where $e \approx 2.71828$.

11-6 Organizer

Objectives: Recognize and extend geometric sequences.

Find the nth term of a geometric sequence.

Power Presentations with PowerPoint®

Warm Up

Find the value of each expression.

1. 2^5 32 **2.** 2^{-5} $\frac{1}{32}$

3. -3^4 -81 **4.** $(-3)^4$ 81

5. $(0.2)^3$ 0.008 **6.** $7(-4)^2$ 112

7. $15\left(\frac{1}{3}\right)^3$ $\frac{5}{9}$

8. $12(-0.4)^3$ -0.768

Also available on transparency

Math Humor

Q: What type of dress did the rectangle wear to the prom?

A: A dress with geometric sequins.

California Standards

Preview of Algebra II
Preparation for 22.0

11-6 Geometric Sequences

California Standards

Preview of Algebra II
Preparation for 22.0 Students find the general term and the sums of arithmetic series and **of both finite and infinite geometric series.**

Vocabulary
geometric sequence
common ratio

Who uses this?
Bungee jumpers can use geometric sequences to calculate how high they will bounce.

The table shows the heights of a bungee jumper's bounces.

Bounce	1	2	3
Height (ft)	200	80	32

The height of the bounces shown in the table above form a *geometric sequence.* In a **geometric sequence** , the ratio of successive terms is the same number r, called the **common ratio** .

EXAMPLE 1 Extending Geometric Sequences

Find the next three terms in each geometric sequence.

A $1, 3, 9, 27, \ldots$

Step 1 Find the value of r by dividing each term by the one before it.

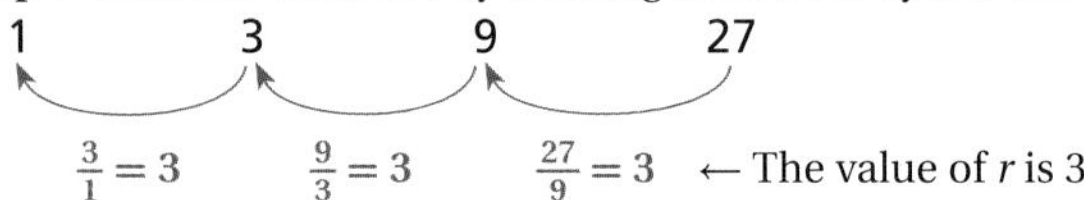

$\frac{3}{1} = 3$ $\frac{9}{3} = 3$ $\frac{27}{9} = 3$ ← The value of r is 3.

Step 2 Multiply each term by 3 to find the next three terms.

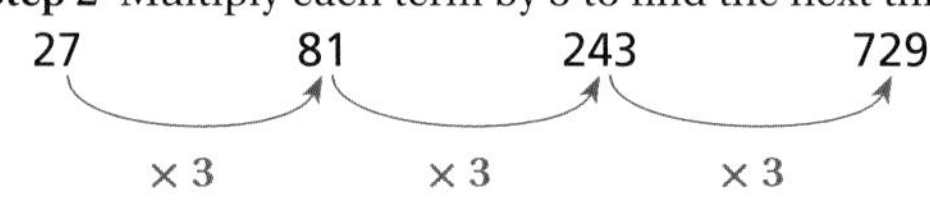

The next three terms are 81, 243, and 729.

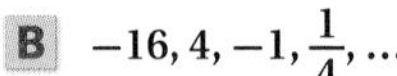

When the terms in a geometric sequence alternate between positive and negative, the value of r is negative.

B $-16, 4, -1, \frac{1}{4}, \ldots$

Step 1 Find the value of r by dividing each term by the one before it.

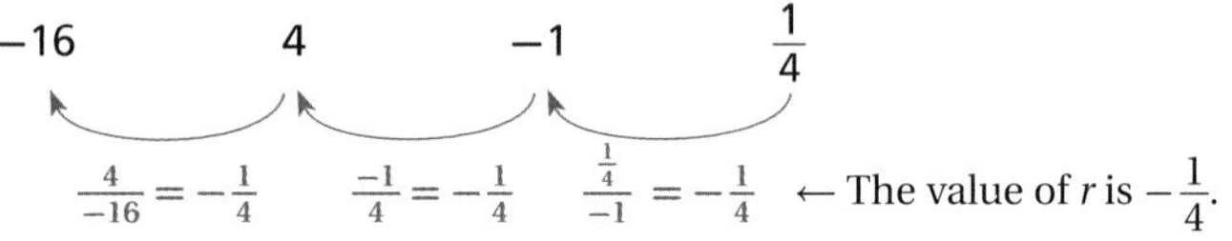

-16 4 -1 $\frac{1}{4}$

$\frac{4}{-16} = -\frac{1}{4}$ $\frac{-1}{4} = -\frac{1}{4}$ $\frac{\frac{1}{4}}{-1} = -\frac{1}{4}$ ← The value of r is $-\frac{1}{4}$.

Step 2 Multiply each term by $-\frac{1}{4}$ to find the next three terms.

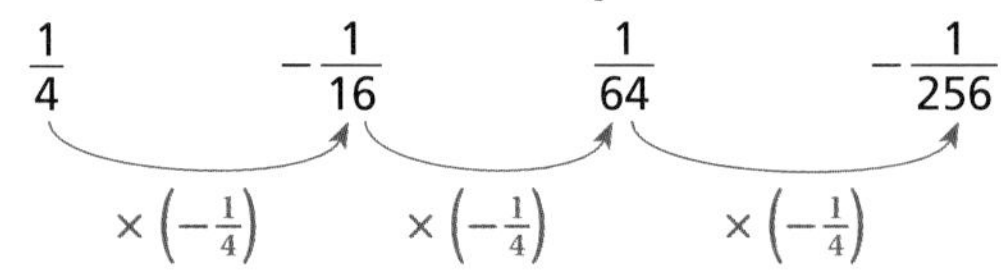

$\frac{1}{4}$ $-\frac{1}{16}$ $\frac{1}{64}$ $-\frac{1}{256}$

$\times\left(-\frac{1}{4}\right)$ $\times\left(-\frac{1}{4}\right)$ $\times\left(-\frac{1}{4}\right)$

The next three terms are $-\frac{1}{16}$, $\frac{1}{64}$, and $-\frac{1}{256}$.

1 Introduce

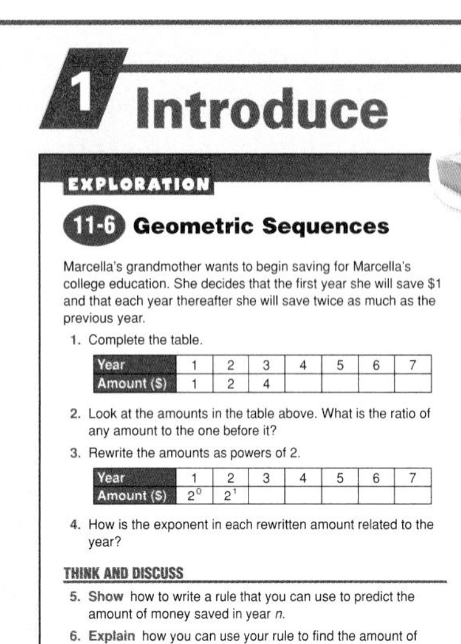

EXPLORATION

11-6 Geometric Sequences

Marcella's grandmother wants to begin saving for Marcella's college education. She decides that the first year she will save $1 and that each year thereafter she will save twice as much as the previous year.

1. Complete the table.

Year	1	2	3	4	5	6	7
Amount ($)	1	2	4				

2. Look at the amounts in the table above. What is the ratio of any amount to the one before it?
3. Rewrite the amounts as powers of 2.

Year	1	2	3	4	5	6	7
Amount ($)	2^0	2^1					

4. How is the exponent in each rewritten amount related to the year?

THINK AND DISCUSS

5. **Show** how to write a rule that you can use to predict the amount of money saved in year n.
6. **Explain** how you can use your rule to find the amount of money saved in year 10.

Motivate

Have students solve the following problem:

You are given 1 cent on the first of 20 days. Each day you will receive twice the amount as the previous day. How much will you receive on the 20th day? $5242.88

Ask students how they figured out the answer. Possible answer: I wrote the amount received for the first day and then doubled the amount for the next 19 days.

Explorations and answers are provided in *Alternate Openers: Explorations Transparencies*

Find the next three terms in each geometric sequence.

1a. 5, −10, 20, −40, ... **80, −160, 320**

1b. 512, 384, 288, ... **216, 162, 121.5**

Recall that the variable a is often used to represent terms in a sequence. The variable a_4 (read "a sub 4") is the fourth term in a sequence. To designate any term, or the nth term, you write a_n, where n can be any natural number.

1	2	3	4...	n	← Position
↓	↓	↓	↓		
3	6	12	24...		← Term
a_1	a_2	a_3	a_4	a_n	

The sequence above starts with the first term, 3. The common ratio r is 2. You can use the first term, 3, and the common ratio, 2, to write a rule for finding a_n.

Words	Numbers	Algebra
1st term	3	a_1
2nd term = 1st term times common ratio	$3 \cdot 2^1 = 6$	$a_1 \cdot r^1$
3rd term = 1st term times common ratio squared	$3 \cdot 2 \cdot 2 = 3 \cdot 2^2 = 12$	$a_1 \cdot r^2$
4th term = 1st term times common ratio cubed	$3 \cdot 2 \cdot 2 \cdot 2 = 3 \cdot 2^3 = 24$	$a_1 \cdot r^3$
nth term = 1st term times common ratio to the power $(n - 1)$	$3 \cdot 2^{n-1}$	$a_1 \cdot r^{n-1}$

The pattern in the table shows that to get the nth term, multiply the first term by the common ratio raised to the power $(n - 1)$.

Finding the nth Term of a Geometric Sequence

The nth term of a geometric sequence with **common ratio r** and **first term a**, is

$$a_n = a_1 r^{n-1}$$

EXAMPLE 2 Finding the nth Term of a Geometric Sequence

A **The first term of a geometric sequence is 128, and the common ratio is 0.5. What is the 10th term of the sequence?**

$a_n = a_1 r^{n-1}$ *Write the formula.*

$a_{10} = 128(0.5)^{10-1}$ *Substitute 128 for a_1, 10 for n, and 0.5 for r.*

$= 128(0.5)^9$ *Simplify the exponent.*

$= 0.25$ *Use a calculator.*

The 10th term of the sequence is 0.25.

B **For a geometric sequence, $a_1 = 8$ and $r = 3$. Find the 5th term of this sequence.**

$a_n = a_1 r^{n-1}$ *Write the formula.*

$a_5 = 8(3)^{5-1}$ *Substitute 8 for a_1, 5 for n, and 3 for r.*

$= 8(3)^4$ *Simplify the exponent.*

$= 648$ *Use a calculator.*

The 5th term of the sequence is 648.

2 Teach

Guided Instruction

After reviewing operations with exponents, show students a geometric sequence and how it can be extended with continued multiplication by r. Choose a sequence and show how the nth term can be found by multiplying the first term by $r(n - 1)$ times. In other words, the nth term is the product of the first term and the common ratio raised to the power $n - 1$.

Universal Access

Advanced Learners/GATE

Display the following sequence:
3, 9, 27, 81, 243,...
Under each term, write a_1, a_2, a_3, a_4, and a_5. Write a_n directly below a_1 and ask how a_2 can be written in terms of n. a_{n+1} Then write the rule for finding the common ratio, r: divide each term by the one before it. Ask how the rule can be written algebraically. $r = \frac{a_{n+1}}{a_n}$ Show students that any two consecutive terms can be used; it can be the third and fourth terms or the fifth and sixth terms.

COMMON ERROR ALERT

When finding a common ratio, students might divide in the wrong order. For instance, in **Example 1B,** students might divide −16 by 4 and so on to get a common ratio of −4. Tell them they are really finding what each term is being *multiplied* by to get the next term, so the inverse operation (division), used in reverse, will produce r.

Power Presentations with PowerPoint®

Additional Examples

Example 1

Find the next three terms in each geometric sequence.

A. 1, 4, 16, 64,...
256, 1024, 4096

B. $-9, 3, -1, \frac{1}{3}, -\frac{1}{9}, \ldots$
$\frac{1}{27}, -\frac{1}{81}, \frac{1}{243}$

Example 2

A. The first term of a geometric sequence is 500 and the common ratio is 0.2. What is the 7th term of the sequence?
0.032

B. For a geometric sequence, $a_1 = 5$ and $r = 2$. Find the 6th term of this sequence. 160

C. What is the 9th term of the geometric sequence 2, −6, 18, −54,...? 13,122

Also available on transparency

INTERVENTION

Questioning Strategies

EXAMPLE 1

- What makes the terms in some geometric sequences alternate signs?
- How do you find r when given part of a geometric sequence?

EXAMPLE 2

- When finding the nth term of a geometric sequence, why is r raised to $n - 1$, not n?

Teaching Tip

Visual Write the formula for a geometric sequence as *term wanted = first term × common ratio*$^{\text{(number of term wanted)} - 1}$.

Power Presentations with PowerPoint®

Additional Examples

Example 3

A ball is dropped from a tower. The table shows the heights of the ball's bounces, which form a geometric sequence. What is the height of the 6th bounce?

9.375 cm

Bounce	Height (cm)
1	300
2	150
3	75

Also available on transparency

INTERVENTION

Questioning Strategies

EXAMPLE 3

- How can you tell whether the common ratio will be greater than one or less than one?
- How do you expect the sequence to continue? Why?

Advanced Learners/GATE In **Example 3,** show students how to evaluate $200(0.4)^4$ without a calculator.

$200(0.4)^4 = 200\left(\frac{4}{10}\right)^4 = 2 \cdot 100 \cdot \frac{4^4}{10^4} = 2 \cdot 10^2 \cdot \frac{(2^2)^4}{10^4} = \frac{2 \cdot 2^8}{10^2} = \frac{2^9}{100} = \frac{512}{100} = 5.12.$

Caution!

When writing a function rule for a sequence with a negative common ratio, remember to enclose r in parentheses.

$-2^{12} \neq (-2)^{12}$

C What is the 13th term of the geometric sequence 8, −16, 32, −64, ... ?

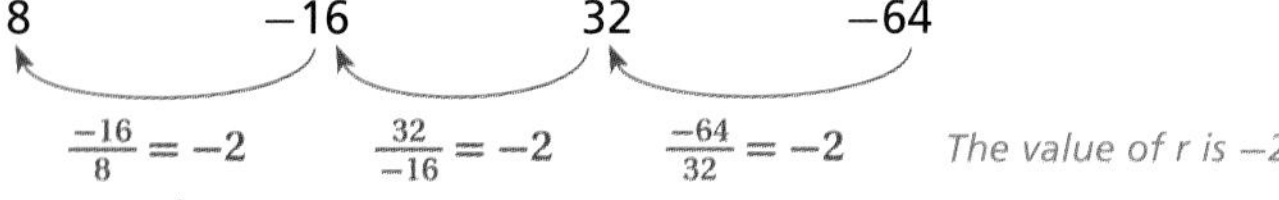

$\frac{-16}{8} = -2 \quad \frac{32}{-16} = -2 \quad \frac{-64}{32} = -2$ *The value of r is −2.*

$a_n = a_1 r^{n-1}$ *Write the formula.*

$a_{13} = 8(-2)^{13-1}$ *Substitute 8 for a_1, 13 for n, and −2 for r.*

$= 8(-2)^{12}$ *Simplify the exponent.*

$= 32{,}768$ *Use a calculator.*

The 13th term of the sequence is 32,768.

2. What is the 8th term of the geometric sequence 1000, 500, 250, 125, ... ? **7.8125**

EXAMPLE 3 ***Sports Application***

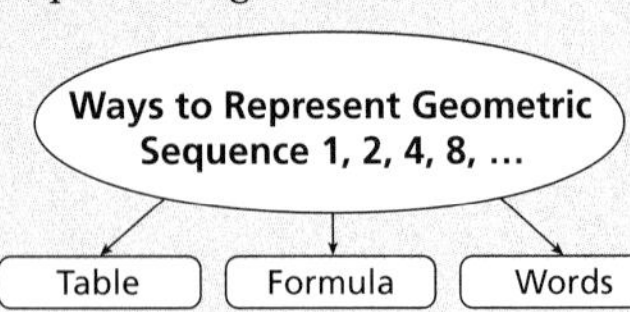

A bungee jumper jumps from a bridge. The diagram shows the jumper's height above the ground at the top of each bounce. The heights form a geometric sequence. What is the jumper's height at the top of the 5th bounce?

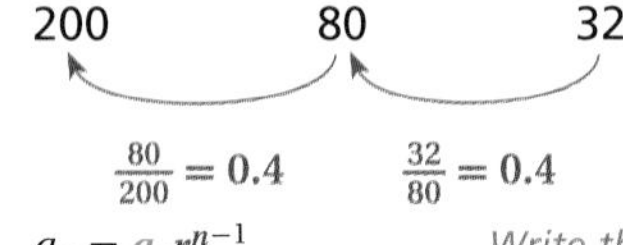

$\frac{80}{200} = 0.4 \quad \frac{32}{80} = 0.4$

$a_n = a_1 r^{n-1}$ *Write the formula.*

$a_5 = 200(0.4)^{5-1}$ *Substitute 200 for a_1, 5 for n, and 0.4 for r.*

$= 200(0.4)^4$ *Simplify the exponent.*

$= 5.12$ *Use a calculator.*

The height of the 5th bounce is 5.12 feet.

3. The table shows a car's value for 3 years after it is purchased. The values form a geometric sequence. How much will the car be worth in the 10th year? **$1342.18**

Year	Value ($)
1	10,000
2	8,000
3	6,400

THINK AND DISCUSS

1. How do you determine whether a sequence is geometric?
2. **GET ORGANIZED** Copy and complete the graphic organizer. In each box, write a way to represent the geometric sequence.

3 Close

Summarize

Tell students that they have learned about two kinds of sequences in this course: arithmetic and geometric. Arithmetic sequences have common differences and geometric sequences have common ratios. Common ratios are found by dividing each term by the term before it. Have students state in their own words how to find any term in a geometric sequence.

FORMATIVE ASSESSMENT and INTERVENTION

***Diagnose Before* the Lesson**
11-6 Warm Up, TE p. 732

***Monitor During* the Lesson**
Check It Out! Exercises, SE pp. 733–734
Questioning Strategies, TE p. 733–734

***Assess After* the Lesson**
11-6 Lesson Quiz, TE p. 737
Alternative Assessment, TE p. 737

Answers to *Think and Discuss*

1. Possible answer: Divide each term after the first by the preceding term. If the quotients are all the same, the sequence is geometric.
2. See p. A9.

11-6 Exercises

Preparation for Algebra II **22.0**; **1A24.1, 1A25.1**

go.hrw.com
Homework Help Online
KEYWORD: MA8CA 11-6
Parent Resources Online
KEYWORD: MA8CA Parent

GUIDED PRACTICE

1. **Vocabulary** What is the *common ratio* of a geometric sequence? **the value that each term is multiplied by to get the next term**

SEE EXAMPLE 1 p. 732

Find the next three terms in each geometric sequence.

2. 2, 4, 8, 16, ... **32, 64, 128**
3. 400, 200, 100, 50, ... **25, 12.5, 6.25**
4. 4, −12, 36, −108, ... **324, −972, 2916**

SEE EXAMPLE 2 p. 733

5. The first term of a geometric sequence is 1, and the common ratio is 10. What is the 10th term of the sequence? **1,000,000,000**
6. What is the 11th term of the geometric sequence 3, 6, 12, 24, ... ? **3072**

SEE EXAMPLE 3 p. 734

7. **Sports** In the NCAA men's basketball tournament, 64 teams compete in round 1. Fewer teams remain in each following round, as shown in the graph, until all but one team have been eliminated. The numbers of teams in each round form a geometric sequence. How many teams compete in round 5? **4**

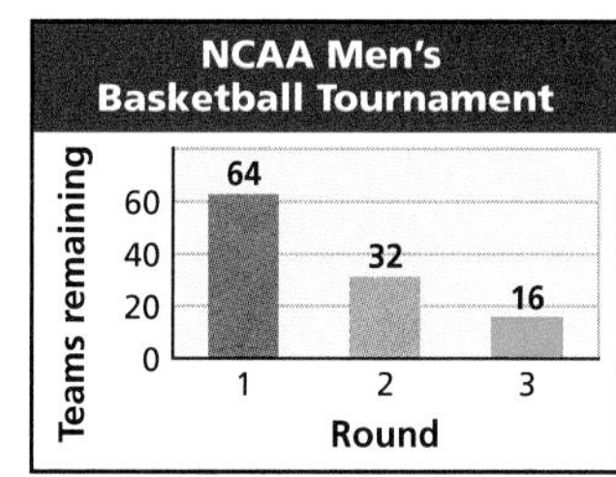

PRACTICE AND PROBLEM SOLVING

Independent Practice

For Exercises	See Example
8–13	1
14–15	2
16	3

Extra Practice
Skills Practice p. EP23
Application Practice p. EP34

Find the next three terms in each geometric sequence.

8. −2, 10, −50, 250, ...
9. 32, 48, 72, 108, ...
10. 625, 500, 400, 320, ...
11. 6, 42, 294, ...
12. 6, −12, 24, −48, ...
13. 40, 10, $\frac{5}{2}$, $\frac{5}{8}$, ...
14. The first term of a geometric sequence is 18 and the common ratio is 3.5. What is the 5th term of the sequence? **2701.125**
15. What is the 14th term of the geometric sequence 1000, 100, 10, 1, ... ? **0.0000000001, or 1×10^{-10}**
16. **Physical Science** A ball is dropped from a height of 500 meters. The table shows the height of each bounce, and the heights form a geometric sequence. How high does the ball bounce on the 8th bounce? Round your answer to the nearest tenth of a meter. **83.9 m**

Bounce	Height (m)
1	400
2	320
3	256

Find the missing term(s) in each geometric sequence.

17. 20, 40, **80**, **160**, ...
18. **2**, 6, 18, **54**, ...
19. 9, 3, 1, **$\frac{1}{3}$**, ...
20. 3, 12, **48**, 192, **768**, ...
21. 7, 1, **$\frac{1}{7}$**, **$\frac{1}{49}$**, $\frac{1}{343}$, ...
22. **400**, 100, 25, **$\frac{25}{4}$**, $\frac{25}{16}$, ...
23. −3, **6**, −12, 24, **−48** ...
24. **$\frac{1}{9}$**, ▒, 1, −3, 9, ... **$-\frac{1}{3}$**
25. 1, 17, 289, ▒, ... **4913**

Determine whether each sequence could be geometric. If so, give the common ratio.

26. 2, 10, 50, 250, ... **yes; 5**
27. 15, 5, $\frac{5}{3}$, $\frac{5}{9}$, ... **yes; $\frac{1}{3}$**
28. 6, 18, 24, 38, ... **no**
29. 9, 3, −1, −5, ... **no**
30. 7, 21, 63, 189, ... **yes; 3**
31. 4, 1, −2, −4, ... **no**

11-6 Exercises

Assignment Guide

Assign *Guided Practice* exercises as necessary.

If you finished Examples **1–3**
Proficient 8–40, 42–46, 55–66
Advanced 8–16 even, 17–66

Homework Quick Check
Quickly check key concepts.
Exercises: 8, 14, 16, 24, 32

Diversity Exercise 7 is about a basketball tournament. Have students discuss the different types of tournaments they have participated in that have a similar type of elimination system.

Answers

8. −1250, 6250, −31,250
9. 162, 243, 364.5
10. 256, 204.8, 163.84
11. 2058, 14,406, 100,842
12. 96, −192, 384
13. $\frac{5}{32}$, $\frac{5}{128}$, $\frac{5}{512}$

Exercise 43 involves using a common ratio to find terms in a geometric sequence. This exercise prepares students for the Concept Connection on page 762.

Answers

39. 12, 3, $\frac{3}{4}$, $\frac{3}{16}$

40. The terms of a geometric sequence are given by $a_1, a_1r, a_1r^2, a_1r^3, \ldots, a_1r^{n-1}, \ldots,$ where n is the term number. Doubling the value of r results in $a_1, a_1(2r), a_1(2r)^2, a_1(2r)^3, \ldots, a_1(2r)^{n-1}, \ldots,$ which is equivalent to $a_1, 2a_1r, 2^2a_1r^2, 2^3a_1r^3, \ldots, 2^{n-1}, a_1r^{n-1}, \ldots.$ The original terms have each been multiplied by 2^{n-1}.

41a, 41b. See p. A26.

42. Divide each term by the term before it to find the value of r. Then use the formula $a_n = a_1r^{n-1}$, where a_1 is the first term of the sequence.

54. Susanna assumed the sequence was geometric with $r = 2$. She used the formula to find $a_8 = 128$. Paul did not assume the sequence was geometric. Instead he noticed a pattern of "add 1, add 2, and so on." He continued this pattern by adding 3, adding 4, etc., until he got the 8th term of 29. Both Susanna and Paul could be considered correct because the type of sequence was not specified.

58–60. See p. A26.

32a. Yes, it is a geom. seq. with $r = 2$.

b. Possible answer: Plan 1; Under Plan 2, the cost for the 10th week alone is \$512, which is more than the cost for the entire summer under Plan 1.

32. **Multi-Step** Billy earns money by mowing lawns for the summer. He offers two payment plans, as shown at right.
   a. Do the payments for plan 2 form a geometric sequence? Explain.
   b. If you were one of Billy's customers, which plan would you choose? (Assume that the summer is 10 weeks long.) Explain your choice.

Billy's Better Lawns
Weekly Lawn Care Service
TWO WAYS TO PAY!
Plan 1: Pay \$150 for the entire summer.
Plan 2: Pay \$1 the 1ST week, \$2 the 2ND week, \$4 the 3RD week, \$8 the 4TH week, and so on.

33. **Measurement** When you fold a piece of paper in half, the thickness of the folded piece is twice the thickness of the original piece. A piece of copy paper is about 0.1 mm thick.
   a. How thick is a piece of copy paper that has been folded in half 7 times? **1.28 cm**
   b. Suppose that you could fold a piece of copy paper in half 12 times. How thick would it be? Write your answer in centimeters. **40.96 cm**

List the first four terms of each geometric sequence.

34. $a_1 = 3, a_n = 3(2)^{n-1}$ **3, 6, 12, 24**
35. $a_1 = -2, a_n = -2(4)^{n-1}$ **−2, −8, −32, −128**
36. $a_1 = 5, a_n = 5(-2)^{n-1}$ **5, −10, 20, −40**
37. $a_1 = 2, a_n = 2(2)^{n-1}$ **2, 4, 8, 16**
38. $a_1 = 2, a_n = 2(5)^{n-1}$ **2, 10, 50, 250**
39. $a_1 = 12, a_n = 12\left(\frac{1}{4}\right)^{n-1}$

40. **Reasoning** Use deductive reasoning to show that if the value of r is doubled in a geometric sequence, then each term is multiplied by 2^{n-1}, where n represents the term number.

For help with deductive reasoning, see p. 99, p. 169, and p. 311.

41. **Geometry** The steps below describe how to make a geometric figure by repeating the same process over and over on a smaller and smaller scale.
   Step 1 (stage 0) Draw a large square.
   Step 2 (stage 1) Divide the square into four equal squares.
   Step 3 (stage 2) Divide each small square into four equal squares.
   Step 4 Repeat Step 3 indefinitely.
   a. Draw stages 0, 1, 2, and 3.
   b. How many small squares are in each stage? Organize your data relating stage and number of small squares in a table.
   c. Does the data in part **b** form a geometric sequence? Explain. **yes; $r = 4$**
   d. Write a rule to find the number of small squares in stage n. **$a_n = 4(4)^{n-1}$, or 4^n**

42. **Write About It** Write a series of steps for finding the nth term of a geometric sequence when you are given the first several terms.

43. This problem will prepare you for the Concept Connection on page 762.
   a. Three years ago, the annual tuition at a university was \$3000. The following year, the tuition was \$3300, and last year, the tuition was \$3630. If the tuition has continued to grow in the same manner, what is the tuition this year? What do you expect it to be next year? **\$3993; \$4392.30**
   b. What is the common ratio? **1.1**
   c. What would you predict the tuition was 4 years ago? How did you find that value? **\$2727.27; divide tuition 3 years ago (\$3000) by 1.1 (the common ratio).**

11-6 PRACTICE A
11-6 PRACTICE C
11-6 PRACTICE B

LESSON 11-6 **Practice B**
Geometric Sequences

Find the next three terms in each geometric sequence.

1. −5, −10, −20, −40, … **−80, −160, −320**
2. 7, 56, 448, 3584… **28,672, 229,376, 1,835,008**
3. −10, 40, −160, 640, … **−2560, 10,240, −40,960**
4. 40, 10, $\frac{5}{2}$, $\frac{5}{8}$, … **$\frac{5}{32}$, $\frac{5}{128}$, $\frac{5}{512}$**
5. The first term of a geometric sequence is 6 and the common ratio is −8. Find the 7th term. **1,572,864**
6. The first term of a geometric sequence is −3 and the common ratio is $\frac{1}{2}$. Find the 6th term. **$-\frac{3}{32}$**
7. The first term of a geometric sequence is −0.25 and the common ratio is −3. Find the 10th term. **4920.75**
8. What is the 12th term of the geometric sequence −4, −12, −36, …? **−708,588**
9. What is the 10th term of the geometric sequence 2, −6, 18, …? **−39,366**
10. What is the 6th term of the geometric sequence 50, 10, 2, …? **0.016**
11. A shoe store is discounting shoes each month. A pair of shoes cost \$80. The table shows the discount prices for several months. Find the cost of the shoes after 8 months. Round your answer to the nearest cent.

Month	Price
1	\$80.00
2	\$72.00
3	\$64.80

\$38.26

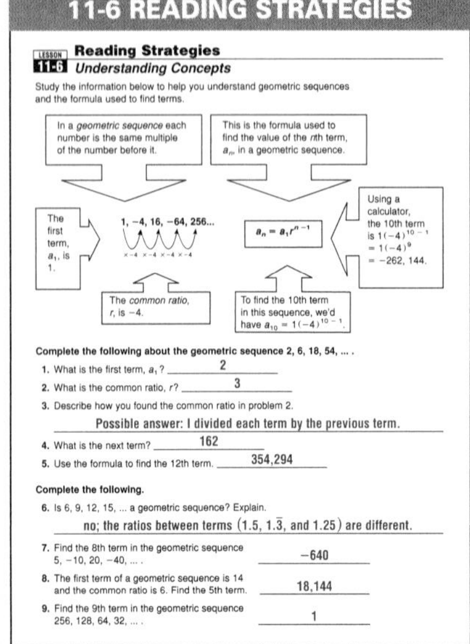

11-6 READING STRATEGIES

LESSON 11-6 **Reading Strategies**
Understanding Concepts

Study the information below to help you understand geometric sequences and the formula used to find terms.

In a *geometric sequence* each number is the same multiple of the number before it.

This is the formula used to find the value of the nth term, a_n, in a geometric sequence.

The first term, a_1, is 1.

1, −4, 16, −64, 256…
×−4 ×−4 ×−4 ×−4

$a_n = a_1r^{n-1}$

Using a calculator, the 10th term is $1(-4)^{10-1} = 1(-4)^9 = -262,144$.

The *common ratio*, r, is −4.

To find the 10th term in this sequence, we'd have $a_{10} = 1(-4)^{10-1}$.

Complete the following about the geometric sequence 2, 6, 18, 54, … .

1. What is the first term, a_1? **2**
2. What is the common ratio, r? **3**
3. Describe how you found the common ratio in problem 2. **Possible answer: I divided each term by the previous term.**
4. What is the next term? **162**
5. Use the formula to find the 12th term. **354,294**

Complete the following.

6. Is 6, 9, 12, 15, … a geometric sequence? Explain. **no; the ratios between terms (1.5, $1.\overline{3}$, and 1.25) are different.**
7. Find the 8th term in the geometric sequence 5, −10, 20, −40, … . **−640**
8. The first term of a geometric sequence is 14 and the common ratio is 6. Find the 5th term. **18,144**
9. Find the 9th term in the geometric sequence 256, 128, 64, 32, … . **1**

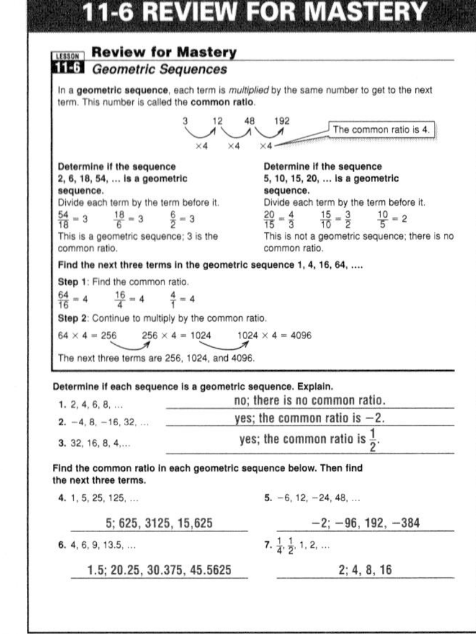

11-6 REVIEW FOR MASTERY

LESSON 11-6 **Review for Mastery**
Geometric Sequences

In a **geometric sequence**, each term is *multiplied* by the same number to get to the next term. This number is called the **common ratio**.

3 12 48 192
×4 ×4 ×4
The common ratio is 4.

Determine if the sequence 2, 6, 18, 54, … is a geometric sequence.
Divide each term by the term before it.
$\frac{54}{18} = 3$ $\frac{18}{6} = 3$ $\frac{6}{2} = 3$
This is a geometric sequence; 3 is the common ratio.

Determine if the sequence 5, 10, 15, 20, … is a geometric sequence.
Divide each term by the term before it.
$\frac{20}{15} = \frac{4}{3}$ $\frac{15}{10} = \frac{3}{2}$ $\frac{10}{5} = 2$
This is not a geometric sequence; there is no common ratio.

Find the next three terms in the geometric sequence 1, 4, 16, 64, ….

Step 1: Find the common ratio.
$\frac{64}{16} = 4$ $\frac{16}{4} = 4$ $\frac{4}{1} = 4$

Step 2: Continue to multiply by the common ratio.
$64 \times 4 = 256$ $256 \times 4 = 1024$ $1024 \times 4 = 4096$

The next three terms are 256, 1024, and 4096.

Determine if each sequence is a geometric sequence. Explain.

1. 2, 4, 6, 8, … **no; there is no common ratio.**
2. −4, 8, −16, 32, … **yes; the common ratio is −2.**
3. 32, 16, 8, 4,… **yes; the common ratio is $\frac{1}{2}$.**

Find the common ratio in each geometric sequence below. Then find the next three terms.

4. 1, 5, 25, 125, … **5; 625, 3125, 15,625**
5. −6, 12, −24, 48, … **−2; −96, 192, −384**
6. 4, 6, 9, 13.5, … **1.5; 20.25, 30.375, 45.5625**
7. $\frac{1}{4}$, $\frac{1}{2}$, 1, 2, … **2; 4, 8, 16**

Multiple Choice For Exercises 44–46, choose the best answer.

44. Which of the following could be a geometric sequence?

(A) $\frac{1}{2}, 1, \frac{3}{2}, 2, \ldots$ (C) $3, 8, 13, 18, \ldots$

(B) $-2, -6, -10, -14, \ldots$ **(D)** $5, 10, 20, 40, \ldots$

45. Which equation represents the nth term in the geometric sequence $2, -8, 32, -128, \ldots$?

(A) $a_n = (-4)^n$ (B) $a_n = (-4)^{n-1}$ (C) $a_n = 2(-4)^n$ **(D)** $a_n = 2(-4)^{n-1}$

46. The frequency of a musical note, measured in hertz (Hz), is called its pitch. The pitches of the A keys on a piano form a geometric sequence, as shown.

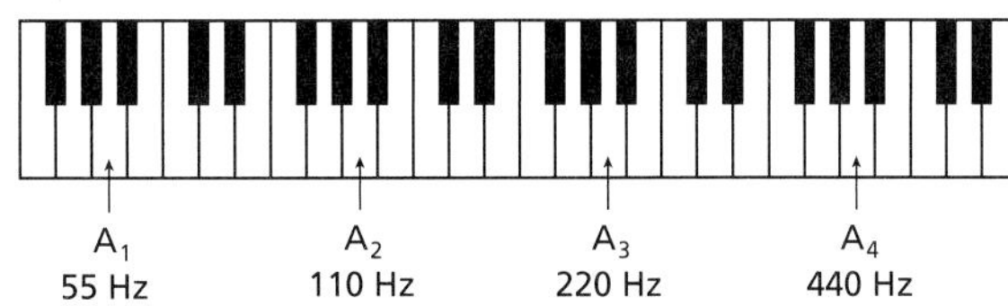

What is the frequency of A_7?

(A) 880 Hz (B) 1760 Hz **(C)** 3520 Hz (D) 7040 Hz

CHALLENGE AND EXTEND

Find the next three terms in each geometric sequence.

47. $x, x^2, x^3, \ldots$ **x^4, x^5, x^6**

48. $2x^2, 6x^3, 18x^4, \ldots$ **$54x^5, 162x^6, 486x^7$**

49. $\frac{1}{y^3}, \frac{1}{y^2}, \frac{1}{y}, \ldots$ **$1, y, y^2$**

50. $\frac{1}{(x+1)^2}, \frac{1}{x+1}, 1, \ldots$ **50. $x+1, (x+1)^2, (x+1)^3$**

51. The 10th term of a geometric sequence is 0.78125. The common ratio is –0.5. Find the first term of the sequence. **–400**

52. The first term of a geometric sequence is 12 and the common ratio is $\frac{1}{2}$. Is 0 a term in this sequence? Explain.

52. No; each term of the seq. is found by multiplying the prev. term by the common ratio $\frac{1}{2}$. $\frac{1}{2}$ of any pos. number is always another pos. number.

53. A geometric sequence starts with 14 and has a common ration of 0.4. Colin finds that another number in the sequence is 0.057344. Which term in the sequence did Colin find? **the 7th term**

54. The first three terms of a sequence are 1, 2, and 4. Susanna said the 8th term of this sequence is 128. Paul said the 8th term is 29. Explain how the students found their answers. Why could these both be considered correct answers?

SPIRAL STANDARDS REVIEW

4.0, 6.0, 20.0

Solve each inequality and graph the solutions. *(Lesson 3-4)*

55. $3(b-4) > 18$ **$b > 10$**

–5 0 5 10 15 20 25 30

56. $-12 + x \le -8$ **$x \le 4$**

–8 –6 –4 –2 0 2 4 6 8

57. $c + \frac{2}{3} < \frac{1}{3}$ **$c < -\frac{1}{3}$**

–6 –4 –2 0 2

Graph the solutions of each linear inequality. *(Lesson 6-5)*

58. $y < 2x - 4$

59. $3x + y > 6$

60. $-y \le 2x + 1$

Solve by using the Quadratic Formula. Check your answer. *(Lesson 9-8)*

61. $3x^2 - 4x = -1$ **$1, \frac{1}{3}$**

62. $5x^2 + 1 = 6x$ **$1, \frac{1}{5}$**

63. $\frac{1}{2}x^2 + \frac{3}{2}x = 14$ **$4, -7$**

64. $2x^2 - 5 = 5x$ **$\approx 3.27, \approx -0.77$**

65. $2x^2 = -8x + 3$ **$\approx 0.35, \approx -4.35$**

66. $-8x^2 + 2x + 3 = 0$

66. $-\frac{1}{2}, \frac{3}{4}$

Teaching Tip

Multiple Choice The incorrect choices, **A, B,** and **C,** in **Exercise 44** are arithmetic sequences. They have common differences, not common ratios.

In **Exercise 45,** choices **A** and **B** can be quickly eliminated because they do not include the first term, 2. To help distinguish between **C** and **D,** have students substitute 1 for n, which will result in the first term.

Journal

Have students explain the difference between the rules used to create the following sequences:

3, 6, 9, 12, 15,...

3, 6, 12, 24, 48,...

ALTERNATIVE ASSESSMENT

Have students write the first five terms of a geometric sequence for which r is greater than one. Then have them write the first five terms of a geometric sequence for which r is less than one. Last, have them find the 10th and 20th terms of each of their sequences by using the formula taught in the lesson.

Power Presentations with PowerPoint®

11-6 Lesson Quiz

Find the next three terms in each geometric sequence.

1. 3, 15, 75, 375,...
1875, 9375, 46,875

2. $5, -1, \frac{1}{5}, -\frac{1}{25}, \frac{1}{125}, \ldots$
$-\frac{1}{625}, \frac{1}{3125}, -\frac{1}{15{,}625}$

3. The first term of a geometric sequence is 300 and the common ratio is 0.6. What is the 7th term of the sequence?
13.9968

4. What is the 15th term of the geometric sequence 4, –8, 16, –32, 64,...? 65,536

5. The table shows a car's value for 3 years after it is purchased. The values form a geometric sequence. How much will the car be worth after 8 years? $5770.39

Year	Value ($)
1	18,000
2	15,300
3	13,005

Also available on transparency

11-6 PROBLEM SOLVING

LESSON 11-6 **Problem Solving**
Geometric Sequences

Write the correct answer.

1. A ball is dropped from 400 feet. The table shows the height of each bounce.

Bounce	Height (ft)
1	280
2	196
3	137.2

Find the height of the ball on the 6th bounce. Round your answer to the nearest tenth of a foot.

47.1 feet

2. A plant starts with 1 branch. Every year, each branch becomes 3 branches. A sketch of the plant for the first 3 years is shown. How many branches will the plant have in year 10?

Year 1 Year 2 Year 3

19,683 branches

How many branches would the plant have in year 10 if the plant had 5 branches the first year? (Each branch still becomes 3 branches every year.)

98,415 branches

3. Jeanette started selling bagels to offices in her area. Her sales for the first 3 months are shown in the table.

Month	Sales ($)
1	$200.00
2	$230.00
3	$264.50

If this trend continues, find the amount of Jeanette's sales in Month 8.

$532

The table shows the number of houses in a new subdivision. Use the table to answer questions 4–7. Select the best answer.

Month	Houses
1	3
2	6
3	12
4	24

4. The number of houses forms a geometric sequence. What is r?
A 0.5 C 3
(B) 2 D 6

5. Assuming that the trend continues, how many houses would be in the subdivision in Month 6?
F 36 H 60
G 48 **(J) 96**

6. Management decides the subdivision is complete when the number of houses reaches 48. When will this happen?
(A) Month 5 C Month 7
B Month 6 D Month 8

7. Suppose the number of houses tripled every month. How many more houses would be in the subdivision in Month 4? (The number of houses in Month 1 is still 3.)
F 48 H 72
(G) 57 J 81

11-6 CHALLENGE

LESSON 11-6 **Challenge**
Series

A **sequence** is a list of numbers that often forms a pattern. You have worked with arithmetic sequences and geometric sequences.

A **series** is the sum of the terms of a sequence. You can either find a *partial sum* of a few terms or determine what happens when you sum infinitely many terms. (You'll look at infinite series in Algebra 2.)

The Greek capital letter sigma (Σ) is often used to represent summation in mathematics. Numbers above and below sigma tell you which terms to sum.

For example, $\sum_{n=1}^{5}$ represents the partial sum of the 1st to 5th terms.

Find the partial sums of these arithmetic series.

1. $\sum_{n=1}^{5} 4 + (n-1)(3) = \underbrace{4}_{n=1} + \underbrace{7}_{n=2} + \underbrace{10}_{n=3} + \underbrace{13}_{n=4} + \underbrace{16}_{n=5} =$ **50**

2. $\sum_{n=1}^{8} -10 + (n-1)(2) = \underbrace{-10}_{n=1} + \underbrace{-8}_{n=2} + \underbrace{-6}_{n=3} + \underbrace{-4}_{n=4} + \underbrace{-2}_{n=5} + \underbrace{0}_{n=6} + \underbrace{2}_{n=7} + \underbrace{4}_{n=8}$
$=$ **–24**

3. $\sum_{n=1}^{6} 23 + (n-1)(-5) =$ **$23 + 18 + 13 + 8 + 3 + (-2)$** $=$ **63**

4. $\sum_{n=1}^{4} \frac{1}{2} + (n-1)\left(\frac{1}{8}\right) =$ **$\frac{1}{2} + \frac{5}{8} + \frac{3}{4} + \frac{7}{8}$** $=$ **$\frac{11}{4}$ or $2\frac{3}{4}$**

5. $\sum_{n=5}^{10} -7 + (n-1)(-1.2) =$ **$-11.8 + (-13) + (-14.2) + (-15.4) + (-16.6) + (-17.8)$** $=$ **–88.8**

Caution!

Find the partial sums of these geometric series.

6. $\sum_{n=1}^{5} 4(3)^{n-1} = \underbrace{4}_{n=1} + \underbrace{12}_{n=2} + \underbrace{36}_{n=3} + \underbrace{108}_{n=4} + \underbrace{324}_{n=5} =$ **484**

7. $\sum_{n=1}^{8} -10(2)^{n-1} = \underbrace{-10}_{n=1} + \underbrace{-20}_{n=2} + \underbrace{-40}_{n=3} + \underbrace{-80}_{n=4} + \underbrace{-160}_{n=5} + \underbrace{-320}_{n=6} + \underbrace{-640}_{n=7} + \underbrace{-1280}_{n=8}$
$=$ **–2550**

8. $\sum_{n=1}^{6} 3(-2)^{n-1} =$ **$3 + (-6) + 12 + (-24) + 48 + (-96)$** $=$ **–63**

9. $\sum_{n=1}^{4} 16\left(\frac{1}{4}\right)^{n-1} =$ **$16 + 4 + 1 + \frac{1}{4}$** $=$ **$\frac{85}{4}$ or $21\frac{1}{4}$**

10. $\sum_{n=5}^{10} -6\left(-\frac{2}{3}\right)^{n-1} =$ **$-\frac{32}{27} + \frac{64}{81} + \left(-\frac{128}{243}\right) + \frac{256}{729} + \left(-\frac{512}{2187}\right) + \frac{1024}{6561}$** $=$ **$\frac{-4256}{6561} \approx -0.649$**

11-7 Organizer

Objectives: Evaluate exponential functions.

Identify and graph exponential functions.

Online Edition
Tutorial Videos, Graphing Calculator, TechKeys

Power Presentations with PowerPoint®

Warm Up

Simplify each expression. Round to the nearest whole number if necessary.

1. 3^2 9 **2.** 5^4 625

3. $2(3)^3$ 54 **4.** $\frac{2}{3}(3)^4$ 54

5. $-5(2)^5$ -160 **6.** $-\frac{1}{2}(4)^3$ -32

7. $100(0.5)^2$ 25

8. $3000(0.95)^8$ 1990

Also available on transparency

Math Humor

Exponential Function: Why is my energy level falling?

Doctor: Your common ratio is below one. Your energy levels will rise if your common ratio is above one.

California Standards

Preview of Algebra II 🔑 12.0

11-7 Exponential Functions

California Standards

Preview of Algebra II
🔑 **12.0 Students** know the laws of fractional exponents, **understand exponential functions,** and use these functions in problems involving exponential growth and decay.

Vocabulary
exponential function

Who uses this?
Scientists model populations with exponential functions.

The table and the graph show an insect population that increases over time.

Time (days)	Population
0	2
1	6
2	18
3	54

(× 3 between each successive population)

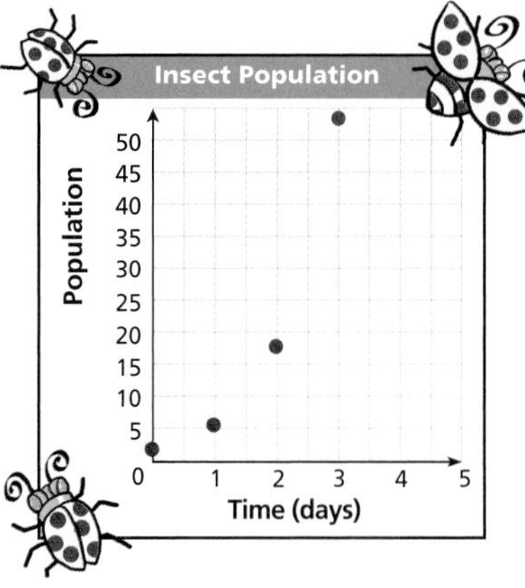

A function rule that describes the pattern above is $f(x) = 2(3)^x$. This type of function, in which the independent variable appears in an exponent, is an **exponential function**. Notice that 2 is the starting population and 3 is the amount by which the population is multiplied each day.

Know it! Note

Exponential Functions

An exponential function has the form $f(x) = ab^x$, where $a \neq 0$, $b \neq 1$, and $b > 0$.

EXAMPLE 1 Evaluating an Exponential Function

A **The function $f(x) = 2(3)^x$ models an insect population after x days. What will the population be on the 5th day?**

$f(x) = 2(3)^x$ *Write the function.*

$f(5) = 2(3)^5$ *Substitute 5 for x.*

$= 2(243)$ *Evaluate 3^5.*

$= 486$ *Multiply.*

There will be 486 insects on the 5th day.

B **The function $f(x) = 1500(0.995)^x$, where x is the time in years, models a prairie dog population. How many prairie dogs will there be in 8 years?**

$f(x) = 1500(0.995)^x$

$f(8) = 1500(0.995)^8$ *Substitute 8 for x.*

≈ 1441 *Use a calculator. Round to the nearest whole number.*

There will be about 1441 prairie dogs in 8 years.

Helpful Hint

In Example 1B, round your answer to the nearest whole number because there can only be a whole number of prairie dogs.

CHECK IT OUT! **1.** The function $f(x) = 8(0.75)^x$ models the width of a photograph in inches after it has been reduced by 25% x times. What is the width of the photograph after it has been reduced 3 times? **3.375 in.**

1 Introduce

EXPLORATION

11-7 Exponential Functions

A biologist is studying bacteria growth. He begins with 10 bacteria in a Petri dish. The number of bacteria doubles each hour.

1. Complete the middle column of the table to show the rate of bacteria growth.

Hour	Bacteria	Exponential Form
0	10	$10(2)^0$
1	20	$10(2)^1$
2		
3		
4		
5		

2. Complete the right-hand column of the table, which shows the number of bacteria written as a power of 2.
3. Look for a pattern in the table to help you write an equation for the number of bacteria *B* in terms of the number of hours *h*.

THINK AND DISCUSS

4. **Explain** how to use your equation to find the number of bacteria after 15 hours.
5. **Describe** how your equation would be different if the biologist had started with 12 bacteria.

Motivate

Write 6, 12, 24, 48 . . . on the board. Tell students that this is a geometric sequence with a common ratio of 2. Explain that in this lesson they will study functions that are very similar to geometric sequences. But unlike geometric sequences, which have discrete terms, these new functions will be continuous. The graphs of these new functions will be unbroken.

Explorations and answers are provided in *Alternate Openers: Explorations Transparencies.*

Exponential functions have *constant ratios*. As the x-values increase by a constant amount, the y-values are multiplied by a constant amount. This amount is the constant ratio and is the value of b in $f(x) = ab^x$.

x	$y = 2(3)^x$
1	6
2	18
3	54
4	162

(+1 for each step in x; ×3 for each step in y)

EXAMPLE 2 Identifying an Exponential Function

Tell whether each set of ordered pairs satisfies an exponential function. Explain your answer.

A $\{(-1, 1.5), (0, 3), (1, 6), (2, 12)\}$

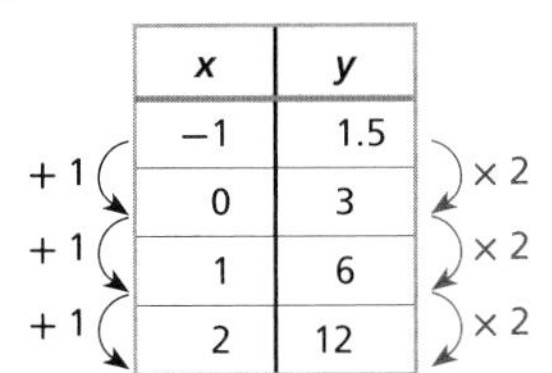

x	y
−1	1.5
0	3
1	6
2	12

(+1, +1, +1; ×2, ×2, ×2)

This is an exponential function. As the x-values increase by a constant amount, the y-values are multiplied by a constant amount.

B $\{(-1, -9), (1, 9), (3, 27), (5, 45)\}$

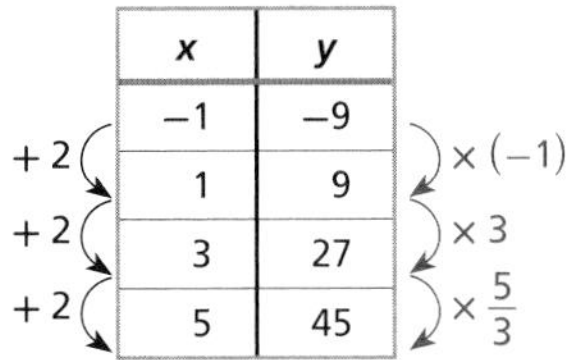

x	y
−1	−9
1	9
3	27
5	45

(+2, +2, +2; $\times(-1)$, ×3, $\times\frac{5}{3}$)

This is *not* an exponential function. As the x-values increase by a constant amount, the y-values are *not* multiplied by a constant amount.

CHECK IT OUT! **Tell whether each set of ordered pairs satisfies an exponential function. Explain your answer.**

2a. $\{(-1, 1), (0, 0), (1, 1), (2, 4)\}$

2b. $\{(-2, 4), (-1, 2), (0, 1), (1, 0.5)\}$

2a. No; as the x-values change by a constant amount, the y-values are not multiplied by a constant amount.

2b. Yes; as the x-values change by a constant amount, the y-values are multiplied by a constant amount.

To graph an exponential function, choose several values of x (positive, negative, and 0) and generate ordered pairs. Plot the points and connect them with a smooth curve.

EXAMPLE 3 Graphing $y = ab^x$ with $a > 0$ and $b > 1$

Graph $y = 3(4)^x$.

Choose several values of x and generate ordered pairs.

x	$y = 3(4)^x$
−1	0.75
0	3
1	12
2	48

Graph the ordered pairs and connect with a smooth curve.

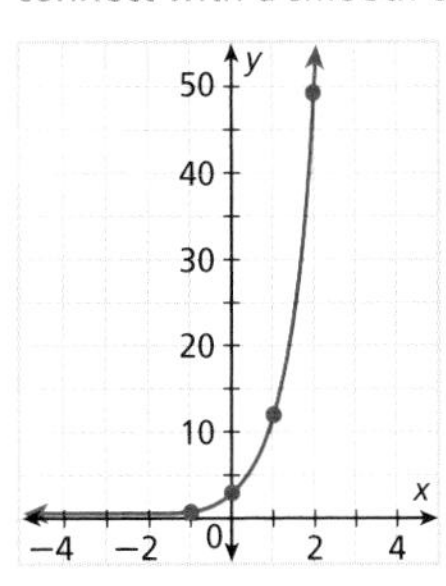

3a.

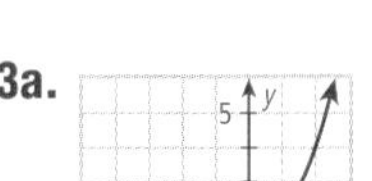

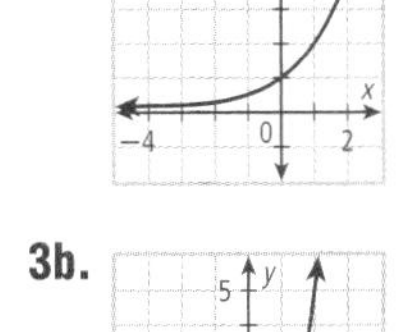

3b.

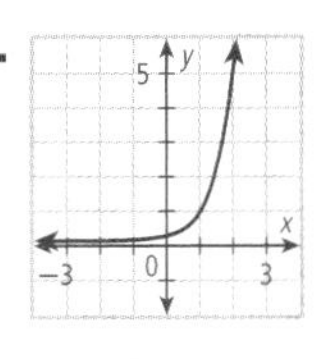

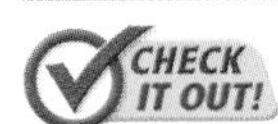

CHECK IT OUT! **Graph each exponential function.**

3a. $y = 2^x$ **3b.** $y = 0.2(5)^x$

COMMON ERROR ALERT

When generating ordered pairs for exponential functions, students may multiply a by b and then raise that product to x. Remind students to use the correct order of operations.

Power Presentations with PowerPoint®

Additional Examples

Example 1

A. The function $f(x) = 500(1.035)^x$ models the amount of money in a certificate of deposit after x years. How much money will there be in 6 years? $614.63

B. The function $f(x) = 200{,}000(0.98)^x$, where x is the time in years, models the population of a city. What will the population be in 7 years? about 173,625

Example 2

Tell whether each set of ordered pairs satisfies an exponential function. Explain your answer.

A. $\{(0, 4), (1, 12), (2, 36), (3, 108)\}$ Yes; as the x-values change by a constant amount, the y-values are multiplied by a constant amount.

B. $\{(-1, -64), (0, 0), (1, 64), (2, 128)\}$ No; as the x-values change by a constant amount, the y-values are not multiplied by a constant amount.

Example 3

Graph $y = 0.5(2)^x$.

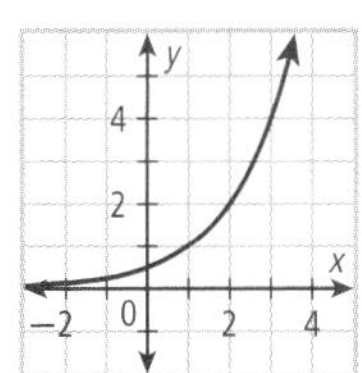

Also available on transparency

2 Teach

Guided Instruction

In **Example 1,** point out that b in an exponential function corresponds to r in a geometric sequence. Explain that these predictions are accurate only if all conditions remain the same throughout the given time period.

When graphing exponential functions, explain that $b = 1$ represents no change (no growth or decline–the graph is linear), so $b > 1$ represents growth and $b < 1$ represents decline.

Universal Access

Through Graphic Organizers

To show why the exponent in a geometric sequence has 1 subtracted from the variable but an exponential function does not, create the following chart, which corresponds to **Example 1A.**

1st Term	2nd Term	3rd Term	4th Term	5th Term	6th Term
2	6	18	54	162	486
After 0 days	After 1 day	After 2 days	After 3 days	After 4 days	After 5 days

INTERVENTION

Questioning Strategies

EXAMPLES 1–2

- How do you know the exponent applies to b and not ab?

EXAMPLE 3

- What are the domain and range of an exponential function if both a and b are positive?

Power Presentations with PowerPoint®

Additional Examples

Example 4

Graph $y = -\frac{1}{4}(2)^x$.

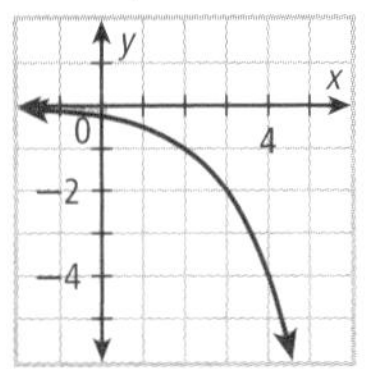

Example 5

Graph each exponential function.

A. $y = -1\left(\frac{1}{4}\right)^x$

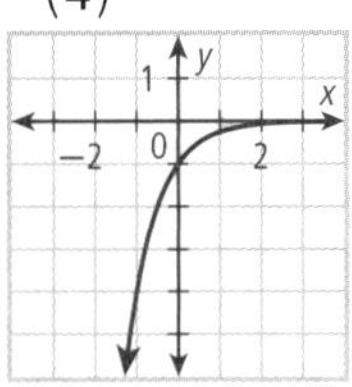

B. $y = 4(0.6)^x$

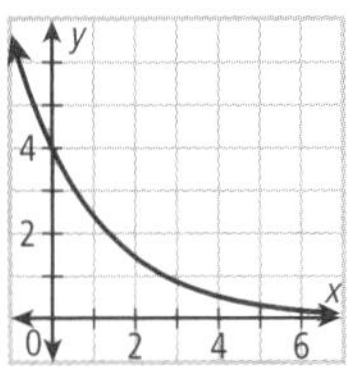

Also available on transparency

INTERVENTION

Questioning Strategies

EXAMPLES **4–5**

- How can the values of a and b tell you which direction the graph takes and in which quadrants the graph is located?

Inclusion Point out to students that, unlike linear functions, b in an exponential function is not the y-intercept.

4a.

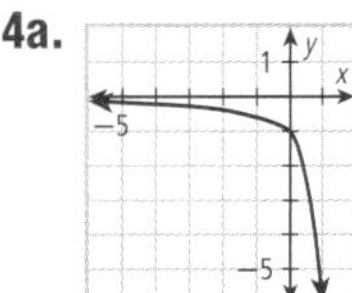

4b.

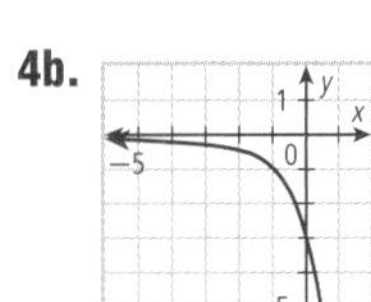

EXAMPLE 4 Graphing $y = ab^x$ with $a < 0$ and $b > 1$

Graph $y = -5(2)^x$.

Choose several values of x and generate ordered pairs.

x	$y = -5(2)^x$
−1	−2.5
0	−5
1	−10
2	−20

Graph the ordered pairs and connect with a smooth curve.

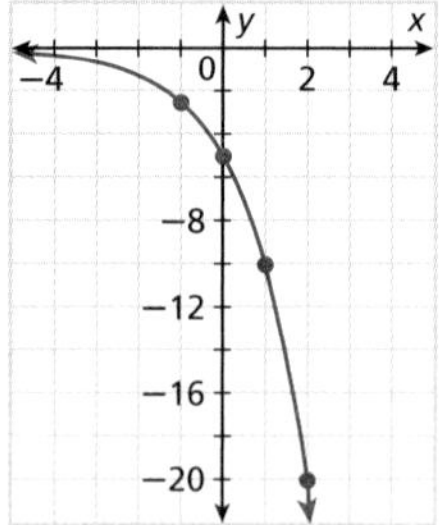

4a. Graph $y = -6^x$.

4b. Graph $y = -3(3)^x$.

EXAMPLE 5 Graphing $y = ab^x$ with $0 < b < 1$

Graph each exponential function.

A $y = 3\left(\frac{1}{2}\right)^x$

Choose several values of x and generate ordered pairs.

x	$y = 3\left(\frac{1}{2}\right)^x$
−1	6
0	3
1	1.5
2	0.75

Graph the ordered pairs and connect with a smooth curve.

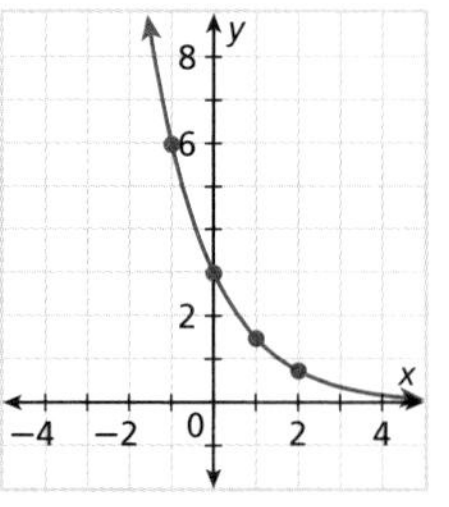

B $y = -2(0.4)^x$

Choose several values of x and generate ordered pairs.

x	$y = -2(0.4)^x$
−2	−12.5
−1	−5
0	−2
1	−0.8

Graph the ordered pairs and connect with a smooth curve.

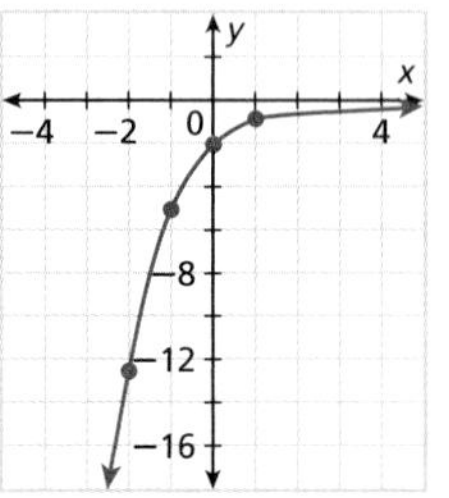

5a.

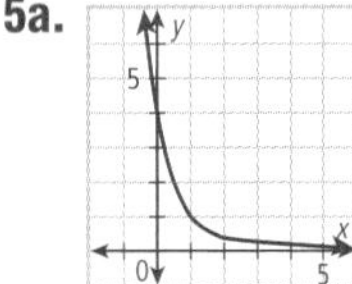

5b.

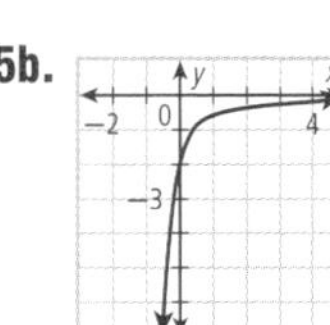

CHECK IT OUT! Graph each exponential function.

5a. $y = 4\left(\frac{1}{4}\right)^x$

5b. $y = -2(0.1)^x$

Teacher to Teacher

As students study exponential functions, it is critical that they understand why the base $b > 1$ makes the graph of $y = ab^x$ (where a is positive) increase while the base $0 < b < 1$ makes it decrease.

Students need plenty of real-world examples to help them understand the connection between the common ratio and the base b. For example, you can discuss what happens if you multiply something over and over by 5, as in $y = 5^x$, versus multiplying it over and over by $\frac{1}{5}$, as in $y = \left(\frac{1}{5}\right)^x$.

Once students understand how the base b affects the graph of $y = ab^x$, where $a > 0$, they can more easily remember how $a < 0$ affects the graph of $y = ab^x$ by thinking of it as a reflection across the x-axis.

Jennifer Bauer
East Haven, CT

The box summarizes the general shapes of exponential function graphs.

Graphs of Exponential Functions

$a > 0$, $a < 0$ For $y = ab^x$, if $b > 1$, then the graph will have one of these shapes.	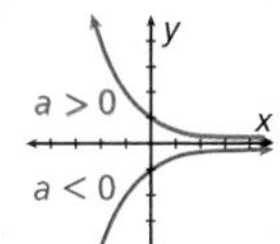 For $y = ab^x$, if $0 < b < 1$, then the graph will have one of these shapes.

EXAMPLE 6 ***Statistics Application***

In the year 2000, the world population was about 6 billion, and it was growing by 1.21% each year. At this growth rate, the function $f(x) = 6(1.0121)^x$ gives the population, in billions, x years after 2000. Using this model, in about what year will the population reach 7 billion?

Enter the function into the Y= editor of a graphing calculator.

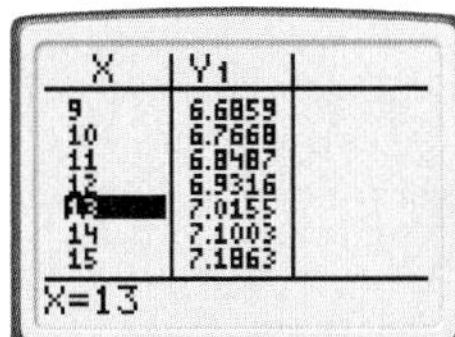

Press 2nd GRAPH (TABLE). Use the arrow keys to find a y-value as close to 7 as possible. The corresponding x-value is 13.

The world population will reach 7 billion in about 2013.

Caution!

The function values give the population *in billions*, so a y-value of 7 means 7 billion.

6. An accountant uses $f(x) = 12{,}330(0.869)^x$, where x is the time in years since the purchase, to model the value of a car. When will the car be worth $2000? **after about 13 yr**

THINK AND DISCUSS

1. How can you find the constant ratio of a set of exponential data?
2. **GET ORGANIZED** Copy and complete the graphic organizer. In each box, give an example of an appropriate exponential function and sketch its graph.

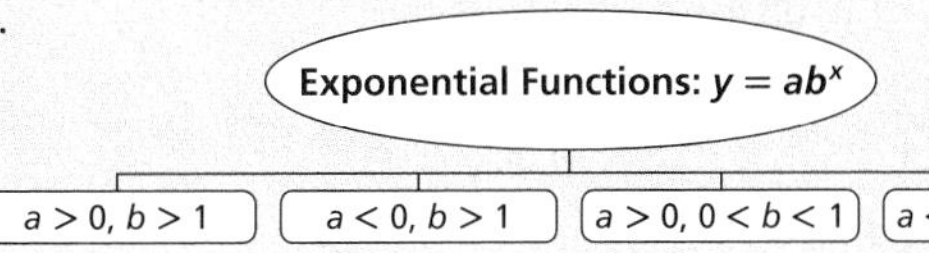

Teaching Tip **Multiple Representations** In **Example 6,** students could also graph the function and trace as close to $y = 7$ as possible.

Power Presentations with PowerPoint®

Additional Examples

Example 6

In 2000, each person in India consumed an average of 13 kg of sugar. Sugar consumption in India is projected to increase by 3.6% per year. At this growth rate, the function $f(x) = 13(1.036)^x$ gives the average yearly amount of sugar, in kilograms, consumed per person x years after 2000. Using this model, in about what year will sugar consumption average about 18 kg per person? 2009

Also available on transparency

INTERVENTION

Questioning Strategies

EXAMPLE 6

- Why is the x-value not the answer to the question?
- What types of conditions could change this prediction?

3 Close

Summarize

Write $f(x) = ab^x$ on the board. Point out the initial amount a, the common ratio b, and the independent variable x. Remind students that the independent variable always serves as the exponent in an exponential function. Then review the different shapes of exponential graphs. If a is positive, then the range is all positive numbers greater than 0, with an increasing graph for values of b greater than one. If a is negative, the graph is reflected across the x-axis.

FORMATIVE ASSESSMENT

and INTERVENTION 

***Diagnose Before* the Lesson**
11-7 Warm Up, TE p. 738

***Monitor During* the Lesson**
Check It Out! Exercises, SE pp. 738–741
Questioning Strategies, TE p. 739–741

***Assess After* the Lesson**
11-7 Lesson Quiz, TE p. 744
Alternative Assessment, TE p. 744

Answers to *Think and Discuss*

1. Possible answer: Make a table of values. Use x-values that change by the same amount each time as you move down the column. Then divide each y-value, starting with the second row, by the y-value before it. The quotient is the common ratio.
2. See p. A9.

11-7 Exercises

Assignment Guide

Assign *Guided Practice* exercises as necessary.

If you finished Examples **1–2**
Proficent 18–24, 35, 38–42
Advanced 18–24, 35, 38–42

If you finished Examples **1–6**
Proficent 18–34 even, 35–47, 52–56
Advanced 18–34 even, 35–56

Homework Quick Check
Quickly check key concepts.
Exercises: 18, 22, 26, 28, 32, 34, 40

Answers

3. As the x-values change by a constant amount, the y-values are not multiplied by a constant amount.
4. As the x-values change by a constant amount, the y-values are multiplied by a constant amount.
5. 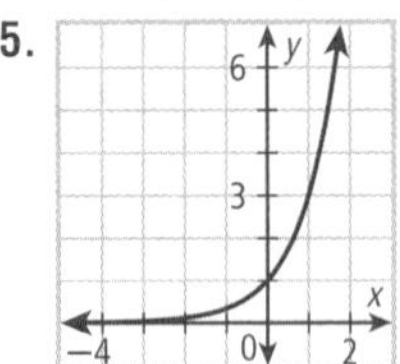

6. 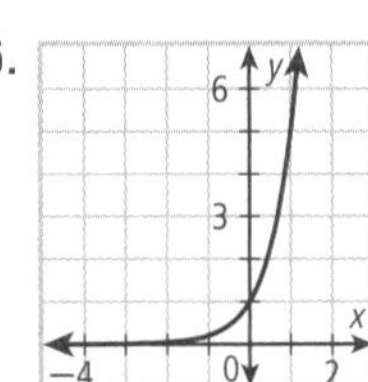

7–16. See pp. A26–A27.

21. Yes; as the x-values change by a constant amount, the y-values are multiplied by a constant amount.
22. No; as the x-values change by a constant amount, the y-values are not multiplied by a constant amount.
23. No; as the x-values change by a constant amount, the y-values are not multiplied by a constant amount.
24. Yes; as the x-values change by a constant amount, the y-values are multiplied by a constant amount.

11-7 Exercises

California Standards Practice
Preview of Algebra II 12.0; 1A24.1

go.hrw.com
Homework Help Online
KEYWORD: MA8CA 11-7
Parent Resources Online
KEYWORD: MA8CA Parent

GUIDED PRACTICE

1. **Vocabulary** Tell whether $y = 3x^4$ is an *exponential function.* Explain your answer. **No; there is no variable in the exponent.**

SEE EXAMPLE 1 p. 738

2. **Physical Science** The function $f(x) = 50{,}000(0.975)^x$, where x represents the underwater depth in meters, models the intensity of light below the water's surface in lumens per square meter. What is the intensity of light 200 meters below the surface? Round your answer to the nearest whole number. **316 lumens/m²**

SEE EXAMPLE 2 p. 739

Tell whether each set of ordered pairs satisfies an exponential function. Explain your answer.

3. $\{(-1, -1), (0, 0), (1, -1), (2, -4)\}$ **no**
4. $\{(0, 1), (1, 4), (2, 16), (3, 64)\}$ **yes**

SEE EXAMPLE 3 p. 739

Graph each exponential function.

5. $y = 3^x$
6. $y = 5^x$
7. $y = 10(3)^x$
8. $y = 5(2)^x$

SEE EXAMPLE 4 p. 740

9. $y = -2(3)^x$
10. $y = -4(2)^x$
11. $y = -3(2)^x$
12. $y = 2(3)^x$

SEE EXAMPLE 5 p. 740

13. $y = -\left(\frac{1}{4}\right)^x$
14. $y = \left(\frac{1}{3}\right)^x$
15. $y = 2\left(\frac{1}{4}\right)^x$
16. $y = -2(0.25)^x$

SEE EXAMPLE 6 p. 741

17. The function $f(x) = 57.8(1.02)^x$ gives the approximate number of passenger cars, in millions, in the United States x years after 1960. Using this model, in about what year will the number of passenger cars reach 200 million? **about 2023**

PRACTICE AND PROBLEM SOLVING

Independent Practice

For Exercises	See Example
18–20	1
21–24	2
25–27	3
28–30	4
31–33	5
34	6

Extra Practice
Skills Practice p. EP23
Application Practice p. EP34

18. **Sports** If a golf ball is dropped from a height of 27 feet, the function $f(x) = 27\left(\frac{2}{3}\right)^x$ gives the height in feet of each bounce, where x is the bounce number. What will be the height of the 4th bounce? **$5\frac{1}{3}$ ft**
19. Suppose the depth of a lake can be described by the function $y = 334(0.976)^x$, where x represents the number of weeks from today. Today, the depth of the lake is 334 ft. What will the depth be in 6 weeks? Round your answer to the nearest whole number. **289 ft**
20. **Physical Science** A ball rolling down a slope travels continuously faster. Suppose the function $y = 1.3(1.41)^x$ describes the speed of the ball in inches per minute. How fast will the ball be rolling in 15 minutes? Round your answer to the nearest hundredth. **225.02 in./min**

Tell whether each set of ordered pairs satisfies an exponential function. Explain your answer.

21. $\{(-2, 9), (-1, 3), (0, 1), \left(1, \frac{1}{3}\right)\}$
22. $\{(-1, 0), (0, 1), (1, 4), (2, 9)\}$
23. $\{(-1, -5), (0, -3), (1, -1), (2, 1)\}$
24. $\{(-3, 6.25), (-2, 12.5), (-1, 25), (0, 50)\}$

11-7 READING STRATEGIES

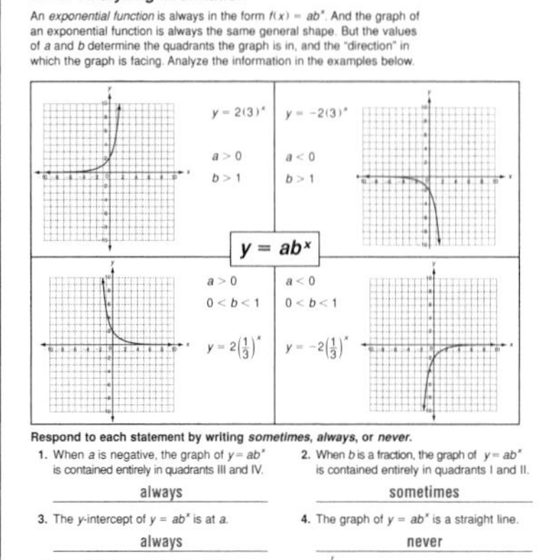

LESSON 11-7 Reading Strategies
Analyzing Information

An *exponential function* is always in the form $f(x) = ab^x$. And the graph of an exponential function is always the same general shape. But the values of a and b determine the quadrants the graph is in, and the "direction" in which the graph is facing. Analyze the information in the examples below.

Respond to each statement by writing *sometimes, always,* or *never*.

1. When a is negative, the graph of $y = ab^x$ is contained entirely in quadrants III and IV. always
2. When b is a fraction, the graph of $y = ab^x$ is contained entirely in quadrants I and II. sometimes
3. The y-intercept of $y = ab^x$ is at a. always
4. The graph of $y = ab^x$ is a straight line. never
5. Complete the table of values and sketch the graph of $y = -3(2)^x$.

x	y
−1	$-\frac{3}{2}$
0	−3
1	−6
2	−12

11-7 REVIEW FOR MASTERY

LESSON 11-7 Review for Mastery
Exponential Functions

An **exponential function** has the independent variable as the exponent.

$y = 3^x$ and $y = -2(0.5)^x$ are exponential functions.

A set of ordered pairs satisfies an exponential function if the y-values are multiplied by a constant amount as the x-values change by a constant amount.

Tell whether the following ordered pairs satisfy an exponential function.

x	y
3	4
5	12
7	36
9	108

Think 4 × ? = 12.
Think 12 × ? = 36.
Think 36 × ? = 108.

The x-values increase by the constant amount 2.

Each y-value is multiplied by the constant amount 3.

This is an exponential function.

x	y
1	2
2	4
3	6
4	8

Think 2 × ? = 4.
Think 4 × ? = 6.
Think 6 × ? = 8.

The x-values increase by the constant amount 1.

The y-value is multiplied by 2, then 1.5, then $1.\overline{3}$. There is no constant ratio.

This is not an exponential function.

The population of a school can be described by the function $f(x) = 1500(1.02)^x$, where x represents the number of years since the school was built. What will be the population of the school in 12 years?

$f(x) = 1500(1.02)^x$
$f(12) = 1500(1.02)^{12}$ *Substitute 12 for x.*
≈ 1902 *Round number of people to the nearest whole number.*

Tell whether the ordered pairs satisfy an exponential function.

1.

x	y
−1	1.5
−2	3
−3	6
−4	12

yes

2.

x	y
1	1
2	2
3	6
4	24

no

3.

x	y
−2	−2
−1	−10
0	−50
1	−250

yes

4. If a rubber ball is dropped from a height of 10 feet, the function $f(x) = 20(0.6)^x$ gives the height in feet of each bounce, where x is the bounce number. What will be the height of the 5th bounce? Round to the nearest tenth of a foot. 1.6 feet
5. A population of pigs is expected to increase at a rate of 4% each year. If the original population is 1000, the function $f(x) = 1000(1.04)^x$ gives the population in x years. What will be the population in 12 years? ≈1601

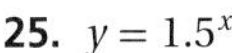

Graph each exponential function.

25. $y = 1.5^x$ **26.** $y = \frac{1}{3}(3)^x$ **27.** $y = 100(0.7)^x$

28. $y = -2(4)^x$ **29.** $y = -1(5)^x$ **30.** $y = -\frac{1}{2}(4)^x$

31. $y = 4\left(\frac{1}{2}\right)^x$ **32.** $y = -2\left(\frac{1}{3}\right)^x$ **33.** $y = 0.5(0.25)^x$

Technology

Early silicon chips were about the size of your pinky finger and held one transistor. Today, chips the size of a baby's fingernail hold over 100 million transistors.

34. Technology Moore's law states that the maximum number of transistors that can fit on a silicon chip doubles every two years. The function $f(x) = 42(1.41)^x$ models the number of transistors, in millions, that can fit on a chip, where x is the number of years since 2000. Predict what year it will be when a chip can hold 1 billion transistors. **about 2009**

35. Multi-Step A computer randomly creates three different functions. The functions are $y = (3.1x + 7)^2$, $y = 4.8(2)^x$, and $y = \frac{1}{5}(6)^x$.

a. Identify which function or functions are exponential. $\mathbf{y = 4.8(2)^x,\ y = \frac{1}{5}(6)^x}$

b. Josie input an x-value into one of the exponential functions, and the computer returned a y-value of 38.4. Which function did Josie use? $\mathbf{y = 4.8(2)^x}$

c. Evaluate $y = 4.8(2)^x$ for $x = 0$ and $x = 4$ **4.8; 76.8**

d. Evaluate $y = \frac{1}{5}(6)^x$ for $x = 0$ and $x = 4$ **0.2; 259.2**

e. What can Josie tell about the difference between the graphs of the two exponential functions from the answers to part **c** and **d**?

36. Contests As a promotion, a clothing store draws the name of one of its customers each week. The prize is a coupon for the store. If the winner is not present at the drawing, he or she cannot claim the prize, and the amount of the coupon increases for the following week's drawing. The function $f(x) = 20(1.2)^x$ gives the amount of the coupon in dollars after x weeks of the prize going unclaimed.

a. What is the amount of the coupon after 2 weeks of the prize going unclaimed? **a. $28.80**

b. After how many weeks of the prize going unclaimed will the amount of the coupon be greater than $100? **after 9 weeks**

c. What is the original amount of the coupon? **$20**

d. Find the percent increase each week. **20%**

37. Critical Thinking In the definition of exponential function, the value of b cannot be 1, and the value of a cannot be 0. Why?

37. If the value of b were 1, the function would be constant. If the value of a were 0, the function would be the constant function $y = 0$.

Graphing Calculator Graph each group of functions on the same screen. How are their graphs alike? How are they different?

38. $y = 2^x, y = 3^x, y = 4^x$ **39.** $y = \left(\frac{1}{2}\right)^x, y = \left(\frac{1}{3}\right)^x, y = \left(\frac{1}{4}\right)^x$

Evaluate each of the following for the given value of x.

40. $f(x) = 4^x;\ x = 3$ **64**

41. $f(x) = -(0.25)^x;\ x = 1.5$ **−0.125**

42. $f(x) = 0.4(10)^x;\ x = -3$ **0.0004, or 4×10^{-4}**

43. This problem will prepare you for the Concept Connection on page 762.

a. The annual tuition at a community college since 2001 is modeled by the equation $C = 2000(1.08)^n$, where C is the tuition cost and n is the number of years since 2001. What was the tuition cost in 2001? **$2000**

b. What is the annual percentage of tuition increase? **8%**

c. Find the tuition cost in 2006. **$2938.66**

CONCEPT CONNECTION **Exercise 43** involves evaluating exponential functions. This exercise prepares students for the Concept Connection on page 762.

Answers

25.

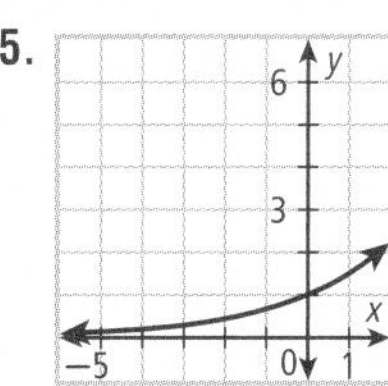

26.

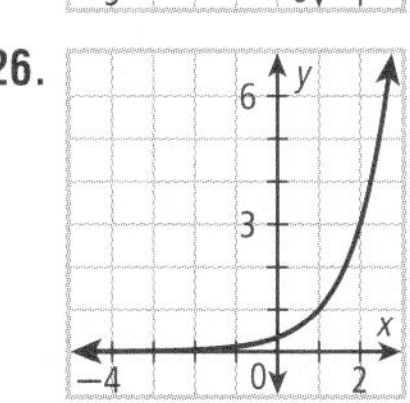

27.

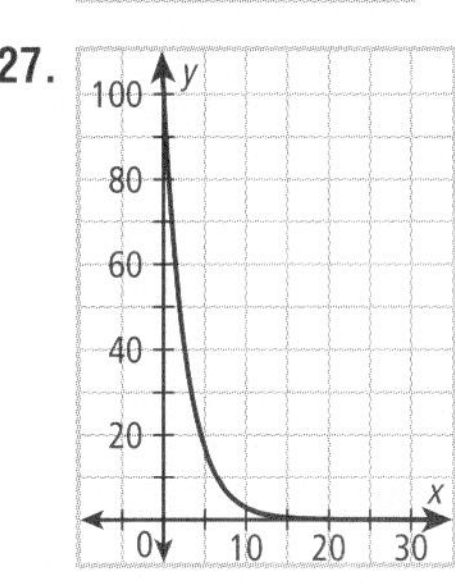

28.

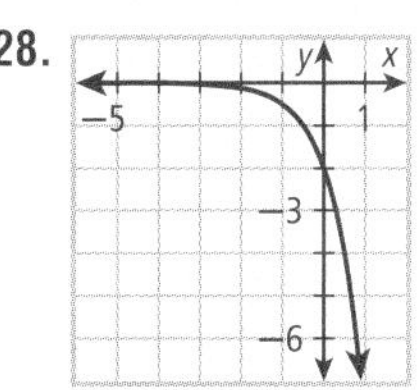

29–33. See p. A27.

35e. Possible answer: The graph of $y = \frac{1}{5}(6)^x$ increases faster.

38, 39. See p. A27.

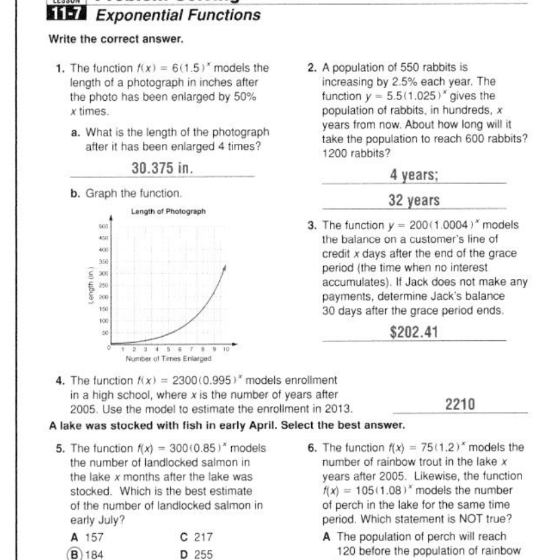

11-7 PROBLEM SOLVING

LESSON 11-7 **Problem Solving**
Exponential Functions

Write the correct answer.

1. The function $f(x) = 6(1.5)^x$ models the length of a photograph in inches after the photo has been enlarged by 50% x times.
   a. What is the length of the photograph after it has been enlarged 4 times? **30.375 in.**
   b. Graph the function.

2. A population of 550 rabbits is increasing by 2.5% each year. The function $y = 5.5(1.025)^x$ gives the population of rabbits, in hundreds, x years from now. About how long will it take the population to reach 600 rabbits? 1200 rabbits? **4 years; 32 years**

3. The function $y = 200(1.0004)^x$ models the balance on a customer's line of credit x days after the end of the grace period (the time when no interest accumulates). If Jack does not make any payments, determine Jack's balance 30 days after the grace period ends. **$202.41**

4. The function $f(x) = 2300(0.995)^x$ models enrollment in a high school, where x is the number of years after 2005. Use the model to estimate the enrollment in 2013. **2210**

A lake was stocked with fish in early April. Select the best answer.

5. The function $f(x) = 300(0.85)^x$ models the number of landlocked salmon in the lake x months after the lake was stocked. Which is the best estimate of the number of landlocked salmon in early July?
   A 157 (B) 184 C 217 D 255

6. The function $f(x) = 75(1.2)^x$ models the number of rainbow trout in the lake x years after 2005. Likewise, the function $f(x) = 105(1.08)^x$ models the number of perch in the lake for the same time period. Which statement is NOT true?
   A The population of perch will reach 120 before the population of rainbow trout does.
   B In 2009, the number of rainbow trout will exceed the number of perch.
   (C) In 2007, the number of rainbow trout will be less than 100.
   D In 10 years, there will be at least twice as many rainbow trout as perch.

7. The function $f(x) = 400(1.05)^x$ models the number of bass x months after the lake was stocked. During what month will the population reach 600?
   F September G October H November (J) December

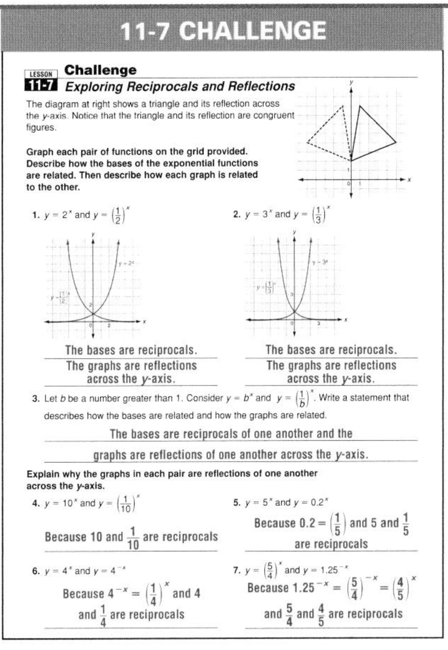

11-7 CHALLENGE

LESSON 11-7 **Challenge**
Exploring Reciprocals and Reflections

The diagram at right shows a triangle and its reflection across the y-axis. Notice that the triangle and its reflection are congruent figures.

Graph each pair of functions on the grid provided. Describe how the bases of the exponential functions are related. Then describe how each graph is related to the other.

1. $y = 2^x$ and $y = \left(\frac{1}{2}\right)^x$
   The bases are reciprocals. The graphs are reflections across the y-axis.

2. $y = 3^x$ and $y = \left(\frac{1}{3}\right)^x$
   The bases are reciprocals. The graphs are reflections across the y-axis.

3. Let b be a number greater than 1. Consider $y = b^x$ and $y = \left(\frac{1}{b}\right)^x$. Write a statement that describes how the bases are related and how the graphs are related.
   The bases are reciprocals of one another and the graphs are reflections of one another across the y-axis.

Explain why the graphs in each pair are reflections of one another across the y-axis.

4. $y = 10^x$ and $y = \left(\frac{1}{10}\right)^x$
   Because 10 and $\frac{1}{10}$ are reciprocals

5. $y = 5^x$ and $y = 0.2^x$
   Because $0.2 = \left(\frac{1}{5}\right)$ and 5 and $\frac{1}{5}$ are reciprocals

6. $y = 4^x$ and $y = 4^{-x}$
   Because $4^{-x} = \left(\frac{1}{4}\right)^x$ and 4 and $\frac{1}{4}$ are reciprocals

7. $y = \left(\frac{5}{4}\right)^x$ and $y = 1.25^{-x}$
   Because $1.25^{-x} = \left(\frac{5}{4}\right)^{-x} = \left(\frac{4}{5}\right)^x$ and $\frac{5}{4}$ and $\frac{4}{5}$ are reciprocals

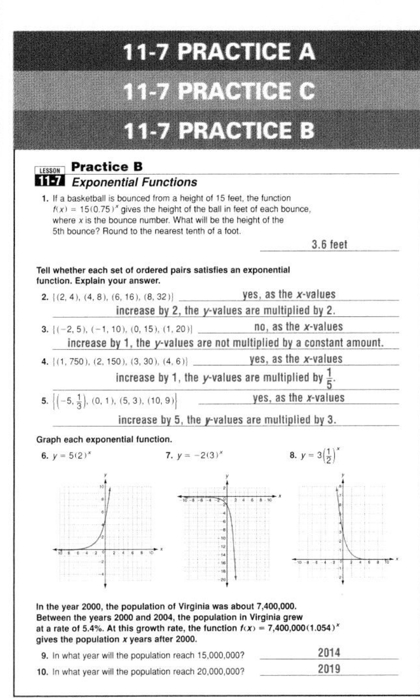

11-7 PRACTICE A

11-7 PRACTICE C

11-7 PRACTICE B

LESSON 11-7 **Practice B**
Exponential Functions

1. If a basketball is bounced from a height of 15 feet, the function $f(x) = 15(0.75)^x$ gives the height of the ball in feet of each bounce, where x is the bounce number. What will be the height of the 5th bounce? Round to the nearest tenth of a foot. **3.6 feet**

Tell whether each set of ordered pairs satisfies an exponential function. Explain your answer.

2. $\{(2, 4), (4, 8), (6, 16), (8, 32)\}$ **yes, as the x-values increase by 2, the y-values are multiplied by 2.**

3. $\{(-2, 5), (-1, 10), (0, 15), (1, 20)\}$ **no, as the x-values increase by 1, the y-values are not multiplied by a constant amount.**

4. $\{(1, 750), (2, 150), (3, 30), (4, 6)\}$ **yes, as the x-values increase by 1, the y-values are multiplied by $\frac{1}{5}$.**

5. $\left\{\left(-5, \frac{1}{3}\right), (0, 1), (5, 3), (10, 9)\right\}$ **yes, as the x-values increase by 5, the y-values are multiplied by 3.**

Graph each exponential function.

6. $y = 5(2)^x$ 7. $y = -2(3)^x$ 8. $y = 3\left(\frac{1}{2}\right)^x$

In the year 2000, the population of Virginia was about 7,400,000. Between the years 2000 and 2004, the population in Virginia grew at a rate of 5.4%. At this growth rate, the function $f(x) = 7{,}400{,}000(1.054)^x$ gives the population x years after 2000.

9. In what year will the population reach 15,000,000? **2014**

10. In what year will the population reach 20,000,000? **2019**

 **Multiple Choice** Remind students who chose **A** or **B** in **Exercise 45** that the range of an exponential function is restricted to either values greater than or less than 0. Students who chose **D** may have forgotten that the domain of an exponential function is all real numbers.

Students who chose **C** in **Exercise 46** raised 1.4 to the power of $x - 1$.

 ***Journal***

Have students describe two ways of identifying an exponential function.

ALTERNATIVE ASSESSMENT

Sketch the four basic shapes of exponential graphs on the board. Then, for each one, have students write an exponential function whose graph has a similar shape.

Power Presentations with PowerPoint®

 **11-7 Lesson Quiz**

Tell whether each set of ordered pairs satisfies an exponential function. Explain your answer.

1. $\{(0, 0), (1, -2), (2, -16), (3, -54)\}$ No; for a constant change in x, y is not multiplied by the same value.
2. $\{(0, -5), (1, -2.5), (2, -1.25), (3, -0.625)\}$ Yes; for a constant change in x, y is multiplied by the same value.
3. Graph $y = -0.5(3)^x$.

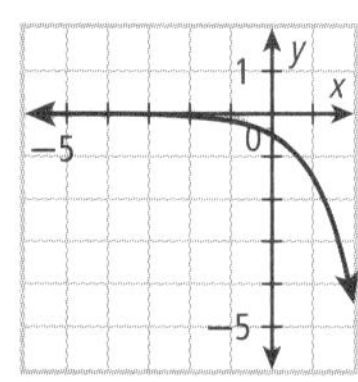

4. The function $y = 11.6(1.009)^x$ models residential energy consumption in quadrillion Btu where x is the number of years after 2003. What will residential energy consumption be in 2013? $\approx$12.7 quadrillion Btu
5. In 2000, the population of Texas was about 21 million, and it was growing by about 2% per year. At this growth rate, the function $f(x) = 21(1.02)^x$ gives the population, in millions, x years after 2000. Using this model, in about what year will the population reach 30 million? 2018

Also available on transparency 

44. **Write About It** Your employer offers two salary plans. With plan A, your salary is given by $y = 10{,}000(2x)$, where x is the number of years you have worked for the company. With plan B, your salary is given by $y = 10{,}000(2)^x$. Which plan would you choose? Why?

Multiple Choice For Exercises 45–47, choose the best answer.

45. Which graph shows an exponential function?

Ⓐ 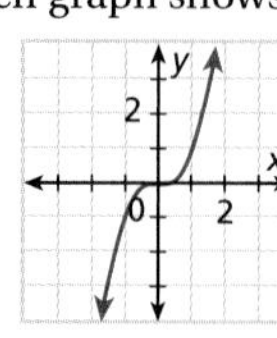

 Ⓒ 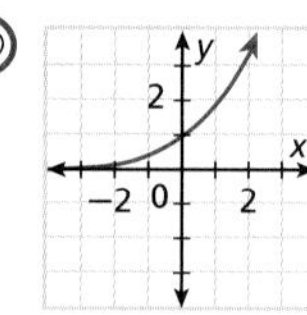

 Ⓑ 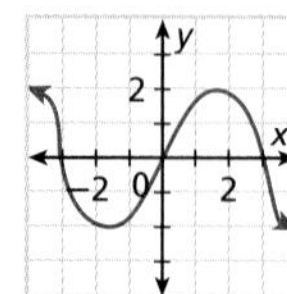

Ⓓ 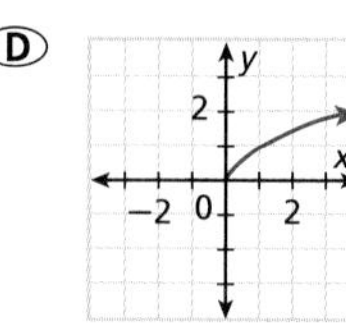

46. The function $f(x) = 15(1.4)^x$ represents the area in square inches of a photograph after it has been enlarged x times by a factor of 140%. What is the area of the photograph after it has been enlarged 4 times?

Ⓐ 5.6 square inches　Ⓒ 41.16 square inches
Ⓑ 57.624 square inches　Ⓓ 560 square inches

47. If n represents the stage number, which expression could represent the number of squares in the nth stage?

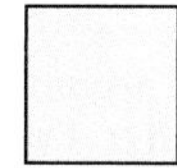
Stage 0

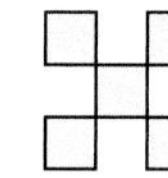
Stage 1

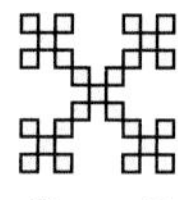
Stage 2

Ⓐ $5n$　Ⓑ $2.5 \cdot 2^n$　Ⓒ 25^{n-1}　Ⓓ 5^n

CHALLENGE AND EXTEND

Solve each equation. Check your answer.

48. $4^x = 64$ **3**　49. $\left(\frac{1}{3}\right)^x = \frac{1}{27}$ **3**　50. $2^x = \frac{1}{16}$ **−4**

51. **Reasoning** Graph the following functions: $y = 2(2)^x$, $y = 3(2)^x$, $y = -2(2)^x$. Then use inductive reasoning to make a conjecture about the relationship between the value of a and the y-intercept of $y = ab^x$.

SPIRAL STANDARDS REVIEW

 4.0, 11.0, 14.0

52. The average of Roger's three test scores must be at least 90 to earn an A in his science class. Roger has scored 88 and 89 on his first two tests. Write and solve an inequality to find what he must score on the third test to earn an A. *(Lesson 3-4)*

52. $\frac{88 + 89 + x}{3} \geq 90$; $x \geq 93$

Find the missing term in each perfect-square trinomial. *(Lesson 8-5)*

53. $x^2 + 10x + ▒$ **25**　54. $4x^2 + ▒ + 64$ **32x**　55. $▒ + 42x + 49$ **9x²**

56. Solve $x^2 + 4x = 5$ by completing the square. Check your answer. *(Lesson 9-7)* **1, −5**

Answers

44. Possible answer: The following table shows how much money you could earn with each plan.

Year	Salary w/ Plan A ($)	Salary w/ Plan B ($)
0	0	10,000
1	20,000	20,000
2	40,000	40,000
3	60,000	80,000

I would choose plan B because plan A doesn't pay you anything for the first year and because after 3 years, plan B pays more money.

51.

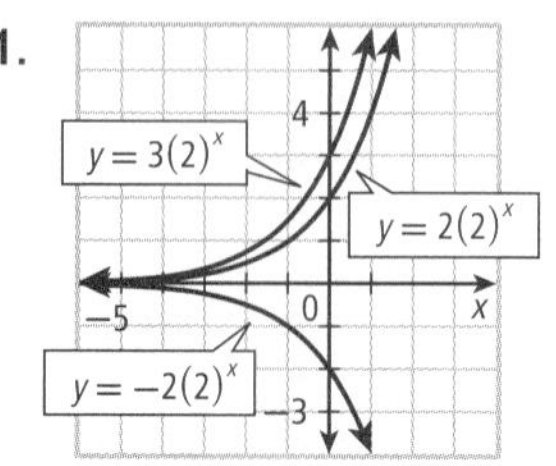

The value of a is the y-intercept.

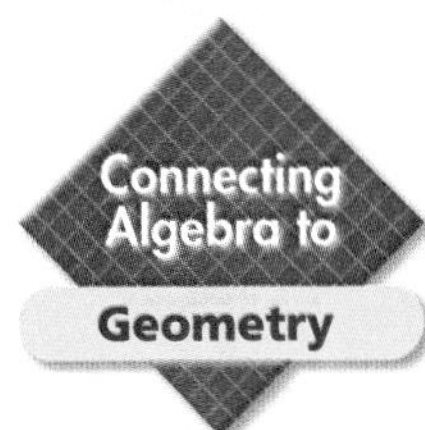

Changing Dimensions

What happens to the volume of a three-dimensional figure when you repeatedly double the dimensions?

California Standards

Reinforcement of 7MG2.3 Compute the length of the perimeter, the surface area of the faces and **the volume of a three-dimensional object** built from rectangular solids. **Understand that when the lengths of all dimensions are multiplied by a scale factor,** the surface area is multiplied by the square of the scale factor and **the volume is multiplied by the cube of the scale factor.**

Recall these formulas for the volumes of common three-dimensional figures.

Cube $V = s^3$

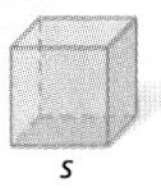

Rectangular Prism $V = \ell wh$

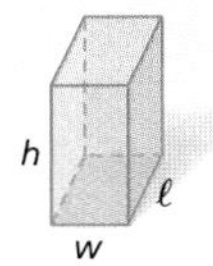

Pyramid $V = \frac{1}{3}(\text{area of base}) \cdot h$

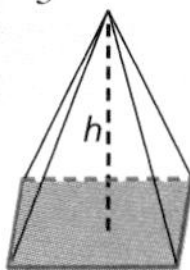

Changing the dimensions of three-dimensional figures results in geometric sequences.

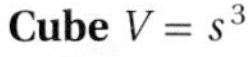

Example

Find the volume of a cube with a side length of 3 cm. Double the side length and find the new volume. Repeat two more times. Show the patterns for the side lengths and volumes as geometric sequences. Identify the common ratios.

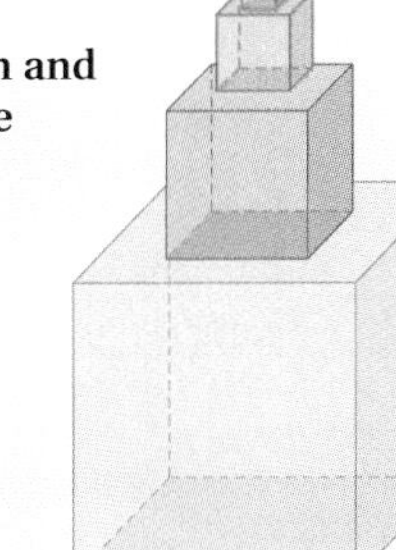

Cube	Side Length (cm)	Volume (cm³)
1	3	27
2	6 (×2)	216 (×8)
3	12 (×2)	1,728 (×8)
4	24 (×2)	13,824 (×8)

The side lengths and the volumes form geometric sequences. The sequence of the side lengths has a common ratio of 2. The sequence of the volumes has a common ratio of 2^3, or 8.

The patterns in the example above are a specific instance of a general rule.

> When the dimensions of a solid figure are multiplied by k, the volume of the figure is multiplied by k^3.

Try This

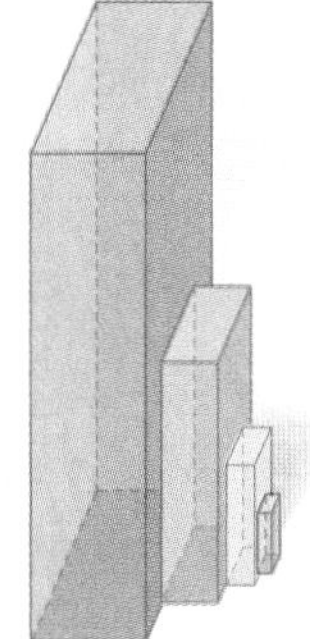

1. The large rectangular prism at right is 8 in. wide, 16 in. long, and 32 in. tall. The dimensions are multiplied by $\frac{1}{2}$ to create each next smaller prism. Show the patterns for the dimensions and the volumes as geometric sequences. Identify the common ratios.
2. A pyramid has a height of 8 cm and a square base of 3 cm on each edge. Triple the dimensions two times. Show the patterns for the dimensions and the volumes as geometric sequences. Identify the common ratios.

Answers

1. widths: 8, 4, 2, 1; common ratio: $\frac{1}{2}$;
   lengths: 16, 8, 4, 2; common ratio: $\frac{1}{2}$
   heights: 32, 16, 8, 4; common ratio: $\frac{1}{2}$,
   volumes: 4096, 512, 64, 8; common ratio: $\frac{1}{8}$
2. heights: 8, 24, 72; common ratio: 3
   edge of bases: 3, 9, 27; common ratio: 3
   volumes: 24, 648, 17,496; common ratio: 27

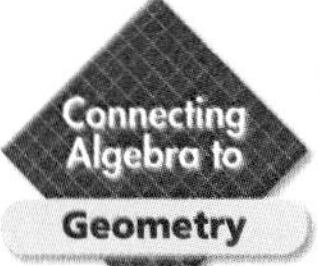

Organizer

See Skills Bank page SB21

Objective: Express with geometric sequences how the changing dimensions of solid figures affects volume.

Teach

Remember

Students review and apply volume formulas for common solids.

INTERVENTION For additional review and practice with volume formulas, see Skills Bank page SB21.

Visual Ask students what they notice about the sets of figures on the lesson pages. If no one realizes it, point out that each set shows a group of similar figures.

Close

Assess

The edges of a cube are multiplied by 5. What happens to the volume of the cube? The volume is multiplied by $5^3 = 125$.

Reinforcement of 7MG2.3

Organizer

Use with Lesson 11-8

Objective: Fold and cut paper to model exponential growth and decay.

Materials: notebook paper, scissors

Teach

Discuss

Remind students that $2^0 = 1$ and $2^{-n} = \frac{1}{2^n}$.

In **Activity 1,** the exponent equals the number of folds. In **Activity 2,** the exponent equals the opposite of the number of cuts.

Close

Key Concept

Multiplying repeatedly by numbers greater than 1 causes a quantity to increase, while multiplying repeatedly by numbers between 0 and 1 causes a quantity to decrease.

Assessment

Journal For each activity, have students explain what b represents in the exponential function $f(x) = b^x$.

California Standards

Algebra 1 2.0

11-8

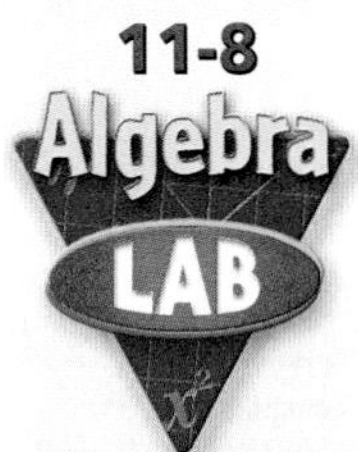

Model Growth and Decay

Use with Lesson 11-8

You can fold and cut paper to model quantities that increase or decrease exponentially.

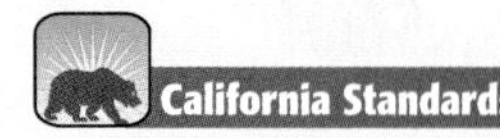

2.0 Students understand and use such operations as taking the opposite, finding the reciprocal, taking a root, and raising to a fractional power. **They understand and use the rules of exponents.**

Activity 1

1. Copy the table at right.
2. Fold a piece of notebook paper in half. Then open it back up. Count the number of regions created by the fold. Record your answer in the table.
3. Now fold the paper in half twice. Record the number of regions created by the folds in the table.
4. Repeat this process for 3, 4, and 5 folds.

Folds	Regions
0	1
1	**2**
2	**4**
3	**8**
4	**16**
5	**32**

Try This

1. When the number of folds increases by 1, the number of regions ___?___. **doubles**
2. For each row of the table, write the number of regions as a power of 2. $\mathbf{2^0, 2^1, 2^2, 2^3, 2^4, 2^5}$
3. Write an exponential expression for the number of regions formed by n folds. $\mathbf{2^n}$
4. If you could fold the paper 8 times, how many regions would be formed? **256**
5. How many times would you have to fold the paper to make 512 regions? **9**

Activity 2

1. Copy the table at right.
2. Begin with a square piece of paper. The area of the paper is 1 square unit. Cut the paper in half. Each piece has an area of $\frac{1}{2}$ square unit. Record the result in the table.
3. Cut one of those pieces in half again, and record the area of one of the new, smaller pieces in the table.
4. Repeat this process for 3, 4, and 5 cuts.

Cuts	Area
0	1
1	$\mathbf{\frac{1}{2}}$
2	$\mathbf{\frac{1}{4}}$
3	$\mathbf{\frac{1}{8}}$
4	$\mathbf{\frac{1}{16}}$
5	$\mathbf{\frac{1}{32}}$

Try This

6. When the number of cuts increases by 1, the area ___?___. **is divided in half**
7. For each row of the table, write the area as a power of 2. $\mathbf{2^0, 2^{-1}, 2^{-2}, 2^{-3}, 2^{-4}, 2^{-5}}$
8. Write an exponential expression for the area after n cuts. $\mathbf{2^{-n}}$
9. What would be the area after 7 cuts? $\mathbf{\frac{1}{128}}$
10. How many cuts would you have to make to get an area of $\frac{1}{256}$ square unit? **8**

11-8 Exponential Growth and Decay

California Standards

Preview of Algebra II
12.0 Students know the laws of fractional exponents, **understand exponential functions, and use these functions in problems involving exponential growth and decay.**

Vocabulary
exponential growth
compound interest
exponential decay
half-life

Why learn this?
Exponential growth and decay describe many real-world situations, such as the value of an investment. (See Example 1.)

Exponential growth occurs when a quantity increases by the same rate r in each time period t. When this happens, the value of the quantity at any given time can be calculated as a function of the rate and the original amount.

Know it! Note

Exponential Growth

An exponential growth function has the form $y = a(1 + r)^t$, where $a > 0$.
- y represents the final amount.
- a represents the original amount.
- r represents the rate of growth expressed as a decimal.
- t represents time.

EXAMPLE 1 Exponential Growth

The original value of an investment is \$1400, and the value increases by 9% each year. Write an exponential growth function to model this situation. Then find the value of the investment in 25 years.

Helpful Hint
In Example 1, round to the nearest hundredth because the problem deals with money. This means you are rounding to the nearest cent.

Step 1 Write the exponential growth function for this situation.

$y = a(1 + r)^t$	*Write the formula.*
$= 1400(1 + 0.09)^t$	*Substitute 1400 for a and 0.09 for r.*
$= 1400(1.09)^t$	*Simplify.*

Step 2 Find the value in 25 years.

$y = 1400(1.09)^t$	
$= 1400(1.09)^{25}$	*Substitute 25 for t.*
$\approx 12{,}072.31$	*Use a calculator and round to the nearest hundredth.*

The value of the investment in 25 years is \$12,072.31.

CHECK IT OUT!
1. An investment is increasing in value at a rate of 8% per year, and its value in 2000 was \$1200. Write an exponential growth function to model this situation. Then find the investment's value in 2006. $y = 1200(1.08)^t$; **\$1904.25**

11-8 Organizer

Objective: Solve problems involving exponential growth and decay.

Algebra Lab
In *Chapter 11 Resource File*

Online Edition
Tutorial Videos, Interactivity

Power Presentations with PowerPoint®

Warm Up

Simplify each expression.
1. $(4 + 0.05)^2$ 16.4025
2. $25(1 + 0.02)^3$ 26.5302
3. $1 + \frac{0.03}{4}$ 1.0075
4. The first term of a geometric sequence is 3 and the common ratio is 2. What is the 5th term of the sequence? 48
5. The function $f(x) = 2(4)^x$ models an insect population after x days. What is the insect population after 3 days? 128 insects

Also available on transparency

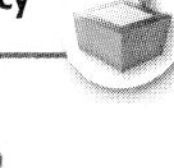

Math Humor

Q: Why was the banker's son sent to the principal's office?
A: He had high interest in another student's test paper.

1 Introduce

EXPLORATION

11-8 Exponential Growth and Decay

Kendrick puts \$200 in a savings account that earns 4% interest each year.
1. How much interest will Kendrick earn in the first year?
2. What is the total amount of money that Kendrick will have at the end of the first year?
3. In the second year, Kendrick will receive 4% interest on the total amount of money you found in Problem 2. How much interest will that be?
4. Complete the table.

Year	Process: Beginning Amount × 1.04	Exponential Form	Total (\$)
1	200(1.04)	200(1.04)	
2	[200(1.04)](1.04)	$200(1.04)^2$	
3			
4			
5			

THINK AND DISCUSS
5. Describe any patterns you see in the table.
6. Show how to write an equation for the total amount of money A that Kendrick will have in year t.

Motivate

Review the formula for simple interest I: $I = Prt$, where P is the principal, or original amount, r is the interest rate as a decimal, and t is time.

Have students compute the simple interest on \$200 invested at 4% for 20 years. \$160

Explorations and answers are provided in *Alternate Openers: Explorations Transparencies.*

California Standards
Preview of Algebra II 12.0

A common application of exponential growth is *compound interest*. Recall that simple interest is earned or paid only on the principal. **Compound interest** is interest earned or paid on *both* the principal and previously earned interest.

Know it! Note

Compound Interest

$A = P\left(1 + \frac{r}{n}\right)^{nt}$

A represents the balance after *t* years.

P represents the principal, or original amount.

r represents the annual interest rate expressed as a decimal.

n represents the number of times interest is compounded per year.

t represents time in years.

EXAMPLE 2 ***Finance Application***

Write a compound interest function to model each situation. Then find the balance after the given number of years.

A **\$1000 invested at a rate of 3% compounded quarterly; 5 years**

Step 1 Write the compound interest function for this situation.

$A = P\left(1 + \frac{r}{n}\right)^{nt}$ *Write the formula.*

$= 1000\left(1 + \frac{0.03}{4}\right)^{4t}$ *Substitute 1000 for P, 0.03 for r, and 4 for n.*

$= 1000(1.0075)^{4t}$ *Simplify.*

Step 2 Find the balance after 5 years.

$A = 1000(1.0075)^{4(5)}$ *Substitute 5 for t.*

$= 1000(1.0075)^{20}$

≈ 1161.18 *Use a calculator and round to the nearest hundredth.*

The balance after 5 years is \$1161.18.

B **\$18,000 invested at a rate of 4.5% compounded annually; 6 years**

Step 1 Write the compound interest function for this situation.

$A = P\left(1 + \frac{r}{n}\right)^{nt}$ *Write the formula.*

$= 18{,}000\left(1 + \frac{0.045}{1}\right)^{t}$ *Substitute 18,000 for P, 0.045 for r, and 1 for n.*

$= 18{,}000(1.045)^{t}$ *Simplify.*

Step 2 Find the balance after 6 years.

$A = 18{,}000(1.045)^{6}$ *Substitute 6 for t.*

$\approx 23{,}440.68$ *Use a calculator and round to the nearest hundredth.*

The balance after 6 years is \$23,440.68.

Reading Math

For compound interest,
- *annually* means "once per year" ($n = 1$).
- *quarterly* means "4 times per year" ($n = 4$).
- *monthly* means "12 times per year" ($n = 12$).

CHECK IT OUT! **Write a compound interest function to model each situation. Then find the balance after the given number of years.**

2a. \$1200 invested at a rate of 3.5% compounded quarterly; 4 years

2b. \$4000 invested at a rate of 3% compounded monthly; 8 years

2a. $A = 1200(1.00875)^{4t}$; **\$1379.49**

2b. $A = 4000(1.0025)^{12t}$; **\$5083.47**

Power Presentations with PowerPoint®

Additional Examples

Example 1

The original value of a painting is \$9000 and the value increases by 7% each year. Write an exponential growth function to model this situation. Then find the painting's value in 15 years.
$y = 9000(1.07)^t$; \$24,831.28

Example 2

Write a compound interest function to model each situation. Then find the balance after the given number of years.

A. \$1200 invested at a rate of 2% compounded quarterly; 3 years $A = 1200(1.005)^{4t}$; \$1274.01

B. \$15,000 invested at a rate of 4.8% compounded monthly; 2 years. $A = 15{,}000(1.004)^{12t}$; \$16,508.22

Also available on transparency

INTERVENTION

Questioning Strategies

EXAMPLE 1

- How is the formula for exponential growth similar to the standard form of an exponential function?
- How is this formula like that for finding the *n*th term of a geometric sequence?

EXAMPLE 2

- How is compound interest different from simple interest?
- In the formula for compound interest, why is *r* divided by *n*? Why is *t* multiplied by *n*?

Teaching Tip **Language Support** Have students find different definitions of *compound*. Examples may include a substance formed by two or more ingredients, to combine, or to make stronger and more intense. Relate these definitions to the meaning of *compound interest*. ENGLISH LANGUAGE LEARNERS

2 Teach

Guided Instruction

Before presenting the formula for compound interest, have students find the total after 1, 2, 3, and 4 years for \$1000 that earns 5% compound interest per year. \$1050; \$1102.50; \$1157.63; \$1215.51 Based on these calculations, challenge students to write an expression for the total after *t* years. $1000(1.05)^t$ Then present the formula and compare it with the expression. Explain that interest may be compounded more than once per year. Because *r* is an annual rate, *r* is divided by *n* when $n \neq 1$. The exponent is the number of time periods *nt*.

Teaching Tip **Math Background** Students benefit from connecting new knowledge to previously acquired knowledge. Show them that the half-life formula is essentially a geometric sequence with first term *P* and common ratio 0.5.

Exponential decay occurs when a quantity decreases by the same rate r in each time period t. Just like exponential growth, the value of the quantity at any given time can be calculated by using the rate and the original amount.

Exponential Decay

An exponential decay function has the form $y = a(1 - r)^t$, where $a > 0$.

y represents the final amount.

a represents the original amount.

r represents the rate of decay as a decimal.

t represents time.

Notice an important difference between exponential growth functions and exponential decay functions. For exponential growth, the value inside the parentheses will be greater than 1 because r is added to 1. For exponential decay, the value inside the parentheses will be less than 1 because r is subtracted from 1.

EXAMPLE 3 Exponential Decay

Helpful Hint

In Example 3, round your answer to the nearest whole number because there can only be a whole number of people.

The population of a town is decreasing at a rate of 1% per year. In 2000 there were 1300 people. Write an exponential decay function to model this situation. Then find the population in 2008.

Step 1 Write the exponential decay function for this situation.

$y = a(1 - r)^t$ — *Write the formula.*

$= 1300(1 - 0.01)^t$ — *Substitute 1300 for a and 0.01 for r.*

$= 1300(0.99)^t$ — *Simplify.*

Step 2 Find the population in 2008.

$y = 1300(0.99)^8$ — *Substitute 8 for t.*

≈ 1200 — *Use a calculator and round to the nearest whole number.*

The population in 2008 will be approximately 1200 people.

CHECK IT OUT! **3.** The fish population in a local stream is decreasing at a rate of 3% per year. The original population was 48,000. Write an exponential decay function to model this situation. Then find the population after 7 years. $y = 48{,}000(0.97)^t$; 38,783

A common application of exponential decay is *half-life*. The **half-life** of a substance is the time it takes for one-half of the substance to decay into another substance.

Half-life

$A = P(0.5)^t$

A represents the final amount.

P represents the original amount.

t represents the number of half-lives in a given time period.

COMMON ERROR ALERT

When writing compound interest functions, students may forget to multiply t by n. Remind students that the exponent is the number of times the interest is compounded, which is not necessarily the number of years.

Power Presentations with PowerPoint®

Additional Examples

Example 3

The population of a town is decreasing at a rate of 3% per year. In 2000, there were 1700 people. Write an exponential decay function to model this situation. Then find the population in 2012. $y = 1700(0.97)^t$; 1180

Also available on transparency

INTERVENTION

Questioning Strategies

EXAMPLE 3

- How is the formula for exponential decay similar to the formula for exponential growth? How is it different?

Teaching Tip **Inclusion** Students often believe that problems associated with a particular formula cannot be solved without using the formula. These students may then attempt to memorize formulas at the expense of understanding. Point out to students that if they understand the background of a particular formula, they will not need to memorize it to solve a problem. Instead they will be able to reconstruct the formula using information given in the problem.

Universal Access

Through Modeling

Tell students the definition of *half-life*. Before presenting the formula, help students complete the table by using the definition. (The table describes 80 g of a substance whose half-life is 15 h.)

Half-lives	Time passed (h)	Amount left (g)
1	15	$\frac{1}{2}$ of 80 = 40
2	30	$\frac{1}{2}$ of 40 = 20
3	45	$\frac{1}{2}$ of 20 = 10

Have students write an equation based on the table for the amount A after t half-lives. $A = 80(0.5)^t$ (Students may add more rows to the table to help see the pattern.) Then present the formula and point out how the above equation corresponds to each part.

Through Critical Thinking

Have students complete the following:

$800 \times (1 - 0.55) = 800 \times 0.45 = 360$

$800 \times (1 - 0.05) = 800 \times 0.95 = 760$

$800 \times 1 = 800$

$800 \times (1 + 0.45) = 800 \times 1.45 = 1160$

$800 \times (1 + 0.95) = 800 \times 1.95 = 1560$

Point out that answers are less than 800 for $1 - r$ and greater than 800 for $1 + r$. Therefore, r is added to 1 in growth problems and subtracted from 1 in decay problems.

Power Presentations with PowerPoint®

Additional Examples

Example 4

Astatine-218 has a half-life of 2 seconds.

A. Find the amount left from a 500-gram sample of astatine-218 after 10 seconds. 15.625 g

B. Find the amount left from a 500-gram sample of astatine-218 after 1 minute. 0.00000047 g

Also available on transparency

INTERVENTION
Questioning Strategies

EXAMPLE 4

- How is the formula for half-life similar to a geometric sequence? Why is b always 0.5?
- How do you find the value of t in the half-life formula?

Advanced Learners/GATE In **Example 4A,** show students how to simplify $40(0.5)^4$ without using a calculator. $40(0.5)^4 = 40\left(\frac{1}{2}\right)^4 = 40\,\frac{1}{2^4} = 40 \cdot \frac{1}{16} = \frac{40}{16} = \frac{5}{2} = 2.5$

EXAMPLE 4 ***Science Application***

Fluorine-20 has a half-life of 11 seconds.

A **Find the amount of fluorine-20 left from a 40-gram sample after 44 seconds.**

Step 1 Find t, the number of half-lives in the given time period.

$\frac{44\text{ s}}{11\text{ s}} = 4$ — *Divide the time period by the half-life. The value of t is 4.*

Step 2 $A = P(0.5)^t$ — *Write the formula.*

$= 40(0.5)^4$ — *Substitute 40 for P and 4 for t.*

$= 2.5$ — *Use a calculator.*

There are 2.5 grams of fluorine-20 remaining after 44 seconds.

B **Find the amount of fluorine-20 left from a 40-gram sample after 2.2 minutes. Round your answer to the nearest hundredth.**

Step 1 Find t, the number of half-lives in the given time period.

$2.2(60) = 132$ — *Find the number of seconds in 2.2 minutes.*

$\frac{132\text{ s}}{11\text{ s}} = 12$ — *Divide the time period by the half-life. The value of t is $\frac{132}{11} = 12$.*

Step 2 $A = P(0.5)^t$ — *Write the formula.*

$= 40(0.5)^{12}$ — *Substitute 40 for P and 12 for t.*

≈ 0.01 — *Use a calculator. Round to the nearest hundredth.*

There is about 0.01 gram of fluorine-20 remaining after 2.2 minutes.

4a. Cesium-137 has a half-life of 30 years. Find the amount of cesium-137 left from a 100-milligram sample after 180 years. **1.5625 mg**

4b. Bismuth-210 has a half-life of 5 days. Find the amount of bismuth-210 left from a 100-gram sample after 5 weeks. (*Hint:* Change 5 weeks to days.) **0.78125 g**

THINK AND DISCUSS

1. Describe three real-world situations that can be described by exponential growth or exponential decay functions.
2. The population of a town after t years can be modeled by $P = 1000(1.02)^t$. Is the population increasing or decreasing? By what percentage rate?
3. An exponential function is a function of the form $y = ab^x$. Explain why both exponential growth functions and exponential decay functions are exponential functions.

4. **GET ORGANIZED** Copy and complete the graphic organizer.

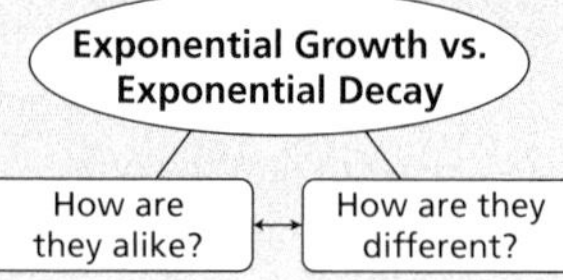

3 Close

Summarize

Write $y = ab^x$ on the board. Below it, write and identify by name the four formulas covered in the lesson. Have students compare each one with the standard form of an exponential function, identifying a and b. Have them also identify each as growth or decay.

FORMATIVE ASSESSMENT and INTERVENTION

***Diagnose Before* the Lesson**
11-8 Warm Up, TE p. 747

***Monitor During* the Lesson**
Check It Out! Exercises, SE pp. 747–750
Questioning Strategies, TE p. 748–750

***Assess After* the Lesson**
11-8 Lesson Quiz, TE p. 754
Alternative Assessment, TE p. 754

Answers to *Think and Discuss*

1. Possible answers: interest earned on an investment, population growth or decline, radioactive decay
2. increasing; by 2% per year
3. An exponential growth function has the form $y = a(1 + r)^t$. The base $(1 + r)$ corresponds to the base b. The exponent t corresponds to the exponent x. An exponential decay function has the form $y = a(1 - r)^t$. The base $(1 - r)$ corresponds to the base b. The exponent t corresponds to the exponent x.
4. See p. A10.

Preview of Algebra II 12.0; 1A25.2

GUIDED PRACTICE

1. **Vocabulary** The function $y = 0.68(2)^x$ is an example of ___?___. (*exponential growth* or *exponential decay*) **exponential growth**

SEE EXAMPLE 1 p. 747

Write an exponential growth function to model each situation. Then find the value of the function after the given amount of time.

2. The cost of tuition at a college is $12,000 and is increasing at a rate of 6% per year; 4 years. $y = 12{,}000\,(1.06)^t$; $15,149.72
3. The number of student-athletes at a local high school is 300 and is increasing at a rate of 8% per year; 5 years. $y = 300(1.08)^t$; 441

SEE EXAMPLE 2 p. 748

Write a compound interest function to model each situation. Then find the balance after the given number of years.

4. $1500 invested at a rate of 3.5% compounded annually; 4 years $A = 1500(1.035)^t$; $1721.28
5. $4200 invested at a rate of 2.8% compounded quarterly; 6 years $A = 4200(1.007)^{4t}$; $4965.43

SEE EXAMPLE 3 p. 749

Write an exponential decay function to model each situation. Then find the value of the function after the given amount of time.

6. The value of a car is $18,000 and is depreciating at a rate of 12% per year; 10 years. $y = 18{,}000\,(0.88)^t$; $5013.02
7. The amount (to the nearest hundredth) of a 10-mg dose of a certain antibiotic decreases in your bloodstream at a rate of 16% per hour; 4 hours. $y = 10(0.84)^t$; 4.98 mg

SEE EXAMPLE 4 p. 750

8. Bismuth-214 has a half-life of approximately 20 minutes. Find the amount of bismuth-214 left from a 30-gram sample after 1 hour. **3.75 g**
9. Mendelevium-258 has a half-life of approximately 52 days. Find the amount of mendelevium-258 left from a 44-gram sample after 156 days. **5.5 g**

PRACTICE AND PROBLEM SOLVING

Independent Practice

For Exercises	See Example
10–13	1
14–17	2
18–19	3
20	4

Extra Practice
Skills Practice p. EP23
Application Practice p. EP34

Write an exponential growth function to model each situation. Then find the value of the function after the given amount of time.

10. Annual sales for a company are $149,000 and are increasing at a rate of 6% per year; 7 years. $y = 149{,}000\,(1.06)^t$; $224,040.91
11. The population of a small town is 1600 and is increasing at a rate of 3% per year; 10 years. $y = 1600(1.03)^t$; 2150
12. A new savings account starts at $700 and increases at 1.2% yearly; 8 years. $A = 700(1.012)^t$; $770.09
13. Membership of a local club grows at a rate of 7.8% yearly and currently has 30 members; 6 years. $A = 30(1.078)^t$; 47 members

Write a compound interest function to model each situation. Then find the balance after the given number of years.

14. $28,000 invested at a rate of 4% compounded annually; 5 years $A = 28{,}000(1.04)^t$; $34,066.28
15. $7000 invested at a rate of 3% compounded quarterly; 10 years $A = 7000(1.0075)^{4t}$; $9438.44
16. $3500 invested at a rate of 1.8% compounded monthly; 4 years $A = 3500(1.0015)^{12t}$; $3761.09
17. $12,000 invested at a rate of 2.6% compounded annually; 15 years

17. $A = 12{,}000(1.026)^t$; $17,635.66

11-8 Exercises

Assignment Guide

Assign *Guided Practice* exercises as necessary.

If you finished Examples **1–2**
Proficient 10–17, 29, 30
Advanced 10–17, 29, 37

If you finished Examples **1–4**
Proficient 10–20, 22–34 even, 35–48, 50–54 even, 55–60
Advanced 10–20, 22–34 even, 36–60

Homework Quick Check
Quickly check key concepts.
Exercises: 10, 14, 18, 20, 24, 30, 40

Teaching Tip

Communicating Math In **Exercise 34,** help students find t by writing the exponent as $\frac{\text{time period}}{\text{half-life}}$. Then they can substitute 3500 for the numerator and 5700 for the denominator. Show students that the answer is reasonable by considering that one half-life is not yet finished. Therefore, half of the 15 grams is not yet gone.

Science Link Exercise 34 involves carbon-14 dating, one common method of dating ancient objects. Scientists also use other isotopes to date objects. Some isotopes' half-lives are millions of years!

Write an exponential decay function to model each situation. Then find the value of the function after the given amount of time.

18. The population of a town is 18,000 and is decreasing at a rate of 2% per year; 6 years.

18. $y = 18{,}000(0.98)^t$; 15,945

19. The value of a book is $58 and decreases at a rate of 10% per year; 8 years.

19. $y = 58(0.9)^t$; $24.97

20. The half-life of bromine-82 is approximately 36 hours. Find the amount of bromine-82 left from an 80-gram sample after 6 days. $y = 80(0.5)^t$; 5 g

Identify each of the following functions as exponential growth or decay. Then give the rate of growth or decay as a percent.

21. $y = 3(1.61)^t$ growth; 61%
22. $y = 39(0.098)^t$ decay; 90.2%
23. $y = a\left(\frac{2}{3}\right)^t$
24. $y = a\left(\frac{3}{2}\right)^t$
25. $y = a(1.1)^t$ growth; 10%
26. $y = a(0.8)^t$ decay; 20%
27. $y = a\left(\frac{5}{4}\right)^t$ growth; 25%
28. $y = a\left(\frac{1}{2}\right)^t$ decay; 50%

23. decay; $33\frac{1}{3}\%$

24. growth; 50%

Write an exponential growth or decay function to model each situation. Then find the value of the function after the given amount of time.

29. The population of a country is 58,000,000 and grows by 0.1% per year; 3 years. $y = 58{,}000{,}000(1.001)^t$; 58,174,174
30. An antique car is worth $32,000, and its value grows by 7% per year; 5 years. $y = 32{,}000(1.07)^t$; $44,881.66
31. An investment of $8200 loses value at a rate of 2% per year; 7 years. $y = 8200(0.98)^t$; $7118.63
32. A new car is worth $25,000, and its value decreases by 15% each year; 6 years. $y = 25{,}000(0.85)^t$; $9428.74
33. The student enrollment in a local high school is 970 students and increases by 1.2% per year; 5 years. $y = 970(1.012)^t$; 1030
34. **Archaeology** Carbon-14 dating is a way to determine the age of very old organic objects. Carbon-14 has a half-life of about 5700 years. An organic object with $\frac{1}{2}$ as much carbon-14 as its living counterpart died 5700 years ago. In 1999, archaeologists discovered the oldest bridge in England near Testwood, Hampshire. Carbon dating of the wood revealed that the bridge was 3500 years old. Suppose that when the bridge was built, the wood contained 15 grams of carbon-14. How much carbon-14 would it have contained when it was found by the archaeologists? Round to the nearest hundredth. 9.80 g

A computer-generated image of what the bridge at Testwood might have looked like

35. **///ERROR ANALYSIS///** Two students were asked to find the value of a $1000-item after 3 years. The item was depreciating (losing value) at a rate of 40% per year. Which is incorrect? Explain the error.

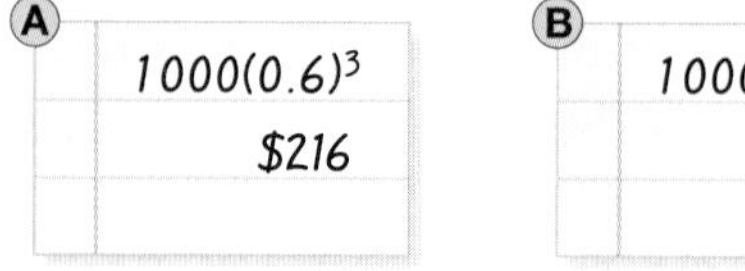

B; possible answer: student B did not subtract the rate from 1.

36. **Critical Thinking** The value of a certain car can be modeled by the function $y = 20{,}000(0.84)^t$, where t is time in years. Will the value ever be zero? Explain.

36. Possible answer: There is no value of t for which $y = 0$. However, when the car's value becomes very small (e.g., less than 1 cent), it would probably be considered to have zero value.

37. The value of a rare baseball card increases every year at a rate of 4%. Today, the card is worth $300. The owner expects to sell the card as soon as the value is over $600. How many years will the owner wait before selling the card? Round your answer to the nearest whole number. 18 years

11-8 PRACTICE A

11-8 PRACTICE C

11-8 PRACTICE B

LESSON 11-8 **Practice B**
Exponential Growth and Decay

Write an exponential growth function to model each situation. Then find the value of the function after the given amount of time.

1. Annual sales for a fast food restaurant are $650,000 and are increasing at a rate of 4% per year; 5 years $y = 650{,}000(1.04)^x$ ≈$790,824.39
2. The population of a school is 800 students and is increasing at a rate of 2% per year; 6 years $y = 800(1.02)^x$ ≈901
3. During a certain period of time, about 70 northern sea otters had an annual growth rate of 18%; 4 years $y = 70(1.18)^x$ ≈136

Write a compound interest function to model each situation. Then find the balance after the given number of years.

4. $50,000 invested at a rate of 3% compounded monthly; 6 years $y = 50{,}000(1.0025)^{12t}$ ≈$59,847.42
5. $43,000 invested at a rate of 5% compounded annually; 3 years $y = 43{,}000(1.05)^t$ ≈$49,777.88
6. $65,000 invested at a rate of 6% compounded quarterly; 12 years $y = 65{,}000(1.015)^{4t}$ ≈$132,826.09

Write an exponential decay function to model each situation. Then find the value of the function after the given amount of time.

7. The population of a town is 2500 and is decreasing at a rate of 3% per year; 5 years $y = 2500(0.97)^x$ ≈2147
8. The value of a company's equipment is $25,000 and decreases at a rate of 15% per year; 8 years $y = 25{,}000(0.85)^x$ ≈$6812.26
9. The half-life of Iodine-131 is approximately 8 days. Find the amount of Iodine-131 left from a 35 gram sample after 32 days. 2.1875 grams

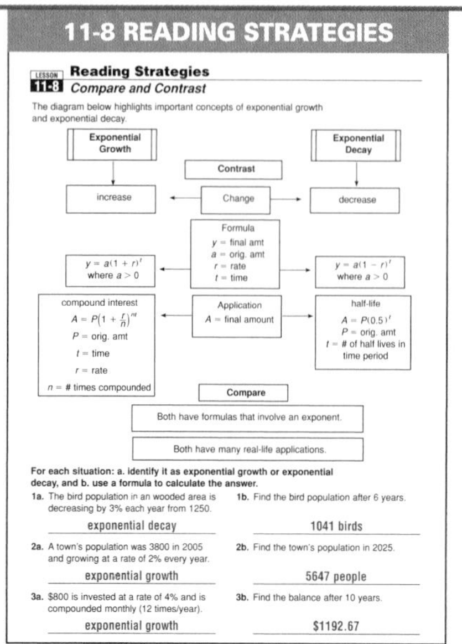
11-8 READING STRATEGIES

LESSON 11-8 **Reading Strategies**
Compare and Contrast

The diagram below highlights important concepts of exponential growth and exponential decay.

Exponential Growth | **Contrast** | **Exponential Decay**

increase ← Change → decrease

$y = a(1 + r)^t$ where $a > 0$ ← Formula: y = final amt, a = orig. amt, r = rate, t = time → $y = a(1 - r)^t$ where $a > 0$

compound interest $A = P\left(1 + \frac{r}{n}\right)^{nt}$, P = orig. amt, t = time, r = rate, n = # times compounded ← Application: A = final amount → half-life $A = P(0.5)^t$, P = orig. amt, t = # of half lives in time period

Compare

Both have formulas that involve an exponent.

Both have many real-life applications.

For each situation: a. identify it as exponential growth or exponential decay, and b. use a formula to calculate the answer.

1a. The bird population in an wooded area is decreasing by 3% each year from 1250. exponential decay
1b. Find the bird population after 6 years. 1041 birds
2a. A town's population was 3800 in 2005 and growing at a rate of 2% every year. exponential growth
2b. Find the town's population in 2025. 5647 people
3a. $800 is invested at a rate of 4% and is compounded monthly (12 times/year). exponential growth
3b. Find the balance after 10 years. $1192.67

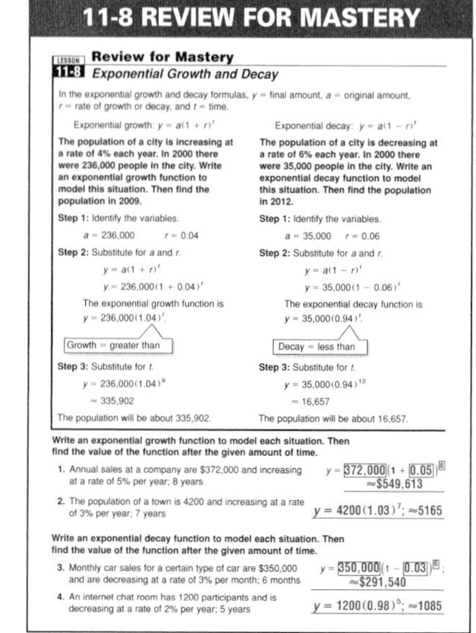
11-8 REVIEW FOR MASTERY

LESSON 11-8 **Review for Mastery**
Exponential Growth and Decay

In the exponential growth and decay formulas, y = final amount, a = original amount, r = rate of growth or decay, and t = time.

Exponential growth: $y = a(1 + r)^t$

The population of a city is increasing at a rate of 4% each year. In 2000 there were 236,000 people in the city. Write an exponential growth function to model this situation. Then find the population in 2009.

Step 1: Identify the variables.
$a = 236{,}000$ $r = 0.04$

Step 2: Substitute for a and r.
$y = a(1 + r)^t$
$y = 236{,}000(1 + 0.04)^t$
The exponential growth function is $y = 236{,}000(1.04)^t$.
Growth = greater than

Step 3: Substitute for t.
$y = 236{,}000(1.04)^9$
$\approx 335{,}902$
The population will be about 335,902.

Exponential decay: $y = a(1 - r)^t$

The population of a city is decreasing at a rate of 6% each year. In 2000 there were 35,000 people in the city. Write an exponential decay function to model this situation. Then find the population in 2012.

Step 1: Identify the variables.
$a = 35{,}000$ $r = 0.06$

Step 2: Substitute for a and r.
$y = a(1 - r)^t$
$y = 35{,}000(1 - 0.06)^t$
The exponential decay function is $y = 35{,}000(0.94)^t$.
Decay = less than

Step 3: Substitute for t.
$y = 35{,}000(0.94)^{12}$
$\approx 16{,}657$
The population will be about 16,657.

Write an exponential growth function to model each situation. Then find the value of the function after the given amount of time.

1. Annual sales at a company are $372,000 and increasing at a rate of 5% per year; 8 years $y = 372{,}000(1 + 0.05)^8$ ≈$549,613
2. The population of a town is 4200 and increasing at a rate of 3% per year; 7 years $y = 4200(1.03)^7$; ≈5165

Write an exponential decay function to model each situation. Then find the value of the function after the given amount of time.

3. Monthly car sales for a certain type of car are $350,000 and are decreasing at a rate of 3% per month; 6 months $y = 350{,}000(1 - 0.03)^6$; ≈$291,540
4. An internet chat room has 1200 participants and is decreasing at a rate of 2% per year; 5 years $y = 1200(0.98)^5$; ≈1085

38. This problem will prepare you for the Concept Connection on page 762.
   a. The annual tuition at a prestigious university was $20,000 in 2002. It generally increases at a rate of 9% each year. Write a function to describe the cost as a function of the number of years since 2002. Use 2002 as year zero when writing the function rule. $y = 20{,}000(1.09)^t$
   b. What do you predict the cost of tuition will be in 2008? **$33,542**
   c. Use a table of values to find the first year that the cost of the tuition will be more than twice the cost in 2002. **2011**

39. **Multi-Step** At bank A, $600 is invested with an interest rate of 5% compounded annually. At bank B, $500 is invested with an interest rate of 6% compounded quarterly. Which account will have a larger balance after 10 years? 20 years? **A; B**

40. **Estimation** The graph shows the decay of 100 grams of sodium-24. Use the graph to estimate the number of hours it will take the sample to decay to 10 grams. Then estimate the half-life of sodium-24. **50 h; 15 h**

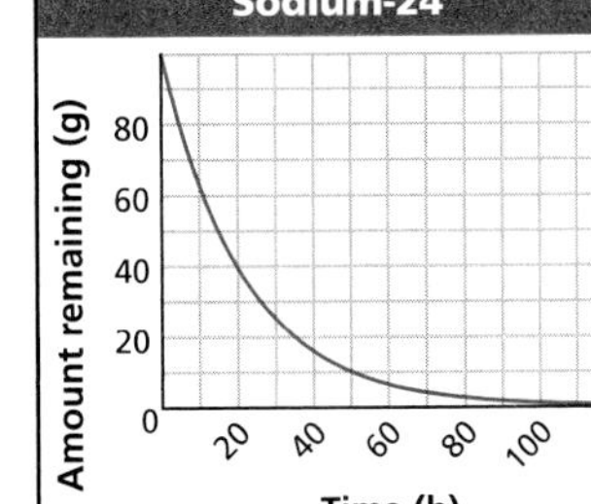

41. **Graphing Calculator** Use a graphing calculator to graph $y = 10(1 + r)^x$ for $r = 10\%$ and $r = 20\%$. Compare the two graphs. How does the value of r affect the graphs?

42. Possible answer: $400 is invested at a rate of 8% compounded annually.

42. **Write About It** Write a real-world situation that could be modeled by $y = 400(1.08)^t$.

43. **Write About It** Write a real-world situation that could be modeled by $y = 800(0.96)^t$. **Possible answer: The population is 800 and decreasing at a rate of 4% per year.**

44. **Critical Thinking** The amount of water in a container doubles every minute. After 6 minutes, the container is full. Your friend says it was half full after 3 minutes. Do you agree? Why or why not? **No; possible answer: the sample doubles every minute, so the container is half full 1 min before it is full. This would be after 5 min.**

Multiple Choice For Exercises 45–47, choose the best answer.

45. A population of 500 is decreasing by 1% per year. Which function models this situation?
   (A) $y = 500(0.01)^t$ (B) $y = 500(0.1)^t$ (C) $y = 500(0.9)^t$ **(D)** $y = 500(0.99)^t$

46. Which function is NOT an exponential decay model?
   (A) $y = 5\left(\frac{1}{3}\right)^x$ **(B)** $y = -5\left(\frac{1}{3}\right)^x$ (C) $y = 5(3)^{-x}$ (D) $y = 5(3^{-1})^x$

47. Stephanie wants to save $1000 for a down payment on a car that she wants to buy in 3 years. She opens a savings account that pays 5% interest compounded annually. About how much should Stephanie deposit now to have enough money for the down payment in 3 years?
   (A) $295 (B) $333 (C) $500 **(D)** $865

48. **Short Response** In 2000, the population of a town was 1000 and was growing at a rate of 5% per year.
   a. Write an exponential growth function to model this situation. $y = 1000(1.05)^t$
   b. In what year will the population be 1300? Show how you found your answer. **about 2005**

CONCEPT CONNECTION **Exercise 38** involves writing an exponential function and using it to make a prediction. This exercise prepares students for the Concept Connection on page 762.

Teaching Tip **Multiple Choice** In **Exercise 45,** the value of a is the same for each function. Only the value of b is different. Students who chose **A** may have forgotten to subtract the rate of decay from 1.

In **Exercise 46,** students should be looking for a value of b that is greater than 1. Students who chose **D** may have forgotten how to simplify expressions with negative exponents.

Students can solve **Exercise 47** by writing the compound interest formula, substituting the given numbers, and solving for A. After simplifying, the equation to be solved is $1000 = 1.157625A$.

Answers

38c.

Year	Tuition ($)
2002	20,000
2003	21,800
2004	23,762
2005	25,900.58
2006	28,231.63
2007	30,772.48
2008	33,542.00
2009	36,560.78
2010	39,851.25
2011	43,437.87

41.

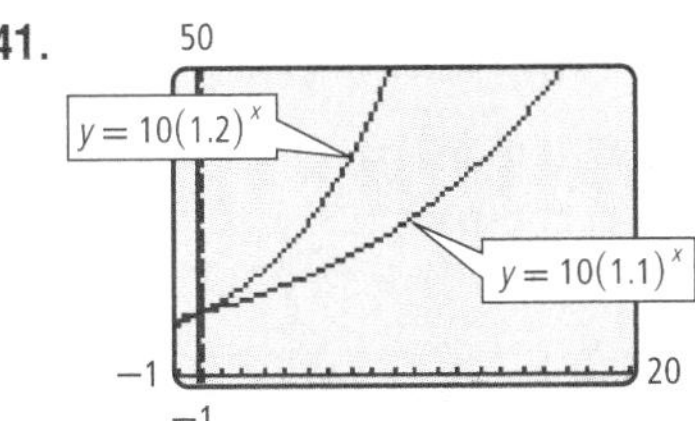

The graph when r is 20% rises faster than when r is 10%. The greater the value of r, the faster the graph will rise.

11-8 PROBLEM SOLVING

LESSON 11-8 Problem Solving
Exponential Growth and Decay

Write the correct answer.

1. A condo in Austin, Texas, was worth $80,000 in 1990. The value of the condo increased by an average of 3% each year. Write an exponential growth function to model this situation. Then find the value of the condominium in 2005.
   $y = 80{,}000(1.03)^t$
   $124,637

2. Markiya deposited $500 in a savings account. The annual interest rate is 2%, and the interest is compounded monthly. Write a compound interest function to model this situation. Then find the balance in Markiya's account after 4 years.
   $y = 500\left(1 + \frac{0.02}{12}\right)^{12t}$
   $541.61

3. The population of a small Midwestern town is 4500. The population is decreasing at a rate of 1.5% per year. Write an exponential decay function to model this situation. Then find the number of people in the town after 25 years.
   $y = 4500(0.985)^t$
   3084

4. Twelve students at a particular high school passed an advanced placement test in 2000. The number of students who passed the test increased by 16.4% each year thereafter. Find the number of students who passed the test in 2004.
   22

Half-lives range from less than a second to billions of years. The table below shows the half-lives of several substances. Select the best answer.

Half-Lives	
Nitrogen-16	7 s
Technetium-99	6 h
Sulfur-35	87 days
Tritium	12.3 yr
Uranium-238	4.5 billion yrs

5. About how many grams of a 500 g sample of Technetium-99 is left after 2 days?
   (A) 1.95 g C 31.25 g
   B 7.81 g D 62.5 g

6. Which equation can be used to find how much of a 50 g sample of Nitrogen-16 is left after 7 minutes?
   F $A = 50(0.5)^1$ H $A = 50(0.5)^{42}$
   G $A = 50(0.5)^7$ **(J)** $A = 50(0.5)^{60}$

7. How many billions of years will it take 1000 grams of Uranium-238 to decay to just 125 grams?
   A 0.125 C 9
   B 3 **(D)** 13.5

8. A researcher had 37.5 g left from a 600 g sample of Sulfer-35. How many half-lives passed during that time?
   (F) 4 H 7
   G 5 J 16

9. Look at problem 8. How many days passed during that time?
   A 7 **(C)** 348
   B 16 D 435

11-8 CHALLENGE

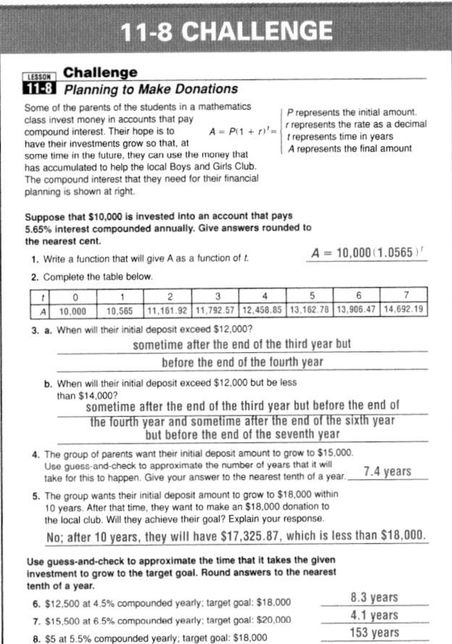

LESSON 11-8 Challenge
Planning to Make Donations

Some of the parents of the students in a mathematics class invest money in accounts that pay compound interest. Their hope is to have their investments grow so that, at some time in the future, they can use the money that has accumulated to help the local Boys and Girls Club. The compound interest that they need for their financial planning is shown at right.

$A = P(1 + r)^t =$ P represents the initial amount. r represents the rate as a decimal t represents time in years A represents the final amount

Suppose that $10,000 is invested into an account that pays 5.65% interest compounded annually. Give answers rounded to the nearest cent.

1. Write a function that will give A as a function of t. $A = 10{,}000(1.0565)^t$

2. Complete the table below.

t	0	1	2	3	4	5	6	7
A	10,000	10,565	11,161.92	11,792.57	12,458.85	13,162.78	13,906.47	14,692.19

3. a. When will their initial deposit exceed $12,000?
   sometime after the end of the third year but before the end of the fourth year
   b. When will their initial deposit exceed $12,000 but be less than $14,000?
   sometime after the end of the third year but before the end of the fourth year and sometime after the end of the sixth year but before the end of the seventh year

4. The group of parents want their initial deposit amount to grow to $15,000. Use guess-and-check to approximate the number of years that it will take for this to happen. Give your answer to the nearest tenth of a year. 7.4 years

5. The group wants their initial deposit amount to grow to $18,000 within 10 years. After that time, they want to make an $18,000 donation to the local club. Will they achieve their goal? Explain your response.
   No; after 10 years, they will have $17,325.87, which is less than $18,000.

Use guess-and-check to approximate the time that it takes the given investment to grow to the target goal. Round answers to the nearest tenth of a year.

6. $12,500 at 4.5% compounded yearly; target goal: $18,000 — 8.3 years
7. $15,500 at 6.5% compounded yearly; target goal: $20,000 — 4.1 years
8. $5 at 5.5% compounded yearly; target goal: $18,000 — 153 years

CHALLENGE AND EXTEND

49. You invest \$700 at a rate of 6% compounded quarterly. Use a graph to estimate the number of years it will take for your investment to increase to \$2300. **about 20 yr**

50. Omar invested \$500 at a rate of 4% compounded annually. How long will it take for Omar's money to double? How long would it take if the interest were 8% compounded annually? **18 yr; 9 yr**

51. An 80-gram sample of a radioactive substance decayed to 10 grams after 300 minutes. Find the half-life of the substance. **100 min, or 1 h 40 min**

52. Praseodymium-143 has a half-life of 2 weeks. The original measurement for the mass of a sample was lost. After 6 weeks, 15 grams of praseodymium-143 remain. How many grams was the original sample? **120 g**

53. Phillip invested some money in a business 8 years ago. Since then, his investment has grown at an average rate of 1.3% compounded quarterly. Phillip's investment is now worth \$250,000. How much was his original investment? Round your answer to the nearest dollar. **\$225,344**

54. **Personal Finance** Anna has a balance of \$200 that she owes on her credit card. She plans to make a \$30 payment each month. There is also a 1.5% finance charge (interest) on the remaining balance each month. Copy and complete the table to answer the questions below. You may add more rows to the table as necessary.

Month	Balance (\$)	Monthly Payment (\$)	Remaining Balance (\$)	1.5% Finance Charge (\$)	New Balance (\$)
1	200	30	170	2.55	172.55
2	172.55	30	**142.55**	**2.14**	**144.69**
3	**144.69**	30	**114.69**	**1.72**	**116.41**
4	**116.41**	30	**86.41**	**1.30**	**87.71**

a. How many months will it take Anna to pay the entire balance? **7 mo**

b. By the time Anna pays the entire balance, how much total interest will she have paid? **\$9.01**

SPIRAL STANDARDS REVIEW

2.0

Write and solve a proportion for each situation. *(Lesson 2-5)*

55. A daffodil that is 1.2 feet tall casts a shadow that is 1.5 feet long. At the same time, a nearby lamppost casts a shadow that is 20 feet long. The daffodil's height and its shadow are in the same proportion as the lamppost and its shadow. What is the height of the the lamppost? **16 ft**

56. A green rectangular throw pillow measures 20 inches long by 10 inches wide. A proportionally similar yellow throw pillow is 12 inches long. What is the width of the yellow pillow? **6 in.**

Simplify. *(Lesson 7-3)*

57. $(x^5)^4$ $\mathbf{x^{20}}$

58. $(c^6)^3 \cdot (c^2)^{-3}$ $\mathbf{c^{12}}$

59. $pq^7 \cdot p^3q \cdot p^2q^8$ $\mathbf{p^6q^{16}}$

60. The function $f(x) = 0.10(2)^x$ gives the total fine in dollars for a library book that is x days overdue. What is the fine if a book is 4 days overdue? How many days overdue is a book if the fine is \$12.80? *(Lesson 11-7)* **\$1.60; 7 days**

Answer

54.

5	87.71	30	57.71	0.87	58.58
6	58.58	30	28.58	0.43	29.01
7	29.01	29.01	0	0	0

Journal

Have students explain what each number represents in the population decay function $P = 6000(0.99)^4$.

ALTERNATIVE ASSESSMENT

Have students write and solve four different word problems, one for each of the four formulas taught in the lesson. For each problem, they must explain how each part of the appropriate formula corresponds to the problem situation.

Power Presentations with PowerPoint®

11-8 Lesson Quiz

1. The number of employees at a certain company is 1440 and is increasing at a rate of 1.5% per year. Write an exponential growth function to model this situation. Then find the number of employees in the company after 9 years. $y = 1440(1.015)^t$; 1646

Write a compound interest function to model each situation. Then find the balance after the given number of years.

2. \$12,000 invested at a rate of 6% compounded quarterly; 15 years $A = 12{,}000(1.015)^{4t}$; \$29,318.64

3. \$500 invested at a rate of 2.5% compounded annually; 10 years $A = 500(1.025)^t$; \$640.04

4. The deer population of a game preserve is decreasing by 2% per year. The original population was 1850. Write an exponential decay function to model the situation. Then find the population after 4 years. $y = 1850(0.98)^t$; 1706

5. Iodine-131 has a half-life of about 8 days. Find the amount left from a 30-gram sample of iodine-131 after 40 days. 0.9375 g

Also available on transparency

11-9 Linear, Quadratic, and Exponential Models

Preview of Algebra II
12.0 Students know the laws of fractional exponents, **understand exponential functions,** and use these functions in problems involving exponential growth and decay.
Extension of 1A7.0 Students verify that a point lies on a line, given an equation of the line. **Students are able to derive linear equations by using the point-slope formula.**

Why learn this?
Different situations in sports can be described by linear, quadratic, or exponential models.

The sports data below show three kinds of variable relationships—linear, quadratic, and exponential.

Linear

Training Heart Rate	
Age (yr)	Beats/min
20	170
30	161.5
40	153
50	144.5

Quadratic

Volleyball Height	
Time (s)	Height (ft)
0.4	10.44
0.8	12.76
1	12
1.2	9.96

Exponential

Volleyball Tournament	
Round	Teams Left
1	16
2	8
3	4
4	2

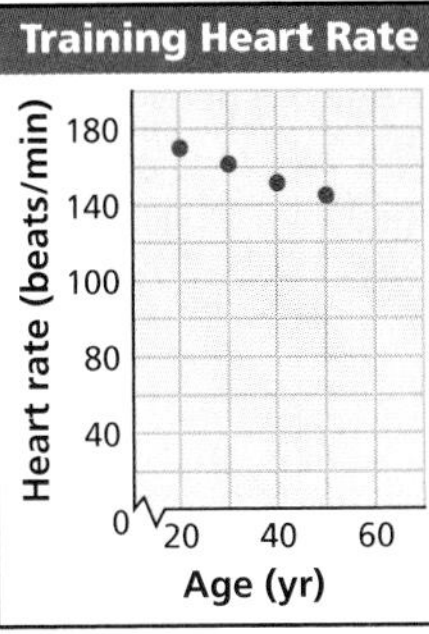

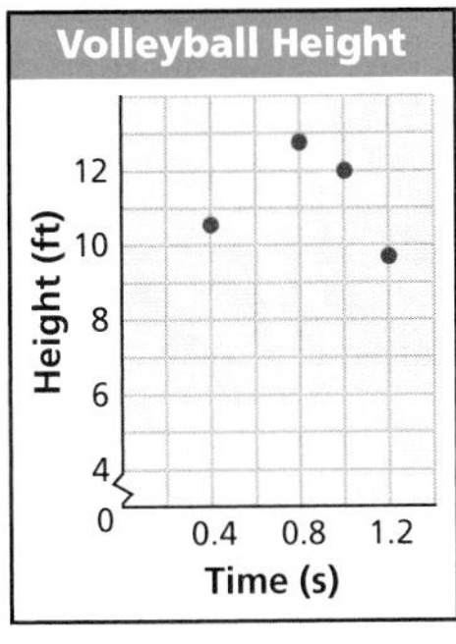

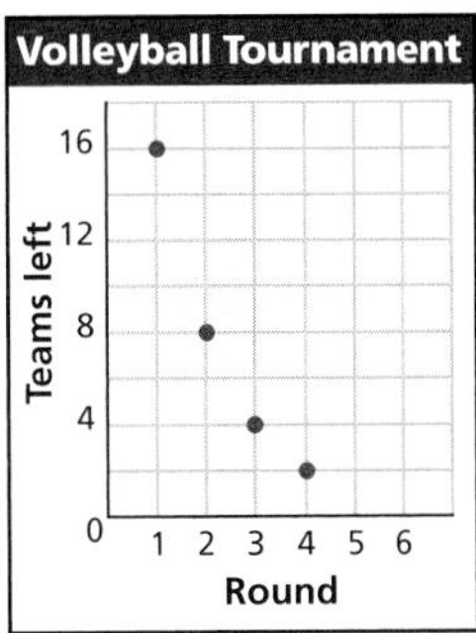

In the real world, people often gather data and then must decide what kind of relationship (if any) they think best describes their data.

EXAMPLE 1 Graphing Data to Choose a Model

Graph the data set. Which kind of model best describes the data?

°C	0	5	10	15	20
°F	32	41	50	59	68

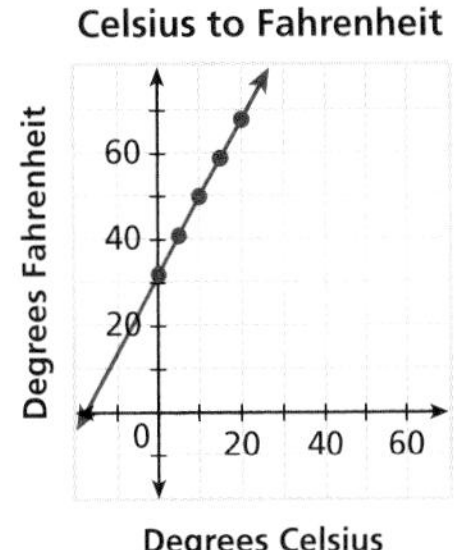

Plot the data points and connect them.
The data appear to be linear.

Graph each data set. Which kind of model best describes the data?

1a. $\{(-3, 0.30), (-2, 0.44), (0, 1), (1, 1.5), (2, 2.25), (3, 3.38)\}$

1b. $\{(-3, -14), (-2, -9), (-1, -6), (0, -5), (1, -6), (2, -9), (3, -14)\}$

1a.
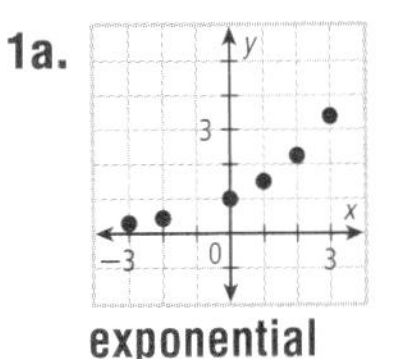

exponential

1b.
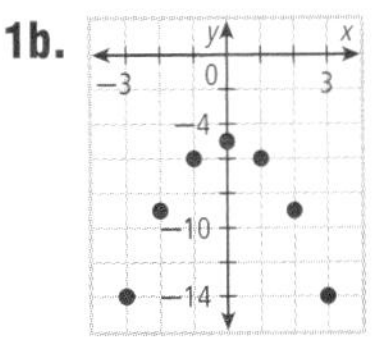

quadratic

11-9 Organizer

Objectives: Compare linear, quadratic, and exponential models.

Given a set of data, decide which type of function models the data and write an equation to describe the function.

Power Presentations with PowerPoint®

Warm Up

1. Find the slope and the y-intercept of the line that passes through (4, 20) and (20, 24). $\frac{1}{4}$; 19

The population of a town is decreasing at a rate of 1.8% per year. In 1990, there were 4600 people.

2. Write an exponential decay function to model this situation. $y = 4600(0.982)^t$
3. Find the population in 2010. 3199

Also available on transparency

Teacher: Why are you so dressed up?
Student: You said we'd be modeling today.

1 Introduce

EXPLORATION

11-9 Linear, Quadratic, and Exponential Models

You will need a graphing calculator for this Exploration.

1. To enter the data from the table below into your calculator, press STAT and select 1:Edit... . Then enter the values from the table in lists L1 and L2.

x	y
0	5
1	2
2	1
3	2
4	5

2. To plot the data points, press Y= and select Plot 1 at the top of the screen. Then press GRAPH.
3. Based on the shape of the graph, what type of function do you think models the data? Why?
4. Repeat the process for the data in this table.

x	y
1	7.2
2	5.8
3	4.6
4	3.7
5	2.9

THINK AND DISCUSS

5. **Explain** what type of function you think models the data in Problem 4.

Motivate

Display the following table and have students list information they remember about each type of function.

Linear	Quadratic	Exponential
Possible answers: graph is a line, has a slope	Possible answers: graph is a parabola, opens up or down	Possible answers: graph is a curve, variable is in exponent

Explorations and answers are provided in *Alternate Openers: Explorations Transparencies.*

Preview of Algebra II 12.0; Extension of 1A7.0

Power Presentations with PowerPoint®

Additional Examples

Example 1

Graph each data set. Which kind of model best describes the data?

A.

Time (h)	Bacteria
0	24
1	96
2	384
3	1536
4	6144

exponential

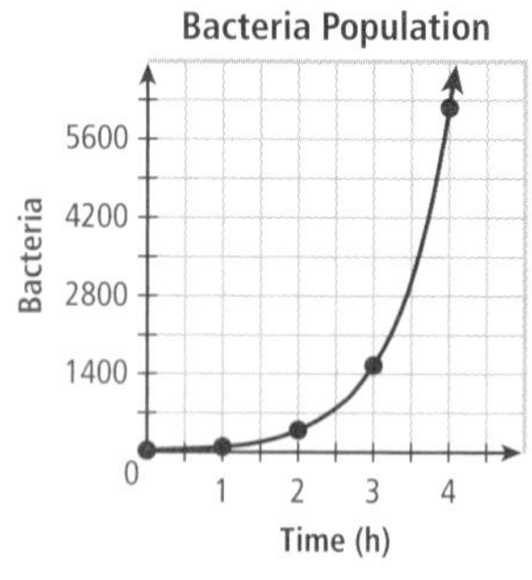

B.

Boxes	Reams of Paper
1	10
5	50
20	200
50	500

linear

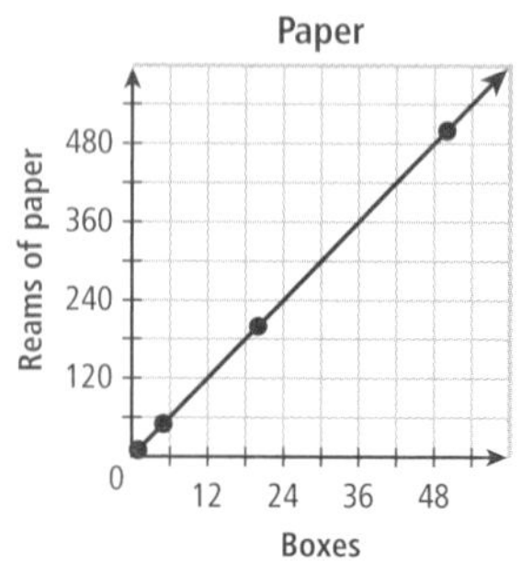

Also available on transparency

INTERVENTION

Questioning Strategies

EXAMPLE 1

- What does the graph of a linear function look like?
- How are the graphs of quadratic and exponential functions similar? How are they different?

Another way to decide which kind of relationship (if any) best describes a data set is to use patterns. Look at a table or list of ordered pairs in which there is a constant change in x-values.

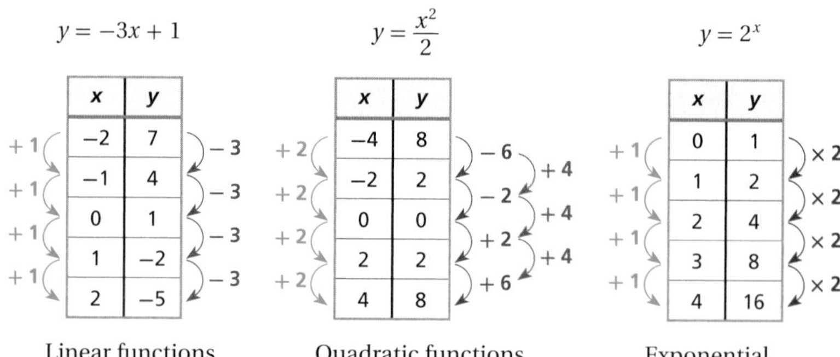

$y = -3x + 1$

x	y
−2	7
−1	4
0	1
1	−2
2	−5

Linear functions have constant first differences.

$y = \frac{x^2}{2}$

x	y
−4	8
−2	2
0	0
2	2
4	8

Quadratic functions have constant second differences.

$y = 2^x$

x	y
0	1
1	2
2	4
3	8
4	16

Exponential functions have a **constant ratio.**

EXAMPLE 2 **Using Patterns to Choose a Model**

Look for a pattern to determine which kind of model best describes the data.

A

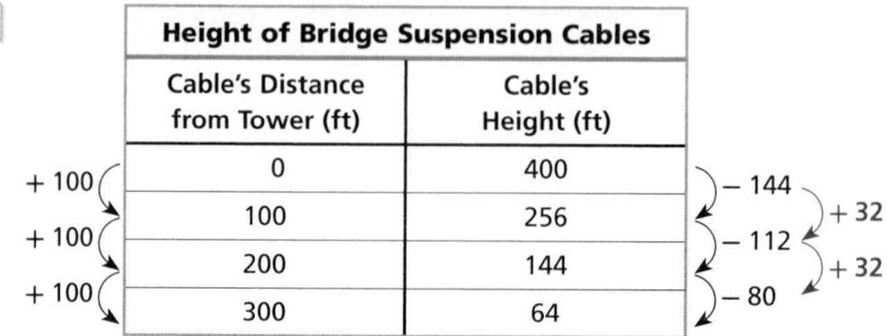

Height of Bridge Suspension Cables	
Cable's Distance from Tower (ft)	**Cable's Height (ft)**
0	400
100	256
200	144
300	64

For every constant change in distance of +100 feet, there is a constant second difference of +32.

The data appear to be quadratic.

B

Value of a Car	
Car's Age (yr)	**Value ($)**
0	20,000
1	17,000
2	14,450
3	12,282.50

+1, +1, +1; × 0.85, × 0.85, × 0.85

For every constant change in age of +1 year, there is a constant ratio of 0.85.

The data appear to be exponential.

When solving problems like those in Example 2, be sure there is a constant change in the x-values.

CHECK IT OUT! 2. Look for a pattern in the data set $\{(-2, 10), (-1, 1), (0, -2), (1, 1), (2, 10)\}$ to determine which kind of model best describes the data. **quadratic**

2 Teach

Guided Instruction

Show how to choose a model graphically and then by looking at patterns. **Check It Out Problem 3** involves finding the slope and y-intercept of a linear function. These skills may need to be reviewed. This lesson does not include finding a function to model quadratic data; that is beyond the scope of this book. Interested or advanced students can find the function for **Example 2A** on a graphing calculator by entering the data into two lists and using the **QuadReg** feature.

Inclusion When graphing, students might choose the wrong model if their graph is sloppy or if they do not graph all the points. For example, points that appear to be parabolic may actually be exponential. Tell students that when in doubt, they should look for patterns.

Critical Thinking Remind students that $y \neq 0$ in an exponential function. If the data set includes $y = 0$, then the function must be linear or quadratic.

After deciding which model best fits the data, you can write a function. Recall the general forms of linear, quadratic, and exponential functions.

General Forms of Functions

LINEAR	QUADRATIC	EXPONENTIAL
$y = mx + b$	$y = ax^2 + bx + c$	$y = ab^x$

EXAMPLE 3 Problem-Solving Application

PROBLEM SOLVING

Use the data in the table to describe how the ladybug population is changing. Then write a function that models the data. Use your function to predict the ladybug population after one year.

Ladybug Population	
Time (mo)	Ladybugs
0	10
1	30
2	90
3	270

1 Understand the Problem

The **answer** will have three parts—a description, a function, and a prediction.

2 Make a Plan

Determine whether the data is linear, quadratic, or exponential. Use the general form to write a function. Then use the function to find the population after one year.

3 Solve

Step 1 Describe the situation in words.

	Ladybug Population		
	Time (mo)	Ladybugs	
+1	0	10	×3
+1	1	30	×3
+1	2	90	×3
	3	270	

Each month, the ladybug population is multiplied by 3. In other words, the population triples each month.

Step 2 Write the function.

There is a constant ratio of 3. The data appear to be exponential.

$y = ab^x$ *Write the general form of an exponential function.*

$y = a(3)^x$ *Substitute the constant ratio, 3, for b.*

$10 = a(3)^0$ *Choose an ordered pair from the table, such as (0, 10). Substitute for x and y.*

$10 = a(1)$ *Simplify. $3^0 = 1$*

$10 = a$ *The value of a is 10.*

$y = 10(3)^x$ *Substitute 10 for a in $y = a(3)^x$.*

Helpful Hint

You can choose any given ordered pair to substitute for x and y. However, choosing an ordered pair that contains 0 will often result in easier calculations.

Power Presentations with PowerPoint®

Additional Examples

Example 2

Look for a pattern in each data set to determine which kind of model best describes the data.

A.

Height of Golf Ball	
Time (s)	Height (ft)
0	4
1	68
2	100
3	100
4	68

quadratic

B.

Money in CD	
Time (yr)	Amount ($)
0	1000.00
1	1169.86
2	1368.57
3	1601.04

exponential

Example 3

Use the data in the table to describe how the number of people changes. Then write a function that models the data. Use your function to predict the number of people who received the e-mail after one week.

E-mail Forwarding	
Time (days)	Number of People Who Received the E-mail
0	8
1	56
2	392
3	2744

increasing by a factor of 7 each day; $y = 8(7)^x$; 6,588,344

Also available on transparency

Universal Access
Through Cooperative Learning

Break students into small groups. Assign each group one of the following kinds of models: linear, quadratic, or exponential. Tell students to prepare a 5-minute presentation that covers:

- characteristics of their model
- how to recognize when their model best describes a set of data
- examples of real-life situations that tend to fit their model

INTERVENTION
Questioning Strategies

EXAMPLE 2

- How can you use the pattern in the table to predict the contents of the next row?

EXAMPLE 3

- How can you use the function to predict other data values?
- How accurate is this prediction?

Visual Students may get a better understanding of exponential functions if they attempt to draw a tree diagram of the situation. For the data in **Example 3,** they should start by drawing 10 circles for 10 bugs and then draw 3 circles for each of those 10 circles, and so on.

Step 3 Predict the ladybug population after one year.

$y = 10(3)^x$ *Write the function.*

$= 10(3)^{12}$ *Substitute 12 for x (1 year = 12 mo).*

$= 5{,}314{,}410$ *Use a calculator.*

There will be 5,314,410 ladybugs after one year.

Look Back

You chose the ordered pair $(0, 10)$ to write the function. Check that every other ordered pair in the table satisfies your function.

$y = 10(3)^x$	
30	$10(3)^1$
30	$10(3)$
30	30 ✓

$y = 10(3)^x$	
90	$10(3)^2$
90	$10(9)$
90	90 ✓

$y = 10(3)^x$	
270	$10(3)^3$
270	$10(27)$
270	270 ✓

CHECK IT OUT! **3.** Use the data in the table to describe how the oven temperature is changing. Then write a function that models the data. Use your function to predict the temperature after 1 hour.

The oven temperature decreases by 50°F every 10 min; $y = -5x + 375$; 75°F

Oven Temperature				
Time (min)	0	10	20	30
Temperature (°F)	375	325	275	225

Student to Student

Checking Units

I used to get a lot of answers wrong because of the units. If a question asked for the value of something after 1 year, I would always just substitute 1 into the function.

I finally figured out that you have to check what x is. If x represents months and you're trying to find the value after 1 year, then you have to substitute 12, not 1, because there are 12 months in a year.

Michael Gambhir
Warren High School

THINK AND DISCUSS

1. Do you think that every data set will be able to be modeled by a linear, quadratic, or exponential function? Why or why not?

2. In Example 3, is it certain that there will be 5,314,410 ladybugs after one year? Explain.

3. GET ORGANIZED Copy and complete the graphic organizer. In each box, list some characteristics and sketch a graph of each type of model.

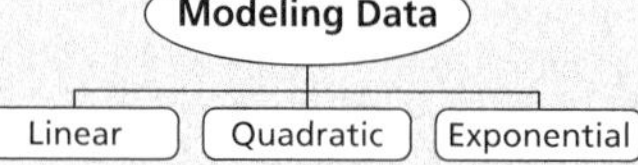

3 Close

Summarize

Ask students which model best fits each of the following situations:

- With a constant change in x, the differences between the first differences are constant. quadratic
- With a constant change in x, there is a constant ratio in the y-values. exponential
- The graph forms a parabola. quadratic
- With a constant change in x, the second differences are zero. linear

FORMATIVE ASSESSMENT and INTERVENTION

***Diagnose Before* the Lesson**
11-9 Warm Up, TE p. 755

***Monitor During* the Lesson**
Check It Out! Exercises, SE pp. 755–758
Questioning Strategies, TE p. 756–757

***Assess After* the Lesson**
11-9 Lesson Quiz, TE p. 761
Alternative Assessment, TE p. 761

Answers to *Think and Discuss*

Possible answers:

1. No; most real-world data probably will not fit exactly into one of these patterns.
2. No; this is just a prediction based on the assumption that the observed trends will continue, which they may or may not do.
3. See p. A10.

11-9 Exercises

California Standards Practice
Preview of Algebra II 22.0; Extension of 1A7.0; 25.2

go.hrw.com
Homework Help Online
KEYWORD: MA8CA 11-9
Parent Resources Online
KEYWORD: MA8CA Parent

GUIDED PRACTICE

SEE EXAMPLE 1 p. 755

Graph each data set. Which kind of model best describes the data?

1. $\{(-1, 4), (-2, 0.8), (0, 20), (1, 100), (-3, 0.16)\}$ **exponential**
2. $\{(0, 3), (1, 9), (2, 11), (3, 9), (4, 3)\}$ **quadratic**
3. $\{(2, -7), (-2, -9), (0, -8), (4, -6), (6, -5)\}$ **linear**

SEE EXAMPLE 2 p. 756

Look for a pattern in each data set to determine which kind of model best describes the data.

4. $\{(-2, 1), (-1, 2.5), (0, 3), (1, 2.5), (2, 1)\}$ **quadratic**
5. $\{(-2, 0.75), (-1, 1.5), (0, 3), (1, 6), (2, 12)\}$ **exponential**
6. $\{(-2, 2), (-1, 4), (0, 6), (1, 8), (2, 10)\}$ **linear**

SEE EXAMPLE 3 p. 757

7. **Consumer Economics** Use the data in the table to describe the cost of grapes. Then write a function that models the data. Use your function to predict the cost of 6 pounds of grapes.

Total Cost of Grapes

Amount (lb)	1	2	3	4
Cost ($)	1.79	3.58	5.37	7.16

Grapes cost $1.79/lb; $y = 1.79x$; $10.74

PRACTICE AND PROBLEM SOLVING

Independent Practice

For Exercises	See Example
8–10	1
11–13	2
14	3

Extra Practice
Skills Practice p. EP23
Application Practice p. EP34

Graph each data set. Which kind of model best describes the data?

8. $\{(-3, -5), (-2, -8), (-1, -9), (0, -8), (1, -5), (2, 0), (3, 7)\}$ **quadratic**
9. $\{(-3, -1), (-2, 0), (-1, 1), (0, 2), (1, 3), (2, 4), (3, 5)\}$ **linear**
10. $\{(0, 0.1), (2, 0.9), (3, 2.7), (4, 8.1)\}$ **exponential**

Look for a pattern in each data set to determine which kind of model best describes the data.

11. $\{(-2, 5), (-1, 4), (0, 3), (1, 2), (2, 1)\}$ **linear**
12. $\{(-2, 12), (-1, 15), (0, 16), (1, 15), (2, 12)\}$ **quadratic**
13. $\{(-2, 8), (-1, 4), (0, 2), (1, 1), (2, 0.5)\}$ **exponential**

14. **Business** Use the data in the table to describe how the company's sales are changing. Then write a function that models the data. Use your function to predict the amount of sales after 10 years.

Company Sales

Year	0	1	2	3
Sales ($)	25,000	30,000	36,000	43,200

14. The company's sales are increasing by 20% each year; $y = 25{,}000(1.2)^x$; $154,793.41.

15. **Multi-Step** Jay's hair grows about 6 inches each year. Write a function that describes the length ℓ in inches that Jay's hair will grow for each year k. Which kind of model best describes the function? **$\ell = 6k$; linear**

11-9 Exercises

Assignment Guide

Assign *Guided Practice* exercises as necessary.

If you finished Examples **1–2**
Proficient 8–13, 16–18, 21, 22
Advanced 8–13, 16–18, 21, 22

If you finished Examples **1–3**
Proficient 8–19, 23–29, 32–50,
Advanced 8–19, 23, 25–50

Homework Quick Check
Quickly check key concepts.
Exercises: 8, 10, 12, 14, 18, 20

Inclusion In **Exercise 10,** there is not a constant change in *x*. Have students focus on the last three points and then use that to find *y* when *x* is 1. Students should then check whether the pattern works for all four points.

Answers

1.
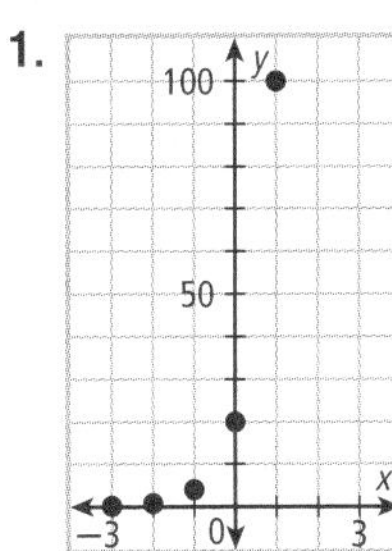

2.
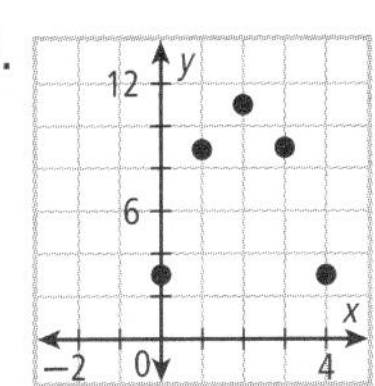

3.
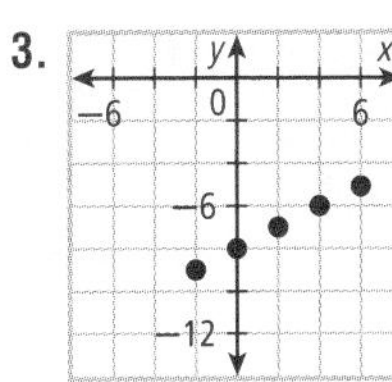

8.
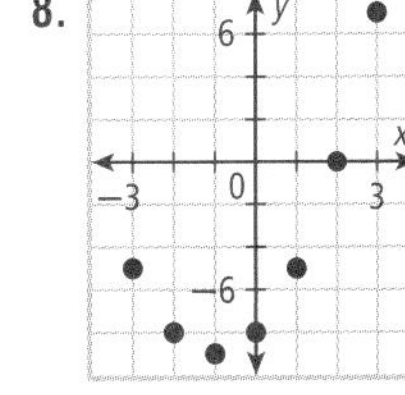

9.
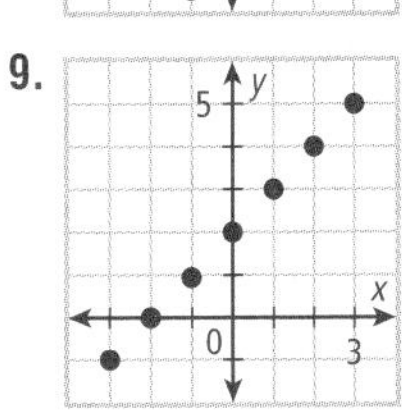

10.
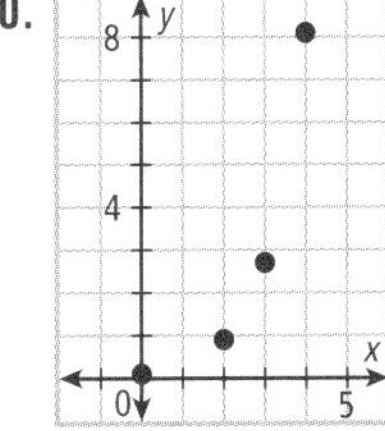

Exercise 26 involves writing a function rule to describe data. This exercise prepares students for the Concept Connection on page 762.

Answers

26a. college 1: linear; college 2: exponential

b. college 1: $y = 200x + 2000$; college 2: $y = 2000(1.1)^x$

c. Both have the same tuition ($2000) in 2004.

d. For college 1, $200 is added each year, so 2000 + 200 = 2200. For college 2, 10% is added each year, so 2000 + (0.1)(2000) = 2200.

Tell which kind of model best describes each situation.

16. The height of a plant at weekly intervals over the last 6 weeks was 1 inches, 1.5 inches, 2 inches, 2.5 inches, 3 inches., and 3.5 inches. **linear**

17. The number of games a baseball player played in the last four years was 162, 162, 162, and 162. **linear**

18. The height of a ball in a certain time interval was recorded as 30.64 feet, 30.96 feet, 31 feet, 30.96 feet, and 30.64 feet. **quadratic**

Write a function to model each set of data.

19.

x	−1	0	1	2	4
y	0.05	0.2	0.8	3.2	51.2

20.

x	−2	0	2	4	8
y	5	4	3	2	0

Tell which kind of model best describes each graph.

21.

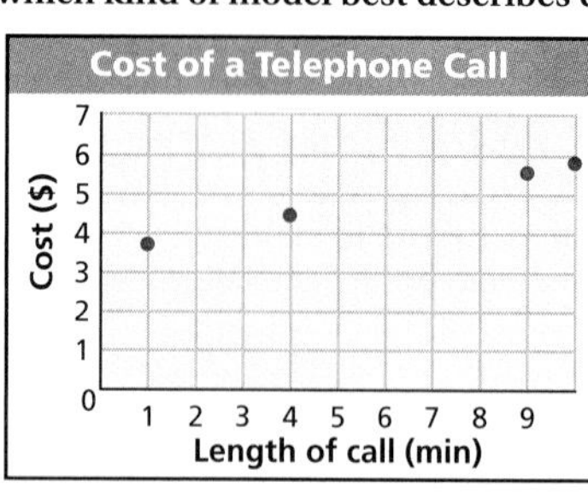

22.

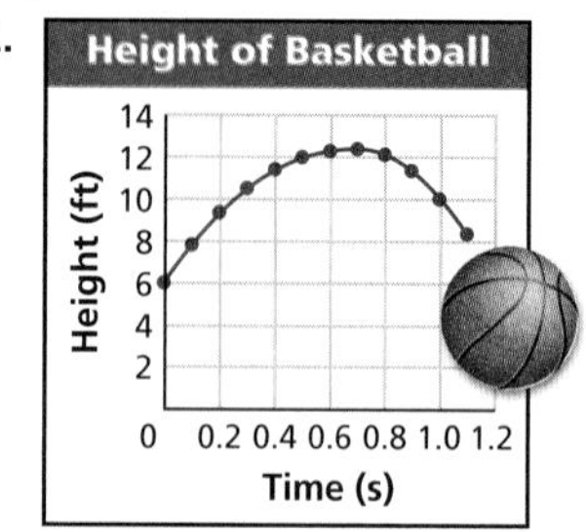

19. $y = 0.2(4)^x$

20. $y = -\frac{1}{2}x + 4$

21. linear

22. quadratic

23. Possible answer: (0, 3), (1, 6), (2, 12), (3, 24); for a constant change in x of +1, there is a common ratio of 2.

23. **Write About It** Write a set of data that you could model with an exponential function. Explain why the exponential model would work.

24. **///ERROR ANALYSIS///** A student concluded that the data set would best be modeled by a quadratic function. Explain the student's error.

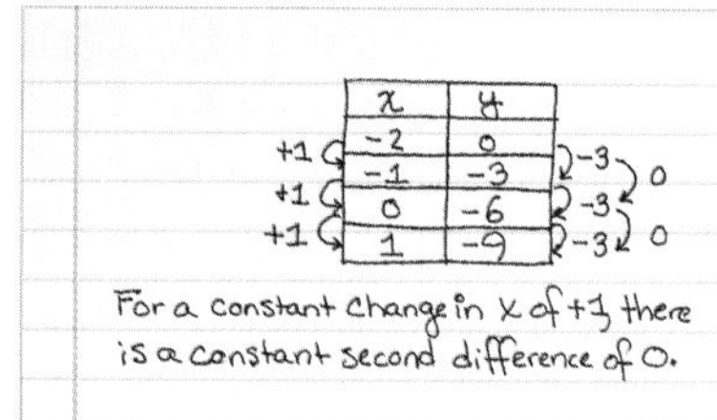

x	y
−2	0
−1	−3
0	−6
1	−9

For a constant change in x of +1 there is a constant second difference of 0.

24. Possible answer: The first differences are constant, so there is no need to check the second differences. A linear function would best model the data.

25. **Critical Thinking** Sometimes the graphs of quadratic data and exponential data can look very similar. Describe how you can tell them apart.
Possible answer: Make a table of ordered pairs and see whether the y-values show a pattern of constant second differences or constant ratios.

CONCEPT CONNECTION

26. This problem will prepare you for the Concept Connection on page 762.

a. Examine the two models that represent annual tuition for two colleges. Describe each model as linear, quadratic, or exponential.

b. Write a function rule for each model.

c. Both models have the same values for 2004. What does this mean?

d. Why do both models have the same value for year 1?

Years After 2004	Tuition at College 1 ($)	Tuition at College 2 ($)
0	2000.00	2000.00
1	2200.00	2200.00
2	2400.00	2420.00
3	2600.00	2662.00
4	2800.00	2928.20

11-9 PRACTICE A

11-9 PRACTICE C

11-9 PRACTICE B

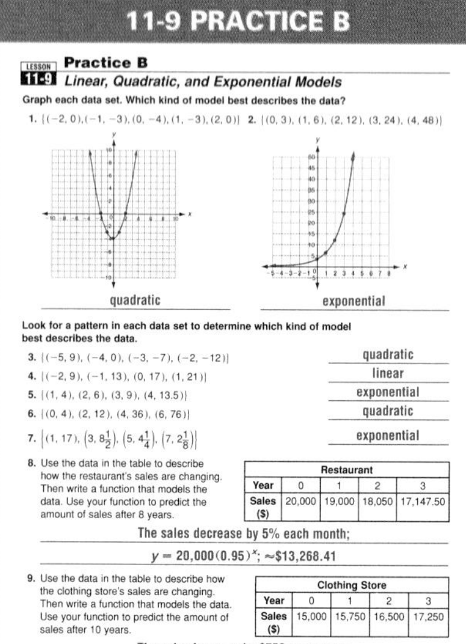

Practice B
11-9 *Linear, Quadratic, and Exponential Models*

Graph each data set. Which kind of model best describes the data?

1. {(−2, 0), (−1, −3), (0, −4), (1, −3), (2, 0)} 2. {(0, 3), (1, 6), (2, 12), (3, 24), (4, 48)}

quadratic exponential

Look for a pattern in each data set to determine which kind of model best describes the data.

3. {(−5, 9), (−4, 0), (−3, −7), (−2, −12)} quadratic
4. {(−2, 9), (−1, 13), (0, 17), (1, 21)} linear
5. {(1, 4), (2, 6), (3, 9), (4, 13.5)} exponential
6. {(0, 4), (2, 12), (4, 36), (6, 76)} quadratic
7. $\{(1, 17), (3, 8\frac{1}{2}), (5, 4\frac{1}{4}), (7, 2\frac{1}{8})\}$ exponential

8. Use the data in the table to describe how the restaurant's sales are changing. Then write a function that models the data. Use your function to predict the amount of sales after 8 years.

Restaurant				
Year	0	1	2	3
Sales ($)	20,000	19,000	18,050	17,147.50

The sales decrease by 5% each month;
$y = 20{,}000(0.95)^x$; ~$13,268.41

9. Use the data in the table to describe how the clothing store's sales are changing. Then write a function that models the data. Use your function to predict the amount of sales after 10 years.

Clothing Store				
Year	0	1	2	3
Sales ($)	15,000	15,750	16,500	17,250

The sales increase by $750 every year;
$y = 750x + 15{,}000$; $22,500

11-9 READING STRATEGIES

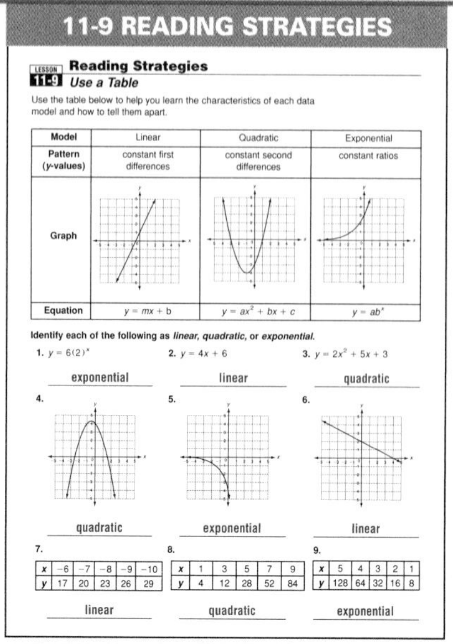

Reading Strategies
11-9 *Use a Table*

Use the table below to help you learn the characteristics of each data model and how to tell them apart.

Model	Linear	Quadratic	Exponential
Pattern (y-values)	constant first differences	constant second differences	constant ratios
Graph			
Equation	$y = mx + b$	$y = ax^2 + bx + c$	$y = ab^x$

Identify each of the following as *linear, quadratic,* or *exponential.*

1. $y = 6(2)^x$ exponential
2. $y = 4x + 6$ linear
3. $y = 2x^2 + 5x + 3$ quadratic

4. quadratic 5. exponential 6. linear

7.

x	−6	−7	−8	−9	−10
y	17	20	23	26	29

linear

8.

x	1	3	5	7	9
y	4	12	28	52	84

quadratic

9.

x	5	4	3	2	1
y	128	64	32	16	8

exponential

11-9 REVIEW FOR MASTERY

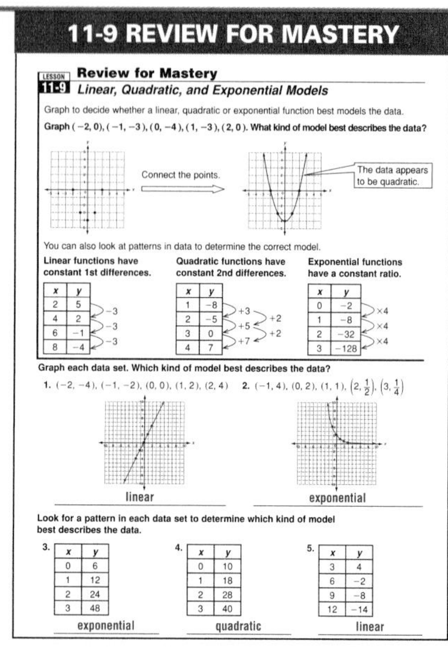

Review for Mastery
11-9 *Linear, Quadratic, and Exponential Models*

Graph to decide whether a linear, quadratic or exponential function best models the data.

Graph {(−2, 0), (−1, −3), (0, −4), (1, −3), (2, 0)}. What kind of model best describes the data?

Connect the points. The data appears to be quadratic.

You can also look at patterns in data to determine the correct model.

Linear functions have constant 1st differences. Quadratic functions have constant 2nd differences. Exponential functions have a constant ratio.

Graph each data set. Which kind of model best describes the data?

1. {(−2, −4), (−1, −2), (0, 0), (1, 2), (2, 4)} 2. $\{(-1, 4), (0, 2), (1, 1), (2, \frac{1}{2}), (3, \frac{1}{4})\}$

linear exponential

Look for a pattern in each data set to determine which kind of model best describes the data.

3.

x	y
0	6
1	12
2	24
3	48

exponential

4.

x	y
0	10
1	18
2	28
3	40

quadratic

5.

x	y
3	4
6	−2
9	−8
12	−14

linear

Multiple Choice For Exercises 27–29, choose the best answer.

27. Which function best models the data: $\{(-4, -2), (-2, -1), (0, 0), (2, 1), (4, 2)\}$?

Ⓐ $y = \left(\frac{1}{2}\right)^x$ Ⓑ $y = \frac{1}{2}x^2$ **Ⓒ** $y = \frac{1}{2}x$ Ⓓ $y = \left(\frac{1}{2}x\right)^2$

28. A city's population is increasing at a rate of 2% per year. Which type of model describes this situation?

Ⓐ Exponential Ⓑ Quadratic Ⓒ Linear Ⓓ None of these

29. Which data set is best modeled by a linear function?

Ⓐ $\{(-2, 0), (-1, 2), (0, -4), (1, -1), (2, 2)\}$

Ⓑ $\{(-2, 2), (-1, 4), (0, 6), (1, 16), (2, 32)\}$

Ⓒ $\{(-2, 2), (-1, 4), (0, 6), (1, 8), (2, 10)\}$

Ⓓ $\{(-2, 0), (-1, 5), (0, 7), (1, 5), (2, 0)\}$

CHALLENGE AND EXTEND

30. **Finance** An accountant estimates that a certain new automobile worth \$18,000 will lose value at a rate of 16% per year.

a. Make a table that shows the worth of the car for years 0, 1, 2, 3, and 4. What is the real-world meaning of year 0? **the year when the car is new**

b. Which type of model best represents the data in your table? Explain. **exponential**

c. Write a function for your data. $y = 18{,}000(0.84)^x$

d. What is the value of the car after $5\frac{1}{2}$ years? **\$6899.36**

e. What is the value of the car after 8 years? **\$4461.77**

30a.

Year	Value (\$)
0	18,000
1	15,120
2	12,700.80
3	10,668.67
4	8961.68

31. **Pet Care** The table shows general guidelines for the weight of a Great Dane at various ages.

Great Dane	
Age (mo)	Weight (kg)
2	12
4	23
6	33
8	40
10	45

a. None of the three models in this lesson—linear, quadratic, or exponential—fits this data exactly. Which of these is the *best* model for the data? Explain your choice.

b. What would you predict for the weight of a Great Dane who is 1 year old? **about 48 kg**

c. Do you think you could use your model to find the weight of a Great Dane at any age? Why or why not?

31a. Possible answer: quadratic; the second differences are approximately constant at −2.

31c. No; this quadratic model will begin to decrease although the dog's weight will either continue to grow or eventually remain constant.

SPIRAL STANDARDS REVIEW

 2.0

Find each root. (Lesson 11-5)

32. $\sqrt{169}$ **13** 33. $\sqrt[3]{216}$ **6** 34. $\sqrt{400}$ **20** 35. $\sqrt[4]{81}$ **3**

36. $\sqrt[5]{32}$ **2** 37. $\sqrt{121}$ **11** 38. $\sqrt{49}$ **7** 39. $\sqrt{625}$ **25**

Solve by using square roots. Check your answer. (Lesson 9-6)

40. $4x^2 = 100$ ± 5 41. $10 - x^2 = 10$ 0 42. $16x^2 + 5 = 86$ $\pm\frac{9}{4}$

Simplify. All variables represent nonnegative numbers. (Lesson 11-2)

43. $\sqrt{24}$ $2\sqrt{6}$ 44. $\sqrt{108}$ $6\sqrt{3}$ 45. $\sqrt{\frac{4}{12}}$ $\frac{\sqrt{3}}{3}$ 46. $\sqrt{\frac{21}{50}}$ $\frac{\sqrt{42}}{10}$

47. $\sqrt{\frac{x^7}{x^3}}$ x^2 48. $\sqrt{\frac{25r^9}{16r}}$ $\frac{5r^4}{4}$ 49. $\sqrt{242}$ $11\sqrt{2}$ 50. $\sqrt{112}$ $4\sqrt{7}$

Teaching Tip

Multiple Choice In **Exercise 27,** remind students that a variable in a linear function, like the variable in choice **C,** has an exponent of one, which is usually not written.

Journal

Have students write a data set that could be modeled by an exponential function. Then have them explain how to write the function rule and how to use it to make predictions.

ALTERNATIVE ASSESSMENT

Have students create a data set that can best be modeled by a quadratic function. Have them explain why a quadratic model fits their data better than either a linear or exponential model.

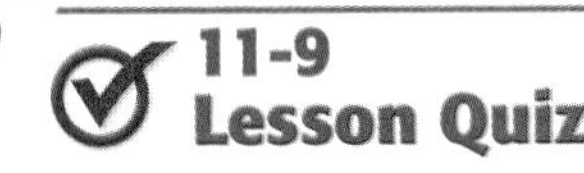

Power Presentations with PowerPoint®

11-9 Lesson Quiz

Which kind of model best describes each set of data?

1.

Time (s)	Height of Ball (ft)
0	200
1	184
2	136
3	56

quadratic

2.

Value of Townhouse	
Age (yr)	Value (\$)
0	100,000
1	102,000
2	104,040
3	106,121

exponential

3. Use the data in the table to describe how the amount of water is changing. Then write a function that models the data. Use your function to predict the amount of water in the pool after 3 hours.

Water in a Swimming Pool	
Time (min)	Amount of Water (gal)
10	327
20	342
30	357
40	372

increasing by 15 gal every 10 min; $y = 1.5x + 312$; 582 gal

Also available on transparency

11-9 PROBLEM SOLVING

LESSON 11-9 **Problem Solving**
Linear, Quadratic, and Exponential Models

Write the correct answer.

1. The table shows the height of a baseball for different times after it was thrown. Graph the data. Which kind of model best describes the data?

Height of Baseball					
Time (s)	0	1	2	3	4
Height (ft)	5	53	69	53	5

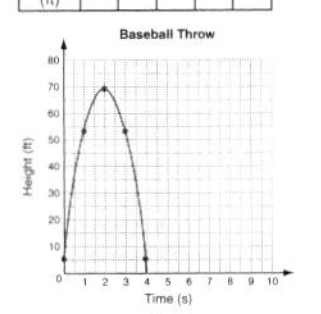

Baseball Throw (graph: Height (ft) vs. Time (s))

quadratic

2. The table shows the cost of peaches. Look for a pattern and determine which kind of model best describes the data. Then write a function that models the data.

Cost of Peaches				
Pounds	1	2	3	4
Cost (\$)	1.29	2.58	3.87	5.16

linear

$y = 1.29x$

3. The table shows the number of computers in a school for four years.

Number of Computers				
Year	'00	'01	'02	'03
Computers	14	28	56	112

Write a function to model the data. Then use the function to predict how many computers the school will have in 2006 if the pattern continues.

$y = 14(2)^x$; 896

The chart shows the ticket sales for movies on two different screens at one theater over four days. Select the best answer.

	Screen 1	Screen 2
Day 1	400	3000
Day 2	440	2400
Day 3	480	1920
Day 4	520	1536

4. Which kind of model best describes the ticket sales for the movie on screen 1?

Ⓐ linear C exponential B quadratic D none of these

5. Which function describes the data for screen 1?

F $y = 40x^2$ H $y = 400x$ **Ⓖ** $y = 40x + 400$ J $y = 400(40)^x$

6. Which kind of model best describes the ticket sales for the movie on screen 2?

A linear **Ⓒ** exponential B quadratic D none of these

7. Which function describes the data for screen 2?

F $y = -600x + 3000$ G $y = 600x^2 + 2400$ **Ⓗ** $y = 3000(0.8)^x$ J $y = 3000(1.25)^x$

11-9 CHALLENGE

LESSON 11-9 **Challenge**
Highway Traffic

If you've ridden in a car on a highway, you've probably noticed that the speed of traffic slows down when there are more cars on the road. The data at right was gathered to research this phenomenon.

Traffic Density (vehicles/mi)	Average Speed (mi/h)
20.4	38.8
26.5	34.0
29.5	31.8
30.0	28.8
97.0	12.3
106.2	10.6
106.7	11.4
107.2	10.3
121.7	8.5
123.9	9.8
130.5	8.6
141.3	7.7

None of the models you have studied fits this data exactly. Furthermore, the values of the independent variable don't change by a constant amount, so you can't check for constant differences or constant ratios. You'll use a graphing calculator to find models instead.

1. Enter the data into lists **L1** and **L2** on your calculator, and make a scatter plot. (Review Technology Lab 4-5 on page 262 of your textbook if you forgot how.) Sketch the scatter plot below.

2. Based on the shape of the scatter plot, which kind of model do you think will best describe the data? **exponential or quadratic**

3. Press STAT and select the **CALC** menu. Select **LinReg(ax+b)** and press ENTER to find a linear model. Write the equation here, rounding to the thousandths. $y = -0.251x + 39.469$

4. Press Y=, enter the equation for the linear model, and press GRAPH. Sketch the line on your graph above.

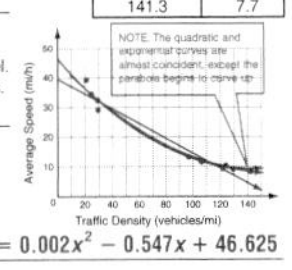

(graph: Average Speed (mi/h) vs. Traffic Density (vehicles/mi)) NOTE: The quadratic and exponential curves are almost coincident, except the parabola begins to curve up.

5. Repeat step 3, but select **QuadReg** to find a quadratic model. Write the equation here. $y = 0.002x^2 - 0.547x + 46.625$

6. Graph the quadratic equation, and sketch it above.

7. Repeat step 3, but select **ExpReg** to find an exponential model. Write the equation here. $y = 46.700(0.987)^x$

8. Graph the exponential equation, and sketch it above.

9. From the graphs of the three models, which model(s) seems to fit best? Explain your choice(s). **Exponential or quadratic; either model is a good fit for the curvature of the scatter plot.**

10. Use each model to predict the average speed of traffic when the traffic density is 180 vehicles per mile.

linear: **−5.711 mi/h** quadratic: **12.965 mi/h** exponential: **4.430 mi/h**

11. From your answers to question 10, which model(s) seems to fit best? Explain your choice(s). **Exponential only as traffic density continues to increases, the linear model gives negative speeds and the quadratic model gives increasing speeds.**

CONCEPT CONNECTION

Organizer

Objective: Assess students' ability to apply concepts and skills in Lessons 11-6 through 11-9 in a real-world format.

Problem	Text Reference
1	Lesson 11-9
2	Lessons 11-7, 11-8
3	Lessons 11-7, 11-8
4	Lessons 11-7, 11-8
5	Lessons 11-7, 11-8

Answers

2.

X	Y1
20	1961.5
21	2138.1
22	2330.5
23	2540.3
24	2768.9
25	3018.1
26	3289.7

X=26

4000

Y1=350(1.09)^X

X=26 Y=3289.7053

0 30

4, 5. For tables and graphs, see p. A27.

Preview of Algebra II 12.0

SECTION 11B

Exponential Functions

1. $y = 350(1.09)^x$; y = tuition (dep.); x = years since 1980 (indep.)

Dollars for Scholars In 1980, the average annual tuition at two-year colleges was $350. Since then, the cost of tuition has increased by an average of 9% each year.

1. Write a function rule that models the annual growth in tuition at two-year colleges since 1980. Let 1980 be year zero in your function. Identify the variables, and tell which is independent and which is dependent.
2. Use your function to determine the average annual tuition in 2006. Use a table and a graph to support your answer. **$3289.71**
3. Use your function to predict the average annual tuition at two-year colleges for the year you plan to graduate from high school. **Answers will vary.**
4. In what year is the average annual tuition twice as much as in 1980? Use a table and a graph to support your answer. **about 1988**
5. In what year does the average annual tuition reach $1000? Use a table and a graph to support your answer. **1993**

INTERVENTION

Scaffolding Questions

1. Explain why it is best to use 1980 as year zero. This is the first year with given data.
2. What is the annual growth factor as a decimal? 1.09
3. How do you find your x-value? the year I graduate from high school minus 1980
4. What is the starting value for tuition? $350
5. Describe how the tuition amounts change with each additional year. Each year the cost is 9% more than the previous year.

Extension

How would the function change if the annual growth rate were 12%? The function would be $y = 350(1.12)^x$.

How would the graph change with this growth rate? It would increase more rapidly.

CHAPTER 11

SECTION 11B

Quiz for Lessons 11-6 Through 11-9

11-6 Geometric Sequences

Find the next three terms in each geometric sequence.

1. 3, 6, 12, 24, ... **48, 96, 192**
2. −1, 2, −4, 8, ... **−16, 32, −64**
3. −2400, −1200, −600, −300, ... **−150, −75, −37.5**
4. The first term of a geometric sequence is 2 and the common ratio is 3. What is the 8th term of the sequence? **4374**
5. The table shows the distance swung by a pendulum during its first three swings. The values form a geometric sequence. What will be the length of the 7th swing? **262.144 cm**

Swing	Length (cm)
1	1000
2	800
3	640

11-7 Exponential Functions

6. The function $f(x) = 3(1.1)^x$ gives the length (in inches) of an image after being enlarged by 10% x times. What is the length of the image after it has been enlarged 4 times? Round your answer to the nearest hundredth. **4.39 in.**

Graph each exponential function.

7. $y = 3^x$
8. $y = 2(2)^x$
9. $y = -2(4)^x$
10. $y = -(0.5)^x$
11. The function $f(x) = 40(0.8)^x$ gives the amount of a medication in milligrams present in a patient's system x hours after taking a 40-mg dose. In how many hours will there be less than 2 mg of the drug in a patient's system? **14 h**

11-8 Exponential Growth and Decay

Write a function to model each situation. Then find the value of the function after the given amount of time.

12. Fiona's salary is \$30,000, and she expects to receive a 3% raise each year; 10 years.
13. \$2000 is invested at a rate of 4.5% compounded monthly; 3 years.
14. A \$1200 computer is losing value at a rate of 20% per year; 4 years.
15. Strontium-90 has a half-life of 29 years. About how much strontium-90 will be left from a 100-mg sample after 290 years? Round your answer to the nearest thousandth. **0.098 mg**

11-9 Linear, Quadratic, and Exponential Models

Graph each data set. Which kind of model best describes the data?

16. $\{(-2, 5), (3, 10), (0, 1), (1, 2), (0.5, 1.25)\}$ **quadratic**
17. $\{(0, 3), (2, 12), (-1, 1.5), (-3, 0.375), (4, 48)\}$ **exponential**

Look for a pattern in each data set to determine which kind of model best describes the data.

18. $\{(-2, -6), (-1, -5), (0, -4), (1, -3), (2, -2)\}$ **linear**
19. $\{(-2, -24), (-1, -12), (0, -6), (1, -3)\}$ **exponential**
20. Use the data in the table to describe how the value of the stamp is changing. Then write a function that models the data. Use your function to predict the value of the stamp in 11 years. **The value of the stamp is increasing by 20% each year; $y = 5(1.2)^x$; \$37.15.**

Value of Collectible Stamp				
Year	0	1	2	3
Value (\$)	5.00	6.00	7.20	8.64

READY TO GO ON? SECTION 11B

Organizer

Objective: Assess students' mastery of concepts and skills in Lessons 11-6 through 11-9.

Resources

Assessment Resources
Section 11B Quiz

Test & Practice Generator
One-Stop Planner®

INTERVENTION

Resources

Ready to Go On? Intervention and Enrichment **Worksheets**

Ready to Go On? **CD-ROM**

Ready to Go On? **Online**

my.hrw.com

Answers

7–10. See p. A27.

12. $y = 30{,}000(1.03)^x$; \$40,317.49

13. $y = 2000(1.00375)^{12x}$; \$2288.50

14. $y = 1200(0.8)^x$; \$491.52

16, 17. For graphs, see p. A27.

READY TO GO ON? Diagnose and Prescribe

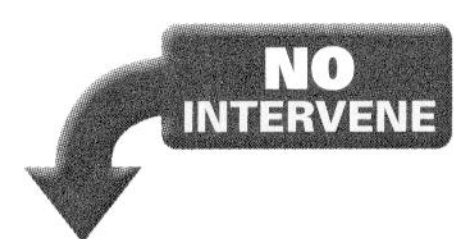

NO INTERVENE

Ready to Go On? Intervention	Worksheets (Ready to Go On? Intervention, Section 11B)	CD-ROM	Online
Lesson 11-6 Prep for 2A22.0	11-6 Intervention	Activity 11-6	Diagnose and Prescribe Online
Lesson 11-7 Preview of 2A12.0	11-7 Intervention	Activity 11-7	
Lesson 11-8 Preview of 2A12.0	11-8 Intervention	Activity 11-8	
Lesson 11-9 Ext. of 1A7.0	11-9 Intervention	Activity 11-9	

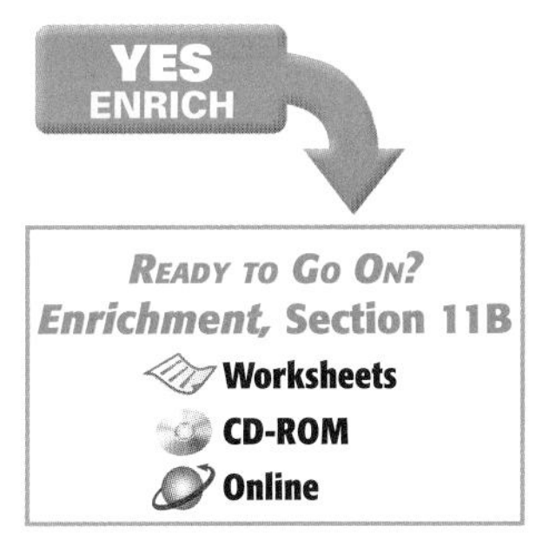

YES ENRICH

Ready to Go On? Enrichment, Section 11B
Worksheets
CD-ROM
Online

Study Guide: Review

Organizer

Objective: Help students organize and review key concepts and skills in Chapter 11.

Online Edition
Multilingual Glossary

Resources

PuzzlePro
One-Stop Planner®

Multilingual Glossary **Online**
go.hrw.com
KEYWORD: MA8CA Glossary

Lesson Tutorial Videos
CD-ROM

Test & Practice Generator
One-Stop Planner®

Answers

1. square-root function
2. exponential decay
3. common ratio
4. exponential function
5. 4.74 cm
6. $x \geq 0$
7. $x \geq -4$
8. $x \geq 0$
9. $x \geq -2$
10. $x \geq \frac{4}{3}$
11. $x \geq -3$
12. $x \geq \frac{7}{2}$
13. $x \geq -\frac{18}{5}$
14. $x \geq \frac{3}{4}$
15. $x \geq 1$
16. 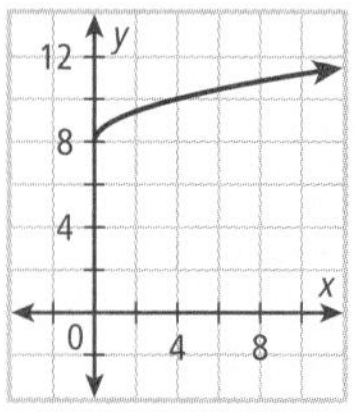
17.

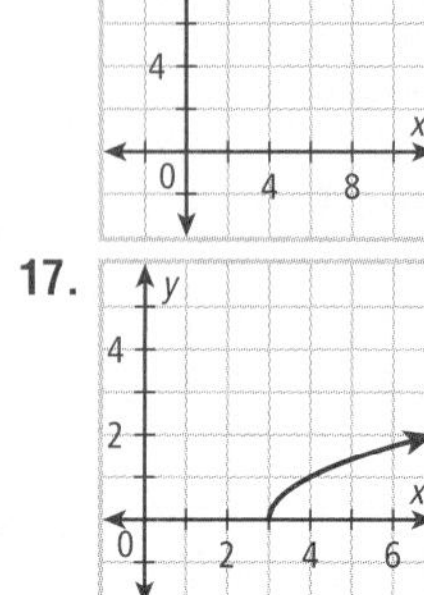

CHAPTER 11 Study Guide: Review

Vocabulary

Complete the sentences below with vocabulary words from the list above.

1. $y = \sqrt{2x}$ is an example of a(n) ___?___.
2. A(n) ___?___ function has the form $y = a(1 - r)^t$, where $a > 0$.
3. In the formula $a_n = a_1 r^{n-1}$, the variable r represents the ___?___.
4. $f(x) = 2^x$ is an example of a(n) ___?___.

11-1 Square-Root Functions *(pp. 700–704)*

Ext. of 1A2.0

EXAMPLE

■ **Graph $y = 3\sqrt{x - 2}$.**

Step 1 Find the domain of the function.

$x - 2 \geq 0$ *The radicand must be greater*
$x \geq 2$ *than or equal to 0.*

Step 2 Generate ordered pairs.

x	$y = 3\sqrt{x - 2}$
2	0
3	3
6	6
11	9
18	12

Choose x-values greater than or equal to 2 that form a perfect square under the radical sign.

Step 3 Plot and connect the points.

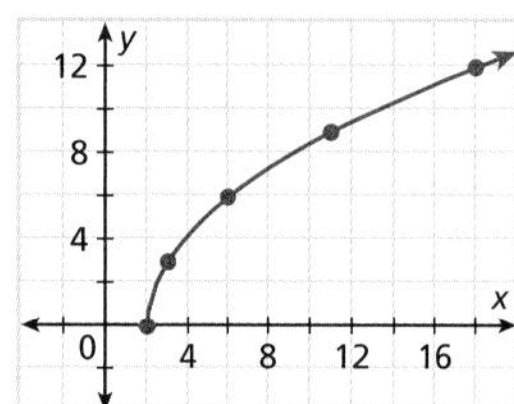

EXERCISES

5. If you know the surface area S of a cube, you can use the formula $\ell = \sqrt{\frac{S}{6}}$ to find the length ℓ of a side. What is the side length of a cube whose surface area is 135 cm^2? Round your answer to the nearest hundredth of a centimeter.

Find the domain of each square-root function.

6. $y = \sqrt{x} + 5$
7. $y = \sqrt{x + 4}$
8. $y = 8 - \sqrt{3x}$
9. $y = 2\sqrt{x + 2}$
10. $y = 1 + \sqrt{3x - 4}$
11. $y = \sqrt{2x + 6}$
12. $y = \sqrt{2x - 7}$
13. $y = \sqrt{5x + 18}$
14. $y = \sqrt{4x - 3}$
15. $y = 3\sqrt{x - 1}$

Graph each square-root function.

16. $y = \sqrt{x} + 8$
17. $y = \sqrt{x - 3}$
18. $y = -\sqrt{2x}$
19. $y = \sqrt{x} - 1$
20. $y = 2\sqrt{x + 3}$
21. $y = \sqrt{5 - x}$
22. $y = \sqrt{7 - 4x}$
23. $y = 3\sqrt{x - 1}$
24. $y = 1 + \sqrt{x + 1}$
25. $y = \frac{1}{2}\sqrt{x - 2}$

18.

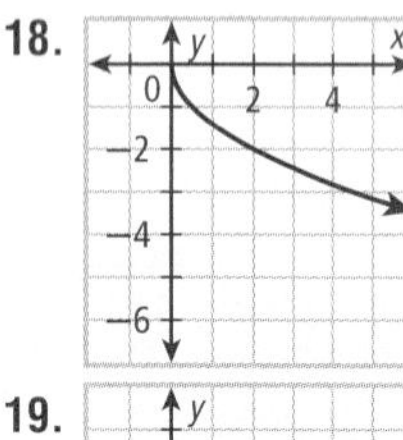

19.

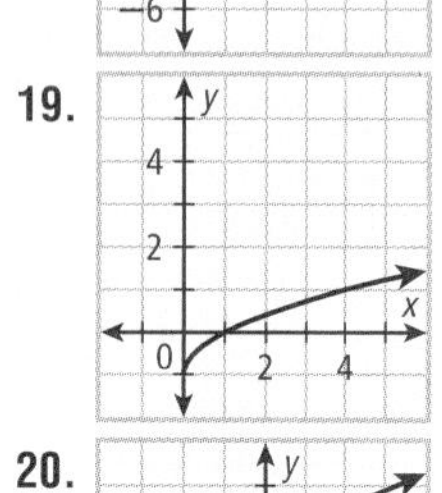

20.

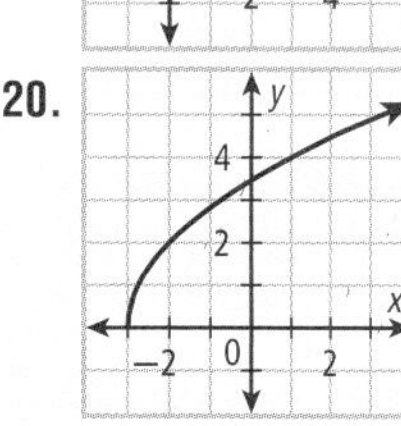

21.

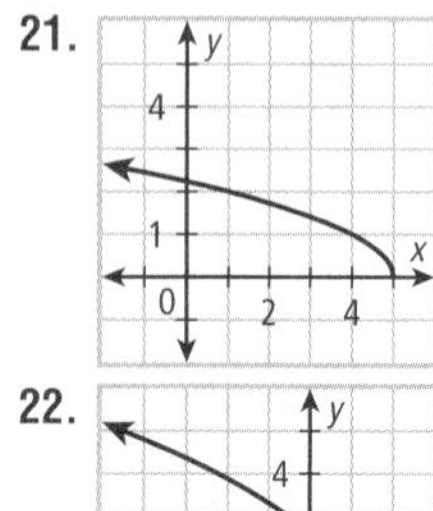

22.

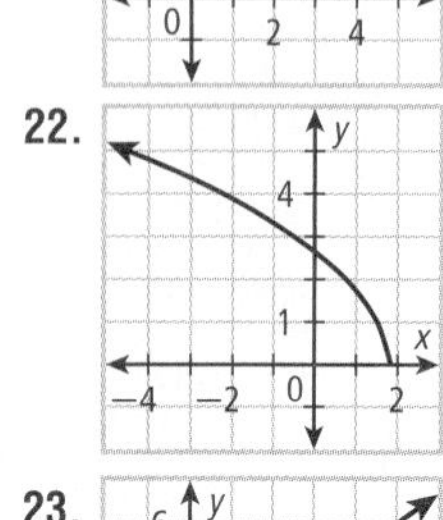

23.

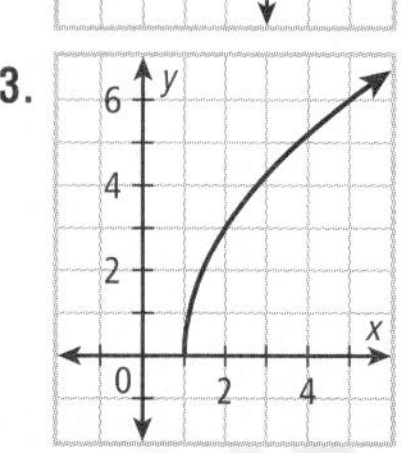

24.

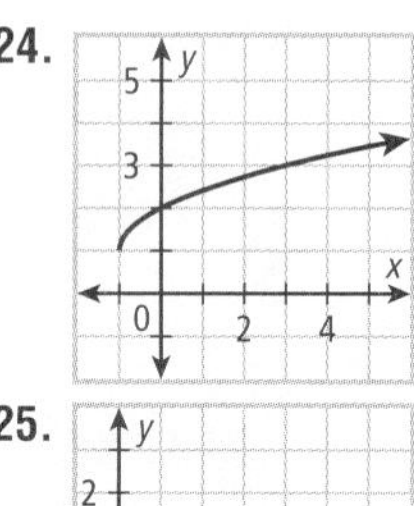

25.

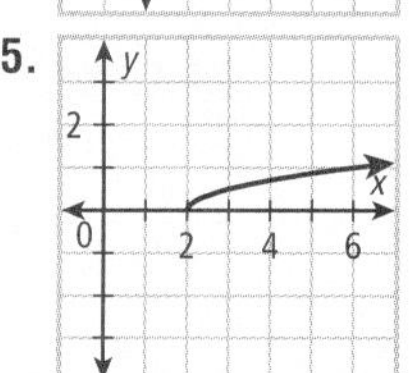

11-2 Radical Expressions *(pp. 705–710)*

Ext. of 1A2.0

EXAMPLE

Simplify. All variables represent nonnegative numbers.

■ $\sqrt{50x^4}$

$\sqrt{(25)(2)x^4}$ — *Factor the radicand.*

$\sqrt{25}\sqrt{2}\sqrt{x^4}$ — *Use the Product Property.*

$5x^2\sqrt{2}$ — *Simplify.*

■ $\sqrt{\dfrac{m^3}{4}}$

$\dfrac{\sqrt{m^3}}{\sqrt{4}}$ — *Use the Quotient Property.*

$\dfrac{\sqrt{m^2}\sqrt{m}}{\sqrt{4}}$ — *Use the Product Property.*

$\dfrac{m\sqrt{m}}{2}$ — *Simplify.*

EXERCISES

Simplify. All variables represent nonnegative numbers.

26. $\sqrt{121}$ **27.** $\sqrt{n^4}$

28. $\sqrt{(x+3)^2}$ **29.** $\sqrt{\dfrac{75}{3}}$

30. $\sqrt{36d^2}$ **31.** $\sqrt{y^6x}$

32. $\sqrt{12}$ **33.** $\sqrt{32ab^5}$

34. $\sqrt{\dfrac{5}{4}}$ **35.** $\sqrt{\dfrac{t^3}{100t}}$

36. $\sqrt{\dfrac{8}{18}}$ **37.** $\sqrt{\dfrac{32p^4}{49}}$

38. $\sqrt{\dfrac{s^2t^9}{s^4}}$ **39.** $\sqrt{\dfrac{72b^6}{225}}$

11-3 Adding and Subtracting Radical Expressions *(pp. 711–715)*

Ext. of 1A2.0

EXAMPLE

■ Simplify $\sqrt{50x} - \sqrt{2x} + \sqrt{12x}$.

$\sqrt{50x} - 1\sqrt{2x} + \sqrt{12x}$

$\sqrt{(25)(2)x} - 1\sqrt{2x} + \sqrt{(4)(3)x}$

$\sqrt{25}\sqrt{2x} - 1\sqrt{2x} + \sqrt{4}\sqrt{3x}$

$5\sqrt{2x} - 1\sqrt{2x} + 2\sqrt{3x}$

$4\sqrt{2x} + 2\sqrt{3x}$

EXERCISES

Simplify each expression. All variables represent nonnegative numbers.

40. $6\sqrt{7} + 3\sqrt{7}$ **41.** $4\sqrt{3} - \sqrt{3}$

42. $3\sqrt{2} + 2\sqrt{3}$ **43.** $9\sqrt{5t} - 8\sqrt{5t}$

44. $\sqrt{50} - \sqrt{18}$ **45.** $\sqrt{12} + \sqrt{20}$

46. $\sqrt{20x} - \sqrt{80x}$ **47.** $4\sqrt{54} - \sqrt{24}$

11-4 Multiplying and Dividing Radical Expressions *(pp. 716–721)*

Ext. of 1A2.0

EXAMPLES

■ Multiply $(\sqrt{3}+6)^2$. Write the product in simplest form.

$(\sqrt{3}+6)^2$

$(\sqrt{3}+6)(\sqrt{3}+6)$ — *Expand the expression.*

$3 + 6\sqrt{3} + 6\sqrt{3} + 36$ — *Use the FOIL method.*

$39 + 12\sqrt{3}$ — *Simplify.*

■ Simplify the quotient $\frac{\sqrt{5}}{\sqrt{3}}$.

$\dfrac{\sqrt{5}}{\sqrt{3}}\left(\dfrac{\sqrt{3}}{\sqrt{3}}\right) = \dfrac{\sqrt{15}}{3}$ — *Rationalize the denominator.*

EXERCISES

Multiply. Write each product in simplest form. All variables represent nonnegative numbers.

48. $\sqrt{2}\sqrt{7}$ **49.** $3\sqrt{2x}\sqrt{14}$

50. $\sqrt{2}(4-\sqrt{8})$ **51.** $(8+\sqrt{7})^2$

Simplify each quotient. All variables represent nonnegative numbers.

52. $\dfrac{4}{\sqrt{5}}$ **53.** $\dfrac{a\sqrt{9}}{\sqrt{2}}$

54. $\dfrac{\sqrt{8}}{2\sqrt{6}}$ **55.** $\dfrac{\sqrt{5}}{\sqrt{2n}}$

Answers

26. 11
27. n^2
28. $x + 3$
29. 5
30. $6d$
31. $y^3\sqrt{x}$
32. $2\sqrt{3}$
33. $4b^2\sqrt{2ab}$
34. $\dfrac{\sqrt{5}}{2}$
35. $\dfrac{t}{10}$
36. $\dfrac{2}{3}$
37. $\dfrac{4p^2\sqrt{2}}{7}$
38. $\dfrac{t^4\sqrt{t}}{s}$
39. $\dfrac{2b^3\sqrt{2}}{5}$
40. $9\sqrt{7}$
41. $3\sqrt{3}$
42. $3\sqrt{2} + 2\sqrt{3}$
43. $\sqrt{5t}$
44. $2\sqrt{2}$
45. $2\sqrt{3} + 2\sqrt{5}$
46. $-2\sqrt{5x}$
47. $10\sqrt{6}$
48. $\sqrt{14}$
49. $6\sqrt{7x}$
50. $4\sqrt{2} - 4$
51. $71 + 16\sqrt{7}$
52. $\dfrac{4\sqrt{5}}{5}$
53. $\dfrac{3a\sqrt{2}}{2}$
54. $\dfrac{\sqrt{3}}{3}$
55. $\dfrac{\sqrt{10n}}{2n}$

Answers

56. $x = 64$
57. $x = 8$
58. $x = 3$
59. $x = 25$
60. $x = -81$
61. $x = 100$
62. $x = 3$
63. $\varnothing$
64. $x = 4$
65. $x = 6$
66. $x = 7$
67. $x = \frac{19}{2}$
68. $x = 12$
69. $x = 3$
70. $x = 4$
71. $x = 5$
72. 81, 243, 729
73. 48, −96, 192
74. 5, 2.5, 1.25
75. −256, −1024, −4096
76. 7,812,500
77. 19,131,876
78. Yes; as the x-values change by a const. amt., the y-values are multiplied by a const. amt.
79. No; as the x-values change by a const. amt., the y-values are not multiplied by a const. amt.
80.

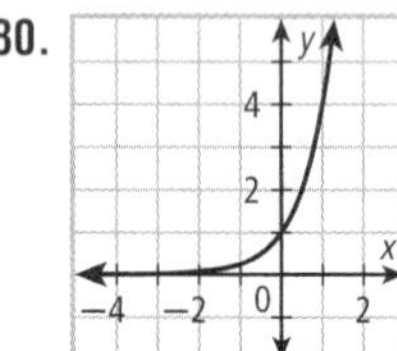

81.

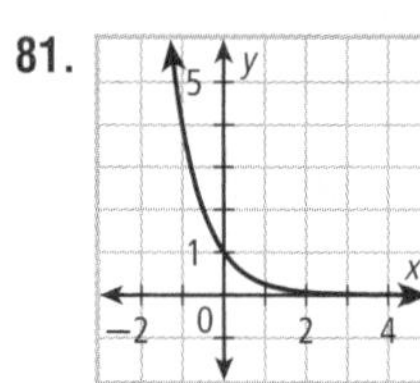

11-5 Solving Radical Equations (pp. 722–729)

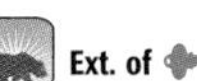
Ext. of 1A2.0

EXAMPLE

■ Solve $\sqrt{4x+1} - 8 = -3$. Check your answer.

$\sqrt{4x+1} - 8 = -3$

$\sqrt{4x+1} = 5$ *Add 8 to both sides.*

$\left(\sqrt{4x+1}\right)^2 = (5)^2$ *Square both sides.*

$4x + 1 = 25$

$4x = 24$ *Subtract 1 from both sides.*

$x = 6$ *Divide both sides by 4.*

Check $\sqrt{4x+1} - 8 = -3$

$\sqrt{4(6)+1} - 8$	-3
$\sqrt{25} - 8$	-3
$5 - 8$	-3
-3	-3 ✓

EXERCISES

Solve each equation. Check your answer.

56. $\sqrt{x} = 8$
57. $\sqrt{2x} = 4$
58. $\sqrt{x+6} = 3$
59. $-3\sqrt{x} = -15$
60. $3\sqrt{-x} = 27$
61. $\frac{4\sqrt{x}}{5} = 8$
62. $\sqrt{x+1} = \sqrt{3x-5}$
63. $\sqrt{x-2} + 4 = 3$
64. $12 = 4\sqrt{2x+1}$
65. $\sqrt{x-5} = \sqrt{7-x}$
66. $\sqrt{x+2} = 3$
67. $\sqrt{2x-3} = 4$
68. $4\sqrt{x-3} = 12$
69. $\sqrt{x+6} = x$
70. $\sqrt{3x+4} = x$
71. $\sqrt{2x+6} = x - 1$

11-6 Geometric Sequences (pp. 732–737)

Prep for 2A22.0

EXAMPLE

■ What is the 10th term of the geometric sequence −6400, 3200, −1600, 800, …?

Find the common ratio by dividing consecutive terms.

$\frac{3200}{-6400} = -0.5 \quad \frac{-1600}{3200} = -0.5$

$a_n = a_1 r^{n-1}$ *Write the formula.*

$a_{10} = -6400(-0.5)^{10-1}$ *Substitute.*

$= -6400(-0.5)^9$ *Simplify.*

$= 12.5$

EXERCISES

Find the next three terms in each geometric sequence.

72. 1, 3, 9, 27, …
73. 3, −6, 12, −24, …
74. 80, 40, 20, 10, …
75. −1, −4, −16, −64, …
76. The first term of a geometric sequence is 4 and the common ratio is 5. What is the 10th term?
77. What is the 15th term of the geometric sequence 4, 12, 36, 108, …?

11-7 Exponential Functions (pp. 738–744)

Preview of 2A12.0

EXAMPLE

■ Tell whether the ordered pairs $\{(1,4), (2,16), (3,36), (4,64)\}$ satisfy an exponential function. Explain.

x	y
1	4
2	16
3	36
4	64

As the x-values increase by a constant amount, the y-values are not multiplied by a constant amount. This function is not exponential.

EXERCISES

Tell whether each set of ordered pairs satisfies an exponential function. Explain.

78. $\{(0, 1), (2, 9), (4, 81), (6, 729)\}$
79. $\{(-2, -8), (-1, -4), (0, 0), (1, 4)\}$

Graph each exponential function.

80. $y = 4^x$
81. $y = \left(\frac{1}{4}\right)^x$

11-8 Exponential Growth and Decay *(pp. 747–754)*

Preview of 2A12.0

EXAMPLE

- **The value of a piece of antique furniture has been increasing at a rate of 2% per year. In 1990, its value was $800. Write an exponential growth function to model the situation. Then find the value of the furniture in the year 2010.**

Step 1 $y = a(1 + r)^t$ *Write the formula.*

$y = 800(1 + 0.02)^t$ *Substitute.*

$y = 800(1.02)^t$ *Simplify.*

Step 2 $y = 800(1.02)^{20}$ *Substitute 20 for t.*

≈ 1188.76 *Simplify and round.*

The furniture's value will be $1188.76.

EXERCISES

82. The number of students in the book club is increasing at a rate of 15% per year. In 2001, there were 9 students in the book club. Write an exponential growth function to model the situation. Then find the number of students in the book club in the year 2008.

83. The population of a small town is decreasing at a rate of 4% per year. In 1970, the population was 24,500. Write an exponential decay function to model the situation. Then find the population in the year 2020.

11-9 Linear, Quadratic, and Exponential Models *(pp. 755–761)*

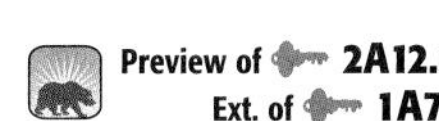

EXAMPLE

- **Use the data in the table to describe how Jasmin's debt is changing. Then write a function that models the data. Use your function to predict Jasmin's debt after 8 years.**

Jasmin's Debt	
Years	**Debt ($)**
1	130
2	260
3	520
4	1040

(+1 between successive years; ×2 between successive debts)

Jasmin's debt doubles every year.

For a constant change in time (+1), there is a constant ratio of 2, so the data is exponential.

$y = ab^x$ *Write the general form.*

$y = a(2)^x$ *Substitute 2 for b.*

$130 = a(2)^1$ *Substitute (1, 130) for x and y.*

$a = 65$ *Solve for a.*

$y = 65(2)^x$ *Replace a and b in $y = ab^x$.*

$y = 65(2)^8$ *Substitute 8 for x.*

$y = 16{,}640$ *Simplify with a calculator.*

Jasmin's debt in 8 years will be $16,640.

EXERCISES

Graph each data set. Which kind of model best describes the data?

84. $\{(-2, -12), (-1, -3), (0, 0), (1, -3), (2, -12)\}$

85. $\{(-2, -2), (-1, 2), (0, 6), (1, 10), (2, 14)\}$

86. $\left\{\left(-2, -\frac{1}{4}\right), \left(-1, -\frac{1}{2}\right), (0, -1), (1, -2), (2, -4)\right\}$

Look for a pattern in each data set to determine which kind of model best describes the data.

87. $\{(0, 2), (1, 6), (2, 18), (3, 54), (4, 162)\}$

88. $\{(0, 0), (2, -20), (4, -80), (6, -180), (8, -320)\}$

89. $\{(-8, 5), (-4, 3), (0, 1), (4, -1), (8, -3)\}$

90. Write a function that models the data. Then use your function to predict how long the humidifier will produce steam with 10 quarts of water.

Input and Output of a Humidifier	
Water Volume (qt)	**Steam Time (h)**
3	4.5
4	6
5	7.5
6	9

Answers

82. $y = 9(1.15)^t$; 24

83. $y = 24{,}500(0.96)^t$; 3182

84.

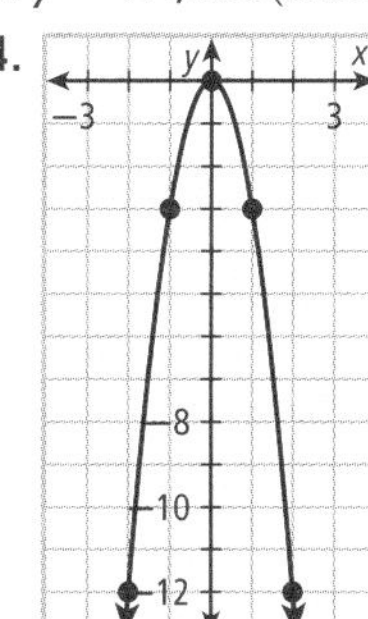

quadratic

85.

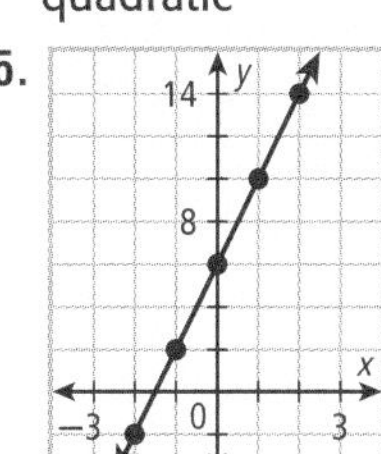

linear

86.

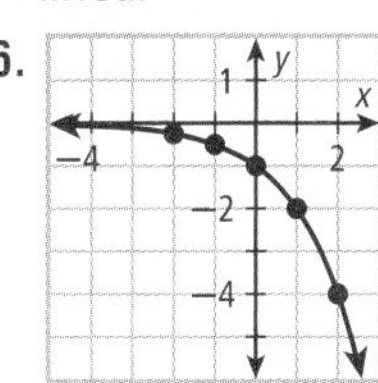

exponential

87. exponential

88. quadratic

89. linear

90. $y = 1.5x$; 15 h

Study Guide: Review 767

Organizer

Objective: Assess students' mastery of concepts and skills in Chapter 11.

Online Edition

Resources

Assessment Resources

Chapter 11 Tests

- Free Response (Levels A, B, C)
- Multiple Choice (Levels A, B, C)
- Performance Assessment

***IDEA Works!* CD-ROM**

Modified Chapter 11 Test

Test & Practice Generator One-Stop Planner®

Answers

4. 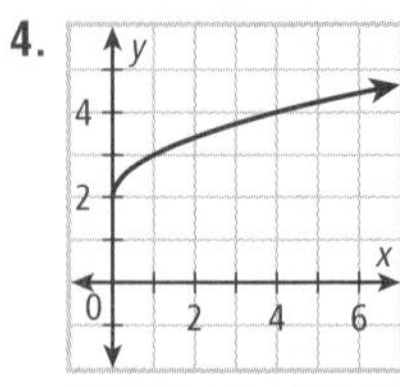

5. 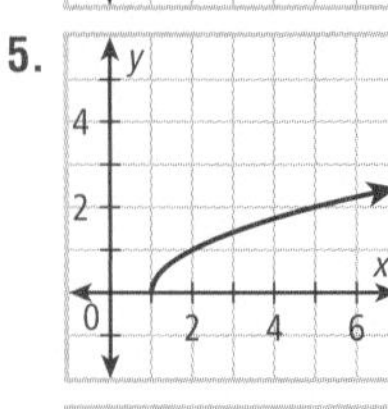

6. 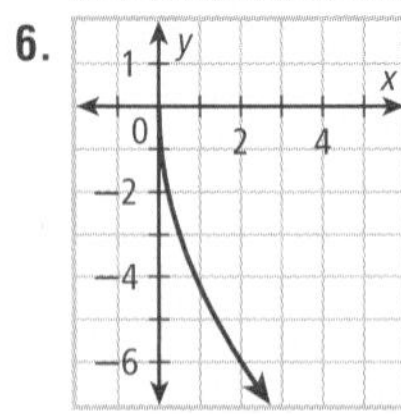

CHAPTER TEST

Find the domain of each square-root function.

1. $y = 6 + \sqrt{x}$ **$x \geq 0$**
2. $y = -2\sqrt{x+9}$ **$x \geq -9$**
3. $y = x + \sqrt{3x-3}$ **$x \geq 1$**

Graph each square-root function.

4. $y = \sqrt{x} + 2$
5. $y = \sqrt{x-1}$
6. $y = -3\sqrt{2x}$

Simplify. All variables represent nonnegative numbers.

7. $\sqrt{27}$ **$3\sqrt{3}$**
8. $\sqrt{75m^4}$ **$5m^2\sqrt{3}$**
9. $\sqrt{\frac{x^6}{y^2}}$ **$\frac{x^3}{y}$**
10. $\sqrt{\frac{p^9}{144p}}$ **$\frac{p^4}{12}$**
11. $4\sqrt{10} - 2\sqrt{10}$ **$2\sqrt{10}$**
12. $5\sqrt{3y} + \sqrt{3y}$ **$6\sqrt{3y}$**
13. $\sqrt{8} - \sqrt{50}$ **$-3\sqrt{2}$**
14. $2\sqrt{75} - \sqrt{32} + \sqrt{48}$ **$14\sqrt{3} - 4\sqrt{2}$**
15. $\sqrt{2}\sqrt{3m}$ **$\sqrt{6m}$**
16. $\frac{\sqrt{128d}}{\sqrt{5}}$ **$\frac{8\sqrt{10d}}{5}$**
17. $\sqrt{3}(\sqrt{21} - 2)$ **$3\sqrt{7} - 2\sqrt{3}$**
18. $(\sqrt{3} - 2)(\sqrt{3} + 4)$ **$-5 + 2\sqrt{3}$**

Solve each equation. Check your answer.

19. $\sqrt{2x} = 6$ **18**
20. $\sqrt{3x+4} - 2 = 5$ **15**
21. $\frac{2\sqrt{x}}{3} = 8$ **144**
22. $\sqrt{5x+1} = \sqrt{2x-2}$ **$\varnothing$**

Find the next three terms in each geometric sequence.

23. 2, 6, 18, 54, ... **162, 486, 1458**
24. 4800, 2400, 1200, 600, ... **300, 150, 75**
25. −4, 20, −100, 500, ... **−2500, 12,500, −62,500**

26. **Communication** If school is cancelled, the school secretary calls 2 families. Each of those families calls 2 other families. In the third round of calls, each of the 4 families calls 2 more families. If this pattern continues, how many families are called in the seventh round of calls? **128**

Graph each exponential function.

27. $y = -2(4)^x$
28. $y = 3(2)^x$
29. $y = 4\left(\frac{1}{2}\right)^x$
30. $-\left(\frac{1}{3}\right)^x$

31. A teacher is repeatedly enlarging a diagram on a photocopier. The function $f(x) = 3(1.25)^x$ represents the length of the diagram, in centimeters, after x enlargements. What is the length after 5 enlargements? Round to the nearest centimeter. **9 cm**

32. Chelsea invested \$5600 at a rate of 3.6% compounded quarterly. Write a compound interest function to model the situation. Then find the balance after 6 years. **$A = 5600(1.009)^{4t}$; \$6943.46**

33. The number of trees in a forest is decreasing at a rate of 5% per year. The forest had 24,000 trees 15 years ago. Write an exponential decay function to model the situation. Then find the number of trees now. **$y = 24{,}000(0.95)^t$; 11,119 trees**

Look for a pattern in each data set to determine which kind of model best describes the data.

34. $\{(-10, -17), (-5, -7), (0, 3), (5, 13), (10, 23)\}$ **linear**
35. $\{(1, 3), (2, 9), (3, 27), (4, 81), (5, 243)\}$ **exponential**

36. Use the data in the table to describe how the bacteria population is changing. Then write a function that models the data. Use your function to predict the bacteria population after 10 hours. **The bacteria pop. is tripling every hour; $y = 6(3)^x$; 354,294**

Bacteria Population				
Time (h)	0	1	2	3
Bacteria	6	18	54	162

27. 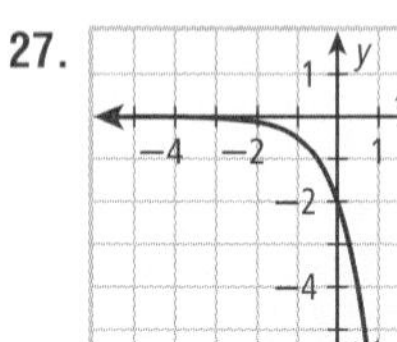

28. 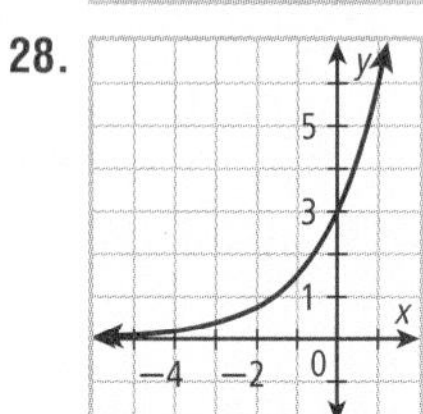

29. 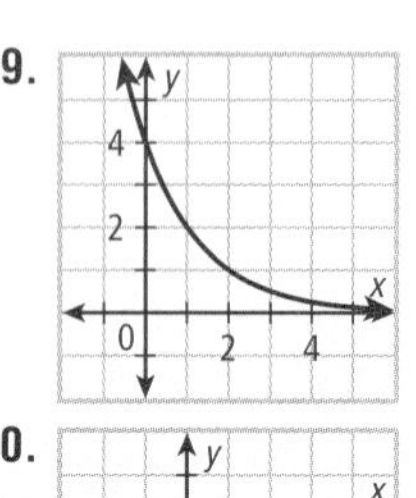

30. 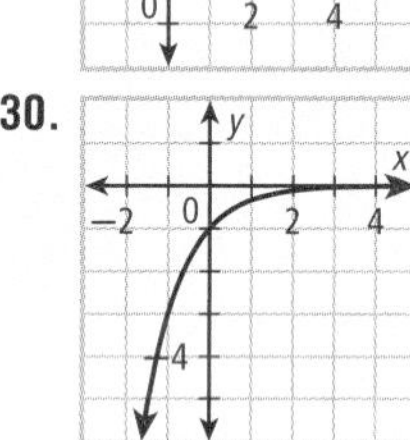

COLLEGE ENTRANCE EXAM PRACTICE

CHAPTER 11

FOCUS ON SAT MATHEMATICS SUBJECT TESTS

Colleges use standardized test scores to confirm what your academic record indicates. Because courses and instruction differ from school to school, standardized tests are one way in which colleges try to compare students fairly when making admissions decisions.

You will need to use a calculator on the SAT Mathematics Subject Tests. If you do not already have a graphing calculator, consider getting one because it may give you an advantage when solving some problems. Spend time getting used to your calculator before the test.

You may want to time yourself as you take this practice test. It should take you about 6 minutes to complete.

1. What is the domain of $y = \sqrt{x - 4}$?
   (A) $x \geq -2$
   (B) $x \geq 2$
   (C) $x \geq -4$
   (D) $x \geq 4$
   (E) $x > 4$

2. $\dfrac{\sqrt{8}\sqrt{3}}{\sqrt{5}} =$
   (A) $2\sqrt{3}$
   (B) $\dfrac{2\sqrt{3}}{5}$
   (C) $\sqrt{12}$
   (D) $\dfrac{4\sqrt{30}}{5}$
   (E) $\dfrac{2\sqrt{30}}{5}$

3. If $\dfrac{\sqrt{6 - 3x}}{5} = 3$, what is the value of x?
   (A) -3
   (B) -13
   (C) -73
   (D) -77
   (E) -89

4. The third term of a geometric sequence is 32 and the fifth term is 512. What is the eighth term of the sequence?
   (A) 544
   (B) 1232
   (C) 8192
   (D) 32,768
   (E) 2,097,152

5. A band releases a new CD and tracks its sales. The table shows the number of copies sold each week (in thousands). Which type of function best models this data?

CD Sales	
Week	Copies Sold (thousands)
1	129.5
2	155
3	179.5
4	203
5	225.5
6	247

   (A) Linear function
   (B) Quadratic function
   (C) Exponential function
   (D) Square-root function
   (E) Absolute-value function

COLLEGE ENTRANCE EXAM PRACTICE

CHAPTER 11

Organizer

Objective: Provide practice for college entrance exams such as the SAT Mathematics Subject Tests.

Online Edition

Resources

College Entrance Exam Practice

Questions on the SAT Mathematics Subject Tests (Levels 1 and 2) represent the following math content areas:

	Level	
	1	2
Algebra	30%	18%
Plane Euclidean Geometry	20%	0%
Coordinate Geometry	12%	12%
Three-dimensional Geometry	6%	8%
Trigonometry	8%	20%
Functions	12%	24%
Statistics/Probability	6%	6%
Miscellaneous	6%	12%

Items on this page focus on:
- Algebra
- Functions

Text References:

Item	1	2	3	4	5
Lesson	11-1	11-4	11-5	11-6	11-9

Multiple Choice

1. Students who chose **E** may not know that 0 can be a value of the radicand. Students who chose **A** may have mistakenly simplified the function as $\sqrt{x}$ − 2 and confused domain values and range values.
2. Students who chose **D** may have incorrectly found $\sqrt{8}$ to be $4\sqrt{2}$.
3. Students who chose **B** may have squared both sides of the equation first but forgot to square the denominator. Remind students to check their solutions to radical equations, not only because there might be extraneous roots but to avoid simple mistakes like this.
4. Students who chose **B** found the eighth term of the arithmetic sequence with the same third and fifth terms. Students who chose **E** found the ratio of a_5 to a_3 and used that as the common ratio for the sequence.
5. Students who chose **A** may have thought the first differences were close enough to being the same that a linear model would fit. However, there is a constant second difference of 1, so a quadratic model is the best fit.

Organizer

Objective: Provide opportunities to learn and practice common test-taking strategies.

Teaching Tip **Multiple Choice** This Strategy for Success focuses on choosing the best answer when there are multiple correct answers or no correct answers. Remind students that they must check *all* of the answers if the answer is "all of the above." Encourage students to combine the strategies for all of the above and none of the above with other strategies they have learned, such as eliminating answer choices and working backward from the answer.

Multiple Choice: *None of the Above* or *All of the Above*

In some multiple-choice test items, one of the options is *None of the above* or *All of the above*. To answer these types of items, first determine whether each of the other options is true or false. If you find that more than one option is true, then the correct choice is likely to be *All of the above*. If none of the options are true, the correct choice is *None of the above*.

If you do not know how to solve the problem and have to guess, *All of the above* is most often correct, and *None of the above* is usually incorrect.

EXAMPLE 1

Which of the following quadratic polynomials has two roots?

Ⓐ $x^2 - 5x - 14$ Ⓒ $14x^2 + 3 - 23x$

Ⓑ $3x^2 + 14x + 13$ Ⓓ All of the above

Notice that choice D is All of the above. This means that you must look at each option. As you consider each option, mark it true or false in your test booklet.

A You could solve each related quadratic equation to answer this question. But you don't need to find the actual roots, just the number of them. Using the discriminant will save time. For a quadratic equation $ax^2 + bx + c = 0$, the discriminant is $b^2 - 4ac$.

Write the related quadratic equation in choice A in standard form: $x^2 - 5x - 14 = 0$.

$a = 1$ $b = -5$ $c = -14$ $b^2 - 4ac = 81$

When the discriminant is positive, the equation has two solutions. Therefore, the polynomial has two roots. Choice A is true.

B Write the related equation in standard form: $3x^2 + 14x + 13 = 0$

$a = 3$ $b = 14$ $c = 13$ $b^2 - 4ac = 40$

The discriminant is positive, so the equation has two solutions and the polynomial has two roots. Choice B is also true. The answer is likely to be Choice D, *All of the above,* but you should also check whether Choice C is true.

C Write the related equation in standard form: $14x^2 - 23x + 3 = 0$

$a = 14$ $b = -23$ $c = 3$ $b^2 - 4ac = 361$

The discriminant is positive. Choice C is true as well.

Because A, B, and C are all true, the correct response is D, *All of the above.*

Be careful of problems that contain more than one negative word, such as *no, not,* or *never.* Read the problem and each option twice before selecting an answer.

Read each test item and answer the questions that follow.

Item A

The mean score on a test is 68. Which CANNOT be true?

Ⓐ Every score is 68.

Ⓑ Half of the scores are 68, and half of the scores are 0.

Ⓒ Half of the scores are 94, and half of the scores are 42.

Ⓓ None of the above

1. What is the definition of *mean*?
2. If you find that an option is true, is that the correct response? Explain.
3. Willie determined that A and C could both be true, so he chose D as his response. Do you agree? Why or why not?

Item B

What is the probability of rolling a 2 on a number cube?

Ⓐ $16.\overline{6}\%$

Ⓑ $1 - P(\text{rolling } 1, 3, 4, 5, \text{ or } 6)$

Ⓒ $\frac{1}{6}$

Ⓓ All of the above

4. What is the complement of rolling a 2? Is choice B correct? Explain.
5. If you roll a number cube, how many possible outcomes are there? How does this information help you solve this problem?
6. Is the value given in choice C equivalent to any other choice? If so, which one(s)?
7. How many choices are true? What is the correct response to the test item?

Item C

Which expression is equivalent to $(8x - 4z) - (5z + x)$?

Ⓐ $8x - 4z - 5z + x$

Ⓑ $9x - 9z$

Ⓒ $8x - 4z - 5z - x$

Ⓓ None of the above

8. Kyle finds that choices A and B are both false. To save time, he selects choice D as his answer because he figures it is likely that choice C will also be false. Do you think Kyle made a wise decision? Why or why not?
9. Determine whether choices A, B, and C are true, and then give the correct response to this test item.

Item D

Which point is on the line that passes through $(1, 5)$ and $(2, 0)$?

Ⓐ $(-3, 5)$

Ⓑ $(-1, -15)$

Ⓒ $(0, 10)$

Ⓓ All of the above

10. What information do you need in order to determine whether a point lies on a line? How can you use the information given in the problem to find this?
11. How can you determine whether choice D is the correct response to the test item?

Answers to Test Items

A. B

B. D

C. C

D. C

Answers

Possible answers:

1. the sum of all the values in the set divided by the number of values in the set
2. No; the question asks which statements cannot be true.
3. No; "None of the above" would mean that all of the statements must be true, but choice **B** is not true.
4. Not rolling a 2, or rolling a 1, 3, 4, 5, or 6; yes; the probability of an event is 1 minus the probability of the complement of that event.
5. 6; the probability of rolling a 2 will be 1 outcome out of 6, so choice **C** is correct.
6. yes; **A**
7. 3 (**A, B,** and **C**); **D**
8. No; choice **C** is correct.
9. Only choice **C** is true; the correct response is **C.**
10. the equation of the line; use the two given points to find the slope and then use the point-slope formula
11. Determine whether or not the values in choices **B, A,** and **C** are equivalent.

California Standards

Algebra 1 7.0

MASTERING THE STANDARDS

Organizer

Objective: Provide review and practice for Chapters 1–11.

PREMIER **Online Edition**

Resources

Assessment Resources

Chapter 11 Cumulative Test

Focus on California Standards Benchmark Tests and Intervention

***California Standards Practice* CD-ROM**

go.hrw.com
KEYWORD: MA8CA Practice

California Standards

Standard	Items
1.0	3
2.0	4, 10
5.0	17
7.0	14
8.0	5
9.0	7, 15
10.0	9, 18b
11.0	8
12.0	1
14.0	18c
15.0	16
17.0	11
20.0	12
21.0	2, 13
22.0	6
23.0	18a

MASTERING THE STANDARDS

go.hrw.com
Standards Practice Online
KEYWORD: MA8CA Practice

CUMULATIVE ASSESSMENT, CHAPTERS 1–11

Multiple Choice

1. Which of the following is the simplified form of the expression $\frac{x^2 - 3x + 2}{x^2 - 4}$?

Ⓐ $\frac{x-1}{x-2}$ Ⓒ $\frac{x+1}{x+2}$

Ⓑ $\frac{x-1}{x+2}$ Ⓓ $\frac{x+1}{x-2}$

2. Which of these is the graph of $y = x^2 - 2x - 3$?

Ⓐ
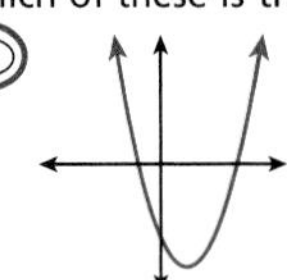

Ⓑ
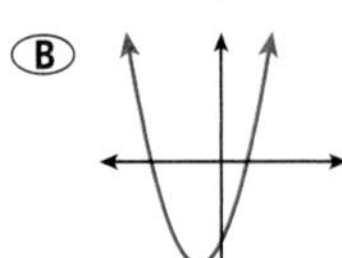

Ⓒ
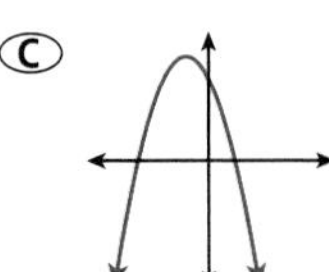

Ⓓ
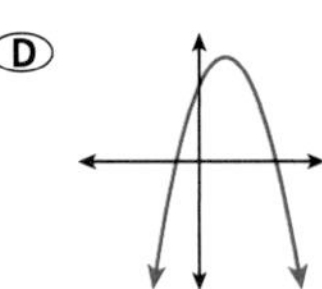

3. Which property is illustrated by the equation $3(w + 4) = 3w + 12$?

Ⓐ Associative Property of Addition

Ⓑ Associative Property of Multiplication

Ⓒ Commutative Property of Multiplication

Ⓓ Distributive Property

4. Which expression is equivalent to $\left(m^2 m^{\frac{1}{2}}\right)^6$?

Ⓐ $m^{\frac{5}{2}}$ Ⓒ $m^{\frac{15}{2}}$

Ⓑ m^6 Ⓓ m^{15}

5. Which line passes through the point $(-4, -3)$ and is perpendicular to the line $3x + y = -5$?

Ⓐ $3x + y = -15$

Ⓑ $3x - y = -15$

Ⓒ $x - 3y = 5$

Ⓓ $x + 3y = 5$

6. Leah graphed a quadratic function that intersected the x-axis at two points. Which function could she have graphed?

Ⓐ $y = x^2 - 6x + 9$

Ⓑ $y = x^2 + 2x - 24$

Ⓒ $y = x^2 + 10x + 25$

Ⓓ $y = x^2 + x + 4$

7. What is the solution to the system of equations below?

$$\begin{cases} 2x - y = 2 \\ y = 3x - 5 \end{cases}$$

Ⓐ (4, 6) Ⓒ (2, 1)

Ⓑ (3, 4) Ⓓ (0, 2)

8. What is the complete factorization of $2x^3 + 18x$?

Ⓐ $2x(x^2 + 9)$

Ⓑ $2x(x + 3)^2$

Ⓒ $2x(x + 3)(x - 3)$

Ⓓ $2(x^3 + 18)$

9. What is the product of $2x - 5$ and $3x + 2$?

Ⓐ $6x^2 - 4x - 10$

Ⓑ $6x^2 - 11x - 10$

Ⓒ $6x^2 - 15x - 10$

Ⓓ $6x^2 - 19x - 10$

Multiple Choice Students who chose **B** in **Item 4** may have multiplied the exponents inside the parentheses instead of adding.

Students who chose **A** or **C** in **Item 7** found solutions to only one of the equations. Remind students that the ordered pair must be a solution for both equations.

Students who chose **B** in **Item 11** may have forgotten that rational functions have excluded values because the denominator cannot equal 0.

When a test item gives an equation to be solved, it may be quicker to work backward from the answer choices by substituting them into the equation. If time remains, check your answer by solving the equation.

10. Which shows the product of 5.1×10^4 and 3×10^9 written in scientific notation?

Ⓐ 1.53×10^{12}

Ⓑ 1.53×10^{14}

Ⓒ 15.3×10^{12}

Ⓓ 15.3×10^{13}

11. Which functions have all real numbers as their domain?

I $y = \frac{1}{x+1}$

II $y = (x+1)^2$

III $y = |x+1|$

Ⓐ I only

Ⓑ I and II

Ⓒ II and III

Ⓓ I, II, and III

Gridded Response

12. Use the Quadratic Formula to find the positive solution of $3x^2 - 8x - 2 = 0$. Round your answer to the nearest tenth. **2.9**

13. The graph of $f(x)$ is shown below. How many zeros does $f(x)$ have? **2**

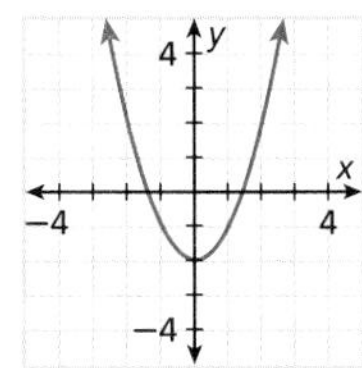

14. Scott is finding the equation of the line that has an x-intercept of −4 and a y-intercept of 3. He writes the equation in the form $Ax + By = 12$. What value should he use for B? **4**

15. Tonya graphs the lines described by $x + 2y = -2$ and $-x + 3y = -8$. What is the x-coordinate of the point of intersection of the lines? **2**

Short Response

16. A chemist has 400 milliliters of a solution that is 50% alcohol. She wants to add alcohol to the solution to make a solution that is 75% alcohol.

a. Write an equation that you can use to find out how many milliliters of alcohol the chemist should add to the solution. Be sure to explain what any variables represent.

b. Solve the equation to determine the number of milliliters of alcohol the chemist should add. Show your work. **400 mL**

17. Ella and Mia went on a camping trip. The total cost for their trip was $124, which the girls divided evenly. Ella paid for 4 nights at the campsite and $30 for supplies. Mia paid for 2 nights at the campsite and $46 for supplies.

a. Write an equation that could be used to find the cost of one night's stay at the campsite. Explain what each variable in your equation represents.

b. Solve your equation from part **a** to find the cost of one night's stay at the campsite. Show your work. **$8.00**

Extended Response

18. The figure gives the dimensions of a rectangular flower bed.

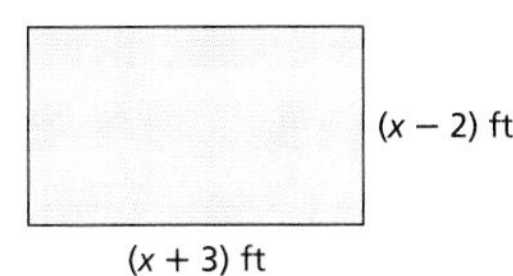

a. The area of the flower bed is 24 ft². Use the formula for the area of a rectangle to write an equation based on the figure.

b. Multiply the binomials in your equation and simplify to write a new equation in the form $ax^2 + bx + c = 0$.

c. Solve the equation. Show your work. Do all of the solutions make sense in this situation? Explain.

d. What are the length and width of the flower bed? **8 ft; 3 ft**

Short-Response Rubric

Items 16–17

2 Points = The student's answer is an accurate and complete execution of the task or tasks.

1 Point = The student's answer contains attributes of an appropriate response but is flawed.

0 Points = The student's answer contains no attributes of an appropriate response.

Extended-Response Rubric

Item 18

4 Points = The student writes the correct equation in part **a,** correctly simplifies and writes a new equation in part **b,** solves the equation correctly in part **c,** and finds the correct length and width in part **d.**

3 Points = The student writes the correct equation in part **a,** correctly simplifies and writes a new equation in part **b,** incorrectly solves but explains how to use the equation in part **c,** and finds the length and width of the flower bed in part **d** (wrong length and width, but correct for the student's equation).

2 Points = The student writes the correct equation in part **a,** simplifies and writes a new equation with minor errors in part **b,** solves but does not explain how to use the equation in part **c,** and finds the length and width of the flower bed in part **d** (wrong length and width, but correct for the student's equation).

1 Point = The student writes a completely incorrect equation in part **a** and attempts to answer all parts, but struggles because part of his or her equation doesn't make sense.

0 Points = The student does not attempt all parts of the problem.

Answers

16a. $\frac{200 + a}{400 + a} = 0.75$, where a is the number of milliliters of alcohol added

17a. $4n + 30 = 2n + 46$; n represents the cost of one night's stay at the campsite.

18a. $(x + 3)(x - 2) = 24$

b. $x^2 + x - 30 = 0$

c. $x = -6, 5$; -6 does not make sense in this situation since the dimensions of the flower bed cannot be negative.

Student Handbook

Student Handbook

Extra Practice

Extra Practice

Chapter 1 ■ Skills Practice

Lesson 1-1

Give two ways to write each algebraic expression in words. See p. A28.

1. $x + 8$ 2. $6(y)$ 3. $g - 4$ 4. $\frac{12}{h}$

Evaluate each expression for the replacement set {2, 4, 5.5}.

5. $8 + a$ 10, 12, 13.5 6. $\frac{a}{8}$ 0.25, 0.5, 0.6875 7. $8 - a$ 6, 4, 2.5 8. $8a$ 16, 32, 44

Write an algebraic expression for each verbal expression. Then evaluate the algebraic expression for the given values of y.

	Verbal	Algebraic	$y = 9$	$y = 6$
9.	y reduced by 4	$y - 4$	5	2
10.	the quotient of y and 3	$y \div 3$	3	2
11.	5 more than y	$y + 5$	14	11
12.	the sum of y and 2	$y + 2$	11	8

Lesson 1-2

Add or subtract using a number line.

13. $-7 - 9$ -16 14. $-2.2 + 4.3$ 2.1 15. $-5\frac{1}{2} - 2\frac{1}{2}$ -8 16. $3.4 - 6.5$ -3.1

Subtract.

17. $12 - 47$ -35 18. $1.3 - 9.2$ -7.9 19. $1\frac{1}{3} - 4\frac{2}{3}$ $-3\frac{1}{3}$

Compare. Write <, >, or =.

20. $-5 - (-8) > -4 - 9$ 21. $|-6 - (-2)| > 7 - 4$ 22. $-2 - 5 = 7 - 14$

Evaluate the expression $g - (-7)$ for each value of g.

23. $g = 121$ 128 24. $g = 1.25$ 8.25 25. $g = -\frac{2}{5}$ $6\frac{3}{5}$ 26. $g = -8\frac{1}{3}$ $-1\frac{1}{3}$

Lesson 1-3

Find the value of each expression.

27. $-24 \div (-8)$ 3 28. $5(-9)$ -45 29. $-5.2 \div -1.3$ 4

30. $\frac{2}{7} \div \left(-\frac{6}{7}\right)$ $-\frac{1}{3}$ 31. $0 \div \left(-\frac{4}{5}\right)$ 0 32. $\frac{9}{10} \div 0$ undef.

Evaluate each expression for $x = -8$, $y = 6$, and $z = -4$.

33. xy -48 34. yz -24 35. $\frac{y}{z}$ $-1\frac{1}{2}$ 36. $\frac{z}{x}$ $\frac{1}{2}$

Let a represent a positive number, b represent a negative number, and z represent zero. Tell whether each expression is positive, negative, zero, or undefined.

37. ab neg. 38. $-bz$ zero 39. $-\frac{a}{b}$ pos. 40. $\frac{ab}{z}$ undef.

Lesson 1-4

Write each expression as repeated multiplication. Then simplify the expression.

41. 3^3 $3 \cdot 3 \cdot 3$; 27 42. -2^4 $-(2 \cdot 2 \cdot 2 \cdot 2)$; -16 43. $(-5)^3$ $-5 \cdot (-5) \cdot (-5)$; -125 44. $(-1)^5$ See p. A28.

Write each expression using a base and an exponent.

45. $5 \cdot 5 \cdot 5 \cdot 5 \cdot 5$ 5^5 46. $4 \cdot 4 \cdot 4$ 4^3 47. $2 \cdot 2 \cdot 2 \cdot 2$ 2^4

Write the exponent that makes each equation true.

48. $2^{■} = 16$ 4 49. $4^{■} = 256$ 4 50. $(-3)^{■} = 81$ 4 51. $-5^{■} = -125$ 3

Chapter 1 ■ Skills Practice

Lesson 1-5

Find each root.

52. $-\sqrt[3]{64}$ -4 53. $\sqrt{144}$ 12 54. $\sqrt{25}$ 5

55. $\sqrt{169}$ 13 56. $\sqrt{225}$ 15 57. $\sqrt[3]{343}$ 7

Compare. Write <, >, or =.

58. $\sqrt{118} < 11$ 59. $6 > \sqrt{35}$ 60. $14 = \sqrt{196}$ 61. $\sqrt{50} > 7$

62. $\sqrt{142} < 12$ 63. $8 < \sqrt{65}$ 64. $\sqrt{102} > 10$ 65. $\sqrt{81} = 9$

Write all classifications that apply to each real number.

66. -44 term. dec., $\mathbb{Z}$, $\mathbb{Q}$ 67. $\sqrt{49}$ $\mathbb{W}$, term. dec., $\mathbb{Z}$, $\mathbb{Q}$ 68. 15.982 $\mathbb{Q}$, term. dec. 69. $\frac{1}{9}$ $\mathbb{Q}$, rep. dec.

Lesson 1-6

Name the property that is illustrated in each equation.

70. $56 + x = x + 56$ Comm. Prop. of Add. 71. $10 \cdot (3 \cdot 11) = (10 \cdot 3) \cdot 11$ Assoc. Prop. of Mult.

72. $(6 + x)5 = 6(5) + x(5)$ Dist. Prop. 73. $(4 + x) + 15 = 4 + (x + 15)$ Assoc. Prop. of Add.

Write each product using the Distributive Property. Then simplify. 74–79. See p. A28.

74. $12(108)$ 75. $7(89)$ 76. $11(33)$

77. $16(1003)$ 78. $8(207)$ 79. $18(999)$

For the set {−2, −1, 0, 1, 2}, find a counterexample to show that each statement is false.

80. The set is closed under addition. Possible answer: $2 + 2 = 4$
81. The set is closed under subtraction. Possible answer: $-2 - 1 = -3$
82. The set is closed under multiplication. Possible answer: $2 \cdot (-2) = -4$
83. The set is closed under division. Possible answer: $1 \div 2 = \frac{1}{2}$

Lesson 1-7

Evaluate each expression for the given value of the variable.

84. $22 - 3g + 5$ for $g = 4$ 15 85. $12 - 30 \div h$ for $h = 6$ 7 86. $\sqrt{(11j + j)} + 6$ for $j = 3$ 12

Simplify each expression.

87. $4 + 12 \div |3 - 9|$ 6 88. $-36 - \sqrt{4 + 15 \div 3}$ -39 89. $\frac{5 - \sqrt{12(3)}}{-4 + \sqrt{2(8)}}$ undef.

90. $-5 + 38 + 5 + 62$ 100 91. $2\frac{1}{3} - 42 + 7\frac{2}{3}$ -32 92. $\frac{1}{5} \cdot 4 \cdot 25$ 20

93. $\frac{\sqrt[3]{27} \div 3}{4(6 - 5) - 3}$ 1 94. $5(9 - 7)^2 + 8$ 28 95. $|10 - 13|^2 - 6$ 3

Simplify each expression by combining like terms.

96. $7a - 3a$ $4a$ 97. $-2b - 12b$ $-14b$ 98. $4c + 5c^2 - c$ $3c + 5c^2$

99. $4x^2 - x + 3x$ $4x^2 + 2x$ 100. $5y - 3y + 5$ $2y + 5$ 101. $-z + 8z^2 - 3z^2$ $5z^2 - z$

102. $2m - 4m^2 + 4m$ $6m - 4m^2$ 103. $6j + 3j + 10j^2$ $10j^2 + 9j$ 104. $4f^2 - 3f + 1$ $4f^2 - 3f + 1$

Use properties and operations to show that the first expression simplifies to the second expression.

105. $6(p - 2) + 3p$; $9p - 12$ 105–106. See p. A28.
106. $-4 + 3r - 7(2s - r)$; $10r - 14s - 4$

Chapter 2 ■ Skills Practice

Lesson 2-1

Solve each equation. Check your answer.

1. $x - 9 = 5$ 14 2. $4 = y - 12$ 16 3. $a + \frac{3}{5} = 7$ $6\frac{2}{5}$

4. $7.3 = b + 3.4$ 3.9 5. $-6 + j = 5$ 11 6. $-1.7 = -6.1 + k$ 4.4

7. $\frac{n}{5} = 15$ 75 8. $-6 = \frac{k}{4}$ -24 9. $\frac{r}{2.6} = 5$ 13

10. $3b = 27$ 9 11. $56 = -7d$ -8 12. $-3.6 = -2f$ 1.8

13. $\frac{1}{4}z = 3$ 12 14. $12 = \frac{4}{5}g$ 15 15. $\frac{1}{3}a = -5$ -15

Write an equation to represent each relationship. Then solve the equation.

16. A number decreased by 7 is equal to 10. $x - 7 = 10$; $x = 17$
17. The sum of 6 and a number is −3. $6 + x = -3$; $x = -9$
18. A number multiplied by 4 is −20. $4x = -20$; $x = -5$
19. The quotient of a number and 5 is 7. $\frac{x}{5} = 7$; $x = 35$

Lesson 2-2

Solve each equation. Check your answer.

20. $2k + 7 = 15$ 4 21. $11 - 5m = -4$ 3 22. $23 = 9 - 2d$ -7

23. $\frac{2}{5}b + 6 = 10$ 10 24. $\frac{f}{3} - 4 = 2$ 18 25. $6n + 4 = 22$ 3

26. $3d - 4 = 11$ 5 27. $3t + t = 28$ 7 28. $\frac{m}{4} + \frac{1}{2} = \frac{3}{4}$ 1

29. $11 = 4c + 3$ 2 30. $6 = 4 + \frac{a}{5}$ 10 31. $7 = -2p + 13$ 3

32. $5q + 4 = 24$ 4 33. $15 - \frac{z}{3} = 21$ -18 34. $8 = 2y - 6$ 7

Write an equation to represent each relationship. Solve each equation.

35. The difference of 11 and 4 times a number equals 3. $11 - 4x = 3$; $x = 2$
36. Thirteen less than 5 times a number is equal to 7. $5x - 13 = 7$; $x = 4$
37. A number times 4 increased by 2 equals 22. $4x + 2 = 22$; $x = 5$
38. Three multiplied by a number all divided by 2 equals 12. $\frac{3x}{2} = 12$; $x = 8$

Lesson 2-3

Solve each equation. Check your answer.

39. $\frac{t - 5}{2} = 4$ 13 40. $\frac{11y + 2}{3} = 8$ 2 41. $\frac{2t + 4}{5} = 2$ 3

42. $a + 4a - 6 = 54$ 12 43. $12 + 5f - 2f = 9$ -1 44. $-n - 8 - 3n = -16$ 2

45. $p(3 + 5) - 4 = 76$ 10 46. $7(h - 2) = 21$ 5 47. $4\left(k - \frac{1}{2}\right) = 42$ 11

48. $6 = \frac{r + 8}{2}$ 4 49. $w - 3w + 8 = 16$ -4 50. $14 = x(13 - 11)$ 7

51. $3(s + 4) = 15$ 1 52. $10 + m - 4m = 4$ 2 53. $\frac{v - 5}{5} = 9$ 50

Write an equation to represent each relationship. Then solve.

54. A number decreased by 2 multiplied by 5 equals 30. $5(x - 2) = 30$; $x = 8$
55. Six plus a number all divided by 4 equals 5. $\frac{6 + x}{4} = 5$; $x = 14$
56. A number times 6 minus 12 added to 4 times the number equals 30. $6x - 12 + 4x = 30$; $x = 4.2$
57. Ten minus a number times 4 is the same as five minus 7. $10 - 4x = 5 - 7$; $x = 3$

Chapter 2 ■ Skills Practice

Lesson 2-4

Solve each equation. Check your answer.

58. $5b - 3 = 4b + 1$ 4 59. $3g + 7 = 11g - 17$ 3

60. $-8 + 4y = y - 6 + 3y - 2$ all real numbers 61. $7 + 3d - 5 = -1 + 2d - 12 + d$ ∅

62. $2s + 6 = 3s - 7$ 13 63. $-3h + 12 - 4h = -7h - 9 - 16$ ∅

64. $6k - 15 - k = 5k - 9 - 6$ all real numbers 65. $c + 22 - \frac{3}{4}c = 5 - \frac{1}{2}c + 17$ 0

Write an equation to represent each relationship. Then solve the equation. See p. A28.

66. Three more than one-half a number is the same as 17 minus three times the number.
67. Two times the difference of a number and 4 is the same as 5 less than the number.
68. A number plus 5 is the same as 3 times the number minus 13.
69. Two times a number minus 9 is equal to 3 minus 4 times the number.

Lesson 2-5

Find each unit rate.

70. A long-distance runner ran 9000 meters in 30 minutes. 300 m/min
71. A hummingbird flapped its wings 770 times in 14 seconds. 55 times/s
72. A car traveled 210 miles in 3 hours. 70 mi/h
73. A printer printed 60 pages in 5 minutes. 12 pages/min

Solve each proportion.

74. $\frac{h}{4} = \frac{5}{6}$ $\frac{20}{6}$ 75. $\frac{5}{m} = \frac{2}{5}$ $\frac{25}{2}$ 76. $\frac{r}{3} = \frac{10}{7}$ $\frac{30}{7}$

77. $\frac{2}{3} = \frac{2x}{8}$ $\frac{16}{6}$ 78. $\frac{5}{x - 3} = \frac{3}{10}$ $\frac{59}{3}$ 79. $\frac{b - 2}{4} = \frac{7}{12}$ $\frac{52}{12}$

80. Find 25% of 60. 15 81. Find 40% of 95. 38

82. What percent of 75 is 15? 20% 83. What percent of 60 is 33? 55%

84. 91 is what percent of 65? 140% 85. 35% of what number is 24.5? 70

86. Find 34% of 50. 17 87. What percent of 95 is 38? 40%

88. 55% of what number is 11? 20 89. Find 115% of 40. 46

Lesson 2-6

Solve for the indicated variable. See p. A28.

90. $q - 3r = 2$ for r 91. $\frac{5 - c}{6} = d - 7$ for c

92. $2x + 3\frac{y}{4} = 5$ for y 93. $2fgh - 3g = 10$ for h

94. $2a + a - r = 5$ for r 95. $3g + 4h = 7$ for g

96. $st - k = 3k$ for s 97. $\frac{11x + y}{4} = y - 1$ for y

98. $\frac{5m}{n} - 3d = 12$ for m 99. $4us + 3c = 8c$ for u.

Lesson 2-7

Solve each equation. Check your answer.

100. $|a| = 13$ ± 13 101. $|x| - 16 = 3$ ± 19 102. $|g + 5| = 11$ $-16, 6$

103. $|7s| - 6 = 8$ ± 2 104. $\left|\frac{f}{2} + 1\right| = 15$ $-32, 28$ 105. $|p - 5| - 12 = -9$ 2, 8

106. $\left|\frac{1}{2} + t\right| - 2 = -\frac{3}{2}$ $0, -1$ 107. $|b + 1| - 17 = -20$ ∅ 108. $|4p| + 5 = 5$ 0

109. $500 = 25|z| + 200$ ± 12 110. $|7j + 14| - 5 = 16$ $-5, 1$ 111. $\frac{|p - 2| - 15}{5} = -1$ $-8, 12$

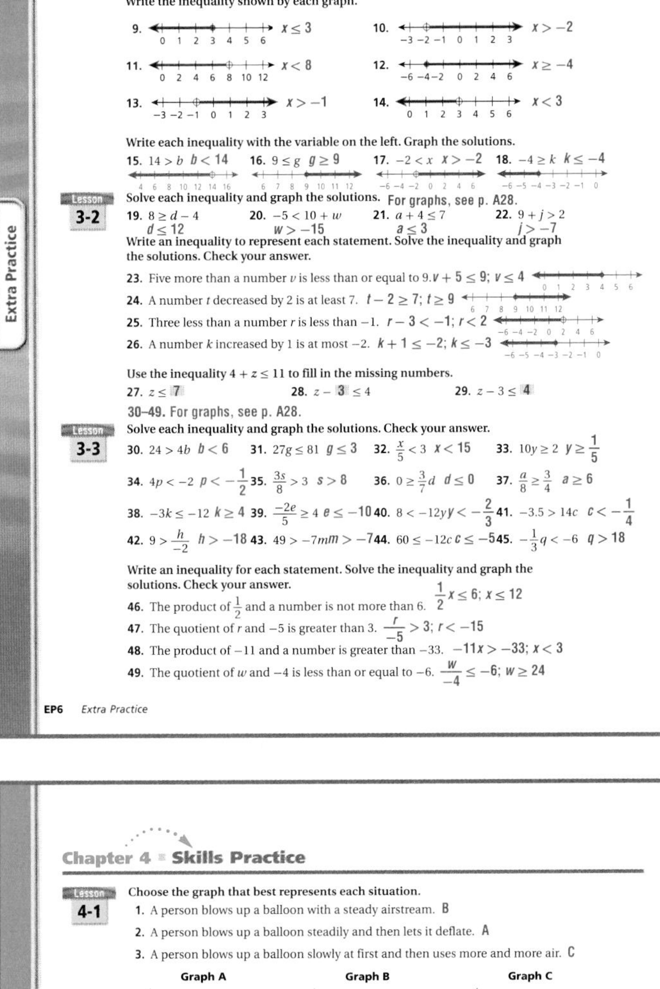

Chapter 3 ▪ Skills Practice

Lesson 3-1

Describe the solutions of each inequality in words. 1–8. See p. A28.

1. $3 + v < -2$ 2. $15 \le k + 4$ 3. $-3 + n > 6$ 4. $1 - 4x \ge -2$

Graph each inequality.

5. $f \ge 2$ 6. $m < -1$ 7. $\sqrt{4^2 + 3^2} > c$ 8. $(-1 - 1)^2 \le p$

Write the inequality shown by each graph.

9. $x \le 3$ 10. $x > -2$

11. $x < 8$ 12. $x \ge -4$

13. $x > -1$ 14. $x < 3$

Write each inequality with the variable on the left. Graph the solutions.

15. $14 > b$ $b < 14$ 16. $9 \le g$ $g \ge 9$ 17. $-2 < x$ $x > -2$ 18. $-4 \ge k$ $k \le -4$

Lesson 3-2

Solve each inequality and graph the solutions. For graphs, see p. A28.

19. $8 \ge d - 4$ $d \le 12$ 20. $-5 < 10 + w$ $w > -15$ 21. $a + 4 \le 7$ $a \le 3$ 22. $9 + j > 2$ $j > -7$

Write an inequality to represent each statement. Solve the inequality and graph the solutions. Check your answer.

23. Five more than a number v is less than or equal to 9. $v + 5 \le 9$; $v \le 4$
24. A number t decreased by 2 is at least 7. $t - 2 \ge 7$; $t \ge 9$
25. Three less than a number r is less than -1. $r - 3 < -1$; $r < 2$
26. A number k increased by 1 is at most -2. $k + 1 \le -2$; $k \le -3$

Use the inequality $4 + z \le 11$ to fill in the missing numbers.

27. $z \le$ 7 28. $z -$ 3 ≤ 4 29. $z - 3 \le$ 4

30–49. For graphs, see p. A28.

Lesson 3-3

Solve each inequality and graph the solutions. Check your answer.

30. $24 > 4b$ $b < 6$ 31. $27g \le 81$ $g \le 3$ 32. $\frac{x}{5} < 3$ $x < 15$ 33. $10y \ge 2$ $y \ge \frac{1}{5}$

34. $4p < -2$ $p < -\frac{1}{2}$ 35. $\frac{3s}{8} > 3$ $s > 8$ 36. $0 \ge \frac{3}{7}d$ $d \le 0$ 37. $\frac{a}{8} \ge \frac{3}{4}$ $a \ge 6$

38. $-3k \le -12$ $k \ge 4$ 39. $\frac{-2e}{5} \ge 4$ $e \le -10$ 40. $8 < -12y$ $y < -\frac{2}{3}$ 41. $-3.5 > 14c$ $c < -\frac{1}{4}$

42. $9 > \frac{h}{-2}$ $h > -18$ 43. $49 > -7m$ $m > -7$ 44. $60 \le -12c$ $c \le -5$ 45. $-\frac{1}{3}q < -6$ $q > 18$

Write an inequality for each statement. Solve the inequality and graph the solutions. Check your answer.

46. The product of $\frac{1}{2}$ and a number is not more than 6. $\frac{1}{2}x \le 6$; $x \le 12$
47. The quotient of r and -5 is greater than 3. $\frac{r}{-5} > 3$; $r < -15$
48. The product of -11 and a number is greater than -33. $-11x > -33$; $x < 3$
49. The quotient of w and -4 is less than or equal to -6. $\frac{w}{-4} \le -6$; $w \ge 24$

EP6 *Extra Practice*

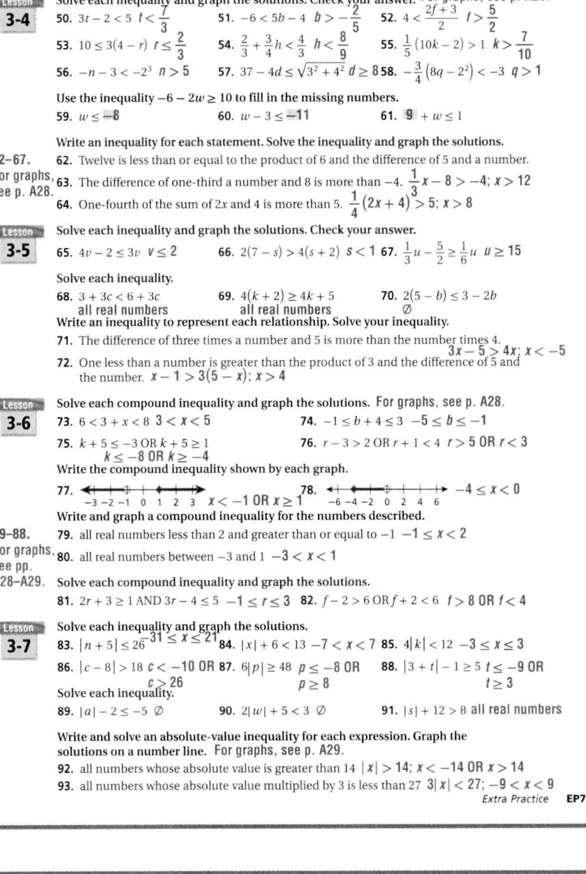

Chapter 3 ▪ Skills Practice

Lesson 3-4

Solve each inequality and graph the solutions. Check your answer. For graphs, see p. A28.

50. $3t - 2 < 5$ $t < \frac{7}{3}$ 51. $-6 < 5b - 4$ $b > -\frac{2}{5}$ 52. $4 < \frac{2f + 3}{2}$ $f > \frac{5}{2}$

53. $10 \le 3(4 - r)$ $r \le \frac{2}{3}$ 54. $\frac{2}{3} + \frac{3}{4}h < \frac{4}{3}$ $h < \frac{8}{9}$ 55. $\frac{1}{5}(10k - 2) > 1$ $k > \frac{7}{10}$

56. $-n - 3 < -2^3$ $n > 5$ 57. $37 - 4d \le \sqrt{3^2 + 4^2}$ $d \ge 8$ 58. $-\frac{3}{4}(8q - 2^2) < -3$ $q > 1$

Use the inequality $-6 - 2w \ge 10$ to fill in the missing numbers.

59. $w \le$ -8 60. $w - 3 \le$ -11 61. 9 $+ w \le 1$

Write an inequality for each statement. Solve the inequality and graph the solutions.

62–67. For graphs, see p. A28.

62. Twelve is less than or equal to the product of 6 and the difference of 5 and a number.
63. The difference of one-third a number and 8 is more than -4. $\frac{1}{3}x - 8 > -4$; $x > 12$
64. One-fourth of the sum of $2x$ and 4 is more than 5. $\frac{1}{4}(2x + 4) > 5$; $x > 8$

Lesson 3-5

Solve each inequality and graph the solutions. Check your answer.

65. $4v - 2 \le 3v$ $v \le 2$ 66. $2(7 - s) > 4(s + 2)$ $s < 1$ 67. $\frac{1}{3}u - \frac{5}{2} \ge \frac{1}{6}u$ $u \ge 15$

Solve each inequality.

68. $3 + 3c < 6 + 3c$ all real numbers 69. $4(k + 2) \ge 4k + 5$ all real numbers 70. $2(5 - b) \le 3 - 2b$ $\varnothing$

Write an inequality to represent each relationship. Solve your inequality.

71. The difference of three times a number and 5 is more than the number times 4. $3x - 5 > 4x$; $x < -5$
72. One less than a number is greater than the product of 3 and the difference of 5 and the number. $x - 1 > 3(5 - x)$; $x > 4$

Lesson 3-6

Solve each compound inequality and graph the solutions. For graphs, see p. A28.

73. $6 < 3 + x < 8$ $3 < x < 5$ 74. $-1 \le b + 4 \le 3$ $-5 \le b \le -1$

75. $k + 5 \le -3$ OR $k + 5 \ge 1$ $k \le -8$ OR $k \ge -4$ 76. $r - 3 > 2$ OR $r + 1 < 4$ $r > 5$ OR $r < 3$

Write the compound inequality shown by each graph.

77. $x < -1$ OR $x \ge 1$ 78. $-4 \le x < 0$

Write and graph a compound inequality for the numbers described.

79–88. For graphs, see pp. A28–A29.

79. all real numbers less than 2 and greater than or equal to -1 $-1 \le x < 2$
80. all real numbers between -3 and 1 $-3 < x < 1$

Solve each compound inequality and graph the solutions.

81. $2r + 3 \ge 1$ AND $3r - 4 \le 5$ $-1 \le r \le 3$ 82. $f - 2 > 6$ OR $f + 2 < 6$ $f > 8$ OR $f < 4$

Lesson 3-7

Solve each inequality and graph the solutions.

83. $|n + 5| \le 26$ $-31 \le x \le 21$ 84. $|x| + 6 < 13$ $-7 < x < 7$ 85. $4|k| < 12$ $-3 \le x \le 3$

86. $|c - 8| > 18$ $c < -10$ OR $c > 26$ 87. $6|p| \ge 48$ $p \le -8$ OR $p \ge 8$ 88. $|3 + t| - 1 \ge 5$ $t \le -9$ OR $t \ge 3$

Solve each inequality.

89. $|a| - 2 \le -5$ $\varnothing$ 90. $2|w| + 5 < 3$ $\varnothing$ 91. $|s| + 12 > 8$ all real numbers

Write and solve an absolute-value inequality for each expression. Graph the solutions on a number line. For graphs, see p. A29.

92. all numbers whose absolute value is greater than 14 $|x| > 14$; $x < -14$ OR $x > 14$
93. all numbers whose absolute value multiplied by 3 is less than 27 $3|x| < 27$; $-9 < x < 9$

Extra Practice EP7

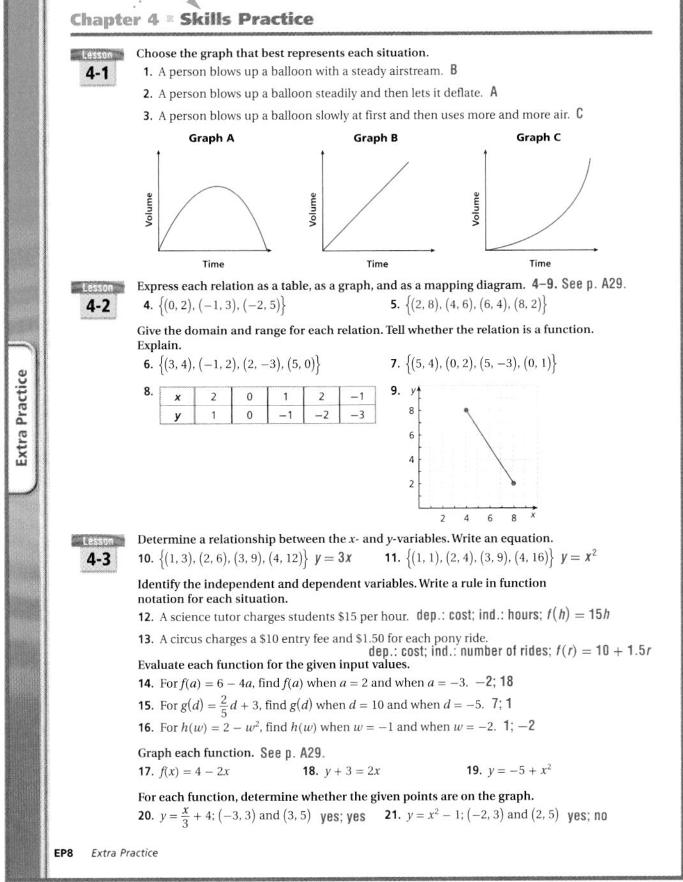

Chapter 4 ▪ Skills Practice

Lesson 4-1

Choose the graph that best represents each situation.

1. A person blows up a balloon with a steady airstream. B
2. A person blows up a balloon steadily and then lets it deflate. A
3. A person blows up a balloon slowly at first and then uses more and more air. C

Lesson 4-2

Express each relation as a table, as a graph, and as a mapping diagram. 4–9. See p. A29.

4. $\{(0, 2), (-1, 3), (-2, 5)\}$ 5. $\{(2, 8), (4, 6), (6, 4), (8, 2)\}$

Give the domain and range for each relation. Tell whether the relation is a function. Explain.

6. $\{(3, 4), (-1, 2), (2, -3), (5, 0)\}$ 7. $\{(5, 4), (0, 2), (5, -3), (0, 1)\}$

8.

x	2	0	1	2	−1
y	1	0	−1	−2	−3

9.

Lesson 4-3

Determine a relationship between the x- and y-variables. Write an equation.

10. $\{(1, 3), (2, 6), (3, 9), (4, 12)\}$ $y = 3x$ 11. $\{(1, 1), (2, 4), (3, 9), (4, 16)\}$ $y = x^2$

Identify the independent and dependent variables. Write a rule in function notation for each situation.

12. A science tutor charges students \$15 per hour. dep.: cost; ind.: hours; $f(h) = 15h$
13. A circus charges a \$10 entry fee and \$1.50 for each pony ride. dep.: cost; ind.: number of rides; $f(r) = 10 + 1.5r$

Evaluate each function for the given input values.

14. For $f(a) = 6 - 4a$, find $f(a)$ when $a = 2$ and when $a = -3$. -2; 18
15. For $g(d) = \frac{2}{5}d + 3$, find $g(d)$ when $d = 10$ and when $d = -5$. 7; 1
16. For $h(w) = 2 - w^2$, find $h(w)$ when $w = -1$ and when $w = -2$. 1; -2

Graph each function. See p. A29.

17. $f(x) = 4 - 2x$ 18. $y + 3 = 2x$ 19. $y = -5 + x^2$

For each function, determine whether the given points are on the graph.

20. $y = \frac{x}{3} + 4$; $(-3, 3)$ and $(3, 5)$ yes; yes 21. $y = x^2 - 1$; $(-2, 3)$ and $(2, 5)$ yes; no

EP8 *Extra Practice*

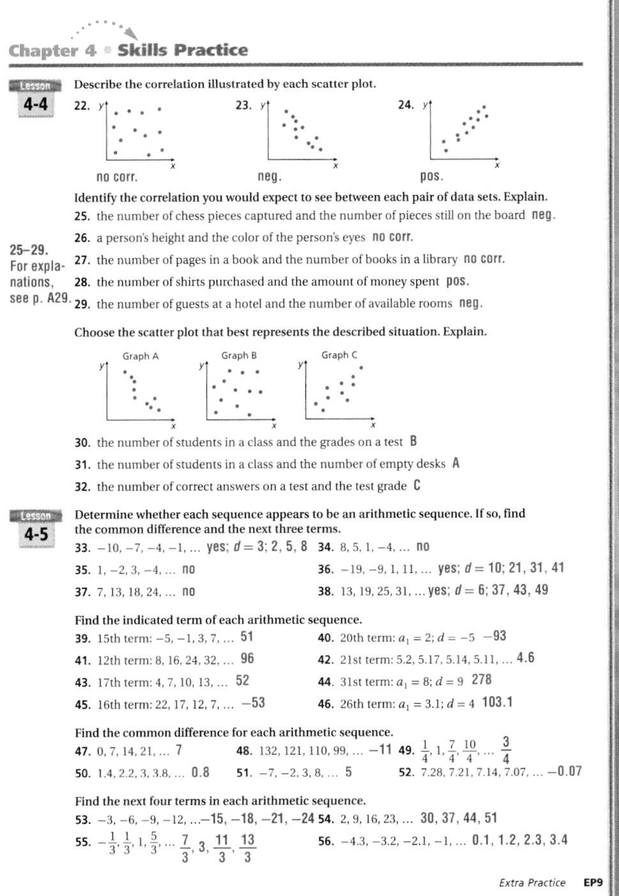

Chapter 4 ▪ Skills Practice

Lesson 4-4

Describe the correlation illustrated by each scatter plot.

22. no corr. 23. neg. 24. pos.

Identify the correlation you would expect to see between each pair of data sets. Explain.

25–29. For explanations, see p. A29.

25. the number of chess pieces captured and the number of pieces still on the board neg.
26. a person's height and the color of the person's eyes no corr.
27. the number of pages in a book and the number of books in a library no corr.
28. the number of shirts purchased and the amount of money spent pos.
29. the number of guests at a hotel and the number of available rooms neg.

Choose the scatter plot that best represents the described situation. Explain.

30. the number of students in a class and the grades on a test B
31. the number of students in a class and the number of empty desks A
32. the number of correct answers on a test and the test grade C

Lesson 4-5

Determine whether each sequence appears to be an arithmetic sequence. If so, find the common difference and the next three terms.

33. $-10, -7, -4, -1, \ldots$ yes; $d = 3$; 2, 5, 8 34. $8, 5, 1, -4, \ldots$ no
35. $1, -2, 3, -4, \ldots$ no 36. $-19, -9, 1, 11, \ldots$ yes; $d = 10$; 21, 31, 41
37. $7, 13, 18, 24, \ldots$ no 38. $13, 19, 25, 31, \ldots$ yes; $d = 6$; 37, 43, 49

Find the indicated term of each arithmetic sequence.

39. 15th term: $-5, -1, 3, 7, \ldots$ 51 40. 20th term: $a_1 = 2$; $d = -5$ -93
41. 12th term: $8, 16, 24, 32, \ldots$ 96 42. 21st term: $5.2, 5.17, 5.14, 5.11, \ldots$ 4.6
43. 17th term: $4, 7, 10, 13, \ldots$ 52 44. 31st term: $a_1 = 8$; $d = 9$ 278
45. 16th term: $22, 17, 12, 7, \ldots$ -53 46. 26th term: $a_1 = 3.1$; $d = 4$ 103.1

Find the common difference for each arithmetic sequence.

47. $0, 7, 14, 21, \ldots$ 7 48. $132, 121, 110, 99, \ldots$ -11 49. $\frac{1}{4}, 1, \frac{7}{4}, \frac{10}{4}, \ldots$ $\frac{3}{4}$
50. $1.4, 2.2, 3, 3.8, \ldots$ 0.8 51. $-7, -2, 3, 8, \ldots$ 5 52. $7.28, 7.21, 7.14, 7.07, \ldots$ -0.07

Find the next four terms in each arithmetic sequence.

53. $-3, -6, -9, -12, \ldots$ $-15, -18, -21, -24$ 54. $2, 9, 16, 23, \ldots$ 30, 37, 44, 51
55. $-\frac{1}{3}, \frac{1}{3}, 1, \frac{5}{3}, \ldots$ $\frac{7}{3}, 3, \frac{11}{3}, \frac{13}{3}$ 56. $-4.3, -3.2, -2.1, -1, \ldots$ 0.1, 1.2, 2.3, 3.4

Extra Practice EP9

Chapter 5 ■ Skills Practice

Lesson 5-1

Graph each linear equation. Then tell whether it represents a function. For graphs, see p. A29.

1. $y = -3x - 5$ yes 2. $y = x$ yes 3. $x = -3$ no

Without graphing, tell whether each point is on the graph of the given line.

4. $11x - 3y = 5$; (1, 2) yes 5. $5x + \frac{1}{2}y = 18$; (3, −6) no
6. $5x + \frac{1}{2}y = 3$; (−1, 4) no 7. $x - 5y = 17$; (7, −2) yes
8. $4x + 2y = 2$; (−2, 5) yes 9. $5x + y = 18$; (3, −3) no
10. $3.5x + 2.4y = 23.6$; (4, 4) yes 11. $\frac{3}{4}x - 3y = 0$; (8, −2) no

Write each equation in standard form and give the values of *A*, *B*, and *C*. Then describe the graph. See p. A29.

12. $12y = 15 - x$ 13. $-4x + 13 = y$ 14. $-\frac{3}{2}y = \frac{7}{5} - \frac{5}{6}x$ 15. $7x = 5y + 2$
16. $7y = 24$ 17. $10 + \frac{1}{2}x = -8y$ 18. $6x = 20 + 4y$ 19. $16 = 13x$

Lesson 5-2

Find the *x*- and *y*-intercepts.

20. 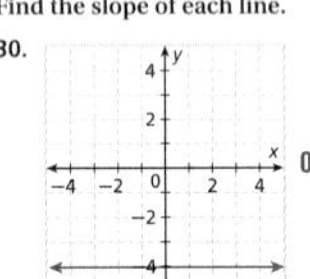 x-int.: 4; y-int.: 2

21. 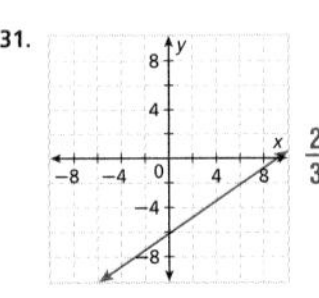 x-int.: 2; y-int: −8

22. $-4x = 2y - 1$ 22. x-int.: $\frac{1}{4}$; y-int.: $\frac{1}{2}$
23. $x - y = 3$ x-int.: 3; y-int: −3
24. $2x - 3y = 12$ x-int.: 6; y-int: −4
25. $2.5x + 2.5y = 5$ x-int.: 2; y-int: 2

Use intercepts to graph the line described by each equation. See p. A29.

26. $15 = -3x - 5y$ 27. $4y = 2x + 8$ 28. $y = 6 - 3x$ 29. $-2y = x + 2$

Lesson 5-3

Find the slope of each line.

30. 0 31. $\frac{2}{3}$

Find the slope of the line that contains each pair of points.

32. (−1, 2) and (−4, 8) −2 33. (2, 6) and (0, 1) $\frac{5}{2}$ 34. (−2, 3) and (4, 0) $-\frac{1}{2}$

Find the slope of the line described by each equation.

35. $2y = 42 - 6x$ −3 36. $3x + 4y = 12$ $-\frac{3}{4}$ 37. $3x = 15 + 5y$ $\frac{3}{5}$

Chapter 5 ■ Skills Practice

Lesson 5-4

Tell whether each equation represents a direct variation. If so, identify the constant of variation.

38. $x - 2y = 0$ yes; $k = \frac{1}{2}$ 39. $x - y = 3$ no 40. $3y = 2x$ yes; $k = \frac{2}{3}$

41. The value of *y* varies directly with *x*, and $y = 2$ when $x = -3$. Find *y* when $x = 6$. −4
42. The value of *y* varies directly with *x*, and $y = -3$ when $x = 9$. Find *y* when $x = 12$. −4
43. The value of *y* varies directly with *x*, and $y = 3$ when $x = 9$. Find *y* when $x = 21$. 7
44. The value of *y* varies directly with *x*, and $y = \frac{1}{2}$ when $x = \frac{1}{4}$. Find *y* when $x = \frac{1}{2}$. 1

Each ordered pair is a solution of a direct variation. Write the equation of direct variation.

45. (1, 4) $y = 4x$ 46. (−2, 12) $y = -6x$ 47. $\left(\frac{1}{2}, -3\right)$ $y = -6x$ 48. (5, 2) $y = \frac{2}{5}x$
49. (8, 12) $y = \frac{3}{2}x$ 50. (7, −2) $y = -\frac{2}{7}x$ 51. (12, −3) $y = -\frac{1}{4}x$ 52. (5, 15) $y = 3x$

Lesson 5-5

Write the equation that describes each line in slope-intercept form.

53. slope = 2, *y*-intercept = −2 $y = 2x - 2$ 54. slope = 0.25, *y*-intercept = 4 $y = 0.25x + 4$
55. slope = −2, *y*-intercept = 3 $y = -2x + 3$ 56. slope = $\frac{1}{3}$, *y*-intercept = 2 $y = \frac{1}{3}x + 2$
57. slope = 7, *y*-intercept = 5 $y = 7x + 5$ 58. slope = $\frac{3}{4}$, *y*-intercept = −12 $y = \frac{3}{4}x - 12$
59. slope = $-\frac{5}{2}$, *y*-intercept = 0 $y = -\frac{5}{2}x$ 60. slope = 0.94, *y*-intercept = 3.7 $y = 0.94x + 3.7$

Write each equation in slope-intercept form. Then graph the line described by the equation. For graphs, see pp. A29–A30.

61. $2y = x - 3$ $y = \frac{1}{2}x - \frac{3}{2}$ 62. $-3x - 2y = 1$ $y = -\frac{3}{2}x - \frac{1}{2}$ 63. $2y - \frac{1}{2}x = 2$ $y = \frac{1}{4}x + 1$

Lesson 5-6

Write an equation in point-slope form for the line with the given slope that contains the given point.

64. slope = 2; (0, 3) $y - 3 = 2(x - 0)$ 65. slope = −1; (1, −1) $y + 1 = -1(x - 1)$ 66. slope = $\frac{1}{2}$; (2, 4) $y - 4 = \frac{1}{2}(x - 2)$
67. slope = $\frac{1}{3}$; (1, 2) $y - 2 = \frac{1}{3}(x - 1)$ 68. slope = −2; (3, 1) $y - 1 = -2(x - 3)$ 69. slope = 3; (−2, −5) $y + 5 = 3(x + 2)$

Write an equation in slope-intercept form for the line through the two points.

70–72. See p. A30.

70. (−1, 1) and (1, −2) 71. (3, 1) and (2, −3) 72. (4, −5) and (2, −1)
73. (5, 6), (2, −3) $y = 3x - 9$ 74. (−1, 3), (6, 31) $y = 4x + 7$ 75. (0, −1), (3, 35) $y = 12x - 1$
76. $\left(\frac{1}{2}, 7\right)$, (4, 35) $y = 8x + 3$ 77. (3, −15), (−2, 10) $y = -5x$ 78. (−6, 1), (1, −13) $y = -2x - 11$

Lesson 5-7

79. Identify which lines are parallel: $y = 3x - 2$; $y = -2$; $y = 3x + 7$; $y = 0$ 79–80. See p. A30.
80. Identify which lines are perpendicular: $y = -2(2x - 1)$; $y = \frac{1}{2}(x + 3)$; $y = \frac{1}{4}(x + 8)$; $y - 4 = 2(3 - 2x)$

Write an equation in slope-intercept form for the line that is parallel to the given line and that passes through the given point.

81. $y = -2x + 3$; (1, 4) $y = -2x + 6$ 82. $y = x - 5$; (2, −4) $y = x - 6$ 83. $y = 3x$; (−1, 5) $y = 3x + 8$

Write an equation in slope-intercept form for the line that is perpendicular to the given line and that passes through the given point.

84. $y = x + 1$; (3, −2) $y = -x + 1$ 85. $y = -4x - 1$; (−1, 0) $y = \frac{1}{4}x + \frac{1}{4}$ 86. $y = 4x + 5$; (2, −1) $y = -\frac{1}{4}x - \frac{1}{2}$

Chapter 6 ■ Skills Practice

Lesson 6-1

Tell whether the ordered pair is a solution of the given system.

1. (1, 3); $\begin{cases} 2x - 3y = -7 \\ -5x + 3y = 4 \end{cases}$ yes 2. (−2, 2); $\begin{cases} 4x + 3y = -2 \\ -2x - 2y = 2 \end{cases}$ no 3. (4, −3); $\begin{cases} -2x - 3y = 1 \\ x + 2y = -2 \end{cases}$ yes

Solve each system by graphing. Check your answer.

4. $\begin{cases} y = x + 1 \\ y = -2x - 2 \end{cases}$ (−1, 0) 5. $\begin{cases} 3x + y = -8 \\ 3y = \frac{1}{2}x - 5 \end{cases}$ (−2, −2) 6. $\begin{cases} x = 2 - 2y \\ -1 = -2x - 3y \end{cases}$ (−4, 3)

Lesson 6-2

Solve each system by substitution. Check your answer.

7. $\begin{cases} y = 12 - 3x \\ y = 2x - 3 \end{cases}$ (3, 3) 8. $\begin{cases} 2x + y = -6 \\ -5x + y = 1 \end{cases}$ (−1, −4) 9. $\begin{cases} y = 11 - 3x \\ -2x + y = 1 \end{cases}$ (2, 5)

10. $\begin{cases} 2x + 3y = 2 \\ -\frac{1}{2}x + 2y = -6 \end{cases}$ (4, −2) 11. $\begin{cases} 3x - 2y = -3 \\ y = 7 - 4x \end{cases}$ (1, 3) 12. $\begin{cases} 4y - 2x = -2 \\ x + 3y = -4 \end{cases}$ (−1, −1)

Two angles whose measures have a sum of 90° are called complementary angles. For Exercises 13–15, *x* and *y* represent complementary angles. Find the measure of each angle.

13. $\begin{cases} x + y = 90 \\ y = 9x - 10 \end{cases}$ $m\angle x = 10°$; $m\angle y = 80°$ 14. $\begin{cases} x + y = 90 \\ y - 4x = 15 \end{cases}$ $m\angle x = 15°$; $m\angle y = 75°$ 15. $\begin{cases} x + y = 90 \\ y = 2x + 15 \end{cases}$ $m\angle x = 25°$; $m\angle y = 65°$

Lesson 6-3

Solve each system by elimination. Check your answer.

16. $\begin{cases} x - 3y = -1 \\ -x + 2y = -2 \end{cases}$ (8, 3) 17. $\begin{cases} -3x - y = 1 \\ 5x + y = -5 \end{cases}$ (−2, 5) 18. $\begin{cases} -x - 3y = -1 \\ 3x + 3y = 9 \end{cases}$ (4, −1)

19. $\begin{cases} 3x - 2y = 2 \\ 3x + y = 8 \end{cases}$ (2, 2) 20. $\begin{cases} 5x - 2y = -15 \\ 2x - 2y = -12 \end{cases}$ (−1, 5) 21. $\begin{cases} -4x - 2y = -4 \\ -4x + 3y = -24 \end{cases}$ (3, −4)

22. $\begin{cases} -3x - 3y = 3 \\ 2x + y = -4 \end{cases}$ (−3, 2) 23. $\begin{cases} 4x - 3y = -1 \\ 2x - 2y = -4 \end{cases}$ (5, 7) 24. $\begin{cases} 3x + 6y = 0 \\ 7x + 4y = 20 \end{cases}$ (4, −2)

Lesson 6-4

Solve each system of linear equations.

25. $\begin{cases} y = 2x + 4 \\ -2x + y = 6 \end{cases}$ ∅ 26. $\begin{cases} -y = 3 - 5x \\ y - 5x = 6 \end{cases}$ ∅ 27. $\begin{cases} y + 2 = 3x \\ 3x - y = -1 \end{cases}$ ∅

28. $\begin{cases} 2y = 6 - 6x \\ 3y + 9x = 9 \end{cases}$ inf. many sol. 29. $\begin{cases} y - 1 = -3x \\ 12x + 4y = 4 \end{cases}$ inf. many sol. 30. $\begin{cases} 4x - 2y = 4 \\ 3y = 6(x - 1) \end{cases}$ inf. many sol.

Classify each system. Give the number of solutions.

31. $\begin{cases} 2y = 2(4x - 3) \\ y - 1 = 4x \end{cases}$ incons.; no sol. 32. $\begin{cases} 3y + 6x = 9 \\ 2(y - 3) = -4x \end{cases}$ consis., dep.; inf. many sol. 33. $\begin{cases} 3x - 13 = 2y \\ -3y = 2x \end{cases}$ consis., indep.; one sol.

Chapter 6 ■ Skills Practice

Lesson 6-5

Solve each system of linear equations.

34. $\begin{cases} x + y = 0 \\ y = 4x + 5 \end{cases}$ (−1, 1) 35. $\begin{cases} 2x - y = 6 \\ 5x + y = 22 \end{cases}$ (4, 2) 36. $\begin{cases} y = 3x + 1 \\ y = -x + 9 \end{cases}$ (2, 7)

Lesson 6-6

Tell whether the ordered pair is a solution of the given inequality.

37. (3, 6); $y > 2x + 4$ no 38. (−2, −8); $y \le 3x - 2$ yes 39. (−3, 3); $y \ge -2x + 5$ no
40. $\left(\frac{1}{2}, -\frac{3}{4}\right)$; $y > \frac{x}{2} - 1$ no 41. (−4, −2); $y \ge 3x + 5$ yes 42. (3, 7); $y \le 3x - 2$ yes
43. (5, 0); $y < -x + 4$ no 44. $\left(\frac{3}{2}, 2\right)$; $y > 4x - 6$ yes 45. (−10, 12); $y \ge -5x - 32$ no

Graph the solutions of each linear inequality. See p. A30.

46. $y > 2x$ 47. $y \le -3x + 2$ 48. $y \ge 2x - 1$ 49. $-y < -x + 4$
50. $y \ge -2x + 4$ 51. $y > -x - 3$ 52. $y < \frac{1}{2}x + 1\frac{1}{2}$ 53. $y \le 4x - (-1)$

Write an inequality to represent each graph.

54. $y \le 5x - 6$ 55. $y \le -\frac{1}{2}x - 1$

Lesson 6-7

Tell whether the ordered pair is a solution of the given system.

56. (2, 5); $\begin{cases} y > 3x - 3 \\ y \ge x + 1 \end{cases}$ yes 57. (3, 9); $\begin{cases} y > -3x - 2 \\ y < 2x + 3 \end{cases}$ no 58. (2, 3); $\begin{cases} y > 2x \\ y \le x - 3 \end{cases}$ no

59. (4, −9); $\begin{cases} y > -3x + 2 \\ y < 2x - 16 \end{cases}$ yes 60. (−3, 2); $\begin{cases} y \le -3x - 6 \\ y \ge x + 4 \end{cases}$ yes 61. (1, 7); $\begin{cases} y \ge 5x + 2 \\ y > 5x + 2 \end{cases}$ no

Graph each system of linear inequalities. Give two ordered pairs that are solutions and two that are not solutions. 62–70. See p. A30.

62. $\begin{cases} x + 4y < 2 \\ 2y > 3x + 8 \end{cases}$ 63. $\begin{cases} y \le 6 - 2x \\ x - 2y < -2 \end{cases}$ 64. $\begin{cases} 2x - 2 > -3y \\ -x + 3y \ge -10 \end{cases}$

Graph each system of linear inequalities.

65. $\begin{cases} y > 2x + 1 \\ y < 2x - 2 \end{cases}$ 66. $\begin{cases} y < 3x - 1 \\ y > 3x - 4 \end{cases}$ 67. $\begin{cases} y \ge -x + 2 \\ y \ge -x + 5 \end{cases}$

68. $\begin{cases} y \ge 2x - 3 \\ y \ge 2x + 3 \end{cases}$ 69. $\begin{cases} y > -4x - 2 \\ y \le -4x - 5 \end{cases}$ 70. $\begin{cases} y \ge -2x + 1 \\ y < -2x + 6 \end{cases}$

Chapter 7 ■ Skills Practice

Lesson 7-1 Simplify.

1. 3^{-4} $\frac{1}{81}$ 2. 5^{-3} $\frac{1}{125}$ 3. -4^0 -1 4. -2^{-5} $-\frac{1}{32}$ 5. 6^{-3} $\frac{1}{216}$
6. $(-2)^{-4}$ $\frac{1}{16}$ 7. 1^{-7} 1 8. $(-4)^{-3}$ $-\frac{1}{64}$ 9. $(-5)^0$ 1 10. $(-1)^{-5}$ -1

Evaluate each expression for the given value(s) of the variable(s).

11. x^{-4} for $x = 2$ $\frac{1}{16}$ 12. $(c+3)^{-3}$ for $c = -6$ $-\frac{1}{27}$
13. $3j^{-7}k^{-1}$ for $j = -2$ and $k = 3$ $-\frac{1}{128}$ 14. $(2n-2)^{-4}$ for $n = 3$ $\frac{1}{256}$

Simplify.

15. b^4g^{-5} $\frac{b^4}{g^5}$ 16. $\frac{k^{-3}}{r^5}$ $\frac{1}{k^3r^5}$ 17. $5s^{-3}c^0$ $\frac{5}{s^3}$ 18. $\frac{z^{-4}}{5t^{-2}}$ $\frac{t^2}{5z^4}$
19. $\frac{f^2}{3a^{-4}}$ $\frac{f^2a^4}{3}$ 20. $\frac{-3t^4}{q^{-5}}$ $-3t^4q^5$ 21. $\frac{a^0k^{-4}}{p^2}$ $\frac{1}{k^4p^2}$ 22. $3f^{-1}y^{-5}$ $\frac{3}{fy^5}$

Lesson 7-2 Find the value of each power of 10.

23. 10^{-7} 0.0000001 24. 10^9 1,000,000,000 25. 10^6 1,000,000 26. 10^{-8} 0.00000001

Write each number as a power of 10.

27. 10,000,000 10^7 28. 0.00001 10^{-5} 29. 10,000,000,000,000 10^{13}

Find the value of each expression.

30. 72.19×10^{-2} 0.7219 31. 0.096×10^{-7} 0.0000000096 32. 7384.5×10^6 7,384,500,000

Write each number in scientific notation.

33. 3,605,000 3.605×10^6 34. 0.0063 6.3×10^{-3} 35. 100,500,000 1.005×10^8

Lesson 7-3 Simplify.

36. $3^4 \cdot 3^2$ 3^6 37. $r^7 \cdot r^0$ r^7 38. $(k^4)^4$ k^{16}
39. $(b^4)^3$ b^{12} 40. $(c^3d^2)^3 \cdot (cd^2)^{-2}$ c^7d^2 41. $(-3q^3)^{-2}$ $\frac{1}{9q^6}$

Find the missing exponent in each expression.

42. $a^{\blacksquare}a^6 = a^9$ 3 43. $(a^3b^{\blacksquare})^3 = \frac{a^9}{b^6}$ -2 44. $(a^4b^{-2})^{\blacksquare} \cdot a^3 = \frac{b^4}{a^5}$ -2

Lesson 7-4 Simplify.

45. $\frac{3^{11}}{3^8}$ 27 46. $\frac{4^4 \cdot 5^3}{3^2 \cdot 4^3 \cdot 5^3}$ $\frac{4}{9}$ 47. $\frac{6h^4}{12h^3}$ $\frac{h}{2}$ 48. $\frac{r^6s^5}{r^5s^6}$ $\frac{r}{s}$

Simplify each quotient and write the answer in scientific notation.

49. $(4 \times 10^7) \div (1.6 \times 10^5)$ 2.5×10^2 50. $(10 \times 10^4) \div (2 \times 10^7)$ 5×10^{-3} 51. $(2.5 \times 10^8) \div (5 \times 10^3)$ 5×10^4

Simplify.

52. $\left(\frac{2}{3}\right)^4$ $\frac{16}{81}$ 53. $\left(\frac{x^2y^2}{y^3}\right)^2$ $\frac{x^4}{y^2}$ 54. $\left(\frac{4}{5}\right)^{-3}$ $\frac{125}{64}$ 55. $\left(\frac{2xy^2}{3(xy)^2}\right)^{-3}$ $\frac{27x^3}{8}$

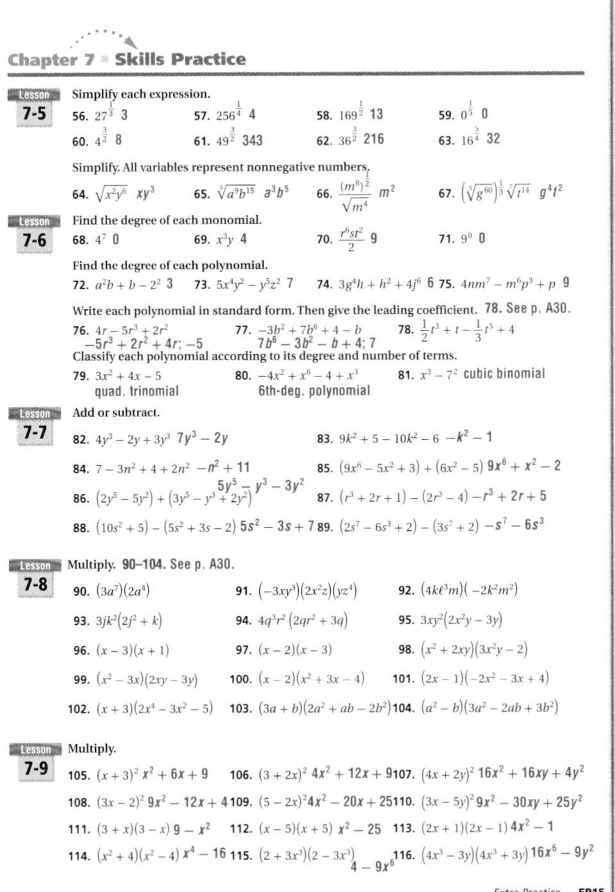

Chapter 7 ■ Skills Practice

Lesson 7-5 Simplify each expression.

56. $27^{\frac{1}{3}}$ 3 57. $256^{\frac{1}{4}}$ 4 58. $169^{\frac{1}{2}}$ 13 59. $0^{\frac{1}{5}}$ 0
60. $4^{\frac{3}{2}}$ 8 61. $49^{\frac{3}{2}}$ 343 62. $36^{\frac{3}{2}}$ 216 63. $16^{\frac{5}{4}}$ 32

Simplify. All variables represent nonnegative numbers.

64. $\sqrt{x^2y^6}$ xy^3 65. $\sqrt[3]{a^9b^{15}}$ a^3b^5 66. $\frac{(m^8)^{\frac{1}{2}}}{\sqrt{m^4}}$ m^2 67. $\left(\sqrt[5]{g^{60}}\right)^{\frac{1}{3}}\sqrt[7]{t^{14}}$ g^4t^2

Lesson 7-6 Find the degree of each monomial.

68. 4^7 0 69. x^3y 4 70. $\frac{r^6st^2}{2}$ 9 71. 9^0 0

Find the degree of each polynomial.

72. $a^2b + b - 2^2$ 3 73. $5x^4y^2 - y^5z^2$ 7 74. $3g^4h + h^2 + 4j^6$ 6 75. $4nm^7 - m^6p^3 + p$ 9

Write each polynomial in standard form. Then give the leading coefficient. 78. See p. A30.

76. $4r - 5r^3 + 2r^2$ $-5r^3 + 2r^2 + 4r$; -5 77. $-3b^2 + 7b^6 + 4 - b$ $7b^6 - 3b^2 - b + 4$; 7 78. $\frac{1}{2}t^3 + t - \frac{1}{3}t^5 + 4$

Classify each polynomial according to its degree and number of terms.

79. $3x^2 + 4x - 5$ quad. trinomial 80. $-4x^2 + x^6 - 4 + x^3$ 6th-deg. polynomial 81. $x^3 - 7^2$ cubic binomial

Lesson 7-7 Add or subtract.

82. $4y^3 - 2y + 3y^3$ $7y^3 - 2y$ 83. $9k^2 + 5 - 10k^2 - 6$ $-k^2 - 1$
84. $7 - 3n^2 + 4 + 2n^2$ $-n^2 + 11$ 85. $(9x^6 - 5x^2 + 3) + (6x^2 - 5)$ $9x^6 + x^2 - 2$
86. $(2y^5 - 5y^2) + (3y^5 - y^3 + 2y^2)$ $5y^5 - y^3 - 3y^2$ 87. $(r^3 + 2r + 1) - (2r^3 - 4)$ $-r^3 + 2r + 5$
88. $(10s^2 + 5) - (5s^2 + 3s - 2)$ $5s^2 - 3s + 7$ 89. $(2s^7 - 6s^3 + 2) - (3s^7 + 2)$ $-s^7 - 6s^3$

Lesson 7-8 Multiply. 90–104. See p. A30.

90. $(3a^7)(2a^4)$ 91. $(-3xy^3)(2x^2z)(yz^4)$ 92. $(4k\ell^3m)(-2k^2m^2)$
93. $3jk^2(2j^2 + k)$ 94. $4q^3r^2(2qr^2 + 3q)$ 95. $3xy^2(2x^2y - 3y)$
96. $(x-3)(x+1)$ 97. $(x-2)(x-3)$ 98. $(x^2 + 2xy)(3x^2y - 2)$
99. $(x^2 - 3x)(2xy - 3y)$ 100. $(x-2)(x^2 + 3x - 4)$ 101. $(2x-1)(-2x^2 - 3x + 4)$
102. $(x+3)(2x^4 - 3x^2 - 5)$ 103. $(3a+b)(2a^2 + ab - 2b^2)$ 104. $(a^2 - b)(3a^2 - 2ab + 3b^2)$

Lesson 7-9 Multiply.

105. $(x+3)^2$ $x^2 + 6x + 9$ 106. $(3+2x)^2$ $4x^2 + 12x + 9$ 107. $(4x+2y)^2$ $16x^2 + 16xy + 4y^2$
108. $(3x-2)^2$ $9x^2 - 12x + 4$ 109. $(5-2x)^2$ $4x^2 - 20x + 25$ 110. $(3x-5y)^2$ $9x^2 - 30xy + 25y^2$
111. $(3+x)(3-x)$ $9 - x^2$ 112. $(x-5)(x+5)$ $x^2 - 25$ 113. $(2x+1)(2x-1)$ $4x^2 - 1$
114. $(x^2+4)(x^2-4)$ $x^4 - 16$ 115. $(2+3x^3)(2-3x^3)$ $4 - 9x^6$ 116. $(4x^3 - 3y)(4x^3 + 3y)$ $16x^6 - 9y^2$

Extra Practice EP15

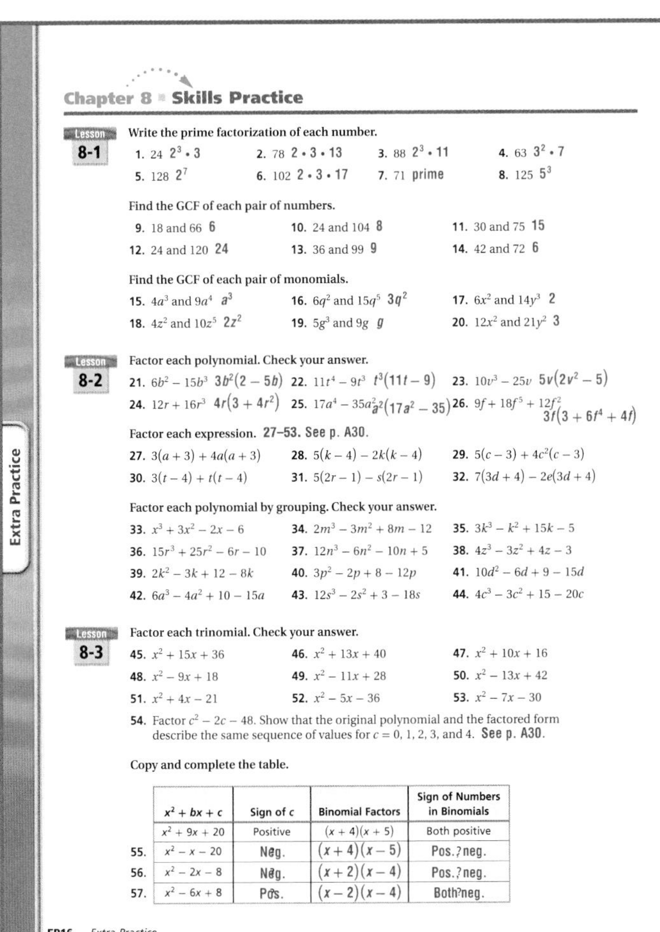

Chapter 8 ■ Skills Practice

Lesson 8-1 Write the prime factorization of each number.

1. 24 $2^3 \cdot 3$ 2. 78 $2 \cdot 3 \cdot 13$ 3. 88 $2^3 \cdot 11$ 4. 63 $3^2 \cdot 7$
5. 128 2^7 6. 102 $2 \cdot 3 \cdot 17$ 7. 71 prime 8. 125 5^3

Find the GCF of each pair of numbers.

9. 18 and 66 6 10. 24 and 104 8 11. 30 and 75 15
12. 24 and 120 24 13. 36 and 99 9 14. 42 and 72 6

Find the GCF of each pair of monomials.

15. $4a^3$ and $9a^4$ a^3 16. $6q^2$ and $15q^5$ $3q^2$ 17. $6x^2$ and $14y^3$ 2
18. $4z^2$ and $10z^5$ $2z^2$ 19. $5g^3$ and $9g$ g 20. $12x^2$ and $21y^2$ 3

Lesson 8-2 Factor each polynomial. Check your answer.

21. $6b^2 - 15b^3$ $3b^2(2 - 5b)$ 22. $11t^4 - 9t^3$ $t^3(11t - 9)$ 23. $10v^3 - 25v$ $5v(2v^2 - 5)$
24. $12r + 16r^3$ $4r(3 + 4r^2)$ 25. $17a^4 - 35a^2$ $a^2(17a^2 - 35)$ 26. $9f + 18f^5 + 12f^2$ $3f(3 + 6f^4 + 4f)$

Factor each expression. 27–53. See p. A30.

27. $3(a+3) + 4a(a+3)$ 28. $5(k-4) - 2k(k-4)$ 29. $5(c-3) + 4c^2(c-3)$
30. $3(t-4) + t(t-4)$ 31. $5(2r-1) - s(2r-1)$ 32. $7(3d+4) - 2e(3d+4)$

Factor each polynomial by grouping. Check your answer.

33. $x^3 + 3x^2 - 2x - 6$ 34. $2m^3 - 3m^2 + 8m - 12$ 35. $3k^3 - k^2 + 15k - 5$
36. $15r^3 + 25r^2 - 6r - 10$ 37. $12n^3 - 6n^2 - 10n + 5$ 38. $4z^3 - 3z^2 + 4z - 3$
39. $2k^2 - 3k + 12 - 8k$ 40. $3p^2 - 2p + 8 - 12p$ 41. $10d^2 - 6d + 9 - 15d$
42. $6a^3 - 4a^2 + 10 - 15a$ 43. $12s^3 - 2s^2 + 3 - 18s$ 44. $4c^3 - 3c^2 + 15 - 20c$

Lesson 8-3 Factor each trinomial. Check your answer.

45. $x^2 + 15x + 36$ 46. $x^2 + 13x + 40$ 47. $x^2 + 10x + 16$
48. $x^2 - 9x + 18$ 49. $x^2 - 11x + 28$ 50. $x^2 - 13x + 42$
51. $x^2 + 4x - 21$ 52. $x^2 - 5x - 36$ 53. $x^2 - 7x - 30$

54. Factor $c^2 - 2c - 48$. Show that the original polynomial and the factored form describe the same sequence of values for $c = 0, 1, 2, 3,$ and 4. See p. A30.

Copy and complete the table.

	$x^2 + bx + c$	Sign of c	Binomial Factors	Sign of Numbers in Binomials
	$x^2 + 9x + 20$	Positive	$(x+4)(x+5)$	Both positive
55.	$x^2 - x - 20$	Neg.	$(x+4)(x-5)$	Pos.; neg.
56.	$x^2 - 2x - 8$	Neg.	$(x+2)(x-4)$	Pos.; neg.
57.	$x^2 - 6x + 8$	Pos.	$(x-2)(x-4)$	Both neg.

EP16 Extra Practice

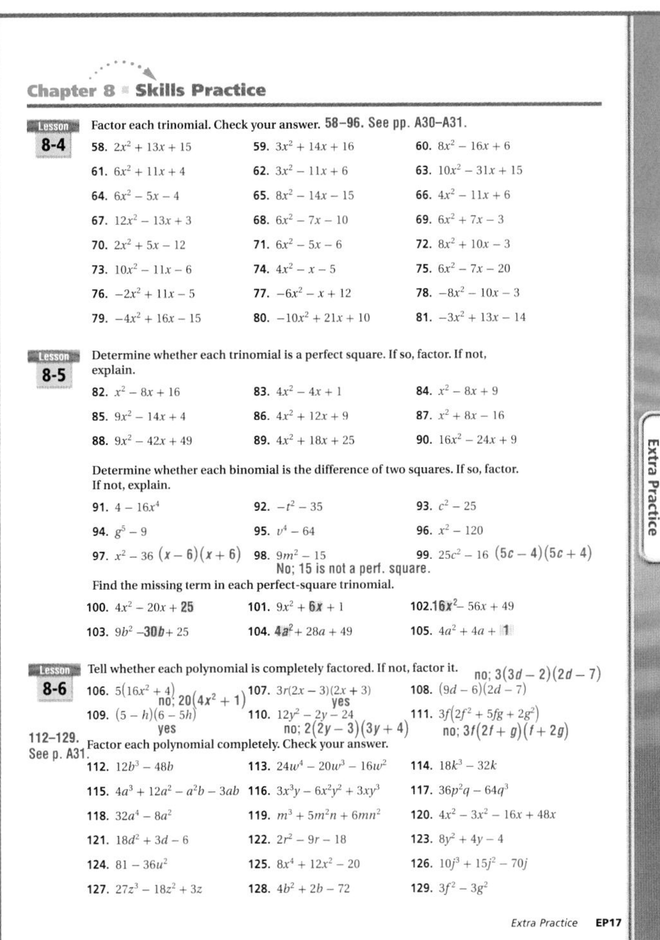

Chapter 8 ■ Skills Practice

Lesson 8-4 Factor each trinomial. Check your answer. 58–96. See pp. A30–A31.

58. $2x^2 + 13x + 15$ 59. $3x^2 + 14x + 16$ 60. $8x^2 - 16x + 6$
61. $6x^2 + 11x + 4$ 62. $3x^2 - 11x + 6$ 63. $10x^2 - 31x + 15$
64. $6x^2 - 5x - 4$ 65. $8x^2 - 14x - 15$ 66. $4x^2 - 11x + 6$
67. $12x^2 - 13x + 3$ 68. $6x^2 - 7x - 10$ 69. $6x^2 + 7x - 3$
70. $2x^2 + 5x - 12$ 71. $6x^2 - 5x - 6$ 72. $8x^2 + 10x - 3$
73. $10x^2 - 11x - 6$ 74. $4x^2 - x - 5$ 75. $6x^2 - 7x - 20$
76. $-2x^2 + 11x - 5$ 77. $-6x^2 - x + 12$ 78. $-8x^2 - 10x - 3$
79. $-4x^2 + 16x - 15$ 80. $-10x^2 + 21x + 10$ 81. $-3x^2 + 13x - 14$

Lesson 8-5 Determine whether each trinomial is a perfect square. If so, factor. If not, explain.

82. $x^2 - 8x + 16$ 83. $4x^2 - 4x + 1$ 84. $x^2 - 8x + 9$
85. $9x^2 - 14x + 4$ 86. $4x^2 + 12x + 9$ 87. $x^2 + 8x - 16$
88. $9x^2 - 42x + 49$ 89. $4x^2 + 18x + 25$ 90. $16x^2 - 24x + 9$

Determine whether each binomial is the difference of two squares. If so, factor. If not, explain.

91. $4 - 16x^4$ 92. $-t^2 - 35$ 93. $c^2 - 25$
94. $g^5 - 9$ 95. $v^4 - 64$ 96. $x^2 - 120$
97. $x^2 - 36$ $(x-6)(x+6)$ 98. $9m^2 - 15$ No; 15 is not a perf. square. 99. $25c^2 - 16$ $(5c-4)(5c+4)$

Find the missing term in each perfect-square trinomial.

100. $4x^2 - 20x +$ 25 101. $9x^2 +$ $6x$ $+ 1$ 102. $16x^2$ $- 56x + 49$
103. $9b^2$ $-30b$ $+ 25$ 104. $4a^2$ $+ 28a + 49$ 105. $4a^2 + 4a +$ 1

Lesson 8-6 Tell whether each polynomial is completely factored. If not, factor it.

106. $5(16x^2 + 4)$ no; $20(4x^2 + 1)$ 107. $3r(2x-3)(2x+3)$ yes 108. $(9d-6)(2d-7)$ no; $3(3d-2)(2d-7)$
109. $(5-h)(6-5h)$ yes 110. $12y^2 - 2y - 24$ no; $2(2y-3)(3y+4)$ 111. $3f(2f^2 + 5fg + 2g^2)$ no; $3f(2f+g)(f+2g)$

Factor each polynomial completely. Check your answer. 112–129. See p. A31.

112. $12b^3 - 48b$ 113. $24w^4 - 20w^3 - 16w^2$ 114. $18k^3 - 32k$
115. $4a^3 + 12a^2 - a^2b - 3ab$ 116. $3x^3y - 6x^2y^2 + 3xy^3$ 117. $36p^2q - 64q^3$
118. $32a^4 - 8a^2$ 119. $m^3 + 5m^2n + 6mn^2$ 120. $4x^2 - 3x^2 - 16x + 48x$
121. $18d^2 + 3d - 6$ 122. $2r^2 - 9r - 18$ 123. $8y^2 + 4y - 4$
124. $81 - 36u^2$ 125. $8x^4 + 12x^2 - 20$ 126. $10j^3 + 15j^2 - 70j$
127. $27z^3 - 18z^2 + 3z$ 128. $4b^2 + 2b - 72$ 129. $3f^2 - 3g^2$

Extra Practice EP17

Extra Practice

Chapter 9 ▪ Skills Practice

Lesson 9-1 Without graphing, tell whether each point is on the graph of the given equation.

1. $y = x^2 - 16$; (5, 9) yes 2. $y = \frac{1}{2}x^2 + 2x$; (4, 14) no
3. $y = -3x^2 + 4x + 16$; (−2, 20) no 4. $y = x^2 - 8x$; (−3, 33) yes
5. $y = \frac{1}{4}x^2 - x$; (6, 3) yes 6. $y - 9 = 3x^2$; (−1, 6) no

Graph each quadratic function. See p. A31.

7. $y = 2x^2$ 8. $y = -3x^2 + 1$ 9. $y = -\frac{1}{2}x^2 + 5$ 10. $y = x^2 - 3$

Tell whether the graph of each quadratic function opens upward or downward.

11. $y = -3x^2$ down 12. $y = \frac{2}{3}x^2$ up 13. $y = x^2 + 2$ up 14. $y = -4x^2 + 2x$ down

Identify the vertex of each parabola. Then find the domain and range.

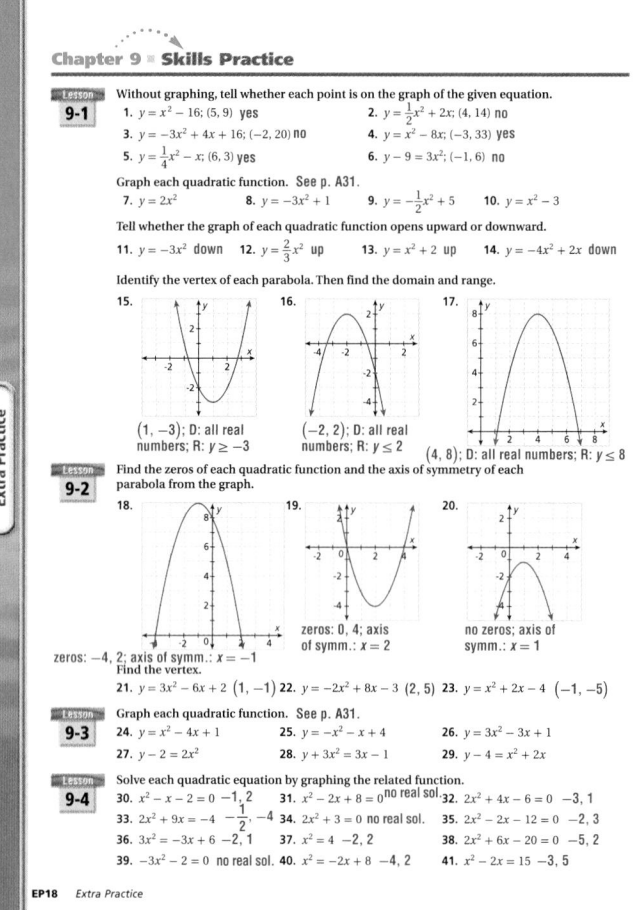

15. (1, −3); D: all real numbers; R: $y \geq -3$
16. (−2, 2); D: all real numbers; R: $y \leq 2$
17. (4, 8); D: all real numbers; R: $y \leq 8$

Lesson 9-2 Find the zeros of each quadratic function and the axis of symmetry of each parabola from the graph.

18. zeros: −4, 2; axis of symm.: $x = -1$
19. zeros: 0, 4; axis of symm.: $x = 2$
20. no zeros; axis of symm.: $x = 1$

Find the vertex.

21. $y = 3x^2 - 6x + 2$ (1, −1) 22. $y = -2x^2 + 8x - 3$ (2, 5) 23. $y = x^2 + 2x - 4$ (−1, −5)

Lesson 9-3 Graph each quadratic function. See p. A31.

24. $y = x^2 - 4x + 1$ 25. $y = -x^2 - x + 4$ 26. $y = 3x^2 - 3x + 1$
27. $y - 2 = 2x^2$ 28. $y + 3x^2 = 3x - 1$ 29. $y - 4 = x^2 + 2x$

Lesson 9-4 Solve each quadratic equation by graphing the related function.

30. $x^2 - x - 2 = 0$ −1, 2 31. $x^2 - 2x + 8 = 0$ no real sol. 32. $2x^2 + 4x - 6 = 0$ −3, 1
33. $2x^2 + 9x = -4$ $-\frac{1}{2}$, −4 34. $2x^2 + 3 = 0$ no real sol. 35. $2x^2 - 2x - 12 = 0$ −2, 3
36. $3x^2 = -3x + 6$ −2, 1 37. $x^2 = 4$ −2, 2 38. $2x^2 + 6x - 20 = 0$ −5, 2
39. $-3x^2 - 2 = 0$ no real sol. 40. $x^2 = -2x + 8$ −4, 2 41. $x^2 - 2x = 15$ −3, 5

Chapter 9 ▪ Skills Practice

Lesson 9-5 Use the Zero Product Property to solve each equation. Check your answer.

42. $(x + 3)(x - 2) = 0$ −3, 2 43. $(x - 4)(x + 2) = 0$ −2, 4 44. $(x)(x - 4) = 0$ 0, 4
45. $(2x + 6)(x - 2) = 0$ −3, 2 46. $(3x - 1)(x + 3) = 0$ −3, $\frac{1}{3}$ 47. $(x)(2x - 4) = 0$ 0, 2

Solve each quadratic equation by factoring. Check your answer.

48. $x^2 + 5x + 6 = 0$ −3, −2 49. $x^2 - 3x - 4 = 0$ −1, 4 50. $x^2 + x - 12 = 0$ −4, 3
51. $x^2 + x - 6 = 0$ −3, 2 52. $x^2 - 6x + 5 = 0$ 1, 5 53. $x^2 + 4x - 12 = 0$ −6, 2
54. $x^2 = 6x - 9$ 3 55. $2x^2 + 4x = 6$ −3, 1 56. $x^2 + 2x = -1$ −1
57. $3x^2 = 3x + 6$ −1, 2 58. $x^2 = x + 12$ −3, 4 59. $4x^2 + 8x + 4 = 0$ −1

Lesson 9-6 Solve using square roots. Check your answer.

60. $x^2 = 169$ ±13 61. $x^2 = 121$ ±11 62. $x^2 = 289$ ±17
63. $x^2 = -64$ no real sol. 64. $x^2 = 81$ ±9 65. $x^2 = -441$ no real sol.
66. $4x^2 - 196 = 0$ ±7 67. $0 = 3x^2 - 48$ ±4 68. $24x^2 + 96 = 0$ no real sol.
69. $10x^2 - 75 = 15$ ±3 70. $0 = 4x^2 + 144$ no real sol. 71. $5x^2 - 105 = 20$ ±5

Solve. Round to the nearest hundredth.

72. $4x^2 = 160$ ±6.32 73. $0 = 3x^2 - 66$ ±4.69 74. $250 - 5x^2 = 0$ ±7.07
75. $0 = 9x^2 - 72$ ±2.83 76. $48 - 2x^2 = 42$ ±1.73 77. $6x^2 = 78$ ±3.61

Lesson 9-7 Complete the square to form a perfect-square trinomial.

78. $x^2 - 8x +$ 16 79. $x^2 + x + \frac{1}{4}$ 80. $x^2 + 10x +$ 25
81. $x^2 - 5x + \frac{25}{4}$ 82. $x^2 + 6x +$ 9 83. $x^2 - 7x + \frac{49}{4}$

Solve by completing the square.

84. $x^2 + 6x = 91$ −13, 7 85. $x^2 + 10x = -16$ −8, −2 86. $x^2 - 4x = 12$ −2, 6
87. $x^2 - 8x = -12$ 2, 6 88. $x^2 - 12x = -35$ 5, 7 89. $-x^2 - 6x = 5$ −5, −1
90. $-x^2 - 4x + 77 = 0$ −11, 7 91. $-x^2 = 10x + 9$ −9, −1 92. $-x^2 + 63 = -2x$ −7, 9

Lesson 9-8 Solve using the Quadratic Formula. Round to the nearest hundredth if necessary. Check your answer.

93. $x^2 + 3x - 4 = 0$ −4, 1 94. $x^2 - 2x - 8 = 0$ −2, 4 95. $x^2 + 2x - 3 = 0$ −3, 1
96. $x^2 - x - 10 = 0$ ≈−2.70, ≈3.70 97. $2x^2 - x - 4 = 0$ ≈−1.19, ≈1.69 98. $2x^2 + 3x - 3 = 0$ ≈−2.19, ≈0.69

Solve using at least two different methods. Check your answer.

99. $3x^2 - 8x - 16 = 0$ $-\frac{4}{3}$, 4 100. $x^2 - 49 = 0$ ±7 101. $x^2 - 2x + 1 = 0$ 1
102. $x^2 - 3x - 10 = 0$ −2, 5 103. $x^2 + \frac{7}{2}x = 2$ −4, $\frac{1}{2}$ 104. $12 = x^2 - 4x$ −2, 6

Lesson 9-9 Find the number of solutions of each equation.

105. $x^2 + 4x + 1 = 0$ 2 106. $2x^2 - 3x + 2 = 0$ 0 107. $x^2 - 5x + 2 = 0$ 2
108. $2x^2 - 4x + 2 = 0$ 1 109. $x^2 + 2x - 5 = 0$ 2 110. $2x^2 - 2x - 3 = 0$ 2

Find the number of x-intercepts of each function by using the discriminant.

111. $y = 5x^2 + 10x - 6$ 2 112. $y = 3x^2 + 12x + 4$ 2 113. $y = x^2 + 5 - 4x$ 0
114. $y = 3x^2 + 6x + 3$ 1 115. $y = x + 5x^2 + 9$ 0 116. $y = 18 + 6x + \frac{1}{2}x^2$ 2

Chapter 10 ▪ Skills Practice

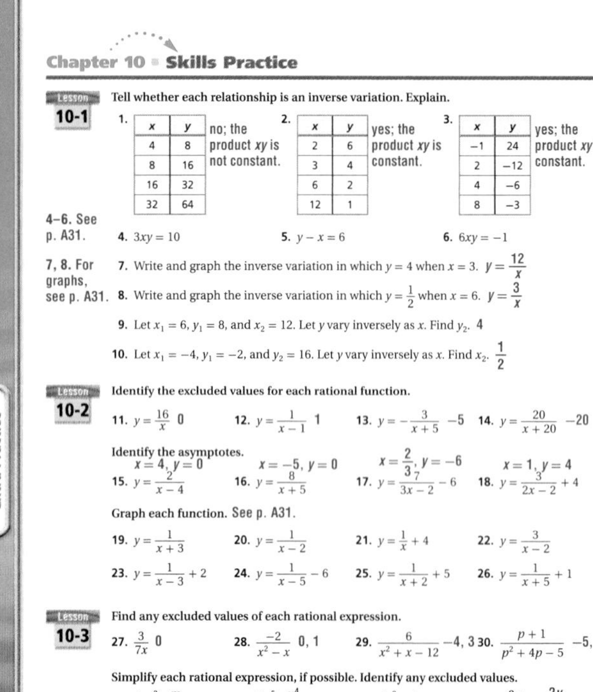

Lesson 10-1 Tell whether each relationship is an inverse variation. Explain.

1.

x	y
4	8
8	16
16	32
32	64

no; the product xy is not constant.

2.

x	y
2	6
3	4
6	2
12	1

yes; the product xy is constant.

3.

x	y
−1	24
2	−12
4	−6
8	−3

yes; the product xy is constant.

4–6. See p. A31.

4. $3xy = 10$ 5. $y - x = 6$ 6. $6xy = -1$

7, 8. For graphs, see p. A31.

7. Write and graph the inverse variation in which $y = 4$ when $x = 3$. $y = \frac{12}{x}$
8. Write and graph the inverse variation in which $y = \frac{1}{2}$ when $x = 6$. $y = \frac{3}{x}$
9. Let $x_1 = 6$, $y_1 = 8$, and $x_2 = 12$. Let y vary inversely as x. Find y_2. 4
10. Let $x_1 = -4$, $y_1 = -2$, and $y_2 = 16$. Let y vary inversely as x. Find x_2. $\frac{1}{2}$

Lesson 10-2 Identify the excluded values for each rational function.

11. $y = \frac{16}{x}$ 0 12. $y = \frac{1}{x - 1}$ 1 13. $y = -\frac{3}{x + 5}$ −5 14. $y = \frac{20}{x + 20}$ −20

Identify the asymptotes.

15. $y = \frac{2}{x - 4}$ $x = 4$, $y = 0$ 16. $y = \frac{8}{x + 5}$ $x = -5$, $y = 0$ 17. $y = \frac{7}{3x - 2} - 6$ $x = \frac{2}{3}$, $y = -6$ 18. $y = \frac{3}{2x - 2} + 4$ $x = 1$, $y = 4$

Graph each function. See p. A31.

19. $y = \frac{1}{x + 3}$ 20. $y = \frac{1}{x - 2}$ 21. $y = \frac{1}{x} + 4$ 22. $y = \frac{3}{x - 2}$
23. $y = \frac{1}{x - 3} + 2$ 24. $y = \frac{1}{x - 5} - 6$ 25. $y = \frac{1}{x + 2} + 5$ 26. $y = \frac{1}{x + 5} + 1$

Lesson 10-3 Find any excluded values of each rational expression.

27. $\frac{3}{7x}$ 0 28. $\frac{-2}{x^2 - x}$ 0, 1 29. $\frac{6}{x^2 + x - 12}$ −4, 3 30. $\frac{p + 1}{p^2 + 4p - 5}$ −5, 1

Simplify each rational expression, if possible. Identify any excluded values.

31. $\frac{4m^2}{12m}$ $\frac{m}{3}$; $m \neq 0$ 32. $\frac{7x^5}{28x}$ $\frac{x^4}{4}$; $x \neq 0$ 33. $\frac{4x^2 - 8x}{x - 2}$ $4x$; $x \neq 2$ 34. $\frac{2y}{y - 1}$ $\frac{2y}{y - 1}$; $y \neq 1$
35. $\frac{5x^3 + 20x^2}{x + 4}$ $5x^2$; $x \neq -4$ 36. $\frac{a + 1}{a - 2}$ $\frac{a + 1}{a - 2}$; $a \neq 2$ 37. $\frac{3y^3 + 3y}{y^2 + 1}$ $3y$; no excl. values 38. $\frac{x^3 + 4x}{x^2 + 4}$ x; no excl. values

Simplify each rational expression, if possible.

39. $\frac{b + 2}{b^2 + 5b + 6}$ $\frac{1}{b + 3}$ 40. $\frac{x - 3}{x^2 - 6x + 9}$ $\frac{1}{x - 3}$ 41. $\frac{y^2 - 4y - 5}{y^2 - 2y - 3}$ $\frac{y - 5}{y - 3}$ 42. $\frac{(m + 2)^2}{m^2 - 6m - 16}$ $\frac{m + 2}{m - 8}$
43. $\frac{x^2 - 9}{x^2 + x - 12}$ $\frac{x + 3}{x + 4}$ 44. $\frac{2 - m}{3m^2 - 6m}$ $-\frac{1}{3m}$ 45. $\frac{x - 4}{12x^2 - 3x^3}$ $-\frac{1}{3x^2}$ 46. $\frac{6 - 3x}{x^2 - 6x + 8}$ $-\frac{3}{x - 4}$

Chapter 10 ▪ Skills Practice

Lesson 10-4 Multiply. Simplify your answer. 53–58. See p. A32.

47. $\frac{4a^3}{b^3} \cdot \frac{ab}{6a^2}$ $\frac{2a^2}{3b^2}$ 48. $\frac{x - 3}{2} \cdot \frac{8}{4x - 12}$ 1 49. $\frac{x - 2}{x - 5} \cdot \frac{2x - 10}{3}$ $\frac{2(x - 2)}{3}$
50. $\frac{a^2b^3}{6a^3c} \cdot \frac{9b^2}{12b^5c^2}$ $\frac{1}{8ac^3}$ 51. $\frac{3x}{2x + 4} \cdot \frac{3x + 6}{9}$ $\frac{x}{2}$ 52. $\frac{1}{2x + 4}(x^2 - 2x - 8)$ $\frac{x - 4}{2}$
53. $\frac{3x}{4x - 20}(x^2 + x - 30)$ 54. $\frac{4r^3 + 8r}{r^3} \cdot \frac{r}{3r^2 + 6}$ 55. $\frac{a^2 - 3a - 10}{a^2 - a - 6} \cdot \frac{a^2 - 2a - 3}{a - 5}$
56. $\frac{4b^2 + 4}{b - 1} \cdot \frac{b^2 - 1}{8b^2 + 8}$ 57. $\frac{pq + 2q}{pq + 1} \cdot \frac{3pq + 3}{pq^2 + 2q^2}$ 58. $\frac{r^2 + 3r + 2}{4r + 4} \cdot \frac{2r + 6}{r^2 - 2r - 8}$

Divide. Simplify your answer.

59. $\frac{3x^2y^3}{x^3z^2} \div \frac{6y^4}{x^2z^5}$ $\frac{xz^3}{2y}$ 60. $\frac{x^2 + 4x + 3}{3x^3 + 9x^2} \div (x^2 - 1)$ $\frac{1}{3x^2(x - 1)}$ 61. $\frac{p - 1}{p^2 + 4p - 5} \div \frac{p^2 - 2p}{p^2 + 3p - 10}$ $\frac{1}{p}$

Lesson 10-5 Add. Simplify your answer.

62. $\frac{3x}{4x^3} + \frac{5x}{4x^3}$ $\frac{2}{x^2}$ 63. $\frac{x^2 + 1}{x - 1} + \frac{1 - 3x}{x - 1}$ $x - 2$ 64. $\frac{2x^2}{x^2 - 2x - 3} + \frac{2x}{x^2 - 2x - 3}$ $\frac{2x}{x - 3}$

Subtract. Simplify your answer.

65. $\frac{5}{6y^4} - \frac{2}{6y^4}$ $\frac{1}{2y^4}$ 66. $\frac{5a^2 + 1}{a^2 - a - 6} - \frac{15a + 1}{a^2 - a - 6}$ $\frac{5a}{a + 2}$ 67. $\frac{m^2 + 2m}{m^2 - 9} - \frac{m + 12}{m^2 - 9}$ $\frac{m + 4}{m + 3}$

Find the LCM of the given expressions.

68. $8x^5y^8$, $6x^4y^9$ $24x^5y^9$ 69. $x^2 - 4$, $x^2 + 7x + 10$ $(x + 2)(x - 2)(x + 5)$ 70. $d^2 - 2d - 3$, $d^2 + d - 12$ $(d + 1)(d - 3)(d + 4)$

Add or subtract. Simplify your answer.

71. $\frac{5}{y^2} - \frac{3}{4y^2}$ $\frac{17}{4y^2}$ 72. $\frac{5}{x^2 - x - 6} + \frac{1}{x + 2}$ $\frac{1}{x - 3}$ 73. $\frac{3x}{x - 2} - \frac{x}{2 - x}$ $\frac{4x}{x - 2}$

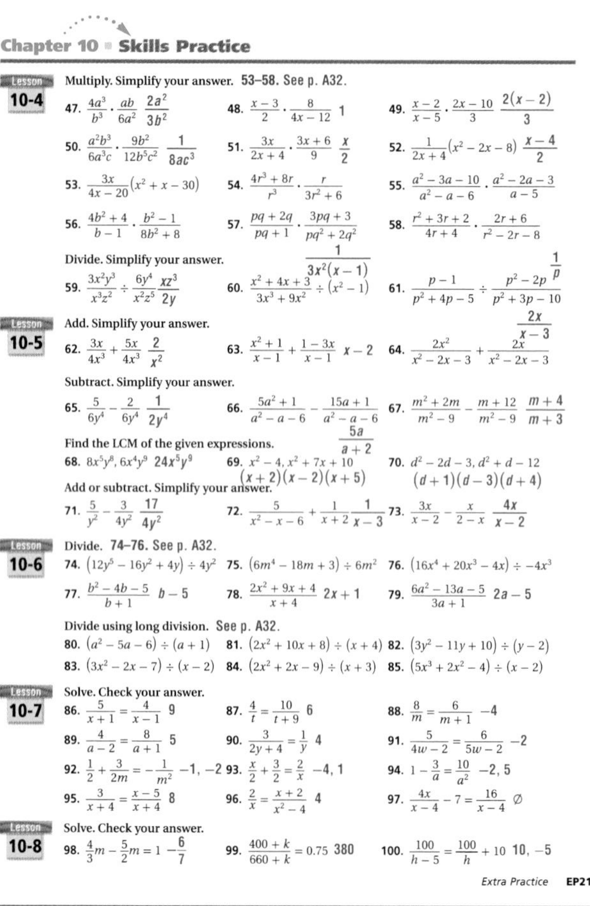

Lesson 10-6 Divide. 74–76. See p. A32.

74. $(12y^5 - 16y^2 + 4y) \div 4y^2$ 75. $(6m^4 - 18m + 3) \div 6m^2$ 76. $(16x^4 + 20x^3 - 4x) \div -4x^3$
77. $\frac{b^2 - 4b - 5}{b + 1}$ $b - 5$ 78. $\frac{2x^2 + 9x + 4}{x + 4}$ $2x + 1$ 79. $\frac{6a^2 - 13a - 5}{3a + 1}$ $2a - 5$

Divide using long division. See p. A32.

80. $(a^2 - 5a - 6) \div (a + 1)$ 81. $(2x^2 + 10x + 8) \div (x + 4)$ 82. $(3y^2 - 11y + 10) \div (y - 2)$
83. $(3x^2 - 2x - 7) \div (x - 2)$ 84. $(2x^2 + 2x - 9) \div (x + 3)$ 85. $(5x^3 + 2x^2 - 4) \div (x - 2)$

Lesson 10-7 Solve. Check your answer.

86. $\frac{5}{x + 1} = \frac{4}{x - 1}$ 9 87. $\frac{4}{t} = \frac{10}{t + 9}$ 6 88. $\frac{8}{m} = \frac{6}{m + 1}$ −4
89. $\frac{4}{a - 2} = \frac{8}{a + 1}$ 5 90. $\frac{3}{2y + 4} = \frac{1}{y}$ 4 91. $\frac{5}{4w - 2} = \frac{6}{5w - 2}$ −2
92. $\frac{1}{2} + \frac{3}{2m} = -\frac{1}{m^2}$ −1, −2 93. $\frac{x}{2} + \frac{3}{2} = \frac{2}{x}$ −4, 1 94. $1 - \frac{3}{a} = \frac{10}{a^2}$ −2, 5
95. $\frac{3}{x + 4} = \frac{x - 5}{x + 4}$ 8 96. $\frac{2}{x} = \frac{x + 2}{x^2 - 4}$ 4 97. $\frac{4x}{x - 4} - 7 = \frac{16}{x - 4}$ ∅

Lesson 10-8 Solve. Check your answer.

98. $\frac{4}{3}m - \frac{5}{2}m = 1 - \frac{6}{7}$ 99. $\frac{400 + k}{660 + k} = 0.75$ 380 100. $\frac{100}{h - 5} = \frac{100}{h} + 10$ 10, −5

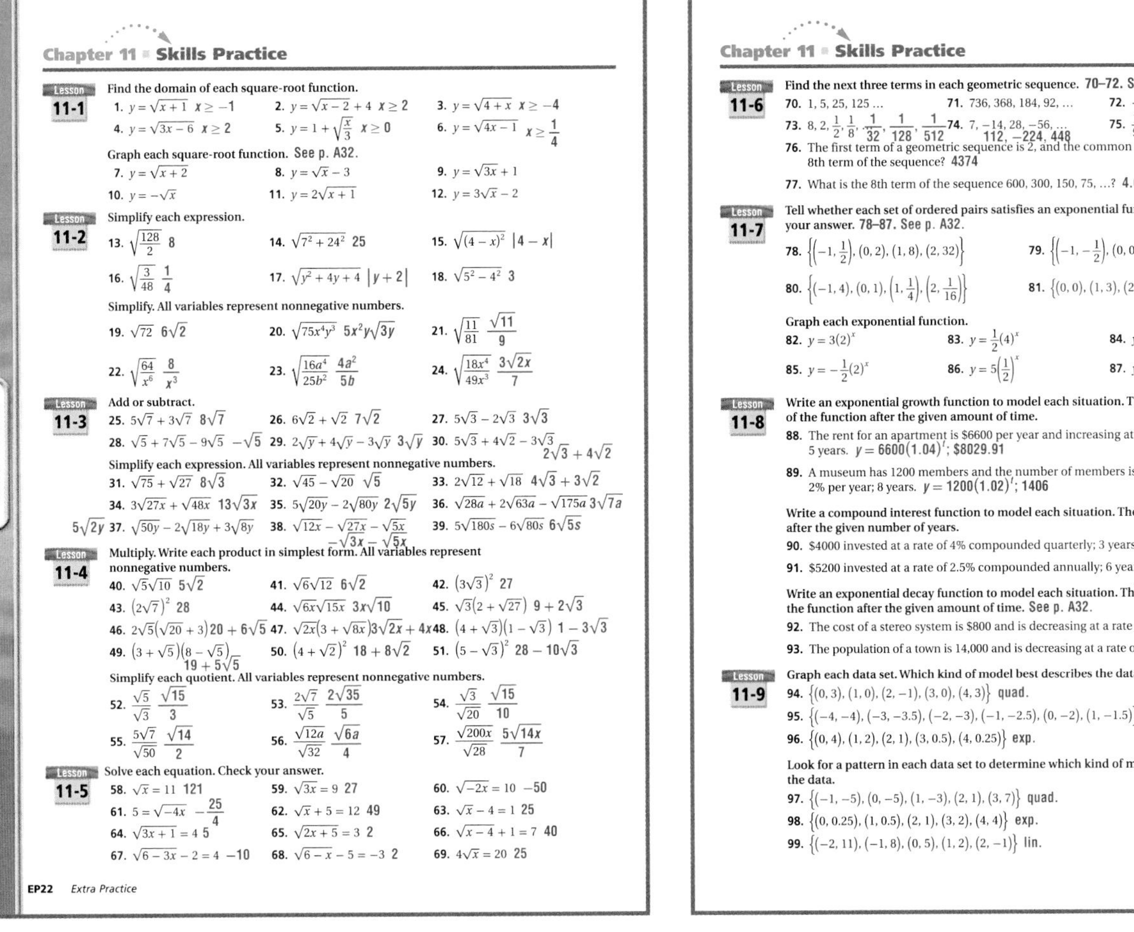

Chapter 11 ■ Skills Practice

Lesson 11-1 Find the domain of each square-root function.

1. $y = \sqrt{x+1}$ $x \geq -1$
2. $y = \sqrt{x-2} + 4$ $x \geq 2$
3. $y = \sqrt{4+x}$ $x \geq -4$
4. $y = \sqrt{3x-6}$ $x \geq 2$
5. $y = 1 + \sqrt{\frac{x}{3}}$ $x \geq 0$
6. $y = \sqrt{4x-1}$ $x \geq \frac{1}{4}$

Graph each square-root function. See p. A32.

7. $y = \sqrt{x+2}$
8. $y = \sqrt{x} - 3$
9. $y = \sqrt{3x} + 1$
10. $y = -\sqrt{x}$
11. $y = 2\sqrt{x+1}$
12. $y = 3\sqrt{x} - 2$

Lesson 11-2 Simplify each expression.

13. $\sqrt{\frac{128}{2}}$ 8
14. $\sqrt{7^2 + 24^2}$ 25
15. $\sqrt{(4-x)^2}$ $|4 - x|$
16. $\sqrt{\frac{3}{48}}$ $\frac{1}{4}$
17. $\sqrt{y^2 + 4y + 4}$ $|y + 2|$
18. $\sqrt{5^2 - 4^2}$ 3

Simplify. All variables represent nonnegative numbers.

19. $\sqrt{72}$ $6\sqrt{2}$
20. $\sqrt{75x^4y^3}$ $5x^2y\sqrt{3y}$
21. $\sqrt{\frac{11}{81}}$ $\frac{\sqrt{11}}{9}$
22. $\sqrt{\frac{64}{x^6}}$ $\frac{8}{x^3}$
23. $\sqrt{\frac{16a^4}{25b^2}}$ $\frac{4a^2}{5b}$
24. $\sqrt{\frac{18x^4}{49x^3}}$ $\frac{3\sqrt{2x}}{7}$

Lesson 11-3 Add or subtract.

25. $5\sqrt{7} + 3\sqrt{7}$ $8\sqrt{7}$
26. $6\sqrt{2} + \sqrt{2}$ $7\sqrt{2}$
27. $5\sqrt{3} - 2\sqrt{3}$ $3\sqrt{3}$
28. $\sqrt{5} + 7\sqrt{5} - 9\sqrt{5}$ $-\sqrt{5}$
29. $2\sqrt{y} + 4\sqrt{y} - 3\sqrt{y}$ $3\sqrt{y}$
30. $5\sqrt{3} + 4\sqrt{2} - 3\sqrt{3}$ $2\sqrt{3} + 4\sqrt{2}$

Simplify each expression. All variables represent nonnegative numbers.

31. $\sqrt{75} + \sqrt{27}$ $8\sqrt{3}$
32. $\sqrt{45} - \sqrt{20}$ $\sqrt{5}$
33. $2\sqrt{12} + \sqrt{18}$ $4\sqrt{3} + 3\sqrt{2}$
34. $3\sqrt{27x} + \sqrt{48x}$ $13\sqrt{3x}$
35. $5\sqrt{20y} - 2\sqrt{80y}$ $2\sqrt{5y}$
36. $\sqrt{28a} + 2\sqrt{63a} - \sqrt{175a}$ $3\sqrt{7a}$
37. $\sqrt{50y} - 2\sqrt{18y} + 3\sqrt{8y}$ $5\sqrt{2y}$
38. $\sqrt{12x} - \sqrt{27x} - \sqrt{5x}$ $-\sqrt{3x} - \sqrt{5x}$
39. $5\sqrt{180s} - 6\sqrt{80s}$ $6\sqrt{5s}$

Lesson 11-4 Multiply. Write each product in simplest form. All variables represent nonnegative numbers.

40. $\sqrt{5}\sqrt{10}$ $5\sqrt{2}$
41. $\sqrt{6}\sqrt{12}$ $6\sqrt{2}$
42. $(3\sqrt{3})^2$ 27
43. $(2\sqrt{7})^2$ 28
44. $\sqrt{6x}\sqrt{15x}$ $3x\sqrt{10}$
45. $\sqrt{3}(2 + \sqrt{27})$ $9 + 2\sqrt{3}$
46. $2\sqrt{5}(\sqrt{20} + 3)$ $20 + 6\sqrt{5}$
47. $\sqrt{2x}(3 + \sqrt{8x})$ $3\sqrt{2x} + 4x$
48. $(4 + \sqrt{3})(1 - \sqrt{3})$ $1 - 3\sqrt{3}$
49. $(3 + \sqrt{5})(8 - \sqrt{5})$ $19 + 5\sqrt{5}$
50. $(4 + \sqrt{2})^2$ $18 + 8\sqrt{2}$
51. $(5 - \sqrt{3})^2$ $28 - 10\sqrt{3}$

Simplify each quotient. All variables represent nonnegative numbers.

52. $\frac{\sqrt{5}}{\sqrt{3}}$ $\frac{\sqrt{15}}{3}$
53. $\frac{2\sqrt{7}}{\sqrt{5}}$ $\frac{2\sqrt{35}}{5}$
54. $\frac{\sqrt{3}}{\sqrt{20}}$ $\frac{\sqrt{15}}{10}$
55. $\frac{5\sqrt{7}}{\sqrt{50}}$ $\frac{\sqrt{14}}{2}$
56. $\frac{\sqrt{12a}}{\sqrt{32}}$ $\frac{\sqrt{6a}}{4}$
57. $\frac{\sqrt{200x}}{\sqrt{28}}$ $\frac{5\sqrt{14x}}{7}$

Lesson 11-5 Solve each equation. Check your answer.

58. $\sqrt{x} = 11$ 121
59. $\sqrt{3x} = 9$ 27
60. $\sqrt{-2x} = 10$ -50
61. $5 = \sqrt{-4x}$ $-\frac{25}{4}$
62. $\sqrt{x} + 5 = 12$ 49
63. $\sqrt{x} - 4 = 1$ 25
64. $\sqrt{3x+1} = 4$ 5
65. $\sqrt{2x+5} = 3$ 2
66. $\sqrt{x-4} + 1 = 7$ 40
67. $\sqrt{6-3x} - 2 = 4$ -10
68. $\sqrt{6-x} - 5 = -3$ 2
69. $4\sqrt{x} = 20$ 25

Chapter 11 ■ Skills Practice

Lesson 11-6 Find the next three terms in each geometric sequence. 70–72. See p. A32.

70. 1, 5, 25, 125 ...
71. 736, 368, 184, 92, ...
72. −2, 6, −18, 54, ...
73. 8, 2, $\frac{1}{2}$, $\frac{1}{8}$, ... $\frac{1}{32}$, $\frac{1}{128}$, $\frac{1}{512}$
74. 7, −14, 28, −56, ... 112, −224, 448
75. $\frac{1}{9}$, $\frac{1}{3}$, 1, 3, ... 9, 27, 81
76. The first term of a geometric sequence is 2, and the common ratio is 3. What is the 8th term of the sequence? 4374
77. What is the 8th term of the sequence 600, 300, 150, 75, ...? 4.6875

Lesson 11-7 Tell whether each set of ordered pairs satisfies an exponential function. Explain your answer. 78–87. See p. A32.

78. $\left\{\left(-1, \frac{1}{2}\right), (0, 2), (1, 8), (2, 32)\right\}$
79. $\left\{\left(-1, -\frac{1}{2}\right), (0, 0), \left(1, \frac{1}{2}\right), (2, 4)\right\}$
80. $\left\{(-1, 4), (0, 1), \left(1, \frac{1}{4}\right), \left(2, \frac{1}{16}\right)\right\}$
81. $\{(0, 0), (1, 3), (2, 12), (3, 27)\}$

Graph each exponential function.

82. $y = 3(2)^x$
83. $y = \frac{1}{2}(4)^x$
84. $y = -3^x$
85. $y = -\frac{1}{2}(2)^x$
86. $y = 5\left(\frac{1}{2}\right)^x$
87. $y = -2(0.25)^x$

Lesson 11-8 Write an exponential growth function to model each situation. Then find the value of the function after the given amount of time.

88. The rent for an apartment is $6600 per year and increasing at a rate of 4% per year; 5 years. $y = 6600(1.04)^t$; $8029.91
89. A museum has 1200 members and the number of members is increasing at a rate of 2% per year; 8 years. $y = 1200(1.02)^t$; 1406

Write a compound interest function to model each situation. Then find the balance after the given number of years.

90. $4000 invested at a rate of 4% compounded quarterly; 3 years $A = 4000(1.01)^{4t}$; $4507.30
91. $5200 invested at a rate of 2.5% compounded annually; 6 years $A = 5200(1.025)^t$; $6030.41

Write an exponential decay function to model each situation. Then find the value of the function after the given amount of time. See p. A32.

92. The cost of a stereo system is $800 and is decreasing at a rate of 6% per year; 5 years.
93. The population of a town is 14,000 and is decreasing at a rate of 2% per year; 10 years.

Lesson 11-9 Graph each data set. Which kind of model best describes the data? For graphs, see pp. A32–A33.

94. $\{(0, 3), (1, 0), (2, -1), (3, 0), (4, 3)\}$ quad.
95. $\{(-4, -4), (-3, -3.5), (-2, -3), (-1, -2.5), (0, -2), (1, -1.5)\}$ lin.
96. $\{(0, 4), (1, 2), (2, 1), (3, 0.5), (4, 0.25)\}$ exp.

Look for a pattern in each data set to determine which kind of model best describes the data.

97. $\{(-1, -5), (0, -5), (1, -3), (2, 1), (3, 7)\}$ quad.
98. $\{(0, 0.25), (1, 0.5), (2, 1), (3, 2), (4, 4)\}$ exp.
99. $\{(-2, 11), (-1, 8), (0, 5), (1, 2), (2, -1)\}$ lin.

Extra Practice

Chapter 1 ■ Applications Practice

Biology Use the following information for Exercises 1 and 2. *(Lesson 1-1)*

In general, every cell in the human body contains 46 chromosomes.

1. Write an expression for the number of chromosomes in c cells. $46c$
2. Find the number of chromosomes in 8, 15, and 50 cells. 368; 690; 2300
3. On a winter day in Fairbanks, Alaska, the temperature dropped from 12°F to −16°F. How many degrees did the temperature drop? *(Lesson 1-2)* 28°F
4. **Geography** The elevation of the Dead Sea in Jordan is −411 meters. The greatest elevation on Earth is Mt. Everest, at 8850 meters. What is the difference in elevation between these two locations? *(Lesson 1-2)* 9261 m
5. Jeremy is raising money for his school by selling magazine subscriptions. Each subscription costs $16.75. During the first week, he sells 12 subscriptions. How much money does he raise? *(Lesson 1-3)* $201
6. As a service charge, Nadine's checking account is adjusted by −$3 each month. What is the total amount of the adjustment over the course of one year? *(Lesson 1-3)* −$36
7. To go from one figure to the next in the sequence of figures, each square is split into four smaller squares. How many squares will be in Figure 5? *(Lesson 1-4)* 1024

8. When you fold a sheet of paper in half and then open it, the crease creates 2 regions. Folding the paper in half 2 times creates 4 regions. How many regions do you create when you fold a sheet of paper in half 5 times? *(Lesson 1-4)* 32
9. Dan began his stamp collection with just 5 stamps in the first year. Every year thereafter, his collection grew 5 times as large as the year before. How many stamps were in Dan's collection after 4 years? *(Lesson 1-4)* 625
10. An art museum exhibits a square painting that has an area of 75 square feet. Find its side length to the nearest tenth. *(Lesson 1-5)* 8.7 ft
11. **Travel** The base of the Washington Monument in Washington, D.C., is a square with an area of 336 yards. Find the length of one side of the monument's base to the nearest tenth. *(Lesson 1-5)* 18.3 yd

Use the following information for Exercises 12 and 13. *(Lesson 1-6)*

The display case in a shoe store has a row of men's boots and a row of women's boots. There are 8 pairs of boots per row.

12. Write an expression that can be used to find the total number of pairs of boots. $8m + 8w$
13. Write an equivalent expression using the Distributive Property. $8(m + w)$
14. The toll to cross a bridge is $2 for cars, $5 for trucks, and $10 for buses. The total amount of money collected can be found using the expression $2C + 5T + 10B$. Use the table to find the total amount of money collected between 10 A.M. and 11 A.M. *(Lesson 1-7)* $338

Bridge Tolls, 10 A.M. to 11 A.M.	
Type of Vehicle	Number
Car C	104
Truck T	20
Bus B	3

15. The expression $\frac{5}{9}(F - 32)$ converts a temperature F in degrees Fahrenheit to a temperature in degrees Celsius. Convert 77°F to degrees Celsius. *(Lesson 1-7)* 25°C

Use the following information for Exercises 16 and 17. *(Lesson 1-7)*

An airplane has 12 rows of seats in first class and 35 rows of seats in coach. Each row has the same number of seats.

16. The total number of seats in the plane is $12x + 35x$, where x is the number of seats in a row. Simplify the expression. $47x$
17. Find the total number of seats in a plane that has 6 seats per row. 282

Chapter 2 ■ Applications Practice

1. **Economics** In 2004, the average price of an ounce of gold was $47 more than the average price in 2003. The 2004 price was $410. Write and solve an equation to find the average price of an ounce of gold in 2003. *(Lesson 2-1)* $x + 47 = 410$; $363
2. During a renovation, 36 seats were removed from a theater. The theater now seats 580 people. Write and solve an equation to find the number of seats in the theater before the renovation. *(Lesson 2-1)* $x - 36 = 580$; 616
3. A case of juice drinks contains 12 bottles and costs $18. Write and solve an equation to find the cost of each drink. *(Lesson 2-1)* $12x = 18$; $1.50
4. **Astronomy** Objects weigh about 3 times as much on Earth as they do on Mars. A rock weighs 42 kg on Mars. Write and solve an equation to find the rock's weight on Earth. *(Lesson 2-1)* $42 = \frac{1}{3}x$; 126 kg
5. The county fair's admission fee is $8 and each ride costs $2.50. Sonia spent a total of $25.50. How many rides did she go on? *(Lesson 2-2)* 7
6. At the beginning of a block party, the temperature was 84°. During the party, the temperature dropped 3° every hour. At the end of the party, the temperature was 66°. How long was the party? *(Lesson 2-2)* 6 h
7. The students at a dance school are divided evenly among six teachers. This semester, there are 15 new students at the school, giving each teacher 20 students. How many students were at the school last semester? *(Lesson 2-3)* 105
8. Olga always orders the same meal at her favorite restaurant. She leaves a $2 tip after each meal. After 4 meals, Olga has paid a total of $44. How much does each meal cost? *(Lesson 2-3)* $9
9. **Consumer Economics** A health insurance policy costs $700 per year, plus a $15 payment for each visit to the doctor's office. A different plan costs $560 per year, but each office visit is $50. Find the number of office visits for which the two plans have the same total cost. *(Lesson 2-4)* 4
10. The ratio of students to adults on a school camping trip is 9:2. There are 6 adults on the trip. How many students are there? *(Lesson 2-5)* 27
11. Paul has 8 jazz CDs. The jazz CDs are 5% of his collection. How many CDs does Paul have? *(Lesson 2-5)* 160
12. **Sports** Last season, a baseball team had 32 players on their active roster, 3 of whom were catchers. To the nearest percent, what percent of the players were catchers? *(Lesson 2-5)* 9%
13. **Geometry** The formula $A = \frac{1}{2}bh$ gives the area A of a triangle with base b and height h. *(Lesson 2-6)*
    a. Solve $A = \frac{1}{2}bh$ for h. $h = \frac{2A}{b}$
    b. Find the height of a triangle with an area of 30 square feet and a base of 6 feet. 10 ft
14. The volume of a rectangular prism can be found by using the formula $V = Ah$, where V represents the volume in units cubed, A represents the area of the base in units squared, and h represents the height of the prism. Solve the equation for A. What is the area of the base of a prism with volume 54 in. and height 4.5 in.? *(Lesson 2-6)* $A = \frac{V}{h}$; 12 in^2
15. Charles is hanging a poster on his wall. He wants the top of the poster to be 84 inches from the floor but would be happy for it to be 3 inches higher or lower. Write and solve an absolute-value equation to find the maximum and minimum acceptable heights. *(Lesson 2-7)* $|x - 84| = 3$; 87 in.; 81 in.
16. Write and solve an absolute-value equation that represents two numbers x that are 4.5 units from 12 on the number line. *(Lesson 2-7)* $|x - 12| = 4.5$; 16.5; 7.5
17. Lily has entered a contest where she must guess within 2% of the actual cost of the prize. The actual cost of the prize is $135. Write and solve an absolute-value equation to find the maximum and minimum prices that Lily can guess to win the prize. *(Lesson 2-7)* $|x - 135| = 2.7$; $137.70; $132.30

Chapter 3 ■ Applications Practice 1–4. See p. A33.

1. At a food-processing factory, each box of cereal must weigh at least 15 ounces. Define a variable and write an inequality for the acceptable weights of the cereal boxes. Graph the solutions. *(Lesson 3-1)*

2. In order to qualify for a discounted entry fee at a museum, a visitor must be less than 13 years old. Define a variable and write an inequality for the ages that qualify for the discounted entry fee. Graph the solutions. *(Lesson 3-1)*

3. A restaurant can seat no more than 102 customers at one time. There are already 96 customers in the restaurant. Write and solve an inequality to find out how many additional customers could be seated in the restaurant. *(Lesson 3-2)*

4. **Meteorology** A hurricane is a tropical storm with a wind speed of at least 74 mi/h. A meteorologist is tracking a storm whose current wind speed is 63 mi/h. Write and solve an inequality to find out how much greater the wind speed must be in order for this storm to be considered a hurricane. *(Lesson 3-2)*

Hobbies Use the following information for Exercises 5–7. *(Lesson 3-3)*

When setting up an aquarium, it is recommended that you have no more than one inch of fish per gallon of water. For example, in a 30-gallon tank, the total length of the fish should be at most 30 inches.

Freshwater Fish	
Name	Length (in.)
Red tail catfish	3.5
Blue gourami	1.5

5. Write an inequality to show the possible numbers of blue gourami you can put in a 10-gallon aquarium. $0 \le 1.5x \le 10$

6. Find the possible numbers of blue gourami you can put in a 10-gallon aquarium. 0, 1, 2, 3, 4, 5, or 6

7. Find the possible numbers of red tail catfish you can put in a 20-gallon aquarium. 0, 1, 2, 3, 4, or 5

8. The admission fee at an amusement park is $12, and each ride costs $3.50. The park also offers an all-day pass with unlimited rides for $33. For what numbers of rides is it cheaper to buy the all-day pass? *(Lesson 3-4)* greater than 6 rides

9. The table shows the cost of Internet access at two different cafes. For how many hours of access is the cost at Web World? *(Lesson 3-5)* greater than 16 h

Internet Access	
Cafe	Cost
Cyber Station	$12 one-time membership fee $1.50 per hour
Web World	No membership fee $2.25 per hour

10. Larissa is considering two summer jobs. A job at the mall pays $400 per week plus $15 for every hour of overtime. A job at the movie theater pays $360 per week plus $20 for every hour of overtime. How many hours of overtime would Larissa have to work in order for the job at the movie theater to pay a higher salary than the job at the mall? *(Lesson 3-5)* greater than 8 h

11. **Health** For maximum safety, it is recommended that food be stored at a temperature between 34°F and 40°F inclusive. Write a compound inequality to show the temperatures that are within the recommended range. Graph the solutions. *(Lesson 3-6)* See p. A33.

12. **Physical Science** Color is determined by the wavelength of light. Wavelengths are measured in nanometers (nm). Our eyes see the color green when light has a wavelength between 492 nm and 577 nm inclusive. Write a compound inequality to show the wavelengths that produce green light. Graph the solutions. *(Lesson 3-6)* See p. A33.

13. Alison is running two miles. She ran the first mile in 8 min and wants to run a second mile within 0.75 min of the first mile time. Write and solve an absolute-value inequality to find the range of times for which Alison is aiming. *(Lesson 3-7)* $|x - 8| < 0.75$; $7.25 < x < 8.75$

Chapter 4 ■ Applications Practice 1–4, 7–8. See p. A33.

1. Donnell drove on the highway at a constant speed and then slowed down as she approached her exit. Sketch a graph to show the speed of Donnell's car. Tell whether the graph is continuous or discrete. *(Lesson 4-1)*

2. Lori is buying mineral water for a party. The bottles are available in six-packs. Sketch a graph showing the number of bottles Lori will have if she buys 1, 2, 3, 4, or 5 six-packs. Tell whether the graph is continuous or discrete. *(Lesson 4-1)*

3. **Health** To exercise effectively, it is important to know your maximum heart rate. You can calculate your maximum heart rate in beats per minute by subtracting your age from 220. *(Lesson 4-2)*

 a. Express the age x and the maximum heart rate y as a relation in table form by showing the maximum heart rate for people who are 20, 30, 35, and 40 years old.

 b. Is this relation a function? Why or why not?

4. **Sports** The table shows the number of games won by four baseball teams and the number of home runs each team hit. Is this relation a function? Explain. *(Lesson 4-2)*

Season Statistics	
Wins	Home Runs
95	185
93	133
80	140
93	167

5. Michael uses 5.5 cups of flour for each loaf of bread that he bakes. He plans to bake a maximum of 4 loaves. Write a function rule to describe the number of cups of flour used. Find a reasonable domain and range for the function. *(Lesson 4-3)* $f(x) = 5.5x$; D: {0, 1, 2, 3, 4}; R: {0, 5.5, 11, 16.5, 22}

6. A gym offers the following special rate. New members pay a $425 initiation fee and then pay $90 per year for 1, 2, or 3 years. Write a function rule to describe the situation. Find a reasonable domain and range for the function. *(Lesson 4-3)* $f(x) = 425 + 90x$; D: {1, 2, 3}; R: {$515, $605, $695}

7. The function $y = 3.5x$ describes the number of miles y that the average turtle can walk in x hours. Graph the function. Use the graph to estimate how many miles a turtle can walk in 4.5 hours. *(Lesson 4-3)*

8. **Earth Science** The Kangerdlugssuaq glacier in Greenland is flowing into the sea at the rate of 1.6 meters per hour. The function $y = 1.6x$ describes the number of meters y that flow into the sea in x hours. Graph the function. Use the graph to estimate the number of meters that flow into the sea in 8 hours. *(Lesson 4-3)*

9. The scatter plot shows a relationship between the number of lemonades sold in a day and the day's high temperature. Based on this relationship, predict the number of lemonades that will be sold on a day when the high temperature is 96°F. *(Lesson 4-4)* 48

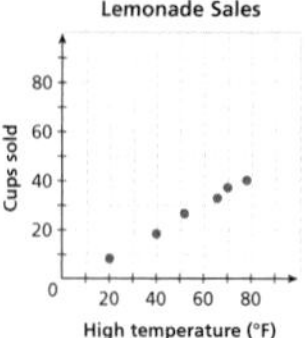

10. The Elmwood Public Library has 85 Spanish books in its collection. Each month, the librarian plans to order 8 new Spanish books. How many Spanish books will the library have after 15 months? *(Lesson 4-5)* 205

11. Nikki purchases a card that she can use to ride the bus in her town. The card costs $45, and each time she rides the bus $1.50 is deducted from the value of the card. How much money will be left on the card after Nikki has taken 12 bus rides? *(Lesson 4-5)* $27

Chapter 5 ■ Applications Practice 1–3. See p. A33.

1. Jennifer is having prints made of her photographs. Each print costs $1.50. The function $f(x) = 1.50x$ gives the total cost of the x prints. Graph this function and give its domain and range. *(Lesson 5-1)*

2. Rolando is serving on jury duty. He is paid $40, plus $15 for each day that he serves. The function $f(x) = 15x + 40$ gives Rolando's total pay for x days. Graph this function and give its domain and range. *(Lesson 5-1)*

3. The Chang family lives 400 miles from Denver. They drive to Denver at a constant speed of 50 mi/h. The function $f(x) = 400 - 50x$ gives their distance in miles from Denver after x hours. *(Lesson 5-2)*

 a. Graph this function and find the intercepts.

 b. What does each intercept represent?

4. Judith and Marie are helping their friends change the light bulbs on a wall fixture. They placed the base of the ladder 3 feet from the wall. The top of the ladder meets the wall 8 ft above the ground. What is the slope of the ladder? *(Lesson 5-3)* $\frac{8}{3}$

5. Danny's kite is 45 ft in the air. The slope of the string is $\frac{9}{2}$. How far away is Danny from the spot on the ground directly below the kite? *(Lesson 5-3)* 10 ft

6. The graph shows the temperature of an oven at different times. Find the slope of the line. Then tell what the slope represents. *(Lesson 5-3)* See p. A33.

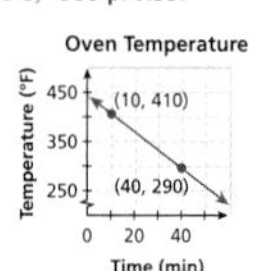

7. **Sports** Competitive race-walkers move at a speed of about 9 miles per hour. Write a direct variation equation for the distance y that a race-walker will cover in x hours. Then graph. *(Lesson 5-4)* See p. A33.

8. A bicycle rental costs $10 plus $1.50 per hour. The cost as a function of the number of hours is shown in the graph. *(Lesson 5-5)*

 a. Write an equation that represents the cost of a bicycle rental as a function of the number of hours. $y = 1.5x + 10$

 b. Identify the slope and y-intercept and describe their meanings in this situation. See p. A33.

 c. Find the cost of renting a bike for 6 hours. $19

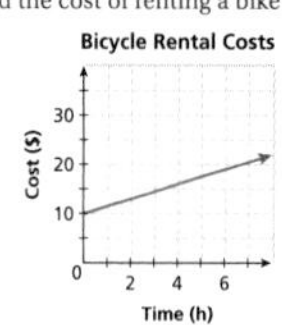

9. A hot-air balloon is moving at a constant rate. Its altitude is a linear function of time, as shown in the table. Write an equation in slope-intercept form that represents this function. Then find the balloon's altitude after 25 minutes. *(Lesson 5-6)* $y = -5x + 250$; 125 m

Balloon's Altitude	
Time (min)	Altitude (m)
0	250
7	215
12	190

10. **Geometry** Show that the points $A(2, 3)$, $B(3, 1)$, $C(-1, -1)$, and $D(-2, 1)$ are the vertices of a rectangle. *(Lesson 5-7)* See p. A34.

11. Write an equation describing the line that is parallel to the y-axis and 8 units to the left of the y-axis. *(Lesson 5-7)* $x = -8$

12. Write an equation describing the line that is parallel to the x-axis and 5 units above the x-axis. *(Lesson 5-7)* $y = 5$

Chapter 6 ■ Applications Practice

1. Net Sounds, an online music store, charges $12 per CD plus $3 for shipping and handling. Web Discs charges $10 per CD plus $9 for shipping and handling. For how many CDs will the cost be the same? What will that cost be? *(Lesson 6-1)* 3; $39

2. At Rocco's Restaurant, a large pizza costs $12 plus $1.25 for each additional topping. At Pizza Palace, a large pizza costs $15 plus $0.75 for each additional topping. For how many toppings will the cost be the same? What will that cost be? *(Lesson 6-1)* 6; $19.50

Use the following information for Exercises 3 and 4. *(Lesson 6-2)*

The coach of a baseball team is deciding between two companies that manufacture team jerseys. One company charges a $60 setup fee and $25 per jersey. The other company charges a $200 setup fee and $15 per jersey.

3. For how many jerseys will the cost at the two companies be the same? What will that cost be? 14; $410

4. The coach is planning to purchase 20 jerseys. Which company is the better option? Why? See p. A34.

5. **Geometry** The length of a rectangle is 5 inches greater than the width. The sum of the length and width is 41 inches. Find the length and width of the rectangle. *(Lesson 6-2)* 23 in.; 18 in.

6. At a movie theater, tickets cost $9.50 for adults and $6.50 for children. A group of 7 moviegoers pays a total of $54.50. How many adults and how many children are in the group? *(Lesson 6-3)* 3 adults, 4 children

7. **Sports** The table shows the time it took two runners to complete the Boston Marathon in several different years. If the patterns continue, will Shanna ever complete the marathon in the same number of minutes as Maria? Explain. *(Lesson 6-4)* See p. A34.

Marathon Times (min)				
	2003	2004	2005	2006
Shanna	190	182	174	166
Maria	175	167	159	151

8. Jordan leaves his house and rides his bike at 10 mi/h. After he goes 4 miles, his brother Tim leaves the house and rides in the same direction at 12 mi/h. If their rates stay the same, will Tim ever catch up to Jordan? Explain. *(Lesson 6-4)* See p. A34.

9. A 25% saltwater solution is mixed with a 45% saltwater solution to make 25 liters of a 37% solution. How many liters of each solution were mixed? *(Lesson 6-5)* 10 L of the 25% sol.; 15 L of the 45% sol.

10. The sum of the digits of a two-digit number is 4. When the digits are reversed, the new number is 18 less than the original number. What is the original number? *(Lesson 6-5)* 31

11–14. See p. A34.

11. Charmaine is buying almonds and cashews for a reception. She wants to spend no more than $18. Almonds cost $4 per pound, and cashews cost $5 per pound. Write a linear inequality to describe the situation. Graph the solutions. Then give two combinations of nuts that Charmaine could buy. *(Lesson 6-6)*

12. Luis is buying T-shirts to give out at a school fund-raiser. He must spend less than $100 for the shirts. Child shirts cost $5 each, and adult shirts cost $8 each. Write a linear inequality to describe the situation. Graph the solutions. Then give two combinations of shirts that Luis could buy. *(Lesson 6-6)*

13. Nicholas is buying treats for his dog. Beef cubes cost $3 per pound, and liver cubes cost $2 per pound. He wants to buy at least 2 pounds of each type of treat, and he wants to spend no more than $14. Graph all possible combinations of the treats that Nicholas could buy. List two possible combinations. *(Lesson 6-7)*

14. **Geometry** The perimeter of a rectangle is at most 20 inches. The length and the width are each at least 3 inches. Graph all possible combinations of lengths and widths that result in such a rectangle. List two possible combinations. *(Lesson 6-7)*

Chapter 7 ■ Applications Practice

1. The eye of a bee is about 10^{-3} m in diameter. Simplify this expression. *(Lesson 7-1)* **0.001 m**

2. A typical stroboscopic camera has a shutter speed of 10^{-6} seconds. Simplify this expression. *(Lesson 7-1)* **0.000001 s**

3. **Space Exploration** During a mission that took place in August, 2005, the Space Shuttle *Discovery* traveled a total distance of 9.3×10^6 km. The Space Shuttle's velocity was 28,000 km/h. *(Lesson 7-2)*
   a. Write the total distance that the Space Shuttle traveled in standard form. **9,300,000 km**
   b. Write the Space Shuttle's velocity in scientific notation. **2.8×10^4 km**

4. There are approximately 10,000,000 grains in a pound of salt. Write this number in scientific notation. *(Lesson 7-2)* **1×10^7**

5. A high-speed centrifuge spins at a speed of 2×10^4 rotations per minute. How many rotations does it make in one hour? Write your answer in scientific notation. *(Lesson 7-3)* **1.2×10^6**

6. **Astronomy** Earth travels approximately 5.8×10^8 miles as it makes one orbit of the Sun. How far does Earth travel in 50 years? (*Note:* One year is one orbit of the Sun.) Write your answer in scientific notation. *(Lesson 7-3)* **2.9×10^{10} mi**

7. **Geography** In 2005, the population of Indonesia was 2.4×10^8. This was 8 times the population of Afghanistan. What was the population of Afghanistan in 2005? Write your answer in standard form. *(Lesson 7-4)* **30,000,000**

8. The Golden Gate Bridge weighs about 8×10^8 kg. The Eiffel Tower weighs about 1×10^7 kg. How many times heavier is the Golden Gate Bridge than the Eiffel Tower? Write your answer in standard form. *(Lesson 7-4)* **80**

9. Carl has 4 identical cubes lined up in a row and wants to find the total length of the cubes. He knows that the volume of one cube is 343 in³. Use the formula $s = V^{\frac{1}{3}}$ to find the length of one cube. What is the length of the row of cubes? *(Lesson 7-5)* **28 in.**

10. A rock is thrown off a 220-foot cliff with an initial velocity of 50 feet per second. The height of the rock above the ground is given by the polynomial $-16t^2 - 50t + 220$, where t is the time in seconds after the rock has been thrown. What is the height of the rock above the ground after 2 seconds? *(Lesson 7-6)* **56 ft**

11. The sum of the first n natural numbers is given by the polynomial $\frac{1}{2}n^2 + \frac{1}{2}n$. Use this polynomial to find the sum of the first 9 natural numbers. *(Lesson 7-6)* **45**

12. **Biology** The population of insects in a meadow depends on the temperature. A biologist models the population of insect A with the polynomial $0.02x^2 + 0.5x + 8$ and the population of insect B with the polynomial $0.04x^2 - 0.2x + 12$, where x represents the temperature in degrees Fahrenheit. *(Lesson 7-7)*
    a. Write a polynomial that represents the total population of both insects. **$0.06x^2 + 0.3x + 20$**
    b. Write a polynomial that represents the difference of the populations of insect B and insect A. **$0.02x^2 - 0.7x + 4$**

13. **Geometry** The length of the rectangle shown is 1 inch longer than 3 times the width.
    a. Write a polynomial that represents the area of the rectangle. **$3x^2 + x$**
    b. Find the area of the rectangle when the width is 4 inches. *(Lesson 7-8)* **52 in²**

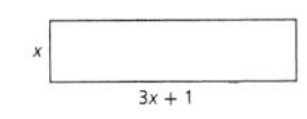

14. A cabinet maker starts with a square piece of wood and then cuts a square hole from its center as shown. Write a polynomial that represents the area of the remaining piece of wood. *(Lesson 7-9)* **$6x + 27$**

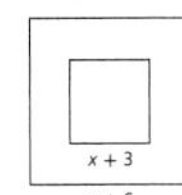

Chapter 8 ■ Applications Practice

1. Ms. Andrews's class has 12 boys and 18 girls. For a class picture, the students will stand in rows on a set of steps. Each row must have the same number of students, and each row will contain only boys or girls. How many rows will there be if Ms. Andrews puts the maximum number of students in each row? *(Lesson 8-1)* **5**

2. A museum director is planning an exhibit of Native American baskets. There are 40 baskets from North America and 32 baskets from South America. The baskets will be displayed on shelves so that each shelf has the same number of baskets. Baskets from North and South America will not be placed together on the same shelf. How many shelves will be needed if each shelf holds the maximum number of baskets? *(Lesson 8-1)* **9**

3. The area of a rectangular painting is $(3x^2 + 5x)$ ft². Factor this polynomial to find expressions for the dimensions of the painting. *(Lesson 8-2)* **Possible dimensions are x ft and $(3x + 5)$ ft**

4. **Geometry** The surface area of a cylinder with radius r and height h is given by the expression $2\pi r^2 + 2\pi rh$. Factor this expression. *(Lesson 8-2)* **$2\pi r(r + h)$**

5. The area of a rectangular classroom in square feet is given by $x^2 + 9x + 18$. The width of the classroom is $(x + 3)$ ft. What is the length of the classroom? *(Lesson 8-3)* **$(x + 6)$ ft**

Gardening Use the following information for Exercises 6 and 7.

A rectangular flower bed has a width of $(x + 4)$ ft. The bed will be enlarged by increasing the length, as shown. *(Lesson 8-3)*

6. The original flower bed has an area of $(x^2 + 9x + 20)$ ft². What is its length? **$(x + 5)$ ft**

7. The enlarged flower bed will have an area of $(x^2 + 12x + 32)$ ft². What will be the new length of the flower bed? **$(x + 8)$ ft**

8. A rectangular poster has an area of $(6x^2 + 19x + 15)$ in². The width of the poster is $(2x + 3)$ in. What is the length of the poster? *(Lesson 8-4)* **$(3x + 5)$ in.**

9. **Physical Science** The height of an object thrown upward with a velocity of 38 feet per second from an initial height of 5 feet can be modeled by the polynomial $-16t^2 + 38t + 5$, where t is the time in seconds. Factor this expression. Then use the factored expression to find the object's height after $\frac{1}{2}$ second. *(Lesson 8-4)* **$-1(8t + 1)(2t - 5)$; 20 ft**

10. A rectangular pool has an area of $(9x^2 + 30x + 25)$ ft². The dimensions of the pool are of the form $ax + b$, where a and b are whole numbers. Find an expression for the perimeter of the pool. Then find the perimeter when $x = 5$. *(Lesson 8-5)* **$12x + 20$; 80**

11. **Geometry** The area of a square is $9x^2 - 24x + 16$. Find the length of each side of the square. Is it possible for x to equal 1 in this situation? Why or why not? *(Lesson 8-5)* **11. See p. A34.**

Architecture Use the following information for Exercises 12–14. *(Lesson 8-6)*

An architect is designing a rectangular hotel room. A balcony that is 5 feet wide runs along the length of the room, as shown in the figure.

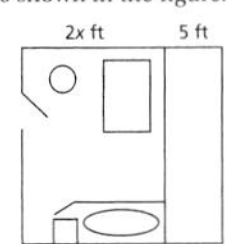

12. The area of the room, including the balcony, is $(4x^2 + 12x + 5)$ ft². Tell whether the polynomial is fully factored. Explain. **No; it can be factored as $(2x + 5)(2x + 1)$.**

13. Find the length and width of the room (including the balcony). **$(2x + 5)$ ft; $(2x + 1)$ ft**

14. How long is the balcony when $x = 9$? **19 ft**

Chapter 9 ■ Applications Practice

1. The height in feet of a football x seconds after it is kicked into the air is modeled by the function $y = -16x^2 + 36x$. *(Lesson 9-1)*
   a. In this situation, what is a reasonable domain? **$x \geq 0$**
   b. How long is the football in the air? **2.25 s**

2. The height of the curved roof of a camping tent can be modeled by $f(x) = -0.5x^2 + 3x$, where x is the width in feet. Find the height of the tent at its tallest point. *(Lesson 9-2)* **4.5 ft**

3. **Engineering** A small bridge passes over a stream. The height in feet of the bridge's curved arch support can be modeled by $f(x) = -0.25x^2 + 2x + 1.5$, where the x-axis represents the level of the water. Find the height of the arch support. *(Lesson 9-2)* **5.5 ft**

4. **Sports** The height in meters of a football that is kicked from the ground is approximated by $f(x) = -5x^2 + 20x$, where x is the time in seconds after the ball is kicked. Find the ball's maximum height and the time it takes the ball to reach this height. Then find how long the ball is in the air. *(Lesson 9-3)* **20 m; 2 s; 4 s**

5. A model rocket is launched into the air with an initial velocity of 144 feet per second. The quadratic function $y = -16x^2 + 144x$ models the height of the rocket after x seconds. How long is the rocket in the air? *(Lesson 9-4)* **9 s**

6. A gymnast jumps on a trampoline. The quadratic function $y = -16x^2 + 24x$ models her height in feet above the trampoline after x seconds. How long is the gymnast in the air? *(Lesson 9-4)* **1.5 s**

7. A child standing on a rock tosses a ball into the air. The height of the ball above the ground is modeled by $h = -16t^2 + 28t + 8$, where h is the height in feet and t is the time in seconds. Find the time it takes the ball to reach the ground. *(Lesson 9-5)* **2 s**

8. A fireworks rocket is shot directly up from the edge of a rooftop. The height of the rocket above the ground is modeled by $h = -16t^2 + 40t + 24$, where h is the height in feet and t is the time in seconds. Find the time it takes the rocket to hit the ground. *(Lesson 9-5)* **3 s**

9. **Geometry** The base of the triangle in the figure is five times the height. The area of the triangle is 400 in². Find the height of the triangle to the nearest tenth. *(Lesson 9-6)* **12.6 in.**

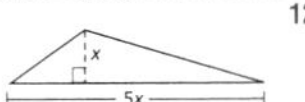

10. The length of a rectangular swimming pool is 8 feet greater than the width. The pool has an area of 240 ft². Find the length and width of the pool. *(Lesson 9-7)* **12 ft; 20 ft**

11. **Geometry** One base of a trapezoid is 4 ft longer than the other base. The height of the trapezoid is equal to the shorter base. The trapezoid's area is 80 ft². Find the height. $\left(\textit{Hint: } A = \frac{1}{2}h(b_1 + b_2)\right)$ *(Lesson 9-7)* **8 ft**

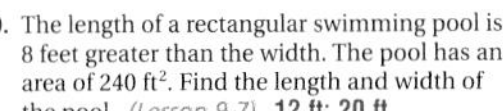

12. A referee tosses a coin into the air at the start of a football game to decide which team will get the ball. The height of the coin above the ground is modeled by $h = -16t^2 + 12t + 4$, where h is the height in feet and t is the time in seconds after the coin is tossed. Will the coin reach a height of 8 feet? Use the discriminant to explain your answer. *(Lesson 9-9)* **See p. A34.**

13. When Marshall came home from school, he kicked his shoe off of his foot into the air. The height of the shoe in feet can be modeled by the quadratic function $h = -0.8s^2 + 2s$, where s is the number of seconds after the shoe is kicked. *(Lesson 9-8)*
    a. Find the height of the shoe after 1 second. **1.2 ft**
    b. For how long is the shoe in the air? **2.5 s**
    c. Find the maximum height of the shoe. **1.25 ft**

Chapter 10 ■ Applications Practice

1. The inverse variation $xy = 200$ relates the number of words per minute x at which a person types to the number of minutes y that it takes to type a 200-word paragraph. Determine a reasonable domain and range and then graph this inverse variation. Use the graph to estimate how many minutes it would take to type the paragraph at a rate of 60 words per minute. *(Lesson 10-1)* **See p. A34.**

2. **Business** The owner of a deli finds that the number of sandwiches sold in one day varies inversely as the price of the sandwiches. When the price is \$4.50, the deli sells 60 sandwiches. How many sandwiches can the owner expect to sell when the price is \$3.60? *(Lesson 10-1)* **75**

3. A gardener has \$30 in his budget to buy packets of seeds. He receives 3 free packets of seeds with his order. The number of packets y he can buy is $y = \frac{30}{x} + 3$, where x is the price per packet. Describe the reasonable domain and range values. Then graph the function. *(Lesson 10-2)* **See p. A34.**

4. Ashley wants to save \$1000 for a trip to Europe. She puts aside x dollars per month, and her grandmother contributes \$10 per month. The number of months y it will take to save \$1000 is $y = \frac{1000}{x + 10}$. Describe the reasonable domain and range values. Then graph the function. *(Lesson 10-2)* **See p. A34.**

5. **Geometry** Find the ratio of the area of a circle to the circumference of the circle. (*Hint:* For a circle, $A = \pi r^2$ and $C = 2\pi r$.) For what radius is this ratio equal to 1? *(Lesson 10-3)* **$\frac{r}{2}$; $r = 2$**

6. **Geometry** For a cylinder with radius r and height h, the volume is $V = \pi r^2 h$, and the surface area is $S = 2\pi r^2 + 2\pi rh$. What is the ratio of the volume to the surface area for a cylinder? What is this ratio when $r = h = 1$? *(Lesson 10-3)* **$\frac{rh}{2(r + h)}$; $\frac{1}{4}$**

7. A committee consists of five more women than men. The chairperson randomly chooses one person to serve as secretary and a different person to serve as treasurer. Write and simplify an expression that represents the probability that both people who are chosen are men. What is the probability of choosing two men if there are 6 men on the committee? *(Lesson 10-4)* **See p. A34.**

8. **Transportation** A delivery truck makes a delivery to a town 150 miles away traveling r miles per hour. On the return trip, the delivery truck travels 20% faster. Write and simplify an expression for the truck's round-trip delivery time in terms of r. Then find the round-trip delivery time if the truck travels 55 mi/h on its way to the delivery. *(Lesson 10-5)* **$\frac{275}{r}$; 5 h**

9. **Recreation** Jordan is hiking 2 miles to a vista point at the top of a hill and then back to his campsite at the base of the hill. His downhill rate is 3 times his uphill rate, r. Write and simplify an expression in terms of r for the time that the round-trip hike will take. Then find how long the hike will take if Jordan's uphill rate is 2 mi/h. *(Lesson 10-5)* **$\frac{8}{3r}$; $1\frac{1}{3}$ h**

10. **Geometry** The volume of a rectangular prism is the area of the base times the height. A rectangular prism has a volume given by $(2x^2 + 7x + 5)$ cm³ and a height given by $(x + 1)$ cm. What is the area of the base of the rectangular prism? *(Lesson 10-6)* **$2x + 5$**

11. Tanya can deliver newspapers to all of the houses on her route in 1 hour. Her brother, Nick, can deliver newspapers along the same route in 2 hours. How long will it take to deliver the newspapers if they work together? *(Lesson 10-7)* **$\frac{2}{3}$ h, or 40 min**

12. **Agriculture** Grains are harvested using a combine. A farm has two combines—one that can harvest the wheat field in 9 hours and another that can harvest the wheat field in 11 hours. How long will it take to harvest the wheat field using both combines? *(Lesson 10-8)* **$4\frac{19}{20}$ h, or 4 h 57 min**

Skills Bank

Chapter 11 ■ Applications Practice

1. The function $f(x) = \sqrt{1.44x}$ gives the approximate distance in miles to the horizon as observed by a person whose eye level is x feet above the ground. Jamal stands on a tower so that his eyes are 180 ft above the ground. What is the distance to the horizon? Round your answer to the nearest tenth. *(Lesson 11-1)* **16.1 mi**

2. **Geometry** Given the surface area, S, of a sphere, the formula $r = \sqrt{\frac{S}{4\pi}}$ can be used to find the sphere's radius. What is the radius of a sphere with a surface area of 100 m^2? Use 3.14 for π. Round your answer to the nearest hundredth of a meter. *(Lesson 11-1)* **2.82 m**

3. **Cooking** A chef has a square baking pan with sides 8 inches long. She wants to know if an 11-inch fish can fit in the pan. Find the length of the diagonal of the pan. Give the answer as a radical expression in simplest form. Then estimate the length to the nearest tenth of an inch. Tell whether the fish will fit in the pan. *(Lesson 11-2)* **$8\sqrt{2}$ in. ≈ 11.3 in.; yes**

4. Alicia wants to put a fence around the irregular garden plot shown. Find the perimeter of the plot. Give your answer as a radical in simplest form. *(Lesson 11-3)* **$11\sqrt{3}$ m**

$\sqrt{12}$ m
$\sqrt{27}$ m
$\sqrt{3}$ m
$\sqrt{75}$ m

5. **Physical Science** The velocity of an object in meters per second is given by $\frac{\sqrt{2}\sqrt{E}}{\sqrt{m}}$, where E is kinetic energy in Joules and m is mass in kilograms. What is the velocity of an object that has 40 Joules of kinetic energy and a mass of 10 kilograms? Give the answer as a radical expression in simplest form. Then estimate the velocity to the nearest tenth. *(Lesson 11-4)* **$2\sqrt{2}$ m/s ≈ 2.8 m/s**

6. A rectangular window has an area of 40 ft^2. The window is 8 feet long and its height is $\sqrt{x+2}$ ft. What is the value of x? What is the height of the window? *(Lesson 11-5)* **$x = 23$; 5 ft**

7. Scientists who are developing a vaccine track the number of new infections of a disease each year. The values in the table form a geometric sequence. To the nearest whole number, how many new infections will there be in the 6th year? *(Lesson 11-6)* **2848**

Year	Number of New Infections
1	12,000
2	9000
3	6750

8. **Finance** For a savings account that earns 5% interest each year, the function $f(x) = 2000(1.05)^x$ gives the value of a \$2000 investment after x years. *(Lesson 11-7)*
   a. Find the investment's value after 5 years. **\$2552.56**
   b. Approximately how many years will it take for the investment to be worth \$3100? **9**

9. **Chemistry** Cesium-137 has a half-life of 30 years. Find the amount left from a 200-gram sample after 150 years. *(Lesson 11-8)* **6.25 g**

10. The cost of tuition at a dance school is \$300 a year and is increasing at a rate of 3% a year. Write an exponential growth function to model the situation and find the cost of tuition after 4 years. *(Lesson 11-8)* **$y = 300(1.03)^t$; \$337.65**

11. Use the data in the table to describe how the price of the company's stock is changing. Then write a function that models the data. Use your function to predict the price of the company's stock after 7 years. *(Lesson 11-9)* **See p. A34.**

Stock Prices				
Year	0	1	2	3
Price (\$)	10.00	11.00	12.20	13.31

12. Use the data in the table to describe the rate at which Susan reads. Then write a function that models the data. Use your function to predict the number of pages Susan will read in 6 hours. *(Lesson 11-9)*

Total Number of Pages Read				
Time (h)	1	2	3	4
Pages	48	96	144	192

Susan reads 48 pages per hour; $y = 48x$; 288

Skills Bank

Place Value

The number 5,304,293,087,201.286 is shown in the place-value chart below.

Trillions	Billions	Millions	Thousands	Ones	.	Tenths	Hundredths	Thousandths
5,	304,	293,	087,	201	.	2	8	6

EXAMPLE 1 Use the place-value chart to find the place value of the underlined digit.

A 5,30<u>4</u>,293,087,201.286 — billions

B 5,304,2<u>9</u>3,087,201.286 — ten millions

C 5,304,293,087,201.28<u>6</u> — thousandths

Expanded form shows a number as the sum of the values of each digit.

EXAMPLE 2 Write 16,752,045.12 in expanded form.

10,000,000 + 6,000,000 + 700,000 + 50,000 + 2,000 + 40 + 5 + 0.1 + 0.02

PRACTICE

Use the place-value chart to find the place value of the underlined digit.

1. 22.3<u>8</u> **hundredths**
2. 1,2<u>3</u>8,400 **ten thousands**
3. <u>2</u>,809,354.003 **millions**

Write each number in expanded form.

4. 899,456 **800,000 + 90,000 + 9,000 + 400 + 50 + 6**
5. 1645.445 **1000 + 600 + 40 + 5 + 0.4 + 0.04 + 0.005**
6. 3,009,844,002,359 **3,000,000,000,000 + 9,000,000,000 + 800,000,000 + 40,000,000 + 4,000,000 + 2,000 + 300 + 50 + 9**

Times Tables

You can use a multiplication table to multiply and to write *number families*. A **number family** is a group of related number sentences that use the same numbers.

EXAMPLE 1

Find 8 • 9.

Find where the 8's row and the 9's column intersect.

8 • 9 = 72

EXAMPLE 2

Write a multiplication and division number family for 8, 9, and 72.

8 • 9 = 72
9 • 8 = 72
72 ÷ 9 = 8
72 ÷ 8 = 9

×	1	2	3	4	5	6	7	8	9	10	11	12
1	1	2	3	4	5	6	7	8	9	10	11	12
2	2	4	6	8	10	12	14	16	18	20	22	24
3	3	6	9	12	15	18	21	24	27	30	33	36
4	4	8	12	16	20	24	28	32	36	40	44	48
5	5	10	15	20	25	30	35	40	45	50	55	60
6	6	12	18	24	30	36	42	48	54	60	66	72
7	7	14	21	28	35	42	49	56	63	70	77	84
8	8	16	24	32	40	48	56	64	72	80	88	96
9	9	18	27	36	45	54	63	72	81	90	99	108
10	10	20	30	40	50	60	70	80	90	100	110	120
11	11	22	33	44	55	66	77	88	99	110	121	132
12	12	24	36	48	60	72	84	96	108	120	132	144

PRACTICE

Multiply. Write a multiplication and division number family for each set of numbers. **See p. A34.**

1. 4 • 8
2. 5 • 12
3. 3 • 11
4. 8 • 7
5. 9 • 6
6. 12 • 12

Compare and Order Rational Numbers

7NS1.1

You can compare and order rational numbers by graphing them on the number line.

EXAMPLE Order 0.25, $\frac{3}{4}$, 0.1, and $\frac{4}{5}$ from least to greatest.

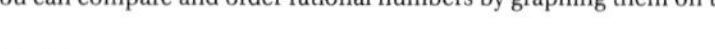

$\frac{3}{4} = 0.75$

$\frac{4}{5} = 0.8$

On the number line, the values increase from left to right: 0.1, 0.25, $\frac{3}{4}$, $\frac{4}{5}$.

PRACTICE

Order each set of numbers from least to greatest.

1. 2.6, $2\frac{2}{5}$, $2\frac{1}{2}$ **$2\frac{2}{5}$, $2\frac{1}{2}$, 2.6**
2. 0.45, $\frac{3}{8}$, $\frac{4}{9}$ **$\frac{3}{8}$, $\frac{4}{9}$, 0.45**
3. 0.55, $\frac{2}{3}$, 0.6 **0.55, 0.6, $\frac{2}{3}$**
4. 5.25, $5\frac{1}{3}$, 5.05, 5.5 **5.05, 5.25, $5\frac{1}{3}$, 5.5**
5. 0.4, $\frac{3}{5}$, $\frac{1}{4}$, 0.42 **$\frac{1}{4}$, 0.4, 0.42, $\frac{3}{5}$**
6. $\frac{5}{8}$, $\frac{4}{9}$, 0.6, $\frac{6}{7}$ **$\frac{4}{9}$, 0.6, $\frac{5}{8}$, $\frac{6}{7}$**

Inverse Operations

Inverse operations "undo" each other. Addition and subtraction are inverse operations. Multiplication and division are inverse operations.

EXAMPLE Use inverse operations to check each answer.

A $567 - 180 \stackrel{?}{=} 487$

487 + 180 *Use addition to check subtraction.*
667
667 ≠ 567
incorrect

B $110 \div 11 \stackrel{?}{=} 10$

10 • 11 *Use multiplication to check division.*
110
110 = 110
correct

PRACTICE

Use inverse operations to check each answer.

1. 51 + 25 = 86 **incorrect**
2. 14 • 4 = 48 **incorrect**
3. 144 ÷ 4 = 36 **correct**
4. 345 − 72 = 273 **correct**
5. 134 + 653 = 787 **correct**
6. 364 ÷ 7 = 52 **correct**
7. 500 − 428 = 82 **incorrect**
8. 6 • 25 = 150 **correct**

Mental Math

Mental math strategies include using the Distributive Property, using the Commutative Property, and using facts about powers of 10.

EXAMPLE Use mental math to solve each problem.

A 6 • 17

Break 17 into 10 + 7. Then use the Distributive Property.

$6 \cdot 17 = 6(10 + 7)$
$= 6(10) + 6(7)$
$= 60 + 42$
$= 102$

B 225 + 78 + 75

Use the Commutative Property to add or multiply numbers in a different order.

$225 + 78 + 75 = 225 + 75 + 78$
$= 300 + 78$
$= 378$

C 132 • 100,000

Count the number of zeros in 100,000. Move the decimal point that many places right.

$132 \cdot 100{,}000 = 13{,}200{,}000$
$= 13{,}200{,}000$

PRACTICE

Use mental math to solve each problem.

1. 3987 • 10,000 **39,870,000**
2. 5 • 29 **145**
3. 950 + 273 + 50 **1273**
4. 12 • 41 **492**
5. 25 • 42 • 4 **4200**
6. 4.5 • 100 • 2 **900**

Divisibility

A number is divisible by another number if their quotient is a whole number with no remainder.

You can use the divisibility rules below to determine whether one number is divisible by another without having to perform any division. These rules are particularly useful when you are working with large numbers.

A number is divisible by...	Divisible	Not divisible
2 if the last digit is an even number.	72	131
3 if the sum of the digits is divisible by 3.	123	916
4 if the last two digits form a number divisible by 4.	1024	823
5 if the last digit is 0 or 5.	100	52
6 if the number is divisible by 2 and 3.	120	592
9 if the sum of the digits is divisible by 9.	1692	9059
10 if the last digit is 0.	460	205

PRACTICE

Determine whether each number is divisible by 2, 3, 4, 5, 6, 9, or 10.

1. 266 **2**
2. 654 **2, 3, 6**
3. 894 **2, 3, 6**
4. 10,020 **2, 3, 4, 5, 6, 10**
5. 4688 **2, 4**
6. 2269 **none**
7. 363 **3**
8. 76,708 **2, 4**
9. 481 **none**
10. 1552 **2, 4**

Factoring Numbers

Whole numbers that are multiplied to find a product are called **factors** of that product. A number is divisible by its factors.

$3 \cdot 5 = 15$ (3 and 5 are the Factors; 15 is the Product)

$15 \div 3 = 5$
$15 \div 5 = 3$ ← 15 is divisible by 3 and 5.

EXAMPLE List all of the factors of each number.

A 24

Begin listing factors in pairs.

$24 = 1 \cdot 24$	*1 and 24 are factors.*
$24 = 2 \cdot 12$	*2 and 12 are factors.*
$24 = 3 \cdot 8$	*3 and 8 are factors.*
$24 = 4 \cdot 6$	*4 and 6 are factors.*
	5 is not a factor.
$24 = 6 \cdot 4$	*6 and 4 have already been listed, so stop here.*

The factors of 24 are 1, 2, 3, 4, 6, 8, 12, and 24.

B 15

Begin listing factors in pairs.

$15 = 1 \cdot 15$	*1 and 15 are factors.*
	2 is not a factor.
$15 = 3 \cdot 5$	*3 and 5 are factors.*
	4 is not a factor.
$15 = 5 \cdot 3$	*5 and 3 have already been listed, so stop here.*

The factors of 15 are 1, 3, 5, and 15.

C 17

Begin listing factors in pairs.

$17 = 1 \cdot 17$	*1 and 17 are factors.*
	17 is not divisible by any other whole numbers.

The factors of 17 are 1 and 17.

PRACTICE

List all of the factors of each number.

1. 12 1, 2, 3, 4, 6, 12
2. 21 1, 3, 7, 21
3. 52 1, 2, 4, 13, 26, 52
4. 81 1, 3, 9, 17, 81
5. 34 1, 2, 17, 34
6. 82 1, 2, 41, 82
7. 67 1, 67
8. 87 1, 3, 29, 87
9. 75 1, 3, 5, 15, 25, 75

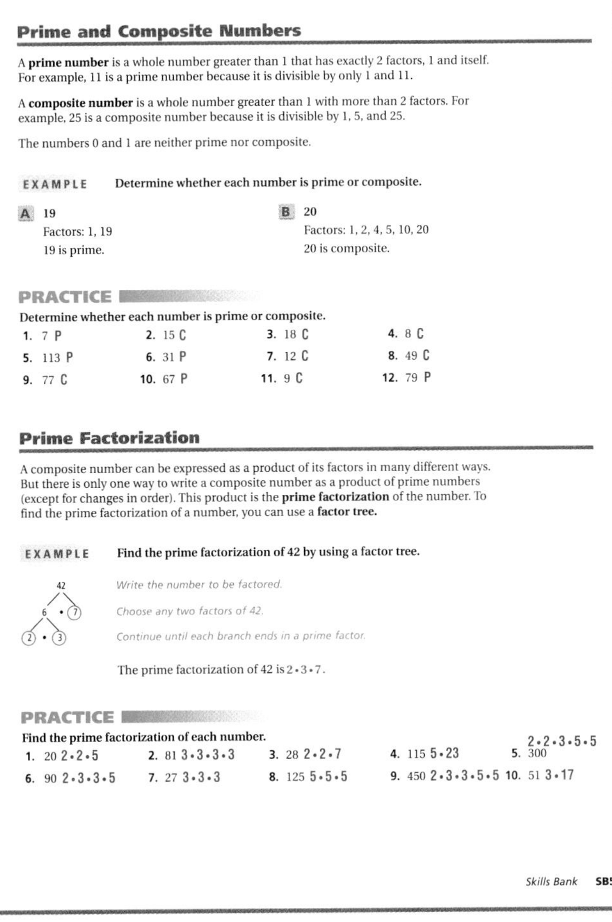

Prime and Composite Numbers

A **prime number** is a whole number greater than 1 that has exactly 2 factors, 1 and itself. For example, 11 is a prime number because it is divisible by only 1 and 11.

A **composite number** is a whole number greater than 1 with more than 2 factors. For example, 25 is a composite number because it is divisible by 1, 5, and 25.

The numbers 0 and 1 are neither prime nor composite.

EXAMPLE Determine whether each number is prime or composite.

A 19
Factors: 1, 19
19 is prime.

B 20
Factors: 1, 2, 4, 5, 10, 20
20 is composite.

PRACTICE

Determine whether each number is prime or composite.

1. 7 P
2. 15 C
3. 18 C
4. 8 C
5. 113 P
6. 31 P
7. 12 C
8. 49 C
9. 77 C
10. 67 P
11. 9 C
12. 79 P

Prime Factorization

A composite number can be expressed as a product of its factors in many different ways. But there is only one way to write a composite number as a product of prime numbers (except for changes in order). This product is the **prime factorization** of the number. To find the prime factorization of a number, you can use a **factor tree.**

EXAMPLE Find the prime factorization of 42 by using a factor tree.

Write the number to be factored.
Choose any two factors of 42.
Continue until each branch ends in a prime factor.

The prime factorization of 42 is $2 \cdot 3 \cdot 7$.

PRACTICE

Find the prime factorization of each number.

1. 20 $2 \cdot 2 \cdot 5$
2. 81 $3 \cdot 3 \cdot 3 \cdot 3$
3. 28 $2 \cdot 2 \cdot 7$
4. 115 $5 \cdot 23$
5. 300 $2 \cdot 2 \cdot 3 \cdot 5 \cdot 5$
6. 90 $2 \cdot 3 \cdot 3 \cdot 5$
7. 27 $3 \cdot 3 \cdot 3$
8. 125 $5 \cdot 5 \cdot 5$
9. 450 $2 \cdot 3 \cdot 3 \cdot 5 \cdot 5$
10. 51 $3 \cdot 17$

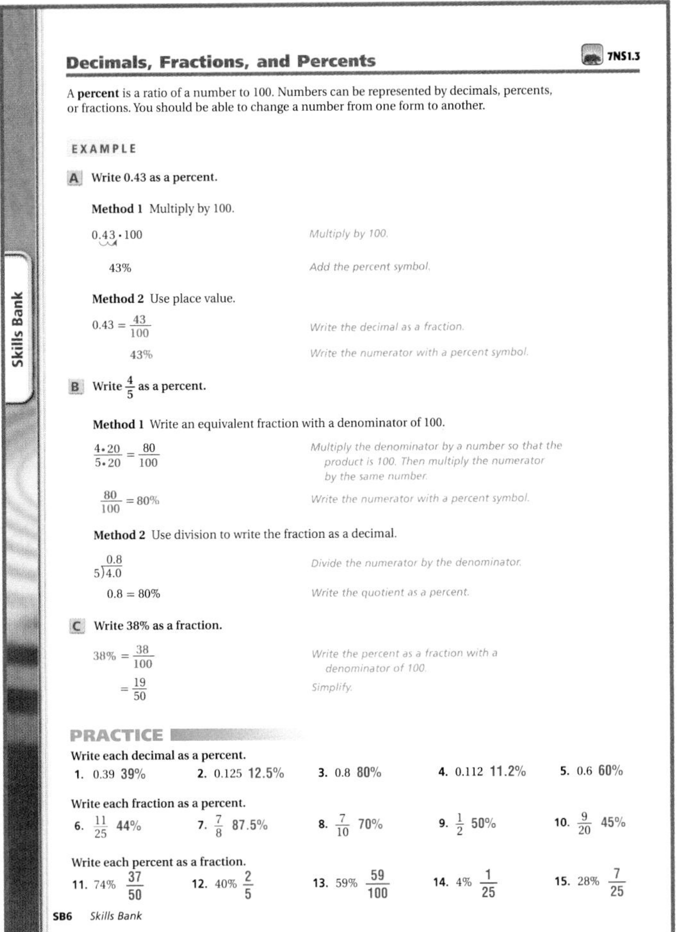

Decimals, Fractions, and Percents

7NS1.3

A **percent** is a ratio of a number to 100. Numbers can be represented by decimals, percents, or fractions. You should be able to change a number from one form to another.

EXAMPLE

A Write 0.43 as a percent.

Method 1 Multiply by 100.

$0.43 \cdot 100$ *Multiply by 100.*

43% *Add the percent symbol.*

Method 2 Use place value.

$0.43 = \frac{43}{100}$ *Write the decimal as a fraction.*

43% *Write the numerator with a percent symbol.*

B Write $\frac{4}{5}$ as a percent.

Method 1 Write an equivalent fraction with a denominator of 100.

$\frac{4 \cdot 20}{5 \cdot 20} = \frac{80}{100}$ *Multiply the denominator by a number so that the product is 100. Then multiply the numerator by the same number.*

$\frac{80}{100} = 80\%$ *Write the numerator with a percent symbol.*

Method 2 Use division to write the fraction as a decimal.

$5\overline{)4.0}$ = 0.8 *Divide the numerator by the denominator.*

$0.8 = 80\%$ *Write the quotient as a percent.*

C Write 38% as a fraction.

$38\% = \frac{38}{100}$ *Write the percent as a fraction with a denominator of 100.*

$= \frac{19}{50}$ *Simplify.*

PRACTICE

Write each decimal as a percent.

1. 0.39 39%
2. 0.125 12.5%
3. 0.8 80%
4. 0.112 11.2%
5. 0.6 60%

Write each fraction as a percent.

6. $\frac{11}{25}$ 44%
7. $\frac{7}{8}$ 87.5%
8. $\frac{7}{10}$ 70%
9. $\frac{1}{2}$ 50%
10. $\frac{9}{20}$ 45%

Write each percent as a fraction.

11. 74% $\frac{37}{50}$
12. 40% $\frac{2}{5}$
13. 59% $\frac{59}{100}$
14. 4% $\frac{1}{25}$
15. 28% $\frac{7}{25}$

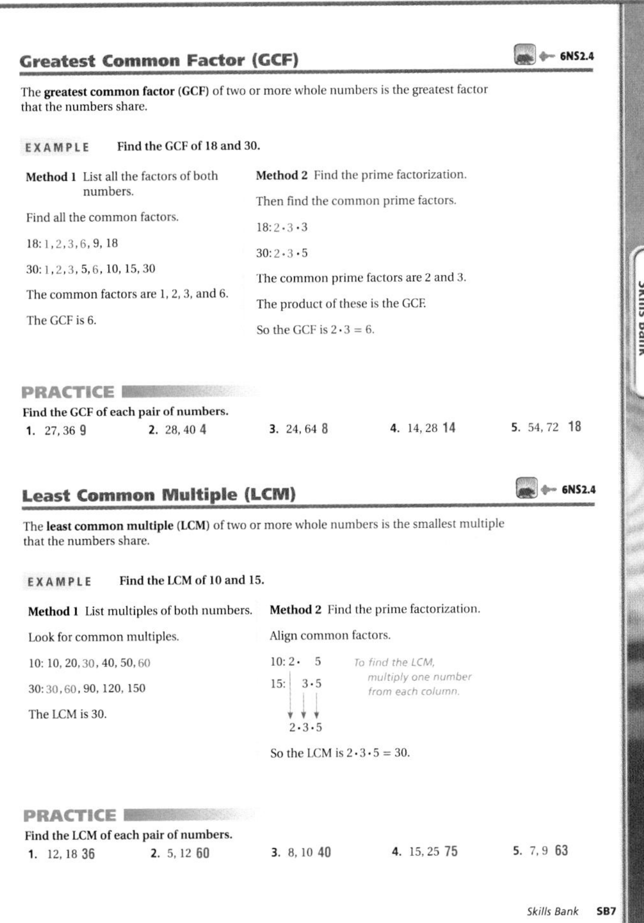

Greatest Common Factor (GCF)

6NS2.4

The **greatest common factor (GCF)** of two or more whole numbers is the greatest factor that the numbers share.

EXAMPLE Find the GCF of 18 and 30.

Method 1 List all the factors of both numbers.

Find all the common factors.

18: 1, 2, 3, 6, 9, 18

30: 1, 2, 3, 5, 6, 10, 15, 30

The common factors are 1, 2, 3, and 6.

The GCF is 6.

Method 2 Find the prime factorization.

Then find the common prime factors.

$18: 2 \cdot 3 \cdot 3$

$30: 2 \cdot 3 \cdot 5$

The common prime factors are 2 and 3.

The product of these is the GCF.

So the GCF is $2 \cdot 3 = 6$.

PRACTICE

Find the GCF of each pair of numbers.

1. 27, 36 9
2. 28, 40 4
3. 24, 64 8
4. 14, 28 14
5. 54, 72 18

Least Common Multiple (LCM)

6NS2.4

The **least common multiple (LCM)** of two or more whole numbers is the smallest multiple that the numbers share.

EXAMPLE Find the LCM of 10 and 15.

Method 1 List multiples of both numbers.

Look for common multiples.

10: 10, 20, 30, 40, 50, 60

30: 30, 60, 90, 120, 150

The LCM is 30.

Method 2 Find the prime factorization.

Align common factors.

$10: 2 \cdot \quad 5$

$15: \quad 3 \cdot 5$

$2 \cdot 3 \cdot 5$

To find the LCM, multiply one number from each column.

So the LCM is $2 \cdot 3 \cdot 5 = 30$.

PRACTICE

Find the LCM of each pair of numbers.

1. 12, 18 36
2. 5, 12 60
3. 8, 10 40
4. 15, 25 75
5. 7, 9 63

Finding a Common Denominator

7NS2.2

You must often rewrite two or more fractions so that they have the same denominator, or a **common denominator.** One way to find a common denominator is to multiply the denominators. Or you can use the **least common denominator (LCD),** which is the LCM of the denominators.

EXAMPLE **Rewrite $\frac{1}{6}$ and $\frac{4}{9}$ so that they have a common denominator.**

Method 1 Multiply the denominators: $6 \cdot 9 = 54$

$\frac{1}{6} = \frac{5 \cdot 9}{6 \cdot 9} = \frac{45}{54}$ $\quad \frac{4}{9} = \frac{4 \cdot 6}{9 \cdot 6} = \frac{24}{54}$ *Rewrite each fraction using the common denominator.*

Method 2 Find the LCD. The LCM of the denominators, 6 and 9, is 18. So the LCD is 18.

$\frac{1}{6} = \frac{5 \cdot 3}{6 \cdot 3} = \frac{15}{18}$ $\quad \frac{4}{9} = \frac{4 \cdot 2}{9 \cdot 2} = \frac{8}{18}$ *Rewrite each fraction using the LCD.*

Two ways to write $\frac{1}{6}$ and $\frac{4}{9}$ with a common denominator are $\frac{45}{54}$ and $\frac{24}{54}$ or $\frac{15}{18}$ and $\frac{8}{18}$.

PRACTICE

Rewrite each pair of fractions so that they have a common denominator. **Possible answers given.**

1. $\frac{1}{3}, \frac{3}{4}$ $\quad$ **$\frac{4}{12}, \frac{9}{12}$**
2. $\frac{1}{2}, \frac{5}{8}$ $\quad$ **$\frac{4}{8}, \frac{5}{8}$**
3. $\frac{3}{4}, \frac{1}{6}$ $\quad$ **$\frac{9}{12}, \frac{2}{12}$**
4. $\frac{1}{4}, \frac{3}{14}$ $\quad$ **$\frac{14}{56}, \frac{12}{56}$**
5. $\frac{5}{6}, \frac{3}{5}$ $\quad$ **$\frac{25}{30}, \frac{18}{30}$**

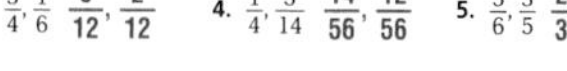

Adding and Subtracting Fractions

7NS1.2, 7NS2.2

To add or subtract fractions, first make sure they have a common denominator. Then add or subtract the numerators and keep the common denominator.

EXAMPLE **Add or subtract. Write your answer in simplest form.**

A $\frac{7}{10} - \frac{3}{10}$

$\frac{7}{10} - \frac{3}{10} = \frac{7-3}{10} = \frac{4}{10} = \frac{2}{5}$ *Subtract the numerators. Keep the denominator.*

B $\frac{5}{6} + \frac{3}{8}$

Step 1 Find the LCD. The LCD is 24.

Step 2 Rewrite the factions using the LCD: $\frac{5}{6} = \frac{5 \cdot 4}{6 \cdot 4} = \frac{20}{24}$ $\quad \frac{3}{8} = \frac{3 \cdot 3}{8 \cdot 3} = \frac{9}{24}$

Step 3 Add: $\frac{20}{24} + \frac{9}{24} = \frac{29}{24}$ *Add the numerators. Keep the denominator.*

PRACTICE

Add or subtract. Write your answer in simplest form.

1. $\frac{3}{5} + \frac{1}{5}$ $\quad$ **$\frac{4}{5}$**
2. $\frac{8}{9} - \frac{5}{9}$ $\quad$ **$\frac{1}{3}$**
3. $\frac{3}{8} + \frac{1}{4}$ $\quad$ **$\frac{5}{8}$**
4. $\frac{8}{9} - \frac{4}{5}$ $\quad$ **$\frac{4}{45}$**
5. $\frac{7}{10} - \frac{3}{8}$ $\quad$ **$\frac{13}{40}$**

Multiplying and Dividing Fractions

7NS1.2

When multiplying or dividing fractions, you do *not* need to find a common denominator.

To multiply fractions, multiply the numerators and then multiply the denominators. Write your answer in simplest form.

EXAMPLE 1 **Multiply $\frac{3}{4} \cdot \frac{2}{5}$. Write your answer in simplest form.**

$\frac{3}{4} \cdot \frac{2}{5}$

$= \frac{3 \cdot 2}{4 \cdot 5}$ *Multiply numerators and denominators.*

$= \frac{6}{20}$

$= \frac{3}{10}$ *Write in simplest form.*

Two numbers are **reciprocals** if their product is 1. To find the reciprocal of a fraction, switch the numerator and denominator. Remember that whole numbers can be written with a denominator of 1. For example, $8 = \frac{8}{1}$. Switch the numerator and the denominator to find the reciprocal: $\frac{1}{8}$.

Dividing by a fraction is the same as multiplying by its reciprocal. So, to divide fractions, multiply the first fraction by the reciprocal of the second fraction.

EXAMPLE 2 **Divide $\frac{2}{3} \div \frac{1}{5}$. Write your answer in simplest form.**

$\frac{2}{3} \div \frac{1}{5}$

$= \frac{2}{3} \cdot \frac{5}{1}$ *Rewrite division as multiplication by the reciprocal.*

$= \frac{2 \cdot 5}{3 \cdot 1}$ *Multiply numerators and denominators.*

$= \frac{10}{3}$ *Write in simplest form.*

PRACTICE

Multiply or divide. Write your answer in simplest form.

1. $\frac{1}{5} \cdot \frac{3}{5}$ $\quad$ **$\frac{3}{25}$**
2. $\frac{7}{8} \cdot \frac{4}{5}$ $\quad$ **$\frac{7}{10}$**
3. $\frac{7}{12} \div \frac{1}{2}$ $\quad$ **$\frac{7}{6}$**
4. $\frac{2}{9} \div \frac{6}{7}$ $\quad$ **$\frac{7}{27}$**
5. $\frac{1}{2} \cdot \frac{4}{7}$ $\quad$ **$\frac{2}{7}$**
6. $\frac{3}{5} \div \frac{4}{5}$ $\quad$ **$\frac{3}{4}$**
7. $\frac{6}{15} \cdot \frac{5}{12}$ $\quad$ **$\frac{1}{6}$**
8. $\frac{5}{8} \div \frac{3}{4}$ $\quad$ **$\frac{5}{6}$**
9. $\frac{2}{5} \div \frac{6}{7}$ $\quad$ **$\frac{7}{15}$**
10. $\frac{1}{3} \cdot \frac{3}{8}$ $\quad$ **$\frac{1}{8}$**

Discounts and Markups

7NS1.7

A **discount** is an amount by which an original price is reduced. A **markup** is an amount by which a wholesale price is increased.

EXAMPLE

A **Admission to the museum is \$8. Students receive a 15% discount. How much is the discount? How much do students pay?**

100% − 15% = 85% *Subtract the percent discount from 100%.*

0.85(\$8.00) = \$6.80 *Find 85% of \$8.00. The result is the student price.*

\$8.00 − \$6.80 = \$1.20 *Subtract \$6.80 from \$8.00. The result is the amount of the discount.*

The amount of the discount is \$1.20. Students pay \$6.80.

B **The wholesale cost of a DVD is \$7. The markup is 75%. What is the amount of the markup? What is the selling price?**

100% + 75% = 175% *Add the percent markup to 100%.*

1.75(\$7.00) = \$12.25 *Find 175% of \$7.00. The result is the selling price.*

\$12.25 − \$7.00 = \$5.25 *Subtract \$7.00 from \$12.25. The result is the amount of the markup.*

The amount of the markup is \$5.25. The selling price is \$12.25.

PRACTICE

1. What is the final price on a \$185 leather jacket that is on sale for 40% off? **\$111**
2. A video game has a 70% markup. The wholesale cost is \$9. What is the selling price? **\$15.30**

Commission

7NS1.7

A **commission** is money paid to a person or a company for making a sale. Usually the commission is a percent of the sale amount.

EXAMPLE

Ms. Barnes earns a base salary of \$42,000 plus a 1.5% commission on sales. Her total sales one year were \$700,000. Find her total pay for that year.

42,000 + 1.5% of 700,000 *total pay = base salary + commission*

= 42,000 + (0.015)(700,000) *Write the percent as a decimal.*

= 42,000 + 10,500 *Multiply.*

= 52,500 *Add.*

Ms. Barnes's total pay was \$52,500.

PRACTICE

1. A telemarketer earns \$350 per week plus a 12% commission on sales. Find his total pay for a week in which his sales are \$940. **\$462.80**

Simple Interest

7NS1.7

Interest is the amount of money charged for borrowing money, or the amount of money earned when saving or investing money. **Principal** is the amount borrowed or invested. **Simple interest** is interest paid only on the principal.

Simple interest paid annually: $I = Prt$ where I is the amount of interest.

P is the principal.

r is the interest rate per year as a decimal.

t is the time in years.

EXAMPLE **Find the simple interest paid annually for 2 years on a \$900 loan at 16% per year.**

$I = Prt$ *Write the formula for simple interest.*

$I = (900)(0.16)(2)$ *Substitute. Write the percent as a decimal.*

$I = 288$ *Multiply.*

The amount of interest is \$288.

PRACTICE

1. Find the simple interest earned after 2 years on an investment of \$3000 at 4.5% earned annually. **\$270**

Percent Change

7NS1.6

Percent change is an increase or decrease given as a percent of the original amount. **Percent increase** describes an amount that has grown. **Percent decrease** describes an amount that has been reduced.

EXAMPLE

A **Find the percent increase or decrease from 25 to 49.**

$\frac{\text{amount of change}}{\text{original amount}} = \frac{49 - 25}{25} = \frac{24}{25} = 0.96 = 96\%$

From 25 to 49 is a 96% increase.

B **Find the percent increase or decrease from 50 to 45.**

$\frac{\text{amount of change}}{\text{original amount}} = \frac{50 - 45}{50} = \frac{5}{50} = \frac{1}{10} = 10\%$

From 50 to 45 is a 10% decrease.

PRACTICE

Find each percent increase or decrease.

1. from 200 to 110 **45% decrease**
2. from 25 to 30 **20% increase**
3. from 80 to 115 **43.75% increase**
4. from 10 to 8 **20% decrease**

Translate from Words to Math

7AF1.1

Some words indicate certain math operations. Common math words and phrases are shown below. Some are listed in more than one column, so always read the problem carefully.

Addition	Subtraction	Multiplication	Division
add, plus, total, sum, more, more than, increased by, in all, combined	subtract, minus, difference, less, less than, more, more than, decreased by	multiply, times, of, product, per, for each, total	divide, divided by, quotient, divide equally, per, percent

EXAMPLE

A **Caroline saved \$42 in September, \$25 in October, and \$$d$ in November. How much money did she save in all?**

The words "in all" indicate addition.

$42 + 25 + d = 67 + d$

Caroline saved $(67 + d)$ dollars in all.

B **Jamal bought g gallons of gas for \$1.98 per gallon. What is the total amount he paid?**

The word "per" could mean multiplication or division. But "total" indicates multiplication.

$g \cdot 1.98 = 1.98g$

Jamal paid a total of \$1.98g.

PRACTICE

1. Sarah worked h hours this week and earned a total of \$112.50. How much does she earn per hour? What words tell you which operation to use? **$\frac{\$112.50}{h}$; per**
2. Lance biked m miles on Monday. On Thursday he biked 5.75 miles less than he did on Monday. How far did he bike on Thursday? What words tell you which operation to use? **$(m - 5.75)$ mi; less**

Cubic Functions

7AF3.1

In a **cubic function**, the greatest power of any variable term is 3. The simplest cubic function is $y = x^3$. Its graph is shown at right. Cubic equations can be solved by graphing the related function and finding the x-value when $y = 0$.

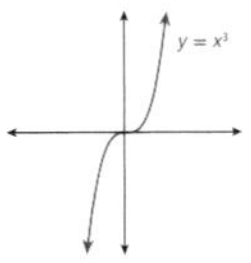

EXAMPLE **Graph $y = 2x^3$. Use the graph to solve $2x^3 = 0$.**

Create a table of ordered pairs. Then plot each point and connect them with a smooth curve.

To solve $2x^3 = 0$, find the value of x when $y = 0$. The solution is $x = 0$.

x	$y = 2x^3$	(x, y)
−2	$2(-2)^3 = 2(-8) = -16$	(−2, −16)
−1	$2(-1)^3 = 2(-1) = -2$	(−1, −2)
0	$2(0)^3 = 2(0) = 0$	(0, 0)
1	$2(1)^3 = 2(1) = 2$	(1, 2)
2	$2(2)^3 = 2(8) = 16$	(2, 16)

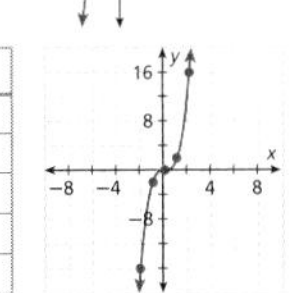

PRACTICE

Graph each cubic function. **See p. A34.**

1. $y = x^3 - 2$
2. $y = \frac{1}{2}x^3$
3. $y = x^3 + 1$
4. $y = -x^3$

Measurement

7MG1.1

The measurements for time are the same worldwide.

1 min = 60 s; 1 h = 60 min; 1 day = 24 h

1 wk = 7 days; 1 yr = 12 mo; 1 yr = 365 days

1 yr = 52 wk; 1 leap yr = 366 days

The **customary system** of measurement is used in the United States.

Length: 12 in. = 1 ft; 3 ft = 1 yd; 5280 ft = 1 mi

Capacity: 8 oz = 1 c; 2 c = 1 pt; 2 pt = 1 qt; 1 gal = 4 qt

Weight: 16 oz = 1 lb; 2000 lb = 1 ton

The **metric system** is used elsewhere and in science worldwide.

Length: 1 mm = 0.001 m; 1 cm = 10 mm; 1 m = 100 cm; 1 km = 1000 m

Capacity: 1 mL = 0.001 L; 1 kL = 1000 L

Mass: 1 g = 1000 mg; 1 kg = 1000 g

Use the table below to convert from metric to customary measurements.

Length	Capacity	Mass/Weight	Temperature
1 cm ≈ 0.394 in.	1 L ≈ 1.057 qt	1 g ≈ 0.0353 oz	$F = \left(\frac{9}{5} \cdot C\right) + 32$
1 m ≈ 3.281 ft	1 L ≈ 0.264 gal	1 kg ≈ 2.205 lb	
1 m ≈ 1.094 yd	1 L ≈ 4.227 c	1 kg ≈ 0.001 ton	
1 km ≈ 0.621 mi	1 mL ≈ 0.338 fl oz	1 metric T ≈ 1.102 ton	

Use the table below to convert from customary to metric measurements.

Length	Capacity	Weight/Mass	Temperature
1 in. ≈ 2.540 cm	1 qt ≈ 0.946 L	1 oz ≈ 28.350 g	$C = \frac{5}{9} \cdot (F - 32)$
1 ft ≈ 0.305 m	1 gal ≈ 3.785 L	1 lb ≈ 0.454 kg	
1 yd ≈ 0.914 m	1 c ≈ 0.237 L	1 ton ≈ 907.185 kg	
1 mi ≈ 1.609 km	1 fl oz ≈ 29.574 mL	1 ton ≈ 0.907 metric ton	

EXAMPLE

A **Write <, =, or >.**

35 in. ▒ 1 yd

35 in. ▒ 3 ft *1 yd = 3 ft*

35 in. < 36 in. *3 ft = 36 in.*

35 in. < 1 yd

B **Convert 32 km/h to mi/h.**

1 km/h ≈ 0.621 mi/h

32 km/h ≈ 32 · 0.621 mi/h

32 km/h ≈ 19.872 mi/h

C **Convert 25°C to °F.**

$F = \left(\frac{9}{5} \cdot 25\right) + 32$

$F = 45 + 32$

$F = 77°F$

PRACTICE

Write <, >, or =.

1. 3 lb **>** 40 oz
2. 200 cm **=** 2 m
3. 6 c **<** 2 qt

Convert.

4. 15 mi/h to km/h **24.135 km/h**
5. 2 weeks to hours **336 h**
6. 32 fl oz to mL **946.368 mL**
7. 95°F to °C **35°C**
8. 14 tons to kg **12,700.59 kg**

Complementary and Supplementary Angles

6MG2.1

Complementary angles are angles whose measures add to 90°. ∠1 and ∠2 are complementary.

Supplementary angles are angles whose measures add to 180°. ∠3 and ∠4 are supplementary.

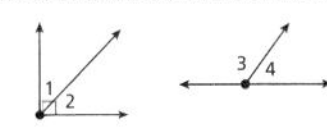

Complementary and supplementary angles may or may not be *adjacent* (have a ray in common).

EXAMPLE

A **The angles shown are complementary. Find the unknown angle measure.**

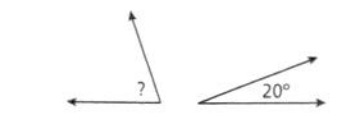

90 − 20 = 70°

B **The two angles that form a draw bridge are supplementary. One angle measures 30°. What is the measure of the other angle?**

180 − 30 = 150

The other angle measures 150°.

PRACTICE

1. Find the complement and supplement of a 48° angle. **complement: 42°; supplement: 132°**

Tell whether each pair of angles is complementary, supplementary, or neither.

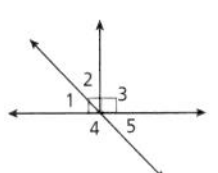

2. ∠1 and ∠4 **supplementary**
3. ∠2 and ∠3 **neither**
4. ∠1 and ∠2 **complementary**
5. ∠4 and ∠5 **supplementary**

Vertical Angles

6MG2.1

When two lines intersect, each pair of nonadjacent angles forms a pair of **vertical angles**. Vertical angles always have the same measure. In the section of fencing shown, there are two pairs of vertical angles: ∠1 and ∠3, ∠4 and ∠2.

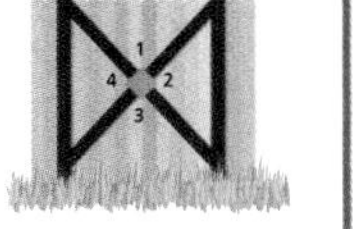

EXAMPLE **Find the measures of ∠BEC, ∠AEB, and ∠DEC.**

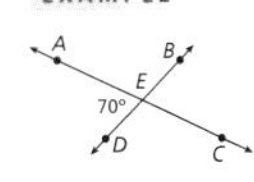

m∠BEC = 70° *∠AED and ∠BEC are vertical.*

m∠AEB = 110° *∠AED and ∠AEB are supplementary.*

m∠DEC = 110° *∠AEB and ∠DEC are vertical.*

PRACTICE

1. Name two pairs of vertical angles. **∠VZW and ∠YZX; ∠VZY and ∠WZX**

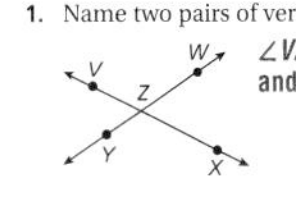

2. Find m∠PTS, m∠PTQ, and m∠QTR. **m∠PTS = 65°; m∠PTQ = 115°; m∠QTR = 65°**

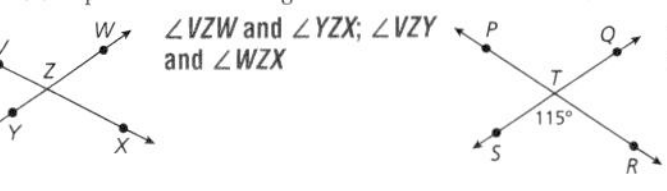

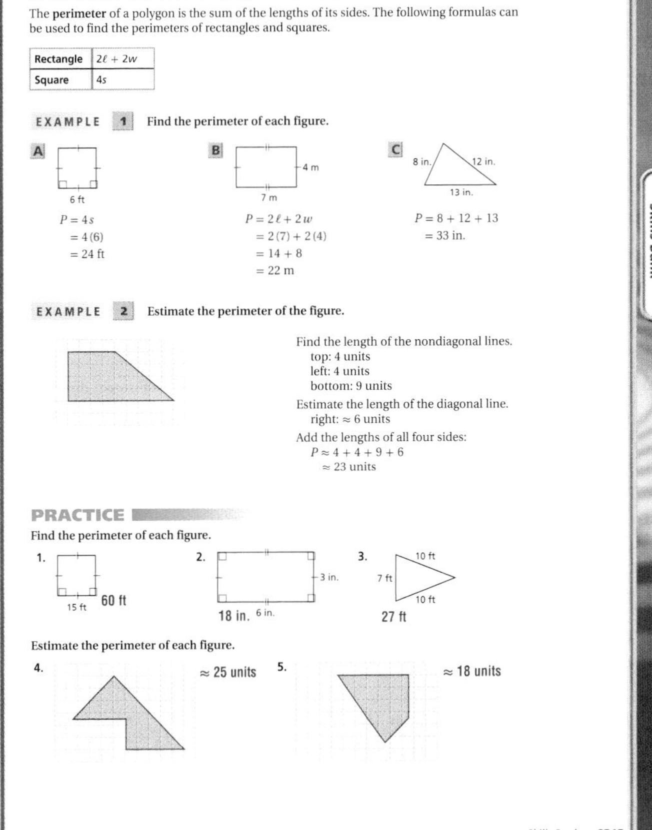

Perimeter

7MG2.1

The **perimeter** of a polygon is the sum of the lengths of its sides. The following formulas can be used to find the perimeters of rectangles and squares.

Rectangle	$2\ell + 2w$
Square	$4s$

EXAMPLE 1 **Find the perimeter of each figure.**

A (6 ft)

$P = 4s$
$= 4(6)$
$= 24$ ft

B (4 m, 7 m)

$P = 2\ell + 2w$
$= 2(7) + 2(4)$
$= 14 + 8$
$= 22$ m

C (8 in., 12 in., 13 in.)

$P = 8 + 12 + 13$
$= 33$ in.

EXAMPLE 2 **Estimate the perimeter of the figure.**

Find the length of the nondiagonal lines.
top: 4 units
left: 4 units
bottom: 9 units

Estimate the length of the diagonal line.
right: ≈ 6 units

Add the lengths of all four sides:
$P \approx 4 + 4 + 9 + 6$
≈ 23 units

PRACTICE

Find the perimeter of each figure.

1. (15 ft) **60 ft**
2. (3 in., 6 in.) **18 in.**
3. (10 ft, 7 ft, 10 ft) **27 ft**

Estimate the perimeter of each figure.

4. **≈ 25 units**
5. **≈ 18 units**

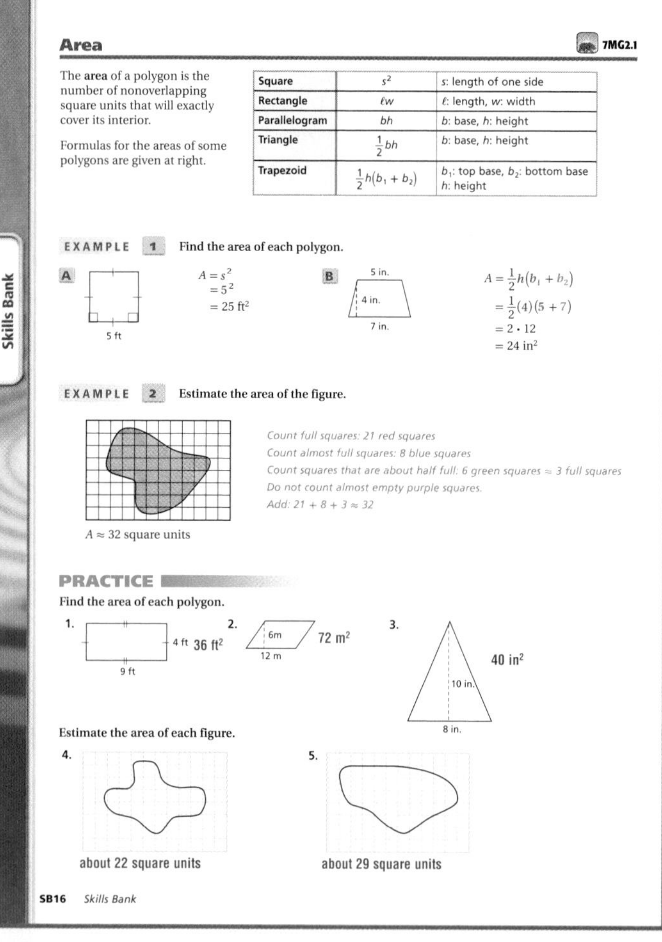

Area

7MG2.1

The **area** of a polygon is the number of nonoverlapping square units that will exactly cover its interior.

Formulas for the areas of some polygons are given at right.

Square	s^2	s: length of one side
Rectangle	ℓw	ℓ: length, w: width
Parallelogram	bh	b: base, h: height
Triangle	$\frac{1}{2}bh$	b: base, h: height
Trapezoid	$\frac{1}{2}h(b_1 + b_2)$	b_1: top base, b_2: bottom base; h: height

EXAMPLE 1 Find the area of each polygon.

A (5 ft)
$A = s^2$
$= 5^2$
$= 25 \text{ ft}^2$

B (5 in., 4 in., 7 in.)
$A = \frac{1}{2}h(b_1 + b_2)$
$= \frac{1}{2}(4)(5 + 7)$
$= 2 \cdot 12$
$= 24 \text{ in}^2$

EXAMPLE 2 Estimate the area of the figure.

Count full squares: 21 red squares
Count almost full squares: 8 blue squares
Count squares that are about half full: 6 green squares ≈ 3 full squares
Do not count almost empty purple squares.
Add: 21 + 8 + 3 ≈ 32

$A \approx 32$ square units

PRACTICE

Find the area of each polygon.

1. (4 ft, 9 ft) **36 ft²**
2. (6m, 12 m) **72 m²**
3. (10 in., 8 in.) **40 in²**

Estimate the area of each figure.

4. **about 22 square units**
5. **about 29 square units**

SB16 *Skills Bank*

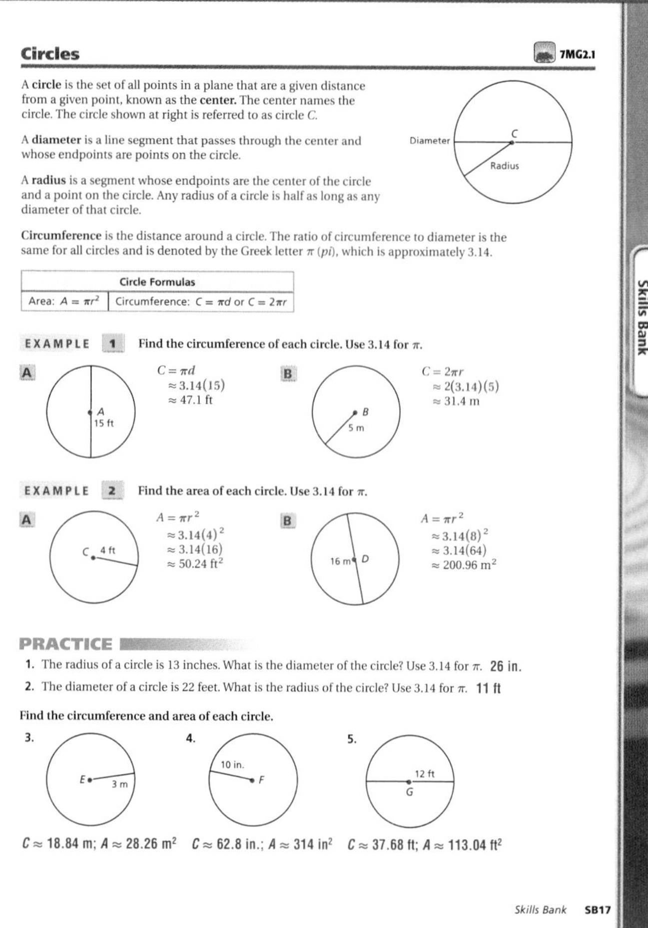

Circles

7MG2.1

A **circle** is the set of all points in a plane that are a given distance from a given point, known as the **center.** The center names the circle. The circle shown at right is referred to as circle C.

A **diameter** is a line segment that passes through the center and whose endpoints are points on the circle.

A **radius** is a segment whose endpoints are the center of the circle and a point on the circle. Any radius of a circle is half as long as any diameter of that circle.

Circumference is the distance around a circle. The ratio of circumference to diameter is the same for all circles and is denoted by the Greek letter π (*pi*), which is approximately 3.14.

Circle Formulas	
Area: $A = \pi r^2$	Circumference: $C = \pi d$ or $C = 2\pi r$

EXAMPLE 1 Find the circumference of each circle. Use 3.14 for π.

A (A, 15 ft)
$C = \pi d$
$\approx 3.14(15)$
≈ 47.1 ft

B (B, 5 m)
$C = 2\pi r$
$\approx 2(3.14)(5)$
≈ 31.4 m

EXAMPLE 2 Find the area of each circle. Use 3.14 for π.

A (C, 4 ft)
$A = \pi r^2$
$\approx 3.14(4)^2$
$\approx 3.14(16)$
$\approx 50.24 \text{ ft}^2$

B (16 m, D)
$A = \pi r^2$
$\approx 3.14(8)^2$
$\approx 3.14(64)$
$\approx 200.96 \text{ m}^2$

PRACTICE

1. The radius of a circle is 13 inches. What is the diameter of the circle? Use 3.14 for π. **26 in.**
2. The diameter of a circle is 22 feet. What is the radius of the circle? Use 3.14 for π. **11 ft**

Find the circumference and area of each circle.

3. (E, 3 m) **$C \approx 18.84$ m; $A \approx 28.26 \text{ m}^2$**
4. (10 in., F) **$C \approx 62.8$ in.; $A \approx 314 \text{ in}^2$**
5. (12 ft, G) **$C \approx 37.68$ ft; $A \approx 113.04 \text{ ft}^2$**

Skills Bank SB17

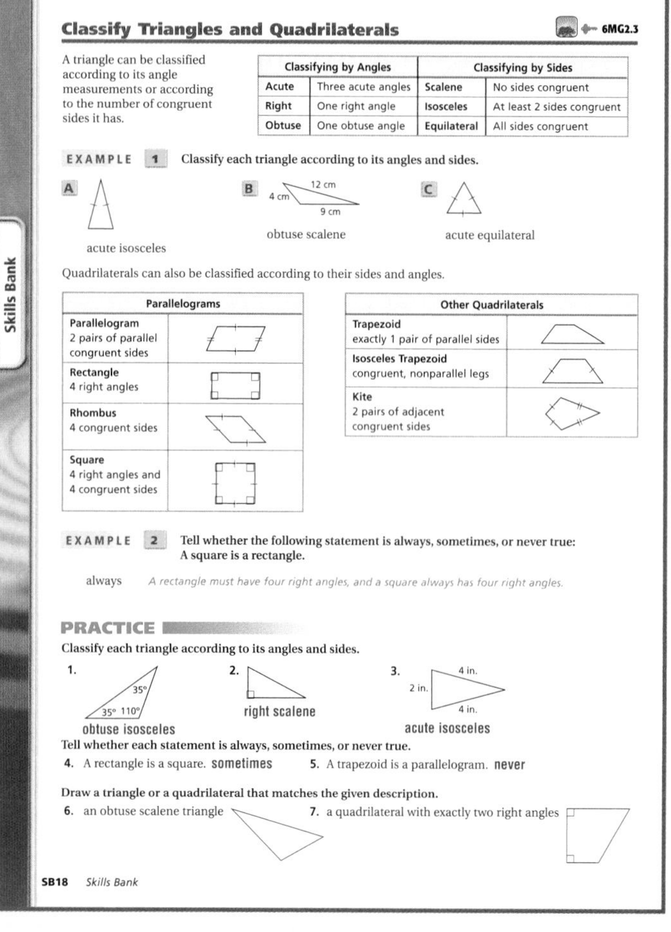

Classify Triangles and Quadrilaterals

6MG2.3

A triangle can be classified according to its angle measurements or according to the number of congruent sides it has.

Classifying by Angles		Classifying by Sides	
Acute	Three acute angles	Scalene	No sides congruent
Right	One right angle	Isosceles	At least 2 sides congruent
Obtuse	One obtuse angle	Equilateral	All sides congruent

EXAMPLE 1 Classify each triangle according to its angles and sides.

A acute isosceles

B (12 cm, 4 cm, 9 cm) obtuse scalene

C acute equilateral

Quadrilaterals can also be classified according to their sides and angles.

Parallelograms
Parallelogram 2 pairs of parallel congruent sides
Rectangle 4 right angles
Rhombus 4 congruent sides
Square 4 right angles and 4 congruent sides

Other Quadrilaterals
Trapezoid exactly 1 pair of parallel sides
Isosceles Trapezoid congruent, nonparallel legs
Kite 2 pairs of adjacent congruent sides

EXAMPLE 2 Tell whether the following statement is always, sometimes, or never true: A square is a rectangle.

always *A rectangle must have four right angles, and a square always has four right angles.*

PRACTICE

Classify each triangle according to its angles and sides.

1. (35°, 35°, 110°) **obtuse isosceles**
2. **right scalene**
3. (4 in., 2 in., 4 in.) **acute isosceles**

Tell whether each statement is always, sometimes, or never true.

4. A rectangle is a square. **sometimes**
5. A trapezoid is a parallelogram. **never**

Draw a triangle or a quadrilateral that matches the given description.

6. an obtuse scalene triangle
7. a quadrilateral with exactly two right angles

SB18 *Skills Bank*

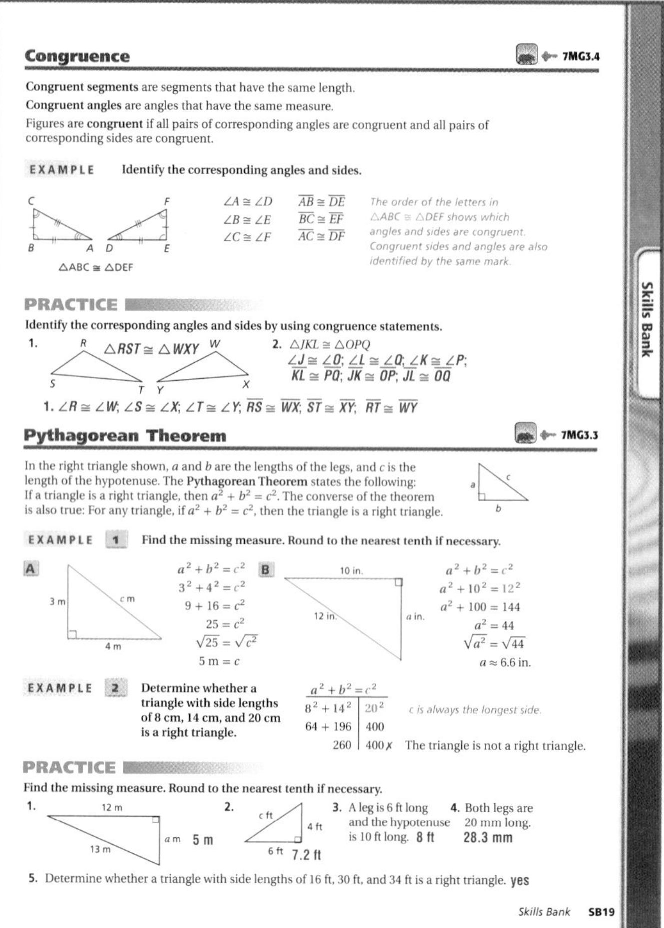

Congruence

7MG3.4

Congruent segments are segments that have the same length.

Congruent angles are angles that have the same measure.

Figures are **congruent** if all pairs of corresponding angles are congruent and all pairs of corresponding sides are congruent.

EXAMPLE Identify the corresponding angles and sides.

$\triangle ABC \cong \triangle DEF$

$\angle A \cong \angle D$ $\quad \overline{AB} \cong \overline{DE}$
$\angle B \cong \angle E$ $\quad \overline{BC} \cong \overline{EF}$
$\angle C \cong \angle F$ $\quad \overline{AC} \cong \overline{DF}$

The order of the letters in △ABC ≅ △DEF shows which angles and sides are congruent. Congruent sides and angles are also identified by the same mark.

PRACTICE

Identify the corresponding angles and sides by using congruence statements.

1. **$\triangle RST \cong \triangle WXY$**
2. $\triangle JKL \cong \triangle OPQ$ **$\angle J \cong \angle O$; $\angle L \cong \angle Q$; $\angle K \cong \angle P$; $\overline{KL} \cong \overline{PQ}$; $\overline{JK} \cong \overline{OP}$; $\overline{JL} \cong \overline{OQ}$**

1. **$\angle R \cong \angle W$; $\angle S \cong \angle X$; $\angle T \cong \angle Y$; $\overline{RS} \cong \overline{WX}$; $\overline{ST} \cong \overline{XY}$; $\overline{RT} \cong \overline{WY}$**

Pythagorean Theorem

7MG3.3

In the right triangle shown, a and b are the lengths of the legs, and c is the length of the hypotenuse. The **Pythagorean Theorem** states the following: If a triangle is a right triangle, then $a^2 + b^2 = c^2$. The converse of the theorem is also true: For any triangle, if $a^2 + b^2 = c^2$, then the triangle is a right triangle.

EXAMPLE 1 Find the missing measure. Round to the nearest tenth if necessary.

A (3 m, 4 m, c m)
$a^2 + b^2 = c^2$
$3^2 + 4^2 = c^2$
$9 + 16 = c^2$
$25 = c^2$
$\sqrt{25} = \sqrt{c^2}$
$5 \text{ m} = c$

B (10 in., 12 in., a in.)
$a^2 + b^2 = c^2$
$a^2 + 10^2 = 12^2$
$a^2 + 100 = 144$
$a^2 = 44$
$\sqrt{a^2} = \sqrt{44}$
$a \approx 6.6$ in.

EXAMPLE 2 Determine whether a triangle with side lengths of 8 cm, 14 cm, and 20 cm is a right triangle.

$a^2 + b^2$	$= c^2$
$8^2 + 14^2$	20^2
$64 + 196$	400
260	400 ✗

c is always the longest side.

The triangle is not a right triangle.

PRACTICE

Find the missing measure. Round to the nearest tenth if necessary.

1. (12 m, 13 m, a m) **5 m**
2. (c ft, 4 ft, 6 ft) **7.2 ft**
3. A leg is 6 ft long and the hypotenuse is 10 ft long. **8 ft**
4. Both legs are 20 mm long. **28.3 mm**
5. Determine whether a triangle with side lengths of 16 ft, 30 ft, and 34 ft is a right triangle. **yes**

Skills Bank SB19

Three-Dimensional Figures

7MG3.6

Polyhedrons are three-dimensional figures made up of polygons which are called **faces.** The sides where faces intersect are **edges.** Any point where three or more edges intersect is a **vertex.**

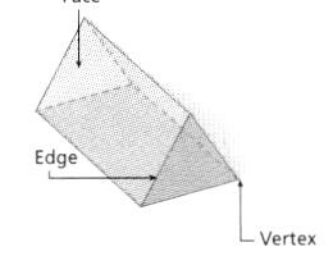

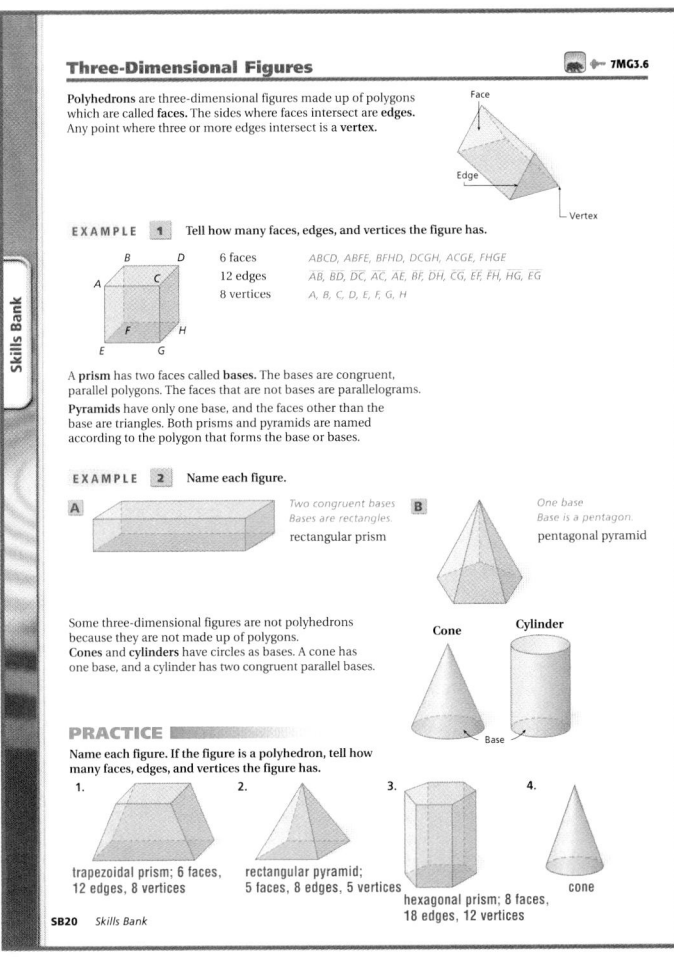

EXAMPLE 1 Tell how many faces, edges, and vertices the figure has.

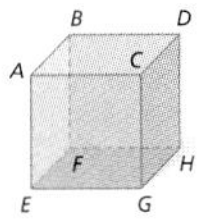

6 faces — *ABCD, ABFE, BFHD, DCGH, ACGE, FHGE*
12 edges — $\overline{AB}, \overline{BD}, \overline{DC}, \overline{AC}, \overline{AE}, \overline{BF}, \overline{DH}, \overline{CG}, \overline{EF}, \overline{FH}, \overline{HG}, \overline{EG}$
8 vertices — *A, B, C, D, E, F, G, H*

A **prism** has two faces called **bases.** The bases are congruent, parallel polygons. The faces that are not bases are parallelograms.

Pyramids have only one base, and the faces other than the base are triangles. Both prisms and pyramids are named according to the polygon that forms the base or bases.

EXAMPLE 2 Name each figure.

A 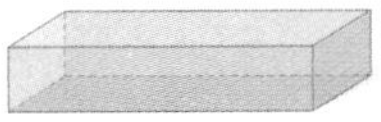
Two congruent bases
Bases are rectangles.
rectangular prism

B 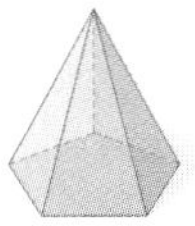
One base
Base is a pentagon.
pentagonal pyramid

Some three-dimensional figures are not polyhedrons because they are not made up of polygons. **Cones** and **cylinders** have circles as bases. A cone has one base, and a cylinder has two congruent parallel bases.

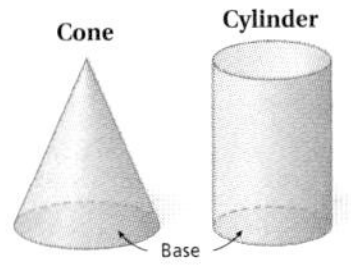

PRACTICE

Name each figure. If the figure is a polyhedron, tell how many faces, edges, and vertices the figure has.

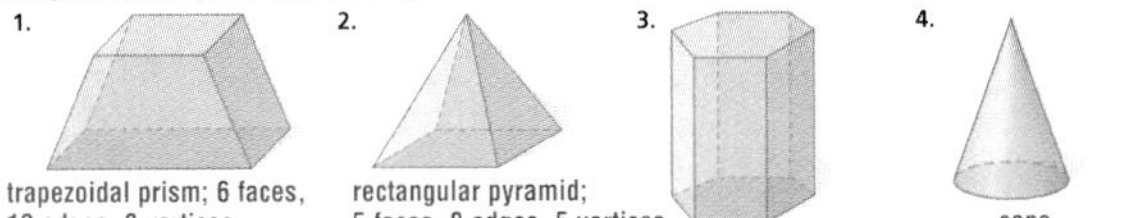

1. trapezoidal prism; 6 faces, 12 edges, 8 vertices
2. rectangular pyramid; 5 faces, 8 edges, 5 vertices
3. hexagonal prism; 8 faces, 18 edges, 12 vertices
4. cone

Volume

7MG2.1

The **volume** of a three-dimensional figure is the number of nonoverlapping cubic units that will exactly fill its interior. The formulas for the volumes of some types of three-dimensional figures are given in the table.

Notice that a cube is listed in the table. A cube is a prism, so the formula for a prism can be used; however, since all sides in a cube are congruent, the formula s^3 is more convenient.

Prism	Bh	*B*: area of base *h*: height of prism
Cube	s^3	*s*: length of one side
Pyramid	$\frac{1}{3}Bh$	*B*: area of base *h*: height of pyramid
Cylinder	$\pi r^2 h$	*r*: radius *h*: height
Cone	$\frac{1}{3}\pi r^2 h$	*r*: radius *h*: height

EXAMPLE 1 Find the volume of each figure. Use 3.14 for π.

A 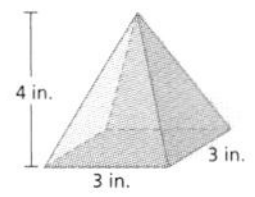

$$V = \frac{1}{3}Bh = \frac{1}{3}(9)(4) = 3(4) = 12 \text{ in}^3$$

B 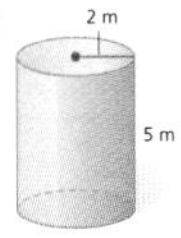

$$V = \pi r^2 h \approx 3.14(2)^2(5) \approx 3.14(4)(5) \approx 62.8 \text{ m}^3$$

EXAMPLE 2 Estimate the volume of the figure.

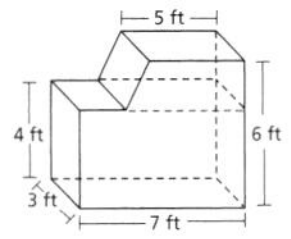

Find the volume of the rectangular prism (bottom part):
$Bh = 21(4) = 84$

Estimate the top part as a rectangular prism with $w = 3$ ft, $\ell = 5$ ft, and $h = 6 \text{ ft} - 4 \text{ ft} = 2$ ft.
$Bh = 15(2) = 30$

Add the volumes of the two prisms:
$84 + 30 = 114$

The volume is approximately 114 ft^3.

PRACTICE

Find or estimate the volume of each figure. Use 3.14 for π.

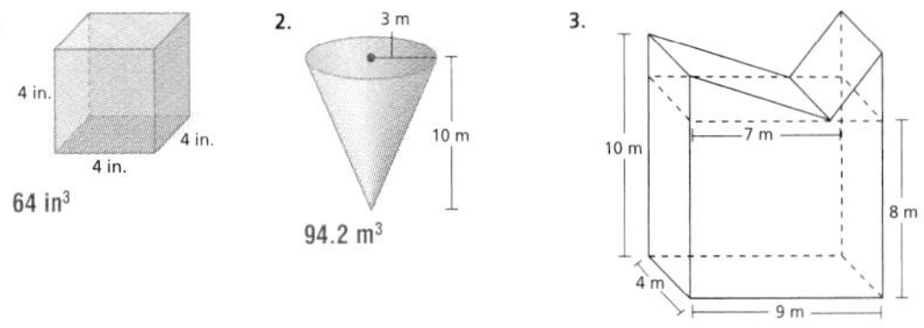

1. 64 in^3
2. 94.2 m^3
3. between 288 m^3 and 360 m^3

Surface Area

7MG2.1

The **surface area** of a three-dimensional figure is the sum of the areas of its surfaces.

Formulas for the surface areas of some three-dimensional figures are given in the table.

Prism	$2B + Ph$	*B*: area of base *P*: perimeter of base *h*: height
Pyramid	$B + \frac{1}{2}P\ell$	*B*: area of base *P*: perimeter of base ℓ: slant height
Cube	$6s^2$	*s*: length of one side
Cylinder	$2\pi r^2 + 2\pi rh$	*r*: radius; *h*: height
Cone	$\pi r^2 + \pi r\ell$	*r*: radius; ℓ: slant height

EXAMPLE 1 Find the surface area of each figure. Use 3.14 for π.

A 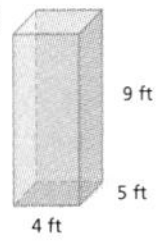

$$S = 2B + Ph = 2(20) + 18(9) = 40 + 162 = 202 \text{ ft}^2$$

B 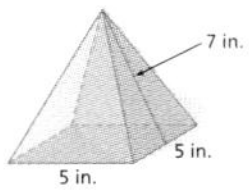

$$S = B + \frac{1}{2}P\ell = 25 + \frac{1}{2}(20)(7) = 25 + 70 = 95 \text{ in}^2$$

C 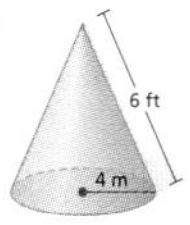

$$S = \pi r^2 + \pi r\ell \approx 3.14(4)^2 + 3.14(4)(6) \approx 50.24 + 75.36 \approx 125.6 \text{ m}^2$$

EXAMPLE 2 The net of a prism is shown below. Estimate the surface area of the prism.

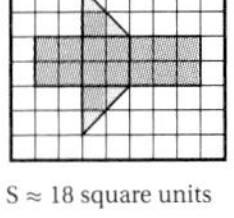

Count full squares: 16 red squares
Count squares that are about half full: 4 blue squares ≈ 2 full squares
Add: 16 + 2 = 18

S ≈ 18 square units

PRACTICE

Find or estimate the surface area of each figure. Use 3.14 for π.

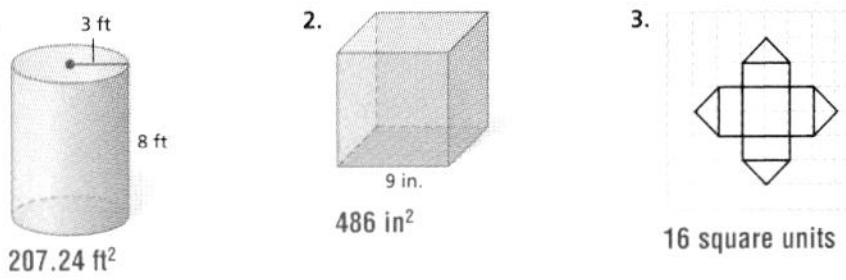

1. 207.24 ft^2
2. 486 in^2
3. 16 square units

The Coordinate Plane

The **coordinate plane** is formed by the intersection of two perpendicular number lines called **axes.** The point of intersection, called the **origin,** is at 0 on each number line. The horizontal number line is called the ***x*-axis,** and the vertical number line is called the ***y*-axis.**

Points on the coordinate plane are described using ordered pairs. An **ordered pair** consists of an ***x*-coordinate** and a ***y*-coordinate** and is written (x, y). Points are often named with a capital letter.

The axes divide the coordinate plane into four **quadrants.** Points that lie on an axis are not in any quadrant.

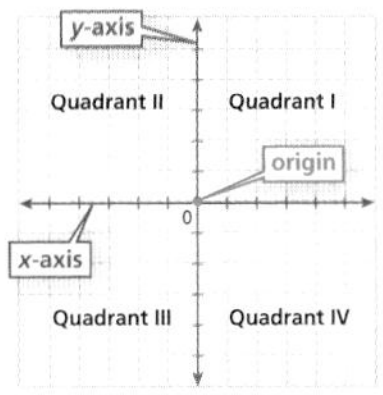

EXAMPLE 1 Graph each point.

A $M(3, 4)$
Start at the origin.
Move 3 units right and 4 units up.

B $N(-2, 0)$
Start at the origin.
Move 2 units left.

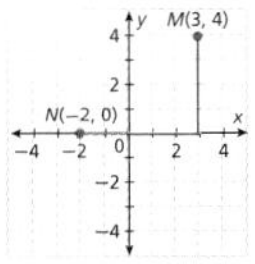

EXAMPLE 2 Name the quadrant in which each point lies.

A *P*
Quadrant III

B *Q*
Quadrant II

C *R*
no quadrant (*x*-axis)

D *S*
Quadrant IV

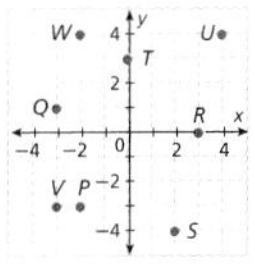

PRACTICE

Graph each point.

1. $R(2, -3)$
2. $S(0, 2)$
3. $T(-2, 6)$
4. $J(4, 5)$
5. $K(-3, 2)$
6. $L(6, 0)$

1–6. 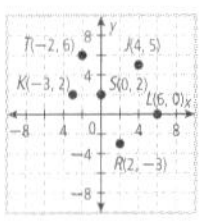

Use the graph in Example 2 to name the quadrant in which each point lies.

7. *T* none
8. *U* Q I
9. *V* Q III

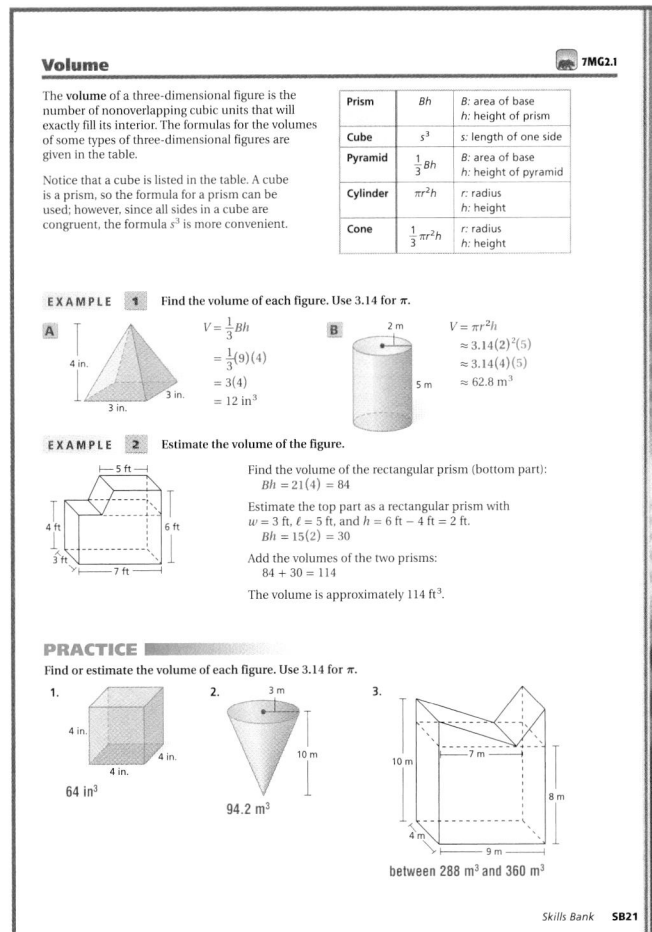

Transformations in the Coordinate Plane

7MG3.2

A **transformation** is a change in the size or position of a figure. If the **preimage,** or original figure, is named *ABC*, then the transformed figure, or **image,** is named *A′B′C′*. Transformations include **translations** (slides), **reflections** (flips), and **rotations** (turns), for which preimages and images are congruent.

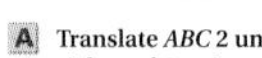

EXAMPLE 1

A **Translate *ABC* 2 units right and 1 unit up.**

B **Reflect *ABC* across the *y*-axis.**

C **Rotate *ABC* 90° clockwise about point *A*.**

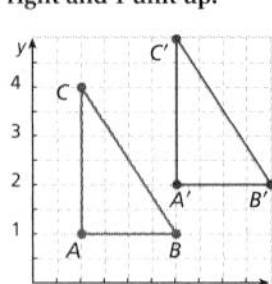

Move each vertex 2 units right and 1 unit up.

The y-axis is a line of symmetry.

A′ is the same as A. Maintain the same side lengths on the image.

EXAMPLE 2 **Could *ABCD* be transformed into *A′B′C′D′*? Explain.**

The figures are congruent, so a translation, rotation, or reflection is possible. Study the figures. If A′ B′ C′ D′ is translated 1 unit right, both figures would be symmetric about the x-axis.

ABCD can be transformed into *A′B′C′D′* by reflecting it across the *x*-axis and translating it 1 unit left.

PRACTICE

1. Translate *ABCD* 2 units left and 4 units down.

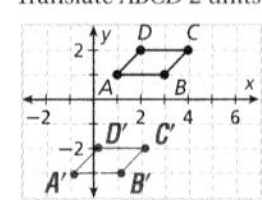

2. Graph $A(1, -2)$, $B(3, -2)$, and $C(2, -4)$. Rotate *ABC* 90° counterclockwise about *A* and reflect it across the *x*-axis.

Use the graph for Exercises 3 and 4.

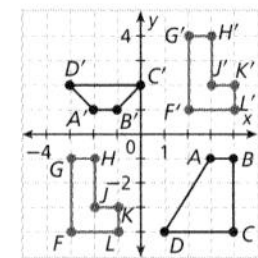

3. Could *ABCD* be transformed into *A′B′C′D′*? Explain. **No; they are not the same shape.**
4. Could *FGHJKL* be transformed into *F′G′H′J′K′L′*? Explain. **Yes; translate 5 units up and 5 right.**

Measures of Central Tendency

6SDAP1.1

Measures of central tendency are values that represent a data set and can be considered typical of the set. These measures are the *mean, median,* and *mode.*

	It is...	Find by...
Mean	The average.	Adding the data values and dividing by the number of values.
Median	The "middle value."	First ordering the data values from least to greatest. If there are an *odd* number of values, the median is the middle number. If there are an *even* number of values, the median is the mean of the two middle values.
Mode	The value or values that occur most often. If every value occurs the same number of times, the data set has no mode.	Choosing the value or values that occur more often than any other.

EXAMPLE **Find the mean, median, and mode of each data set.**

A **18, 22, 13, 16, 15, 18, 10**

mean:

$\frac{18 + 22 + 13 + 16 + 15 + 18 + 10}{7} = \frac{112}{7} = 16$

The mean is 16.

median:

Order the data values from least to greatest. There are an odd number of values. Choose the middle number.

10, 13, 15, (16), 18, 18, 22

The median is 16.

mode:

Every value occurs once except 18, which occurs twice.

The mode is 18.

B **These are the number of people who attended a seminar each of four days: 102, 96, 88, 109.**

mean: $\frac{102 + 96 + 88 + 109}{4} = \frac{395}{4} = 98.75$

The mean is 98.75.

median:

Order the data values from least to greatest. There are an even number of values. Find the mean of the two middle numbers.

88, (96, 102), 109

$\frac{96 + 102}{2} = \frac{198}{2} = 99$

The median is 99.

mode:

Every value occurs once.

There is no mode.

PRACTICE

Find the mean, median, and mode of each data set.

1.

High Temperatures (°F)						
Sun	Mon	Tue	Wed	Thu	Fri	Sat
85	81	83	85	86	82	84

mean: 83.71°F; median: 84°F; mode: 85°F

2. These are the ages of the students in an after-school club: 14, 15, 14, 16, 15, 17, 14, 15. **mean: 15; median: 15; modes: 14 and 15**
3. Jenny took a survey of her classmates to find out how much they each paid for their notebooks. Here are their responses: 85¢, 55¢, 80¢, 85¢, 75¢, 95¢, 85¢, 75¢, 67¢. **mean: 78¢; median: 80¢; mode: 85¢**

Sampling

6SDAP2.5

A **population** is a group that someone is gathering information about.

A **sample** is part of a population. For example, if 5 students are chosen to represent a class of 20 students, the 5 chosen students are a sample of the population of 20 students.

The sample is a **random sample** if every member of the population has an equal chance of being chosen for the sample.

EXAMPLE **Explain whether each sample is random.**

A **Carlos wrote the name of each student in his class on a slip of paper and put the papers into a hat. Then, without looking at the slips, he drew the names of the students who would complete his survey.**

Each name is in the hat once, so each has an equal chance of being selected. The sample is random.

B **Jamal telephoned people on a list of 100 names in the order in which they appeared. He surveyed the first 20 people who answered their phone.**

Names at the beginning of the list have a greater chance of being selected than those at the end of the list, so the sample is not random.

PRACTICE

Explain whether each sample is random.

1. Rebecca surveyed every person in a theater who was sitting in a seat along the aisle. **Not random; people not sitting in an aisle seat have no chance of being chosen.**
2. Inez assigned 50 people a number from 1 to 50. Then she used a calculator to generate 10 random numbers from 1 to 50 and surveyed those with matching numbers. **Random; every person had a number that the calculator could have selected.**

Bias

6SDAP2.5

Bias is error that favors part of a population and/or does not accurately represent the population. Bias can occur from using sampling methods that are not random or from asking confusing or leading questions.

EXAMPLE **Explain why each survey is biased.**

A **Jenn went to a movie theater and asked people who exited if they agree that the theater should be torn down to build office space.**

People usually only go to movies if they enjoy them, so those exiting a movie theater would not want it torn down. People who do not use the theater did not have a chance to answer.

B **A student asked, "A new cafeteria would mean that loud construction would take place for several weeks. Also, the hallways would become even more congested in that area. Do you want a new cafeteria?"**

The question only mentions the bad things that could come from a new cafeteria, not the good ones, such as better food or more seats.

PRACTICE

Explain why each survey is biased. **See p. A35.**

1. A surveyor asked, "Is it not true that you do not oppose the candidate's views?"
2. Brendan asked everyone on his track team how they thought the money from the athletic department fund-raiser should be spent.

Bar Graphs and Histograms

7SDAP1.1

A **bar graph** displays data using vertical or horizontal bars that do not touch.

A **histogram** is a bar graph used to display the frequency of data divided into equal intervals. The bars must be of equal width and should touch, but not overlap.

EXAMPLE **Use the data in the table to make a bar graph.**

Livestock Show Entries					
Animal	Chicken	Goat	Horse	Pig	Sheep
Number	38	10	32	12	25

Step 1 Determine an appropriate scale. The scale must include all data values. The scale is separated into equal parts called intervals.

Step 2 Use the data to determine the lengths of the bars. Draw bars of equal width that do not touch.

Step 3 Title the graph. Label the horizontal and vertical scales.

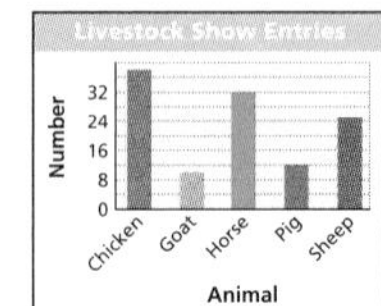

PRACTICE

1. Use the data in the table to make a histogram. **See p. A35.**

Damien's Math Test Scores					
75	84	68	72	59	88
72	77	81	84	60	70

Box and Whisker Plots

7SDAP1.1

A **box-and-whisker plot** is a graph showing the **lower extreme** (the least value), the **upper extreme** (the greatest value), the median, the **lower quartile** (the median of the lower half of the data), and the **upper quartile** (the median of the upper half of the data).

EXAMPLE **Use the data to make a box-and-whisker plot.**

3	4	8	12	7	5	4	12	3	9	9
11	4	14	8	2	10	3	10	11	4	

Step 1 Order the data from least to greatest. Find the lower extreme, the upper extreme, the lower quartile, the **upper quartile,** and the median.

2, 3, 3, 3, 4, 4, 4, 4, 5, 7, 8, 8, 9, 9, 10, 10, 11, 11, 12, 12, 14

Step 2 Draw a number line and plot a point above each value from Step 1. Draw a box through the lower and upper quartiles and a vertical line through the median. Draw lines (whiskers) from the box to the upper and lower extremes.

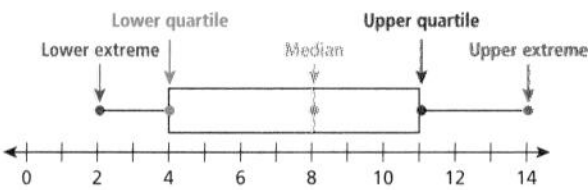

PRACTICE

1. Use the data to make a box-and whisker plot. **See p. A35.**
13, 14, 18, 13, 12, 17, 15, 12, 13, 19, 11, 14, 14, 18, 22, 23

Circle Graphs

7SDAP1.1

A **circle graph** shows parts of a whole. The entire circle represents 100% of the data, and each sector represents a percent of the total.

EXAMPLE **Use the data to make a circle graph.**

Crop	Acres	% of total acres	Degrees of circle
Corn	70	$\frac{70}{200} = 35\%$	$0.35(360) = 126°$
Fallow	50	$\frac{50}{200} = 25\%$	$0.25(360) = 90°$
Mixed vegetables	10	$\frac{10}{200} = 5\%$	$0.05(360) = 18°$
Soybeans	40	$\frac{40}{200} = 20\%$	$0.2(360) = 72°$
Wheat	30	$\frac{30}{200} = 15\%$	$0.15(360) = 54°$

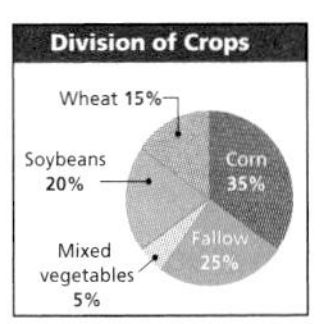

PRACTICE

1. Use the data to make a circle graph.

Degrees Held by Faculty		
PhD	Master's	Bachelor's
7	24	31

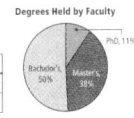

Degrees Held by Faculty: PhD, 11%; Bachelor's, 50%; Master's, 38%

Venn Diagrams

7SDAP1.1

Venn diagrams are used to show relationships between two or more sets of numbers or objects. They show which elements are common between sets.

EXAMPLE **In a group of 15 students, 10 play basketball or baseball, 5 play basketball, and 3 play both sports. Draw a Venn diagram. How many students play baseball?**

Draw two overlapping ovals, one for each sport. Three students will be in the overlapping region. Since 5 students play basketball, and 3 of them also play baseball, 2 students play only basketball.

There are 10 student players in all, and 5 are already represented in the graph. Therefore, the remaining 5 play only baseball.

Adding the 3 students who also play basketball, a total of 8 students play baseball.

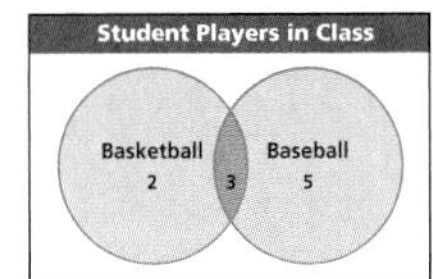

PRACTICE

In a group of 138 people, 55 own a cat, 27 own a cat and a dog, and 42 own neither pet.

1. How many people own only a cat? **28**
2. How many people own a dog? **68**

Theoretical Probability

6SDAP3.3

An **experiment** is an activity involving chance that can have different results. Flipping a coin and rolling a number cube are examples of experiments.

The different results that can occur are called **outcomes** of the experiment. If you are flipping a coin, "heads" is a possible outcome. An **event** is an outcome or set of outcomes in an experiment. **Probability** is a measure of how likely a particular event is to occur. The higher the probability, the more likely the event will occur.

When all possible outcomes have the same chance of occurring, the outcomes are said to be **equally likely.** The **theoretical probability** of an event is the ratio of the number of ways the event can occur to the total number of equally likely outcomes.

$$\text{Theoretical probability} = \frac{\text{number of ways the event can occur}}{\text{total number of equally likely outcomes}}$$

EXAMPLE 1 **Find the theoretical probability of rolling a 3 on a fair number cube.**

$$\text{Theoretical probability} = \frac{\text{number of ways the event can occur}}{\text{total number of equally likely outcomes}}$$

$= \frac{1}{6}$ ← There is one 3 on a number cube. ← There are 6 equally likely outcomes on a number cube.

$= 0.1\overline{6}$

$= 16\frac{2}{3}\%$

The **complement of an event** is the set of all possible outcomes that are not included in the event. The sum of the probabilities of an event and its complement is 1, or 100%, because every event will either happen or not happen.

EXAMPLE 2 **The weather forecaster predicts a 20% chance of snow. What is the probability that it will not snow?**

$P(\text{snow}) + P(\text{not snow}) = 100\%$ *Either it will snow or it will not snow.*

$20\% + P(\text{not snow}) = 100\%$ *P(snow) = 20%*

$-20\% \qquad -20\%$ *Subtract 20% from both sides.*

$P(\text{not snow}) = 80\%$

PRACTICE

An experiment consists of rolling a fair number cube. Find the theoretical probability of each outcome.

1. rolling a 1 or a 6 **$33.\overline{3}\%$**
2. rolling an even number **50%**
3. rolling a multiple of 3 **$33.\overline{3}\%$**
4. rolling a number greater than 5 **$16.\overline{6}\%$**
5. A jar has green, blue, purple, and white marbles. The probability of choosing a green marble is 0.2, the probability of choosing blue is 0.3, and the probability of choosing purple is 0.1. What is the probability of choosing white? **0.4**

Experimental Probability

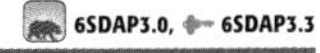
6SDAP3.0, 6SDAP3.3

Performing an experiment is one way to estimate the probability of an event. If an experiment is repeated many times, the **experimental probability** of an event is the ratio of the number of times the event occurs to the total number of times the experiment is performed. Each time that the experiment is performed is a **trial**. The more trials performed, the more accurate the experimental probability will be.

$$\text{Experimental probability} = \frac{\text{number of times the event occurs}}{\text{total number of trials}}$$

EXAMPLE **Ian tossed a coin 30 times and recorded whether the result was "heads" or "tails." Based on Ian's results, what is the experimental probability that the next toss will be "heads"?**

Heads	~~||||~~ ~~||||~~ ~~||||~~ |
Tails	~~||||~~ ~~||||~~ ||||

$$\text{Experimental probability} = \frac{\text{number of times the event occurs}}{\text{total number of trials}}$$

$P(\text{heads}) = \frac{16}{30}$

$= \frac{8}{15}$

The experimental probability that Ian's next toss will be "heads" is $\frac{8}{15}$.

PRACTICE

Jennifer has a bag of marbles. She removed one marble, recorded the color, and placed it back in the bag. She repeated this process several times and recorded her results in the table.

Use the table for Exercises 1 and 2.

White	~~||||~~
Red	|||
Yellow	~~||||~~
Black	~~||||~~ ~~||||~~ ||

1. Based on Jennifer's results, find the experimental probability that a marble selected from the bag will be red. **12%**
2. Find the experimental probability that a marble selected from the bag will NOT be black. **52%**
3. One game of bowling consists of ten frames. Elise usually rolls 3 strikes in each game. What is the experimental probability that Elise will roll a strike in a particular frame? **30%**
4. A manufacturer inspects 800 light bulbs and finds that 796 of them have no defects. What is the experimental probability that a randomly chosen light bulb from this manufacturer will have no defects? **99.5%**
5. Ms. Bleakman checks 32 papers and finds 2 with no name. What is the experimental probability that a paper chosen at random will have no name? **6.25%**
6. A tennis player served the ball 16 times and 2 of those serves were aces (unreturned serves). What is the experimental probability that the player's next serve will be an ace? **12.5%**

Compound Events

6SDAP3.1

A **compound event** consists of two or more single events.

EXAMPLE **Christine rolls a fair number cube and then tosses a fair coin. Find the probability that the number cube will show an even number and that the coin will show "heads."**

	1	2	3	4	5	6
H	1,H	2,H	3,H	4,H	5,H	6,H
T	1,T	2,T	3,T	4,T	5,T	6,T

Use a table to list all possible outcomes. Circle or highlight the outcomes with an even number and "heads."

$$P(\text{even, heads}) = \frac{\text{3 ways outcome can occur}}{\text{12 equally likely outcomes}}$$

$= \frac{3}{12}$

$= \frac{1}{4}$

In the Example, a table was used to list the possible outcomes. Another way to list outcomes of a compound event is to use a **tree diagram.**

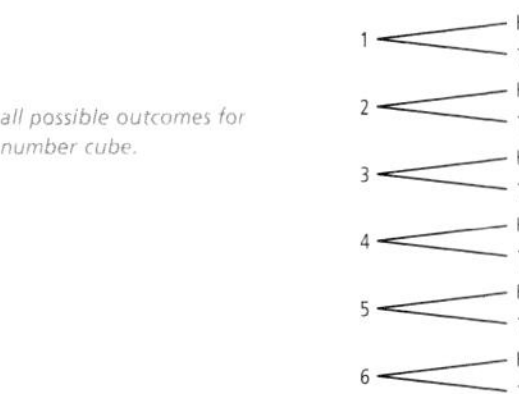

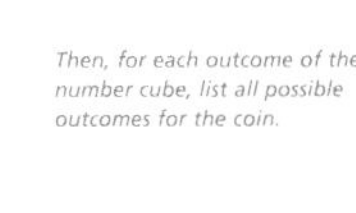

Then, for each outcome of the number cube, list all possible outcomes for the coin.

PRACTICE

Use the spinner for Exercises 1–3.

1. If you spin the spinner twice, what is the probability that it will land on blue on the first spin and on green on the second spin? $\frac{1}{16}$
2. What is the probability that the spinner will land on either red or yellow on the first spin and on blue on the second spin? $\frac{1}{8}$
3. What is the probability that the spinner will land on the same color twice in a row? $\frac{1}{16}$

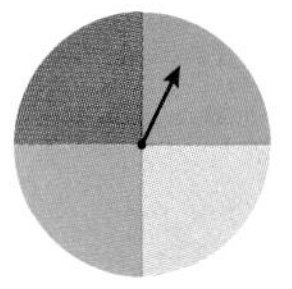

Selected Answers

Independent and Dependent Events

6SDAP3.4, 6SDAP3.5

For two **independent events,** the occurrence of one event has no effect on the probability that the second event will occur. To find the probability that two independent events will occur, multiply the individual probabilities.

Probability of Two Independent Events

$P(A \text{ and } B) = P(A) \cdot P(B)$

EXAMPLE 1 **An experiment consists of randomly selecting a marble from a bag, replacing it, and then selecting another marble. The bag contains 7 blue marbles and 3 red marbles. What is the probability of selecting a red marble and then a blue marble?**

Because the first marble selected is replaced, the number of possible outcomes for each selection is the same. These events are independent.

$P(\text{red, blue}) = P(\text{red}) \cdot P(\text{blue})$

$= \frac{3}{10} \cdot \frac{7}{10}$

$= \frac{21}{100}$

$= 21\%$

For two **dependent events,** the occurrence of one event has an effect on the probability that the second event will occur. To find the probability that two dependent events will occur, multiply probabilities as shown below.

Probability of Two Dependent Events

$P(A \text{ and } B) = P(A) \cdot P(B \text{ after } A)$

EXAMPLE 2 **There are 7 pink flowers and 5 yellow flowers in a bunch. Jane selects a flower at random, and then Leah selects a flower at random from the remaining flowers. What is the probability that Jane selects a pink flower and Leah selects a yellow flower?**

Because the first flower selected is not replaced, the number of possible outcomes for each selection is different. These events are dependent.

$P(\text{pink, yellow}) = P(\text{pink}) \cdot P(\text{yellow after pink})$

$= \frac{7}{12} \cdot \frac{5}{11}$

Jane selects one of 7 pink flowers from 12 total flowers. Then Leah selects one of 5 yellow flowers from 11 remaining flowers.

$= \frac{35}{132}$

$\approx 26.5\%$

PRACTICE

1. A coin is flipped 4 times. What is the probability of flipping 4 heads in a row? $\frac{1}{16}$
2. A snack cart has 6 bags of pretzels and 10 bags of trail mix. Grant selects a bag at random, and then Iris selects a bag at random. What is the probability that Grant selects pretzels and Iris selects trail mix? $\frac{1}{4}$

Skills Bank

Selected Answers

Chapter 1

1-1

Check It Out! 1a. Possible answers: 4 decreased by n; n less than 4 **1b.** Possible answers: the quotient of t and 5; t divided by 5 **1c.** Possible answers: the sum of 9 and q; q added to 9 **1d.** Possible answers: the product of 3 and h; 3 times h **2a.** $65t$ **2b.** $m + 5$ **3a.** $\frac{4}{3}$; 2; 6 **3b.** 13; 12; 6 **3c.** 2.15; 3.15; 9.15 **4a.** $63s$ **4b.** 756 bottles; 1575 bottles; 3150 bottles

Exercises 1. variable **3.** Possible answers: the quotient of f and 3; f divided by 3 **5.** Possible answers: 9 decreased by y; y less than 9 **7.** Possible answers: the sum of t and 12; t increased by 12 **9.** Possible answers: x decreased by 3; the difference of x and 3 **11.** $w + 4$ **13.** 12, 16, 36 **15.** 6, 8, 18 **17.** Possible answers: the product of 5 and p; 5 groups of p **19.** Possible answers: the sum of 3 and x; 3 increased by x **21.** Possible answers: negative 3 times s; the product of negative 3 and s **23.** Possible answers: 14 decreased by t; the difference of 14 and t **25.** $t + 20$ **27.** 1, 7, 12 **29.** 1, 4, $\frac{13}{2}$ **31a.** $h - 40$, **31b.** 0; 4; 8; 12 **33.** $2x$ **35.** $y + 10$ **37.** $9w$; 9 in^2; 72 in^2; 81 in^2; 99 in^2 **39.** 13; 14; 15; 16 **41.** 6; 10; 13; 15 **43a.** $47.84 + m$; **43b.** $58.53 - s$ **45.** $x + 7$; 19; 21 **46.** $\frac{x}{2}$; 6; 7 **47.** $x + 3$; 15; 17 **49.** A **51.** 36 **53.** 1 **55.** 45° **57.** 90° **59.** $\frac{1}{2}$ **61.** 1

1-2

Check It Out! 1a. 4 **1b.** −10 **1c.** 1.5 **2a.** −12 **2b.** −35.8 **2c.** −16 **3a.** −8 **3b.** 4 **3c.** −2 **4.** 13,018 ft

Exercises 1. opposite **3.** −8.5 **5.** $9\frac{1}{4}$ **7.** 1 **9.** −13 **11.** $-1\frac{3}{5}$ **13.** 4 **15.** $-11\frac{3}{4}$ **17.** −30 **19.** 14 **21.** $-\frac{1}{2}$ **23.** 23°F **25.** 0.75 **27.** $-12\frac{2}{5}$ **29.** −12 **31.** 37 **33.** 0 **35.** $\frac{1}{10}$ **37.** > **39.** > **41.** < **43.** 11,331 ft **45.** always **47.** A **51.** A **53.** −9 **55.** 2 **59.** 12,660.5 ft **61.** 44 in^2 **63.** 13 cm **65.** 12 **67.** 4

1-3

Check It Out! 1a. −7 **1b.** 44 **1c.** −42 **2a.** $\frac{1}{12}$ **2b.** $-\frac{1}{4}$ **2c.** $-\frac{1}{2}$ **3a.** 0 **3b.** 0 **3c.** 0 **4.** 7.875 mi

Exercises 1. Switch the numerator and denominator. The reciprocal of $\frac{1}{2}$ is $\frac{2}{1}$, or 2. **3.** −121 **5.** 7 **7.** 2 **9.** undefined **11.** 0 **13.** about $210,000,000 **15.** −32 **17.** $\frac{9}{10}$ **19.** −3 **21.** 0 **23.** 0 **25.** −15°F **27.** −4 **29.** −62 **31.** 18.75 **33.** 1 **35.** −12 **37.** $\frac{3}{2}$ **39.** negative **41.** negative **43.** positive **45.** undefined **47.** 1 **49.** $\frac{1}{2}$ **51.** $-\frac{1}{5}$ **53.** $\frac{9}{8}$ **55.** 15 h per semester **57.** < **59.** > **61.** = **63a.** positive **63b.** negative **63c.** The product of two negative numbers is positive. The product of that positive number and a negative number is negative. **63d.** no **65.** $75\left(\frac{1}{15}\right)$ **67.** $-121\left(\frac{1}{11}\right)$ **69.** sometimes **71.** The product of two negative numbers is positive and the product of a negative number and a positive number is negative. You know that the product is positive and one factor is negative, so the second factor must also be negative. **73.** B **75.** Clarinets: 1 half note = $\frac{1}{2}$ whole note, 8 half notes = 4 whole notes. Find the number of quarter notes that have the same length as 4 whole notes. $4 \div \frac{1}{4} = 16$; the flutes play 16 quarter notes. **77.** $\frac{25}{49}$ **79.** 5 **81.** 1 **83.** $-\frac{27}{64}$ **89.** $85 **91.** 12.6 **93.** 6.3 **95.** −6 **97.** 8

1-4

Check It Out! 1a. 2^2 **1b.** x^3 **2a.** −125 **2b.** −36 **2c.** $\frac{27}{64}$ **3a.** 8^2 **3b.** $(-3)^3$ **4.** $2^8 = 256$

Exercises 1. the number of times to use the base as a factor **3.** 2^3 **5.** 49 **7.** −32 **9.** 9^2 **11.** $(-4)^3$ **13.** 3^4 **15.** $3^5 = 243$ **17.** 3^3 **19.** 27 **21.** −16 **23.** 7^2 **25.** $(-2)^3$ **27.** 4^3 **29.** $2^4 = 16$ **31.** < **33.** = **35.** = **37.** > **39.** 8; $2 \cdot 2 \cdot 2 = 8$ **41.** −64; $(-4)(-4)(-4) = -64$ **43.** −1; $(-1)(-1)(-1) = -1$ **45.** $\frac{1}{27}$; $\left(\frac{1}{3}\right)\left(\frac{1}{3}\right)\left(\frac{1}{3}\right) = \frac{1}{27}$ **47a.** 36 in^2 **47b.** 9 in^2 **47c.** 27 in^2 **49.** 6^2 **51.** $(-1)^4$ **53.** $\left(\frac{1}{9}\right)^3$ **55.** between 8000 cm^3 and 15,625 cm^3 **57.** 2 **59.** 4 **61.** 2 **63.** 4 **65a.** 100, 1000, 10,000 **65b.** The exponent is the same as the number of zeros in the number. **67.** C **69.** B **71.** 64 **73.** 65,536 **75a.** $4 \cdot 4$; $4 \cdot 4 \cdot 4$ **75b.** $4 \cdot 4 \cdot 4 \cdot 4 \cdot 4 = 4^5$ **77.** 5 **79.** Possible answers: 5 minus x; x less than 5 **81.** Possible answers: c divided by d; the quotient of c and d **83.** $\frac{5}{2}$ **85.** 280

1-5

Check It Out! 1a. 2 **1b.** −5 **1c.** 3 **2a.** $\frac{2}{3}$ **2b.** $\frac{1}{2}$ **2c.** $-\frac{2}{7}$ **3.** about 5.1 ft **4a.** $\mathbb{Q}$, rep. dec. **4b.** $\mathbb{Q}$, term. dec., $\mathbb{Z}$ **4c.** irr. **4d.** $\mathbb{N}$, $\mathbb{W}$, $\mathbb{Z}$, $\mathbb{Q}$, term. dec.

Exercises 3. −15 **5.** 5 **7.** −3 **9.** −4 **11.** $\frac{2}{3}$ **13.** $\frac{3}{8}$ **15.** $\frac{1}{4}$ **17.** $-\frac{1}{5}$ **19.** $\mathbb{Q}$, term. dec., $\mathbb{Z}$ **21.** irr. **23.** 11 **25.** −10 **27.** $\frac{1}{5}$ **29.** $-\frac{1}{2}$ **31.** about 14.9 yd **33.** $\mathbb{Q}$, term. dec., $\mathbb{Z}$, $\mathbb{W}$, $\mathbb{N}$ **35.** irr. **37.** > **39.** < **41.** 45; $\mathbb{Q}$, term. dec., $\mathbb{Z}$, $\mathbb{W}$, $\mathbb{N}$ **43.** 34.625; $\mathbb{Q}$, term. dec. **45.** always **47.** always **51.** 18 **53.** A **55.** D **57.** 0.9 **59.** −0.1 **61.** 4 **63.** 65 **65a.** No **67.** $\frac{1}{2}$ **69.** $-\frac{3}{16}$ **71.** $-\frac{7}{2}$ **73.** $-\frac{8}{125}$ **75.** 64

1-6

Check It Out! 1a. Comm. Prop. of Add. **1b.** Assoc. Prop. of Add. **1c.** Comm. Prop. of Mult. **2.** Possible answer: $6 \div 2 \neq 2 \div 6$ **3a.** $9(50) + 9(2)$; 468 **3b.** $12(100) - 12(2)$; 1176 **3c.** $7(30) + 7(4)$; 238 **4a.** Possible answer: −2 and −1 are negative integers, but $(-2)(-1) = 2$, which is not a negative integer. **4b.** Possible answer: 15 is a whole number, but $\sqrt{15}$ is not a whole number.

Selected Answers

Exercises 1. Associative **3.** Assoc. Prop. of Add. **5.** Comm. Prop. of Mult. **7.** $14(1000) + 14(2)$; 14,028 **9.** $9(40) - 9(2)$; 342 **11.** $12(100) + 12(12)$; 1344 **15.** Comm. Prop. of Add. **17.** Assoc. Prop. of Mult. **19.** Comm. Prop. of Mult. **23.** $8(30) - 8(1)$; 232 **25.** $6(50) + 6(3)$; 318 **27.** $3(150) - 3(1)$; 447 **31a.** Amy: 98:21; Julie: 81:12; Mardi: 83:39 **31b.** Julie, Mardi, Amy **33.** Dist. Prop. **35.** Dist. Prop. **37a.** 336 ft^2 **37b.** 336 ft^2 **37c.** By the Dist. Prop., $8 \cdot 12 + 8 \cdot 14 + 8 \cdot 16 = 8(12 + 14 + 16)$. **41.** A **43.** yes **45.** no **47.** −5; 61 **49.** yes **51.** 1, −1, −2 **53.** 27, 45, 54 **55.** 4^2 **57.** 3^3 **59.** −9 **61.** $\frac{2}{3}$

1-7

Check It Out! 1a. 48 **1b.** 1 **1c.** 21 **2.** 400 **3a.** $100p$ **3b.** $-28.5t$ **3c.** $2m^2 + m^3$ **4.** $6(x - 4) + 9$

$6(x) - 6(4) + 9$	Dist. Prop.
$6x - 24 + 9$	Multiply.
$6x - 15$	Combine like terms.

Exercises 3. 15 **5.** −3 **7.** −22 **9.** $16x$ **11.** $6a$ **13.** $20x^2 + x$ **19.** −17 **21.** 47 **23.** −10 **25.** −14 **27.** $\frac{1}{4}$ **29.** $12x$ **31.** x **33.** $8x^2 - 2x$ **35.** $13y - 10$ **37.** $4(y + 6) + 9$

$4y + 24 + 9$	Dist. Prop.
$4y + 33$	Combine like terms.

41a. 55 **41b.** 498 **41c.** 250 **41d.** 10 **41e.** 30 **41f.** 70 **43.** 1 **45.** 14 **47.** 92 **49.** $6p + 9$ **51a.** $\frac{57.823}{6}$ **51b.** 9.637 **55a.** equal **55b.** 96π **55c.** $2(16\pi) + 96\pi = 128\pi$ **57.** D **59.** 4 **61.** 1 **63.** $12x + 116$ **65.** $-3b - 7$ **69a.** Dist. Prop. **69b.** Multiply **71.** $-6\frac{1}{3}$ **73.** −2.4 **75.** 324 **77.** $\frac{1}{4}$ **79.** 18 **81.** −11

Study Guide: Review

1. constant **2.** whole numbers **3.** coefficient **4.** term **5.** $1.99g$ **6.** $t + 3$ **7.** −5; 0; 5 **8.** −5; 0; 5 **9.** −4; 1; 6 **10.** $150 \div m$; 30; 25; 15 **11.** −14 **12.** −4.6 **13.** $4\frac{1}{2}$ **14.** −1 **15.** −24 **16.** 14.3 **17.** 5 **18.** 2231 ft **19.** 90 **20.** 0 **21.** −15.2 **22.** −8 **23.** 0 **24.** undefined **25.** 9 **26.** $-\frac{2}{3}$ **27.** $\frac{15}{7}$ **28.** 3,650,000 steps **29.** $4 \cdot 4 \cdot 4 = 64$ **30.** $(-3)(-3)(-3) = -27$ **31.** $(-3)(-3)(-3)(-3) = 81$ **32.** $-1 \cdot 5 \cdot 5 = -25$ **33.** $\left(\frac{2}{3}\right)\left(\frac{2}{3}\right)\left(\frac{2}{3}\right) = \frac{8}{27}$ **34.** $\left(-\frac{4}{5}\right)\left(-\frac{4}{5}\right) = \frac{16}{25}$ **35.** 2^4 **36.** $(-10)^3$ **37.** $(-8)^2$ **38.** 12^1 **39.** 729 in^3 **40.** 6 **41.** 14 **42.** −13 **43.** −12 **44.** $\frac{5}{6}$ **45.** $\frac{1}{3}$ **46.** 4 **47.** $\frac{9}{11}$ **48.** 3 **49.** rational number, terminating decimal, integer, whole number, natural number **50.** rational number, terminating decimal, integer, whole number **51.** rational number, terminating decimal, integer **52.** rational number, terminating decimal **53.** irrational number **54.** rational number, repeating decimal **55.** rational number, terminating decimal, integer, whole number **56.** rational number, terminating decimal **57.** rational number, terminating decimal **58.** 3.6 ft **59.** 3.9 ft **60.** Associative Property of Addition **61.** Associative Property of Multiplication **62.** Commutative Property of Addition **63.** Commutative Property of Multiplication **64.** Possible answer: $6 \div 3 \neq 3 \div 6$ **65.** $3(20) + 3(7)$; 81 **66.** $6(10) + 6(2)$; 72 **67.** $8(10) + 8(7)$; 136 **68.** $7(20) + 7(2)$; 154 **69.** Possible answer: $\sqrt{2} \cdot \sqrt{2} = 2$ **70.** 40 **71.** 270 **72.** 31 **73.** 3 **74.** 35.5 **75.** 40 **76.** $6 **77.** $4x$ **78.** $7y^2$ **79.** $4x + 24$ **80.** $2x^2 + 2$ **81.** $-4y + 3y^2$ **82.** $8y - a$ **83.** $8.84

84.

	Statements	Reasons
1.	$2(x + 5) - 3$	
2.	$2x + 2(5) - 3$	Distributive Property
3.	$2x + 10 - 3$	Multiply.
4.	$2(x) + 2(5) - 3$	Combine like terms.

85.

	Statements	Reasons
1.	$(5 + y - 3) + 4y$	
2.	$(5 - 3 + y) + 4y$	Commutative Property of Addition
3.	$(2 + y) + 4y$	Combine like terms.
4.	$2 + (y + 4y)$	Associative Property of Addition
5.	$2 + 5y$	Combine like terms.
6.	$5y + 2$	Commutative Property of Addition

Chapter 2

2-1

Check It Out! 1a. 8.8 **1b.** 0 **1c.** 8 **2a.** 50 **2b.** −20 **2c.** 56 **3a.** 9.3 **3b.** 2 **3c.** 612 **4.** $\frac{m}{3} = 10{,}000$; 30,000 ft

Exercises 3. 21 **5.** −30 **7.** 0.6 **9.** 19 **11.** 7 **13.** 5 **15.** 32 **17.** 14 **19.** −9 **21.** 9 **23.** 17 **25.** 0 **27.** 5 **29.** 24 **31.** −3 **33.** −36 **35.** 2.1 **37.** 15 **39.** $-\frac{7}{2}$ **41.** 30 **43.** −12 **45.** $80 = 10a$; 8 mg **47.** $x - 13 = 7$; $x = 20$ **49.** $x + 8 = 16$; $x = 8$ **51.** $30{,}246 = a + 17{,}366$; 12,880 ft **55a.** 2000 acres **55b.** 5000 acres **55c.** Divide 780 by 7. **57.** $42 + x = 90$; $x = 48$ **59.** A **61a.** $6x = 4.80$ **61b.** $0.80 **63.** $\frac{29}{12}$ **65.** $\frac{1}{4}$ **67.** 22 **69.** −78 **71.** $-\frac{3}{4}$ **73.** 15 m **75.** 10 cm **77.** $12(40) + 12(3)$; 516

2-2

Check It Out! 1a. 1 **1b.** 6 **1c.** 0 **2a.** $\frac{55}{4}$ **2b.** $\frac{1}{2}$ **2c.** 15 **3a.** $60 **3b.** 2

Exercises 1. 2 **3.** 66 **5.** 2 **7.** $\frac{1}{2}$ **9.** 52 **11.** $\frac{17}{5}$ **13.** 15 passes **15.** 4 **17.** 5 **19.** −9 **21.** $\frac{1}{4}$ **23.** 1 **25.** 3 **27.** $2x - 7 = 19$; $x = 13$ **29.** $30 + 5x = 80$; $x = 10$ **31.** $64 + 3x = -2$; $x = -22$ **33a.** $1963 - 5s = 1863$; $s = 20$ **33b.** 3 **35.** 8 **37.** 4.5 **39.** −10 **41.** 10 **43.** 4.5 **45.** 3 **47.** $5k - 70 = 60$; 26 in.

49a.

Cost of Fighting Fire	
Acres	Cost ($)
100	22,500
200	45,000
500	112,500
1000	225,000
1500	337,500
n	$225n$

49b. $c = 225n$ **53.** D **55.** −6 **57.** 2 **59.** 5 **61a.** 1.65 **61b.** 3.3 **61c.** c doubles **63.** integer, rational, terminating decimal **65.** terminating decimal, rational **67.** $9(20) + 9(8)$; 252 **69.** $13(20) + 13(1)$; 273 **71.** $7(10) + 7(9)$; 133 **73.** $8(30) + 8(3)$; 264 **75.** 21 **77.** 0 **79.** 28 **81.** −42

2-3

Check It Out! 1a. $-\frac{11}{5}$ **1b.** 6 **2a.** $-\frac{5}{6}$ **2b.** −5 **2c.** 8 **3a.** 2 **3b.** 4 **3c.** 8 **4a.** $50 **4b.** $18.15

Exercises 1. 5 **3.** $\frac{4}{3}$ **5.** 3 **7.** 22 **9.** 3 **11.** 3 **13.** 16 **15.** −5 **17.** 30 **19.** 6 **21.** $\frac{27}{2}$ **23.** 7 **25.** 100 **27.** −13 **29.** $\frac{8}{3}$ **31.** $-\frac{2}{5}$ **33.** 16 **35.** Amanda: $20; Casey: $10 **37.** −1 **39.** 10 **41.** −3 **43.** $x = 2$ **45.** $d = -\frac{17}{3}$ **47.** $16 + 7 - 4x = 3$; $x = 5$ **49.** $\frac{1}{2}x + 2(x - 5) = 0$; $x = 4$ **51.** $2x + 115 = 180$; $x = 32.5$ **53.** −2 **55.** −10 **57.** 1 **59.** $\frac{25}{6}$ **61.** 2, 3 **63.** 102 and 104 **67.** Dist. Prop., Comm. Prop. of Add., Comm. Prop. of Mult., Assoc. Prop. of Add. **69.** D **71.** $10 **73.** 8 **75.** $\frac{29}{2}$ **77.** 2 **79.** Comm. Prop. of Add. **81.** $8m$ **83.** $118v$ **85.** $12c + x$ **87.** 3 **89.** −6

2-4

Check It Out! 1a. −2 **1b.** 2 **2a.** 4 **2b.** −2 **3a.** ∅ **3b.** all real numbers **4.** 10 years old

Exercises 3. 1 **5.** 40 **7.** $-\frac{2}{3}$ **9.** 3 **11.** ∅ **13.** all real numbers **15.** 6 **17.** 6 **19.** 2.85 **21.** 10 **23.** 6 **25.** 14 **27.** $\frac{3}{4}$ **29.** −4 **31.** ∅ **33a.** 15 weeks **33b.** 180 lb **35.** always **37.** −4 **39.** 7 **41.** −3 **43.** 2 **45.** 1 **47.** $-\frac{7}{5}$ **49.** 4 **51.** ∅ **53.** 9 **59.** A **61.** C **63.** 2 **65.** ∅ **67.** −20 **69.** 6, 7, 8 **71.** $1.68 **73.** $3y$ cm **75.** −63 **77.** 4 **79.** 2 **81.** −125 **83.** 15 **85.** 3

2-5

Check It Out! 1. 15 **2a.** $7.50/h **2b.** 6 envelopes/min **3a.** −20 **3b.** 5.75 **4a.** 12 **4b.** 320 **5a.** about 0.2 in. **5b.** 6 in.

Exercises 1. The ratios are equal. **3.** $48 **5.** 50 rotations/s **7.** 24 **9.** 6 **11.** −7.5 **13.** 30 **15.** 65.55 **17.** 65.5% **19.** $\frac{3}{5} = \frac{h}{4.9}$; 2.94 m **21.** 72 **23.** $403.90/oz **25.** 10 **27.** −1 **29.** 31.5 **31.** 63 **33.** 300% **35.** 4 **37.** 2 **39.** 49%; 51% **41a.** 40% **41b.** action **41c.** 3% **41d.** 36.9% **45.** D **47.** 40°; 50° **49.** 17.2%

51.

$$\frac{3}{x} = \frac{5}{x-1}$$
$$(x)\frac{3}{x} = (x)\frac{5}{x-1}$$
$$3 = \frac{5x}{x-1}$$
$$3(x-1) = \frac{5x}{x-1}(x-1)$$
$$3(x-1) = 5x$$

53. −27 **55.** $-\frac{1}{32}$ **57.** 10^2 **59.** −5 **65.** 8

2-6

Check It Out! 1. about 1.46 h **2.** $i = f + gt$ **3a.** $t = \frac{5-b}{2}$ **3b.** $V = \frac{m}{D}$

Exercises 1. A literal equation contains more than one variable. A formula shows how to determine the value of one variable when you know the value(s) of one or more other variables. So a formula always contains more than one variable, making it a literal equation. **3.** $w = \frac{V}{\ell h}$ **5.** $m = 4n + 8$ **7.** $a = \frac{10}{b+c}$ **9.** $I = A - P$ **11.** $x = \frac{k+5}{y}$ **13.** $\frac{x-2}{z} = y$ **15.** $x = 5(a + g)$ **17.** $x = \frac{y-b}{m}$ **19.** $T = \frac{PV}{nR}$ **21.** $T = M + R$ **23.** $b = \frac{c-2a}{2}$ **25.** $r = 7 - ax$ **27.** $x = \frac{5-4y}{3}$ **31.** $a = \frac{t-g}{-0.0035}$ **35.** C **37.** D **39.** $a = \frac{5}{2}\left(c + \frac{3}{4}b\right)$ **41.** $d = 500\left(t - \frac{1}{2}\right)$ **43.** $s = \frac{v^2 - u^2}{2a}$ **45.** 120 s **47.** 12 **49.** −6 **51.** 20 **53.** 12

2-7

Check It Out! 1a. −7, 7 **1b.** −5.5, 10.5 **2a.** ∅ **2b.** 4 **3.** $|x - 134| = 0.18$; min. height: 133.82 m; max. height: 134.18 m

Exercises 1. −6, 6 **3.** −2, 2 **5.** $-\frac{3}{2}, \frac{1}{2}$ **7.** ∅ **9.** ∅ **11.** 2.8 **13.** $|x - 207| = 2$; mile markers 205 and 209 **15.** −9, 13 ft **17.** −2, 2 **19.** 18.8, 65.28 **21.** $-\frac{14}{3}$, 4 **23.** 0 **25.** 0 **27.** $\frac{2}{3}$ **29.** $|x - 5| = 0.001$; 4.999 mm; 5.001 mm **31.** $|x - 7| = 2$; 5, 9 **33.** $|x - 1500| = 75$; 1575 bricks; 1425 bricks **35.** $|x| = 3$ **37.** $|x - 2| = 3$ **39.** sometimes **41.** always **43a.** $|t - 24| = 5$ **43b.** 19; 29 **43c.** yes **43d.** The measurements are correct to within 5 mi/h. **47.** C **49.** B **51.** Div. Prop. of Eq.; Subtr. Prop. of Eq.; Div. Prop. of Eq. **53.** 9.5 **55.** 15 **57.** 6 **59.** 9 **61.** $m = 7 - 5n$ **63.** $y = \frac{1-3x}{2}$ **65.** $e = \frac{5}{c+d}$

Study Guide: Review

1. literal equation **2.** ratio **3.** 36 **4.** −2 **5.** −21 **6.** 18 **7.** $\frac{9}{8}$ **8.** $\frac{7}{3}$ **9.** $t = 5.1$ **10.** $x = 25.5$ **11.** 7 **12.** $s = -7$ **13.** $f = 120$ **14.** $m = 15$ **15.** $j = 72$ **16.** $n = 36$ **17.** $k = 0.875$ **18.** $c = 12.5$ **19.** $27 + s = 108$; 81 **20.** $213 **21.** 17.5 **22.** −5 **23.** $z = 6$ **24.** $h = 4$ **25.** $k = 40$ **26.** $f = -\frac{3}{2}$ **27.** $h = \frac{16}{3}$ **28.** $k = 3$ **29.** $t = 13$ **30.** $a = -4$ **31.** $x = 2$ **32.** $x = 1$ **33.** 92 **34.** $a = 13$ **35.** $y = -6$ **36.** 15 **37.** $x = 6$ **38.** $h = 3$ **39.** $z = 2$ **40.** $w = -0.4$ **41.** $x = -2$ **42.** 18 **43.** 1 **44.** 41; 123°; 57° **45.** $5; $2 **46.** $x = -2$ **47.** $r = -2$ **48.** 1 **49.** $-\frac{2}{3}$ **50.** ∅ **51.** all real numbers **52.** $x = 3.5$ **53.** $c = \frac{18}{7}$ **54.** $x = 7$ **55.** $x = 6$ **56.** $n = -2$ **57.** $x = 3$ **58.** 9 **59.** $\frac{16}{1}$ **60.** $n = 1.6$ **61.** $x = 54$ **62.** 1.37 ft **63.** 5.29 **64.** 3105 **65.** 66.7% **66.** 400% **67.** 133.3 **68.** 240 **69.** 80% **70.** $n = \frac{360}{c}$ **71.** $a = \frac{2S}{n} - \ell$ **72.** $x = \frac{225 - y}{0.25}$ **73.** 3.7 gal **74.** $x = 15, -27$ **75.** $y = 7, -3$ **76.** $y = 9, -9$ **77.** $x = 17.4, -6.6$ **78.** $g = -4, -8$ **79.** $x = \frac{5}{7}, -\frac{5}{7}$ **80.** $|x - 5| = 55$; min. speed: 50 mi/h; max. speed: 60 mi/h

Chapter 3

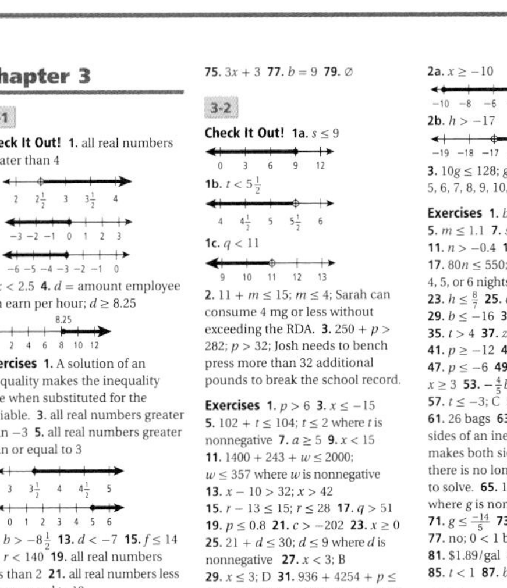

3-1

Check It Out! 1. all real numbers greater than 4 **2a.** **2b.** **2c.** **3.** $x < 2.5$ **4.** d = amount employee can earn per hour; $d \geq 8.25$

Exercises 1. A solution of an inequality makes the inequality true when substituted for the variable. **3.** all real numbers greater than -3 **5.** all real numbers greater than or equal to 3 **7.** **9.** **11.** $b > -8\frac{1}{2}$ **13.** $d < -7$ **15.** $f \leq 14$ **17.** $r < 140$ **19.** all real numbers less than 2 **21.** all real numbers less than or equal to 12 **23.** **25.** **27.** $v < -11$ **29.** $x > -3.3$ **31.** $z \geq 9$ **33.** y = years of experience; $y \geq 5$ **35.** h is less than -5. **37.** r is greater than or equal to -2. **39.** $p \leq 17$ **41.** $f > 0$ **43.** p = profits; $p < 10{,}000$ **45.** e = elevation; $e \leq 5000$ **47.** x represents the age in years of a child at a childcare center when x is positive. **49.** x represents the number of millions of albums sold by a popular band. **51.** D **53.** C **55a.** $125 - s \geq 90$; $s \leq 35$ **55b.** **55c.** $s + 15 \leq 35$; $s \leq 20$ where s is nonnegative **59.** D **61.** C **63.** any numbers such that $|x| < |y|$ **65.** < **67.** any number between 0.35 and 1.27 **69.** Draw an empty circle at 5. Then draw arrows going left and right from 5. **71.** 10 **73.** 7 **75.** $3x + 3$ **77.** $b = 9$ **79.** $\varnothing$

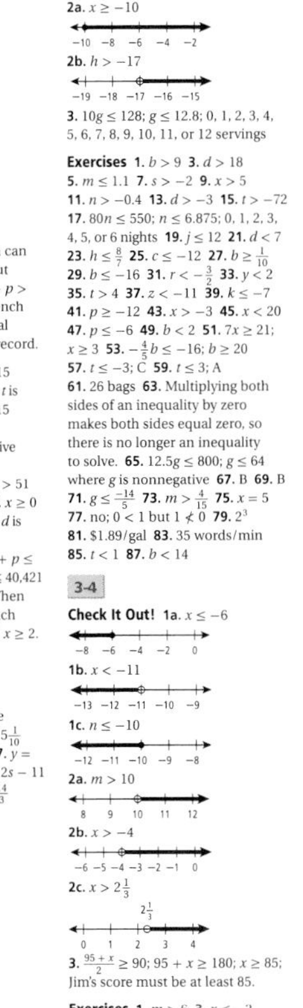

3-2

Check It Out! 1a. $s \leq 9$ **1b.** $t < 5\frac{1}{2}$ **1c.** $q < 11$ **2.** $11 + m \leq 15$; $m \leq 4$; Sarah can consume 4 mg or less without exceeding the RDA. **3.** $250 + p > 282$; $p > 32$; Josh needs to bench press more than 32 additional pounds to break the school record.

Exercises 1. $p > 6$ **3.** $x \leq -15$ **5.** $102 + t \leq 104$; $t \leq 2$ where t is nonnegative **7.** $a \geq 5$ **9.** $x < 15$ **11.** $1400 + 243 + w \leq 2000$; $w \leq 357$ where w is nonnegative **13.** $x - 10 > 32$; $x > 42$ **15.** $r - 13 \leq 15$; $r \leq 28$ **17.** $q > 51$ **19.** $p \leq 0.8$ **21.** $c > -202$ **23.** $x \geq 0$ **25.** $21 + d \leq 30$; $d \leq 9$ where d is nonnegative **27.** $x < 3$; B **29.** $x \leq 3$; D **31.** $936 + 4254 + p \leq 45{,}611$; $5190 + p \leq 45{,}611$; $p \leq 40{,}421$ where p is nonnegative **33.** When you isolate the variable in each inequality, you get $x \geq 2$ and $x \geq 2$. **35a.** $411 + 411 = 882$ miles **35b.** $822 + m \leq 1000$ **35c.** $m \leq 178$, but m cannot be negative. **37.** A **39.** D **41.** $r \leq 5\frac{1}{10}$ **43.** sometimes **45.** always **47.** $y = 3 - \frac{2}{3}x$ **49.** $a = \frac{c}{2+b}$ **51.** $k = 2s - 11$ **53.** 4, -4 **55.** 5, -5 **57.** 4, $-\frac{14}{3}$ **55.** $x \geq -1$

3-3

Check It Out! 1a. $k > 6$ **1b.** $q \leq -10$ **1c.** $g > 36$ **2a.** $x \geq -10$ **2b.** $h > -17$ **3.** $10g \leq 128$; $g \leq 12.8$; 0, 1, 2, 3, 4, 5, 6, 7, 8, 9, 10, 11, or 12 servings

Exercises 1. $b > 9$ **3.** $d > 18$ **5.** $m \leq 1.1$ **7.** $s > -2$ **9.** $x > 5$ **11.** $n > -0.4$ **13.** $d > -3$ **15.** $t > -72$ **17.** $80n \leq 550$; $n \leq 6.875$; 0, 1, 2, 3, 4, 5, or 6 nights **19.** $j \leq 12$ **21.** $d < 7$ **23.** $h \leq \frac{8}{7}$ **25.** $c \leq -12$ **27.** $b \geq \frac{1}{10}$ **29.** $b \leq -16$ **31.** $r < -\frac{3}{2}$ **33.** $y < 2$ **35.** $t > 4$ **37.** $z < -11$ **39.** $k \leq -7$ **41.** $p \geq -12$ **43.** $x > -3$ **45.** $x < 20$ **47.** $p \leq -6$ **49.** $b < 2$ **51.** $7x \geq 21$; $x \geq 3$ **53.** $-\frac{4}{5}b \leq -16$; $b \geq 20$ **57.** $t \leq -3$; C **59.** $t \leq 3$; A **61.** 26 bags **63.** Multiplying both sides of an inequality by zero makes both sides equal zero, so there is no longer an inequality to solve. **65.** $12.5g \leq 800$; $g \leq 64$ where g is nonnegative **67.** B **69.** B **71.** $g \leq \frac{-14}{5}$ **73.** $m > \frac{4}{15}$ **75.** $x = 5$ **77.** no; $0 < 1$ but $1 \nless 0$ **79.** 2^3 **81.** \$1.89/gal **83.** 35 words/min **85.** $t < 1$ **87.** $b < 14$

3-4

Check It Out! 1a. $x \leq -6$ **1b.** $x < -11$ **1c.** $n \leq -10$ **2a.** $m > 10$ **2b.** $x > -4$ **2c.** $x > 2\frac{1}{3}$ **3.** $\frac{95+x}{2} \geq 90$; $95 + x \geq 180$; $x \geq 85$; Jim's score must be at least 85.

Exercises 1. $m > 6$ **3.** $x \leq -2$ **5.** $x > -16$ **7.** $x \geq -9$ **9.** $x > -\frac{1}{2}$ **11.** $x \leq 19$ **13.** $x > 1$

15. $300 + 0.1x > 1200$; sales of more than \$9000 **17.** $x \leq 1$ **19.** $w < -2$ **21.** $x < -6$ **23.** $f < -4.5$ **25.** $w > 0$ **27.** $v > \frac{2}{3}$ **29.** $x > -5$ **31.** $x < -2$ **33.** $a \geq 11$ **35.** $x > 3$ **37.** $29.99 < 19.99 + 0.35x$; $x > 28.57$; starting at 29 min **39.** $x \leq 2$ **41.** $x < 4$ **43.** $x < -6$ **45.** $r < 8$ **47.** $x < 7$ **49.** $p \geq 18$ **51.** $\frac{1}{2}x + 9 < 33$; $x < 48$ **53.** $4(x + 12) \leq 16$; $x \leq -8$ **55.** $x \geq 4$; B **57.** $x \leq -2$; A **59.** $225 + 400 < 275 + 15m$; $23\frac{1}{3} < m$; 24 months or more **61a.**

Number	Process	Cost
1	350 + 3	353
2	350 + 3(2)	356
3	350 + 3(3)	359
10	350 + 3(10)	380
n	350 + 3n	350 + 3n

61b. $c = 350 + 3n$ **61c.** $350 + 3n \leq 500$; $n \leq 50$; 50 CDs or fewer **65.** B **67.** 59 **69.** $x > 5$ **71.** $x > 0$ **73.** $x \geq 0$ **75.** $-3x > 0$; $x < 0$ **77.** 7 **79.** $\frac{2}{3}$ **81.** -1 **83.** $25 + 2m = 10 + 2.5m$; $m = 30$ **85.** $a \geq 6$

3-5

Check It Out! 1a. $x \leq -2$ **1b.** $t < -1$ **2.** more than 160 flyers **3a.** $r \leq 2$ **3b.** $x < 3$ **4a.** no solutions **4b.** all real numbers

Exercises 1. $x < 3$ **3.** $x < 2$ **5.** $c < -2$ **7.** $100 + 4p < 7p$; $p > 33.33$; they'll have to sell at least 34 pizzas. **9.** $p < -17$ **11.** $x > 3$ **13.** $t < 6.8$ **15.** $\varnothing$ **17.** all real numbers **19.** $\varnothing$ **21.** $y > -2$ **23.** $b \geq -7$ **25.** $m > 5$ **27.** $x \geq 2$ **29.** $w \geq 6$ **31.** $r \geq -4$ **33.** $\varnothing$ **35.** all real numbers **37.** all real numbers **39.** $t < -7$ **41.** $x > 3$ **43.** $x < 2$ **45.** $x > -2$ **47.** $x \leq -6$ **49.** $s > 26.67$; 27 s **51a.** $400 + 4.50n$ **51b.** $12n$ **51c.** $400 + 4.50n < 12n$; $n > 53\frac{1}{3}$; 54 CDs or more **53.** $5x - 10 < 6x - 8$; $x > -2$ **55.** $\frac{3}{4}x \geq x - 5$; $x \leq 20$ **57.** no **59.** x can never be greater than itself plus 1. **61.** D **63.** A **67.** $x < -3$ **69.** $w \geq -1\frac{6}{7}$ **73.** $\frac{2}{5} = \frac{w}{65}$; $w = 26$ in. **75.** y = years; $y \geq 14$

3-6

Check It Out! 1. $1.0 \leq c \leq 3.0$ **2a.** $1 < x < 5$ **2b.** $-3 \leq n < 2$ **3a.** $r < 10$ OR $r > 14$ **3b.** $x \geq 3$ OR $x < -1$ **4a.** $-9 < y < -2$ **4b.** $x \leq -3$ OR $x \geq 2$

Exercises 1. intersection **3.** $-5 < x < 5$ **5.** $0 < x < 3$ **7.** $x < -8$ OR $x > 4$ **9.** $n < 1$ OR $n > 4$ **11.** $-5 \leq a \leq -3$ **13.** $c < 1$ OR $c \geq 9$ **15.** $16 \leq k \leq 50$ **17.** $3 \leq n \leq 6$ **19.** $2 < x < 6$ **21.** $x < 0$ OR $x > 3$ **23.** $x < -3$ OR $x > 2$ **25.** $q < 0$ OR $q \geq 2$ **27.** $-2 < s < 1$ **29a.** $225 + 80n$ gives the cost of the studio and technicians. They will spend between \$200 and \$550. **29b.** $-0.3125 \leq n \leq 4.0625$; n cannot be negative. **29c.** They need to raise an additional \$155. **31.** $1 \leq x \leq 2$ **33.** $-10 \leq x \leq 10$ **35.** $t < 0$ OR $t > 100$ **37.** $-2 < x < 5$ **39.** $a < 0$ OR $a > 1$ **41.** $n < 2$ OR $n > 5$ **43.** $7 \leq m \leq 60$ **47.** D **49.** B **51.** $0.5 < c < 3$ **53.** $s \leq 6$ OR $s \geq 9$ **55.** $-1 \leq x \leq 3$ **57.** $4x - 5$

$4(x - 3) + 7$	
$4x - 12 + 7$	Distribute 4.
$4x - 5$	Combine like terms.

59. $3a + 3$

$6a - 3(a - 1)$	
$6a - 3a + 3$	Distribute 3.
$3a + 3$	Combine like terms.

61. 3 **63.** $d = rt$; 126.8 mi **65.** $x > -1$

3-7

Check It Out! 1a. $-3 \leq x \leq 3$ **1b.** $-15 \leq x \leq 9$ **2a.** $x \leq -2$ OR $x \geq 2$ **2b.** $x \leq -6$ OR $x \geq 1$ **3.** $|p - 125| \leq 75$; $50 \leq p \leq 200$ **4a.** all real numbers **4b.** $\varnothing$

Exercises 1. $-3 \leq x \leq 3$ **3.** $-2 < x < 2$ **5.** $4 < x < 6$ **7.** $x < -22$ OR $x > 22$ **9.** $x \leq -4$ OR $x \geq 4$ **11.** $x \leq 1$ OR $x \geq 5$ **13.** $|x - 55| \leq 25$; $30 \leq x \leq 80$ **15.** $\varnothing$ **17.** all real numbers **19.** $\varnothing$ **21.** $2 < x < 4$ **23.** $-3 < x < 3$ **25.** $-6 < x < 0$ **27.** $x \leq -10$ OR $x \geq 10$ **29.** $x \leq -10$ OR $x \geq 6$ **31.** $x < -1$ OR $x > 2$ **33.** $\varnothing$ **35.** all real numbers **37.** $\varnothing$ **39.** always **41.** sometimes **43.** $|x - 2| \leq 3$; $-1 \leq x \leq 5$ **45.** $|a| \leq 2$ **47.** $|c| \geq 6\frac{1}{2}$ **49a.** 10,010 Hz **49b.** $|x - 10{,}010| \leq 9990$ **51.** $|n - 23| > 12$ **53.** $k \leq 1$; the inequality is equivalent to $|x| < k - 1$, and this has no solutions when the expression on the right side is less than or equal to 0 (i.e., when $k - 1 \leq 0$ or $k \leq 1$). **55.** B **57.** B **61.** $1\frac{1}{2}$ **63.** $2\frac{1}{2}$ **65.** all real numbers less than 2 **67.** all real numbers greater than or equal to -6 **69.** $0 < x < 4$ **71.** $x < 1$ OR $x > 4$

Study Guide: Review

1. inequality **2.** union **3.** compound inequality **4.** intersection **5.** solution of an inequality **6.** **7.** **8.**

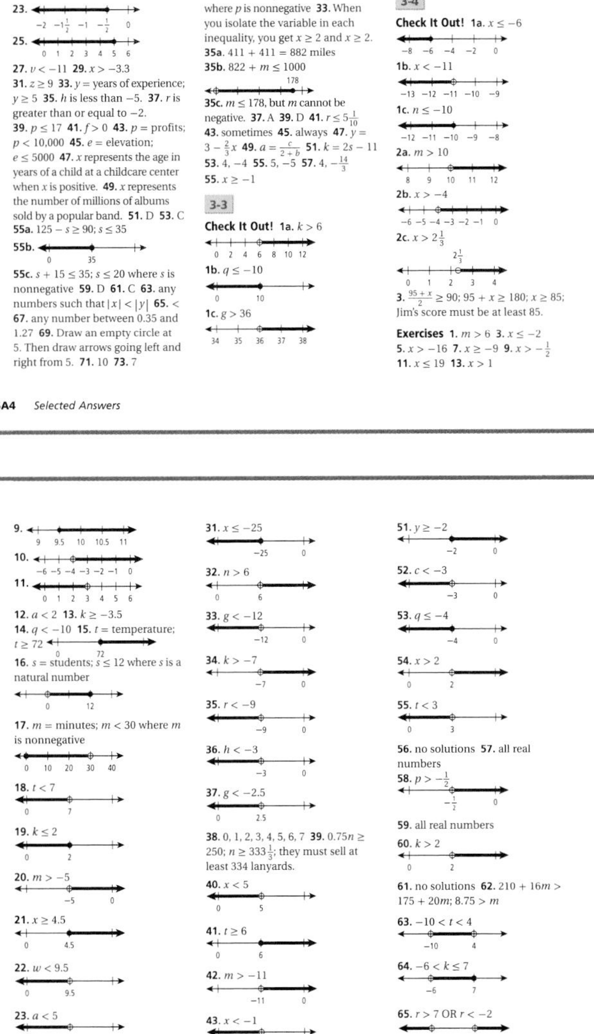

9. **10.** **11.** **12.** $a < 2$ **13.** $k \geq -3.5$ **14.** $q < -10$ **15.** t = temperature; $t \geq 72$ **16.** s = students; $s \leq 12$ where s is a natural number **17.** m = minutes; $m < 30$ where m is nonnegative **18.** $t < 7$ **19.** $k \leq 2$ **20.** $m > -5$ **21.** $x \geq 4.5$ **22.** $w < 9.5$ **23.** $a < 5$ **24.** $h < 1$ **25.** $v < -2$ **26.** $4.5 + m \geq 10$; $m \geq 5.5$; Tammy must run 5.5 mi or more. **27.** $32 + d \leq 50$; $d \leq 18$; Rob can spend \$18 or less. **28.** $a \leq 5$ **29.** $t > -3$ **30.** $p > 8$ **31.** $x \leq -25$ **32.** $n > 6$ **33.** $g < -12$ **34.** $k > -7$ **35.** $r < -9$ **36.** $h < -3$ **37.** $g < -2.5$ **38.** 0, 1, 2, 3, 4, 5, 6, 7 **39.** $0.75n \geq 250$; $n \geq 333\frac{1}{3}$; they must sell at least 334 lanyards. **40.** $x < 5$ **41.** $t \geq 6$ **42.** $m > -11$ **43.** $x < -1$ **44.** $h > -3$ **45.** $x > 1\frac{1}{2}$ **46.** $b \leq 10$ **47.** $y > 3\frac{1}{2}$ **48.** $n > -15$ **49.** 0, 1, 2, 3, 4, 5, 6, 7, 8, 9, 10, 11, 12, or 13 **50.** $m < -1$ **51.** $y \geq -2$ **52.** $c < -3$ **53.** $q \leq -4$ **54.** $x > 2$ **55.** $t < 3$ **56.** no solutions **57.** all real numbers **58.** $p > -\frac{1}{2}$ **59.** all real numbers **60.** $k > 2$ **61.** no solutions **62.** $210 + 16m > 175 + 20m$; $8.75 > m$ **63.** $-10 < t < 4$ **64.** $-6 < k \leq 7$ **65.** $r > 7$ OR $r < -2$ **66.** $\varnothing$ **67.** $-2 < p \leq 5$ **68.** all real numbers **69.** $68 \leq t \leq 84$ **70.** $102 \leq n \leq 183.6$ **71.** $-22 \leq x \leq 22$ **72.** $x < -12$ OR $x > 4$ **73.** $-4 \leq x \leq 4$ **74.** $-18 < x < 0$

75. $x \leq -3$ OR $x \geq 3$ **76.** $-3 < x < 3$ **77.** $x < -13.9$ OR $x > 13.9$ **78.** $-12.5 < x < 2.1$ **79.** $x \leq 5$ OR $x \geq 9$ **80.** $x \leq -4$ OR $x \geq 4$ **81.** $\varnothing$ **82.** $-16.8 \leq x \leq 5.8$ **83.** $|d - 72| \leq 4$, $68 \leq d \leq 76$

Chapter 4

4-1

Check It Out! 1. graph C **2a.** discrete; **2b.** continuous; **3.** Possible answer: When the number of students reaches a certain point, the number of pizzas bought increases.

Exercises 1. continuous **3.** graph B **5.** graph C **11.** graph A **13.** continuous; **19.** The point of intersection represents the time of day when you will be the same distance from the base of the mountain on both the hike up and the hike down. **23.** C **27.** Container C **29.** -8 **31.** $\frac{1}{9}$ **33.** $n - 5 = -2$; 3 **35.** -23, 15

4-2

Check It Out! 1.

x	y
1	3
2	4
3	5

2a. D: $\{6, 5, 2, 1\}$; R: $\{-4, -1, 0\}$ **2b.** D: $\{1, 4, 8\}$; R: $\{1, 4\}$ **3a.** D: $\{-6, -4, 1, 8\}$; R: $\{1, 2, 9\}$; function; each domain value is paired with exactly one range value. **3b.** D: $\{2, 3, 4\}$; R: $\{-5, -4, -3\}$; not a function; the domain value 2 is paired with both -5 and -4.

Exercises

3.

x	y
1	1
1	2

5.

x	y
−7	7
−3	3
−1	1
5	−5

7. D: $\{-5, 0, 2, 5\}$; R: $\{-20, -8, 0, 7\}$ **9.** D: $\{2, 3, 5, 6, 8\}$; R: $\{4, 9, 25, 36, 81\}$ **11.** D: $\{1\}$; R: $\{-2, 0, 3, 8\}$; not a function; the domain value 1 is paired with several different range values. **13.** D: $\{-2, -1, 0, 1, 2\}$; R: $\{1\}$; function; each element in the domain is paired with exactly one element in the range.

15.

x	y
−2	−4
−1	−1
0	0
1	−1
2	−4

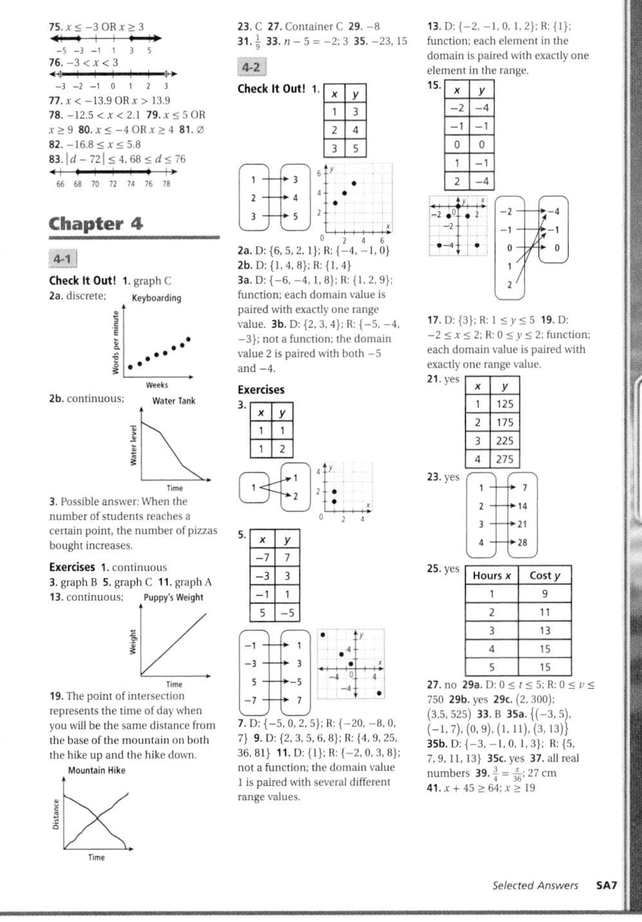

17. D: $\{3\}$; R: $1 \leq y \leq 5$ **19.** D: $-2 \leq x \leq 2$; R: $0 \leq y \leq 2$; function; each domain value is paired with exactly one range value.

21. yes

x	y
1	125
2	175
3	225
4	275

23. yes

25. yes

Hours x	Cost y
1	9
2	11
3	13
4	15
5	15

27. no **29a.** D: $0 \leq t \leq 5$; R: $0 \leq v \leq 750$ **29b.** yes **29c.** (2, 300); (3.5, 525) **33.** B **35a.** $\{(-3, 5), (-1, 7), (0, 9), (1, 11), (3, 13)\}$ **35b.** D: $\{-3, -1, 0, 1, 3\}$; R: $\{5, 7, 9, 11, 13\}$ **35c.** yes **37.** all real numbers **39.** $\frac{3}{4} = \frac{x}{36}$; 27 cm **41.** $x + 45 \geq 64$; $x \geq 19$

4-3

Check It Out! **1.** $y = 3x$ **2a.** yes **2b.** yes

3a. ind. var.: hours; dep. var.: cost; $f(x) = 28x$ **3b.** ind. var.: pounds; dep. var.: cost; $f(x) = 1.69x$ **3c.** ind. var.: people; dep. var.: cost; $f(x) = 6 + 29.99x$ **4.** $h(1) = 1$; $h(-3) = -7$

Exercises **1.** dependent **3.** $y = x - 2$ **5.** yes **7.** yes **9.** yes

11. ind. var.: hours; dep. var.: cost; $f(h) = 75h$ **13.** $f(0) = 2$; $f(1) = 9$ **15.** $h(27) = -1$; $h(-15) = -15$ **17.** $y = -x$ **19.** yes **21.** yes

23. yes **25.** yes

27. ind. var.: days late; dep. var.: total cost; $f(x) = 3.99 + 0.99x$ **29.** ind. var.: gallons of gas; dep. var.: miles; $f(x) = 28x$ **31.** $g(1) = 7$; $g(2) - 10$ **33.** yes; no **35.** yes; no **37a.** yes; ind. var.: hours; dep. var.: distance; $f(h) = 630h$ **37b.** 7560 mi

39.

x	0	1	2	3
$h(x)$	0	2	6	12

41. D: all real numbers; R: all real numbers **43.** D: all real numbers; R: all real numbers **45.** D: all real numbers; R: $y \geq -5$ **47.** -10 **49.** Rashid must multiply $150 by the number of months he saves for, not add the number of months to 150. **51a.** $v = 1250t$ **51b.** ind. var.: time; dep. var.: volume **51c.** 8 h **53.** B **55.** the same; x-value; x-value; y-values; x-value; more than one **61.** 6 **63.** 1 **65.** ∅ **67.** all real numbers **69.** all real numbers **71.** D: $\{-3, -1, 0, 1, 3\}$; R: $\{4, 2, 0, -4\}$; function; each domain value is paired with exactly one range value.

4-4

Check It Out!

1. Football Team Scores

2. positive correlation **3a.** No correlation; the temperature in Houston has nothing to do with the number of cars sold in Boston. **3b.** Positive correlation; as the number of family members increases, more food is needed, so the grocery bill increases too. **3c.** Negative correlation; as the number of times you sharpen your pencil increases, the length of the pencil decreases. **4.** Graph A; it cannot be graph B because graph B shows negative minutes; it cannot be graph C because graph C shows the temperature of the pie increasing, a positive correlation. **5.** about 75 rolls

Exercises **3.** no **5.** positive correlation **7.** negative correlation **9.** positive correlation **11.** Graph A **15.** positive correlation **17.** positive correlation **19.** Graph A **23.** positive correlation **25.** B

27a. Juan's Trip

27b. Positive correlation; as time increases, the number of miles also increases. **29.** C **35.** $5(n + 2) = 2n - 8$, $n = -6$ **37.** no solution **39.** yes **41.** yes

4-5

Check It Out! **1a.** yes; $d = \frac{1}{2}; \frac{5}{4}, \frac{7}{4}, \frac{9}{4}$ **1b.** no **1c.** yes; $d = -3$; $-8, -11, -14$ **2a.** -343 **2b.** 19.6 **3.** 750 lb

Exercises **1.** common difference **3.** yes; $d = -0.7$; $-0.7, -1.4, -2.1$ **5.** no **7.** -53 **9.** no **11.** yes; $d = -9$; $-58, -67, -76$ **13.** 5.9 **15.** 9500 mi

17. $\frac{1}{4}$ **19.** -2.2 **21.** 0.07 **23.** $-\frac{3}{8}, -\frac{1}{2}, -\frac{5}{8}, -\frac{3}{4}$ **25.** $-0.2, -0.7, -1.2, -1.7$ **27.** $-0.3, -0.1, 0.1, 0.3$ **29.** 22 **31.** 122 **33a.** It could be arithmetic because you pay $2 per lap, so the common difference could be 2. **33b.** $11, $13, $15; $a_n = 2n + 7$ **33c.** $37 **33d.** no **35.** -104.5 **37.** $\frac{20}{3}$ **39a.** $a_n = 6 + 3(n - 1)$ **39b.** 48 **39c.** $7800 **39d.** $a_n = 7 + 3(n - 1)$; $8200 **41a.**

Time Interval	Mile Marker
1	520
2	509
3	498
4	487
5	476
6	465

41b. $a_n = 520 + (n - 1)(-11)$ **41c.** number of miles per interval **41d.** 421 **43.** A **45.** 20th and 21st terms **47a.** session 16; yes; she increases the amount she runs by 1.5 miles each time **47b.** Thursday **49.** 16 **51.** $t < -2$ OR $t > 2$ **53.** negative correlation

Study Guide: Review

1. domain **2.** negative correlation **3.** term **4.** continuous **5.** continuous

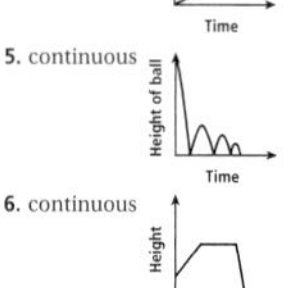

6. continuous

7. Possible answer: A family buys a fish tank and some fish. After two weeks, they buy some more fish. After two more weeks, they buy even more fish. **8.** Possible answer: A monkey swings from a high branch to a lower branch. He climbs along the branch. Then he jumps to a higher branch and takes a nap.

9.

x	-1	0	2
y	0	1	1

10.

x	-2	-1	2	3
y	-1	1	3	4

11. D: $\{-4, -2, 0, 2\}$; R: $\{-1, 1, 3, 5\}$ **12.** D: $\{-2, -1, 0, 1, 2\}$; R: $\{-1, 0\}$ **13.** D: $\{0, 1, 4\}$; R: $\{-2, -1, 0, 1, 2\}$ **14.** D: $-4 \leq x \leq 3$; R: $-3 \leq y \leq 5$ **15.** D: $\{-5, -3, -1, 1\}$; R: $\{-3, -2, -1, 0\}$; function; every element of the domain is assigned to exactly one element in the range. **16.** D: $\{-4, -2, 0, 2\}$; R: $\{-2, 1\}$; function; each element of the domain is assigned to exactly one element in the range. **17.** D: $\{1, 2, 3, 4\}$; R: $\{-1, 0, 1, 2, 3\}$; not a function; the x-value 1 is assigned to the y-value 3 and the y-value -1. **18.** $\{(1, 5.00), (2, 6.50), (3, 8.00), (4, 9.50), (5, 11.00)\}$; yes; each x-value has exactly one y-value. **19.** yes; each element in the domain is assigned to exactly one element in the range.

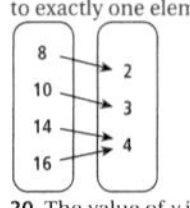

20. The value of y is 7 less than x; $y = x - 7$ **21.** The value of y is $\frac{1}{2}$ times x; $y = \frac{1}{2}x$ **22.** The value of y is 9 times x; $y = 9x$ **23.** independent variable: number of cakes; dependent variable: cost; $f(c) = 6c$ **24.** independent variable: number of CDs Raul will buy; dependent variable: number of CDs Tim will buy; $g(n) = 2n$ **25.** 14 **26.** -11 **27.** 6, -1 **28.** $k(4) = 15$; $k(-6) = 25$ **29.** $w(16) = -1.5$; $w(12.25) = -2$

30. yes

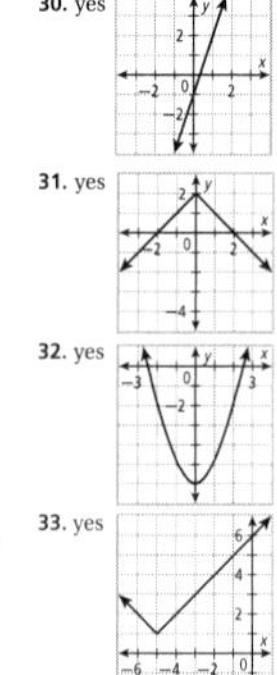

31. yes **32.** yes **33.** yes

34. D: all real numbers; R: all real numbers **35.** D: all real numbers; R: all real numbers **36.** D: all real numbers; R: $y \geq -6$ **37.** D: all real numbers; R: $y \geq 5$

38.

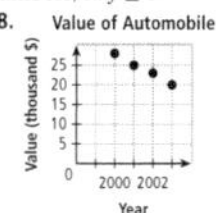

Negative correlation; as the time increases, the value of the automobile decreases. **39.** Possible answer: 33 **40.** yes; -6; $-4, -10, -16$ **41.** no **42.** no **43.** yes; 2.5; 2, 4.5, 7 **44.** 105 **45.** -62 **46.** 20 **47.** $420 **48.** -15.5°C

Chapter 5

5-1

Check It Out! **1a.** yes **1b.** yes **1c.** no **2a.** no **2b.** yes **2c.** yes **3a.** $5x - y = 9$; $A = 5, B = -1, C = 9$; nonhoriz., nonvert. line **3b.** $0x + y = 12$; $A = 0, B = 1, C = 12$; horiz. line **3c.** $x + 0y = 2$; $A = 1, B = 0, C = 2$; vert. line **4.** D: $\{0, 1, 2, 3, \ldots\}$ R: $\{\$10, \$13, \$16, \$19, \ldots\}$

Exercises **1.** no **3.** no **5.** yes **7.** no **9.** yes **11.** $2x + 3y = 5$; $A = 2, B = 3, C = 5$; nonhoriz., nonvert. line **13.** $x - 5y = -3$; $A = 1, B = -5, C = -3$; nonhoriz., nonvert. line **15.** D: $x \geq 0$; R: $y \geq 0$ **17.** yes **19.** yes **21.** yes **23.** no **25.** no **27.** no **29.** $-2x + 4y = 0$; $A = -2, B = 4, C = 0$; nonhoriz., nonvert. line **31.** $3x + 0y = 3$; $A = 3, B = 0, C = 3$; vert. line **33.** The equation will be either $Ax = 1$ or $Bx = 1$; the graph will be either a vertical or horizontal line. **35.** yes **37.** yes **39.** yes; $-4x + y = 2$; $A = -4$; $B = 1$; $C = 2$ **41.** no **43.** yes; $x = 7$; $A = 1$; $B = 0$; $C = 7$; **45.** yes; $3x - y = 1$; $A = 3$; $B = -1$; $C = 1$ **47.** yes; $5x - 2y = -3$; $A = 5$, $B = -2$, $C = -3$ **49.** no

51. **53.** **55.** **57.**

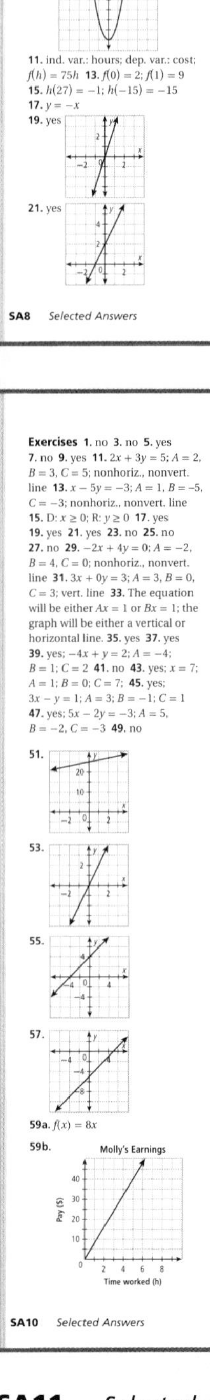

59a. $f(x) = 8x$

59b. Molly's Earnings

59c. yes **61a.** Juan's Workout

61b. The graph forms a line. **63.** no **65.** C **69.** linear **71.** not linear **73.** -1 **75.** $\frac{1}{9}$ **77.** 2 **79.** ∅ **81.** $-22 \leq x \leq 24$ **83.** ∅

5-2

Check It Out! **1a.** x-int.: -2; y-int.: 3 **1b.** x-int.: -10; y-int.: 6 **1c.** x-int.: 4; y-int.: 8 **2a.** x-int.: 30; y-int.: 20;

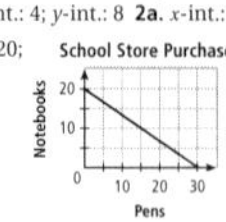

2b. x-int.: pens that can be purchased if no notebooks are purchased; y-int.: notebooks that can be purchased if no pens are purchased.

3a. **3b.**

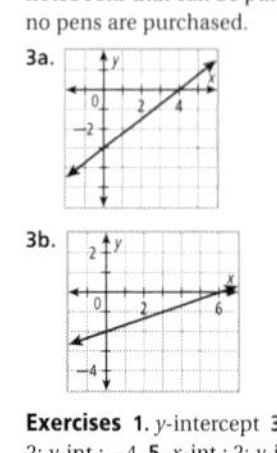

Exercises **1.** y-intercept **3.** x-int.: 2; y-int.: -4 **5.** x-int.: 2; y-int.: -1 **7.** x-int.: 2; y-int.: 8 **9.** **11.**

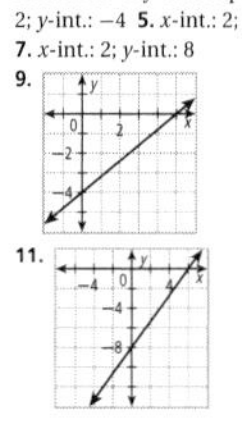

13. x-int.: -1; y-int.: 3 **15.** x-int.: -4; y-int.: 2 **17.** x-int.: -4; y-int.: 2 **19.** x-int.: 2; y-int.: 8 **21.** x-int.: $\frac{1}{8}$; y-int.: -1

23a.

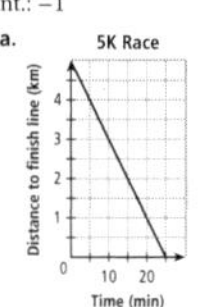

x-int.: 25; y-int.: 5 **23b.** x-int.: total time to run race (when distance to finish line is 0); y-int.: total length of race (when time is 0)

25. **27.** **29.**

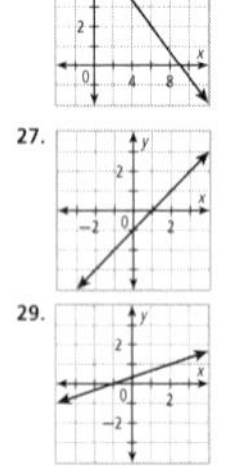

31a. x-int.: 600; y-int.: 7.5 **31b.** x-int.: number of years after 1800 when there will be no acres of tropical forest; y-int.: million acres of tropical forest in 1800

33a.

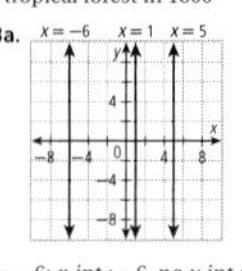

$x = -6$: x-int.: -6, no y-int.; $x = 1$: x-int.: 1, no y-int.; $x = 5$: x-int.: 5, no y-int. **33b.** $y = -3$: no x-int., y-int.: -3; $y = 2$: no x-int., y-int.: 2; $y = 7$: no x-int., y-int.: 7

33c. Horiz.: For $y = c$, the y-int. is c, and there is no x-int. Vert.: For $x = k$, the x-int. is k, and there is no y-int. **35.** A **37.** B **41.** A

43. **45.**

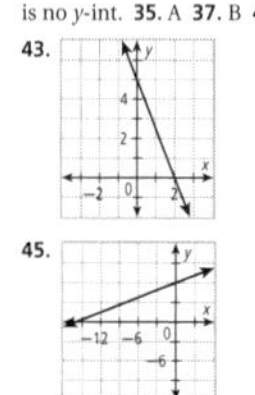

47. 600 in^3 **49.** $m \geq -6$ **51.** yes

5-3

Check It Out! **1.** $-\frac{1}{2}$ **2a.** undefined **2b.** 0 **3a.** $m = 0$ **3b.** $m = 3$ **4a.** undefined **4b.** positive **5.** $m = \frac{1}{2}$; the height of the plant is increasing at a rate of 1 cm every 2 days. **6.** $m = -\frac{2}{3}$

Exercises **1.** rise **3.** $\frac{1}{2}$ **5.** 0 **7.** 1 **9.** $-\frac{1}{2}$ **11.** 2 **13.** negative **15.** 10; the money earned is increasing at a rate of $10/h. **17.** -4 **19.** $\frac{9}{5}$ **21.** undefined **23.** 0 **25.** positive **27.** zero **29.** $-\frac{9}{5000}$; the boiling point is decreasing at a rate of 9 °F for each 5000 ft above sea level. **31.** $-\frac{13}{5}$ **33.** $\frac{17}{18}$ **35a.** In 165 s, about 425 files were scanned. **37.** 10 **41a.** -1 **44b.** For each year that a person ages, the maximum heart rate decreases by 1 beat/min. **43.** D **45.** $-\frac{b}{a}$ **47.** $\frac{3 - 2y}{2}$ **49.** $x = \frac{1}{2}$ **51.** $k = 4.85$ **53.** $f = 41$ **55.** yes **57.** x-int.: -3; y-int.: -9

5-4

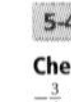

Check It Out! **1a.** no **1b.** yes; $-\frac{3}{4}$ **c.** yes; -3 **2a.** no; possible answer: the value of $\frac{y}{x}$ is not the same for each ordered pair. **2b.** yes; possible answer: the value of $\frac{y}{x}$ is the same for each ordered pair. **2c.** no; possible answer: the value of $\frac{y}{x}$ is not the same for each ordered pair. **3.** 90

4. $y = 4x$

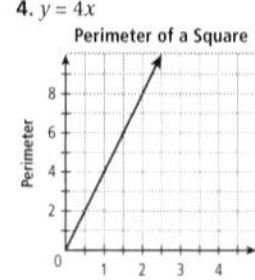

Exercises **1.** direct variation **3.** yes **5.** no **7.** 18 **9.** $y = 5x$ **11.** yes **13.** yes **15.** -16 **17.** $y = 2.50x$ **19.** no **21.** $y = -3x$ **23.** $y = 4x$ **25.** $y = 2x$ **27.** $y = 7x$ **29.** $k = -\frac{2}{9}x$ **31.** $k = \frac{4}{3}x$ **33.** $y = -6x$ **35.** $y = \frac{2}{7}x$ **37a.** $y = 15x$

36b.

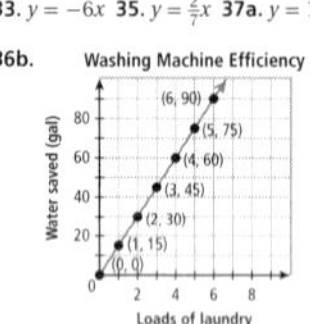

36c. 1560 gal **41.** C **43.** B **45a.** 4 gal **45b.** no **45c.** 750 gal; 250 gal **47.** 6 **49.** D: $\{1, 2, 3, 4\}$; R: $\{-5, -4, -3, -2\}$; yes **51.** D: $\{-3, -2, -1, -2\}$; R: $\{9, 6, 3, 0\}$; no **53.** 2

5-5

Check It Out!

1a. **1b.**

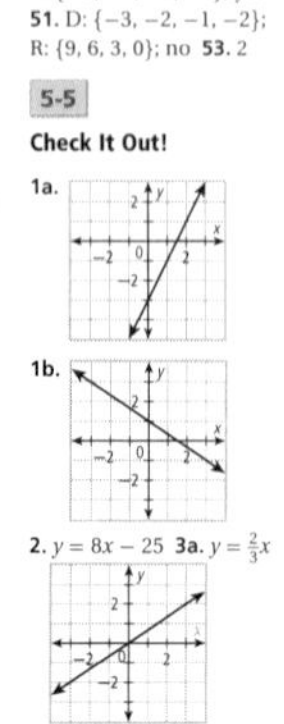

2. $y = 8x - 25$ **3a.** $y = \frac{2}{3}x$ **3b.** $y = -3x + 5$ **3c.** $y = -4$

4a. $y = 18x + 200$ **4b.** slope: 18; cost per person; y-int.: 200; fee **4c.** $3800

Exercises **1.** **3.**

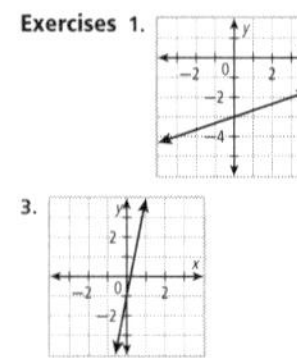

5. $y = 8x + 2$ **7.** $y = -3$ **9.** $y = \frac{2}{5}x - 6$ **11.** $y = -2x + 4$

13. **15.**

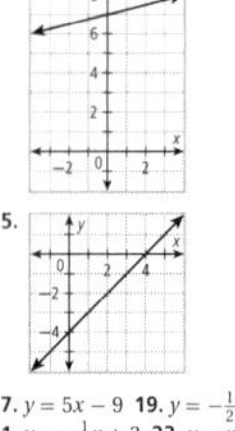

17. $y = 5x - 9$ **19.** $y = -\frac{1}{2}x + 7$ **21.** $y = -\frac{1}{2}x + 3$ **23.** $y = x + 6$ **25.** $y = \frac{7}{2}$ **27.** $y = \frac{1}{2}x + 4$ **29.** $y = -2x + 8$ **31.** student A **35.** impossible **37.** A **41.** B **43.** B **45.** $y = \frac{1}{3}x - 3$ **47.** -6 **49.** $3x + 4 \leq 10$ **51.** $n \leq 8$ **53.** $t < -3$ **55.** x-int.: 3; y-int.: 6

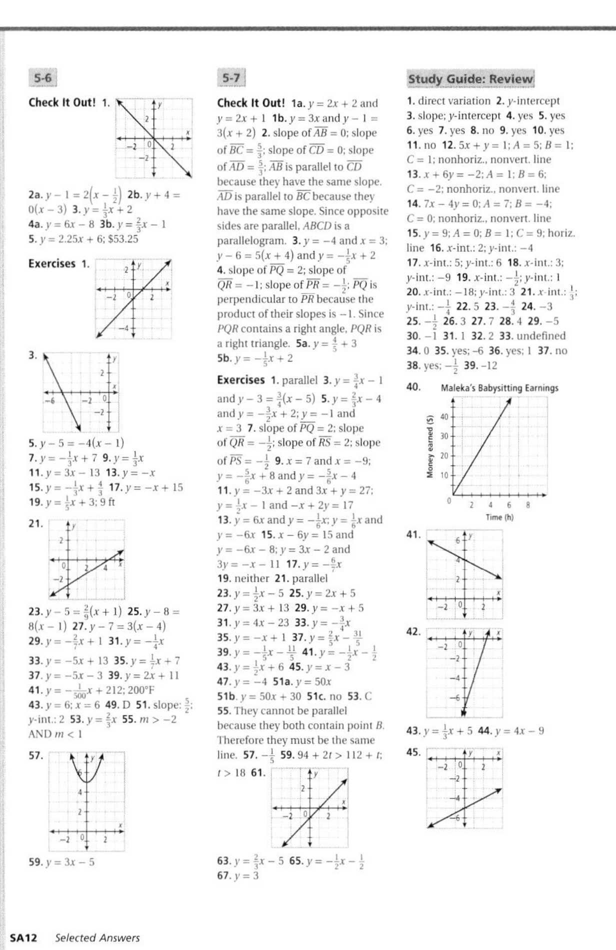

5-6

Check It Out! 1. [graph]

2a. $y - 1 = 2\left(x - \frac{1}{2}\right)$ **2b.** $y + 4 = 0(x - 3)$ **3.** $y = \frac{1}{3}x + 2$
4a. $y = 6x - 8$ **3b.** $y = \frac{2}{3}x - 1$
5. $y = 2.25x + 6$; $53.25

Exercises 1. [graph]

3. [graph]

5. $y - 5 = -4(x - 1)$
7. $y = -\frac{1}{3}x + 7$ **9.** $y = \frac{1}{3}x$
11. $y = 3x - 13$ **13.** $y = -x$
15. $y = -\frac{1}{3}x + \frac{4}{3}$ **17.** $y = -x + 15$
19. $y = \frac{1}{5}x + 3$; 9 ft

21. [graph]

23. $y - 5 = \frac{2}{9}(x + 1)$ **25.** $y - 8 = 8(x - 1)$ **27.** $y - 7 = 3(x - 4)$
29. $y = -\frac{2}{7}x + 1$ **31.** $y = -\frac{1}{4}x$
33. $y = -5x + 13$ **35.** $y = \frac{1}{7}x + 7$
37. $y = -5x - 3$ **39.** $y = 2x + 11$
41. $y = -\frac{1}{500}x + 212$; 200°F
43. $y = 6$; $x = 6$ **49.** D **51.** slope: $\frac{5}{2}$; y-int.: 2 **53.** $y = \frac{2}{3}x$ **55.** $m > -2$ AND $m < 1$

57. [graph]

59. $y = 3x - 5$

5-7

Check It Out! 1a. $y = 2x + 2$ and $y = 2x + 1$ **1b.** $y = 3x$ and $y - 1 = 3(x + 2)$ **2.** slope of $\overline{AB} = 0$; slope of $\overline{BC} = \frac{5}{3}$; slope of $\overline{CD} = 0$; slope of $\overline{AD} = \frac{5}{3}$; $\overline{AB}$ is parallel to $\overline{CD}$ because they have the same slope. $\overline{AD}$ is parallel to $\overline{BC}$ because they have the same slope. Since opposite sides are parallel, $ABCD$ is a parallelogram. **3.** $y = -4$ and $x = 3$; $y - 6 = 5(x + 4)$ and $y = -\frac{1}{5}x + 2$
4. slope of $\overline{PQ} = 2$; slope of $\overline{QR} = -1$; slope of $\overline{PR} = -\frac{1}{2}$; $\overline{PQ}$ is perpendicular to $\overline{PR}$ because the product of their slopes is −1. Since PQR contains a right angle, PQR is a right triangle. **5a.** $y = \frac{4}{5} + 3$
5b. $y = -\frac{1}{5}x + 2$

Exercises 1. parallel **3.** $y = \frac{3}{4}x - 1$ and $y - 3 = \frac{3}{4}(x - 5)$ **5.** $y = \frac{2}{3}x - 4$ and $y = -\frac{3}{2}x + 2$; $y = -1$ and $x = 3$ **7.** slope of $\overline{PQ} = 2$; slope of $\overline{QR} = -\frac{1}{2}$; slope of $\overline{RS} = 2$; slope of $\overline{PS} = -\frac{1}{2}$ **9.** $x = 7$ and $x = -9$; $y = -\frac{5}{6}x + 8$ and $y = -\frac{5}{6}x - 4$
11. $y = -3x + 2$ and $3x + y = 27$; $y = \frac{1}{2}x - 1$ and $-x + 2y = 17$
13. $y = 6x$ and $y = -\frac{1}{6}x$; $y = \frac{1}{6}x$ and $y = -6x$ **15.** $x - 6y = 15$ and $y = -6x - 8$; $y = 3x - 2$ and $3y = -x - 11$ **17.** $y = -\frac{6}{7}x$
19. neither **21.** parallel
23. $y = \frac{1}{2}x - 5$ **25.** $y = 2x + 5$
27. $y = 3x + 13$ **29.** $y = -x + 5$
31. $y = 4x - 23$ **33.** $y = -\frac{3}{4}x$
35. $y = -x + 1$ **37.** $y = \frac{2}{5}x - \frac{31}{5}$
39. $y = -\frac{1}{5}x - \frac{11}{5}$ **41.** $y = -\frac{1}{2}x - \frac{1}{2}$
43. $y = \frac{1}{2}x + 6$ **45.** $y = x - 3$
47. $y = -4$ **51a.** $y = 50x$
51b. $y = 50x + 30$ **51c.** no **53.** C
55. They cannot be parallel because they both contain point B. Therefore they must be the same line. **57.** $-\frac{1}{5}$ **59.** $94 + 2t > 112 + t$; $t > 18$ **61.** [graph]

63. $y = \frac{2}{3}x - 5$ **65.** $y = -\frac{1}{2}x - \frac{1}{2}$
67. $y = 3$

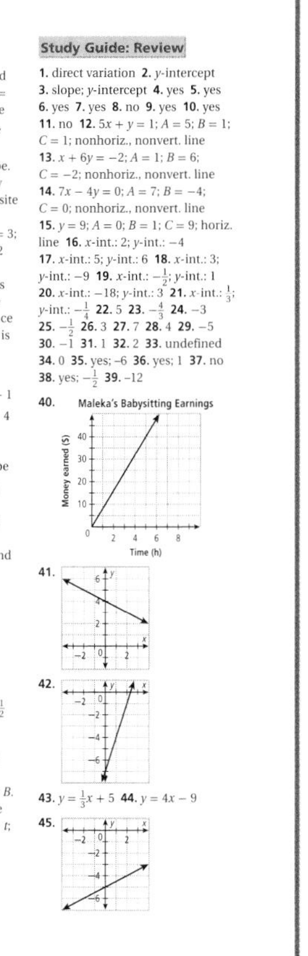

Study Guide: Review

1. direct variation **2.** y-intercept
3. slope; y-intercept **4.** yes **5.** yes
6. yes **7.** yes **8.** no **9.** yes **10.** yes
11. no **12.** $5x + y = 1$; $A = 5$; $B = 1$; $C = 1$; nonhoriz., nonvert. line
13. $x + 6y = -2$; $A = 1$; $B = 6$; $C = -2$; nonhoriz., nonvert. line
14. $7x - 4y = 0$; $A = 7$; $B = -4$; $C = 0$; nonhoriz., nonvert. line
15. $y = 9$; $A = 0$; $B = 1$; $C = 9$; horiz. line **16.** x-int.: 2; y-int.: −4
17. x-int.: 5; y-int.: 6 **18.** x-int.: 3; y-int.: −9 **19.** x-int.: $-\frac{1}{2}$; y-int.: 1
20. x-int.: −18; y-int.: 3 **21.** x-int.: $\frac{1}{3}$; y-int.: $-\frac{1}{4}$ **22.** 5 **23.** $-\frac{4}{3}$ **24.** −3
25. $-\frac{1}{2}$ **26.** 3 **27.** 7 **28.** 4 **29.** −5
30. −1 **31.** 1 **32.** 2 **33.** undefined
34. 0 **35.** yes; −6 **36.** yes; 1 **37.** no
38. yes; $-\frac{1}{2}$ **39.** −12

40. Maleka's Babysitting Earnings [graph: Money earned ($) vs. Time (h)]

41. [graph]

42. [graph]

43. $y = \frac{1}{3}x + 5$ **44.** $y = 4x - 9$
45. [graph]

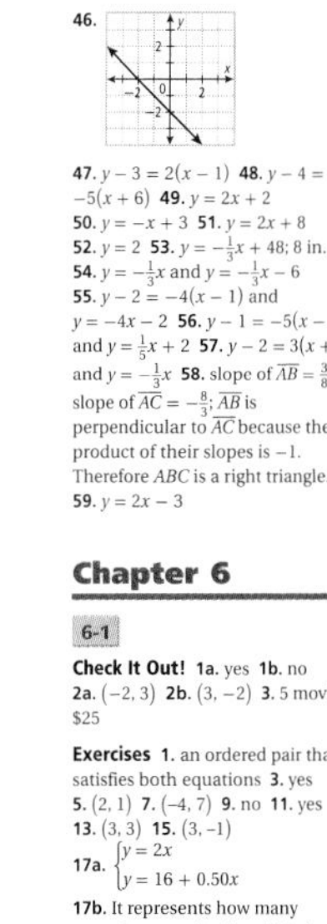

46. [graph]

47. $y - 3 = 2(x - 1)$ **48.** $y - 4 = -5(x + 6)$ **49.** $y = 2x + 2$
50. $y = -x + 3$ **51.** $y = 2x + 8$
52. $y = 2$ **53.** $y = -\frac{1}{3}x + 48$; 8 in.
54. $y = -\frac{1}{3}x$ and $y = -\frac{1}{3}x - 6$
55. $y - 2 = -4(x - 1)$ and $y = -4x - 2$ **56.** $y - 1 = -5(x - 6)$ and $y = \frac{1}{5}x + 2$ **57.** $y - 2 = 3(x + 1)$ and $y = -\frac{1}{3}x$ **58.** slope of $\overline{AB} = \frac{3}{8}$; slope of $\overline{AC} = -\frac{8}{3}$; $\overline{AB}$ is perpendicular to $\overline{AC}$ because the product of their slopes is −1. Therefore ABC is a right triangle.
59. $y = 2x - 3$

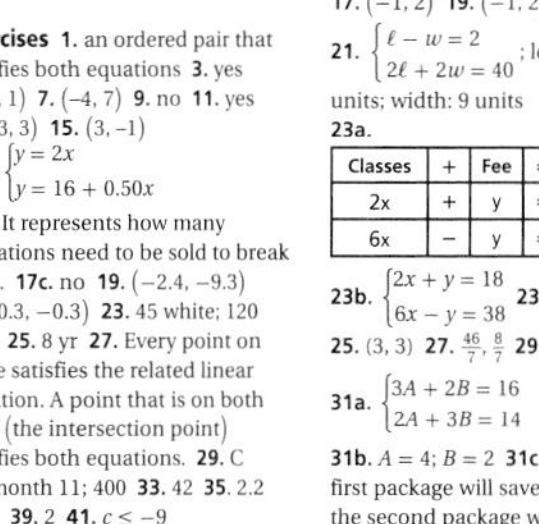

Chapter 6

6-1

Check It Out! 1a. yes **1b.** no
2a. (−2, 3) **2b.** (3, −2) **3.** 5 movies; $25

Exercises 1. an ordered pair that satisfies both equations **3.** yes
5. (2, 1) **7.** (−4, 7) **9.** no **11.** yes
13. (3, 3) **15.** (3, −1)
17a. $\begin{cases} y = 2x \\ y = 16 + 0.50x \end{cases}$
17b. It represents how many carnations need to be sold to break even. **17c.** no **19.** (−2.4, −9.3)
21. (0.3, −0.3) **23.** 45 white; 120 pink **25.** 8 yr **27.** Every point on a line satisfies the related linear equation. A point that is on both lines (the intersection point) satisfies both equations. **29.** C
31. month 11; 400 **33.** 42 **35.** 2.2
37. 1 **39.** 2 **41.** $c \le -9$

6-2

Check It Out! 1a. (−2, 1)
1b. (0, 2) **1c.** (3, −10) **2.** (−1, 6)
3a. 10 months **3b.** $860; the first option; the first option is cheaper for the first 9 months; the second option is cheaper after 10 months.

Exercises 1. (9, 35) **3.** (3, 8)
5. $\left(-\frac{15}{2}, -12\right)$ **7a.** 3 months; $136
7b. Green Lawn **9.** (−4, 2)
11. $\left(\frac{1}{2}, \frac{1}{2}\right)$ **13.** (1, 5) **15.** (3, −2)
17a. 6 months; $360 **17b.** the second option **19.** (2, −2)
21. (8, 6) **23.** (−9, −14.8) **25.** 4; 66
27. $\begin{cases} x + y = 1000 \\ 0.05x + 0.06y = 58 \end{cases}$; $200 at 5%; $800 at 6% **29.** $m\angle x = 60°$; $m\angle y = 30°$ **31.** $m\angle x = 29°$; $m\angle y = 61°$ **35a.** $\begin{cases} 2x + y = 26 \\ x = y - 8 \end{cases}$
35b. book: $6; backpack: $14 **37.** D
39. $\begin{cases} n + u = 378 \\ 4n = 5u \end{cases}$; 210 new cars; 168 used cars **41.** $x = 2$; $y = 1$; $z = 4$
43. yes **45.** yes **47.** x-int.: 15; y-int.: −5 **49.** no **51.** no

6-3

Check It Out! 1. (−2, 4) **2.** (4, 1)
3a. (2, 0) **3b.** (3, 4) **4.** 9 lilies; 4 tulips

Exercises 1. (−4, 1) **3.** (−2, −4)
5. (−6, 30) **7.** (3, 2) **9.** (4, −3)
11. (−1, −2) **13.** (1, 5) **15.** $\left(6, -\frac{1}{2}\right)$
17. (−1, 2) **19.** (−1, 2)
21. $\begin{cases} \ell - w = 2 \\ 2\ell + 2w = 40 \end{cases}$; length: 11 units; width: 9 units
23a.

Classes	+	Fee	=	Total Price
2x	+	y	=	18
6x	−	y	=	38

23b. $\begin{cases} 2x + y = 18 \\ 6x - y = 38 \end{cases}$ **23c.** 7; 4
25. (3, 3) **27.** $\frac{46}{7}, \frac{8}{7}$ **29.** $\frac{15}{7}, \frac{9}{7}$
31a. $\begin{cases} 3A + 2B = 16 \\ 2A + 3B = 14 \end{cases}$
31b. $A = 4$; $B = 2$ **31c.** Buying the first package will save $8; buying the second package will save $7.
33. A **35a.** $\begin{cases} s + n = 358 \\ 1.50s + 3.25n = 752.25 \end{cases}$
35b. $s = 235$; $n = 123$ **37.** $x = 4$; $y = -1$; $z = 10$ **39.** pen = $2; notebook = $6; bag = $9 **41.** $y = 3x$
43. $y = 2x - 9$ **45.** $y = \frac{1}{2}x + 10$
47. (4, 9)

6-4

Check It Out! 1. no solution
2. infinitely many solutions
3a. consistent, dependent; infinitely many solutions **3b.** consistent, independent; one solution
3c. inconsistent; no solution
4. Yes; the graphs of the two equations have different slopes so they intersect.

Exercises 1. consistent **3.** no sol.
5. inf. many solutions **7.** inf. many solutions **9.** inconsis.; no sol.
11. yes **13.** no solution **15.** no solution **17.** inf. many solutions
19. inf. many solutions **21.** consis., indep.; one sol. **23.** yes **25.** There are infinitely many answers for the cost of each video game and DVD. The system is consistent and dependent. **27.** They will always have the same amount; both started with 2 and add 4 every year.
29. The graph will be 2 parallel lines. **31.** student A **33.** D
35. $p = q$; $p \ne q$ **37.** 11 km
39. −3.5, 8.5 **41.** $-\frac{13}{3}$, 1
43. (−2, −4)

6-5

Check It Out! 1. 1.5 mi/h; 9 mi
2. 25 g of the 9% solution; 5 g of the 15% solution **3.** 89

Exercises 1. 1 mi/h; 5 mi/h **3.** 59
5. 300 mL of each
7a.

	Quarters	+	Dimes	=	Total
Number of Coins	q	+	d	=	250
Value in Dollars	0.25q	+	0.1d	=	39.25

7b. $\begin{cases} q + d = 250 \\ 0.25q + 0.1d = 39.25 \end{cases}$
7c. 95 quarters; 155 dimes
9a. $f + 4$; $d + 4$
9b. $\begin{cases} f = d + 32 \\ f + 4 = 5(d + 4) \end{cases}$
9c. father: 36; daughter: 4 **11.** 49
13a. $\begin{cases} a + c = 100 \\ 13a + 8c = 1100 \end{cases}$
13b. 60 adults'; 40 children's
13c. 80 adults'; 20 children's **17.** D
19. Maya: 25; David: 20

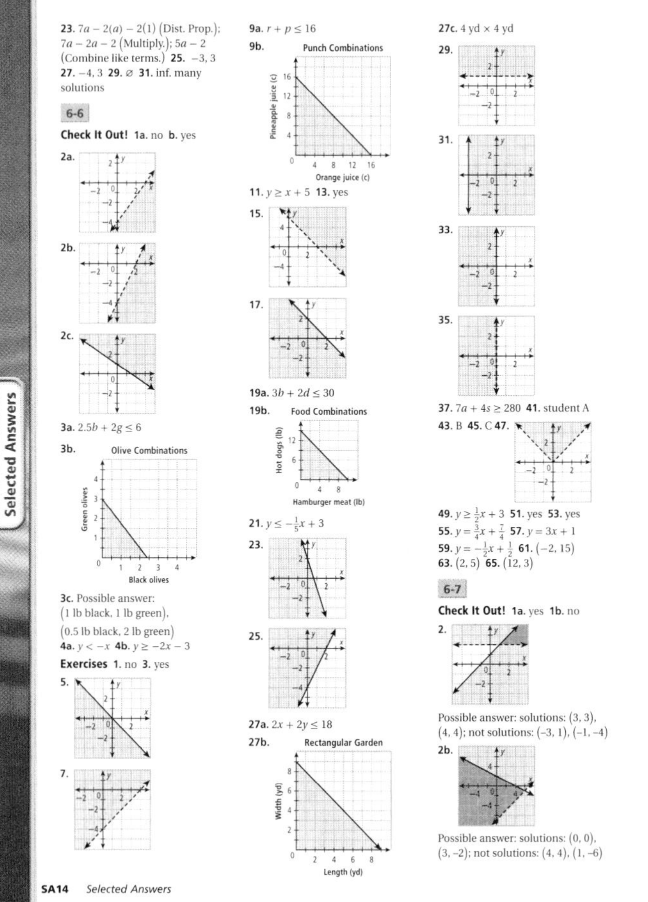

23. $7a - 2(a) - 2(1)$ (Dist. Prop.); $7a - 2a - 2$ (Multiply.); $5a - 2$ (Combine like terms.) **25.** −3, 3
27. −4, 3 **29.** ∅ **31.** inf. many solutions

6-6

Check It Out! 1a. no **b.** yes

2a. [graph]

2b. [graph]

2c. [graph]

3a. $2.5b + 2g \le 6$

3b. Olive Combinations [graph: Green olives vs. Black olives]

3c. Possible answer: (1 lb black, 1 lb green), (0.5 lb black, 2 lb green)
4a. $y < -x$ **4b.** $y \ge -2x - 3$

Exercises 1. no **3.** yes

5. [graph]

7. [graph]

9a. $r + p \le 16$
9b. Punch Combinations [graph: Pineapple juice (c) vs. Orange juice (c)]

11. $y \ge x + 5$ **13.** yes

15. [graph]

17. [graph]

19a. $3b + 2d \le 30$
19b. Food Combinations [graph: Hot dogs (lb) vs. Hamburger meat (lb)]

21. $y \le -\frac{1}{5}x + 3$

23. [graph]

25. [graph]

27a. $2x + 2y \le 18$
27b. Rectangular Garden [graph: Width (yd) vs. Length (yd)]

27c. 4 yd × 4 yd

29. [graph]

31. [graph]

33. [graph]

35. [graph]

37. $7a + 4s \ge 280$ **41.** student A
43. B **45.** C **47.** [graph]

49. $y \ge \frac{1}{2}x + 3$ **51.** yes **53.** yes
55. $y = \frac{3}{4}x + \frac{7}{4}$ **57.** $y = 3x + 1$
59. $y = -\frac{1}{2}x + \frac{1}{2}$ **61.** (−2, 15)
63. (2, 5) **65.** (12, 3)

6-7

Check It Out! 1a. yes **1b.** no
2. [graph]

Possible answer: solutions: (3, 3), (4, 4); not solutions: (−3, 1), (−1, −4)
2b. [graph]

Possible answer: solutions: (0, 0), (3, −2); not solutions: (4, 4), (1, −6)

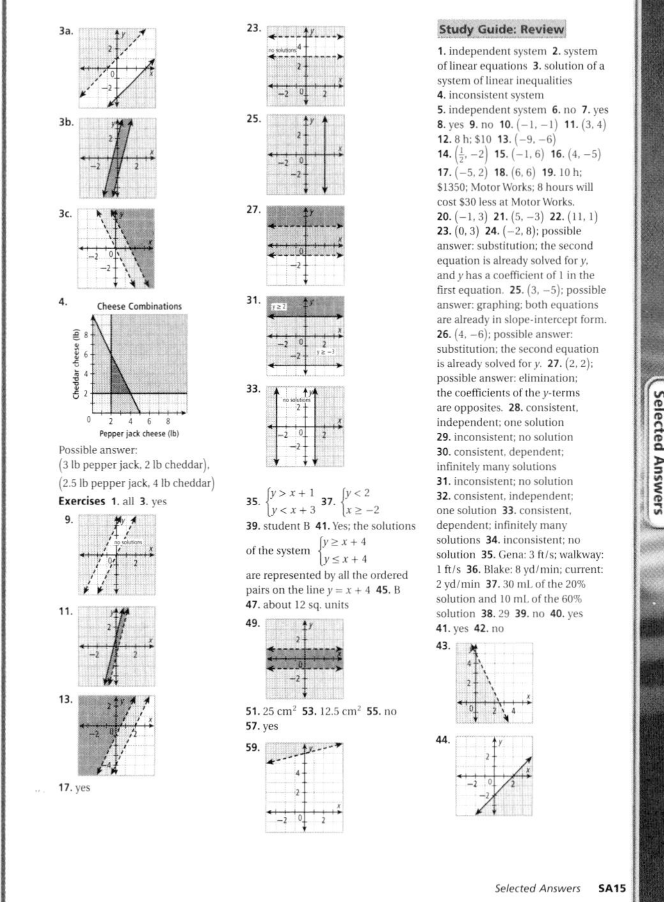

3a. [graph]

3b. [graph]

3c. [graph]

4. Cheese Combinations [graph: Cheddar cheese (lb) vs. Pepper jack cheese (lb)]

Possible answer: (3 lb pepper jack, 2 lb cheddar), (2.5 lb pepper jack, 4 lb cheddar)

Exercises 1. all **3.** yes

9. [graph: no solutions]

11. [graph]

13. [graph]

17. yes

23. [graph: no solutions]

25. [graph]

27. [graph]

31. [graph: $y \ge 2$, $y \ge -3$]

33. [graph: no solutions]

35. $\begin{cases} y > x + 1 \\ y < x + 3 \end{cases}$ **37.** $\begin{cases} y < 2 \\ x \ge -2 \end{cases}$
39. student B **41.** Yes; the solutions of the system $\begin{cases} y \ge x + 4 \\ y \le x + 4 \end{cases}$ are represented by all the ordered pairs on the line $y = x + 4$ **45.** B
47. about 12 sq. units
49. [graph]

51. 25 cm² **53.** 12.5 cm² **55.** no
57. yes
59. [graph]

Study Guide: Review

1. independent system **2.** system of linear equations **3.** solution of a system of linear inequalities
4. inconsistent system
5. independent system **6.** no **7.** yes
8. yes **9.** no **10.** (−1, −1) **11.** (3, 4)
12. 8 h; $10 **13.** (−9, −6)
14. $\left(\frac{1}{2}, -2\right)$ **15.** (−1, 6) **16.** (4, −5)
17. (−5, 2) **18.** (6, 6) **19.** 10 h; $1350; Motor Works; 8 hours will cost $30 less at Motor Works.
20. (−1, 3) **21.** (5, −3) **22.** (11, 1)
23. (0, 3) **24.** (−2, 8); possible answer: substitution; the second equation is already solved for y, and y has a coefficient of 1 in the first equation. **25.** (3, −5); possible answer: graphing; both equations are already in slope-intercept form.
26. (4, −6); possible answer: substitution; the second equation is already solved for y. **27.** (2, 2); possible answer: elimination; the coefficients of the y-terms are opposites. **28.** consistent, independent; one solution
29. inconsistent; no solution
30. consistent, dependent; infinitely many solutions
31. inconsistent; no solution
32. consistent, independent; one solution **33.** consistent, dependent; infinitely many solutions **34.** inconsistent; no solution **35.** Gena: 3 ft/s; walkway: 1 ft/s **36.** Blake: 8 yd/min; current: 2 yd/min **37.** 30 mL of the 20% solution and 10 mL of the 60% solution **38.** 29 **39.** no **40.** yes
41. yes **42.** no
43. [graph]

44. [graph]

45. 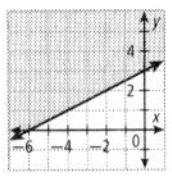

46. 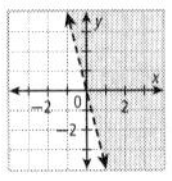

47. 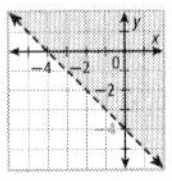

48. 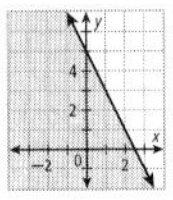

49. Let x = slices of pizza and y = bottles of soda; $2x + 1y \geq 450$

Possible answer: (200, 50), (150, 150) **50.** no **51.** yes
52. Possible answer: solutions: (−6, 6), (−10, 0); not solutions: (0, 0), (4, −4) 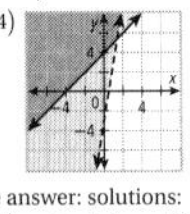

53. Possible answer: solutions: (0, 0), (−5, 0); not solutions: (8, 0) (3, −3) 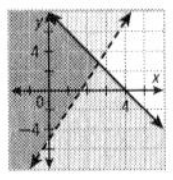

54. Possible answer: solutions: (−6, 2), (−8, 1); not solutions: (0, 0), (4, 1) 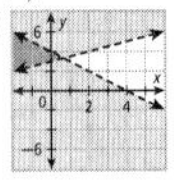

55. 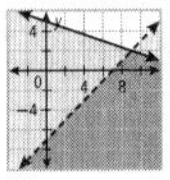

Possible answer: solutions: (8, −8), (9, 0); not solutions: (0, 0), (0, −4)

56. 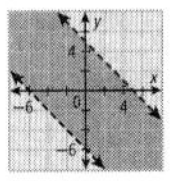

57. 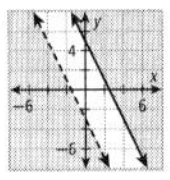

Chapter 7

7-1

Check It Out! **1.** $\frac{1}{125}$ m **2a.** $\frac{1}{10,000}$ **2b.** $\frac{1}{16}$ **2c.** $-\frac{1}{32}$ **2d.** $-\frac{1}{32}$ **3a.** $\frac{1}{64}$ **3b.** 2 **4a.** $\frac{2}{m^3}$ **4b.** $\frac{1}{7r^3}$ **4c.** g^4h^6

Exercises **1.** $\frac{1}{10,000,000}$ m **3.** 1 **5.** $\frac{1}{27}$ **7.** $-\frac{1}{512}$ **9.** 1 **11.** $\frac{1}{16}$ **13.** $\frac{1}{256}$ **15.** $-\frac{1}{32}$ **17.** $\frac{3}{k^4}$ **19.** $x^{10}d^3$ **21.** $\frac{g^6}{f^4}$ **23.** $\frac{p^7}{q}$ **25.** 1 **27.** $\frac{1}{81}$ **29.** $-\frac{1}{36}$ **31.** 1 **33.** $-\frac{1}{3}$ **35.** 4 **37.** $\frac{1}{256}$ **39.** 1 **41.** $\frac{1}{144}$ **43.** $\frac{1}{k^4}$ **45.** $\frac{b^3}{2}$ **47.** $-\frac{5}{x^3}$ **49.** $\frac{2g^{10}}{7}$ **51.** s^5t^{12} **53.** 1 **55.** $\frac{1}{q^2}$ **57.** $\frac{h^3}{6m^2k}$ **59.** $\frac{1}{16}$ **61.** $-\frac{1}{6}$ **63.** 3 **65.** $\frac{1}{81}$ **67.** $\frac{a^3}{b^2}$ **69.** $\frac{w^2}{y}$ **71.** $-\frac{5}{y^6}$ **73.** $2a^3b$ **75.** $\frac{1}{3x^8y^{12}}$ **77.** red blood cell: $\frac{1}{125,000}$ m; white blood cell: $\frac{3}{250,000}$ m; platelet: $\frac{3}{1,000,000}$ m **79.** never **81.** sometimes **83.** sometimes **87.** 81 **89.** 1 **91.** −3 **93.** −1 **95.** D **97.** A **99.** $\frac{1}{a^n}$; a^{-n} is the same as $\frac{1}{a^n}$ and b^0 is 1. So you have $\frac{1}{a^n} \cdot 1$, or simply $\frac{1}{a^n}$.

101.

n	1^n	$(-1)^n$
−1	1	−1
−2	1	1
−3	1	−1
−4	1	1
−5	1	−1

$(1)^n = 1$; $(-1)^n = -1$ if n is odd, and $(-1)^n = 1$ if n is even. **103.** −2 **105.** 4 **107.** 28 **109.** ind.: number of days; dep.: total cost; $f(x) = 10x + 30$ **111.** $y = \frac{1}{3}x + 5$

7-2

Check It Out! **1a.** 0.01 **1b.** 100,000 **1c.** 10,000,000,000 **2a.** 10^8 **2b.** 10^{-4} **2c.** 10^{-1} **3a.** 85,340,000 **3b.** 0.00163 **4a.** 1.43×10^5 km **4b.** 13,000 m/s **5.** 2×10^{-12}, 4×10^{-3}, 5.2×10^{-3}, 3×10^{14}, 4.5×10^{14}, 4.5×10^{30}

Exercises **1.** A number written in scientific notation is a product with 2 parts: a decimal greater than or equal to 1 and less than 10 and a power of 10. **3.** 0.00001 **5.** 100,000,000 **7.** 10^{-6} **9.** 650,300,000 **11.** 0.092 **13.** 5.85×10^{-3}, 2.5×10^{-1}, 8.5×10^{-1}, 3.6×10^8, 8.5×10^8 **15.** 0.000000001 **17.** 100,000,000,000,000 **19.** 10^6 **21.** 92,000 **23.** 0.00042 **25.** 10,000,000,000,000 **27.** 1.23×10^{-3}, 1.32×10^{-3}, 3.12×10^{-3}, 2.13×10^{-1}, 2.13×10^1, 3.12×10^2 **29.** 2.7×10^7 **31.** 2.35×10^5 **33.** 6×10^{-7} **35.** 4.12×10^{-2} **37.** yes **39.** no **41.** yes **43.** yes **45a.** 490,000,000; 740,000,000; 1,329,000,000 **45b.** Zorah's observation is correct. **47.** 10^{-3} **49a.** 300,000,000 **49c.** 6.8×10^{-7} **51.** A **53.** about 7 times **55.** $m \geq 45$ **57.** $n > 50$ **59.** (−2, 1) **61.** (−4, 2) **63.** (7, 1) **65.** 1

7-3

Check It Out! **1a.** 7^{12} **1b.** 3×5^{10} **1c.** $\frac{m^5}{n^4}$ **1d.** $\frac{1}{x^7}$ **2.** 6.696×10^8 mi **3a.** 3^{20} **3b.** 1 **3c.** a^{18} **4a.** $64p^3$ **4b.** $25t^4$ **4c.** $\frac{1}{y^4}$

Exercises **1.** 2^5 **3.** n^8 **5.** 7.5×10^8 mi **7.** y^{32} **9.** $\frac{1}{3^4}$, or $\frac{1}{81}$

11. x^7y^{13} **13.** $36k^2$ **15.** $-8x^{15}$ **17.** b^{10} **19.** 6^8 **21.** $\frac{x}{y^3}$ **23.** 2^9, or 512 **25.** $\frac{1}{x^2}$ **27.** $\frac{a^{12}}{b^5}$ **29.** $27x^3$ **31.** $p^{28}q^{14}$ **33.** $-256x^{12}$ **35.** 6 **37.** 3 **39.** 8 **41.** $2x^3$ **43.** $2m^{10}n^6$ **45.** $108x^{13}$ **47.** $125x^6$ **49.** $3a^6$ **51.** 10^3, or 1000 **53.** Earth: 9.3×10^7 mi; Mars: 1.4136×10^8 mi; Jupiter: 4.836×10^8 mi; Saturn: 8.928×10^8 mi **55a.** Exponents are multiplied but should be added; x^6. **55b.** Exponents are added but should be multiplied; x^{20} **55c.** Exponent is written as a power but should be multiplied; x^6 **57.** $\frac{a^7}{b^5}$ **59.** $15m^{12}n^9$ **61.** $9s^2t^7$ **63.** t^7 **65a.** 9^3, or 729. Round −3.031 to −3. **65b.** 0.0245 **69.** $17k^2$ **71.** $6x^4$ **73.** $15a^2b^3$ **75a.** 6×10^{-7} m **75b.** 3×10^8 m/s **75c.** Assoc. and Comm. Properties of Mult. **77.** $(6ab)^2$ **79.** $\left(\frac{1}{2kmn}\right)^2$ **81.** C **83.** A **85.** 3^{2x} **87.** $x + 1$ **89.** x^{3y+3z} **91.** x^{x^2} **93.** $x = 4$ **95.** $x = 4$ **97.** 1.728 cm³ **99.** $8 + 6x = 71 + 3$; 11 **101.** $|x - 120| = 12$; 108°F; 132°F **103.** 0.000495 **105.** 6,000,000

7-4

Check It Out! **1a.** 4 **1b.** $\frac{1}{y^3}$ **1c.** $\frac{n^3}{m^5}$ **1d.** $\frac{3}{16}$ **2.** 1.1×10^{-2} **3.** $12,800 **4a.** $\frac{2^6}{3^4}$, or $\frac{64}{81}$ **4b.** $\frac{a^5b^{20}}{c^{10}d^{15}}$ **4c.** $\frac{a^3}{b^3}$ **5a.** $\frac{9^3}{4^3}$, or $\frac{729}{64}$ **5b.** $\frac{b^8c^{12}}{16a^4}$ **5c.** $\frac{t}{s^4}$

Exercises **1.** 25 **3.** 3 **5.** 7×10^2 **7.** 1 **9.** $\frac{4}{25}$ **11.** $\frac{1}{a^6b^4}$ **13.** $\frac{16}{9}$ **15.** $\frac{2b^2}{3a^2}$ **17.** 27 **19.** x^5 **21.** 5×10^{-7} **23.** 7×10^{-3} **25.** 2×10^{27} kg **27.** $\frac{a^{12}}{b^6}$ **29.** $\frac{y^3}{x^6}$ **31.** $\frac{y^{25}}{x^{10}}$ **33.** $\frac{196}{9x^2}$ **35.** $2d^2$ **37.** $\frac{3x^5}{4}$ **39.** $\frac{c^4}{a^4}$ **41.** $\frac{25}{p^2}$ **43.** $\frac{1}{100}$ **45.** −1 **47.** 2000: 3×10^1; 1995: 2.84×10^1; 1990: 2.65×10^1 **51.** 3 **53.** 3; 4 **55.** B **57.** A **59.** 3 **63.** 1 **65.** 12 **67.** $x = -\frac{1}{2}$ **69.** 1 **71.** $-125x^{12}$

7-5

Check It Out! **1a.** 3 **1b.** 15 **2a.** 8 **2b.** 1 **2c.** 81 **3.** 1944 **4a.** xy^3 **4b.** xy

Exercises **1.** 5 **3.** 4 **5.** 3 **7.** 6 **9.** 5 **11.** 10 **13.** 4 **15.** 32 **17.** 125 **19.** 256 **21.** 0 **23.** x^2y **25.** x^3y^3 **27.** a^2 **29.** 1 **31.** 10 **33.** 8 **35.** 2 **37.** 2 **39.** 14 **41.** 8 **43.** 8 **45.** 64 **47.** 1000 **49.** 243 **51.** $2g$ **53.** $2m$ **55.** $3x^2$ **57.** ab^4 **59.** a^8b **61.** 1 **63.** 0 **65.** 625 **67.** 3 **69.** $\frac{2}{3}$ **71.** $\frac{1}{4}$ **73.** $\frac{4}{9}$ **75.** $\frac{8}{343}$ **77.** $\frac{1}{27}$ **79.** $\frac{16}{625}$ **81.** 1.86 in. **83.** $n^{\frac{2}{3}}$ will be less than n because $\frac{2}{3} < 1$. $n^{\frac{3}{2}}$ will be greater than n because $\frac{3}{2} > 1$. **85a.** 10 in. **85b.** The distance doubles (20 in.). **87.** B **89.** C **91.** a **93.** x^3 **95.** 3 **97.** 36π cm²; both volume and surface area are described by 36π (although the units are different). **99.** −1 **101.** $n < 3$ **103.** $y \leq -2$ **105.** D: {−2, −1, −0, 1}; R: {0, 1, 2, 3}; function; each domain value is paired with exactly one range value. **107.** D: $1 \leq x \leq 4$; R: $2 \leq y \leq 4$; function; each domain value is paired with exactly one range value.

7-6

Check It Out! **1a.** 3 **1b.** 1 **1c.** 3 **2a.** $x^5 + 9x^3 - 4x^2 + 16$; 1 **2b.** $-3y^8 + 18y^5 + 14y$; −3 **3a.** constant monomial **3b.** cubic polynomial **3c.** 8th degree trinomial **4.** 1606 ft **5.** yes

Exercises **1.** d **3.** a **5.** 3 **7.** 0 **9.** $-8a^9 + 9a^8$; −8 **11.** $3x^2 + 2x - 1$; 3 **13.** $5c^4 + 5c^3 + 3c^2 - 4$; 5 **15.** linear binomial **17.** quartic polynomial **19.** quartic trinomial **21.** no **23.** yes **25.** yes **27.** 4 **29.** 6 **31.** 7 **33.** 1 **35.** $4.9t^3 - 4t^2 + t + 2.5$; 4.9 **37.** $x^{10} + x^7 - x^5 + x^3 - x$; 1 **39.** $5x^3 + 3x^2 + 5x - 4$; 5 **41.** $-d^3 + 3d^2 + 4d + 5$; −1 **43.** $-x^5 - x^3 + 4x^2 + 1$; −1 **45.** linear monomial **47.** quadratic trinomial **49.** quartic trinomial **51.** quadratic monomial **53.** yes **55.** yes **57.** no **59.** always **61.** never **63a.** 58.05 in³ **63b.** 66 in³ **63c.** 0 **63d.** yes **65.** −48; 0; 3270 **75.** A **77.** C **79a.** 58 cm; 65 cm **79b.** 50.310 cm **79c.** The first three terms of the polynomial will equal 0, so just look at the constant. **81.** $90 - m - 2m = 45$; 15 min **83.** inconsistent; no solutions **85.** consistent and independent; one solution **87.** $\frac{x^2}{y^5}$ **89.** $\frac{p^8}{16}$

7-7

Check It Out! **1a.** $5s^2 + 6$ **1b.** $20z^4 - 6$ **1c.** $x^8 + 6y^8$ **1d.** b^3c^2 **2.** $12a^3 + 15a^2 - 16a$ **3.** $-2x^2 - x$ **4.** $-0.05x^2 + 46x - 3200$

Exercises **1.** $-3a^2 + 9a$ **3.** $0.26r^4 + 0.32r^3$ **5.** $3b^3c$ **7.** $23n^3 + 3n + 15$ **9.** $9x^2 - x - 6$ **11.** $4c^4 + 8c + 6$ **13.** $-3r + 11$ **15.** $8a^2 + 5a + 9$ **17.** $12n^2 + 6n - 3m$ **19.** $d^5 + 1$ **21.** $5x$ **23.** $2x^3 - 5$ **25.** $10t^2 + t$ **27.** $x^5 + x^4$ **29.** $-2t^3 + 8t^2$ **31.** $-6m^3 + 2m^2 + 5m + 3$ **33.** $4w^2 + 6w + 4$ **35.** $t - 5$ **37.** $2n - 2$ **39.** $6x^2 - x - 1$ **41.** $-u^3 + 3u^2 + 3u + 6$ **43.** $x = \frac{3}{2}$, or 1.5 **45.** B **47.** $3x + 6$ **49.** $6x + 14$ **51.** $2x^2 + x - 5$ **53a.** 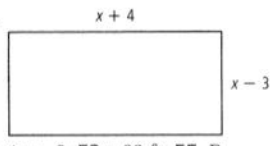

53b. $4x + 2$ **53c.** 62 ft **55.** B **57.** $3x^2 - 2$ **63.** $d \geq -7$ **65.** $t < 0$ **67.** $y = \frac{1}{4}x + 3$ **69.** b^{11} **71.** $9z^{12}$

7-8

Check It Out! **1a.** $18x^5$ **1b.** $10r^2t^4$ **1c.** $4x^5y^5z^7$ **2a.** $8x^2 + 2x + 6$ **2b.** $15a^3b + 3ab^2$ **2c.** $5r^3s^2 - 15r^2s^3$ **3a.** $a^2 - a - 12$ **3b.** $x^2 - 6x + 9$ **3c.** $2a^2 + 7ab^2 - 4b^4$ **4a.** $x^3 - x^2 - 6x + 18$ **4b.** $3x^3 - 4x^2 + 11x + 10$ **5a.** $x^2 - 4x$ **5b.** 12 m²

Exercises **1.** $14x^6$ **3.** $3r^5s^5t^5$ **5.** $21x^7y^3$ **7.** $4x^2 + 8x + 4$ **9.** $6a^5b^2 + 2a^4b^3$ **11.** $10x^3y^4 - 5x^2y^2$ **13.** $x^2 - x - 2$ **15.** $x^2 - 4x + 4$ **17.** $4a^4 - 2ab - 12a^3b^2 + 6b^3$ **19.** $x^3 + 3x^2 - 7x + 15$ **21.** $-6x^4 + 12x^3 + 4x^2 - 18x + 20$ **23.** $x^3 - 4x^2 - 4x - 5$ **25a.** $2x^2 - 3x$ **25b.** 20 in² **27.** $-12r^5s^5$ **29.** $10a^4$ **31.** $-6a^5b^6$ **33.** $-12a^7b^7c^8$ **35.** $9s^2 + 54s$ **37.** $27x^3 - 12x^2$ **39.** $10s^3t^3 - 15s^2t^5$ **41.** $-10x^3 + 15x^2 + 5x$ **43.** $-14x^6y^3 + 7x^5y^4$ **45.** $x^2 + 8x + 16$ **47.** $5x^2 + 13x - 6$ **49.** $10x^2 - x - 2$ **51.** $7x^2 - 52x - 32$ **53.** $x^3 - x^2 - x + 10$ **55.** $-10x^4 + 2x^3 + 20x^2 - 19x + 3$ **57.** $8x^5 - 2x^4 - 12x^3 + 17x^2 - 21$ **59.** $x^3 - 3x - 2$ **61.** $-x^3 + 3x^2 - 3x + 1$ **63.** $16x^2 - 48x + 36$

65a. 3; 2; $10x^5 + 5x^3$; 5 **65b.** 2; 2; $x^4 - x^3 + 2x^2 - 2x$; 4 **65c.** 1; 3; $x^4 - 5x^3 + 6x^2 + x - 3$; 4 **65d.** $m + n$ **67.** $12x^2 + 12x + 3$ **69a.** $2x^2$ **69b.** 800 m² **71.** $2x^2 - 7x - 30$ **73.** $8x^2 - 16xy + 6y^2$ **75.** $6x^2 - 9x - 6$ **77.** $x^3 + 3x^2$ **79.** $2x^3 - 7x^2 - 10x + 24$ **81.** $8p^3 - 36p^2q + 54pq^2 - 27q^3$ **85.** $x = 0$ **87.** C **89.** D **91.** $-x^2 - 6$ **93a.** $x^2 - 1$ **93b.** $8x + 16$ **95.** $x^3 + 3x^2 + 2x$ **97.** $a = 2$

99. 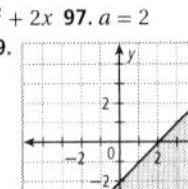

101. 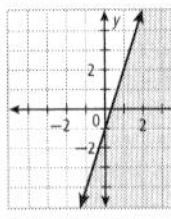

103. x^4y^3 **105.** a^4b^6

7-9

Check It Out! **1a.** $x^2 + 12x + 36$ **1b.** $25a^2 + 10ab + b^2$ **1c.** $1 + 2c^3 + c^6$ **2a.** $x^2 - 14x + 49$ **2b.** $9b^2 - 12bc + 4c^2$ **2c.** $a^4 - 8a^2 + 16$ **3a.** $x^2 - 64$ **3b.** $9 - 4y^4$ **3c.** $81 - r^2$ **4.** 25

Exercises **3.** $4 + 4x + x^2$ **5.** $4x^2 + 24x + 36$ **7.** $4a^2 + 28ab + 49b^2$ **9.** $x^2 - 4x + 4$ **11.** $64 - 16x + x^2$ **13.** $49a^2 - 28ab + 4b^2$ **15.** $x^2 - 36$ **17.** $4x^4 - 9$ **19.** $4x^2 - 25y^2$ **21.** $x^2 + 6x + 9$ **23.** $x^4 + 2x^2y^2 + y^4$ **25.** $4 + 12x + 9x^2$ **27.** $s^4 - 14s^2 + 49$ **29.** $a^2 - 16a + 64$ **31.** $9x^2 - 24x + 16$ **33.** $a^2 - 100$ **35.** $49x^2 - 9$ **37.** $25a^4 - 81$ **39.** $\pi x^2 + 8\pi x + 16\pi$ **41.** $x^2 + 2xy + y^2$ **43.** $x^4 - 16$ **45.** $x^4 - 8x^2 + 16$ **47.** $1 + 2x + x^2$ **49.** $x^6 - 2a^3x^3 + a^6$ **51.** $36a^2 - 25b^2$ **53.** 4; 4 **55.** 25; 25 **57.** 9; 9 **59.** −5; −5 **61.** 840 **65.** 1, 4, 9, 16, 25, 36, 49, 64, 81, 100 **67.** B **69.** D **71.** $x^3 + 4x^2 - 16x - 64$ **73.** Since $x^2 + bx + c$, then $x^2 + bx + c = (x + y)(x + y)$, where y is an integer. After using FOIL, $(x + y)(x + y) = x^2 + (2y)x + y^2$ and $x^2 + (2y)x + y^2 = x^2 + (b)x + c$. You can see that $c = y^2$, or $\sqrt{c} = \pm y$, and $b = 2y$, or $b = \pm 2\sqrt{c}$.

75. 13 cm

77. 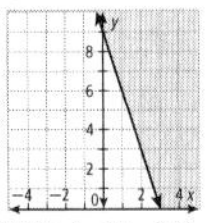

79. $12x^2 + 6x$ **81.** $-3p^3 - 8p$

Study Guide: Review

1. cubic **2.** standard form of a polynomial **3.** monomial **4.** trinomial **5.** scientific notation **6.** $\frac{1}{32}$ in. **7.** 1 **8.** 1 **9.** $\frac{1}{125}$ **10.** $\frac{1}{10,000}$, or 0.0001 **11.** $\frac{1}{16}$ **12.** $\frac{1}{256}$ **13.** $\frac{27}{4}$ **14.** $\frac{1}{m^2}$ **15.** b **16.** $-\frac{1}{2x^2y^4}$ **17.** $2b^6c^4$ **18.** $\frac{3a^2}{4c^2}$ **19.** $\frac{s^3}{qr^2}$ **20.** 10,000,000 **21.** 0.00001 **22.** 10^2 **23.** 10^{-11} **24.** 325,000 **25.** 1800 **26.** 0.17 **27.** 0.000299 **28.** 5.8×10^{-7}, 6.3×10^{-3}, 2.2×10^2, 1.2×10^4 **29.** $38,500,000,000 **30.** 5^9 **31.** $2^3 \cdot 3^4$ **32.** b^{10} **33.** r^5 **34.** x^{12} **35.** 1 **36.** $\frac{1}{2^3}$, or $\frac{1}{8}$ **37.** $\frac{1}{5^4}$, or $\frac{1}{625}$ **38.** $\frac{1}{16b^6}$ **39.** $g^{12}h^8$ **40.** x^4y^2 **41.** $-x^4y^2$ **42.** x^6y^{15} **43.** j^6k^9 **44.** $\frac{1}{5}$ **45.** m^8n^{30} **46.** 8×10^{11} **47.** 9×10^7 **48.** 1×10^{10} **49.** 2.8×10^{15} **50.** 6×10^1 **51.** 1.8×10^{-8} **52.** 3.55×10^7 **53.** 64 **54.** m^5 **55.** $\frac{7}{32}$ **56.** $6b$ **57.** t^3v^4 **58.** 16 **59.** 5×10^1 **60.** 2.5×10^7 **61.** 9 **62.** 7 **63.** 16 **64.** 8 **65.** z^2 **66.** $5x^2$ **67.** x^4y^3 **68.** m^2n^4 **69.** 0 **70.** 3 **71.** 6 **72.** 1 **73.** $3n^2 + 2n - 4$; 3 **74.** $-a^6 - a^4 + 3a^3 + 2a$; −1 **75.** linear binomial **76.** quintic monomial **77.** quartic trinomial **78.** constant monomial **79.** $-4t + 3$ **80.** $-6x^6 - x^5$ **81.** $3h^3 - 3h^2 + 5$ **82.** $2m^2 - 5m - 1$ **83.** $p^2 + 5p + 8$ **84.** $-7z^2 - z + 10$ **85.** $3g^2 + 2g + 4$ **86.** $-x^2 + 4x + 8$ **87.** $8r^2$ **88.** $6a^6b$ **89.** $18x^3y^2$ **90.** $3s^6t^{14}$ **91.** $2x^2 - 8x + 12$ **92.** $-3a^2b^2 + 6a^3b^2 - 15a^2b$ **93.** $a^2 - 3a - 18$ **94.** $b^2 - 6b - 27$ **95.** $x^2 - 12x + 20$ **96.** $t^2 - 1$ **97.** $8q^2 + 34q + 30$ **98.** $20g^2 - 37g + 8$ **99.** $p^2 - 8p + 16$ **100.** $x^2 + 24x + 144$ **101.** $m^2 + 12m + 36$ **102.** $9c^2 + 42c + 49$ **103.** $4r^2 - 4r + 1$ **104.** $9a^2 - 6ab + b^2$ **105.** $4n^2 - 20n + 25$ **106.** $h^2 - 26h + 169$ **107.** $x^2 - 1$ **108.** $z^2 - 225$ **109.** $c^4 - d^2$ **110.** $9k^4 - 49$

Chapter 8

8-1

Check It Out! **1a.** $2^3 \cdot 5$ **1b.** $3 \cdot 11$ **1c.** 7^2 **1d.** 19 **2a.** 4 **2b.** 5 **3a.** $9g^2$ **3b.** 1 **3c.** 1 **4.** 7

Exercises **3.** $3^2 \cdot 2^2$ **5.** $3^3 \cdot 2$ **7.** 7 (prime) **9.** $3 \cdot 5^2$ **11.** 7 **13.** 7 **15.** 18 **17.** x^2 **19.** 2 **21.** 1 **23.** $2 \cdot 3^2$ **25.** $2^2 \cdot 3$ **27.** 17 **29.** 7^2 **31.** 9 **33.** 10 **35.** 2 **37.** $9s$ **39.** $3w^2$ **41.** $3x$ **43.** 5 **45.** $4x^2$ **47.** $2n$ **51.** 15 rows **53.** 8 and 20; 4 **55.** 63 and 105; 21 **57.** 54 and 72; 18 **59.** 36; 2; 9; 3; $2^3 \cdot 3^2$ **61.** 105; 5; 7; $2 \cdot 3 \cdot 5 \cdot 7$ **63.** 2; 2; 27; 3; $2^2 \cdot 3^3$ **65.** 24; 2; 6; 3; $2^4 \cdot 3$ **67.** 2; 2; 10; 5; $2^3 \cdot 5$ **69a.** $2t + t^2$ **69b.** t **71.** A **73.** $4n$ **75.** 25 **77.** xy **79.** $1 \cdot 20$; $2 \cdot 10$; $4 \cdot 5$; $20 \cdot 1$; $10 \cdot 2$; $5 \cdot 4$ **83.** $y = 9$ and $y = 8$ **85.** $3x^2 + 14x - 3$

8-2

Check It Out! **1a.** $b(5 + 9b^2)$ **1b.** cannot be factored **1c.** $-y^2(18y + 7)$ **1d.** $2x^2(4x^2 + 2x - 1)$ **2.** $2x$ cm; $(x + 2)$ cm **3a.** $(4s - 5)(s + 6)$ **3b.** $(7x + 1)(2x + 3)$ **3c.** cannot be factored **3d.** $(5x - 2)^2$ **4a.** $(2b^2 + 3)(3b + 4)$ **4b.** $(4r + 1)(r^2 + 6)$ **5a.** $(5x^2 - 4)(3 - 2x)$ **5b.** $(8 - x)(y - 1)$

Exercises **1.** $5a(3 - a)$ **3.** $7(-5x + 6)$ **5.** $2h(6h^3 + 4h - 3)$ **7.** $m(9m + 1)$ **9.** $3(12f + 6f^2 + 1)$ **11.** $(2b + 5)(b + 3)$ **13.** cannot be factored **15.** $(x^2 + 2)(x + 4)$ **17.** $(7r^2 + 6)(r - 5)$ **19.** $(2b^2 + 5)(2b - 3)$ **21.** $2(r - 2)(r - 3)$ **23.** $(2m^2 - 3)(m - 3)$ **25.** $(7q - 2)(2q - 3)$ **27.** $9y(y + 5)$ **29.** $-d^2(4d^2 - d + 3)$ **31.** $x^2(-14x^2 + 5)$ **33.** $7c(3c + 2)$ **35.** $P(1 + rt)$ **37.** cannot be factored **39.** $(-3 + 4b)(b + 2)$ **41.** $(6y + 1)(y - 7)$ **43.** $(2a^2 + 3)(a - 4)$ **45.** $(n^2 + 5)(n - 2)$ **47.** $(6x^2 + 1)(x + 3)$ **49.** $(2m^2 - 3)(m - 1)$

51. $(b^2 - 2)(b + 4)$ **53.** $(2f^2 - 5)(3f - 4)$ **55.** $3v$ **57.** $2k$ **59.** 2; binomial; $x(x + 5)$ **61.** 3; trinomial; $a^2(a^2 + a + 1)$ **63a.** $100x^3$; $200x^2$; $400x$ **63b.** $100x^3 + 200x^2 + 400x + 800$ **63c.** $100(x^2 + 4)(x + 2)$; $1603.12 **69a.** Comm. Prop. of Add. **b.** Assoc. Prop. of Add. **c.** Distrib. Prop. **d.** Distrib. Prop. **71.** D **73.** C **75.** $-9ab(8ab + 5)$ **77.** $(a + c)(b + d)$ **79.** $(x^2 + 3)(x - 4)$ **81.** $\overline{AB}$ and $\overline{CD}$ are both horiz., so they have the same slope and are parallel. The slope of both $\overline{AD}$ and $\overline{BC}$ is 4, so they are parallel. Two pairs of parallel sides define a parallelogram. **83.** (−1, 6) **85.** 5^2 **87.** $\frac{x^5}{z^3}$

8-3

Check It Out! **1a.** $(x + 4)(x + 6)$ **1b.** $(x + 4)(x + 3)$ **2a.** $(x + 6)(x + 2)$ **2b.** $(x - 2)(x - 3)$ **2c.** $(x + 6)(x + 7)$ **2d.** $(x - 8)(x - 5)$ **3a.** $(x + 5)(x - 3)$ **3b.** $(x - 4)(x - 2)$ **3c.** $(x - 10)(x + 2)$

4.

n	$n^2 - 7n + 10$
0	$0^2 - 7(0) + 10 = 10$
1	$1^2 - 7(1) + 10 = 4$
2	$2^2 - 7(2) + 10 = 0$
3	$3^2 - 7(3) + 10 = -2$
4	$4^2 - 7(4) + 10 = -2$

n	$(n - 5)(n - 2)$
0	$(0 - 5)(0 - 2) = 10$
1	$(1 - 5)(1 - 2) = 4$
2	$(2 - 5)(2 - 2) = 0$
3	$(3 - 5)(3 - 2) = -2$
4	$(4 - 5)(4 - 2) = -2$

Exercises
1. $(x + 4)(x + 9)$ **3.** $(x + 4)(x + 10)$ **5.** $(x + 3)(x + 2)$ **7.** $(x + 2)(x + 8)$ **9.** $(x - 3)(x - 8)$ **11.** $(x - 1)(x - 6)$ **13.** $(x + 9)(x - 3)$ **15.** $(x - 9)(x + 5)$ **17.** $(x - 2)(x + 1)$

19.

n	$n^2 + 6n - 7$
0	$0^2 + 6(0) - 7 = -7$
1	$1^2 + 6(1) - 7 = 0$
2	$2^2 + 6(2) - 7 = 9$
3	$3^2 + 6(3) - 7 = 20$
4	$4^2 + 6(4) - 7 = 33$

n	$(n + 7)(n - 1)$
0	$(0 + 7)(0 - 1) = -7$
1	$(1 + 7)(1 - 1) = 0$
2	$(2 + 7)(2 - 1) = 9$
3	$(3 + 7)(3 - 1) = 20$
4	$(4 + 7)(4 - 1) = 33$

21. $(x + 3)(x + 10)$ **23.** $(x + 5)(x + 8)$ **25.** $(x + 4)(x + 12)$ **27.** $(x + 2)(x + 14)$ **29.** $(x - 1)(x - 5)$ **31.** $(x - 4)(x - 8)$ **33.** $(x + 7)(x - 3)$ **35.** $(x - 13)(x + 1)$ **37.** $(x - 7)(x + 5)$ **39.** C **41.** D **45.** $(x - 2)(x - 9)$ **47.** $(x + 1)(x + 9)$ **49.** $(x + 6)(x + 7)$ **51.** $(x + 2)(x + 9)$ **53.** $(x - 3)(x + 8)$ **55.** $(x - 5)(x + 9)$ **57.** approximately 1.5 **59a.** length: $(x + 2)$ ft; width: $(x + 1)$ ft **59b.** length: $(x + 3)$ ft; width: $(x + 5)$ ft **59c.** The length will increase by 1 ft. The width will increase by 4 ft. **61.** $x^2 + 6x + 8$; $(x + 4)(x + 2)$ **67a.** $d = t^2$ **67b.** $d = 4t$ **67c.** $t(t - 4)$ **69.** true **71.** false **73.** 4 **75.** 4 **77a.** $(x + 10)$ ft **b.** $\ell = (x + 14)$ ft; $w = (x + 6)$ ft **c.** $A = (x^2 + 20x + 84)$ ft² **79.** D **81.** C **83.** $(x^2 + 9)(x^2 + 9)$ **85.** $(d^2 + 21)(d^2 + 1)$ **87.** $(de - 5)(de + 4)$ **89.** 16; 11; 29 **91a.** $(x + 7)$ ft **91b.** $(4x + 26)$ ft **91c.** $92.00 **91d.** $36.96 **91e.** $128.96 **93.** (7, 5) **95.** x^5 **97.** t^{12} **99.** $(x + 2)(x^2 + 5)$ **101.** $(p - 2)(2p^3 + 7)$

8-4

Check It Out! **1a.** $(3x + 1)(2x + 3)$ **1b.** $(3x + 4)(x - 2)$ **2a.** $(2x + 5)(3x + 1)$ **2b.** $(3x - 4)(3x - 1)$ **2c.** $(3x + 4)(x + 3)$ **3a.** $(3x - 1)(2x + 3)$ **3b.** $(4n + 3)(n - 1)$ **4a.** $-1(2x + 3)(3x + 4)$ **4b.** $-1(3x + 2)(x + 5)$

Exercises **1.** $(2x + 5)(x + 2)$ **3.** $(5x - 3)(x + 2)$ **5.** $(3x + 4)(x - 6)$ **7.** $(x + 2)(5x + 1)$ **9.** $(4x - 5)(x - 1)$ **11.** $(5x + 4)(x + 1)$ **13.** $(2a - 1)(2a + 5)$ **15.** $(2x - 3)(x + 2)$ **17.** $(10x + 1)(x - 1)$ **19.** $(2x + 3)(4 - x)$ **21.** $-1(5x + 3)(x - 2)$ **23.** $-1(2x - 1)(2x + 5)$ **25.** $(3x + 2)(3x + 1)$ **27.** $(n + 2)(3n + 2)$ **29.** $(4c - 5)(c - 3)$ **31.** $(2x + 5)(4x + 1)$ **33.** $(5x - 6)(x + 3)$ **35.** $(10n - 7)(n - 1)$ **37.** $(7x + 1)(x + 2)$ **39.** $(3x - 4)(x - 5)$ **41.** $(x - 7)(4x - 3)$ **43.** $(4y - 1)(3y + 5)$ **45.** $(2x - 1)(2x + 3)$ **47.** $(3x + 5)(x - 3)$ **49.** $-1(2x - 3)(2x + 5)$ **51.** $-1(3x - 2)(x + 1)$ **53.** $2x^2 - 5x + 2$; $(x - 2)(2x - 1)$ **55.** $(9n + 8)(n + 1)$ **57.** $(2x - 1)(2x - 5)$ **59.** $(3x + 8)(x + 2)$ **61.** $(3x + 4)(2x - 3)$ **63.** $(2x - 3)(2x - 3)$ **65.** $(6x - 1)(2x - 1)$ **67.** $(15x + 8)(x + 1)$ **69.** not factorable **73.** $4x(x + 2) + 1(x + 2)$ $(4x + 1)(x + 2)$ **75a.** $-16t^2 + 20t + 6$ **75b.** $-2(4t + 1)(2t - 3)$ **75c.** 10 ft **77a.** $2t^2 - 10t + 8 = 0$ **77b.** $2(t - 1)(t - 4)$ **77c.** When $t = 1$ or $t = 4$, one of the factors in part **b** is equal to 0, making the product equal to 0. **79.** B **81.** C **83.** B **85.** A **87.** $(2x + 1)(2x + 1)$ **89.** $(9x + 1)(9x + 1)$ **91.** $(5x + 2)(5x + 2)$ **93.** −7; −5; 5; 7 **95.** −6; 6 **101.** $(x + 1)(x - 9)$

8-5

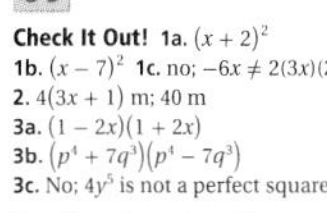

Check It Out! **1a.** $(x+2)^2$ **1b.** $(x-7)^2$ **1c.** no; $-6x \neq 2(3x)(2)$ **2.** $4(3x+1)$ m; 40 m **3a.** $(1-2x)(1+2x)$ **3b.** $(p^4+7q^3)(p^4-7q^3)$ **3c.** No; $4y^5$ is not a perfect square.

Exercises **1.** yes; $(x-2)^2$ **3.** yes; $(3x-2)^2$ **5.** yes; $(x-3)^2$ **7.** $4(x+12)$; 88 yd **9.** yes; $(s+4)(s-4)$ **11.** yes; $(2x^2+3y)(2x^2-3y)$ **13.** yes; $(x^3+3)(x^3-3)$ **15.** no **17.** no; $10x \neq 2(5x)(2)$ **19.** yes; $(4x-5)^2$ **21.** yes; $(1+2x)(1-2x)$ **23.** no **25.** yes; $(9-10x^2)(9+10x^2)$ **27.** 49 **29.** $4y^2$ **31.** $(10x+9y)(10x-9y)$; difference of 2 squares **33.** $(2r^3+5s^3)(2r^3-5s^3)$; difference of 2 squares **35.** $(x^7+12)(x^7-12)$; difference of 2 squares **37.** Multiply a binomial by itself. Choose 2 perfect squares, find 2 times the product of their square roots, and then write these 3 expressions as a sum. **39.** $c = 32$ **41a.** $5z-4$ **41b.** $20z-16$ **41c.** 11; 44; 121 **43a.** 0; 0; 100; 100; 0 **43b.** 16; 16; 36; 36; −24 **43c.** 25; 25; 25; 25; −25 **43d.** 36; 36; 16; 16; −24 **43e.** 100; 100; 0; 0; 0 **45.** $a-b$; $a+b$ **47.** C **49.** 1 **51a.** $a=2$; $b=(v+2)$ **51b.** $[2+(v+2)][2-(v+2)] = (v+4)(-v) = -v^2-4v$ **53.** $a=3y$; $b=4$; $(3y-4)(9y^2+12y+16)$ **54.** $a=n^2$; $b=2$; $(n^2-2)(n^4+2n+4)$ **55.** D: {5, 4, 3, 2}; R: {2, 1, 0, −1}; yes **57.** D: {2}; R: {−8, −2, 4, 10}; no **59.** $6a^3+14a^2-10a$ **61.** $t^2-8t+16$ **63.** $(x+3)(x-4)$

8-6

Check It Out! **1a.** yes **1b.** no; $4(x+1)^2$ **2a.** $4x(x+2)^2$ **2b.** $2y(x-y)(x+y)$ **3a.** $(3x+4)(x+1)$ **3b.** $2p^3(p+6)(p-1)$ **3c.** $3q^4(3q+4)(q+2)$ **3d.** $2(x^4+9)$

Exercises **1.** yes **3.** yes **5.** no; $4(2p^2+1)(2p^2-1)$ **7.** $3x^3(x+2)(x-2)$ **9.** $2p(2q+1)^2$ **11.** $mn(n^2+m)(n^2-m)$ **13.** $3x^2(2x-3)(x+1)$ **15.** $(p^3+1)(p^2+3)$ **17.** unfactorable **19.** no; $2xy(y^2-4y+5)$ **22.** yes **23.** yes **25.** $-4x(x-3)^2$ **27.** $5(d-3)(d-9)$ **29.** $2x(7x+5y)(7x-5y)$ **31.** unfactorable **33.** $(p^2+4)(p+2)(p-2)$ **34.** $2m^4(m-6)(2m-3)$ **37.** $x^2+12x+36=(x+6)^2$ **39.** $s^2-16s+28=(s-2)(s-14)$ **41.** $b^2-49=(b+7)(b-7)$ **45.** $(3x-1)(x+7)$ **47.** $(3x+y-3)(3x-y-7)$ **49a.** $4x^2-100=4(x^2-25)=4(x-5)(x+5)$ **49b.** $4x^2-100=(2x+10)(2x-10)=2(x+5)(2)(x-5)=4(x+5)(x-5)$ **53.** 8 **55.** C **57.** C **59a.** $V=8p[\pi(3p+1)^2]$ **59b.** $r=(3p+1)$ cm **59c.** $h=8$ cm; $V=128\pi$ cm^3 **61.** $h^2(h^4+1)(h^2+1)$ **63.** $x^{n+3}(x^2+x+1)$ **65.** D: {−1, 0, 1, 2}; R: {−2, 1, 4, 7}; function; each element in the domain is assigned to exactly 1 element in the range. **67.** $y=-5x+4$ and $y=\frac{1}{5}x+2$ **70.** $(2x-1)(2x+3)$ **71.** $(3x+2)(2x-5)$

Study Guide: Review

1. prime factorization **2.** greatest common factor **3.** $2^2 \cdot 3$ **4.** $2^2 \cdot 5$ **5.** 2^5 **6.** prime **7.** $2^3 \cdot 5$ **8.** 2^6 **9.** $2 \cdot 3 \cdot 11$ **10.** $2 \cdot 3 \cdot 19$ **11.** 5 **12.** 12 **13.** 1 **14.** 27 **15.** 4 **16.** 3 **17.** $2x$ **18.** $9b^2$ **19.** $25r$ **20.** 6 boxes; 13 rows **21.** $5x(1-3x^2)$ **22.** $16(-b+2)$ **23.** $-7(2v+3)$ **24.** $4(a^2-3a-2)$ **25.** $5g(g^2-3)(g^2+1)$ **26.** $10(4p^2-p+3)$ **27.** $(6x+5)$ ft by x ft **28.** $(2x+9)(x-4)$ **29.** $(t-6)(3t+5)$ **30.** $(5-3n)(6-n)$ **31.** $(b+2)(b+4)$ **32.** $(x^2+7)(x-3)$ **33.** $(n^2+1)(n-4)$ **34.** $(2b+5)(3b-4)$ **35.** $(2h^2-7)(h+7)$ **36.** $(3t+1)(t+6)$ **37.** $(5m^2-1)(2m+3)$ **38.** $(4p-3)(2p^2+1)$ **39.** $-1(r-5)(r-2)$ **40.** $(b^2-5)(b-3)$ **41.** $(t+4)(-t^2+6)$ **42.** $-1(3h-1)(h-4)$ **43.** $-1(d-1)^2$ **44.** $(2-b)(5b-6)$ **45.** $(t+1)(5-t)$ **46.** $(2b^2+5)(4-b)$ **47.** $-1(3r-1)(r-1)$ **48.** left rectangle: $2x^2+3x$; right rectangle: $8x+12$; combined: $2x^2+8x+3x+12$; $(2x+3)(x+4)$ **49.** $(x+1)(x+5)$ **50.** $(x+2)(x+4)$ **51.** $(x+3)(x+5)$ **52.** $(x-6)(x-2)$ **53.** $(x+5)^2$ **54.** $(x-2)(x-11)$ **55.** $(x+4)(x+20)$ **56.** $(x-6)(x-20)$ **57.** $(x+12)(x-7)$ **58.** $(x+3)(x-8)$ **59.** $(x+4)(x-7)$ **60.** $(x-1)(x+5)$ **61.** $(x+3)(x-2)$ **62.** $(x+5)(x-4)$ **63.** $(x-8)(x+6)$ **64.** $(x-9)(x+4)$ **65.** $(x-12)(x+6)$ **66.** $(x-10)(x+7)$ **67.** $(x+20)(x-6)$ **68.** $(x+7)(x-1)$ **69.** $(y+3)$ m **70.** $(2x+1)(x+5)$ **71.** $(3x+7)(x+1)$ **72.** $(2x-1)(x-1)$ **73.** $(3x+2)(x+2)$ **74.** $(5x+3)(x+5)$ **75.** $(2x-3)(3x-5)$ **76.** $(4x+5)(x+2)$ **77.** $(3x+4)(x+2)$ **78.** $(7x-2)(x-5)$ **79.** $(3x+2)(3x+4)$ **80.** $(2x+1)(x-1)$ **81.** $(3x+1)(x-4)$ **82.** $(2x-1)(x-5)$ **83.** $(7x+2)(x-3)$ **84.** $(5x+1)(x-2)$ **85.** $-1(2x-1)(3x+2)$ **86.** $(6x+5)(x-1)$ **87.** $(3x-2)(2x+7)$ **88.** $-1(2x+1)(2x-5)$ **89.** $-1(2x-3)(5x+2)$ **90.** $12x^2-11x-5$; $(4x-5)(3x+1)$ **91.** yes; $(x+6)^2$ **92.** no; $5x \neq 2(x)(5)$ **93.** no; $-2x \neq 2(2x)(1)$ **94.** yes; $(3x+2)^2$ **95.** no; $8x \neq 2(4x)(2)$ **96.** yes; $(x+7)^2$ **97.** yes; $(10x-9)(10x+9)$ **98.** No; 2 is not a perfect square. **99.** No; 5 and 10 are not perfect squares. **100.** yes; $-(12+x^3)(-12-x^3)$ **101.** no; terms must be subtracted **102.** yes; $25(2p-q)(2p+q)$ **103.** $(x-5)(x+5)$; difference of 2 squares **104.** $(x+10)^2$; perfect-square trinomial

105. $(j-k^2)(j+k^2)$; difference of 2 squares **106.** $(3x-7)^2$; perfect-square trinomial **107.** $(9x+8)^2$; perfect-square trinomial **108.** $(4b^2-11c^3)(4b^2+11c^3)$; difference of 2 squares **109.** no; $2(2x+3)(x+1)$ **110.** yes **111.** no; $(b^2+9)(b-3)(b+3)$ **112.** yes **113.** $4(x-4)(x+4)$ **114.** $3b^3(b-4)(b+2)$ **115.** $a^2b^3(a-b)(a+b)$ **116.** $t^4(t^8+1)(t^4+1)(t^2+1)(t+1)(t-1)$ **117.** $5(x+3)(x+1)$ **118.** $2x^2(x-5)(x+5)$ **119.** $2(s+4)(t+4)$ **120.** $5m(5m+2)(m-4)$ **121.** $4x(4x^2+1)(2x-3)$ **122.** $6s^2t(s+t)^2$ **123.** $2(m+3)(m-3)(5m+2)$

Chapter 9

9-1

Check It Out! **1a.** yes **1b.** yes **1c.** no

2a.

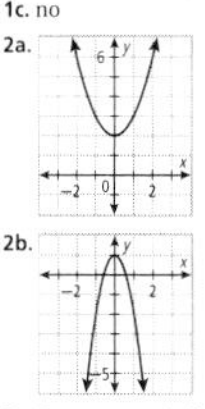

2b.

3a. Because $a < 0$, the parabola opens downward. **3b.** Because $a > 0$, the parabola opens upward. **4a.** vertex: $(-2, 5)$; maximum: 5 **4b.** vertex: $(3, -1)$; minimum: −1 **5a.** D: all real numbers; R: $y \geq -4$ **5b.** D: all real numbers; R: $y \leq 3$

Exercises **1.** minimum **3.** no **5.** yes **7.** yes

9.

11.

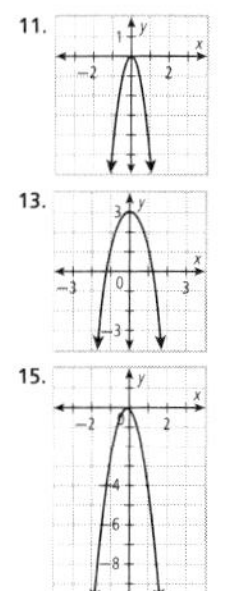

13.

15.

17. upward; $a > 0$ **19.** upward; $a > 0$ **21.** downward; $a < 0$ **23.** $(-3, -4)$; minimum: −4 **25.** D: all real numbers; R: $y \leq 4$ **27.** D: all real numbers; R: $y \geq -4$ **29.** yes **31.** no **33.** no

35.

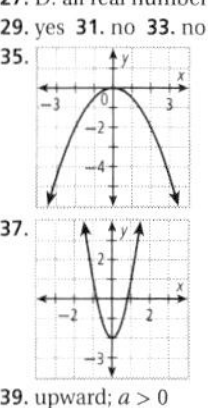

37.

39. upward; $a > 0$ **41.** vertex: $(0, -5)$; minimum: −5 **43.** D: all real numbers; R: $y \leq 0$ **45.** D: all real numbers; R: $y \geq -2$ **47.** never **49.** always **51.** sometimes **53.** no **55.** yes **57.** yes **59a.** about 0.375 s **59b.** about 2.25 m **59c.** The independent variable x represents the time since the volleyball is served, so this only makes sense for nonnegative numbers. **61.** quadratic **63.** quadratic **65.** neither **67.** linear

69a.

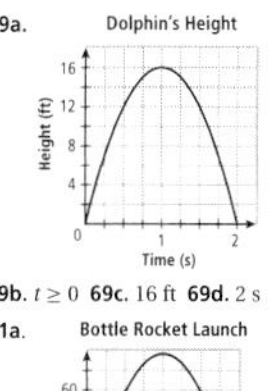

69b. $t \geq 0$ **69c.** 16 ft **69d.** 2 s

71a. Bottle Rocket Launch

71b. maximum; the greatest height reached by the rocket **73.** C

75. yes

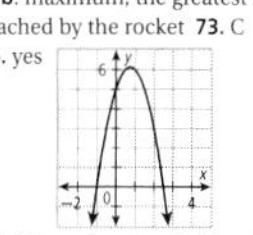

77. $f(x)=x^2-4 \rightarrow$ D: all real numbers; R: $y \geq -4$; $f(x)=-(x+2)^2 \rightarrow$ D: all real numbers; R: $y \leq 0$ **79.** $(-2)^4$ **81.** $42\frac{3}{4}$ mi **83.** ind. var.: hours; dep. var.: pay; $f(x)=9x$

9-2

Check It Out! **1a.** no zeros **1b.** 3 **2a.** $x=-3$ **2b.** $x=1$ **3.** $x=-\frac{1}{4}$ **4.** $(2, -14)$ **5.** 7 ft

Exercises **1.** An x-intercept is a value of x where $f(x)=0$. **3.** −1 **5.** no zeros **7.** $x=2$ **9.** $x=-2$ **11.** $x=-\frac{3}{4}$ **13.** $(1, 8)$ **15.** $(-2, -11)$ **17.** $(3, 10)$ **19.** no zeros **21.** −8, −2 **23.** $x=6$ **25.** $x=-\frac{1}{2}$ **27.** $x=5$ **29.** $(-3.5, -12.25)$ **31.** $(4, 32)$ **33.** $\left(\frac{1}{4}, 2\frac{1}{16}\right)$ **35.** The equation for the axis of symmetry is $x=-\frac{b}{2a}$. If $b=0$, then the axis of symmetry is $x=0$, or the y-axis. **37.** 0 **39.** 2 **41.** B **43.** 2 **45.** 25 ft; 100 ft **47.** yes **49.** x^2+6x **51.** yes

9-3

Check It Out!

1a.

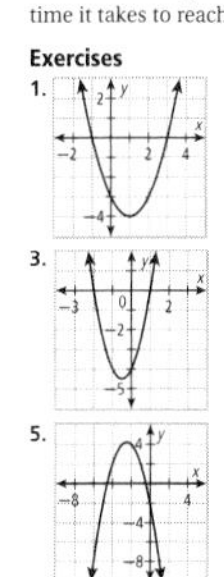

1b.

2. maximum height: 9 ft at 0.75 s; time it takes to reach the pool: 1.5 s

Exercises

1.

3.

5.

7. maximum height: 144 ft at 3 s; time in the air: 6 s

9.

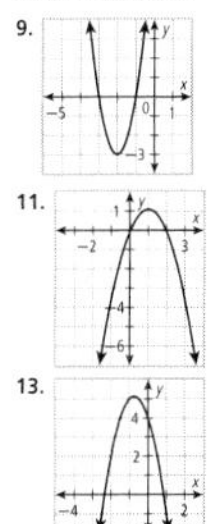

11.

13.

15. $x=4$; $(4, -16)$ **17.** $x=0$; $(0, 4)$ **19.** $x=-\frac{1}{2}$; $\left(-\frac{1}{2}, -\frac{15}{4}\right)$

21.

23.

25.

27a. Falling Sunglasses

27b. D: $\{x: 0 \leq x \leq 3.16\}$; R: $\{y: 0 \leq x \leq 50\}$ **27c.** 3.16 s **29.** $(-1, 4)$; reflect the given point across the axis of symmetry. **31.** 12 cm/s **33.** $(-1, 6)$; the axis of symmetry is a vertical line through the vertex. So its equation is $x=0$. Reflect the point $(1, 6)$ across the axis of symmetry. **35a.** $h(t)=-16t^2+45t+50$ **35b.** $(1.4, 81.6)$

35c. Bottle Rocket

35d. The vertex represents the time, 1.4 s, that the water bottle has spent in the air when it reaches its highest point, 81.6 ft. **37.** A **39.** D **41.** −1; the axis of symmetry is $x=1$. The given zero is 2 units from the axis of symmetry. The other zero is the same number of units from the axis of symmetry but on the opposite side. **43.** 3; 6 **45.** none; 3 **47.** $(3, -1)$ **49.** no

9-4

Check It Out! **1a.** $x=-4$ **1b.** no zeros **1c.** $x=-2$ or $x=2$ **2a.** 1, −2 **2b.** $\frac{1}{3}$ **2c.** no real roots **3.** 2 s

Exercises **1.** −2, 2 **3.** no real solutions **5.** −3, 3 **7.** 3 **9.** −4, −1 **11.** −1, −7 **13.** 5 s **15.** no real solutions **17.** $x=-5$ **19.** 1 **21.** −3, 3 **23.** about 9.5 s **25.** sometimes **27.** sometimes

29.

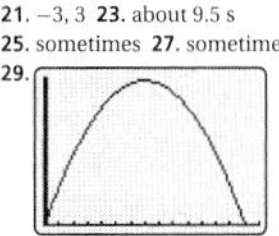

784 ft; 14 s **31.** −3, 4 **33.** −1 **35.** no real solutions **39a.** 5 s **39b.** 100 ft **39c.** 2.5 s **39d.** 84 ft; yes **41.** B **43.** $x \approx 2.3$ or $x \approx 1$ **45.** $x \approx -1$ or $x \approx 0.75$ **47.** $y=\frac{1}{2}x+2$ **49.** $y=1$ **51.** 20 **53.** $\frac{y^6}{x^9}$ **55.** $\frac{9t^2}{16s^2}$ **57.** $-125k^3$

9-5

Check It Out! **1a.** 0, −4 **1b.** −4, 3 **2a.** 3 **2b.** 1, −5 **2c.** $-\frac{5}{3}$ **2d.** $\frac{1}{3}$, 1 **3.** 1.5 s

Exercises **1.** −2, 8 **3.** −7, −9 **5.** −11, 0 **7.** −6, 2 **9.** 2, 3 **11.** −8, −2 **13.** 4 **15.** 6 **17.** 8 **19.** 1 s **21.** −4, −7 **23.** 0, 9 **25.** $-\frac{1}{2}$, $\frac{1}{3}$ **27.** −2, 4 **29.** −5 **31.** −2 **33.** 1 **35.** 1 **37.** 1 **39.** B **41.** 6 m **43.** 6 s **45.** no **47a.** 3 s **47b.** 64 ft **47c.** yes **49.** A **51.** $3x$ **53.** $(m, 0)$ and $(n, 0)$ **55.** −8 **57.** 15 **59.** $5m=65$; 13 **61.** 4, −3

9-6

Check It Out! **1a.** ±11 **1b.** 0 **1c.** ∅ **2a.** ∅ **2b.** $\pm\frac{1}{6}$ **3a.** ±9.49 **3b.** ±5.66 **3c.** ∅ **4.** 45 ft

Exercises **1.** ±15 **3.** ∅ **5.** ∅ **7.** ±5 **9.** ∅ **11.** ±2 **13.** ±5.20 **15.** ±4.47 **17.** ±13 **19.** ∅ **21.** ∅ **23.** $\pm\frac{2}{9}$ **25.** $\pm\frac{5}{8}$ **27.** $\pm\frac{13}{7}$ **29.** ±4.69 **31.** ±10.20 **33.** ±7.07 **35.** 6.1 s **37.** $a=-6$ and $b=-3$ or $a=6$ and $b=3$ **39.** about 2.5 s **41.** always **43.** 3.75 s **45a.** a must be greater than 0. **45b.** a must be equal to 0. **45c.** a must be less than 0. **47.** no; $x=\pm\frac{\sqrt{2}}{2}$, irrational **49.** yes; $x=\pm\frac{1}{2}$, rational **53.** C **55.** $\pm\frac{1}{4}$ **57.** $\pm\frac{8}{11}$ **59.** 13 **61.** $y=4x-7$ and $-y=4(2-x)$ **63.** −6, 1 **65.** −4, 3 **67.** −9, 1

9-7

Check It Out! **1a.** 36 **1b.** $\frac{25}{4}$ **1c.** 16 **2a.** −9, −1 **2b.** $4 \pm \sqrt{21}$ **3a.** $-\frac{1}{3}$, 2 **3b.** no real solutions **4.** 16.4 ft by 24.4 ft

Exercises **3.** 4 **5.** −5, −1 **7.** −6, 5 **9.** 1, 9 **11.** $\frac{-5 \pm 3\sqrt{5}}{2}$ **13.** no real solutions **15.** $4 \pm \sqrt{10}$ **17.** 7.2 m; 11.2 m **19.** 1 **21.** −2, 12 **23.** −13, −2 **25.** −6, 8 **27.** −2, 3 **29.** $\frac{-1 \pm \sqrt{5}}{2}$ **31.** $\frac{-15 \pm \sqrt{105}}{2}$ **33.** 4 in. **35.** $1 \pm \sqrt{7}$ **37.** −3, $\frac{1}{2}$ **39.** −10, 2 **41.** 81 **43.** $\frac{49}{4}$ **45.** 9 **47a.** $(10+2x)(34+2x)=640$ **47b.** 3 ft **49.** If $(x+2)^2=81$, then $x+2=9$ or $x+2=-9$. The correct answer is $x=7$ or $x=-11$. **51.** $-6 \pm 3\sqrt{3}$ **53.** −6 **55.** no real roots **57.** no real roots **61a.** $-16t^2+64t+32=0$ **61b.** 4 **61c.** ≈4.4 s **63.** B **65.** B **67.** $-\frac{3}{2}$, $\frac{2}{3}$ **69.** $-\frac{2}{3}-\frac{\sqrt{7}}{3}$, $-\frac{2}{3}+\frac{\sqrt{7}}{3}$ **71.** 0, $-\frac{b}{a}$

73.

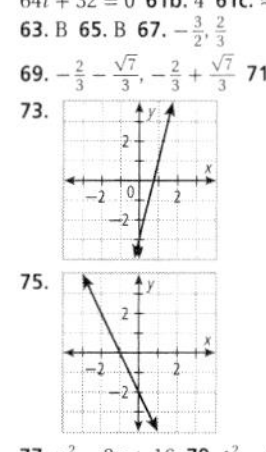

75.

77. $x^2-8x+16$ **79.** $t^2-8t+16$ **81.** $64b^4-4$ **83.** ±1 **85.** ±4 **87.** ±15 **89.** ±1.55 **91.** ±5.10 **93.** ±1.48

9-8

Check It Out! **1a.** 2, $-\frac{1}{3}$ **1b.** 2, $-\frac{1}{5}$ **2.** ≈0.13, ≈3.87 **3a.** −2, −5 **3b.** −2, 7 **3c.** ≈−4.39, ≈2.39

Exercises **1.** 1, 4 **3.** −1, 7 **5.** $-\frac{4}{3}$, 2 **7.** ≈±1.73 **9.** ≈0.30, ≈6.70 **11.** ≈5.32, ≈−1.32 **13.** ≈3, −4 **15.** $-\frac{1}{2}$, 1 **17.** 1, $-\frac{7}{2}$ **19.** 4, $\frac{1}{3}$ **21.** $\frac{1}{3}$, −1 **23.** ≈±1.29 **25.** −1, −3 **27.** 3, −4 **29.** −3, −4 **31.** $-\frac{3}{2}$, −2 **33.** −3, −4 **35.** $9x^2-12x+4=0$; $\frac{2}{3}$ **37.** $2x^2-2x-4=0$; 2, −1 **39.** $4x^2+7x-2=0$; $\frac{1}{4}$, −2 **41.** $7.2x^2+3.6x=0$; 0, $-\frac{1}{2}$ **43.** $\frac{7}{2}$, −3 **45.** 5 **47.** $-\frac{3}{2}$, 6 **51a.** no **51b.** no **51c.** ≈−0.36, 5 **53.** $a=1$, $b=1$, $c=7$ **55.** $a=10$, $b=-17$, $c=2$ **57.** $a=0.5$, $b=1.5$, $c=3.7$ **59.** $a=\frac{1}{2}$, $b=\frac{3}{4}$, $c=1$ **61.** $a=24$, $b=29$, $c=-13$ **65.** 1, $-\frac{3}{2}$ **67.** $-\frac{1}{3}$, 1 **69.** $\pm\sqrt{3}$ **71.** −\$56.25 **73.** C **75.** A **77.** yes **79.** $x \leq 8$ **81.** $(r^3+t)(s^2+5)$ **83.** $(n^4-2)(n-6)$ **85.** −10, 4 **87.** −6, 1 **89.** 5, −1

9-9

Check It Out! **1a.** 0 **1b.** 1 **2a.** 0 **2b.** 2 **3.** No; for the equation $45=-16t^2+20t+0$, the discriminant is negative, so the weight will not ring the bell.

Exercises **1.** no **3.** 1 **5.** 0 **7.** 2 **9.** 0 **11.** 0 **13.** 0 **15.** 0 **17.** 2 **19.** 1 **21.** 0 **23.** 1 **25.** 2 **27.** 1 **29.** 0 **31.** 2 **33.** no **35.** −5, 3 **37.** 0, −10 **39.** 6, −5 **41.** 2 solutions; 8, −1 **43.** 2 x-intercepts; 9 −4 **45.** 1 x-intercept; $-\frac{2}{3}$ **47a.** ≈1.76 s **47b.** 2 **47c.** no **49a.** no **49b.** yes **49c.** 5.24 s **51.** A **55.** $8x^2-19x-34=0$; 2 solutions; ≈−1.19, ≈3.57 **57.** $8x^2-6x+39=0$; ∅ **59.** $2x^2+4x+4=0$; ∅ **61.** $a=\frac{31.5+28.7+19.2+21.3+36.5}{5}$; 27.44 **63.** $y=\frac{1}{2}x+8$ **65.** $y=3x+2$ **67.** $y=\frac{3}{4}x-5$ **69.** $(b^2+2)(b-4)$ **71.** ≈−1.92, ≈3.92 **73.** 5, 8

Study Guide: Review

1. vertex **2.** minimum; maximum **3.** zero of a function **4.** discriminant of a quadratic equation **5.** completing the square **6.** yes **7.** no **8.** yes **9.** no

10.

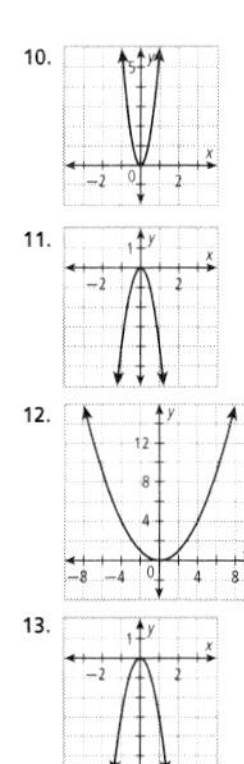

11.

12.

13.

14. Upward; the value of a is positive. **15.** Downward; the value of a is negative. **16.** $(-2, -4)$; minimum: −4 **17.** −5 and 2 **18.** −1 and 2 **19.** $x=6$; $(6, 4)$ **20.** $x=-1$; $(-1, -18)$

21.

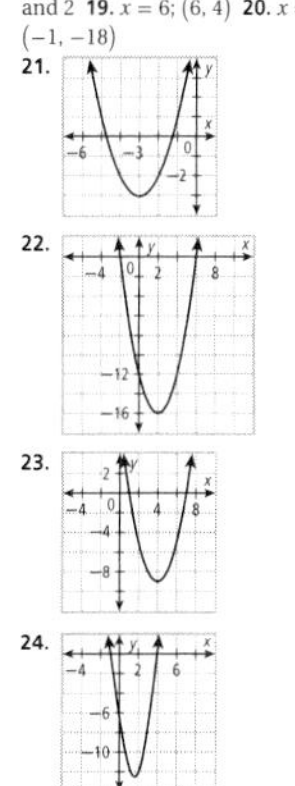

22.

23.

24.

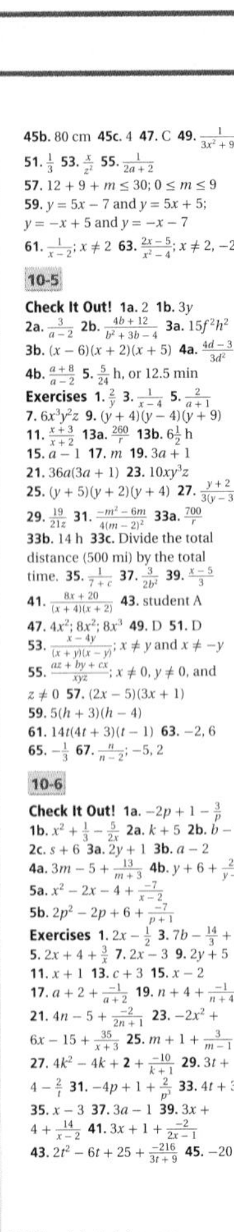

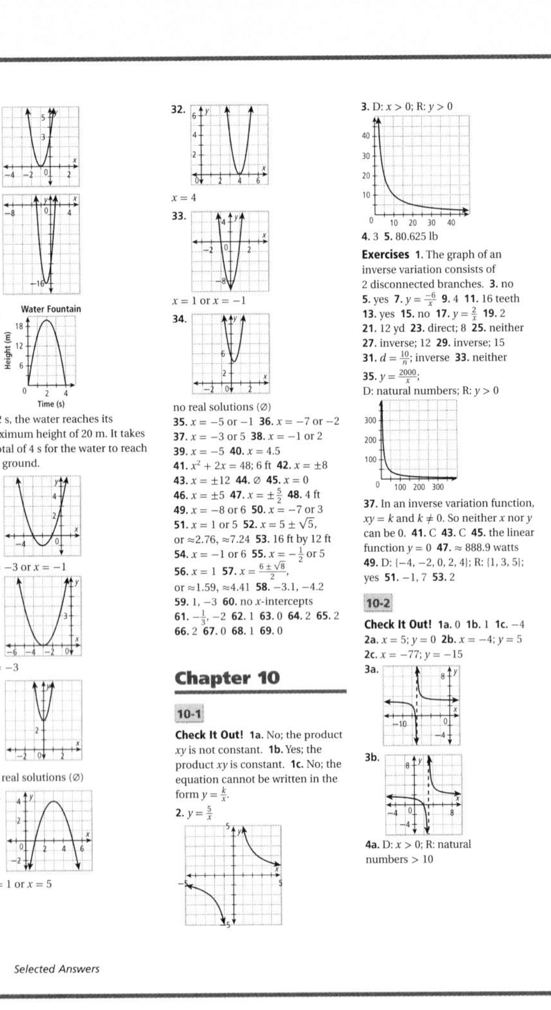

25. 26. 27. Water Fountain

In 2 s, the water reaches its maximum height of 20 m. It takes a total of 4 s for the water to reach the ground.

28. $x = -3$ or $x = -1$

29. $x = -3$

30. no real solutions (∅)

31. $x = 1$ or $x = 5$

32. $x = 4$

33. $x = 1$ or $x = -1$

34. no real solutions (∅)

35. $x = -5$ or -1 **36.** $x = -7$ or -2 **37.** $x = -3$ or 5 **38.** $x = -1$ or 2 **39.** $x = -5$ **40.** $x = 4.5$ **41.** $x^2 + 2x = 48$; 6 ft **42.** $x = \pm 8$ **43.** $x = \pm 12$ **44.** ∅ **45.** $x = 0$ **46.** $x = \pm 5$ **47.** $x = \pm\frac{5}{2}$ **48.** 4 ft **49.** $x = -8$ or 6 **50.** $x = -7$ or 3 **51.** $x = 1$ or 5 **52.** $x = 5 \pm \sqrt{5}$, or ≈ 2.76, ≈ 7.24 **53.** 16 ft by 12 ft **54.** $x = -1$ or 6 **55.** $x = -\frac{1}{2}$ or 5 **56.** $x = 1$ **57.** $x = \frac{6 \pm \sqrt{8}}{2}$, or ≈ 1.59, ≈ 4.41 **58.** $-3.1, -4.2$ **59.** $1, -3$ **60.** no x-intercepts **61.** $-\frac{1}{3}, -2$ **62.** 1 **63.** 0 **64.** 2 **65.** 2 **66.** 2 **67.** 0 **68.** 1 **69.** 0

Chapter 10

10-1

Check It Out! 1a. No; the product xy is not constant. **1b.** Yes; the product xy is constant. **1c.** No; the equation cannot be written in the form $y = \frac{k}{x}$.

2. $y = \frac{5}{x}$

3. D: $x > 0$; R: $y > 0$

4. 3 **5.** 80.625 lb

Exercises 1. The graph of an inverse variation consists of 2 disconnected branches. **3.** no **5.** yes **7.** $y = \frac{-6}{x}$ **9.** 4 **11.** 16 teeth **13.** yes **15.** no **17.** $y = \frac{2}{x}$ **19.** 2 **21.** 12 yd **23.** direct; 8 **25.** neither **27.** inverse; 12 **29.** inverse; 15 **31.** $d = \frac{10}{n}$; inverse **33.** neither **35.** $y = \frac{2000}{x}$; D: natural numbers; R: $y > 0$

37. In an inverse variation function, $xy = k$ and $k \neq 0$. So neither x nor y can be 0. **41.** C **43.** C **45.** the linear function $y = 0$ **47.** ≈ 888.9 watts **49.** D: $\{-4, -2, 0, 2, 4\}$; R: $\{1, 3, 5\}$; yes **51.** $-1, 7$ **53.** 2

10-2

Check It Out! 1a. 0 **1b.** 1 **1c.** -4 **2a.** $x = 5$; $y = 0$ **2b.** $x = -4$; $y = 5$ **2c.** $x = -77$; $y = -15$

3a. 3b.

4a. D: $x > 0$; R: natural numbers > 10

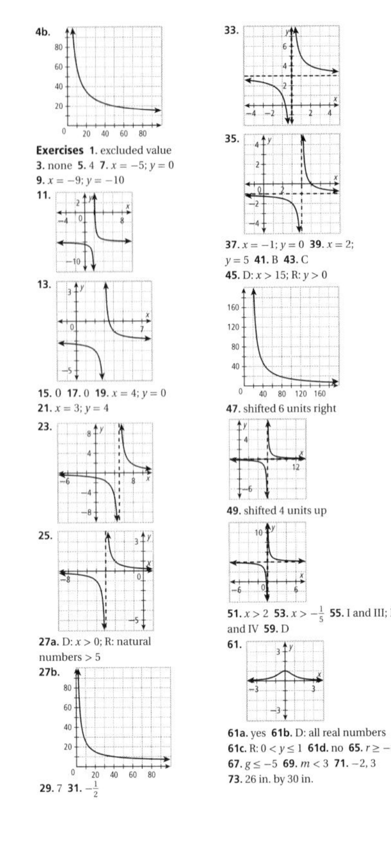

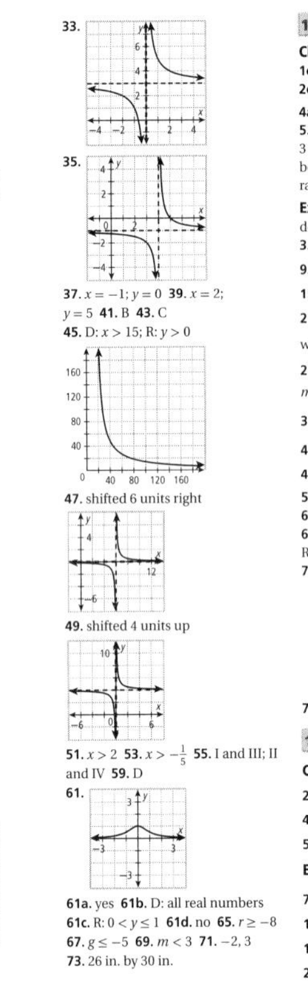

4b.

Exercises 1. excluded value **3.** none **5.** 4 **7.** $x = -5$; $y = 0$ **9.** $x = -9$; $y = -10$

11. 13.

15. 0 **17.** 0 **19.** $x = 4$; $y = 0$ **21.** $x = 3$; $y = 4$

23. 25.

27a. D: $x > 0$; R: natural numbers > 5

27b.

29. 7 **31.** $-\frac{1}{2}$

33. 35.

37. $x = -1$; $y = 0$ **39.** $x = 2$; $y = 5$ **41.** B **43.** C **45.** D: $x > 15$; R: $y > 0$

47. shifted 6 units right

49. shifted 4 units up

51. $x > 2$ **53.** $x > -\frac{1}{5}$ **55.** I and III; II and IV **59.** D

61.

61a. yes **61b.** D: all real numbers **61c.** R: $0 < y \leq 1$ **61d.** no **65.** $r \geq -8$ **67.** $g \leq -5$ **69.** $m < 3$ **71.** $-2, 3$ **73.** 26 in. by 30 in.

10-3

Check It Out! 1a. none **1b.** $0, -5$ **1c.** $-3, -4$ **2a.** $\frac{m}{3}$; $m \neq 0$ **2b.** $6p$ **2c.** $\frac{3n}{n-2}$; $n \neq 2$ **3a.** $\frac{1}{r+5}$ **3b.** $\frac{b-5}{b+5}$ **4a.** $-\frac{3}{4+x}$ **4b.** $-\frac{1}{x+1}$ **4c.** $\frac{3}{x+11}$ **5.** The barrel cactus with a radius of 3 inches has less chance of survival because its surface-area-to-volume ratio is greater.

Exercises 1. Both the numerator and denominator are polynomials. **3.** 0, 8 **5.** $\frac{a}{2}$; $a \neq 0$ **7.** $\frac{2}{y+3}$; $y \neq -3$ **9.** $\frac{h}{h+2}$; $h \neq -2$ **11.** $\frac{1}{b+1}$ **13.** $\frac{c+2}{c-4}$ **15.** $\frac{j-5}{j-3}$ **17.** $-\frac{2}{8+n}$ **19.** $\frac{-5}{r+6}$ **21.** $-\frac{5}{10+q}$ **23a.** $\frac{b_2}{b_1+b_2}$ **23b.** They will be the same: $\frac{b_2}{b_1+b_2}$. **25.** 0 **27.** $-\frac{1}{2}, 4$ **29.** already simplified; $m \neq 4$ **31.** $\frac{t}{8}$; $t \neq 0$ **33.** $\frac{z-1}{z+1}$ **35.** $\frac{p-7}{p-5}$ **37.** $\frac{2}{x-4}$ **39.** $-\frac{1}{b+7}$ **41a.** $\frac{2(\ell w + \ell h + wh)}{\ell wh}$ **41b.** box A **43.** $\frac{p+6}{12}$ **45.** $\frac{1}{3}$ **47.** $\frac{3w+7}{3}$ **49.** 1 **51.** $-\frac{5+x}{x+2}$ **53a.** $\frac{6}{s}$ **53b.** 3 **53c.** 1 **57.** A **59.** sometimes **61.** sometimes **63.** $\frac{a-3}{a+5}$ **65.** ± 14 **67.** $-2, 0$ **69.** D: $\{4, 5, 25, 29\}$; R: $\{-7, 2, 22\}$

71.

73. $\frac{5}{h^3}$ **75.** already simplified

10-4

Check It Out! 1a. $-\frac{9}{4}$ **1b.** $\frac{5x^2y^4}{6}$ **2.** $\frac{3m-15}{m-6}$ **3a.** $\frac{n+4}{n^2+2n}$ **3b.** $\frac{p^2-p-20}{p^3+16p}$ **4a.** $\frac{3x-15}{x^5}$ **4b.** $\frac{2w^8}{v^2x^3}$ **4c.** $\frac{x}{x^2+5x+6}$ **5.** ≈ 0.23

Exercises 1. $\frac{6h}{5jk^2}$ **3.** $\frac{2x-4}{3}$ **5.** $\frac{a}{6}$ **7.** $3y - 6$ **9.** $\frac{m^2-10m}{2}$ **11.** $a^3 + 10a^2 + 25a$ **13.** $\frac{a+6b}{b^2}$ **15.** $\frac{1}{2}$ **17.** $\frac{2r+28}{r-4}$ **19.** b **21.** $\frac{1}{3x-15}$ **23.** $-\frac{3p^8q^2}{7r^4}$ **25.** $\frac{10y+20}{3y+15}$ **27.** $4m^2 - 4m$ **29.** $\frac{3n^2-3n}{n+8}$ **31.** 1 **33.** $-\frac{1}{2a^3}$ **35a.** $\frac{x^2}{4(4x^2+8x-1)}$ **35b.** $\frac{9}{236}$ **37.** B **39.** $\frac{1}{2m}$ **41.** $\frac{1}{16x}$ **43.** 1 **45a.** 64 cm

45b. 80 cm **45c.** 4 **47.** C **49.** $\frac{1}{3x^2+9x}$ **51.** $\frac{1}{3}$ **53.** $\frac{x}{z^2}$ **55.** $\frac{1}{2a+2}$ **57.** $12 + 9 + m \leq 30$; $0 \leq m \leq 9$ **59.** $y = 5x - 7$ and $y = 5x + 5$; $y = -x + 5$ and $y = -x - 7$ **61.** $\frac{1}{x-2}$; $x \neq 2$ **63.** $\frac{2x-5}{x^2-4}$; $x \neq 2, -2$

10-5

Check It Out! 1a. 2 **1b.** $3y$ **2a.** $\frac{3}{a-2}$ **2b.** $\frac{4b+12}{b^2+3b-4}$ **3a.** $15f^2h^2$ **3b.** $(x-6)(x+2)(x+5)$ **4a.** $\frac{4d-3}{3d^2}$ **4b.** $\frac{a+8}{a-2}$ **5.** $\frac{5}{24}$ h, or 12.5 min

Exercises 1. $\frac{2}{y}$ **3.** $\frac{1}{x-4}$ **5.** $\frac{2}{a+1}$ **7.** $6x^3y^2z$ **9.** $(y+4)(y-4)(y+9)$ **11.** $\frac{x+3}{x+2}$ **13a.** $\frac{260}{r}$ **13b.** $6\frac{1}{2}$ h **15.** $a - 1$ **17.** m **19.** $3a + 1$ **21.** $36a(3a+1)$ **23.** $10xy^3z$ **25.** $(y+5)(y+2)(y+4)$ **27.** $\frac{y+2}{3(y-3)}$ **29.** $\frac{19}{21z}$ **31.** $\frac{-m^2-6m}{4(m-2)^2}$ **33a.** $\frac{700}{r}$ **33b.** 14 h **33c.** Divide the total distance (500 mi) by the total time. **35.** $\frac{1}{7+c}$ **37.** $\frac{3}{2b^2}$ **39.** $\frac{x-5}{3}$ **41.** $\frac{8x+20}{(x+4)(x+2)}$ **43.** student A **47.** $4x^2$; $8x^2$; $8x^3$ **49.** D **51.** D **53.** $\frac{x-4y}{(x+y)(x-y)}$; $x \neq y$ and $x \neq -y$ **55.** $\frac{az+by+cx}{xyz}$; $x \neq 0$, $y \neq 0$, and $z \neq 0$ **57.** $(2x-5)(3x+1)$ **59.** $5(h+3)(h-4)$ **61.** $14t(4t+3)(t-1)$ **63.** $-2, 6$ **65.** $-\frac{1}{3}$ **67.** $\frac{n}{n-2}$; $-5, 2$

10-6

Check It Out! 1a. $-2p + 1 - \frac{3}{p}$ **1b.** $x^2 + \frac{1}{3} - \frac{5}{2x}$ **2a.** $k + 5$ **2b.** $b - 7$ **2c.** $s + 6$ **3a.** $2y + 1$ **3b.** $a - 2$ **4a.** $3m - 5 + \frac{13}{m+3}$ **4b.** $y + 6 + \frac{20}{y-3}$ **5a.** $x^2 - 2x - 4 + \frac{-7}{x-2}$ **5b.** $2p^2 - 2p + 6 + \frac{-7}{p+1}$

Exercises 1. $2x - \frac{1}{2}$ **3.** $7b - \frac{14}{3} + \frac{8}{b}$ **5.** $2x + 4 + \frac{3}{x}$ **7.** $2x - 3$ **9.** $2y + 5$ **11.** $x + 1$ **13.** $c + 3$ **15.** $x - 2$ **17.** $a + 2 + \frac{-1}{a+2}$ **19.** $n + 4 + \frac{-1}{n+4}$ **21.** $4n - 5 + \frac{-2}{2n+1}$ **23.** $-2x^2 + 6x - 15 + \frac{35}{x+3}$ **25.** $m + 1 + \frac{3}{m-1}$ **27.** $4k^2 - 4k + 2 + \frac{-10}{k+1}$ **29.** $3t + 4 - \frac{2}{t}$ **31.** $-4p + 1 + \frac{2}{p^3}$ **33.** $4t + 3$ **35.** $x - 3$ **37.** $3a - 1$ **39.** $3x + 4 + \frac{14}{x-2}$ **41.** $3x + 1 + \frac{-2}{2x-1}$ **43.** $2t^2 - 6t + 25 + \frac{-216}{3t+9}$ **45.** -20

47. $2x - 5 + \frac{3}{x+1}$ **49a.** The values of y are negative and decreasing. **49b.** The values of y are positive and decreasing. **49c.** The function is not defined at $x = 5$. **51.** $0.5m + 1$ **53a.** $y = \frac{12x}{x-12}$ **53b.** The function is undefined at $x = 12$. **57.** C **59.** B **61.** $3x - \frac{1}{2y} + \frac{2y}{x}$ **63.** $x + 2$ **65.** 3 m **67.** 3 weeks **69.** $4(x+1)$ **71.** $2k^2 + 5k + 2$

10-7

Check It Out! 1a. 2 **1b.** 1 **1c.** $-\frac{7}{6}$ **2a.** -4 **2b.** -4 **2c.** 1, 3 **3.** $22\frac{2}{9}$ min, or ≈ 22 min 13 s **4a.** 5 **4b.** 1, 5 **4c.** 4

Exercises 1. rational equation **3.** 8 **5.** -20 **7.** 5 **9.** 3 **11.** $-\frac{5}{2}$ **13.** 18 **15.** 1, 6 **17.** $-7, 1$ **19.** $-1, 5$ **21.** ∅ **23.** -6 **25.** -1 **27.** 4 **29.** ∅ **31.** ∅ **33.** 3, 6 **35.** 2, 4 **37.** -1 **39.** 2 **41.** ∅ **43.** 2 **45.**

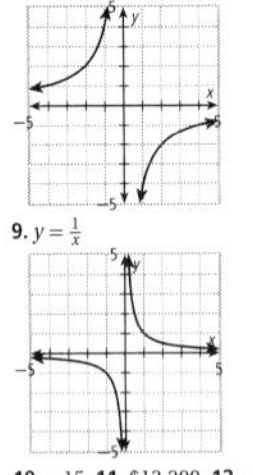

	Karla	Andrew
Books	12	18
Stacks	x	$x-2$
Books per Stack	$\frac{12}{x}$	$\frac{18}{x-2}$

47. no **49.** B **51.** D **53.** 3 **55.** $y = 3x + 1$ and $y = 3x - 1$ are parallel. **57.** $y = x - 2$ and $y = x + 3$ are parallel; $y = -x - 3$ is perpendicular to both $y = x - 2$ and $y = x + 3$. **59.** (4, 7) **61.** $(-5, -6)$

10-8

Check It Out! 1. $22\frac{2}{9}$ min, or about 22 min 13 s **2.** 750 mL **3.** 5 h

Exercises 1. $1\frac{7}{8}$ h **3.** 4 h **5.** 4 h **7.** 60 mi/h

9a.

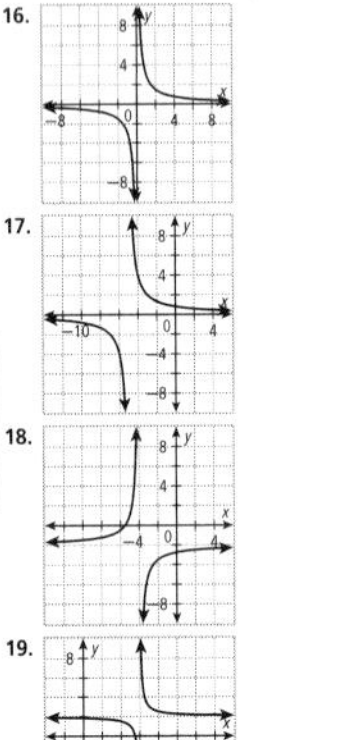

	Area (m^2)	Length (m)	Width (m)
Rectangle A	96	ℓ	$\frac{96}{\ell}$
Rectangle B	96	2ℓ	$\frac{96}{2\ell}$

9b. $\frac{96}{\ell} = \frac{96}{2\ell} + 4$ **9c.** length: 12 m; width: 8 m **11.** -2 or 2 **13a.** $\frac{1}{12} = \frac{1}{x} + \frac{1}{x-10}$ **13b.** 30 cm **13c.** 20 cm **17.** B **19.** Eddie: 6 h; Luke: 3 h; Ryan: 4 h **21.** yes **23.** yes **25.** yes **27.** yes; $(2x+3)^2$ **29.** no **31.** no **33.** $x + 1$ **35.** $x + 4$ **37.** $x - 6$

Study Guide: Review

1. rational expression **2.** rational function **3.** rational equation **4.** inverse variation **5.** discontinuous function **6.** Yes; the product xy is constant. **7.** No; the product xy is not constant.

8. $y = -\frac{4}{x}$

9. $y = \frac{1}{x}$

10. -15 **11.** $13,200 **12.** -4; $x = -4$; $y = 0$ **13.** -1; $x = -1$; $y = 3$ **14.** -3; $x = -3$; $y = -4$ **15.** $\frac{7}{4}$; $x = \frac{7}{4}$; $y = 5$

16. 17. 18. 19.

20. D: $x > 0$; R: $y > 0$

21. 0 **22.** 7 **23.** 0, 1 **24.** $-1, 5$ **25.** $5, -5$ **26.** 4, 7 **27.** $\frac{1}{3r}$; $r \neq 0$ **28.** $\frac{1}{2k-3}$; $k \neq 0$ and $k \neq \frac{3}{2}$ **29.** $\frac{1}{x-2}$; $x \neq -6$ and $x \neq 2$ **30.** $\frac{-2}{x+3}$; $x \neq \pm 3$ **31.** $\frac{3}{x-1}$; $x \neq -5$ and $x \neq 1$ **32.** $\frac{x+3}{x-5}$; $x \neq -6$ and $x \neq 5$ **33.** $\frac{4}{\pi}$ **34.** $\frac{2b^2+2b}{3}$ **35.** $\frac{4x^2-12x}{3}$ **36.** $\frac{15b^2}{2}$ **37.** $\frac{-3c^3}{4d^2}$ **38.** $\frac{b+2}{2b^2+8b}$ **39.** $\frac{n^2+3n+2}{n^2-n-42}$ **40.** $\frac{1}{b-3}$ **41.** $\frac{y^2}{3}$ **42.** $\frac{12n^3}{m}$ **43.** $\frac{x^2+2x-3}{4x^2-16}$ **44.** $10a^2b^2$ **45.** $10x(x-3)$ **46.** $\frac{b^2+8}{2b}$ **47.** $\frac{3x^2+2x-4}{x^2-2}$ **48.** $\frac{8p-2}{p^2-4p+2}$ **49.** $\frac{5b-1}{7-b}$ **50.** $\frac{-10}{n^2-1}$ **51.** $\frac{7m+2}{10m^2}$ **52.** $\frac{h^2+5h-1}{h-5}$ **53.** $\frac{40}{3r}$ **54.** $x - \frac{2}{x} + \frac{5}{x^2}$ **55.** $x + 2$ **56.** $3n + 1$ **57.** $x + 2$ **58.** $x + 6$ **59.** $3b^2 + 6b + 8 + \frac{18}{b-2}$ **60.** $-4x^2 + 10x - 17 + \frac{34}{x+2}$ **61.** $-\frac{3}{4}$ **62.** $\frac{12}{7}$ **63.** $-\frac{18}{11}$ **64.** $-\frac{7}{6}$ **65.** $-\frac{2}{3}$ **66.** $-\frac{1}{3}, 1$ **67.** -3 **68.** ± 1 **69.** $-\frac{1}{12}$ **70.** -2 **71.** 4, 5 **72.** $-12, 1$ **73.** -19 **74.** 0 **75.** $7\frac{1}{5}$ h, or 7 h 12 min **76.** 80 mL

Chapter 11

11-1

Check It Out! 1a. 40 ft/s **1b.** 30.98 ft/s **2.** $x \geq \frac{1}{2}$

3.

Exercises 1. There is no variable under the square-root sign. **3.** $x \geq -6$ **5.** $x \geq 0$ **7.** $x \geq -3$

9.

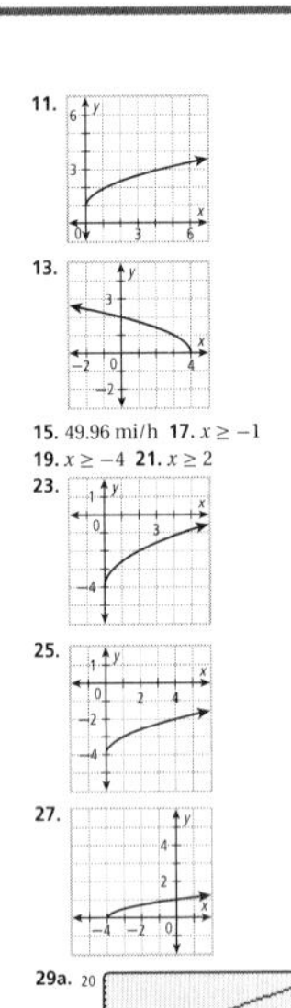

11. 13.

15. 49.96 mi/h **17.** $x \geq -1$ **19.** $x \geq -4$ **21.** $x \geq 2$

23. 25. 27.

29a.

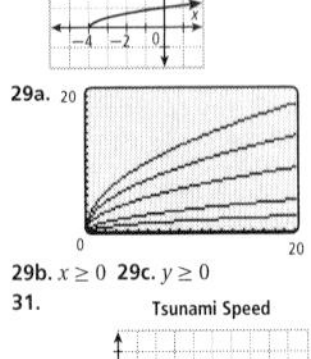

29b. $x \geq 0$ **29c.** $y \geq 0$

31.

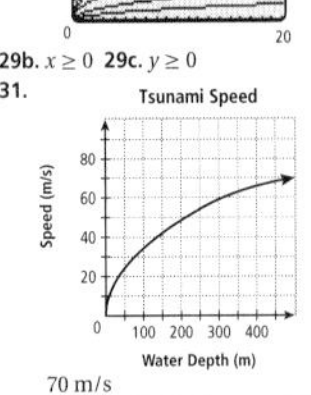

70 m/s

35. no **37.** A **39.** C **41.** $x \leq -5$ OR $x \geq 5$ **43.** $x \leq -4$ OR $x \geq \frac{3}{2}$ **45.** D: $x \leq 3$; R: $y \leq 4$ **49a.** When $x = 2$ or $x = 4$, the expression under the square-root sign is negative. **49b.** 3, 1 **51.** $y = -\frac{1}{2}x + 2$ **53.** $9x^2 - 6x + 1$ **55.** $a^2 - 2ab^2c + b^4c^2$ **57.** $9r^2 - 4s^2$ **59.** $x - 14$ **61.** $2r + 1$ **63.** $3s + 4$

11-2

Check It Out! 1a. 8 **1b.** 7 **1c.** 13 **1d.** $|3 - x|$ **2a.** $8\sqrt{2}$ **2b.** $xy\sqrt{x}$ **2c.** $4a\sqrt{3b}$ **3a.** $\frac{2}{3}$ **3b.** $\frac{6}{x^2}$ **3c.** $\frac{y^3}{2}$ **4a.** $\frac{2\sqrt{5}}{7}$ **4b.** $\frac{z^2\sqrt{z}}{5y}$ **4c.** $\frac{p^3}{q^5}$ **5.** $60\sqrt{2}$ ft; 84.9 ft

Exercises 1. $3x - 6$ **3.** 7 **5.** $6\sqrt{5}$ **7.** $18\sqrt{2}$ **9.** $4x^2y\sqrt{2y}$ **10.** $10a\sqrt{2b}$ **12.** $\frac{\sqrt{7}}{4}$ **13.** $\frac{\sqrt{6}}{7}$ **15.** $\frac{\sqrt{x}}{3}$ **17.** $\frac{6\sqrt{3}}{7}$ **19.** $\frac{16\sqrt{2}}{9}$ **21.** $\frac{5x\sqrt{2}}{13}$ **23.** $5\sqrt{41}$ mi; 32 mi **25.** 20 **27.** 9 **29.** $|x + 1|$ **31.** $|x - 3|$ **33.** $20\sqrt{10}$ **35.** $8rs\sqrt{5}$ **37.** $\frac{3\sqrt{5}}{2}$ **39.** $\frac{\sqrt{14}}{3}$ **41.** $\frac{x\sqrt{x}}{y^3}$ **43.** $\frac{8s\sqrt{3}}{7}$ **45.** $-20\sqrt{3}$ **47.** $15x\sqrt{7}$ **49.** x **51.** $\frac{x^3\sqrt{x}}{3}$ **53.** $\sqrt{36}$; 6 **55.** $\sqrt{50}$; $5\sqrt{2}$ **57.** $\sqrt{3}$ **59.** $\sqrt{20}$; $2\sqrt{5}$ **61.** 42 ft; length of missing side ≈ 17.2 ft, which will need to be rounded up to 18. $10 + 14 + 18 = 42$ ft **63a.** $v = 8\sqrt{h}$; 93.6 ft/s **63b.** Pythagorean Theorem **63c.** 171.4 ft **65.** Sears: $\frac{10\sqrt{87}}{3}$ mi; 31.1 mi
Empire: $\frac{50\sqrt{3}}{3}$ mi; 28.9 mi
Aon: $\frac{4\sqrt{426}}{3}$ mi; 27.5 mi
67. C **69.** C **71.** $x\sqrt{x+1}$ **73a.** $|x|$ **73b.** x^2 **73c.** $|x^3|$ **73d.** x^4 **73e.** $|x^5|$ **73f.** x^n; $|x^n|$ **75.** yes **77.** no **79.** $x \geq 2$ **81.** $x \geq 1$ **83.** $x \leq 6$

11-3

Check It Out! 1a. $-\sqrt{7}$ **1b.** $3\sqrt{3}$ **1c.** $8\sqrt{n}$ **1d.** $\sqrt{2s} + 8\sqrt{5s}$ **2a.** $5\sqrt{6}$ **2b.** $12\sqrt{3} - 3\sqrt{2}$ **2c.** $5\sqrt{3y}$ **3.** $10\sqrt{b}$ in.

Exercises 3. $10\sqrt{5}$ **5.** $3\sqrt{7} + 5\sqrt{2}$ **7.** $5\sqrt{6a} + 6\sqrt{5a}$ **9.** $13\sqrt{3}$ **11.** $-\sqrt{5x}$ **13.** $8\sqrt{2t} - 4\sqrt{3t}$ **15.** $6\sqrt{3}$ **17.** $-3\sqrt{11}$ **19.** $-4\sqrt{n}$ **21.** $7\sqrt{7}$ **23.** $12\sqrt{2}$ **25.** $3\sqrt{7x} - 12\sqrt{3x}$ **27.** $3\sqrt{5j}$ **29.** $2\sqrt{3m}$ **31.** $12\sqrt{7}$ **33.** 0 **35.** $7\sqrt{3}$ **37.** $7\sqrt{2}$ **39a.** $3\sqrt{11}$; $2\sqrt{11}$; $5\sqrt{11}$ **39b.** $10\sqrt{11}$ **39c.** Because the areas found in parts **a** and **b** must be equal, the model shows that $3\sqrt{11} + 2\sqrt{11} + 5\sqrt{11} = (3 + 2 + 5)\sqrt{11} = 10\sqrt{11}$. **41.** $2\sqrt{3} + 5\sqrt{5} + 5$ **43.** $8\sqrt{7x} - \sqrt{70x}$ **45.** $35\sqrt{5k}$ **47.** $5\sqrt{3} + 5\sqrt{5}$

51. 9 **53.** 18 **55.** $36x^2$ **57.** $16\sqrt{3}$ in.; $8\sqrt{3}$ in.; $24\sqrt{3}$ in. **59.** B **61.** A **63.** $\sqrt{x}(x+2)$ **65.** 0 **67.** $(x+2)\sqrt{x-1}$ **69.** $3\sqrt{x+1} - x\sqrt{x+2}$ **71.** $m_{AB} = 1$, $m_{BC} = \frac{1}{6}$, $m_{CD} = 1$, $m_{AD} = \frac{1}{6}$. Since $m_{AB} = m_{CD}$, $\overline{AB} \parallel \overline{CD}$. Since $m_{BC} = m_{AD}$, $\overline{BC} \parallel \overline{AD}$. Because both pairs of opposite sides are parallel, *ABCD* is a parallelogram. **73.** −3, 1 **75.** 9, −2 **77.** $x \geq -3$

11-4

Check It Out! 1a. $5\sqrt{2}$ **1b.** 63 **1c.** $2m\sqrt{7}$ **2a.** $4\sqrt{3} - 3\sqrt{6}$ **2b.** $5\sqrt{2} + 4\sqrt{15}$ **3a.** $83 + 18\sqrt{2}$ **3b.** $17 - \sqrt{3}$ **4a.** $\frac{\sqrt{65}}{5}$ **4b.** $\frac{\sqrt{21a}}{6}$ **4c.** $\frac{8\sqrt{35}}{7}$

Exercises 1. $\sqrt{6}$ **3.** 125 **5.** $3\sqrt{30a}$ **7.** $2\sqrt{6} + \sqrt{42}$ **9.** $\sqrt{35} - \sqrt{21}$ **11.** $5\sqrt{3} + 4\sqrt{5}$ **13.** $12 + 7\sqrt{2}$ **15.** $-5 - 2\sqrt{3}$ **17.** $81 - 30\sqrt{2}$ **19.** $\frac{\sqrt{26}}{2}$ **21.** $\frac{\sqrt{33}}{18}$ **23.** $\frac{2\sqrt{7}}{7}$ **25.** $\frac{\sqrt{5x}}{5x}$ **27.** $3\sqrt{10}$ **29.** 8 **31.** $6d\sqrt{7}$ **33.** $4\sqrt{5} - 5\sqrt{2}$ **35.** $2\sqrt{3} - 2\sqrt{5}$ **37.** $3 + 12\sqrt{3}$ **39.** $75 + 19\sqrt{15}$ **41.** $10 - \sqrt{2}$ **43.** $67 + 16\sqrt{3}$ **45.** $\frac{5\sqrt{6}}{2}$ **47.** $\frac{\sqrt{3x}}{x}$ **49.** $\frac{7\sqrt{2x}}{2}$ **51.** $2\sqrt{y}$ **53.** 180 in² **55.** $(6\sqrt{10} - 2\sqrt{5})$ cm² **57.** $\sqrt{30}$ **59.** $-5 - 2\sqrt{3}$ **61.** $3\sqrt{2}$ **63.** $134\sqrt{3} + 96$ **65.** $x - 2\sqrt{xy} + y$ **67.** $3 + 2\sqrt{3x} + x$ **69.** $\frac{\pi\sqrt{6}}{4}$ s ≈ 1.9 s **71.** 269.5 ft² **75.** B **77.** D **79.** $-4\sqrt{3} + 4\sqrt{5}$ **81.** $-5 - 2\sqrt{6}$ **83.** $2 - \sqrt{3}$ **85.** $2\sqrt{6} + 2\sqrt{5}$ **87.** $x < 8$ **89.** $x \geq 2$ **91.** $(3x+1)(2x+3)$ **93.** $3(x+5)^2$ **95.** $4x(2x+1)(x-3)$ **97.** $\frac{3\sqrt{2}}{2}$ **99.** $\frac{5a^2\sqrt{2}}{3}$

11-5

Check It Out! 1a. 36 **1b.** 3 **1c.** $\frac{1}{3}$ **2a.** 9 **2b.** 18 **2c.** 3 **3a.** 121 **3b.** 64 **3c.** 100 **4a.** 2 **4b.** $\frac{11}{2}$ **5a.** ∅ **5b.** ∅ **5c.** 4 **6.** 8; 3 cm

Exercises 1. no **3.** −8 **5.** −144 **7.** 27 **9.** 50 **11.** −2 **13.** 9 **15.** 64 **17.** 16 **19.** 16 **21.** $\frac{4}{9}$ **23.** 100 **25.** 5 **27.** 13 **29.** 6 **31.** 2 **33.** ∅ **35.** 4 **37.** 2 **39.** ∅ **41.** 48 **43.** −25 **45.** 71 **47.** −8 **49.** 36 **51.** −16 **53.** 8 **55.** 9 **57.** 2 **59.** −5 **61.** 5 **63.** 1 **65.** 1 **67.** $x = 144$; 12 in. **69.** $\sqrt{x} - 3 = 4$; 49 **71.** $x = \sqrt{x+6}$; 3 **73.** 3 in. by 1 in. **75a.** 54.88 joules **75b.** 0 joules **77.** 1690 ft **79.** $x = 25$; $y = 16$

81. sometimes **83.** student B **85.** $x \leq 0$ since the square root is only defined for nonnegative values. $k \geq 0$ since the value of the square root must be nonnegative. **87.** A **89.** C **91.** A **93.** 1, 2 **95.** 2 **97.** 0

99a.

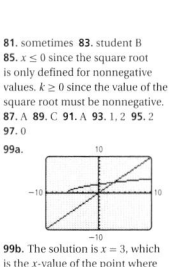

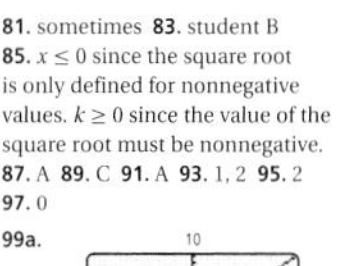

99b. The solution is $x = 3$, which is the *x*-value of the point where the graphs intersect. **101.** D: {−6, 1, 3, 5}; R: {2, 3, 4} **103.** D: {3, 4, 6, 7, 9}; R: {−8, −5, 0, 1, 2} **105.** (3, 11) **107.** (5, −3)

109.

11-6

Check It Out! 1a. 80, −160, 320 **1b.** 216, 162, 121.5 **2.** 7.8125 **3.** $1342.18

Exercises 1. the value that each term is multiplied by to get the next term **3.** 25, 12.5, 6.25 **5.** 1,000,000,000 **7.** 4 **9.** 162, 243, 364.5 **11.** 2058; 14,406; 100,842 **13.** $\frac{5}{32}, \frac{5}{128}, \frac{5}{512}$ **15.** 0.0000000001, or 1×10^{-10} **17.** 80; 160 **19.** $\frac{1}{3}$ **21.** $\frac{1}{7}$; $\frac{1}{49}$ **23.** 6; −48 **25.** 4913 **27.** yes; $\frac{1}{3}$ **29.** no **31.** no **33a.** 1.28 cm **33b.** 40.96 cm **35.** −2, −8, −32, −128 **37.** 2, 4, 8, 16 **39.** 12, 3, $\frac{3}{4}$, $\frac{3}{16}$

41a. Stage 0:

Stage 1:

Stage 2:

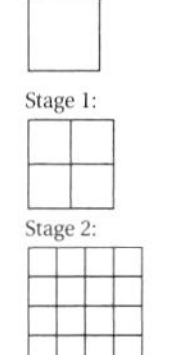

Stage 3:

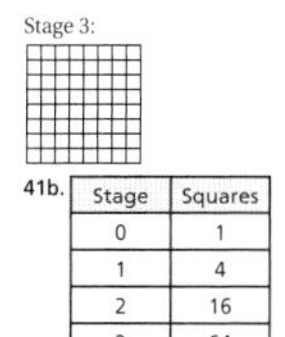

41b.

Stage	Squares
0	1
1	4
2	16
3	64

41c. yes; $r = 4$ **41d.** $a_n = 4(4)^{n-1}$, or 4^n **43a.** $3993; $4392.30 **43b.** 1.1 **43c.** $2727.27; divide tuition 3 years ago ($3000) by 1.1 (the common ratio) **45.** D **47.** x^4, x^5, x^6 **49.** 1, y, y^2 **51.** −400 **53.** the 7th term **55.** $b > 10$ **57.** $c < -\frac{1}{3}$

59.

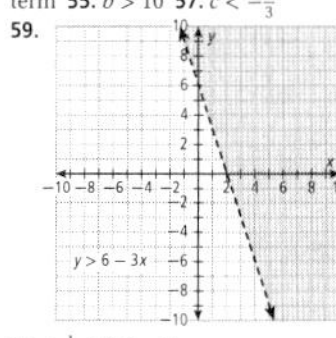

61. 1, $\frac{1}{3}$ **63.** 4, −7 **65.** ≈ 0.35, ≈ −4.35

11-7

Check It Out! 1. 3.375 in. **2a.** No; as the *x*-values change by a constant amount, the *y*-values are not multiplied by a constant amount. **2b.** Yes; as the *x*-values change by a constant amount, the *y*-values are multiplied by a constant amount.

3a.

3b.

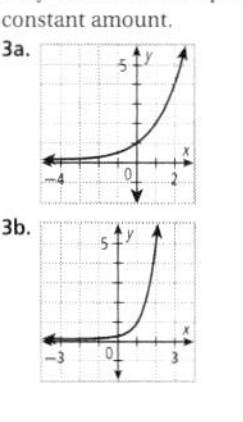

4a.

4b.

5a.

5b.

6. after about 13 yr

Exercises 1. no **3.** no

5.

7.

9.

11.

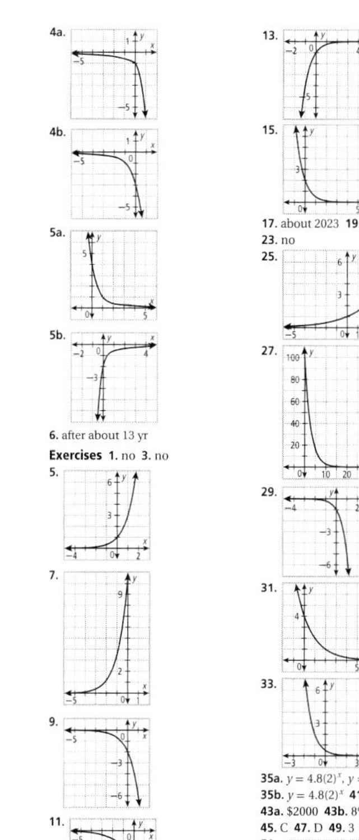

13.

15.

17. about 2023 **19.** 289 ft **21.** yes **23.** no

25.

27.

29.

31.

33.

35a. $y = 4.8(2)^x$, $y = \frac{1}{5}(6)^x$ **35b.** $y = 4.8(2)^x$ **41.** −0.125 **43a.** $2000 **43b.** 8% **43c.** $2938.66 **45.** C **47.** D **49.** 3

51.

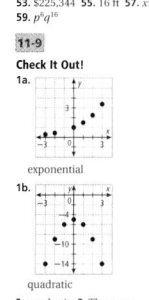

The value of *a* is the *y*-intercept.

53. 25 **55.** $9x^2$

11-8

Check It Out! 1. $y = 1200(1.08)^t$; $1904.25 **2a.** $A = 1200(1.00875)^{4t}$; $1379.49 **2b.** $A = 4000(1.0025)^{12t}$; $5083.47 **3.** $y = 48{,}000(0.97)^t$; 38,783 **4a.** 1.5625 mg **4b.** 0.78125 g

Exercises 1. exponential growth **3.** $y = 300(1.08)^t$; 441 **5.** $A = 4200(1.007)^{4t}$; $4965.43 **7.** $y = 10(0.84)^t$; 4.98 mg **9.** 5.5 g **11.** $y = 1600(1.03)^t$; 2150 **13.** $A = 30(1.078)^t$; 47 members **15.** $A = 7000(1.0075)^{4t}$; $9438.44 **17.** $A = 12{,}000(1.026)^t$; $17,635.66 **19.** $y = 58(0.9)^t$; $24.97 **21.** growth; 61% **23.** decay; $33\frac{1}{3}$% **25.** growth; 10% **27.** growth; 25% **29.** $y = 58{,}000{,}000(1.001)^t$; 58,174,174 **31.** $y = 8200(0.98)^t$; $7118.63 **33.** $y = 970(1.012)^t$; 1030 **35.** B **37.** 18 yr **39.** A; B

41.

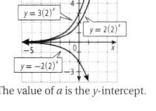

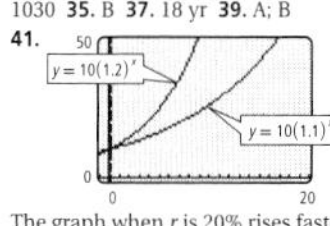

The graph when *r* is 20% rises faster than when *r* is 10%. The greater the value of *r*, the faster the graph will rise. **45.** D **47.** D **49.** about 20 yr **51.** 100 min, or 1 h 40 min **53.** $225,344 **55.** 16 ft **57.** x^{20} **59.** p^6q^{16}

11-9

Check It Out!

1a.

exponential

1b.

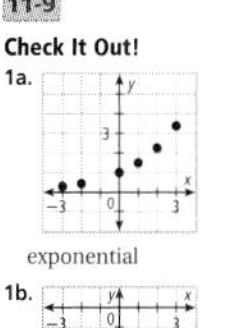

quadratic

2. quadratic **3.** The oven temperature decreases by 50°F every 10 min; $y = -5x + 375$; 75°F

Exercises

1.

exponential

3.

linear

5. exponential **7.** Grapes cost $1.79/lb; $y = 1.79x$; $10.74

9.

linear

11. linear **13.** exponential **15.** $\ell = 6k$; linear **17.** linear **19.** $y = 0.2(4)^x$ **21.** linear **27.** C **29.** C **33.** 6 **35.** 3 **37.** 11 **39.** 25 **41.** 0 **43.** $2\sqrt{6}$ **45.** $\frac{\sqrt{3}}{3}$ **47.** x^2 **49.** $11\sqrt{2}$

Study Guide: Review

1. square-root function **2.** exponential decay **3.** common ratio **4.** exponential function **5.** 4.74 cm **6.** $x \geq 0$ **7.** $x \geq -4$ **8.** $x \geq 0$ **9.** $x \geq -2$ **10.** $x \geq \frac{4}{3}$ **11.** $x \geq -3$ **12.** $x \geq \frac{7}{2}$ **13.** $x \geq -\frac{18}{5}$ **14.** $x \geq \frac{3}{4}$ **15.** $x \geq 1$

16.

17.

18.

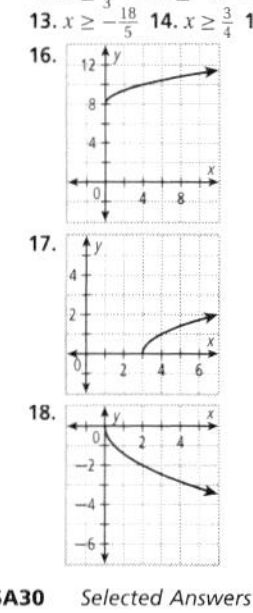

19.

20.

21.

22.

23.

24.

25.

26. 11 **27.** n^2 **28.** $x + 3$ **29.** 5 **30.** $6d$ **31.** $y^3\sqrt{x}$ **32.** $2\sqrt{3}$ **33.** $4b^2\sqrt{2ab}$ **34.** $\frac{\sqrt{5}}{2}$ **35.** $\frac{t}{10}$ **36.** $\frac{2}{3}$ **37.** $\frac{4p^2\sqrt{2}}{7}$ **38.** $\frac{t^4\sqrt{t}}{s}$ **39.** $\frac{2b^3\sqrt{2}}{5}$ **40.** $9\sqrt{7}$ **41.** $3\sqrt{3}$ **42.** $3\sqrt{2} + 2\sqrt{3}$ **43.** $\sqrt{5t}$ **44.** $2\sqrt{2}$ **45.** $2\sqrt{3} + 2\sqrt{5}$ **46.** $-2\sqrt{5x}$ **47.** $10\sqrt{6}$ **48.** $\sqrt{14}$ **49.** $6\sqrt{7x}$ **50.** $4\sqrt{2} - 4$ **51.** $71 + 16\sqrt{7}$ **52.** $\frac{4\sqrt{5}}{5}$ **53.** $\frac{3a\sqrt{2}}{2}$ **54.** $\frac{\sqrt{3}}{3}$ **55.** $\frac{\sqrt{10n}}{2n}$ **56.** $x = 64$ **57.** $x = 8$ **58.** $x = 3$ **59.** $x = 25$ **60.** $x = -81$ **61.** $x = 100$ **62.** $x = 3$ **63.** ∅

64. $x = 4$ **65.** $x = 6$ **66.** $x = 7$ **67.** $x = \frac{19}{2}$ **68.** $x = 12$ **69.** $x = 3$ **70.** $x = 4$ **71.** $x = 5$ **72.** 81, 243, 729 **73.** 48, −96, 192 **74.** 5, 2.5, 1.25 **75.** −256, −1024, −4096 **76.** 7,812,500 **77.** 19,131,876 **78.** Yes; as the *x*-values change by a constant amount, the *y*-values are multiplied by a constant amount. **79.** No; as the *x*-values change by a constant amount, the *y*-values are not multiplied by a constant amount.

80.

81.

82. $y = 9(1.15)^t$; 24 **83.** $y = 24{,}500(0.96)^t$; 3182

84.

quadratic

85.

linear

86.

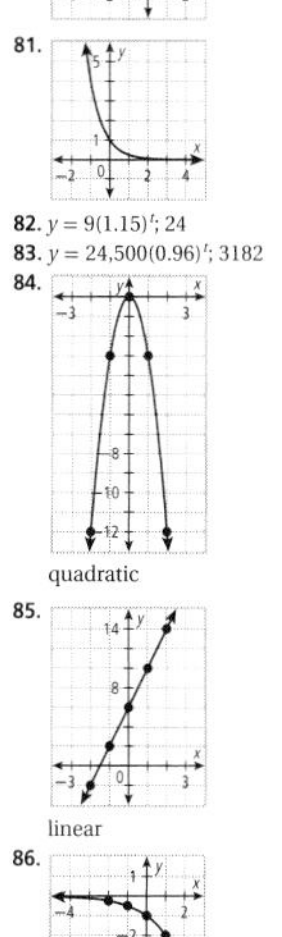

exponential

87. exponential **88.** quadratic **89.** linear **90.** $y = 1.5x$; 15 h

Graphic Organizer Answers

Possible answers given.

Chapter 1

Lesson 1-1

	Words	Algebra
Addition	3 more than x	$x + 3$
Subtraction	1 less than y	$y - 1$
Multiplication	The product of 2 and n	$2n$
Division	The quotient of x and 4	$x \div 4$

Lesson 1-2

Points	Sum	Difference
A, B	Neg.	Neg.
B, A	Neg.	Pos.
C, B	Neg.	Pos.
D, A	Pos.	Pos.

Lesson 1-3

Multiplying and Dividing Numbers	
Multiplication	Division
pos • pos = pos	pos ÷ pos = pos
pos • neg = neg	pos ÷ neg = neg
neg • pos = neg	neg ÷ pos = neg
neg • neg = pos	neg ÷ neg = pos

Lesson 1-4

	Even Exponent	Odd Exponent
Positive Base	$3^2 = 9$ Positive	$3^3 = 27$ Positive
Negative Base	$(-3)^2 = 9$ Positive	$(-3)^3 = -27$ Negative

Lesson 1-5

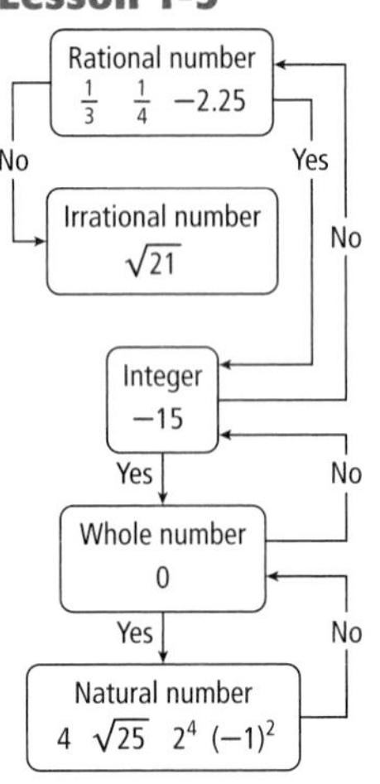

Lesson 1-6

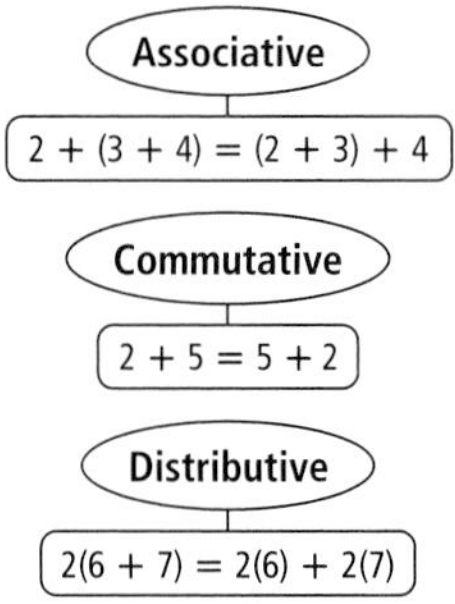

Lesson 1-7

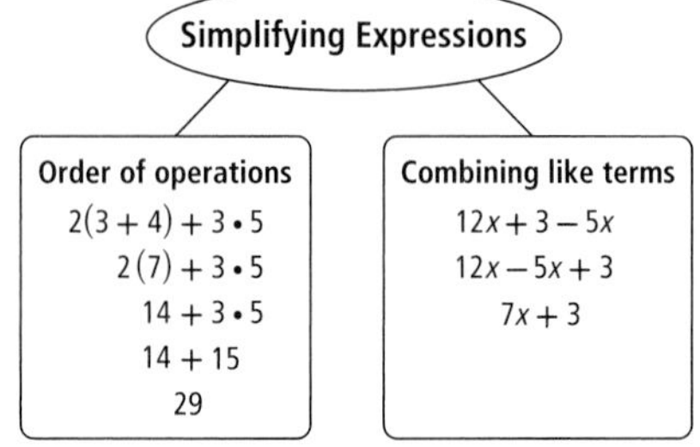

Chapter 2

Lesson 2-1

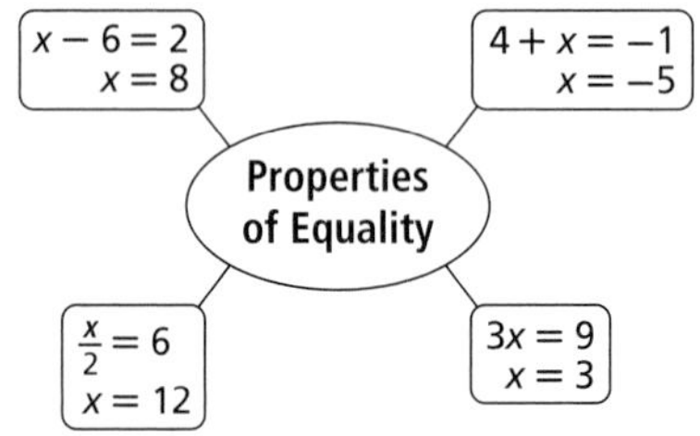

Lesson 2-2

Solving Two-Step Equations	
$2x + 1 = 9$ $2x = 8$ $x = 4$	$\frac{x}{3} - 2 = 1$ $\frac{x}{3} = 3$ $x = 9$

Lesson 2-3

Solving Multi-Step Equations	
$2(x + 5) = 16$ $2(x) + 2(5) = 16$ $2x + 10 = 16$ $2x = 6$ $x = 3$	$\frac{x-4}{3} = 12$ $3\left(\frac{x-4}{3}\right) = 3(12)$ $x - 4 = 36$ $x = 40$

Lesson 2-4

An equation with variables on both sides can have...

- One solution: $5x - 4 = 4x + 5$
- No solution: $5x - 4 = 5x - 3$
- Many solutions: $5x - 4 = 5x - 4$

Lesson 2-5

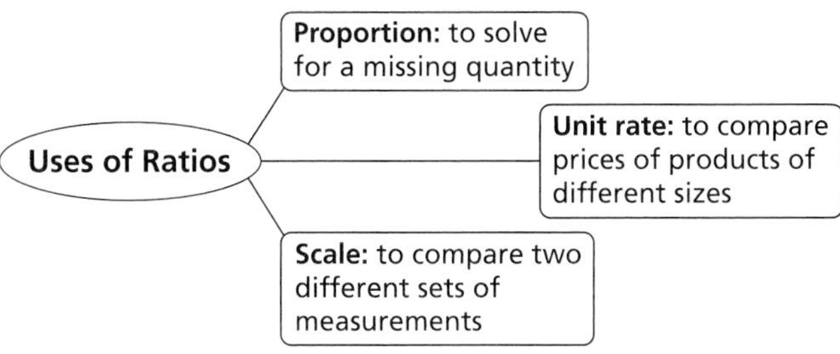

Lesson 2-6

Common Formulas	
Subject	**Formula**
Geometry	$P = 4s$; $s = \frac{P}{4}$ (perimeter of a square is 4 times the side length)
Physical science	$F = ma$; $m = \frac{F}{a}$; $a = \frac{F}{m}$ (force equals mass times acceleration)
Earth science	$K = C + 273$; $C = K - 273$ (temperature in kelvins is Celsius temperature plus 273)

Lesson 2-7

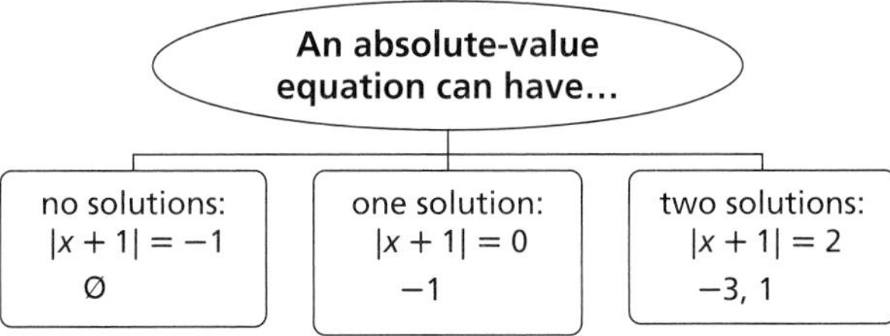

Chapter 3

Lesson 3-1

Inequality	Graph
$x > 1$	−1 0 1 2 3 4 5
$x \leq -3$	−5 −4 −3 −2 −1 0 1

Lesson 3-2

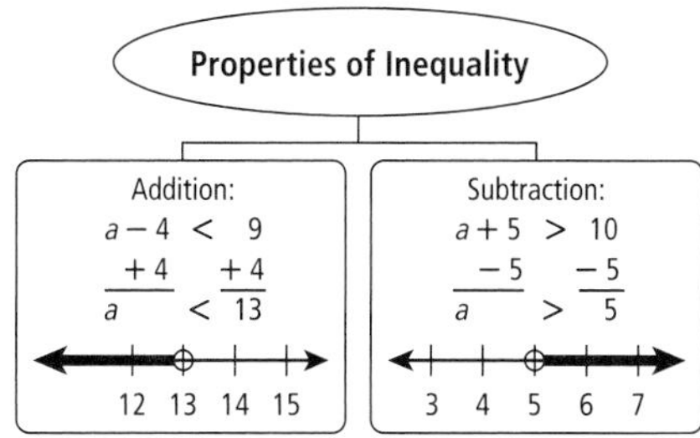

Lesson 3-3

Solving Inequalities by Using Multiplication and Division		
	By a positive number	**By a negative number**
Divide	$2x < 8$ $\frac{2x}{2} < \frac{8}{2}$ $x < 4$	$-3x > 9$ $\frac{-3x}{-3} < \frac{9}{-3}$ $x < -3$
Multiply	$\frac{x}{4} \leq 4$ $\frac{x}{4}(4) \leq 4(4)$ $x \leq 16$	$\frac{x}{-5} \geq 2$ $\frac{x}{-5}(-5) \leq 2(-5)$ $x \leq -10$

Lesson 3-4

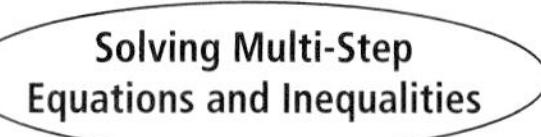

How are they alike? To solve multi-step equations or inequalities, follow the order of operations to simplify the expressions on both sides of the equal sign or inequality symbol, and then undo each operation.

How are they different? When solving multi-step inequalities, you must reverse the inequality symbol if you multiply or divide both sides by a negative number. There are many solutions of an inequality but usually only one solution of an equation.

Lesson 3-5

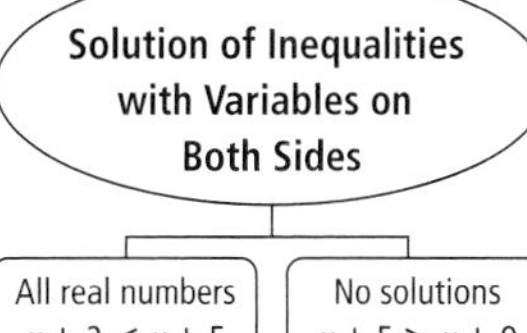

- All real numbers: $x + 2 < x + 5$
- No solutions: $x + 5 > x + 9$

Lesson 3-6

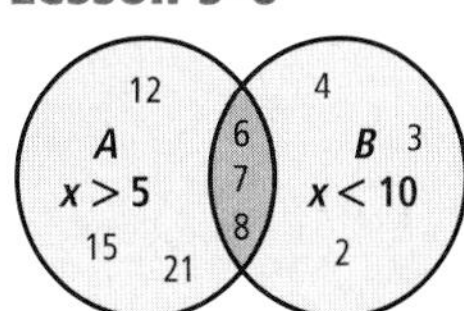

$x > 5$ AND $x < 10$	$x > 5$ OR $x < 10$
6 7 8	2 3 4 6 7 8 12 15 21

Lesson 3-7

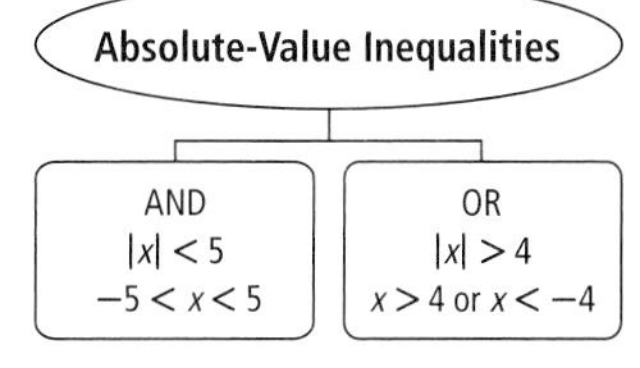

Chapter 4

Lesson 4-1

Key Words for Graph Segments

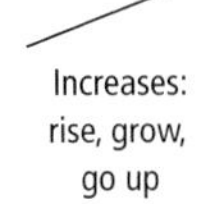

Increases: rise, grow, go up	Decreases: drop, go down	Stays the same: unchanged, constant

Lesson 4-2

A relation is …	
a function if … there is exactly one range element for each domain element.	not a function if … there is more than one range element for a domain element.

Lesson 4-3

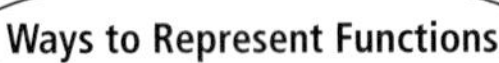

Ways to Represent Functions

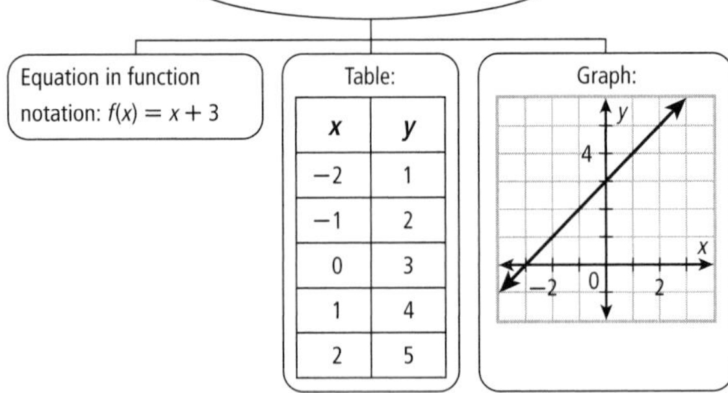

Equation in function notation: $f(x) = x + 3$

Table:

x	y
−2	1
−1	2
0	3
1	4
2	5

Graph:

Lesson 4-4

	As a graph	Example
Positive Correlation		the total price of an ice cream cone and the number of scoops
Negative Correlation		the amount of water in a watering can and the number of flowers watered
No Correlation		the number of magazines a person has and the size of the person's shoes

Lesson 4-5

Finding the *n*th Term of an Arithmetic Sequence → 1. Find the common difference. → 2. Write a rule to find the *n*th term.

Chapter 5

Lesson 5-1

Determining Whether an Equation is Linear

From its graph: All the points form a line.

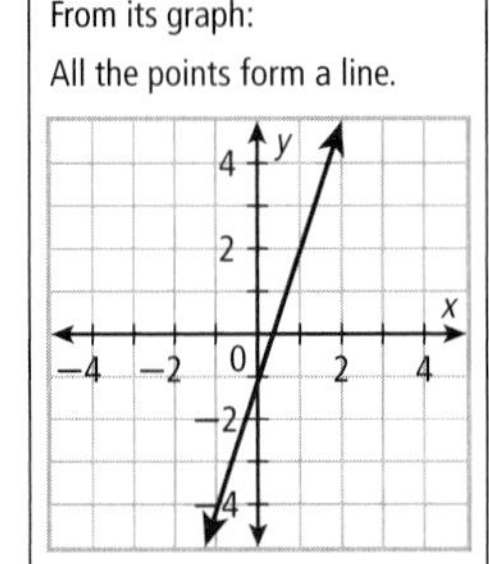

From its equation: It can be written in standard form, $Ax + By = C$, where A and B are not both 0.

Example: $4x + 2y = -2$

From a list of ordered pairs: When graphed, the ordered pairs lie on a line. Example: (0, 6), (1, 3), (2, 0)

Lesson 5-2

Graphing $Ax + By = C$ Using Intercepts

1. Find the x-intercept by letting y equal 0 and solving for x. → 2. Find the y-intercept by letting x equal 0 and solving for y. → 3. Graph the line by plotting the points containing the intercepts and then connecting the points with a straight line.

Lesson 5-3

Finding Slope

From a graph: Begin at any point on the line. Count rise and run to another point on the line. Slope is the ratio of rise to run.	From an equation: Find the x- and y-intercepts. Substitute the points containing the intercepts into the slope formula.

Lesson 5-4

Recognizing a Direct Variation		
From an Equation: The equation can be written in the form $y = kx$ for some nonzero value of k.	From Ordered Pairs: An equation describing the ordered pairs can be written in the form $y = kx$. Also, the ratio $\frac{y}{x}$ is constant for each ordered pair.	From a Graph: The graph is a line through (0, 0).

Lesson 5-5

Graphing the Line Described by $y = mx + b$

1. Plot the point (0, b). → 2. Find a second point on the line by using the slope m to move horizontally and vertically from (0, b). → 3. Draw the line connecting the two points.

Lesson 5-6

Writing the Equation of a Line

- If you know two points on the line: Use the two points in the slope formula to find the slope. Then use the slope and one of the points to write the equation in point-slope form.
- If you know the slope and y-intercept: If the slope is m and the y-intercept is b, then the equation is $y = mx + b$.
- If you know the slope and a point on the line: Use the slope and the point to write the equation in point-slope form.

Lesson 5-7

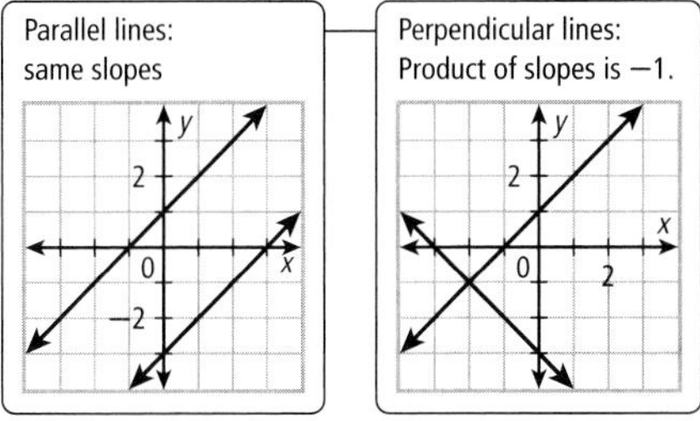

Chapter 6

Lesson 6-1

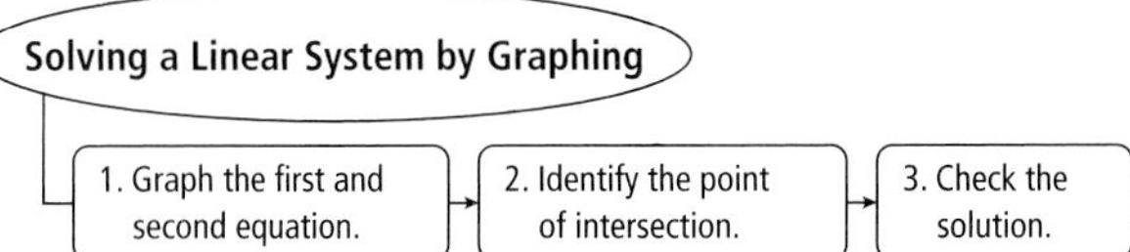

Solving a Linear System by Graphing
1. Graph the first and second equation.
2. Identify the point of intersection.
3. Check the solution.

Lesson 6-2

The solution for each is (5, 3).

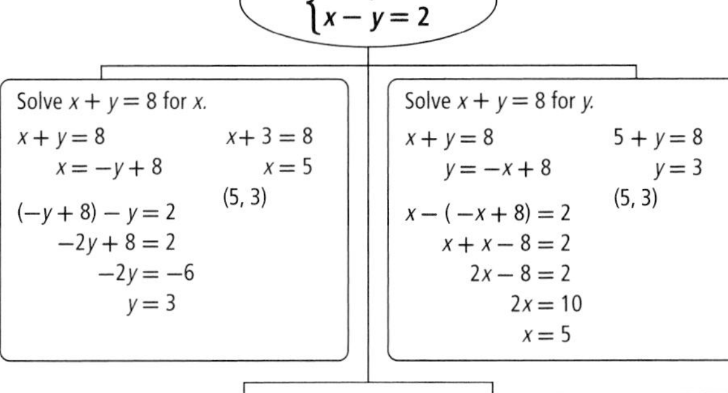

$$\begin{cases} x + y = 8 \\ x - y = 2 \end{cases}$$

Solve $x + y = 8$ for x.

$x + y = 8$
$x = -y + 8$
$(-y + 8) - y = 2$
$-2y + 8 = 2$
$-2y = -6$
$y = 3$

$x + 3 = 8$
$x = 5$
(5, 3)

Solve $x + y = 8$ for y.

$x + y = 8$
$y = -x + 8$
$x - (-x + 8) = 2$
$x + x - 8 = 2$
$2x - 8 = 2$
$2x = 10$
$x = 5$

$5 + y = 8$
$y = 3$
(5, 3)

Solve $x - y = 2$ for x.

$x - y = 2$
$x = y + 2$
$(y + 2) + y = 8$
$2y + 2 = 8$
$2y = 6$
$y = 3$

$x - 3 = 2$
$x = 5$
(5, 3)

Solve $x - y = 2$ for y.

$x - y = 2$
$-y = -x + 2$
$y = x - 2$
$x + (x - 2) = 8$
$2x - 2 = 8$
$2x = 10$
$x = 5$

$5 - y = 2$
$-y = -3$
$y = 3$
(5, 3)

Lesson 6-3

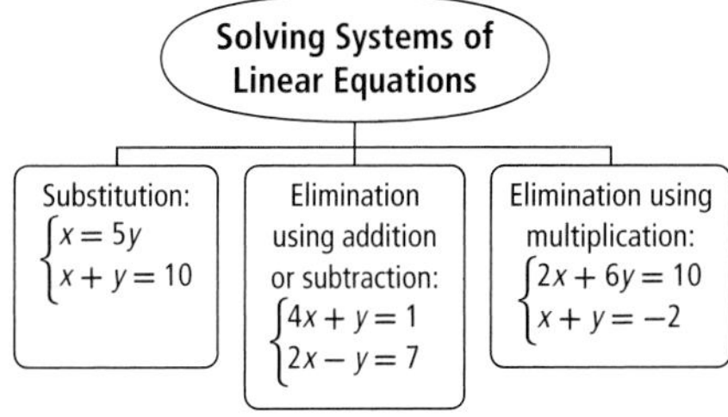

Lesson 6-4

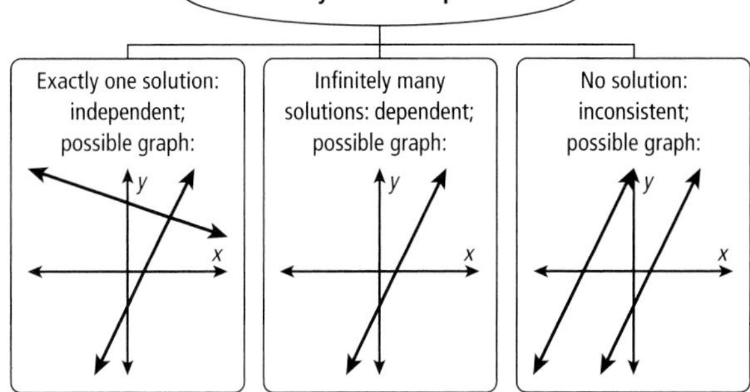

Lesson 6-5

Applications of Systems of Equations

- **Rate Problem** A plane flying against the wind takes 2.5 hours to make a one-way trip of 750 miles. Returning with the wind, the trip takes 2 hours. What is the wind speed and the speed of the plane with no wind? 37.5 mi/h; 337.5 mi/h
- **Mixture Problem** A 1.5% acid solution is mixed with a 4% acid solution. How many ounces of each solution are needed to make 60 ounces of a 2.5% acid solution? 36 oz of the 1.5% solution; 24 oz of the 4% solution
- **Number-Digit Problem** The sum of the digits of a two-digit number is 6. When the digits are reversed, the new number is 18 more than the original number. What is the original number? 24

Lesson 6-6

Inequality	$y < 5x + 2$	$y > 7x - 3$	$y \leq 9x + 1$	$y \geq -3x - 2$
Symbol	$<$	$>$	$\leq$	$\geq$
Boundary Line	Dashed	Dashed	Solid	Solid
Shading	Below	Above	Below	Above

Lesson 6-7

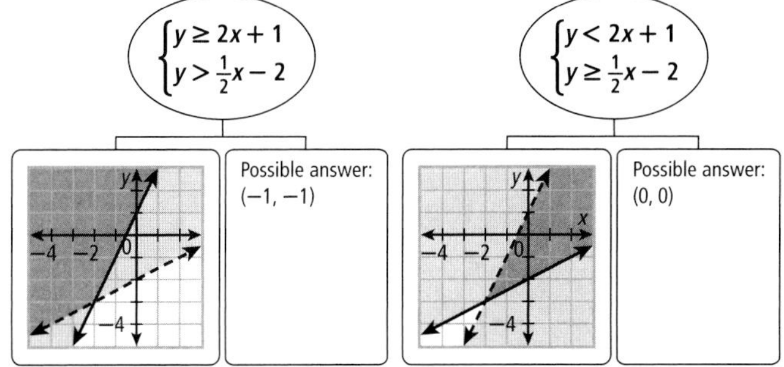

Additional Answers

Chapter 7

Lesson 7-1

Simplifying Expressions with Negative Exponents

For a negative exponent in the numerator, move the power to the denominator and change the negative exponent to a positive exponent; possible answer: $2^{-3} = \frac{1}{2^3}$.	For a negative exponent in the denominator, move the power to the numerator and change the negative exponent to a positive exponent; possible answer: $\frac{4}{x^{-5}} = 4x^5$.

Lesson 7-2

Powers of 10 and Scientific Notation

A negative exponent corresponds to moving the decimal point to the left.	A positive exponent corresponds to moving the decimal point to the right.

Lesson 7-3

Multiplication Properties of Exponents		
Product of Powers Property	Power of a Power Property	Power of a Product Property
$a^m a^n = a^{m+n}$	$(a^m)^n = a^{mn}$	$(ab)^n = a^n b^n$

Lesson 7-4

If a and b are nonzero real numbers and m and n are integers, then...		
$\frac{a^m}{a^n} = a^{m-n}$ $\frac{7^5}{7^3} = 7^{5-3} = 7^2 = 49$	$\left(\frac{a}{b}\right)^n = \frac{a^n}{b^n}$ $\left(\frac{2}{3}\right)^3 = \frac{2^3}{3^3} = \frac{8}{27}$	$\left(\frac{a}{b}\right)^{-n} = \left(\frac{b}{a}\right)^n$ $\left(\frac{3}{4}\right)^{-2} = \left(\frac{4}{3}\right)^2 = \frac{4^2}{3^2} = \frac{16}{9}$

Lesson 7-5

Fractional Exponent	Definition	Numerical Example
$b^{\frac{1}{n}}$	A number raised to the power of $\frac{1}{n}$ is equal to the nth root of that number.	$36^{\frac{1}{2}} = \sqrt{36} = 6$
$b^{\frac{m}{n}}$	A number raised to the power of $\frac{m}{n}$ is equal to the nth root of that number raised to the mth power.	$36^{\frac{3}{2}} = \left(\sqrt{36}\right)^3 = 6^3 = 216$

Lesson 7-6

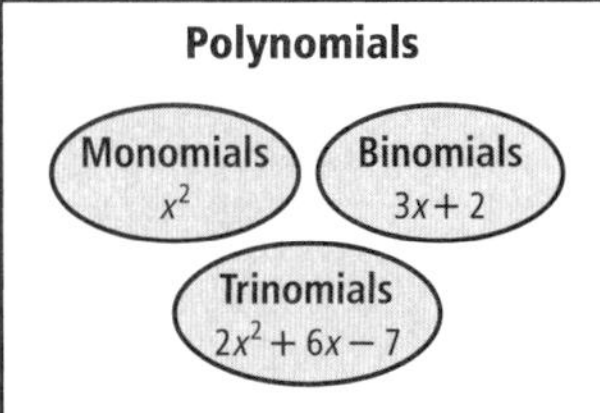

Lesson 7-7

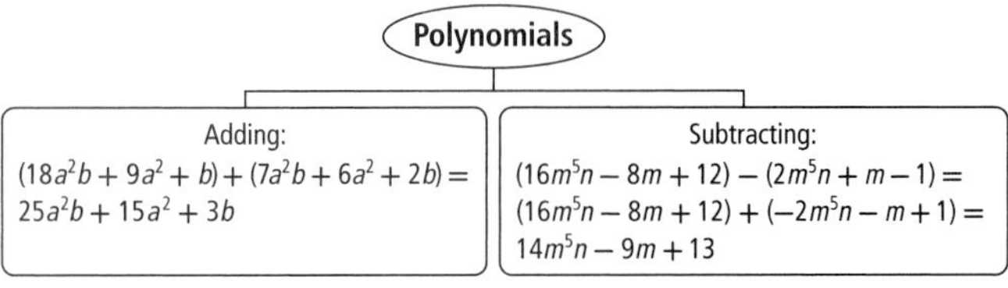

Polynomials
Adding:
$(18a^2b + 9a^2 + b) + (7a^2b + 6a^2 + 2b) =$
$25a^2b + 15a^2 + 3b$
Subtracting:
$(16m^5n - 8m + 12) - (2m^5n + m - 1) =$
$(16m^5n - 8m + 12) + (-2m^5n - m + 1) =$
$14m^5n - 9m + 13$

Lesson 7-8

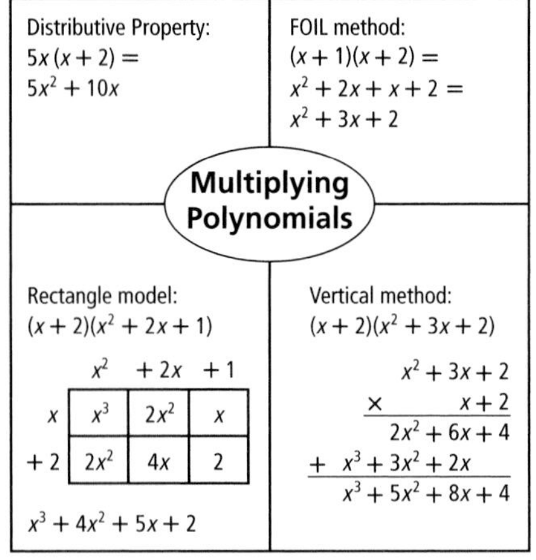

Distributive Property:
$5x(x + 2) =$
$5x^2 + 10x$
FOIL method:
$(x + 1)(x + 2) =$
$x^2 + 2x + x + 2 =$
$x^2 + 3x + 2$
Multiplying Polynomials
Rectangle model:
$(x + 2)(x^2 + 2x + 1)$
x^2 $+2x$ $+1$
x x^3 $2x^2$ x
$+2$ $2x^2$ $4x$ 2
$x^3 + 4x^2 + 5x + 2$
Vertical method:
$(x + 2)(x^2 + 3x + 2)$
$x^2 + 3x + 2$
$\times \quad x + 2$
$2x^2 + 6x + 4$
$+ \ x^3 + 3x^2 + 2x$
$x^3 + 5x^2 + 8x + 4$

Lesson 7-9

Special Products of Binomials		
Perfect-Square Trinomials		Difference of Two Squares
$(a + b)^2 = a^2 + 2ab + b^2$ $(x + 4)^2 = x^2 + 8x + 16$	$(a - b)^2 = a^2 - 2ab + b^2$ $(x - 4)^2 = x^2 - 8x + 16$	$(a + b)(a - b) = a^2 - b^2$ $(x + 4)(x - 4) = x^2 - 16$

Chapter 8

Lesson 8-1

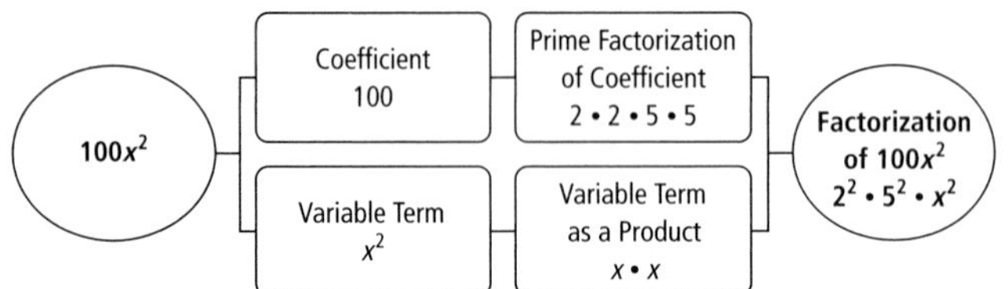

Lesson 8-2

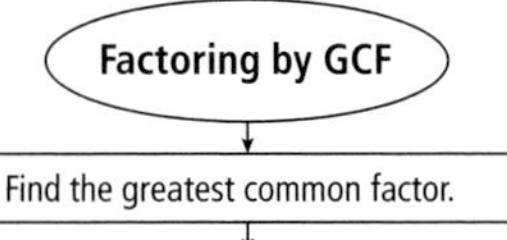

1. Find the greatest common factor.
2. Write each term as a product using the GCF.
3. Use the Distributive Property to factor out the GCF.
4. Check by multiplying.

Lesson 8-3

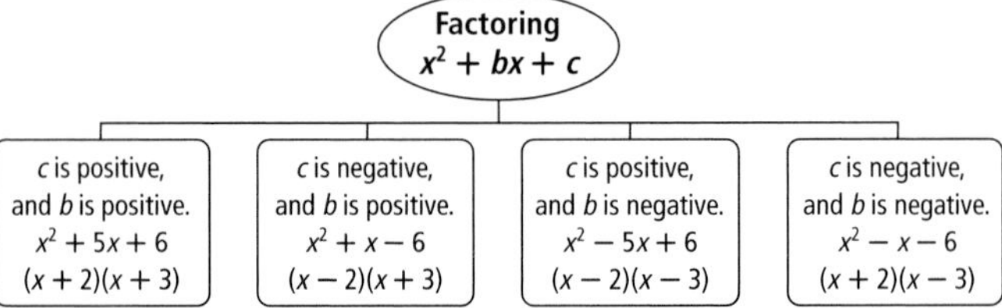

Additional Answers

Lesson 8-4

Factoring $ax^2 + bx + c$	
$c > 0$	
$b > 0$	$b < 0$
$3x^2 + 10x + 8 = (3x + 4)(x + 2)$	$3x^2 - 10x + 8 = (3x - 4)(x - 2)$
$c < 0$	
$b < 0$	$b > 0$
$3x^2 - 10x - 8 = (3x + 2)(x - 4)$	$3x^2 + 10x - 8 = (3x - 2)(x + 4)$

Lesson 8-5

Special Product	Factored Form
Perfect-square trinomial with positive coefficient of middle term: $x^2 + 2x + 1$	$(x + 1)^2$
Perfect-square trinomial with negative coefficient of middle term: $x^2 - 2x + 1$	$(x - 1)^2$
Difference of two squares: $x^2 - 1$	$(x - 1)(x + 1)$

Lesson 8-6

Factoring Methods	
Polynomial	**Method**
1. $16x^4 - 25y^8$	**A.** Factoring out the GCF
2. $x^2 + 10x + 25$	**B.** Factoring by grouping
3. $9t^2 + 27t + 18t^4$	**C.** Unfactorable
4. $a^2 + 3a - 7a - 21$	**D.** Difference of two squares
5. $100b^2 + 81$	**E.** Perfect-square trinomial

Chapter 9

Lesson 9-1

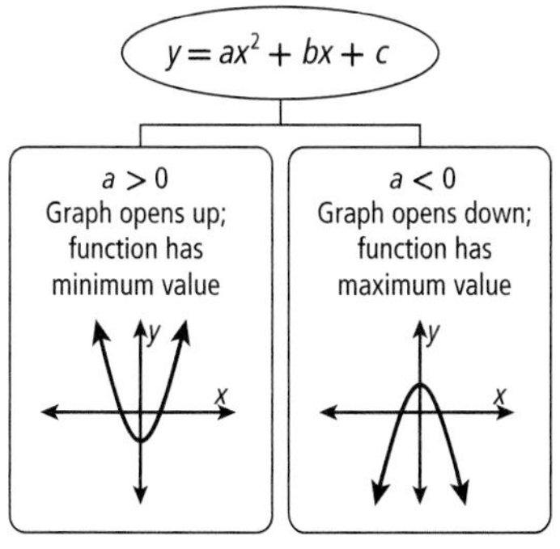

$y = ax^2 + bx + c$
$a > 0$
Graph opens up; function has minimum value
$a < 0$
Graph opens down; function has maximum value

Lesson 9-2

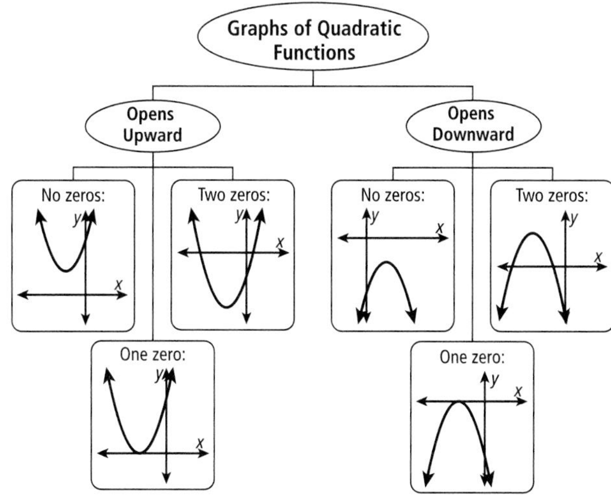

Lesson 9-3

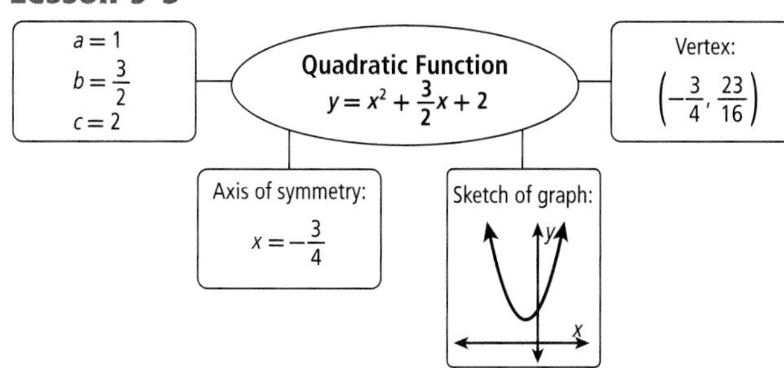

Lesson 9-4

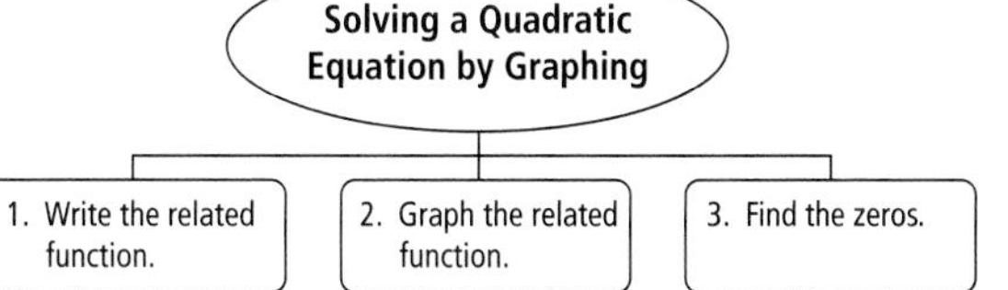

Solving a Quadratic Equation by Graphing
1. Write the related function.
2. Graph the related function.
3. Find the zeros.

Lesson 9-5

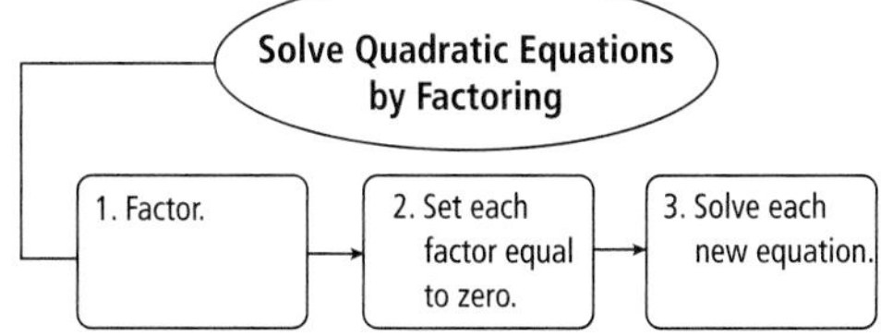

Lesson 9-6

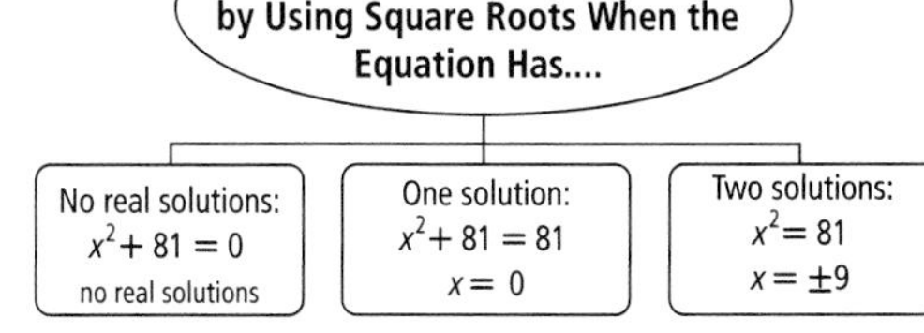

Lesson 9-7

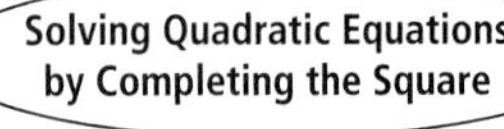

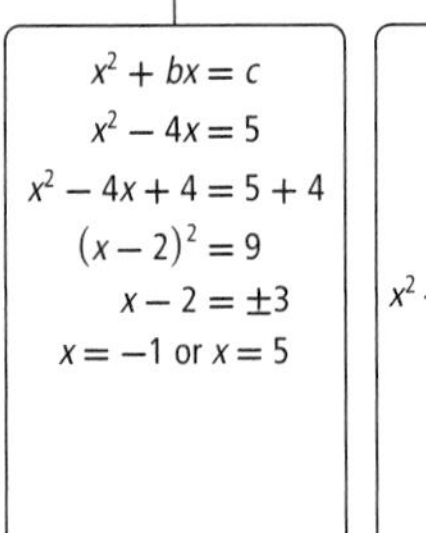

$x^2 + bx = c$
$x^2 - 4x = 5$
$x^2 - 4x + 4 = 5 + 4$
$(x-2)^2 = 9$
$x - 2 = \pm 3$
$x = -1$ or $x = 5$

$ax^2 + bx = c$
$2x^2 - 3x = 2$
$x^2 - \frac{3}{2}x = 1$
$x^2 - \frac{3}{2}x + \frac{9}{16} = 1 + \frac{9}{16}$
$\left(x - \frac{3}{4}\right)^2 = \frac{25}{16}$
$x - \frac{3}{4} = \pm\frac{5}{4}$
$x = -\frac{1}{2}$ or $x = 2$

$x^2 + bx + c = 0$
$2x^2 + 4x - 20 = 0$
$x^2 + 2x - 10 = 0$
$x^2 + 2x = 10$
$x^2 + 2x + 1 = 10 + 1$
$(x+1)^2 = 11$
$x + 1 = \pm\sqrt{11}$
$x = -1 - \sqrt{11}$ or
$x = -1 + \sqrt{11}$

Lesson 9-8

Equation	$x^2 + 5 = -20$	$x^2 + 6x + 9 = 0$	$3x^2 - 7 + 11 = 0$
Method	using square roots	factoring	Quadratic Formula

Lesson 9-9

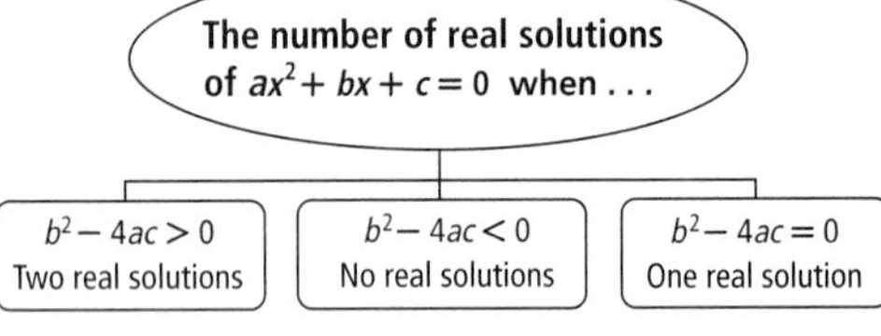

The number of real solutions of $ax^2 + bx + c = 0$ when . . .
$b^2 - 4ac > 0$ Two real solutions
$b^2 - 4ac < 0$ No real solutions
$b^2 - 4ac = 0$ One real solution

Chapter 10

Lesson 10-1

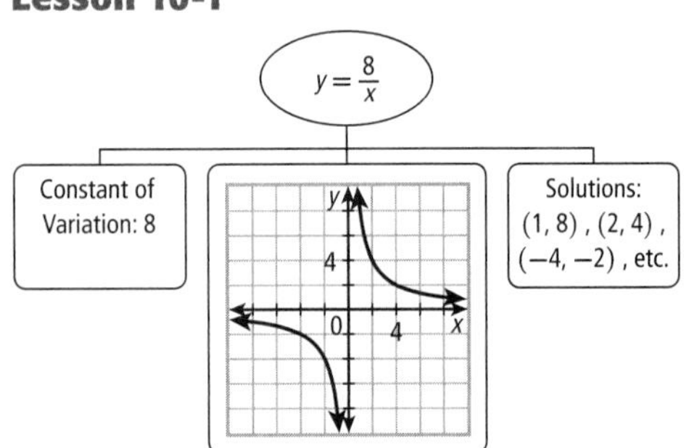

Lesson 10-2

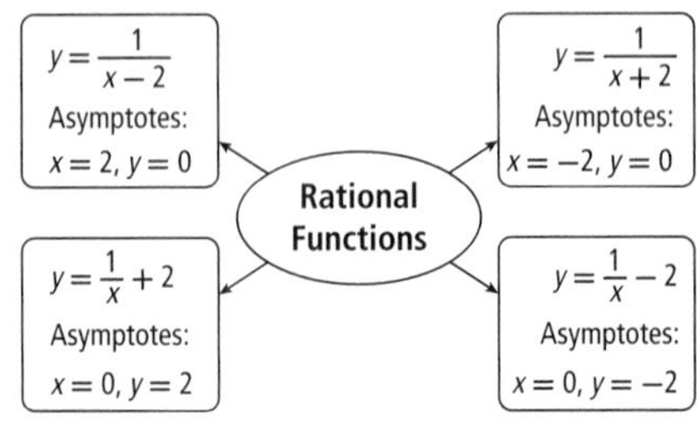

Lesson 10-3

Using Properties of Exponents: $\frac{5x^4}{x^2} = 5x^2$

Using Opposite Binomials: $\frac{4-x}{x-4} = -1$

Ways of Simplifying Rational Expressions

Factoring the Numerator: $\frac{4x^2 - 4x}{8x} = \frac{x-1}{2}$

Factoring the Denominator: $\frac{x-3}{x^2 - 6x + 9} = \frac{1}{x-3}$

Lesson 10-4

Rational Expressions

Multiplying: Multiply numerators, multiply denominators, and then simplify.

Dividing: Multiply the first expression by the reciprocal of the second expression.

Lesson 10-5

Adding

Similarities: In both, write each expression with a common denominator, add, and simplify.

Differences: In rational expressions, you may need to combine like terms.

Subtracting

Similarities: In both, write each expression with a common denominator, subtract, and simplify.

Differences: In rational expressions, you may need to combine like terms.

Lesson 10-6

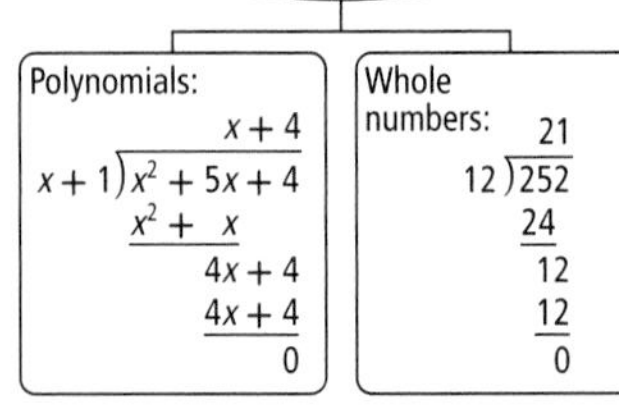

Additional Answers

Lesson 10-7

Solving Rational Equations

Solve by using cross products:

$$\frac{3}{x} = \frac{2}{x+1}$$
$$3(x+1) = 2x$$
$$3x + 3 = 2x$$
$$x = -3$$

Solve by using the LCD:

$$\frac{7}{x-1} - \frac{4}{x-1} = \frac{6}{x}$$
$$\frac{x}{x}\left(\frac{7}{x-1} - \frac{4}{x-1}\right) = \frac{6}{x}\left(\frac{x-1}{x-1}\right)$$
$$\frac{7x}{x^2-x} - \frac{4x}{x^2-x} = \frac{6(x-1)}{x^2-x}$$
$$7x - 4x = 6(x-1)$$
$$3x = 6x - 6$$
$$x = 2$$

Lesson 10-8

Applications of Rational Equations

Work Problem	Mixture Problem	Rate Problem
Janet can wash a car in 40 minutes. Navi can wash the same car in 60 minutes. How long will it take to wash the car if they work together? 24 min	A chemist has 100 mL of a solution that is half hydrochloric acid. How many milliliters of hydrochloric acid should be added to get a solution that is 90% hydrochloric acid? 400 mL	Train A goes 40 mi/h faster than Train B. It takes Train A 2 hours less time than Train B to go 160 miles. How long does it take Train A to make the trip? 2 h

Chapter 11

Lesson 11-1

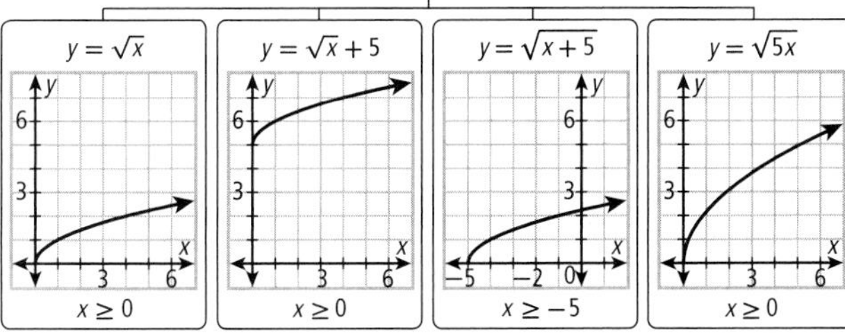

Lesson 11-2

	Product Property of Square Roots	Quotient Property of Square Roots
Words	If $a \geq 0$ and $b \geq 0$, then $\sqrt{ab} = \sqrt{a}\sqrt{b}$.	If $a \geq 0$ and $b > 0$, then $\sqrt{\frac{a}{b}} = \frac{\sqrt{a}}{\sqrt{b}}$.
Example	$\sqrt{4 \cdot 16} = \sqrt{4}\sqrt{16} = 2 \cdot 4 = 8$	$\sqrt{\frac{49}{81}} = \frac{\sqrt{49}}{\sqrt{81}} = \frac{7}{9}$

Lesson 11-3

Like Radicals

Definition: Radical expressions that have the same radicand and the same index

Examples: $\sqrt{7}$ and $2\sqrt{7}$; $2\sqrt{x}$ and $-7\sqrt{x}$

Nonexamples: $\sqrt{2}$ and $\sqrt{3}$; $\sqrt{10x}$ and $\sqrt{100x}$

Lesson 11-4

Multiplying Radical Expressions

Multiplying two square roots:	Using the Distributive Property:	Using FOIL:
$\sqrt{6}\sqrt{12} = \sqrt{6(12)}$ $= \sqrt{72} = \sqrt{36(2)}$ $= 6\sqrt{2}$	$\sqrt{2}(\sqrt{5} - \sqrt{2})$ $= \sqrt{2}\sqrt{5} - \sqrt{2}\sqrt{2}$ $= \sqrt{10} - 2$	$(2 + \sqrt{3})(4 - \sqrt{3})$ $= 8 - 2\sqrt{3} + 4\sqrt{3} - 3$ $= 5 + 2\sqrt{3}$

Lesson 11-5

Solving Radical Equations

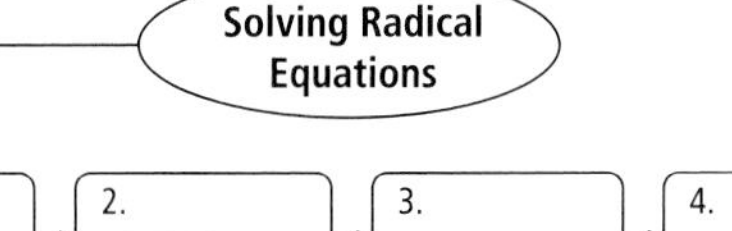

1. $4\sqrt{x+2} = 12$
2. $\sqrt{x+2} = 3$
3. $x + 2 = 9$
4. $x = 7$

Lesson 11-6

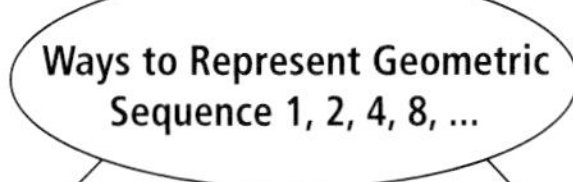

Table

Position	Term
1	1
2	2
3	4
4	8

Formula

$$a_n = 1(2)^{n-1}$$

Words

Start with 1 and multiply each term by 2 to get the next term.

Lesson 11-7

Exponential Functions: $y = ab^x$

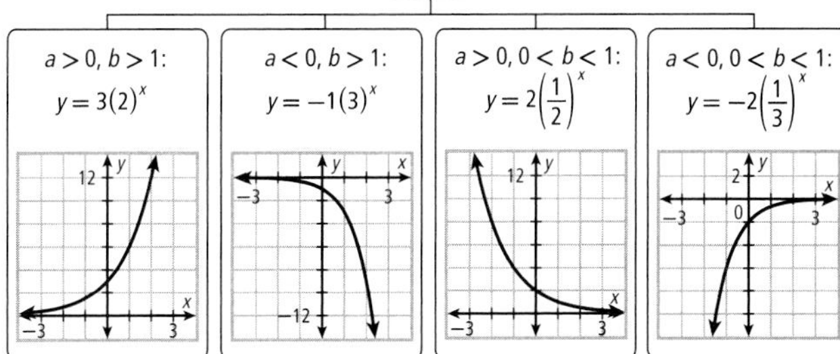

Additional Answers

Lesson 11-8

Exponential Growth vs. Exponential Decay

How are they alike?
Both are exponential functions, have a domain of all real numbers, have a range of all real numbers greater than 0, and represent a change in quantity by the same rate over time.

How are they different?
One increases over time and the other decreases over time, in one you add the rate to 1 and in the other you subtract the rate from 1.

Lesson 11-9

Modeling Data

Linear: Points lie on a line; for a constant change in *x*, the first differences are constant.

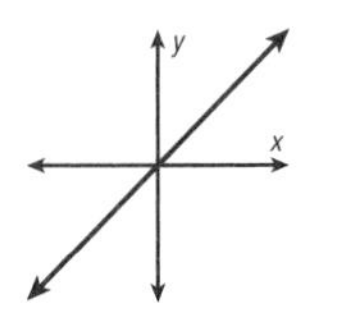

Exponential: Smooth curve that extends infinitely either up to the right, up to the left, down to the right, or down to the left; for a constant change in *x*, there is a constant ratio.

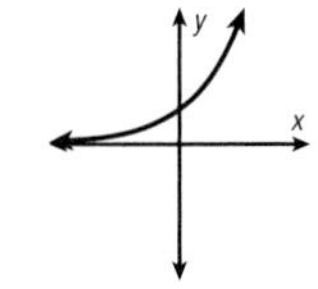

Quadratic: Points lie on a parabola and are symmetric with a vertical line through the vertex; for a constant change in *x*, the second differences are constant.

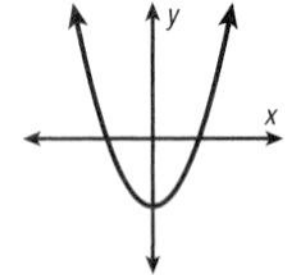

Additional Answers continue on p. A12.

Notes

Additional Answers

Chapter 1

1-1 *Exercises*

23, 24. Possible answers given.

23. 14 decreased by t; the difference of 14 and t

24. the sum of x and 0.5; x increased by 0.5

33. $2x$; possible answer: Jim has twice as many aunts as Carly, who has x aunts.

34. $17 - b$; possible answer: Sarah started with 17 apples, but lost b of them.

35. $y + 10$; possible answer: April had y CDs and then got 10 more.

1A *Ready to Go On?*

1–4. Possible answers given.

1. the sum of 4 and n; 4 increased by n

2. the difference of m and 9; 9 less than m

3. g divided by 2; the quotient of g and 2

4. 4 times z; the product of 4 and z

1B *Ready to Go On?*

32. $3(x + 2) - 3x$; $3x + 3(2) - 3x$ (Dist. Prop.); $3x + 6 - 3x$ (Multiply.); $6 + 3x - 3x$ (Comm. Prop. of Add.); $6 + (3x - 3x)$ (Assoc. Prop. of Add.); $6 + 0$ (Combine like terms.); 6 (Combine like terms.)

33. $x - 6x^2 + 3x + 4x^2$; $x + 3x - 6x^2 + 4x^2$ (Comm. Prop. of Add.); $(x + 3x) + (-6x^2 + 4x^2)$ (Assoc. Prop. of Add.); $4x - 2x^2$ (Combine like terms.)

34. $-2(3x + 2y + 4x - 5y)$; $-2(3x) - 2(2y) - 2(4x) - 2(-5y)$ (Dist. Prop.); $-6x + (-4y) + (-8x) + 10y$ (Multiply.); $-6x - 4y - 8x + 10y$ (Def. of subt.); $-6x - 8x - 4y + 10y$ (Comm. Prop. of Add.); $(-6x - 8x) + (-4y + 10y)$ (Assoc. Prop. of Add.); $-14x + 6y$ (Combine like terms.)

Chapter 2

Logical Reasoning

1.

Statements	Reasons
1. $x - 2 = 4$	Given
2. $x = 6$	Add. Prop of Eq. (Add 2 to both sides.)

If $x - 2 = 4$, then $x = 6$.
Hypothesis: $x - 2 = 4$;
Conclusion: $x = 6$

2.

Statements	Reasons
1. $x + 6 = 16$	Given
2. $x = 10$	Subtr. Prop of Eq. (Subtract 6 from both sides.)

If $x + 6 = 16$, then $x = 10$.
Hypothesis: $x + 6 = 10$;
Conclusion: $x = 10$

3.

Statements	Reasons
1. $-5x = 25$	Given
2. $x = -5$	Div. Prop. of Eq. (Divide both sides by -5.)

If $-5x = 25$, then $x = -5$.
Hypothesis: $-5x = 25$;
Conclusion: $x = -5$

4.

Statements	Reasons
1. $\frac{x}{4} = 13$	Given
2. $x = 52$	Mult. Prop. of Eq. (Multiply both sides by 4.)

If $\frac{x}{4} = 13$, then $x = 52$.
Hypothesis: $\frac{x}{4} = 13$;
Conclusion: $x = 52$

5.

Statements	Reasons
1. $-2x + 5 = 9$	Given
2. $-2x = 4$	Subtr. Prop. of Eq. (Subtract 5 from both sides.)
3. $x = -2$	Div. Prop. of Eq. (Divide both sides by -2.)

If $-2x + 5 = 9$, then $x = -2$.
Hypothesis: $-2x + 5 = 9$;
Conclusion: $x = -2$

6.

Statements	Reasons
1. $6x - 5 = 2x - 21$	Given
2. $4x - 5 = -21$	Subtr. Prop. of Eq. (Subtract $2x$ from both sides.)
3. $4x = -16$	Add. Prop. of Eq. (Add 5 to both sides.)
4. $x = -4$	Div. Prop. of Eq. (Divide both sides by 4.)

If $6x - 5 = 2x - 21$, then $x = -4$.
Hypothesis: $6x - 5 = 2x - 21$;
Conclusion: $x = -4$

7.

Statements	Reasons
1. $6(x - 5) = 10$	Given
2. $6x - 30 = 10$	Dist. Prop.
3. $6x = 40$	Add. Prop. of Eq. (Add 30 to both sides.)
4. $x = \frac{20}{3}$	Div. Prop. of Eq. (Divide both sides by 6.)

If $6(x - 5) = 10$, then $x = \frac{20}{3}$.
Hypothesis: $6(x - 5) = 10$;
Conclusion: $x = \frac{20}{3}$

8.

Statements	Reasons
1. $6x + 1 + x = 10 - 12$	Given
2. $7x + 1 = -2$	Combine like terms.
3. $7x = -3$	Subtr. Prop. of Eq. (Subtract 1 from both sides.)
4. $x = -\frac{3}{7}$	Div. Prop. of Eq. (Divide both sides by 7.)

If $6x + 1 + x = 10 - 12$, then $x = -\frac{3}{7}$.
Hypothesis: $6x + 1 + x = 10 - 12$;
Conclusion: $x = -\frac{3}{7}$

9. In Step 2, the Subtr. Prop. of Eq. should have been used (subtract 1 from both sides).

Statements	Reasons
1. $5x + 1 = 7$	Given
2. $5x = 6$	Subtr. Prop. of Eq. (Subtract 1 from both sides.)
3. $x = \frac{6}{5}$	Div. Prop. of Eq. (Divide both sides by 5.)

Logical Reasoning

2.

Statements	Reasons
1. a and b are even.	Given
2. a and b are each divisible by 2: $a = 2m$ and $b = 2n$.	Def. of even number
3. $ab = 2m(2n)$	Substitute $2m$ for a and $2n$ for b.
4. $ab = 2(2mn)$	Comm. and Assoc. Prop. of Mult.
5. Because ab is divisible by 2, ab is even.	Def. of even number

Chapter 3

3-2 *Exercises*

34. Both inequalities have all numbers greater than 1 as solutions. $x + 2 \geq 3$ also includes 1. The graph of $x + 2 > 3$ has an empty circle at 1, but the graph of $x + 2 \geq 3$ has a solid circle at 1.

35a. $411 + 411 = 822$ miles

b. $822 + m \leq 1000$

c. $m \leq 178$, but m cannot be negative

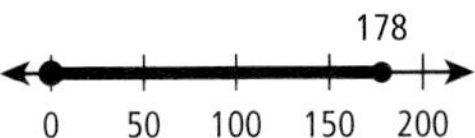

46. If $x + b > c$, then $x > c - b$ (Subtr. Prop. of Ineq.). Also, $x > 0$, so $c - b > 0$, or $c = b$ (Add. Prop. of Ineq.), which is the same as $b = c$.

3-3 *Exercises*

31. $r < -\frac{3}{2}$

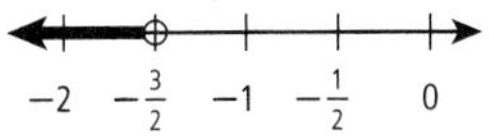

-2 $-\frac{3}{2}$ -1 $-\frac{1}{2}$ 0

32. $p < -0.1$

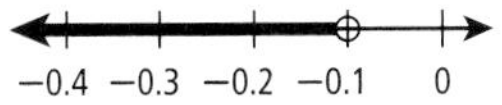

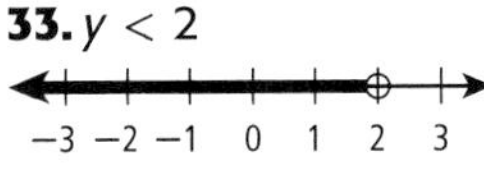

33. $y < 2$

−3 −2 −1 0 1 2 3

34. $f > -30$

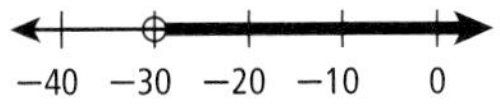

−40 −30 −20 −10 0

35. $t > 4$

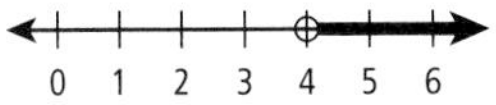

0 1 2 3 4 5 6

36. $w \leq -2.4$

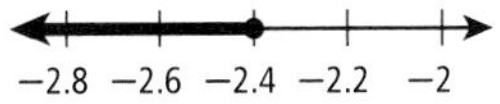

−2.8 −2.6 −2.4 −2.2 −2

37. $z < -11$

−13 −12 −11 −10 −9

38. $f < -3$

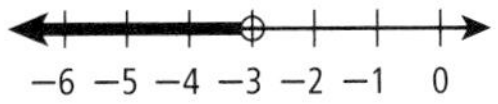

−6 −5 −4 −3 −2 −1 0

39. $k \leq -7$

−9 −8 −7 −6 −5

40. $b > 3.5$

3 3.5 4 4.5 5

41. $p \geq -12$

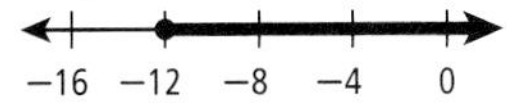

−16 −12 −8 −4 0

43. $x > -3$

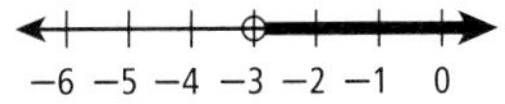

−6 −5 −4 −3 −2 −1 0

44. $t \leq 8$

0 2 4 6 8 10 12

45. $x < 20$

0 10 20 30 40

46. $p \geq -30$

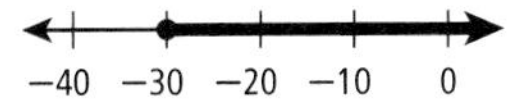

−40 −30 −20 −10 0

47. $p \leq -6$

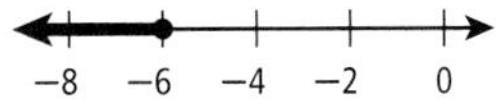

−8 −6 −4 −2 0

48. $t > -\frac{1}{6}$

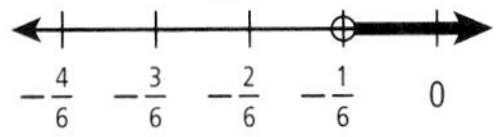

$-\frac{4}{6}$ $-\frac{3}{6}$ $-\frac{2}{6}$ $-\frac{1}{6}$ 0

49. $b < 2$

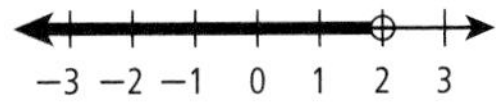

−3 −2 −1 0 1 2 3

50. $r < 60$

0 20 40 60 80

51.

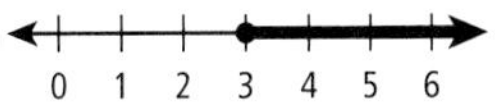

0 1 2 3 4 5 6

52.

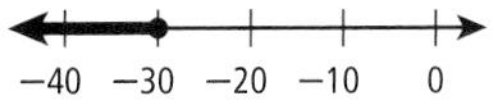

−40 −30 −20 −10 0

53.

0 10 20 30 40

54.

0 20 40 60 80

3A *Ready To Go On?*

1. all real numbers greater than −2

2. all real numbers less than or equal to 8

3. all real numbers greater than or equal to 3

4. all real numbers greater than 1

15. $k \leq 2$

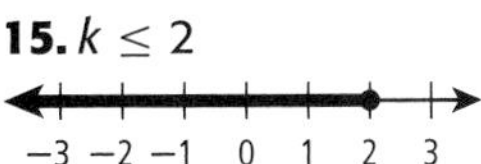

16. $p < 7$

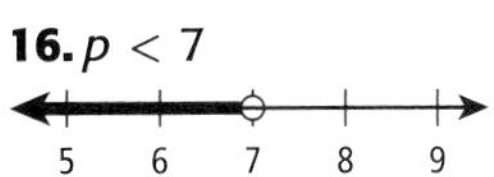

17. $r \geq -4$

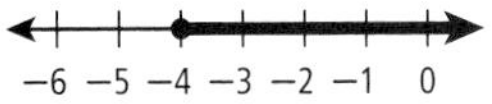

−6 −5 −4 −3 −2 −1 0

18. $p < -3$

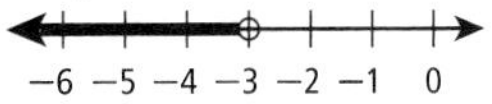

−6 −5 −4 −3 −2 −1 0

21.

−3 −2 −1 0 1 2 3

22.

−12 −9 −6 −3 0

23.

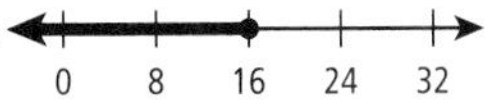

0 8 16 24 32

24.

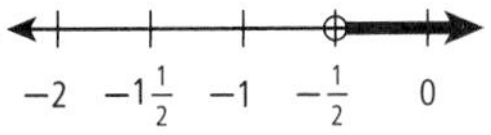

-2 $-1\frac{1}{2}$ -1 $-\frac{1}{2}$ 0

3-4 *Exercises*

25. $w > 0$

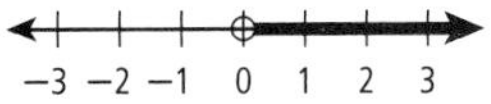

−3 −2 −1 0 1 2 3

26. $p > -5$

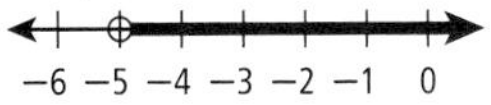

−6 −5 −4 −3 −2 −1 0

27. $v > \frac{2}{3}$

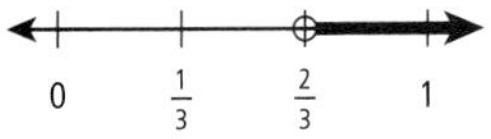

0 $\frac{1}{3}$ $\frac{2}{3}$ 1

28. $x > -9$

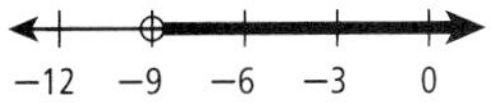

−12 −9 −6 −3 0

29. $x > -5$

−6 −5 −4 −3 −2 −1 0

30. $h \geq 17$

15 16 17 18 19

31. $x < -2$

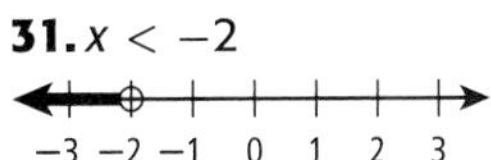

Additional Answers

32. $x < -8$

−16 −12 −8 −4 0

33. $a \geq 11$

9 10 11 12 13

34. $x < 19$

17 18 19 20 21

35. $x > 3$

0 1 2 3 4 5 6

36. $q \leq 16$

0 8 16 24 32

38. $x > 1$

−3 −2 −1 0 1 2 3

39. $x \leq 2$

−3 −2 −1 0 1 2 3

40. $x > 18$

16 17 18 19 20

41. $x < 4$

0 1 2 3 4 5 6

42. $x < 0$

−3 −2 −1 0 1 2 3

43. $x < -6$

−8 −6 −4 −2 0

44. $m \leq -\frac{1}{8}$

$-\frac{1}{2}$ $-\frac{3}{8}$ $-\frac{1}{4}$ $-\frac{1}{8}$ 0

45. $r < 8$

0 4 8 12 16

46. $n \leq 1.8$

1.8

0 0.5 1 1.5 2

47. $x < 7$

5 6 7 8 9

48. $n > 3.5$

2 2.5 3 3.5 4

49. $p \geq 18$

0 6 12 18 24 30

68.

0 1 2 3 4 5 6

69.

0 1 2 3 4 5 6

70.

−3 −2 −1 0 1 2 3

71.

−3 −2 −1 0 1 2 3

72.

−3 −2 −1 0 1 2 3

73.

−3 −2 −1 0 1 2 3

74.

0

75.

−3 −2 −1 0 1 2 3

76.

−3 −2 −1 0 1 2 3

84.

−6 −5 −4 −3 −2 −1 0

85.

0 2 4 6 8

86.

0 1 2 3 4 5 6

Logical Reasoning

2.

Statements	Reasons
1. $x - 9 \leq -12$	Given
2. $x \leq -3$	Add. Prop of Ineq. (Add 9 to both sides.)

If $x - 9 \leq -12$, then $x \leq -3$.
Hypothesis: $x - 9 \leq -12$;
Conclusion: $x \leq -3$

3.

Statements	Reasons
1. $8x > 64$	Given
2. $x > 8$	Div. Prop. of Ineq. (Divide both sides by 8.)

If $8x > 64$, then $x > 8$.
Hypothesis: $8x > 64$;
Conclusion: $x > 8$

4.

Statements	Reasons
1. $\frac{x}{12} \leq -7$	Given
2. $x \leq -84$	Mult. Prop. of Ineq. (Multiply both sides by 12.)

If $\frac{x}{12} \leq -7$, then $x \leq -84$.
Hypothesis: $\frac{x}{12} \leq -7$;
Conclusion: $x \leq -84$

5.

Statements	Reasons
1. $2x + 15 < 29$	Given
2. $2x < 14$	Subtr. Prop. of Ineq. (Subtract 15 from both sides.)
3. $x < 7$	Div. Prop. of Ineq. (Divide both sides by 2.)

If $2x + 15 < 29$, then $x < 7$.
Hypothesis: $2x + 15 < 29$;
Conclusion: $x < 7$

6.

Statements	Reasons
1. $5(3 + x) < 20$	Given
2. $15 + 5x < 20$	Dist. Prop.
3. $5x < 5$	Subtr. Prop. of Ineq. (Subtract 15 from both sides.)
4. $x < 1$	Div. Prop. of Ineq. (Divide both sides by 5.)

If $5(3 + x) < 20$, then $x < 1$.
Hypothesis: $5(3 + x) < 20$;
Conclusion: $x < 1$

7.

Statements	Reasons
1. $16 - x \geq 3x + 8 - 5x$	Given
2. $16 - x \geq (3x - 5x) + 8$	Assoc. and Comm. Prop. of Add.
3. $16 - x \geq -2x + 8$	Combine like terms.
4. $16 + x \geq 8$	Add. Prop. of Ineq. (Add $2x$ to both sides.)
5. $x \geq -8$	Subtr. Prop. of Ineq. (Subtract 16 from both sides.)

If $16 - x \geq 3x + 8 - 5x$, then $x \geq -8$.
Hypothesis: $16 - x \geq 3x + 8 - 5x$;
Conclusion: $x \geq -8$

8.

Statements	Reasons
1. $-4(x+3) > 6(3-x)$	Given
2. $-4x - 12 > 18 - 6x$	Dist. Prop.
3. $2x - 12 > 18$	Add. Prop. of Ineq. (Add $6x$ to both sides.)
4. $2x > 30$	Add. Prop. of Ineq. (Add 12 to both sides.)
5. $x > 15$	Div. Prop. of Ineq. (Divide both sides by 2.)

If $-4(x+3) > 6(3-x)$, then $x > 15$.
Hypothesis: $-4(x+3) > 6(3-x)$;
Conclusion: $x > 15$

9. In Step 2, the terms $3x$ and $-4x$ were combined incorrectly; $3x - 4x = -x$, not x.

Statements	Reasons
1. $3x + 9 - 4x \geq 15$	Given
2. $(3x - 4x) + 9 \geq 15$	Assoc. and Comm. Prop. of Add.
3. $-x + 9 \geq 15$	Combine like terms.
4. $-x \geq 6$	Subtr. Prop. of Ineq. (Subtract 9 from both sides.)
5. $x \leq -6$	Div. Prop. of Ineq. (Divide both sides by -1. Reverse the inequality symbol.)

3-6 *Exercises*

20.

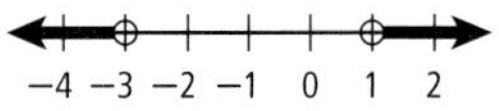

21.

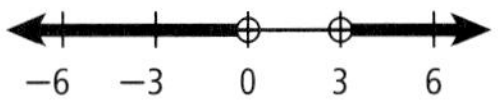

22.

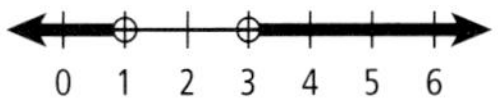

23.

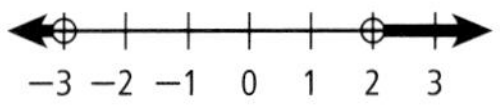

3-7 *Exercises*

20. $-4 \leq x \leq 4$

21. $2 < x < 4$

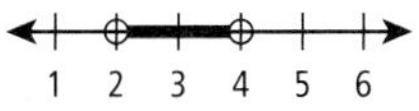

22. $-3 \leq x \leq 7$

23. $-3 < x < 3$

24. $0 \leq x \leq 4.8$

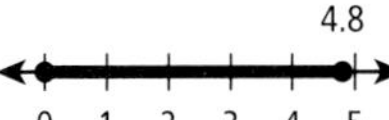

25. $-6 < x < 0$

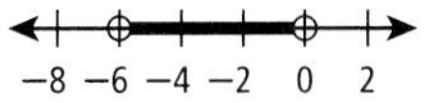

26. $x < -1$ OR $x > 3$

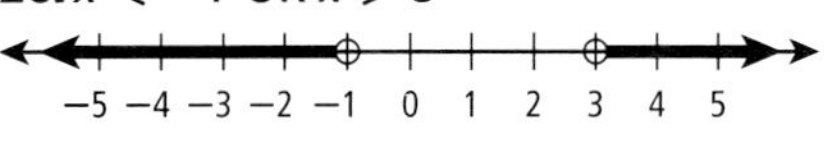

27. $x \leq -10$ OR $x \geq 10$

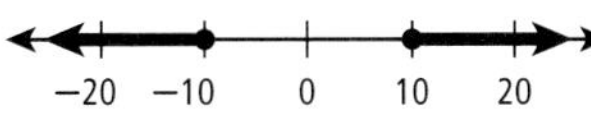

28. $x < -1$ OR $x > 9$

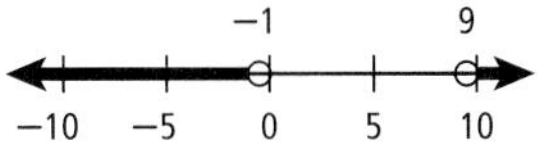

29. $x \leq -10$ OR $x \geq 6$

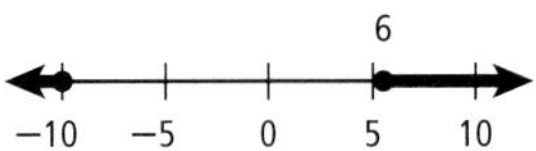

30. $x < 3$ OR $x > 5$

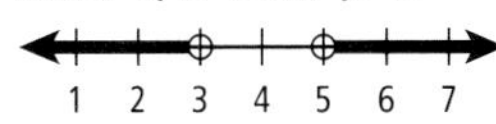

31. $x < -1$ OR $x > 2$

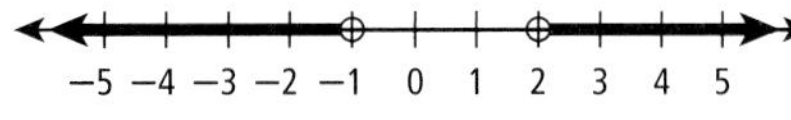

32. $|x - 175| \leq 12$; $163 \leq x \leq 187$

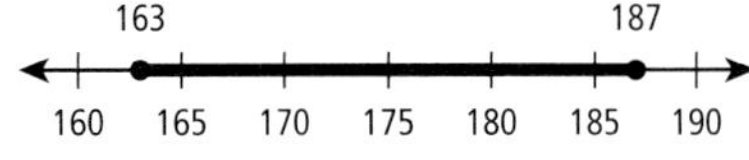

53. $k \leq 1$; the inequality is equivalent to $|x| < k - 1$, and this has no solutions when the expression on the right side is less than or equal to 0 (i.e., when $k - 1 \leq 0$ *or* $k \leq 1$).

54. The difference between a number and -6 must be less than 5.
$|x - (-6)| < 5$
$|x + 6| < 5$

65. all real numbers less than 2

66. all real numbers less than 7

67. all real numbers greater than or equal to -6

68. all real numbers less than or equal to -7

69. $0 < x < 4$

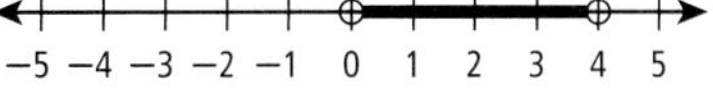

70. $-2 \leq x \leq 4$

71. $x < 1$ OR $x > 4$

72. $x \leq -1$ OR $x \geq 2$

3B *Ready To Go On?*

1.

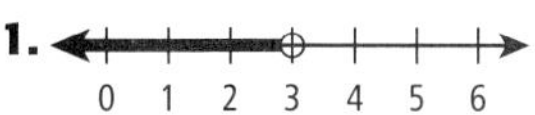

2.

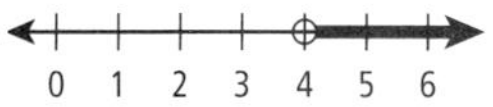

3.

9.

10.

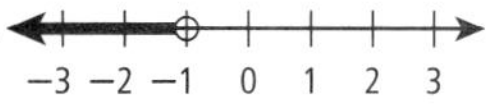

11.

17.

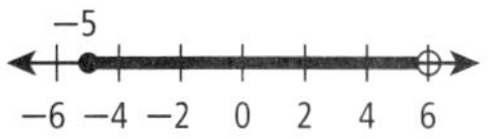

18.

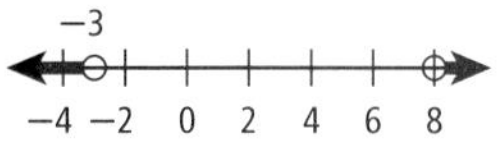

20.

22. $-3 \leq x \leq 3$

23. $-28 < x < 14$

24. $x \leq -7$ OR $x \geq 7$

29.

Chapter 4

Are You Ready?

6–13.

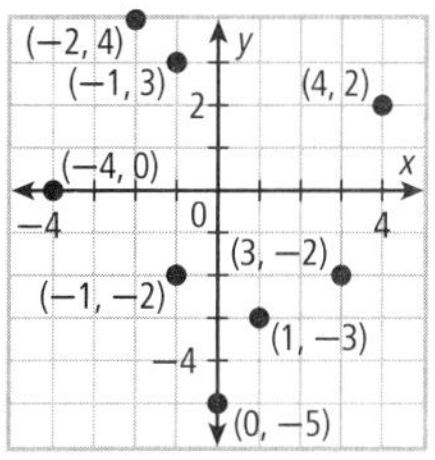

4-1 *Exercises*

19. The point of intersection represents the time of day when you will be the same distance from the base of the mountain on both the hike up and the hike down.

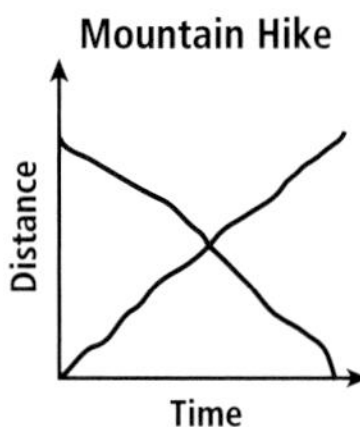

20. Both graphs would start from the origin and then rise. The graph for the brick would increase rapidly and then drop suddenly to zero. The graph for the rolled ball would increase less rapidly and then slowly drop to zero.

21. Possible answer: The number of eggs in stock in a grocery store on different days could be represented by a graph of distinct points. The depth of a scuba diver during a dive could be represented by a connected graph.

22a.

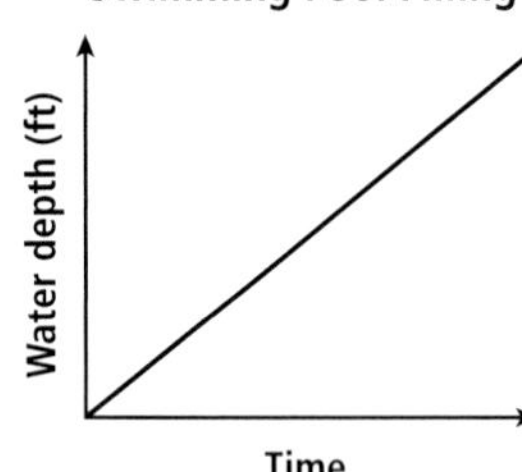

22b.

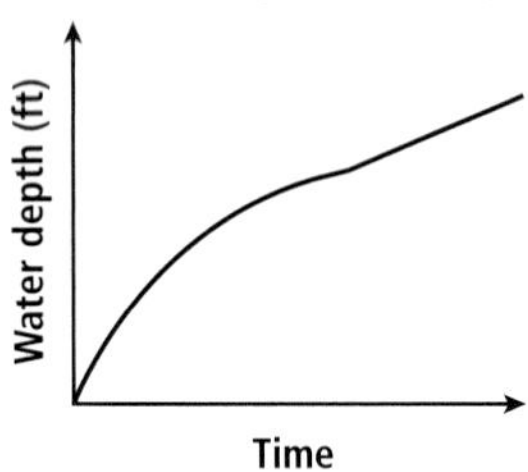

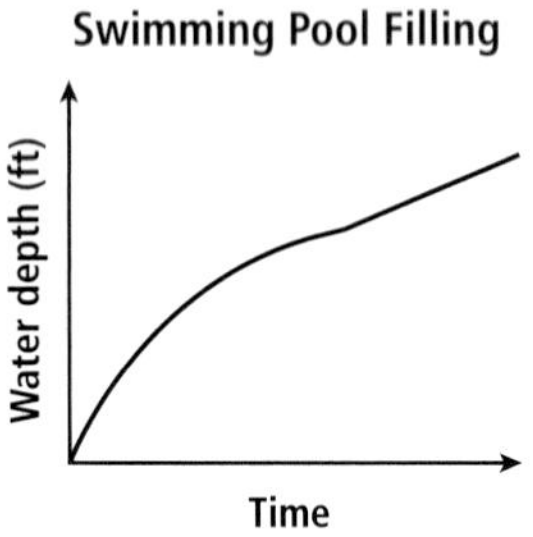

4-2 *Exercises*

3.

x	y
1	1
1	2

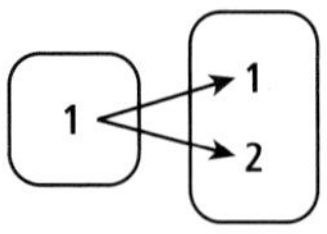

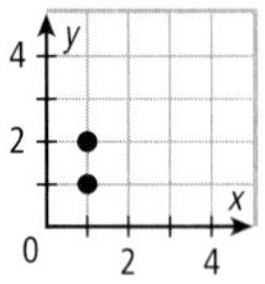

4.

x	y
−1	1
−2	$\frac{1}{2}$
−3	$\frac{1}{3}$
−4	$\frac{1}{4}$

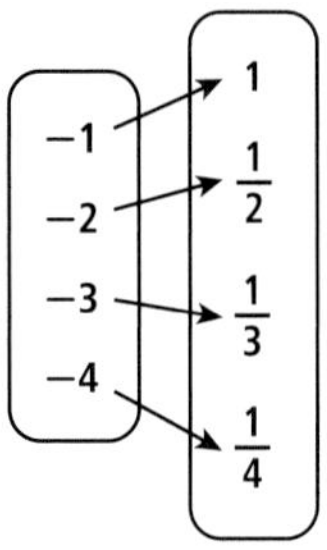

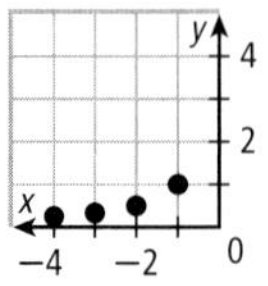

5.

x	y
−7	7
−3	3
−1	1
5	−5

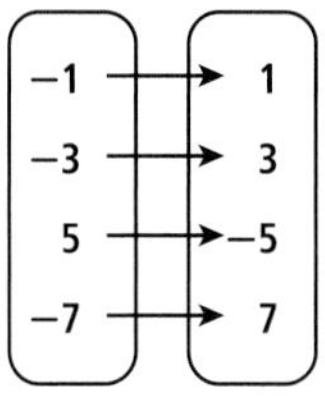

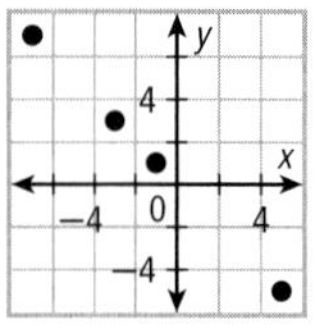

6.

x	y
0	0
2	−4
2	−2

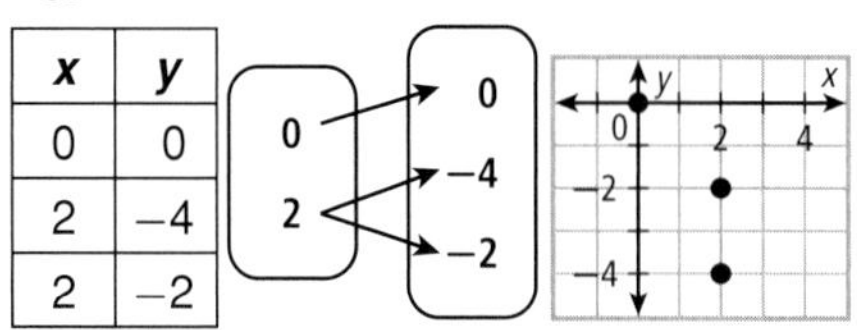

26a. {(60, 360), (120, 720), (180, 1080), (240, 1440), (300, 1800)}

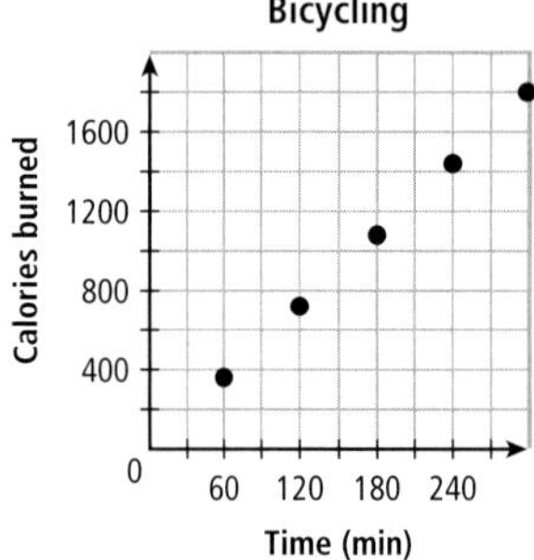

b. D: {60, 120, 180, 240, 300}; R: {360, 720, 1080, 1440, 1800}

c. Yes; each domain value is paired with exactly one range value.

4-3 *Exercises*

21. 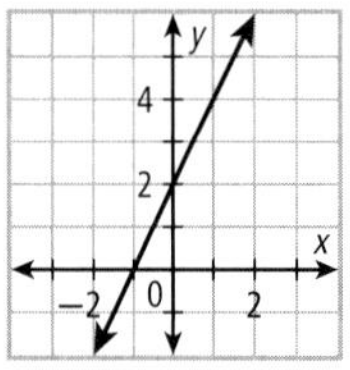 yes

22. yes

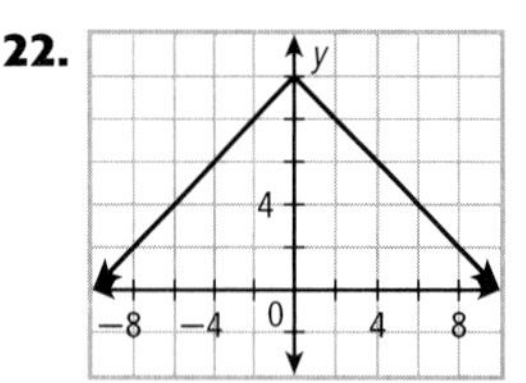

23. yes

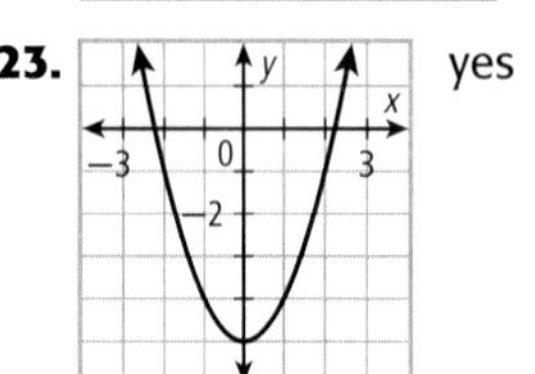

24. yes

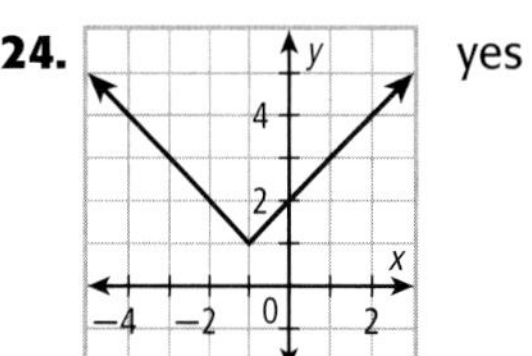

25. yes

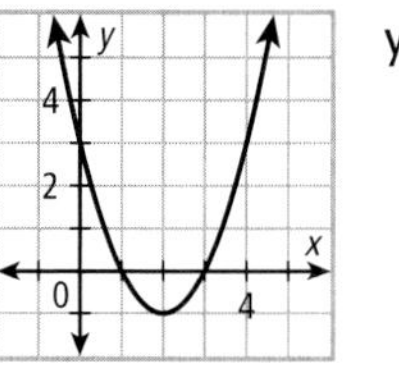

26. 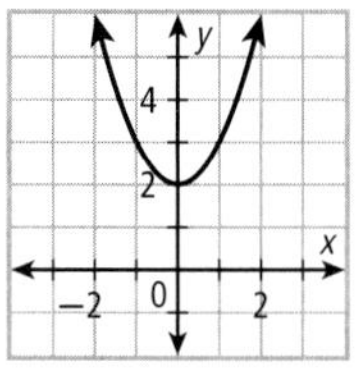 yes

58. Possible answer: The domain value 0 is paired with range values 2 and −2.

59. Possible answer: The domain value 0 is paired with range values 6 and −6.

60. Possible answer: The domain value 2 is paired with range values 1 and −1.

4-3 *Technology Lab*

1.

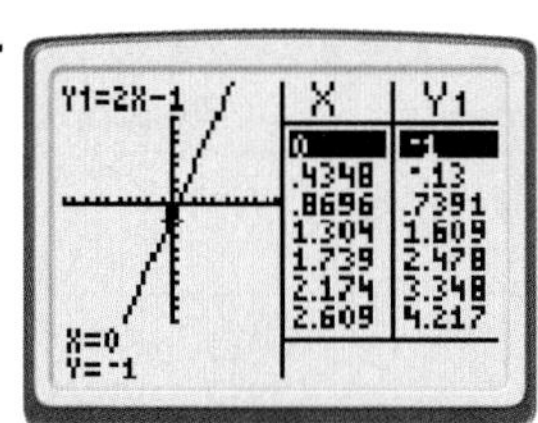

2.

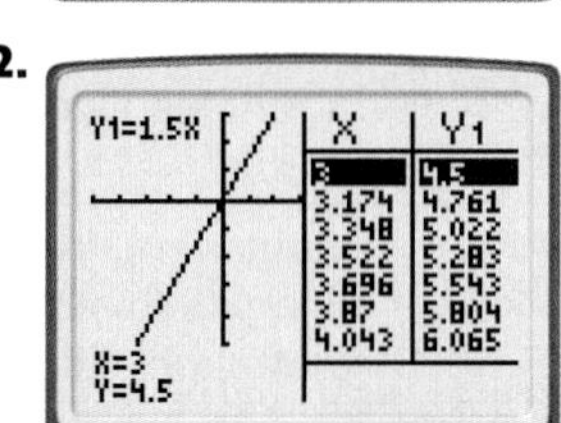

3.

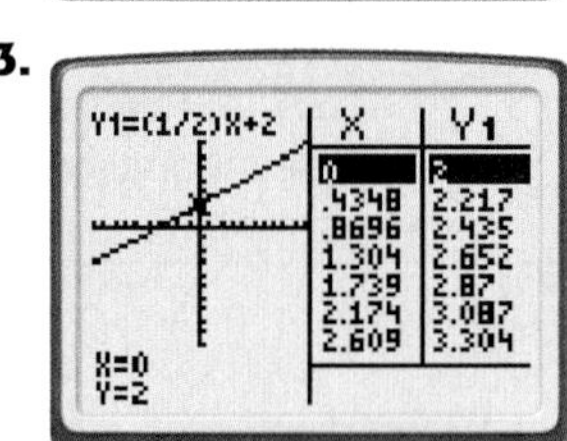

4A *Ready to Go On?*

3. Quiz Score

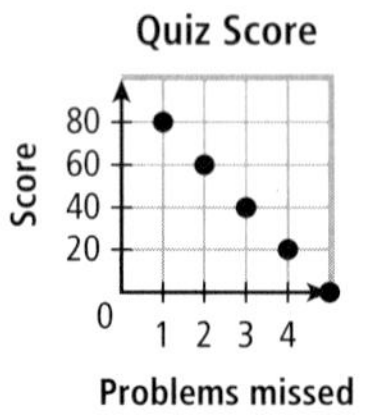

5. D: {−2, −1, 0, 2, 3}; R: {3}; function; each element in the domain is assigned to exactly 1 element in the range.

6. D: $\{-4 \le x \le 2\}$; R: $\{0 \le y \le 4\}$; function; each element in the domain is assigned to exactly one element in the range.

12.

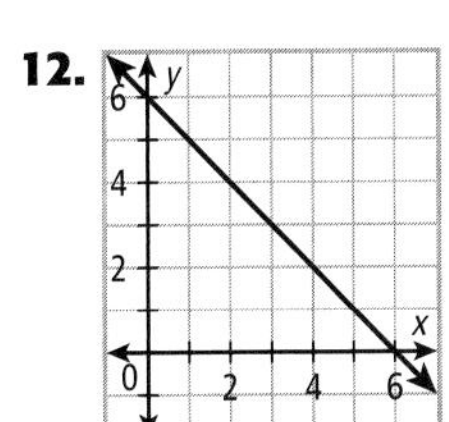

13.

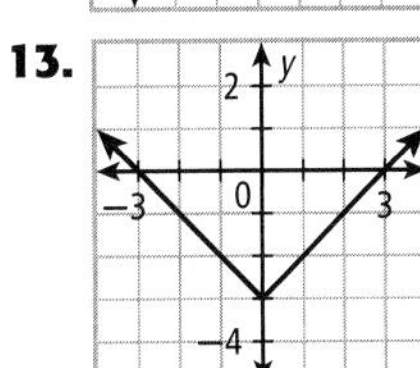

14.

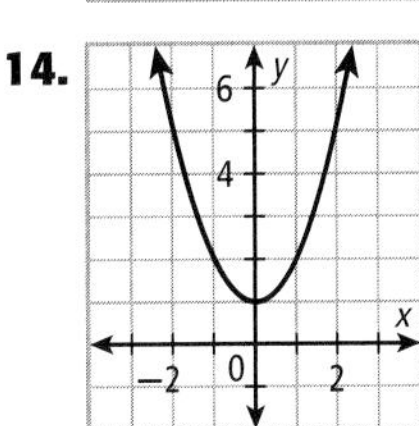

Chapter 5

Are You Ready?

5–12.

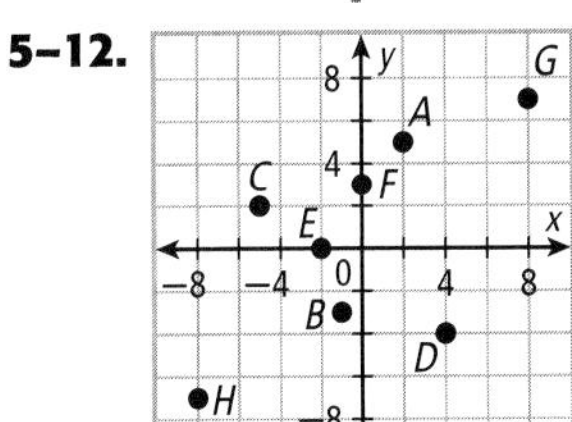

5-1 *Exercises*

2.

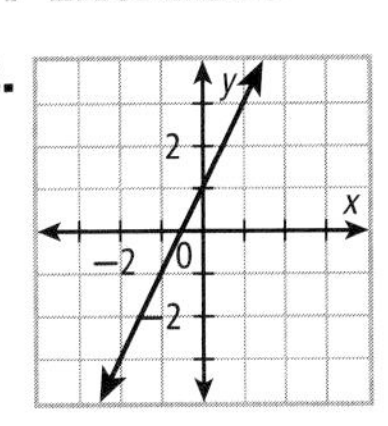

3.

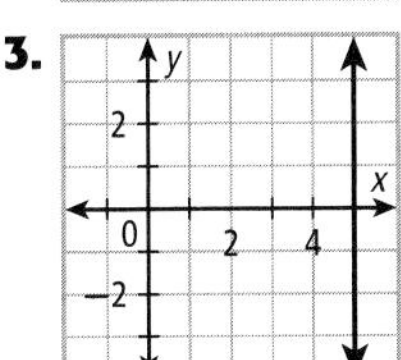

4.

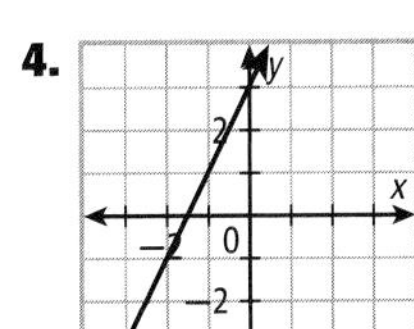

15.

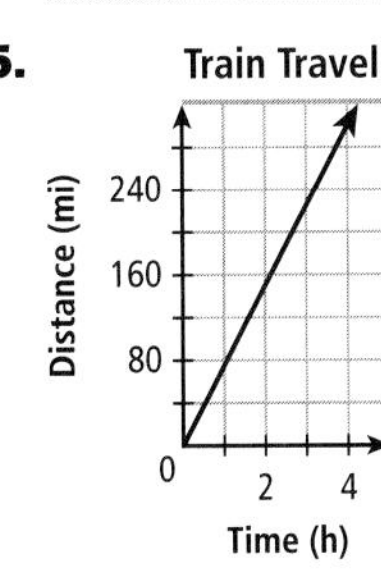

D: $x \geq 0$; R: $y \geq 0$

16.

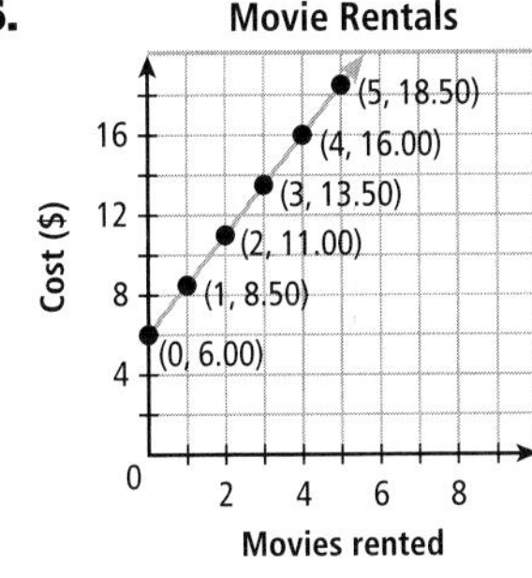

D: {0, 1, 2, 3, ...}

R: {$6.00, $8.50, $11.00, $13.50, ...}

17.

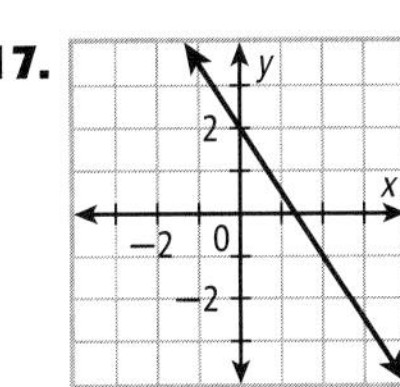

18.

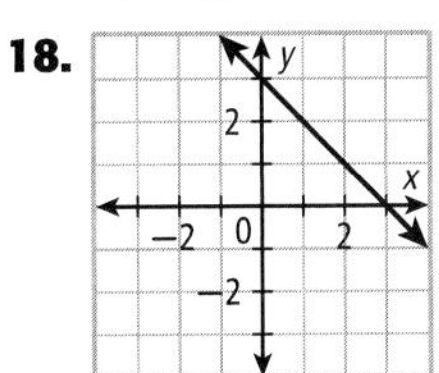

19.

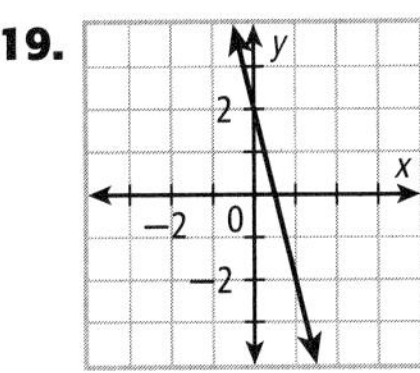

50.

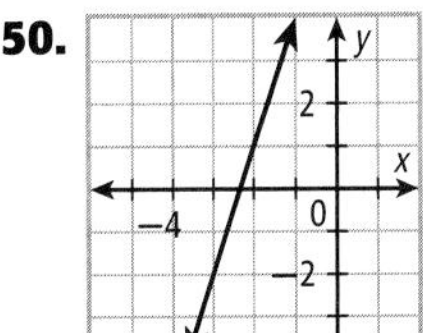

51.

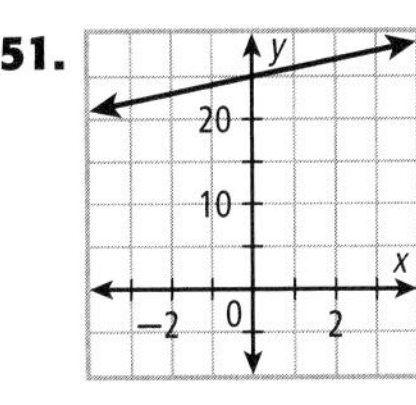

52.

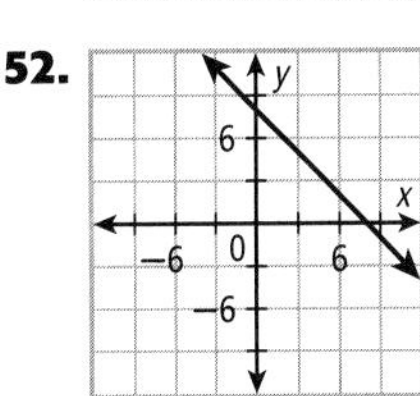

53.

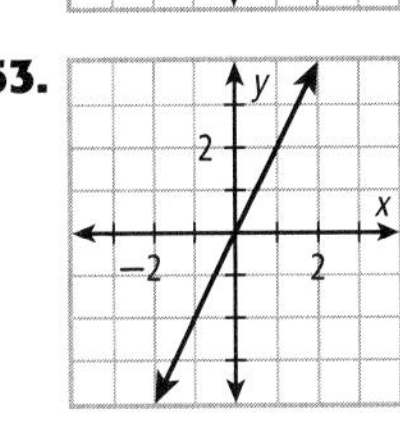

54.

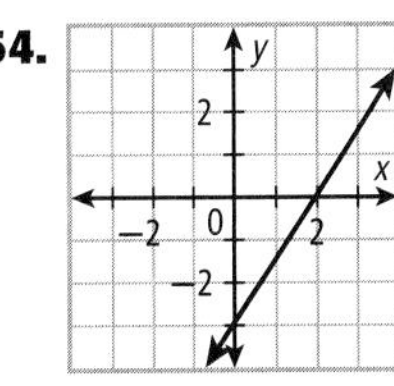

55.

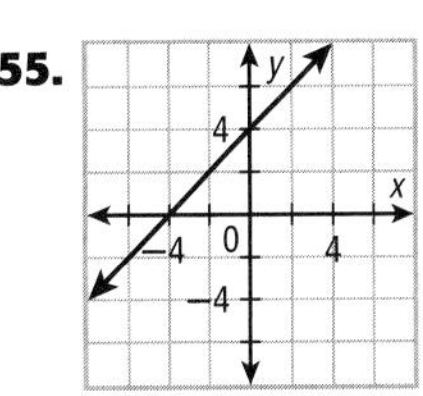

56.

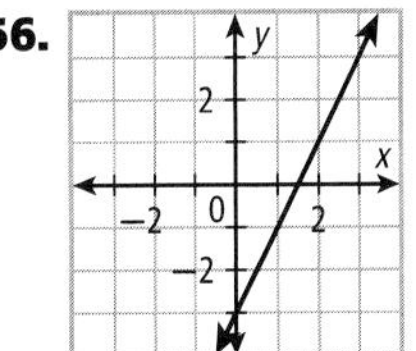

57.

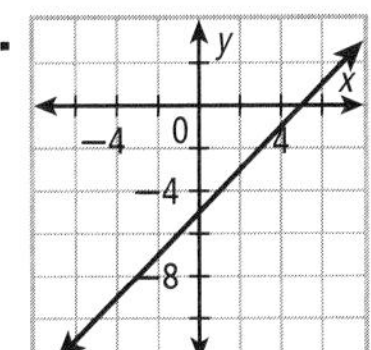

59b.

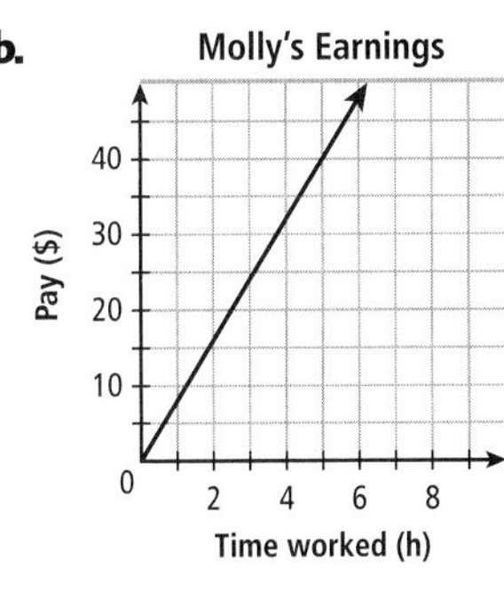

D: $x \geq 0$; R: $y \geq 0$

60. Possible answer:

x	$y = 2x - 1$
−2	−5
−1	−3
0	−1
1	1
2	3

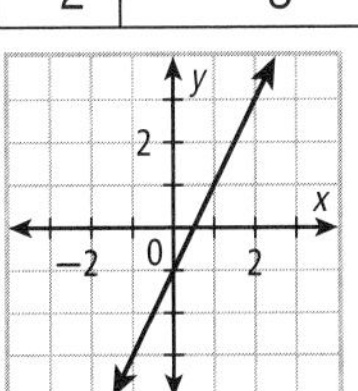

The table gives some ordered pairs (x, y) that satisfy the equation $y = 2x - 1$. The graph is a representation of all ordered pairs (x, y) that satisfy $y = 2x - 1$.

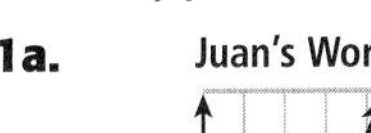

61a.

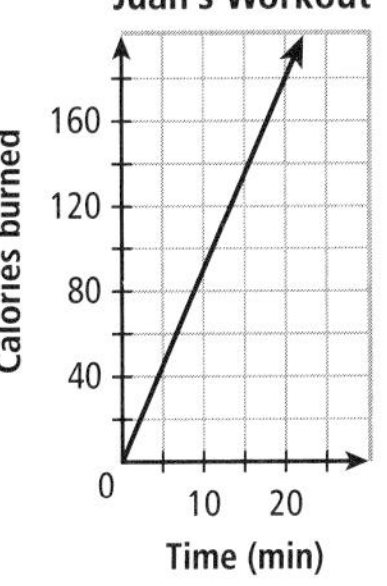

5-2 *Exercises*

9.

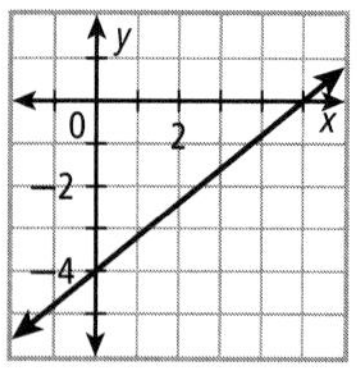

10.

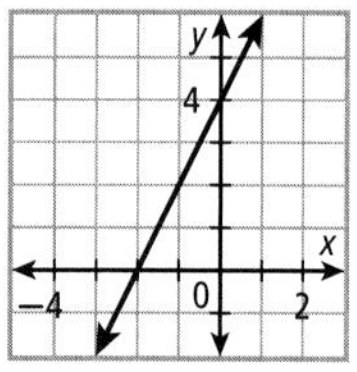

11.

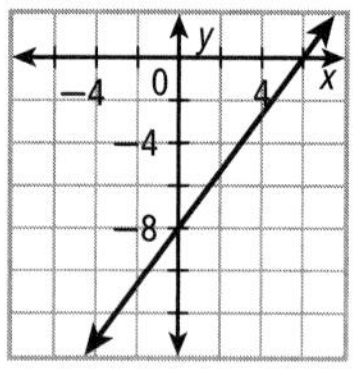

12.

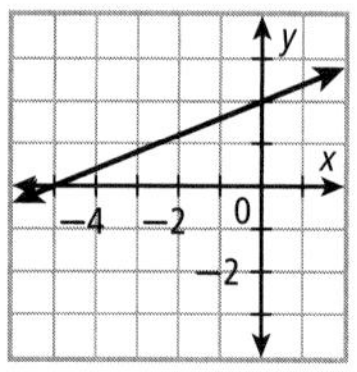

22a. Bass Population

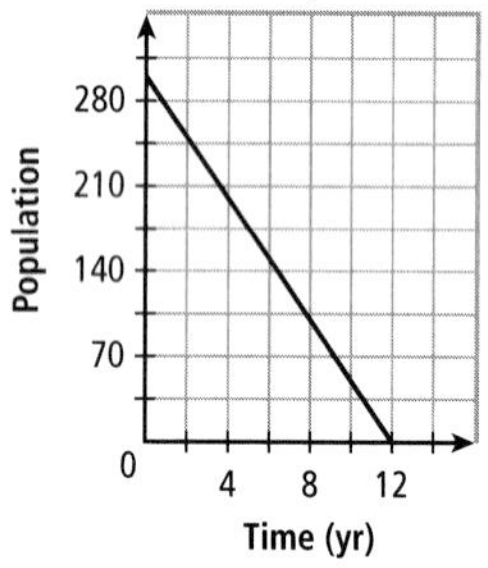

x-int.: 12; y-int.: 300

b. x-int.: time when bass pop. is 0; y-int.: number of bass originally put in lake

23a. 5K Race

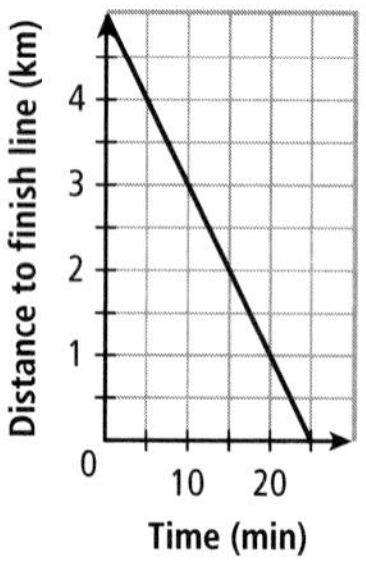

x-int.: 25; y-int.: 5

b. x-int.: total time to run race (when dist. to finish line is 0); y-int.: total length of race (when time is 0)

28.

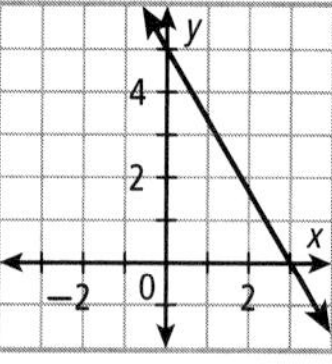

29.

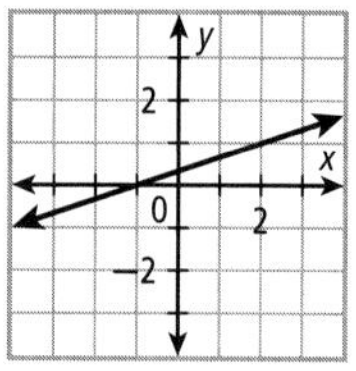

31b. x-int.: number of years after 1800 when there will be no acres of tropical forest; y-int.: million acres of tropical forest in 1800

32a. Account Balance

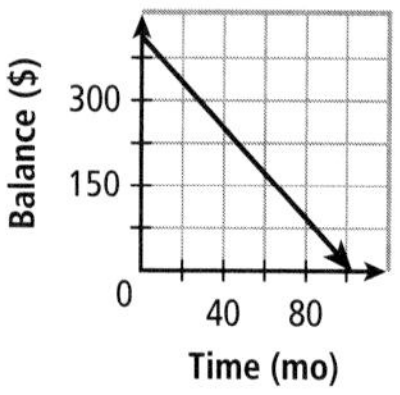

D: {0, 1, 2, 3, …};
R: {\$412, \$408, \$404, \$400, …}

x-int.: 103; y-int.: 412; y-int.: balance when employee noticed account; x-int.: number of months from that time until account has \$0

33a. $x = -6$ $x = 1$ $x = 5$

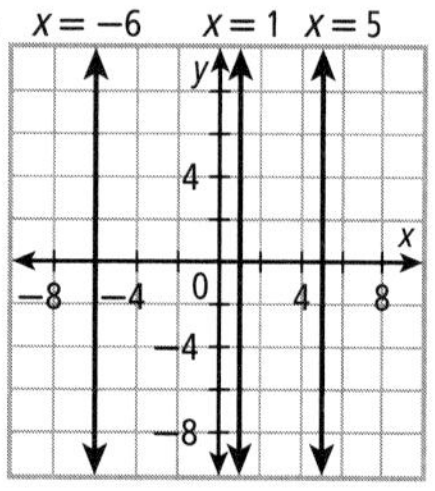

$x = -6$: x-int.: −6, no y-int.; $x = 1$: x-int.: 1, no y-int.; $x = 5$: x-int.: 5, no y-int.

b.

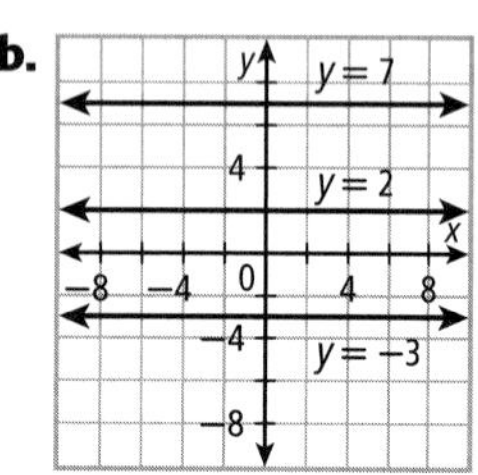

$y = -3$: no x-int., y-int.: −3; $y = 2$: no x-int., y-int.: 2; $y = 7$: no x-int., y-int.: 7

5-4 *Exercises*

22. $y = \frac{1}{4}x$

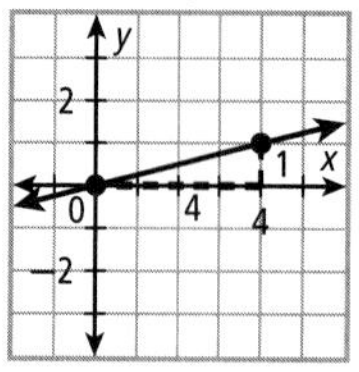

$k = \frac{1}{4}$; graph shows slope $= \frac{1}{4}$

23. $y = 4x$

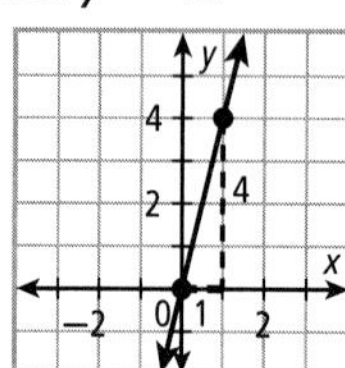

$k = 4$; graph shows slope = 4

24. $y = 3x$

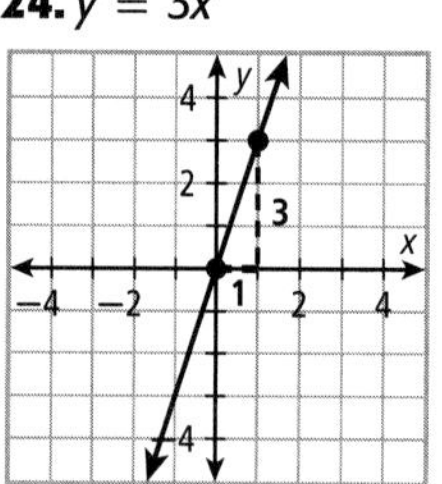

$k = 3$; graph shows slope = 3

25. $y = 2x$

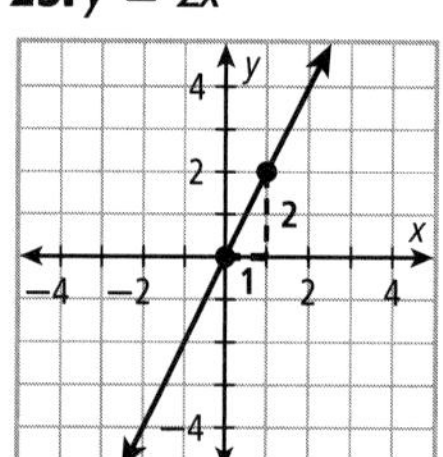

$k = 2$; graph shows slope = 2

26. $y = -8x$

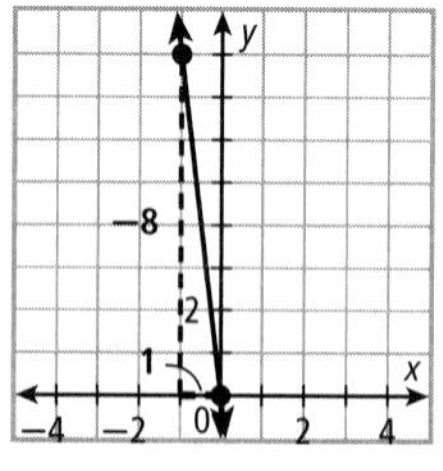

$k = -8$; graph shows slope = −8

27. $y = 7x$

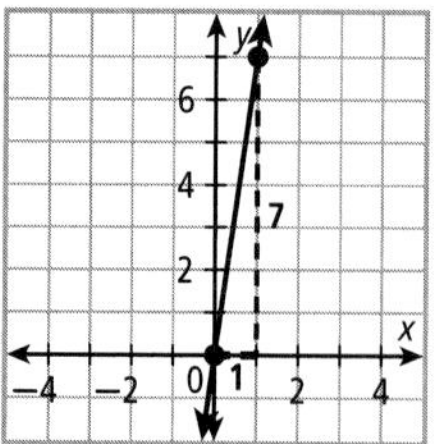

$k = 7$; graph shows slope = 7

28. $y = -\frac{9}{2}x$

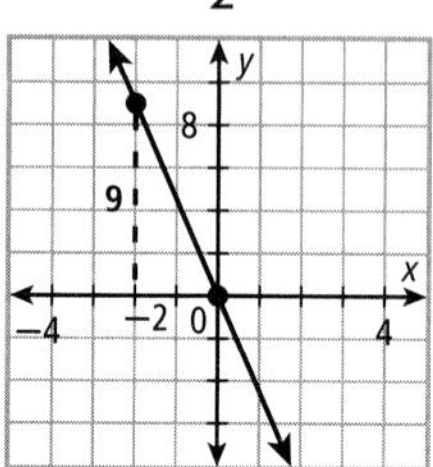

$k = -\frac{9}{2}$; graph shows slope $= -\frac{9}{2}$

29. $y = -\frac{2}{9}x$

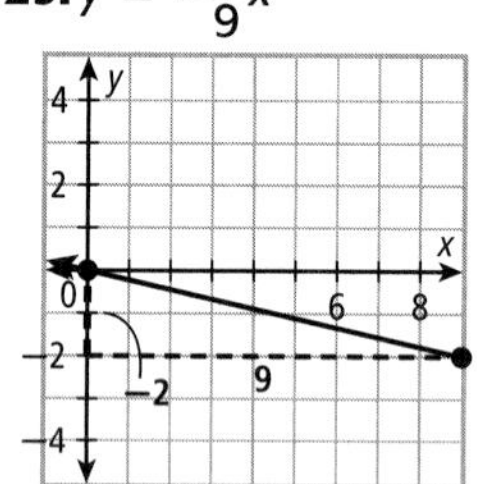

$k = -\frac{2}{9}$; graph shows slope $= -\frac{2}{9}$

30. $y = \frac{3}{2}x$

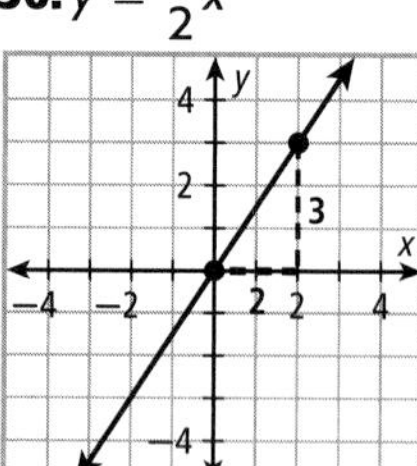

$k = \frac{3}{2}$; graph shows slope $= \frac{3}{2}$

31. $y = \frac{4}{3}x$

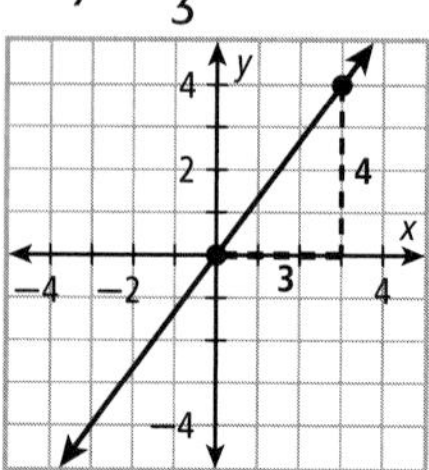

$k = \frac{4}{3}$; graph shows slope $= \frac{4}{3}$

32. $y = \frac{1}{5}x$

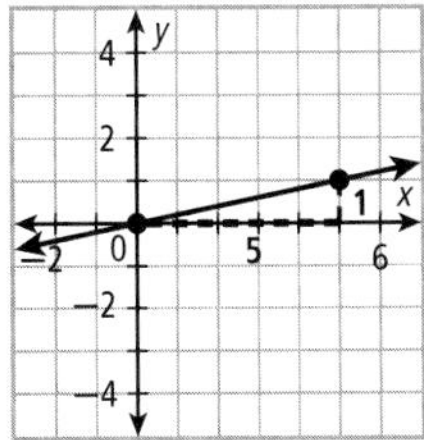

$k = \frac{1}{5}$; graph shows slope $= \frac{1}{5}$

33. $y = -6x$

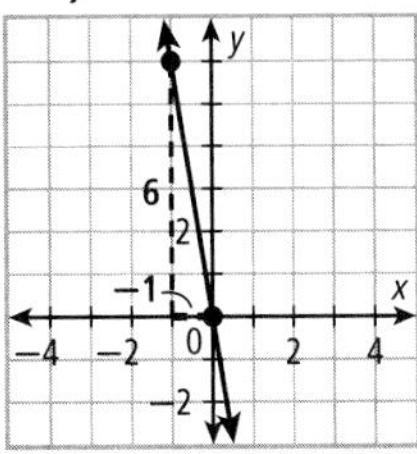

$k = -6$; graph shows slope $= -6$

34. $y = -\frac{1}{2}x$

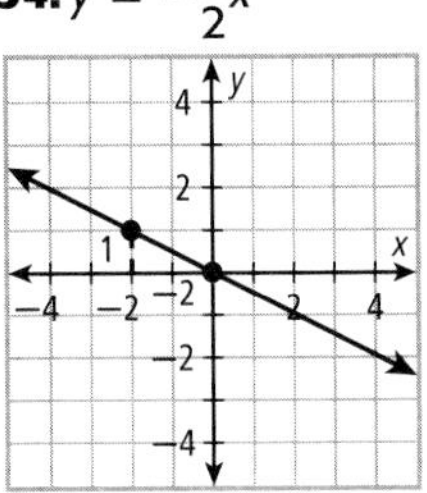

$k = \frac{1}{2}$; graph shows slope $= \frac{1}{2}$

35. $y = \frac{2}{7}x$

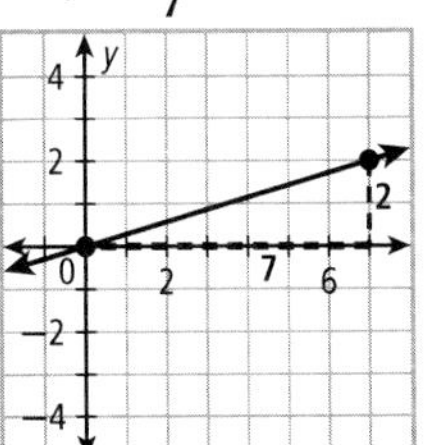

$k = \frac{2}{7}$; graph shows slope $= \frac{2}{7}$

37b.

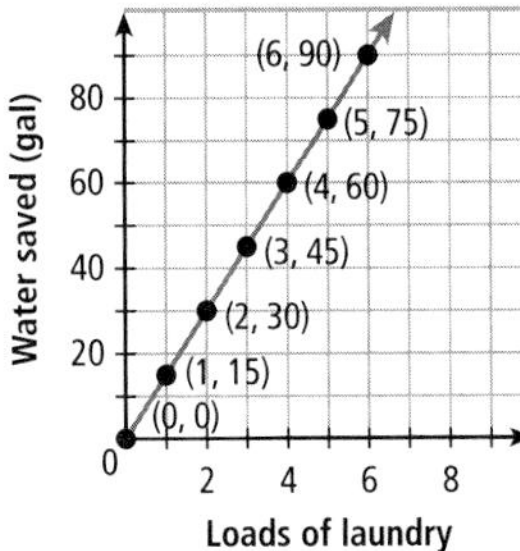

No; possible answer: Mischa cannot wash a fraction of a load of laundry, so only points whose x-coord. is a whole number make sense in this situation.

38. Possible answer: In a direct variation, $y = kx$. If you double x, then the right side of the equation becomes $k(2x)$, or $2kx$. In other words, the right side has been multiplied by 2. To keep the balance, you must also double the left side, and you get $2y$. Therefore $2y = 2kx$ or $2y = k(2x)$

46. Possible answer:

Statements	Reasons
$ax + by = c$	Given
$by = c - ax$	Subt. Prop. of Eq.
$y = \frac{c - ax}{b}$	Div. Prop. of Eq.
$y = \frac{c}{b} - \frac{ax}{b}$	Distrib. Prop.
$y = \frac{c}{b} - \frac{a}{b}x$	Assoc. Prop of Mult.
$y = -\frac{a}{b}x + \frac{c}{b}$	Comm. Prop. of Add.
The above is a dir. var.	Given
$\frac{c}{b} = 0$	Def. of dir. var.
$c = 0$	Mult. Prop. of Eq.

5A *Ready to Go On?*

1.

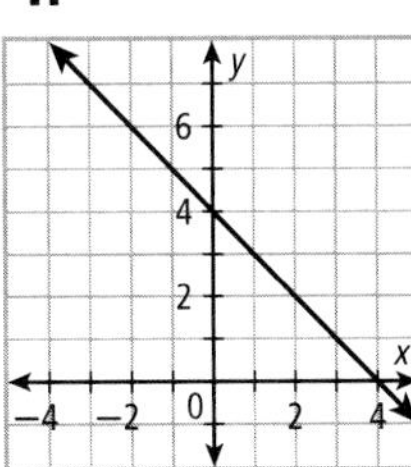

2.

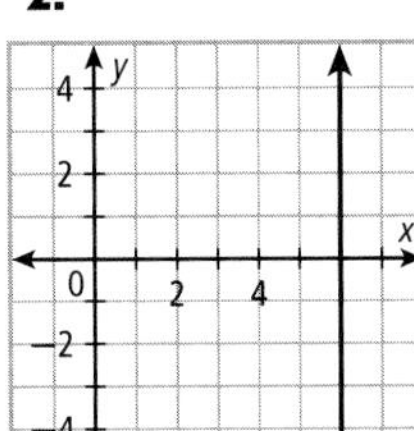

3.

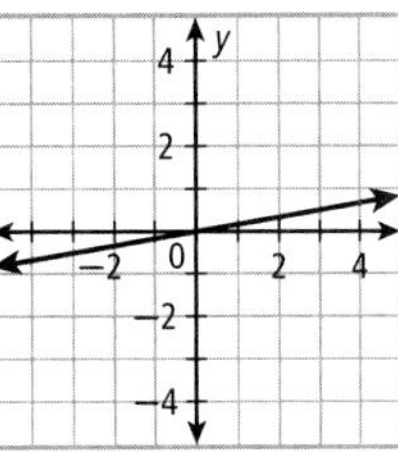

4.

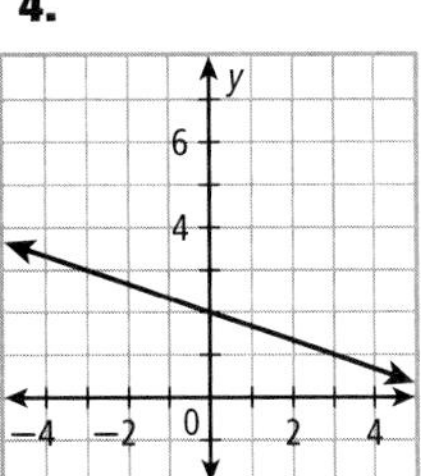

9.

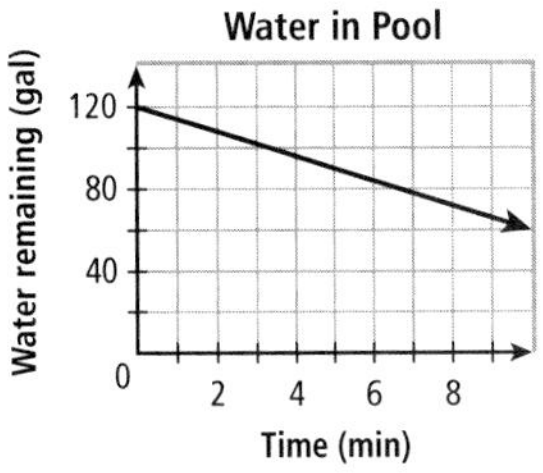

Water in Pool

Water remaining (gal): 120, 80, 40, 0; Time (min): 2, 4, 6, 8

x-int.: 20; y-int.: 120; x-int.: time when there will be no water left in pool; y-int.: orig. amount of water in pool

10.

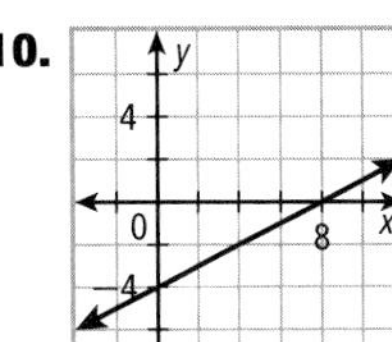

11.

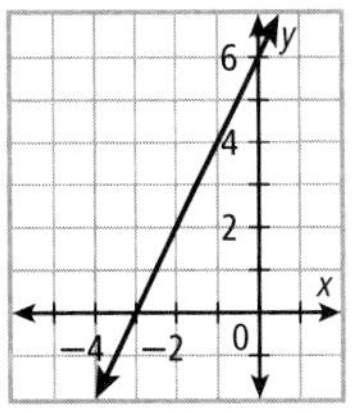

12.

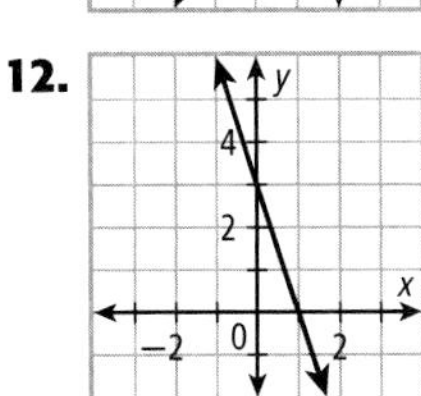

5-5 *Exercises*

9. $y = \frac{2}{5}x - 6$

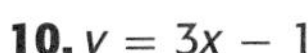
10. $y = 3x - 1$

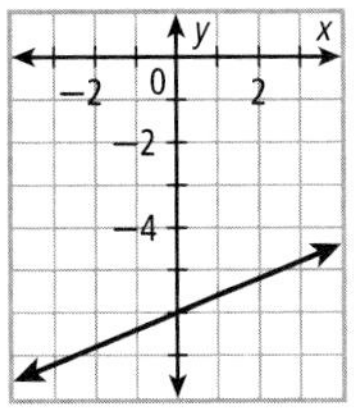

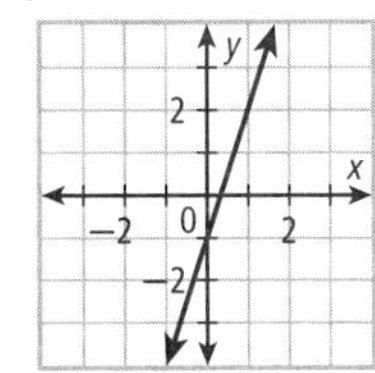

11. $y = -2x + 4$

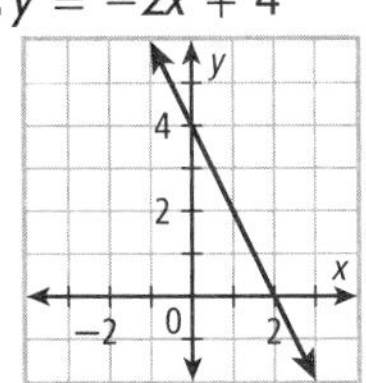

13.

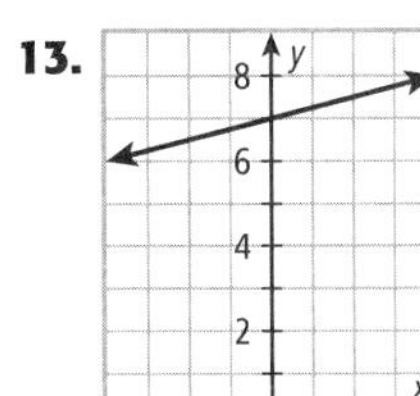

14.

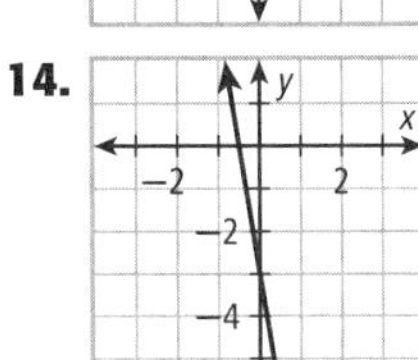

15.

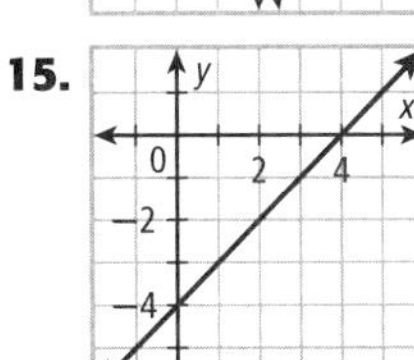

16.

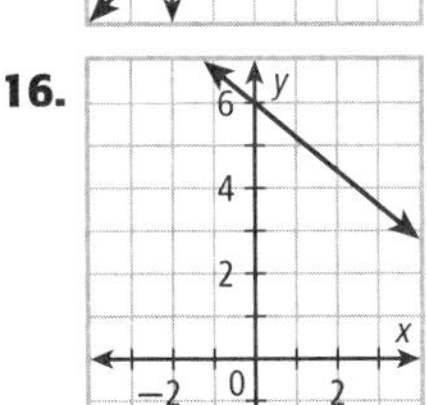

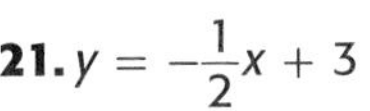
21. $y = -\frac{1}{2}x + 3$

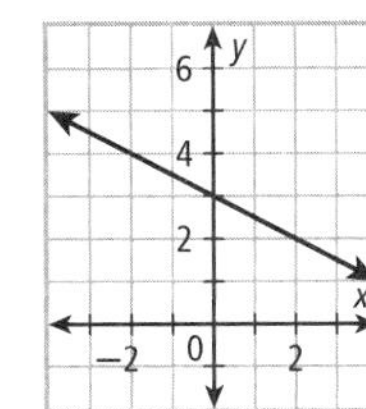

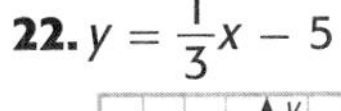
22. $y = \frac{1}{3}x - 5$

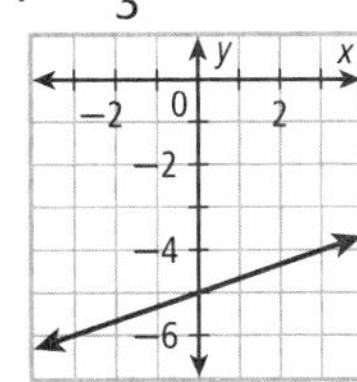

Additional Answers

23. $y = x + 6$

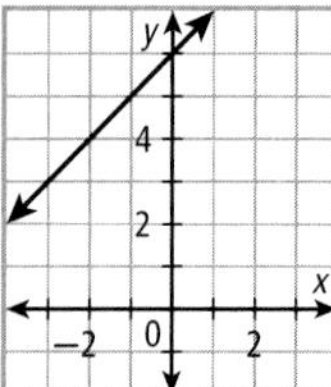

24. $y = -2x + 4$

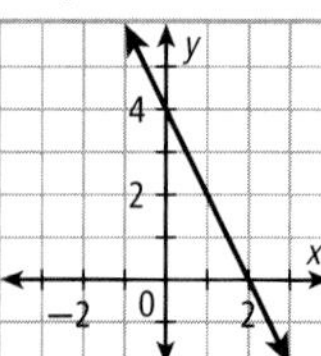

25. $y = \frac{7}{2}$

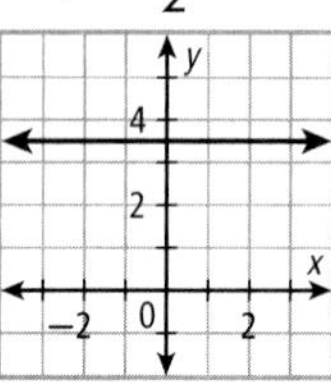

26. $y = -4x + 9$

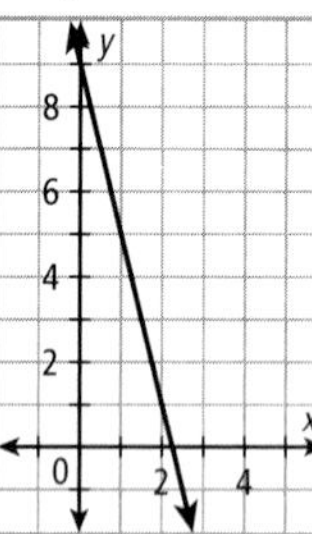

27. $y = \frac{1}{2}x + 4$

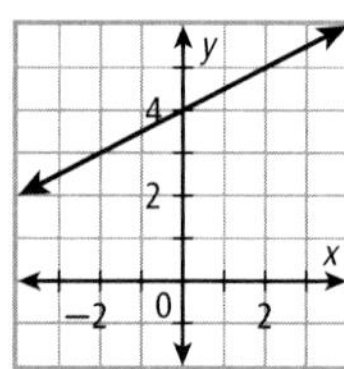

28. $y = -\frac{2}{3}x + 2$

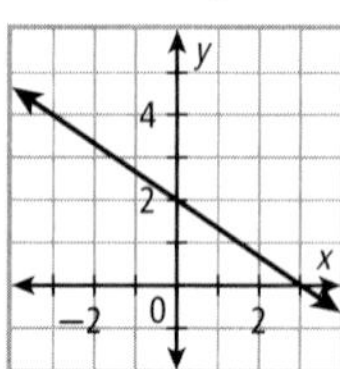

29. $y = -2x + 8$

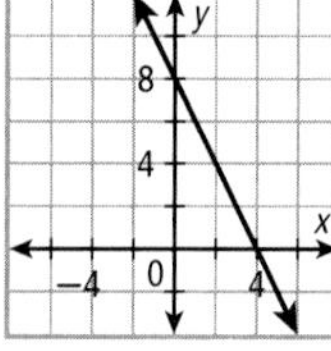

5-6 *Exercises*

56.

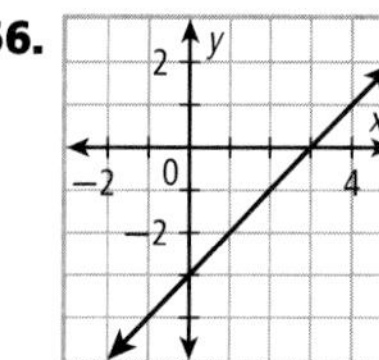

57.

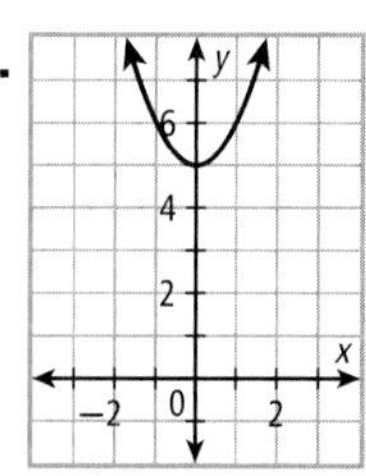

58.

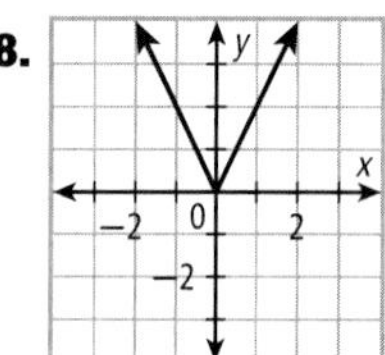

5-7 *Exercises*

55. If the line containing A and B has the same slope as the line containing B and C, then either line AB is par. to line BC or they are the same line. They cannot be par. because they both contain C. Therefore they must be the same line.

58. The slope of one diagonal is $\frac{a-0}{a-0} = \frac{a}{a} = 1$. The slope of the other diagonal is $\frac{0-a}{a-0} = \frac{-a}{a} = -1$. The product of the slopes is -1, so the diagonals are perp.

60.

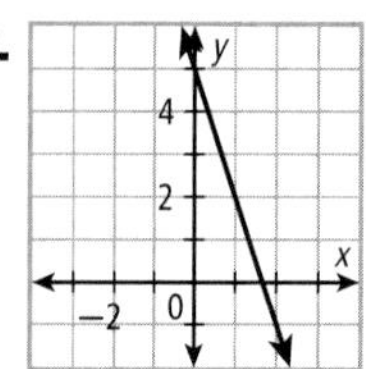

61.

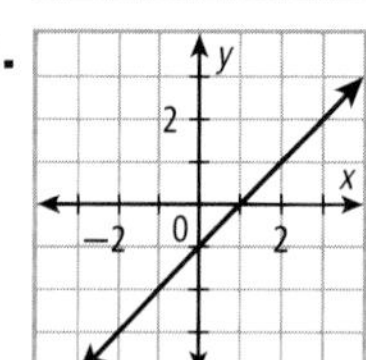

62.

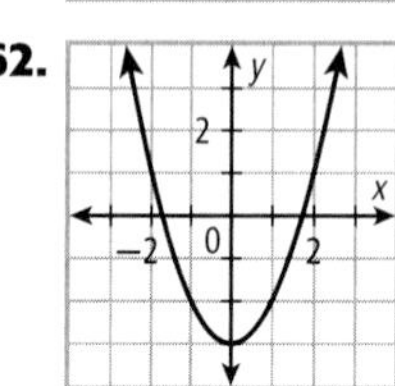

5B *Ready to Go On?*

1.

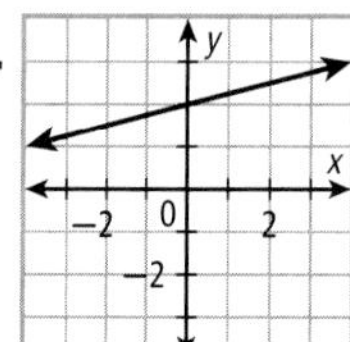

2.

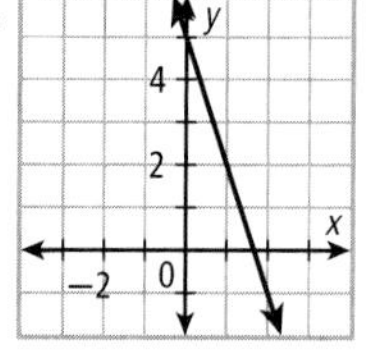

3.

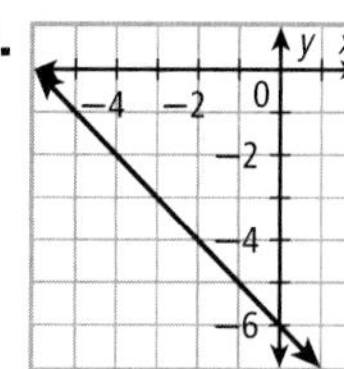

4.

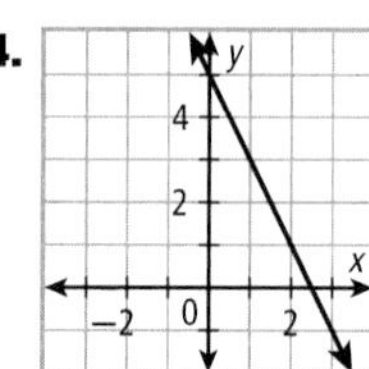

5.

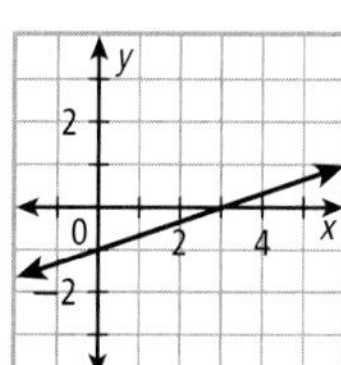

6.

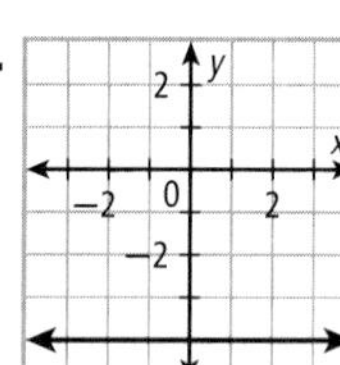

8.

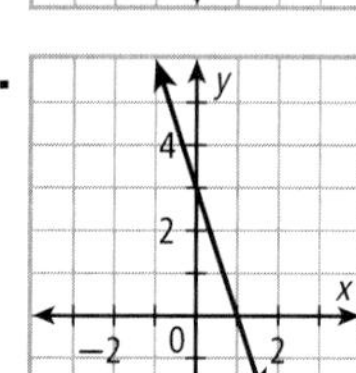

9.

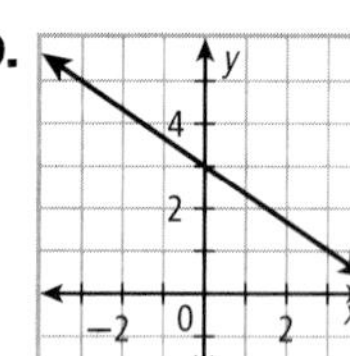

10.

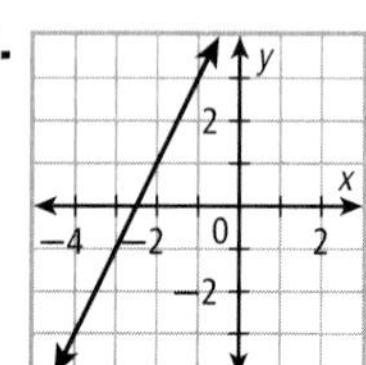

Chapter 6

Are You Ready?

6. 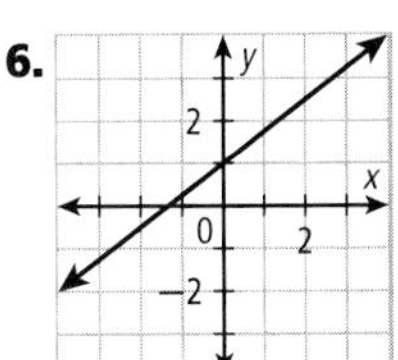

7. 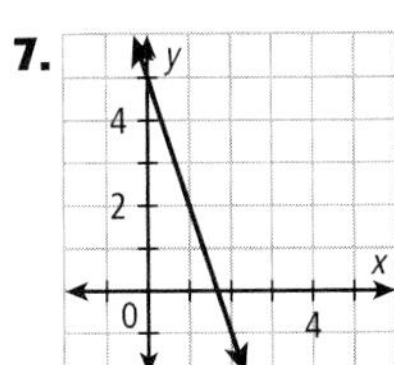

8. 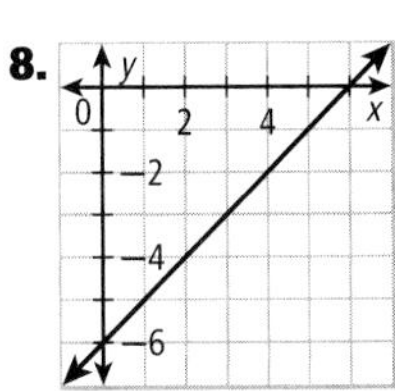

9. 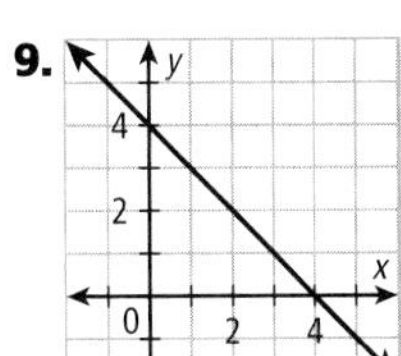

10. 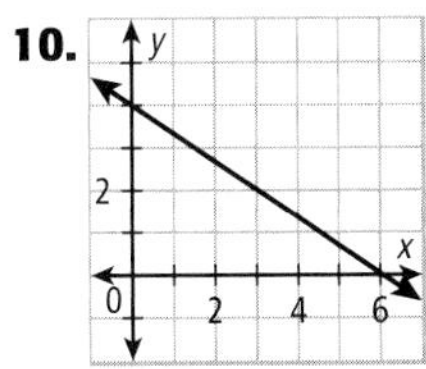

11. 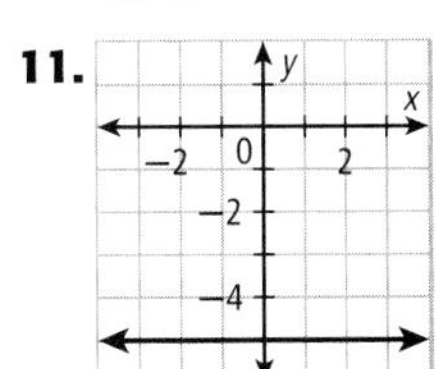

30. 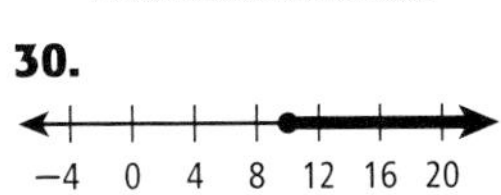

31. 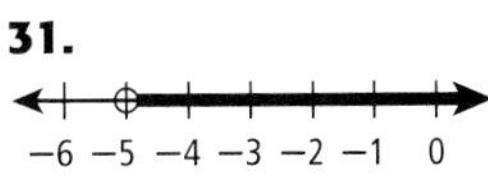

32. 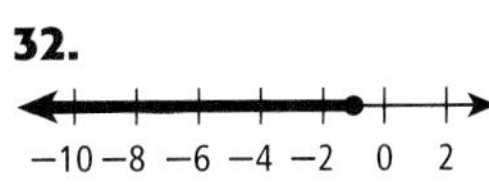

33. 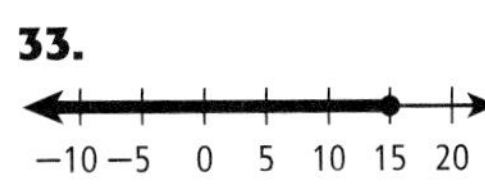

6-4 *Exercises*

30a. $c = 50 + 1.1b$; $c = 40 + 1.1b$

b. Never; the slope, or cost of the buttons, is the same, and the initial costs, or *y*-intercepts, are different.

c. For the same price, the *y*-intercept would have to be changed to 40. Possible answers: The *y*-intercept may be lowered to a value less than 40, or the slope may be changed to a value less than 1.1.

6-6 *Exercises*

8. 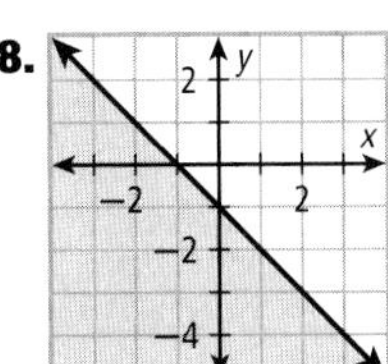

9a. $x + y \leq 16$

b. 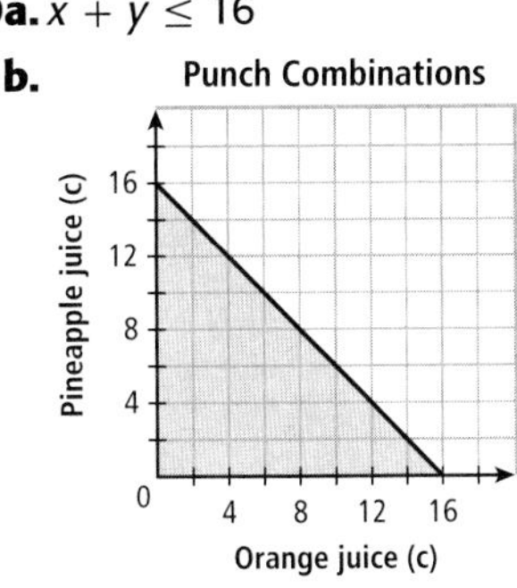

c. Possible answer: (2 c orange, 2 c pineapple), (4 c orange, 10 c pineapple)

15. 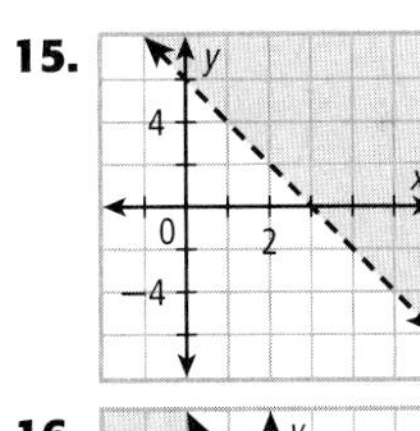

16. 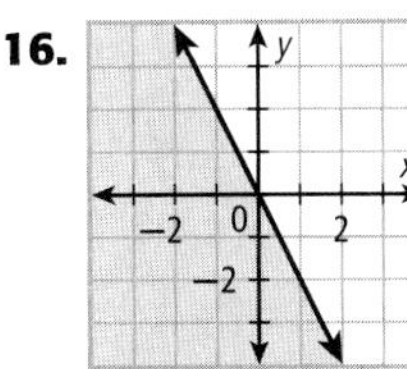

17. 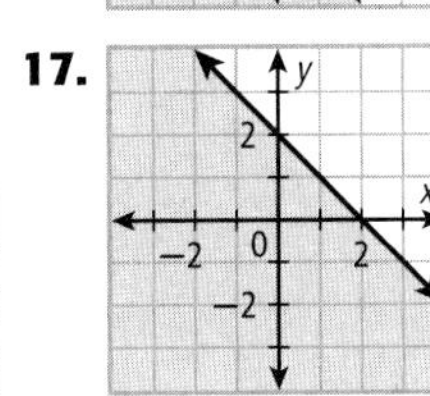

18. 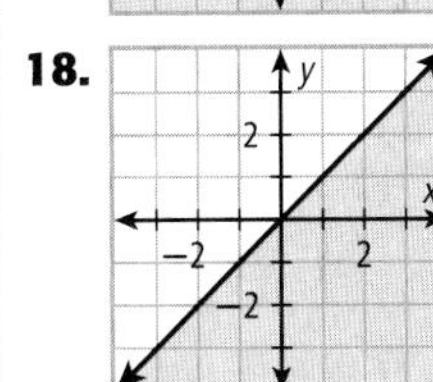

19a. $3x + 2y \leq 30$

b. 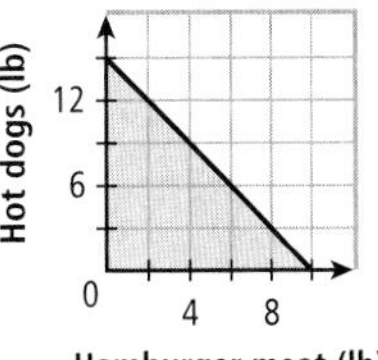

c. Possible answer: (3 lb ham., 2 lb hot dogs), (5 lb ham., 6 lb hot dogs)

27b. Possible answer: (length: 3 yd, width: 1 yd), (length: 1 yd, width: 6 yd), (length: 6 yd, width: 2 yd)

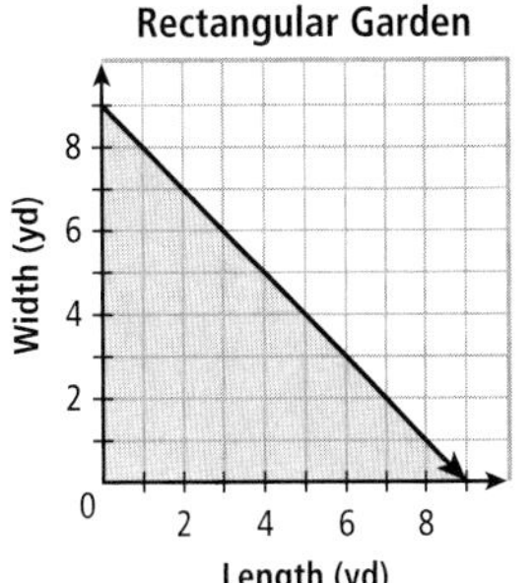

28. $15x + 11y \leq 77$; possible answer: (2, 2.5); you cannot buy half a fish.

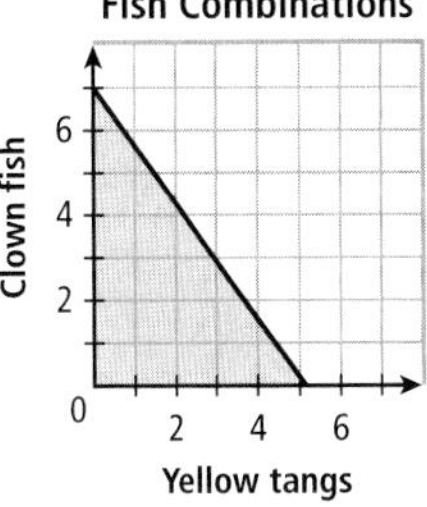

29. 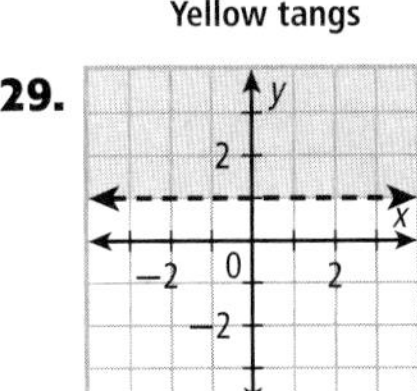

30. 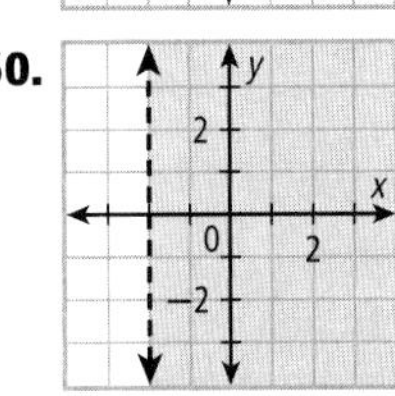

31. **32.** 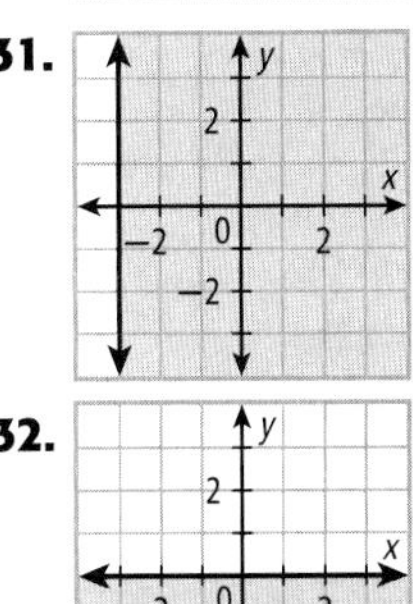

33. 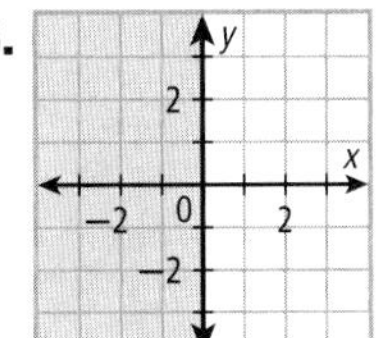

34. 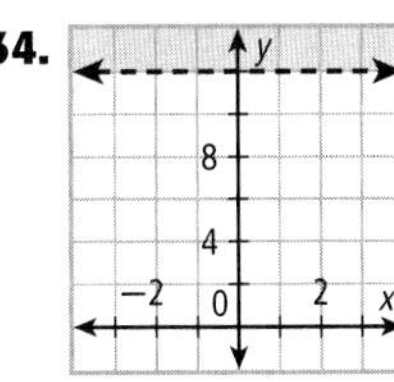

35. 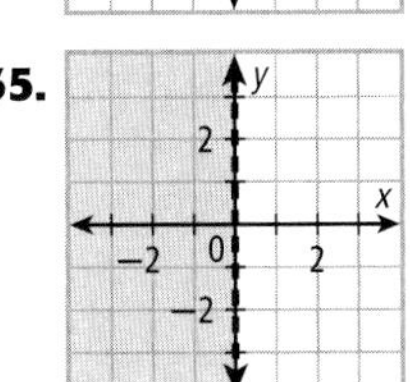

36. 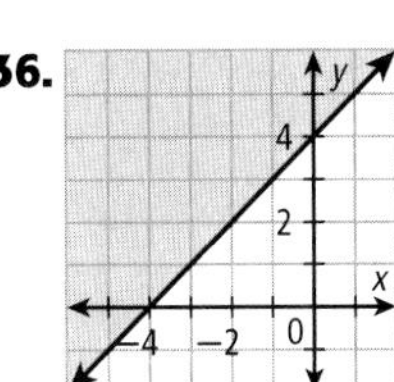

37. $7a + 4s \geq 280$; possible answer: (40, 10), (40, 20), (20, 100)

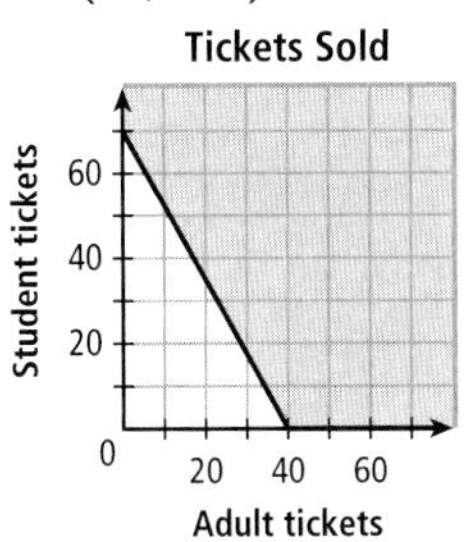

40b. 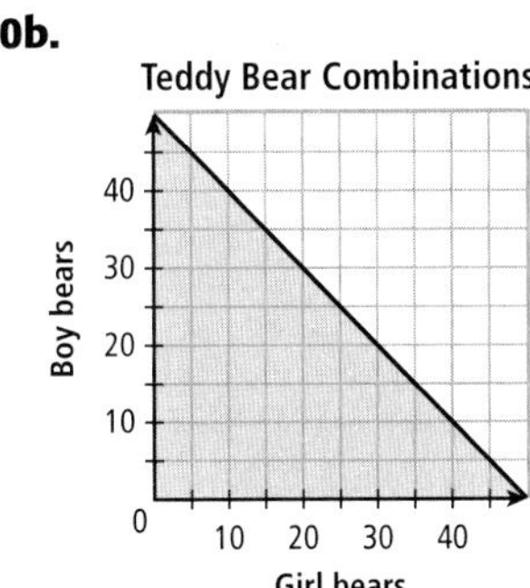 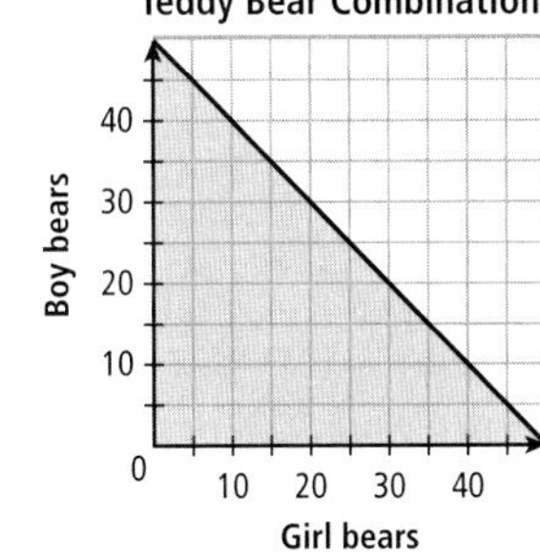

6-7 *Exercises*

7. 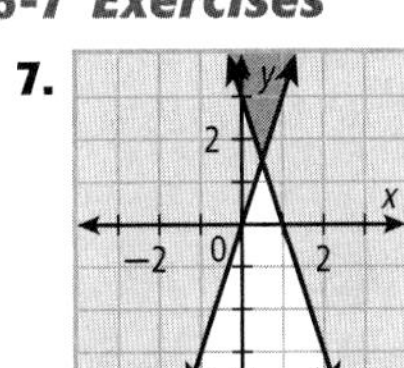

Possible answer: solutions: (0.5, 3), (1, 3); not solutions: (0, 0), (−1, 2)

8.

Possible answer: solutions: (0, 0), (1, 1); not solutions: (3, 0), (−3, −4)

9.

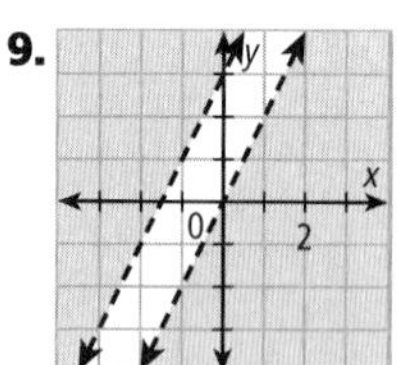

10.

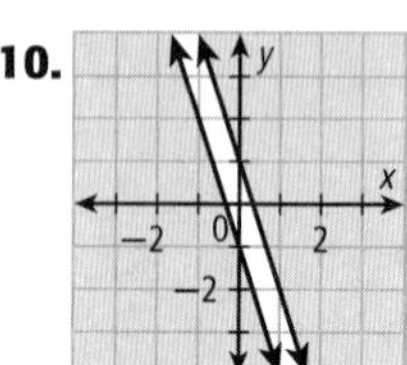

11.

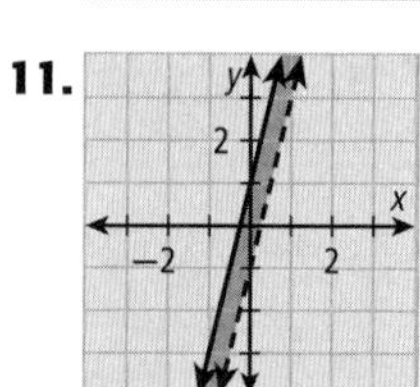

12.

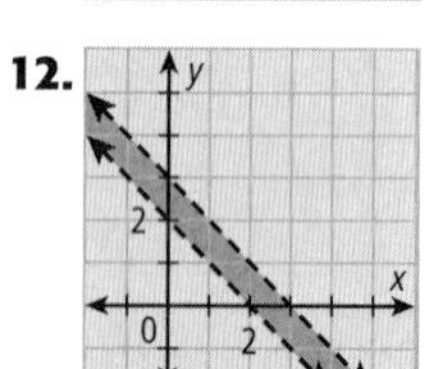

13.

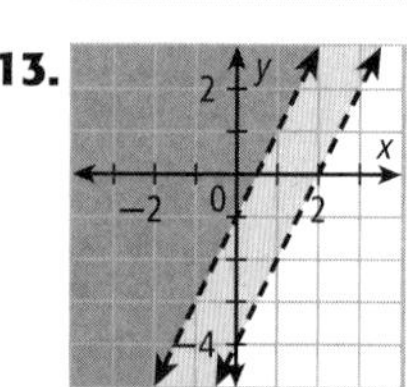

14.

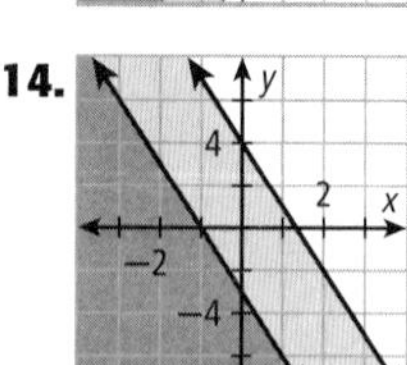

19.

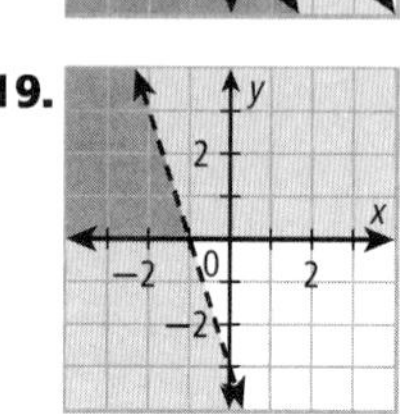

Possible answer: solutions: (−2, 0), (−3, 1); not solutions: (0, 0), (1, 4)

20.

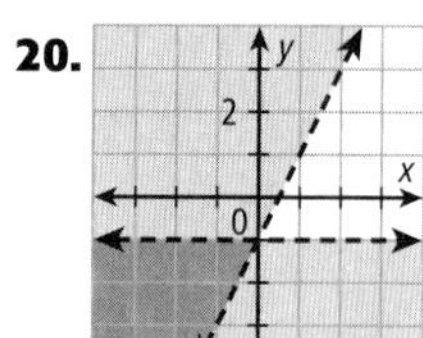

Possible answer: solutions: (−2, −2), (−3, −2); not solutions: (0, 0), (1, −4)

21.

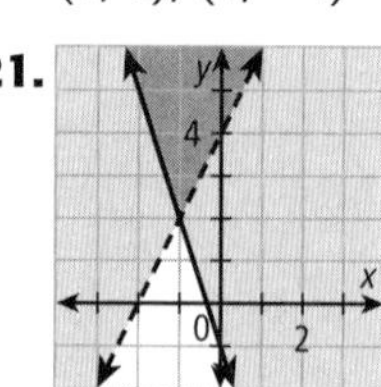

Possible answer: solutions: (−1, 3), (0, 5); not solutions: (0, 0), (1, 4)

22.

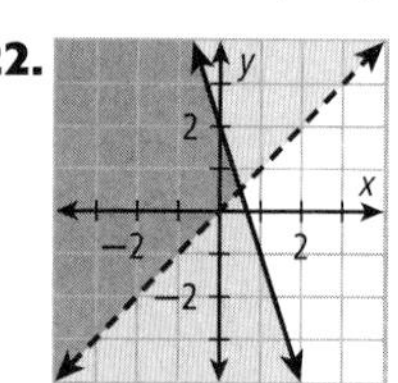

Possible answer: solutions: (−2, 0), (−3, 1); not solutions: (0, 0), (1, 4)

23.

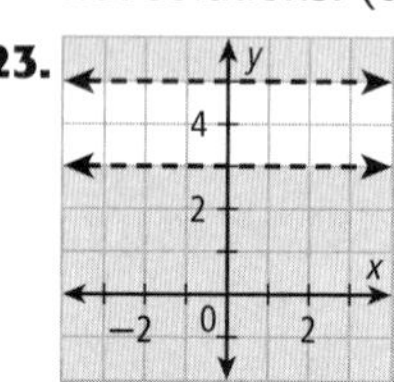

24.

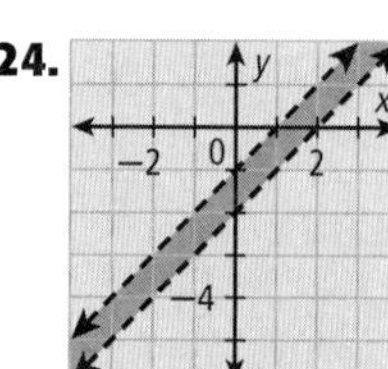

25.

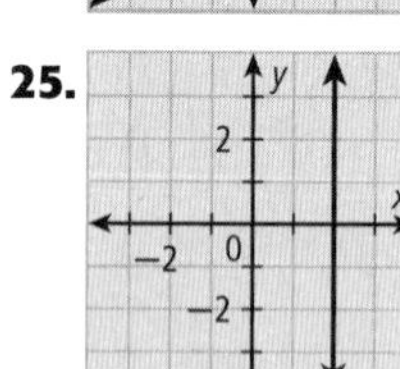

26.

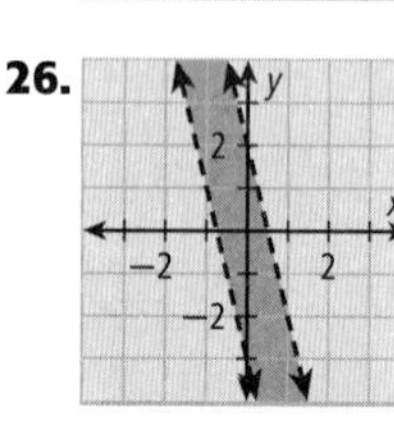

27.

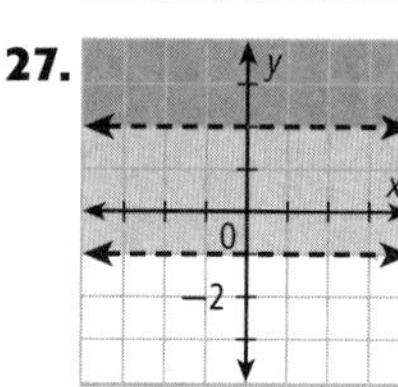

28.

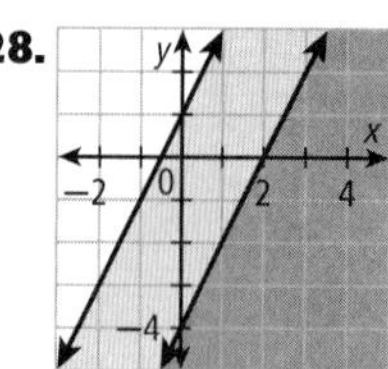

30.

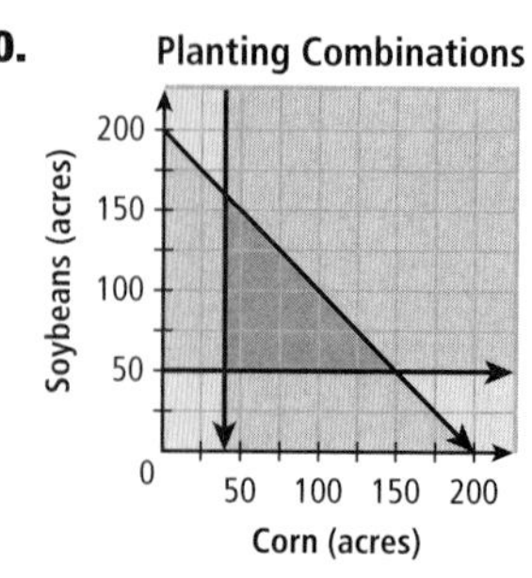

Reasonable solutions are positive rational numbers; possible answer: (60, 80), (100, 60)

31.

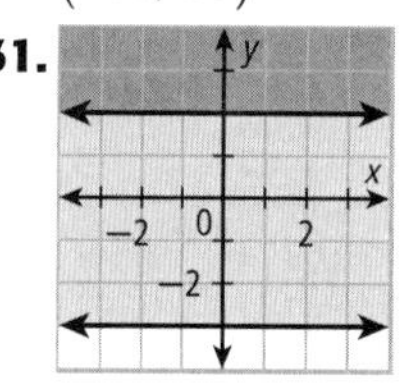

32.

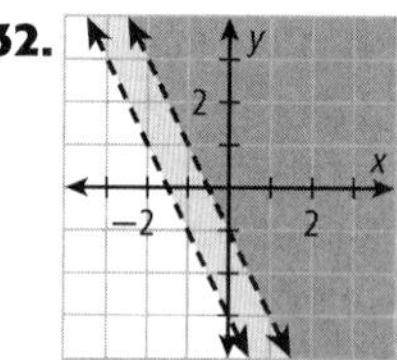

33.

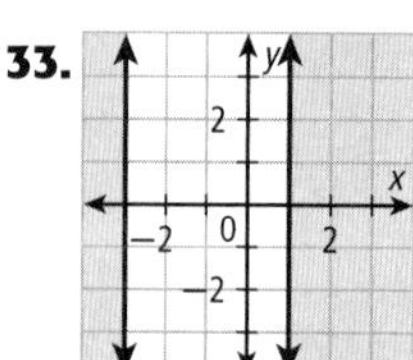

34.

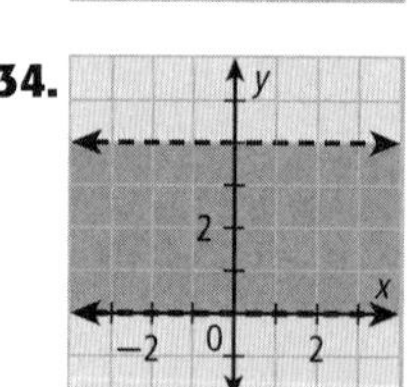

38.

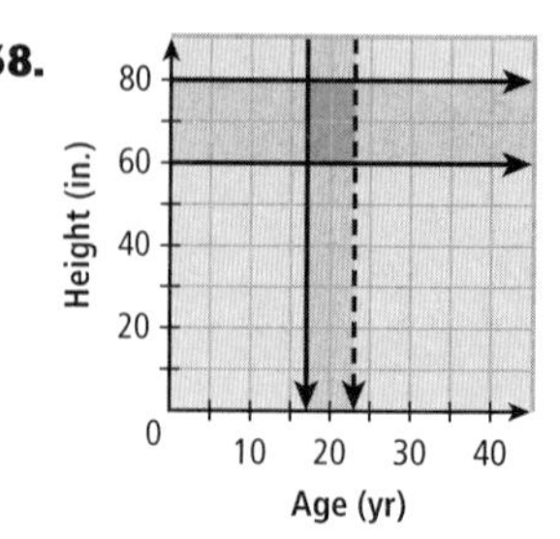

Possible answer: (20, 70), (19, 75), (18, 69)

40.

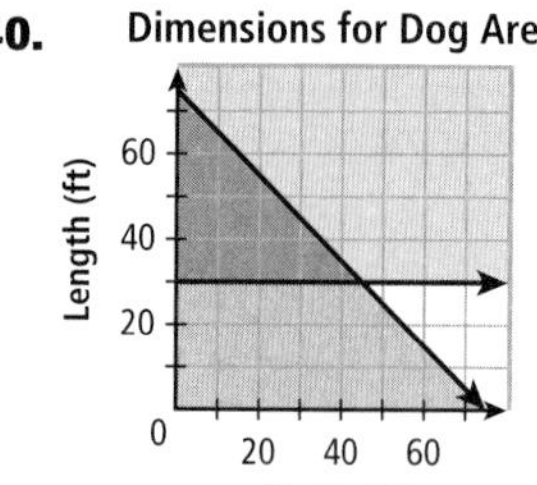

41. Yes; the solutions of the system

$$\begin{cases} y \geq x + 4 \\ y \leq x + 4 \end{cases}$$

are represented by all the ordered pairs on the line $y = x + 4$.

42a. $x + y \leq 40$

b. $15x + 12y \geq 540$

c.

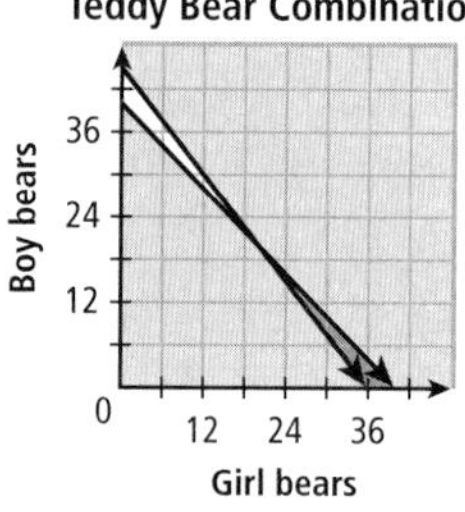

6B *Ready to Go On?*

4.

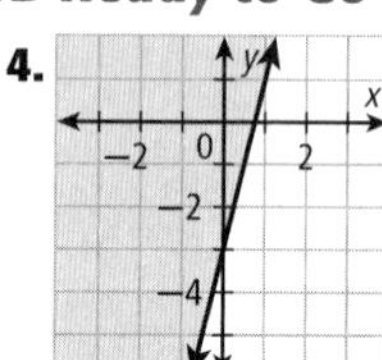

5.

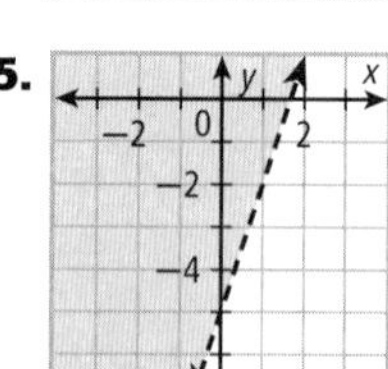

6.

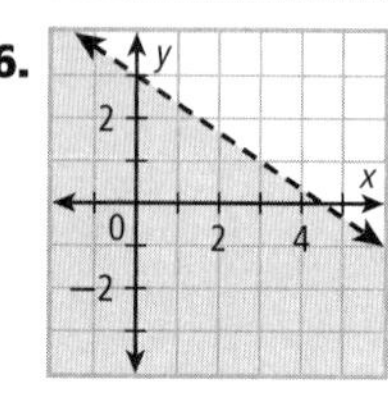

7.

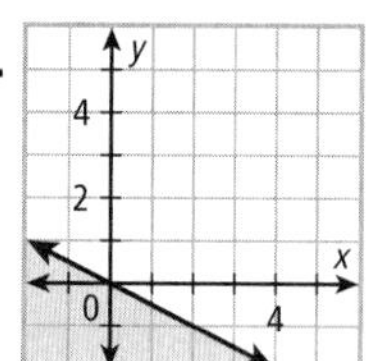

8. $30x + 15y \leq 150$

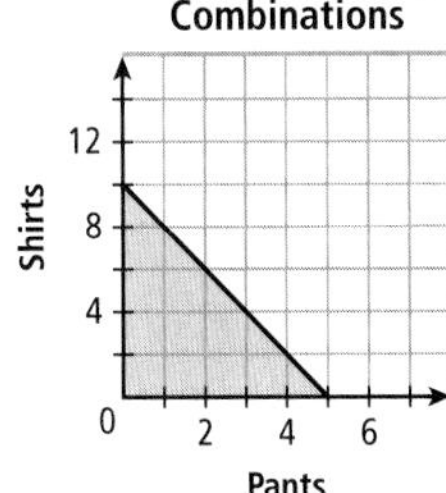

Possible answer: (4, 2), (3, 2), (2, 6)

15. Possible answer: solutions: (0, 0), (2, 2); not solutions: (−6, 0), (−4, 4)

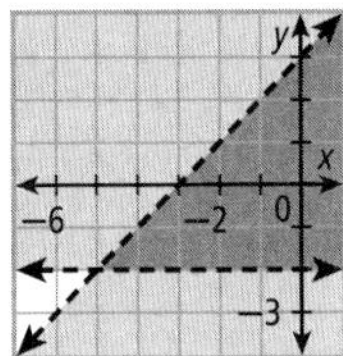

16. Possible answer: solutions: (2, 0), (2, −2); not solutions: (6, 0), (−4, 0)

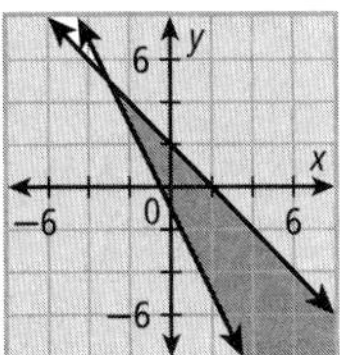

17. Possible answer: solutions: (−6, 6), (−5, 0); not solutions: (2, 0), (4, 8)

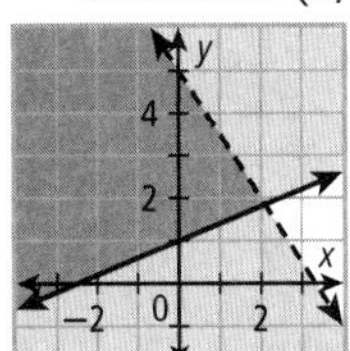

21. Let x = pounds of mangos, and y = pounds of apples.

$$\begin{cases} x \leq 45 \\ y \leq 50 \\ 4x + 3y \geq 300 \end{cases};$$

possible answer: (45, 40), (42, 50)

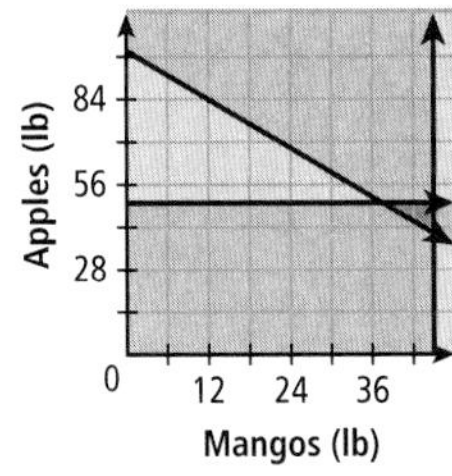

Chapter 7

7-7 Exercises

66.

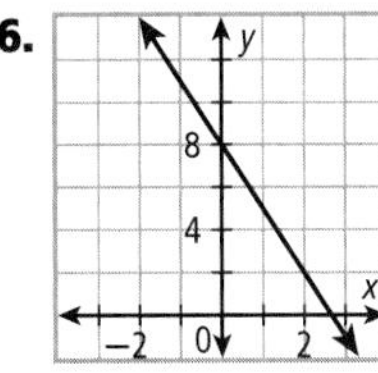

67.

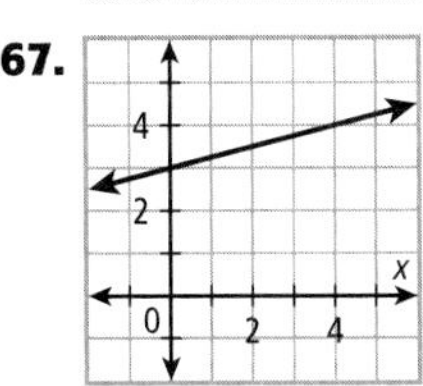

68.

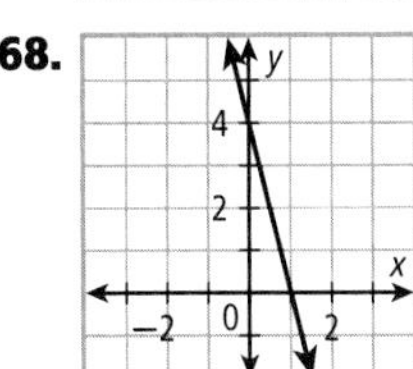

7-8 Exercises

99.

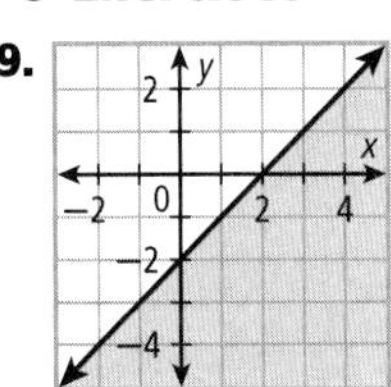

100.

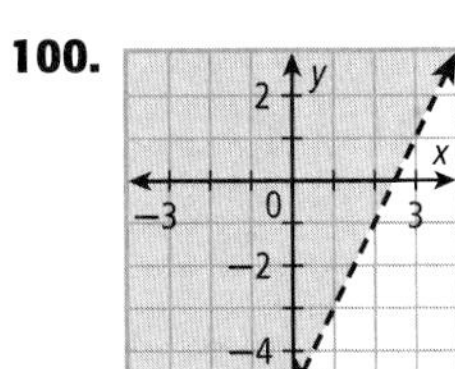

101.

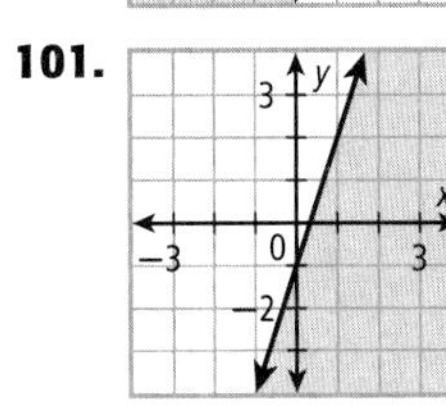

7B Ready To Go On?

21. $9k^2 + 30k + 25$
22. $8x^5 + 2x^3y + 12x^2y + 3y^2$
23. $9p^4 + 21p^3 - 23p^2 - 15p$
25. $d^2 + 18d + 81$
26. $4t^2 + 12t + 9$
27. $4x^2 + 20xy + 25y^2$
28. $m^2 - 8m + 16$
29. $a^2 - 2ab + b^2$
30. $9w^2 - 6w + 1$
31. $c^2 - 4$
32. $25r^2 - 36$

Chapter 8

8-3 Exercises

19.

n	$n^2 + 6n - 7$	$(n + 7)(n - 1)$
0	$0^2 + 6(0) - 7 = -7$	$(0 + 7)(0 - 1) = -7$
1	$1^2 + 6(1) - 7 = 0$	$(1 + 7)(1 - 1) = 0$
2	$2^2 + 6(2) - 7 = 9$	$(2 + 7)(2 - 1) = 9$
3	$3^2 + 6(3) - 7 = 20$	$(3 + 7)(3 - 1) = 20$
4	$4^2 + 6(4) - 7 = 33$	$(4 + 7)(4 - 1) = 33$

38.

n	$n^2 - 12n - 45$	$(n - 15)(n + 3)$
0	$0^2 - 12(0) - 45 = -45$	$(0 - 15)(0 + 3) = -45$
1	$1^2 - 12(1) - 45 = -56$	$(1 - 15)(1 + 3) = -56$
2	$2^2 - 12(2) - 45 = -65$	$(2 - 15)(2 + 3) = -65$
3	$3^2 - 12(3) - 45 = -72$	$(3 - 15)(3 + 3) = -72$
4	$4^2 - 12(4) - 45 = -77$	$(4 - 15)(4 + 3) = -77$

56.

n	$n^2 + 11n + 28$	$(n + 4)(n + 7)$
0	$0^2 + 11(0) + 28 = 28$	$(0 + 4)(0 + 7) = 28$
1	$1^2 + 11(1) + 28 = 40$	$(1 + 4)(1 + 7) = 40$
2	$2^2 + 11(2) + 28 = 54$	$(2 + 4)(2 + 7) = 54$
3	$3^2 + 11(3) + 28 = 70$	$(3 + 4)(3 + 7) = 70$
4	$4^2 + 11(4) + 28 = 88$	$(4 + 4)(4 + 7) = 88$

8-4 Exercises

19. $-1(2x + 3)(x - 4)$
20. $-1(2n - 1)(2n + 9)$
21. $-1(5x + 3)(x - 2)$
22. $-1(x - 2)(6x - 1)$
23. $-1(2x - 1)(2x + 5)$
24. $-1(5x + 9)(x - 2)$
25. $(3x + 2)(3x + 1)$
26. $(2x + 5)(x + 1)$
27. $(n + 2)(3n + 2)$
28. $(10d + 7)(d + 1)$
29. $(4c - 5)(c - 3)$
30. $2(3x + 1)(x + 2)$
31. $(2x + 5)(4x + 1)$
32. $(3x - 2)(2x - 3)$
33. $(5x - 6)(x + 3)$
34. $(2x + 7)(3x + 1)$
35. $(10n - 7)(n - 1)$
36. $(3x + 2)(x + 3)$
37. $(7x + 1)(x + 2)$
38. $(3n + 1)(n + 1)$
39. $(3x - 4)(x - 5)$
40. $(3x + 4)(2x + 1)$
41. $(x - 7)(4x - 3)$
42. $(5x + 3)(2x + 5)$
43. $(4y - 1)(3y + 5)$
44. $(3x - 2)(x + 4)$
45. $(2x - 1)(2x + 3)$
46. $(2n + 1)(n - 4)$
47. $(3x + 5)(x - 3)$
48. $(n + 1)(3n - 4)$
49. $-1(2x - 3)(2x + 5)$
50. $-1(x - 4)(3x - 4)$
51. $-1(3x - 2)(x + 1)$
52. $12x^2 + 27x + 6$; 3 $(4x + 1)(x + 2)$
53. $2x^2 - 5x + 2$; $(x - 2)(2x - 1)$
54. $5x^2 + 31x - 28$; $(x + 7)(5x - 4)$
55. $(9n + 8)(n + 1)$
56. $(2x + 1)(x - 4)$
57. $(2x - 1)(2x - 5)$
58. cannot be factored
59. $(3x + 8)(x + 2)$
60. $-1(3x - 1)(x + 4)$
61. $(3x + 4)(2x - 3)$
62. $(5a + 3)(2a + 1)$
63. $(2x - 3)(2x - 3)$

8A Ready To Go On?

27.

n	$n^2 + 3n - 4$	$(n+4)(n-1)$
0	$0^2 + 3(0) - 4 = -4$	$(0+4)(0-1) = -4$
1	$1^2 + 3(1) - 4 = 0$	$(1+4)(1-1) = 0$
2	$2^2 + 3(2) - 4 = 6$	$(2+4)(2-1) = 6$
3	$3^2 + 3(3) - 4 = 14$	$(3+4)(3-1) = 14$
4	$4^2 + 3(4) - 4 = 24$	$(4+4)(4-1) = 24$

28. $(2x+1)(x+5)$

29. $(3n+7)(n+3)$

30. $(5y+3)(y-2)$

31. $(2g-2)(2g-3)$

32. $6(p-4)(p+1)$

33. $(4d-3)(3d+4)$

8B Ready To Go On?

11. yes; $(5m + 2m^3)(5m - 2m^3) = m^2(5 + 2m^2)(5 - 2m^2)$

12. no; terms must be subtracted.

13. $(r^2 - t)(r^2 + t)$

21. $3x(x-2)^2$

22. $4m(2m+1)(2m-1)$

23. $5xy(x+3)(x-3)$

24. unfactorable

25. $3(c+7)(c-3)$

26. $x(x+3)(x-3)(x^2+9)$

27. $(\ell^2 - 36)$; $(\ell + 6)(\ell - 6)$

28. $a^2 - 8a + 16$; $(a-4)^2$

29. $2v^2 + 2v - 12$; $2(v+3)(v-2)$

30. $3h^3 + 3h^2 - 6h$; $3h(h+2)(h-1)$

31. $(9x)(8x) - (8y)(4y)$; $8(3x - 2y)(3x + 2y)$

Chapter 9

Are You Ready?

5.

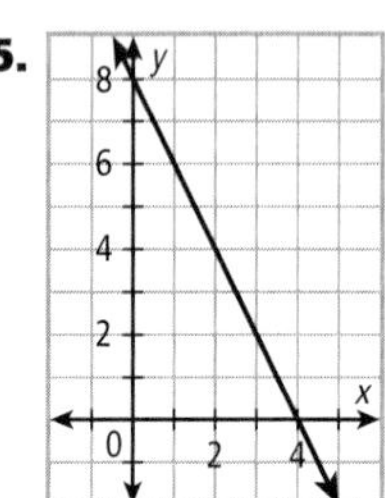

6.

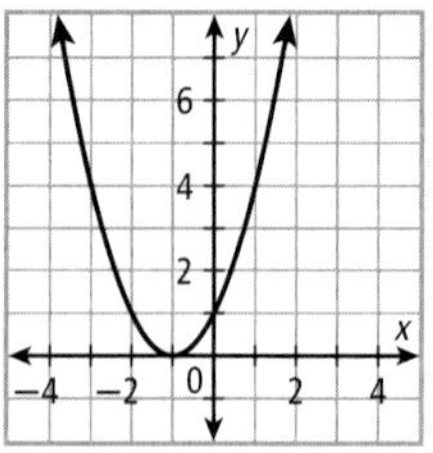

7.

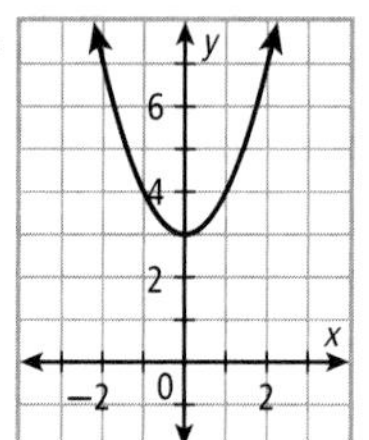

8.

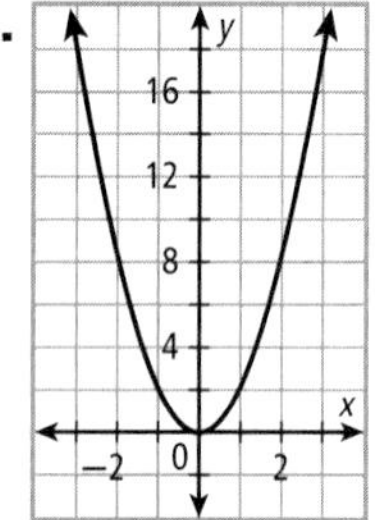

9-1 Exercises

14.

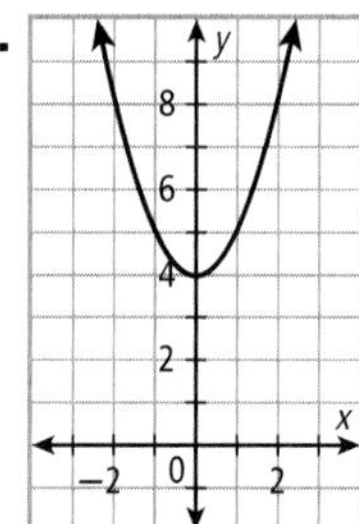

15.

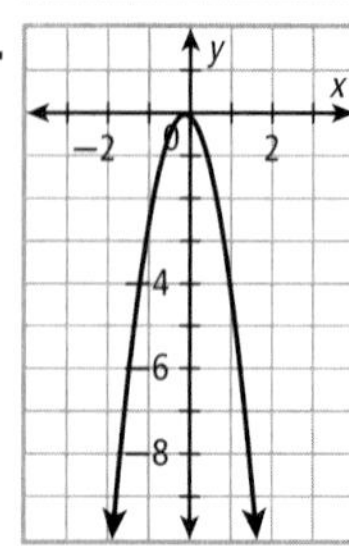

9-3 Exercises

21.

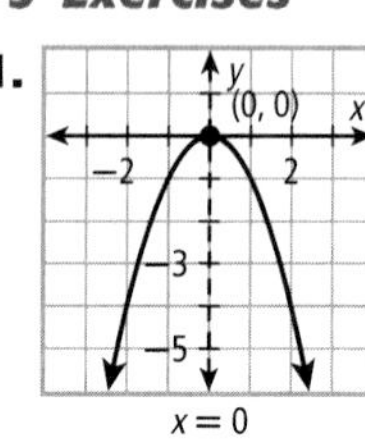

22.

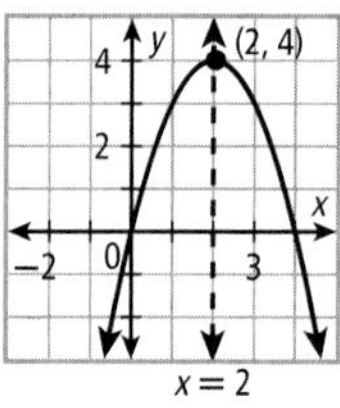

23.

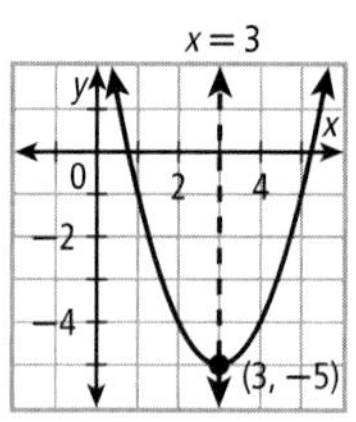

24.

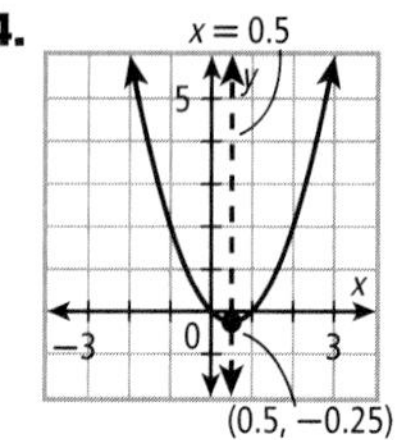

25.

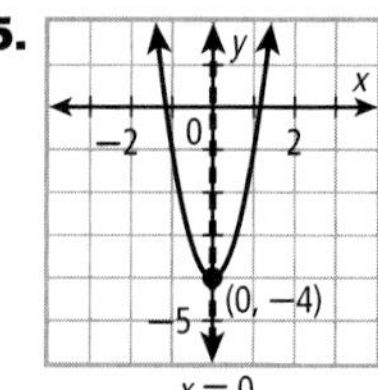

26.

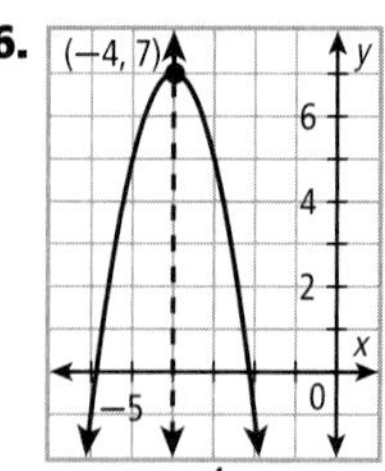

27a.

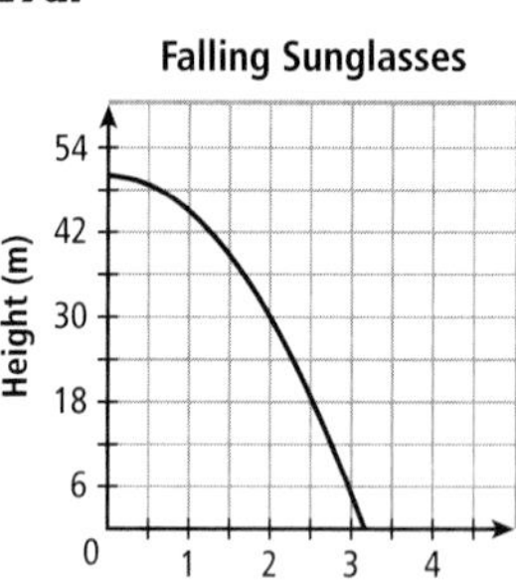

35c.

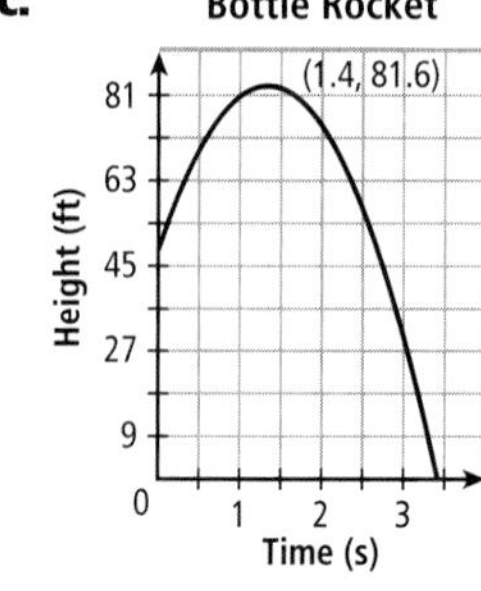

d. The vertex represents the time, 1.4 s, that the water bottle rocket has spent in the air when it reaches its highest point, 81.6 ft.

9A Ready To Go On?

10.

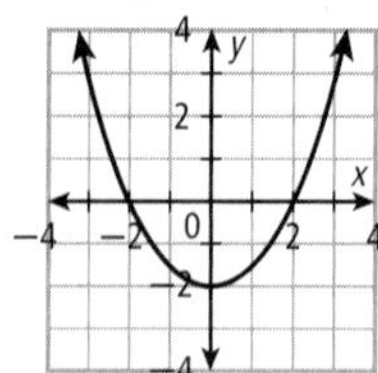

D: all real numbers

R: $y \geq -2$

21.

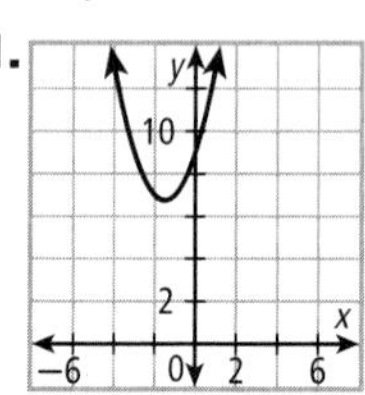

22.

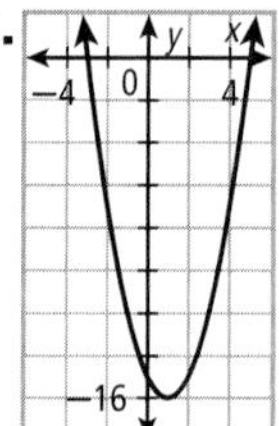

23.

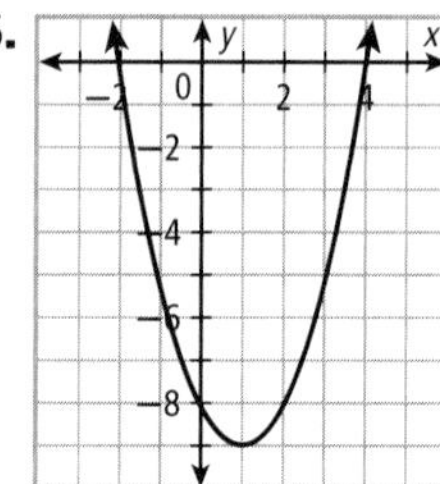

24.

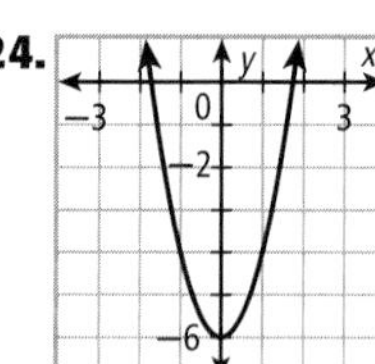

25.

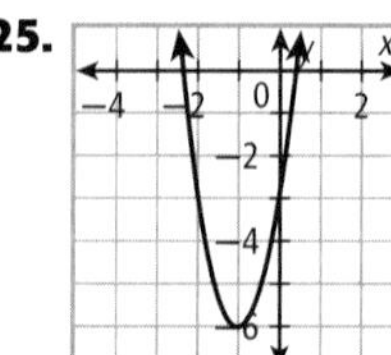

26.

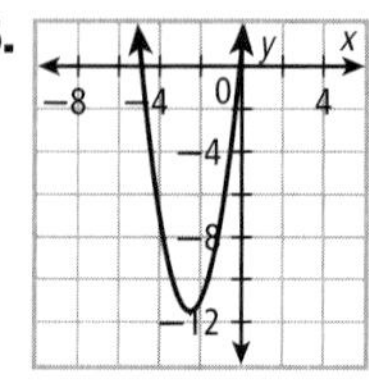

Chapter 10

10-2 *Exercises*

10.

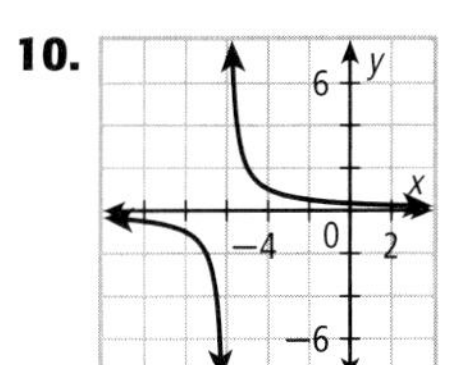

11.

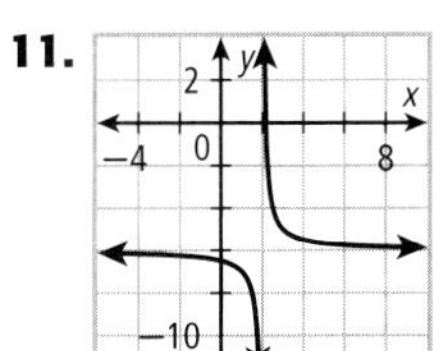

12.

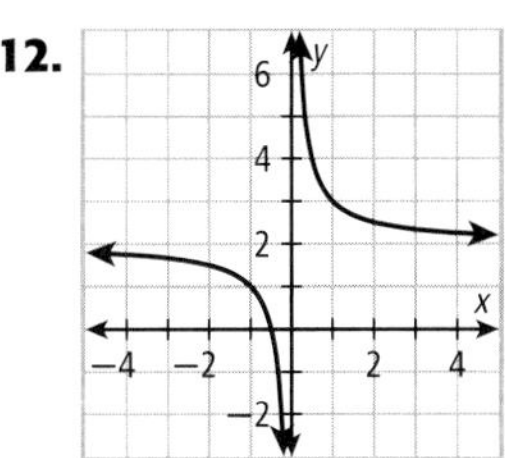

13.

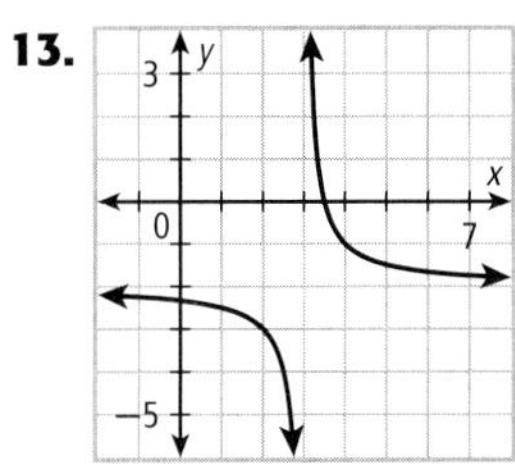

23.

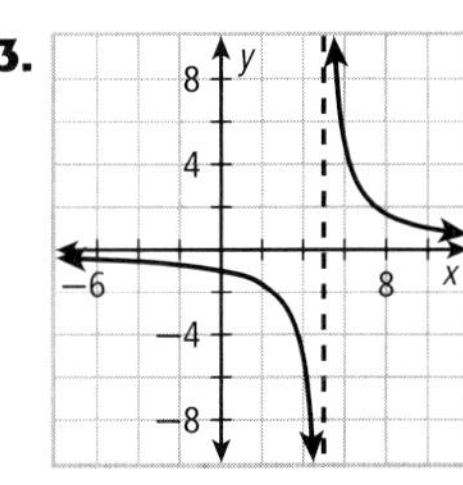

24.

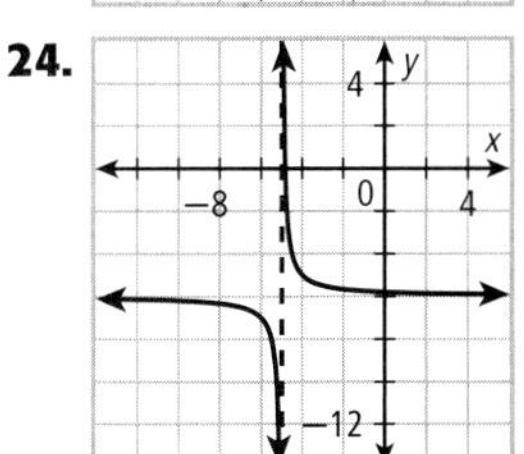

25.

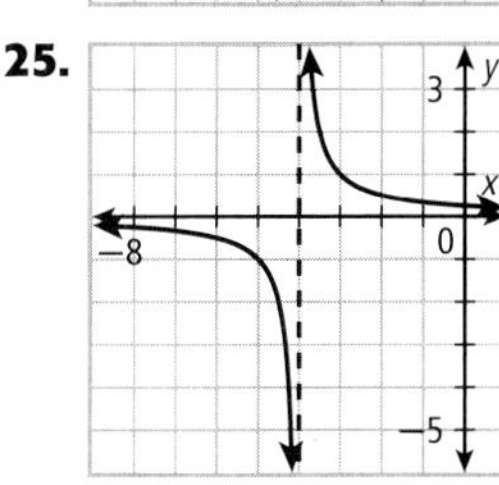

26.

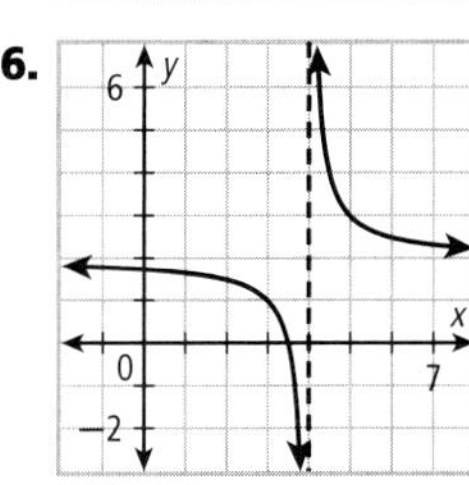

27b.

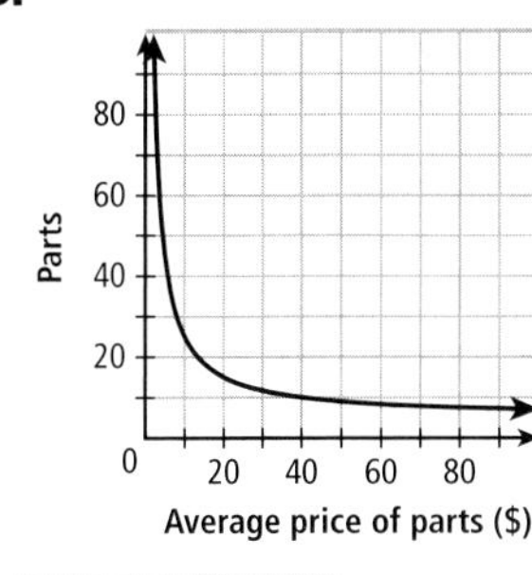

32.

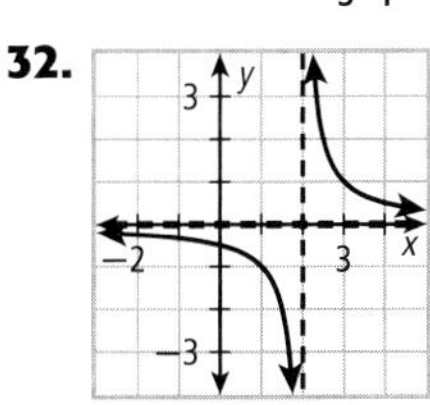

33.

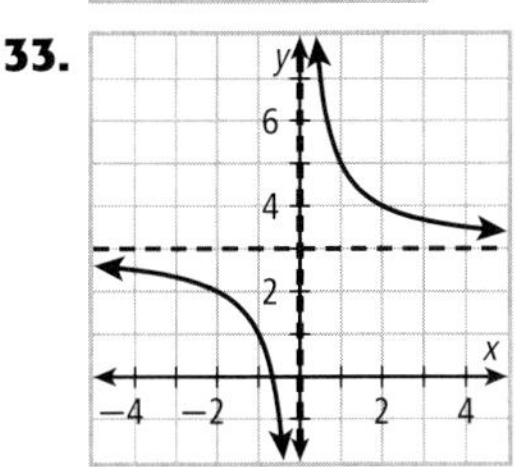

34.

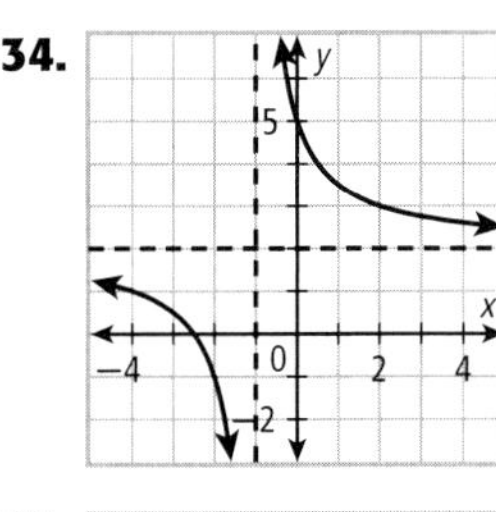

35.

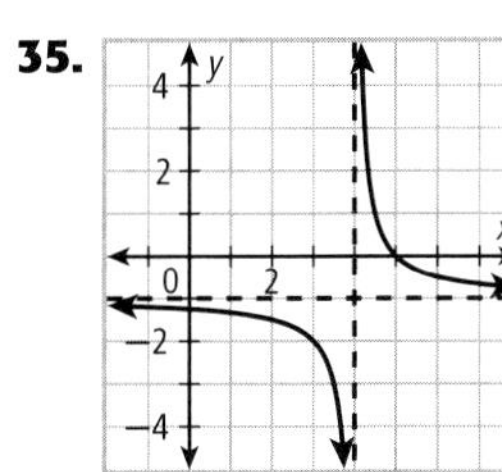

36.

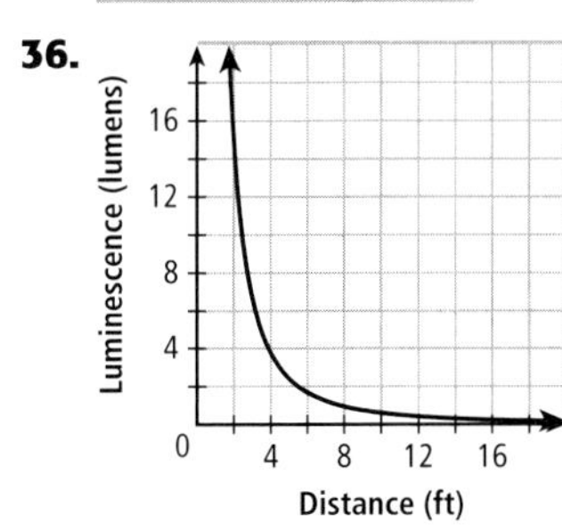

45. *D*: $x > 15$; R: nonnegative values

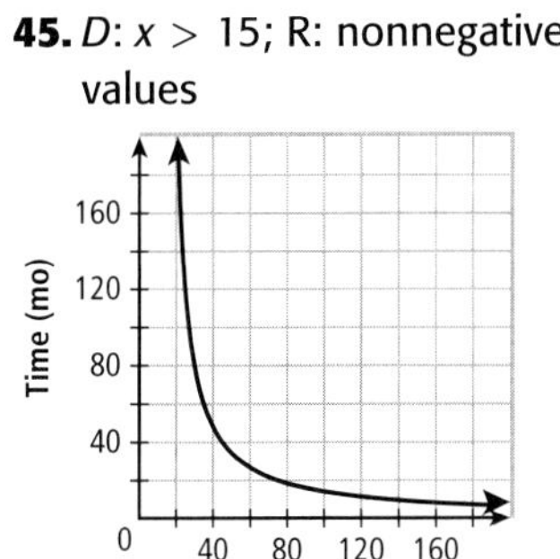

46a.

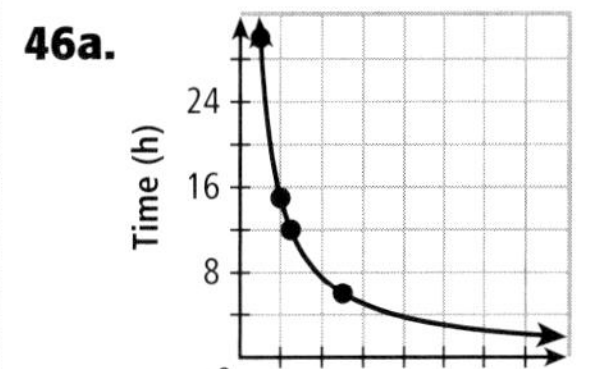

56c.

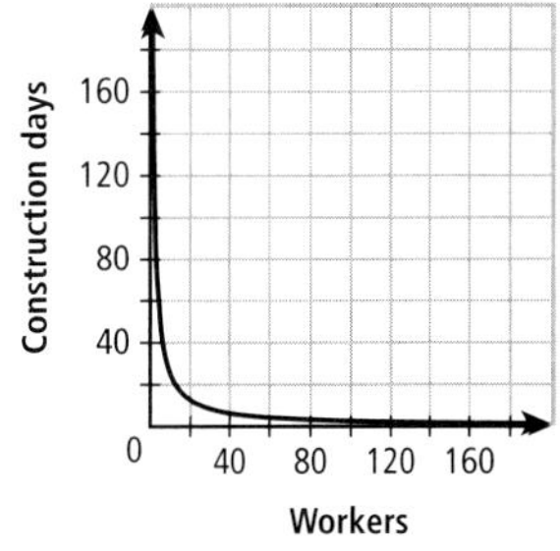

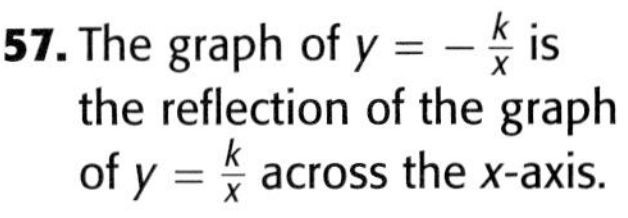

57. The graph of $y = -\frac{k}{x}$ is the reflection of the graph of $y = \frac{k}{x}$ across the *x*-axis.

a.

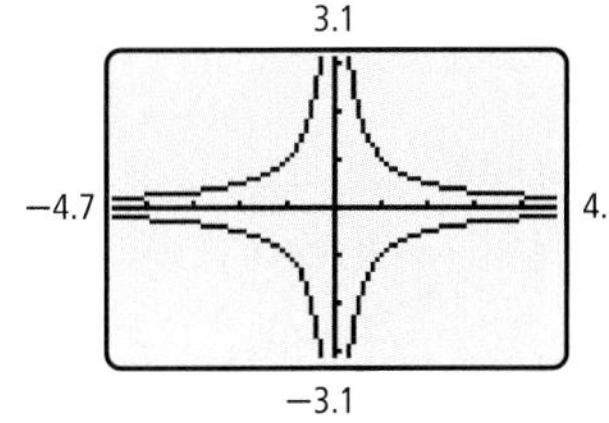

b.

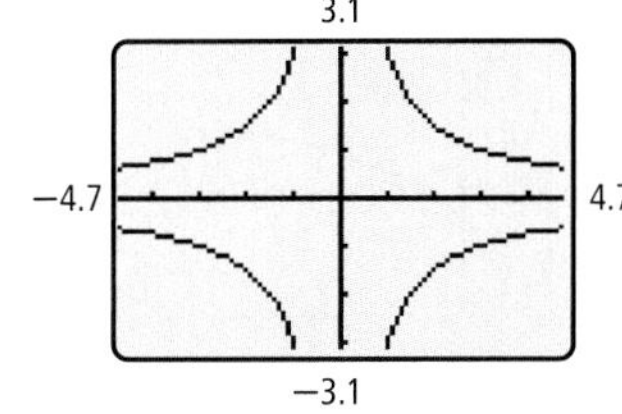

c.

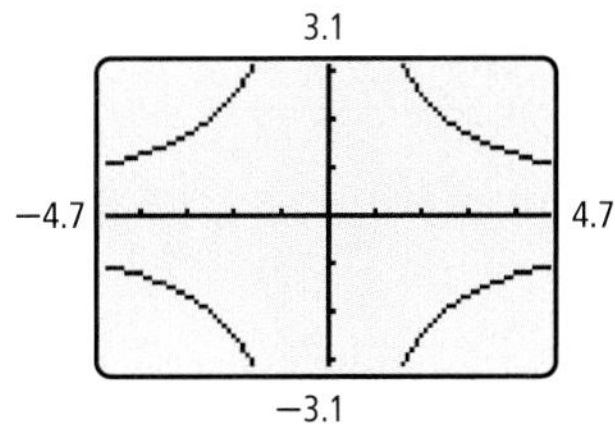

60.

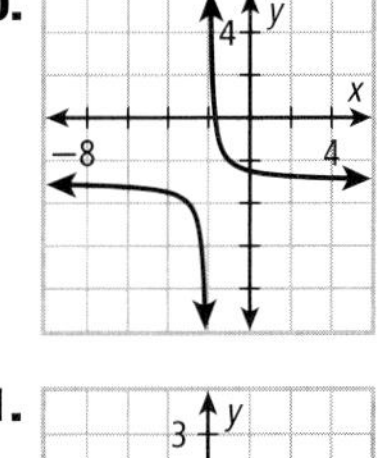

61.

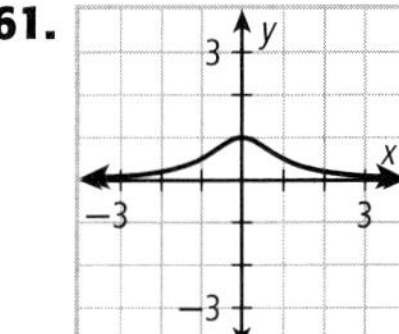

10A *Ready To Go On?*

5. constant product

6. cannot be written in the form $y = \frac{k}{x}$

7.

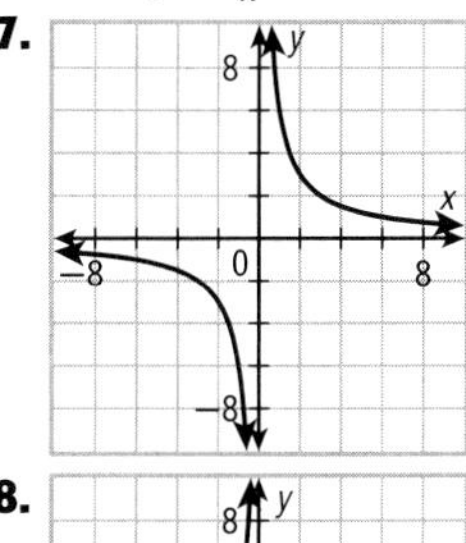

8.

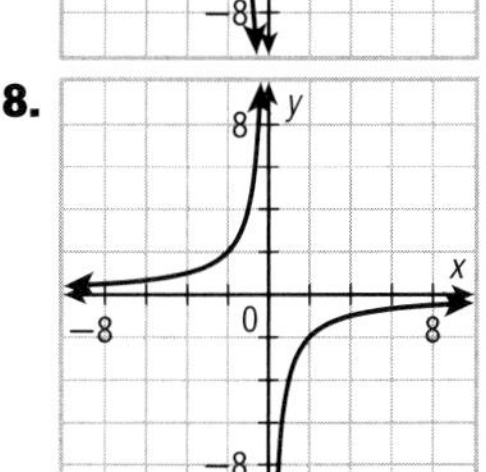

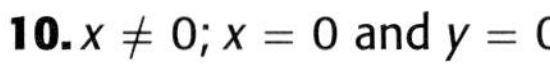

10. $x \neq 0$; $x = 0$ and $y = 0$

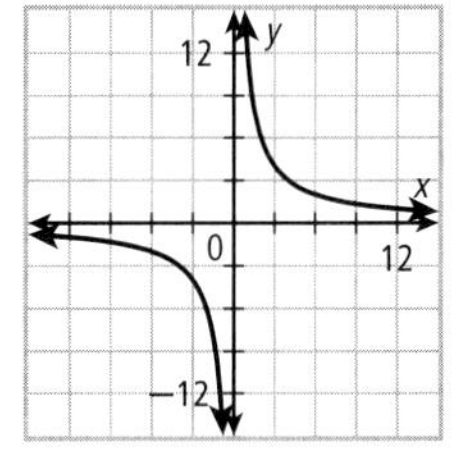

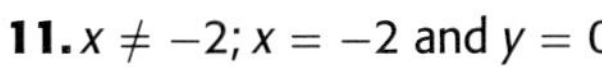

11. $x \neq -2$; $x = -2$ and $y = 0$

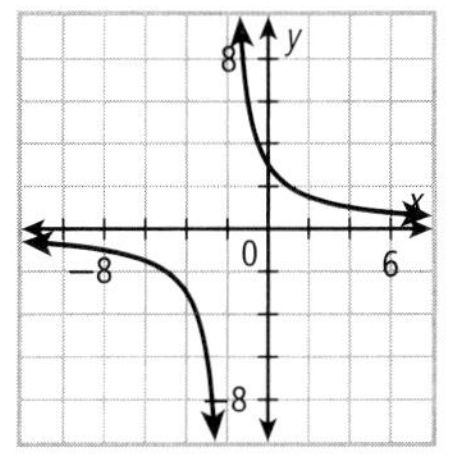

12. $x \neq 1$; $x = 1$ and $y = 0$

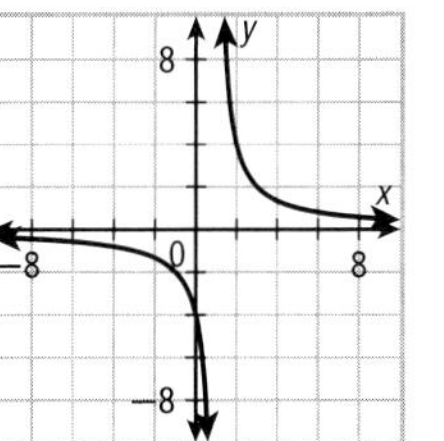

13. $x \neq -1$; $x = -1$ and $y = -3$

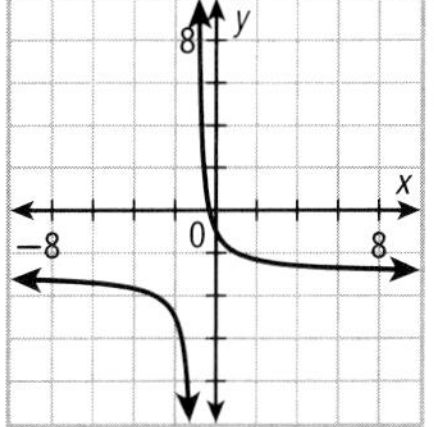

14.

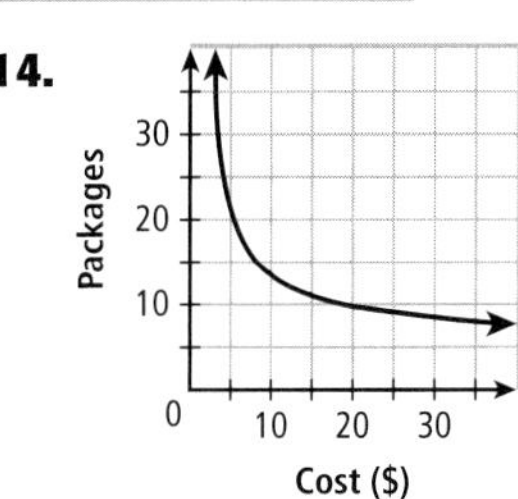

Additional Answers

Chapter 11

Are You Ready?

25.
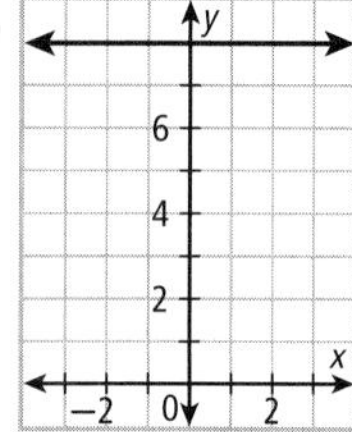

26.
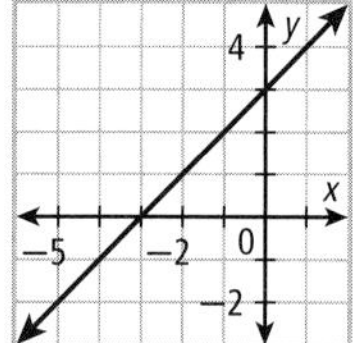

27.
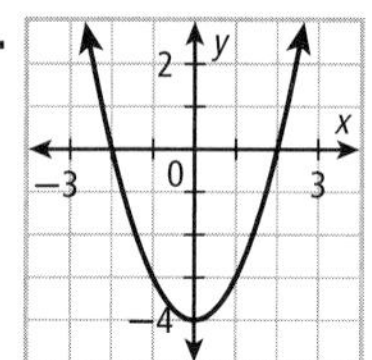

28.
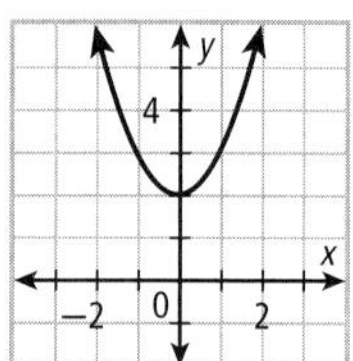

11-1 *Exercises*

9.
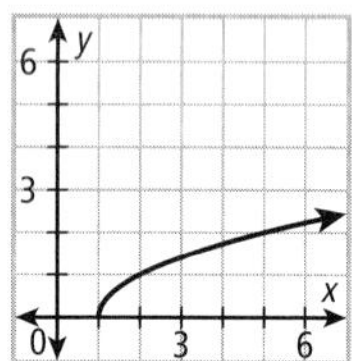

10.
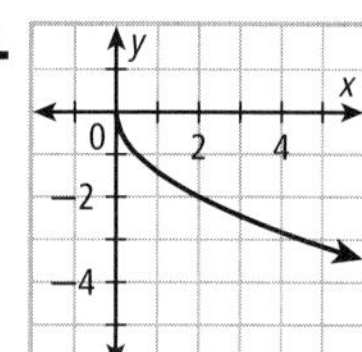

11.
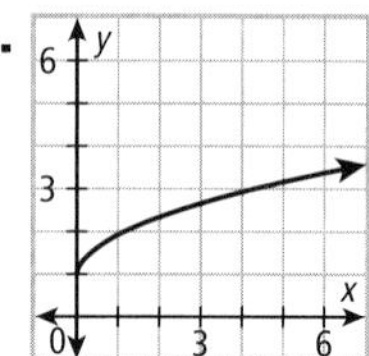

12.
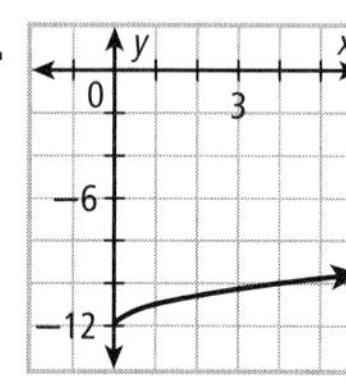

13.
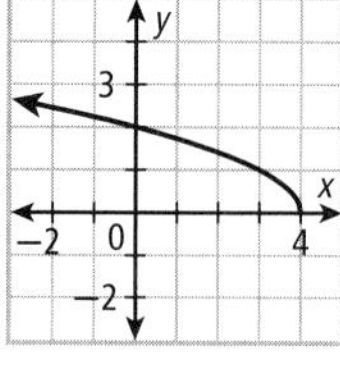

14.
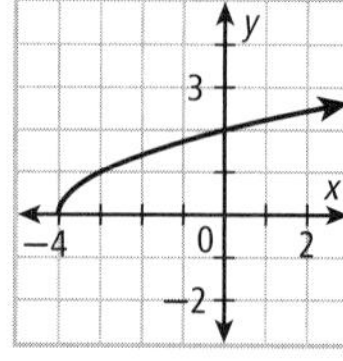

22.
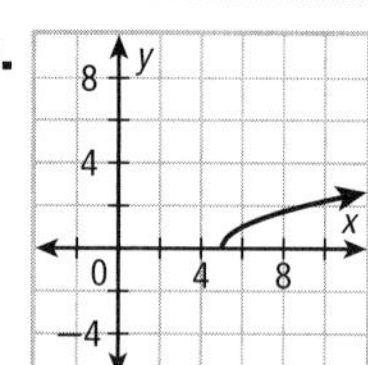

23.
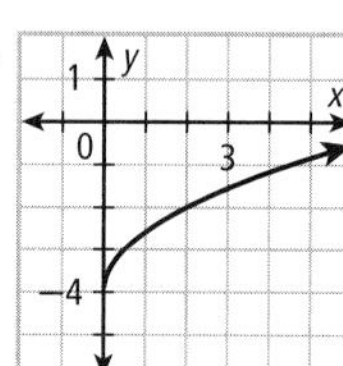

24.
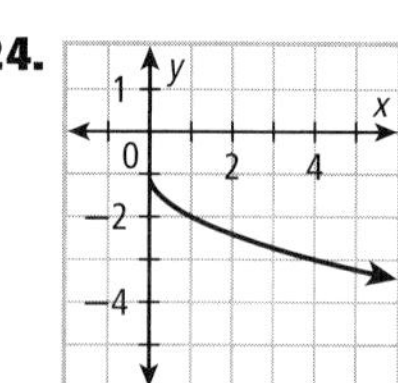

25.
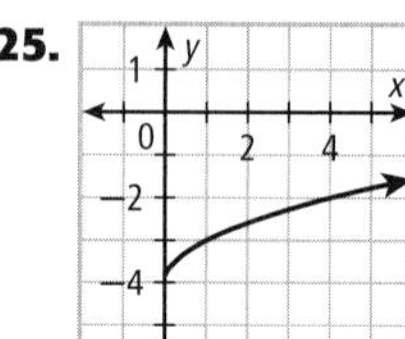

26.
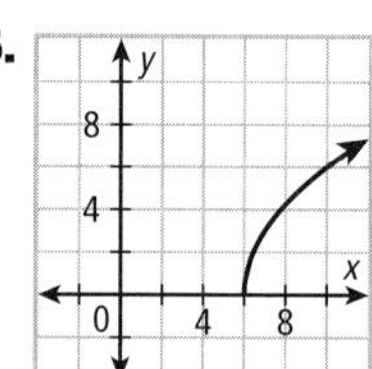

27.
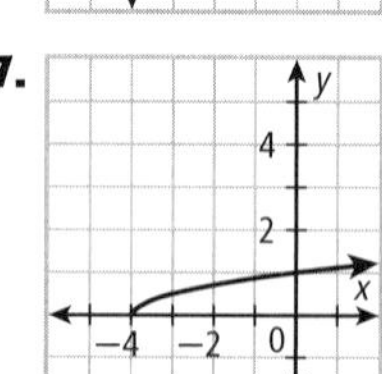

31.
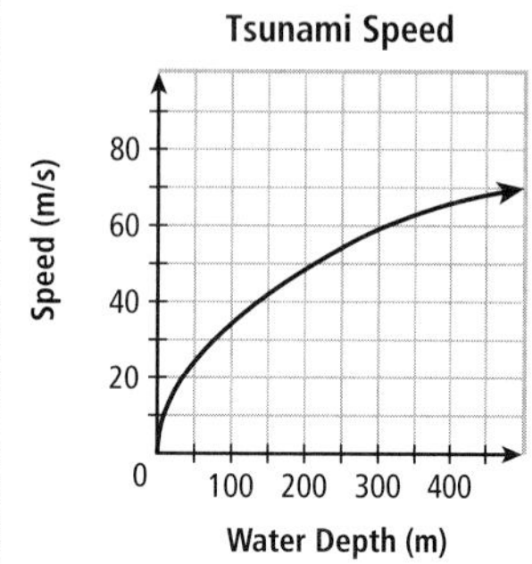

33. No; the domain of a square root function is limited to values that make the value under the square root sign non-negative. A function with a limited domain cannot have a range of all real numbers.

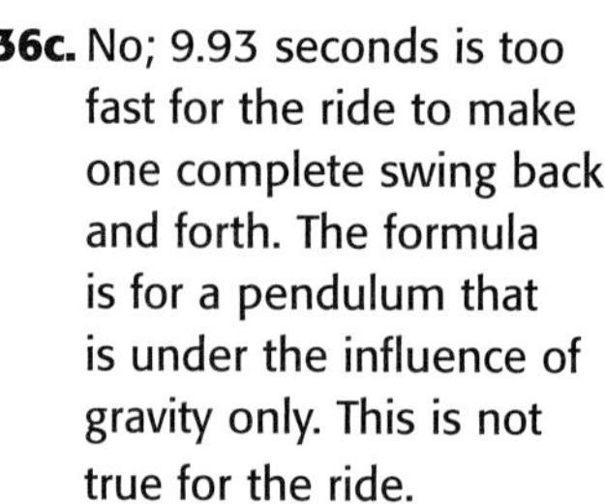

36c. No; 9.93 seconds is too fast for the ride to make one complete swing back and forth. The formula is for a pendulum that is under the influence of gravity only. This is not true for the ride.

50.
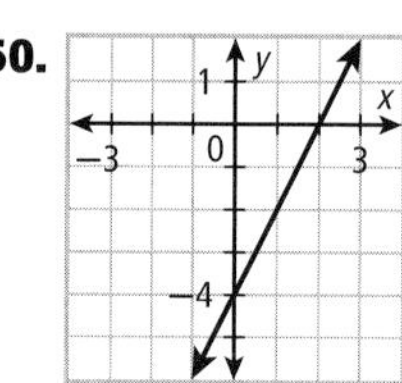

51.
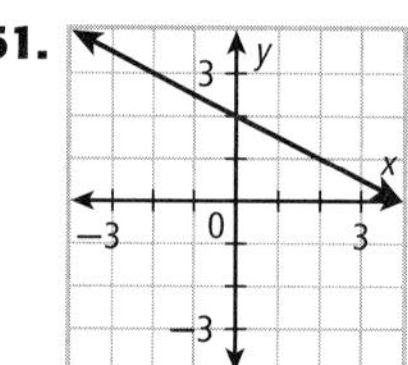

52.
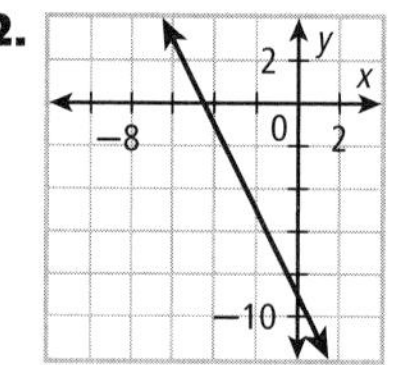

11A *Ready To Go On?*

5.
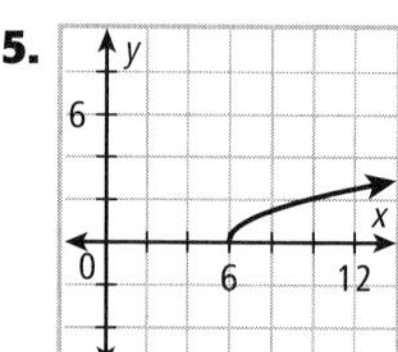

6.
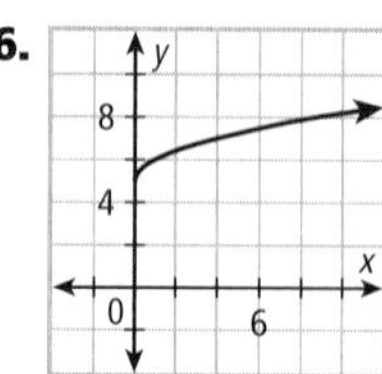

7.
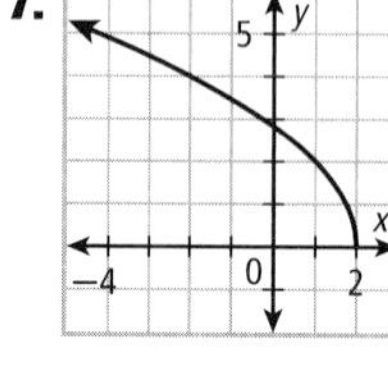

11-6 *Exercises*

41a. Stage 0:

Stage 1:
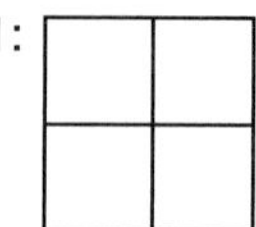

Stage 2:
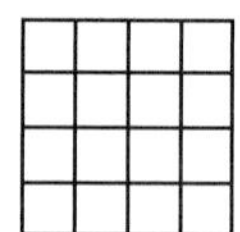

Stage 3:
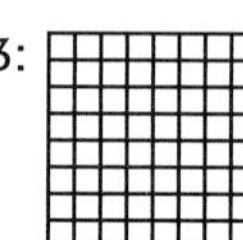

b.
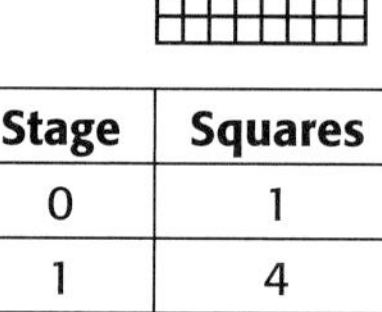

Stage	Squares
0	1
1	4
2	16
3	64

58.
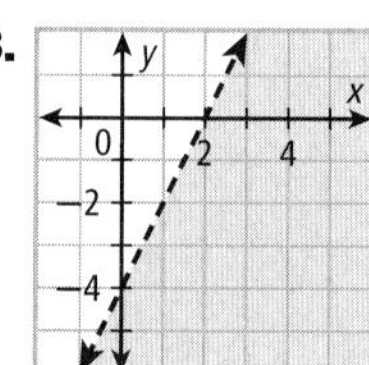

59.
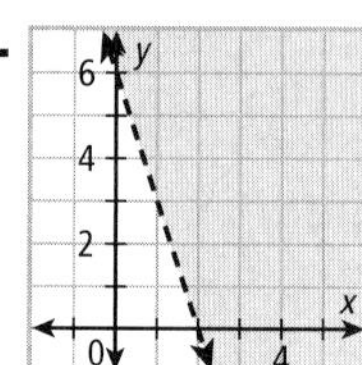

60.
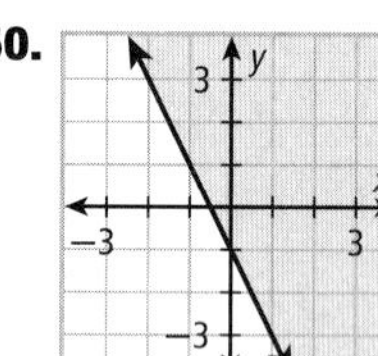

Lesson 11-7

7.
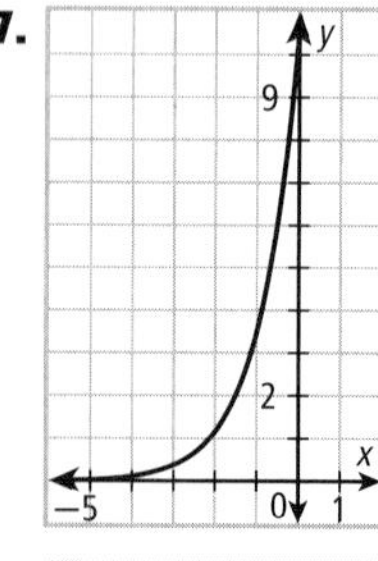

8.
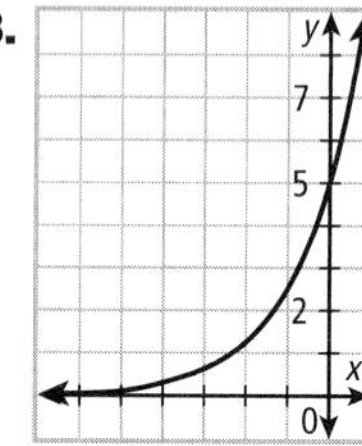

9.

10.

11.

12.

13.

14.

15.

16.

29.

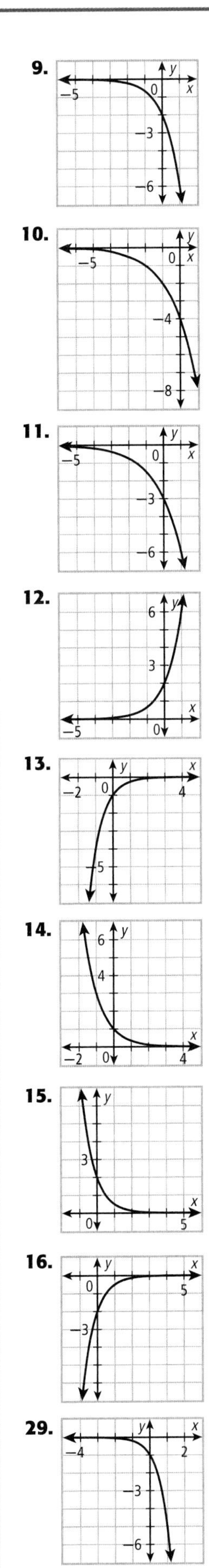

30.

31.

32.

33.

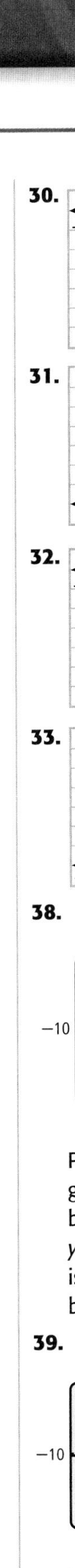

38.

Possible answer: The graphs have the same basic shape and the same y-intercept; each graph is steeper than the one before it.

39.

Possible answer: The graphs have the same basic shape and the same y-intercept; each graph is steeper than the one before it.

11B *Concept Connection*

4.

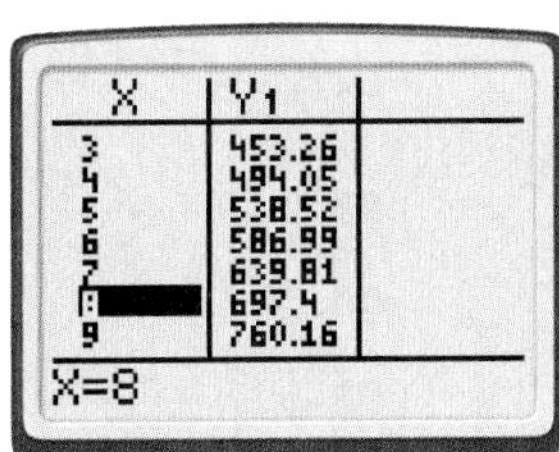

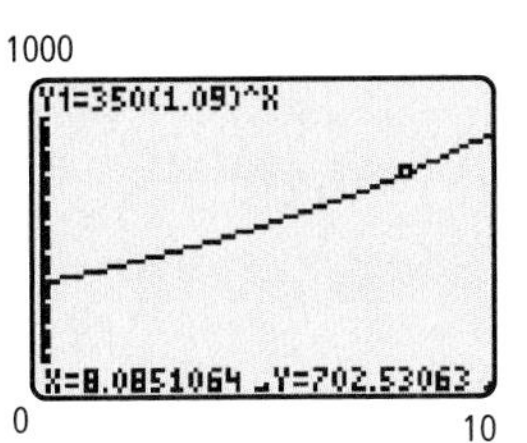

5.

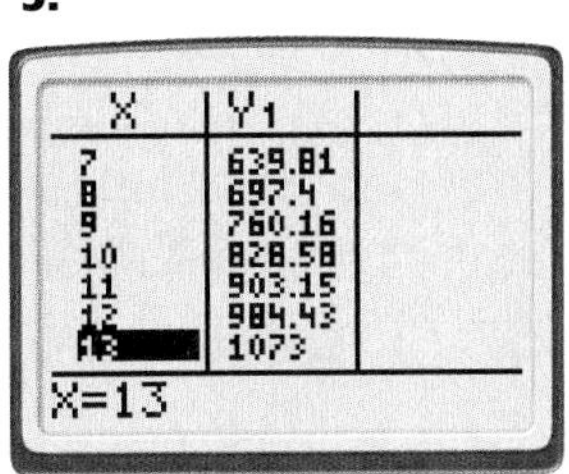

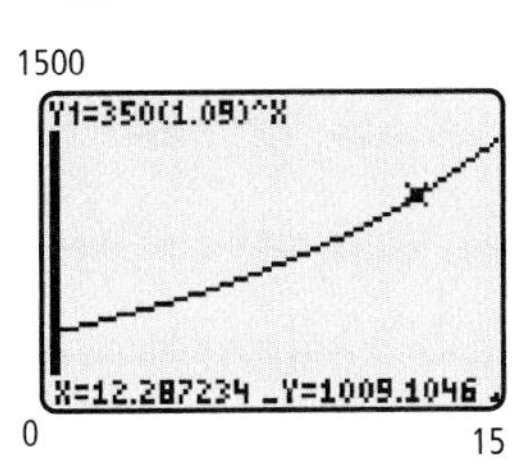

11B *Ready To Go On?*

7.

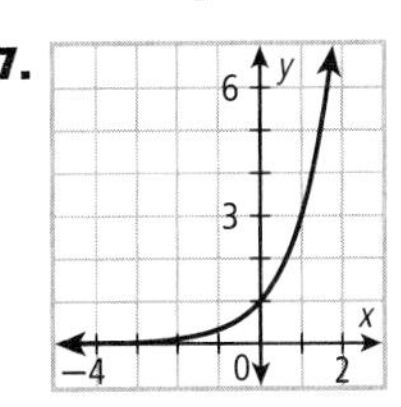

8.

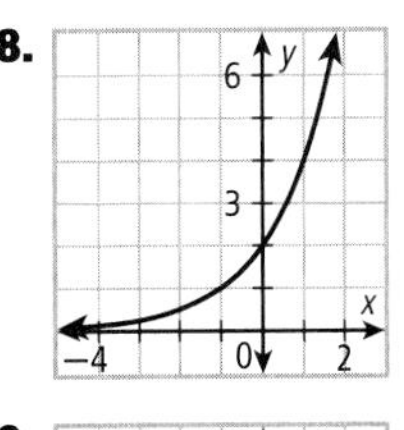

9.

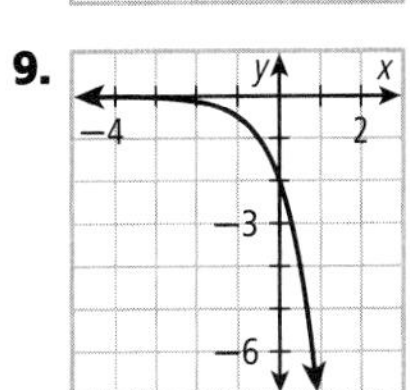

10.

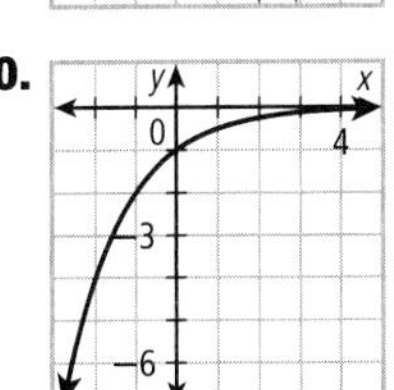

16.

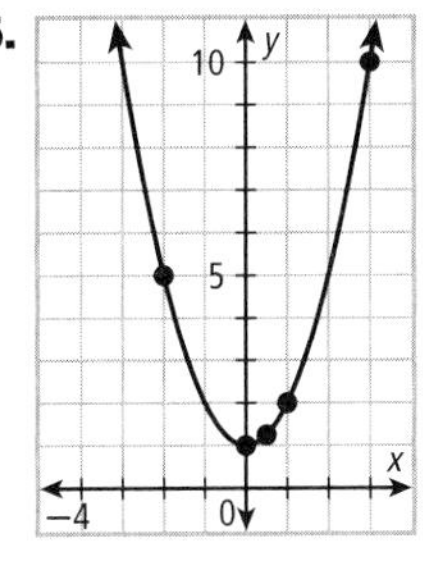

17.

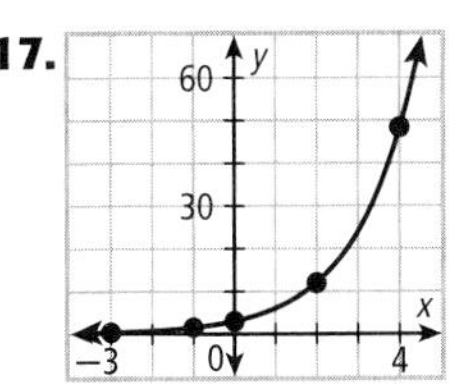

Extra Practice Skills

Chapter 1

1–4. Possible answers given.

1. 8 more than x; the sum of x and 8

2. 6 times y; the product of 6 and y

3. the difference of g and 4; 4 less than g

4. the quotient of 12 and h; 12 divided by h

44. $-1 \cdot (-1) \cdot (-1) \cdot (-1) \cdot (-1); -1$

74. $12(100 + 8); 12(100) + 12(8);$ $1200 + 96 = 1296$

75. $7(100 - 11); 7(100) - 7(11);$ $700 - 77 = 623$

76. $11(30 + 3); 11(30) + 11(3);$ $330 + 33 = 363$

77. $16(1000 + 3); 16(1000) + 16(3);$ $16000 + 48 = 16{,}048$

78. $8(200 + 7); 8(200) + 8(7);$ $1600 + 56 = 1656$

79. $18(1000 - 1); 18(1000) - 18(1);$ $18000 - 18; 17{,}982$

105.

Statements	Reasons
1. $6(p - 2) + 3p$	
2. $6(p) + 6(-2) + 3p$	Dist. Prop.
3. $6p + (-12) + 3p$	Multiply.
4. $6p + 3p + (-12)$	Comm. Prop. of Add.
5. $(6p + 3p) + (-12)$	Assoc. Prop. of Add.
6. $9p - 12$	Combine like terms.

106.

Statements	Reasons
1. $-4 + 3r - 7(2s - r)$	
2. $-4 + 3r - 7(2s) - 7(-r)$	Dist. Prop.
3. $-4 + 3r - 14s + 7r$	Multiply.
4. $3r + 7r - 14s - 4$	Comm. Prop. of Add.
5. $(3r + 7r) - 14s - 4$	Assoc. Prop. of Add.
6. $10r - 14s - 4$	Combine like terms.

Chapter 2

66. $\frac{1}{2}x + 3 = 17 - 3x; x = 4$

67. $2(x - 4) = x - 5; x = 3$

68. $x + 5 = 3x - 13; x = 9$

69. $2x - 9 = 3 - 4x; x = 2$

90. $r = \frac{2 - q}{-3}$

91. $c = -6d + 47$

92. $y = \frac{20 - 8x}{3}$

93. $h = \frac{10 + 3g}{2fg}$

94. $r = 3a - 5$

95. $g = \frac{7 - 4h}{3}$

96. $s = \frac{4k}{t}$

97. $y = \frac{11x + 4}{3}$

98. $m = \frac{12n + 3dn}{5}$

99. $u = \frac{5c}{4s}$

Chapter 3

1. all real numbers less than -5

2. all real numbers greater than or equal to 11

3. all real numbers greater than 9

4. all real numbers less than or equal to $\frac{3}{4}$

5.

6. −3 −2 −1 0 1 2 3

7. 0 1 2 3 4 5 6

8. 0 2 4 6 8 10 12

19. 8 9 10 11 12 13 14

20. −16 −15 −14 −13 −12 −11 −10

21. 0 1 2 3 4 5 6

22. −8 −7 −6 −5 −4 −3 −2

30. 0 2 4 6 8 10 12

31. 0 1 2 3 4 5 6

32. 10 11 12 13 14 15 16

33. $-\frac{1}{5}$ 0 $\frac{1}{5}$ $\frac{2}{5}$ $\frac{3}{5}$ $\frac{4}{5}$ 1

34. $-\frac{3}{2}$ −1 $-\frac{1}{2}$ 0 $\frac{1}{2}$ 1 $\frac{3}{2}$

35. 6 7 8 9 10 11 12

36. −3 −2 −1 0 1 2 3

37. 0 2 4 6 8 10 12

38. 0 2 4 6 8 10 12

39. −12 −10 −8 −6 −4 −2 0

40. $-\frac{5}{3}$ $-\frac{4}{3}$ −1 $-\frac{2}{3}$ $-\frac{1}{3}$ 0 $\frac{1}{3}$

41. $-\frac{1}{2}$ $-\frac{1}{4}$ 0 $\frac{1}{4}$ $\frac{1}{2}$ $\frac{3}{4}$ 1

42. −22 −20 −18 −16 −14 −12 −10

43. −10 −9 −8 −7 −6 −5 −4

44. −10 −9 −8 −7 −6 −5 −4

45. 10 12 14 16 18 20 22

46. 8 10 12 14 16 18 20

47. −18 −17 −16 −15 −14 −13 −12

48. 0 1 2 3 4 5 6

49. 18 20 22 24 26 28 30

50. 1 $\frac{4}{3}$ $\frac{5}{3}$ 2 $\frac{7}{3}$ $\frac{8}{3}$ 3

51. −1 $-\frac{4}{5}$ $-\frac{3}{5}$ $-\frac{2}{5}$ $-\frac{1}{5}$ 0 $\frac{1}{5}$

52. 0 $\frac{1}{2}$ 1 $\frac{3}{2}$ 2 $\frac{5}{2}$ 3

53. $-\frac{1}{3}$ 0 $\frac{1}{3}$ $\frac{2}{3}$ 1 $\frac{4}{3}$ $\frac{5}{3}$

54. $\frac{4}{9}$ $\frac{5}{9}$ $\frac{2}{3}$ $\frac{7}{9}$ $\frac{8}{9}$ 1 $\frac{10}{9}$

55. $\frac{2}{5}$ $\frac{1}{2}$ $\frac{3}{5}$ $\frac{7}{10}$ $\frac{4}{5}$ $\frac{9}{10}$ 1

56. 3 4 5 6 7 8 9

57. 6 7 8 9 10 11 12

58. −3 −2 −1 0 1 2 3

62. $12 \le 6(5 - x); x \le 3;$

0 1 2 3 4 5 6

63. 8 10 12 14 16 18 20

64. 0 2 4 6 8 10 12

65. −6 −4 −2 0 2 4 6

66. −3 −2 −1 0 1 2 3

67. 12 13 14 15 16 17 18

73. 0 1 2 3 4 5 6

74. −6 −5 −4 −3 −2 −1 0

75. −12 −10 −8 −6 −4 −2 0

76. 0 1 2 3 4 5 6

79. −3 −2 −1 0 1 2 3

80. −3 −2 −1 0 1 2 3

81.  −3 −2 −1 0 1 2 3

82. 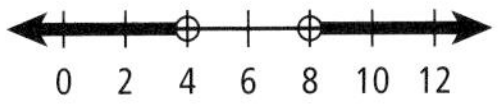 0 2 4 6 8 10 12

83.  −60 −40 −20 0 20 40 60

84.  −8 −6 −4 −2 0 2 4 6 8

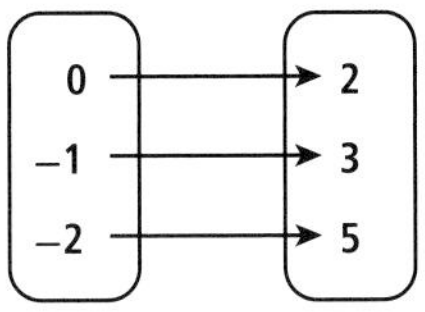

85.  −4 −3 −2 −1 0 1 2 3 4

86. 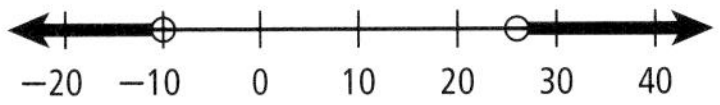 −20 −10 0 10 20 30 40

87. 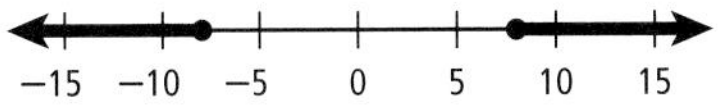 −15 −10 −5 0 5 10 15

88. 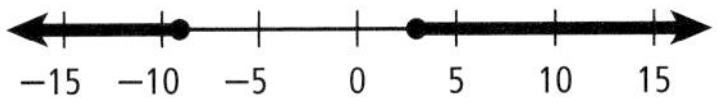 −15 −10 −5 0 5 10 15

92. 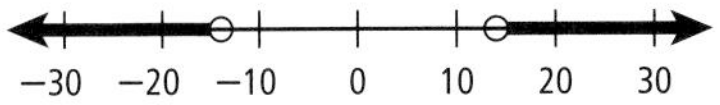 −30 −20 −10 0 10 20 30

93.  −15 −10 −5 0 5 10 15

Chapter 4

4.

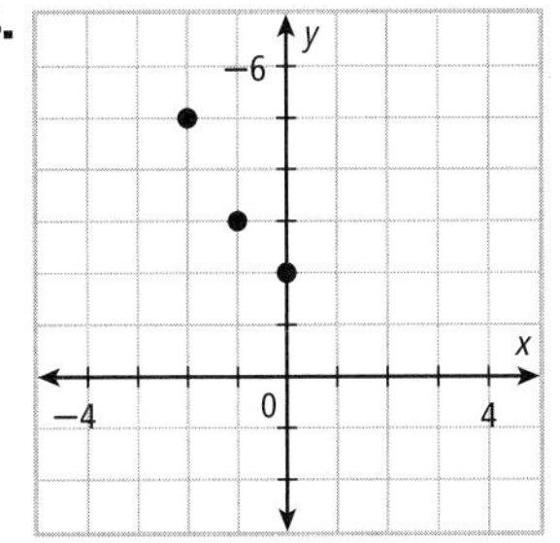

x	y
0	2
−1	3
−2	5

0 → 2
−1 → 3
−2 → 5

5.

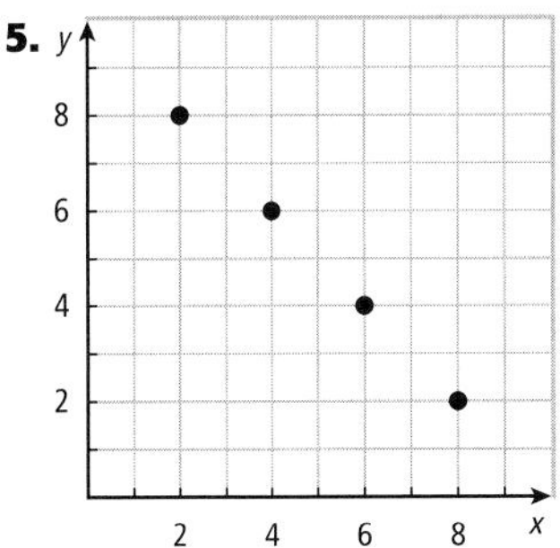

x	y
2	8
4	6
6	4
8	2

2 → 8
4 → 6
6 → 4
8 → 2

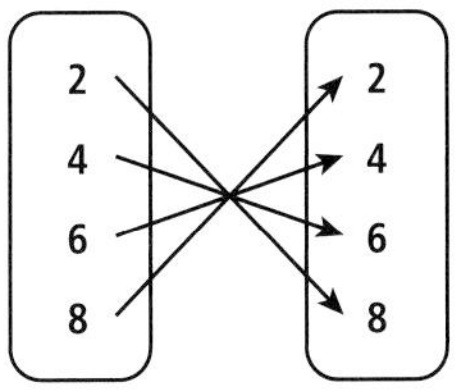

6. D: {−1, 3, 2, 5}; R: {−3, 0, 2, 4}; yes; each domain value is paired with exactly one range value.

7. D: {0, 5}; R: {−3, 1, 2, 4}; no; the domain value 5 is paired with more than one range value.

8. D: {−1, 0, 1, 2}; R: {−3, −2, −1, 0, 1}; no; the domain value 2 is paired with more than one range value.

9. D: $\{4 \le x \le 8\}$; R: $\{2 \le y \le 8\}$; yes; each domain value is paired with exactly one range value.

17.

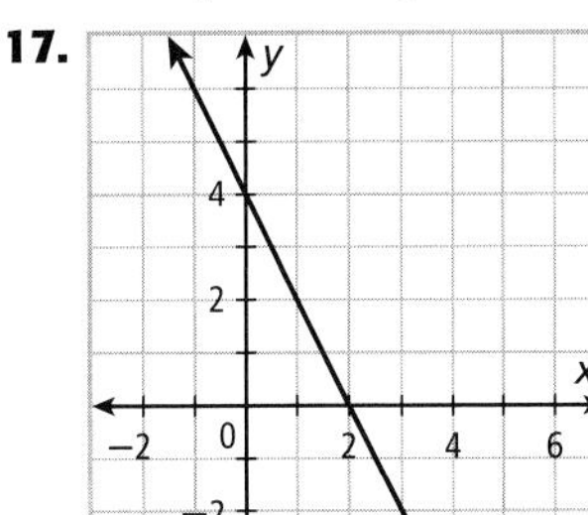

18.

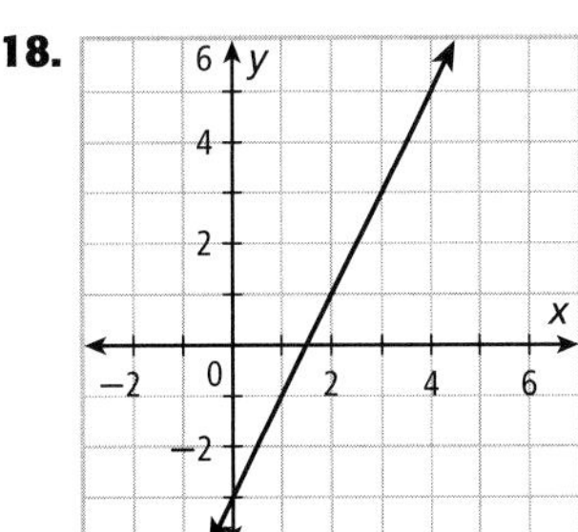

19.

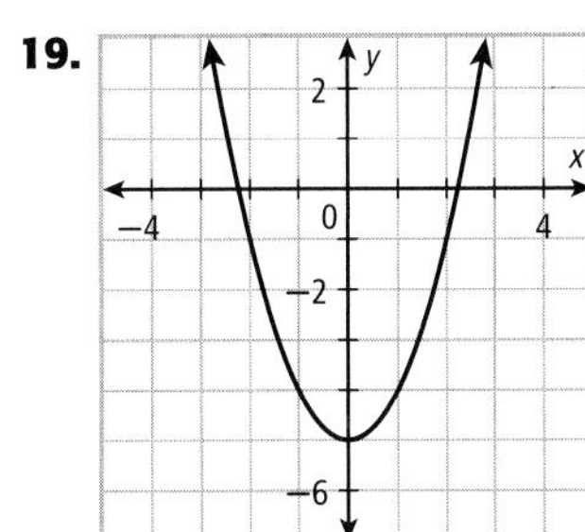

25. As more pieces are captured, the fewer there are on the board.

26. There is no relationship between a person's height and eye color.

27. There is no relationship between pages in a book and books in the library.

28. As more shirts are purchased, more money is spent.

29. As more guests come to the hotel, fewer rooms remain.

Chapter 5

1.

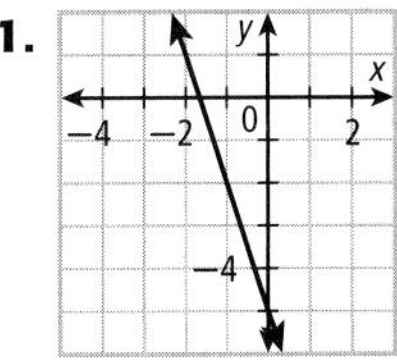

2.

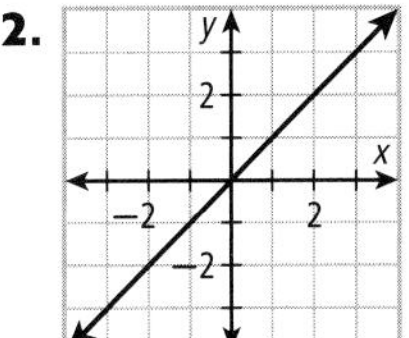

3.

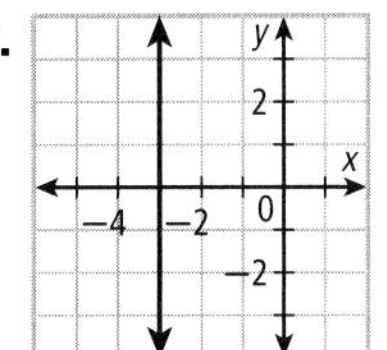

12. $x + 12y = 15$; $A = 1$, $B = 12$, $C = 15$; nonhoriz., nonvert. line

13. $4x + y = 13$; $A = 4$, $B = 1$, $C = 13$; nonhoriz., nonvert. line

14. $\frac{5}{6}x - \frac{3}{2}y = \frac{7}{5}$; $A = \frac{5}{6}$, $B = \frac{3}{2}$, $C = \frac{7}{5}$; nonhoriz., nonvert. line

15. $7x - 5y = 2$; $A = 7$, $B = -5$, $C = 2$; nonhoriz., nonvert. line

16. $0x + 7y = 24$; $A = 0$, $B = 7$, $C = 24$; horiz. line

17. $\frac{1}{2}x + 8y = -10$; $A = \frac{1}{2}$, $B = 8$, $C = -10$; nonhoriz., nonvert. line

18. $6x - 4y = 20$; $A = 6$, $B = -4$, $C = 20$; nonhoriz., nonvert. line

19. $13x + 0y = 16$; $A = 13$, $B = 0$, $C = 16$; vert. line

26.

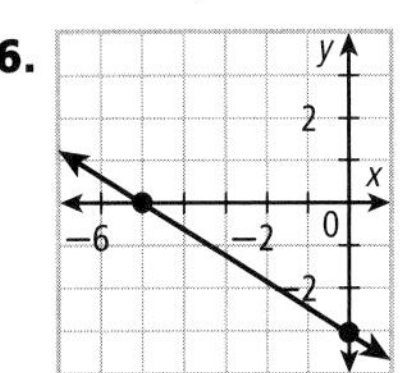

27.

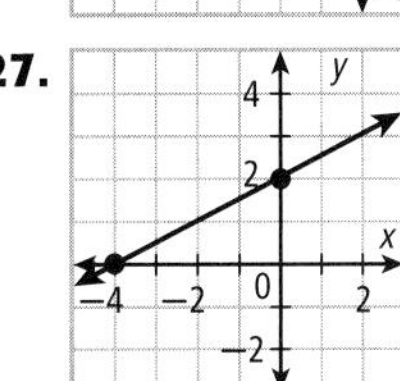

28.

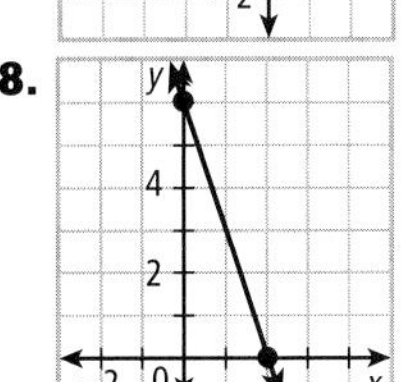

29.

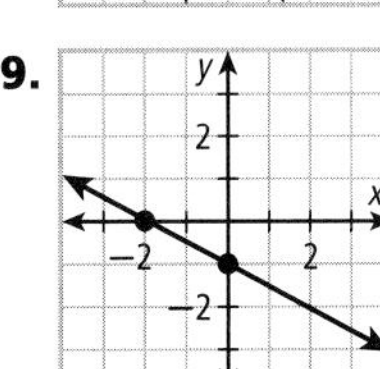

61.

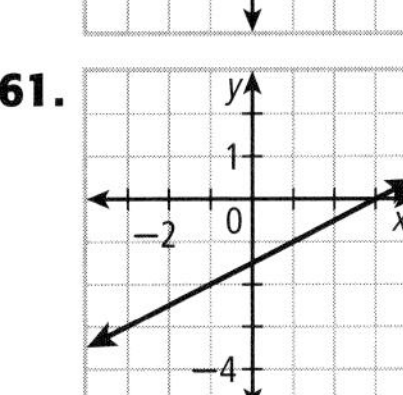

62.

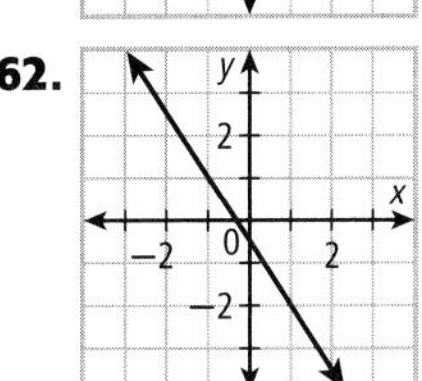

Additional Answers

63.

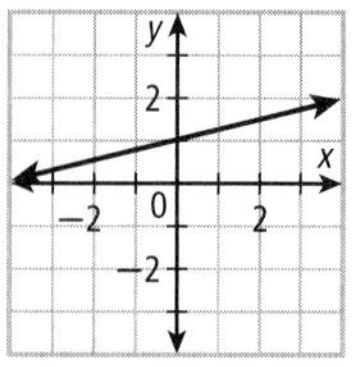

70. $y = -\frac{3}{2}x - \frac{1}{2}$

71. $y = 4x - 11$

72. $y = -2x + 3$

79. $y = 3x - 2$ and $y = 3x + 7$

80. $y = \frac{1}{4}(x + 8)$ is perp. to $y = -2(2x - 1)$ and $y - 4 = 2(3 - 2x)$.

Chapter 6

46.

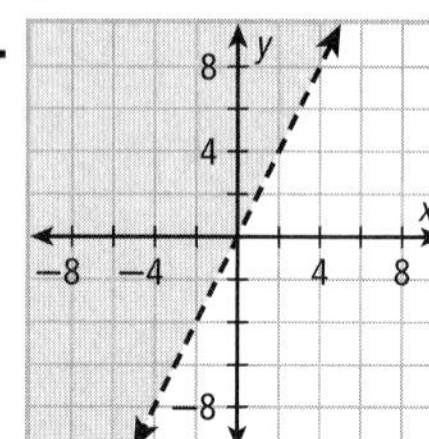

47.

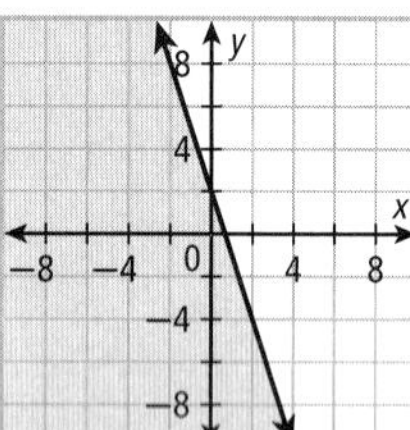

48.

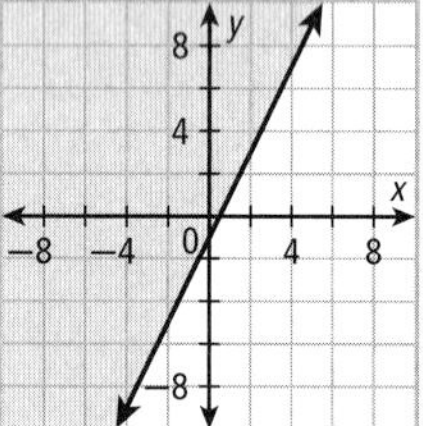

49.

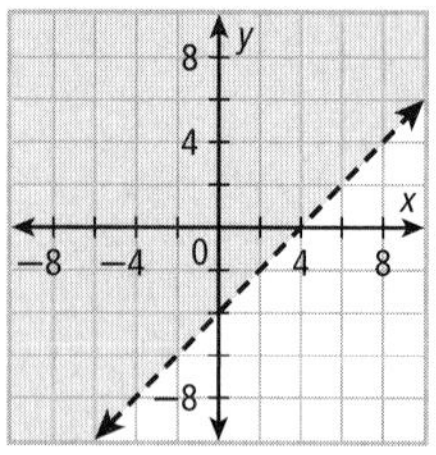

50.

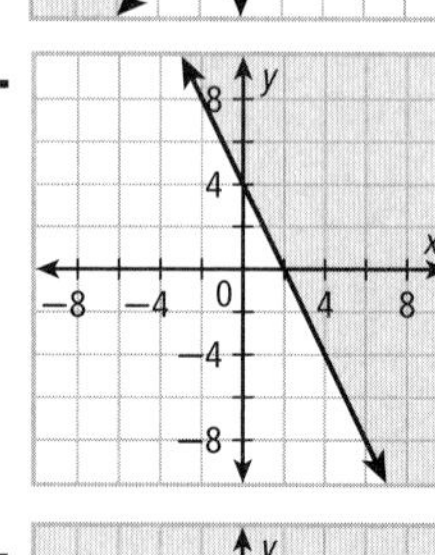

51.

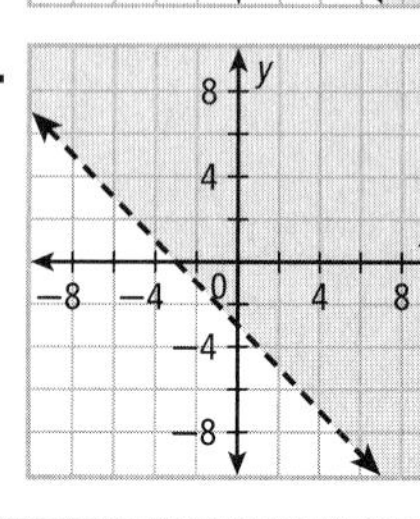

52.

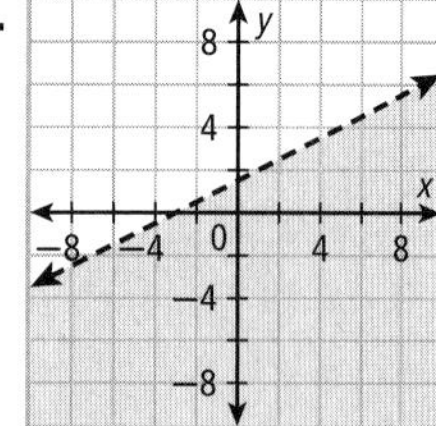

53.

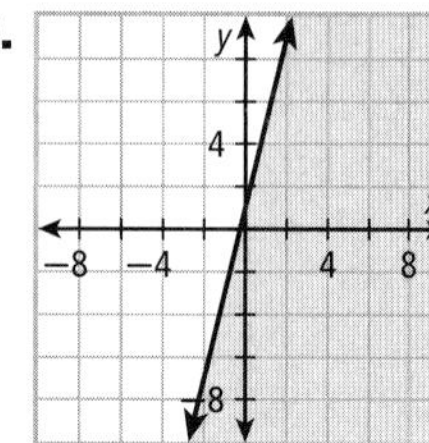

62.

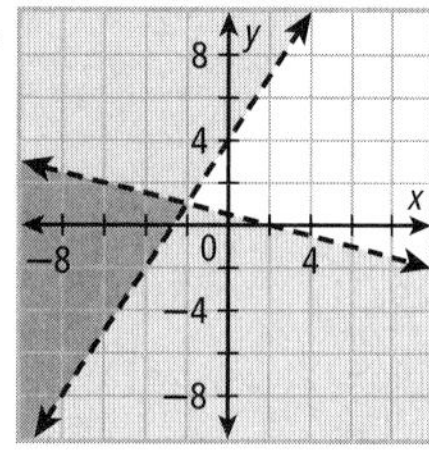

solutions: (−10, 0) and (−12, 1); not solutions: (0, 0) and (6, −2)

63.

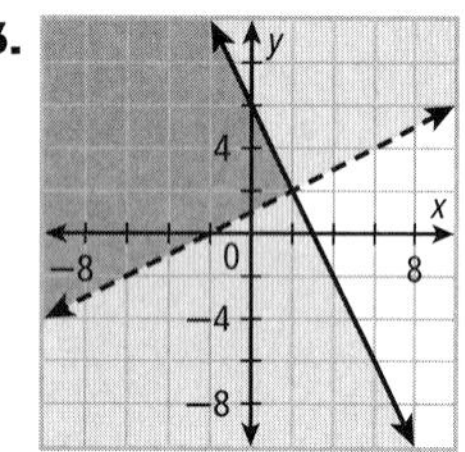

solutions: (−2, 6) and (0, 2); not solutions: (8, 0) and (0, 8)

64.

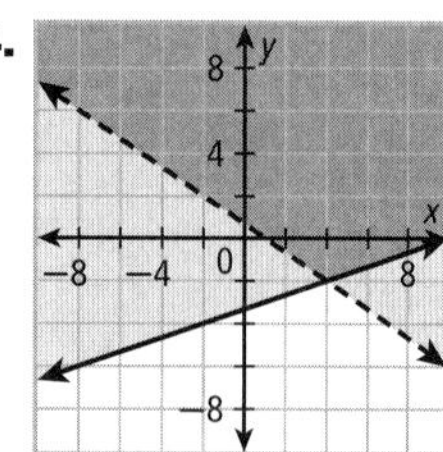

solutions: (4, 0) and (2, 2); not solutions: (−2, 0) and (6, −6)

65.

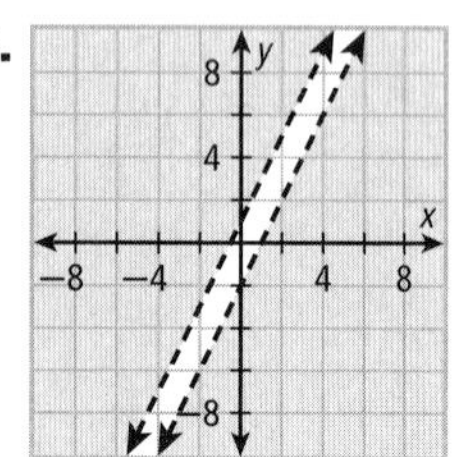

66.

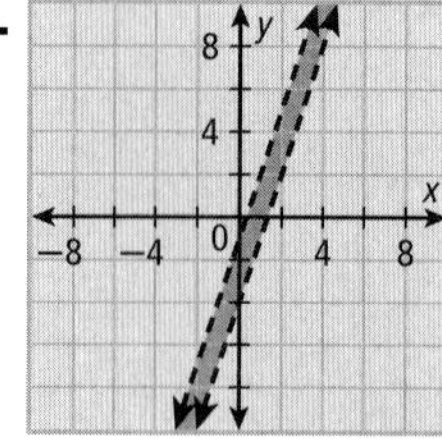

67.

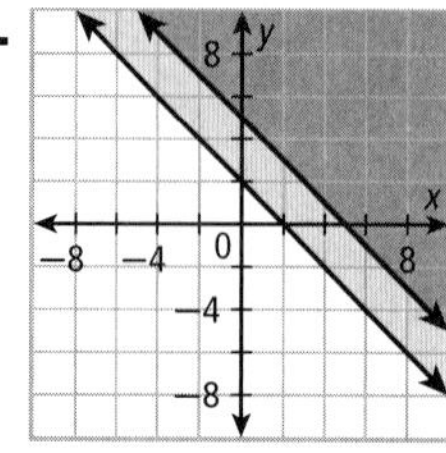

68.

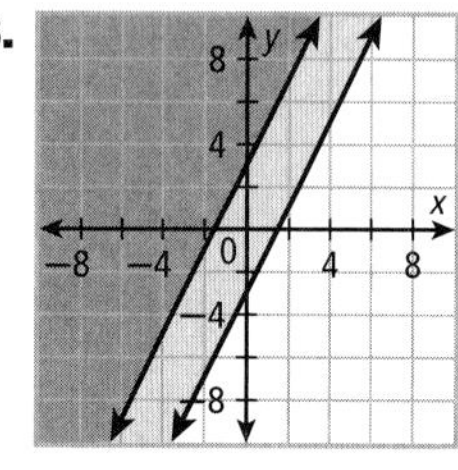

69.

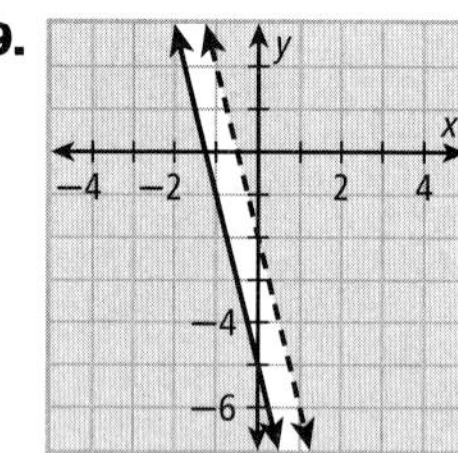

70.

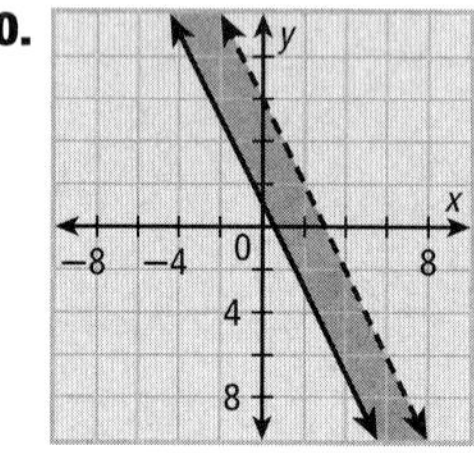

Chapter 7

78. $-\frac{1}{3}t^5 + \frac{1}{2}t^3 + t + 4; -\frac{1}{3}$

90. $6a^{11}$

91. $-6x^3y^4z^5$

92. $-8k^3\ell^3m^3$

93. $6j^3k^2 + 3jk^3$

94. $8q^4r^4 + 12q^4r^2$

95. $6x^3y^3 - 9xy^3$

96. $x^2 - 2x - 3$

97. $x^2 - 5x + 6$

98. $3x^4y + 6x^3y^2 - 2x^2 - 4xy$

99. $2x^3y - 9x^2y + 9xy$

100. $x^3 + x^2 - 10x + 8$

101. $-4x^3 - 4x^2 + 11x - 4$

102. $2x^5 + 6x^4 - 3x^3 - 9x^2 - 5x - 15$

103. $6a^3 + 5a^2b - 5ab^2 - 2b^3$

104. $3a^4 - 2a^3b - 3a^2b + 3a^2b^2 + 2ab^2 - 3b^3$

Chapter 8

27. $(3 + 4a)(a + 3)$

28. $(5 - 2k)(k - 4)$

29. $(5 + 4c^2)(c - 3)$

30. $(3 + t)(t - 4)$

31. $(5 - s)(2r - 1)$

32. $(7 - 2e)(3d + 4)$

33. $(x + 3)(x^2 - 2)$

34. $(2m - 3)(m^2 + 4)$

35. $(3k - 1)(k^2 + 5)$

36. $(3r + 5)(5r^2 - 2)$

37. $(2n - 1)(6n^2 - 5)$

38. $(4z - 3)(z^2 + 1)$

39. $(2k - 3)(k - 4)$

40. $(3p - 2)(p - 4)$

41. $(5d - 3)(2d - 3)$

42. $(3a - 2)(2a^2 - 5)$

43. $(6s - 1)(2s^2 - 3)$

44. $(4c - 3)(c^2 - 5)$

45. $(x + 3)(x + 12)$

46. $(x + 5)(x + 8)$

47. $(x + 2)(x + 8)$

48. $(x - 3)(x - 6)$

49. $(x - 4)(x - 7)$

50. $(x - 6)(x - 7)$

51. $(x - 3)(x + 7)$

52. $(x + 4)(x - 9)$

53. $(x + 3)(x - 10)$

54.

c	$c^2 - 2c - 48$	$(c - 8) \cdot (c + 6)$
0	−48	−48
1	−49	−49
2	−48	−48
3	−45	−45
4	−40	−40

58. $(2x + 3)(x + 5)$

59. $(x + 2)(3x + 8)$

60. $(4x - 2)(2x - 3)$

61. $(2x + 1)(3x + 4)$

62. $(3x - 2)(x - 3)$

63. $(5x - 3)(2x - 5)$

64. $(3x - 4)(2x + 1)$

65. $(4x + 3)(2x - 5)$

66. $(x - 2)(4x - 3)$

67. $(3x - 1)(4x - 3)$

68. $(6x + 5)(x - 2)$

69. $(2x + 3)(3x - 1)$

70. $(2x - 3)(x + 4)$

71. $(3x + 2)(2x - 3)$

72. $(4x - 1)(2x + 3)$

73. $(5x + 2)(2x - 3)$

74. $(4x - 5)(x + 1)$

75. $(3x + 4)(2x - 5)$

76. $-1(2x - 1)(x - 5)$

77. $-1(3x - 4)(2x + 3)$

78. $-1(4x + 3)(2x + 1)$

79. $-1(2x - 5)(2x - 3)$

80. $-1(5x + 2)(2x - 5)$

81. $-1(3x - 7)(x - 2)$

82. $(x - 4)^2$

83. $(2x - 1)^2$

84. no; $-8x \neq 2(x \cdot 3)$

85. no; $-14x \neq 2(3x \cdot 2)$

86. $(2x + 3)^2$

87. No; -16 is not a perfect square.

88. $(3x - 7)^2$

89. no; $18x \neq 2(2x \cdot 5)$

90. $(4x - 3)^2$

91. $(2 - 4x^2)(2 + 4x^2)$

92. No; 35 is not a perfect square.

93. $(c - 5)(c + 5)$

94. No; g^5 is not a perfect square.

95. $(v^2 - 8)(v^2 + 8)$

96. No; 120 is not a perfect square.

112. $12b(b - 2)(b + 2)$

113. $4w^2(3w - 4)(2w + 1)$

114. $2k(3k + 4)(3k - 4)$

115. $a(4a - b)(a + 3)$

116. $3xy(x - y)^2$

117. $4q(3p - 4q)(3p + 4q)$

118. $8a^2(2a - 1)(2a + 1)$

119. $m(m + 2n)(m + 3n)$

120. $x(x + 32)$

121. $3(2d - 1)(3d + 2)$

122. $(2r + 3)(r - 6)$

123. $4(2y - 1)(y + 1)$

124. $9(3 - 2u)(3 + 2u)$

125. $4(2x^2 + 5)(x + 1)(x - 1)$

126. $5j(2j + 7)(j - 2)$

127. $3z(3z - 1)^2$

128. $2(2b + 9)(b - 4)$

129. $3(f + g)(f - g)$

Chapter 9

7.

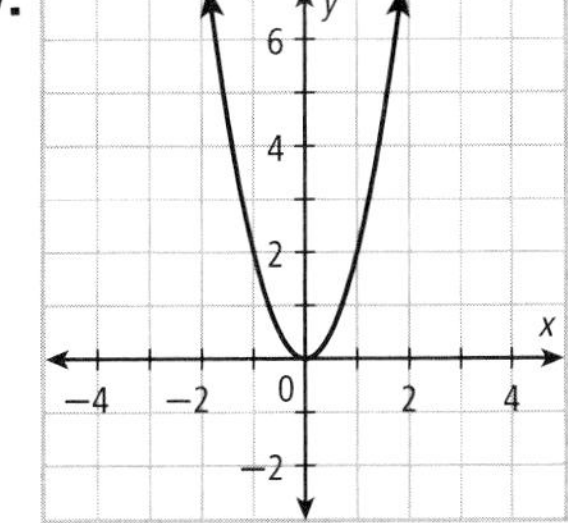

8.

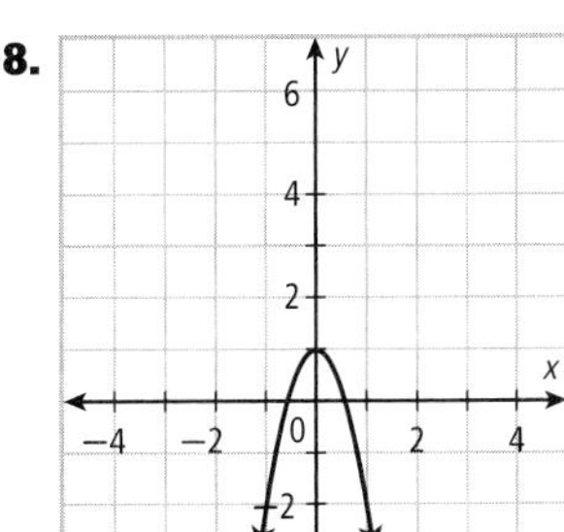

9.

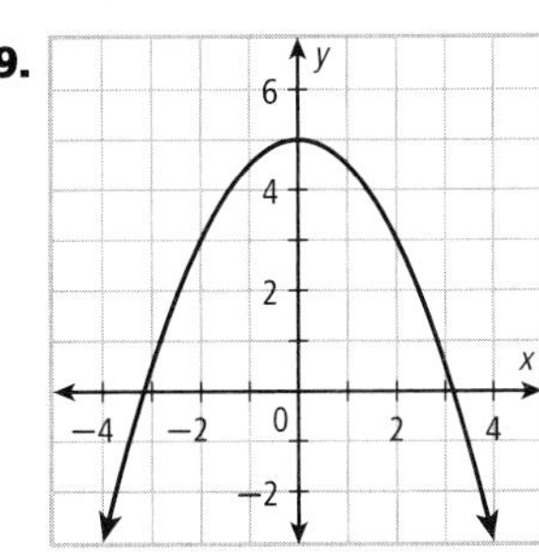

10.

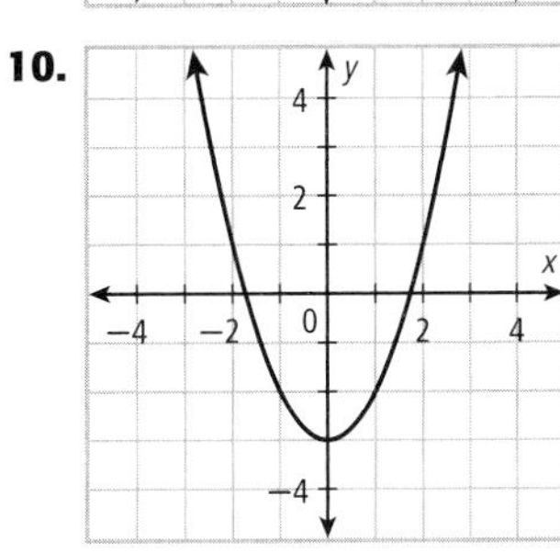

24.

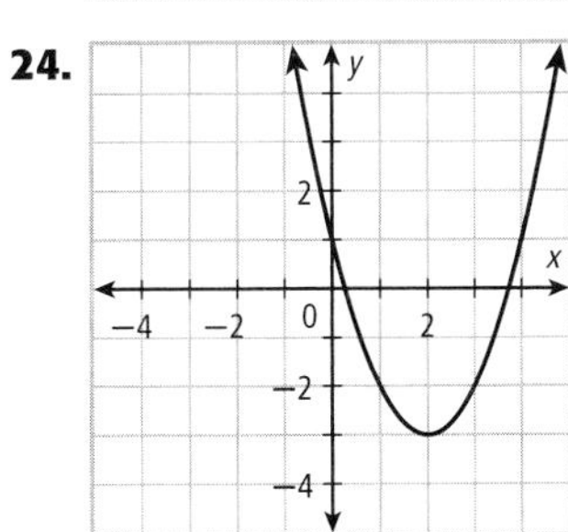

25.

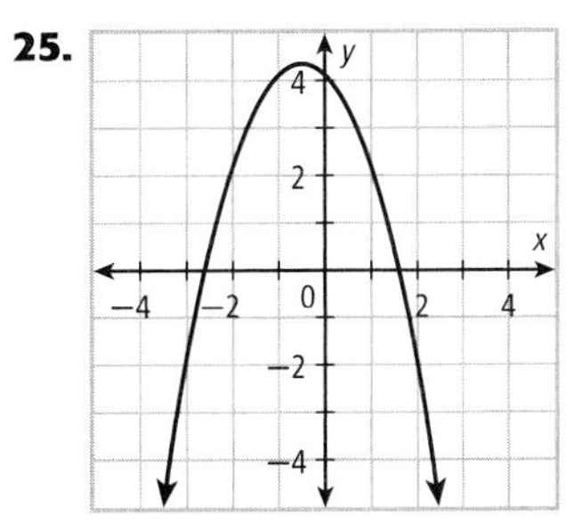

26.

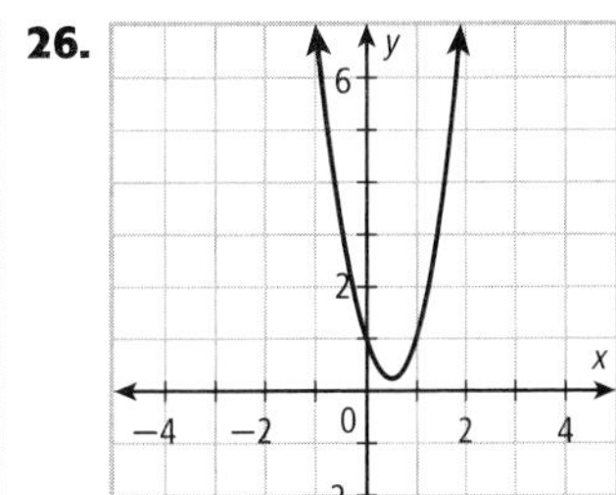

27.

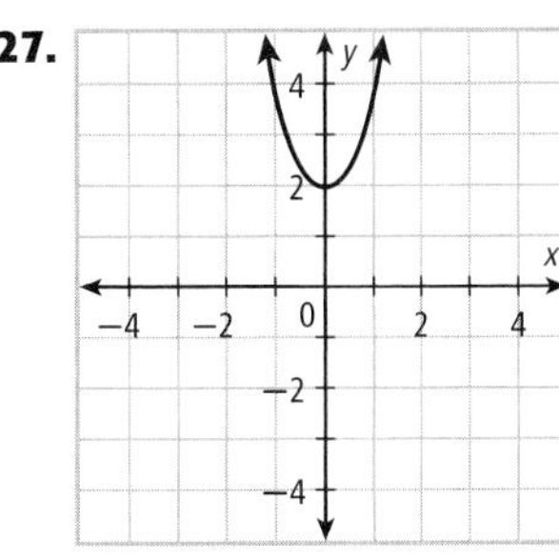

28.

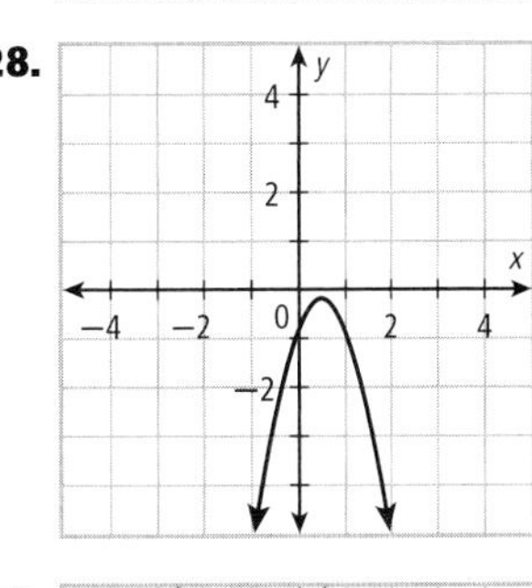

29.

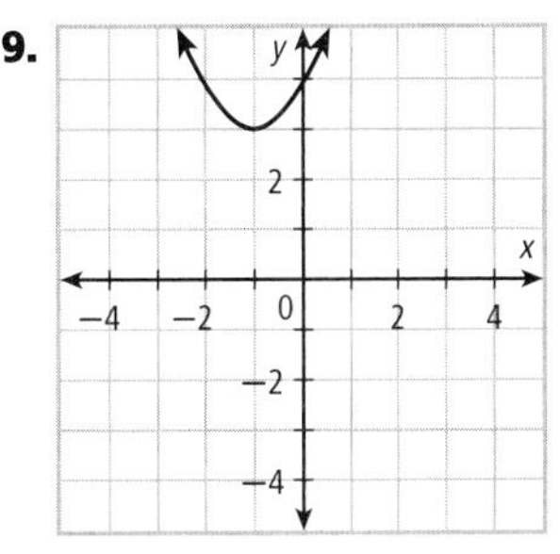

Chapter 10

4. yes; xy equals $\frac{10}{3}$.

5. no; the product xy is not constant.

6. yes; xy equals $-\frac{1}{6}$.

7.

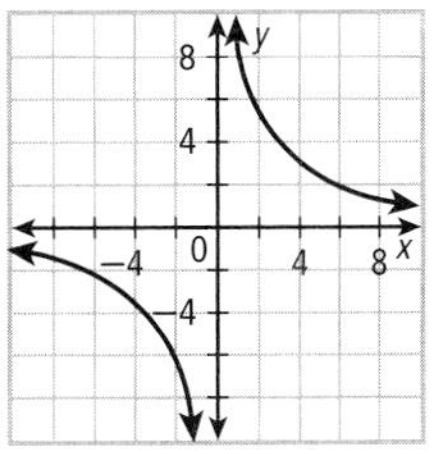

8.

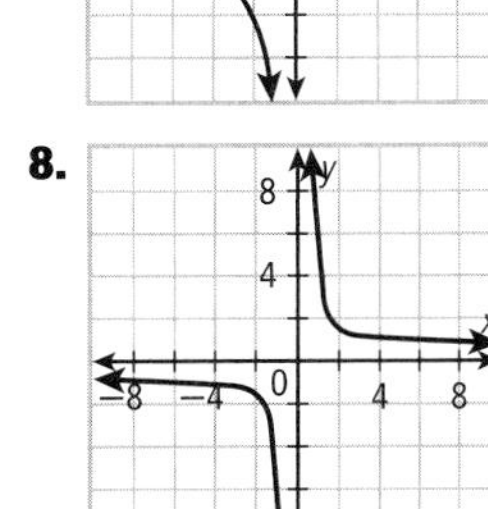

19.

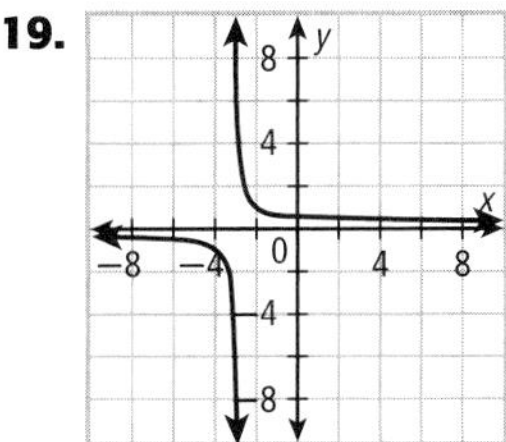

20.

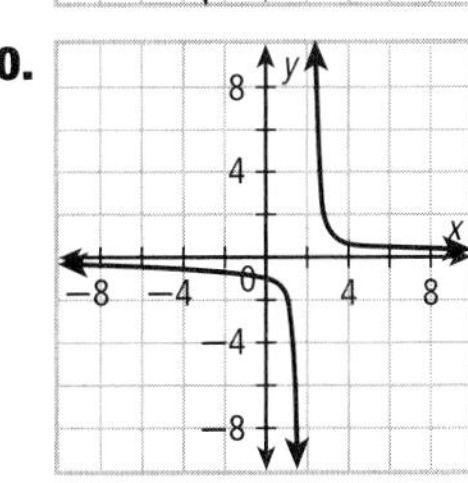

21.

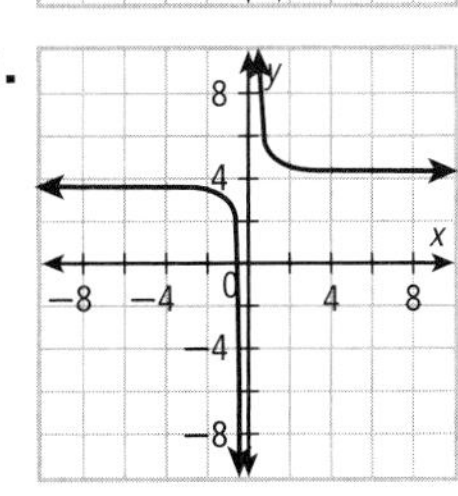

22.

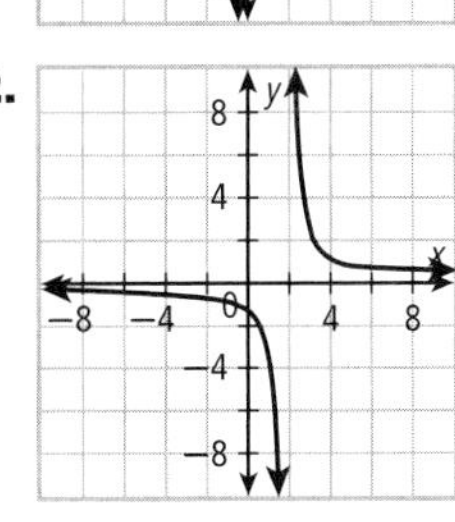

23.

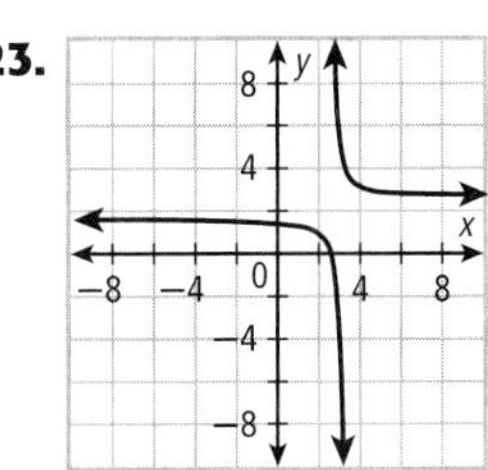

24.

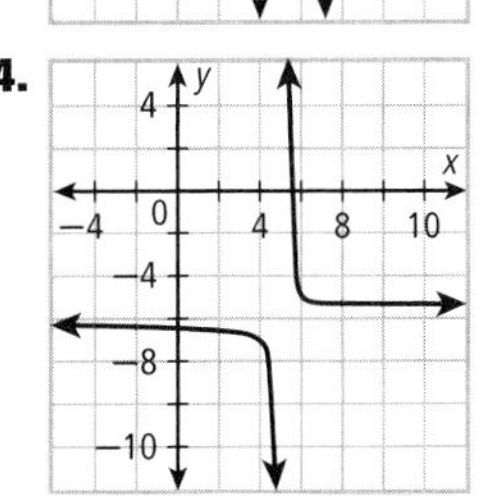

25.

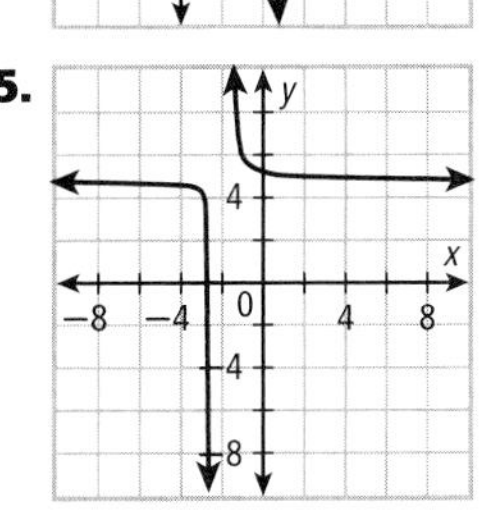

26.

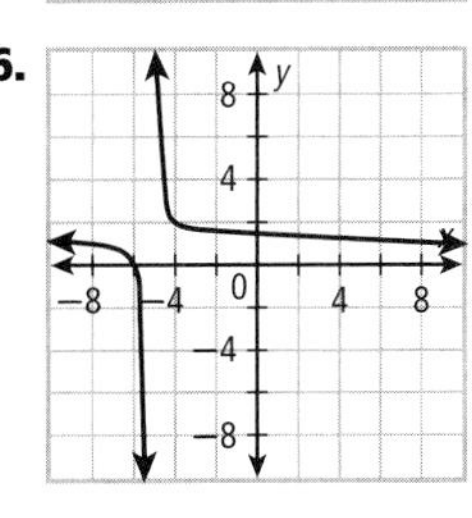

53. $\frac{3x(x + 6)}{4}$

54. $\frac{4}{3r}$

55. $a + 1$

56. $\frac{b + 1}{2}$

57. $\frac{3}{q}$

58. $\frac{r + 3}{2(r - 4)}$

74. $3y^3 - 4 + \frac{1}{y}$

75. $m^2 - \frac{3}{m} + \frac{1}{2m^2}$

76. $-4x - 5 + \frac{1}{x^2}$

80. $a - 6$

81. $2x + 2$

82. $3y - 5$

83. $3x + 4 + \frac{1}{x - 2}$

84. $2x - 4 + \frac{3}{x + 3}$

85. $5x^2 + 12x + 24 + \frac{44}{x - 2}$

Chapter 11

7. 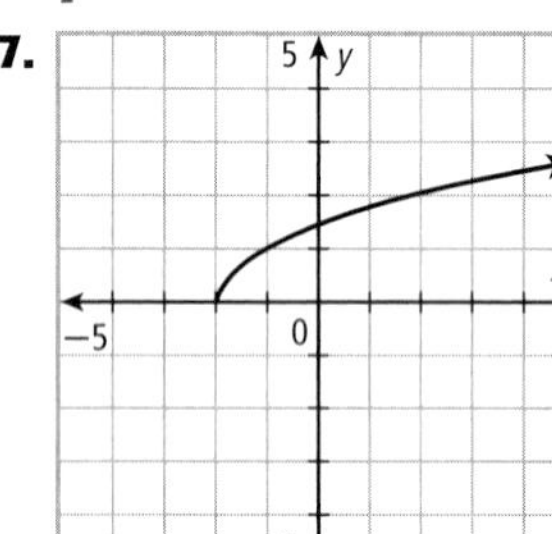

8. 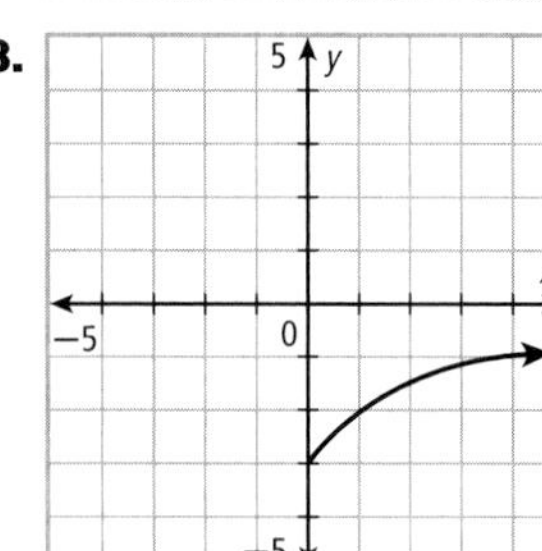

9. 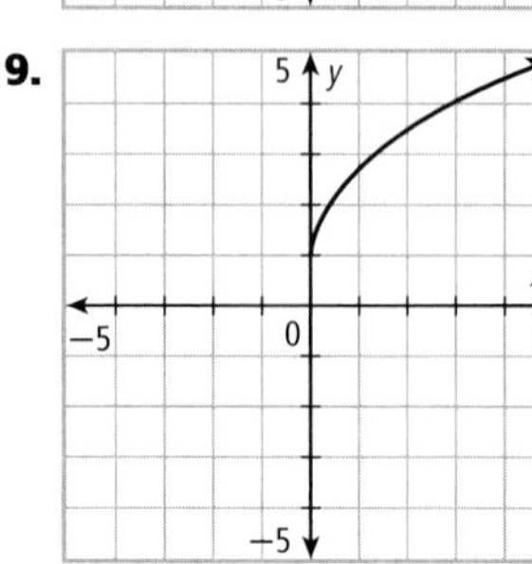

10. 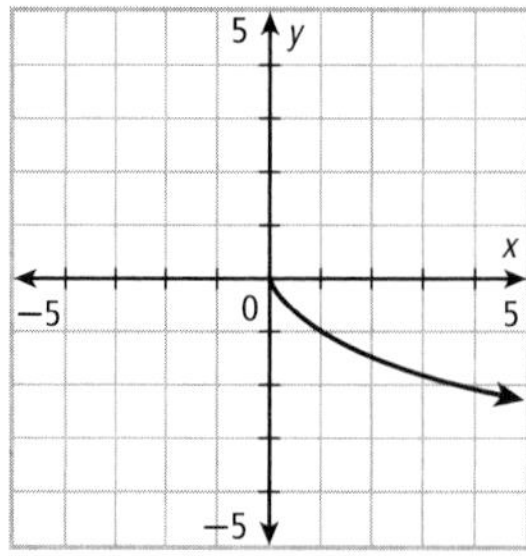

11. 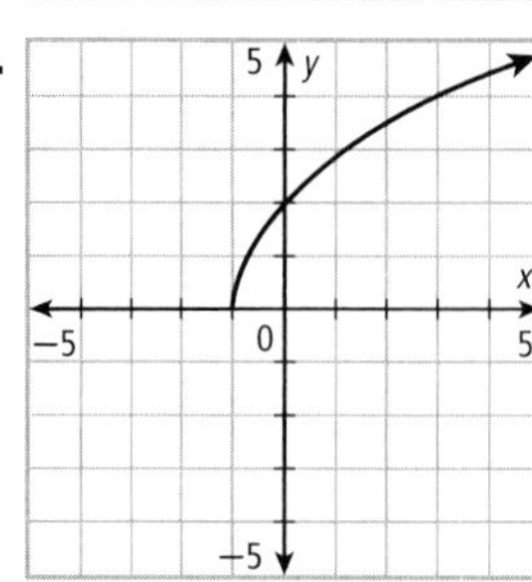

12. 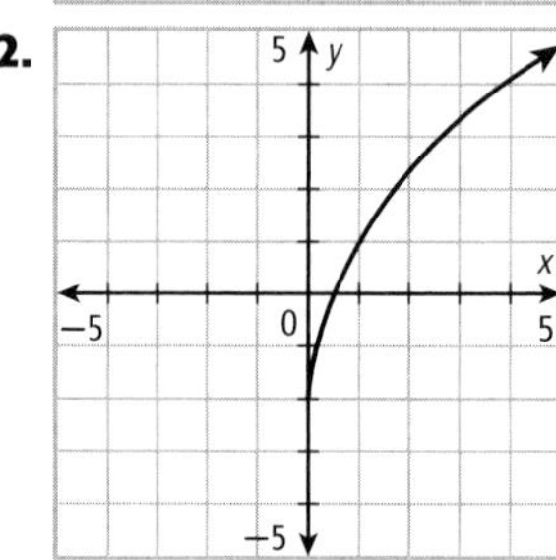

70. 625; 3,125; 15,625

71. 46, 23, 11.5

72. −162, 486, −1,458

78. Yes; as the *x*-values increase by a constant amount, the *y*-values are multiplied by a constant amount.

79. No; as the *x*-values increase by a constant amount, the *y*-values are not multiplied by a constant amount.

80. Yes; as the *x*-values increase by a constant amount, the *y*-values are multiplied by a constant amount.

81. No; as the *x*-values increase by a constant amount, the *y*-values are not multiplied by a constant amount.

82. 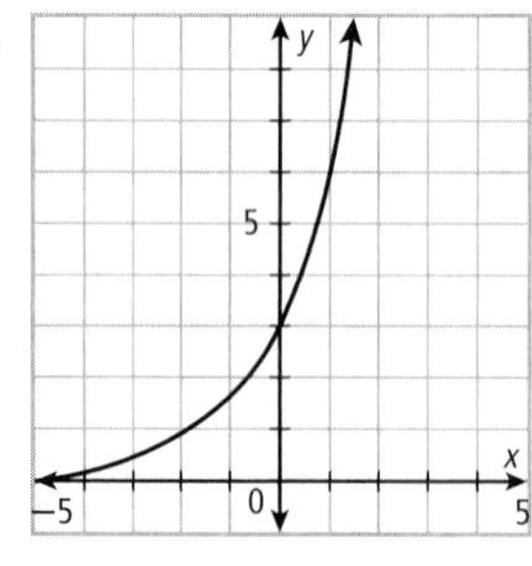

83. 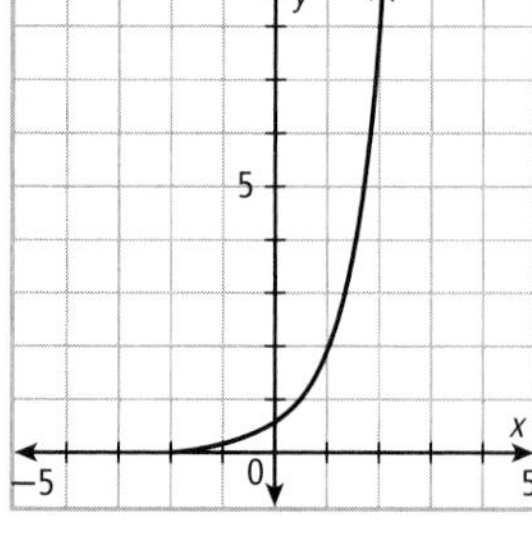

84. 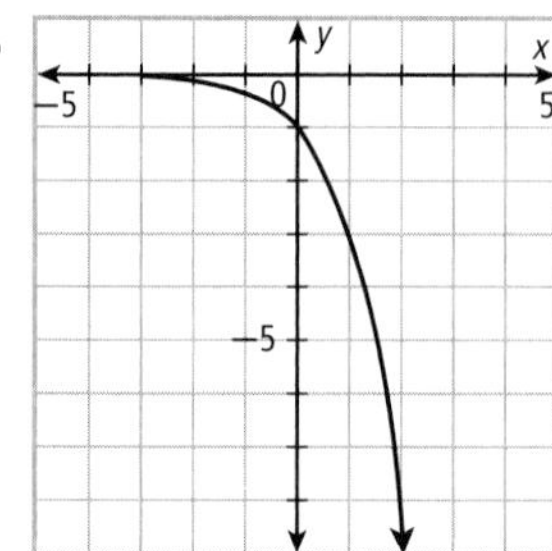

85. 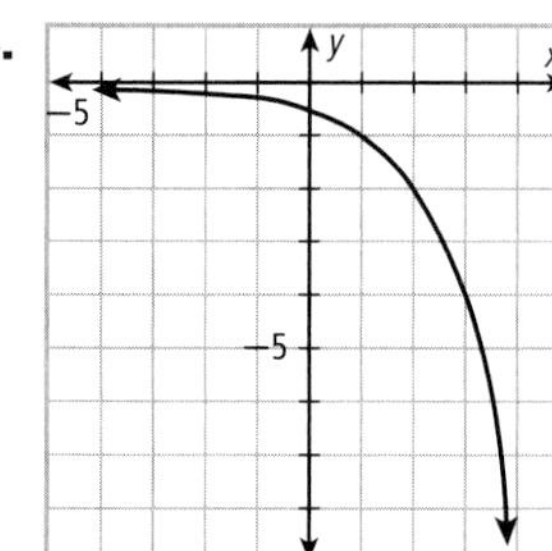

86. 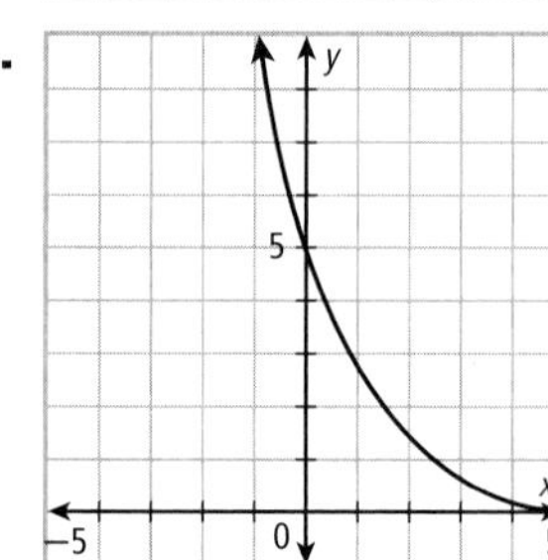

87. 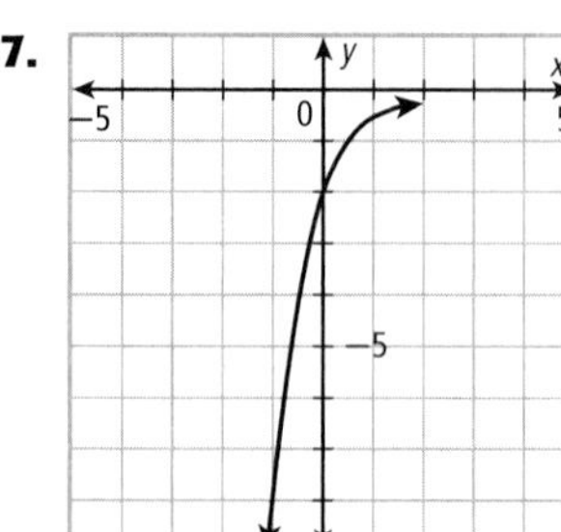

92. $y = 800(0.94)^t$; \$587.12

93. $y = 14{,}000(0.98)^t$; 11,439

94. 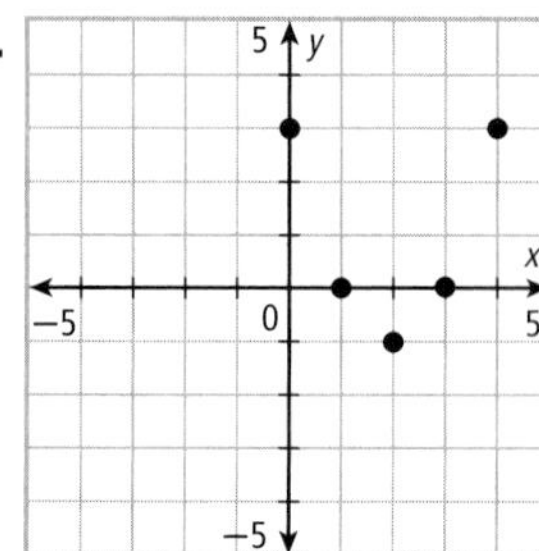

95.

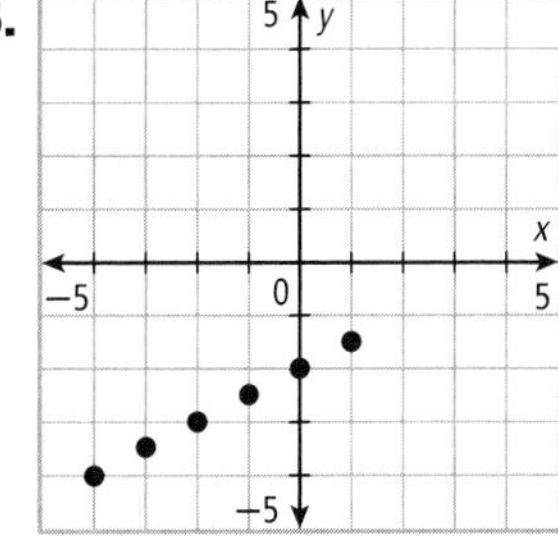

96.

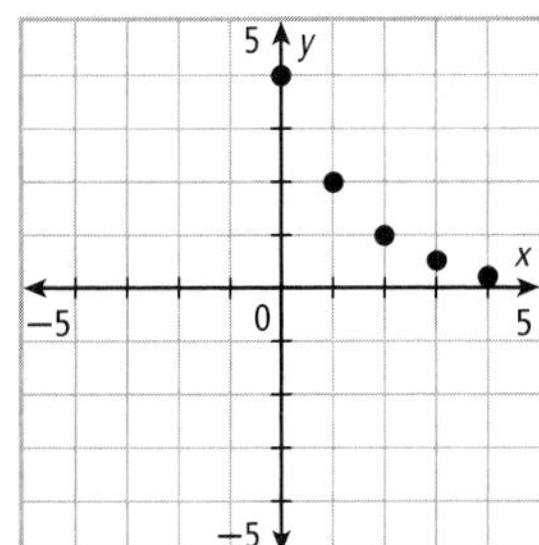

Extra Practice Applications

Chapter 3

1. Let x represent the weight of a box in ounces; $0 < x \geq 15$

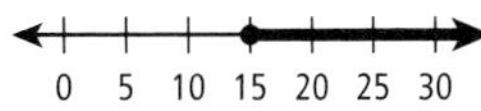

2. Let x be the age of a visitor to the museum; $0 < x < 13$

3. $96 + x \leq 102$; 0, 1, 2, 3, 4, 5, or 6 additional customers could be seated.

4. $63 + x \geq 74$; the wind speed must be at least 11 mi/h greater.

11. $34 \leq x \leq 40$

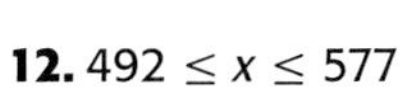

12. $492 \leq x \leq 577$

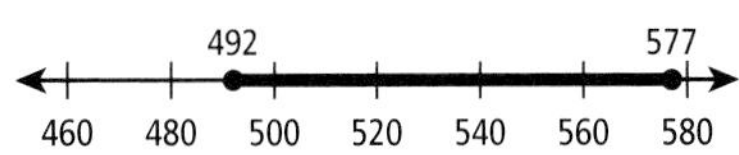

Chapter 4

1. continuous

Speed of Donnell's Car

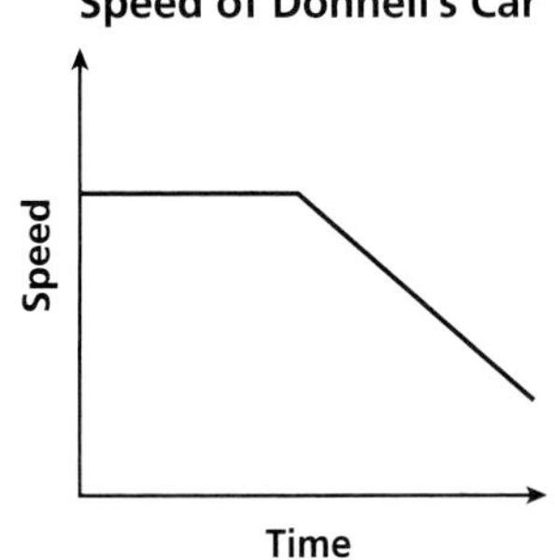

2. discrete

Bottles of Mineral Water

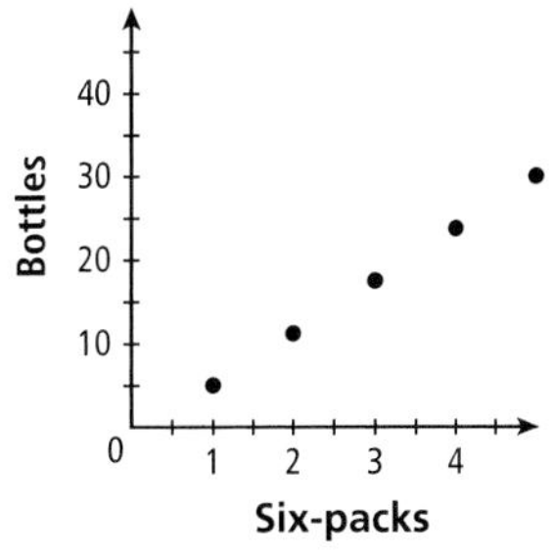

3a.

x	y
20	200
30	190
35	185
40	180

b. Yes; each domain value is paired with only one range value.

4. No; one of the domain values (93) is paired with more than one range value.

7. 15.75 mi

Turtle's Walking Speed

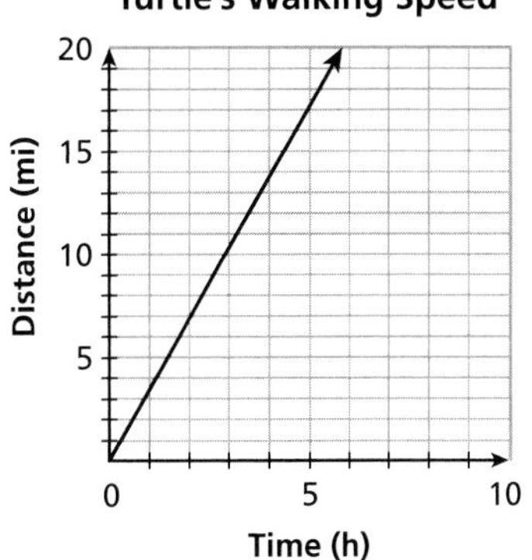

8. 12.8 m

Kangerdlugssuaq Glacier

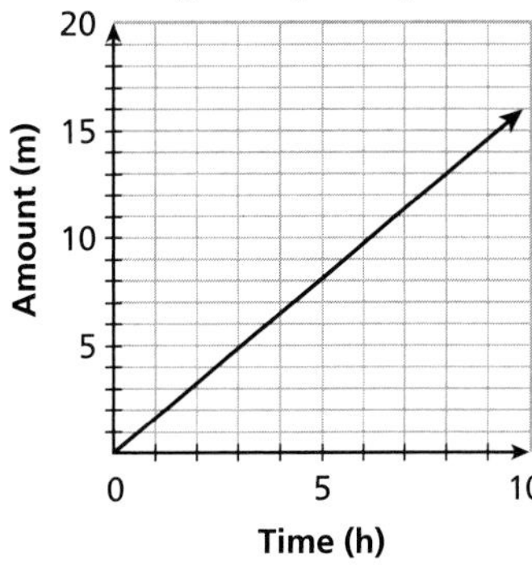

Chapter 5

1. D: {0, 1, 2, 3, ...};
R: {\$0, \$1.50, \$3.00, \$4.50, ...}

Cost of Prints

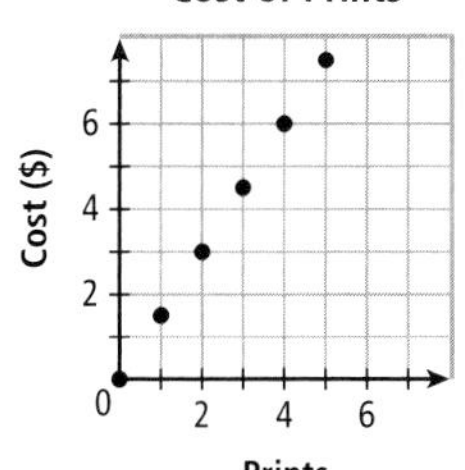

2. D: {0, 1, 2, 3, ...};
R: {\$40, \$55, \$70, \$85, ...}

Jury Duty Pay

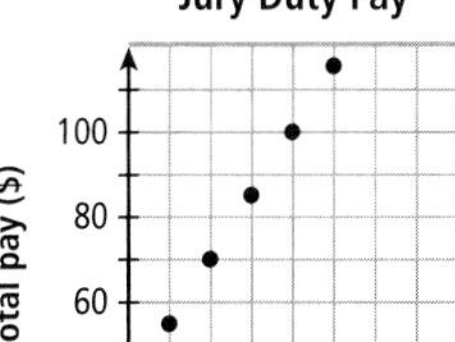

3a. Chang Family Trip

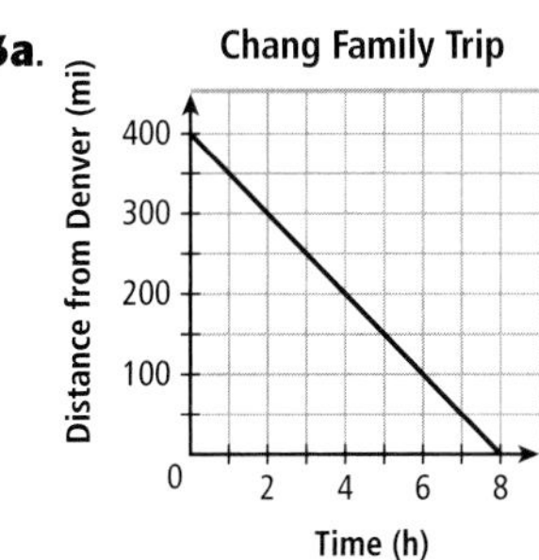

b. y-intercept: 400; this is the starting distance from Denver. x-intercept: 8; this is the time required to reach Denver (8 h).

6. −4; the oven cools at a rate of 4°F per minute.

7. $y = 9x$

Speed of a Race-Walker

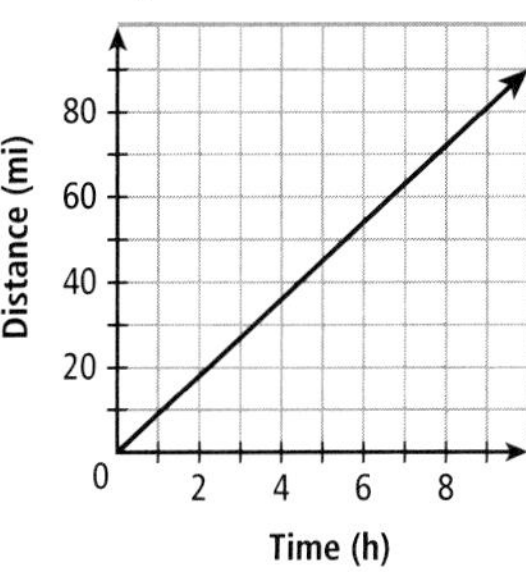

8b. The y-intercept is 10. This is the cost for 0 hours, or the initial rental fee. The slope is 1.5. This is the rate of change of the cost: \$1.50 per hour.

10. slope of $\overline{AB}$ = slope of $\overline{DC} = -2$; slope of $\overline{AD}$ = slope of $\overline{BC} = \frac{1}{2}$. Therefore, $\overline{AB} \perp \overline{BC}$, $\overline{BC} \perp \overline{DC}$, $\overline{DC} \perp \overline{AD}$, and $\overline{AD} \perp \overline{AB}$, so the figure has four right angles and is a rectangle.

Chapter 6

4. The company with the \$200 setup fee is cheaper if more than 14 jerseys are purchased.

7. No; Shanna's time is given by $y = 190 - 8x$, and Maria's time is given by $y = 175 - 8x$, where x is the number of years after 2003. The graphs are two parallel lines. There is no solution to the system of equations, so the two times will never be equal.

8. Yes; Jordan's distance is given by $y = 10x + 4$, and Tim's distance is given by $y = 12x$, where x is the number of hours since Tim left the house. This is a consistent and independent system, so there is a solution. Tim will catch up to Jordan in 2 hours.

11. $4x + 5y \leq 18$, where x is the number of pounds of almonds and y is the number of pounds of cashews; Possible combinations: 2 pounds of almonds, 2 pounds of cashews; 3 pounds of almonds, 1 pound of cashews

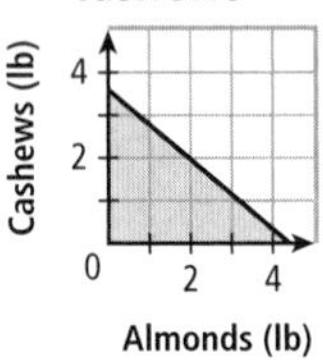

12. $5x + 8y < 100$, where x is the number of child shirts and y is the number of adult shirts; Possible combinations: 16 child shirts, 2 adult shirts; 8 child shirts, 6 adult shirts

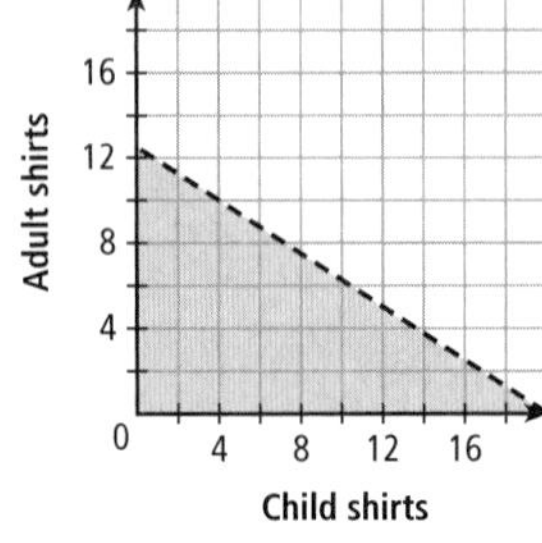

13. Possible combinations: 3 lb of beef cubes, 2 lb of liver cubes; 2 lb of beef cubes, 3 lb of liver cubes

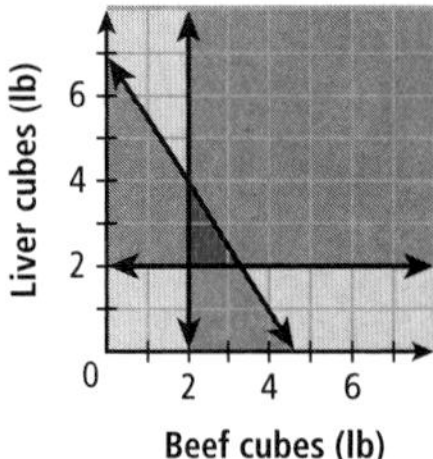

14. Possible combinations: length: 5 in., width: 5 in.; length: 6 in., width: 4 in.

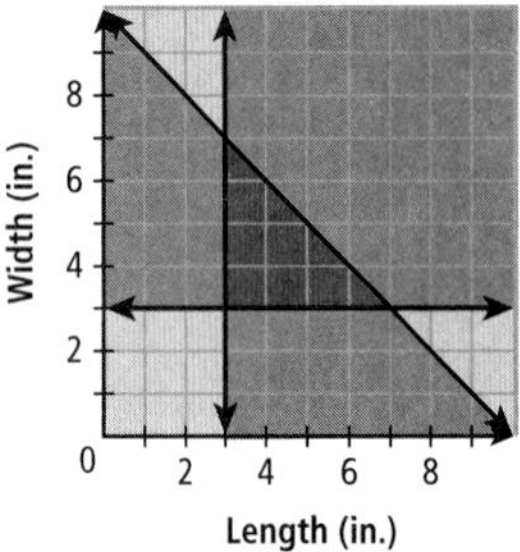

Chapter 8

11. $3x - 4$; no; the length of the sides cannot be negative.

Chapter 9

12. No; if the coin reached a height of 8 ft, there would be a real solution to the equation $-16t^2 + 12t + 4 = 8$ or $-16t^2 + 12t - 4 = 0$. The discriminant is $b^2 - 4ac = 12^2 - 4(-16)(-4) = 144 - 256 = -112$.

Since the discriminant is negative, the equation has no real solutions.

Chapter 10

1. D: $0 < x < 200$; R: $1 < y < 200$; 3 min

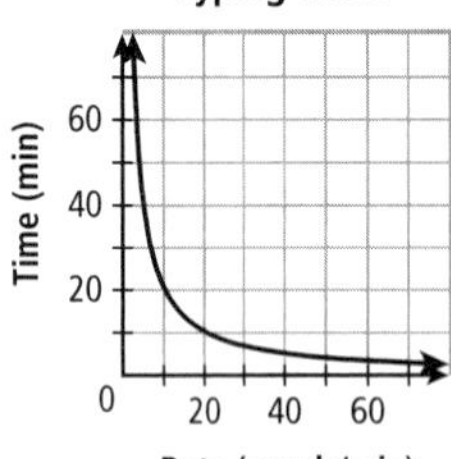

3. D: $x > 0$; R: whole numbers $y > 3$

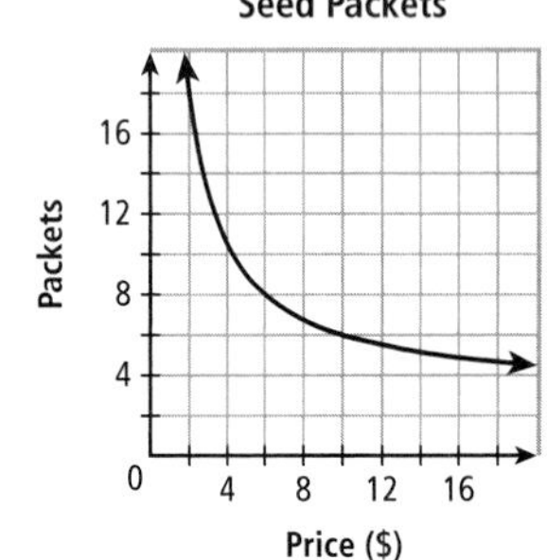

4. D: $x \geq 0$; R: $0 < y \leq 100$

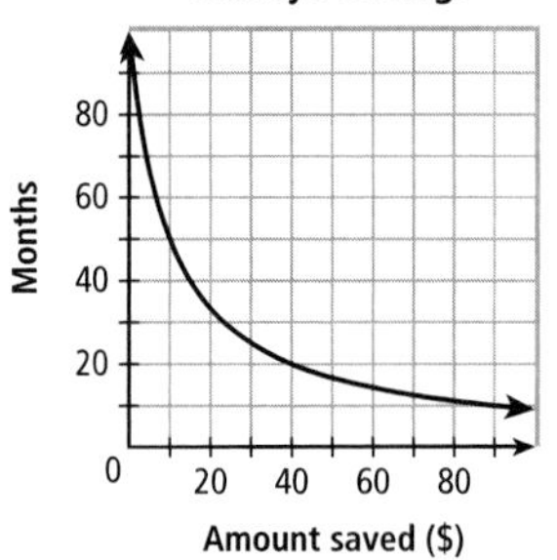

7. $\dfrac{x(x-1)}{2(2x+5)(x+2)}$, where x is the number of men; $\frac{15}{136}$

Chapter 11

11. The stock price increases by 10% per year; $y = 10(1.1)^x$; \$19.49

Skills Bank

Times Tables

1. 32; $4 \cdot 8 = 32$; $8 \cdot 4 = 32$; $32 \div 8 = 4$; $32 \div 4 = 8$

2. 60; $5 \cdot 12 = 60$; $12 \cdot 5 = 60$; $60 \div 12 = 5$; $60 \div 5 = 12$

3. 33; $3 \cdot 11 = 33$; $11 \cdot 3 = 33$; $33 \div 11 = 3$; $33 \div 3 = 11$

4. 56; $8 \cdot 7 = 56$; $7 \cdot 8 = 56$; $56 \div 7 = 8$; $56 \div 8 = 7$

5. 54; $9 \cdot 6 = 54$; $6 \cdot 9 = 54$; $54 \div 6 = 9$; $54 \div 9 = 6$

6. 144; $12 \cdot 12 = 144$; $144 \div 12 = 12$

Cubic Functions

1.

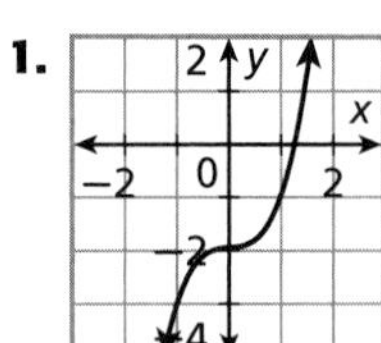

2.

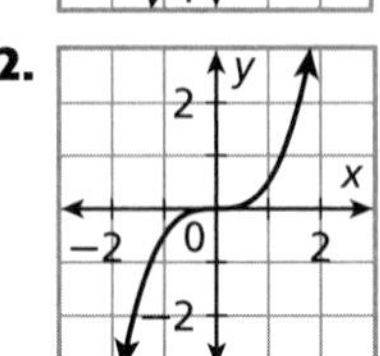

3.

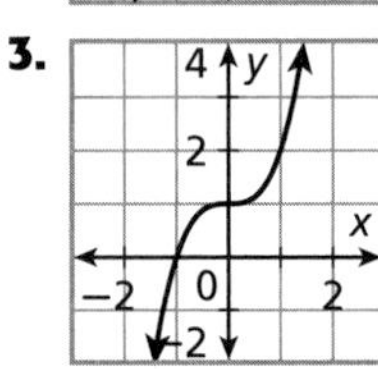

4.

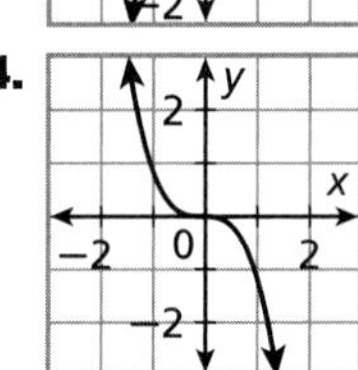

Bias

1. Someone may not understand what his or her answer really means because the question was worded in a confusing way.
2. The track team would want the money to benefit their own team, not others. Athletes on other teams did not have a chance to answer.

Bar Graphs and Histograms

1. **Damien's Math Test Scores**

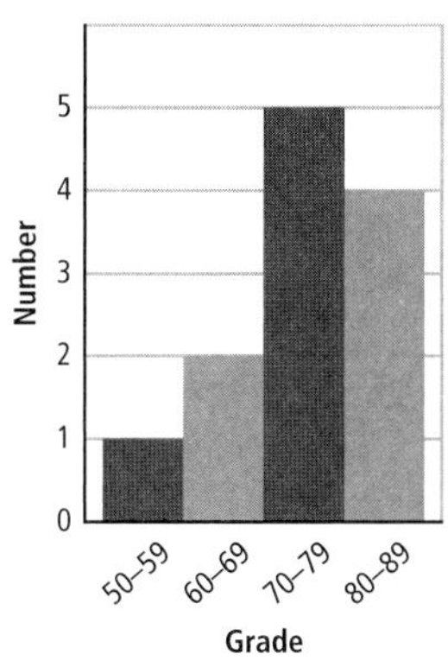

Box-and-Whisker Plots

1.

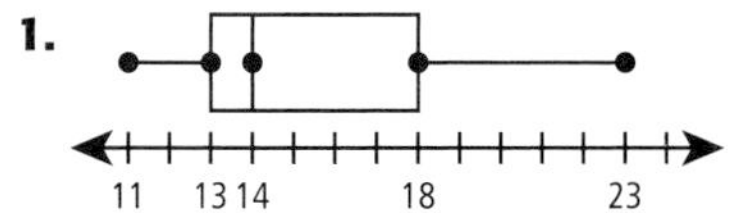

Notes

Glossary/Glosario

ENGLISH	SPANISH	EXAMPLES
absolute value (p. 14) The absolute value of x is the distance from zero to x on the number line, denoted $\lvert x \rvert$. $\lvert x \rvert = \begin{cases} x & \text{if } x \geq 0 \\ -x & \text{if } x < 0 \end{cases}$	**valor absoluto** El valor absoluto de x es la distancia de cero a x en la recta numérica, y se expresa $\lvert x \rvert$. $\lvert x \rvert = \begin{cases} x & \text{si } x \geq 0 \\ -x & \text{si } x < 0 \end{cases}$	$\lvert 3 \rvert = 3$ $\lvert -3 \rvert = 3$
absolute-value equation (p. 114) An equation that contains a variable within an absolute value.	**ecuación de valor absoluto** Ecuación que contiene una variable dentro de un valor absoluto.	$\lvert x + 4 \rvert = 7$
absolute-value inequality (p. 178) An inequality that contains a variable within an absolute value.	**desigualdad de valor absoluto** Desigualdad que contiene una variable dentro de un valor absoluto.	$\lvert x + 4 \rvert > 7$
acute angle (p. SB63) An angle that measures greater than 0° and less than 90°.	**ángulo agudo** Ángulo que mide más de 0° y menos de 90°.	
acute triangle (p. SB18) A triangle with three acute angles.	**triángulo acutángulo** Triángulo con tres ángulos agudos.	
Addition Property of Equality (p. 72) For real numbers a, b, and c, if $a = b$, then $a + c = b + c$.	**Propiedad de igualdad de la suma** Dados los números reales a, b y c, si $a = b$, entonces $a + c = b + c$.	$\begin{array}{r} x - 6 = 8 \\ \underline{+6 \quad +6} \\ x \quad = 14 \end{array}$
Addition Property of Inequality (p. 142) For real numbers a, b, and c, if $a < b$, then $a + c < b + c$. Also holds true for $>$, $\leq$, $\geq$, and $\neq$.	**Propiedad de desigualdad de la suma** Dados los números reales a, b y c, si $a < b$, entonces $a + c < b + c$. Es válido también para $>$, $\leq$, $\geq$ y $\neq$.	$\begin{array}{r} x - 6 < 8 \\ \underline{+6 \quad +6} \\ x \quad < 14 \end{array}$
additive inverse (p. 15) The opposite of a number. Two numbers are additive inverses if their sum is zero. *See also* opposite.	**inverso aditivo** El opuesto de un número. Dos números son inversos aditivos si su suma es cero. *Ver tambien* opuesto.	The additive inverse of 5 is −5. The additive inverse of −5 is 5.
algebraic expression (p. 6) An expression that contains at least one variable.	**expresión algebraica** Expresión que contiene por lo menos una variable.	$2x + 3y$ $4x$
algebraic order of operations *See* order of operations.	**orden algebraico de las operaciones** *Ver* orden de las operaciones.	
AND (p. 170) A logical operator representing the intersection of two sets.	**Y** Operador lógico que representa la intersección de dos conjuntos.	$A = \{2, 3, 4, 5\}$ $B = \{1, 3, 5, 7\}$ The set of values that are in A AND B is $A \cap B = \{3, 5\}$.

Glossary/Glosario **G1**

ENGLISH	SPANISH	EXAMPLES
angle (p. SB14) A figure formed by two rays with a common endpoint.	**ángulo** Figura formada por dos rayos con un extremo común.	A
area (p. SB16) The number of nonoverlapping unit squares of a given size that will exactly cover the interior of a plane figure.	**área** Cantidad de cuadrados unitarios de un determinado tamaño no superpuestos que cubren exactamente el interior de una figura plana.	5 2 The area is 10 square units.
arithmetic sequence (p. 234) A sequence whose successive terms differ by the same nonzero constant d, called the *common difference*.	**sucesión aritmética** Sucesión cuyos términos sucesivos difieren en la misma constante distinto de cero d, denominado *diferencia común*.	4, 7, 10, 13, 16, ... + 3 + 3 + 3 + 3 $d = 3$
Associative Property of Addition (p. 42) For all real numbers a, b, and c, $(a + b) + c = a + (b + c)$.	**Propiedad asociativa de la suma** Dados tres números reales cualesquiera a, b y c, $(a + b) + c = a + (b + c)$.	$(5 + 3) + 7 = 5 + (3 + 7)$
Associative Property of Multiplication (p. 42) For all real numbers a, b, and c, $(a \cdot b) \cdot c = a \cdot (b \cdot c)$.	**Propiedad asociativa de la multiplicación** Dados tres números reales cualesquiera a, b y c, $(a \cdot b) \cdot c = a \cdot (b \cdot c)$.	$(5 \cdot 3) \cdot 7 = 5 \cdot (3 \cdot 7)$
asymptote (p. 634) A line that a graph gets closer to as the value of a variable becomes extremely large or small.	**asíntota** Línea recta a la cual se aproxima una gráfica a medida que el valor de una variable se hace sumamente grande o pequeño.	y 4 asymptote x −4 0 4
average *See* mean.	**promedio** *Ver* media.	
axis of the coordinate plane (p. SB23) One of two perpendicular number lines, called the x-axis and the y-axis, used to define the location of a point in the coordinate plane.	**eje del plano cartesiano** Una de las dos rectas numéricas perpendiculares, denominadas eje x y eje y, utilizadas para definir la ubicación de un punto en el plano cartesiano.	y-axis 0 x-axis
axis of symmetry (p. 554) A line that divides a plane figure or a graph into two congruent reflected halves.	**eje de simetría** Línea que divide una figura plana o una gráfica en dos mitades reflejadas congruentes.	$x = 3$ Axis of symmetry 4 2 x 0 (3, 0) 4

G2 Glossary/Glosario

B

ENGLISH	SPANISH	EXAMPLES

bar graph (p. SB27) A graph that uses vertical or horizontal bars to display data.

gráfica de barras Gráfica con barras horizontales o verticales para mostrar datos.

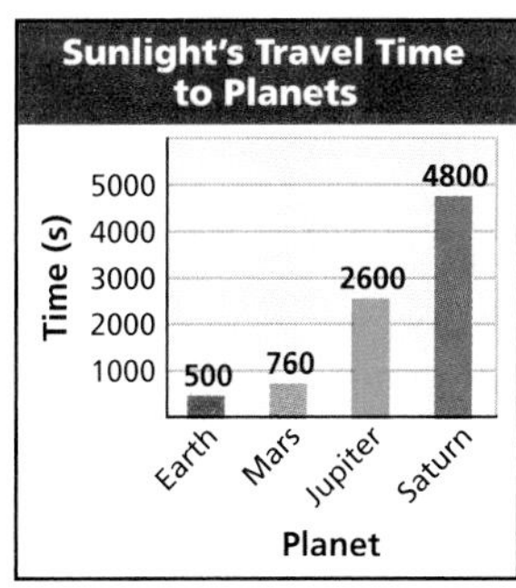

base of an exponential function (p. 738) The value of b in a function of the form $f(x) = ab^x$, where a and b are real numbers with $a \neq 0$, $b > 0$, and $b \neq 1$.

base de una función exponencial Valor de b en una función del tipo $f(x) = ab^x$, donde a y b son números reales con $a \neq 0$, $b > 0$ y $b \neq 1$.

In the function $f(x) = 5(2)^x$, the base is 2.

base of a power (p. 26) The number in a power that is used as a factor.

base de una potencia Número de una potencia que se utiliza como factor.

$3^4 = 3 \cdot 3 \cdot 3 \cdot 3 = 81$
3 is the base.

bias (p. SB26) An error that favors part of a population and/or does not accurately represent the population.

muestra no representativa Error que favorece a una parte de una población y/o no representa con exactitud a la población.

To find out about the exercise habits of average Americans, a fitness magazine surveyed its readers about how often they exercise. The population is all Americans and the sample is readers of the fitness magazine. This sample will likely be biased because readers of fitness magazines may exercise more often than other people do.

binomial (p. 431) A polynomial with two terms.

binomio Polinomio con dos términos.

$x + y$

$2a^2 + 3$

$4m^3n^2 + 6mn^4$

boundary line (p. 364) A line that divides the coordinate plane into two half-planes.

línea de límite Línea que divide el plano cartesiano en dos semiplanos.

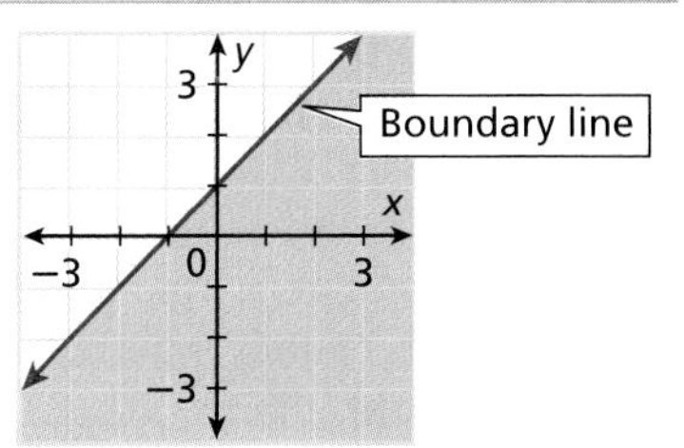

box-and-whisker plot (p. SB27) A method of showing how data is distributed by using the median, quartiles, and extreme values; also called a *box plot*.

gráfica de mediana y rango Método para mostrar la distribución de datos utilizando la mediana, los cuartiles y los valores extremos; también llamado *gráfica de caja*.

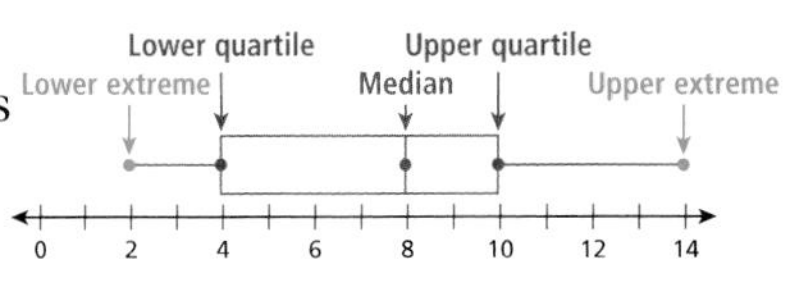

Glossary/Glosario G3

C

ENGLISH	SPANISH	EXAMPLES
Cartesian coordinate system *See* coordinate plane.	**sistema de coordenadas cartesianas** *Ver* plano cartesiano.	
center of a circle (p. SB17) The point inside a circle that is the same distance from every point on the circle.	**centro de un círculo** Punto dentro de un círculo que se encuentra a la misma distancia de todos los puntos del círculo.	*A*
circle (p. SB17) The set of points in a plane that are a fixed distance from a given point called the center of the circle.	**círculo** Conjunto de puntos en un plano que se encuentran a una distancia fija de un punto determinado denominado centro del círculo.	
circle graph (p. SB28) A way to display data by using a circle divided into non-overlapping sectors.	**gráfica circular** Forma de mostrar datos mediante un círculo dividido en sectores no superpuestos.	Residents of Mesa, AZ 65+ 13% Under 18 27% 45–64 19% 18–24 11% 25–44 30%
circumference (p. SB17) The distance around a circle.	**circunferencia** Distancia alrededor de un círculo.	Circumference
closure (p. 44) A set of numbers is said to be closed, or to have closure, under a given operation if the result of the operation on any two numbers in the set is also in the set.	**cerradura** Se dice que un conjunto de números es cerrado, o tiene cerradura, respecto de una operación determinada, si el resultado de la operación entre dos números cualesquiera del conjunto también está en el conjunto.	The set of integers is closed under addition because the sum of any two integers is also an integer. The set of whole numbers is not closed under subtraction because the difference of any two whole numbers may not be another whole number; for example, $2 - 4 = -2$.
coefficient (p. 49) A number multiplied by a variable.	**coeficiente** Número multiplicado por una variable.	In the expression $2x + 3y$, 2 is the coefficient of x and 3 is the coefficient of y.
commission (p. SB10) Money paid to a person or company for making a sale, usually a percent of the sale amount.	**comisión** Dinero que se paga a una persona o empresa por realizar una venta; generalmente se trata de un porcentaje del total de la venta.	
common difference (p. 234) In an arithmetic sequence, the nonzero constant difference of any term and the previous term.	**diferencia común** En una sucesión aritmética, diferencia constante distinta de cero entre cualquier término y el término anterior.	In the arithmetic sequence 3, 5, 7, 9, 11, …, the common difference is 2.
common factor (p. 479) A factor that is common to all terms of an expression or to two or more expressions.	**factor común** Factor que es común a todos los términos de una expresión o a dos o más expresiones.	Expression: $4x^2 + 16x^3 - 8x$ Common factor: $4x$ Expressions: 12 and 18 Common factors: 2, 3, and 6

G4 Glossary/Glosario

ENGLISH	SPANISH	EXAMPLES
common ratio (p. 732) In a geometric sequence, the constant ratio of any term and the previous term.	**razón común** En una sucesión geométrica, la razón constante entre cualquier término y el término anterior.	In the geometric sequence 32, 16, 8, 4, 2, . . ., the common ratio is $\frac{1}{2}$.
Commutative Property of Addition (p. 46) For any two real numbers a and b, $a + b = b + a$.	**Propiedad conmutativa de la suma** Dados dos números reales cualesquiera a y b, $a + b = b + a$.	$3 + 4 = 4 + 3 = 7$
Commutative Property of Multiplication (p. 46) For any two real numbers a and b, $a \cdot b = b \cdot a$.	**Propiedad conmutativa de la multiplicación** Dados dos números reales cualesquiera a y b, $a \cdot b = b \cdot a$.	$3 \cdot 4 = 4 \cdot 3 = 12$
complementary angles (p. SB14) Two angles whose measures have a sum of 90°.	**ángulos complementarios** Dos ángulos cuyas medidas suman 90°.	37° B 53° A
complement of an event (p. SB29) The set of all outcomes that are not the event.	**complemento de un suceso** El conjunto de todos los resultados que no están en el suceso.	In the experiment of rolling a number cube, the complement of rolling a 3 is rolling a 1, 2, 4, 5, or 6.
completing the square (p. 591) A process used to form a perfect-square trinomial. To complete the square of $x^2 + bx$, add $\left(\frac{b}{2}\right)^2$.	**completar el cuadrado** Proceso utilizado para formar un trinomio cuadrado perfecto. Para completar el cuadrado de $x^2 + bx$, hay que sumar $\left(\frac{b}{2}\right)^2$.	$x^2 + 6x + \square$ Add $\left(\frac{6}{2}\right)^2 = 9$. $x^2 + 6x + 9$
composite figure (p. 78) A plane figure made up of triangles, rectangles, trapezoids, circles, and other simple shapes, or a three-dimensional figure made up of prisms, cones, pyramids, cylinders, and other simple three-dimensional figures.	**figura compuesta** Figura plana compuesta por triángulos, rectángulos, trapecios, círculos y otras figuras simples, o figura tridimensional compuesta por prismas, conos, pirámides, cilindros y otras figuras tridimensionales simples.	
composite number (p. SB5) A whole number greater than 1 with more than two positive factors.	**número compuesto** Número cabal mayor que 1 que tiene más de dos factores positivos.	4, 6, 8, and 9 are composite numbers.
compound event (p. SB32) An event made up of two or more simple events.	**suceso compuesto** Suceso formado por dos o más sucesos simples.	In the experiment of tossing a coin and rolling a number cube, the event of the coin showing heads and the number cube showing 3 is a compound event.
compound inequality (p. 170) Two inequalities that are combined into one statement by the word *and* or *or*.	**desigualdad compuesta** Dos desigualdades unidas en un enunciado por la palabra *y* u *o*.	$x \geq 2$ AND $x < 7$ (also written $2 \leq x < 7$) 0 2 4 6 8 $x < 2$ OR $x > 6$ 0 2 4 6 8

Glossary/Glosario G5

ENGLISH	SPANISH	EXAMPLES
compound interest (p. 748) Interest earned or paid on both the principal and previously earned interest. The formula for compound interest is $A = P\left(1 + \frac{r}{n}\right)^{nt}$, where A is the final amount, P is the principal, r is the interest rate expressed as a decimal, n is the number of times interest is compounded, and t is the time.	**interés compuesto** Intereses ganados o pagados sobre el capital y los intereses ya devengados. La fórmula de interés compuesto es $A = P\left(1 + \frac{r}{n}\right)^{nt}$, donde A es la cantidad final, P es el capital, r es la tasa de interés expresada como un decimal, n es la cantidad de veces que se capitaliza el interés y t es el tiempo.	If \$100 is put into an account with an interest rate of 5% compounded monthly, then after 2 years, the account will have $100\left(1 + \frac{0.05}{12}\right)^{12 \cdot 2} = \$110.49$.
compound statement (p. 170) Two statements that are connected by the word *and* or *or*.	**enunciado compuesto** Dos enunciados unidos por la palabra *y* u *o*.	The sky is blue and the grass is green. I will drive to school or I will take the bus.
conclusion (p. 38) The part of a conditional statement following the word *then*.	**conclusión** Parte de un enunciado condicional que sigue a la palabra *entonces*.	If $x + 1 = 5$, then $\underbrace{x = 4}_{\text{Conclusion}}$.
conditional statement (p. 38) A statement that can be written in "if-then" form.	**enunciado condicional** Enunciado que se puede expresar como "si *p*, entonces *q*."	If $x + 1 = 5$, then $x = 4$.
cone (p. SB20) A three-dimensional figure with a circular base lying in one plane plus a vertex not lying in that plane. The remaining surface of the cone is formed by joining the vertex to points on the circle by line segments.	**cono** Figura tridimensional con una base circular que está en un plano, más un vértice que no está en ese plano. El resto de la superficie del cono se forma uniendo el vértice con los puntos del círculo por medio de segmentos de recta.	
congruent (p. SB19) Having the same size and shape, denoted by $\cong$.	**congruente** Que tiene el mismo tamaño y la misma forma, expresado por $\cong$.	P Q R S $\overline{PQ} \cong \overline{RS}$
congruent angles (p. SB19) Angles that have the same measure.	**ángulos congruentes** Ángulos que tienen la misma medida.	C A B D E F $\angle ABC \cong \angle DEF$
congruent segments (p. SB19) Segments that have the same length.	**segmentos congruentes** Segmentos que tienen la misma longitud.	P Q R S $\overline{PQ} \cong \overline{SR}$
conjecture (p. 233) A statement that is believed to be true.	**conjetura** Enunciado que se supone verdadero.	A sequence begins with the terms 2, 4, 6, 8, 10. A reasonable conjecture is that the next term in the sequence is 12.
conjugate of an irrational number (p. 721) The conjugate of a number in the form $a + \sqrt{b}$ is $a - \sqrt{b}$.	**conjugado de un número irracional** El conjugado de un número en la forma $a + \sqrt{b}$ es $a - \sqrt{b}$.	The conjugate of $1 + \sqrt{2}$ is $1 - \sqrt{2}$.

Glossary/Glosario

G6 Glossary/Glosario

ENGLISH	SPANISH	EXAMPLES
consistent system (p. 350) A system of equations or inequalities that has at least one solution.	**sistema consistente** Sistema de ecuaciones o desigualdades que tiene por lo menos una solución.	$\begin{cases} x + y = 6 \\ x - y = 4 \end{cases}$ solution: (5, 1)
constant (p. 6) A value that does not change.	**constante** Valor que no cambia.	3, 0, π
constant of variation (p. 282) The constant *k* in direct and inverse variation equations.	**constante de variación** La constante *k* en ecuaciones de variación directa e inversa.	$y = 5x$ ↑ constant of variation
continuous graph (p. 201) A graph made up of connected lines or curves.	**gráfica continua** Gráfica compuesta por líneas rectas o curvas conectadas.	
contradiction (p. 484) Two statements that cannot both be true at the same time.	**contradicción** Dos enunciados que no pueden ser verdaderos al mismo tiempo.	$x + 1 = 2$ $x + 1 = 0$
converse of a conditional statement (p. 39) The statement formed by exchanging the hypothesis and conclusion of a conditional statement.	**reciproco de enunciado condicional** Enunciado que se forma intercambiando la hipótesis y la conclusion de un enunciado condicional.	Statement: If $n + 1 = 3$, then $n = 2$. Converse: If $n = 2$, then $n + 1 = 3$.
coordinate (p. SB23) A number used to identify the location of a point. On a number line, one coordinate is used. In the coordinate plane, two coordinates — called the *x*-coordinate and the *y*-coordinate — are used.	**coordenada** Número utilizado para identificar la ubicación de un punto. En una recta numérica se utiliza una coordenada. En el plano cartesiano se utilizan dos coordenadas, denominadas coordenada *x* y coordenada *y*.	 The coordinate of *A* is 2. The coordinates of *B* are (−2, 3).
coordinate plane (p. SB23) A plane that is divided into four regions by a horizontal line called the *x*-axis and a vertical line called the *y*-axis.	**plano cartesiano** Plano dividido en cuatro regiones por una línea horizontal denominada eje *x* y una línea vertical denominada eje *y*.	
correlation (p. 224) A measure of the strength and direction of the relationship between two variables or data sets.	**correlación** Medida de la fuerza y dirección de la relación entre dos variables o conjuntos de datos.	

Glossary/Glosario G7

ENGLISH	SPANISH	EXAMPLES
corresponding angles of polygons (p. SB19) Angles in the same position in two different polygons that have the same number of angles.	**ángulos correspondientes de los polígonos** Ángulos que tienen la misma posición relativa en dos polígonos diferentes que tienen el mismo número de ángulos.	A B C D E F $\angle A$ and $\angle D$ are corresponding angles.
corresponding sides of polygons (p. SB19) Sides in the same position in two different polygons that have the same number of sides.	**lados correspondientes de los polígonos** Lados que tienen la misma posición en dos polígonos diferentes que tienen el mismo número de lados.	A B C D E F $\overline{AB}$ and $\overline{DE}$ are corresponding sides.
counterexample (p. 43) An example that proves that a conjecture or statement is false.	**contraejemplo** Ejemplo que demuestra que una conjetura o enunciado es falso.	15 is a counterexample to the statement that all odd numbers are prime, because 15 is odd but not prime.
Cross Product Property (p. 103) For any real numbers *a*, *b*, *c*, and *d*, where $b \neq 0$ and $d \neq 0$, if $\frac{a}{b} = \frac{c}{d}$, then $ad = bc$.	**Propiedad de productos cruzados** Dados los números reales *a*, *b*, *c* y *d*, donde $b \neq 0$ y $d \neq 0$, si $\frac{a}{b} = \frac{c}{d}$, entonces $ad = bc$.	If $\frac{4}{6} = \frac{10}{x}$, then $4x = 60$, so $x = 15$.
cross products (p. 103) In the statement $\frac{a}{b} = \frac{c}{d}$, bc and ad are the cross products.	**productos cruzados** En el enunciado $\frac{a}{b} = \frac{c}{d}$, bc y ad son productos cruzados.	$\frac{1}{2} = \frac{3}{6}$ Cross products: $2 \cdot 3 = 6$ and $1 \cdot 6 = 6$
cube (p. SB20) A prism with six square faces.	**cubo** Prisma con seis caras cuadradas.	
cube in numeration (p. 26) The third power of a number.	**cubo en numeración** Tercera potencia de un número.	8 is the cube of 2 because $2^3 = 8$
cube root (p. 32) A number, written as $\sqrt[3]{x}$, whose cube is *x*.	**raíz cúbica** Número, expresado como $\sqrt[3]{x}$, cuyo cubo es *x*.	$\sqrt[3]{64} = 4$, because $4^3 = 64$; 4 is the cube root of 64.
cubic function (p. SB12) A function in which the greatest power of any variable term is 3.	**función cúbica** Función en la que la mayor potencia de cualquier variable es 3.	$y = x^3$
cubic polynomial (p. 431) A polynomial of degree 3.	**polinomio cúbico** Polinomio de grado 3.	$x^3 + 4x^2 - 6x + 2$
customary system of measurement (p. SB13) The system of measurement often used in the United States.	**sistema usual de medidas** El system de medidas que se usa comúnmente en Estados Unidos.	inches, feet, miles, ounces, pounds, tons, cups, quarts, gallons
cylinder (p. SB20) A three-dimensional figure with two parallel congruent circular bases. The third surface of the cylinder consists of all parallel circles of the same radius whose centers lie on the segment joining the centers of the bases.	**cilindro** Figura tridimensional con dos bases circulares paralelas y congruentes. La tercera superficie del cilindro consiste en todos los circulos paralelos del mismo radio cuyo centro está en el segmento que une los centros de la bases.	

Glossary/Glosario

G8 Glossary/Glosario

ENGLISH	SPANISH	EXAMPLES
data (p. SB26) Information gathered from a survey or experiment.	**datos** Información reunida en una encuesta o experimento.	
deductive reasoning (p. 99) The process of using logic to draw conclusions.	**razonamiento deductivo** Proceso en el que se utiliza la lógica parar sacar conclusions.	
degree of a monomial (p. 430) The sum of the exponents of the variables in the monomial.	**grado de un monomio** Suma de los exponentes de las variables del monomio.	$4x^2y^5z^3$ Degree: $2 + 5 + 3 = 10$ $5 = 5x^0$ Degree: 0
degree of a polynomial (p. 430) The degree of the term of the polynomial with the greatest degree.	**grado de un polinomio** Grado del término del polinomio con el grado máximo.	$3x^2y^2 + 4xy^5 - 12x^3y^2$ Degree 4 Degree 6 Degree 5 Degree 6
dependent events (p. SB31) Events for which the occurrence or nonoccurrence of one event affects the probability of the other event.	**sucesos dependientes** Dos sucesos son dependientes si el hecho de que uno de ellos ocurra o no afecta la probabilidad del otro suceso.	From a bag containing 3 red marbles and 2 blue marbles, drawing a red marble, and then drawing a blue marble without replacing the first marble are dependent events.
dependent system (p. 351) A system of equations that has infinitely many solutions.	**sistema dependiente** Sistema de ecuaciones que tiene infinitamente muchas soluciones.	$\begin{cases} x + y = 2 \\ 2x + 2y = 4 \end{cases}$
dependent variable (p. 216) A variable whose value depends on the value of a variable called the independent variable.	**variable dependiente** Variable cuyo valor depende del valor de una variable llamada variable independiente.	A math tutor charges \$35 per hour. In this situation, the total fee is the dependent variable. It depends on the number of tutoring hours.
diameter (p. SB17) A segment that has endpoints on a circle and that passes through the center of the circle; also the length of that segment.	**diámetro** Segmento que atraviesa el centro de un círculo y cuyos extremos están sobre la circunferencia; longitud de dicho segmento.	
difference of two cubes (p. 520) A polynomial of the form $a^3 - b^3$, which may be written as the product $(a - b)(a^2 + ab + b^2)$.	**diferencia de dos cubos** Polinomio del tipo $a^3 - b^3$, que se puede expresar como el producto $(a - b)(a^2 + ab + b^2)$.	$x^3 - 8 = (x - 2)(x^2 + 2x + 4)$
difference of two squares (p. 457) A polynomial of the form $a^2 - b^2$, which may be written as the product $(a + b)(a - b)$.	**diferencia de dos cuadrados** Polinomio del tipo $a^2 - b^2$, que se puede expresar como el producto $(a + b)(a - b)$.	$x^2 - 4 = (x + 2)(x - 2)$

Glossary/Glosario G9

ENGLISH	SPANISH	EXAMPLES
direct variation (p. 282) A linear relationship between two variables, x and y, that can be written in the form $y = kx$, where k is a nonzero constant.	**variación directa** Relación lineal entre dos variables, x e y, que puede expresarse en la forma $y = kx$, donde k es una constante distinta de cero.	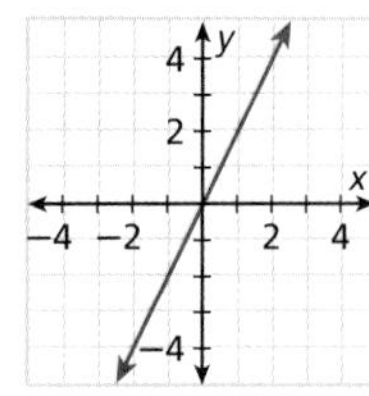 $y = 2x$
discontinuous function (p. 634) A function whose graph has one or more jumps, breaks, or holes.	**función discontinua** Función cuya gráfica tiene uno o más saltos, interrupciones u hoyos.	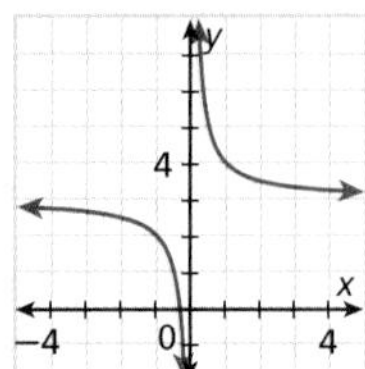
discount (p. SB10) An amount by which an original price is reduced.	**descuento** Cantidad por la que se reduce un precio original.	
discrete graph (p. 201) A graph made up of unconnected points.	**gráfica discreta** Gráfica compuesta de puntos no conectados.	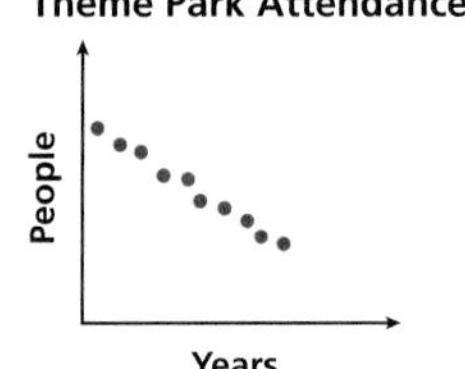
discriminant (p. 605) The discriminant of the quadratic equation $ax^2 + bx + c = 0$ is $b^2 - 4ac$.	**discriminante** El discriminante de la ecuación cuadrática $ax^2 + bx + c = 0$ es $b^2 - 4ac$.	The discriminant of $2x^2 - 5x - 3$ is $(-5)^2 - 4(2)(-3)$ or 49.
Distance Formula (p. 588) In the coordinate plane, the distance from (x_1, y_1) to (x_2, y_2) is $d = \sqrt{(x_2 - x_1)^2 + (y_2 - y_1)^2}$.	**Fórmula de distancia** En el plano cartesiano, la distancia desde (x_1, y_1) hasta (x_2, y_2) es $d = \sqrt{(x_2 - x_1)^2 + (y_2 - y_1)^2}$.	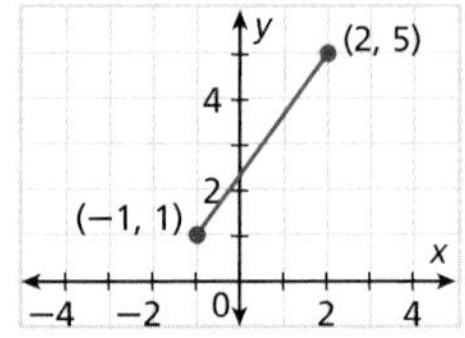 The distance from $(2, 5)$ to $(-1, 1)$ is $d = \sqrt{(-1 - 2)^2 + (1 - 5)^2}$ $= \sqrt{(-3)^2 + (-4)^2}$ $= \sqrt{9 + 16} = \sqrt{25} = 5$.
Distributive Property (p. 47) For all real numbers a, b, and c, $a(b + c) = ab + ac$, and $(b + c)a = ba + ca$.	**Propiedad distributiva** Dados los números reales a, b y c, $a(b + c) = ab + ac$, y: $(b + c)a = ba + ca$.	$3(4 + 5) = 3 \cdot 4 + 3 \cdot 5$ $(4 + 5)3 = 4 \cdot 3 + 5 \cdot 3$
Division Property of Equality (p. 73) For real numbers a, b, and c, where $c \neq 0$, if $a = b$, then $\frac{a}{c} = \frac{b}{c}$.	**Propiedad de igualdad de la división** Dados los números reales a, b y c, donde $c \neq 0$, si $a = b$, entonces $\frac{a}{c} = \frac{b}{c}$.	$4x = 12$ $\frac{4x}{4} = \frac{12}{4}$ $x = 3$

G10 *Glossary/Glosario*

ENGLISH	SPANISH	EXAMPLES
Division Property of Inequality (p. 148) For real numbers a, b, and c, where $c > 0$, if $a < b$, then $\frac{a}{c} < \frac{b}{c}$. For real numbers a, b, and c, where $c < 0$, if $a < b$, then $\frac{a}{c} > \frac{b}{c}$. Also holds true for $>$, $\leq$, $\geq$, and $\neq$.	**Propiedad de desigualdad de la división** Dados los números reales a, b, y c, donde $c > 0$, si $a < b$, entonces $\frac{a}{c} < \frac{b}{c}$. Dados los números reales a, b, y c, donde $c < 0$, si $a < b$, entonces $\frac{a}{c} > \frac{b}{c}$. Es válido también para $>$, $\leq$, $\geq$, y $\neq$.	$4x \geq 12$ $\frac{4x}{4} \geq \frac{12}{4}$ $x \geq 3$ $-4x \geq 12$ $\frac{4x}{-4} \leq \frac{12}{-4}$ $x \leq -3$
domain (p. 206) The set of all first coordinates (or x-values) of a relation or function.	**dominio** Conjunto de todos los valores de la primera coordenada (o valores de x) de una función o relación.	The domain of the function $f(x) = \sqrt{x}$ is $x \geq 0$.

E

ENGLISH	SPANISH	EXAMPLES
edge (p. SB20) A segment that is the intersection of two faces of a polyhedron.	**artista** Segmento que constituye la intersección de dos caras de un poliedro.	Edge
element (p. 76) Each member in a set.	**elemento** Cada miembro en un conjunto.	For the set {1, 3, 6, 9}, the elements are 1, 3, 6, and 9.
elimination method (p. 343) A method used to solve systems of equations in which one variable is eliminated by adding or subtracting two equations of the system.	**eliminación** Método utilizado para resolver sistemas de ecuaciones por el quale se elimina una variable sumando o restando dos ecuaciones del sistema.	
empty set (p. 93) The set with no elements denoted ∅ or { }.	**conjunto vacío** Conjunto sin elementos expresado ∅ o { }.	The solution set of $\lvert x \rvert < 0$ is the empty set.
equally likely outcomes (p. SB29) Outcomes are equally likely if they have the same probability of occurring. If an experiment has n equally likely outcomes, then the probability of each outcome is $\frac{1}{n}$.	**resultados igualmente probables** Los resultados son igualmente probables si tienen la misma probabilidad de ocurrir. Si un experimento tiene n resultados igualmente probables, entonces la probabilidad de cada resultado es $\frac{1}{n}$.	If a fair coin is tossed, then $P(\text{heads}) = P(\text{tails}) = \frac{1}{2}$. So the outcome "heads" and the outcome "tails" are equally likely.
equation (p. 72) A mathematical statement that two expressions are equal.	**ecuación** Enunciado matemático que indica que dos expresiones son iguales.	$x + 4 = 7$ $2 + 3 = 6 - 1$ $(x - 1)^2 + (y + 2)^2 = 4$
equilateral triangle (p. SB18) A triangle with three congruent sides.	**triángulo equilátero** Triángulo con tres lados congruentes.	
equivalent equations (p. 79) Equations that have the same solution set.	**ecuaciones equivalentes** Ecuaciones con la misma solución.	$x = 5$ and $x + 2 = 7$ are equivalent equations.
equivalent inequalities (p. 142) Inequalities that have the same solution set.	**desigualdades equivalentes** Desigualdades con la misma solución.	$x > 5$ and $x + 2 > 7$ are equivalent inequalities.

Glossary/Glosario G11

ENGLISH	SPANISH	EXAMPLES
evaluate (p. 7) To find the value of an algebraic expression by substituting a number for each variable and simplifying by using the order of operations.	**evaluar** Calcular el valor de una expresión algebraica sustituyendo cada variable por un número y simplificando mediante el orden de las operaciones.	Evaluate $2x + 7$ for $x = 3$. $2x + 7$ $2(3) + 7$ $6 + 7$ 13
event (p. SB29) An outcome or set of outcomes in a probability experiment.	**suceso** Resultado o conjunto de resultados en un experimento de probabilidad.	In the experiment of rolling a number cube, the event "an odd number" consists of the outcomes 1, 3, and 5.
excluded values (p. 634) Values of x for which a function or expression is not defined.	**valores excluidos** Valores de x para los cuales no está definida una función o expresión.	The excluded values of $f(x) = \dfrac{(x+2)}{(x-1)(x+4)}$ are $x = 1$ and $x = -4$, which would make the denominator equal to 0.
experiment (p. SB29) An activity involving chance that can have different results.	**experimento** Actividad que implica probabilidad y puede tener diferentes resultados.	Tossing a coin 10 times and noting the number of heads.
experimental probability (p. SB30) The ratio of the number of times an event occurs to the number of trials, or times, that an activity is performed.	**probabilidad experimental** Razón entre la cantidad de veces que ocurre un suceso y la cantidad de pruebas, o veces, que se realiza una actividad.	Kendra attempted 27 free throws and made 16 of them. The experimental probability that she will make her next free throw is $P(\text{free throw}) = \dfrac{\text{number made}}{\text{number attempted}} = \dfrac{16}{27} \approx 0.59$.
exponent (p. 26) The number that indicates how many times the base in a power is used as a factor.	**exponente** Número que indica la cantidad de veces que la base de una potencia se utiliza como factor.	$3^4 = 3 \cdot 3 \cdot 3 \cdot 3 = 81$ 4 is the exponent.
exponential decay (p. 749) An exponential function of the form $f(x) = ab^x$ in which $0 < b < 1$. If r is the rate of decay in decimal form, then the function can be written $y = a(1 - r)^t$, where a is the initial amount and t is the time.	**decremento exponencial** Función exponencial del tipo $f(x) = ab^x$ en la cual $0 < b < 1$. Si r es la tasa decremental en forma decimal, entonces la función se puede expresar como $y = a(1 - r)^t$, donde a es la cantidad inicial y t es el tiempo.	$f(x) = 3\left(\frac{1}{2}\right)^x$ 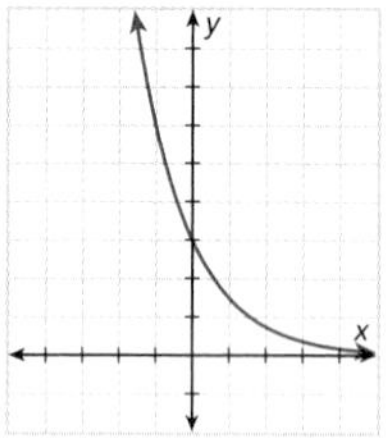
exponential expression (p. 757) An algebraic expression in which the variable is in an exponent with a fixed number as the base.	**expresión exponencial** Expresión algebraica en la que la variable está en un exponente y que tiene un número fijo como base.	2^{x+1}
exponential function (p. 738) A function of the form $f(x) = ab^x$, where a and b are real numbers with $a \neq 0$, $b > 0$, and $b \neq 1$.	**función exponencial** Función del tipo $f(x) = ab^x$, donde a y b son números reales con a $\neq 0$, $b > 0$ y $b \neq 1$.	$f(x) = 3 \cdot 4^x$ 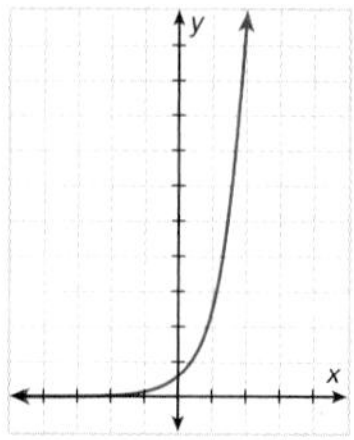

G12 Glossary/Glosario

ENGLISH	SPANISH	EXAMPLES
exponential growth (p. 747) An exponential function of the form $f(x) = ab^x$ in which $b > 1$. If r is the rate of growth in decimal form, then the function can be written $y = a(1 + r)^t$, where a is the initial amount and t is the time.	**crecimiento exponencial** Función exponencial del tipo $f(x) = ab^x$ en la que $b > 1$. Si r es la tasa de crecimiento en forma decimal, entonces la función se puede expresar como $y = a(1 + r)^t$, donde a es la cantidad inicial y t es el tiempo.	$f(x) = 2^x$ 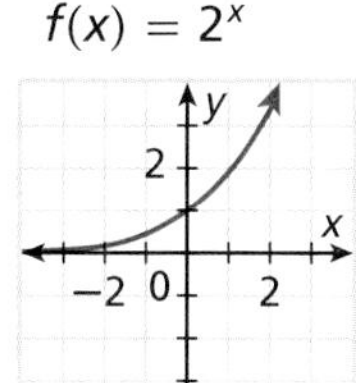
expression (p. 6) A mathematical phrase that contains operations, numbers, and/or variables.	**expresión** Frase matemática que contiene operaciones, números y/o variables.	$6x + 1$
extraneous solution (p. 675) A solution of a derived equation that is not a solution of the original equation.	**solución extraña** Solución de una ecuación derivada que no es una solución de la ecuación original.	To solve $\sqrt{x} = -2$, square both sides; $x = 4$. ***Check*** $\sqrt{4} = -2$ is false, so 4 is an extraneous solution.

F

ENGLISH	SPANISH	EXAMPLES
face of a polyhedron (p. SB20) A flat surface of the polyhedron.	**cara de un poliedro** Superficie plana de un poliedro.	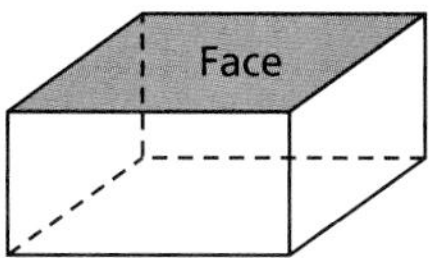
factor (p. 478) A number or expression that is multiplied by another number or expression to get a product. *See also* factoring.	**factor** Número o expresión que se multiplica por otro número o expresión para obtener un producto. *Ver también* factoreo.	$12 = 3 \cdot 4$ 3 and 4 are factors of 12. $x^2 - 1 = (x - 1)(x + 1)$ $(x - 1)$ and $(x + 1)$ are factors of $x^2 - 1$.
factoring (p. 478) The process of writing a number or algebraic expression as a product.	**factorización** Proceso por el que se expresa un número o expresión algebraica como un producto.	$x^2 - 4x - 21 = (x - 7)(x + 3)$
factor tree (p. SB5) A diagram showing how a whole number breaks down into its prime factors.	**árbol de factores** Diagrama que muestra cómo se descompone un número cabal en sus factores primo.	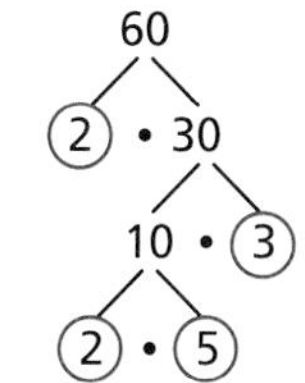
first differences (p. 756) The differences between y-values of a function for evenly spaced x-values.	**primeras diferencias** Diferencias entre los valores de y de una función para valores de x espaciados uniformemente.	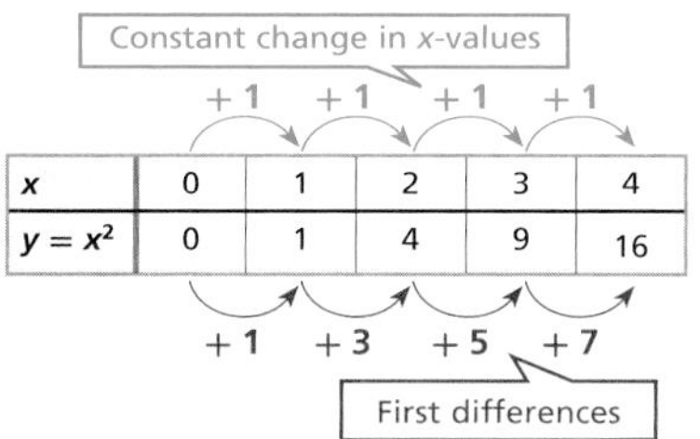
first quartile *See* lower quartile.	**primer cuartil** *Ver* cuartil inferior.	

Glossary/Glosario **G13**

ENGLISH	SPANISH	EXAMPLES
FOIL (p. 447) A mnemonic (memory) device for a method of multiplying two binomials: Multiply the **First** terms. Multiply the **Outer** terms. Multiply the **Inner** terms. Multiply the **Last** terms.	**FOIL** Regla mnemotécnica para recordar el método de multiplicación de dos binomios: Multiplicar los términos **Primeros** (*First*). Multiplicar los términos **Externos** (*Outer*). Multiplicar los términos **Internos** (*Inner*). Multiplicar los términos **Últimos** (*Last*).	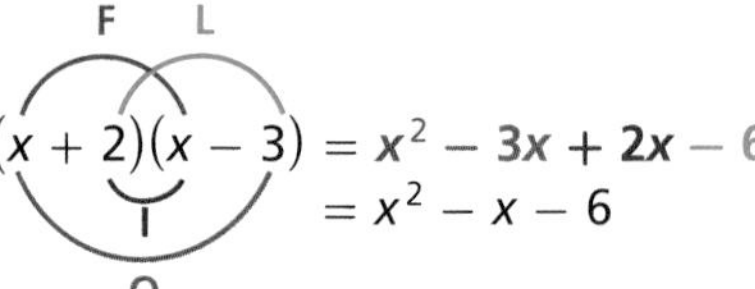 $(x+2)(x-3) = x^2 - 3x + 2x - 6$ $= x^2 - x - 6$
formula (p. 109) A literal equation that states a rule for a relationship among quantities.	**fórmula** Ecuación literal que establece una regla para una relación entre cantidades.	$A = \pi r^2$
fractional exponent (p. 423) An exponent that can be expressed as $\frac{m}{n}$ such that if m and n are integers, then $b^{\frac{m}{n}} = \sqrt[n]{b^m} = \left(\sqrt[n]{b}\right)^m$.	**exponente fraccionario** Exponente que se puede expresar como $\frac{m}{n}$ tal que si m y n son números enteros, entonces $b^{\frac{m}{n}} = \sqrt[n]{b^m} = \left(\sqrt[n]{b}\right)^m$.	$64^{\frac{1}{6}} = \sqrt[6]{64}$
function (p. 207) A relation in which every domain value is paired with exactly one range value.	**función** Relación en la que a cada valor de dominio corresponde exactamente un valor de rango.	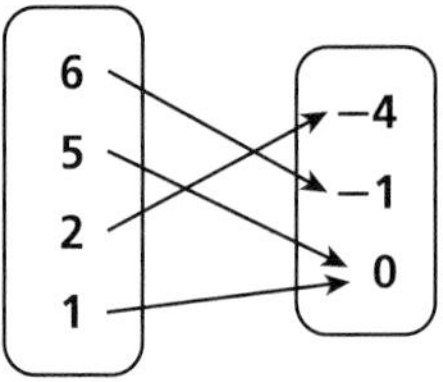
function notation (p. 216) If x is the independent variable and y is the dependent variable, then the function notation for y is $f(x)$, read "f of x," where f names the function.	**notación de función** Si x es la variable independiente e y es la variable dependiente, entonces la notación de función para y es $f(x)$, que se lee "f de x," donde f nombra la función.	equation: $y = 2x$ function notation: $f(x) = 2x$

G

ENGLISH	SPANISH	EXAMPLES
geometric sequence (p. 732) A sequence in which the ratio of successive terms is a constant r, called the common ratio, where $r \neq 0$ and $r \neq 1$.	**sucesión geométrica** Sucesión en la que la razón de los términos sucesivos es una constante r, denominada razón común, donde $r \neq 0$ y $r \neq 1$.	1, 2, 4, 8, 16, ... $\cdot 2 \;\; \cdot 2 \;\; \cdot 2 \;\; \cdot 2$ $r = 2$
graph of a function (p. 214) The set of points in the coordinate plane with coordinates (x, y), where x is in the domain of the function f and $y = f(x)$.	**gráfica de una función** Conjunto de los puntos de el plano cartesiano con coordenadas (x, y), donde x está en el dominio de la función f e $y = f(x)$.	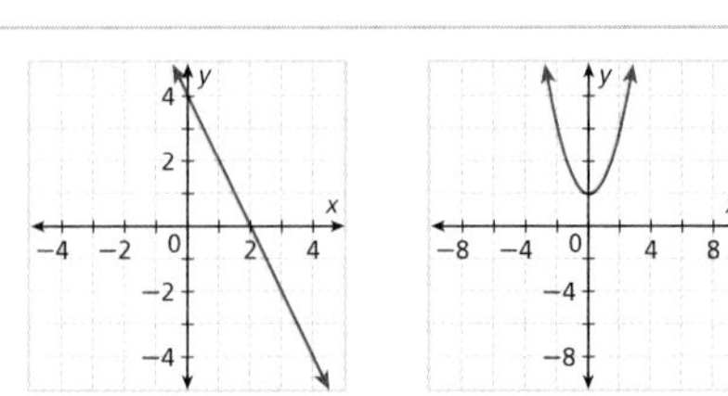
graph of an inequality in one variable (p. 137) The set of points on the number line that are solutions of the inequality.	**gráfica de una desigualdad en una variable** Conjunto de los puntos de la recta numérica que representan soluciones de la desigualdad.	$x \geq 2$ 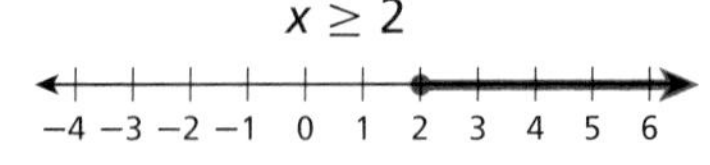

G14 *Glossary/Glosario*

ENGLISH	SPANISH	EXAMPLES
graph of an inequality in two variables (p. 364) The set of points in the coordinate plane whose coordinates (x, y) are solutions of the inequality.	**gráfica de una desigualdad en dos variables** Conjunto de los puntos de el plano cartesiano cuyas coordenadas (x, y) son soluciones de la desigualdad.	$y \leq x + 1$ 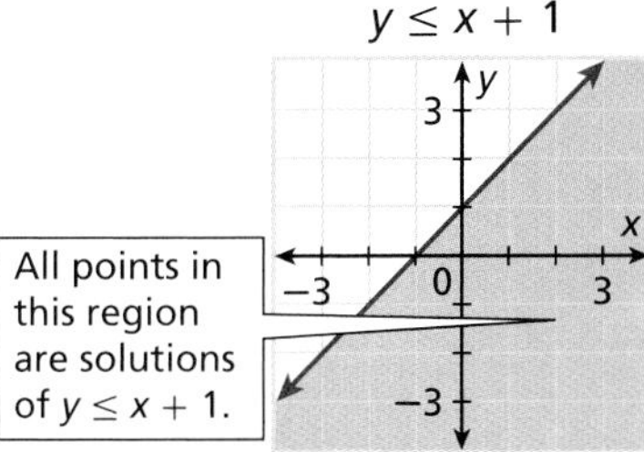
graph of an ordered pair (p. SB23) For the ordered pair (x, y), the point in the coordinate plane that is a horizontal distance of x units from the origin and a vertical distance of y units from the origin.	**gráfica de un par ordenado** Dado el par ordenado (x, y), punto en el plano cartesiano que está a una distancia horizontal de x unidades desde el origen y a una distancia vertical de y unidades desde el origen.	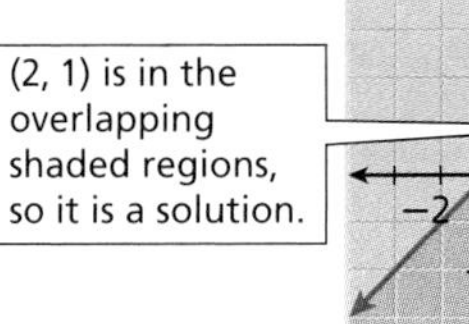 $(2, -4)$
graph of a system of linear inequalities (p. 371) The region in the coordinate plane consisting of points whose coordinates are solutions to all of the inequalities in the system.	**gráfica de un sistema de desigualdades lineales** Región de el plano cartesiano que consta de puntos cuyas coordenadas son soluciones de todas las desigualdades del sistema.	(2, 1) is in the overlapping shaded regions, so it is a solution.
greatest common factor (GCF) (p. 479, p. SB7) For two or more numbers, the largest whole number that divides evenly into each number. For two or more monomials that contain variables, the product of the largest integer and the largest power of each variable that divide evenly into each term.	**máximo común divisor (MCD)** Dados dos o más números, el número cabal mayor que divide exactamente cada número. Dados dos o más monomios que contienen variables, el producto del entero mayor y la potencia mayor de cada variable que divide exactamente cada término.	The GCF of 27 and 45 is 9. The GCF of $4x^3y$ and $6x^2y$ is $2x^2y$.
grouping symbols (p. 48) Symbols such as parentheses ( ), brackets [ ], and braces { } that separate part of an expression. A fraction bar, absolute-value symbols, and radical symbols may also be used as grouping symbols.	**símbolos de agrupación** Símbolos tales como paréntesis ( ), corchetes [ ] y llaves { } que separan parte de una expresión. La barra de fracciones, los símbolos de valor absoluto y los símbolos de radical también se pueden utilizar como símbolos de agrupación.	$6 + \{3 - [(4 - 3) + 2] + 1\} - 5$ $6 + \{3 - [1 + 2] + 1\} - 5$ $6 + \{3 - 3 + 1\} - 5$ $6 + 1 - 5$ 2

H

ENGLISH	SPANISH	EXAMPLES
half-life (p. 749) The half-life of a substance is the time it takes for one-half of the substance to decay into another substance.	**vida media** La vida media de una sustancia es el tiempo que tarda la mitad de la sustancia en desintegrarse y transformarse en otra sustancia.	Carbon-14 has a half-life of 5730 years, so 5 g of an initial amount of 10 g will remain after 5730 years.
half-plane (p. 364) The part of the coordinate plane on one side of a line, which may include the line.	**semiplano** La parte del plano cartesiano de un lado de una línea, que puede incluir la línea.	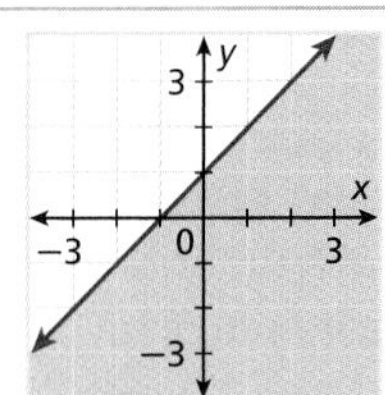

Glossary/Glosario G15

ENGLISH	SPANISH	EXAMPLES
Heron's Formula (p. 710) A triangle with side lengths a, b, and c has area $A = \sqrt{s(s-a)(s-b)(s-c)}$, where s is one-half the perimeter, or $s = \frac{1}{2}(a+b+c)$.	**fórmula de Herón** Un triángulo con longitudes de lado a, b y c tiene un área $A = \sqrt{s(s-a)(s-b)(s-c)}$, donde s es la mitad del perímetro ó $s = \frac{1}{2}(a+b+c)$.	
histogram (p. SB27) A bar graph used to display data grouped in class intervals. The width of each bar is proportional to the class interval, and the area of each bar is proportional to the frequency.	**histograma** Gráfica de barras utilizada para mostrar datos agrupados en intervalos de clases. El ancho de cada barra es proporcional al intervalo de clase y el área de cada barra es proporcional a la frecuencia.	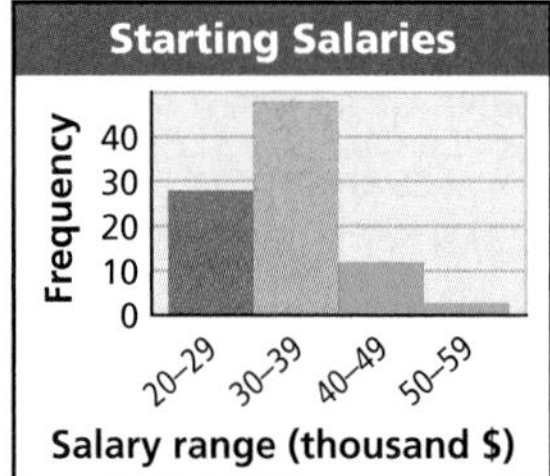
horizontal line (p. 273) A line described by the equation $y = b$, where b is the y-intercept.	**línea horizontal** Línea descrita por la ecuación $y = b$, donde b es la intersección con el eje y.	$y = 4$ 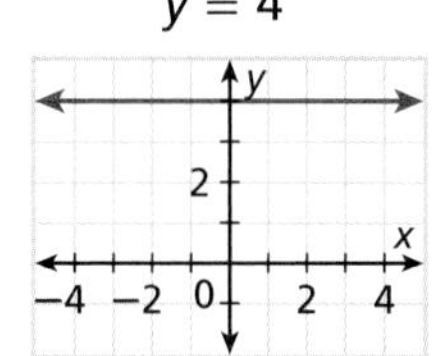
hypotenuse (p. SB19) The side opposite the right angle in a right triangle.	**hipotenusa** Lado opuesto al ángulo recto de un triángulo rectángulo.	hypotenuse
hypothesis (p. 38) The part of a conditional statement following the word *if*.	**hipótesis** La parte de un enunciado condicional que sigue a la palabra *si*.	If $x + 1 = 5$, then $x = 4$. (Hypothesis: $x + 1 = 5$)

I

ENGLISH	SPANISH	EXAMPLES
identity (p. 93) An equation that is true for all values of the variables.	**identidad** Ecuación verdadera para todos los valores de las variables.	$3 = 3$ $2(x - 1) = 2x - 2$
image (p. SB24) A shape that results from a transformation of a figure known as the preimage.	**imagen** Forma resultante de la transformación de una figura conocido como imagen original.	Preimage, Image $\triangle ABC \rightarrow \triangle A'B'C'$
inconsistent system (p. 350) A system of equations or inequalities that has no solution.	**sistema inconsistente** Sistema de ecuaciones o desigualdades que no tiene solución.	$\begin{cases} x + y = 0 \\ x + y = 1 \end{cases}$
independent events (p. SB31) Events for which the occurrence or nonoccurrence of one event does not affect the probability of the other event.	**sucesos independientes** Dos sucesos son independientes si el hecho de que se produzca o no uno de ellos no afecta la probabilidad del otro suceso.	From a bag containing 3 red marbles and 2 blue marbles, drawing a red marble, replacing it, and then drawing a blue marble are independent events.
independent system (p. 351) A system of equations that has exactly one solution.	**sistema independiente** Sistema de ecuaciones que tiene sólo una solución.	$\begin{cases} x + y = 7 \\ x - y = 1 \end{cases}$ Solution: (4, 3)

G16 *Glossary/Glosario*

ENGLISH	SPANISH	EXAMPLES
independent variable (p. 216) A variable whose value determines the value of a variable called the dependent variable.	**variable independiente** Variable cuyo valor determina el valor de una variable llamada variable dependiente.	A math tutor charges $35 per hour. In this situation, the number of tutoring hours is the independent variable. It determines the total fee.
index (p. 422) In the radical $\sqrt[n]{x}$, which represents the nth root of x, n is the index. In the radical $\sqrt{x}$, the index is understood to be 2.	**índice** En el radical $\sqrt[n]{x}$, que representa la enésima raíz de x, n es el índice. En el radical $\sqrt{x}$, se da por sentado que el índice es 2.	The radical $\sqrt[3]{8}$ has an index of 3.
indirect proof (p. 484) A proof in which the statement to be proved is assumed to be false and then deductive reasoning is used to find a contradiction.	**demostración indirecta** Prueba en la que se supone que el enunciado a demonstrar es falso y se muestra una contradicción.	
inductive reasoning (p. 233) The process of conjecturing that a general rule or statement is true because specific cases are true.	**razonamiento inductivo** Proceso de razonamiento por el que se determina que una regal o enunciado son verdaderos porque ciertos casos especificos son verdaderos.	A sequence begins with the terms 2, 4, 6, 8, 10. You notice that each term is two more than the previous term. You use inductive reasoning to predict that the next term is 12.
inequality (p. 136) A mathematical statement that compares two expressions by using one of the following signs: $<$, $>$, $\leq$, $\geq$, or $\neq$.	**desigualdad** Enunciado matemático que compara dos expresiones utilizando uno de los siguientes signos: $<$, $>$, $\leq$, $\geq$, o $\neq$.	$x \geq 2$ −4 −3 −2 −1 0 1 2 3 4 5 6
input (p. 217) A value that is substituted for the independent variable in a function.	**entrada** Valor que sustituye a la variable independiente en una función.	For the function $f(x) = x + 5$, the input 3 produces an output of 8.
input-output table (p. 213) A table that displays input values of a function or relation together with the corresponding outputs.	**tabla de entrada y salida** Tabla que muestra los valores de entrada de una función o relación junto con las correspondientes salidas.	Input: x = 1, 2, 3, 4 Output: y = 4, 7, 10, 13
integers (p. 33) The set of whole numbers and their opposites.	**enteros** El conjunto de números cabales y sus opuestos.	$\{\ldots, -3, -2, -1, 0, 1, 2, 3, \ldots\}$
intercept *See* x-intercept and y-intercept.	**intersección** *Ver* intersección con el eje x e intersección con el eje y.	
interest (p. SB11) The amount of money charged for borrowing money or the amount of money earned when saving or investing money. *See also* compound interest, simple interest.	**interés** Cantidad de dinero que se cobra por prestar dinero o cantidad de dinero que se gana cuando se ahorra o invierte dinero. *Ver también* interés compuesto, interés simple.	
intersection (p. 171) The intersection of two sets is the set of all elements that are common to both sets, denoted by $\cap$.	**intersección** La intersección de dos conjuntos es el conjunto de todos los elementos que son comunes a ambos conjuntos, expresado por $\cap$.	$A = \{1, 2, 3, 4\}$ $B = \{1, 3, 5, 7, 9\}$ $A \cap B = \{1, 3\}$

Glossary/Glosario

Glossary/Glosario **G17**

ENGLISH	SPANISH	EXAMPLES
inverse operations (p. 72) Operations that undo each other.	**operaciones inversas** Operaciones que se anulan entre sí.	Addition and subtraction of the same quantity are inverse operations: $5 + 3 = 8, 8 - 3 = 5$ Multiplication and division by the same quantity are inverse operations: $2 \cdot 3 = 6, 6 \div 3 = 2$
Inverse Property of Addition (p. 15) For any real number a, $a + (-a) = (-a) + a = 0$.	**propiedad inversa de la suma** Dado cualquier número real a, $a + (-a) = (-a) + a = 0$.	$4 + (-4) = (-4) + 4 = 0$
Inverse Property of Multiplication (p. 21) For any real number a $(a \neq 0)$, $a \cdot \frac{1}{a} = \frac{1}{a} \cdot a = 1$.	**propiedad inversa de la multiplicación** Dado cualquier número real a $(a \neq 0)$, $a \cdot \frac{1}{a} = \frac{1}{a} \cdot a = 1$.	$2 \cdot \frac{1}{2} = \frac{1}{2} \cdot 2 = 1$
inverse variation (p. 627) A relationship between two variables, x and y, that can be written in the form $y = \frac{k}{x}$, where k is a nonzero constant and $x \neq 0$.	**variación inversa** Relación entre dos variables, x e y, que puede expresarse en la forma $y = \frac{k}{x}$, donde k es una constante distinta de cero y $x \neq 0$.	$y = \frac{8}{x}$ 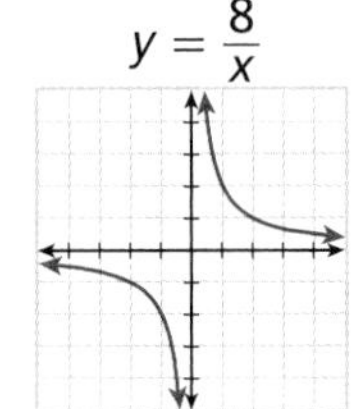
irrational number (p. 33) A real number that cannot be expressed as a ratio of two integers.	**número irracional** Número real que no se puede expresar como una razón de enteros.	$\sqrt{2}, \pi$
isolate the variable (p. 72) A variable is isolated when it appears by itself on one side of an equation and does not appear on the other side.	**despejar la variable** Una variable está despejada cuando aparece sola en uno de los lados de una ecuación y no aparece en el otro lado.	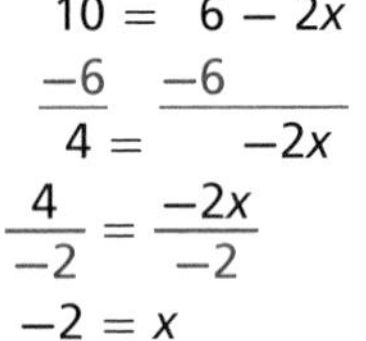 $10 = 6 - 2x$; $\underline{-6 \quad -6}$; $4 = -2x$; $\frac{4}{-2} = \frac{-2x}{-2}$; $-2 = x$
isosceles trapezoid (p. SB18) A trapezoid whose nonparallel sides are congruent.	**trapecio isósceles** Trapecio cuyos lados no paralelos son congruentes.	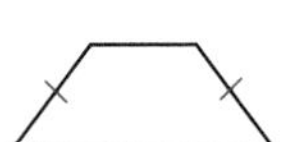
isosceles triangle (p. SB15) A triangle with at least two congruent sides.	**triángulo isósceles** Triángulo que tiene al menos dos lados congruentes.	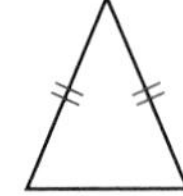

K

kite (p. SB18) A quadrilateral with two pairs of adjacent congruent sides.	**cometa o papalote** Cuadrilátero con dos pares de lados adyacentes congruentes.	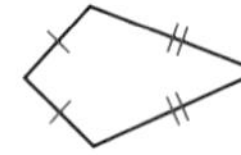

L

leading coefficient (p. 431) The coefficient of the first term of a polynomial in standard form.	**coeficiente principal** Coeficiente del primer término de un polinomio en forma estándar.	$3x^2 + 7x - 2$ Leading coefficient: 3
least common denominator (LCD) (p. 661) The least common multiple of the denominators of two or more rational expressions.	**mínimo común denominador (MCD)** Mínimo común múltiplo de los denominadores de dos o más expresiones racionales.	The LCD of $\frac{3}{4}$ and $\frac{5}{6}$ is 12. The LCD of $\frac{1}{6x^2}$ and $\frac{5}{8x}$ is $24x^2$.

G18 *Glossary/Glosario*

ENGLISH	SPANISH	EXAMPLES
least common multiple (LCM) (p. 660, SB7) For two or more whole numbers, the smallest multiple that the numbers share. For two or more monomials that contain variables, the product of the smallest positive integer and the lowest power of each variable that divide evenly into each term.	**mínimo común múltiplo (MCM)** Dados dos o más números cabales, el múltiplo menor que los números comparten. Dados dos o más monomios que contienen variables, el producto del menor entero positive y la potencia menor de cada variable que divide exactamente cada término.	The LCM of 10 and 18 is 90. The LCM of $6x^2$ and $8x$ is $24x^2$.
leg of a right triangle (p. SB19) One of the two sides of a right triangle that form the right angle.	**cateto de un triángulo rectángulo** Uno de los dos lados de un triángulo rectángulo que forman el ángulo recto.	leg leg
like radicals (p. 711) Radical terms having the same radicand and index.	**radicales semejantes** Términos radicales que tienen el mismo radicando e índice.	$3\sqrt{2x}$ and $\sqrt{2x}$
like terms (p. 49) Terms with the same variables raised to the same exponents.	**términos semejantes** Términos con las mismas variables elevadas a los mismos exponentes.	$3a^3b^2$ and $7a^3b^2$
linear equation in one variable (p. 256) An equation that can be written in the form $ax = b$ where a and b are constants and $a \neq 0$.	**ecuación lineal en una variable** Ecuación que puede expresarse en la forma $ax = b$ donde a y b son constantes y $a \neq 0$.	$x + 1 = 7$
linear equation in two variables (p. 256) An equation that can be written in the form $Ax + By = C$ where A, B, and C are constants and A and B are not both 0.	**ecuación lineal en dos variables** Ecuación que puede expresarse en la forma $Ax + By = C$ donde A, B y C son constantes y A y B no son ambas 0.	$2x + 3y = 6$
linear function (p. 256) A function that can be written in the form $y = mx + b$, where x is the independent variable and m and b are real numbers. Its graph is a line.	**función lineal** Función que puede expresarse en la forma $y = mx + b$, donde x es la variable independiente y m y b son números reales. Su gráfica es una línea.	$y = x - 1$
linear inequality in one variable (p. 364) An inequality that can be written in one of the following forms: $ax < b$, $ax > b$, $ax \leq b$, $ax \geq b$, or $ax \neq b$, where a and b are constants and $a \neq 0$.	**desigualdad lineal en una variable** Desigualdad que puede expresarse de una de las siguientes formas: $ax < b$, $ax > b$, $ax \leq b$, $ax \geq b$ o $ax \neq b$, donde a y b son constantes y $a \neq 0$.	$3x - 5 \leq 2(x + 4)$
linear inequality in two variables (p. 364) An inequality that can be written in one of the following forms: $Ax + By < C$, $Ax + By > C$, $Ax + By \leq C$, $Ax + By \geq C$, or $Ax + By \neq C$, where A, B, and C are constants and A and B are not both 0.	**desigualdad lineal en dos variables** Desigualdad que puede expresarse de una de las siguientes formas: $Ax + By < C$, $Ax + By > C$, $Ax + By \leq C$, $Ax + By \geq C$ o $Ax + By \neq C$, donde A, B y C son constantes y A y B no son ambas 0.	$2x + 3y > 6$

Glossary/Glosario G19

ENGLISH	SPANISH	EXAMPLES
literal equation (p. 110) An equation that contains two or more variables.	**ecuación literal** Ecuación que contiene dos o más variables.	$d = rt$ $A = \frac{1}{2}h(b_1 + b_2)$
lower extreme (p. SB27) The least value in a data set.	**extremo inferior** El valor meno de un conjunto de datos.	For the data set {3, 3, 5, 7, 8, 10, 11, 11, 12}, the lower extreme is 3.
lower quartile (p. SB27) The median of the lower half of a data set. Also called *first quartile.*	**cuartil inferior** Mediana de la mitad inferior de un conjunto de datos. También se llama *primer cuartil.*	Lower half Upper half 18, (23), 28, 49, 36, 42 Lower quartile

M

ENGLISH	SPANISH	EXAMPLES
mapping diagram (p. 206) A diagram that shows the relationship of elements in the domain to elements in the range of a relation or function.	**diagrama de correspondencia** Diagrama que muestra la relación entre los elementos del dominio y los elementos del rango de una función.	Mapping Diagram Domain Range 2 → A, B, C
markup (p. SB10) The amount by which a wholesale cost is increased.	**margen de ganancia** Cantidad que se agrega a un costo mayorista.	
maximum of a function (p. 546) The *y*-value of the highest point on the graph of the function.	**máximo de una función** Valor de *y* del punto más alto en la gráfica de la función.	(0, 2) The maximum of the function is 2.
mean (p. SB25) The sum of all the values in a data set divided by the number of data values. Also called the *average.*	**media** Suma de todos los valores de un conjunto de datos dividida entre el número de valores de datos. También llamada *promedio.*	Data set: 4, 6, 7, 8, 10 Mean: $\frac{4 + 6 + 7 + 8 + 10}{5}$ $= \frac{35}{5} = 7$
measure of central tendency (p. SB25) A measure that describes a data set.	**medida de tendencia dominante** Medida que describe un conjunto de datos.	mean, median, or mode
median (p. SB25) For an ordered data set with an odd number of values, the median is the middle value. For an ordered data set with an even number of values, the median is the average of the two middle values.	**mediana** Dado un conjunto de datos ordenado con un número impar de valores, la mediana es el valor medio. Dado un conjunto de datos con un número par de valores, la mediana es el promedio de los dos valores medios.	8, 9, (9), 12, 15 Median: 9 4, 6, (7, 10), 10, 12 Median: $\frac{7 + 10}{2} = 8.5$
metric system (p. SB13) A decimal system of weights and measures that is used universally in science and commonly throughout the world.	**sistema métrico** Sistema decimal de pesos y medidas empleado universalmente en las ciencias y por lo general en todo el mundo.	centimeters, meters, kilograms, milliliters, liters
minimum of a function (p. 546) The *y*-value of the lowest point on the graph of the function.	**mínimo de una función** Valor de *y* del punto más bajo en la gráfica de la función.	(0, −2) The minimum of the function is −2.

G20 Glossary/Glosario

ENGLISH	SPANISH	EXAMPLES
mode (p. SB25) The value or values that occur most frequently in a data set; if all values occur with the same frequency, the data set is said to have no mode.	**moda** El valor o los valores que se presentan con mayor frecuencia en un conjunto de datos. Si todos los valores se presentan con la misma frecuencia, se dice que el conjunto de datos no tiene moda.	Data: 3, 6, 8, 8, 10 Mode: 8 Data: 2, 5, 5, 7, 7 Modes: 5, 7 Data: 2, 3, 6, 9, 11 No mode
monomial (p. 430) A number, a variable, or a product of numbers and variables with whole-number exponents.	**monomio** Número, variable, o producto de números y variables con exponentes de números cabales, o polinomio con un término.	$3x^2y^4$
Multiplication Property of Equality (p. 73) If a, b, and c are real numbers and $a = b$, then $ac = bc$.	**Propiedad de igualdad de la multiplicación** Si a, b y c son números reales y $a = b$, entonces $ac = bc$.	$\frac{1}{3}x = 7$ $(3)\left(\frac{1}{3}x\right) = (3)(7)$ $x = 21$
Multiplication Property of Inequality (p. 148) For real numbers a, b, and c, where $c > 0$, if $a < b$, then $ac < bc$. For real numbers a, b, and c, where $c < 0$, if $a < b$, then $ac > bc$. Also holds true for $>$, $\leq$, $\geq$, and $\neq$.	**Propiedad de desigualdad de la multiplicación** Dados los números reales a, b, y c, donde $c > 0$, si $a < b$, entonces $ac < bc$. Dados los números reales a, b, y c, donde $c < 0$, si $a < b$, entonces $ac > bc$. Es válido también para $>$, $\leq$, $\geq$, y $\neq$.	$\frac{1}{3}x > 7$ $(3)\left(\frac{1}{3}x\right) > (3)(7)$ $x > 21$ $-x \leq 2$ $(-1)(-x) \geq (-1)(2)$ $x \geq -2$
multiplicative inverse (p. 21) The reciprocal of a number. Two numbers are multiplicative inverses if their product is 1.	**inverso multiplicativo** Recíproco de un número. Dos números son inversos multiplicativos si su producto es 1.	The multiplicative inverse of 5 is $\frac{1}{5}$.

N

ENGLISH	SPANISH	EXAMPLES
natural numbers (p. 33) The set of counting numbers.	**números naturales** El conjunto de números que se utilizan para contar.	$\{1, 2, 3, 4, 5, 6, \ldots\}$
negative correlation (p. 225) Two data sets have a negative correlation if one set of data values increases as the other set decreases.	**correlación negativa** Dos conjuntos de datos tienen una correlación negativa si un conjunto de valores de datos aumenta a medida que el otro conjunto disminuye.	y x
negative exponent (p. 394) For any nonzero real number x and any integer n, $x^{-n} = \frac{1}{x^n}$.	**exponente negativo** Para cualquier número real distinto de cero x y cualquier entero n, $x^{-n} = \frac{1}{x^n}$.	$x^{-2} = \frac{1}{x^2}$; $3^{-2} = \frac{1}{3^2}$
negative number (p. 36) A number that is less than zero. Negative numbers lie to the left of 0 on a number line.	**número negativo** Número menor que cero. Los números negativos se ubican a la izquierda del 0 en una recta numérica.	−2 is a negative number. −4 −3 −2 −1 0 1 2 3 4
negative square root (p. 32) The opposite of the principal square root of a number a, written as $-\sqrt{a}$.	**raíz cuadrada negativa** Opuesto de la raíz cuadrada principal de un número a, que se expresa como $-\sqrt{a}$.	The negative square root of 9 is $-\sqrt{9} = -3$.

Glossary/Glosario G21

ENGLISH	SPANISH	EXAMPLES
net (p. SB22) A diagram of the faces of a three-dimensional figure arranged in such a way that the diagram can be folded to form the three-dimensional figure.	**plantilla** Diagrama de las caras de una figura tridimensional que se puede plegar para formar la figura tridimensional.	10 m, 6 m, 10 m, 6 m
no correlation (p. 225) Two data sets have no correlation if there is no relationship between the sets of values.	**sin correlación** Dos conjuntos de datos no tienen correlación si no existe una relación entre los conjuntos de valores.	y, x
***n*th root** (p. 422) The *n*th root of a number *a*, written as $\sqrt[n]{a}$ or $a^{\frac{1}{n}}$, is a number that is equal to *a* when it is raised to the *n*th power.	**enésima raíz** La enésima raíz de un número *a*, que se escribe $\sqrt[n]{a}$ o $a^{\frac{1}{n}}$, es un número igual a *a* cuando se eleva a la enésima potencia.	$\sqrt[5]{32} = 2$, because $2^5 = 32$.
number line (p. 14) A line used to represent the real numbers. Every point on the number line represents a real number.	**recta numérica** Línea utilizada para representar los números reales. Cada punto de la recta numérica representa un número real.	−4 −3 −2 −1 0 1 2 3 4 5 6
numerical expression (p. 6) An expression that contains only numbers and operations.	**expresión numérica** Expresión que contiene únicamente números y operaciones.	$2 \cdot 3 + (4 - 6)$

O

ENGLISH	SPANISH	EXAMPLES
obtuse angle (p. SB18) An angle that measures greater than 90° and less than 180°.	**ángulo obtuso** Ángulo que mide más de 90° y menos de 180°.	
obtuse triangle (p. SB18) A triangle with one obtuse angle.	**triángulo obtusángulo** Triángulo con un ángulo obtuso.	
opposite (p. 15) The opposite of a number *a*, denoted $-a$, is the number that is the same distance from 0 as *a*, on the opposite side of the number line. The sum of opposites is 0.	**opuesto** El opuesto de un número *a*, expresado $-a$, es el número que se encuentra a la misma distancia de 0 que *a*, del lado opuesto de la recta numérica. La suma de los opuestos es 0.	5 units, 5 units; −6 −5 −4 −3 −2 −1 0 1 2 3 4 5 6; 5 and −5 are opposites.
opposite reciprocal (p. 307) The opposite of the reciprocal of a number. The opposite reciprocal of any nonzero number *a* is $-\frac{1}{a}$.	**recíproco opuesto** Opuesto del recíproco de un número. El recíproco opuesto de *a* es $-\frac{1}{a}$.	The opposite reciprocal of $\frac{2}{3}$ is $-\frac{3}{2}$.
OR (p. 170) A logical operator representing the union of two sets.	**O** Operador lógico que representa la unión de dos conjuntos.	$A = \{2, 3, 4, 5\}$ $B = \{1, 3, 5, 7\}$ The set of values that are in *A* OR *B* is $A \cup B = \{1, 2, 3, 4, 5, 7\}$.
ordered pair (p. SB23) A pair of numbers (x, y) that can be used to locate a point on the coordinate plane. The first number *x* indicates the distance to the left or right of the origin, and the second number *y* indicates the distance above or below the origin.	**par ordenado** Par de números (x, y) que se pueden utilizar para ubicar un punto en el plano cartesiano. El primer número, *x*, indica la distancia a la izquierda o derecha del origen y el segundo número, *y*, indica la distancia hacia arriba o hacia abajo del origen.	B; y; 4; 2; x; −4 −2 0 2 4; The coordinates of *B* are $(-2, 3)$.

Glossary/Glosario

G22 *Glossary/Glosario*

ENGLISH	SPANISH	EXAMPLES
order of operations (p. 48) A process for evaluating expressions: First, perform operations in parentheses or other grouping symbols. Second, evaluate powers and roots. Third, perform all multiplication and division from left to right. Fourth, perform all addition and subtraction from left to right.	**orden de las operaciones** Regla para evaluar las expresiones: Primero, realizar las operaciones entre paréntesis u otros símbolos de agrupación. Segundo, evaluar las potencias y las raíces. Tercero, realizar todas las multiplicaciones y divisiones de izquierda a derecha. Cuarto, realizar todas las sumas y restas de izquierda a derecha.	$2 + 3^2 - (7 + 5) \div 4 \cdot 3$ $2 + 3^2 - 12 \div 4 \cdot 3$ Add inside parentheses. $2 + 9 - 12 \div 4 \cdot 3$ Evaluate the power. $2 + 9 - 3 \cdot 3$ Divide. $2 + 9 - 9$ Multiply. $11 - 9$ Add. 2 Subtract.
origin (p. SB23) The intersection of the x- and y-axes in the coordinate plane. The coordinates of the origin are $(0, 0)$.	**origen** Intersección de los ejes x e y en el plano cartesiano. Las coordenadas de origen son $(0, 0)$.	origin 0
outcome (p. SB29) A possible result of a probability experiment.	**resultado** Resultado posible de un experimento de probabilidad.	In the experiment of rolling a number cube, the possible outcomes are 1, 2, 3, 4, 5, and 6.
output (p. 217) The result of substituting a value for the independent variable in a function.	**salida** Resultado de la sustitución de la variable independiente por un valor en una función.	For the function $f(x) = x^2 + 1$, the input 3 produces an output of 10.

P

ENGLISH	SPANISH	EXAMPLES
parabola (p. 545) The shape of the graph of a quadratic function.	**parábola** Forma de la gráfica de una función cuadrática.	
parallel lines (p. 304) Lines in the same plane that do not intersect.	**líneas paralelas** Líneas en el mismo plano que no se cruzan.	r s
parallelogram (p. 305) A quadrilateral with two pairs of parallel sides.	**paralelogramo** Cuadrilátero con dos pares de lados paralelos.	
Pascal's triangle (p. 526) A triangular arrangement of numbers in which every row starts and ends with 1 and each other number is the sum of the two numbers above it.	**triángulo de Pascal** Arreglo triangular de números en el cual cada fila comienza y termina con 1 y los demás números son la suma de los dos valores que están arriba de cada uno.	1 1 1 1 2 1 1 3 3 1 1 4 6 4 1
percent (p. 103, p. SB6) A ratio that compares a number to 100.	**porcentaje** Razón que compara un número con 100.	$\frac{17}{100} = 17\%$
percent change (p. SB11) An increase or decrease given as a percent of the original amount. *See also* percent decrease, percent increase.	**porcentaje de cambio** Incremento o disminución dada como un porcentaje de la cantidad original. *Ver también* porcentaje de disminución, porcentaje de incremento.	

Glossary/Glosario

Glossary/Glosario G23

ENGLISH	SPANISH	EXAMPLES
percent decrease (p. SB11) A decrease given as a percent of the original amount.	**porcentaje de disminución** Disminución dada como un porcentaje de la cantidad original.	If an item that costs \$8.00 is marked down to \$6.00, the amount of the decrease is \$2.00, so the percent decrease is $\frac{2.00}{8.00} = 0.25 = 25\%$.
percent increase (p. SB11) An increase given as a percent of the original amount.	**porcentaje de incremento** Incremento dado como un porcentaje de la cantidad original.	If an item's wholesale cost of \$8.00 is marked up to \$12.00, the amount of the increase is \$4.00, so the percent increase is $\frac{4.00}{8.00} = 0.5 = 50\%$.
perfect square (p. 32) A number whose positive square root is a whole number.	**cuadrado perfecto** Número cuya raíz cuadrada positiva es un número cabal.	36 is a perfect square because $\sqrt{36} = 6$.
perfect-square trinomial (p. 455) A trinomial whose factored form is the square of a binomial. A perfect-square trinomial has the form $a^2 - 2ab + b^2$ or $a^2 + 2ab + b^2$.	**trinomio cuadrado perfecto** Trinomio cuya forma factorizada es el cuadrado de un binomio. Un trinomio cuadrado perfecto tiene la forma $a^2 - 2ab + b^2$ o $a^2 + 2ab + b^2$.	$x^2 + 6x + 9$ is a perfect-square trinomial, because $x^2 + 6x + 9 = (x + 3)^2$.
perimeter (p. SB15) The sum of the lengths of the sides of a polygon.	**perímetro** Suma de las longitudes de los lados de un poligano.	18 ft 6ft Perimeter = 18 + 6 + 18 + 6 = 48 ft
perpendicular (p. 306) Intersecting to form 90° angles.	**perpendicular** Que se cruza para formar ángulos de 90°.	n m
perpendicular lines (p. 306) Lines that intersect at 90° angles.	**líneas perpendiculares** Líneas que se cruzan en ángulos de 90°.	n m
point-slope form (p. 298) The point-slope form of a linear equation is $y - y_1 = m(x - x_1)$, where m is the slope and (x_1, y_1) is a point on the line.	**forma de punto y pendiente** La forma de punto y pendiente de una ecuación lineal es $y - y_1 = m(x - x_1)$, donde m es la pendiente y (x_1, y_1) es un punto en la línea.	$y - 3 = 2(x - 3)$ The slope is 2. (3, 3) is on the line.
polyhedron (p. SB20) A three-dimensional figure made up of polygons that intersect only at their edges.	**poliedro** Figura tridimensional cerrada formada por polígonos que se cruzan sólo en sus aristas.	
polynomial (p. 430) A monomial or a sum or difference of monomials.	**polinomio** Monomio o suma o diferencia de monomios.	$2x^2 + 3xy - 7y^2$
polynomial long division (p. 667) A method of dividing one polynomial by another.	**división larga polinomial** Método por el que se divide un polinomio entre otro.	$x + 2\,\overline{)\,x^2 + 3x + 5}$ quotient $x + 1$ $-(x^2 + 2x)$ $x + 5$ $-(x + 2)$ 3 $\frac{x^2 + 3x + 5}{x + 2} = x + 1 + \frac{3}{x + 2}$

G24 Glossary/Glosario

ENGLISH	SPANISH	EXAMPLES
population (p. SB26) The whole group being surveyed.	**población** El grupo completo que es objecto de estudio.	In a survey about eating habits of high school students, the population is all high school students.
positive correlation (p. 225) Two data sets have a positive correlation if both sets of data values increase.	**correlación positiva** (p. 264) Dos conjuntos de datos tienen correlación positiva si los valores de ambos conjuntos de datos aumentan.	y, x
positive number (p. 36) A number greater than zero. Positive numbers lie to the right of 0 on a number line.	**número positivo** Número mayor que cero. Los números positivos se ubican a la derecha del 0 en una recta numérica.	2 is a positive number. −4 −3 −2 −1 0 1 2 3 4
positive square root (p. 32) A positive number that is multiplied by itself to form a product is called the positive square root of that product. A positive square root is indicated by the radical sign.	**raiz cuadrada positiva** Un número positivo que se multiplica por sí mismo para obtener un producto se llama raíz cuadrada positiva de ese producto. Una raíz cuadrada positivo se indica con un signo de radical.	The positive square root of 36 is $\sqrt{36} = 6$.
power (p. 26) An expression written with a base and an exponent or the value of such an expression.	**potencia** Expresión escrita con una base y un exponente o el valor de dicha expresión.	$2^3 = 8$, so 8 is the third power of 2.
Power of a Power Property (p. 410) If a is any nonzero real number and m and n are integers, then $(a^m)^n = a^{mn}$.	**Propiedad de la potencia de una potencia** Dado un número real a distinto de cero y los números enteros m y n, entonces $(a^m)^n = a^{mn}$.	$(6^7)^4 = 6^{7 \cdot 4}$ $= 6^{28}$
Power of a Product Property (p. 411) If a and b are any nonzero real numbers and n is an integer, then $(ab)^n = a^n b^n$.	**Propiedad de la potencia de un producto** Dados los números reales a y b distintos de cero y un número entero n, entonces $(ab)^n = a^n b^n$.	$(2 \cdot 4)^3 = 2^3 \cdot 4^3$ $= 8 \cdot 64$ $= 512$
Power of a Quotient Property (p. 416, p. 417) If a and b are any nonzero real numbers and n is an integer, then $\left(\frac{a}{b}\right)^n = \frac{a^n}{b^n}$.	**Propiedad de la potencia de un cociente** Dados los números reales a y b distintos de cero y un número entero n, entonces $\left(\frac{a}{b}\right)^n = \frac{a^n}{b^n}$.	$\left(\frac{3}{5}\right)^4 = \frac{3}{5} \cdot \frac{3}{5} \cdot \frac{3}{5} \cdot \frac{3}{5}$ $= \frac{3 \cdot 3 \cdot 3 \cdot 3}{5 \cdot 5 \cdot 5 \cdot 5}$ $= \frac{3^4}{5^4}$
preimage (p. SB24) The original figure in a transformation.	**imagen original** Figura original en una transformación.	Preimage, Image, A, B, C, A′, B′, C′ $\triangle ABC \rightarrow \triangle A'B'C'$
prime factorization (p. 478, p. SB5) A representation of a number or a polynomial as a product of primes.	**factorización prima** Representación de un número o de un polinomio como producto de números primos.	The prime factorization of 60 is $2 \cdot 2 \cdot 3 \cdot 5$.
prime number (p. 478, p. SB5) A whole number greater than 1 that has exactly two positive factors, itself and 1.	**número primo** Número cabal mayor que 1 que es divisible únicamente entre sí mismo y entre 1.	5 is prime because its only factors are 5 and 1.
principal (p. SB11) An amount of money borrowed or invested.	**capital** Cantidad de dinero que se pide prestado o se invierte.	

Glossary/Glosario **G25**

ENGLISH	SPANISH	EXAMPLES
principal square root (p. 32) The positive square root of a number, indicated by the radical sign.	**raíz principal** Raíz cuadrada positivo de un número, expresada por el signo de radical.	The principal square root of 36 is $\sqrt{36} = 6$.
prism (p. SB20) A three-dimensional figure with two congruent parallel polygonal bases. The remaining edges join corresponding vertices of the bases so that the remaining faces are rectangles.	**prisma** Figura tridimensional con dos bases poligonales congruentes y paralelas. El resto de las aristas se unen a los vértices correspondientes de las bases de manera que las otras sean rectángulos.	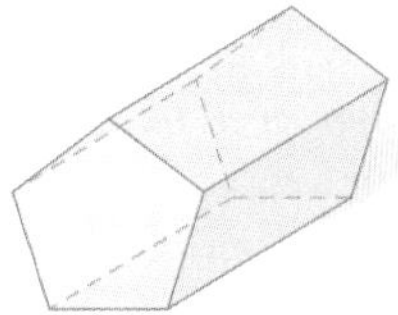
probability (p. SB29) A number from 0 to 1 (or 0% to 100%) that is the measure of how likely an event is to occur.	**probabilidad** Número entre 0 y 1 (o entre 0% y 100%) que describe cuán probable es que ocurra un suceso.	A bag contains 3 red marbles and 4 blue marbles. The probability of randomly choosing a red marble is $\frac{3}{7}$.
Product of Powers Property (p. 408) If a is any nonzero real number and m and n are integers, then $a^m \cdot a^n = a^{m+n}$.	**Propiedad del producto de potencias** Dado un número real a distinto de cero y los números enteros m y n, entonces $a^m \cdot a^n = a^{m+n}$.	$6^7 \cdot 6^4 = 6^{7+4}$ $= 6^{11}$
Product Property of Square Roots (p. 706) For $a \geq 0$ and $b \geq 0$, $\sqrt{ab} = \sqrt{a} \cdot \sqrt{b}$.	**Propiedad del producto de raíces cuadradas** Dados $a \geq 0$ y $b \geq 0$, $\sqrt{ab} = \sqrt{a} \cdot \sqrt{b}$.	$\sqrt{9 \cdot 25} = \sqrt{9} \cdot \sqrt{25}$ $= 3 \cdot 5 = 15$
proportion (p. 102) A statement that two ratios are equal; $\frac{a}{b} = \frac{c}{d}$.	**proporción** Ecuación que establece que dos razones son iguales; $\frac{a}{b} = \frac{c}{d}$.	$\frac{2}{3} = \frac{4}{6}$
pyramid (p. SB20) A three-dimensional figure with a polygonal base lying in one plane plus one additional vertex not lying on that plane. The remaining edges of the pyramid join the additional vertex to the vertices of the base.	**pirámide** Figura tridimensional con una base poligonal en un plano, más un vértice adicional que no está en ese plano. El resto de las aristas de la pirámide unen el vértice adicional a los vértices de la base.	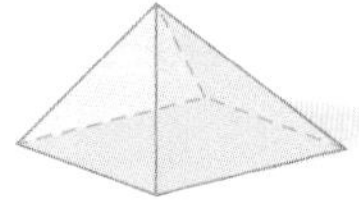
Pythagorean Theorem (p. SB20) For any right triangle, if the legs have lengths a and b and the hypotenuse has length c, then $a^2 + b^2 = c^2$.	**Teorema de Pitágoras** Dado un triángulo rectángulo con catetos de longitudes a y b y una hipotenusa de longitud c, entonces $a^2 + b^2 = c^2$.	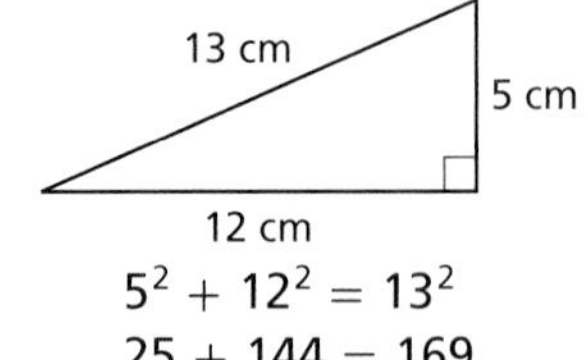 $5^2 + 12^2 = 13^2$ $25 + 144 = 169$
Pythagorean triple (p. 473) A set of three nonzero whole numbers a, b, and c such that $a^2 + b^2 = c^2$.	**Tripleta de Pitágoras** Conjunto de tres números cabales distintos de cero a, b y c tal que $a^2 + b^2 = c^2$.	The numbers 3, 4, and 5 form a Pythagorean triple because $3^2 + 4^2 = 5^2$.

ENGLISH	SPANISH	EXAMPLES
quadrant (p. SB23) One of the four regions into which the x- and y-axes divide the coordinate plane.	**cuadrante** Una de las cuatro regiones en las que los ejes x e y dividen el plano cartesiano.	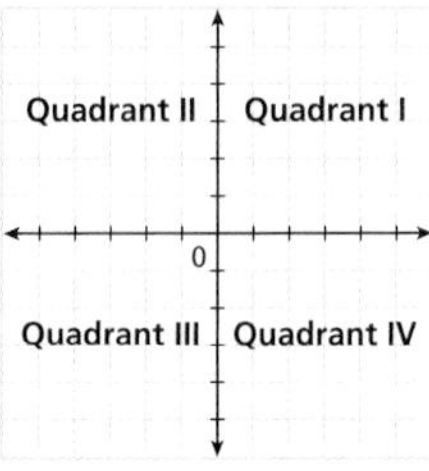

G26 *Glossary/Glosario*

ENGLISH	SPANISH	EXAMPLES
quadratic equation (p. 544) An equation that can be written in the form $ax^2 + bx + c = 0$, where a, b, and c are real numbers and $a \neq 0$.	**ecuación cuadrática** Ecuación que se puede expresar como $ax^2 + bx + c = 0$, donde a, b y c son números reales y $a \neq 0$.	$x^2 + 3x - 4 = 0$ $x^2 - 9 = 0$
Quadratic Formula (p. 598) The formula $x = \frac{-b \pm \sqrt{b^2 - 4ac}}{2a}$, which gives solutions of equations in the form $ax^2 + bx + c = 0$, where $a \neq 0$.	**fórmula cuadrática** La fórmula $x = \frac{-b \pm \sqrt{b^2 - 4ac}}{2a}$, que da soluciones para las ecuaciones del tipo $ax^2 + bx + c = 0$, donde $a \neq 0$.	The solutions of $2x^2 - 5x - 3 = 0$ are given by $x = \frac{-(-5) \pm \sqrt{(-5)^2 - 4(2)(-3)}}{2(2)}$ $= \frac{5 \pm \sqrt{25 + 24}}{4} = \frac{5 \pm 7}{4}$. So $x = 3$ or $x = -\frac{1}{2}$.
quadratic function (p. 544) A function that can be written in the form $f(x) = ax^2 + bx + c$, where a, b, and c are real numbers and $a \neq 0$.	**función cuadrática** Función que se puede expresar como $f(x) = ax^2 + bx + c$, donde a, b y c son números reales y $a \neq 0$.	$f(x) = x^2 - 6x + 8$
quadratic polynomial (p. 431) A polynomial of degree 2.	**polinomio cuadrático** Polinomio de grado 2.	$x^2 - 6x + 8$
quartile (p. SB27) The median of the upper or lower half of a data set. *See also* lower quartile, upper quartile.	**cuartil** La mediana de la mitad superior o inferior de un conjunto de datos. *Ver también* cuartil inferior, cuartil superior.	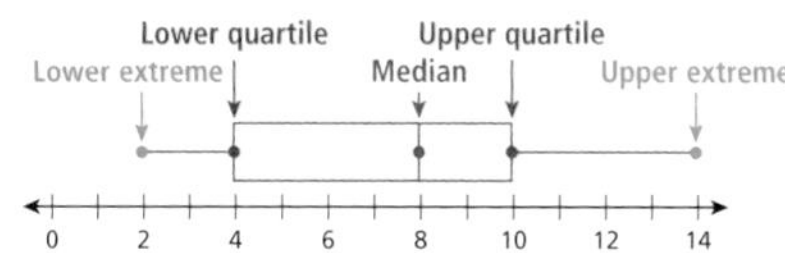
Quotient of Powers Property (p. 415) If a is a nonzero real number and m and n are integers, then $\frac{a^m}{a^n} = a^{m-n}$.	**Propiedad del cociente de potencias** Dado un número real a distinto de cero y los números enteros m y n, entonces $\frac{a^m}{a^n} = a^{m-n}$.	$\frac{6^7}{6^4} = 6^{7-4} = 6^3$
Quotient Property of Square Roots (p. 706) For $a \geq 0$ and $b > 0$, $\sqrt{\frac{a}{b}} = \frac{\sqrt{a}}{\sqrt{b}}$.	**Propiedad del cociente de raíces cuadradas** Dados $a \geq 0$ y $b > 0$, $\sqrt{\frac{a}{b}} = \frac{\sqrt{a}}{\sqrt{b}}$.	$\sqrt{\frac{9}{25}} = \frac{\sqrt{9}}{\sqrt{25}} = \frac{3}{5}$

R

ENGLISH	SPANISH	EXAMPLES
radical equation (p. 722) An equation that contains a variable within a radical.	**ecuación radical** Ecuación que contiene una variable dentro de un radical.	$\sqrt{x + 3} + 4 = 7$
radical expression (p. 705) An expression that contains a radical sign.	**expresión radical** Expresión que contiene un signo de radical.	$\sqrt{x + 3} + 4$
radical symbol (p. 32) The symbol $\sqrt{}$ used to denote a root. The symbol is used alone to indicate a square root or with an index, $\sqrt[n]{}$, to indicate the nth root.	**símbolo de radical** Símbolo $\sqrt{}$ que se utiliza para expresar una raíz. Puede utilizarse solo para indicar una raíz cuadrada, o con un índice, $\sqrt[n]{}$, para indicar la enésima raíz.	$\sqrt{36} = 6$ $\sqrt[3]{27} = 3$

Glossary/Glosario

Glossary/Glosario **G27**

ENGLISH	SPANISH	EXAMPLES
radicand (p. 705) The expression under a radical sign.	**radicando** Número o expresión debajo del signo de radical.	Expression: $\sqrt{x+3}$ Radicand: $x + 3$
radius (p. SB17) A segment whose endpoints are the center of a circle and a point on the circle; the distance from the center of a circle to any point on the circle.	**radio** Segmento cuyos extremos son el centro de un círculo y un punto de la circunferencia; distancia desde el centro de un círculo hasta cualquier punto de la circunferencia.	Radius
random sample (p. SB26) A sample selected from a population so that each member of the population has an equal chance of being selected.	**muestra aleatoria** Muestra seleccionada de una población tal que cada miembro de ésta tenga igual probabilidad de ser seleccionada.	Mr. Hansen chose a random sample of the class by writing each student's name on a slip of paper, mixing up the slips, and drawing five slips without looking.
range of a function or relation (p. 206) The set of all second coordinates (or *y*-values) of a function or relation.	**rango de una función o relación** Conjunto de todos los valores de la segunda coordenada (o valores de *y*) de una función o relación.	The range of $y = x^2$ is $y \geq 0$.
rate (p. 102) A ratio that compares two quantities measured in different units.	**tasa** Razón que compara dos cantidades medidas en diferentes unidades.	$\frac{55 \text{ miles}}{1 \text{ hour}} = 55\text{mi/h}$
rate of change (p. 272) A ratio that compares the amount of change in a dependent variable to the amount of change in an independent variable.	**tasa de cambio** Razón que compara la cantidad de cambio de la variable dependiente con la cantidad de cambio de la variable independiente.	The cost of mailing a letter increased from 22 cents in 1985 to 25 cents in 1988. During this period, the rate of change was $\frac{\text{change in cost}}{\text{change in year}} = \frac{25-21}{1988-1985} = \frac{3}{3}$ $= 1$ cent per year.
ratio (p. 102) A comparison of two numbers or quantities.	**razón** Comparación de dos números o cantidades.	$\frac{1}{2}$ or 1:2
rational equation (p. 674) An equation that contains one or more rational expressions.	**ecuación racional** Ecuación que contiene una o más expresiones racionales.	$\frac{x+2}{x^2+3x-1} = 6$
rational exponent *See* fractional exponent.	**exponente racional** *Ver* exponente fraccionario.	
rational expression (p. 642) A quotient of polynomials.	**expresión racional** Cociente de polinomios.	$\frac{x+2}{x^2+3x-1}$
rational function (p. 634) A function whose rule is a quotient of polynomials.	**función racional** Función cuya regla es un cociente de polinomios.	$f(x) = \frac{x+2}{x^2+3x-1}$
rationalizing the denominator (p. 718) A method of rewriting a fraction by multiplying by another fraction that is equivalent to 1 in order to remove radical terms from the denominator.	**racionalizar el denominador** Método que consiste en escribir nuevamente una fracción multiplicándola por otra fracción equivalente a 1 a fin de eliminar los términos radicales del denominador.	$\frac{1}{\sqrt{2}} \cdot \frac{\sqrt{2}}{\sqrt{2}} = \frac{\sqrt{2}}{2}$

Glossary/Glosario

G28 *Glossary/Glosario*

ENGLISH	SPANISH	EXAMPLES
rational number (p. 33) A number that can be written in the form $\frac{a}{b}$, where a and b are integers and $b \neq 0$.	**número racional** Número que se puede expresar como $\frac{a}{b}$, donde a y b son números enteros y $b \neq 0$.	$3, 1.75, 0.\overline{3}, -\frac{2}{3}, 0$
real numbers (p. 14) The set of all rational or irrational numbers. Every point on the number line represents a real number.	**número real** El conjunto de todos los números racionales o irracionales. Cada punto de la recta numérica representa un número real.	Real Numbers: Rational Numbers (Q): $\frac{27}{4}$, $0.\overline{3}$, $-\frac{10}{11}$, 4.5, $\frac{5}{9}$; Integers (Z): −3, −2, −1; Whole Numbers (W): 0; Natural Numbers (N): 1, 2, 3. Irrational Numbers: $\sqrt{17}$, $-\sqrt{11}$, $\sqrt{2}$, e, π
reciprocal (p. 21) For a real number $a \neq 0$, the reciprocal of a is $\frac{1}{a}$. The product of reciprocals is 1.	**recíproco** Dado el número real $a \neq 0$, el recíproco de a es $\frac{1}{a}$. El producto de los recíprocos es 1.	Number / Reciprocal: 2 / $\frac{1}{2}$; 1 / 1; −1 / −1; 0 / No reciprocal
rectangle (p. SB18) A quadrilateral with four right angles.	**rectángulo** Cuadrilátero con cuatro ángulos rectos.	
rectangular prism (p. SB20) A three-dimensional figure that has three pairs of opposite parallel congruent faces that are rectangles.	**prisma rectangular** Figura tridimensional con tres pares de caras opuestas, y congruentes que son rectangulós.	
rectangular pyramid (p. SB20) A three-dimensional figure with a rectangular base lying in one plane plus one additional vertex not lying on that plane. The remaining edges of the rectangular pyramid join the additional vertex to the vertices of the base.	**pirámide rectangular** Figura tridimensional con una base rectangular en un plano, más un vértice adicional que no está en ese plano. El resto de las aristas de la pirámide rectangular unen el vértice adicional con los vértices de la base.	
reflection (p. SB24) A transformation that reflects, or "flips," a graph or figure across a line, called the line of reflection.	**reflexión** Transformación en la que una gráfica o figura se refleja o se invierte sobre una línea, denominada la línea de reflexión.	A, B, C reflected to A', B', C'
relation (p. 206) A set of ordered pairs.	**relación** Conjunto de pares ordenados.	$\{(0, 5), (0, 4), (2, 3), (4, 0)\}$
repeating decimal (p. 33) A rational number in decimal form that has a block of one or more digits (that are not all zero) after the decimal point that repeat continuously.	**decimal periódico** Número racional en forma decimal que tiene un bloque de uno o más dígitos que se repite continuamente.	$1.\overline{3} = 1.3333...$ $2.\overline{14} = 2.141414...$
replacement set (p. 8) A set of numbers that can be substituted for a variable.	**conjunto de reemplazo** Conjunto de números que pueden sustituir una variable.	
rhombus (p. SB18) A quadrilateral with four congruent sides.	**rombo** Cuadrilátero con cuatro lados congruentes.	
right angle (p. SB63) An angle that measures 90°.	**ángulo recto** Ángulo que mide 90°.	

Glossary/Glosario G29

ENGLISH	SPANISH	EXAMPLES
right triangle (p. SB18) A triangle with one right angle.	**triángulo rectángulo** Triángulo con un ángulo recto.	
rise (p. 272) The difference in the y-values of two points on a line.	**distancia vertical** Diferencia entre los valores de y de dos puntos de una línea.	For the points $(3, -1)$ and $(6, 5)$, the rise is $5 - (-1) = 6$.
rotation (p. SB24) A transformation that rotates or turns a figure about a point called the center of rotation.	**rotación** Transformación que rota o gira una figura sobre un punto llamado centro de rotación.	
run (p. 272) The difference in the x-values of two points on a line.	**distancia horizontal** Diferencia entre los valores de x de dos puntos de una línea.	For the points $(3, -1)$ and $(6, 5)$, the run is $6 - 3 = 3$.

S

ENGLISH	SPANISH	EXAMPLES
sample (p. SB26) A part of a group being surveyed.	**muestra** Parte de un grupo que es objeto de estudio.	In a survey about eating habits of high school students, a sample is a group of 100 randomly chosen high school students.
scale (p. 104) The ratio between two corresponding measurements.	**escala** Razón entre dos medidas correspondientes.	1 cm:5 mi
scale drawing (p. 104) A drawing that uses a scale to represent an object as smaller or larger than the actual object.	**dibujo a escala** Dibujo que utiliza una escala para representar un objeto como más pequeño o más grande que el objeto original.	A blueprint is an example of a scale drawing.
scale model (p. 104) A three-dimensional model that uses a scale to represent an object as smaller or larger than the actual object.	**modelo a escala** Modelo tridimensional que utiliza una escala para representar un objeto como más pequeño o más grande que el objeto real.	
scalene triangle (p. SB18) A triangle with no congruent sides.	**triángulo escaleno** Triángulo sin lados congruentes.	
scatter plot (p. 224) A graph with points plotted to show a possible relationship between two sets of data.	**diagrama de dispersión** Gráfica con puntos que se usa para demostrar una relación posible entre dos conjuntos de datos.	
scientific notation (p. 401) A method of writing very large or very small numbers, by using powers of 10, in the form $m \times 10^n$, where $1 \leq m < 10$ and n is an integer.	**notación científica** Método que consiste en escribir números muy grandes o muy pequeños utilizando potencias de 10 del tipo $m \times 10^n$, donde $1 \leq m < 10$ y n es un número entero.	$12{,}560{,}000{,}000{,}000 = 1.256 \times 10^{13}$ $0.0000075 = 7.5 \times 10^{-6}$

G30 Glossary/Glosario

ENGLISH	SPANISH	EXAMPLES

second differences (p. 756) The differences between first differences of a function for evenly spaced x-values.

segundas diferencias Las diferencias entre las primeras diferencias de una función para valores de x espaciados uniformemente.

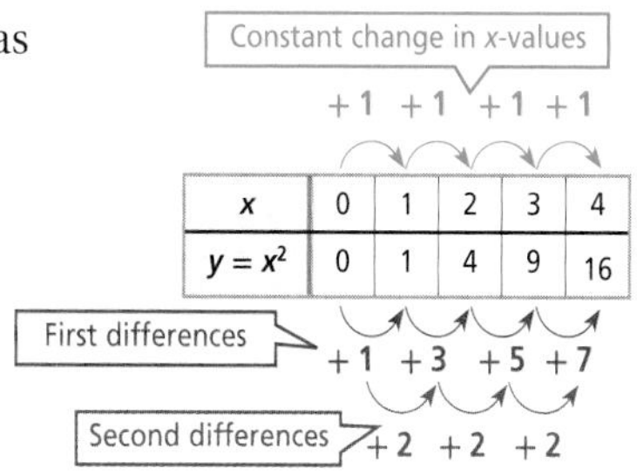

---

sequence (p. 234) A list of numbers that may form a pattern.

sucesión Lista de números que forman un patrón.

1, 2, 4, 8, 16, ...

---

set-builder notation (p. 142) A notation for a set that uses a rule to describe the properties of the elements of the set.

notación de conjuntos Notación para un conjunto que se vale de una regla para describir las propiedades de los elementos del conjunto.

$\{x : x > 3\}$ is read "The set of all x such that x is greater than 3."

---

simple interest (p. SB11) A fixed percent of the principal. For principal P, interest rate r (expressed as a decimal), and time t in years, the simple interest is $I = Prt$.

interés simple Porcentaje fijo del capital. Dado el capital P, la tasa de interés r (expresada como un decimal) y el tiempo t expresado en años, el interés simple es $I = Prt$.

If \$100 is put into an account with a simple interest rate of 5%, then after 2 years, the account will have earned $I = 100 \cdot 0.05 \cdot 2 = \$10$ in interest.

---

simplest form of an exponential expression (p. 408) An exponential expression is in simplest form if it meets the following criteria:

1. There are no negative exponents.
2. The same base does not appear more than once in a product or quotient.
3. No powers, products, or quotients are raised to powers.
4. Numerical coefficients in a quotient do not have any common factor other than 1.

forma simplificada de una expresión exponencial Una expresión exponencial está en forma simplificada si reúne los siguientes requisitos:

1. No hay exponentes negativos.
2. La misma base no aparece más de una vez en un producto o cociente.
3. No se elevan a potencias productos, cocientes ni potencias.
4. Los coeficientes numéricos en un cociente no tienen ningún factor común que no sea 1.

Not Simplest Form	Simplest Form
$7^8 \cdot 7^4$	7^{12}
$(x^2)^{-4} \cdot x^5$	$\frac{1}{x^3}$
$\frac{a^5b^9}{(ab)^4}$	ab^5

---

simplest form of a rational expression (p. 643) A rational expression is in simplest form if the numerator and denominator have no common factors.

forma simplificada de una expresión racional Una expresión racional está en forma simplificada cuando el numerador y el denominador no tienen factores comunes.

$$\frac{x^2 - 1}{x^2 + x - 2} = \frac{(x-1)(x+1)}{(x+1)(x+2)} = \frac{x-1}{x+2}$$

↑ Simplest form

---

simplest form of a square-root expression (p. 705) A square-root expression is in simplest form if it meets the following criteria:

1. No perfect squares are in the radicand.
2. No fractions are in the radicand.
3. No square roots appear in the denominator of a fraction.

See also rationalizing the denominator.

forma simplificada de una expresión de raíz cuadrada Una expresión de raíz cuadrada está en forma simplificada si reúne los siguientes requisitos:

1. No hay cuadrados perfectos en el radicando.
2. No hay fracciones en el radicando.
3. No aparecen raíces cuadradas en el denominador de una fracción.

Ver también racionalizar el denominador.

Not Simplest Form	Simplest Form
$\sqrt{180}$	$6\sqrt{5}$
$\sqrt{216a^2b^2}$	$6ab\sqrt{6}$
$\frac{\sqrt{7}}{\sqrt{2}}$	$\frac{\sqrt{14}}{2}$

Glossary/Glosario

Glossary/Glosario **G31**

ENGLISH	SPANISH	EXAMPLES
simplify (p. 48) To perform all indicated operations.	**simplificar** Realizar todas las operaciones indicadas.	$13 - 20 + 8$ $-7 + 8$ 1
slope (p. 272) A measure of the steepness of a line. If (x_1, y_1) and (x_2, y_2) are any two points on the line, the slope of the line, represented by m, is $m = \frac{y_2 - y_1}{x_2 - x_1}$.	**pendiente** Medida de la inclinación de una línea. Dados dos puntos (x_1, y_1) y (x_2, y_2) en una línea, la pendiente de la línea, denominada m, se representa con la ecuación $m = \frac{y_2 - y_1}{x_2 - x_1}$.	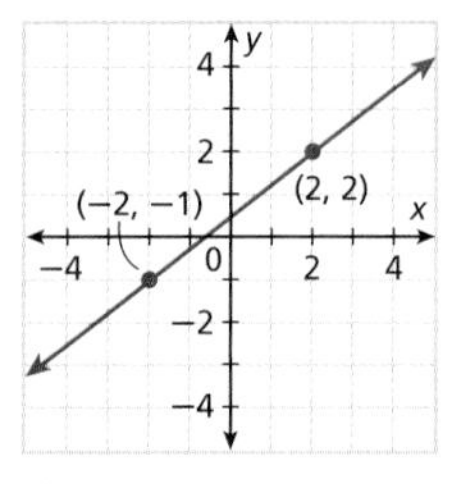 $m = \frac{y_2 - y_1}{x_2 - x_1} = \frac{-1 - 2}{-2 - 2} = \frac{3}{4}$
slope-intercept form (p. 291) The slope-intercept form of a linear equation is $y = mx + b$, where m is the slope and b is the y-intercept.	**forma de pendiente-intersección** La forma de pendiente-intersección de una ecuación lineal es $y = mx + b$, donde m es la pendiente y b es la intersección con el eje y.	$y = -2x + 4$ The slope is -2. The y-intercept is 4.
solution of an equation in one variable (p. 72) A value or values that make the equation true.	**solución de una ecuación en una variable** Valor o valores que hacen que la ecuación sea verdadera.	Equation: $x + 2 = 6$ Solution: $x = 4$
solution of an equation in two variables (p. 213) An ordered pair or ordered pairs that make the equation true.	**solución de una ecuación en dos variables** Un par ordenado o pares ordenados que hacen que la ecuación sea verdadera.	Equation: $x + y = 6$ Solution: $(4, 2)$ (one possible solution)
solution of an inequality in one variable (p. 136) A value or values that make the inequality true.	**solución de una desigualdad en una variable** Valor o valores que hacen que la desigualdad sea verdadera.	Inequality: $x + 2 < 6$ Solution: $x < 4$
solution of an inequality in two variables (p. 364) An ordered pair or ordered pairs that make the inequality true.	**solución de una desigualdad en dos variables** Un par ordenado o pares ordenados que hacen que la desigualdad sea verdadera.	Inequality: $3x + 2y \geq 6$ 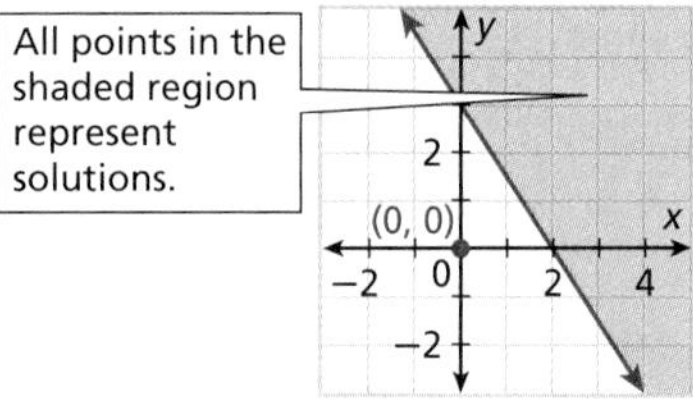
solution of a system of equations in two variables (p. 329) Any ordered pair that satisfies all the equations in the system.	**solución de un sistema de ecuaciones en dos variables** Cualquier par ordenado que resuelva todas las ecuaciones del sistema.	$\begin{cases} x + y = -1 \\ -x + y = -3 \end{cases}$ Solution: $(1, -2)$
solution of a system of inequalities in two variables (p. 371) Any ordered pair that satisfies all the inequalities in the system.	**solución de un sistema de desigualdades en dos variables** Cualquier par ordenado que resuelva todas las desigualdades del sistema.	$\begin{cases} y \leq x + 1 \\ y < -x + 4 \end{cases}$ 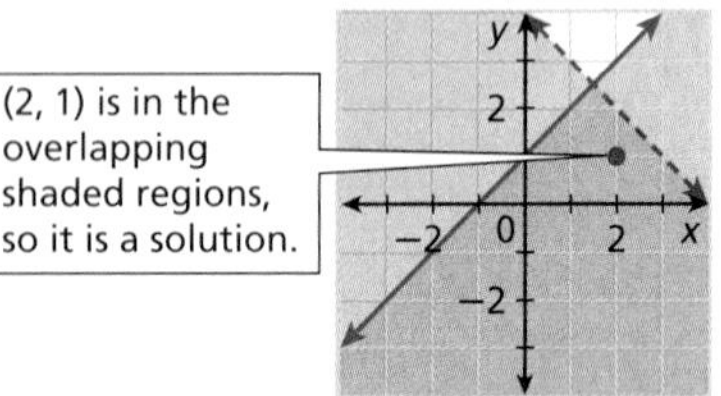
solution set (p. 72) The set of all solutions of a particular problem.	**conjunto solución** Conjunto de todas las soluciones de un problema en particular.	Inequality: $x + 3 \geq 5$ Solution set: $\{x : x \geq 2\}$ −4 −3 −2 −1 0 1 2 3 4 5 6

G32 Glossary/Glosario

ENGLISH	SPANISH	EXAMPLES
square (p. SB18) A quadrilateral with four congruent sides and four right angles.	**cuadrado** Cuadrilátero con cuatro lados congruentes y cuatro ángulos rectos.	
square in numeration (p. 26) The second power of a number.	**cuadrado en numeración** La segunda potencia de un número.	16 is the square of 4 because $4^2 = 16$.
square root (p. 32) A number that is multiplied by itself to form a product is called a square root of that product.	**raíz cuadrada** El número que se multiplica por sí mismo para formar un producto se denomina la raíz cuadrada de ese producto.	The square roots of 16 are 4 and −4 because $4^2 = 4 \cdot 4 = 16$ and $(-4)^2 = -4 \cdot (-4) = 16$.
square-root function (p. 700) A function whose rule contains a variable under a square-root sign.	**función de raíz cuadrada** Función cuya regla contiene una variable bajo un signo de raíz cuadrada.	$y = \sqrt{3x} - 5$
standard form of a linear equation (p. 258) $Ax + By = C$, where A, B, and C are real numbers and A and B are not both 0.	**forma estándar de una ecuación lineal** $Ax + By = C$, donde A, B y C son números reales y A y B no son ambas 0.	$2x + 3y = 6$
standard form of a polynomial (p. 431) A polynomial in one variable is written in standard form when the terms are in order from greatest degree to least degree.	**forma estándar de un polinomio** Un polinomio de una variable se expresa en forma estándar cuando los términos se ordenan de mayor a menor grado.	$4x^5 - 2x^4 + x^2 - x + 1$
standard form of a quadratic equation (p. 577) $ax^2 + bx + c = 0$, where a, b, and c are real numbers and $a \neq 0$.	**forma estándar de una ecuación cuadrática** $ax^2 + bx + c = 0$, donde a, b y c son números reales y $a \neq 0$.	$2x^2 + 3x - 1 = 0$
substitution method (p. 336) A method used to solve systems of equations by solving an equation for one variable and substituting the resulting expression into the other equation(s).	**sustitución** Método utilizado para resolver sistemas de ecuaciones resolviendo una ecuación para una variable y sustituyendo la expresión resultante en las demás ecuaciones.	
Subtraction Property of Equality (p. 72) If a, b, and c are real numbers and $a = b$, then $a - c = b - c$.	**Propiedad de igualdad de la resta** Si a, b y c son números reales y $a = b$, entonces $a - c = b - c$.	$\begin{aligned} x + 6 &= 8 \\ -6 &\quad -6 \\ x &= 2 \end{aligned}$
Subtraction Property of Inequality (p. 142) For real numbers a, b, and c, if $a < b$, then $a - c < b - c$. Also holds true for $>$, $\leq$, $\geq$, and $\neq$.	**Propiedad de desigualdad de la resta** Dados los números reales a, b y c, si $a < b$, entonces $a - c < b - c$. Es válido también para $>$, $\leq$, $\geq$ y $\neq$.	$\begin{aligned} x + 6 &< 8 \\ -6 &\quad -6 \\ x &< 2 \end{aligned}$
supplementary angles (p. SB14) Two angles whose measures have a sum of 180°.	**ángulos suplementarios** Dos ángulos cuyas medidas suman 180°.	30° 150°

Glossary/Glosario

Glossary/Glosario G33

ENGLISH	SPANISH	EXAMPLES
surface area (p. SB22) The total area of all faces and curved surfaces of a three-dimensional figure.	**área total** Área total de todas las caras y superficies curvas de una figura tridimensional.	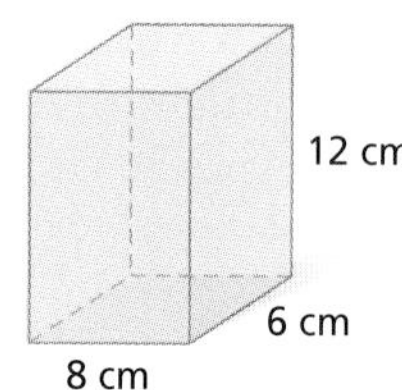 Surface area $= 2(8)(12) + 2(8)(6) + 2(12)(6)$ $= 432 \text{ cm}^2$
system of linear equations (p. 329) A set of two or more linear equations containing two or more variables.	**sistema de ecuaciones lineales** Conjunto de dos o más ecuaciones lineales con dos o más variables.	$\begin{cases} 2x + 3y = -1 \\ x - 3y = 4 \end{cases}$
system of linear inequalities (p. 371) A set of two or more linear inequalities containing two or more variables.	**sistema de desigualdades lineales** Conjunto de dos o más desigualdades lineales con dos o más variables.	$\begin{cases} 2x + 3y > -1 \\ x - 3y \leq 4 \end{cases}$

ENGLISH	SPANISH	EXAMPLES
term of an expression (p. 49) The parts of the expression that are added or subtracted.	**término de una expresión** Parte de una expresión que debe sumarse o restarse.	$3x^2 + 6x - 8$ 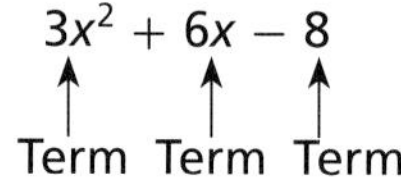
term of a sequence (p. 234) An element or number in the sequence.	**término de una sucesión** Elemento o número de una sucesión.	5 is the third term in the sequence 1, 3, 5, 7, ...
terminating decimal (p. 33) A rational number in decimal form that has a finite number of digits after the decimal point.	**decimal finito** Número racional en forma decimal que tiene un número finito de dígitos después del punto decimal.	1.5, 2.75, 4.0
theoretical probability (p. SB29) The ratio of the number of equally likely outcomes in an event to the total number of possible outcomes.	**probabilidad teórica** Razón entre el número de resultados igualmente probables de un suceso y el número total de resultados posibles.	In the experiment of rolling a number cube, the theoretical probability of rolling an odd number is $\frac{3}{6} = \frac{1}{2}$.
third quartile *See* upper quartile.	**tercer cuartil** *Ver* cuartil superior.	
transformation (p. SB24) A change in the position, size, or shape of a figure or graph.	**transformación** Cambio en la posición, tamaño o forma de una figura o gráfica.	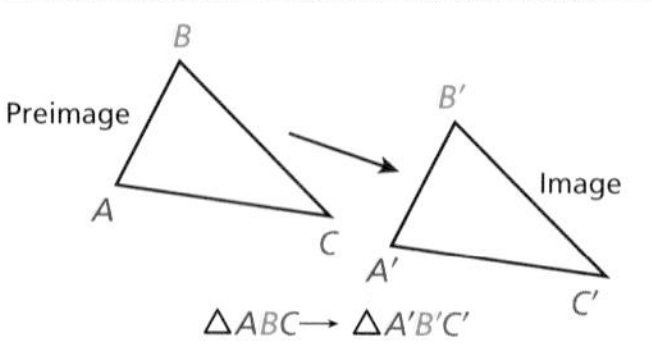
translation (p. SB24) A transformation that shifts or slides every point of a figure or graph the same distance in the same direction.	**traslación** Transformación en la que todos los puntos de una figura o gráfica se mueven la misma distancia en la misma dirección.	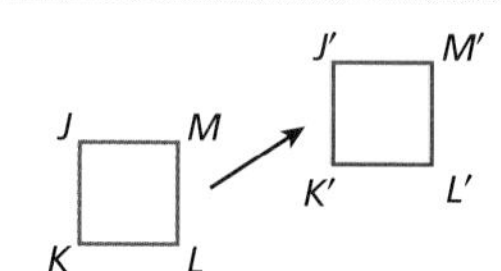
trapezoid (p. SB18) A quadrilateral with exactly one pair of parallel sides.	**trapecio** Cuadrilátero con sólo un par de lados paralelos.	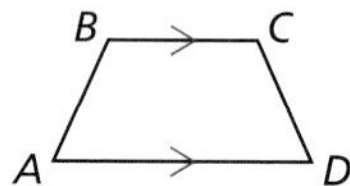

G34 *Glossary/Glosario*

ENGLISH	SPANISH	EXAMPLES
tree diagram (p. SB32) A branching diagram that shows all possible combinations or outcomes of an experiment.	**diagrama de árbol** Diagrama con ramificaciones que muestra todas las combinaciones o resultados posibles de un experimento.	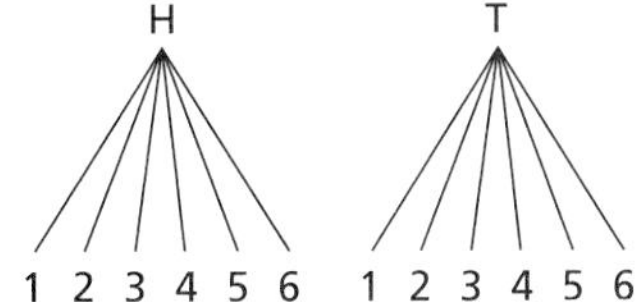 The tree diagram shows the possible outcomes when tossing a coin and rolling a number cube.
trend line (p. 227) A line on a scatter plot that helps show the correlation between data sets more clearly.	**línea de tendencia** Línea en un diagrama de dispersión que sirve para mostrar la correlación entre conjuntos de datos más claramente.	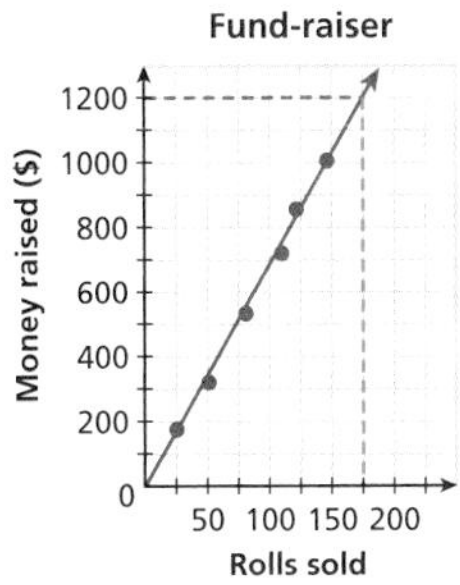
trial (p. SB30) In probability, a single repetition or observation of an experiment.	**prueba** En probabilidad, una sola repetición u observación de un experimento.	In the experiment of rolling a number cube, each roll is one trial.
triangle (p. 177) A three-sided polygon.	**triángulo** Polígono de tres lados.	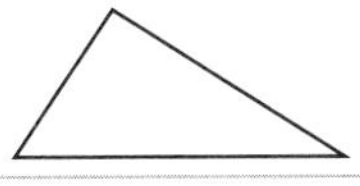
triangular prism (p. SB20) A three-dimensional figure with two congruent parallel triangular bases whose other faces are rectangles.	**prisma triangular** Figura tridimensional con dos bases triangulares paralelas y congruentes cuyas otras caras son rectángulos.	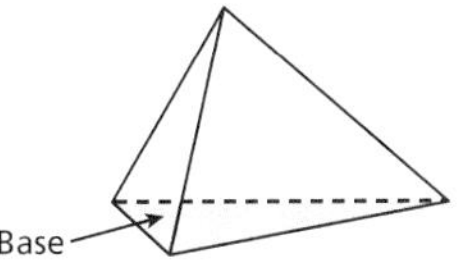
triangular pyramid (p. SB20) A three-dimensional figure with a triangular base lying in one plane plus one additional vertex not lying on that plane. The remaining edges of the triangular pyramid join the additional vertex to the vertices of the base.	**pirámide triangular** Figura tridimensional con una base triangular en un plano, más un vertice adicional que no está en ese plano. El resto de las aristas de la pirámide triangular unen el vértice adicional con los vértices de la base.	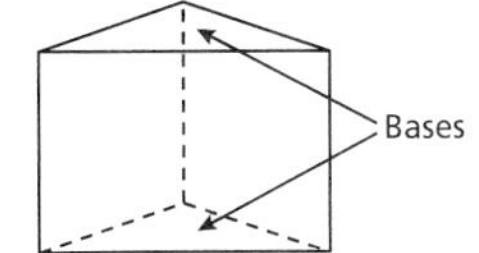
trinomial (p. 431) A polynomial with three terms.	**trinomio** Polinomio con tres términos.	$4x^2 + 3xy - 5y^2$

U

ENGLISH	SPANISH	EXAMPLES
union (p. 172) The union of two sets is the set of all elements that are in either set, denoted by ∪.	**unión** La unión de dos conjuntos es el conjunto de todos los elementos que se encuentran en ambos conjuntos, expresado por ∪.	$A = \{1, 2, 3, 4\}$ $B = \{1, 3, 5, 7, 9\}$ $A \cup B = \{1, 2, 3, 4, 5, 7, 9\}$
unit rate (p. 102) A rate in which the second quantity in the comparison is one unit.	**tasa unitaria** Tasa en la que la segunda cantidad de la comparación es una unidad.	$\frac{30 \text{ mi}}{1 \text{ h}} = 30 \text{ mi/h}$
unlike radicals (p. 711) Radicals with different radicands or indices.	**radicales distintos** Radicales con diferentes radicandos o indices.	$2\sqrt{2}$ and $2\sqrt{3}$ $\sqrt{5}$ and $\sqrt[5]{5}$

Glossary/Glosario G35

ENGLISH	SPANISH	EXAMPLES
unlike terms (p. 49) Terms with different variables or the same variables raised to different powers.	**términos distintos** Términos con variables diferentes o las mismas variables elevadas a potencias diferentes.	$4xy^2$ and $6x^2y$
upper extreme (p. SB27) The greatest value in a data set.	**extremo superior** El valor mayor de un conjunto de datos.	For the data set {3, 3, 5, 7, 8, 11, 11, 12}, the upper extreme is 12.
upper quartile (p. SB27) The median of the upper half of a data set. Also called *third quartile.*	**cuartil superior** La mediana de la mitad superior de un conjunto de datos. También se llama *tercer cuartil.*	Lower half: 18, 23, 28, Upper half: 49, (36), 42 — Upper quartile

V

ENGLISH	SPANISH	EXAMPLES
value of a function (p. 217) The result of replacing the independent variable with a number and simplifying.	**valor de una función** Resultado de reemplazar la variable independiente por un número y luego simplificar.	The value of the function $f(x) = x + 1$ for $x = 3$ is 4.
value of an expression (p. 7) The result of replacing the variables in an expression with numbers and simplifying.	**valor de una expresión** Resultado de reemplazar las variables de una expresión por un número y luego simplificar.	The value of the expression $x + 1$ for $x = 3$ is 4.
value of a variable (p. 7) A number used to replace a variable.	**valor de una variable** Número utilizado para reemplazar una variable.	When you evaluate the expression $x + 2$ for $x = 3$, the value of the variable is 3.
variable (p. 6) A symbol used to represent a quantity that can change.	**variable** Símbolo utilizado para representar una cantidad que puede cambiar.	In the expression $2x + 3$, x is the variable.
Venn diagram (p. SB28) A diagram used to show relationships between two or more sets.	**diagrama de Venn** Diagrama utilizado para mostrar la relación entre dos o más conjuntos.	Brand A; Both; Brand B; Neither: 15
vertex of a cone (p. SB20) The point opposite the base of the cone.	**vértice de un cono** Punto opuesto a la base del cono.	Vertex
vertex of a parabola (p. 546) The highest or lowest point on the parabola.	**vértice de una parábola** Punto más alto o más bajo de una parábola.	(0, −2) The vertex is (0, −2).
vertex of a polyhedron (p. SB20) Any point on the polyhedron where three or more edges intersect.	**vértice de un poliedro** Punto que representa la intersección de tres o más caras.	Vertex

G36 Glossary/Glosario

Glossary/Glosario

ENGLISH	SPANISH	EXAMPLES
vertical angles (p. SB14) A pair of nonadjacent angles formed by two intersecting lines.	**ángulos opuestos por el vértice** Par de ángulos no adyacentes formados por dos líneas que se cruzan.	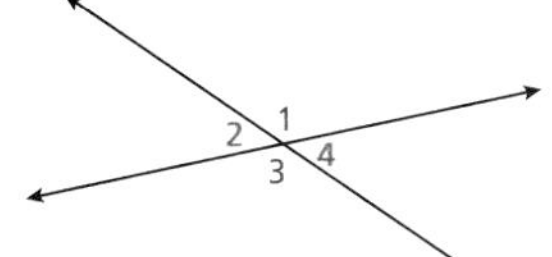 $\angle 1$ and $\angle 3$ are vertical angles. $\angle 2$ and $\angle 4$ are vertical angles.
vertical line (p. 273) A line whose equation is $x = a$, where a is the x-intercept.	**línea vertical** Línea cuya ecuación es $x = a$, donde a es la intersección con el eje x.	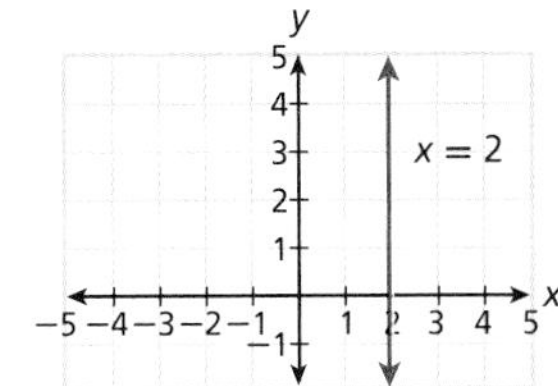
vertical-line test (p. 214) A test used to determine whether a relation is a function. If any vertical line crosses the graph of a relation more than once, the relation is not a function.	**prueba de la línea vertical** Prueba utilizada para determinar si una relación es una función. Si una línea vertical corta la gráfica de una relación más de una vez, la relación no es una función.	Function 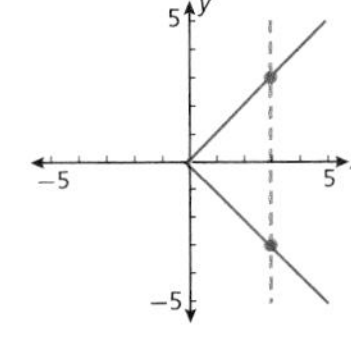 Not a function
volume (p. SB21) The number of nonoverlapping unit cubes of a given size that will exactly fill the interior of a three-dimensional figure.	**volumen** Cantidad de cubos unitarios no superpuestos de un determinado tamaño que llenan exactamente el interior de una figura tridimensional.	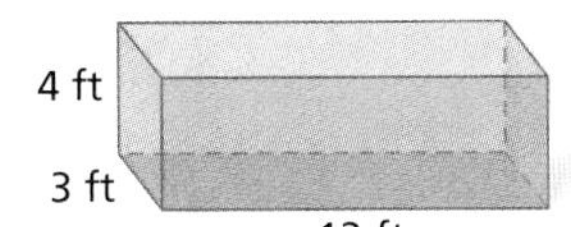 Volume $= (3)(4)(12) = 144 \text{ ft}^3$

W

whole numbers (p. 33) The set of natural numbers and zero.	**números cabales** Conjunto de los números naturales y cero.	$\{0, 1, 2, 3, 4, 5, \ldots\}$

X

***x*-axis** (p. SB23) The horizontal axis in the coordinate plane.	**eje *x*** Eje horizontal en el plano cartesiano.	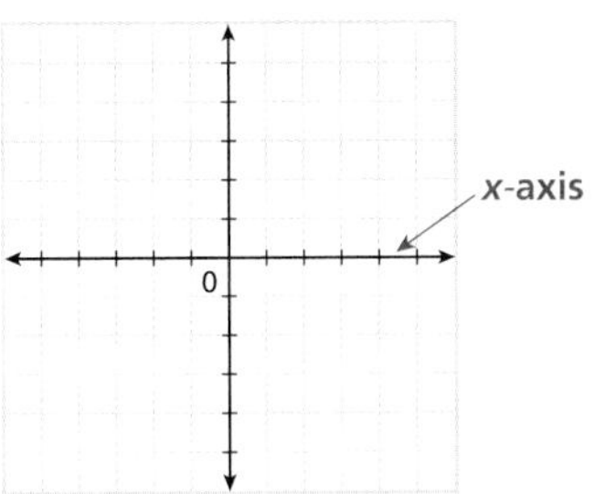
***x*-coordinate** (p. SB23) The first number in an ordered pair, which indicates the horizontal distance of a point from the origin on the coordinate plane.	**coordenada *x*** Primer número de un par ordenado, que indica la distancia horizontal de un punto desde el origen en un plano cartesiano.	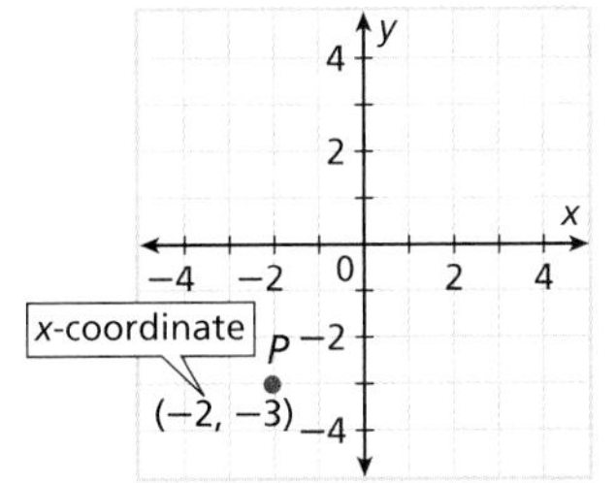

Glossary/Glosario

Glossary/Glosario G37

ENGLISH	SPANISH	EXAMPLES
x-intercept (p. 263) The x-coordinate(s) of the point(s) where a graph intersects the x-axis.	**intersección con el eje x** Coordenada(s) x de uno o más puntos donde una gráfica corta el eje x.	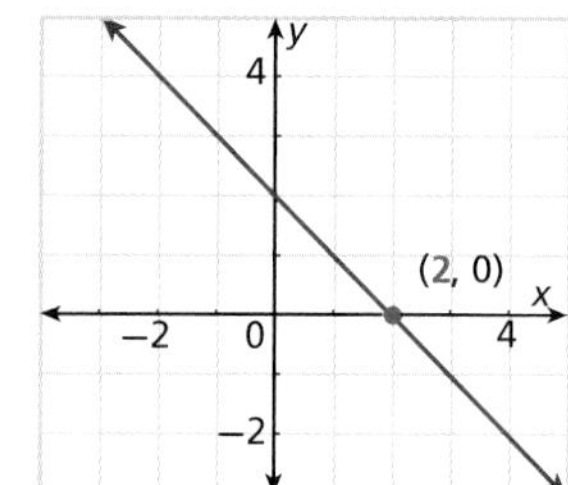 The x-intercept is 2.

ENGLISH	SPANISH	EXAMPLES
y-axis (p. SB23) The vertical axis in the coordinate plane.	**eje y** Eje vertical en el plano cartesiano.	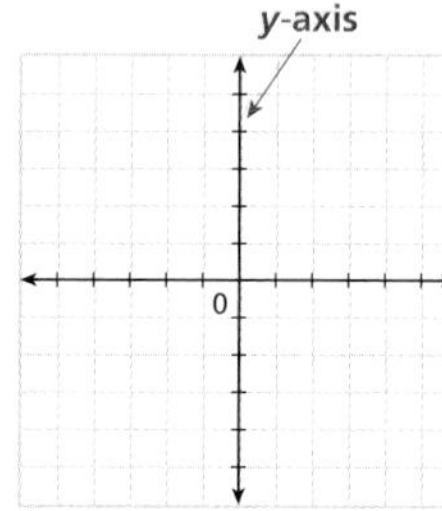
y-coordinate (p. SB23) The second number in an ordered pair, which indicates the vertical distance of a point from the origin on the coordinate plane.	**coordenada y** Segundo número de un par ordenado, que indica la distancia vertical de un punto desde el origen en un plano cartesiano.	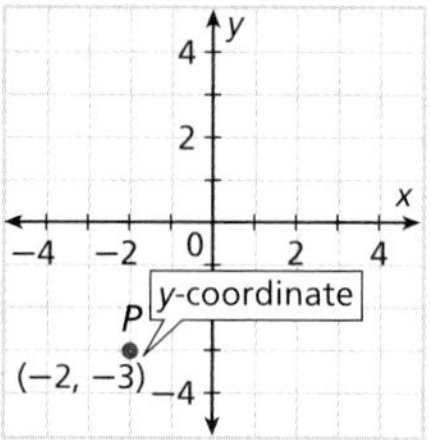
y-intercept (p. 263) The y-coordinate(s) of the point(s) where a graph intersects the y-axis.	**intersección con el eje y** Coordenada(s) y de uno o más puntos donde una gráfica corta el eje y.	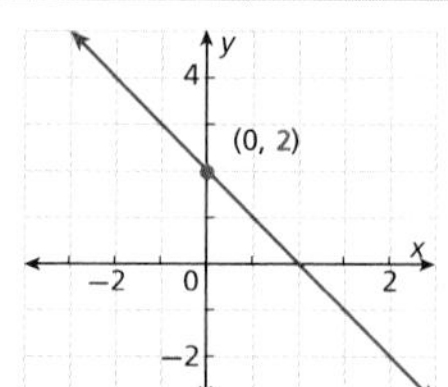 The y-intercept is 2.

ENGLISH	SPANISH	EXAMPLES
zero exponent (p. 394) For any nonzero real number x, $x^0 = 1$.	**exponente cero** Dado un número real distinto de cero x, $x^0 = 1$.	$5^0 = 1$
zero of a function (p. 553) For the function f, any number x such that $f(x) = 0$.	**cero de una función** Dada la función f, todo número x tal que $f(x) = 0$.	The zeros are −3 and 1.
Zero Product Property (p. 576) For real numbers p and q, if $pq = 0$, then $p = 0$ or $q = 0$.	**Propiedad del producto cero** Dados los números reales p y q, si $pq = 0$, entonces $p = 0$ o $q = 0$.	If $(x - 1)(x + 2) = 0$, then $x - 1 = 0$ or $x + 2 = 0$. So $x = 1$ or $x = -2$.

G38 Glossary/Glosario

Index

Index

D

Index

Index

Index

N

Q

R

Index

S

T

Index

Credits

Abbreviations used: (t) top, (c) center, (b) bottom, (l) left, (r) right, (bkgd) background

Staff

Bruce Albrecht, Nancy Behrens, Tica Chitrarachis, Lorraine Cooper, Marc Cooper, Jennifer Craycraft, Martize Cross, Nina Degollado, Julie Dervin, Michelle Dike, Lydia Doty, Sam Dudgeon, Kelli R. Flanagan, Stephanie Friedman, Jeff Galvez, Pam Garner, Diannia Green, Tracie Harris, Liz Huckestein, Jevara Jackson, Simon Key, Jane A. Kirschman, Kadonna Knape, Cathy Kuhles, Jill M. Lawson, Liann Lech, Jeff Mapua, Susan Mussey, Kim Nguyen, Manda Reid, Michael Rinella, Annette Saunders, Kay Selke, Robyn Setzen, Patricia Sinnott, Victoria Smith, Dawn Marie Spinozza, Jeannie Taylor, Karen Vigil, April Warn, Kira J. Watkins, Sherri Whitmarsh, David W. Wynn

Photo

All photos Sam Dudgeon/HRW unless otherwise noted.

Title Page: (windsurfer), DY Riess MD/Alamy; (Joshua Tree), Frank Krahmer/zefa/Corbis; (buildings), Toyohiro Yamada/Getty Images; (Big Sur), David Muench/CORBIS; (bridge), George Steinmetz/Corbis.

Front Matter: iii (border), PhotoDisc; iv (bl), Courtesy of Lee Haines; iv (br), Courtesy of Robin Scarcella; v (bl), Courtesy of Charlie Bialowas; v (br), Courtesy of Wendy Taub-Hoglund; vii (border), Charles O'Rear/CORBIS; viii (border), Jan Butchofsky-Houser/CORBIS; ix (border), Randy Faris/CORBIS; x (border), Tom and Pat Leeson; xi (border), Ron Stroud/Masterfile; xii (border), Noah Graham/NBAE via Getty Images; xiii (starry border), ©Royalty-Free/Corbis; xiii (observatory), Bill Ross/CORBIS OUTLINE; xv (border), ©Royalty Free/CORBIS; xvi (border), Tom Paiva/Getty Images; xvii (border), QT Luong/Terra Galleria Photography; xiv (border), ©Mark Gibson Photography.

Chapter One: 2–3 (all), Charles O'Rear/CORBIS; 6 (tr), ©Ray Roberts/Alamy Photos; 6 (sky), PhotoDisc/Getty Images; 8 (tc), Sam Dudgeon/HRW; 8 (c), Sam Dudgeon/HRW; 10 (bl), AP Photo/NASA Haughton-Mars Project 2001, Pascal Lee; 10 (tl), ©Royalty Free/CORBIS; 14 (tr), ©Paul A. Souders/CORBIS; 18 (c), John Sullivan/Ribbit Photography; 18 (bl), ©Royalty Free/CORBIS; 20 (c), ©Craig Aurness/CORBIS; 20 (tc), Derek & Garry Walker/Adams/PictureQuest/Jupiter Images; 22 (cr), ©Dave G. Houser/CORBIS; 24 (cl), Wes Skiles/Karst Productions, Inc.; 24 (bl), ©Royalty Free/CORBIS; 26 (tr), ©Ted Horowitz/CORBIS; 29 (br), Michael Abbey/Photo Researchers, Inc.; 30 (cl), ©2007 The Josef and Anni Albers Foundation/Artist Rights Society (ARS), New York/The Newark Museum/Art Resource, NY; 30 (bl), ©Royalty Free/CORBIS; 30 (cr), PhotoDisc/Getty Images; 36 (bl), ©Royalty Free/CORBIS; 37 (tr), Stephanie Friedman/HRW; 40 (tl), ©Royalty Free/CORBIS; 40 (cr), ©Federico Cabello/SuperStock; 43 (tl), ©BananaStock Ltd.; 46 (bl), PhotoDisc/gettyimages; 49 (tr), AP/Wide World Photos; 52 (tl), Clive Brunskill/Getty Images; 52 (bl), PhotoDisc/gettyimages; 56 (tl), PhotoDisc/gettyimages; 56 (cr), Sam Dudgeon/HRW.

Chapter Two: 68–69 (bkgd), Jan Butchofsky-Houser/CORBIS; 74 (bl), RubberBall/Alamy; 76 (l), ©2001 MBARI; 76 (bl), ©Image Ideas, Inc.; 83 (tl), ©Robert W. Kelley/Time Life Pictures/Getty Images; 83 (cr), ©Corel; 83 (bl), ©Image Ideas, Inc.; 89 (bl), ©Image Ideas, Inc.; 92 (tc), ©Ingram Publishing; 96 (bl), ©Image Ideas, Inc.; 97 (tl), ©Royalty-Free/CORBIS; 98 (bl), Rob Melnychuk/gettyimages; 100 (tl), ©Image Ideas, Inc.; 100 (cr), John Coletti/Index Stock Imagery/Jupiterimages; 100 (b), Brand X Pictures/Jupiterimages; 109 (tr), ©Ezra Shaw/Getty Images; 112 (cr), Aflo Foto Agency/Alamy; 113 (cr), Pixar Animation Studios/ZUMA Press; 116 (tr), Dallas and John Heaton/Stock Connection/Jupiterimages; 118 (cr), David Guttenfelder/AP/Wide World Photos; 120 (cr), Sylvia Pitcher Photolibrary/Alamy; 120 (bl), waring abbott /Alamy.

Chapter Three: 132–133 (bkgd), Randy Faris/CORBIS; 136 (tr), ©Charles Crust; 137 (bl), Digital Vision/gettyimages; 140 (bl), ©Creatas; 146 (tl), Buzz Orr/The Gazette/AP/Wide World Photos; 146 (cr), PhotoDisc/gettyimages; 146 (bl), ©Creatas; 148 (tr), on-page credit; 152 (bl), ©Creatas; 152 (cl), David Brooks/San Diego Union Tribune/Zuma Press/Newscom; 154 (tl), ©Creatas; 156 (tr), ©Peter Beck/CORBIS; 158 (tr), Paul Sakuma/AP/Wide World Photos; 160 (bl), ©Brand X Pictures; 162 (tr), ©Ariel Skelley/CORBIS; 166 (cl), Brad Mitchell/Alamy; 166 (bl), ©Brand X Pictures; 168 (bl), ©Jose Luis Pelaez, Inc./CORBIS; 170 (tr), ©Michele Westmorland/CORBIS; 170 (br), Sam Dudgeon/HRW; 175 (tl), ©Brand X Pictures; 175 (cl), Richard Megna/Fundamental Photographs; 182 (bl), ©Brand X Pictures; 184 (tl), ©Brand X Pictures; 184 (br), Peter Beavis/Taxi/Getty Images; 184 (cr), (bl), PhotoDisc/Getty Images; 186 (b), Jill Stephenson/Alamy.

Chapter Four: 196–197 (bkgd), Tom and Pat Leeson; 200 (tr), ©Royalty-Free/CORBIS; 204 (cl), ©Bettmann/CORBIS; 204 (bl), Sam Dudgeon/HRW; 205 (all), Sam Dudgeon/HRW; 206 (tr), Aflo Sport; 208 (cl), ©Comstock Images/Alamy Photos; 211 (tl), Sam Dudgeon/HRW; 213 (tr), RubberBall/Alamy; 219 (tl), ©Bettmann/CORBIS; 219 (bl), Sam Dudgeon/HRW; 222 (br), Big Cheese Photo/Alamy Photos; 222 (tl), Sam Dudgeon/HRW; 224 (tr), David Welling/Animals Animals; 229 (bl), Roy Toft; 230 (bl), comstock.com; 234 (tr), ©COMSTOCK, Inc.; 238 (cl), Cal Poly College of Engineering/Design by Jeffrey Gordon Smith Landscape Architecture, Los Osos, California; 238 (bl), comstock.com; 240 (tl), comstock.com; 240 (bl), AP Photo/Daniel Hulshizer.

Chapter Five: 252–253 (bkgd), Ron Stroud/Masterfile; 261 (bl), Victoria Smith/HRW; 264 (tl), ©LWA-Dann Tardif/CORBIS; 264 (cr), ©Buddy Mays/CORBIS; 267 (tl), ©John and Lisa Merrill/CORBIS; 268 (tl), Victoria Smith/HRW; 272 (tr), ©Patrick Eden/Alamy Photos; 278 (cl), Garry Black/Masterfile; 279 (tl), Victoria Smith/HRW; 282 (tr), ©Royalty-Free/Corbis; 284 (bl), Genevieve Vallee/Alamy; 286 (cl), Courtesy NASA/JPL-Caltech; 286 (bl), Victoria Smith/HRW; 288 (tl), Victoria Smith/HRW; 288 (br), ©Rick Gomez/CORBIS; 288 (tr), ©age fotostock/SuperStock; 295 (bl), ©Brand X Pictures; 297 (tr), ©Pixtal/SuperStock; 302 (tl), Jake Norton; 302 (bl), ©Brand X Pictures; 303 (bl), image100/Alamy; 309 (bl), ©Brand X Pictures; 312 (tl), ©Brand X Pictures; 312 (b), ©Tim Pannell/CORBIS; 312 (tr), Andy Christiansen/HRW.

Chapter Six: 324–325 (bkgd), Noah Graham/NBAE via Getty Images; 332 (bl), Victoria Smith/HRW; 333 (tl), ©Lee Snider/Photo Images/CORBIS; 334 (bl), ©R. Holz/CORBIS; 336 (tr), ON-PAGE CREDIT; 338 (bl), ©Michael Pole/SuperStock; 341 (bl), Victoria Smith/HRW; 343 (tr), Photofusion Picture Library/Alamy; 346 (tl), Victoria Smith/HRW; 348 (cl), ©UNICOVER CORPORATION 1986; 348 (bl), Victoria Smith/HRW; 354 (bl), Victoria Smith/HRW; 354 (cl), Brad Tanas/Del Air Rockhounds; 356 (tr), Reimar Gaertner/Alamy; 357 (tl), Peter Van Steen/HRW; 357 (cl), Stephanie Friedman/HRW; 360 (bl), Victoria Smith/HRW; 362 (tl), Victoria Smith/HRW; 362 (cr), David Madison ©2005; 362 (b), ©Les Stone/CORBIS; 369 (tl), Max Gibbs/photolibrary.com; 369 (bl), Nathan Kaey/HRW; 369 (cl), PhotoDisc Blue/Getty Images; 371 (tr), ©Justin Pumfrey/Taxi/Getty Images; 375 (cl), ©Reuters/CORBIS; 375 (bl), Nathan Kaey/HRW; 378 (all), Nathan Kaey/HRW.

Chapter Seven: 390–391 (starry bkgd), ©Royalty-Free/Corbis; 390-391 (observatory), Bill Ross/CORBIS OUTLINE; 394 (tr), Advertising Archive; 397 (cr), B. G. Thomson/Photo Researchers, Inc.; 398 (cl), ©PHOTOTAKE Inc./Alamy; 400 (tr), Arscimed/Photo Researchers, Inc.; 402 (tr), Courtesy NASA/JPL-Caltech; 403 (br), ©Visuals Unlimited/Getty Images; 404 (tl), Cern/Photo Researchers, Inc.; 408 (tr), D. Parker/Photo Researchers, Inc.; 410 (bl), ©BananaStock Ltd.; 428 (br), Robert Flusic/PhotoDisc/Getty Images; 430 (tr), ©Jeff Hunter/Getty Images; 434 (tl), ©Don Johnston/Stone/Getty Images; 434 (bl), ©Comstock, Inc.; 441 (frame), ©1998 Image Farm Inc.; 441 (teens), Artville/Getty Images; 442 (bl), ©Comstock,

Credits

Photo

All Teacher-to-Teacher photos courtesy of the teachers.

Chapter One TE wrap: Page 2 (tl), Royalty Free/CORBIS; (bl), PhotoDisc/gettyimages

Chapter Two TE wrap: Page 68 (tl), Image Ideas, Inc.; (tl), Creatas

Chapter Three TE wrap: Page 132 (cl), Brand X Pictures; (tl), Sam Dudgeon/HRW

Chapter Four TE wrap: Page 196 (cl), comstock.com

Chapter Five TE wrap: Page 252 (tl), Victoria Smith/HRW; (cl), Brand X Pictures

Chapter Six TE wrap: Page 324 (tl), Victoria Smith/HRW; (cl), Nathan Kaey/HRW

Chapter Seven TE wrap: Page 390 (cl), Comstock, Inc.

Chapter Eight TE wrap: Page 474 (tl), Royalty-Free/Corbis; (cl), Stockbyte

Chapter Nine TE wrap: Page 540 (tl), Sam Dudgeon/HRW; (cl-ball), PhotoDisc/Getty Images; (cl-tees), COMSTOCK, Inc.

Chapter Ten TE wrap: Page 650 (tl), PhotoDisc/Getty Images

Chapter Eleven TE wrap: Page 696 (tl), Brand X Pictures

Inc.; 450 (cr), Royalty-Free/Corbis; 452 (cl), Philippe Desmazes/AFP/Getty Images; 452 (tl), ©Comstock, Inc.; 455 (tr), Juniors Bildarchiv/Alamy; 458 (cl), Dale Jorgensen/SuperStock; 460 (tr), Molly Eckler - puzzle, photo by Victoria Smith/HRW; 460 (bl), ©Ruggero Vanni/CORBIS; 462 (tl), ©Comstock, Inc.; 462 (tr), SuperStock; 462 (b), Ryan McVay/PhotoDisc/Getty Images.

Chapter Eight: 474–475 (bkgd), ©Mark Gibson Photography; 482 (tl), Photo by Jolesch Photography. ©2004 Drum Corps International. All rights reserved.; 483 (t), ©Royalty-Free/Corbis; 487 (tr), PhotoDisc/Getty Images; 488 (br), Victoria Smith/HRW; 488 (bc), Victoria Smith/HRW; 491 (b), Carl & Ann Purcell/CORBIS; 492 (bl), ©Royalty-Free/Corbis; 492 (cl), David R. Frazier Photolibrary, Inc./Alamy; 493 (cr), Sam Dudgeon/HRW; 496 (tr), Travel-Shots/Alamy; 501 (cl), Composition 17, 1919 (oil on canvas) by Doesburg, Theo van (1883-1931) ©Haags Gemeentemuseum, The Hague, Netherlands/The Bridgeman Art Library Nationality/copyright status: Dutch/out of copyright; 501 (bl), ©Royalty-Free/Corbis; 503 (bl), Janine Wiedel Photolibrary/Alamy; 505 (tr), AP Photo/Peter Cosgrove; 508 (tl), ©Stockbyte; 510 (bl), ©Royalty-Free/Corbis; 512 (tl), ©Royalty-Free/Corbis; 512 (br), ©Peter Adams/Getty Images; 515 (cr), ©Yann Arthus-Bertrand/CORBIS; 519 (tl), ©Stockbyte; 522 (tl), A. & J. Visage/Peter Arnold, Inc.; 526 (tl), ©Stockbyte; 526 (cl), Sheila Terry/Science Photo Library/Photo Researchers, Inc.; 528 (tl), ©Stockbyte; 528 (br), David Young Wolff/Photoedit.

Chapter Nine: 540–541 (bkgd), ©Royalty Free/CORBIS; 550 (bl), Sam Dudgeon/HRW; 553 (tr), Roy Ooms/Masterfile; 558 (cl), Ambient Images Inc./Alamy; 559 (tl), Sam Dudgeon/HRW; 560 (tr), ©Michael S. Yamashita/CORBIS; 564 (tl), AP Photo/Fabio Muzzi; 564 (bl), Sam Dudgeon/HRW; 566 (all), Sam Dudgeon/HRW; 568 (tr), MedioImages/SuperStock; 572 (cl), ©Theo Allofs/CORBIS; 572 (bl), PhotoDisc/Getty Images; 572 (bc), ©COMSTOCK, Inc.; 576 (tr), Dynamic Graphics Group/IT Stock Free/Alamy; 580 (cr), imagebroker/Alamy; 580 (bl), PhotoDisc/Getty Images; 580 (bc), ©COMSTOCK, Inc.; 586 (cl), Loren Winters/Visuals Unlimited; 586 (bl), PhotoDisc/Getty Images; 586 (bc), ©COMSTOCK, Inc.; 596 (bl), PhotoDisc/Getty Images; 596 (bl), ©COMSTOCK, Inc.; 601 (c), Comstock Images/Alamy; 603 (bl), PhotoDisc/Getty Images; 603 (bl), ©COMSTOCK, Inc.; 603 (b), Robyn Beck/AFP/Getty Images; 608 (bl), PhotoDisc/Getty Images; 608 (bl), ©COMSTOCK, Inc.; 610 (tl), PhotoDisc/Getty Images; 610 (tc), ©COMSTOCK, Inc.; 610 (tr), Stuart Franklin/Getty Images; 610 (b), Robert Laberge/Getty Images.

Chapter Ten: 622–623 (bkgd), Tom Paiva/Getty Images; 627 (tr), MedioImages/Alamy; 632 (tl), AP Photo/Robert F. Bukaty; 632 (bl), PhotoDisc/Getty Images; 640 (bl), PhotoDisc/Getty Images; 640 (bl), PhotoDisc/Getty Images; 642 (tr), Gerald C. Kelley/Photo Researchers, Inc.; 644 (bl), ©Paul Barton/CORBIS; 645 (tl), ©SuperStock; 647 (cl), AP Photo/Lou Krasky; 647 (bl), PhotoDisc/Getty Images; 650 (tl), PhotoDisc/Getty Images; 650 (br), AP Photo/Tyler Morning Telegraph, Tom Worner; 650 sky PhotoDisc/Getty Images; 652 (tr), ©Stock Connection Distribution/Alamy; 659 (tr), Philippe Blondel/Photo Researchers, Inc.; 664 (tl), Photo Researchers, Inc.; 667 (tc), AP Photo/Dolores Ochoa; 667 (cr), ©Nigel Francis/Robert Harding/Alamy Photos; 672 (l), Dell-Winston School Solar Car Challenge; 679 (tr), ©Tom Stewart/CORBIS; 684 (b), ©Dynamic Graphics Group/i2i/ Alamy; 684 (movie screen), Ralph Nelson/Imagine Entertainment/ZUMA/CORBIS.

Chapter Eleven: 696–697 (bkgd), QT Luong/Terra Galleria Photography; 700 (tr), NASA; 703 (tl), AP Photo/Andy Eames; 703 (bl), ©Brand X Pictures; 705 (tr), Steve Gottlieb/PictureQuest/Jupiter Images; 709 (bl), ©Brand X Pictures; 714 (bl), ©Brand X Pictures; 716 (tr), ON-PAGE CREDIT; 720 (tl), ©Richard Cummins/SuperStock; 720 (bl), ©Brand X Pictures; 722 (t), AP Photo/Gregory Smith; 727 (bl), John Warden/SuperStock; 728 (bl), ©Brand X Pictures; 730 (cr), Walker/PictureQuest/Jupiter Images; 730 (tl), ©Brand X Pictures; 730 (bc), AP Photo/Anna Branthwaite; 732 (tr), Randy Lincks/Masterfile; 743 (tl), Lucidio Studio, Inc./Alamy; 747 (tr), D. Hurst/Alamy; 752 (cr), Tom Goskar/Wessex Archaeology Ltd.; 757 (tr), Stephen Dalton/Photo Researchers, Inc.; 758 (cl), age fotostock; 762 (c), Laimute Druskis/Stock Boston/IPN; 762 (bc), ©D. Hurst/Alamy; 762 (br), ©Brian Hagiwara/Brand X Pictures/Alamy.

Back Matter: 788 (tl), PhotoDisc/Getty Images; 789 (b), PhotoDisc/Getty Images.

Symbols

Relation Symbols

$<$	is less than
$>$	is greater than
$\leq$	is less than or equal to
$\geq$	is greater than or equal to
$\neq$	is not equal to
$\approx$	is approximately equal to
$\cong$	is congruent to

Real Numbers

$\mathbb{R}$	the set of real numbers
$\mathbb{Q}$	the set of rational numbers
$\mathbb{Z}$	the set of integers
$\mathbb{W}$	the set of whole numbers
$\mathbb{N}$	the set of natural numbers

Geometry

$\angle ABC$	angle ABC
$m\angle ABC$	the measure of angle ABC
$\triangle ABC$	triangle ABC
$\overline{AB}$	segment AB

Other

$\pm$	plus or minus
$\lvert -4 \rvert$	the absolute value of -4
$\{$	system
π	pi; $\pi \approx 3.14$ or $\pi \approx \frac{22}{7}$
$\varnothing$	empty set
$f(x)$	function notation; f of x
a_n	the nth term of a sequence
$P(\text{event})$	the probability of an event

Table of Measures

METRIC

Length

1 kilometer (km) = 1000 meters (m)
1 meter = 100 centimeters (cm)
1 centimeter = 10 millimeters (mm)

Capacity and Volume

1 liter (L) = 1000 milliliters (mL)

Mass and Weight

1 kilogram (kg) = 1000 grams (g)
1 gram = 1000 milligrams (mg)

CUSTOMARY

Length

1 mile (mi) = 5280 feet (ft)
1 yard = 3 feet (ft)
1 foot = 12 inches (in.)

Capacity and Volume

1 gallon (gal) = 4 quarts (qt)
1 quart = 2 pints (pt)
1 pint = 2 cups (c)
1 cup = 8 fluid ounces (fl oz)

Mass and Weight

1 ton = 2000 pounds (lb)
1 pound = 16 ounces (oz)

TIME

1 year (yr) = 365 days (d)
1 year = 12 months (mo)
1 year = 52 weeks (wk)
1 week = 7 days
1 day = 24 hours (h)
1 hour = 60 minutes (min)
1 minute = 60 seconds (s)